SCHOLARSHIPS,

FELLOWSHIPS

AND LOANS

DISCARD

ISSN 1058-5699

SCHOLARSHIPS, FELLOWSHIPS AND LOANS

A GUIDE TO EDUCATION-RELATED FINANCIAL AID PROGRAMS FOR STUDENTS AND PROFESSIONALS

Volume Two

Sponsors and Their Scholarships: I–T

Thirty-Eighth Edition

GALE
A Cengage Company

Scholarships, Fellowships and Loans, 38th Edition

Project Editor: Anthony Boussie

Editorial Support Services: Scott Flaugher

Composition and Electronic Prepress:
Charlie Montney

Manufacturing: Cynde Lentz

Gale
27500 Drake Rd.
Farmington Hills, MI, 48331-3535

ISBN-13: 978-0-02-867033-1 (3 vol. set)
ISBN-13: 978-0-02-867034-8 (vol. 1)
ISBN-13: 978-0-02-867035-5 (vol. 2)
ISBN-13: 978-0-02-867036-2 (vol. 3)

ISSN 1058-5699

This title is also available as an e-book.
ISBN-13: 978-0-02-867038-6
Contact your Gale sales representative for ordering information.

Printed in the United States of America
1 2 3 4 5   25 24 23 22 21

Contents

This edition of *Scholarships, Fellowships and Loans (SFL)* provides access to over 3,400 sources of education-related financial aid for students and professionals at all levels. *SFL's* scope ranges from undergraduate and vocational/technical education through post-doctoral and professional studies. Students and others interested in education funding will find comprehensive information on a variety of programs in all educational areas, including:

- Architecture
- Area and Ethnic Studies
- Art
- Business
- Communications
- Computer Science
- Education
- Engineering
- Health Science
- Humanities
- Industrial Arts
- Language

- Law
- Literature
- Liberal Arts
- Library Science
- Life Science
- Medicine
- Mathematics
- Performing Arts
- Philosophy
- Physical Sciences
- Social Sciences
- Theology and Religion

SFL Provides Detailed Information on Awards

SFL provides all the information students need to complete their financial aid search. Entries include: administering organization name and address; purpose of award; qualifications and restrictions; selection criteria; award amount and number of awards granted; application details and deadlines; detailed contact information.

Additionally, look for the section on federal financial aid following the User's Guide for a quick summary of programs sponsored by the U.S. government, as well as information on the AmeriCorps program. There is also a section that lists higher education agencies by state.

Five Indexes Allow Quick and Easy Access to Awards

Whether you are a high school student looking for basic undergraduate financial aid, a scientist investigating research grants, or a professional attempting to finance additional career training, SFL aids your search by providing access to awards through the following indexes:

Field of Study Index categorizes awards by very specific subject fields.

Legal Resident Index targets awards restricted to applicants from specific geographic locations.

Place of Study Index provides a handy guide to awards granted for study within specific states, provinces, or countries.

Special Recipient Index lists awards that are reserved for candidates who qualify by virtue of their gender, organizational affiliation, minority or ethnic background.

Sponsor and Scholarship Index provides a complete alphabetical listing of all awards and their administering organizations.

Catchwords

SFL includes catchwords of the organization on each corresponding page, to aid the user in finding a particular entry.

As we make our way through difficult economic times, there is a growing need for a more highly-trained and educated work force. From political discussions and debates to reports from future-oriented think tanks and other groups, there is agreement that postsecondary education is a key to success. Yet how are students and their families to afford the already high (and constantly rising) cost of higher education? Searching for financial aid can be very tedious and difficult, even though hundreds of millions of dollars in aid reportedly go unclaimed every year.

Scholarships, Fellowships and Loans (SFL), the most comprehensive single directory of education-related financial aid available, can save you time, effort, and money by helping you to focus your search within the largest pool of awards and avoid pursuing aid for which you do not qualify. In most cases, the detailed descriptions contain enough information to allow you to decide if a particular scholarship is right for you to begin the application process. *SFL* lists over 8,900 major awards available to U.S. and Canadian students for study throughout the world. Included are:

- scholarships, fellowships, and grants, which do not require repayment;

- loans, which require repayment either monetarily or through service;

- scholarship loans, which are scholarships that become loans if the recipient does not comply with the award's terms;

- internships and work study programs, which provide training, work experience, and (usually) monetary compensation; and

- awards and prizes that recognize excellence in a particular field.

Also included are other forms of assistance offered by associations, corporations, religious groups, fraternal organizations, foundations, and other private organizations and companies. *SFL* includes a broad representation of government-funded awards at the national and state levels, as well as a representative sampling of lesser-known and more narrowly focused awards, such as those of a strictly local nature or programs sponsored by small organizations. Some financial aid programs administered and funded by individual colleges or universities are included in *SFL*. Both need- and merit-based awards are included. Competition-based awards and prizes are included when they offer funds that support study or research and are intended to encourage further educational or professional growth.

Students of All Types Can Benefit

Traditional students as well as those returning to school, non-degree learners, those in need of retraining, and established professionals can use the funding sources listed in *SFL* for formal and non-formal programs of study at all levels:

- high school
- vocational
- undergraduate
- graduate
- postgraduate
- doctorate
- postdoctorate
- professional development

Content and Arrangement

Scholarships, Fellowships and Loans is organized into a main section containing descriptive listings of award programs and their administering organizations, and five indexes.

The main section, Sponsors and Their Scholarships, is arranged alphabetically by name of administering organization. Entries for each organization's awards appear immediately following the entry on the organization. Each entry contains detailed contact and descriptive information, often providing users with all the information they need to make a decision about applying.

The indexes provide a variety of specific access points to the information contained within the organization and award listings, allowing users to easily identify awards of interest.

Practical Tips on How to Find Financial Aid

While there are many education-related financial aid programs for students of all types and study levels, the competition for available funds is steadily increasing. You will improve the likelihood of meeting your financial aid goals if you:

- carefully assess your particular needs and preferences;

- consider any special circumstances or conditions that might qualify you for aid; and

- carefully research available aid programs.

The following pages list some general guidelines for making your way through the search and application process.

Start Your Search Early

Any search for financial aid is likely to be more successful if you begin early. If you allow enough time to complete all of the necessary steps, you will be more likely to identify a wide variety of awards for which you qualify with plenty of time to meet their application deadlines. This can increase your chances of obtaining aid.

Some experts recommend that you start this process up to two years before you think you will need financial assistance. While you will probably be able to obtain some support if you allow less time, you might overlook some important opportunities.

Some awards are given on a first-come, first-served basis, and if you do not file your application early enough, the aid will already be distributed. In many cases, if your application is late you will not be considered, even if you have met all of the other criteria.

An early start will also allow you to identify organizations that offer scholarships to members or participants, such as student or professional associations, in time to establish membership or otherwise meet their qualifying criteria.

Assess Your Needs and Goals

The intended recipients for financial aid programs and the purposes for which awards are established can vary greatly. Some programs are open to almost anyone, while others are restricted to very specific categories of recipients. The majority of awards fall somewhere in between. Your first step in seeking financial aid is to establish your basic qualifications as a potential recipient. The following are some general questions to ask yourself to help define your educational and financial needs and goals:

- What kinds of colleges or universities interest me?

- What careers or fields of study interest me?

- Do I plan to earn a degree?

- Am I only interested in financial aid that is a gift, or will I consider a loan or work study?

- In what parts of the country am I willing to live and study?

Leave No Stone Unturned

After you have defined your goals, the next step is to identify any special factors that might make you eligible for aid programs offered only to a restricted group. Examine this area carefully, and remember that even minor or unlikely connections may be worth checking. The most common qualifications and restrictions involve:

- citizenship

- community involvement or volunteer work

- creative or professional accomplishment

- employer

- financial need

- gender

- merit or academic achievement

- military or veteran status

- organization membership (such as a union, association, or fraternal group)

- place of residence

- race or ethnic group

- religious affiliation

With many awards, you may be eligible if your spouse, parents, or guardians meet certain criteria by status or affiliations. You should be aware of your parents' affiliations even if you don't live with one (or both) of them, or if they are deceased. And given enough lead time, it may be possible for you (or your parents) to join a particular organization, or establish necessary residence, in time for you to be eligible for certain funds.

Contact Financial Aid Offices

Most colleges, universities, and other educational institutions offer their own financial aid programs. Their financial aid offices may also have information on privately sponsored awards that are specifically designated for students at those institutions. Contact their respective financial aid offices to request applications and details for all of the aid programs they sponsor and/or administer.

Use *SFL* to Identify Awards Sponsored by Private Organizations and Corporations

Scholarships, Fellowships and Loans (SFL) is the most comprehensive single source of information on major education-related financial aid programs sponsored and administered by private organizations and companies for use by students and professionals. Using *SFL* as a starting point, you can quickly compile a substantial list of financial aid programs for which you may qualify by following these simple steps:

- Compile an initial list of awards offered in your field of study.
- If you have already chosen your field of study, look in the Field of Study Index to find listings of awards grouped by more precise disciplines (such as Accounting or Journalism). If you choose this approach, your initial list is likely to be shorter but more focused. Eliminate awards that cannot be used at your chosen level of study or that do not meet your financial needs. Are you an undergraduate only interested in scholarships? Are you a graduate student willing to participate in an internship or take out a loan? Consult the User's Guide to determine which of the study level categories and award types apply to your particular situation. Both indexes clearly note the study levels at which awards may be used. The Field of Study Index also lists the type of financial aid provided.
- Eliminate awards by citizenship, residence, and other restrictions (minority status, ethnic background, gender, organizational affiliation) that make you ineligible.
- If your list is based on the Field of Study Index, you will need to look under the section for qualifications in each descriptive listing to see what requirements apply.
- Read the descriptive listings for each of the award programs left on your list. The descriptive listings should contain all the information you need to decide if you qualify and should apply for each of the awards on your list.

Expand Your List of Possibilities

If you are willing to take the initiative and do a little extra digging, you should be able to add to your list of institution-related and privately sponsored programs. In most cases, the best possibilities fall into these two areas:

Government Agencies and Programs. The Sponsors and Their Scholarships main section includes a broad representation of award programs sponsored by federal and state governments. Since these listings are not meant to be exhaustive, you should be able to identify additional programs by contacting the government agencies responsible for education-related financial aid programs listed here. On the federal level, contact the U.S. Department of Education at 400 Maryland Ave., SW, Washington, DC 20202, or on their website at https://www.ed.gov, for up-to-date information on U.S. Government award programs. For a broad overview of federal financial aid, consult the Federal Programs section. Similarly, you may contact your state department of education for details on what is offered in your particular state. Please see the State Higher Education Agencies section for state-by-state listings.

Local Sources of Awards. A surprisingly large number of financial aid programs are sponsored by small and/or lo-cal organizations. *SFL* contains a representative sampling of such programs to encourage you to seek similar programs in your own geographic area. High school guidance counselors are often aware of local programs as well, and they can usually tell you how to get in touch with the sponsoring or administering organizations. Local newspapers are also rich sources of information on financial aid programs.

Allow Enough Time for the Application Process

The amount of time needed to complete the application process for individual awards will vary, so you should pay close attention to application deadlines. Some awards carry application deadlines that require you to apply a year or more before your studies will begin. In general, allow plenty of time to:

- Write for official applications. You may not be considered for some awards unless you apply with the correct forms.
- Read all instructions carefully.
- Take note of application deadlines.
- Accurately and completely file all required supporting material, such as essays, school transcripts, and financial records. If you fail to answer certain questions, you may be disqualified even if you are a worthy candidate.
- Give references enough time to submit their recommendations. Teachers in particular get many requests for letters of recommendation and should be given as much advance notice as possible.

Make Sure You Qualify

Finally, don't needlessly submerge yourself in paperwork. If you find you don't qualify for a particular award, don't apply for it. Instead, use your time and energy to find and apply for more likely sources of aid.

Available in Electronic Format

Scholarships, Fellowships and Loans is also available online as part of Gale Directory Library and Gale eBooks. For more information, call 1-800-877-GALE.

Comments and Suggestions Welcome

We welcome reader suggestions regarding new and previously unlisted organizations and awards. Please send your suggestions to:

Scholarships, Fellowships and Loans

Gale, a Cengage Company

27500 Drake Rd.

Farmington Hills, MI 48331-3535

Phone: (248) 699-4253

Toll-free: 800-347-4253

Fax: (248) 699-8070

Email: Anthony.Boussie@cengage.com

Scholarships, Fellowships and Loans is comprised of a main section containing descriptive listings on award programs and their administering organizations, and five indexes that aid users in identifying relevant information. Each of these sections is described in detail below.

Sponsors and Their Scholarships

SFL contains two types of descriptive listings:

- brief entries on the organizations that sponsor or administer specific award programs
- descriptive entries on the award programs themselves

Entries are arranged alphabetically by administering organization; awards administered by each organization follow that organization's listings. Entries contain detailed contact and descriptive information. Users are strongly encouraged to read the descriptions carefully and pay particular attention to the various eligibility requirements before applying for awards.

The following sample organization and award entries illustrate the kind of information that is or might be included in these entries. Each item of information is preceded by a number, and is explained in the paragraph with the same number on the following pages.

Sample Entry

❚ 1 ❚ 3445
❚ 2 ❚ Microscopy Society of America
❚ 3 ❚ 4 Barlows Landing Rd., Ste. 8 Woods Hole, MA 02543
❚ 4 ❚ Ph: (508) 563-1155
❚ 5 ❚ Fax: (508) 563-1211
❚ 6 ❚ Free: 800-538-3672
❚ 7 ❚ E-mail: businessofficemsa.microscopy.com
❚ 8 ❚ URL: http://www.msa.microscopy.com
❚ 9 ❚ 3446
❚ 10 ❚ MSA Presidential Student Awards
❚ 11 ❚ (Graduate, Undergraduate/
❚ 12 ❚ Award

   ❚ 13 ❚ Purpose: To recognize outstanding original research by students. ❚ 14 ❚ Focus: Biological Clinical Sciences—Microscopy, Physical Sciences—Microscopy. ❚ 15 ❚ Qualif.: Candidate may be of any nationality, but must be enrolled at a recognized college or university in the United States at the time of the MSA annual meeting. ❚ 16 ❚ Criteria: Selection is done based on the applicant's

career objectives, academic record, and financial need. ❚ 17 ❚ Funds Avail.: Registration and round-trip travel to the MSA annual meeting, plus a stipend to defray lodging and other expenses. ❚ 18 ❚ Duration: Annual. ❚ 19 ❚ Number awarded: 5. ❚ 20 ❚ To Apply: Write to MSA for application form and guidelines. ❚ 21 ❚ Deadline: March 15. ❚ 22 ❚ Remarks: Established in 1979. ❚ 23 ❚ Contact: Alternate phone number: 800-538-EMSA.

Descriptions of Numbered Elements

❚ 1 ❚ **Organization Entry Number.** Administering organizations are listed alphabetically. Each entry is followed by an alphabetical listing of its awards. All entries (organization and award) are numbered in a single sequence. These numbers are used as references in the indexes.

❚ 2 ❚ **Organization Name.** The name of the organization administering the awards that follow.

❚ 3 ❚ **Mailing Address.** The organization's permanent mailing address is listed when known; in some cases an award address is given.

❚ 4 ❚ **Telephone Number.** The general telephone number for the administering organization. Phone numbers pertaining to specific awards are listed under "Contact" in the award description.

❚ 5 ❚ **Fax Number.** The facsimile number for the administering organization. Fax numbers pertaining to specific awards are included under "Contact" in the award description.

❚ 6 ❚ **Toll-free Number.** The toll-free number for the administering organization. Toll-free numbers pertaining to specific awards are included under "Contact" in the award description.

❚ 7 ❚ **E-mail Address.** The electronic mail address for the administering organization. Electronic mail addresses pertaining to specific awards are included under "Contact" in the award description.

❚ 8 ❚ **URL and Social Media.** The web address(es) for the administering organization.

❚ 9 ❚ **Award Entry Number.** Awards are listed alphabetically following the entry for their administering organizations. All entries (organization and award) are numbered in a single sequence. These numbers are used as references in the indexes.

❚ 10 ❚ **Award Name.** Names of awards are always listed. Organization titles or acronyms have been added to generic award names (for example, MSA Undergraduate Scholarships, Canadian Council Fiction Writing Grant, etc.) to avoid confusion.

❚ 11 ❚ Study Level. The level of study for which the award may be used. One or more of the following terms will be listed:

- All: not restricted to a particular level.
- High School: study at the secondary level.
- Vocational: study leading to postsecondary awards, certificates, or diplomas requiring less than two years of study.
- 2 Year: study leading to a bachelor's degree within two years
- 4 Year: study leading to a bachelor's degree within four years
- Undergraduate: study immediately beyond the secondary level, including associate, colleges and universities, junior colleges, technical institutes leading to a bachelor's degree, and vocational technical schools.
- Graduate: study leading to an M.A., M.S., LL.B., LL.M., and other intermediate degrees.
- Master's: study leading specifically to a master's degree, such as a M.A., M.S., or M.B.A.
- Postgraduate: study beyond the graduate level not specifically leading to a degree.
- Doctorate: study leading to a Ph.D., Ed.D., Sc.D., M.D., D.D.S., D.O., J.D., and other terminal degrees.
- Postdoctorate: study beyond the doctorate level; includes awards intended for professional development when candidates must hold a doctoral degree to qualify.
- Professional Development: career development not necessarily restricted by study.

❚ 12 ❚ Award Type. The type or category of award. One or more of the following terms will be listed:

- Award: generally includes aid given in recognition and support of excellence, including awards given through music and arts competitions. Non-monetary awards and awards given strictly for recognition are not included.
- Fellowship: awards granted for graduate- or postgraduate-level research or education that do not require repayment.
- Grant: includes support for research, travel, and creative, experimental, or innovative projects.
- Internship: training and work experience programs. Internships that do not include compensation of some type are not included.
- Loan: aid that must be repaid either monetarily or through service. Some loans are interest-free, others are not.
- Prize: funds awarded as the result of a competition or contest. Prizes that are not intended to be used for

study or to support professional development are not included.

- Scholarships: support for formal educational programs that does not require repayment.
- Scholarship Loan: a scholarship that becomes a loan if the recipient does not comply with the terms.
- Work Study: combined study and work program for which payment is received.
- Other: anything that does not fit the other categories, such as a travel award.

❚ 13 ❚ Purpose. The purpose for which the award is granted is listed here when known.

❚ 14 ❚ Focus. The field(s) of study that the recipient must be pursuing.

❚ 15 ❚ Qualif. Information regarding applicant eligibility. Some examples of qualification requirements include the following: academic record, citizenship, financial need, organizational affiliation, minority or ethnic background, residency, and gender.

❚ 16 ❚ Criteria Information concerning selection criteria.

❚ 17 ❚ Funds Avail. The award dollar amounts are included here along with other relevant funding information, such as the time period covered by the award, a breakdown of expenses covered (e.g., stipends, tuition and fees, travel and living allowances, equipment funds, etc.), the amount awarded to the institution, loan repayment schedules, service-in-return-for-funding agreements, and other obligations.

❚ 18 ❚ Duration. Frequency of the award.

❚ 19 ❚ Number awarded. Typical number of awards distributed.

❚ 20 ❚ To Apply. Application guidelines, requirements, and other information.

❚ 21 ❚ Deadline. Application due dates, notification dates (the date when the applicant will be notified of receipt or denial of award), disbursement dates, and other relevant dates.

❚ 22 ❚ Remarks. Any additional information concerning the award.

❚ 23 ❚ Contact. When contact information differs from that given for the administering organization, relevant addresses, telephone and fax numbers, and names of specific contact persons are listed here. When the address is that of the administering organization, the entry number for the organization is provided.

Indexes

Field of Study Index classifies awards by one or more of 450 specific subject categories, allowing users to easily target their search by specific area of study. Citations are arranged alphabetically under all appropriate subject terms. Each citation is followed by the study level and award type, which appear in parentheses and can be used to narrow the search even further.

Legal Residence Index lists awards that are restricted by the applicant's residence of legal record. Award citations are arranged alphabetically by country and subarranged by region, state or province (for U.S. and Canada). Each citation is followed by the study level and award type, which appear in parentheses and can be used to eliminate inappropriate awards.

Place of Study Index lists awards that carry restrictions on where study can take place. Award citations are arranged alphabetically under the following geographic headings:

- United States
- United States—by Region
- United States—by State
- Canada
- Canada—by Province
- International
- International—by Region
- International—by Country

Each citation is followed by the study level and award type, which appear in parentheses.

Special Recipient Index lists awards that carry restrictions or special qualifying factors relating to applicant affiliation. This index allows users to quickly identify awards relating to the following categories:

- African American
- Asian American
- Association Membership
- Disabled
- Employer Affiliation
- Ethnic Group Membership
- Fraternal Organization Membership
- Hispanic American
- Military
- Minority
- Native American
- Religious Affiliation
- Union Affiliation
- Veteran

Awards are listed under all appropriate headings. Each citation includes information on study level and award type, which appear in parentheses and can be used to further narrow the search. Users interested in awards restricted to particular minorities should also look under the general Minorities heading, which lists awards targeted for minorities but not restricted to any particular minority group.

Sponsor and Scholarship Index lists, in a single alphabetic sequence, all of the administering organizations, awards, and acronyms included in *SFL*.

Federal Programs

Federal aid for college students is available through a variety of programs administered by the U.S. Department of Education. Most colleges and universities participate in federal programs, but there are exceptions. Contact a school's financial aid office to find out if it is a participating institution. If it participates, the student works with financial aid counselors to determine how much aid can be obtained.

Aid for students comes in three forms: grants (gifts to the student), loans (which must be repaid), and work-study jobs (a job for the student while enrolled in which his/her pay is applied to his school account). These types of aid are further explained below. More information can be found at https://www.ed.gov.

Grants

Pell Grants are intended to provide funds for any undergraduate student (who does not already have a degree) who wishes to attend college regardless of family financial background. They are available through the financial aid office at the school. The maximum Pell Grant award for the 2020-2021 award year (July 1, 2020 to June 30, 2021) is $6,345.

Federal Supplemental Educational Opportunity Grants (FSEOG) are intended for students with exceptional financial need, these grants are typically for smaller amounts (between $100 and $4,000) than Pell Grants. They are available on a limited basis.

Loans

Student loans are available a variety of ways. Loans may not be taken out for more than the cost of attendance at the school, which is determined by the financial aid administrator. Grants and other forms of aid are taken into consideration when determining the amount a student will be allowed to borrow. Loan amounts may be reduced if a student receives other forms of aid. Loans are divided into two types, subsidized and unsubsidized:

Subsidized loans: the federal government pays the interest on the loan until after schooling is complete.

Unsubsidized loans: the student incurs the interest charges while in school, but payment of the charges may be deferred until schooling is complete. The advantage of unsubsidized loans is that there are usually fewer restrictions against obtaining them. Amounts available through these programs vary depending on academic level. The total debt a student or a student's parents may accumulate for that student is $31,000 for a dependent undergraduate student, $57,500 for an independent undergraduate student (with a limit of $23,000 in subsidized loans), and $138,500 for a graduate or professional student (with a limit of $65,500 in subsidized loans) or $224,000 for health professionals.

Available Funding Programs Direct Loan Program

These low-interest loans bypass lending institutions such as banks. They are a direct arrangement between the government and the student (administered by the school). There are four repayment options for the Direct Loan program: the Income Contingent Repayment Plan, the Extended Repayment Plan, the Graduated Repayment Plan, and the Standard Repayment Plan.

Direct subsidized loans may be taken out for a maximum of $3,500 by incoming freshmen, $4,500 for sophomores, and $5,500 for juniors and seniors. The amounts for independent undergraduate students range from $9,500 to $12,500 per year for direct loans. Independent students face some restrictions on the amount of subsidized funds they can receive from the program. At least half of the funds borrowed through the Direct Loan program by independent students must come from unsubsidized loans. Graduate students may borrow up to $20,500 directly in unsubsidized loans.

Direct PLUS Loans Direct PLUS loans are federal loans that graduate or professional degree students and parents of dependent undergraduate students can use to help pay education expenses. The U.S. Department of Education makes Direct PLUS loans to eligible borrowers through schools participating in the program. The Maximum amount to be borrowed is the cost of attending the shool minus other forms of aid already obtained. For 2020-2021 the fixed rate for a Direct PLUS loan is 5.30%.

With the Direct PLUS loan, students or parents fill out a Direct PLUS Loan Application, available at the school's financial aid office. The funds are disbursed to the school. Students and parents may choose from three repayment plans: Standard, Extended, or Graduated.

Perkins Loan Program Under federal law, the authorty for schools to make new Perkins Loans ended on Sept. 30, 2017, and final disbursements were permitted through June 30, 2018. As a result, students can no longer receive Perkins Loans. A borrower who received a Perkins Loan can learn more about managing the repayment of the loan by contacting either the school that made the loan or the school's loan servicer.

Federal Work-Study Program Work-study is an arrangement that allows students to work on campus while they are enrolled to help pay their expenses. The federal government pays the majority of the student's wages, although the department where the student works also contributes. The employment must be relevant to the student's field of study and only so much time per semester may be devoted to the job. If the student earns the amount of aid prior to the end of the semester, work is terminated for the duration of the award period.

Other Considerations

Application: Applying for federal student aid is free. All federal aid is obtained by first completing a Free Application for Federal Student Aid (FAFSA). After the application is submitted, it will be processed by the Department of Education. The student then receives a Student Aid Report (SAR), which contains a figure for Expected Family Contribution. This is the amount that the student should plan on providing from non-federal sources in order to attend school.

Dependency: If a student is eligible for independent status, more money may be available in the form of loans. The interest rates and the programs for repayment, however, are the same. Independent status provides more financial aid for students who do not have the benefit of parental financial contributions.

Deadline: FAFSA deadlines are set by federal and state agencies, as well as individual schools, and vary widely. Applicants are encouraged to apply as soon as possible after January 1 of the year they plan to enroll, but no earlier.

Special Circumstances: The financial aid counselor at the school will often listen to extenuating circumstances such as unexpected medical expenses, private education expenses for other family members, or recent unemployment when evaluating requests for assistance.

Contact Information for Federal Financial Aid Programs

Call (800)433-3243 to have questions answered; (319) 337-5665 to find out if your application has been processed; (800) 730-8913 (TTY) if you are hearing impaired; (800) 647-8733 to report fraud, waste, or abuse of federal student aid funds; or visit https://www.ed.gov for application forms, guidelines, and general information.

President Clinton launched this volunteer community service program in September 1993 through the *National and Community Service Trust Act*, aimed at helping college-bound young people pay for their education while serving their communities. AmeriCorps volunteers receive minimum wage, health benefits, and a grant toward college for up to two years.

Funds for the program are distributed by the federal government in the form of grants to qualifying organizations and community groups with the goal of achieving direct results in addressing the nation's critical education, human services, public safety, and environmental needs at the community level. The program provides meaningful opportunities for Americans to serve their country in organized efforts, fostering citizen responsibility, building community, and providing educational opportunities for those who make a substantial commitment to service.

The AmeriCorps programs are run by not-for-profit organizations or partnerships, institutions of higher learning, local governments, school or police districts, states, Native American tribes, and federal agencies. Examples of participating programs include Habitat for Humanity, the American Red Cross, Boys and Girls Clubs, and local community centers and places of worship. Volunteers have nearly 1,000 different groups from which to choose. The AmeriCorps Pledge: "I will get things done for America to make our people safer, smarter, and healthier. I will bring Americans together to strengthen our communities. Faced with apathy, I will take action. Faced with conflict, I will seek a common ground. Faced with adversity, I will persevere. I will carry this commitment with me this year and beyond. I am an AmeriCorps Member and I am going to get things done."

Eligibility and Selection for Service in AmeriCorps

Citizens and legal resident aliens who are 17 years of age or older are eligible to serve in AmeriCorps before, during, or after post-secondary education. In general, participants must be high school graduates or agree to achieve their GED prior to receiving education awards. Individual programs select service participants on a nondiscriminatory and nonpolitical basis. There are national and state-wide recruiting information systems and a national pool of potential service volunteers.

Term of Service

One full-time term of service is a minimum of 1,700 hours over the course of one year or less; or a part-time term, which can range from 300 hours to 900 hours. Short-term service (such as a summer program) provides eligibility for reduced part-time status.

Compensation

You will receive a modest living allowance, health insurance, student loan deferment, and training. After you complete your term of service, you will receive an education award to help pay for your education. Serve part-time and you will receive a portion of the full amount. The amount is tied to the maximum amount of the U.S. Department of Education's Pell Grant. Since the amount of a Pell Grant can change from year to year, the amount of an education award can vary from year to year. Currently, AmeriCorps members may earn up to the value of two full-time education awards and have seven years from the date they earned each award to use it. For fiscal 2021, which began October 1, 2020, the award is $6,345 for a year of full-time service, and is pro rated for part-time service.

How Can I Use an Award?

These awards may be used to repay qualified existing or future student loans, to pay all or part of the cost of attending a qualified institute of higher education (including some vocational programs), or to pay expenses while participating in an approved school-to-work program. Awards must be used within seven years of completion of service.

Contact

Individuals interested in participating in AmeriCorps national service programs should apply directly. For basic program information, individuals can call the AmeriCorps Information Hotline at 1-800-942-2677 or visit their Web site at https://www.nationalservice.gov/programs/americorps.

State Higher Education Agencies

The following is an alphabetic state-by-state listing of agencies located in the United States. Many of these agencies administer special federal award programs, as well as state-specific awards, such as the Tuition Incentive Program (TIP) offered by the state of Michigan for low-income students to receive free tuition at community colleges. Financial aid seekers should contact the agency in their home state for more information.

ALABAMA

Alabama Comm. on Higher Education
100 N. Union St.
P.O. Box 302000
Montgomery, AL 36104
(334)242-1998
https://ache.edu

ALASKA

Alaska Comm. on Postsecondary Education
P.O. Box 110505
Juneau, AK 99811-0505
(907)465-2962
https://acpesecure.alaska.gov

ARIZONA

Arizona Comm. for Postsecondary Education
2020 N. Central Ave.,
Ste. 650
Phoenix, AZ 85004-4503
(602)542-7230
https://highered.az.gov

ARKANSAS

Arkansas Div. of Higher Education
423 Main St., Ste. 400
Little Rock, AR 72201
(501)371-2000
https://www.adhe.edu

CALIFORNIA

California Student Aid Comm.
PO Box 419027
Rancho Cordova, CA 95741-9027
(888)224-7268
https://www.csac.ca.gov

COLORADO

Colorado Dept. of Higher Education
1600 Broadway, Ste. 2200
Denver, CO 80202
(303)862-3001
https://highered.colorado.gov

CONNECTICUT

Connecticut Office of Higher Education
450 Columbus Blvd. Ste. 707
Hartford, CT 06103-1841
(860)947-1800
www.ctohe.org

DELAWARE

Delaware Dept. of Higher Education Scholarship Incentive Program
The Townsend Building
401 Federal St., Ste. 2
Dover, DE 19901-3639
(302)735-4000
https://www.doe.k12.de.us/Page/316

DISTRICT OF COLUMBIA

District of Columbia Office of the State Superintendent of Education
1050 First Street, NE
Washington, DC 20002
(202)727-6436
https://osse.dc.gov

FLORIDA

Office of Student Financial Assistance
Dept. of Education
325 W. Gaines St.

Turlington Bldg., Ste. 1514
Tallahassee, FL 32399-0400
(800)366-3475
www.floridastudentfinancialaid.org

GEORGIA

Georgia Student Finance Comm.
2082 E. Exchange Pl.
Tucker, GA 30084
(800)505-4732
https://gsfc.georgia.gov

HAWAII

Hawaii Board of Regents
2444 Dole St.,
Bachman Hall, Rm. 209
Honolulu, HI 96822
(808)956-8213
www.hawaii.edu/offices/bor/

IDAHO

Idaho State Board of Education
PO Box 83720
Boise, ID 83720-0037
(208)334-2270
https://www.boardofed.idaho.gov

ILLINOIS

Illinois Student Assistance Comm.
1755 Lake Cook Rd.
Deerfield, IL 60015-5209
(800)899-4722
https://www.isac.org

INDIANA

Indiana Comm. for Higher Education
101 W. Ohio St., Ste. 300
Indianapolis, IN 46204-4206

(888)528-4719
https://www.in.gov/che

IOWA

Iowa College Student Aid Comm.
475 SW Fifth St., Ste. D
Des Moines, IA 50309
(877)272-4456
https://www.iowacollegeaid.gov

KANSAS

Kansas Board of Regents
1000 SW Jackson St., Ste. 520
Topeka, KS 66612-1368
(785)430-4240
https://www.kansasregents.org

KENTUCKY

Kentucky Higher Education Assistance Authority
P.O. Box 798
Frankfort, KY 40602-0798
(800)928-8926
https://www.kheaa.com/website/kheaa/home

LOUISIANA

Louisiana Office of Student Financial Assistance
602 N. Fifth St.
Baton Rouge, LA 70802
(225)219-1012
https://mylosfa.la.gov

MAINE

Finance Authority of Maine (FAME)
5 Community Dr.
P.O. Box 949
Augusta, ME 04332-0949
(207)623-3263
https://www.famemaine.com

MARYLAND

Maryland Higher Education Comm.
6 N. Liberty St.
Baltimore, MD 21201
(410)767-3300
https://mhec.state.md.us/Pages/default.aspx

MASSACHUSETTS

Massachusetts Dept. of Higher Education
One Ashburton Pl., Rm. 1401
Boston, MA 02108-1696

(617)994-6950
https://www.mass.edu/home.asp

MICHIGAN

MI Student Aid
Student Scholarships and Grants
P.O. Box 30462
Lansing, MI 48909-7962
(888)447-2687
https://www.michigan.gov/mistudentaid

MINNESOTA

Minnesota Office of Higher Education
1450 Energy Park Dr., Ste. 350
St. Paul, MN 55108-5227
(651)642-0567
www.ohe.state.mn.us/index.cfm

MISSISSIPPI

Mississippi Institutions of Higher Learning
3825 Ridgewood Rd.
Jackson, MS 39211
(601)432-6198
www.ihl.state.ms.us

MISSOURI

Missouri Dept. of Higher Education
301 W. High St.
Jefferson City, MO 65101
(573)751-2361
https://dhewd.mo.gov/

MONTANA

Montana Board of Regents
Office of Commissioner of Higher Education
Montana University System
560 N. Park, 4th Fl.
PO Box 203201
Helena, MT 59620-3201
(406)449-9124
https://www.mus.edu

NEBRASKA

Nebraska Coordinating Comm. for Postsecondary Education
P.O. Box 95005
Lincoln, NE 68509-5005
(402)471-2847
https://ccpe.nebraska.gov

NEVADA

Nevada Department of Education
700 E. Fifth St.
Carson City, NV 89701
(775)687-9115
www.doe.nv.gov

Las Vegas Office
2080 E. Flamingo Rd., Ste. 210
Las Vegas, NV 89119
(702)486-6458

NEW HAMPSHIRE

New Hampshire Dept. of Education
101 Pleasant St.
Concord, NH 03301-3494
(603)271-3494
https://www.education.nh.gov/

NEW JERSEY

Higher Education Student Assistance Authority
P.O. Box 545
Trenton, NJ 08625-0545
(800)792-8670
https://www.hesaa.org/Pages/Default.aspx

NEW MEXICO

New Mexico Higher Education Dept.
2044 Galisteo St., Ste. 4
Santa Fe, NM 87505-2100
(505)476-8400
https://hed.state.nm.us

NEW YORK

New York State Higher Education Svcs. Corp.
99 Washington Ave.
Albany, NY 12255
(888)697-4372
https://www.hesc.ny.gov

NORTH CAROLINA

North Carolina State Education Assistance Authority
PO Box 14103
Research Triangle Park, NC 27709

(919)549-8614
www.ncseaa.edu

NORTH DAKOTA

North Dakota University System
10th Fl., State Capitol
600 E. Boulevard Ave., Dept. 215
Bismarck, ND 58505-0230
(701)328-2960
https://www.ndus.edu

OHIO

Ohio Department of Higher Education
25 S. Front St.
Columbus, OH 43215
(614)466-6000
https://www.ohiohighered.org

OKLAHOMA

Oklahoma State Regents for Higher Education
655 Research Pkwy.
Suite 200
Oklahoma City, OK 73104
(405)225-9100
https://www.okhighered.org

OREGON

Oregon Student Access Comm.
1500 Valley River Dr., Ste. 100
Eugene, OR 97401
(541)687-7400
https://oregonstudentaid.gov

PENNSYLVANIA

Pennsylvania Higher Education Assistance Agency
1200 N. 7th St.
Harrisburg, PA 17102-1444
(800)692-7392
https://www.pheaa.org

RHODE ISLAND

Rhode Island Office of the Postsecondary Commissioner
560 Jefferson Blvd., Ste. 100
Warwick, RI 02886-1304

(401)736-1100
https://www.riopc.edu

SOUTH CAROLINA

South Carolina Comm. on Higher Education
1122 Lady St., Ste. 300
Columbia, SC 29201
(803)737-2260
https://www.che.sc.gov/

SOUTH DAKOTA

South Dakota Board of Regents
306 E. Capitol Ave., Ste. 200
Pierre, SD 57501
(605)773-3455
https://www.sdbor.edu/Pages/default.aspx

TENNESSEE

Tennessee Higher Education Comm.
312 Rosa Parks Ave., 9th Floor
Nashville, TN 37243
(615)741-3605
https://www.tn.gov/thec.html

TEXAS

Texas Higher Education Coordinating Board
1200 E. Anderson Ln.
Austin, TX 78752
(512)427-6101
https://www.highered.texas.gov

UTAH

Utah System of Higher Education
Two Gateway
60 South 400 West
Salt Lake City, UT 84101-1284
(800)418-8757
https://ushe.edu

VERMONT

Vermont Student Assistance Corp.
10 E. Allen St.
P.O. Box 2000

Winooski, VT 05404
(800)642--3177
https://www.vsac.org/

VIRGINIA

State Council of Higher Education for Virginia
James Monroe Bldg.
101 N. 14th St., 10th Fl.
Richmond, VA 23219
(804)225-2600
https://www.schev.edu

WASHINGTON

Washington Student Achievement Council
917 Lakeridge Way SW
Olympia, WA 98502
(360)753-7800
https://wsac.wa.gov

WEST VIRGINIA

West Virginia Higher Education Policy Comm.
1018 Kanawha Blvd., E., Ste. 700
Charleston, WV 25301
(304)558-2101
www.wvhepc.edu

WISCONSIN

Wisconsin Higher Education Aids Board
P.O. Box 7885
Madison, WI 53707-7885
(608)267-2206
heab.state.wi.us

WYOMING

Wyoming Community College Comm.
2300 Capitol Ave., 5th Fl., Ste. B
Cheyenne, WY 82002
(307)777-7763
https://communitycolleges.wy.edu

U.S. State Abbreviations

AK	Alaska
AL	Alabama
AR	Arkansas
AZ	Arizona
CA	California
CO	Colorado
CT	Connecticut
DC	District of Columbia
DE	Delaware
FL	Florida
GA	Georgia
GU	Guam
HI	Hawaii
IA	Iowa
ID	Idaho
IL	Illinois
IN	Indiana
KS	Kansas
KY	Kentucky
LA	Louisiana
MA	Massachusetts
MD	Maryland
ME	Maine
MI	Michigan
MN	Minnesota
MO	Missouri
MS	Mississippi
MT	Montana
NC	North Carolina
ND	North Dakota
NE	Nebraska
NH	New Hampshire
NJ	New Jersey
NM	New Mexico
NV	Nevada
NY	New York
OH	Ohio
OK	Oklahoma
OR	Oregon
PA	Pennsylvania
PR	Puerto Rico
RI	Rhode Island
SC	South Carolina
SD	South Dakota
TN	Tennessee
TX	Texas
UT	Utah
VA	Virginia
VI	Virgin Islands
VT	Vermont
WA	Washington
WI	Wisconsin
WV	West Virginia
WY	Wyoming

Canadian Province Abbreviations

AB	Alberta
BC	British Columbia
MB	Manitoba
NB	New Brunswick
NL	Newfoundland and Labrador
NS	Nova Scotia
NT	Northwest Territories
ON	Ontario
PE	Prince Edward Island
QC	Quebec
SK	Saskatchewan
YT	Yukon Territory

Other Abbreviations

ACT	American College Testing Program
B.A.	Bachelor of Arts
B.Arch.	Bachelor of Architecture
B.F.A.	Bachelor of Fine Arts
B.S.	Bachelor of Science
B.Sc.	Bachelor of Science
CSS	College Scholarship Service
D.D.S.	Doctor of Dental Science/Surgery
D.O.	Doctor of Osteopathy
D.Sc.	Doctor of Science
D.S.W.	Doctor of Social Work
D.V.M.	Doctor of Veterinary Medicine
D.V.M.S.	Doctor of Veterinary Medicine and Surgery
D.V.S.	Doctor of Veterinary Science
FAFSA	Free Application for Federal Student Aid
FWS	Federal Work Study
GED	General Education Development Certificate
GPA	Grade Point Average
GRE	Graduate Record Examination
J.D.	Doctor of Jurisprudence
LL.B.	Bachelor of Law
LL.M.	Master of Law
LSAT	Law School Admission Test
M.A.	Master of Arts
M.Arch.	Master of Architecture
M.B.A.	Master of Business Administration
M.D.	Doctor of Medicine
M.Div.	Master of Divinity
M.F.A.	Master of Fine Arts
MIA	Missing in Action
M.L.S.	Master of Library Science
M.N.	Master of Nursing
M.S.	Master of Science
M.S.W.	Master of Social Work
O.D.	Doctor of Optometry
Pharm.D.	Doctor of Pharmacy
Ph.D.	Doctor of Philosophy
POW	Prisoner of War
PSAT	Preliminary Scholastic Aptitude Test
ROTC	Reserve Officers Training Corps
SAR	Student Aid Report
SAT	Scholastic Aptitude Test
Sc.D.	Doctor of Science
TDD	Telephone Device for the Deaf
Th.d.	Doctor of Theology
U.N.	United Nations
U.S.	United States

5672 ■ Ice Skating Institute (ISI)

6000 Custer Rd., Bldg. 9
Plano, TX 75023
Ph: (972)735-8800
Fax: (972)735-8815
E-mail: info@skateisi.org
URL: www.skateisi.com
Social Media: www.facebook.com/skateisi
twitter.com/skatingisi

5673 ■ Ice Skating Institute of America Education Foundation Scholarships *(Undergraduate/Scholarship)*

Purpose: To promote the intellectual growth of ISI member skaters. **Focus:** General studies/Field of study not specified. **Qualif.:** Applicants must have completed at least three years of high school or equivalent, with a minimum 3.0 grade point average (based on a 4.0 system) during the last two years; must be a current individual or professional member of the ice skating institute and have been for a minimum of four years; must have participated in the ISI recreational skater program at an ISI administrative member (rink or club) program for a minimum of four years; must have participated in ISI group classes or ISI endorsed competitions within the last two years; must have completed 120 hours of volunteer service, of which at least 60 hours must be in association with an ISI member facility; must enroll and carry the minimum number of credit hours necessary to be a full time undergraduate student; teachers or instructors must be a current professional member of the ice skating institute, teaching the ISI program at an ISI administrative member (rink or club); instructor status must be verified by the ISI administrative member. **Criteria:** Final selection will be made by the Trustees of the ISIA Education Foundation.

Funds Avail.: $4,000. **Duration:** Entire length of undergraduate study. **Number Awarded:** Varies. **To Apply:** Applicants must submit an official transcript including grades through the last reporting period prior to application and an official recording of SAT/ACT scores, to the ISIA education foundation; must be accompanied by a typed statement of 500 words or less. should receive an ISIA education foundation scholarship. **Deadline:** February 1. **Contact:** Email: scholarships@isiafoundation.org.

5674 ■ Idaho Community Foundation (ICF)

210 W State St.
Boise, ID 83702
Ph: (208)342-3535
Fax: (208)342-3577
E-mail: info@idahocf.org
URL: www.idahocf.org
Social Media: www.facebook.com/IdahoCF
www.instagram.com/idahocf
www.linkedin.com/company/idaho-community-foundation

5675 ■ Alois and Marie Goldmann Scholarship *(Graduate/Scholarship)*

Purpose: To promote greater understanding of the Holocaust among high school students in Idaho. **Focus:** General studies/Field of study not specified. **Qualif.:** Applicants must be senior students in an accredited high school or home school in Idaho; must have plans to attend an accredited Idaho Institution of higher learning during the academic year. **Criteria:** Recipients are selected based on originality of an essay or research paper; minimum C grade point average, scholastic achievement, financial need and extracurricular or community activities.

Funds Avail.: Approximately $1,000. **Duration:** Annual. **Number Awarded:** 1. **To Apply:** Applicants must submit a formal research paper, bibliography and references; Essay or Paper must be 2 - 6 pages in length (1 - 3 pages double sided); one-inch margins and 10-12 point font. **Deadline:** March 1. **Remarks:** Established in 1997. **Contact:** Goldmann Scholarship Committee, c/o Idaho Community Foundation, 210 W. State St., Boise, ID, 83702; Phone: 208-342-3535; Questions: Elly Davis; Email: edavis@idcomfdn.org.

5676 ■ Mike Crapo Math and Science Scholarship Fund *(Undergraduate/Scholarship)*

Purpose: To assist Idaho students who are interested in pursuing math and science degrees at Idaho college and universities. **Focus:** Mathematics and mathematical sciences. **Qualif.:** Applicants must be students, pursuing math and science degrees at Idaho colleges and universities, that are residents of Idaho and enrolled as a full-time student at the freshman level at a public or private four-year college or university in the state of Idaho; must also have a cumulative GPA of 3.0 or above for all class work prior to the application. **Criteria:** Recipients are selected based on financial need and academic performance.

Funds Avail.: No specific amount. **Duration:** Annual. **To Apply:** Applicants must submit most recent unofficial high schooltranscript; short statement of educational goals; two letters of recommendation. **Deadline:** March 15. **Contact:** Email scholarships@idahocf.org or call (208)342-3535.

Awards are arranged alphabetically below their administering organizations

5677 ▪ Idaho Nursing and Health Professions Scholarship Fund *(Undergraduate/Scholarship)*

Purpose: To assist recipients with educational expenses at any Idaho accredited nursing program. **Focus:** Nursing. **Qualif.:** Applicant must be a student that has been accepted by an accredited Idaho nursing or health professions program, including but not limited to respiratory therapy, physical therapy, and others. **Criteria:** Selection will be given to a student in the top third of the academic ranking of the class. Demonstrated financial need as documented on the standard FAFSA report.

Funds Avail.: No specific amount. **Duration:** Annual. **To Apply:** Applicants must submit a completed application form; an official high school transcript; short statement of educational goals; one letter of reference from higher educational institution you are attending; copy of FAFSA Report; essay on why you chose nursing or a health profession as your career path. **Deadline:** March 15. **Contact:** Phone: 208-342-3535; Email: scholarships@idahocf.org.

5678 ▪ Idaho Society of CPA's Scholarships *(Other/Scholarship)*

Purpose: To attract the best and brightest students to the profession pursuing an accounting degree at an Idaho school. **Focus:** Accounting. **Criteria:** Recipients are selected based on GPA or academic standing, individual achievement as evidenced through participation in outside and activities, leadership roles, work experience and sincere desire for further education or training.

Funds Avail.: $1,000. **Duration:** Annual. **Number Awarded:** 3. **To Apply:** Applicants must submit a completed application form along with most recent college or university transcript and copy of most recent grades (if not reflected on transcript); letter of recommendation from an instructor you have taken an accounting course from. **Remarks:** Established in 2003. **Contact:** Fax: 208.344.8984.

5679 ▪ Jim Poore Memorial Scholarship Fund *(Undergraduate/Scholarship)*

Purpose: To encourage and promote the attainment of higher education goals for students who have demonstrated an aptitude for and an interest in writing. **Focus:** Writing. **Criteria:** Preference given to students attending or planning to attend University of Idaho or Boise State University.

Duration: Annual. **To Apply:** Applicants must submit a completed application form along with most recent college or university transcript and copy of most recent grades (if not reflected on transcript); have not attended school recently must submit their last grade transcripts along with a history of employment; extra-curricular and community activities with a signature line at the bottom to certify participation; a 300 word short story, news article, or opinion piece. **Deadline:** march 15. **Contact:** Lisa Bearg; Phone: 208-342-3535; Email: lbearg@idcomfdn.org.

5680 ▪ Roger C. Sathre Memorial Scholarship Fund *(Graduate/Scholarship)*

Purpose: To recognize and encourage outstanding Idaho students pursuing first certificates or degree in professional-technical education or professional-technical teacher education at Idaho Schools. **Focus:** General studies/Field of study not specified. **Criteria:** Recipients are selected based on financial need.

Duration: Annual. **To Apply:** Applicants must submit a completed application form along with most recent college or university transcript and copy of most recent grades (if

not reflected on transcript); two letter of recommendation; FAFSA Student Aid Report. **Deadline:** March 15. **Contact:** Lisa Bearg; Phone: 208-342-3535; Email: lbearg@idcomfdn.org.

5681 ▪ W. L. Shattuck Scholarship *(Undergraduate, Graduate, High School/Scholarship)*

Purpose: To further the education of students at an accredited college, university or technical college. **Focus:** General studies/Field of study not specified. **Qualif.:** Applicants must be high school graduate students of Idaho Falls School District 91 or 93, who are not younger than 16 years of age or older than 26, and accepted and enrolled in an accredited higher education or technical education program. **Criteria:** Recipients are selected based on financial need.

Duration: Annual. **Number Awarded:** 1. **To Apply:** Applicants must submit a completed application form; an official high school transcript; two letters of recommendation; resume and short statement of educational goals; must also submit the names and addresses of higher education or technical education programs to be attended. **Deadline:** March 15. **Contact:** Email:scholarships@idahocf.org.

5682 ▪ Idaho Nursery and Landscape Association (INLA)
PO Box 2065
Idaho Falls, ID 83403
URL: www.inlagrow.org
Social Media: www.facebook.com/inlagrow

5683 ▪ Idaho Nursery and Landscape Association Scholarships *(Undergraduate/Scholarship)*

Purpose: To encourage the study of Horticulture, Floriculture, Plant Pathology, Landscape Design, Turfgrass Management, Botany and allied subjects that pertain to the Green Industry. **Focus:** Horticulture. **Qualif.:** Applicants must be Idaho residents and students in an accredited two or four-year program in the State of Idaho pursuing studies in the Green Industry. **Criteria:** Selection will based on scholastic record, students' ability and sincerity in pursuing employment in the Green Industry.

Funds Avail.: $750. **Duration:** Annual. **Number Awarded:** Varies. **To Apply:** Applicants must submit "one-page, typed" essay stating their reasons for interest in this particular field of endeavor, future plans and goals; must submit a letter of recommendation from someone in the community who will evaluate citizenship; must submit school transcript and letter of recommendation from a professor in the applicant's major field of study. **Deadline:** December 15. **Remarks:** Established in 1986. **Contact:** Ann Bates, Executive Director, PO Box 2065, Idaho Falls, ID, 83403; Email: abates@inlagrow.org.

5684 ▪ Idaho Society of Certified Public Accountants (ISCPA)
1649 W Shoreline Dr., Ste. 202
Boise, ID 83702
Ph: (208)344-6261
Fax: (208)344-8984
Free: 800-388-3635
E-mail: info@idcpa.org
URL: www.idcpa.org
Social Media: www.facebook.com/IDCPA

Awards are arranged alphabetically below their administering organizations

www.linkedin.com/company/idaho-society-of-cpas-iscpa-
twitter.com/ISCPA1
www.youtube.com/user/iscpa100

5685 ■ Idaho Society of CPA's Scholarships *(Other/ Scholarship)*

Purpose: To attract the best and brightest students to the profession pursuing an accounting degree at an Idaho school. **Focus:** Accounting. **Criteria:** Recipients are selected based on GPA or academic standing, individual achievement as evidenced through participation in outside and activities, leadership roles, work experience and sincere desire for further education or training.

Funds Avail.: $1,000. **Duration:** Annual. **Number Awarded:** 3. **To Apply:** Applicants must submit a completed application form along with most recent college or university transcript and copy of most recent grades (if not reflected on transcript); letter of recommendation from an instructor you have taken an accounting course from. **Remarks:** Established in 2003. **Contact:** Fax: 208.344.8984.

5686 ■ Idaho State Board of Education

650 W State St., 3rd Fl.
Boise, ID 83702
Ph: (208)334-2270
Fax: (208)334-2632
E-mail: board@osbe.idaho.gov
URL: boardofed.idaho.gov

5687 ■ Tschudy Family Scholarship *(Undergraduate/ Scholarship)*

Purpose: To encourage educational pursuits among less capable students by providing educational assistance. **Focus:** General studies/Field of study not specified. **Qualif.:** Applicants must be Enroll as a full-time academic student; Be an Idaho resident; Be a graduating Emmett High School senior or have graduated within the last seven years from Emmett High School. **Criteria:** selection will be Emmett High School seniors or recent graduates Requires a 2.6 GPA. selected based on academic merit, integrity and financial need.

Funds Avail.: $500. **Duration:** Annual. **Number Awarded:** 2. **To Apply:** Applicants must complete a general application available on the website. **Deadline:** February 15.

5688 ■ Idaho State Broadcasters Association (ISBA)

c/o Connie Searles, President & Executive Director
1674 W Hill Rd., Ste. 3
Boise, ID 83702-4741
URL: www.idahobroadcasters.org

5689 ■ ISBA Scholarship Program *(Undergraduate/ Scholarship)*

Purpose: To further the interests of broadcasters in Idaho. **Focus:** Broadcasting. **Criteria:** Selection will be based on the committee's criteria.

Funds Avail.: $1,000. **Duration:** Annual. **Number Awarded:** 2. **To Apply:** Applicants must submit a completed application form, letter of recommendation from the GM of an ISBA member station, transcripts and an essay

(one page is sufficient) explaining the applicant's reasons for applying for the scholarship as well as career plans. **Deadline:** March 15. **Contact:** ISBA, 1674 Hill Rd., Ste. 3, Boise, ID, 83702; Email: isba@qwestoffice.net.

5690 ■ IEEE - Photonics Society

445 Hoes Ln.
Piscataway, NJ 08854
URL: photonicssociety.org
Social Media: www.facebook.com/PhotonicsSociety
twitter.com/ieeephotonics

5691 ■ IEEE - Photonics Society Graduate Student Fellowship *(Graduate/Fellowship)*

Purpose: To provide grants to outstanding society student members who are pursuing graduate education within the field of interest. **Focus:** Electronics. **Qualif.:** Applicants must be an active IEEE Photonics Society student member pursuing a graduate education within the Photonics Society field of interest; should normally be in their penultimate year of study at the time of applying.

Funds Avail.: $1,000 each. **Duration:** Annual. **Number Awarded:** Up to 10. **To Apply:** Applicants must submit Cover letter to include name, address, email, IEEE member number, expected date of submission of the thesis, and a listing of any activities related to Photonics Society, along with the names and contact information of two references; one-page CV, including all degrees received and dates; One copy of educational transcripts; A 300-word statement of purpose describing the student's research project and interests; Two reference letters from individuals familiar with the student's research and educational credentials; Note that additional information and submissions over the specified word count will not be forwarded to the evaluating committee. **Deadline:** May 30.

5692 ■ Illinois Association of Chamber of Commerce Executives (IACCE)

PO Box 9436
Springfield, IL 62791-9436
Ph: (217)585-2995
E-mail: lisa@iacce.org
URL: www.iacce.org
Social Media: www.facebook.com/IACCE4me
www.linkedin.com/company/iacce
twitter.com/iacce

5693 ■ Illinois Association of Chamber of Commerce Executives Scholarships *(Professional development/Scholarship)*

Purpose: To provide training that will help the members to continue their education. **Focus:** General studies/Field of study not specified. **Qualif.:** Applicants must be a members of the IACCE. **Criteria:** Selection will be based on the committee's criteria.

Duration: Annual. **To Apply:** Applicants must complete the application form; resume of professional and education experiences; and letter of reference from Chamber's current board president or executives. **Contact:** IACCE - Scholarship Committee, PO Box 9436, Springfield, IL, 62791-9436; Phone: 217-585-2995; Email: lisa@iacce.org.

Awards are arranged alphabetically below their administering organizations

5694 ■ Illinois Business Education Association (IBEA)

3610 Hennepin Dr.
Joliet, IL 60431
Ph: (815)483-4056
E-mail: ibea@ibea.org
URL: www.ibea.org
Social Media: www.facebook.com/IllinoisIBEA
twitter.com/ibeatweets
www.youtube.com/IBEATube1

5695 ■ The Dora J. Beattie IBEA Scholarship
(Undergraduate/Scholarship)

Purpose: To provide financial assistance to qualified students enrolled in an Illinois teacher education program. **Focus:** Business; Computer and information sciences; Education; Marketing and distribution.

Funds Avail.: $5,000. **Duration:** Annual. **Deadline:** May 15.

5696 ■ The Gloria Bousley Graduate Scholarship
(Graduate/Scholarship)

Purpose: To provide financial assistance to qualified students enrolled in an Illinois teacher education program. **Focus:** Business. **Qualif.:** Applicants must be IBEA member who are enrolled in an Illinois college or university business teacher education program or related business area with an emphasis in business education at the graduate level.

Funds Avail.: Up to $2,500. **Duration:** Annual. **Number Awarded:** 1. **Deadline:** May 15.

5697 ■ Illinois City County Management Association (ILCMA)

Center for Governmental Studies
Northern Illinois University
DeKalb, IL 60115
Ph: (815)753-5424
Fax: (815)753-7278
E-mail: info@ilcma.org
URL: www.ilcma.org

5698 ■ James M. Banovetz Illinois Local Government Fellowships *(Graduate, Undergraduate/ Fellowship)*

Purpose: To finance studies leading to a Master's in Public Administration (MPA) or equivalent degree. **Focus:** Public administration. **Qualif.:** Applicants must be graduate students, in good academic standing, at an institution of higher learning in Illinois who are accepted into a degree program that is designed to prepare them to enter the field of city/county management, and have completed at least nine hours of coursework, not including internship or capstone hours, necessary to complete their degree. **Criteria:** Selection will be selected on the basis of their commitment to serve the public through a career in either municipal or county management.

Funds Avail.: $2,000. **Duration:** Annual. **To Apply:** Applicants should submit the complete fellowship application consists of: completed application form; a sealed letter of recommendation from their graduate dean or program director; a sealed recommendation letter from their supervisor; and transcripts of grades from their undergraduate and graduate institutions (photocopies are acceptable). **Deadline:** May 10. **Remarks:** The award was established in honor of James m. Banovetz. **Contact:** Dawn Peters; Phone: 815-753-0923; Email: dpeters@niu.edu.

5699 ■ Illinois Lakes Management Association (ILMA)

PO Box 20655
Springfield, IL 62708
Free: 800-338-6976
URL: www.ilma-lakes.org
Social Media: www.facebook.com/Illinois-Lakes -Management-Association-ILMA-173941715951432

5700 ■ Illinois Lake Management Association Undergraduate/Graduate Scholarships *(Graduate, Undergraduate/Scholarship)*

Purpose: To financially assist students who want to pursue their studies in lake management and watershed ecosystem. **Focus:** Water resources. **Criteria:** Applicants will be selected based on the primary selection criteria: (1) academic achievements; (2) major field of study; (3) statement of career goals and student special interest.

Funds Avail.: $1,000. **Duration:** Annual. **To Apply:** Applicants must complete the application form available on the website; must attach 2 letter of recommendation; must provide official transcripts; must include a project description, budget, and description of how the scholarship money will be spent. **Deadline:** December 31. **Contact:** Illinois Lake Management Association, PO Box 20655, Springfield, IL, 62708.

5701 ■ Robert Esser Student Achievement Scholarship *(Graduate, Undergraduate/Scholarship)*

Purpose: To financially assist students who want to pursue their studies in lake management and watershed ecosystem. **Focus:** Water resources. **Criteria:** Selection will be based on the Scholarship Committee; will consider academic achievement, major field of study, statement of career goals and student special interests.

Funds Avail.: $500. **Duration:** Annual. **Number Awarded:** 1. **Deadline:** December 31. **Contact:** Illinois Lake Management Association, PO Box 20655, Springfield, IL, 62708; Email:ilma@ilma-lakes.org.

5702 ■ Illinois Landscape Contractors Association (ILCA)

2625 Butterfield Rd., Ste. 104S
Oak Brook, IL 60523-1234
Ph: (630)472-2851
Fax: (630)472-3150
E-mail: information@ilca.net
URL: www.ilca.net
Social Media: www.facebook.com/ illinoislandscapecontractorsassociation
www.instagram.com/ilcalandscape
twitter.com/ILCAlandscape

5703 ■ Illinois Landscape Contractors Association Scholarships *(Undergraduate/Scholarship)*

Purpose: To support the education of students pursuing a career in horticulture. **Focus:** Horticulture.

Funds Avail.: One $10,000; two $5,000; one $2,500. **To Apply:** Applicants must submit a completed application

Awards are arranged alphabetically below their administering organizations

form; a letter describing their goals and aspirations in the field of horticulture, a transcript of records; must attach evaluation/letters from employers, internships, work study or any horticulture/landscape experience. **Deadline:** March 31.

5704 ◼ Illinois Section of the American Water Works Association (ISAWWA)

545 S Randall Rd.
Saint Charles, IL 60174
Ph: (866)521-3595
Free: 866-521-3595
URL: www.isawwa.org
Social Media: www.facebook.com/illinoisawwa
twitter.com/isawwa

5705 ◼ JDRF Outreach Scholarship *(Undergraduate, Master's, Doctorate/Scholarship)*

Purpose: To support the general public on the essential functions and importance of the water industry, the water cycle and water treatment, and career paths in the water industry. **Focus:** Water resources; Water supply industry. **Qualif.:** Applicants must be enrolled or accepted into a water-related secondary, continuing-education, or enrichment program for the academic year. Secondary education includes water system operator training programs, water-related technical school, community college, four-year college, Master's and Doctoral programs. **Criteria:** Selection will be based on the committee's criteria.

Funds Avail.: $5,000. **Duration:** Annual. **To Apply:** Applicants may contact the AWWA Illinois section for the application process and other information. **Deadline:** January 31. **Contact:** Email: laurie@isawwa.org; Phone; 866-521-3595, ext. 1.

5706 ◼ Illinois Society of Professional Engineers (ISPE)

100 E Washington St.
Springfield, IL 62701
Ph: (217)544-7424
Fax: (217)528-6545
E-mail: info@illinoisengineer.com
URL: www.illinoisengineer.com
Social Media: www.facebook.com/IllinoisEngineer
www.linkedin.com/company/illinois-society-of-professional
  -engineers?trk=biz-companies-cym
twitter.com/ilengineers

5707 ◼ ISPE Foundation Scholarship *(Undergraduate/Scholarship)*

Purpose: To provide financial assistance for the education of students who are sons or daughters of ISPE members. **Focus:** Engineering. **Qualif.:** Applicants must be attending an Illinois university; enrolled in an engineering program accredited by the Accreditation Board of Engineering and Technology (ABET); must have at least junior standing; must have a B average or better in courses which are credited toward the engineering degree; must show evidence of financial need. **Criteria:** Recipients are judged based on financial need, extracurricular activities, interest in engineering and the applicants' essays.

Funds Avail.: $1,000. **Duration:** Annual. **To Apply:** Applicants must submit official transcripts of all college and

university work; two letters of reference from the department chair or department faculty member and from past employer or other character reference; and typewritten essay in 200 words or less discussing why they want to become a professional engineer. **Deadline:** April 1. **Contact:** ISPE Foundation, Inc, 100 East Washington St., Springfield, IL, 62701; Email: Info@IllinoisEngineer.com.

5708 ◼ Illinois State Dental Society (ISDS)

1010 S 2nd St.
Springfield, IL 62704-3005
Ph: (217)525-1406
Fax: (217)525-8872
E-mail: info@isds.org
URL: www.isds.org
Social Media: www.facebook.com/
  IllinoisStateDentalSociety
www.linkedin.com/company/illinois-state-dental-society
twitter.com/IllinoisDental

5709 ◼ Paul W. Clopper Scholarship Grant for Junior Dental Students *(Undergraduate/Scholarship)*

Purpose: To provide support to qualified dental students who are succeeding academically and who have committed themselves to community involvement. **Focus:** Dental laboratory technology. **Qualif.:** Applicants must be incoming junior students in the fall semester of dental school. **Criteria:** Selection will be based on the committee's criteria.

Funds Avail.: $3,000. **Duration:** Annual. **Number Awarded:** 3. **To Apply:** Applicants must complete and submit the application form available at the website.

5710 ◼ Illinois Student Assistance Commission (ISAC)

1755 Lake Cook Rd.
Deerfield, IL 60015-5209
Fax: (847)831-8549
Free: 800-899-4722
E-mail: isac.studentservices@illinois.gov
URL: www.isac.org
Social Media: www.facebook.com/ILStudentAssistance
www.instagram.com/isacfinaid
www.linkedin.com/company/state-of-illinois---illinois-student
  -assistance-commission
twitter.com/ISACFinAid
www.youtube.com/user/ISACvid

5711 ◼ Allied Health Care Professional Scholarship *(Undergraduate/Scholarship)*

Purpose: To provide Award to students studying to be nurse practitioners, physician assistants, and certified nurse midwives. **Focus:** Health sciences; Midwifery; Nursing. **Qualif.:** Applicant must be a nurse practitioner, physician assistant or certified nurse midwives; recipients must fulfill an obligation to practice full time in a designated shortage area as an allied health care professional in Illinois for one year for each year of scholarship funding received. **Criteria:** Previous experience with medically under served populations; greatest financial need; academic capabilities.

Funds Avail.: $7,500. **Duration:** Up to two years. **To Apply:** Submit completed application. **Deadline:** June 30. **Contact:** Bronwyn Jones-Leach; Phone: 217-782-1624.

Awards are arranged alphabetically below their administering organizations

5712 ■ Illinois Special Education Teacher Tuition Waiver Scholarship (SETTW) *(Undergraduate/Scholarship)*

Purpose: To provide support to teacher or an academically talented student pursuing a career in special education, you may be eligible for the Illinois Special Education Teacher Tuition Waiver Program. **Focus:** Education, Special. **Qualif.:** Applicants must be a U.S. citizen or an eligible non-citizen; must be an Illinois resident; must have graduated from an approved high school in the academic year in the upper half of their graduating class according to performance-based academic data provided by the high school; or graduated from an approved high school prior to the academic year in which the award is made; must hold a valid teaching certificate that is not in the discipline of special education; must be enrolled or accepted for enrollment at one of the eligible public four-year colleges in Illinois as an undergraduate or graduate student seeking initial certification in any area of special education; must be enrolled in a program of special education within ten days after the beginning of the term for which the waiver was initially awarded; must comply with federal Selective Service registration requirements. **Criteria:** Selection will be based on the committee's criteria.

Funds Avail.: No specific amount. **Duration:** Annual. **To Apply:** Applicants must complete ISAC application for the Illinois SETTW Program. **Contact:** ISAC, Dept. D, 1755 Lake Cook Rd., Deerfield, IL, 60015-5209; Fax: 847-831-8549; E-mail: isac.studentservices@illinois.gov.

5713 ■ Illinois Student Assistance Commission Medical Student Scholarship *(Undergraduate/Scholarship)*

Purpose: To increase the number of primary care physicians practicing in areas of Illinois that have an insufficient number of physicians in the specialties of family practice, general internal medicine, general pediatrics and obstetrics/gynecology. **Focus:** Medical technology; Medicine, Osteopathic. **Qualif.:** Applicants must be enrolled in an approved allopathic or osteopathic medical school in Illinois; must agree to work in an identified physician-shortage area in Illinois; must be Illinois residents. **Criteria:** Demonstrate financial need and good academic standing.

Funds Avail.: $950 per month. **Duration:** Annual. **To Apply:** Details available online at: www.dph.illinois.gov/topics-services/life-stages-populations/rural-underserved-populations/scholarship/medical-student. **Deadline:** May 15. **Contact:** Phone: Center for Rural Health, 217-782-1624.

5714 ■ Illinois Student Assistance Commission Nursing Education Scholarship *(Undergraduate, Graduate, College/Scholarship)*

Purpose: To provide financial support to a qualified individual intending to pursue a career in professional or practical nursing education in Illinois. **Focus:** Nursing. **Qualif.:** Applicant must be a U.S citizen or an eligible non-citizen; must be an Illinois resident; be enrolled, or accepted for enrollment, on at least a half-time basis in an approved program of practical nursing education at an eligible Illinois college; must have a satisfactory academic progress as determined by the college; agree to the nurse employment or nurse educator employment obligation. **Criteria:** Financial need.

Funds Avail.: No specific amount. **Duration:** Annual. **To Apply:** Applicants must submit a completed application, a copy of your enrollment or acceptance letter to an approved nursing program or official transcripts; a copy of driver's license, birth certificate, or documentation you are a naturalized citizen, or documentation you are a lawful permanent resident of the U.S.; current Student Aid Report (SAR); copy of your current Illinois nursing license; signed Confirmation and Release form. **Deadline:** April 30. **Contact:** E-mail: dph.nesp@illinois.gov; Phone: 217-782-1624; URL: www.isac.org/students/during-college/types-of-financial-aid/scholarships/nursing-education-scholarship-program.html.

5715 ■ Minority Teachers of Illinois Scholarship (MTI) *(Undergraduate/Scholarship)*

Purpose: To provide financial support to the minority individuals intending to pursue their careers as a preschool, elementary or secondary school teacher. **Focus:** Teaching. **Qualif.:** Applicants must be a U.S citizen or an eligible non citizen; must be a resident of Illinois; must be either a African American/Black, Hispanic American, Asian American or of Native American origin; must be a high school graduate, or hold a General Educational Development certificate; must be enrolled at least on a part-time basis as an undergraduate or graduate student; must be enrolled or accepted for enrollment at a qualified Illinois institution of higher education in a course of study which, upon completion, qualifies to be certified as a preschool, elementary or secondary school teacher by the Illinois State Board of Education, including alternative teacher certification; must maintain a cumulative grade point average of 2.5 on a 4.0 scale; must maintain a satisfactory academic progress as determined by the college; must comply with federal Selective Service registration requirements. **Criteria:** Selection will be based on the committee's criteria.

Funds Avail.: No specific amount. **Duration:** Annual. **Number Awarded:** Varies. **To Apply:** Applicants must submit the complete application form for the Teacher Education Scholarship Programs (available online); must sign the application's Teaching Agreement or Promissory Note promising to fulfill the teaching commitment or repay funds received plus interest. **Deadline:** March 1. **Contact:** ISAC, Dept. D, 1755 Lake Cook Rd., Deerfield, IL, 60015-5209; Fax: 847-831-8549; E-mail: isac.studentservices@illinois.gov.

5716 ■ Imagine America Foundation (IAF)
14200 Park Meadow Dr., Ste. 117s
Chantilly, VA 20151
Ph: (571)267-3010
URL: www.imagine-america.org
Social Media: www.facebook.com/Imagine-America-Foundation-118864293578
www.linkedin.com/company/imagine-america-foundation
twitter.com/iafoundation

5717 ■ Imagine America College Scholarships for High School Students *(Undergraduate/Scholarship)*

Purpose: To support students to pursue postsecondary career education at hundreds of career schools across the United States. **Focus:** General studies/Field of study not specified. **Criteria:** Recipients are selected based on financial need.

Funds Avail.: $1,000. **Duration:** Annual.

Awards are arranged alphabetically below their administering organizations

5718 ■ Imagine America Military Awards Program
(Undergraduate/Scholarship)

Purpose: To help military servicepersons receive career education and make the transition from military to civilian life. **Focus:** General studies/Field of study not specified. **Funds Avail.:** $1,000.

5719 ■ Imagine America Scholarships for Adults
(Undergraduate/Scholarship)

Purpose: To help non-traditional students to pursue a career education at hundreds of career schools across the United States. **Focus:** General studies/Field of study not specified. **Funds Avail.:** $1,000.

5720 ■ Immerse Education
15 19 Bakers Row
London EC1R 3DG, United Kingdom
Ph: 44 20 8123 6988
URL: www.immerse.education
Social Media: www.facebook.com/immerseedu
www.instagram.com/immerseeducation
twitter.com/immerse_edu

5721 ■ Immerse Education University Scholarship
(Undergraduate, University, College/Scholarship)

Purpose: To engage and secure the future of young professionals and provide opportunities for all students in all fields of academia. **Focus:** General studies/Field of study not specified. **Qualif.:** Applicant must be enrolling as a full-time student at an accredited college or university for completion of an undergraduate degree. Students of all nationalities are welcome to apply. **Criteria:** Selection is based on the submitted essay.

Funds Avail.: $1,000 (2); $500 (1). **Duration:** Annual. **Number Awarded:** 3. **To Apply:** Applicant must write a 1,000-word essay on a given prompt; complete online application, supply verification of enrollment at a college or university. **Deadline:** May 1. **Contact:** E-mail: enquiries@immerse.education; URL: www.immerse.education/usa-university-scholarships/.

5722 ■ Immigration and Ethnic History Society (IEHS)
History Dept.
Marquette University
PO Box 1881
Milwaukee, WI 53201-1881
URL: www.iehs.org
Social Media: www.facebook.com/IEHSPage
twitter.com/IEHS1965

5723 ■ John Higham Research Fellowship
(Postdoctorate/Fellowship)

Purpose: To provide travel grants to graduate students to be used toward costs of attending the OAH/IEHS Annual Meeting. **Focus:** History, American; Immigration. **Qualif.:** Applicants must be graduate students writing doctoral dissertations for a Ph.D. in American history. **Criteria:** Selection will be based on the committee's criteria.

Funds Avail.: $1,000 to $1,500. **Duration:** Annual. **Number Awarded:** 3. **To Apply:** Applicants should submit

project proposal of no more than 1, 000 words describing the research project and detailing how the funds will be used; updated curriculum vitae with a list of the names and addresses of references; two signed letters of recommendation on official letterhead submitted independently by referees. **Deadline:** December 1. **Remarks:** The grants are given in memory of John Higham (1920-2003), past president of the OAH and an important figure in immigration, ethnic, and intellectual history. **Contact:** Julian Lim, Arizona State University, Committee Chair jlim42@asu.edu.

5724 ■ ImmunoGen+ Inc.
1100 Dennison Ave.
Columbus, OH 43201
Ph: (614)884-4400
Fax: (614)884-4484
E-mail: cgehring@lifecarealliance.org
URL: www.lifecarealliance.org/programs/coda
Social Media: www.facebook.com/diabetesohio
www.instagram.com/lifecarealliance/
www.linkedin.com/company/lifecare-alliance/
twitter.com/diabetesohio

5725 ■ The Youth Scholarship Program
(Undergraduate/Scholarship)

Purpose: To provide scholarships to those students with diabetes. **Focus:** Diabetes. **Qualif.:** Applicants must be full-time undergraduate students with diabetes in the Central Ohio area; must demonstrate exemplary adjustment to living with diabetes; show financial need; and demonstrate involvement in extracurricular activities which help others and foster personal growth. **Criteria:** Selection will be based on the committee's criteria.

Funds Avail.: No specific amount. **Duration:** Annual. **To Apply:** Applicants must submit a completed application form.

5726 ■ Imprex
2916 Malmo Rd.
Arlington Heights, IL 60004
Ph: (847)364-4930
Fax: (847)364-4963
E-mail: sales@imprex.net
URL: www.imprex.net

5727 ■ Imprex Scholarship *(College, University/Scholarship)*

Purpose: To help students afford a college degree. **Focus:** General studies/Field of study not specified. **Qualif.:** Applicant must be a U.S. citizen pursuing an undergraduate degree at a college or university in the United States. **Criteria:** Selection will be based on the best essay submitted.

Funds Avail.: $1,000 (1); $250 (2). **Duration:** Annual. **Number Awarded:** 3. **To Apply:** Applicant must write an essay and fill out the application at www.imprex.net/scholarship. **Deadline:** December 1.

5728 ■ In-Plant Printing and Mailing Association (IPMA)
103 North Jefferson St.
Kearney, MO 64060

Awards are arranged alphabetically below their administering organizations

Ph: (816)919-1691
E-mail: ipmainfo@ipma.org
URL: www.ipma.org
Social Media: www.facebook.com/ipma.headquarters
www.instagram.com/ipmahq
www.linkedin.com/company/in-plant-printing-and-mailing
 -association-ipma-
twitter.com/ipmahq
www.youtube.com/channel/UCtVGu4PAx6hYmWebcf3Ia0w

5729 ■ James M. Brahney Scholarship *(Professional development/Scholarship)*

Purpose: To promote education in the field of in-house print, mail, and management. **Focus:** Art; Communications. **Qualif.:** Applicant must be related to, or a member in good standing with IPMA; any IPMA member, a child of a member, or a grandchild of a member, is eligible; family members for post-secondary funding must be high school graduates, with a cumulative GPA of 3.0 or higher (4.0 scale); applicants must be accepted to a post-secondary institution and pursuing a degree or in a training program related to the graphic arts, printing, design or mailing; examples might include vocational printing and design, graphic arts management, graphic design, web and app development, marketing, management or industrial education, to name a few. **Criteria:** Selection will be based on IPMA members in good standing applying for Conference assistance can only be used to supplement attendance to the IPMA Annual Conference.

Funds Avail.: $1,000. **Duration:** Annual. **To Apply:** Applicants must submit a letter of application, official transcripts (High School or College), completed application form and 3 letters of reference. **Deadline:** March 31. **Remarks:** The scholarship is presented in memory of James M. Brahney, a founder of IPMA and its first international president. **Contact:** IPMA Awards Program, Brahney Scholarship, 103 N Jefferson St., Kearney, MO, 64060; Phone: 816-919-1691.

5730 ■ Incorporated Society of Irish American Lawyers (ISIAL)

c/o Jennifer A. Cupples, President
ALTIOR LAW, 401 S Old Woodward, Ste. 460
Birmingham, MI 48009
Ph: (248)594-5252
E-mail: president@irish-lawyers.org
URL: www.irish-lawyers.org

5731 ■ Thomas P. Thornton Scholarship *(Undergraduate, Graduate/Scholarship)*

Purpose: To support law school students of Irish descent. **Focus:** Law. **Qualif.:** Applicants must be law students with a minimum 2.5 GPA and Irish ancestry; must have financial need. **Criteria:** Selection will be based on the committee's criteria.

Funds Avail.: $2,000. **Duration:** Annual. **Number Awarded:** 1. **To Apply:** Applicants must submit their resume and a letter stating why they should be awarded the scholarship; must also include information pertaining to their Irish heritage and financial need, and must attach a copy of transcript of grades from the latest semester. Application and supporting documents should be mailed to the contact. **Contact:** Frances Murphy, 18301 E. 8 Mile Road, Suite 100, Eastpointe, MI 48201-3326; E-mail: fran@franmurphylaw.com.

5732 ■ Independent Accountants Association of Illinois (IAAI)

PO Box 9140
Springfield, IL 62791-9140
Free: 800-313-2274
E-mail: illinoisaccountants@gmail.com
URL: www.illinoisaccountants.com
Social Media: www.facebook.com/IAAI-Independent
 -Accountants-Association-of-Illinois-523188227834525
twitter.com/IL_Accountants

5733 ■ IAAI Scholarship Foundation Accounting Scholarships *(Undergraduate/Scholarship)*

Purpose: To support deserving college students who have indicated a firm intention of pursuing their accounting studies at a successful conclusion and plan to enter the accounting profession. **Focus:** Accounting. **Qualif.:** Applicants must be residential college students interested in pursuing a career in the field of accounting throughout the State of Illinois and attending an Illinois college, community college, or university.

Funds Avail.: $1,000. **Duration:** Annual. **Number Awarded:** 2. **To Apply:** Applicants should complete the scholarship application. Submit official transcripts from colleges attended, along with a letter of recommendation from an accounting professor or head of the accounting department. Documents may be submitted together or separately. **Deadline:** June 30. **Contact:** URL: www.illinoisaccountants.com/resources/scholarship.

5734 ■ Independent Lubricant Manufacturers Association (ILMA)

675 N. Washington St., Ste 275
Alexandria, VA 22314
Ph: (703)684-5574
Fax: (703)350-4919
E-mail: ilma@ilma.org
URL: www.ilma.org
Social Media: www.facebook.com/ILMAConnects
www.linkedin.com/company/independent-lubricant
 -manufacturers-association-ilma-
twitter.com/ILMAtweets
www.youtube.com/channel/UCOqmIJwTCY
 -h7qgNXK01hSQ

5735 ■ ILMA foundation Scholarship Program *(Undergraduate/Scholarship)*

Purpose: To provide financial assistance to deserving students. **Focus:** General studies/Field of study not specified. **Qualif.:** Applicants must be a citizen in a North American country; must attend or be enrolled in a college or university in North America; must be registered as an undergraduate full-time student (12 credit hours or more per semester, 9 credit hours per trimester or more); must have a minimum of 3.0 cumulative GPA. **Criteria:** Selection of applicants will be based on financial need and GPA. Preference will be given to those with major in Math, Science or Engineering; relationship to ILMA member company.

Funds Avail.: $3,000 each. **Duration:** Four years. **To Apply:** Applicants must have a letter of recommendation from teacher or advisor; must submit an essay on how the scholarship will benefit future education endeavors; and any special circumstances i.e., applicant is the first child to

Awards are arranged alphabetically below their administering organizations

go to college, comes from a single parent household, or need-based financial assistance. **Deadline:** June 30.

5736 ■ Independent Order of Foresters

789 Don Mills Rd.
Toronto, ON, Canada M3C 1T9
URL: my.foresters.com
Social Media: www.facebook.com/Foresters

5737 ■ Foresters Competitive Scholarship

*(Undergraduate, Vocational/Occupational, Four Year College, Two Year College/Scholarship)***Focus:** General studies/Field of study not specified. **Qualif.:** Applicants must be enrolling in a minimum two-year, full-time undergraduate program of study at an eligible institution in the United States or Canada in Fall 2019; must have a minimum GPA of 2.8 or 70%.

Funds Avail.: $2,000 each. **Duration:** Annual. **Number Awarded:** up to 250. **To Apply:** Applicants must have the a) Community Service, Recommendation Letter and Essay: 65% b) Grades: 35%. **Deadline:** February 27. **Contact:** Foresters Member Services; Phone: 800-444-3043; E-mail: myforesters@foresters.com; ISTS; E-mail: foresters@applyISTS.com; Phone: 866-258-0626.

5738 ■ Independent Professional Seed Association (IPSA)

12 W Dickson Str. Ste. 1488
Fayetteville, AR 72701
Free: 888-888-5058
URL: ipseed.org
Social Media: www.facebook.com/ipsa.seed
www.instagram.com/independent_seeds
www.linkedin.com/company/independent-professional-seed
twitter.com/IndieProSeed

5739 ■ Myron "Ted" Asplin Foundation Scholarships

(Professional development/Scholarship)

Purpose: To support and encourage the agriculture by supporting and encouraging the education of future ag professionals. **Focus:** Agricultural sciences. **Qualif.:** Applicants must be high school seniors as well as active college students; must be majoring in an Agriculture related degree to be considered. **Criteria:** Selection will be based on a combination of academic achievement, community and agricultural involvement. All applications will be reviewed by the IPSA Scholarship Awards Committee and the Board of Directors of the Independent Professional Seed Association.

Funds Avail.: $2,000. **Duration:** Annual. **To Apply:** Applicants should submit complete application online, the most recent student transcripts and 2 letters of recommendation must be uploaded for each applicant. PDF is the preferred version. must be completed in full including complete contact information with name, address, email, cell phone. Incomplete applications will be disregarded. **Deadline:** April 30. **Remarks:** The award was established in memory of Myron "Ted" Asplin. **Contact:** URL: ipseed.org/ipsa-affairs/scholarships; E-mail: Todd Martin, todd@ipseed.org; or Julianne Thompson, julianne@ipseed.org.

5740 ■ Independent Professional Seed Association Student Recognition Awards *(Undergraduate/Scholarship)*

Purpose: To promote education in the field of agriculture. **Focus:** Agriculture, Economic aspects. **Qualif.:** Applicants must be high school seniors as well as active college students; must be majoring in an Agriculture related degree to be considered. **Criteria:** Selection will be science related fields (Agronomy, Crop, Soil, Engineering), and Business fields (Agriculture Business, Economics, Marketing); preference will be given to active college students pursuing ag-related fields.

Funds Avail.: $2,000. **Duration:** Annual. **To Apply:** Applicants should submit complete application in full; complete contact information is required for consideration; save document using their name as the document name. Make sure to include; completed application; most recent student transcript; two reference letters with contact information (phone number and email). **Deadline:** March 31. **Remarks:** The Award was created in 1997 with donations from Independent Corn Breeders Association. Established in 1997. **Contact:** IPSA, P.O. Box 241312, Omaha, NE 68124-5312; Ph. 402-991-3550 Fax: 877-415-1306 info@independentseeds.com.

5741 ■ Independent University Alumni Association at Lowell

PO Box 242
Lowell, MA 01853-0242
Ph: (978)934-6530
URL: iuaal.wordpress.com

5742 ■ Gehring Memorial Foundation Scholarships
(Graduate, Undergraduate/Scholarship)

Purpose: To support graduate and undergraduate students who are pursuing education at Lowell. **Focus:** General studies/Field of study not specified. **Qualif.:** Applicants must be a Lowell graduate or undergraduate student. **Criteria:** Selection is based on scholarship record, personality, and ability in leadership, extracurricular activities, and financial need.

Funds Avail.: No specific amount. **To Apply:** Applicants must submit a completed application form together with the required supporting materials.

5743 ■ Barnett D. Gordon Scholarships *(Graduate, Undergraduate/Scholarship)*

Purpose: To support graduate and undergraduate students who are pursuing education at Lowell. **Focus:** General studies/Field of study not specified. **Qualif.:** Applicant must be a Lowell graduate or undergraduate student. **Criteria:** Selection is based on the application.

To Apply: Applicants must submit a completed application form together with the required supporting materials.

5744 ■ Independent University Alumni Association Scholarships *(Graduate, Undergraduate/Scholarship)*

Purpose: To support graduate and undergraduate students who are pursuing education at Lowell. **Focus:** General studies/Field of study not specified. **Qualif.:** Applicant must be a member of an underrepresented group (American Indian/Native, African American/Black, Hispanic American/Latino); a U.S. citizen at the time of application; must sign up to take the GRE at the time of application; be admitted into a GEM member university graduate program before the Fellowship is awarded; a senior, masters student or graduate of an engineering or applied science program accredited by the Accreditation Board for Engineering and Technology (ABET) at the time of application; have a cumulative GPA of 3.0/4.0; and must contractually agree to

Awards are arranged alphabetically below their administering organizations

intern with a GEM employer member at least once early on or before the start of the PhD program. **Criteria:** Selection is based on the application.

To Apply: Applicants must submit a completed application form together with the required supporting materials. **Contact:** Independent University Alumni Association at Lowell, at the above address.

5745 ■ Joseph Kaplan Fund *(Graduate, Undergraduate/Scholarship)*

Purpose: To support graduate and undergraduate students who are pursuing education at Lowell. **Focus:** General studies/Field of study not specified. **Qualif.:** Applicant must be a graduate in physics or equivalent major from an accredited university or college in North America; have an undergraduate GPA of greater than 3.5. **Criteria:** Selection is based on the application.

To Apply: Applicants must submit a completed application form together with the required supporting materials.

5746 ■ Jacob Ziskind Memorial Fund for Upperclassmen *(Graduate, Undergraduate/Scholarship)*

Purpose: To support graduate and undergraduate students who are pursuing education at Lowell. **Focus:** General studies/Field of study not specified. **Qualif.:** Applicants must be a Lowell graduate or undergraduate upperclassman student. **Criteria:** Selection is based on the application.

Funds Avail.: No specific amount. **To Apply:** Applicants must submit a completed application form together with the required supporting materials. **Contact:** Independent University Alumni Association at Lowell, at the above address.

5747 ■ Indiana Bar Foundation (IBF)
615 N. Alabama St., Ste. 426
Indianapolis, IN 46204
Ph: (317)269-2415
Fax: (317)536-2271
E-mail: info@inbf.org
URL: inbf.org
Social Media: www.facebook.com/INBarFoundation
www.linkedin.com/company/indiana-bar-foundation
twitter.com/INBarFoundation
www.youtube.com/channel/UC6jTd5TlttVbkP6QMo2l2DQ

5748 ■ Joseph T. Helling Scholarship Fund
(Undergraduate/Scholarship)

Purpose: To provide scholarships to young attorneys in Indiana in order to give them the opportunity to participate in the Indiana State Bar Association's annual meeting. **Focus:** Law. **Qualif.:** Applicant/nominee must be actively practicing law in Indiana, admitted to the practice of law less than five years and must also be a member of the Indiana State Bar Association.

Funds Avail.: No specific amount. **Duration:** Annual. **Number Awarded:** 1. **To Apply:** Applicants must submit a completed application/nomination form. Applicants must also submit a concise typewritten paragraph describing the accomplishments, contributions and/or initiatives of the nominee in the areas addressed by the award criteria indicating the significance of their impact. **Deadline:** July 1. **Remarks:** Established by Nancy J. Gargula, Cynthia L. Chandler, and Douglas J. Helling in honor of their father,

Joseph T. Helling. **Contact:** Director of Development & Communications; Phone: 317-269-7864; E-mail: tbrowning@inbf.org.

5749 ■ Indiana Broadcasters Association (IBA)
PO Box 902
Carmel, IN 46082
Fax: (317)218-4548
E-mail: iba@indianabroadcasters.org
URL: www.indianabroadcasters.org

5750 ■ Indiana Broadcasters Association College Scholarship Program *(Undergraduate/Scholarship)*

Purpose: To support worthy students who are pursuing a degree in the field of broadcasting. **Focus:** Broadcasting. **Qualif.:** Applicants must have an overall 3.0 GPA on a 4.0 scale; must be a current, full-time college student with plans to continue as a full-time college student in the 2020 fall semester. **Criteria:** Recipients are selected based on academic performance.

Funds Avail.: No specific amount. **Duration:** Annual. **Deadline:** February 15. **Contact:** Indiana Broadcasters Association P.O. Box 902 Carmel, IN 46032-or-emailed from the college/university to sam@indianabroadcasters.org.

5751 ■ Indiana FFA Association
1 N Capital, Ste. 600
Indianapolis, IN 46204
Ph: (317)407-7926
URL: inffa.org/association
Social Media: twitter.com/IndianaFFA

5752 ■ Indiana FFA Association State Fair Scholarship *(Undergraduate/Scholarship)*

Purpose: To support individuals who benefited themselves and the Indiana FFA by contributing to the Indiana FFA Pavilion and its activities at the State Fair. **Focus:** General studies/Field of study not specified. **Qualif.:** Applicants must be active FFA members.

Funds Avail.: $500. **Duration:** Annual. **To Apply:** Applicants must complete and submit the application form available online and must provide some required materials. **Deadline:** May 15.

5753 ■ Indiana Library Federation (ILF)
941 E 86th St., Ste. 260
Indianapolis, IN 46240
Ph: (317)257-2040
E-mail: askus@ilfonline.org
URL: www.ilfonline.org

5754 ■ Esther Schlundt Memorial Scholarship Fund
(Graduate, Undergraduate/Scholarship)

Purpose: To foster the professional growth of its members and the promotion of all libraries in Indiana. **Focus:** Library and archival sciences. **Qualif.:** Applicants must be entering or currently enrolled in an ALA-accredited graduate degree program in library and information science; or must be entering or currently enrolled in an Indiana State Library-approved library certification program. **Criteria:** Recipients are selected based on academic performance, Interest in librarianship as a profession, Personality and Character,

Awards are arranged alphabetically below their administering organizations

Economic need, References and/or a personal interview. **Funds Avail.:** $750; $1,000. **To Apply:** Applicants must submit three letters of recommendation from which one must come from a librarian, short essay, personal interview video. Masters candidates must submit (a) transcript or copy of official grade report for any library science courses already completed, (b) transcripts of all undergraduate education and (c) transcripts from other graduate work may be included, but not required. Public library certification candidates must submit (a) a copy of the approved public library certification program, (b) transcripts from undergraduate education and/or high school and (c) transcript or copy of official grade report for any course already taken toward library certification. School library candidates must submit (a) transcript or copy of official grade report for any library science courses already completed, (b) transcripts of all undergraduate or graduate work completed. Library assistant candidates must submit (a) transcript or copy of official grade report for any library science courses already completed, including completion of at least 20 of the 60 required credits, (b) transcripts of all undergraduate or graduate work completed, (c) must demonstrate a C or better GPA at the end of their most recent semester. **Deadline:** June 30.

5755 ■ Sue Marsh Weller Memorial Scholarship Fund *(Graduate/Scholarship)*

Purpose: To provide financial assistance to the needs of the members for their professional growth. **Focus:** Library and archival sciences. **Qualif.:** Applicants must be entering or currently enrolled in an ALA-accredited program of graduate study specializing in children librarianship; must be legal residents of Indiana; must accept employment in an Indiana library within one year after completing their library education; and must continue to work in an Indiana library for at least one year after accepting employment. If recipients are unable to comply with these conditions, scholarship must be repaid as a loan. **Criteria:** Recipients are selected based on interest in librarianship as a profession; personality and character; academic record; economic need; and references and/or a personal interview.

Funds Avail.: Up to $1,000. **To Apply:** Applicants must submit three letters of recommendation from which one must come from a librarian, short essay, personal interview video. Masters candidates must submit (a) transcript or copy of official grade report for any library science courses already completed, (b) transcripts of all undergraduate education and (c) transcripts from other graduate work may be included, but not required. Public library certification candidates must submit (a) a copy of the approved public library certification program, (b) transcripts from undergraduate education and/or high school and (c) transcript or copy of official grade report for any course already taken toward library certification. School library candidates must submit (a) transcript or copy of official grade report for any library science courses already completed, (b) transcripts of all undergraduate or graduate work completed. Library assistant candidates must submit (a) transcript or copy of official grade report for any library science courses already completed, including completion of at least 20 of the 60 required credits, (b) transcripts of all undergraduate or graduate work completed, (c) must demonstrate a C or better GPA at the end of their most recent semester. **Deadline:** June 30.

5756 ■ Indiana State University (ISU)
200 N 7th St.
Terre Haute, IN 47809-1902

Free: 800-468-6478
E-mail: admissions@indstate.edu
URL: www.indstate.edu
Social Media: www.facebook.com/IndianaState
www.instagram.com/indianastateuniversity
www.linkedin.com/school/indiana-state-university
twitter.com/indianastate
www.youtube.com/user/IndianaStateU

5757 ■ Indiana State University Academic Excellence Scholarship *(Undergraduate/Scholarship)*

Purpose: To support incoming ISU students in their pursuit of higher education. **Focus:** General studies/Field of study not specified. **Qualif.:** Applicants must have a cumulative grade point average of at least 3.8 on a 4.0 scale; a 1270 SAT (Evidence-Based Reading and Writing and Math) or 27 ACT (composite); ranking in the top 10% of the senior class. **Criteria:** Selection will be based on the committee's criteria.

Funds Avail.: $3,000 a year. **Duration:** up to three years. **Deadline:** December 1 (fall); December 15 (spring). **Contact:** University Scholarship Office, 318 N Sixth St., Terre Haute, In, 47809; Phone: 800-468-6478; Email: scholarships@indstate.edu.

5758 ■ Indiana State University Incentive Scholarship *(Undergraduate/Scholarship)*

Purpose: To support incoming ISU students in their pursuit of higher education. **Focus:** General studies/Field of study not specified. **Qualif.:** Applicants must be residents outside Indiana and not qualify for a reduced tuition rate offered through the Illinois Student Scholarship, Kentucky Student Scholarship, Midwest Consortium Scholarship, or Ohio Student Scholarship; they also must have a cumulative high school grade point average of at least 3.0 on a 4.0 scale and earn a college-prep diploma.

Funds Avail.: $5,000 a year. **Duration:** Annual; up to three years. **Number Awarded:** Varies. **Contact:** University Scholarship Office, 318 N Sixth St., Terre Haute, In, 47809; Phone: 800-468-6478; Email: scholarships@indstate.edu.

5759 ■ Indiana State University President's Scholarships *(Undergraduate/Scholarship)*

Purpose: To support incoming ISU students in their pursuit of higher education. **Focus:** General studies/Field of study not specified. **Qualif.:** Applicants should be incoming freshmen who are admitted to the ISU by December 1 and must have the combination of two of the following three: a cumulative grade point average of at least 3.8 on a 4.0 scale; a 1270 SAT (Evidence-Based Reading and Writing and Math) or 27 ACT (composite); ranking in the top 10% of the senior class. **Criteria:** Selection will be listed below will be eligible to register to attend a winter interview competition.

Funds Avail.: No specific amount. **Duration:** Annual; up to three years. **Deadline:** December 15. **Remarks:** No additional application required.

5760 ■ Indiana State University Rural Health Scholarship *(Undergraduate/Scholarship)*

Purpose: To prepare and support students from rural Indiana to go back to their hometown as a primary care physician. **Focus:** Medicine. **Qualif.:** Applicants should be residents of Indiana and be incoming freshmen who are admitted to the ISU by December 1 and must have the

Awards are arranged alphabetically below their administering organizations

combination of two of the following three: a cumulative GPA of at least 3.5 on a 4.0 scale; an 1270 SAT (Evidence-Based Reading and Writing and Math) or a 27 ACT, and reside in rural Indiana. **Criteria:** Selection is highly competitive and based upon academic and personal accomplishments, as well as performance in a winter interview competition.

Funds Avail.: No specific amount. **Duration:** up to three years. **Number Awarded:** 10. **Deadline:** December 1. **Remarks:** The program is developed by Indiana State University and Indiana University School of Medicine. **Contact:** University Scholarship Office, 318 N Sixth St., Terre Haute, In, 47809; Phone: 800-468-6478; Email: scholarships@indstate.edu.

5761 ■ Indiana State University Transfer Student Scholarships *(Undergraduate/Scholarship)*

Purpose: To support transfer students in their pursuit of higher education. **Focus:** General studies/Field of study not specified. **Qualif.:** Applicants must be Indiana and out-of-state residents, including on-campus and online-only students. All incoming transfer students who are admitted to the University by the deadline listed below will be automatically considered for the scholarship. enroll as full-time students each semester (minimum of 12 credits). **Criteria:** Selection will be based on the committee's criteria.

Funds Avail.: No specific amount. **Number Awarded:** Varies. **To Apply:** Applicants who are admitted to the University will be automatically qualified for the scholarship. The application for admission serves as the scholarship application.

5762 ■ ISU Gongaware Scholarship *(Undergraduate/ Scholarship)*

Purpose: To support incoming ISU students in their pursuit of higher education. **Focus:** Insurance and insurance-related fields; Risk management. **Qualif.:** Applicants should be admitted as incoming freshmen who are admitted to the ISU and must have the combination of two of the following three: a cumulative GPA of at least 3.5 on a 4.0 scale; a 1140 SAT (Evidence-Based Reading and Writing and Math) or 23 ACT; and ranking in the top 15% of their senior class. **Criteria:** Selection will be based on the committee's criteria.

Funds Avail.: Amount varies. **Duration:** Annual; up to three years. **Number Awarded:** 4. **Deadline:** December 1. **Contact:** University Scholarship Office, 318 N Sixth St., Terre Haute, In, 47809; Phone: 800-468-6478; Email: scholarships@indstate.edu.

5763 ■ ISU Networks Scholarship *(Undergraduate/ Scholarship)*

Purpose: To support those who are pursuing business-related education. **Focus:** Business administration; Finance. **Qualif.:** Applicants should be admitted as incoming freshmen who are admitted to the ISU-Scott College of Business and must have the combination of two of the following three: a cumulative GPA of at least 3.5 on a 4.0 scale. an 1140 SAT (evidence-based reading and writing and math) or 23 ACT; and ranking in the top 15% of the senior high school class. **Criteria:** Selection shall be based on the demonstrated leadership in high school and in the community, be an incoming freshman majoring in business; intend to prepare for a career in the financial services industry - all business majors qualify.

Funds Avail.: $33,000 4-year Full Tuition Scholarship and $3,000 Professional Development Account. **Duration:** An-

nual. **To Apply:** Applicants must submit the completed application form; including an official high school transcript will receive preferred consideration. **Deadline:** December 15. **Contact:** Contact: 800-468-6478 Email: admissions@ indstate.edu, business@indstate.edu.

5764 ■ Noyce Scholarships for Secondary Math and Science Education *(Undergraduate/Scholarship)*

Purpose: To support transfer students in their pursuit of higher education and teaching of secondary mathematics and science education. **Focus:** Education, Secondary; Mathematics and mathematical sciences; Science. **Qualif.:** Applicants must be transfer students and have a cumulative grade point average of 2.75 and a 3.0 cumulative grade point average in all science and mathematics course work. **Criteria:** Selection will be based on the committee's criteria.

Funds Avail.: Amount varies. **Duration:** Annual. **Number Awarded:** Varies. **To Apply:** Applicants who are admitted to the University will be automatically qualified for the scholarship. The application for admission serves as the scholarship application.

5765 ■ Phi Theta Kappa Scholarship *(Undergraduate/Scholarship)*

Purpose: To support students who are members of the Phi Theta Kappa in their pursuit of higher education. **Focus:** Art; Science. **Qualif.:** Applicants must be Indiana or out-of-state residents; must have a cumulative grade point average of at least 3.5 on a 4.0 scale; earned an Associate's Degree; an active membership in Phi Theta Kappa. **Criteria:** Selection will be listed below, and submit proof of their membership will be considered. To be awarded this scholarship, students must be entering ISU fall semester.

Funds Avail.: Approximately $18,000. **Duration:** up to one year. **Number Awarded:** 10. **Deadline:** June 1. **Contact:** University Scholarship Office, 318 N Sixth St., Terre Haute, In, 47809; Phone: 800-468-6478; Email: scholarships@ indstate.edu.

5766 ■ Warren M. Anderson Scholarship *(Undergraduate/Scholarship)*

Purpose: To support the educational pursuit of under-represented minority students. **Focus:** General studies/ Field of study not specified. **Qualif.:** Applicants must be Indiana and out-of-state residents who are underrepresented minorities with a cumulative GPA of 3.5 on a 4.0 scale.

Funds Avail.: No specific amount. **Duration:** Annual; up to three years. **Number Awarded:** 10. **Deadline:** February 1. **Contact:** University Scholarship Office, 318 N Sixth St., Terre Haute, In, 47809; Phone: 800-468-6478; Email: scholarships@indstate.edu.

5767 ■ Indiana State University Alumni Association (ISUAA)
200 North Seventh Street
Terre Haute, IN 47809
Ph: (812)237-6100
E-mail: alumni@indstatefoundation.org
URL: www.indstate.edu
Social Media: www.facebook.com/indstatealumni
twitter.com/Indstatealumni

5768 ■ Indiana State University Academic Promise Scholarships *(Undergraduate/Scholarship)*

Purpose: To support students for showing academic promise and for them to obtain higher education degree.

Awards are arranged alphabetically below their administering organizations

Focus: General studies/Field of study not specified. **Qualif.:** Applicants must be enrolled as full-time students each semester (minimum of 12 credits) and successfully complete a minimum of 30 credit hours each academic year. This will enable them to successfully progress toward graduation within four years. They must also achieve a minimum cumulative grade point average of 3.00. **Criteria:** Selection will be based on the committee's criteria.

To Apply: Applicants may visit the website to verify the application process and other pieces of information.

5769 ■ Indiana State University Creative and Performing Arts Awards (Undergraduate/Scholarship)

Purpose: To support students in their pursuit of higher education in creative and performing arts. **Focus:** Art; Dance; Education, Physical; English language and literature; Music; Theater arts. **Qualif.:** Applicants must be Indiana and out-of-state residents and have at least a 2.5 cumulative grade point average on a 4.0 scale; To be awarded this award, students must be entering ISU fall semester. **Criteria:** Selection is based on academic and personal accomplishments.

Funds Avail.: $3,000 per year. **Duration:** Annual. **Number Awarded:** Varies. **To Apply:** Applicants should contact the department of the area in which they are applying for specific information. **Deadline:** March 1. **Contact:** Art: 812-237-3697; Music: 812-237-27771; English Creative Writing: 812-237-3161; Theater: 812-237-3339.

5770 ■ ISU Child of Alumni Book Voucher Awards (Undergraduate/Scholarship)

Purpose: To support the educational pursuits of dependents of alumni. **Focus:** General studies/Field of study not specified. **Qualif.:** Applicants must be enrolled full-time with 12 or more credit hours in both fall and spring semesters at ISU. **Criteria:** Selection will be based on the committee's criteria.

Funds Avail.: $500 ($250 in fall and another in spring). **Duration:** Annual. **To Apply:** Applicants may visit the website to verify the application process and other pieces of information. **Contact:** 200 North Seventh Street, Terre Haute, IN 47809. Phone: (812)237-6100. Email: admissions@indstate.edu, alumni@indstatefoundation.org.

5771 ■ Indigenous Bar Association (IBA)

70 Pineglen Cres.
Ottawa, ON, Canada K2G 0G8
Fax: (613)224-1529
E-mail: achalmers@indigenousbar.ca
URL: www.indigenousbar.ca
Social Media: www.facebook.com/
  IndigenousBarAssociation
twitter.com/IBA_Canada

5772 ■ Indigenous Bar Association Law Student Scholarship (Undergraduate/Scholarship)

Purpose: To provide assistance to qualified individuals who want to pursue their education. **Focus:** Law. **Qualif.:** Applicants must be an Indigenous law student currently enrolled in law school who, at a minimum, has substantially completed their first year of legal studies; must have demonstrated interest in serving the Indigenous community and the creator with honor and integrity. **Criteria:** Selection will be based on financial need, academic merit and commitment to Indigenous legal matters; preference and prior-

ity will be given to Indigenous students currently enrolled in law school, students enrolled in other professional legal studies may also be considered for the scholarship.

Funds Avail.: $2,000. **Duration:** Annual. **Number Awarded:** 2. **Deadline:** June 30. **Remarks:** Established in 2003. **Contact:** Anne Chalmers, 70 Pineglen Crescent, Ottawa, ON K2G 0G8; E-mail: achalmers@indigenousbar.ca.

5773 ■ Indspire

50 Generations Dr., Ste. 100
Six Nations of the Grand River
Ohsweken, ON, Canada N0A 1M0
Fax: (866)433-3159
Free: 855-463-7747
E-mail: info@indspire.ca
URL: indspire.ca
Social Media: www.facebook.com/Indspire
www.instagram.com/indspire.ca/
www.linkedin.com/company/Indspire
twitter.com/Indspire

5774 ■ Indspire Health Careers Bursary and Scholarships (Graduate, Undergraduate/Scholarship)

Purpose: To support students pursuing accredited health studies leading to employment in the health professions and who have demonstrated the potential for academic success. **Focus:** Biology; Chemistry; Dentistry; Medical laboratory technology; Medicine; Nursing; Pharmacy. **Qualif.:** Applicants must be Canadian residents First Nation (status and non-status), Metis, or Inuit students enrolled in a full-time post-secondary study. **Criteria:** Selection is based on financial need, academic performance, connection to the aboriginal community and commitment to the field of study.

Funds Avail.: No specific amount. **Duration:** Annual. **To Apply:** Application must be completed online at: indspire.ca/programs/students/bursaries-scholarships/. **Deadline:** August 1; November 1; February 1. **Contact:** Suzanne Bradley; Email: education@indspire.ca.

5775 ■ Indspire Post-Secondary Education Scholarships (PSE) (Graduate, Undergraduate, Vocational/Occupational, Two Year College, Four Year College/Scholarship)

Purpose: To meet the increasing needs of First Nations, Inuit, and Metis students for financial support and to assist them in the pursuit of excellence in every discipline. **Focus:** General studies/Field of study not specified. **Qualif.:** Applicants must be Canadian residents First Nation (status and non-status), Metis, or Inuit students enrolled in full- and part-time studies in college, university, skilled trades, apprenticeships, and technology programs. **Criteria:** Selection is based on financial need, academic performance, connection to the aboriginal community, and commitment to the field of study.

Funds Avail.: No specific amount. **Duration:** Annual. **To Apply:** Application should be completed online at: indspire.ca/programs/students/bursaries-scholarships/. **Deadline:** August 1; November 1; February 1. **Contact:** Suzanne Bradley; Email: education@indspire.ca.

5776 ■ Oil & Gas, Trades & Technology (OGTT) Bursary and Scholarship Awards (OGTT) (Undergraduate/Scholarship)

Purpose: To provide financial support to aboriginal people interested in pursuing studies in the Oil and Gas trades

Awards are arranged alphabetically below their administering organizations

and technology sector in Alberta and Alberta Aboriginal apprentices. **Focus:** Industry and trade. **Qualif.:** Applicant must be a Canadian resident aboriginal who is either First Nation (status or non-status), Inuit, or Metis; accepted or has applied for part-time or full-time studies in Alberta at an accredited training institute, college or university; an aboriginal across Canada taking Certificate, Diploma or Applied Degree Programs in Alberta. **Criteria:** Selection is based on demonstrated financial need; involvement with the aboriginal community; suitability and commitment to trades; and academic performance.

Funds Avail.: No specific amount. **Duration:** Annual. **To Apply:** Application must be completed online at: indspire.ca/programs/students/bursaries-scholarships/. **Deadline:** August 1; November 1; February 1. **Contact:** Suzanne Bradley; Email: education@indspire.ca.

5777 ■ Industrial Designers Society of America (IDSA)
555 Grove St., Ste. 200
Herndon, VA 20170
Ph: (703)707-6000
Fax: (703)787-8501
URL: www.idsa.org
Social Media: www.facebook.com/IDSA.org
www.instagram.com/idsadesign
www.linkedin.com/company/idsa-the-industrial-designers
 -society-of-america
twitter.com/IDSA

5778 ■ Gianninoto Industrial Design Graduate Scholarship *(Graduate, Undergraduate/Scholarship)*

Purpose: To promote and support excellence in the industrial design field. **Focus:** Industrial design. **Qualif.:** Applicants must be in their final year of study in an undergraduate industrial design program and currently applying to graduate school; must be currently enrolled in an industrial design graduate program or a practicing professional applying to return to graduate school; must be a member of an IDSA student chapter; must be a US citizen or US resident.

Funds Avail.: $1,500. **Duration:** Annual. **Remarks:** Established in 1932.

5779 ■ Industrial Supply Association (ISA)
100 N 20th St., Ste. 400
Philadelphia, PA 19103
Ph: (215)320-3862
Fax: (215)963-9785
Free: 877-460-2365
E-mail: info@isapartners.org
URL: www.isapartners.org

5780 ■ Gary L. Buffington Memorial Scholarships *(Undergraduate/Scholarship)*

Purpose: To recognize members who embody the values fostered by Gary L. Buffington while performing his duty for the industry. **Focus:** Education, Industrial. **Qualif.:** Applicant must be a rising senior in an established college or university industrial distribution channel. **Criteria:** Recipient will be selected based on criteria of high educational performance, leadership and community service.

Funds Avail.: $10,000. **To Apply:** Applicant must submit a completed application.

5781 ■ Influenster
435 Hudson St.,Ste 400.
New York, NY 10014
Ph: (917)210-2981
URL: www.influenster.com
Social Media: www.facebook.com/influenster
instagram.com/influenster
pinterest.com/influenster
twitter.com/influenster
youtube.com/user/Influenster

5782 ■ Influenster Code Like a Girl Scholarships *(Undergraduate, Graduate/Scholarship)*

Purpose: To elevate the status of female students pursuing an undergraduate or graduate degree and who aspire to become a coder, programmer or developer some day. **Focus:** Computer and information sciences; Engineering. **Qualif.:** Applicants must be lawfully authorized to work on a full-time basis in the United States without any form of sponsorship; must be female students majoring in computer science, information science, engineering, or a related field; must be enrolled full-time in their third, fourth or fifth year; must have a minimum 3.40 cumulative GPA on a 4.0 scale. **Criteria:** Selection will be based on the following criteria; computer science, information science, engineering, or a related field.

Funds Avail.: $1,000. **Number Awarded:** 5. **To Apply:** Applicants must submit all components of the Influenster application including the written essay topic, "Discuss a tool in the realm of technology that you wish you could reinvent, tweak, or collaborate on and why?"; must also attach a valid resume and transcript as proof of enrollment. **Deadline:** November 5.

5783 ■ Information Age Publishing Inc. (IAP)
7500 E McCormick Pky.
Scottsdale, AZ 85258
Ph: (704)752-9125
Fax: (704)752-9113
E-mail: infoage@infoagepub.com
URL: www.infoagepub.com
Social Media: www.facebook.com/
 InformationAgePublishing
twitter.com/infoagepub

5784 ■ Information Age Publishing HMJ Scholarship award *(Doctorate, Graduate/Scholarship)*

Purpose: To assist students with their graduate education finances. **Focus:** General studies/Field of study not specified. **Qualif.:** Applicants must be nominated by faculty. **Criteria:** Selection is based on the nomination letter.

Funds Avail.: No specific amount. **To Apply:** Any full-time tenure track faculty member may nominate a student. Nominating letter should include: the nominating faculty member's name, rank, department and college affiliation; the nominated student's name, department and college affiliation, and email address; and a brief description of the student's need.

5785 ■ Infusion Nurses Society (INS)
1 Edgewater Drive Suite 209
Norwood, MA 02062
Ph: (781)440-9408

Awards are arranged alphabetically below their administering organizations

Fax: (781)440-9409
E-mail: ins@ins1.org
URL: www.ins1.org
Social Media: www.facebook.com/InfusionNursesSociety
www.instagram.com/infusionnursessociety/
www.linkedin.com/company/103319
www.linkedin.com/company/infusion-nurses-society
twitter.com/ins1org

5786 ■ Gardner Foundation Education Scholarship
(Professional development/Scholarship)

Purpose: To support and recognize a commitment to continuing education. **Focus:** Health care services; Nursing. **Qualif.:** Applicants must be member of Infusion Nurses Society (INS). **Criteria:** Selection will be based on the Scholarship Committees' review on the application materials.

Funds Avail.: $1,000. **Duration:** Annual. **Number Awarded:** Up to 2. **To Apply:** Applicants must submit a completed application form available at the website; an evidence of acceptance into a collegiate program; and (two-page, double-spaced) summary of professional goals and how continuing education (collegiate, post-collegiate) will enhance their practice. **Contact:** Completed applications to: The Gardner Foundation/INS; One Edgewater Drive Suite 209; Norwood, MA 02062; ins@ins1.org.

5787 ■ Leslie Baranowski Scholarship for Professional Excellence *(Professional development/ Scholarship)*

Purpose: To support and recognize a commitment to improving and enhancing the quality of infusion care through leadership activities. **Focus:** Health care services; Nursing. **Qualif.:** Applicants must be member of Infusion Nurses Society (INS). **Criteria:** Selection will be based on the Scholarship Committees' review on the application materials.

Funds Avail.: $2,500. **Duration:** Annual. **Number Awarded:** Up to 2. **To Apply:** Applicants must submit a completed application form; (two-page, double-spaced) summary on how they would use the scholarship award to demonstrate/facilitate leadership in the community of infusion. **Contact:** Completed applications to: The Gardner Foundation/INS; One Edgewater Drive Suite 209; Norwood, MA 02062; ins@ins1.org.

5788 ■ INKAS Armored Vehicle Manufacturing
3605 Weston Rd.
Toronto, ON, Canada M9L 1V7
E-mail: info@inkas.ca
URL: inkasarmored.com
Social Media: www.facebook.com/inkas.armored.vehicles
www.instagram.com/inkas.armored
www.linkedin.com/company/inkasgroup
twitter.com/inkasvehicles
www.youtube.com/user/inkasvehicles

5789 ■ INKAS Rising Star Scholarship *(University/ Scholarship)*

Purpose: To award students who show excellence in engineering or business fields of study. **Focus:** Business; Engineering. **Qualif.:** Applicant must be a citizen or permanent resident of Canada, or a U.S. citizen or Green Card holder; have a minimum 75 percent average or equal

GPA; and be a full-time student in business or engineering at an accredited Canadian or U.S. university. **Criteria:** Selection is based on the submitted essay.

Funds Avail.: 1,500 Canadian Dollars. **Duration:** Annual. **Number Awarded:** 2. **To Apply:** Application and essay can be submitted online at inkasarmored.com/inkas-rising-star-scholarship-program/. **Deadline:** January 10.

5790 ■ Insite Solutions
3650 Rogers Rd. 298
Wake Forest, NC 27587
Ph: (919)569-6765
Fax: (919)569-6764
URL: stop-painting.com
Social Media: facebook.com/stoppainting
pinterest.com/stoppaintingcom
twitter.com/stoppainting
youtube.com/user/InSiteSolutionsLLC

5791 ■ Stop-Painting.com Scholarships
(Undergraduate/Scholarship)

Purpose: To support students who exemplify exceptional responsibility, leadership skills, and a key understanding of Stop-Paintings products and ethos. **Focus:** General studies/Field of study not specified. **Qualif.:** Applicants must be students currently enrolled in an accredited college, university or other related technical program. **Criteria:** Selection will be made by an independent reviewer, who will judge essays on creativity, originality, writing quality and understanding of the topic.

Funds Avail.: $1,000. **To Apply:** Applicants may obtain an application form online; must complete and submit the application form including their essay; the essay must be between 500-1,000 words, explaining the importance of organization and how visual cues help simplify efforts, either in the work place or life in general. **Deadline:** June 15 Fall Semester); November 15 (Spring semester).

5792 ■ Institut Canadien d' études Juridiques Supérieures
1601 Bayview Ave.
Toronto, ON, Canada M4G 4G8
Ph: (416)429-3292
Fax: (416)429-9805
E-mail: info@canadian-institute.com
URL: canadian-institute.com

5793 ■ Canadian Institute for Advanced Legal Studies French Language Scholarships *(Graduate, Advanced Professional/Scholarship)*

Purpose: To support students for whom a scholarship would make a significant difference in French-language European university for graduate studies. **Focus:** Law. **Criteria:** Selection will be based on academic record and the proposed program of study.

Funds Avail.: 20,000 Canadian Dollars. **Duration:** Annual. **Number Awarded:** Varies. **To Apply:** Applicants must submit a curriculum vitae; a personal statement indicating why the applicant chose graduate studies in law and why the applicant is suited to undertake such studies; a copy of transcripts for undergraduate and graduate studies, for

Awards are arranged alphabetically below their administering organizations

studies in law or for a Bar Admission Course, as applicable; a maximum of three letters of reference; and a statement of tuition fees and anticipated living and travel expenses. **Contact:** Mr. Randall J. Hofley, Vice President, Canadian Institute for Advanced Legal Studies, PO Box 43538, Leaside Post Office, 1601 Bayview Ave., Toronto, Ontario, M4G 4G8; Phone: 416-429-3292; Fax: 416-429-9805; Email: info@canadian-institute.com.

5794 ■ Right Honourable Paul Martin Sr. Scholarships *(Graduate/Scholarship)*

Purpose: To provide financial assistance for students of graduate studies in law at the University of Cambridge, England. **Focus:** Law. **Qualif.:** Applicants must be graduate of law from a Canadian university; attendees at a Bar Admission Course in Canada; or an articling students in Canada; and must be accepted into the University of Cambridge and a college of the University of Cambridge for graduate studies in law. **Criteria:** Selection will be based on the committee's criteria.

Funds Avail.: No specific amount. **Duration:** Annual. **To Apply:** Applications must include: curriculum vitae; a personal statement indicating why the Applicants wishes to undertake graduate studies in law at the University of Cambridge and why the Applicants is suited to undertake such studies; a copy of transcripts for undergraduate and graduate studies, for studies in law and for a Bar Admissions Course, as applicable; and a maximum of three letters of reference. Applications must be submitted by mail, fax or electronic mail no later than the deadline. **Deadline:** December 3. **Contact:** Lynn Morrison, Executive Secretary, Canadian Institute for Advanced Legal Studies, PO Box 43538, Leaside Post Office, 1601 Bayview Ave., Toronto, Ontario, M4G 4G8; Phone: 416-429-3292; Fax: 416-429-9805; Email: info@canadian-institute.com.

5795 ■ Institut de Recherche Robert-Sauve en Sante et en Securite du Travail (IRSST)

505, Boul. De Maisonneuve West
Montreal, QC, Canada H3A 3C2
Ph: (514)288-1551
E-mail: communications@irsst.qc.ca
URL: www.irsst.qc.ca
Social Media: www.facebook.com/IRSST-Occupational
  -Health-and-Safety-Research-207703664186
www.instagram.com/irsst
www.linkedin.com/company/irsst
twitter.com/IRSST
www.youtube.com/user/IRSST

5796 ■ Doctoral Scholarship Outside Québec *(Doctorate/Scholarship)*

Purpose: To financially assist graduate students who want to enhance their research programs which deal with the prevention of industrial accidents and occupational diseases or the rehabilitation of affected workers. **Focus:** Occupational safety and health. **Criteria:** Selection of applicants will be based on the following scholarship criteria: (1) Applicant's performance; (2) Scientific merit of the research project; (3) Quality and relevance of the research environment.

Funds Avail.: $25,950. **Duration:** Annual. **To Apply:** Applicants must complete the application form available on the website; must submit the official transcripts of all university grades including those for completed programs

and those under way; must provide an evaluation form from each of two scientists other than the research supervisor who have participated in the applicant's education; must provide a letter of recommendation written by the research supervisor. **Deadline:** October 21.

5797 ■ IRSST Doctoral Scholarship *(Doctorate/ Scholarship)*

Purpose: To financially assist graduate students who want to enhance their research programs which deal with the prevention of industrial accidents and occupational diseases or the rehabilitation of affected workers. **Focus:** Occupational safety and health. **Criteria:** Selection will be based on the following scholarship criteria: applicant's performance; scientific merit of the research project; quality and relevance of the research environment.

Funds Avail.: $19,950. **Duration:** Annual. **Number Awarded:** 1. **To Apply:** Applicants must complete the application form available on the website; must submit the official transcripts of all university grades, including those for completed programs and those under way; must provide an evaluation form from each of two scientists other than the research supervisor, who have participated in the applicant's education; must provide a letter of recommendation written by the research supervisor. **Deadline:** October 21.

5798 ■ IRSST Doctoral Scholarships Supplement *(Doctorate/Scholarship)*

Purpose: To financially assist graduate students who want to enhance their research programs which deal with the prevention of industrial accidents and occupational diseases or the rehabilitation of affected workers. **Focus:** Occupational safety and health. **Criteria:** Selection will be based on the following scholarship criteria: applicant's performance; scientific merit of the research project; quality and relevance of the research environment.

Funds Avail.: $5,250. **Duration:** Annual. **To Apply:** Applicants must complete the application form available on the website; must submit the official transcripts of all university grades, including those for completed programs and those under way; must provide an evaluation form from each of two scientists other than the research supervisor, who have participated in the applicant's education; must provide a letter of recommendation written by the research supervisor. **Deadline:** October 21.

5799 ■ IRSST Master's Scholarships *(Master's/ Scholarship)*

Purpose: To financially assist graduate students who want to enhance their research programs which deal with the prevention of industrial accidents and occupational diseases or the rehabilitation of affected workers. **Focus:** Occupational safety and health. **Criteria:** Selection will be based on the following scholarship criteria: applicant's performance; scientific merit of the research project; quality and relevance of the research environment.

Funds Avail.: $16,625. **Duration:** Biennial. **To Apply:** Applicants must complete the application form available on the website; must submit the official transcripts of all university grades, including those for completed programs and those under way; must provide an evaluation form from each of two scientists other than the research supervisor, who have participated in the applicant's education; must provide a letter of recommendation written by the research supervisor.

Awards are arranged alphabetically below their administering organizations

5800 ■ IRSST Master's Scholarships Supplement
(Master's/Scholarship)

Purpose: To financially assist graduate students who want to enhance their research programs which deal with the prevention of industrial accidents and occupational diseases or the rehabilitation of affected workers. **Focus:** Occupational safety and health. **Criteria:** Selection will be based on the following scholarship criteria: applicant's performance; scientific merit of the research project; quality and relevance of the research environment.

Funds Avail.: $4,375. **Duration:** Annual. **To Apply:** Applicants must complete the application form available on the website; must submit the official transcripts of all university grades, including those for completed programs and those under way; must provide an evaluation form from each of two scientists other than the research supervisor, who have participated in the applicant's education; must provide a letter of recommendation written by the research supervisor. **Deadline:** October 21.

5801 ■ IRSST postdoctoral fellowship
(Postdoctorate/Fellowship)

Purpose: To financially assist graduate students who want to enhance their research programs which deal with the prevention of industrial accidents and occupational diseases or the rehabilitation of affected workers. **Focus:** Occupational safety and health. **Criteria:** Selection will be based on the following scholarship criteria: applicant's performance; scientific merit of the research project; quality and relevance of the research environment.

Funds Avail.: $45,000. **Duration:** Annual. **To Apply:** Applicants must complete the application form available on the website; must submit the official transcripts of all university grades, including those for completed programs and those under way; must provide an evaluation form from each of two scientists other than the research supervisor, who have participated in the applicant's education; must provide a letter of recommendation written by the research supervisor; a proof of Canadian citizenship and a copy of valid Quebec health insurance card. **Deadline:** October.

5802 ■ Postdoctoral Fellowship in Québec
(Postdoctorate/Fellowship)

Purpose: To financially assist graduate students who want to enhance their research programs which deal with the prevention of industrial accidents and occupational diseases or the rehabilitation of affected workers. **Focus:** Occupational safety and health. **Criteria:** Selection of applicants will be based on the following scholarship criteria: (1) Applicant's performance; (2) Scientific merit of the research project; (3) Quality and relevance of the research environment.

Funds Avail.: $55,000. **Duration:** Annual. **To Apply:** Applicants must complete the application form available on the website; must submit the official transcripts of all university grades, including those for completed programs and those under way; must provide an evaluation form from each of two scientists other than the research supervisor, who have participated in the applicant's education; must provide a letter of recommendation written by the research supervisor.

5803 ■ Institut Royal d'Architecture du Canada (IRAC)
55 rue Murray St., Ste. 330
Ottawa, ON, Canada K1N 5M3

URL: www.raic.org

5804 ■ Arthur Buckwell Memorial Scholarship
(Undergraduate/Scholarship)

Purpose: To provide support to a student at the School of Architecture at the University of Manitoba. **Focus:** Architecture.

Funds Avail.: $1,500. **Duration:** Annual. **Remarks:** Established in 1993.

5805 ■ Ernest Wilby Memorial Scholarship
(Undergraduate/Scholarship)

Purpose: To support student entering the year before the final year of their main architectural course, who shows definite promise and talent in their work and who requires assistance to continue the course. **Focus:** Architecture. **Qualif.:** Applicant must be a student entering the year before the final year of their main architectural course, who shows definite promise and talent in their work and who requires assistance to continue the course. **Criteria:** The selection is made by the School staff.

Funds Avail.: 1,000 Canadian dollars. **Duration:** Annual. **Number Awarded:** 1. **To Apply:** The application process is online. **Remarks:** The award was established in the will of Mrs. Ernest Wilby as a memorial to her late husband who was a Fellow of the RAIC and resided in Windsor, Ontario. Established in 1966.

5806 ■ Institut des Sciences Mathematiques (ISM)
University of Quebec in Montreal
Montreal, QC, Canada H2X 3Y7
Ph: (514)987-3000
Fax: (514)987-8935
E-mail: ism@uqam.ca
URL: ism.uqam.ca/~ism/?language=default

5807 ■ CRM-ISM Postdoctoral Fellowship
(Postdoctorate/Fellowship)

Purpose: To support promising researchers who have recently obtained or are expected to obtain a PhD in the mathematical science. **Focus:** Mathematics and mathematical sciences. **Qualif.:** Candidate must be supported by a scientific group. Exceptionally, support from individual professors will be accepted if, for example, the candidate's field of research is poorly represented by scientific groups. **Criteria:** Selection is based on the excellence of the file, integration of the person into a research team, guaranteed funding from a team.

5808 ■ ISM Scholarships for Graduate Studies
(Graduate/Scholarship)

Purpose: To support students who wish to complete a PhD in mathematics. **Focus:** Mathematics and mathematical sciences. **Qualif.:** Applicants must be enrolled to a graduate study program in mathematics at one of the member universities and cumulative GPA must be at least 3.5. **Criteria:** Selection is based on excellent academic record and research aptitude and experience.

Funds Avail.: No specific amount. **To Apply:** Applicants must submit up-to-date university transcripts (graduate and undergraduate); a curriculum vitae; and two letters of recommendation. The Applicants must submit application materials to host departments.

Awards are arranged alphabetically below their administering organizations

5809 ■ Institute of Actuaries of Australia (IAAUST)
50 Carrington St., Level 2
Sydney, NSW 2000, Australia
URL: www.actuaries.asn.au

5810 ■ A. H. Pollard Travelling PhD Scholarships
(Postdoctorate/Scholarship)

Purpose: To provide assistance to a member of the institute who are studying for a PhD degree in an actuarial or related field. **Focus:** Education. **Qualif.:** Applicants must be permanent residents of Australia; must be members of the Actuaries Institute; must be enrolled for a PhD degree in a recognized university in any country; must be undertaking a PhD course relevant to actuaries or the actuarial profession. **Criteria:** Selection will be based on the committees' criteria.

Funds Avail.: $8,000. **Duration:** Annual. **To Apply:** Applicants must submit full details of their academic records from their undergraduate or other degree, including details of any prizes or awards won; a written reference from their masters degree supervisor or other academic familiar with their previous studies and able to comment on their research potential; details of published paper; outline of PhD research; standard C.V. including details of outside interests.

5811 ■ Institute for Anarchist Studies (IAS)
PO Box 90454
Portland, OR 97290
E-mail: anarchiststudies@gmail.com
URL: www.anarchist-studies.org
Social Media: www.facebook.com/
    InstituteForAnarchistStudies
twitter.com/narchiststudies

5812 ■ Institute for Anarchist Studies Grants for Radical Writers and Translators *(Professional development/Grant)*

Purpose: To support writers and translators in the development of theoretical tools, contemporary anarchist theory and practice. **Focus:** Translating; Writing. **Qualif.:** Applicants must be essay writers and translators. **Criteria:** Selection will be evaluated based on a content of the submitted work, ability to complete the project intellectual experiences and, publishing plans.

Funds Avail.: Total of $3,250. **Duration:** Annual. **Number Awarded:** Around 2 to 4. **Remarks:** Established in 1996.

5813 ■ Institute for Diversity and Health Equity
155 N Wacker Ave.
Chicago, IL 60606
Ph: (312)422-2630
URL: www.diversityconnection.org
Social Media: www.facebook.com/Institute.for.Diversity
www.linkedin.com/company/
    institutefordiversityinhealthmanagement
twitter.com/IFD_AHA

5814 ■ Cathy L. Brock Memorial Scholarships
(Graduate/Scholarship)

Purpose: To provide financial support to help fund graduate education for students preparing for a career as health administrators. **Focus:** Health education; Health services administration. **Qualif.:** Applicants must be first or second year graduate students pursuing a degree in healthcare administration or a comparable degree program (MBA, MPH, MHA, MPA, MSN or BSN); must demonstrate financial need and a commitment to community service; must excel academically (minimum 3.0 GPA); must be member of a federally classified ethnic minority group and have proof of U.S. citizenship. **Criteria:** Selection is based on leadership potential, academic achievement, community involvement, commitment to health care administration, financial need and overall professional maturity.

Funds Avail.: $1,000. **Duration:** Annual. **Number Awarded:** 1. **To Apply:** Applicants are required to complete the application online. **Remarks:** Named in memory of Cathy L. Brock, Director of Operations for the American Hospital Association's (AHA) Health Research and Educational Trust. **Contact:** Chris O. Biddle, Membership and Education Specialist; Phone: 312-422-2658; E-mail: cbiddle@aha.org.

5815 ■ Elliott C. Roberts Scholarships *(Graduate/Scholarship)*

Purpose: To provide financial support to help fund graduate education for students preparing for a career as health administrators. **Focus:** Health education; Health services administration. **Qualif.:** Applicants must be first or second year graduate students pursuing a degree in healthcare administration or a comparable degree program (MBA, MPH, MHA, MPA, MSN or BSN); must demonstrate financial need and a commitment to community service; must excel academically (minimum 3.0 GPA); must be member of a federally classified ethnic minority group and have proof of U.S. citizenship. **Criteria:** Selection is based on leadership potential, academic achievement, community involvement, commitment to health care administration, financial need and overall professional maturity.

Funds Avail.: $1,000. **Duration:** Annual. **Number Awarded:** 1. **To Apply:** Applicants are required to complete the application online. **Remarks:** The scholarship was established in memory of Elliott C. Roberts. **Contact:** E-mail: cbiddle@aha.org.

5816 ■ Institute of Electrical and Electronics Engineers (IEEE)
3 Park Ave., 17th Fl.
New York, NY 10016-5997
Ph: (212)419-7900
Fax: (212)752-4929
E-mail: contactcenter@ieee.org
URL: www.ieee.org
Social Media: www.facebook.com/IEEE.org
www.instagram.com/ieeeorg
www.linkedin.com/company/ieee
twitter.com/IEEEorg
www.youtube.com/user/IEEEorg

5817 ■ Charles LeGeyt Fortescue Scholarship
(Graduate/Scholarship, Award, Monetary)

Purpose: To provide students a one year of full-time graduate work in electrical at an engineering school of recognized standing located in the U.S. **Focus:** Electronics. **Qualif.:** Applicant must be a resident of the United States of America, have majored in the field of electrical engineering, and have received a bachelor's degree from an engineer-

Awards are arranged alphabetically below their administering organizations

ing college of recognized standing; the scholarship will be awarded to a first-year, full-time graduate student only; in the event the college is conducting a combined B.S. and M.S. degree program, the student in the penultimate year would be eligible for the award, which would apply in the final year of the program.

Funds Avail.: Up to $24,000. **Duration:** Annual. **Number Awarded:** 1. **To Apply:** Applicants must complete the entire application form and submit certified transcripts from all colleges/universities attended; provide letters of recommendation from three college/university professors who are familiar with their work; the complete name, title, and address of the reference must be clearly noted on the letter; letters of recommendation should address the following areas: the applicant's ability to perform graduate work; originality and creativity; character; diligence and social responsibility; ability to lead; ability to communicate; where the reference would rank the applicant among recent students in the field. **Deadline:** May 4. **Remarks:** The Award is given in honor of Charles LeGeyt. Established in 1939.

5818 ■ Institute of Food Technologists (IFT)

525 W Van Buren St., Ste. 1000
Chicago, IL 60607
Ph: (312)782-8424
Fax: (312)782-8348
Free: 800-438-3663
E-mail: info@ift.org
URL: www.ift.org
Social Media: www.facebook.com/IFTfoodscience
twitter.com/#!/IFT
www.youtube.com/user/IFTlive

5819 ■ Feeding Tomorrow Scholarships *(Graduate, Undergraduate/Scholarship)*

Purpose: To support and encourage outstanding research and education in food science and technology. **Focus:** Food science and technology.

Duration: Annual. **Deadline:** May 28. **Contact:** Jaime Gutshall; Phone: 312-604-0256; E-mail: jgutshall@ift.org; Scholarship America by emailing feedingtomorrow@ scholarshipamerica.org or by calling +1.507.931.1682.

5820 ■ Institute for Health Metrics and Evaluation (IHME)

2301 5th Ave., Ste. 600
Seattle, WA 98121
Ph: (206)897-2800
Fax: (206)897-2899
E-mail: ihme@healthdata.org
URL: www.healthdata.org
Social Media: www.facebook.com/IHMEUW
www.instagram.com/ihme_uw
www.linkedin.com/company/institute-for-health-metrics-and
  -evaluation
twitter.com/ihme_uw

5821 ■ Institute for Health Metrics and Evaluation Post Bachelor Fellowship (PBF) *(Graduate/ Fellowship)*

Purpose: To provide opportunities for recent college graduates with strong quantitative skills to train with faculty and

senior researchers on a variety of global health projects. **Focus:** Public health. **Qualif.:** Applicants must have a Bachelor's degree and proven quantitative and analytical skills, with high academic potential and a strong interest in pursuing an academic or professional career related to global health. **Criteria:** Selection will be based on the committee's criteria.

Funds Avail.: Amount varies. **Duration:** Annual. **To Apply:** Applicants must submit a resume (two-page limit); official copy of academic transcripts; one letter of reference from a professor or professional familiar with the applicant's coursework or research; and a brief personal statement (500-word max) on how the applicant's skills, experience and long-term career goals contribute to their candidacy. **Remarks:** To provides many different opportunities for research at the post-doctoral level. Hear from alumni about their experiences. **Contact:** Email: pbfs@healthdata.org.

5822 ■ Institute for Health Metrics and Evaluation Post Graduate Fellowships (PGF) *(Doctorate, Postdoctorate/Fellowship)*

Purpose: To provide opportunities both for self-directed research and interdisciplinary collaboration in health metrics. **Focus:** Public health. **Qualif.:** Applicants must have a PhD or MD; have a strong quantitative background, with advanced research experience, especially with data analysis and statistical methods. **Criteria:** Selection includes a phone interview and final interview, usually held at IHME offices.

Funds Avail.: No specific amount. **Duration:** One year. **To Apply:** Applicants must submit accepted on a rolling basis. Candidates are selected through a tiered process, and admissions decisions are made on a rolling basis. **Contact:** Institute for Health Metrics and Evaluation, at the above address or Email: pgf@healthmetricsandevaluation.org.

5823 ■ Institute for Humane Studies (IHS)

George Mason University
3434 Washington Blvd., MS 1C5
Arlington, VA 22201
Ph: (703)993-4880
Free: 800-697-8799
E-mail: questions@theihs.org
URL: www.theihs.org
Social Media: www.facebook.com/
  InstituteforHumaneStudies
twitter.com/theihs

5824 ■ Humane Studies Fellowship *(Graduate/ Fellowship)*

Purpose: To provide financial assistance to support the work of outstanding students interested in exploring the principles, practices and institutions necessary for a free society through their academic work. **Focus:** General studies/Field of study not specified. **Qualif.:** Applicants must be enrolled full time in a PhD program at any institution for the 2021-2022 academic year. Have a research interest that contributes to the advancement of classical liberal scholarship.

Funds Avail.: up to $15,000. **Duration:** Annual. **To Apply:** Applicants must submit applications online including: completed application form; curriculum vitae; a recent writing sample of 3, 000 words or fewer (if preferred writing sample is longer than 3, 000 words, a partial sample of that work is acceptable); an electronic transcript from current

Awards are arranged alphabetically below their administering organizations

(or most recent) institution; unofficial transcripts are acceptable. **Deadline:** December 1.

5825 ■ Institute of Industrial and Systems Engineers (IISE)

3577 Parkway Ln., Ste. 200
Norcross, GA 30092
Ph: (770)449-0460
Fax: (770)441-3295
Free: 800-494-0460
URL: www.iise.org
Social Media: www.facebook.com/iisenet
www.instagram.com/iisenet
twitter.com/iisenet
www.youtube.com/c/iisechannel

5826 ■ A.O. Putnam Memorial Scholarship
(Undergraduate/Scholarship)

Purpose: To support the education of industrial engineering students for academic excellence and campus leadership. **Focus:** Engineering, Industrial. **Qualif.:** Applicants must be undergraduate students enrolled in any school in the United States and its territories, Canada and Mexico, provided that the school's industrial engineering program or equivalent is accredited by an agency or organization recognized by IIE and the students are pursuing a course of study in industrial engineering; must be overall point-hour average of 3.40 on a scale of 0 – 4.00; must have a graduation date of May/June 2022 or later. **Criteria:** Selection will be based on scholastic ability, character, leadership, potential service to the industrial engineering profession and need for financial assistance; preference will be given to Applicants who have demonstrated an interest in management consulting.

Funds Avail.: $3,000. **Duration:** Annual. **Number Awarded:** 1. **To Apply:** Applicants must be nominated by IE department heads and mailed to the Institute headquarters by the deadline fixed by the Institute. After the review of nominations, eligible candidates will receive an application package that must be completed and sent back to IIE. **Deadline:** November 15. **Contact:** Bonnie Cameron, headquarters operations administrator; Phone: 770-449-0461, ext. 105; Email: bcameron@iienet.org.

5827 ■ John S.W. Fargher, Jr. Scholarship
(Graduate/Scholarship)

Purpose: To support students academic excellence and noteworthy contribution to the development of the industrial engineering profession. **Focus:** Engineering, Industrial. **Qualif.:** Applicants must be graduate students enrolled in any school in the United States and its territories, provided that the school's engineering program or equivalent is accredited by an accrediting agency recognized by IISE and the students are pursuing a course of study in industrial engineering or engineering management. **Criteria:** Selection will be selected based on GPA, IISE student chapter involvement and nomination letter.

Funds Avail.: $2,000. **Duration:** Annual. **Number Awarded:** 1. **To Apply:** Applicants must submit a nomination letter, along with an official transcript to IISE. **Deadline:** November 15. **Contact:** Bonnie Cameron, Headquarters Operations Administrator; Phone: 770-449-0461, ext. 105; Email: bcameron@iienet.org.

5828 ■ Dwight D. Gardner Scholarship
(Undergraduate/Scholarship)

Purpose: To support students pursuing an advanced degree in industrial engineering. **Focus:** Engineering, Industrial. **Qualif.:** Applicants must be undergraduate students enrolled in any school in the United States and its territories, Canada and Mexico, provided that the school's engineering program or equivalent is accredited by an agency or organization recognized by IIE and the student is pursuing a course of study in industrial engineering; must be active Institute member and have an overall average of 3.40 on a scale of 0-4.00; must have a graduation date of May/June 2022 or later. **Criteria:** Recipient will be selected based on scholastic ability, character, leadership, potential service to the industrial engineering profession and need for financial assistance; preference will be given to Applicants who have demonstrated an interest in management consulting.

Funds Avail.: $3,500, $3,000. **Duration:** Annual. **Number Awarded:** 6. **To Apply:** Candidates must be nominated by IE department heads and mailed to the Institute headquarters. After the review of nominations, eligible candidates will receive an application package that must be completed and sent back to IIE. **Deadline:** November 15. **Contact:** Bonnie Cameron, headquarters operations administrator; Phone: 770-449-0461, ext. 105; Email: bcameron@iienet.org.

5829 ■ Gilbreth Memorial Fellowship *(Graduate/Fellowship)*

Purpose: To support students pursuing an advanced degree in industrial engineering or its equivalent. **Focus:** Engineering, Industrial. **Qualif.:** Applicants must be graduate students enrolled in any school in the United States and its territories, Canada, or Mexico, pursuing an advanced degree in industrial engineering or equivalent; must be active Institute members and have an overall average of 3.40 on a scale of 4.00; must enrolled full time in graduate or undergraduate industrial engineering programs; graduate students must have had a 3.40 average as undergraduates to qualify; must have a graduation date of May/June 2022 or later. **Criteria:** Scholarship recipient will be selected based on scholastic ability, character, leadership, potential service to the industrial engineering profession and need for financial assistance; preference will be given to applicants who have demonstrated an interest in management consulting.

Funds Avail.: $3,000. **Duration:** Annual. **Number Awarded:** 3. **To Apply:** Applicants must be nominated by IE department heads and mailed to the Institute headquarters; after review of nominations, eligible candidates will receive an application package that must be completed and sent back to IIE. **Deadline:** November 15. **Contact:** Bonnie Cameron, headquarters operations administrator; Phone: 770-449-0461, ext. 105; Email: bcameron@iienet.org.

5830 ■ IISE Council of Fellows Undergraduate Scholarship *(Undergraduate/Scholarship)*

Purpose: To reward outstanding academic scholarship and leadership at the undergraduate level. **Focus:** Engineering, Industrial. **Qualif.:** Applicants must be undergraduate students enrolled in any school provided that the school's industrial engineering program or equivalent is accredited by an agency or organization recognized by IIE and the students are pursuing a course of study in industrial engineering; enrolled full time in undergraduate industrial engineering programs; must have overall point-hour average of 3.40 on a scale of 0 – 4.00; must have a graduation date of May/June 2022 or later.**Criteria:** Selection shall be based on scholastic ability, character, leadership, potential service to the industrial engineering profession and need for financial assistance.

Awards are arranged alphabetically below their administering organizations

Funds Avail.: $3,500; $1,000. **Duration:** Annual. **Number Awarded:** 1. **To Apply:** Applicants must be nominated by IE department heads and mailed to the Institute headquarters by the deadline fixed by the Institute; after the review of nominations, eligible candidates will receive an application package that must be completed and sent back to IIE. **Deadline:** November 15. **Contact:** Bonnie Cameron, headquarters operations administrator; Phone: 770-449-0461, ext. 105; Email: bcameron@iienet.org.

5831 ■ IISE Presidents Scholarship (Undergraduate/Scholarship)

Purpose: To support student excellence in scholarly activities and leadership of the industrial engineering profession. **Focus:** Engineering, Industrial. **Qualif.:** Applicants must be undergraduate students pursuing a course of study in industrial engineering who are active in a student chapter, and have demonstrated leadership and promoted IISE involvement on campus; must have overall point-hour average of 3.40 on a scale of 0 - 4.00. Graduate students must have had a 3.40 average as undergraduates to qualify; must have a graduation date of May/June 2022 or later. **Criteria:** Selection will be based on the aforementioned Applicants' qualifications and compliance with the application details.

Funds Avail.: $1,000. **Duration:** Annual. **Number Awarded:** 5. **To Apply:** Applicants must be nominated by IE department heads and mailed to the Institute headquarters by the deadline fixed by the Institute. After the review of nominations, eligible candidates will receive an application package that must be completed and sent back to IISE. **Deadline:** November 15. **Contact:** Bonnie Cameron, headquarters operations administrator; Phone: 770-449-0461, ext. 105; Email: bcameron@iienet.org.

5832 ■ John L. Imhoff Scholarship (Graduate, Undergraduate/Scholarship)

Purpose: To support a student pursuing an industrial engineering degree who, by academic, employment and/or professional achievements, has made noteworthy contributions to the development of the industrial engineering profession through international understanding. **Focus:** Engineering, Industrial. **Qualif.:** Applicants must be pursuing a BS in an accredited IE program, or have a BS in IE and pursuing a master's or doctorate degree in an accredited IE program. **Criteria:** Selection will be based on the aforementioned candidates' qualifications and compliance with the application details.

Funds Avail.: $1,000. **Duration:** Annual. **Number Awarded:** 2. **To Apply:** Applicants must submit a completed application form; a written essay describing candidate's international contributions to, or experience in, industrial engineering; and three references reinforcing Applicant's contributions to the industrial engineering profession through international understanding. **Deadline:** November 15. **Contact:** Bonnie Cameron, headquarters operations administrator; Phone: 770-449-0461, ext. 105; Email: bcameron@iienet.org.

5833 ■ Harold and Inge Marcus Scholarship (Undergraduate/Scholarship)

Purpose: To support undergraduate industrial engineering students for academic excellence and noteworthy contribution to the development of the industrial engineering profession. **Focus:** Engineering, Industrial. **Qualif.:** Applicants must be undergraduate students enrolled in any school in the United States, provided that the school's engineering

program is accredited by an agency recognized by IISE and the student is pursuing a course of study in industrial engineering; must be active Institute members as reflected on or before your October chapter roster; enrolled full time in undergraduate industrial engineering programs; overall point-hour average of 3.40 on a scale of 0 – 4.00; must have a graduation date of May/June 2022 or later. **Criteria:** Selection will be based on scholastic ability, character, leadership, potential service to the industrial engineering profession and need for financial assistance.

Funds Avail.: $1,000 each. **Duration:** Annual. **Number Awarded:** 11. **To Apply:** Applicants must be nominated by IE department heads and mailed to the Institute headquarters by the deadline fixed by the Institute. After the review of nominations, eligible candidates will receive an application package that must be completed and sent back to IISE. **Deadline:** November 15. **Contact:** Bonnie Cameron, headquarters operations administrator; Phone: 770-449-0461, ext. 105; Email: bcameron@iienet.org.

5834 ■ Marvin Mundel Memorial Scholarship (Undergraduate/Scholarship)

Purpose: To support the education of industrial engineering students for academic excellence and campus leadership. **Focus:** Engineering, Industrial. **Qualif.:** Applicants must be undergraduate students enrolled in any school in the United States and its territories, Canada and Mexico, provided that the school's industrial engineering program or equivalent is accredited by an agency or organization recognized by IISE and the students are pursuing a course of study in industrial engineering. **Criteria:** Selection will be based on scholastic ability, character, leadership, potential service to the industrial engineering profession and need for financial assistance. Preference will be given to Applicants who have demonstrated an interest in work measurement and methods engineering.

Funds Avail.: $3,000. **Duration:** Annual. **Number Awarded:** 1. **To Apply:** Applicants must be nominated by IE department heads and mailed to the Institute headquarters by the deadline fixed by the Institute. After the review of nominations, eligible candidates will receive an application package that must be completed and sent back to IISE. **Deadline:** November 15. **Contact:** Bonnie Cameron, headquarters operations administrator; Phone: 770-449-0461, ext. 105; Email: bcameron@iienet.org.

5835 ■ E.J. Sierleja Memorial Fellowship (Graduate/Fellowship)

Purpose: To recognize graduate students for academic excellence and campus leadership. **Focus:** Transportation. **Qualif.:** Applicants must be graduate students pursuing advanced studies in the area of transportation. **Criteria:** Selection will be given to students pursuing advanced studies on rail transportation.

Funds Avail.: $2,000. **Duration:** Annual. **Number Awarded:** 1. **To Apply:** Applicants must be nominated by IE department heads. Nominations must be mailed to the Institute headquarters. Candidates must submit a completed application package to IIE. **Deadline:** November 15. **Contact:** Bonnie Cameron, headquarters operations administrator; Phone: 770-449-0461, ext. 105; Email: bcameron@iienet.org.

5836 ■ UPS Scholarship for Female Students (Undergraduate/Scholarship)

Purpose: To support the education of industrial engineering students for academic excellence and campus leader-

Awards are arranged alphabetically below their administering organizations

ship. **Focus:** Engineering, Industrial. **Qualif.:** Applicants must be undergraduate students enrolled in any school in the United States and its territories, Canada and Mexico, provided that the school's industrial engineering program or equivalent is accredited by an agency or organization recognized by IIE and the students are pursuing a course of study in industrial engineering. **Criteria:** Selection shall be based on scholastic ability, character, leadership, potential service to the industrial engineering profession and need for financial assistance. Preference will be given to applicants who have demonstrated an interest in management consulting.

Funds Avail.: $4,000. **Duration:** Annual. **Number Awarded:** 1. **To Apply:** Applicants must be nominated by IE department heads and mailed to the Institute headquarters by the deadline fixed by the Institute; after the review of nominations, eligible candidates will receive an application package that must be completed and sent back to IIE. **Deadline:** November 15. **Contact:** Bonnie Cameron, headquarters operations administrator; Phone: 770-449-0461, ext. 105; Email: bcameron@iienet.org.

5837 ■ UPS Scholarship for Minority Students (Undergraduate/Scholarship)

Purpose: To support the education of industrial engineering students for academic excellence and campus leadership. **Focus:** Engineering, Industrial. **Qualif.:** Applicants must be undergraduate students enrolled in any school in the United States and its territories, Canada and Mexico, provided that the school's industrial engineering program or equivalent is accredited by an agency or organization recognized by IIE and the students are pursuing a course of study in industrial engineering. **Criteria:** Selection shall be based on scholastic ability, character, leadership, potential service to the industrial engineering profession and need for financial assistance. Preference will be given to applicants who have demonstrated an interest in management consulting.

Funds Avail.: $4,000. **Duration:** Annual. **Number Awarded:** 1. **To Apply:** Applicants must be nominated by IE department heads and mailed to the Institute headquarters by the deadline fixed by the Institute; after the review of nominations, eligible candidates will receive an application package that must be completed and sent back to IIE. **Deadline:** November 15. **Contact:** Bonnie Cameron, headquarters operations administrator; Phone: 770-449-0461, ext. 105; Email: bcameron@iienet.org.

5838 ■ Lisa Zaken Award For Excellence (Graduate, Undergraduate/Award, Monetary)

Purpose: To recognize excellence in scholarly activities and leadership related to the industrial engineering profession on campus. **Focus:** Engineering, Industrial. **Qualif.:** Applicants must be undergraduate and graduate students enrolled in any school, and pursuing a course of study in industrial engineering; must also be active in a student chapter having demonstrated leadership, as well as having promoted IIE involvement on campus, and have an overall grade point average of 3.00 on a scale of 0-4.00. **Criteria:** Selection will be selected based on GPA, IISE student chapter involvement and nomination letter.

Funds Avail.: $2,000. **Duration:** Annual. **Number Awarded:** 1. **To Apply:** Candidates must submit a nomination letter, along with an official transcript to IISE. **Deadline:** November 15. **Contact:** Bonnie Cameron, headquarters operations administrator; Phone: 770-449-0461, ext. 105; Email: bcameron@iienet.org.

5839 ■ Institute of International Education, Inc. (IIE)

IIE New York City
809 United Nations Plz.
New York, NY 10017
Ph: (212)883-8200
Fax: (212)984-5452
E-mail: membership@iie.org
URL: www.iie.org
Social Media: www.facebook.com/IIEglobal
instagram.com/iieglobal
www.linkedin.com/company/institute-of-international
 -education
twitter.com/iieglobal
youtube.com/iieglobal

5840 ■ Boren Fellowships (Graduate/Fellowship)

Purpose: To support study and research in areas of the world that are critical to U.S. interests. **Focus:** Area and ethnic studies; International affairs and relations. **Qualif.:** Applicants must be U.S. graduate students planning to add an important international and language component to their graduate education through specialization in area study, language study, or increased language proficiency. These fellowships support study and research in areas of the world that are critical to U.S. interests. **Criteria:** Selection will be based on the committee's criteria.

Funds Avail.: $30,000. **Duration:** Annual; minimum of 12 weeks and maximum of one year. **To Apply:** Applicants may contact the IIE for the application process and other information. **Deadline:** January 30. **Contact:** Email: boren@iie.org; URL: www.borenawards.org; www.iie.org/en/Programs/Boren-Awards-for-International-Study.

5841 ■ Boren Scholarships (Undergraduate, College/Scholarship)

Purpose: To support students who wish to study abroad in areas of the world that are critical to the nation's interests and underrepresented in study abroad. **Focus:** Area and ethnic studies; International affairs and relations. **Qualif.:** Applicants must be American undergraduate students planning to study abroad in areas of the world that are critical to U.S. interests and underrepresented in study abroad. **Criteria:** Selection will be based on the committee's criteria.

Funds Avail.: Up to $20,000. **Duration:** Annual. **To Apply:** Applicants may contact the IIE for the application process and other information. **Deadline:** February 7. **Contact:** Email: boren@iie.org; URL: www.borenawards.org; www.iie.org/en/Programs/Boren-Awards-for-International-Study.

5842 ■ Institute for the International Education of Students (IES)

33 W Monroe St., Ste. 2300
Chicago, IL 60603
Ph: (312)944-1750
Fax: (312)944-1448
Free: 800-995-2300
E-mail: info@iesabroad.org
URL: www.iesabroad.org
Social Media: www.facebook.com/IESabroad
www.instagram.com/iesabroad
www.linkedin.com/school/ies-abroad/
twitter.com/iesabroad

Awards are arranged alphabetically below their administering organizations

www.youtube.com/iesabroad

5843 ■ Institute for the International Education of Students Faculty Fellowships *(Postdoctorate/Fellowship)*

Purpose: To provide assistance to researchers who wish to use the Newberry Library's collections. **Focus:** General studies/Field of study not specified. **Qualif.:** Applicants must be a faculty members from any IES Center; must be an postdoctoral scholars. **Criteria:** Selection will be based on the committee's criteria.

Funds Avail.: $1,200 each. **Duration:** up to 1 month. **Number Awarded:** 2. **To Apply:** Applicants must submit the following Cover Sheet; Project Abstract of no more than 300 words; Project Description of no more than 1500 words; Curriculum Vitae; Three letters of reference. **Deadline:** December 15.

5844 ■ Institute for International Law and Justice (IILJ)

New York University School of Law
139 MacDougal St., 3rd flr.
New York, NY 10012-1076
Ph: (212)998-6709
Fax: (212)995-3825
E-mail: IILJ@nyu.edu
URL: www.iilj.org
Social Media: www.facebook.com/nyuiilj
www.instagram.com/nyuiilj
twitter.com/nyuiilj
www.youtube.com/user/nyuiilj

5845 ■ IILJ Scholarships *(Doctorate/Scholarship)*

Purpose: To promote the study of law. **Focus:** Law. **Qualif.:** Applicants must be law school students with outstanding academic backgrounds and strong international law interests. **Criteria:** Selection will be based on the committee's criteria.

Funds Avail.: No specific amount. **Duration:** Annual. **To Apply:** Applicants must complete the appropriate section of the JD application. Interested applicants are asked to submit a one-page essay, of no more than 500 words, with the JD application. The essay should explain how their approach and commitment to scholarship and to their intended study of international law make them a suitable candidate for the Scholars Program. **Contact:** iilj@juris.law.nyu.edu.

5846 ■ IILJ Visiting Fellowships and Research *(Postdoctorate/Fellowship)*

Purpose: To promote the study of law. **Focus:** Law. **Qualif.:** Applicants must be postdoctoral scholars or professorial visitors holding academic positions in other universities who are in full-time residence at the Law School. Full-time doctoral students of non-law departments of universities in the greater New York area, whose work is directly focused on central concerns of the program, may also be invited to participate informally in activities of the program. **Criteria:** Selection will be on a competitive basis.

Funds Avail.: No specific amount. **To Apply:** Applicants must complete and submit the application to the Hauser Global Law School program office. **Contact:** iilj@juris.law.nyu.edu.

5847 ■ Institute of Management Accountants (IMA)

10 Paragon Dr., Ste. 1
Montvale, NJ 07645-1760

Ph: (201)573-9000
Free: 800-638-4427
E-mail: ima@imanet.org
URL: www.imanet.org
Social Media: www.facebook.com/IMAnetORG
www.instagram.com/imaglobal
www.linkedin.com/company/ima-institute-of-management-accountants
twitter.com/IMA_News
www.youtube.com/user/LinkUpIMA?feature=watch

5848 ■ IMA Memorial Education Fund Scholarships (MEF) *(Graduate, Undergraduate/Scholarship)*

Purpose: To help student members of IMA offset the high cost of education and pursue further studies in preparation for careers in accounting, management and finance. **Focus:** Accounting; Finance; Management. **Qualif.:** Applicant must be IMA student member (membership number must be indicated in the application); must have undergraduate/graduate academic career. **Criteria:** Selection will be based on academic merit; IMA participation; quality of presentation; and strength of recommendation.

Funds Avail.: $1,000-$2,500. **Duration:** Annual. **To Apply:** Applicants must submit (one-page) resume; official university transcripts with school seal enclosed in a sealed envelope; two letters of recommendations (from current or past employer, professor or an IMA member). Should be in an attached form with reference's signature across the envelope seal; and (two-page) written statement indicating: career goals and objectives; reasons for applying the scholarship, statements why the Applicants deserves the award, specific contributions to IMA, suggestions on promoting awareness, increasing membership and certification within IMA. **Deadline:** March 10. **Contact:** Contact Kerry Butkera, IMA research and academic relations administrator, at kbutkera@imanet.org.

5849 ■ Institute of Management Accountants FAR Doctoral Student Grants Program *(Doctorate/Grant)*

Purpose: To financially assist accounting doctoral students who are pursuing research for the advancement of management accounting profession. **Focus:** Accounting. **Qualif.:** Applicants must be an accounting doctoral student. **Criteria:** Proposals will be reviewed and evaluated by the FAR Board of trustees and directors.

Funds Avail.: No specific amount. **To Apply:** Applicants must prepare a research plan; a letter from the researcher's dissertation chair or faculty advisor; and a letter from student indicating: a) completion of the doctoral program; b) plans for submitting the research to academic journal; c) discussion of research; d) budget proposal. Materials should be submitted electronically (PDF or Word document). **Remarks:** Established in 2005. **Contact:** Kip Krumwiede, CMA, CPA, Ph.D., Director of Research; Phone: 201-474-1732; Email: kkrumwiede@imanet.org.

5850 ■ Stuart Cameron and Margaret McLeod Memorial Scholarship (SCMS) *(Graduate, Undergraduate/Scholarship)*

Purpose: To help student members of IMA offset the high cost of education and pursue further studies in preparation for careers in accounting, management and finance. **Focus:** Accounting; Finance; Management. **Qualif.:** Applicant must be IMA student member. **Criteria:** Selection of applicants will be based on academic merit, IMA participation, quality of presentation and other materials provided.

Awards are arranged alphabetically below their administering organizations

Funds Avail.: $5,000. **Duration:** Annual. **To Apply:** Applicants must submit (one-page) resume; official university transcripts with school seal enclosed in a sealed envelope; two letters of recommendations (from current or past employer, professor or an IMA member). Should be in an attached form with reference's signature across the envelope seal; and (two-page) written statement indicating: career goals and objectives; reasons for applying the scholarship, statements why the Applicants deserves the award, specific contributions to IMA, suggestions on promoting awareness, increasing membership and certification within IMA.**Deadline:** March 1. **Remarks:** Established in 1934.

5851 ■ Institute for Operations Research and the Management Sciences (INFORMS)
5521 Research Park Dr., Ste. 200
Catonsville, MD 21228
Ph: (443)757-3500
Fax: (443)757-3515
Free: 800-446-3676
E-mail: informs@informs.org
URL: www.informs.org
Social Media: www.facebook.com/INFORMSpage
www.instagram.com/informs_orms
www.linkedin.com/company/informs_2
twitter.com/INFORMS

5852 ■ Seth Bonder Scholarship for Applied Operations Research in Military Applications *(Doctorate/ Scholarship, Monetary, Recognition, Award)*

Purpose: To promote the development and application of process modeling and operations research analyses to military issues. **Focus:** Management. **Qualif.:** Applicants must be students pursuing doctoral studies in military operations research or a related discipline is eligible, particularly those with two to three years remaining in their programs. **Criteria:** Selection will be basis of excellence, innovation, preparation, and probability of candidate's success. Candidates will be evaluated on the quality of their preparation to undertake a program of applied operations research in the military and/or national security arena. The proposed program of research will be judged according to its potential for making a significant contribution to the field of applied OR in defense-related applications, including military and national security, as well as the likelihood of successful completion.

Funds Avail.: A grant of $4,000; up to $1,000 (USD) of travel funding; additional $2,000 ($US) grant is provided and funded by the Seth Bonder Foundation. **Duration:** Annual. **Number Awarded:** 1. **To Apply:** Applicant must submit Your a curriculum vita; two letters of support (note: in a few cases, when it is needed in order to fully represent the academic and practical strengths of an application, a third letter may be appropriate); a brief statement describing why they are interested in applying operations research to defense-related applications, including military and national security issues; a two-page summary of their proposed program of research. **Deadline:** July 1.

5853 ■ Institute for Public Policy Research (IPPR)
14 Buckingham St., Gnd Fl.
London WC2N 6DF, United Kingdom
Ph: 44 20 74706100

Fax: 44 20 74706111
E-mail: info@ippr.org
URL: www.ippr.org
Social Media: www.facebook.com/ipprUK
www.linkedin.com/company/ippr
twitter.com/ippr

5854 ■ IPPR North Events Internship *(Undergraduate/Internship)*

Purpose: To provide assistance to interns working across the organization providing support for events. **Focus:** Education. **Criteria:** Selection will be based on the committees' criteria.

Duration: Annual; 6 months. **To Apply:** Applicants may contact IPPR for the application process and other information. **Contact:** Please send your completed application form to: intern@ippr.org or by post to: Intern, ippr, 30-32 Southampton St., London WC2E 7RA; Phone: 0207-470-6100.

5855 ■ Amelia Zollner IPPR/UCL Internship Award *(Undergraduate/Internship)*

Purpose: To give assistance to UCL students and recent UCL graduates as a stepping stone to working in policy or politics. **Focus:** Education. **Qualif.:** Applicants must be UCL students or recent UCL graduates. **Criteria:** Selection will be based on the committees' criteria.

Duration: Annual. **To Apply:** Applicants may contact IPPR for the application process and other information. **Remarks:** The award was established in memory of 24-year-old UCL student Amelia Zollner, who tragically died in a cycling accident while working as an intern at IPPR.

5856 ■ Institute for Public Relations (IPR)
PO Box 118400
Gainesville, FL 32611-8400
Ph: (352)392-0280
E-mail: info@instituteforpr.org
URL: www.instituteforpr.org

5857 ■ IPR Pathfinder Award *(Postgraduate/ Recognition)*

Purpose: To honor and recognize an original program of scholarly research that has made a significant contribution to the body of knowledge and practice of public relations. **Focus:** Public relations. **Criteria:** Selection committee is particularly interested in scholarly contributions resulting in the publication of major articles, chapters or books and other outstanding research endeavors that have advanced the field.

Duration: Annual. **Number Awarded:** 1. **Contact:** Email: info@instituteforpr.org.

5858 ■ Ketchum Excellence in Public Relations Research Award *(Graduate/Fellowship, Internship)*

Purpose: To foster the development of new public relations research methods, especially measuring the effectiveness of public relations solutions. **Focus:** Public relations. **Qualif.:** Applicants must be graduate students majoring in communications or research who have completed at least one year of study towards a Masters degree or Ph.D. **Criteria:** Selection will be given to those who exhibit exceptional intellect in the field of public relations research and measurement, and who can serve as valued members of the Ketchum team in the New York office.

Awards are arranged alphabetically below their administering organizations

Funds Avail.: $7,500 for eight-week PR research internship with Ketchum in New York City during summer; $2,500 stipend for the research paper after it has been accepted for publication by IPR. **Duration:** Annual. **Number Awarded:** 1. **To Apply:** Applicants may contact the IIE for the application process and other information. **Contact:** Robert W. Grupp; Phone: 484-557-8401; E-mail: rgrupp@ instituteforpr.org.

5859 ■ Makovsky Best Master's Thesis of the Year Award *(Master's/Award)*

Purpose: To recognize and encourage graduate study and scholarship in public relations through an annual award for an outstanding master's thesis. **Focus:** Public relations. **Qualif.:** Application is open to graduate studies students who are enrolled in master's degree program (MA, MS, MBA, MJ, MPR or any masters program). **Criteria:** Entries are judged on their contribution to the advancement of research-based knowledge in the field of public relations and the degree to which the research is relevant or has an impact on to profession.

Funds Avail.: $1,000-$2,000. **Duration:** Annual. **Number Awarded:** 2 (1 grand winner and 1 winner's faculty advisor). **To Apply:** Applicant must be completed application form from online and submitted; the thesis or written project must be written in English language, submitted in a single pdf-formatted document via email. **Deadline:** May 1. **Contact:** Email: awards@instituteforpr.org.

5860 ■ Institute of Real Estate Management (IREM)

430 N Michigan Ave., Ste. 500
Chicago, IL 60611
Fax: (800)338-4736
Free: 800-837-0706
E-mail: getinfo@irem.org
URL: www.irem.org
Social Media: www.facebook.com/
  InstituteofRealEstateManagement
www.instagram.com/ireminfo
www.linkedin.com/company/institute-of-real-estate
  -management
twitter.com/IREM_info
www.youtube.com/user/IREMinfo

5861 ■ George M. Brooker, CPM Diversity Collegiate Scholarship *(Graduate, Undergraduate/Scholarship)*

Purpose: To attract young people from underrepresented populations into the real estate management business. **Focus:** Management; Real estate. **Qualif.:** Applicants must: be members of a minority (non-Caucasian) group; be citizens of the United States; be beginning in their junior or senior years of undergraduate work or pursuing graduate or post-graduate studies; have declared a major in real estate or a related field; have a minimum GPA of 3.0 on a 4.0 scale within their major; and have completed two courses in real estate or have indicated the intent to complete such courses. **Criteria:** Recipients are chosen based on merit.

Funds Avail.: No specific amount. **Duration:** Semiannual. **Number Awarded:** Varies. **To Apply:** Applicants must submit complete application (available in the website), three letters of recommendation of which one must come from the college dean, written essay (not to exceed 500 words) explaining the applicants' interest in the industry, and a let-

ter of recommendation from local IREM chapter president or officer. **Contact:** IREM Foundation, Attn: Scholarship Program, 430 N. Michigan Avenue, Chicago, IL 60611; Phone: 312-329-6008; Fax: 312-410-7908; E-mail: kholmes@irem.org.

5862 ■ Donald M. Furbush Professional Development Grants *(Other/Grant)*

Purpose: To provide funding for individuals to follow the institute's entire curriculum required to qualify for the CPM designation, ARM certification and Accredited Commercial Manager certification, thus promoting professional development. **Focus:** Management; Real estate. **Qualif.:** Nominees must be of legal age in the country in which the nominee resides; and must be actively employed in the real estate management industry. **Criteria:** Selection is based on commitment to professional excellence, financial need, strength of recommendation and personal commitment in gaining CPM designation.

Funds Avail.: up to $6,000. **To Apply:** Applicants must submit complete application (available in the website). **Deadline:** June 30.

5863 ■ Paul H. Rittle Sr. Professional Development Grants *(Other/Grant)*

Purpose: To provide financial assistance to individuals exploring a career in real estate management. **Focus:** Management; Real estate. **Qualif.:** Applicants must be of legal age and currently employed in some aspect of the real estate field. **Criteria:** Recipients are selected on the basis of financial need; commitment to real estate management as a career; and character as demonstrated by community involvement.

Funds Avail.: $3,000. **Duration:** Quarterly. **Number Awarded:** Varies. **To Apply:** Applicants must submit official application form; employer affidavit and financial status form; personal letter describing the objectives and information of the applicant; for U.S. citizen: a letter support from the local president or officer supporting your application; a copy of applicant's signed federal income tax return and Form W-2 for previous year; for international applicants: letter from employee or client if self-employed and total income indicated in Annual Income Statement for the previous year (if married include your spouse). **Deadline:** Monthly between the 15th and last day of the month except during the last quarter of the year.

5864 ■ Institute of Transportation Engineers (ITE)

1627 Eye St. NW, Ste. 600
Washington, DC 20006
Ph: (202)785-0060
Fax: (202)785-0609
E-mail: ite_staff@ite.org
URL: www.ite.org
Social Media: www.facebook.com/ITEHQ
twitter.com/ITEHQ
www.youtube.com/user/ITEHQ

5865 ■ Institute of Transportation Engineers - Texas District Fellowships *(Graduate/Fellowship)*

Purpose: To support students wishing to pursue a graduate study in transportation engineering. **Focus:** Transportation. **Qualif.:** Applicants must be highest ranked candidates from Texas; course of study must be pursued at one of the universities within the district.

Awards are arranged alphabetically below their administering organizations

Funds Avail.: $1,000. **Duration:** Annual. **Number Awarded:** Up to 2.

5866 ■ Western District fellowship *(Graduate/Fellowship)*

Purpose: To support students wishing to pursue a graduate study in transportation engineering. **Focus:** Transportation. **Qualif.:** Applicant must: be an active ITE Student, Member or Fellow in good standing with ITE; be able to demonstrate contributions to ITE through volunteer activities; b willing to work with their employer, District and Section for financial support of the registration fee. **Criteria:** Selection will be based on the committee criteria.

Funds Avail.: $1,000. **Duration:** Annual. **Number Awarded:** 1. **To Apply:** A completed application packet includes: completed application form submitted by the due date; responses to short essay questions; nomination letter from current or past ITE District or Section officer; support letter from current employer; and support letter from non-employer. **Deadline:** September 16.

5867 ■ Transoft Solutions, Inc. Ahead of the Curve Scholarship (AOTC) *(Graduate, Undergraduate/Scholarship)*

Purpose: To encourage students to pursue studies in transportation and/or traffic engineering. **Focus:** Transportation. **Qualif.:** Applicants must be transportation and/or traffic engineering students within the U.S. or Canada.

Funds Avail.: $2,000. **Duration:** Annual. **Deadline:** April 1.

5868 ■ Institute of Turkish Studies (ITS)

Georgetown University
3300 Whitehaven St. NW, Ste. 3100
Washington, DC 20007
Ph: (202)687-0292
Fax: (202)687-3780
E-mail: itsdirector@turkishstudies.org
URL: www.turkishstudies.org
Social Media: www.facebook.com/instituteofturkishstudies
twitter.com/TurkishStudies

5869 ■ Dissertation Writing Grants *(Graduate/Grant)*

Purpose: To provide partial support for travel and research to Turkey for those who hold a Ph.D. in a social sciences or humanities discipline. **Focus:** Turkish studies. **Qualif.:** Applicants must be graduate students in any field of the social sciences and/or humanities; U.S. citizens or permanent residents at the time of the application; currently enrolled in a Ph.D. degree program in the United States; and, expecting to complete all Ph.D. requirements except their dissertations by June the following year. **Criteria:** Recipients will be selected by the expert panels.

Funds Avail.: $5,000-$15,000. **Duration:** Annual. **To Apply:** Applicants must send a two-page grant application cover sheet (available at the website); a maximum of six pages project proposal, double-space; budget; three letters of recommendation; curriculum vitae; and an academic transcript send by university registrar. Applications and supporting documents must be sent electronically in MS Word or PDF format or by regular mail. **Deadline:** March 29. **Remarks:** Established in 1983. **Contact:** Sinan Ciddi, Institute of Turkish Studies, 3300 Whitehaven St., NW, Ste. 3100, Georgetown University, Washington, DC 20007, United States.

5870 ■ Institute of Turkish Studies Sabbatical Research Grants *(Other/Grant)*

Purpose: To support faculty research during the course of their sabbaticals. **Focus:** Turkish studies. **Qualif.:** Applicants must be faculty member in the field of social sciences and/or humanities; must be U.S. citizens or permanent residents. **Criteria:** Recipients will be selected by the expert panels.

Funds Avail.: $25,000 each. **Duration:** Annual. **Number Awarded:** Varies. **To Apply:** Applicants must send a two-page grant application cover sheet available at the website; a project proposal (maximum of six pages, double-spaced); and a curriculum vitae. Applications must be sent electronically in MS Word or PDF format or by regular mail. **Contact:** Send applications to: Dr. Sinan Ciddi, Intercultural Center 305R, Georgetown University, 37th & O Street, Washington DC, DC 20057-1033, United States.

5871 ■ Post-Doctoral Summer Travel-Research Grants *(Postdoctorate/Grant)*

Purpose: To provide partial support for travel and research to Turkey for those who hold a Ph.D. in a social sciences or humanities discipline. **Focus:** Humanities; Social sciences; Turkish studies. **Qualif.:** Applicants must be U.S. citizens or permanent residents who are currently working in the United States and holding a Ph.D. in social science or humanities; must have received their Ph.D. within the last five years. **Criteria:** Recipients will be selected by the expert panels.

Funds Avail.: No specific amount. **Duration:** Annual. **To Apply:** Applicants must send a (two-page) grant application cover sheet available at the website; a project proposal (maximum of five pages, double-spaced); budget; three letters of recommendation; and a curriculum vitae. Applications and supporting documents must be sent electronically in MS Word or PDF format or by regular mail. **Deadline:** March 30. **Remarks:** Established in 1983. **Contact:** Sinan Ciddi, Institute of Turkish Studies, 3300 Whitehaven St., NW, Ste. 3100, Georgetown University, Washington, DC 20007, United States.

5872 ■ Summer Language Study Grants in Turkey *(Graduate/Grant)*

Purpose: To provide summer travel to Turkey in preparation for graduate research in language study. **Focus:** Humanities; Social sciences; Turkish studies. **Qualif.:** Applicants must be U.S. citizens or permanent residents; graduate students in the field of social science or humanities; and, enrolled in a university within the United States. **Criteria:** Recipients will be selected based on the final decision of the expert panels.

Funds Avail.: $1,000-$3,000. **Duration:** Annual. **To Apply:** Applicants must send a (two-page) grant application cover sheet (available at the website); a project proposal (maximum of three pages, double-spaced); budget; three letters of recommendation; curriculum vitae; academic transcript send by university registrar. Applications and supporting documents must be sent electronically in MS Word or PDF format or by regular mail. **Deadline:** March 30. **Remarks:** Established in 1983. **Contact:** Sinan Ciddi, Institute of Turkish Studies, 3300 Whitehaven S., NW, Ste. 3100, Georgetown University, Washington, DC 20007, United States.

5873 ■ Institute for Women's Policy Research (IWPR)

1200 18th St. NW, Ste. 301
Washington, DC 20036

Awards are arranged alphabetically below their administering organizations

Ph: (202)785-5100
Fax: (202)833-4362
E-mail: iwpr@iwpr.org
URL: www.iwpr.org
Social Media: www.facebook.com/iwpresearch
www.instagram.com/iwpresearch
www.linkedin.com/company/institute-for-women's-policy
  -research
twitter.com/IWPResearch

5874 ■ Mariam K. Chamberlain Fellowship in Women and Public Policy *(Graduate/Fellowship)*

Purpose: To provide fellowship in public policy to a promising scholar each year. **Focus:** Social sciences; Statistics; Women's studies.

Funds Avail.: $33,300. **Duration:** Annual. **Remarks:** The fellowship awarded in honor of pioneering feminist economist Mariam K. Chamberlain. **Contact:** Mary Sykes, Fellowship Coordinator at MKCfellowship@iwpr.org; Address: 1200, 18th St., NW, Ste. 301, Washington, DC 20036.

5875 ■ Institute for Work and Health (IWH)
400 University Ave., Ste. 1800
Toronto, ON, Canada M5G 2E9
URL: www.iwh.on.ca

5876 ■ IWH Mustard Fellowship in Work and Health *(Postgraduate/Fellowship)*

Purpose: To support the development of outstanding new researchers in the field of work and health congruent with the mission of the Institute and o build capacity for innovative multidisciplinary research concerning the relationships between work environments and worker health. **Focus:** Medical research. **Qualif.:** Applicants must have completed a Ph.D. (or equivalent) at the time they begin the Fellowship, in one or more of the fields of social, behavioral, organizational or health sciences, including epidemiology, medicine, and allied medical professions; must be within five years of completion of their PhD, have held no more than one other postdoctoral fellowship (or equivalent), and have not held another academic job as an independent investigator (e.g., assistant professorship); should have an interest in approaching research questions from a multidisciplinary perspective; should have proficiency in relevant qualitative and/or quantitative methods; must hold Canadian citizenship, have permanent residency status in Canada or be eligible for a Canadian work visa at the time of application; may not hold another major salary award in addition to the Mustard Fellowship.

Funds Avail.: $55,000 Canadian Dollars. **Duration:** Annual. **To Apply:** Applicants must submit a cover letter; a curriculum vitae; a transcript of academic records (complete with a description of grading scale employed); a brief abstract of the post-doctoral research proposal, maximum 200 words; a full statement of the proposed program of research to be conducted during the term of the Fellowship, maximum three pages; description should be written by the applicant and should state the scientific and career benefits expected to be derived from the research and its relevance to the mandate of the Institute; three letters of reference (one letter of reference should be from thesis supervisor) reference letters should describe the referee's relationship to the candidate and address the candidate's research skills, initiative and ability to work independently, writing and presentation skills, and provide an overall as-

sessment; reference letters should be sent by referees directly to Lyudmila Mansurova at lmansurova@iwh.on.ca. **Remarks:** In honor of Dr. J. Fraser Mustard, who was the chair of the Institute for Work & Health's first Board of Directors, the Institute created a fellowship in his name in 1999 when he stepped down as the inaugural chair. **Contact:** Lyudmila Mansurova, Administrative Assistant, Office of the President, Institute for Work & Health; Email: lmansurova@iwh.on.ca.

5877 ■ S. Leonard Syme Training Fellowship *(Master's, Doctorate/Fellowship)*

Purpose: To recognize students who show commitment to research that promises to reduce work-related injury, illness and disability in Ontario. **Focus:** Health care services; Medical research. **Qualif.:** Applicant must be currently enrolled or accepted into an accredited graduate studies program at the master's or doctoral level; be enrolled in one of the following IWH-affiliated universities: McMaster University, University of Toronto, University of Waterloo, York University, Ryerson University, Trent University, University of British Columbia, University of Victoria, University of Montreal, University of Lethbridge, Dalhousie University or Lakehead University; be directly supervised or mentored by an IWH scientist or adjunct scientist. **Criteria:** Selection will be evaluated based on scientific merit, innovation, the feasibility of the proposal, and alignment with IWH's Strategic Research Plan.

Funds Avail.: 5,000 Canadian Dollars - 15,000 Canadian Dollars. **Duration:** Annual. **To Apply:** Applicant must be statement of the candidate's research interests and career objectives. Two (2) academic references. The reference form is made available with the online application form. Copies of transcripts from all post-secondary institutions in PDF format (unofficial and student-issued transcripts are permitted; e.g., ROSI screenshots). Curriculum vitae in PDF format. **Remarks:** In appreciation of Dr. S. Leonard Syme's contributions to the Institute for Work & Health (IWH) as chair of its Scientific Advisory Committee from 1995 to 2002, IWH established a research training fellowship in his name in 2002. **Contact:** Lyudmila Mansurova, Administrative Assistant, Office of the President, Institute for Work & Health; Email: lmansurova@iwh.on.ca.

5878 ■ Instituts de Recherche en Sainté du Canada
160 Elgin St., 9th Fl.
Ottawa, ON, Canada K1A 0W9
Ph: (613)941-2672
Fax: (613)954-1800
Free: 888-603-4178
E-mail: info@cihr-irsc.gc.ca
URL: www.cihr-irsc.gc.ca
Social Media: www.facebook.com/
  RechercheEnSanteAuCanada
www.instagram.com/cihr_irsc
www.linkedin.com/company/canadian-institutes-of-health
  -research
twitter.com/irsc_cihr

5879 ■ IHSPR Institute Community Support (ICS) Program *(Undergraduate, Graduate, Postgraduate, Postdoctorate/Prize)*

Purpose: To promote significant contributions by students and trainees in the field of cancer research. **Focus:** Oncology.

Awards are arranged alphabetically below their administering organizations

Funds Avail.: $100,000. **Duration:** Annual. **Contact:** E-mail: icrh.iscr@cihr-irsc.gc.ca; Phone: 613-954-1968.

5880 ■ Insurify
222 3rd St., Ste.4000
Cambridge, MA 02142
Free: 866-373-0443
URL: insurify.com
Social Media: www.facebook.com/insurify
twitter.com/insurify

5881 ■ Insurify Safe Driving Scholarship
(Undergraduate/Scholarship)

Purpose: To support the next generation of innovators with a college scholarship contest. **Focus:** General studies/ Field of study not specified. **Qualif.:** Applicants must be enrolled at any accredited four-year university, two-year college, graduate school, community college, or trade school; must be willing to prove their active student status. **Criteria:** Selection will be based on the written essay of the applicants.

Funds Avail.: $1,000. **To Apply:** Applicants should write a well-developed, thought-provoking essay on one of the topic prompts regarding safe driving. Prompts and application form available at insurify.com/blog/company-news/ scholarship/. **Contact:** Email: scholarship@insurify.com.

5882 ■ Inter-American Foundation (IAF)
1331 Pennsylvania Ave. NW, Ste. 1200 N
Washington, DC 20004-1766
Ph: (202)360-4530
Fax: (703)306-4365
E-mail: inquiries@iaf.gov
URL: www.iaf.gov
Social Media: www.facebook.com/iafgrassroots
www.instagram.com/iafgrassroots
www.linkedin.com/company/59725
www.linkedin.com/company/inter-american-foundation
twitter.com/IAFgrassroots

5883 ■ IAF Fellowships *(Doctorate/Fellowship)*

Purpose: To support dissertation research of doctoral students regarding grassroots development issues in Latin America and the Caribbean. **Focus:** Culture; Government; Latin American studies; Physical sciences; Social sciences. **Criteria:** Fellowships are based on both development and scholarly criteria; selection will be based on the applicants' eligibility and their research proposals.

Funds Avail.: $3,000 research allowance; $1,500 monthly stipend for 12 months. **To Apply:** Applicants should submit their respective research proposals; proposed research should have a focus on grassroots development and only in exceptional cases will the IAF support proposals reflecting a primary interest in macro questions of politics and economics as they relate to the environment of the poor. Applicants may contact the IAF for the other materials necessary for the submission of applications. **Remarks:** The IAF Fellowships are currently administered with the support of the Institute for International Education (IIE). **Contact:** Any inquiries should be addressed to the Institute of International Education at iaffellowships@iie.org.

5884 ■ Intercollegiate Studies Institute (ISI)
3901 Centerville Rd.
Wilmington, DE 19807

Free: 800-526-7022
URL: isi.org
Social Media: www.facebook.com/ISIInc
www.linkedin.com/company/intercollegiate-studies-institute
twitter.com/isi

5885 ■ Henry Salvatori Fellowships *(Graduate/ Fellowship)*

Purpose: To improve the ability of the American people to understand their heritage, to distinguish its principles, and to choose well so that, through self-governance, they may protect their nation and preserve their liberties for themselves and the generations to come. **Focus:** United States studies. **Qualif.:** Applicant must be a U.S. citizen and member of the Intercollegiate Studies Institute; must be a college senior or graduate student; must engage in graduate studies for the purpose of teaching at the college level. **Criteria:** Applicants must meet the requirements specific to the fellowship.

Funds Avail.: $5,000 to $15,000 each. **Duration:** Annual; one year. **Contact:** E-mail: awards@isi.org.

5886 ■ Richard M. Weaver Fellowships *(Graduate/ Fellowship)*

Purpose: To assist motivated future teachers, similar to Professor Weaver, by the need to integrate the idea of liberal education with their teaching efforts, and in doing so, to restore to university studies their distinction and worth. **Focus:** Education. **Qualif.:** Applicant must be a U.S. citizen and member of the Intercollegiate Studies Institute; must be a college senior or graduate student; must engage in graduate studies for the purpose of teaching at the college level.

Funds Avail.: $5,000 to $15,000 each. **Duration:** Annual. **To Apply:** Submit a 1,250 to 2,500 word essay, recent high resolution photo, one page CV or resume, five to ten page autobiography, two academic letters of recommendation, transcripts of all undergraduate and graduate work, brief response to questions available online, completed application. **Deadline:** February 1. **Contact:** Email: awards@isi.org; URL: isi.org/students/fellowship-apply/.

5887 ■ Interior Design Educators Council (IDEC)
1 Parkview Plz., Ste. 800
Oakbrook Terrace, IL 60181
Ph: (630)544-5057
E-mail: info@idec.org
URL: www.idec.org
Social Media: www.facebook.com/idecorg
twitter.com/IDECorg

5888 ■ IDEC Special Project Grant *(Professional development/Grant)*

Purpose: To support individual projects that relate to interior design education and the profession. **Focus:** Education; Interior design. **Qualif.:** Applicant must be IDEC professional member in good standing. **Criteria:** Selection are based upon quality of idea and written abstract; contribution to interior design education and/or the profession; potential for matching or supplemental funds.

Funds Avail.: $3,000. **Duration:** Annual. **To Apply:** Applicant should submit project Form; Proposal abstract (500-word maximum) describing the research initiative or activity; For research projects using human subjects, authors

Awards are arranged alphabetically below their administering organizations

must include a completed IRB application. **Deadline:** January 6.

5889 ■ Intermediaries & Reinsurance Underwriters Association, Inc. (IRU Inc.)

c/o The Beaumont Group, Inc.
3626 E Tremont Ave., Ste. 203
Throggs Neck, NY 10465
Ph: (718)892-0228
E-mail: jwallis@irua.com
URL: www.irua.org
Social Media: linkedin.com/company-beta/2823800
twitter.com/IRUAnews

5890 ■ Intermediaries and Reinsurance Underwriters Association Summer Intern Scholarships Program *(Undergraduate/Scholarship)*

Purpose: To expand the exposure to reinsurance for students/interns through enhanced networking and interaction with existing industry professionals. **Focus:** Insurance and insurance-related fields. **Qualif.:** Applicants must be interns at an IRU member company; must be currently enrolled at a full-time college or university; must be working in any department at their host company. However, the host company must be an IRU member. **Criteria:** Applicants will be evaluated by the Internship Selection Committee.

To Apply: Applications and sample papers will be available for download on the IRU website at www.irua.com. Applicants must also submit a 10-20 page white paper on a specific insurance or reinsurance topic and provide a detailed explanation on that topic's relevance and impact or potential impact to the reinsurance industry.

5891 ■ Intermountain Medical Imaging

2929 E Magic View Dr.
Meridian, ID 83642
Ph: (208)954-8100
URL: www.aboutimi.com
Social Media: facebook.com/IntermountainMedicalImaging
www.linkedin.com/company/intermountain-medical-imaging
twitter.com/aboutIMI
www.youtube.com/channel/UCtiWR
_MQYM8I944JnO8XVdg

5892 ■ Intermountain Medical Imaging Scholarship *(Undergraduate, Community College/Scholarship)*

Purpose: To provide financial help for students seeking to further their career in a medical field. **Focus:** Medicine; Nursing; Radiology. **Qualif.:** Applicant must be a high school senior or college freshman attending or graduated from an Idaho high school; must have at least a 3.0 GPA; must have an interest in going into a healthcare field (MD, DO, PA, NP, nursing, radiology, technologist).

Funds Avail.: $1,000. **Number Awarded:** 1. **To Apply:** Applicant must submit an original 500-word essay on how they made a difference in their community and fill out an online form. **Deadline:** April 30. **Contact:** Email: community@aboutimi.com.

5893 ■ Intermountain Section American Water Works Association

8215 South 1300 West
West Jordan, UT 84088

Ph: (801)712-1619
URL: www.ims-awwa.org

5894 ■ Eva Nieminski Honorary Graduate Science and Engineering Scholarship *(Graduate/Scholarship)*

Purpose: To support students pursuing studies in the field of water quality, supply, and treatment in the Intermountain West. **Focus:** Water resources; Water supply industry. **Qualif.:** Students are eligible to apply who are enrolled in a graduate science or engineering program in the Intermountain West and whose research interests involve water quality, supply, or treatment. Students who have been accepted into such a graduate program but have not yet begun coursework are also eligible to apply. Applicants for this scholarship are considered without consideration of race, gender, color, or creed. Students are eligible to receive. **Criteria:** Selection Criteria Members of the Student Outreach and Scholarship Committee of the Intermountain; Members of the Student Outreach and Scholarship Committee of the Intermountain Section of the American Water Works Association will review all submitted application materials.

Funds Avail.: $1,000. **To Apply:** Applicants will be evaluated based on: The applicant's letters of recommendation The quality of the applicant's essay The applicant's potential to contribute to the field of water quality, supply; Scholarship Application Form (page 3 of this document) Resume Essay on your academic interests and career goals relevant to water quality, supply or treatment in the Intermountain West 2 Letters of Recommendation. **Deadline:** December 5. **Contact:** Email to nicoleb@ims-awwa.org.

5895 ■ IMS AWWA Graduate Science and Engineering Scholarships *(Graduate/Scholarship)*

Purpose: To support students pursuing studies in the field of water quality, supply, and treatment in the Intermountain West. **Focus:** Water resources; Water supply industry. **Qualif.:** Applicants must be pursuing a science or engineering degree in the Intermountain West. Students who have been accepted into a program but have not yet begun coursework are eligible to apply. Applicants for this scholarship are eligible without consideration of race, gender, color, or creed. **Criteria:** Selection will be based on letters of recommendation; the quality of the essay; the potential to contribute to the field of water quality, supply and treatment in the Intermountain West.

Funds Avail.: $1,750. **Duration:** Annual. **To Apply:** Applicants must submit all materials required in the application for scholarship in one document in a pdf format; must complete resume; an essay regarding applicant's academic interests and career goals and how they are relevant to water quality, supply, or treatment in the Intermountain West; must provide two letters of recommendation. **Deadline:** December 5. **Contact:** Email: nicoleb@ims-awwa.org.

5896 ■ International Academy of Aviation and Space Medicine (IAASM)

8 Cambridge
Baie D'Urfe, QC, Canada H9X 2V4
URL: www.iaasm.org

5897 ■ IAASM Aviation Medicine Scholarship *(Professional development/Scholarship)*

Purpose: To enable young physicians commencing a career in aerospace medicine to undertake training in the specialty. **Focus:** Medicine. **Qualif.:** applicant must contact

Awards are arranged alphabetically below their administering organizations

the institution where he/she intends to pursue his/her studies and find out if an English test is required. **Criteria:** Selection is based on basis of depending on the detail of the applications received.

Funds Avail.: Up to $20,000. **Duration:** Annual. **Number Awarded:** Varies. **To Apply:** Individuals wishing to apply for this Scholarship may print a copy of the Scholarship Application Form in English or French. These forms are in PDF format for which you will need Adobe Acrobat Reader or the full Adobe Acrobat program. **Contact:** Dr. Francisco Tejada, Chairman, Scholarship Committee E-Mail: scholarship@iaasm.org.

5898 ■ International Anesthesia Research Society (IARS)

90 New Montgomery St., Ste. 412
San Francisco, CA 94105
Ph: (240)646-7089
E-mail: info@iars.org
URL: www.iars.org

5899 ■ IARS Mentored Research Award (IMRA)
(Professional development/Award, Grant)

Purpose: To support investigations that will further the understanding of clinical practice in anesthesiology and related sciences. **Focus:** Anesthesiology. **Qualif.:** Applicants must be investigators(clinical, translational, basic science) with IARS membership. **Criteria:** Selection will be based on the submitted applications, which will be reviewed on the basis of scientific merit, adequate preliminary data, career potential of the investigators, and importance of the investigation to the specialty of anesthesiology.

Funds Avail.: $175,000 each. **Duration:** Annual; up to two years. **Number Awarded:** 4. **To Apply:** Applicants must check the website for more information. **Contact:** Email: awards@iars.org.

5900 ■ International Association of Administrative Professionals Wings Chapter

Dayton, OH
Ph: (937)898-0826
E-mail: stoffjen@sbcglobal.net
URL: www.iaap-ohio.org/Chapters.htm#Dayton_Wings

5901 ■ IAAP Wings Chapter Scholarships
(Undergraduate/Scholarship)

Purpose: To recognize individuals who are pursuing careers as office professionals. **Focus:** Business. **Qualif.:** Applicant must be from Dayton area and surrounding counties who are pursuing careers as office professionals.

Funds Avail.: No specific amount. **Duration:** Annual.

5902 ■ International Association of Arson Investigators (IAAI)

2111 Baldwin Ave., Ste. 203
Crofton, MD 21114
Ph: (410)451-3473
Fax: (410)451-9049
Free: 800-468-4224
E-mail: iaai@firearson.com
URL: www.firearson.com
Social Media: www.facebook.com/IAAIInc

twitter.com/IAAIhq
www.youtube.com/user/iaaifireinvestigator

5903 ■ John Charles Wilson and Robert Doran Sr. Scholarship *(Undergraduate/Scholarship)*

Purpose: To provide financial assistance to individuals to enhance their education in the fire/explosion profession by attending the IAAI International Training Conference or other IAAI Training events. **Focus:** Fires and fire prevention. **Qualif.:** Applicants must be a current IAAI member or current IAAI Chapter member.

Funds Avail.: $1,000. **Duration:** Annual. **Number Awarded:** Varies. **To Apply:** Applicants must submit a completed application, along with a short narrative on why they are making application for the scholarship program. **Deadline:** August 1. **Contact:** IAAI Foundation Scholarship, 2111 Baldwin Ave., Ste. 204, Crofton, Maryland, 21114; Phone: 410-451-3473; Email: iaaifoundation@firearson.com.

5904 ■ International Association of Arson Investigators Maine Chapter

PO Box 1101
Auburn, ME 04211-1101
E-mail: maineiaai@gmail.com
URL: maineiaai.com
Social Media: www.facebook.com/maineiaai

5905 ■ Joseph C. Menezes Scholarship Fund
(Undergraduate/Scholarship)

Purpose: To provide financial support to individuals who are pursuing studies in the field of Fire Science Degree programs. **Focus:** Fires and fire prevention.

Funds Avail.: No specific amount. **To Apply:** Application must be submit through online form. **Deadline:** April 1. **Contact:** Maine Chapter IAAI Attn: Scholarship Committee PO Box 1101 Auburn, ME 04211-1101.

5906 ■ International Association of Black Actuaries (IABA)

PO Box 270701
West Hartford, CT 06127
Ph: (860)906-1286
Fax: (860)906-1369
E-mail: iaba@blackactuaries.org
URL: www.blackactuaries.org
Social Media: www.instagram.com/blackactuaries/
www.linkedin.com/groups/1218187
twitter.com/BlackActuaries
www.youtube.com/channel/
    UCTbPGTSMQ77Sc7JB3XJL5jw

5907 ■ International Association of Black Actuaries Scholarships *(Undergraduate/Scholarship)*

Purpose: To provide scholarships among undergraduates or graduate level for qualified black students who are interested in pursuing actuarial careers. **Focus:** Actuarial science.

Funds Avail.: $3,000 - $5,000. **Duration:** Annual.

5908 ■ International Association of Chiefs of Police (IACP)

44 Canal Center Plaza Ste. 200
Alexandria, VA 22314

Awards are arranged alphabetically below their administering organizations

Ph: (703)836-6767
Fax: (703)836-4543
Free: 800-843-4227
E-mail: membership@theiacp.org
URL: www.theiacp.org
Social Media: www.facebook.com/TheIACP
www.linkedin.com/company/international-association-of
  -chiefs-of-police
twitter.com/TheIACP
www.youtube.com/user/TheIACP

5909 ■ IACP University and College Police Section Scholarship *(Undergraduate/Scholarship)*

Purpose: To provide scholarship assistance to outstanding students who meet eligibility guidelines set by the section and are pursuing undergraduate degrees from an accredited university or college program relating to any aspect of the criminal justice system. **Focus:** Law enforcement. **Qualif.:** Applicant must be an IACP University & College Section member and have an endorsing letter of reference from an official at the institution where the student is currently enrolled; a verification of enrollment as an undergraduate student at an accredited institution; and an academic grade point average of 3.0 or higher. **Criteria:** Selection will be based on academic ability, leadership, and unlimited growth potential or other supporting characteristics.

Funds Avail.: $1,000. **Duration:** Annual. **Remarks:** Established in 2001.

5910 ■ International Association for Cross-Cultural Psychology (IACCP)

c/o William Gabrenya, IT Officer, Webmaster
School of Psychology Florida Institute of Technology
Melbourne, FL 32901
Ph: (310)825-7526
E-mail: gabrenya@fit.edu
URL: www.iaccp.org
Social Media: www.facebook.com/groups/IACCP
twitter.com/iaccp

5911 ■ Harry and Pola Triandis Doctoral Thesis Award *(Doctorate/Grant)*

Purpose: To promote and facilitate research in the areas of culture and psychology. **Focus:** Psychology. **Criteria:** Selection will be based on committee's criteria.

Funds Avail.: $500. **Duration:** Biennial. **Number Awarded:** 2. **To Apply:** Submit a 1500-word abstract of the doctoral thesis in English. The abstract must contain no information that identifies the applicant, thesis supervisor, or institution. The abstract must include complete details of theory, method, results, and implications for the field. The abstract must be submitted electronically (email attachment, CD, disk, etc.) using a common word processing file format such as Microsoft Word, WordPerfect, or RTF. Include: a letter from the thesis advisor certifying the university acceptance date of the thesis; cover letter with complete applicant contact information, including an address or addresses through with the applicant can be contacted during the evaluation process, telephone numbers, fax number, and e-mail addresses. Following a preliminary evaluation, finalists will be asked to send copies of their complete doctoral thesis, in the language in which it was written, to the evaluation committee. **Deadline:**

October 30. **Remarks:** Established in 2000.

5912 ■ International Association for Dental Research (IADR)

1619 Duke St.
Alexandria, VA 22314-3406
Ph: (703)548-0066
Fax: (703)548-1883
E-mail: research@iadr.org
URL: www.iadr.org
Social Media: www.facebook.com/DentalResearch
www.instagram.com/official_iadr
twitter.com/iadr

5913 ■ IADR John Clarkson Fellowship *(Postdoctorate/Fellowship)*

Purpose: To allow investigators in the field of public dental health to obtain training and experience at a center of excellence. **Focus:** Dentistry. **Qualif.:** Applicants must hold a degree in dentistry or in a scientific discipline (dental, masters, or PhD degrees), and be member of IADR and actively engaged in research in public dental health. **Criteria:** Recipients will be selected based on merit.

Funds Avail.: Up to $15,000 covering accommodation, subsistence and travel. **Duration:** Biennial. **Number Awarded:** 1. **To Apply:** Applications should be made individually and should include the following details: name, address, current place of work, and position; IADR Division/Section membership; full curriculum vitae and reprints of three relevant publications; references from two recognized scientists and the principal Dean/Chair of the institution where the applicant is employed; and an outline (3 pages maximum, single-spaced) by the applicant describing how their experience and interests qualify them as a candidate for the Fellowship, including: detailed description of the subject areas to be covered in the training program; practical use to which the training acquired would be put, proposed duration and dates of the fellowship; institutes and country it is proposed to visit; reasons for selection of particular institutes(s); previous Fellowships/awards; and detailed budget for program. Applications are sent electronically. **Remarks:** The Fellowship is in honor of John Clarkson, who served as Executive Director of IADR/AADR from 1990-97. **Contact:** Anthony Jones; Awards, Fellowships and Grants Coordinator; ajones@iadr.org.

5914 ■ IADR John Gray Fellowship *(Other/Fellowship)*

Purpose: To allow dental or postgraduate students to obtain training and experience in dental or related research. **Focus:** Dentistry. **Qualif.:** Applicants must be registered students in an accredited or acceptable dental school or in a recognized formal postgraduate program; in a training program in the division in which the fellowship is awarded; sponsored by their faculty advisor/direct supervisor or the Dean of the School; must be an IADR member. **Criteria:** Recipients will be selected based on merit.

Funds Avail.: Up to $10,000. **Duration:** Biennial; awarded in odd-numbered years. **Number Awarded:** 1. **To Apply:** Applicants must submit a proposal to the division secretary outlining: the precise title of the subject to be studied; detailed description of the subjects to be covered in the training program; practical use to which the training acquired would be put; proposed duration and dates of the fellowship; institute(s) and country it is proposed to visit;

Awards are arranged alphabetically below their administering organizations

reasons for particular institute(s); previous fellowships or awards; and budget for program. The division officers will select the fellowship recipient and will then send the candidate's name to the Central Office for presentation to the IADR Board of Directors for approval. **Deadline:** January 15. **Remarks:** The Fellowship is in tribute to John A. Gray, former Executive Director of IADR, and is funded out of donations from members and sponsors. **Contact:** Anthony Jones; Awards, Fellowships and Grants Coordinator; ajones@iadr.org.

5915 ■ IADR Toshio Nakao Fellowship (Other/ Fellowship)

Purpose: To allow young investigators in the area of dental materials science to obtain training and experience at a center of excellence. **Focus:** Dentistry. **Qualif.:** Applicants must hold a degree in dentistry or in a scientific discipline; be within five years of obtaining their dental or scientific degree on or at the fellowship proposal deadline; and, be member of IADR and are actively engaged in research. **Criteria:** Recipients will be selected based on merit as evaluated by the IADR Fellowships Committee. Preference will be given to applicants from regions with less developed research programs in the field of materials science.

Funds Avail.: Up to $15,000. **Duration:** Biennial; awarded in odd-numbered years. **Number Awarded:** 1. **To Apply:** Applications should be made individually and should include the following details (in English): name, address, date of birth, current place of work, and position; IADR Division/Section membership; full curriculum vitae with list and reprints of three relevant publications; references from two recognized scientists, one of whom should be from the principal (Dean/Chair) of the institution where the applicant is employed; and an outline by the applicant of how their experience and interests qualify them as a candidate for the fellowship (no more than three single spaced pages), including: detailed description of the subject areas to be covered in the training program; practical use to which the training acquired would be put; proposed duration and dates of the fellowship; institutes and/or country it is proposed to visit; reasons for particular institutes(s); previous fellowships/awards; and budget for program. **Deadline:** February 10. **Remarks:** The Fellowship is in memory of Toshio Nakao, former President of GC Corporation. **Contact:** Anthony Jones; Awards, Fellowships and Grants Coordinator; ajones@iadr.org.

5916 ■ IADR Norton Ross Fellowship (Postgraduate/ Fellowship)

Purpose: To allow dental or postgraduate students to obtain training and experience in dental or related research. **Focus:** Dentistry. **Qualif.:** Applicants must be registered in an accredited or acceptable dental school or in a recognized formal postgraduate program; sponsored by their faculty advisor, direct supervisor, or the Dean of the school; and, IADR member. They may have a college or advanced degree in a discipline other than dentistry. **Criteria:** Recipients will be selected based on merit.

Funds Avail.: $2,800. **Duration:** Biennial; awarded in even-numbered years. **Number Awarded:** 1. **To Apply:** Applicants must submit a proposal directly to their division outlining: the precise title of the subject to be studied; detailed description of the subjects to be covered in the training program; practical use to which the training acquired would be put; proposed duration and dates of the fellowship; institute(s) and country it is proposed to visit; reasons for particular institute(s); previous fellowships or awards; and budget for program. **Remarks:** The awarding

of the fellowship rotates among the IADR Divisions. **Contact:** Anthony Jones; Awards, Fellowships and Grants Coordinator; ajones@iadr.org.

5917 ■ IADR David B. Scott Fellowship (Professional development/Fellowship, Award)

Purpose: To improve knowledge on oral health by advancing and supporting research projects, support and represent the oral health research community, and facilitate the communication and application of research findings. **Focus:** Dental hygiene. **Qualif.:** Applicants must be training dental students registered in an accredited or acceptable dental school, and be sponsored by a dental researcher with the approval of their school's dean; Candidates may not have received their dental degree nor should they be due to receive their degree in the year of the award, and may have a college or advanced degree in a discipline other than the industry; must be IADR member. **Criteria:** Recipients will be selected based on the submitted project proposal as reviewed by the IADR Board of Directors.

Funds Avail.: $2,500. **Duration:** Annual. **Number Awarded:** Varies. **To Apply:** Applicants and their sponsors must submit a research project proposal to the division not exceeding eight pages (including references), typed and double-spaced; Proposal should include aims, objectives and significance of the proposal; rationale and background to the study; materials and methods; statistical treatment of data; facilities and equipment; and budget. **Deadline:** January 15. **Remarks:** Established in 1987. **Contact:** Anthony Jones; Awards, Fellowships and Grants Coordinator; ajones@iadr.org.

5918 ■ International Association of Emergency Managers (IAEM)
201 Park Washington Ct.
Falls Church, VA 22046-4527
Ph: (703)538-1795
Fax: (703)241-5603
E-mail: info@iaem.com
URL: iaem.com
Social Media: www.facebook.com/
  InternationalAssociationOfEmergencyManagers
twitter.com/iaem
www.youtube.com/user/IAEMOfficialChannel

5919 ■ IAEM Scholarship Program (Undergraduate, Graduate/Scholarship)

Purpose: To assist the profession by identifying and developing students with the intellect and technical skills that can advance and enhance emergency management or disaster management. **Focus:** Emergency and disaster services. **Qualif.:** Applicant must be a full-time undergraduate and graduate and part-time graduate student in the field of disaster and emergency management. **Criteria:** Selection will be based on merit.

Funds Avail.: No specific amount. **Duration:** Annual. **Number Awarded:** Varies. **To Apply:** Applicants must submit the following: completed application form; transcripts with official seal; proof of enrollment as full-time undergraduate students; at least three character and personal references; description of applicants' major/program; and two essays indicated in the application form (should be between 1, 000 and 1, 500 words, 12 point type, one inch/2.5 centimeters margins, double spaced, single-sided. The format is approximately 300 words per page. Begin each essay on a

Awards are arranged alphabetically below their administering organizations

new page). **Deadline:** July 31. **Contact:** IAEM Scholarship Program Director Dawn M. Shiley, shiley@iaem.com.

5920 ■ International Association for Food Protection (IAFP)

2900 100th St., Ste. 309
Des Moines, IA 50322-3855
Ph: (515)276-3344
Fax: (515)276-8655
Free: 800-369-6337
E-mail: info@foodprotection.org
URL: www.foodprotection.org
Social Media: www.facebook.com/International-Association
  -for-Food-Protection-134554485526
www.linkedin.com/company/international-association-for
  -food-protection/
twitter.com/IAFPFood

5921 ■ International Association for Food Protection - Student Travel Scholarship Program
(Undergraduate, Graduate/Scholarship)

Purpose: To provide travel funding for full-time students to attend the Annual Meeting of the International Association for Food Protection and to encourage developing scientists to participate in association activities. **Focus:** Food science and technology; Microbiology; Toxicology. **Qualif.:** Applicants must be members of IAFP; must demonstrate an interest in and commitment to food safety and quality as undergraduate or graduate students enrolled full-time in a food science, microbiology, toxicology or other program related to food microbiological or toxicological safety at a college or university at the time of the application deadline.

Funds Avail.: No specific amount. **Duration:** Annual. **Number Awarded:** Up to 20. **To Apply:** Applicants must submit an application in one electronic file that includes the following documents completed application form; statement of interest explaining the interest in food safety and quality, career aspirations, reasons to attend the IAFP Annual Meeting, and current research projects how the project will enhance food safety or quality and who will benefit from the work; one letter of recommendation from faculty member or department head to include outstanding qualifications/contributions made throughout the student's academic career; potential value the students possess toward making significant future contributions in the food safety profession; must also include one-page maximum, additional information list of received awards, honors, travel grants, scholarships, etc.; schools attended; involvement in local affiliate; other relevant supporting materials. **Deadline:** February 18. **Contact:** Email: studenttravel@foodprotection.org.

5922 ■ International Association for Great Lakes Research (IAGLR)

4840 S State Rd.
Ann Arbor, MI 48108
Ph: (734)665-5303
Fax: (734)741-2055
E-mail: office@iaglr.org
URL: www.iaglr.org
Social Media: www.facebook.com/iaglr
www.linkedin.com/company/international-association-for
  -great-lakes-research
twitter.com/iaglr

www.youtube.com/channel/UCJnfE3drxlpr9JQBTMyzBFA

5923 ■ Norman S. Baldwin Fishery Science Scholarship *(Doctorate, Master's/Scholarship)*

Purpose: To promote academic excellence by encouraging young scientists to undertake graduate research in fishery biology and to enter the field of Great Lakes science. **Focus:** Fisheries sciences/management. **Qualif.:** Applicants must be master's or Ph.D. students at the time of application, whose proposed research topic is relevant to Great Lakes fishery research, and who have not previously received the award. **Criteria:** Aeection will be based on the basis of scientific merit, presentation, originality, and contribution to the understanding of Great Lakes fisheries.

Funds Avail.: $3,000 each. **Duration:** Annual. **Number Awarded:** Up to 2. **To Apply:** A complete application is composed of four parts: application form; brief title and extended abstract of proposed research and relevance of the project to fishery science (no more than 2 single spaced pages); current curriculum vitae; letter of endorsement from a supervising professor. **Deadline:** December 1.

5924 ■ IAGLR Scholarship *(Doctorate/Scholarship)*

Purpose: To recognize a promising Ph.D. student whose dissertation research is likely to make a significant contribution to the understanding of large lakes. **Focus:** Environmental science. **Qualif.:** Applicants must be Ph.D. students at the time of application, who are members of IAGLR; and proposed research topic is relevant to large lakes are eligible; student's academic ability, aptitude. **Criteria:** Selection will be based on academic excellence, scientific merit, presentation, originality, and contribution to the understanding of large lakes.

Funds Avail.: $2,000. **Duration:** Annual. **Number Awarded:** Varies. **To Apply:** Applicant must submit a application form; brief title and extended abstract of dissertation research, including a statement of why the research will make a significant contribution to understanding large lakes (no more than 2 single-spaced pages); current curriculum vitae; letter of endorsement from a supervising professor; transcripts for past 2 years. **Deadline:** December 1. **Remarks:** Established in 1986. **Contact:** Email: scholarships@iaglr.org.

5925 ■ Paul W. Rodgers Scholarship
(Undergraduate/Scholarship)

Purpose: To support the advancement of knowledge relating to Great Lakes aquatic ecosystem health and management. **Focus:** Conservation of natural resources. **Qualif.:** Applicants must be students who have knowledge relating to Great Lakes aquatic ecosystem health and management.

Funds Avail.: $10,000. **Duration:** Annual. **Number Awarded:** varies. **Remarks:** Established in 1999.

5926 ■ International Association of Healthcare Central Service Materiel Management (IAHCSMM)

55 W Wacker Dr., Ste. 501
Chicago, IL 60601
Ph: (312)440-0078
Fax: (312)440-9474
Free: 800-962-8274
E-mail: mailbox@iahcsmm.org
URL: www.iahcsmm.org
Social Media: www.facebook.com/IAHCSMM

Awards are arranged alphabetically below their administering organizations

www.linkedin.com/company/iahcsmm
twitter.com/IAHCSMM

5927 ■ IAHCSMM-Purdue University Scholarship
(Professional development/Scholarship)

Purpose: To financially support individuals who are pursuing their educational and individual growth. **Focus:** General studies/Field of study not specified. **Qualif.:** Applicants should be central sterile supply department technicians, central sterile supply department managers/supervisors. **Criteria:** Selection will be based on financial need; interest in pursuing educational and individual growth goals; participation in activities (association, hospital department, community); and years of service in Central Service.

Funds Avail.: No specific amount. **Number Awarded:** 2. **To Apply:** Applicants must submit the online application form with a reference letter and personal essay attached. **Deadline:** February 29. **Contact:** Purdue Online Scholarship Awards; Purdue Online Learning; Ernest C Young Hall, Room 405; West Lafayette, IN 47907-2114.

5928 ■ SPSmedical CS Scholarships *(Other/ Scholarship)*

Purpose: To give individuals the opportunity to work towards certification by providing all the study materials needed to prepare for the certification exam. **Focus:** Medical technology. **Qualif.:** Applicants must be employed in the CS profession for at least six months. **Criteria:** Selection will be based on applicants who will fulfill the requirements.

Funds Avail.: No specific amount. **Duration:** Annual. **Number Awarded:** Various. **To Apply:** Applicants must submit the online application form and submit along with recommendation from supervisor/manager. **Contact:** Send Application to: Crosstex; Attn: Education Department; 6789 W. Henrietta Road; Rush, NY, 14543; (800) 722-1529; Fax: 585-359-0167; E-mail: info@spsmedical.com.

5929 ■ International Association of Law Enforcement Intelligence Analysts (IALEIA)
PO Box 13857
Richmond, VA 23225
Ph: (424)246-8350
Fax: (804)565-2059
URL: www.ialeia.org
Social Media: www.facebook.com/IALEIA
www.pinterest.com/pin/517210338450461599
twitter.com/intellanalysts

5930 ■ Jorge Espejel Contreras IALEIA Scholarship
(Undergraduate/Scholarship)

Purpose: To support students in their pursuit of career in the intelligence field. **Focus:** Criminal justice; Intelligence service; Statistics.

Number Awarded: 1 in 2017. **To Apply:** Applicants must submit scholarship application (see below); essay (1, 500 – 2, 000 words); letter from a faculty advisor or acceptance letter from academic institution, including the name, telephone number, and mailing address of the Registrar for the school you are attending. **Remarks:** The scholarship was established in honor of Jorge Espejel.

5931 ■ Henley-Putnam University Scholarships
(Other/Scholarship)

Purpose: To promote career development and continued education in the intelligence field by providing educational assistance. **Focus:** Intelligence service. **Qualif.:** Applicants must be active IALEIA members or immediate family members of IALEIA members. **Criteria:** Applicants will be evaluated by the IALEIA Director of Training, Education and Career Development and TE&CD committee members.

Funds Avail.: No specific amount. **Duration:** Annual. **Remarks:** The scholarship is made possible by the partnership of the Henley-Putnam University and the IALEIA. **Contact:** Nancy A. Reggio, Director of Admissions, Henley-Putnam University at nreggio@henley-putnam.edu.

5932 ■ International Association of Law Libraries (IALL)
PO Box 5709
Washington, DC 20016
URL: iall.org
Social Media: www.facebook.com/IALL.org
twitter.com/iallofficial?lang=en

5933 ■ IALL Regular Bursaries *(Other/Scholarship)*

Purpose: To enable law librarians who are normally unable to benefit from the association's activities to attend the Annual Course in International Law Librarianship that forms the annual conference of the association. **Focus:** Law. **Qualif.:** Applicants must be in current employment in librarianship with significant legal context to their work; need not be members of the Association and not available to students.

Funds Avail.: Varies. **Duration:** Annual. **Number Awarded:** 3. **To Apply:** Applicants must submit online application form along with copy of resume; personal statement stating the reason for attending the IALL conference; two reference letters (1 must be from your current employer); an itemized estimate of expenses for attending the conference including airfare, ground transportation, hotel and food, documented in English and calculated in $US dollars. **Contact:** David Gee, Chair of the IALL Scholarships; Email: david.gee@sas.ac.uk.

5934 ■ International Association of Lighting Designers (IALD)
440 N Wells St., Ste. 210
Chicago, IL 60654
Ph: (312)527-3677
Fax: (312)527-3680
E-mail: iald@iald.org
URL: www.iald.org
Social Media: www.facebook.com/theIALD
www.linkedin.com/groups/790407/profile
twitter.com/iald
www.youtube.com/theiald

5935 ■ BK Lighting / Ron Naus Scholarship *(Graduate, Undergraduate/Scholarship)*

Purpose: To promote the study of architectural lighting design. **Focus:** Architecture. **Qualif.:** Applicants must be student members of the IALD, or have their applications pending, currently enrolled in an undergraduate or graduate program and pursuing architectural lighting design as their course of study. **Criteria:** Applicants will be judged based on Completeness, Followed Directions, Creativity, Enthusiasm, Strength, Effort.

Funds Avail.: $1,000 USD to $3,000 USD.(BK Lighting / Ron Naus Scholarship &Lighting Design Alliance Scholar-

Awards are arranged alphabetically below their administering organizations

ship); $4,000 USD(Thomas M. Lemons). Scholarship. **Duration:** Annual. **To Apply:** Applicants must complete and submit the following materials: an application form (available at the website); resume; letters of recommendation; statement of personal experience; PDF of your strongest lighting project - three (3) page maximum. **Deadline:** Mid-November to Mid-December.

5936 ■ International Association for Research on Service-Learning and Community Engagement (IARSLCE)

Tulane University Ctr. for Public Service
Alcee Fortier Hall., 6823 St. Charles Ave.
6823 St. Charles Ave.
New Orleans, LA 70118
E-mail: info@researchslce.org
URL: www.researchslce.org
Social Media: www.facebook.com/larslce
 -121503447907092
www.linkedin.com/groups/3659612/profile
twitter.com/IARSLCE

5937 ■ IARSLCE Graduate Student Scholarships *(Graduate/Scholarship)*

Purpose: To support students in their participation in the IARSLCE Conference. **Focus:** Education; Sociology. **Qualif.:** Applicants must either be early graduate or advanced graduate students. **Criteria:** Selection will be based on the IARSLCE's criteria.

Funds Avail.: $500 each. **Duration:** Annual. **Number Awarded:** 10. **To Apply:** Applicants must submit the application packet that includes name, mailing address, phone number, and email address; institution, department, and advisor/program director; date of entry into graduate program and date of anticipated graduation; for the early graduate students, provide a single-spaced statement not to exceed 500 words that clearly identifies research areas of interest and plans for pursuing them; specific examples of how attendance at the conference will benefit the research and graduate education; current involvement with service-learning or community engagement research or practice; for the advanced graduate students: a single-spaced statement not to exceed 500 words that clearly identifies a research project, including research question and methods; specific examples of how attendance at the conference will benefit the current and/or future research, remaining graduate education, and professional goals. **Deadline:** March 23. **Contact:** Email: info@researchslce.org.

5938 ■ International Association for the Study of Pain (IASP)

1510 H St. NW, Ste. 600
Washington, DC 20005-1020
Ph: (202)856-7400
Fax: (202)856-7401
E-mail: iaspdesk@iasp-pain.org
URL: www.iasp-pain.org
Social Media: www.facebook.com/IASP.pain
twitter.com/IASPPAIN

5939 ■ IASP Collaborative Research Grants *(Professional development/Grant)*

Purpose: To support international interdisciplinary collaborations in pain research. **Focus:** Medical research.

Qualif.: Applicant must be the principal investigator in charge of the overall project must have been a member of IASP for the past year from the date of application; the principal investigator should be at a professional level of independence (i.e., a faculty-level academic appointment); the collaborators must be located in at least 2 different countries. **Criteria:** Selection will be based on scientific merit; qualifications of the investigators; evidence of interdisciplinary collaboration.

Funds Avail.: Up to $15,000. **Duration:** Annual. **Number Awarded:** 2. **To Apply:** Applications must be submitted in English via the online application system and include all required documents, as stated in the online application guidelines; short-version curriculum vitae of the principal investigator; evidence of professional independence. **Deadline:** April 4. **Contact:** Phone: 202-856-7400; Email: grants@iasp-pain.org.

5940 ■ IASP Developed-Developing Countries Collaborative Research Grants *(Advanced Professional/Grant)*

Purpose: To recognize and promote international, interdisciplinary collaborations in pain research, specifically between laboratories in a developing country and in a developed country. **Focus:** Medical research. **Qualif.:** Investigators in each country must have been members of IASP for the past year. The principal investigator in charge of the overall project should be at a professional level of independence. At least one participating institute and investigator must be from a developing country. **Criteria:** Evaluations are based on qualifications of the investigators; scientific merit; and evidence of interdisciplinary collaboration.

Funds Avail.: $15,000. **Duration:** Annual. **Number Awarded:** 1. **To Apply:** All applications must be submitted using the online application system. **Deadline:** April 7. **Contact:** grants@iasp-pain.org if you have any questions, or call +1-202-856-7400.

5941 ■ IASP Developing Countries Project: Initiative for Improving Pain Education *(Advanced Professional/Grant)*

Purpose: To improve the scope and availability of essential education for pain clinicians of all disciplines, taking into account specific local needs and to address the need for improved pain education and practice in developing countries by providing support grants. **Focus:** Medical research. **Qualif.:** The principal organizer must be based in a developing country; must have been a member of IASP for the past year; must not have received the same award in the previous year. Applications should be for one-year projects that are ready to begin within three months of the date of submitting this application; must not be in the planning stages; and must have specific beginning and ending dates.

Funds Avail.: Up to $10,000 each. **Duration:** Annual. **Number Awarded:** Varies. **To Apply:** Applications must be completed online; Short version curriculum vitae of the applicant; template is available via online grant application system; template is available via online grant application system. **Deadline:** March 14. **Contact:** Phone: 202-856-7400; Email: grants@iasp-pain.org.

5942 ■ IASP Research Symposium *(Advanced Professional/Grant)*

Purpose: To sponsor research symposia on topics of interest to basic scientists and clinical researchers. **Focus:**

Awards are arranged alphabetically below their administering organizations

Medical research. **Qualif.:** Applicants must be members of IASP.

Funds Avail.: Up to $50,000. **Duration:** Annual. **Remarks:** Established in 1998.

5943 ■ IASP Visiting Professor Grant (Professional development/Grant)

Purpose: To fund travel for a single IASP guest speaker at a chapter meeting or event. **Focus:** Education. **Qualif.:** Applicants must be a current IASP member for at least one year before the grant application is submitted.

Funds Avail.: No specific amount. **Duration:** Biennial. **Number Awarded:** 1. **To Apply:** Applicants may contact IASP for the application process and other information. **Contact:** Send your completed application form to chapters@iasp-pain.org.

5944 ■ John J. Bonica Trainee Fellowship (Professional development/Fellowship)

Purpose: To support training in all aspects of pain research. **Focus:** Medicine. **Qualif.:** Applicants have no restrictions as to the trainee's age; must provide a proof of Ph.D. completion (or equivalent) prior to initiation of the fellowship; trainee will generally be in an early stage of their career; trainees must be IASP members at the time of applying; mentors must be IASP members for at least one year at the time of applying; the mentor must not have served as a mentor for a John J. Bonica Fellowship trainee within the last three years. **Criteria:** Selection will be based on qualifications of the applicant and mentor; usefulness of the training to the research career; research proposal.

Funds Avail.: $50,000. **Duration:** Annual; for 24 months. **Number Awarded:** 1. **To Apply:** Applications can be submitted online; must include curriculum vitae (maximum of four pages); description of the research project (justification of the particular project, the methods employed, and whether the proposed experiments will generate interpretable results); maximum of three pages, 11 pt. font, inch (1.27 cm) margins; at least two letters of recommendation from IASP members (in addition to the mentor's letter). **Remarks:** The Fellowship was established in memory of the founder of IASP, John J. Bonica. Established in 1998. **Contact:** Phone: 202-856-7400; Email: grants@iasp-pain.org.

5945 ■ Phillip A. Spiegel IASP Congress Trainee Scholarship (Graduate, Undergraduate/Scholarship)

Purpose: To support IASP trainees who need financial assistance in furthering their education in the study of pain. **Focus:** General studies/Field of study not specified.

Funds Avail.: No specific amount. **Duration:** Annual. **Number Awarded:** 1. 2018. **To Apply:** Applicants may contact the Association for the application process and other information's. **Remarks:** The scholarship was established by IASP and friends and family of Philip A. Spiegel, a young medical researcher and IASP member. Established in 2011.

5946 ■ International Association of Wildland Fire (IAWF)

1418 Washburn St.
Missoula, MT 59801
Ph: (406)531-8264
URL: www.iawfonline.org
Social Media: www.facebook.com/pages/International
  -Association-of-Wildland-Fire/143152469082255

twitter.com/IAWF

5947 ■ International Association of Wildland Fire Graduate-Level Scholarships (Graduate/Scholarship)

Purpose: To financially assist graduate students in obtaining their graduate level degree in a wildland fire or any related topics. **Focus:** Fires and fire prevention. **Qualif.:** Applicants must be IAWF members who are enrolled full-time in graduate school; must be Master's of Science or Ph.D. students. **Criteria:** Selection of applicants will be based on the criteria of the selection committee.

Funds Avail.: $3,000. **Duration:** Annual. **Number Awarded:** 2.

5948 ■ International Association of Women Police (IAWP)

12600 Kavanaugh Ln.
Bowie, MD 20715
Ph: (301)464-1402
E-mail: iawp@iawp.org
URL: www.iawp.org
Social Media: www.facebook.com/groups/iawpgroup
twitter.com/IAWPinfo
www.youtube.com/user/IAWPvideo

5949 ■ IAWP International Scholarship (Other/Scholarship)

Purpose: To increase the understanding about the roles of women officers in various countries. **Focus:** Law enforcement. **Qualif.:** Applicants must be women and members of the police organization outside U.S. and Canada.

Funds Avail.: $500. **Duration:** Annual. **Number Awarded:** 1. **To Apply:** Applicants must submit the following: a personal information including the name, rank, assignment, police organization and contact information; biography including education, employment history and interest; a letter of support from the applicant's senior officer or administrator indicating how long they have known the applicants and the basis of the recommendation; and a letter of application written by applicants showing why they deserve to receive the scholarship award. **Deadline:** April 30. **Contact:** Linda Mayberry; E-mail: linda-mayberry@hotmail.com; or Cindy Shain; E-mail: cindyshain@aol.com.

5950 ■ International Association of Workforce Professionals (IAWP)

3267 Bee Caves Rd., Ste. 107-104
Austin, TX 78746
Ph: (502)223-4459
E-mail: info@iawponline.org
URL: www.iawponline.org
Social Media: www.facebook.com/pages/category/
  Nonprofit-Organization/International-Association-of
  -Workforce-Professionals-IAWP-782675548504900
www.instagram.com/workforceprofessionals
twitter.com/iawpcenter

5951 ■ W. Scott Boyd Group Grant (Advanced Professional/Grant)

Purpose: To provide financial assistance to IAWP chapters and subchapters, as well as chapters working with their agencies for the presentation of group educational and training programs. **Focus:** General studies/Field of study not specified.

Awards are arranged alphabetically below their administering organizations

Funds Avail.: Amount varies. **Duration:** Annual. **Remarks:** The scholarship established to honor W. Scott Boyd, the second Executive Director of the association, was an exemplary leader of the organization for almost nineteen years, from October 1962 to June 1981.

5952 ■ Logan S. Chambers Individual Scholarship
(Other/Scholarship)

Purpose: To provide financial assistance to IAWP full members who wish to increase their knowledge, skills and abilities in a course of study that pertains to employment and training work, or toward a degree program that relates to job performance and/or promotional possibilities. **Focus:** General studies/Field of study not specified. **Qualif.:** Applicants must be IAWP full member. **Criteria:** Recipients will be selected on a first-come-first-serve basis.

Funds Avail.: Amount varies. **Duration:** Annual. **To Apply:** Application must be submitted along with a description of the class, training or seminar along with who is sponsoring the class, training or seminar; a brief explanation of how this course relates to their work or promotional chances must be submitted. **Remarks:** The scholarship established to honor Logan S. Chambers, a former Executive Director of the International Association of Personnel in Employment Security (IAPES). **Contact:** IAWP Administrative Office, 3267 Bee Caves Rd., Ste. 107-104, Austin, TX 78746.

5953 ■ Freddy L. Jacobs Individual Scholarship
(Undergraduate/Scholarship)

Purpose: To provide financial assistance to IAWP student members or dependents of IAWP full members who wish to increase their knowledge, skills and abilities in the area of leadership or workforce development. **Focus:** General studies/Field of study not specified. **Qualif.:** Applicants must be IAWP student member or dependents of IAWP member; must be pursuing an associate, undergraduate degree or other certification required to complete an extracurricular educational or training to program to obtain high school diploma; applicant seeking this scholarship in the status of "dependent" must meet all five dependency tests set forth in the Internal Revenue Code (26 U.S.C. SS152, et seq.) and IRS Publication 929 - Tax Rules for Children and Dependents. Those tests are (1) Full member of Household or Relationship Test; (2) Citizen or Resident Test; (3) Joint Return Test; (4) Gross Income Test; and (5) Support Test. **Criteria:** Recipients will be selected based on a first-come-first-serve basis.

Funds Avail.: Amount varies. **To Apply:** Applicants must submit the scholarship application form along with proof of completion of the course and attach a brief explanation of how this course will increase their knowledge, skills and abilities in the area of leadership or workforce development. **Remarks:** The scholarship established to honor Freddy Jacobs. **Contact:** IAWP Administrative Office, 3267 Bee Caves Rd., Ste. 107-104, Austin, TX 78746.

5954 ■ International Bowling Media Association (IBMA)
c/o Joan Romero, President
6544 Gloria Ave.
Van Nuys, CA 91406
Ph: (818)787-2310
URL: www.bowlingmedia.org
Social Media: www.facebook.com/groups/IBMAmedia/ about

5955 ■ Chuck Pezzano Scholarship *(College, Graduate/Scholarship)*

Purpose: To provide financial support for students pursuing a career in communications that involves the sport of bowling. **Focus:** Communications; Sports writing. **Qualif.:** Applicants must have a minimum of 3.0/4.0 GPA or equivalent; must be high school or vocational school seniors or college students. **Criteria:** Awards are given based on academic merit, civic and bowling participation.

Funds Avail.: $5,000. **Duration:** Annual. **To Apply:** Applicants must send an application form available at the website; transcript; at least one reference letter; maximum of 500 words essay; and any other information to support your application. **Deadline:** May 15. **Contact:** Contact Brian Hirsch, IBMA Operations Manager, E-mail: operations@bowlingmedia.org.

5956 ■ International Brotherhood of Electrical Workers - Local Union 827
263 Ward St.
East Windsor, NJ 08520
Ph: (609)443-4100
URL: ibew827.com
Social Media: www.facebook.com/IBEW-Local-827 -132679073486188
twitter.com/Local827

5957 ■ Local 827 Peter J. Casey Scholarship
(Undergraduate/Scholarship)

Purpose: To provide educational support for children of IBEW members. **Focus:** General studies/Field of study not specified. **Qualif.:** Applicants must be dependents of IBEW members and be in their senior year of high school. **Criteria:** Selections will be made by the Office of University Undergraduate Admissions Committee based on their criteria.

Funds Avail.: $1,000 each. **Duration:** Annual. **Number Awarded:** 2. **To Apply:** Applicants must call the Local Union Headquarters to request an application form. **Deadline:** January 15. **Contact:** Local Union Headquarters; Phone: 609-443-4100.

5958 ■ International Career Institute (ICI)
Level 14, Lumley House
309 Kent St.
Sydney, NSW 2000, Australia
Ph: 61 1300 131 582
URL: www.ici.edu.au
Social Media: www.facebook.com/ InternationalCareerInstitute
instagram.com/international_career_institute
linkedin.com/company/international-career-institute
twitter.com/icieducation
youtube.com/user/icieducation

5959 ■ ICI Business Leadership Scholarship
(Undergraduate, Graduate, Professional development/ Scholarship)

Purpose: To provide online education options that are flexible enough to work around a job schedule. **Focus:** Business. **Qualif.:** Applicants must be individuals who can demonstrate they are in a leadership role and wish to progress their career.

Awards are arranged alphabetically below their administering organizations

To Apply: Submit essay that highlights your current role and why you wish to follow a particular course of study. **Deadline:** April 1. **Remarks:** ICI will support the recipient in completing an Advanced Diploma level course in his or her chosen discipline. **Contact:** URL: www.ici.net.au/scholarships/business-scholarship/.

5960 ■ ICI Military Scholarship (Undergraduate, Vocational/Occupational/Scholarship)

Purpose: To provide online education that could assist in progressing a military career, such as courses in project and business management, mediation, personal training, and language. **Focus:** General studies/Field of study not specified. **Qualif.:** Applicants must be Navy, Army or Airforce Officers (Regular or Reserve); must provide compelling responses to the select committee via the selection questionnaire; must recognize and encourage the development of leaders in the Australian Defence Force.

To Apply: Submit an essay that highlights your current role in the military and explains why you wish to follow a particular course of study. **Deadline:** March 31. **Contact:** URL: www.ici.net.au/scholarships/military-scholarship/.

5961 ■ International Catacomb Society (ICS)
217 Hanover St., Ste. 130413
Boston, MA 02113
E-mail: info@catacombsociety.org
URL: www.catacombsociety.org

5962 ■ Shohet Scholars Grant Program (SSG)
(Professional development/Grant)

Purpose: To support significant, innovative research that can be completed and reported within the award period as regards to the catacombs. **Focus:** Art, Roman. **Qualif.:** Applicants must be scholars of all institutional affiliations who are US citizens and possess a doctoral degree or equivalent; must be in their early post-doctoral or launching stage of their careers; must be independent, unaffiliated scholars without doctoral credentials but equivalent in experience, competence and accomplishments of other candidates; Non-U.S. citizens may apply if a co-applicant is a legal resident (in possession of a "Green Card"/Form I-551) or native or naturalized citizen of the U.S.A. **Criteria:** Applications will be evaluated by a jury of academic experts who take into account the quality and feasibility of the research project submitted, the time required to meet the objectives sought, the anticipated impact of the findings, and the excellence of the applicant's skills as attested by diplomas obtained, letters of recommendation, and publications, papers, and presentations.

Funds Avail.: $2,000 - $30,000. **Duration:** Annual. **Number Awarded:** Varies. **To Apply:** Applicants must submit an information sheet; curriculum vitae; maximum of 2, 500 words (10 pages, double-spaced) research proposal; 100-word abstract and significance of the proposed research; budget proposal; letters of recommendation from three individuals; and letter from applicants' Department Chairperson or other institutional officer; if applicants will conduct an archaeological fieldwork or project involving items in museum collections, they must submit a statement of permission. **Deadline:** January 15. **Remarks:** Established in 2001.

5963 ■ International Center for Not-for-Profit Law (ICNL)
1126 16th St. NW, Ste. 400
Washington, DC 20036-4837

Ph: (202)452-8600
Fax: (202)452-8555
E-mail: infoicnl@icnl.org
URL: www.icnl.org
Social Media: www.facebook.com/ICNLAlliance
twitter.com/icnlalliance

5964 ■ ICNL Research Fellowships (Advanced Professional, Professional development/Fellowship)

Purpose: To provide opportunities to engage practitioners and scholars to advance the legal environment for civil society by providing them with the support and expertise of ICNL's international staff; access to extensive library of NGO legal materials; and meetings with NGO representatives, academics and others in Washington, DC. **Focus:** Law. **Qualif.:** Applicants must be residents of Benin, Burundi, Malawi, Ghana, The Gambia, Zimbabwe, Bangladesh, Cambodia, Indonesia, Thailand, Colombia, Mexico, Peru, Kosovo, Moldova, Ukraine. **Criteria:** Selection will be based on compliance with eligibility requirements and application procedures; demonstrated interest and experience relating to the legal environment for civil society; quality of the proposed research project, including the significance of the issue to be studied, research methodology/design, feasibility of the project, and likelihood that the Fellowship will help advance the legal framework for civil society in the applicant's country; commitment to continue working on civil society legal issues for a minimum of 12 months upon the applicant's return home, and ability to effect change based upon leadership potential; USAID's concurrence.

Funds Avail.: No specific amount. **Duration:** Annual; up to 4 weeks during June – August. **Number Awarded:** 4. **To Apply:** Applicants must submit the following with reference made to Research Fellowship Summer in the email subject line: application coversheet; proposal; resume, Curriculum Vitae (CV), or other statement of work history and education. **Deadline:** March 30. **Contact:** ICNL Program Assistant Kristian Kopp at kkopp@icnl.org.

5965 ■ International Centre for Diffraction Data (ICDD)
12 Campus Blvd.
Newtown Square, PA 19073-3273
Ph: (610)325-9814
Fax: (610)325-9823
Free: 866-378-9331
E-mail: info@icdd.com
URL: www.icdd.com
Social Media: www.facebook.com/TheICDD
www.instagram.com/theicdd
www.linkedin.com/company/international-centre-for
-diffraction-data
twitter.com/icddicdd
www.youtube.com/user/theicdd

5966 ■ The Ludo Frevel Crystallography Scholarship (Graduate/Scholarship)

Purpose: To encourage promising graduate students to pursue crystallographically oriented research. **Focus:** Mineralogy. **Qualif.:** Applicants must be graduate students enrolled in a graduate degree program with a major interest in crystallography (crystal structure analysis, crystal morphology, modulated structures, correlation of atomic

Awards are arranged alphabetically below their administering organizations

structure with physical properties, systematic classification of crystal structures, phase identification and materials characterization). **Criteria:** Selection is based on the proposal (impact, innovativeness, originality, efficacy of approach, and relationship to crystallography) and the student (recommendation letter, educational track record, prior work and/or research, honors, awards and professional activities).

Funds Avail.: $2,500 each. **Duration:** Annual. **Number Awarded:** 3. **To Apply:** Applicants are required to complete the application online and submit application with font Size: 12 point; Margin: no smaller than 3/4 inch; a description of the candidate's proposed research (limit 2 pages) including purpose and rationale for the research; proposed methodology to be used in the study; references and/or descriptions of the scientific background for the proposed research; a curriculum vitae including; educational preparation (institutions, dates, degrees obtained and in progress, and particularly pertinent coursework); awards, honors received; any research publications and/or presentations given any work experience (dates, employers, positions); professional activities, memberships. **Deadline:** October 16. **Contact:** Stephanie Jennings; Email: sjennings@icdd.com; Phone: 610-325-9814.

5967 ■ International City/County Management Association (ICMA)

777 N Capitol St. NE, Ste. 500
Washington, DC 20002-4201
Ph: (202)962-3680
Fax: (202)962-3500
Free: 800-745-8780
E-mail: customerservices@icma.org
URL: icma.org
Social Media: www.facebook.com/ICMAORG
www.instagram.com/icmaorg
www.linkedin.com/company/icma
twitter.com/icma
www.youtube.com/user/ICMAvideos

5968 ■ ICMA Local Government Management Fellowship (Master's/Fellowship)

Purpose: To generate interest in local government careers among recent master's program graduates. **Focus:** Local government. **Qualif.:** Applicants must be a recent graduate or student enrolled in a public administration, public policy, or related field master's degree program. Satisfy all of the requirements for their degree program by August 31 of the year of the fellowship. Have no formal local government management work experience. Be eligible to work in the United States.

Funds Avail.: Amount varies. **Duration:** Annual. **Contact:** Email: lgmfprogram@icma.org.

5969 ■ International Code Council (ICC)

500 New Jersey Ave. NW, 6th Fl.
Washington, DC 20001
Ph: (202)370-1800
Fax: (202)783-2348
Free: 888-422-7233
URL: www.iccsafe.org
Social Media: www.facebook.com/
InternationalCodeCouncil

www.linkedin.com/company/international-code-council
twitter.com/IntlCodeCouncil
www.youtube.com/user/ICCMEDIA

5970 ■ C.D. Howard Scholarship (Undergraduate/ Scholarship, Monetary, Award)

Purpose: To provide financial assistance to the children of ICC governmental members. **Focus:** General studies/Field of study not specified. **Qualif.:** Applicants must be children of code enforcement agency personnel; jurisdiction authority must be an active Governmental Member of the International Code Council; children must be dependents as defined by the Internal Revenue Service. **Criteria:** Selection will be based on merit and demonstrated need for financial assistance; qualified applicants from the State of Alabama will be given first consideration.

Funds Avail.: $1,000. **Duration:** Annual; up to 4 years. **Number Awarded:** 1. **To Apply:** Applicants must complete the scholarship application; must submit financial information along with the details of any other financial assistance they are receiving; must also provide evidence of satisfactory scholastic achievement including grades, test scores and teacher recommendations. a one-page narrative on why the applicant should be awarded the scholarship is also required. **Deadline:** June 29. **Remarks:** The scholarship is awarded by the Code Officials Association of Alabama in memory of C.D. Howard. **Contact:** International Code Council, Attn: Scholarships, c/o: Karla Price Higgs, 900 Montclair Rd., Birmingham, AL 35213-1206; E-mail: khiggs@iccsafe.org.

5971 ■ ICC General Scholarship Fund (Undergraduate/Scholarship, Monetary, Award)

Purpose: To provide financial assistance to the children of ICC governmental members. **Focus:** General studies/Field of study not specified. **Qualif.:** Applicants must be children of code enforcement agency personnel; jurisdiction authority must be an active Governmental Member of the International Code Council; children must be dependents as defined by the Internal Revenue Service; typically, this includes birth children, stepchildren, legally adopted children or a legal ward financially supported by the employee. **Criteria:** Selection will be based on satisfactory scholastic achievement and demonstrated need for financial assistance.

Funds Avail.: $2,500 each. **Duration:** Annual. **Number Awarded:** 2. **To Apply:** Applications shall be received by the deadline posted each year and submitted to the International Code Council. **Deadline:** June 29. **Contact:** International Code Council, Attn: Scholarships, c/o: Karla Price Higgs, 900 Montclair Rd., Birmingham, AL 35213-1206; E-mail: khiggs@iccsafe.org.

5972 ■ J.W. "Bill" Neese Scholarship (Undergraduate/ Scholarship, Monetary, Award)

Purpose: To provide financial assistance to the children of ICC governmental members. **Focus:** Engineering, Architectural. **Criteria:** The recipients are selected by a committee of volunteers.

Funds Avail.: $1,000. **Duration:** Annual. **Number Awarded:** 1. **To Apply:** Applicants must complete the application form and must submit a one-page narrative on why they deserve the scholarship; two recommendation forms which must be completed by teachers and/or faculty members or employer; an official transcript from the last school attended; copy of act or sat scores; financial

Awards are arranged alphabetically below their administering organizations

information. **Deadline:** July 1. **Remarks:** The scholarship was established by Central Florida Chapter in honor of J.W. Bill Neese. **Contact:** 888-ICC-SAFE (888-422-7233), ext. 5268 or Email:scholarships@iccsafe.org.

5973 ■ Charlie O'Meilia Scholarship *(Undergraduate/ Scholarship, Monetary, Award)*

Purpose: To provide financial assistance to the children of ICC Governmental Members. **Focus:** General studies/Field of study not specified. **Criteria:** Recipients will be selected based on scholastic achievement and demonstrated need for financial assistance; qualified applicants from the State of Florida will be given first consideration.

Funds Avail.: $1,000. **Duration:** Annual; up to 4 years. **To Apply:** Applicants must complete the scholarship application; must submit financial information along with the details of any other financial assistance they are receiving; must also provide evidence of satisfactory scholastic achievement including grades, test scores and teacher recommendations. a one-page narrative on why the applicant should be awarded the scholarship is also required. **Deadline:** June 29. **Remarks:** The scholarship is awarded by the Palm Beach County (Florida) chapter in honor of long-time member Charlie O'Meilia. **Contact:** International Code Council, Attn: Scholarships, c/o: Karla Price Higgs, 900 Montclair Rd., Birmingham, AL 35213-1206; E-mail: khiggs@iccsafe.org.

5974 ■ William J. Tangye Scholarship
(Undergraduate/Scholarship, Monetary, Award)

Purpose: To provide financial assistance for children of ICC members intending to pursue higher education. **Focus:** Engineering, Architectural. **Criteria:** Selection will be based on merit.

Funds Avail.: $2,500. **Duration:** Annual. **Number Awarded:** 1. **To Apply:** Applicants must complete the application form and must submit a one-page narrative on why they deserve the scholarship; two recommendation forms which must be completed by teachers and/or faculty members or employer; an official transcript from the last school attended; copy of act or sat scores; financial information. **Deadline:** July 1. **Remarks:** The scholarship was established in memory of William J. Tangye, the first Chief Executive Officer of the International Code Council. **Contact:** International Code Council, Attn: Scholarships, c/o: Karla Price Higgs, 900 Montclair Rd., Birmingham, AL 35213-1206; E-mail: khiggs@iccsafe.org.

5975 ■ International Coral Reef Society (ICRS)
1105 Wooded Acres Dr., Ste. 260
Waco, TX 76710-5400
Ph: (254)776-3550
E-mail: isrs@sgmeet.com
URL: www.coralreefs.org
Social Media: www.facebook.com/
 InternationalSocietyforReefStudies
www.instagram.com/icrs.students
twitter.com/ICRSreefstudent
www.youtube.com/channel/UCNp56
 _9WtqJ1N2PWGJJU5ew

5976 ■ ICRS Graduate Fellowships *(Doctorate, Graduate/Fellowship)*

Purpose: To assist research students develop skills and address problems related to coral reef ecosystem science

and management. **Focus:** Biology, Marine. **Qualif.:** Applicants must be students or full members of the ISRS; must be in the first or second year or at the beginning of the third year (or at the equivalent stage if part-time) of a research degree.

Funds Avail.: $2,500 each. **Duration:** Annual. **Number Awarded:** 6. **To Apply:** Applicants must submit a research proposal (not exceed six pages) as a PDF document using 12-point font including Key Information, proposal Summary briefly explaining the proposed research in context and indicate the principal research aims or questions which led to the proposal, Proposal Background summarizing the scientific and / or other background to the research, Project Activities proposed to pursue and provide an indicative timetable, methods to be used, explain any experimental design, and state how the data will be analyzed. **Deadline:** February 15. **Contact:** Professor Rupert Ormond, Heriot-Watt University, Edinburgh, Scotland, UK; Email: rupert.ormond.mci@gmail.com.

5977 ■ International Council of Shopping Centers Foundation (ICSC)
1251 Avenue of the Americas,45th floor
New York, NY 10020-1104
Ph: (646)728-3800
E-mail: membership@icsc.org
URL: www.icsc.org
Social Media: www.facebook.com/MyICSC
www.instagram.com/icsc/?hl=en
www.linkedin.com/company/icsc
twitter.com/icsc

5978 ■ Charles Grossman Graduate Scholarship *(Graduate/Scholarship)*

Purpose: To assist and encourage extraordinary students to select retail real estate as their career path. **Focus:** Real estate.

Funds Avail.: $10,000 toward tuition fees. **To Apply:** Applicants must submit application form transcript, resume, and letters of reference; three essays from 500 words limit for essay 1 and 2, 500 words limit for essay 3.

5979 ■ The Harold E. Eisenberg Foundation Scholarship *(Other/Scholarship)*

Purpose: To support graduates and real estate practitioner an educational scholarships. **Focus:** Management; Marketing and distribution. **Qualif.:** Applicant must be an ICSC member based in the U.S. Midwest. **Criteria:** Selection will be based on the committee criteria.

Funds Avail.: $40,000. **Duration:** Annual. **Number Awarded:** 2.

5980 ■ Mary Lou Fiala Fellowship *(Graduate/ Fellowship)*

Purpose: To support an outstanding professional with passion and commitment to retail real estate, and has the potential to make a lasting contribution to the industry. **Focus:** Real estate. **Criteria:** All applications are confidential and are reviewed by a selection committee.

Funds Avail.: No specific amount. **Duration:** Annual. **To Apply:** Applications can be submitted online. **Contact:** Angela Rizzo; Phone: 646-728-3582; Email: arizzo@icsc.org.

5981 ■ John T. Riordan Professional Education Scholarships *(Professional development/Fellowship)*

Purpose: To support retail estate professionals who wants to further their education and career development. **Focus:**

Awards are arranged alphabetically below their administering organizations

Management; Marketing and distribution. **Qualif.:** Applicant must be a member of ICSC; new to a retail real estate or looking to expand knowledge of management, marketing, leasing/or development, design, and construction.

Funds Avail.: No specific amount. **To Apply:** Applicants must submit an application form, resume and letters of reference.

5982 ■ Schurgin Family Foundation Scholarship
(Undergraduate/Scholarship)

Purpose: To provide tuition assistance to undergraduate students who are studying retail real estate or a related field. **Focus:** Real estate. **Qualif.:** Applicant must be a U.S. Citizen who is or will be a junior or senior undergraduate degree-seeking candidate enrolled full time at an accredited college/university; have a minimum of 3.0 GPA; with a strong interest in the industry. **Criteria:** Selection will be based on the committee's criteria.

Funds Avail.: $10,000. **Duration:** Annual. **To Apply:** Applicants must submit application form transcript, resume, and letters of reference; limit for essay 2. **Remarks:** Established in 1979.

5983 ■ International Council on Systems Engineering (INCOSE)
7670 Opportunity Rd., Ste. 220
San Diego, CA 92111-2222
Ph: (858)541-1725
Fax: (858)541-1728
Free: 800-366-1164
E-mail: info@incose.org
URL: www.incose.org
Social Media: www.facebook.com/groups/INCOSE
twitter.com/incose_org

5984 ■ James E. Long Memorial Post Doctoral Fellowship *(Postdoctorate/Fellowship)*

Purpose: To inspire innovative post-doctorate level research that has the potential to produce major improvements in advancing the practice of systems engineering and systems thinking. **Focus:** Systems engineering. **Qualif.:** Applicants must be engaged in promising post-doctoral research at an accredited university or research institute; applicants seeking the award must submit an application; applicants may not receive the award more than once.

Funds Avail.: $5,000. **Duration:** Annual. **To Apply:** Applicants must submit an application package to include complete resume/vitae, a brief bio-sketch, description of the study/research area of interest and a discussion of the contributions and expected outcomes that will benefit applications to advance the state of the practice; must have two professional references familiar with the applicant's research, submit recommendation letters on their behalf outlining the potential benefits and application toward solving complex problems. **Deadline:** June 1. **Remarks:** Established in 2010. **Contact:** Email: foundation@incose.org.

5985 ■ Johns Hopkins University/Applied Physics Laboratory Alexander Kossiakoff Scholarship
(Doctorate, Graduate, Master's/Scholarship)

Purpose: To recognize promising applied systems engineering research by students in a Masters or Doctoral program. **Focus:** Systems engineering. **Qualif.:** Applicant must be a U.S. citizen and must be an admitted student in a Masters or Doctoral Program in Systems Engineering at an accredited university; applicant seeking the award must submit an application; applicants may not receive more than one award. **Criteria:** Selection will be based on the following criteria: rigor and creativity of proposed applied research; potential application to Applied Physics Laboratory systems engineering interests; strength of resume and bio sketch; strength of academic recommendations; additional attributes noted in the applicant's materials that go beyond the application requirements.

Funds Avail.: $5,000. **Duration:** Annual. **To Apply:** Each applicant must submit an application package to include a complete resume/vitae, a brief bio-sketch, description of the study/research areas of interest (at least three to four pages), and a discussion of the contribution and expected outcomes that will benefit applications of interest to the Laboratory; must have two faculty references submit recommendation letters on their behalf. **Deadline:** June 1. **Contact:** Email: holly.witte@incose.org and foundation@incose.org.

5986 ■ Stevens Doctoral Award *(Doctorate/Award)*

Purpose: To honor and recognize innovative doctoral-level research to the field of systems engineering and integration. **Focus:** Systems engineering. **Qualif.:** Applicant must be a qualified PhD student in a degree program with an approved research proposal and may not receive more than one award. **Criteria:** Selection will be based on the advancement of the state-of-the-knowledge in systems engineering and integration; potential for the advancement of the state-of-the-practice of systems engineering and integration within the next five to ten years.

Funds Avail.: $5,000. **Duration:** Annual. **To Apply:** Applicants must complete award application form. **Contact:** Email: foundation@incose.org.

5987 ■ International Dairy-Deli-Bakery Association (IDDBA)
636 Science Dr.
Madison, WI 53711-1073
Ph: (608)310-5000
Fax: (608)238-6330
E-mail: iddba@iddba.org
URL: www.iddba.org
Social Media: www.linkedin.com/company/international
 -dairy-deli-bakery-association/
twitter.com/myiddba

5988 ■ International Dairy-Deli-Bakery Association's Scholarship for Growing the Future *(Graduate, Undergraduate/Scholarship)*

Purpose: To support employees of IDDBA-member companies. **Focus:** Business; Culinary arts; Food service careers. **Qualif.:** Applicant must have been worked 13 hours/week for an IDDBA-member company during the school year; must also have a 2.5 grade-point average on a 4.0 scale, or equivalent which may be waived for first-time returning adult students.

Funds Avail.: Up to $4,000. **To Apply:** Applicants must submit a completed application form together with a transcript; a letter of recommendation that speaks to your work/academic abilities. **Deadline:** April 1. **Contact:** Email: scholarships@iddba.org; Phone: 608-310-5000.

5989 ■ Undergraduate/Graduate Scholarships
(Undergraduate, Graduate/Scholarship)

Purpose: To provide an academic support to high school seniors and current or returning college or vocational/

Awards are arranged alphabetically below their administering organizations

technical school students. **Focus:** Business; Food science and technology; Marketing and distribution. **Qualif.:** Applicants must be current full- or part-time employees of an IDDBA-member company; must work a minimum of 13 hours per week during the school year for an IDDBA-member company; must have academic field of study in a food-related field, business or marketing program; and must have a 2.5 grade-point average on a 4.0 scale, or equivalent. **Criteria:** Selection will be given to supermarket dairy, deli and bakery employees.

Funds Avail.: Up to $2,000. **Duration:** Annual. **Number Awarded:** 2. **To Apply:** Applicants may apply online by visiting the IDDBA's website, or download the application form provided by IDDBA. **Contact:** scholarships@iddba.org.

5990 ■ International Dance Teachers Association (IDTA)
International House
76 Bennett Rd.
East Sussex
Brighton BN2 5JL, United Kingdom
Ph: 44 1273 685652
Fax: 44 1273 674388
URL: www.idta.co.uk
Social Media: www.facebook.com/TheIDTA
www.instagram.com/theidta/
twitter.com/theidta
www.youtube.com/channel/UCnyuPFvoVMFBpk0i8309yuA

5991 ■ IDTA Freestyle Scholarships *(Other/ Scholarship)*

Purpose: To provide assistance for students who wants to pursue a dance career; to further the knowledge about the art of dance and all its forms. **Focus:** Dance. **Qualif.:** Applicants must be members of IDTA. **Criteria:** Selection will be based on the committee's criteria.

Funds Avail.: No specific amount. **Duration:** Annual. **To Apply:** Applicants must contact IDTA for the application details.

5992 ■ International Desalination Association (IDA)
PO Box 387
Topsfield, MA 01983
Ph: (978)887-0410
Fax: (978)887-0411
E-mail: info@idadesal.org
URL: www.idadesal.org
Social Media: www.facebook.com/
internationaldesalinationassociation
www.linkedin.com/company/international-desalination
-association-ida-
twitter.com/idadesal
www.youtube.com/user/idadesal

5993 ■ Channabasappa Memorial Scholarships *(Graduate, Doctorate/Scholarship)*

Purpose: To provide assistance for graduate students intending to further their education in subjects related to desalination. **Focus:** Engineering; Engineering, Hydraulic; Science; Water resources. **Qualif.:** Applicants must have graduated from an accredited university; must be from the

top 10% of their class in science or engineering; applicant must prove full-time admission to a graduate program of doctoral studies in desalination or water re-use and must exhibit leadership and achievement potential; must be an IDA member. **Criteria:** Recipients will be selected based on the undergraduate and graduate transcripts, references and motivation for a career in desalination.

Funds Avail.: $10,000 maximum grant per student. **Duration:** Annual. **To Apply:** Applicants must submit the online application form; statement of purpose, detailing your planned career in desalination or water reuse technologies; proof of acceptance to a doctoral program at an accredited university; official statement on faculty letterhead from your sponsor indicating the nature and scope of your research assignment; evidence of other (if applicable) sources of funding to complete your degree objective; four letters of recommendation, at least one by an IDA member; transcript of your undergraduate academic record indicating grade point average or rank in your class (Official translation must be attached if such documents are not in English). **Deadline:** January 31. **Contact:** E-mail: education@idadesal.org.

5994 ■ IDA Fellowship/Scholarship Programs *(Other/Fellowship)*

Purpose: To promote development in the desalination and water reuse industry. **Focus:** Engineering; Engineering, Hydraulic; Science; Water resources. **Criteria:** Recipients will be selected based on the following: high professional achievements; relevance of the experience; responsible career goals for advancement in the chosen field; potential to make a contribution in the field of water reuse; benefits of the attachment to the applicants; assurance that the applicants will remain connected to the desalination water-reuse industry through future work.

Funds Avail.: $10,000. **Duration:** Biennial. **Contact:** E-mail: education@idadesal.org.

5995 ■ International Door Association (IDA)
529 14th St. NW, Suite 1280
Washington, DC 20045
Ph: (202)591-2457
Fax: (202)591-2445
E-mail: info@doors.org
URL: www.doors.org
Social Media: www.facebook.com/pages/International-Door
-Association/131289850277235
www.instagram.com/intldoorassoc
twitter.com/IntlDoorAssoc
www.youtube.com/user/InternationalDoor

5996 ■ International Door Association Scholarship Foundation Program *(Undergraduate/Scholarship)*

Purpose: To support advanced educational opportunities for scholastically eligible students. **Focus:** General studies/Field of study not specified. **Qualif.:** Applicants must be high school students with senior standing, or enrolled in community college, an associate degree program, vocational school or similar certification/diploma program, undergraduate college or university; have a cumulative grade point average equal to or greater than 3.0 on a 4.0 scale (or equivalent); must be immediate family member, an employee, or an immediate family member of an employee of an IDA Installing/Servicing Dealer Member or an IDA Primary Industry Manufacturer/Vendor Member in

Awards are arranged alphabetically below their administering organizations

good standing. **Criteria:** Selection is based on their grades, community and school involvement, recommendations and character determined through narrative.

Funds Avail.: $2,000 for full-time; for part-time, award amount is to be determined by semester hours or equivalent taken, and not to exceed $1,000. **Duration:** One academic year. **To Apply:** Applicants must complete an IDA Foundation Scholarship application for the specified year and submit it to the Scholarship Committee. Applications are available online starting the month of April with a deadline mid-July. Incomplete applications will not be considered. **Deadline:** July 31. **Remarks:** Scholarship has two criteria: Primary Full-Time and Secondary Part-Time. **Contact:** Contact IDA Headquarters at 202-591-2457, or email to info@doors.org.

5997 ■ International Executive Housekeepers Association (IEHA)
1001 Eastwind Dr., Ste. 302
Westerville, OH 43081-3361
Ph: (847)982-0800
Fax: (614)423-2888
E-mail: excel@ieha.org
URL: www.ieha.org
Social Media: www.facebook.com/IEHAWorldwide
twitter.com/IEHA

5998 ■ IEHA Education/Scholarship Foundation Award *(Undergraduate/Scholarship)*
Purpose: To financially support students who are continuing their education to enhance their knowledge in their chosen field. **Focus:** General studies/Field of study not specified. **Qualif.:** Applicants must be IEHA member enrolled in an undergraduate or associate degree or IEHA approved certification program.

Funds Avail.: No specific amount. **Duration:** Annual. **To Apply:** Applicants must submit an application form, a letter from their school official, official school transcript, and a manuscript describing the reason(s) applying for the scholarship and an explanation letter of career goals. **Deadline:** January 10. **Contact:** IEHA Education Foundation, 1001 Eastwind Dr., Ste. 301, Westerville, OH, 43081-3361.

5999 ■ International Executive Housekeepers Association Spartan Scholarship Award *(Undergraduate/Scholarship)*
Purpose: To provide educational assistance to those who are in need. **Focus:** General studies/Field of study not specified. **Qualif.:** Applicants must be IEHA member or immediate family of an IEHA member. **Criteria:** Selection will be based on the IEHA Education Committee's review of the application materials.

Funds Avail.: $1,500. **To Apply:** Applicants must submit a completed application form and a letter briefly explaining; why they are applying for the funds, what they are to be used for, and what their career goals are. **Deadline:** July 25. **Contact:** IEHA Scholarship Selection Committee, 1001 Eastwind Dr., Ste. 301,Westerville, OH, 43081-3361; Toll-free: 800-200-6342; Fax: 614-895-1248.

6000 ■ International Facility Management Association Foundation (IFMA)
800 Gessner Rd., Ste. 900
Houston, TX 77024-4257
Ph: (713)623-4362
Fax: (713)623-6124
URL: www.ifmafoundation.org
Social Media: www.facebook.com/IFMAFoundation
www.linkedin.com/company/ifma-foundation
twitter.com/FMFoundation

6001 ■ IFMA Foundation Scholarship *(Undergraduate, Graduate/Scholarship)*
Purpose: To fund and promote education and research for the advancement of facility management. **Focus:** Management; Materials handling. **Criteria:** Selection shall be based on achievements/accomplishments, involvement, letter of intent, resume and recommendation.

Funds Avail.: $1,500 to $10,000. **Duration:** Annual. **To Apply:** Applicants must complete and submit the application form; all information must be typed; no handwritten responses will be accepted. **Deadline:** May 15. **Contact:** Amy Arnold, IFMA Foundation Administrator; Email: amy.arnold@ifma.org.

6002 ■ International Federation of Operational Research Societies (IFORS)
c/o Mary Thomas Magrogan, Secretary
7240 Parkway Dr., Ste. 310
Hanover, MD 21076
E-mail: secretary@ifors.org
URL: ifors.org
Social Media: www.facebook.com/iforsofficial

6003 ■ Anna Valicek Award *(Graduate, Master's, Doctorate/Medal, Scholarship)*
Purpose: To recognize an individual for original and innovative research in the application of operations research to airline and/or airline-related business problems. **Focus:** Operations research.

Funds Avail.: $2,500; $1,000. **Duration:** Annual. **Number Awarded:** 2. **Contact:** valicekaward@agifors.org.

6004 ■ International Food Service Executives Association (IFSEA)
PO Box 1125
Placitas, NM 87043
Free: 855-268-1367
URL: www.ifsea.org
Social Media: www.facebook.com/IFSEA.HQ

6005 ■ IFSEA Worthy Goal Scholarships *(Two Year College, Undergraduate, Vocational/Occupational, Four Year College/Scholarship)*
Purpose: To provide assistance to individuals intending to receive food service management or vocational training beyond the high school level. **Focus:** Food service careers. **Qualif.:** Applicants must be enrolled or accepted as a full time student in a Food Service-related major at a 2 or 4 year college or university for the fall term following the award.

Funds Avail.: $500 to $2,500. **Duration:** Annual. **To Apply:** Applicant must submit an application form; provide a personal financial summary of projected 1-year expenses and income/ fundraising beginning with the fall semester or a summary of financial statement; a statement (maximum

Awards are arranged alphabetically below their administering organizations

of 500 words) on personal background focusing on aspects regarding food service and future goals; documentation of work experience, student organizations, transcript of grades, three letters of recommendation, and a statement (maximum of 250 words) on how receiving the scholarship would help the applicant in reaching their goals. **Deadline:** March 15. **Remarks:** Established in 1968. **Contact:** Submission E-mail: johnsojm@morrisville.edu; Questions: Dr. Ernest Boger, Worthy Goal Scholarship Chair at epboger@umes.edu.

6006 ■ International Foodservice Editorial Council (IFEC)
PO Box 581
Pleasant Valley, NY 12569
Ph: (845)723-4434
URL: ifeconline.com
Social Media: www.facebook.com/IFEC56
twitter.com/IFECorg

6007 ■ International Foodservice Editorial Council Scholarship *(Graduate/Scholarship)*

Purpose: To assist students pursuing careers as writers, editors, public relation and marketing communication practitioners and closely related areas within the foodservice industry. **Focus:** Communications; Culinary arts; Food science and technology; Food service careers; Graphic art and design; Hotel, institutional, and restaurant management; Journalism; Nutrition; Photography; Public relations. **Qualif.:** Applicant must be a full-time college student enrolled as of March 15 of the year, working toward an associate's, bachelor's or master's degree; enrollment must be in an accredited post-secondary educational institution in the U.S. Expected graduation date must be no earlier than January 1 of upcoming year. **Criteria:** Recipients will be selected based on academic record, character references, and financial need.

Funds Avail.: $1,500 - $6,000. **Duration:** Annual. **Number Awarded:** 4-6. **To Apply:** Applicants must submit a complete application together with academic transcript and two letters of recommendation from a supervisor, teacher, advisor or other foodservice or communications professional familiar with applicant's skills; application requirements must be typewritten and submitted using U.S. Postal Service's Return Receipt Service. **Deadline:** March 15. **Contact:** E-mail: ifec@ifeconline.com.

6008 ■ International Foundation for Ethical Research (IFER)
53 W Jackson Blvd., Ste. 1552
Chicago, IL 60604
Ph: (312)427-6025
Fax: (312)427-6524
E-mail: ifer@navs.org
URL: www.ifer.org

6009 ■ Graduate Student Fellowships for Alternatives to the Use of Animals in Science *(Graduate, Doctorate/Fellowship)*

Purpose: To provide monetary assistance to graduate students. **Focus:** Science technologies. **Qualif.:** Applicant must be a student enrolled in masters and Ph.D. programs. **Funds Avail.:** A stipend of $12,500 and up to $2,500 for supplies. **Duration:** Annual. **To Apply:** Applications forms

are available in the website. **Deadline:** April 30.

6010 ■ International Franchise Association (IFA)
1900 K St., NW Ste. 700
Washington, DC 20006
Ph: (202)628-8000
Fax: (202)628-0812
URL: www.franchise.org
Social Media: www.facebook.com/IFA.DC
www.linkedin.com/company/international-franchise -association
twitter.com/franchising411
www.youtube.com/user/ifadc

6011 ■ Don Debolt Franchising Scholarship Program *(Undergraduate/Scholarship)*

Purpose: To provide financial support to those students who are acquiring knowledge about franchising. **Focus:** Business. **Qualif.:** Applicants must be a United States Citizens enrolled in an accredited college/university in the U.S; must have competed in the Franchising/Entrepreneurship competition sponsored by DECA within the last year.

Funds Avail.: No specific amount. **Duration:** Annual. **To Apply:** Applicant must submit copy of franchising business plan presented at the DECA Competitive Event along with scholarship form. **Deadline:** October 31. **Remarks:** Named in honor of IFA's past president Don DeBolt, who served from 1995 to 2004.

6012 ■ Franchise Law Diversity Scholarship Awards *(Undergraduate/Scholarship)*

Purpose: To support minority law students in pursuing their careers in franchise and distribution law. **Focus:** Law. **Qualif.:** Applicants must have 2L or 3L status and be enrolled in at least one course oriented towards franchise law.

Funds Avail.: $4,000. **Duration:** Annual.

6013 ■ International Furnishings and Design Association (IFDA)
610 Freedom Business Ctr., Ste. 110
King of Prussia, PA 19406
Ph: (610)992-0011
Fax: (610)992-0021
E-mail: info@ifda.com
URL: www.ifda.com
Social Media: www.facebook.com/IFDAssociation
www.linkedin.com/groups/4458249/profile
twitter.com/IFDAssociation
twitter.com/ifdaphilly

6014 ■ IFDA Student Member Scholarship *(Undergraduate/Scholarship)*

Purpose: To foster educational and philanthropic activities which will benefit individuals and institutions; to promote, develop or enhance the furnishings and design industries and the practice of these professions. **Focus:** Interior design. **Qualif.:** Applicants must be post-secondary students majoring in Interior Design or closely related-field; must have completed four design-related courses and be enrolled at an accredited school or college.

Funds Avail.: No specific amount. **Duration:** Annual.

Awards are arranged alphabetically below their administering organizations

6015 ■ International Furnishings and Design Association Part-time Student Scholarship (Undergraduate/Scholarship)

Purpose: To support students entering and re-entering various professions in the field as well as opportunities for continuing education. **Focus:** Interior design.

Funds Avail.: No specific amount. **Duration:** Annual.

6016 ■ International Grenfell Association (IGA)

430 Topsail Road
Saint John's, NL, Canada A1E 4N1
Ph: (709)745-6162
Fax: (709)745-6163
E-mail: iga@nfld.net
URL: www.grenfellassociation.org
Social Media: www.facebook.com/grenfellassociation
www.instagram.com/grenfellassociation

6017 ■ International Grenfell Association Bursary (Undergraduate, Postgraduate/Scholarship)

Purpose: To support the education of students with financial need who have been accepted into or are currently attending a post-secondary education institution. **Focus:** General studies/Field of study not specified. **Qualif.:** Applicant must be a Canadian citizen in the IGA region (must have graduated from a high school within the region); must not already possess a post-secondary degree; and must complete at least four courses per semester. **Criteria:** Selection will be based on the committee's criteria.

Funds Avail.: Amount varies. **Duration:** Annual. **Number Awarded:** 1. **To Apply:** Application forms and information can be obtained from the Grenfell Scholarship Committee or may be obtained online. Applications must be completed by the student and returned to the committee on or before the deadline. **Deadline:** February 28. **Contact:** Paul Canning, IGA Administrator International Grenfell Association; Phone: 709-745-6162; Fax: 709-745-6163; Email: iga@nfld.net.

6018 ■ International Grenfell Association High School Bursaries (Undergraduate/Scholarship)

Purpose: To support the education of high achievers who are planning to pursue college education. **Focus:** General studies/Field of study not specified. **Qualif.:** Applicant must be a graduating secondary and currently enrolled post-secondary students having graduated from high schools in area served by the Association (the Northern Peninsula and Coastal Labrador). **Criteria:** Selection will be based primarily on financial need.

Funds Avail.: $1,000-$6,000. **Duration:** Annual. **To Apply:** Application form can be downloaded online. **Deadline:** February 28.

6019 ■ International Grenfell Association Post-Secondary Bursaries (Undergraduate/Scholarship)

Purpose: To support the education of high achievers and/or those with financial need who have completed one or more years of post-secondary education with one renewable scholarship. **Focus:** General studies/Field of study not specified. **Qualif.:** Applicants must not already have a degree or diploma.

Funds Avail.: $1,000-$6,000. **Duration:** Annual. **To Apply:** Application form can be downloaded online; must include a letter of reference with the application. **Deadline:** February 28.

6020 ■ International Horn Society (IHS)

PO Box 630158
Lanai City, HI 96763-0158
Ph: (808)565-7273
Fax: (808)565-7273
URL: www.hornsociety.org

6021 ■ Paul Mansur Award (Undergraduate/Scholarship)

Purpose: To provide opportunities for full-time students attending the IHS international symposium to receive a lesson from a world-renowned artist or teacher. **Focus:** Music. **Qualif.:** Applicants must be full-time students 18 years or younger, or 19-26 years old at the time of the symposium (one award for each age group); must be full-time students attending the IHS international symposium to receive a lesson from a world renowned artist or teacher. **Criteria:** Selection will be based on essays which will be evaluated for both content and grammar, so time and care in preparation is encouraged.

Funds Avail.: No specific amount. **To Apply:** Applicant must submit applications to the IHS Executive Secretary, either on print or by email; must provide proof of full-time public or private school, conservatory, or university enrollment; and essay on the subject of how attending and receiving a lesson during the symposium will enhance education; those whose native language is not English may submit application in their native language, but translation is required. **Deadline:** April 1. **Remarks:** The award was named for the longtime Editor of The Horn Call, Emeritus Dean, and IHS Honorary Member, Paul Mansur. **Contact:** E-mail: exec-director@hornsociety.org.

6022 ■ Barry Tuckwell Award (All/Scholarship)

Purpose: To encourage and support worthy horn students to pursue education and performance by attending and participating in masterclasses and workshops throughout the world. **Focus:** Music. **Qualif.:** Applicants must be age 18 to 24. **Criteria:** Recipients will be selected by the appointed Committee of IHS Scholarship Chairs based on combination of ability, character, motivation, goals and opportunities available at the selected venue.

Funds Avail.: $500. **Number Awarded:** 1. **To Apply:** Applicants must submit a completed Tuckwell Scholarship application available online along with two brief essays outlining the applicant's experience, musical training, plan to study and perform at a specific event; a recording of applicant playing one movement of a concerto or sonata (with piano), one etude and two orchestral excerpts; and two letters of recommendation including an assessment of financial need. **Deadline:** December 1. **Remarks:** Established in 1997. **Contact:** IHS Executive Director at exec-director@hornsociety.org.

6023 ■ International Information Systems Security Certification Consortium (ISC2)

311 Park Place Blvd., Ste. 400
Clearwater, FL 33759
Ph: (727)785-0189
Free: 866-331-4722
E-mail: membersupport@isc2.org
URL: www.isc2.org

Awards are arranged alphabetically below their administering organizations

Social Media: www.facebook.com/isc2fb
www.linkedin.com/company/isc2/
twitter.com/ISC2
www.youtube.com/user/ISC2TV

6024 ■ (ISC)2 Foundation Information Security Undergraduate Scholarships *(Undergraduate/Scholarship)*

Purpose: To ease some of the financial burden of aspiring information security professionals. **Focus:** Computer and information sciences; Information science and technology; National security. **Qualif.:** Applicant must be a senior in high school, or an undergraduate student who is currently a junior, freshman, sophomore or senior who will be pursuing an undergraduate degree in the fall with a focus on cybersecurity or information assurance; may be attending full-time or part-time on campus or online; must have a minimum 3.3 GPA on a 4.0 scale. **Criteria:** Selection shall be based on passion, merit, and financial need.

Funds Avail.: $1,000 to $5,000 each. **Duration:** Annual. **Number Awarded:** Up to 20. **To Apply:** Application details are available online: at iamcybersafe.org/s/undergraduate-scholarships. **Deadline:** March 8. **Remarks:** All scholarships are administered by the Center for Cyber Safety and Education. **Contact:** Email: scholarships@isc2.org.

6025 ■ International Institute for Municipal Clerks (IIMC)

8331 Utica Avenue Suite 200
Rancho Cucamonga, CA 91730
Ph: (909)944-4162
Fax: (909)944-8545
Free: 800-251-1639
E-mail: hq@iimc.com
URL: www.iimc.com
Social Media: www.facebook.com/itsmyIIMC
www.instagram.com/iimc_clerks
twitter.com/EDIIMC
www.youtube.com/channel/UCy-olD57ligBZuMiek4hKyw

6026 ■ CMC/MMC Scholarships (CMC) *(Other/Scholarship)*

Purpose: To enhance the job performance of the Clerk in small and large municipalities. **Focus:** General studies/Field of study not specified. **Qualif.:** Applicants must be IIMC member, who are clerks.

Funds Avail.: $400. **Duration:** Annual. **Number Awarded:** More than 1,500. **Deadline:** March 1. **Remarks:** Established in 1986.

6027 ■ MMC Scholarships *(Other/Scholarship)*

Purpose: To support municipal clerks and deputy clerks to improve their professional performance. **Focus:** General studies/Field of study not specified. **Qualif.:** Applicants must be IIMC member, who are clerks.

Funds Avail.: $400. **Duration:** Annual. **Number Awarded:** 1,500. **Deadline:** October 1. **Remarks:** Established in 1986.

6028 ■ International Law Students Association (ILSA)

701 13th St. NW, 12th Fl.
Washington, DC 20005
Ph: (202)729-2470
Fax: (202)639-9355
E-mail: ilsa@ilsa.org
URL: www.ilsa.org
Social Media: www.facebook.com/jessupilsa
www.instagram.com/jessupilsa
www.linkedin.com/company/international-law-students
-association
twitter.com/The_Jessup

6029 ■ ILSA Internships *(Undergraduate/Internship)*

Purpose: To support law students in their career development. **Focus:** Law. **Qualif.:** Applicants must be pursuing an undergraduate degree; must have proficiency in Microsoft PowerPoint, Excel, and Word; must have strong written and verbal communication skills; must be familiar with social media platforms (including Facebook, Twitter, and Instagram). **Criteria:** Selection will be based on ILSA's criteria.

Funds Avail.: No specific amount. **Duration:** Annual. **To Apply:** Applicants must submit a cover letter and resume to the ILSA Executive Office. **Deadline:** September 4. **Contact:** E-mail: ilsa@ilsa.org.

6030 ■ International Life Sciences Institute North America (ILSI)

740 15th St. NW, Ste. 600
Washington, DC 20005
Ph: (202)659-0074
E-mail: ilsina@ilsi.org
URL: www.ilsina.org

6031 ■ ILSI North America Future Leader Award *(Professional development/Grant)*

Purpose: To give promising nutrition and food scientists the opportunity to add to an existing project or to conduct exploratory research that might not receive funding from other sources or add to an existing project. **Focus:** Nutrition. **Criteria:** Consideration will be given to individuals proposing research in the areas of experimental nutrition, nutrition and toxicology, and nutrition and food science.

Funds Avail.: $15,000 per annum. **Duration:** Annual; up to two years.

6032 ■ International Literacy Association (ILA)

258 Chapman Rd., Ste. 203
Newark, DE 19702
Ph: (302)731-1600
Fax: (302)731-1057
Free: 800-336-7323
E-mail: customerservice@reading.org
URL: www.literacyworldwide.org

6033 ■ Jeanne S. Chall Research Fellowship *(Doctorate, Graduate/Fellowship, Grant)*

Purpose: To honor and recognize reading research by promising scholars in areas of beginning reading, readability, reading difficulty, stages of reading development, relation of vocabulary to reading, and diagnosing those with limited ability. **Focus:** Reading. **Qualif.:** Applicants must be a member of the International Reading Association; may either be doctoral students who are planning or

Awards are arranged alphabetically below their administering organizations

beginning their dissertations; or a university based graduate students embarking on independent research studies. **Criteria:** Selection will be based on the committee's criteria.

Funds Avail.: $5,000. **Number Awarded:** 1 in 2018. **To Apply:** Applicants are advised to. visit the website for the online application process and must submit the following requirements: curriculum vitae; research Description; references; applicant may enter cover letter text (do NOT include identifying information). **Deadline:** March 15. **Remarks:** Established in 1998.

6034 ■ Elva Knight Research Grant (Professional development, Graduate/Grant, Award)

Purpose: To support promising research that addresses significant questions for the discipline of reading/literacy research and practice. **Focus:** Reading. **Qualif.:** Applicants must be a member of the International Reading Association. **Criteria:** Selection will be based on the committee's criteria.

Funds Avail.: $5,000. **Duration:** Annual. **Number Awarded:** Varies. **To Apply:** Applicants (and coapplicants) must create a profile by providing the following information in the Scholar One system; Select Manuscript Type (screen will refresh once selected); Full project title (15-word max); Running Head (50-character max); Abstract (150-word max), describing the purpose, method, and potential significance of the proposed research; Application Type (Individual or Group); materials should be uploaded as individual documents. **Deadline:** June 1. **Contact:** Dawn Roberts at ILAAwards@reading.org.

6035 ■ ILA Teacher as Researcher Grant (Professional development/Grant)

Purpose: To support classroom teachers who undertake action research inquiries about literacy and instruction in their classroom. **Focus:** Reading.

Funds Avail.: $5,000. **Duration:** Annual. **Number Awarded:** Up to 2. **Deadline:** January 15.

6036 ■ Nila Banton Smith Research Dissemination Support Grant (Professional development/Grant)

Purpose: To facilitate the dissemination of literacy research to the educational community. **Focus:** Reading. **Qualif.:** Applicants must be members of the International Reading Association. **Criteria:** Applications and proposals will be reviewed by the members of the International Reading Association Studies and Research based on: significance of research questions; rationale for the research; adequacy of methods and data treatment; significance of project impact; clarity of presentation.

Funds Avail.: $5,000. **Duration:** Annual. **Number Awarded:** Varies. **To Apply:** Applicants (and coapplicants) must create a profile by providing the following information in the Scholar One system; Select Manuscript Type (screen will refresh once selected); Full project title (15-word max); Running Head (50-character max); Abstract (150-word max), describing the purpose, method, and potential significance of the proposed research; Application Type (Individual or Group); materials should be uploaded as individual documents. **Deadline:** September 15; June 1. **Contact:** Dawn Roberts at ILAAwards@reading.org.

6037 ■ Helen M. Robinson Grants (Doctorate/Grant)

Purpose: To assist doctoral students at the early stages of their dissertation research in the area of reading and literacy. **Focus:** Reading. **Qualif.:** Applicants must be a member of the International Literacy Association; must be doctoral students in the early stages of the dissertation research in areas of reading and literacy. **Criteria:** Selection will be based on the committee's criteria.

Funds Avail.: $1,200. **Duration:** Annual. **Number Awarded:** 1 in 2018. **To Apply:** Application must be sent online; applicants must Upload the following materials Research Description, References; applicant may enter cover letter text (do NOT include identifying information). **Remarks:** The grant was established in memory of Helen M. Robinson. **Contact:** Wendy Logan; Email: ilaawards@reading.org.

6038 ■ Regie Routman Teacher Recognition Grant (Advanced Professional/Grant, Recognition)

Purpose: To support and honor an outstanding mainstream, elementary classroom teacher dedicated to developing reading and writing skills within students. **Focus:** Education, Elementary. **Qualif.:** Potential nominees need to be IRA members and teach at schools where at least 60% of students are eligible for free or reduced lunch. Teachers must also be able to demonstrate that they are devoted to improving the teaching and learning of reading and writing across the curriculum in grades K-6.

Funds Avail.: $2,500. **Duration:** Annual. **Number Awarded:** 1 in 2018. **To Apply:** Applicant must submit A three-page (maximum) proposal outlining; one-page personal statement (beliefs statement and how your beliefs align with your research-supported practices, including your professional vision for this project; letters of recommendation; applicant may enter cover letter text (not viewable by reviewers) or upload a cover letter (as a Supplementary File NOT for Review). **Deadline:** March 15. **Contact:** Email: ilaawards@reading.org.

6039 ■ Steven A. Stahl Research Grant (Graduate/Grant, Award)

Purpose: To provide opportunity for a graduating students to conduct their classroom research in reading. **Focus:** Reading. **Qualif.:** Applicants (including any coapplicants) must be current members of the International Literacy Association. **Criteria:** Selection will be based on the committee's criteria.

Funds Avail.: $1,000. **Duration:** Annual. **Number Awarded:** 1. **To Apply:** Applicants (and coapplicants) must create a profile by providing the following information in the Scholar One system; Select Manuscript Type (screen will refresh once selected); Full project title (15-word max); Running Head (50-character max); Abstract (150-word max), describing the purpose, method, and potential significance of the proposed research; Application Type (Individual or Group); materials should be uploaded as individual documents. **Deadline:** September 15; June 1. **Contact:** Dawn Roberts at ILAAwards@reading.org.

6040 ■ International Military Community Executives Association (IMCEA)
14080 Nacogdoches Rd.
San Antonio, TX 78247-1944
Ph: (940)463-5145
Fax: (866)369-2435
E-mail: imcea@imcea.org
URL: imcea.org
Social Media: www.facebook.com/IMCEA1
twitter.com/imcea1

Awards are arranged alphabetically below their administering organizations

6041 ■ The Robert W. Brunsman Memorial Scholarship *(Professional development/Scholarship)*

Purpose: To assist MWR professionals in continuing their education. **Focus:** General studies/Field of study not specified. **Qualif.:** Applicants must be IMCEA MWR/Services Professional member in good standing who are currently enrolled in a higher learning institution, whether in-class or on-line. **Criteria:** Selection will be based on the aforementioned Applicant's qualifications and compliance with the application details.

Funds Avail.: $1,000. **Duration:** Annual. **To Apply:** Applicants must mail the application form and attach a two-page, double spaced essay discussing how each area of MWR/Services (clubs, bowling's, golf, child care, etc.) might work together to create synergy and enhance the mission of IMCEA; each area has its own distinct challenges and opportunities; submit the said documents along with a copy of the current college transcript to the Scholarship Committee. **Deadline:** July 1. **Contact:** IMCEA Headquarters - Scholarship, 14080 Nacogdoches Rd., Ste. 329, San Antonio, TX, 78247-1944; Phone: 940-463-5145; Email: imcea@imcea.org.

6042 ■ Roy C. and Dorothy Jean Olson Memorial Scholarship *(Graduate/Scholarship)*

Purpose: To assist young men and women in furthering their education beyond secondary level. **Focus:** General studies/Field of study not specified. **Qualif.:** Applicants must be family members of a current IMCEA Professional member who are graduating from high school and continuing their education, or who are already enrolled in college. **Criteria:** Selection will be based on the aforementioned Applicant's qualifications and compliance with the application details.

Funds Avail.: $1,000. **To Apply:** Applicants must mail the application form, along with the following: a two-page essay discussing the question "How do social networking and media outlets affect the US Military mission in a wartime environment?"; a letter of acceptance to the college or university that the Applicants are planning to attend; and/or, a transcript from the college or university currently attended. **Deadline:** July 1. **Contact:** IMCEA Headquarters - Scholarship, 14080 Nacogdoches Rd., Ste. 329, San Antonio, TX, 78247-1944; Phone: 940-463-5145; Email: imcea@imcea.org.

6043 ■ International Narcotics Interdiction Association (INIA)

PO Box 1757
Spring Hill, TN 37174
Free: 866-780-4642
E-mail: info@inia.org
URL: www.inia.org
Social Media: www.facebook.com/skynarc1997
twitter.com/skynarc1997

6044 ■ INIA Scholarship Program *(Undergraduate/Scholarship)*

Purpose: To support the education the children of INIA members. **Focus:** General studies/Field of study not specified. **Qualif.:** Applicants must be children of INIA members (living or deceased) who will be in their senior year of high school. **Criteria:** Selection will be based on submitted essay which will be judged based on its content, form and grammar.

Funds Avail.: $1,000 each. **Duration:** Annual. **To Apply:** Applicants must submit their completed application form along with an essay not exceeding 500 words on the topic described on the application form; must be accompanied by the signed certification statement indicating that the parent/guardian had monitored the essay; prior to receiving the funds, are required to provide a proof of admission to an accredited institute in a full-time status. **Deadline:** May 15. **Contact:** INIA Scholarship Award, PO Box 1757 Springhill, TN, 37174; Phone: 866-780-4642; Email: info@inia.org.

6045 ■ International Nurses Society on Addictions (INTNSA)

3416 Primm Ln.
Birmingham, AL 35216
Ph: (205)823-6106
E-mail: intnsa@intnsa.org
URL: www.intnsa.org
Social Media: www.youtube.com/channel/UCXSJ5z6AMsBlfOS8MKHxgGQ

6046 ■ Lois Widly Student Scholarships *(Graduate, Undergraduate/Scholarship)*

Purpose: To financially assist IntNSA members to further their professional education. **Focus:** Nursing. **Qualif.:** Applicant must be a current full-time student in a nursing undergraduate or graduate program; must be sponsored by a current IntNSA member. **Criteria:** Selection of applicants will be based on the Scholarship application criteria.

Funds Avail.: $500. **Duration:** Annual. **Number Awarded:** Up to 4; 2 undergraduate and 2 graduate scholarships. **To Apply:** Applicants must complete the application form available online; must submit a recommendation letter; letter of support from their sponsor; and essay about their interest in attending the conference and what they plan to do with the knowledge gained (250-300 word). **Deadline:** June 1. **Contact:** IntNSA, 3416 Primm Ln., Birmingham, AL, 35216; Email: intnsa@intnsa.org.

6047 ■ International Order of the Golden Rule (IOGR)

3520 Executive Center Dr., Ste. 300
Austin, TX 78731
Ph: (512)334-5504
Fax: (512)334-5514
Free: 800-637-8030
E-mail: info@ogr.org
URL: www.ogr.org
Social Media: www.facebook.com/GoldenRuleFH
www.instagram.com/goldenrulefh
twitter.com/GoldenRuleFH

6048 ■ OGR Award of Excellence Scholarships *(Undergraduate/Scholarship)*

Purpose: To support students who have demonstrated excellence in the study of mortuary science. **Focus:** Mortuary science. **Qualif.:** Applicant must be currently enrolled in a mortuary science degree program at an accredited mortuary school; be scheduled to graduate in the current year; have a cumulative GPA of 3.0 or higher; must be involved in community service activities and school activities; must demonstrate excellence in the pursuit of knowledge in mortuary science and commit to working for an independently owned funeral home.

Awards are arranged alphabetically below their administering organizations

Funds Avail.: $3,500; $2,000. **Duration:** Annual. **Number Awarded:** 2. **Deadline:** November 30. **Contact:** OGR Awards of Excellence Fund, 9101 Burnet Rd., Ste. 120, Austin, TX, 78758; Fax: 512-334-5514.

6049 ■ International Order of the King's Daughters and Sons (IOKDS)

34 Vincent Ave.
Chautauqua, NY 14722
Ph: (716)357-4951
Fax: (716)357-3762
E-mail: iokds5@windstream.net
URL: www.iokds.org
Social Media: www.facebook.com/IOKDS
www.instagram.com/iokds_chautauqua
twitter.com/TheKing31863130

6050 ■ IOKDS Health Careers Scholarship *(College, University, Undergraduate, Graduate, Doctorate/ Scholarship)*

Purpose: To contribute to the education of compassionate health care workers. **Focus:** Dentistry; Medical technology; Medicine; Nursing; Occupational therapy; Pharmaceutical sciences; Physical therapy; Speech and language pathology/Audiology. **Qualif.:** Applicants must be medical or dental students who have completed their first year of an accredited medical or dental school program; students in the fields of pharmacy, occupational therapy, physical therapy, speech and language therapy, and medical technologies must have completed a minimum of two years of study; students studying to become registered nurses with an Associate's Degree must have completed their first year of studies at an accredited institution; students pursuing a Bachelor's or Master's Degrees in nursing must have completed two years of study; must be U.S. or Canadian citizens enrolled at accredited institutions in the United States or Canada. **Criteria:** Priority is given to students pursuing their Master's or Doctorate Degrees when those degrees are required for certification.

Duration: Annual. **To Apply:** Application details are available online at iokds.org/scholarships/health-careers-scholarships-2/. Recipients are eligible to receive scholarships for a maximum of three years but they must reapply every year and remain in good academic standing. **Deadline:** March 1. **Contact:** Email: health-careers-director@iokds.org.

6051 ■ IOKDS Native American Scholarships *(Undergraduate, University, College, Vocational/ Occupational/Scholarship)*

Purpose: To assist Native American students in pursuing post-secondary education. **Focus:** General studies/Field of study not specified. **Qualif.:** Applicants must be of Native American ancestry and enrolled in a technical, vocational, or college studies program.

Funds Avail.: $1,000. **Duration:** Annual. **To Apply:** Must submit a tribal application number along with the other requirements. Application details are available online at iokds.org/scholarships/native-american-scholarship-program/. Scholarship is available for more than one year, but recipients must reapply each year. **Deadline:** April 1. **Contact:** Email: Native-American-director@iokds.org.

6052 ■ IOKDS Student Ministry Scholarships *(Master's/Scholarship)*

Purpose: To assist students in pursuing Masters' degrees in Divinity studies. **Focus:** Religion. **Qualif.:** Applicant must be a full-time student in a Master of Divinity program at an Association of Theological Schools in the United States or Canada-accredited college or seminary; must be a citizen of the U.S. or Canada; must have maintained a minimum 3.0 GPA for all undergraduate and graduate studies.

Funds Avail.: $1,000. **Duration:** Annual. **To Apply:** Write two essays, one personal statement including family background and reasons for choosing Masters of Divinity study, one essay regarding a bible verse that is significant to the applicant; provide two letters of recommendation; official transcripts; include stamped, self-addressed envelope in submission packet. **Deadline:** March 1. **Contact:** Email: student-ministry-director@iokds.org; URL: iokds.org/scholarships/student-ministry-scholarships/.

6053 ■ International Organic Inspectors Association (IOIA)

PO Box 6
Broadus, MT 59317
Ph: (406)436-2031
E-mail: ioia@ioia.net
URL: www.ioia.net
Social Media: www.facebook.com/margaret.scoles.3
www.linkedin.com/company/international-organic-inspectors-association/?viewAsMember=true

6054 ■ IOIA Organic Community Initiative Scholarships *(Other/Scholarship)*

Purpose: To provide students a full tuition for an IOIA Inspector training Course. **Focus:** Education, Vocational-technical. **Qualif.:** Applicants must be individuals residing outside of the United States and Canada. **Criteria:** Recipients will be selected based on their potential to effect change in their organic community and financial need.

Funds Avail.: No amount mentioned. **Duration:** Annual. **Number Awarded:** 1. **To Apply:** Applicants must submit a completed application form, cover letter, current resume, and list of three references. **Deadline:** October 1. **Contact:** IOIA, P.O BOX 6, Brodadus, MT, 59317; Email: scholarship@ioia.net.

6055 ■ IOIA Andrew Rutherford Scholarships *(Other/ Scholarship)*

Purpose: To provide students a full tuition for an IOIA Inspector training Course. **Focus:** Education, Vocational-technical. **Qualif.:** Applicants must come from outside of the US or Canada; prospective and experienced inspectors are eligible to apply for the Scholarship. **Criteria:** Selection will be evaluated by the Scholarship Committee.

Funds Avail.: No amount mentioned. **Duration:** Annual. **Deadline:** October 1. **Contact:** Email: scholarship@ioia.net.

6056 ■ International Organization of Black Security Executives (IOBSE)

2340 Powell St., No. 327
Emeryville, CA 94608
Ph: (510)648-4292
E-mail: info@iobse.org
URL: iobse.org
Social Media: www.facebook.com/IOBSE
www.linkedin.com/company/iobse

6057 ■ IOBSE Scholarships *(Undergraduate/ Scholarship)*

Purpose: To assist those students demonstrating an interest in Security as a profession. **Focus:** Security. **Qualif.:**

Awards are arranged alphabetically below their administering organizations

Applicants must be undergraduate students have a high interest in the security profession, demonstrate leadership, and are involved in supporting the community by serving others. **Criteria:** Applicants are judged upon the committee's criteria.

Funds Avail.: $1,500. **Duration:** Annual. **Number Awarded:** 3. **To Apply:** Applicants must submit a resume detailing specific leadership and community roles held; provide one recommendation from campus staff, current employer, or community leader discussing their leadership skills; and complete an interview process. **Contact:** IOBSE Scholarship Applications, 2340 Powell St., Ste. 327, Emeryville, CA, 94608.

6058 ■ International Phonetic Association (IPA)
c/o Dr Michael Ashby, President
Chandler House, 2 Wakefield St.
London WC1N 1PF, United Kingdom
Ph: 44 20 76794090
Fax: 44 20 76794010
E-mail: m.ashby@ucl.ac.uk
URL: www.internationalphoneticassociation.org
Social Media: www.facebook.com/
internationalphoneticassociation
twitter.com/IPAphonetics

6059 ■ Gösta Bruce Scholarship Fund *(Other/Scholarship)*

Purpose: To support student members in presenting their research at the International Congress of Phonetic Sciences. **Focus:** Education. **Qualif.:** Applicants must be current student members of the IPA who are the first or sole author of a paper or poster. (I) student members, (ii) unemployed members, (iii) members under age 35, or (iv) members from countries where funding resources are limited.

Funds Avail.: 100-350 Euros. **Duration:** Annual. **Number Awarded:** 10. **Deadline:** April 15.

6060 ■ International Practice Management Association (IPMA)
Bldg. 5, Ste. 300
3525 Piedmont Rd. NE
Atlanta, GA 30305
Ph: (404)467-6757
E-mail: info@theipma.org
URL: www.theipma.org
Social Media: www.facebook.com/TheIPMA
www.linkedin.com/company/theipma
twitter.com/TheIPMA

6061 ■ Therese A. "Teri" Cannon Educational Scholarship *(Other/Scholarship)*

Purpose: To support and assist members in continuing their education through advanced training. **Focus:** Paralegal studies. **Qualif.:** Applicants must be regular, associate, life or emeritus IPMA members if the cost of IPMA Conference registration fee is not covered by their employer. **Criteria:** Selection will be based on committee's criteria.

Funds Avail.: No specific amount. **Number Awarded:** 1. **To Apply:** Completed application form must be submitted to the awards committee. **Deadline:** September 1. **Remarks:** The scholarship was created to honor Teri Cannon's dedicated service to the IPMA and to recognize her commitment to the education of paralegal and paralegal management. **Contact:** E-mail: awards@theipma.org.

6062 ■ International Precious Metals Institute (IPMI)
5101 N 12th Ave., Ste. C
Pensacola, FL 32504
Ph: (850)476-1156
Fax: (850)476-1548
E-mail: mail@ipmi.org
URL: www.ipmi.org
Social Media: www.facebook.com/International-Precious
-Metals-Institute-IPMI-122471634476706
www.youtube.com/user/TheIPMI

6063 ■ IPMI Richard Rubin Memorial Scholarship Award *(Graduate/Scholarship)*

Purpose: To recognize achievement in precious metals research by a graduate student. **Focus:** Metallurgy.

Funds Avail.: $20,000. **Duration:** Annual. **Deadline:** January 31. **Contact:** Email: mail@ipmi.org; Phone: 850-476-1156.

6064 ■ International Public Management Association for Human Resources (IPMA-HR)
1617 Duke St.
Alexandria, VA 22314
Ph: (703)549-7100
Fax: (703)549-7100
URL: www.ipma-hr.org
Social Media: www.facebook.com/International-Public
-Management-Association-for-Human-Resources-IPMA
-HR-38098732966
www.instagram.com/ipmahr/
www.linkedin.com/company/297501
www.linkedin.com/company/ipma-hr
twitter.com/ipmahr

6065 ■ Graduate Study Fellowship *(Professional development/Fellowship)*

Purpose: To allow recipients to pursue graduate study in public administration, business administration, the law or a related field. **Focus:** Business administration; Law; Public administration. **Qualif.:** Applicants must have a minimum of five years of full-time professional experience of excellent quality and depth; at least two of these years must be in an HR-related area; must have a strong academic record; must have demonstrated leadership, management or creativity; strong commitment to public sector human resources; must have a current national membership in the association of at least one year, other than as student members. **Criteria:** Selection will be based on the committee criteria.

Funds Avail.: $2,000. **Duration:** Annual. **Number Awarded:** 2. **To Apply:** Applicants must provide the following; letter indicating acceptance to graduate school for a law degree or a master's degree in public administration, business administration or a related field; and official copies of all undergraduate and graduate transcripts. **Deadline:** June 1.

6066 ■ International Radio and Television Society Foundation (IRTS)
1697 Broadway, 10th Fl.
New York, NY 10019

Awards are arranged alphabetically below their administering organizations

Ph: (212)867-6650
E-mail: info@irts.org
URL: irtsfoundation.org
Social Media: www.facebook.com/TheIRTS
www.instagram.com/irts.foundation/
www.linkedin.com/company/the-irts-foundation/
twitter.com/irtsfoundation

6067 ■ International Radio and Television Society Foundation Summer Fellowships Program
(Undergraduate, Graduate/Fellowship)

Purpose: To assist students in their professional development. **Focus:** General studies/Field of study not specified. **Qualif.:** Applicants must be college juniors, seniors or graduate students from all majors (including math, computer science, business, marketing, communications, etc.), as of April of the current year. **Criteria:** Selection shall be based on the aforementioned qualifications and compliance with the application details.

Funds Avail.: No specific amount. **Duration:** Annual. **To Apply:** Applicants must complete and submit online application; additional document must also includes one-page resume (Word document or PDF).

6068 ■ International Research and Exchanges Board (IREX)
1275 K St. NW, Ste. 600
Washington, DC 20005
Ph: (202)628-8188
Fax: (202)628-8189
E-mail: communications@irex.org
URL: www.irex.org
Social Media: www.facebook.com/irexinternational
www.linkedin.com/company/irex
twitter.com/irexintl

6069 ■ Educational and Cultural Affairs Alumni Small Grants Program (ECA) *(Other/Grant)*

Purpose: To bring outstanding secondary school teachers from around the globe to the United States to further develop expertise in their subject areas, enhance their teaching skills, and increase their knowledge about the United States. **Focus:** European studies. **Qualif.:** Applicants must be alumni of the Edmund S. Muskie Graduate Fellowship Program (MUSKIE) or the Eurasian Undergraduate Program (UGRAD). **Criteria:** Selection is based on the applications.

Funds Avail.: No specific amount. **Duration:** Annual. **To Apply:** Applicants must contact their local IREX office for application details.

6070 ■ Individual Advanced Research Opportunities Program For Master's Students *(Graduate, Master's/Fellowship)*

Purpose: To support in-depth, primary source research in policy-relevant subjects related to Southeast Europe and Eurasia. **Focus:** European studies. **Qualif.:** Applicants must be U.S. citizens who are currently enrolled in a Master's program. **Criteria:** Selection will be based on the following criteria: overall strength of proposals, reference and proposed methodology; importance of topic towards foreign policy community; value of research to community; demonstrated serious preparatory work; well-argued need to conduct the research; language skills adequate for proposed research; feasibility of project and timeframe; demonstrated career commitment to the field; and few previous opportunities to conduct the research. Preference will be given to research projects on the countries of Central Asia and the Caucasus.

Funds Avail.: $30,000. **To Apply:** Applications can be submitted online. **Deadline:** November 14. **Contact:** iaro@irex.org.

6071 ■ IREX Individual Advanced Research Opportunities Program For Postdoctoral Scholars
(Postdoctorate/Fellowship)

Purpose: To support in-depth, primary source research in policy-relevant subjects related to Southeast Europe and Eurasia. **Focus:** European studies. **Qualif.:** Applicants must be U.S. citizens who are Ph.D. holders. **Criteria:** Selection will be based on the following criteria: overall strength of proposals, reference and proposed methodology; importance of topic towards foreign policy community; value of research to community; demonstrated serious preparatory work; well-argued need to conduct the research; language skills adequate for proposed research; feasibility of project and timeframe; demonstrated career commitment to the field; and few previous opportunities to conduct the research. Preference will be given to research projects on the countries of Central Asia and the Caucasus.

Funds Avail.: No specific amount. **To Apply:** Applicants must complete an application form; must submit a research proposal; five-page curriculum vitae; transcript of records; Professional/Academic Reference and one Language Proficiency Form (to be sent directly by referee). Other information on the research proposal can be verified at the website. **Contact:** E-mail: iaro@irex.org; Phone: 202-628-8188.

6072 ■ IREX Individual Advanced Research Opportunities Program For Pre-doctoral Students
(Doctorate/Fellowship)

Purpose: To support in-depth, primary source research in policy-relevant subjects related to Southeast Europe and Eurasia. **Focus:** European studies. **Qualif.:** Applicants must be U.S. citizens who are currently enrolled in a Ph.D. program. **Criteria:** Selection will be based on the following criteria: overall strength of proposals, reference and proposed methodology; importance of topic towards foreign policy community; value of research to community; demonstrated serious preparatory work; well-argued need to conduct the research; language skills adequate for proposed research; feasibility of project and timeframe; demonstrated career commitment to the field; and few previous opportunities to conduct the research. Preference will be given to research projects on the countries of Central Asia and the Caucasus.

Funds Avail.: No specific amount. **To Apply:** Applicants must complete an application form; must submit a research proposal; five-page curriculum vitae; transcript of records; Professional/Academic Reference and one Language Proficiency Form (to be sent directly by referee). Other information on the research proposal can be verified at the website. **Contact:** E-mail: iaro@irex.org; Phone: 202-628-8188.

6073 ■ IREX Individual Advanced Research Opportunities Program For Professionals *(Other/Fellowship)*

Purpose: To support in-depth, primary source research in policy-relevant subjects related to Southeast Europe and

Awards are arranged alphabetically below their administering organizations

Eurasia. **Focus:** European studies. **Qualif.:** Applicants must be U.S. citizens who have one of the following degrees (MA, MS, MFA, MBA, MPA, MLIS, MPH, JD, or MD). They must not be enrolled as students during the grant period. **Criteria:** Selection will be based on the following criteria: overall strength of proposals, reference and proposed methodology; importance of topic towards foreign policy community; value of research to community; demonstrated serious preparatory work; well-argued need to conduct the research; language skills adequate for proposed research; feasibility of project and timeframe; demonstrated career commitment to the field; and few previous opportunities to conduct the research. Preference will be given to research projects on the countries of Central Asia and the Caucasus.

Funds Avail.: No specific amount. **To Apply:** Applicants must complete an application form; must submit a research proposal; five-page curriculum vitae; transcript of records; Professional/Academic Reference and one Language Proficiency Form (to be sent directly by referee). Other information on the research proposal can be verified at the website. **Contact:** E-mail: iaro@irex.org; Phone: 202-628-8188.

6074 ■ The International Research Foundation for English Language Education

177 Webster St., No. 220
Monterey, CA 93940
Fax: (831)647-6650
E-mail: info@tirfonline.org
URL: tirfonline.org
Social Media: www.facebook.com/tirfonline
www.youtube.com/user/tirfonline

6075 ■ Doctoral Dissertation Grants *(Doctorate/ Grant)*

Purpose: To support students completing their doctoral research on topics related to the foundation's priorities. **Focus:** General studies/Field of study not specified. **Qualif.:** Applicants must be enrolled in a legitimate doctoral program; must be advanced to candidacy and have had a research plan approved by a faculty committee at their university; must have a research supervisor. **Criteria:** Selection will be based on the committee's criteria.

Funds Avail.: $5,000. **To Apply:** Applicants must write a proposal which is clearly related to TIRF's research priorities; must follow specific instructions located in the call for proposals; applicants' research supervisor must submit an official letter of support attesting to the applicants' readiness to complete the doctoral dissertation. **Deadline:** May 27. **Remarks:** Established in 2002.

6076 ■ International Rett Syndrome Foundation (IRSF)

4600 Devitt Dr.
Cincinnati, OH 45246
Ph: (513)874-3020
URL: www.rettsyndrome.org
Social Media: www.facebook.com/RettSyndrome
www.instagram.com/rettsyndromeorg
www.linkedin.com/company/rettsyndrome.org
twitter.com/Rettsyndrome

6077 ■ IRSF Mentored Training Fellowships *(Advanced Professional/Fellowship)*

Purpose: To assist post-doctoral research scientists and clinical scientists establish careers in the fields relevant to

Rett syndrome research. **Focus:** Neuroscience. **Qualif.:** Applicants must be post-doctoral research scientists or clinical scientists.

Funds Avail.: $100,000. **Duration:** Two years. **To Apply:** Applicants is considered Principal Investigator (PI) for the application, and is required to identify a sponsoring mentor.

6078 ■ International Safety Equipment Association (ISEA)

1901 N Moore St., Ste. 808
Arlington, VA 22209-1762
Ph: (703)525-1695
Fax: (703)528-2148
URL: safetyequipment.org
Social Media: www.facebook.com/iseastandards
www.linkedin.com/company/isea-safety
twitter.com/isea_safety

6079 ■ Lincoln C. Bailey Memorial Scholarship Fund *(Undergraduate/Scholarship)*

Purpose: To provide financial assistance to the promising dependent of its members in the final year in college or universities. **Focus:** General studies/Field of study not specified. **Qualif.:** Applicant must be a son, daughter, stepson, stepdaughter, or legally adopted ward of an employee of an ISEA member company, a safety division or that part of a company that holds membership in ISEA, or of an employee of ISEA; must be a full-time student completing sophomore or junior year at an accredited college or university in the United States taking courses leading to a bachelor's degree. **Criteria:** Selection will be based on independent panel, based on academic achievement, extracurricular activity and financial need.

Funds Avail.: No specific amount. **Duration:** Annual. **To Apply:** Applicants must submit transcript and financial information and letters of recommendation. **Deadline:** March 13. **Remarks:** Established in 1989.

6080 ■ International Sanitary Supply Association (ISSA)

3300 Dundee Rd.
Northbrook, IL 60062
Ph: (847)982-0800
Fax: (847)982-1012
Free: 800-225-4772
E-mail: info@issa.com
URL: www.issa.com
Social Media: www.facebook.com/issaworldwide
www.instagram.com/issaworldwide
www.linkedin.com/groups/1799553/profile
www.linkedin.com/company/issaworldwide
twitter.com/issaworldwide

6081 ■ International Sanitary Supply Association Foundation Scholarships *(Undergraduate/ Scholarship)*

Purpose: To provide scholarship assistance to ISSA member company employees and their family members. **Focus:** General studies/Field of study not specified. **Qualif.:** Applicants must be entering or continuing studies at a fully accredited four-year college or university. **Criteria:** Selection will be judged on the basis of merit, individual accomplishments, and evidence of leadership; preference will

Awards are arranged alphabetically below their administering organizations

be given to those with financial need and other special circumstances.

Funds Avail.: $164,000. **Duration:** Annual. **To Apply:** Applicants must provide a resume with personal information; an essay; academic activity and leadership record; official high school or college/university transcript; must also submit official SAT, ACT, GRE, GMAT or LSAT test scores; two evaluations from current or past professors or teaching assistants. **Deadline:** March 1. **Contact:** Mail Completed Scholarship Application to ISSA Foundation; 3300 Dundee Rd., Northbrook, IL 60062.

6082 ■ International Society of Air Safety Investigators (ISASI)

c/o Ann Schull, International Office Manager
107 E Holly Ave., Ste. 11
Sterling, VA 20164
Ph: (703)430-9668
Fax: (703)430-4970
E-mail: isasi@erols.com
URL: www.isasi.org
Social Media: twitter.com/isasiairsafety

6083 ■ The ISASI Rudolf Kapustin Memorial Scholarship (Undergraduate/Scholarship)

Purpose: To encourage and assist college-level students interested in the field of aviation safety and aircraft occurrence investigation. **Focus:** Aviation. **Qualif.:** Applicants must be a member of ISASI and enrolled as a full-time student in a recognized education program, which includes courses in aircraft engineering and/or operations, aviation psychology, aviation safety or aircraft occurrence investigation, etc., with major or minor subjects that focus on aviation safety/investigation. **Criteria:** Selection will be scholarship fund committee will review submitted materials.

Funds Avail.: $2,000. **Duration:** Annual. **To Apply:** Applicants should submit a 1500 (+/- 10%) word paper in English, addressing "the challenges for air safety investigators" or the current conference theme. The papers will be evaluated based on content, original thinking, logic, clarity of expression and topic applicability; grammar and professional presentation will be taken into account; the paper is to be the student's own work and must be countersigned by the student's tutor/academic supervisor as authentic, original work; must submit a letter of recommendation from their professor, academic tutor, or faculty mentor. **Deadline:** April 15.

6084 ■ International Society of Automation (ISA)

67 TW Alexander Dr.
Research Triangle Park, NC 27709
Ph: (919)549-8411
Fax: (919)549-8288
E-mail: info@isa.org
URL: www.isa.org
Social Media: www.facebook.com/
  InternationalSocietyOfAutomation
www.instagram.com/isa_interchange
www.pinterest.com/IntlSocietyofAutomation
twitter.com/ISA_Interchange
www.youtube.com/user/isawebgroup

6085 ■ ISA Aerospace Industries Division - William H. Atkinson Scholarships (Graduate, Undergraduate/Scholarship)

Purpose: To support outstanding students pursuing careers in the area pertinent to the Division's activity. **Focus:** Automotive technology; Systems engineering.

Contact: Dennis Coad; Email: Dennis.l.coad@boeing.com.

6086 ■ ISA Educational Foundation Scholarship (Undergraduate, Graduate/Scholarship)

Purpose: To support students tuition and related expenses and research activities and initiatives. **Focus:** Automotive technology; Systems engineering. **Qualif.:** Applicants must be currently enrolled in a graduate or undergraduate program in an instrumentation, systems, or automation discipline (2-year program or 4-year baccalaureate program or its equivalent); two-year program must have completed at least one academic semester, or 12 semester hours, or its equivalent; four-year degree program must be in sophomore year or higher at the time of application; must be full-time students in an educational institution who have an overall GPA of 3.0 on a 4.0 scale. **Criteria:** Preference is given to students who are enrolled in a degree program in instrumentation, systems, and automation or other closely related field.

Duration: Annual. **To Apply:** Applicants must submit completed application (with Department Head Signature); two reference letters; original transcript (with raised seal); list of awards and honors and extracurricular activities; employment history; and an essay; mail the original and ten copies of the complete application with attachments unfolded in an envelope. **Deadline:** February 24. **Contact:** ISA Educational Foundation - Scholarship Committee, 67 Alexander Dr., Research Triangle Pk., NC 27709 USA.

6087 ■ ISA Executive Board Scholarship (Graduate, Undergraduate/Scholarship)

Purpose: To support college or university students who demonstrate outstanding potential for long-range contribution to the fields of automation and control. **Focus:** Automotive technology; Systems engineering. **Criteria:** Preference is given to applicants with demonstrated leadership capabilities.

Funds Avail.: Amount varies. **Contact:** Scholarship Committee; Phone: 919-549-8411.

6088 ■ ISA Section and District Scholarships - Houston (Graduate, Undergraduate/Scholarship)

Purpose: To support college or university students who demonstrate outstanding potential for long-range contribution to the fields of automation and control. **Focus:** Automotive technology; Systems engineering.

Duration: Annual. **Contact:** Ardis Bartle, Email: ardisbartle@apexmeasurement.com; Mike Huereca, Email: Mike.Huereca@RawsonLP.com; Mary Cannon, Email: mary.cannon@pentair.com.

6089 ■ ISA Section and District Scholarships - Lehigh Valley (Graduate, Undergraduate/Scholarship)

Purpose: To support college or university students who demonstrate outstanding potential for long-range contribution to the fields of automation and control. **Focus:** Automotive technology; Systems engineering.

Contact: Dave Tachovsky; Email: dtach@ptd.net.

Awards are arranged alphabetically below their administering organizations

6090 ■ ISA Section and District Scholarships - Richmond Hopewell *(Graduate, Undergraduate/ Scholarship)*

Purpose: To support college or university students who demonstrate outstanding potential for long-range contribution to the fields of automation and control. **Focus:** Automotive technology; Systems engineering.

Contact: Bill Sneddon; Email: bill.sneddon@qimonda.com.

6091 ■ ISA Section and District Scholarships - Southwestern Wyoming *(Graduate, Undergraduate/ Scholarship)*

Purpose: To promote education in instrumentation, systems, or automation discipline. **Focus:** Automotive technology; Systems engineering. **Qualif.:** Applicant must be currently enrolled in a graduate or undergraduate program in an instrumentation, systems, or automation discipline (2-year program or 4-year baccalaureate program or its equivalent). Two-year program applicants must have completed at least one academic semester or its equivalent. Four-year degree program applicants must be in sophomore year or higher at the time of application. Applicants must be full-time students in an educational institution and have at least an overall GPA of 3.0 on a 4.0 scale. **Criteria:** Preference is given to students who are enrolled in a degree program in instrumentation, systems, and automation or other closely related field.

Funds Avail.: No specific amount. **Duration:** Annual. **To Apply:** Applicants must submit completed application (with Department Head Signature); two reference letters; original transcript (with raised seal); list of awards and honors; extracurricular activities; employment history; and an essay. Mail the original and ten copies of the complete application with attachments unfolded in an envelope. **Deadline:** February 15.

6092 ■ ISA Section and District Scholarships - Texas, Louisiana and Mississippi *(Graduate, Undergraduate/Scholarship)*

Purpose: To promote education in instrumentation, systems, or automation discipline. **Focus:** Automotive technology; Systems engineering. **Qualif.:** Applicant must be currently enrolled in a graduate or undergraduate program in an instrumentation, systems, or automation discipline (2 year program or 4 year baccalaureate program or its equivalent). Two-year program applicants must have completed at least one academic semester or its equivalent. Four-year degree program applicants must be in sophomore year or higher at the time of application. Applicants must be full-time students in an educational institution who have at least an overall GPA of 3.0 on a 4.0 scale. **Criteria:** Preference is given to students who are enrolled in a degree program in instrumentation, systems, and automation or other closely related field.

Funds Avail.: No amount mentioned. **Duration:** Annual. **To Apply:** Applicants must submit a completed application (with Department Head Signature); two reference letters; original transcript (with raised seal); list of awards and honors; extracurricular activities; employment history; and an essay. Mail the original and ten copies of the complete application with attachments unfolded in an envelope. **Deadline:** February 15.

6093 ■ ISA Section and District Scholarships - Wilmington *(Graduate, Undergraduate/Scholarship)*

Purpose: To promote education in instrumentation, systems, or automation discipline. **Focus:** Automotive

technology; Systems engineering. **Qualif.:** Applicant must be currently enrolled in a graduate or undergraduate program in an instrumentation, systems, or automation discipline (2-year program or 4-year baccalaureate program or its equivalent). Two-year program applicants must have completed at least one academic semester or its equivalent. Four-year degree program applicants must be in sophomore year or higher at the time of application. Applicants must be full-time students in an educational institution and have at least an overall GPA of 3.0 on a 4.0 scale. **Criteria:** Preference is given to students who are enrolled in a degree program in instrumentation, systems, and automation or other closely related field.

Funds Avail.: No specific amount. **Duration:** Annual. **To Apply:** Applicants must submit completed application (with Department Head Signature); two reference letters; original transcript (with raised seal); list of awards and honors; extracurricular activities; employment history; and an essay. Mail the original and ten copies of the complete application with attachments unfolded in an envelope. **Deadline:** February 15.

6094 ■ ISA Technical Division Scholarships - Analysis Division *(Graduate, Undergraduate/ Scholarship)*

Purpose: To support outstanding students pursuing careers in the area pertinent to the Division's activity. **Focus:** Automotive technology; Systems engineering.

6095 ■ ISA Technical Division Scholarships - Chemical and Petroleum Industries Division *(College, University/Scholarship)*

Purpose: To support outstanding students pursuing careers in the area pertinent to the Division's activity. **Focus:** Automotive technology; Systems engineering.

Contact: Fares Karadsheh; Email: fares.karadsheh@psctexas.com.

6096 ■ ISA Technical Division Scholarships - Food and Pharmaceutical Industries Division *(Graduate, Undergraduate/Scholarship)*

Purpose: To support outstanding students pursuing careers in the area pertinent to the Division's activity. **Focus:** Automotive technology; Systems engineering.

Contact: Michael Baldauff; Email: michael.baldauff@fujifilm.com.

6097 ■ ISA Technical Division Scholarships - Power Industry Division *(Graduate, Undergraduate/ Scholarship)*

Purpose: To support outstanding students pursuing careers in the area pertinent to the Division's activity. **Focus:** Automotive technology; Systems engineering.

Contact: Mike Skoncey; Email: mskoncey@firstenergy.corp.com.

6098 ■ ISA Technical Division Scholarships - Process Measurement and Control Division *(Graduate, Undergraduate/Scholarship)*

Purpose: To support outstanding students pursuing careers in the area pertinent to the Division's activity. **Focus:** Automotive technology; Systems engineering.

Contact: Murtaza Gandhi at musra.gandi@chevron.com.

6099 ■ ISA Technical Division Scholarships - Pulp and Paper Industry Division *(Graduate, Undergraduate/Scholarship)*

Purpose: To support outstanding students pursuing careers in the area pertinent to the Division's activity. **Focus:** Auto-

Awards are arranged alphabetically below their administering organizations

motive technology; Systems engineering.

Contact: Brad Carlberg; Email: brad.carlberg@bsc-engineering.com.

6100 ■ ISA Technical Division Scholarships - Test Measurement Division *(Graduate, Undergraduate/ Scholarship)*

Purpose: To support outstanding students pursuing careers in the area pertinent to the Division's activity. **Focus:** Automotive technology; Systems engineering.

Contact: J. Brandon Jones; Email: joshua.jones@arnold.af.mil.

6101 ■ ISA Technical Division Scholarships - Water and Wastewater Industries Division *(Graduate, Undergraduate/Scholarship)*

Purpose: To support outstanding students pursuing careers in the area pertinent to the Division's activity. **Focus:** Automotive technology; Systems engineering.

Contact: Mike Fedenyszen; Email: mfedenyszen@vanderweil.com.

6102 ■ Bob and Mary Ives Scholarship *(Graduate, Undergraduate/Scholarship)*

Purpose: To promote education in an instrumentation, systems, or automation discipline. **Focus:** Automotive technology; Systems engineering. **Qualif.:** Applicants must be currently enrolled in a graduate or undergraduate program in an instrumentation, systems, or automation discipline (2-year program or 4-year baccalaureate program or its equivalent); two-year program must have completed at least one academic semester, or 12 semester hours, or its equivalent; four-year degree program must be in sophomore year or higher at the time of application; must be full-time students in an educational institution who have an overall GPA of 3.0 on a 4.0 scale. **Criteria:** Applicants who demonstrate outstanding potential for long-range contribution to the fields of automation and control.

Funds Avail.: No amount mentioned. **Duration:** Annual. **Deadline:** February 24. **Remarks:** The award was established to honor of Robert P. Ives, President of ISA in 2003. Established in 2003.

6103 ■ Norman E. and Mary-Belle Huston Scholarship *(Graduate, Undergraduate/Scholarship)*

Purpose: To promote education in an instrumentation, systems, or automation discipline. **Focus:** Automotive technology; Systems engineering. **Criteria:** Applicants who demonstrate outstanding potential for long-range contribution to the fields of automation and control.

Funds Avail.: No specific amount. **Duration:** Annual. **Deadline:** March 15. **Remarks:** Established in 1979.

6104 ■ International Society for Disease Surveillance
288 Grove Street, Ste. 203
Braintree, MA 02184

6105 ■ ISDS Graduate Student Scholarships *(Doctorate, Graduate/Scholarship)*

Purpose: To provide ISDS members the opportunity to disseminate innovative research and practice and to create network with the broader surveillance community. **Focus:** General studies/Field of study not specified. **Qualif.:** Ap-

plicants must be ISDS members; must be Master's or PhD candidates in surveillance-related field; must be in need of funding to attend the conference. **Criteria:** Applicants will be judged based on methods and science in surveillance, informatics, communication, visualization, and reporting, policy, one health and beyond, public or population health surveillance practice.

Funds Avail.: No specific amount. **To Apply:** Applicants must submit the contact information with name, address, institutional affiliation and position title; proof of student status (scanned copy of unofficial transcript and student ID). **Deadline:** October 29.

6106 ■ International Society of Explosives Engineers (ISEE)
30325 Bainbridge Rd.
Cleveland, OH 44139
Ph: (440)349-4400
Fax: (440)349-3788
E-mail: isee@isee.org
URL: www.isee.org
Social Media: www.facebook.com/ExplosivesEngineers
www.linkedin.com/company-beta/1789194
www.linkedin.com/company/international-society-of
  -explosives-engineers
twitter.com/explosiveseng
www.youtube.com/user/ExplosivesEngineers

6107 ■ SEE Education Foundation Scholarship *(Undergraduate, Graduate, Doctorate/Scholarship)*

Purpose: To support students pursuing a technical undergraduate, graduate or doctorate degree in the fields of education related to the commercial explosives industry. **Focus:** Engineering, Chemical; Engineering, Nuclear. **Qualif.:** Applicants must be pursuing technical, undergraduate, graduate or doctorate degrees in fields of education related to the commercial explosives industry and able to demonstrate financial need. **Criteria:** Selection will be students assessed on their financial need, academic and professional achievements and goals related to the industry.

Funds Avail.: $81,000. **Duration:** Annual. **Number Awarded:** Varies. **To Apply:** Applicants must submit a completed scholarship application together with a documentation of income; two letters of recommendation; college transcript(s); and a personal challenge and goal statement. Applicants must provide contact information for the university financial aid/scholarship representative. First year college students must enclose a letter of acceptance from the university for the upcoming academic year. **Deadline:** Feb. 28, May 8. **Remarks:** The scholarships are offered in various memorial funds. **Contact:** Email: isee@isee.org.

6108 ■ International Society for Human Ethology (ISHE)
1090 Vienna, Austria
URL: www.ishe.org
Social Media: www.facebook.com/ISHE.ORG

6109 ■ Owen F. Aldis Scholarship Fund *(Doctorate/ Scholarship)*

Purpose: To nurture excellence in human ethology by supporting students who are undertaking empirical research in human behavior, drawing on the repertoire of methods

Awards are arranged alphabetically below their administering organizations

developed in biology and the human behavioral sciences. **Focus:** Behavioral sciences. **Qualif.:** Applicants must be students who have not yet formally received their doctorate at the time of the application deadline, in any academic discipline related to human ethology, who are in good standing as certified by their academic advisor or director at a recognized educational or scientific institution.**Criteria:** Selection will be based on the premises that the applicant's respective research proposals on human behavior are able to meet the "scientific quality" and "ethological relevance".

Funds Avail.: Up to $8,000. **Duration:** Annual. **To Apply:** Applications must be submitted in English; application document must be submitted as an MS-Word document; cover sheet; outline of the planned study should cover the following areas: aims, concentrating on innovative aspects; letter from the applicant's institution giving permission for the applicant to conduct the proposed research at that institution; short cv; letter of support from his/her mentor. **Deadline:** January 15. **Remarks:** The scholarship was established to honor Owen Franklin Aldis life and his contribution who taught economics at Yale and worked for an investment firm in New York, before moving to the San Francisco Bay area to pursue a scholarly interest in Skinnerian behavioral psychology. **Contact:** ISHE Secretary; E-mail: mlfisher.99@gmail.com and The Chair of Trustees; E-mail: johnricher@oxhs.co.uk.

6110 ■ International Society for Humor Studies (ISHS)
c/o Martin Lampert, Ph.D., Executive Secretary
Holy Names University
Oakland, CA 94619
Ph: (510)436-1532
E-mail: ishs@hnu.edu
URL: www.humorstudies.org

6111 ■ International Society for Humor Studies Graduate Student Awards (GSA) (Graduate/Award, Scholarship)
Purpose: To recognize outstanding scholars and promising graduate students conducting research in humor studies. **Focus:** Humanities. **Qualif.:** Applicants must be graduate students working toward master's or doctorate degrees and doing noteworthy research within humor studies and/or all ISHS graduate student member planning to attend the Society's annual conference. **Criteria:** Candidates will be evaluated by the ISHS Awards Committee.

Funds Avail.: No amount mentioned. **Duration:** Annual. **Number Awarded:** Varies. **To Apply:** Applicants must submit a letter of intent to compete for a GSA, a description of their research program within humor studies, a presentation proposal, and all required registration materials and fees. **Deadline:** April 15. **Remarks:** Established in 2006.

6112 ■ International Society for Humor Studies Scholarly Contribution Awards (SCA) (Other/Award)
Purpose: To recognize outstanding scholars and promising graduate students conducting research in humor studies. **Focus:** Humanities. **Criteria:** Candidates will be evaluated by the ISHS Awards Committee.

Funds Avail.: No specific amount. **Duration:** Annual. **Remarks:** Established in 2006.

6113 ■ International Society for Infectious Diseases (ISID)
9 Babcock St., 3rd Fl.
Brookline, MA 02446
Ph: (617)277-0551
E-mail: info@isid.org
URL: www.isid.org
Social Media: twitter.com/ISID_org

6114 ■ ISID Small Grants (Postdoctorate, Professional development/Grant)
Purpose: To support and foster the professional development of individuals in the field of human infectious diseases research. **Focus:** Infectious diseases. **Qualif.:** Applicants must be nationals or residents of resource-limited countries, in the early stages of their research career, who have not previously received major research funding or who have not had an opportunity to work or study outside their region. **Criteria:** Selection will be based on the committee's criteria.

Funds Avail.: Up to $6,000. **Duration:** Annual. **Number Awarded:** Up to 5. **To Apply:** Applicants must submit: a completed application form; a research plan; a current curriculum vitae; a letter of recommendation from the sponsoring institution. **Deadline:** April 1. **Contact:** Email: program.coordinator@isid.org.

6115 ■ International Society of Offshore and Polar Engineers (ISOPE)
495 N Whisman Rd., Ste. 300
Mountain View, CA 94043-5711
Ph: (650)254-1871
Fax: (650)254-2038
E-mail: info@isope.org
URL: www.isope.org

6116 ■ ISOPE Offshore Mechanics Scholarships for Outstanding Students (Graduate/Scholarship)
Purpose: To provide students the opportunity to engage in research in the field of Offshore Mechanics, Ocean, Arctic, and Related Engineering fields. **Focus:** Mechanics and repairs. **Qualif.:** Applicants must be graduate students or admitted to a graduate program (verified by the Department Chairman or the supervising professor); must have demonstrated scholastic achievement; must be individuals of integrity, good character and strict morals. **Criteria:** Selection is given to applicants whose papers are accepted at the council-supported technical meetings.

Funds Avail.: $1,000. **Duration:** Annual. **Number Awarded:** 3 to 5. **To Apply:** Applicants must submit official graduate school transcript for current graduate students; letter of recommendation from the thesis supervising faculty; application form. **Deadline:** April 15. **Remarks:** Established in 1989. **Contact:** ISOPE Awards Committee; 495 North Whisman Road, Suite 300, California 94043, USA; Email: info@isope.org.

6117 ■ International Society for Therapeutic Ultrasound (ISTU)
PO Box 17592
Seattle, WA 98127
Ph: (206)310-5148
E-mail: admin@istu.org
URL: www.istu.org
Social Media: www.facebook.com/ISTUofficial
instagram.com/istu2020
linkedin.com/in/international-society-for-therapeutic
-ultrasound-804687185

Awards are arranged alphabetically below their administering organizations

6118 ■ The William and Francis Fry Honorary Fellowship for Contributions to Therapeutic Ultrasound (Professional development/Fellowship)

Purpose: To award individuals who have made outstanding contributions to therapeutic ultrasound. **Focus:** Medicine. **Qualif.:** Applicants must have contributions to therapeutic ultrasound. **Criteria:** Recipients will be selected based on the impact of their contributions.

Funds Avail.: No amount mentioned. **Duration:** Annual. **Remarks:** Established in 2003. **Contact:** URL: istu.org/prizes-and-awards/.

6119 ■ ISTU Student Prizes (Undergraduate/Prize)

Purpose: To recognize students who exhibit strong potential to impact the world of therapeutic ultrasound. **Focus:** Medicine. **Qualif.:** Applicants must be students who have potential in the field of therapeutic ultrasound.

Funds Avail.: No amount mentioned. **Duration:** Annual.

6120 ■ Nadine Barrie Smith Student Award (Undergraduate/Award)

Purpose: To recognize student achievements in the field of therapeutic ultrasound. **Focus:** Medicine. **Qualif.:** Applicants must be interested in the field of therapeutic ultrasound.

Funds Avail.: No amount mentioned. **Duration:** Annual. **Contact:** Diane Eberle, 14750 Sweitzer Ln., Ste. 100, Laurel, MD, 20707.

6121 ■ International Society of Travel and Tourism Educators (ISTTE)

23220 Edgewater St.
Saint Clair Shores, MI 48082
Ph: (586)294-0208
Fax: (586)294-0208
E-mail: joannb@istte.org
URL: www.istte.org
Social Media: www.facebook.com/ISTTE
www.linkedin.com/company/international-society-of-travel
  -and-tourism-educators/?trk=biz-companies-cymlinkedin
  .com
twitter.com/ISTTEDUCATORS

6122 ■ ISTTE Scholarship (Graduate, Undergraduate/Scholarship)

Purpose: To assist students affiliated with ISTTE member schools in their education. **Focus:** Travel and tourism. **Qualif.:** Applicants must be students affiliated with ISTTE member schools during the current academic year. **Criteria:** Selection will be based on the submitted applications, particularly essays. ISTTE member faculty will judge the essays using the following five criteria: comprehension; organization; creativity; conclusions; and writing.

Funds Avail.: $1,000 each. **Duration:** Annual. **Number Awarded:** 4. **To Apply:** Applicants must submit a word-processed, double-spaced, 3-5 page original essay on a topic relevant to this year's conference theme; Our 2017 Conference theme is "The Living Laboratory"; the essay should reflect this theme or other sustainable tourism planning and development niches; including an endorsement by an active ISTTE member from the student's institution; please create a PDF, after the form has been signed; a cover letter (maximum 2 pages), including student's

academic background, experience, aspirations in the travel and tourism industry; the reason(s) for seeking the scholarship; the essay. **Remarks:** The committee will award the scholarships in the following categories: Graduate School; Four-Year College/University; Two-Year College/University; and High School or Non-degree Proprietary School (Certificate). **Contact:** HTM Dept./ School of Business 5 Liberty Street Charleston, SC 29424; Phone: 843-953-5455; Jeremy Clement; Email: clementj@cofc.edu.

6123 ■ International Technology and Engineering Educators Association (ITEEA)

1914 Association Dr., Ste. 201
Reston, VA 20191
Ph: (703)860-2100
Fax: (703)860-0353
E-mail: iteea@iteea.org
URL: www.iteea.org
Social Media: www.facebook.com/iteeastem
instagram.com/iteeastem
linkedin.com/groups/ITEEA-Educators-1787786/about
twitter.com/iteea
youtube.com/user/ITEEASTEM

6124 ■ ITEEA Greer/FTE Grants (Other/Grant)

Purpose: To recognize and encourage individual achievement and ability in any aspect of technology and engineering. **Focus:** Engineering; Teaching; Technology. **Qualif.:** Recipients must be ITEEA members and register for the ITEEA annual conference; must be technology and engineering education teachers or supervisors for secondary education grades 6-12; must not have attended more than three previous ITEEA conferences. **Criteria:** Recipients are selected based on application materials.

Funds Avail.: $1,000. **To Apply:** Applicants must submit the following required materials: (1) applicant's name, address, phone, fax, email, school name, grade level, subject(s) taught, previous ITEEA/ITEA conferences attended, and other pertinent data; (2) brief history of the applicant's professional participation activities, includes curriculum projects, professional association memberships, position held, grants/scholarships received, and awards; (3) explanation of why the applicant is seeking the grant; (4) knowledge/experience the applicants expect to gain from attending the ITEEA conference. **Contact:** GREER/FTEE GRANT, Foundation for Technology and Engineering Educators; Email: iteea@iteea.org.

6125 ■ Litherland/FTEE Undergraduate Scholarships (Undergraduate/Scholarship)

Purpose: To promote the study of technology and engineering education teacher preparation. **Focus:** Technology. **Qualif.:** Applicants must be a member of ITEA; must not be a senior by the application deadline; must be a current, full-time undergraduate majoring in technology education teacher preparation. **Criteria:** Selection will be based on interest in acting, academic ability, need and faculty recommendation.

Funds Avail.: $1,000. **Duration:** Annual. **To Apply:** Applicants must submit the following requirements: letter of application that includes a statement about personal interest in teaching technology and Applicants' address with day and night telephone numbers; resume; a photocopy of Applicants' college transcript; a grade point average of 2.5

Awards are arranged alphabetically below their administering organizations

or more is required; three faculty recommendations. **Deadline:** December 1. **Remarks:** The Foundation for Technology and Engineering Educators proudly announces the Litherland/FTEE Scholarship in honor of Dr. Les Litherland. The scholarship is for an undergraduate student majoring in technology and engineering education teacher preparation. The award is based upon interest in teaching, academic ability, need, and faculty recommendations.

6126 ■ Maley/FTE Scholarships (Graduate/Scholarship)

Purpose: To enhance education and careers in technology and engineering education. **Focus:** Engineering; Teaching; Technology. **Qualif.:** Applicant must be a member of the ITEEA; must be a technology and engineering teacher at any grade level who is beginning and continuing graduate study. **Criteria:** Selection will be based on the application and submitted materials based on the following criteria: evidence of teaching success; plans for action research; recommendation; plans for professional development; the applicant's need.

Funds Avail.: $1,000. **To Apply:** Applicants must submit a letter of application with a clear explanation of plans for the graduate study; plans for action research; the applicant's need; and identification details - school name, grade level, telephone, and home address. Must provide resume not exceeding four pages that describes current position, professional activities, and achievements; must provide a college transcript, and documentation of acceptance into graduate school; must have three recommendation letters from among the following; undergraduate faculty, graduate faculty, school administration. **Deadline:** December 1. **Contact:** Foundation for Technology and Engineering Educators, 1914 Association Dr., Ste., 201 Reston, VA, 20191-1539; Phone: 703-860-2100; Fax: 703-860-0353; Email: iteea@iteea.org.

6127 ■ Maley/FTEE Teacher Professional Development Scholarships (Professional development/Scholarship)

Purpose: To support teachers in their preparation to increase the positive outcomes of technology and engineering education. **Focus:** Technology. **Qualif.:** Applicant must be a member of ITEA; must not be a technology teacher at any grade level who is beginning or continuing graduate study. **Criteria:** Selection will be based on the committee's criteria.

Funds Avail.: $1,000. **Duration:** Annual. **To Apply:** Applicant must submit the following requirements: letter of application with clear explanation of (a) plans for graduate study, (b) plans for action research, (c) the applicant's need, and (d) identification details, including school name, grade level, address, telephone, and home address; resume not exceeding four pages that describes current position, professional activities, and achievements; official college transcript(s); documentation of acceptance into graduate school; and three recommendation letters. **Contact:** Foundation for Technology and Engineering Educators, 1914 Association Dr., Ste., 201 Reston, VA, 20191-1539 Phone: 703-860-2100; Fax: 703-860-0353; Email: iteea@iteea.org.

6128 ■ International Textile and Apparel Association (ITAA)

PO Box 70687
Knoxville, TN 37938-0687
Ph: (865)992-1535
E-mail: info@itaaonline.org

URL: itaaonline.org
Social Media: www.facebook.com/officialinternationaltextileandapparelassociation

6129 ■ ITAA Graduate Student Best Paper Award (Graduate/Award, Monetary)

Purpose: To recognize individuals for their outstanding contributions to the Association. **Focus:** Design; Textile science. **Qualif.:** Applicants must be faculty members. **Criteria:** Selection will be based on the committee's criteria.

Funds Avail.: $500 toward travel and hotel costs. **Number Awarded:** 2. **To Apply:** Applicants must use American Psychological Association; should be in English; including the 150 word abstract, graphics, and references, can be up to 30 pages. **Deadline:** February 1.

6130 ■ International Thomas Merton Society (ITMS)

2001 Newburg Rd.
Louisville, KY 40205
Ph: (502)272-8177
Fax: (502)272-8452
URL: merton.org

6131 ■ Daggy Youth/Student Scholarships (Undergraduate, Professional development/Scholarship)

Purpose: To enable young people to participate in an International Thomas Merton Society Conference. **Qualif.:** Applicants must be young individuals (ages 14-29) who are interested in learning about Thomas Merton. **Criteria:** Selection will be based on committee's criteria.

Funds Avail.: No specific amount. **Duration:** Biennial. **To Apply:** Applicants must submit a statement explaining why they are interested in learning more about Thomas Merton and how they think they would benefit from attending the ITMS Conference; must have the recommendation from a youth minister, campus minister, pastor, teacher, or other qualified adult. **Deadline:** March 15. **Remarks:** The scholarships were established to honor the late Robert E. Daggy, founding member and second President of the ITMS. **Contact:** Jamie Fazio; Email: jfazio1@naz.edu.

6132 ■ ITMS Shannon Fellowships (Graduate, Undergraduate/Fellowship)

Purpose: To enable qualified researchers to visit the Thomas Merton Center archives. **Focus:** General studies/Field of study not specified. **Qualif.:** Applicants must be researchers, students or young scholars without academic affiliation; must be members of the ITMS who are engaged in research for thesis and dissertations. **Criteria:** Selection will be based on the quality of the proposal submitted; the need for consulting archival materials at the site proposed.

Funds Avail.: $750. **Duration:** Annual. **Number Awarded:** Up to 5. **To Apply:** Applicants should include a detailed proposal of 500-750 words explaining the subject and goals of the research and the rationale for consulting primary sources at the Merton collection; a letter of recommendation from a scholar familiar with the qualifications and research interests; a proposed expense budget grants will cover costs of travel to and from collections; expenses for accommodations and food during time of research at archives; costs of photocopying; disclosure of any other sources of funding awarded or applied for, with amounts received or requested. **Deadline:** March 15. **Remarks:** The

Awards are arranged alphabetically below their administering organizations

award was established in honor of William H. Shannon, founding President of the International Thomas Merton Society. **Contact:** ITMS Resident Secretary, Dr. Paul M Pearson, International Thomas Merton Society, Bellarmine University, 2001 Newburg Rd., Louisville. KY. 40205; Email: merton@bellarmine.edu.

6133 ■ Shannon Fellowships *(Professional development/Fellowship)*

Purpose: To enable qualified researchers to visit the Thomas Merton center archives at Bellarmine University in Louisville, Kentucky. **Focus:** Religion. **Qualif.:** Applicants must be members of the ITMS. **Criteria:** Selection will be based on the quality of the proposal submitted; the need for consulting archival materials.

Funds Avail.: $750. **Duration:** Annual. **Number Awarded:** Varies. **To Apply:** Applicants must submit a detailed proposal of 500-750 words explaining the subject and goals of the applicant's research and the rationale for consulting primary sources at the Merton collection selected by the applicant; a letter of recommendation from a scholar familiar with the applicant's qualifications and research interests; a proposed expense budget: grants will cover costs of travel to and from collections; expenses for accommodations and food during time of research at archives; costs of photocopying; disclosure of any other sources of funding awarded or applied for, with amounts received or requested. **Deadline:** March 15.

6134 ■ International Trademark Association (INTA)
675 3rd Ave., 3rd Fl.
New York, NY 10017
Ph: (212)642-1700
Fax: (212)768-7796
E-mail: memberoperations@inta.org
URL: www.inta.org
Social Media: www.facebook.com/GoINTA
www.instagram.com/intaglobal
www.linkedin.com/company/gointa
twitter.com/INTA
www.youtube.com/channel/UCfoSgeaIdEpL1f32YWS5nPw

6135 ■ The Ladas Memorial Award - Student Category *(Undergraduate/Award)*

Purpose: To provide incentives to students and professionals to further develop their interest in the field of trademark law. **Focus:** Law. **Qualif.:** Applicants must be enrolled as either full- or part-time law or graduate students; must provide proof of matriculation, school ID is acceptable; for applicants outside of the United States, university enrollment is acceptable. **Criteria:** Selection will be based on nature, breadth and timeliness of the subject(s) addressed; originality of the subject and thought; extent of the research and scholarship; and quality of writing.

Funds Avail.: $2,500 each. **Duration:** Annual. **Number Awarded:** 2. **To Apply:** Applicants must submit eligible papers, both original unpublished manuscripts and published articles are accepted; subject of the paper must be trademark law or a matter that directly relates to, or affects, trademarks; published articles must have been first published no longer than one year prior to the competition deadline; paper may be co-authored and must be a product of the author's original thought and scholarship; Paper must be limited to twenty-five pages. **Deadline:** January 17.

Contact: Email: ladasaward@inta.org.

6136 ■ International Transplant Nurses Society (ITNS)
8735 W Higgins Rd., Ste. 300
Chicago, IL 60631
Ph: (847)375-6340
Fax: (847)375-6341
E-mail: info@itns.org
URL: www.itns.org
Social Media: www.facebook.com/pages/International -Transplant-Nurses-Society
twitter.com/itnsnurses

6137 ■ ITNS Research Grants *(Other/Grant)*

Purpose: To encourage qualified transplant health care providers to contribute to the advancement of transplantation through research by providing financial aid. **Focus:** Medical research. **Qualif.:** Applicants must be members of ITNS. **Criteria:** Preference will be given to research studies that address scholarly work such as clinical outcomes and quality improvement; program evaluation projects are encouraged.

Funds Avail.: $2,500. **Duration:** Annual. **To Apply:** Applicants must submit a completed application form; four copies of the proposal containing title page, abstract, proposal narrative (maximum of 5 singled-spaced pages), appendices, budget and biographical sketch (maximum of two pages). Scholarship information and instructions are available on the website. **Deadline:** July 1.

6138 ■ International Union of Bricklayers and Allied Craftworkers (BAC)
620 F St. NW
Washington, DC 20004
Ph: (202)783-3788
Free: 888-880-8222
E-mail: askbac@bacweb.org
URL: www.bacweb.org
Social Media: www.facebook.com/IUBAC
www.instagram.com/iubac
twitter.com/IUBAC
www.youtube.com/user/BACInternational

6139 ■ Union Plus Scholarship Program *(Undergraduate/Scholarship)*

Purpose: To assist students pursuing their post-secondary education. **Focus:** General studies/Field of study not specified. **Qualif.:** Applicants must be current or retired members of unions participating in any Union Plus program, their spouses and their dependent children (including foster children, stepchildren, and any other child for whom the individual member provides greater than 50% support) can also apply for a Union Plus Scholarship; must be accepted into an accredited college or university, community college or recognized technical or trade school. **Criteria:** Applicants for scholarships are evaluated according to academic ability, social awareness, financial need and appreciation of labor. Scholarship applications are judged by a committee of impartial post secondary educators.

Duration: Annual. **To Apply:** Application forms are available at the website.

6140 ■ U.S. Bates Scholarship *(Undergraduate/Scholarship)*

Purpose: To assist the children of BAC members in pursuing a college education. **Focus:** General studies/Field of

Awards are arranged alphabetically below their administering organizations

study not specified. **Qualif.:** Applicants must be a son or daughter of U.S BAC member (in good standing) of U.S. BAC locals who will be juniors in high school; must take or plan to take the standardized PSAT exam in the fall of their junior year. **Criteria:** Selection of recipients is administered through the National Merit Scholarship Corporation.

Funds Avail.: $2,500. **Duration:** Annual. **Number Awarded:** 3. **To Apply:** Applicants must apply during their junior year in high school.

6141 ■ International Union of Operating Engineers - Local 564
2120 N Brazosport Blvd. N
Richwood, TX 77531-2306
Ph: (979)480-0003
Fax: (979)480-0509
Free: 800-486-3564
E-mail: lewis@local564.com
URL: www.local564.com
Social Media: www.facebook.com/local564

6142 ■ Local 564 Scholarship Fund (Undergraduate, Vocational/Occupational/Scholarship)

Purpose: To provide support to members' dependent children that are graduating high school Seniors. **Focus:** General studies/Field of study not specified. **Qualif.:** Applicants must be high school seniors and children of a Local 564 member.

Funds Avail.: $500. **Duration:** Annual. **To Apply:** Applicants can contact the sponsoring organization for details.

6143 ■ International Water, Sanitation and Hygiene Foundation (IWSH)
4755 E. Philadelphia St.
Ontario, CA 91761
Ph: (909)472-4100
Fax: (909)472-4241
E-mail: info@iwsh.org
URL: www.iwsh.org
Social Media: www.facebook.com/IWSHFoundation
www.instagram.com/iwsh_foundation
www.linkedin.com/company/iwshfoundation
twitter.com/IWSH_Foundation

6144 ■ IWSH Essay Scholarship Contest
(Undergraduate, College, University, Vocational/Occupational/Scholarship)

Purpose: To help students pay for higher education while also acquainting the uninitiated with the crucial importance the plumbing industry plays in everyday life and introducing students to the global impacts of IWSH projects. **Focus:** General studies/Field of study not specified. **Qualif.:** Applicants must be current high school seniors accepted to, or current students enrolled in, an accredited technical school, community college, trade school, four-year accredited college or university, or an apprenticeship program. International students are eligible. **Criteria:** The scholarship committee will review essays to determine the top three.

Funds Avail.: $500 to $1,000. **Number Awarded:** 3. **To Apply:** Applicants must submit an original essay on the topic given by the sponsor. Essay should be submitted via

email or postal mail along with the following: a copy of applicant's current full-time schedule, school transcripts, or acceptance letter. Essays will be posted on the IWSH website and become the property of IWSH. **Deadline:** April 30. **Contact:** Attn: Leticia Gallegos, Essay Contest; Email: essay@iwsh.org; URL: www.iwsh.org/hidden/iwsh-essay-scholarship-contest.

6145 ■ International Women's Fishing Association (IWFA)
PO Box 31507
Palm Beach Gardens, FL 33420
URL: www.iwfa.org
Social Media: www.facebook.com/International-Womens-Fishing-Association-117302265091920
www.instagram.com/womensfishingassociation

6146 ■ International Women's Fishing Association Scholarship Trust (Graduate/Scholarship)

Purpose: To support students in attaining graduate degrees in marine science. **Focus:** Biology, Marine. **Qualif.:** Applicants must be matriculated at a recognized University; pursuing a study leading to a graduate degree in marine sciences. **Criteria:** Selection is based on character, academic accomplishments, ability and the need for the award.

Duration: Annual. **To Apply:** Applicants must submit a completed application form; transcript of college records; recent photo with reverse sign; letter including: description of research in Marine Science, explanation of choosing graduate institution, career goals and financial need; and letters of recommendation from instructor in major field, advisor or other school officials; and completed summary sheet. **Deadline:** March 1. **Remarks:** Established in 1965. **Contact:** Email: scholarshiptrust@iwfa.org.

6147 ■ International Women's Media Foundation (IWMF)
1625 K St. NW, Ste. 1275
Washington, DC 20006
Ph: (202)496-1992
URL: www.iwmf.org
Social Media: www.facebook.com/IWMFpage
www.instagram.com/theiwmf
twitter.com/IWMF
www.youtube.com/user/Thelwmf

6148 ■ Elizabeth Neuffer Fellowship (Other/Fellowship)

Purpose: To provides academic and professional opportunities to advance the reporting skills of women journalists who focus on human rights and social justice. **Focus:** Journalism. **Qualif.:** Applicants must be female journalists whose work focuses on human rights and social justice, and must have a minimum of three years of experience in journalism. **Criteria:** Selection is based on the applicant's completed applications, the caliber and promise of the applicant's work on human rights and social justice, and on personal statements explaining how the fellowship would be a transformative experience.

Funds Avail.: No specific amount. **Number Awarded:** 1. **To Apply:** Applicants must complete the application form online which includes CV; Interest with Fellowship Goals;

Awards are arranged alphabetically below their administering organizations

Two work samples; Two letters of recommendation. **Deadline:** March 7.

6149 ■ Internet Society

11710 Plaza America Drive, Suite 400
Reston, VA 20190-5108
Ph: (703)439-2120
Fax: (703)326-9881
E-mail: isoc@isoc.org
URL: www.internetsociety.org
Social Media: www.facebook.com/InternetSociety
www.instagram.com/internetsociety
www.linkedin.com/company/internet-society
twitter.com/internetsociety
www.youtube.com/user/InternetSocietyVideo

6150 ■ Internet Society Fellowships to the IETF
(Master's, Postdoctorate/Fellowship)

Purpose: To Provide an opportunity for networking with individuals from around the world with similar technical interests. **Focus:** Computer and information sciences. **Criteria:** Selection will be based on the committee's criteria.

Number Awarded: 9. **To Apply:** Applicants must submit a filled-out application form.

6151 ■ Iota Sigma Pi

PO Box 75
Brentwood, MD 20722
URL: www.iotasigmapi.info
Social Media: www.facebook.com/IotaSigmaPi
twitter.com/IotaSigmaPi

6152 ■ Gladys Anderson Emerson Scholarship
(Undergraduate/Award, Scholarship)

Purpose: To provide financial support to a junior/senior college chemistry major who is an Iota Sigma Pi member. **Focus:** Biochemistry; Chemistry. **Criteria:** Selection will be made by a member of Iota Sigma Pi and must be supported by members of the faculty of the applicant's institution through letters of recommendation.

Funds Avail.: $2,000. **Duration:** Annual. **To Apply:** Applications can be submitted online; an academic history, including official transcripts (scanned) of the student's college record including the grade point average; include transcripts from all institutions attended; if the most recent grades are not included on the official transcript, the department head can write on behalf of the candidate to certify the most recent grades; a personal Statement that describes the candidate, her goals in chemistry, her academic honors and professional memberships, and her college activities, hobbies, talents; evidence of financial need may be presented in the personal statement, if applicable; the personal statement should not exceed 2 pages; at least two letters of recommendation from faculty members who know the candidate's academic history and/or have taught her. **Deadline:** February 15. **Remarks:** Named in the honor of Gladys Anderson Emerson, chairman of the Department of Home Economics and Nutrition at the University of California at Los Angeles. Established in 1987. **Contact:** Kathryn Thomasson, University of North Dakota, Chemistry Department, Abbott Hall Rm. 236, 151 Cornell St., Stop 9024, Grand Forks, ND, 58202-9024; Phone: 701-777-3199; E-mail: studentawards@iotasigmapi.info.

6153 ■ Iowa Association for Energy Efficiency

PO Box 31112
Johnston, IA 50131
Ph: (515)512-3236
E-mail: info@iowaenergy.org
URL: www.iowaenergy.org
Social Media: www.facebook.com/IowaEE
www.linkedin.com/in/iaee-iowa-association-for-energy
 -efficiency-a15bb36b
twitter.com/IowaEE

6154 ■ Iowa Association for Energy Efficiency Scholarship *(Undergraduate/Scholarship)*

Purpose: To promote the art and science of energy efficiency by supporting students pursuing an education related to energy efficiency. **Focus:** Energy-related areas. **Qualif.:** Applicants must have a high school diploma or GED; be currently enrolled in an accredited post-secondary institution in Iowa, with at least one full semester completed and one full semester remaining; pursuing a degree that supports the mission of IAEE; committed to pursuing a career in the energy efficiency industry; and have a GPA of 2.5 or higher.

Funds Avail.: $1,000. **Duration:** Annual. **Number Awarded:** Up to 2. **To Apply:** Applicant must submit the following documents: completed application (Word or PDF version); letters of recommendation (no more than five), focusing on applicant's interest, knowledge, and desire to pursue energy efficiency; one letter must be from the applicants educational institution; and recent copy of transcript. **Deadline:** May 31. **Contact:** Email: csteinbock@iowaenergy.org.

6155 ■ Iowa Association for Justice (IAJ)

505 5th Ave., Ste. 630
Des Moines, IA 50309
Ph: (515)280-7366
Fax: (515)280-3745
E-mail: info@iowajustice.org
URL: www.iowajustice.org
Social Media: www.facebook.com/IowaJustice
twitter.com/IowaJustice

6156 ■ Byard Braley Scholarship *(Undergraduate/Scholarship)*

Purpose: To support and assist injured workers or their family members in the pursuit of further education. **Focus:** General studies/Field of study not specified. **Criteria:** Selection will be based on the committee's criteria; selection committee will consider primarily whether the requested assistance will make a difference based on the applicant's needs and the clarity of their educational plans and goals. The more specific the explanation for how the funds will be used and why they are needed.

Funds Avail.: $500. **Duration:** Semiannual. **To Apply:** Applicants may contact IAJ workers' compensation section for the application process and other information. application to be completed by the sponsoring attorney for consideration of scholarship funds. **Deadline:** July 15; November 15. **Remarks:** The Scholarship Fund was established by a gift from bruce braley to the Iowa Foundation for Justice. **Contact:** IAJ, 505 5th Ave., Ste 630., Des Moines, IA, 50309-2319; Phone: 515-280-7366; Email: info@iowajustice.org.

Awards are arranged alphabetically below their administering organizations

6157 ■ Iowa Choral Directors Association, Inc. (ICDA)

209 Oak Ridge Drive SE
Mount Vernon, IA 52314
E-mail: execsec@iowachoral.org
URL: www.iowachoral.org
Social Media: www.facebook.com/groups/
211220212378393

6158 ■ ICDA Graduate Scholarships *(Graduate/Scholarship)*

Purpose: To provide financial assistance to ICDA members in their pursuit of graduate work. **Focus:** General studies/Field of study not specified. **Qualif.:** Applicants must be active or life members of ACDA/ICDA; must be studying towards graduate degree; must be full-time graduate students or completing a minimum of four-weeks summer term. **Criteria:** Selection will be based on evaluation of submitted documents and specific criteria.

Funds Avail.: Up to $750. **Duration:** Annual. **To Apply:** Applicants must submit a completed application form; a letter stating educational plans and why applicants deserve the award; must submit the tuition costs, validated by the institution. **Deadline:** May 1. **Remarks:** Established in 1986. **Contact:** Joleen Nelson Woods, ICDA Executive Secretary/Treasurer, at the above address.

6159 ■ ICDA Research Grants *(Graduate/Grant)*

Purpose: To provide financial assistance to ICDA members in their pursuit of graduate work. **Focus:** General studies/Field of study not specified. **Qualif.:** Must be an Active or Life member of ACDA/ICDA, pursue a project involving an in-depth study of a particular aspect of the choral art.

Funds Avail.: $500. **Duration:** Annual. **To Apply:** Must provide a breakdown of projected costs, a personal statement of the candidate's worthiness for this award, completed application. A monograph of the candidate's study is required within one calendar year of receiving the grant. **Deadline:** May 1. **Contact:** Sarah Bouska; Email: sbouska@masoncityschools.org or symposium17@iowachoral.org.

6160 ■ Iowa Court Reporters Association (ICRA)

601 Linden St.
Dallas Center, IA 50063-7881
Ph: (515)966-7881
E-mail: info@iacra.org
URL: www.iacra.org
Social Media: www.facebook.com/Iowa-Court-Reporters
-Association-338231539530223
twitter.com/iacra

6161 ■ Mary L. Brown Scholarship DMACC *(Undergraduate/Scholarship)*

Purpose: To promote and advance the interest of individuals engaged in the profession of shorthand reporting throughout the state of Iowa; to develop greater awareness and appreciation for the profession through public education and to promote the shorthand reporting industry. **Focus:** Broadcasting. **Qualif.:** Applicants must be students planning to enroll or currently enrolled in Des Moines Area Community College (CMACC) in a Realtime Reporting Major in either Judicial or Captioning/CART Services. **Criteria:** Recipients are selected based on grades, community and school activities.

Funds Avail.: $1,000. **Duration:** Annual. **To Apply:** Applicants must submit a completed application form along with two letters of recommendation and a 250-word essay. **Deadline:** March 31. **Contact:** ICRA c/o Rachel Ellefson, Vice President, Po Box 217, Mason City, IA, 50402; Email: ellefson.rachel@gmail.om.

6162 ■ Iowa Library Association (ILA)

6919 Vista Dr.
West Des Moines, IA 50266-9309
Ph: (515)282-8192
URL: www.iowalibraryassociation.org
Social Media: www.facebook.com/IowaLibAssoc
twitter.com/IowaLA
www.youtube.com/channel/
UC5Uv8VUSpPRzFymCFOHHRYQ

6163 ■ Iowa Library Association Foundation Scholarships *(Graduate/Scholarship)*

Purpose: To assist outstanding students who are pursuing a graduate degree in school library studies at the University of Northern Iowa. **Focus:** Information science and technology; Library and archival sciences. **Qualif.:** Applicants must have been fully admitted into the graduate program in school library studies at the University of Northern Iowa and enrolled continuously for three semesters of study; must have at least a 3.25 grade point average (on a 4.0 scale) for their undergraduate program of study or previous graduate studies of at least 8 credit hours. **Criteria:** Recipients will be chosen based on demonstrated academic excellence, potential to become a successful librarian, evidence of the ability to work well with others, and demonstrated communication skills; selection shall be made solely on the basis of stated criteria without regard to sex, creed, race, national origin.

Funds Avail.: $1,500. **Duration:** Annual. **To Apply:** Applicants must accomplish proper completion and filing of the application form (available online) and submit along with three letters of recommendation from persons working in the library science/information science field. **Contact:** Ken Jones, ILAF Scholarship Chair, Jones Library Sales, P.O. Box 536, Carlisle, Iowa 50047; Fax: 515-989-4230; Email: joneslib@msn.com.

6164 ■ The Jack Tillson Scholarship Fund *(Graduate/Scholarship)*

Purpose: To assist outstanding students who are pursuing a graduate degree in Library Science or Information Science at the University of Iowa. **Focus:** Information science and technology; Library and archival sciences. **Qualif.:** Must be a library student attending the University of Iowa School of Library Science.

Funds Avail.: $1,500. **Duration:** Annual. **Remarks:** Established in 1987 by Jack Tillson, longtime Executive Assistant to the Iowa Library Association. Established in 1987. **Contact:** The Community Foundation of Greater Des Moines to donate via the Endow Iowa Fund and mention the donation is for the Iowa Library Association Foundation; The Community Foundationf of Greater Des Moines can be reached at 515-883-2626.

6165 ■ Iowa Newspaper Association (INA)

319 E 5th St.
Des Moines, IA 50309-1927
Ph: (515)244-2145

Awards are arranged alphabetically below their administering organizations

Fax: (515)244-4855
URL: www.inanews.com
Social Media: www.facebook.com/Iowa-Newspaper
-Association-Foundation-93267756902
twitter.com/iowanewspaper

6166 ■ INF Scholarships *(Undergraduate/Scholarship)*

Purpose: To support students preparing for a career in the newspaper industry. **Focus:** Journalism. **Qualif.:** Applicants must be Iowa students preparing for an Iowa newspaper career at in-state colleges or universities.

Funds Avail.: No specific amount. **Duration:** Annual.

6167 ■ Iowa Journalism Institute Scholarships *(Graduate, Undergraduate/Scholarship)*

Purpose: To support students preparing for a career in the newspaper industry. **Focus:** Communications; Journalism. **Qualif.:** Applicants must be a undergraduate or graduate of Iowa State University's Greenlee School of Journalism and Communication.

Duration: Annual. **Deadline:** February 14. **Contact:** Jana Shepherd; Phone: 515-422-9051; Email: jshepherd@ inanews.com.

6168 ■ Carter Pitts Scholarships *(Undergraduate/ Scholarship)*

Purpose: To support students preparing for a career in the newspaper industry. **Focus:** Journalism.

Funds Avail.: $500. **Duration:** Annual. **Contact:** Jana Shepherd; Phone: 515-422-9051; Email: jshepherd@ inanews.com.

6169 ■ Iranian American Bar Association (IABA)
5185 MacArthur Blvd. NW, Ste. 624
Washington, DC 20016
E-mail: info@iaba.us
URL: www.iaba.us
Social Media: www.facebook.com/
iranianamericanbarassociation
twitter.com/iabaus

6170 ■ IABA Scholarship *(Graduate/Scholarship)*

Purpose: To support law students for their commitment to the advancement of the Iranian American community. **Focus:** Law. **Qualif.:** Applicant must be of Iranian American heritage; enrolled in or accepted for enrollment in an aba accredited law school; a position to accept the scholarship in the school year for which it is being awarded; a full time student; not be receiving full funding for education from another organization (e.g. members of the armed services attending us military academies, students receiving full reimbursement from an employer). **Criteria:** Applicants will be judged based on merit and financial need.

Funds Avail.: No specific amount. **Duration:** Annual. **Number Awarded:** Varies. **To Apply:** Applicants must submit a duly completed National Scholarship Application Form; a detailed resume; a statement or essay written by the applicants (no more than one single-sided 1.5-spaced typewritten page); and official law school and college transcripts. **Deadline:** March 31. **Contact:** E-mail: scholarship@iaba.us.

6171 ■ Iranian Scholarship Foundation (ISF)
PO Box 320204
Los Gatos, CA 95032

E-mail: info@theisf.org
URL: www.iranianscholarships.com

6172 ■ Dr. Ali Jarrahi Merit Scholarship *(Undergraduate/Scholarship)*

Purpose: To provide assistance to students with outstanding records who are pursuing to enter one of the top universities in the United States. **Focus:** General studies/ Field of study not specified. **Qualif.:** Applicants must be of Iranian descent; must be enrolled or accepted one of the top universities in the United States; must possess and maintain 4.0 GPA or higher; must have portfolio of community service; have minimum SAT score of 2000 or ACT score of 30. **Criteria:** Selection will be based on the submitted application and financial need.

Funds Avail.: No specific amount. **Duration:** Annual. **Number Awarded:** Varies. **To Apply:** Applicants must provide two letters of recommendation, one from a teacher and one from an organization for which the student has performed community service; must write a 750-1000 words essay about their dreams and aspirations; complete application form; copy of IRS form 4506. **Contact:** Iranian Scholarship Foundation, PO Box 320204, Los Gatos, CA, 95032; Email: info@theisf.org.

6173 ■ ISF Excellence in Community Service Scholarship *(Undergraduate/Scholarship)*

Purpose: To provide support to one student with an outstanding record of community service who wants to pursue studies. **Focus:** General studies/Field of study not specified. **Criteria:** Selection will be based on the submitted application and financial need.

Funds Avail.: No specific amount. **Duration:** Annual. **Number Awarded:** 1. **To Apply:** Applicant should include three letters of recommendation: one letter from a teacher or professor; two letters from an organization where applicant has performed community service; transcripts from all of their high school and undergraduate programs, if applicable; a 750-1000 word essay detailing applicant's dreams and aspirations for their studies and career. **Deadline:** May 31. **Contact:** Iranian Scholarship Foundation, Email: info@theisf.org.

6174 ■ ISF Undergraduate Scholarship *(Undergraduate/Scholarship)*

Purpose: To provide financial support to qualified Iranian-American students pursuing higher education. **Focus:** General studies/Field of study not specified. **Criteria:** Selection will be based on financial need.

Funds Avail.: No specific amount. **Duration:** Annual. **To Apply:** Applicants must provide two letters of recommendation, one from a teacher and one from an organization for which the student has performed community service; must write a 750-1000 words essay about their dreams and aspirations; complete application form; copy of IRS form 4506. **Contact:** Iranian Scholarship Foundation, PO Box 320204, Los Gatos, CA, 95032; Email: info@theisf.org.

6175 ■ Islamic Research Foundation International, Inc. (IRFI)
7102 W Shefford Ln.
Louisville, KY 40242-6462
Ph: (502)287-6262
E-mail: irfi@iname.com
URL: www.irfi.org

Awards are arranged alphabetically below their administering organizations

6176 ■ Dr. Mubin Syed And Mrs. Afshan Syed Scholarship Program *(Undergraduate/Scholarship)*

Purpose: To provide one Muslim(boy) and one Muslimah-(girl) funds to gain a four-year college degree and also who are a minority in Bellary and have financial challenges and wants to continue education. **Focus:** Religion. **Qualif.:** Applicants must be Muslim (boy or girl) seeking admission in Bellary colleges for 4 year or above professional course/college through Government quota into Medical, Engineering, Pharmacy, Nursing, Management etc., residents by birth in Bellary District and attended high school and pre-university courses on the same place with no more than Rs. 1 lakh per year of Household income (provide proof of income of parents). **Criteria:** Selection will be verification of documents and student with highest score; exceptional character; extracurricular activities or talent and leadership skills; no other scholarship has been accepted; any false declaration will result in forfeit of the scholarship and prosecution for perjury; the Bijli Foundation Charitable Trust located in Cowl Bazaar, Bellary, Office bearers will investigate the authenticity of documents and personal data submitted.

Funds Avail.: $1,500 or Approximately 60,000 Indian Rupees. **Duration:** Annual. **Number Awarded:** 2. **To Apply:** Applicants must submit the following requirements through online; application form; copy of official entrance test scores and ranking; copy of high school marks sheet and college/diploma marks sheet, officially signed and sealed by Gazette officer or Notary; two letters of recommendation for conduct - one from high school teacher/principal and one from college/diploma teacher/principal on official paper with seal and signature; name, address of college and course selected and contact info for payment to the institution and; proof of income, officially signed and sealed by Gazette officer or Notary. **Contact:** Submit all required documents via email to IRFI@INAME.COM or mail to Chairperson, Awards and Scholarships Committee-Bellary, 7102 W. Shefford Ln., Louisville, KY, 40242-6462, USA.

6177 ■ Islamic Scholarship Fund (ISF)
8407 Central Ave. Ste. 2007
Newark, CA 94560
Ph: (650)995-6782
E-mail: contact@islamicscholarshipfund.org
URL: islamicscholarshipfund.org
Social Media: www.facebook.com/IslamicScholarshipFund
www.instagram.com/islamicscholarshipfund
www.linkedin.com/company/islamic-scholarship-fund
twitter.com/isfscholarships

6178 ■ Islamic Scholarship Fund Scholarship (ISF) *(Graduate, Undergraduate/Scholarship)*

Purpose: To encourage Muslim students to pursue college or post-graduate degrees in humanities, social sciences, liberal arts and law. **Focus:** General studies/Field of study not specified.

Duration: Annual. **To Apply:** Applicants must submit a completed application form; an essay; a resume; official college transcripts; two recommendation letters; video introduction; college transcripts. **Deadline:** March 21.

6179 ■ Islamic Society of North America (ISNA)
6555 S County Road 750 E
Plainfield, IN 46168

Ph: (317)839-8157
E-mail: info@isna.net
URL: www.isna.net
Social Media: www.facebook.com/isnahq
www.instagram.com/isnahq/
twitter.com/isnahq
www.youtube.com/isnavideos

6180 ■ HRH Prince Alwaleed Bin Talal ISNA Fellowships *(Graduate/Fellowship)*

Purpose: To provide support and training in education, philanthropy, and management for Muslim Americans pursuing graduate studies in the United States. **Focus:** Management. **Qualif.:** Applicants must be graduate students or recent graduates from an undergraduate program looking to pursue their Masters degree; must complete all admissions and GRE testing requirements for application to academic program; must be U.S. citizens or have legal permanent residency; able to complete an internship with a U.S. non-profit organization consisting of a minimum of 480 hours; must be available to attend an intensive five-day orientation and training program as well as to assist with work at the ISNA Annual Convention with all expenses paid. **Criteria:** Selection is based on high academic achievement with a preference to applicants with a 3.0 GPA or higher; consistent active participation in public service-oriented activities; evidence of leadership skills and potential for growth; superior analytical and communication skills (oral and written); confirmation of ability to meet program requirements. Based on the application scores, candidates will be interviewed and considered for the funding.

Funds Avail.: $11,000. **Number Awarded:** 10. **To Apply:** Applicants should submit a completed application form; an essay and two letters of recommendation. **Deadline:** March 1.

6181 ■ ISSA Canada
910 Dundas St. W
Whitby, ON, Canada L1P 1P7
URL: issa-canada.com

6182 ■ Sam Tughan Scholarships *(Undergraduate/Scholarship)*

Purpose: To provide scholarship assistance to qualified Canadian students who will be attending college or university in Canada. **Focus:** Medicine. **Qualif.:** Applicant must be a student who will be graduating high school; must be an individual who is already enrolled in a college or university in Canada; must be a young Canadian who has achieved a high level of academic and leadership standards. **Criteria:** Applicant will be judged based on the following criteria: (1) Applicant's ability to read and fully comprehend the terms and conditions of the application procedure; (2) Applicant's ability to ensure that all components of the application - the Applicant Information Form, the 2x3 photo, the essay, the transcripts, the evaluation form and the typed resume - are received by the CSSA Scholarship Foundation office; (3) Applicant's academic achievements as well as school/college activities, volunteerism and social achievements; (4) Quality of the essay - originality, clarity, grammar and presentation.

Funds Avail.: 2,000 Canadian dollars. **Number Awarded:** 7. **To Apply:** Applicant must complete the application form available online; must have a photograph, and official high

Awards are arranged alphabetically below their administering organizations

school or college transcript; must provide an essay on: "Does your school use EcoLogo certified products? If yes, do they believe it is effective against old style cleaning products? What products (brands) do they use? If not, what are the reasons that prevent them from using it?"; must have a typed resume with name, planned occupation or profession, high school information, college or university information, employment history, activity and leadership record, and applicant evaluation form completed by a counselor or teacher.

6183 ■ Ivanhoe Foundation

160 S Lomita
Ojai, CA 93023
Fax: (805)646-8620
E-mail: info@theivanhoefoundation.org
URL: www.theivanhoefoundation.com

6184 ■ Ivanhoe Foundation Fellowship *(Master's/Fellowship)*

Purpose: To support the education of students studying practical Master of Science degree in engineering or science, with an emphasis on water resources. **Focus:** Land management; Waste management; Water resources. **Criteria:** Selection is based on the submitted letter of nomination; priority is given to research in: arid land Management, water conservation, water recycling, waste water treatment, Pathogen & Chemical Remediation, all water related research will be considered.

Funds Avail.: $5,000. **Duration:** Annual. **To Apply:** Applicants should include a letter of nomination must be submitted by the students' professor; information submitted must include a description of the students' thesis and how the work would specifically improve the water resources of impoverished countries; All nominations and pertinent information must be submitted through mail. **Contact:** Selection Committee, The Ivanhoe Foundation, 160 S Lomita, Ojai, CA, 93023; Fax: 805-646-8620; Email: info@theivanhoefoundation.org.

6185 ■ IvyPanda

30 N Gould St., Ste. 4817
Sheridan, WY 82801
Free: 866-236-7979
URL: ivypanda.com
Social Media: www.facebook.com/ivypandacom/
www.instagram.com/ivypanda_studyhelp
www.pinterest.com.au/ivypandacom
twitter.com/smartstudynow
www.youtube.com/channel/
   UC87xQ8CepBSmWeyk14gfxZg/featured

6186 ■ $1,500 Annual Video Contest Scholarship for Students *(High School, College, University/Scholarship)*

Purpose: To assist talented and creative movie making students **Focus:** General studies/Field of study not specified. **Qualif.:** Applicant must be a current high school, college, or university student from any country. **Criteria:** Video will be evaluated by the editorial team based on the following criteria: content/usefulness, engagement, creativity, and production. Videos that meet all of the criteria will be published on the IvyPanda YouTube channel and opened up for online voting.

Funds Avail.: $1,000 (first place); $500 (runner-up). **Duration:** Annual. **Number Awarded:** 2. **To Apply:** 1. Upload your video to one of these file-hosting services: Dropbox, Google Drive. We accept videos on one of the following topics: a) Money-Managing Tips for Students; b) Socializing in College: Your Advice; c) How to Enhance Your Studying With the Use of Digital Age Tools. 2. Subscribe to IvyPandas YouTube channels; like and share the Contest video-description on Twitter, Facebook or Instagram. 3. Send an email to scholarship@ivypanda.com with the direct link to your uploaded video, the screenshots of your subscriptions to IvyPandas YouTube channels, the screenshot of the Contest video-description shared on social media, the detailed answer to the question: "Where did you find out about the IvyPanda Contest?". **Deadline:** October 31.

6187 ■ J & Y Law Firm

1880 Century Park E, Ste. 717
Los Angeles, CA 90067
Ph: (310)407-0766
E-mail: info@jnylaw.com
URL: jnylaw.com
Social Media: www.facebook.com/jandylawfirm
www.linkedin.com/company/j&y-law-firm
twitter.com/JandYlaw
www.youtube.com/channel/
   UCtbdZtdI86OLCU6n9gDPWWw

6188 ■ Distracted Driving Scholarship *(High School, Two Year College, University/Scholarship)*

Purpose: To support high school seniors and college students who are committed to helping their communities by pledging to abstain from distracted driving. **Focus:** General studies/Field of study not specified. **Qualif.:** Applicant must be enrolled in a two- or four-year degree granting program, be at least 18 years old by the start of the fall semester, and have a minimum 3.0 GPA. Applicant must reside and be studying in California. **Criteria:** Selection will be based on the essay submitted; judging will be done by a panel of lawyers looking for clear, articulate, clearly organized, and grammatically correct writing.

Funds Avail.: $1,000. **Number Awarded:** 1. **To Apply:** Applicants must fill out the form on the website and submit a 500 to 1,000 word essay on the following questions: 1. How have you actively abstained from distracted driving and how do you plan on continuing to do so while you are at college?; 2. Have you ever seen your friends participate in distracted driving? What did you do? What are some ways you can teach them the dangers of distracted driving? **Deadline:** May 29. **Contact:** URL: jnylaw.com/distracted-driving-scholarship/.

6189 ■ Jack and Jill Foundation

1930 17th St. NW
Washington, DC 20009
Ph: (202)232-5290
Fax: (202)232-1747
URL: jackandjillfoundation.org
Social Media: www.facebook.com/jackjillfound
www.instagram.com/jackjillfound
twitter.com/JJAFOUNDATION

Awards are arranged alphabetically below their administering organizations

6190 ■ The Jack and Jill of America Foundation's National Scholarship Program *(Undergraduate/ Scholarship)*

Purpose: To provide financial assistance to African American students in preparing them to reach their fullest potential through higher education. **Focus:** General studies/ Field of study not specified. **Qualif.:** Applicants must be African American high school seniors with a minimum GPA of 3.0 who will be pursuing a bachelor's degree at any accredited postsecondary institution in the United States. **Criteria:** Applicants will be evaluated based on scholastic performance and active community service.

Funds Avail.: $1,500 to $2,500. **Duration:** Annual. **Number Awarded:** Varies. **To Apply:** Applicants must submit an essay, resume, academic transcript, letters of recommendation and confirmation of 60 hours or more of active community service. **Contact:** JaiSun McCormick; E-mail: jaisun.mccormick@uncf.org.

6191 ■ Jackson Community Foundation (JCF)
100 S. Jackson Street, Suite 206B
Jackson, MI 49201
Ph: (517)787-1321
E-mail: jcf@jacksoncf.org
URL: www.jacksoncf.org
Social Media: www.facebook.com/jacksoncf.org

6192 ■ Antonia Dellas Memorial Scholarship
(Undergraduate/Scholarship)

Purpose: To support the pursuit of higher education in Jackson County. **Focus:** Education, Special. **Qualif.:** Applicants must be high school senior students with a minimum of 3.25 or above GPA; must be accepted or attending an accredited Michigan college or university; must intend to enroll or are already enrolled in a school of education; college student who holds a GPA of 3.0 or above. **Criteria:** Preference will be given to those majoring in special education.

Funds Avail.: Up to $2,000. **Duration:** Annual. **Number Awarded:** 2. **To Apply:** Applicants must submit a completed application form and provide a proof of financial need. **Deadline:** February 14. **Remarks:** Established by John J. Dellas in memory of his wife, Antonia.

6193 ■ Dennis J. Beck Memorial Scholarship
(Undergraduate/Scholarship)

Purpose: To assist graduating seniors from Jackson County high schools and other Jackson County residents who are attending college. **Focus:** General studies/Field of study not specified. **Qualif.:** Applicant must be resident of Jackson County, Michigan; must be Ethnic Minority (non-Caucasian); must be graduating high school senior, returning learner, or student enrolled in the Jackson College Prison Education Initiative who has completed at least one semester and is housed in a Jackson County Corrections facility; open to any field of study, with special consideration given to manufacturing (including any discipline used in direct support of operating a manufacturing facility).; must demonstrate personal responsibility through work, community or family activities.

Funds Avail.: Up to $1,000. **Duration:** Annual. **Number Awarded:** 2. **To Apply:** Applicants must submit a letter of recommendation; fall high school or college transcript;proof of completion of FAFSA. **Remarks:** Established by the family and friends of Dennis J. Beck, this scholarship honors

his belief that a young person's character, when supported through education, is the foundation of the future.

6194 ■ Bernice Barabash Sports Scholarship
(Graduate/Scholarship)

Purpose: To recognizes youth who participate in hockey while maintaining high academic standards in preparation for future educational enrichment. **Focus:** Sports studies. **Qualif.:** Applicants must be students in grades seven to twelve who hold a minimum of 3.0 GPA; must be an active hockey player during the school year; must be residing in Jackson County; must plan to attend an accredited college or university program or vocational/technical institute; Prior recipients are not eligible to apply. **Criteria:** Recipients are selected based on lottery draw of qualified applicants.

Funds Avail.: $1,000. **Duration:** Annual. **Number Awarded:** 2. **To Apply:** Applicants must submit a completed online application form. **Deadline:** February 14. **Contact:** Dana Ashlock; Phone: 517-787-1321 or E-mail: dashlock@jacksoncf.org.

6195 ■ Bob and Dawn Hardy Automotive Scholarship
(Undergraduate/Scholarship)

Purpose: To support the pursuit of higher education in Jackson County. **Focus:** Automotive technology. **Qualif.:** Applicants must resident of Jackson County, Michigan; must Graduating high school senior, student already enrolled in and taking undergraduate classes, returning learner, or previous recipient; must enrolled full or part-time in Jackson College's Automotive Service Technology Associates or Certificate Program; must cumulative GPA of 2.0 or higher.

Funds Avail.: Up to $3,000. **Duration:** Annual. **Number Awarded:** More than 1. **To Apply:** Applicants must submit 1 letter of recommendation; fall high school or college transcript; proof of completion of FAFSA. **Deadline:** February 14. **Remarks:** The scholarship is used for tuition and fees and required course material such as tools.

6196 ■ Dr. William A. and Marceleine J. Sautter Hanover-Horton Youth of Promise Scholarship
(Graduate/Scholarship)

Purpose: To recognize a Hanover-Horton student for overall achievement and scholastic excellence. **Focus:** General studies/Field of study not specified. **Qualif.:** Applicants must be graduating Hanover-Horton High School senior students who hold a GPA of 3.0; have attended the school for at least one full academic year and demonstrate good character with focused goals; have the plan to be full-time students and carry a minimum of 12 credit hours or equivalent; and, have plan to attend an accredited Michigan college or university.

Funds Avail.: Up to $1,000. **Duration:** Annual. **Number Awarded:** Varies. **Remarks:** The scholarship is used for tuition, books, fees, and/or other academic expenses.

6197 ■ Dorothy and Dick Burgess Scholarship
(Undergraduate/Scholarship)

Purpose: To support the pursuit of higher education in Jackson County. **Focus:** Engineering. **Criteria:** Selection will be interview may be requested at the discretion of the scholarship committee.

Funds Avail.: Up to $4,000. **Duration:** Annual. **Number Awarded:** Up to 3. **To Apply:** Applicants must submit a completed application form and must provide a proof of financial need; proof of acceptance to a smaller, public,

Awards are arranged alphabetically below their administering organizations

and accredited Michigan 2 or 4-year college or university. **Contact:** The scholarship is used for tuition, books, fees, or other academic related costs.

6198 ■ The Eileen J. Smith, R.N. Memorial Scholarship *(Undergraduate/Scholarship)*

Purpose: To support the pursuit of higher education in Jackson County. **Focus:** Health care services. **Criteria:** Interviews may be required at the discretion of the scholarship committee.

Funds Avail.: Upto $1,000. **Duration:** Annual. **Remarks:** Established by Eileen's husband and children. Eileen was a friendly, kind, and generous person. This scholarship is a reminder of the passion and dedication she had for helping others.

6199 ■ The Eleanor A. Ernest Scholarship *(Graduate/Scholarship)*

Purpose: To assist graduating seniors from Jackson County high schools and other Jackson County residents who are attending college. **Focus:** General studies/Field of study not specified.

Funds Avail.: Up to $1,000. **Duration:** Annual. **To Apply:** Applicants must submit a letter of recommendation; fall high school or college transcript;proof of completion of FAFSA. **Deadline:** February 14. **Remarks:** The scholarship is used for tuition and fees.

6200 ■ Melissa Eleanor Ernest Scholarship *(Undergraduate/Scholarship)*

Purpose: To support the pursuit of higher education in Jackson County. **Focus:** Cosmetology. **Criteria:** Recipients are selected based on financial need.

Funds Avail.: Up to $1,500. **Duration:** Annual. **Remarks:** The scholarship was established by family and friends in honor of Melissa Eleanor Ernest who was anticipating a promising career as an Esthetician upon graduation from Douglas J. Aveda Institute before her tragic death.

6201 ■ Faith Speckhard Scholarship *(Graduate/Scholarship)*

Purpose: To recognize a student ho demonstrate motivation in their pursuit of higher education, are actively involved in their community, and have financial need. **Focus:** General studies/Field of study not specified. **Qualif.:** Applicants must be Jackson High School graduating seniors that have a minimum of 2.4 GPA and must be full or part-time students in an accredited college or university; must actively participate in community activities, leadership, and service. **Criteria:** Selection will be based on committee's criteria.

Funds Avail.: Up to $5,000. **Duration:** Annual. **Number Awarded:** 1. **To Apply:** Applicants must submit a completed application form along with proof of acceptance in an accredited college, university, vocational or technical institute and financial need. **Remarks:** The scholarship is used for tuition only.

6202 ■ Martha and Oliver Hansen Memorial Scholarships *(Undergraduate/Scholarship)*

Purpose: To support the pursuit of higher education in Jackson County. **Focus:** Education. **Qualif.:** Applicants must be incoming college junior or senior majoring in education with the intention of teaching in the classroom and resident of Jackson County, Michigan; must attend an accredited Michigan college or university who holds minimum 2.5 GPA or above.

Funds Avail.: Up to $1,000. **Duration:** Annual.

6203 ■ June Danby and Pat Pearse Education Scholarship *(Undergraduate/Scholarship)*

Purpose: To assist graduating seniors from Jackson County high schools and other Jackson County residents who are attending college. **Focus:** Education; Teaching.

Funds Avail.: Up to $1,000. **Duration:** Annual. **To Apply:** Applicants must submit a letter of recommendation; fall high school or college transcript;proof of completion of FAFSA. **Remarks:** The scholarship is used for tuition, books, fees, room and board or other academic-related costs.

6204 ■ Lucille E. McGee Scholarship Endowment Fund *(Undergraduate/Scholarship)*

Purpose: to support Hanover Horton students. **Focus:** General studies/Field of study not specified. **Qualif.:** Applicants must be senior graduating students of Hanover-Horton High School.

6205 ■ The Otis and Florence Lapham Memorial Scholarship *(Graduate/Scholarship)*

Purpose: To support the pursuit of higher education in Hanover-Horton schools. **Focus:** General studies/Field of study not specified. **Qualif.:** Applicants must be senior graduating students of Hanover-Horton High School who hold a minimum of 2.5 GPA; must demonstrate a good work history and have participated in both school and extracurricular activities. **Criteria:** Recipients are selected based on financial need.

Funds Avail.: Up to $1,000. **Duration:** Annual. **Number Awarded:** Varies. **Remarks:** The scholarship is used for tuition only.

6206 ■ Paul Tejada Memorial Scholarship *(Undergraduate/Scholarship)*

Purpose: To assist graduating seniors from Jackson County high schools and other Jackson County residents who are attending college. **Focus:** Health care services; Nursing. **Qualif.:** Applicants must have plans to pursue a course of study leading to a degree in health services administration, nursing or human medicine; must plan to be or be a full time student who maintain a minimum of 12 credit hours with a minimum of 3.0 GPA; resident of Jackson County, Michigan; must be graduating high school senior, previous recipient, home-schooled student, student already enrolled in and taking undergraduate classes, returning learner; Prior recipients must carry at least a 2.0 GPA during their first year of college and a 2.5 thereafter; must demonstrate good citizenship, high moral character and potential leadership.

Funds Avail.: Up to $1,500. **Duration:** Annual; up to 3 times renewable. **Number Awarded:** Varies. **To Apply:** Applicants must submit a letter of recommendation; fall high school or college transcript;proof of completion of FAFSA. **Remarks:** The scholarship was established in memory of Paul Tejada, former President of W.A. Foote Memorial Hospital.

6207 ■ Phillip Guy Richardson Memorial Scholarship *(Undergraduate/Scholarship)*

Purpose: To support the pursuit of higher education in Napoleon High School senior graduate. **Focus:** General studies/Field of study not specified. **Criteria:** Applicants may be interviewed by a committee of community members.

Awards are arranged alphabetically below their administering organizations

Funds Avail.: Up to $2,000. **Duration:** Annual. **Number Awarded:** Up to 3 Years.

6208 ■ Robert P. Ernest Scholarship *(Undergraduate/ Scholarship)*

Purpose: To support the pursuit of higher education in Jackson County. **Focus:** General studies/Field of study not specified.

Funds Avail.: Up to $1,000. **Duration:** Annual. **Remarks:** The scholarship is used for tuition and fees.

6209 ■ Barbara and Howard Thompson Scholarships *(Undergraduate/Scholarship)*

Purpose: To support the pursuit of higher education in Jackson County. **Focus:** History; Political science. **Qualif.:** Applicants must be Jackson High School graduating seniors or previous recipients who have plan to pursue a degree in history and/or political science; must be accepted at an accredited two or four-year college or university; must have 3.0 GPA; must demonstrate good citizenship and leadership qualities and participate in school activities and/or sports.

Funds Avail.: Up to $5,000. **Duration:** Annual.

6210 ■ Sue Walicki Nursing Scholarships *(Undergraduate/Scholarship)*

Purpose: To assist graduating seniors from Jackson County high schools and other Jackson County residents who are attending college. **Focus:** Nursing. **Qualif.:** Applicants must be Jackson County residents; must be graduating high school senior, previous recipient, student already enrolled in and taking undergraduate classes, returning learner, student planning to attend graduate school, student already enrolled in graduate school planning to start, continue, or advance education in the field of nursing or a nursing-related field (such as a Nurse Practitioner, Mid-Wife, or Nurse Anesthetist); must be Full or part time enrollment at an accredited Michigan college or university.

Funds Avail.: Up to $5,000. **Duration:** Annual. **To Apply:** Applicants must submit a proof of acceptance in an accredited Nursing Program and proof of financial need.

6211 ■ William and Beatrice Kavanaugh Memorial Scholarship *(Graduate/Scholarship)*

Purpose: To support Grass Lake High School students to enable them to further their educational goals. **Focus:** General studies/Field of study not specified. **Qualif.:** Applicants must: be graduating students of Grass Lake High school, seniors who attended the school for the full academic year; have a cumulative GPA of 2.8 or higher; have plan to be full-time students and carry at least 12 credit hours or equivalent; must be accepted at an accredited college or university and demonstrate a good citizenship qualities in school and/or community.

Funds Avail.: Up to $1,000. **Duration:** Annual. **Remarks:** The scholarship is used for tuition, fees and/or other academic expenses.

6212 ■ Jamaican Canadian Association
995 Arrow Rd.
Toronto, ON, Canada M9M 2Z5
Ph: (416)746-5772
Fax: (416)746-7035
E-mail: info@jcaontario.org

URL: www.jcaontario.org
Social Media: www.facebook.com/
JamaicanCanadianAssociation
twitter.com/jca_ontario

6213 ■ Dr. Ezra Nesbeth Foundation Scholarship *(Undergraduate/Scholarship)*

Purpose: To provide financial assistance to students from the Caribbean or African community who are pursuing post-secondary studies in Ontario universities/colleges. **Focus:** Business; Computer and information sciences; Health sciences; Technology. **Qualif.:** Applicant must be college or university student studying business, technology, computer science or health science; must have high academic standing (minimum B average); must have completed at least one (1) year of college or university in Canada; must demonstrate strong oral and written communication skills; must be a landed immigrant or Canadian citizen; must be involved in extracurricular activities within the university, Afro-Canadian community, or wider Canadian community. **Criteria:** Demonstrated scholastic ability; applicant's response to the essay question Involvement and leadership in community/campus activities; significant personal achievements beyond scholastic ability which may include personal accomplishments in spite of adversity; references demonstrating the applicant's accomplishments; commitment to career goals.

Funds Avail.: $25,000 Canadian Dollars. **Contact:** Jamaican Canadian Association, 995 Arrow Rd, Toronto, M9M 2Z5; Phone: 416-746-5772.

6214 ■ Dr. Lancelot Brown Dental Scholarships *(Undergraduate/Scholarship)*

Purpose: To provide financial assistance to students from the Caribbean/ African community who are pursuing post-secondary studies in Ontario universities/colleges. **Focus:** Dental hygiene; Dental laboratory technology; Dentistry. **Qualif.:** Must provide proof of status in Canada; be enrolled as a full-time student at an Ontario university, college or other post-secondary institution; Must demonstrate involvement and leadership in campus and/or community activities; must demonstrate financial need; demonstrate remarkable academic performance or progress in high school, except where otherwise noted. **Criteria:** Priority for this scholarship is given to applicants pursuing dental studies (i.e., dentistry, dental hygiene, dental assistant); preference is also given to students with exceptional aptitude in the health sciences and visual arts.

Funds Avail.: No specific amount. **To Apply:** Must include an original or copy of the most recent university/college transcript, or report card from the last semester of high school verifying academic performance; must include a two-page double-spaced essay describing the applicant's academic and career goals; this should include how local community/campus activities in which the applicant is involved will enhance these goals; must provide two letters of recommendation as character references and descriptions of the applicant's performance, potential as a student, leader, and employee or volunteer; must provide a digital photograph (JPEG or PNG format) for applications submitted by e-mail; for applications submitted by mail, applicants must provide two passport sized photographs.

6215 ■ Dr. Mary Anne Chambers Scholarship *(Undergraduate/Scholarship)*

Purpose: To provide financial assistance to students from the Caribbean/ African community who are pursuing post-

Awards are arranged alphabetically below their administering organizations

secondary studies in Ontario universities/colleges. **Focus:** General studies/Field of study not specified. **Qualif.:** Must provide proof of status in Canada; Be enrolled as a full-time student at an Ontario university, college or other post-secondary institution; Must demonstrate involvement and leadership in campus and/or community activities; must demonstrate financial need; demonstrate remarkable academic performance or progress in high school, except where otherwise noted. **Criteria:** Priority for this scholarship is given to applicants facing personal challenges, including the inability to secure the financial resources required to achieve their potential.

Funds Avail.: No specific amount. **To Apply:** Must include an original or copy of the most recent university/college transcript, or report card from the last semester of high school verifying academic performance; must include a two-page double-spaced essay describing the applicant's academic and career goals; this should include how local community/campus activities in which the applicant is involved will enhance these goals; must provide two letters of recommendation as character references and descriptions of the applicant's performance, potential as a student, leader, and employee or volunteer; must provide a digital photograph (JPEG or PNG format) for applications submitted by e-mail; for applications submitted by mail, applicants must provide two passport sized photographs. **Contact:** Jamaican Canadian Association, 995 Arrow Rd, Toronto, M9M 2Z5; Phone: 416-746-5772.

6216 ■ Marcus Mosiah Garvey Scholarships (Undergraduate/Scholarship)

Purpose: To provide financial assistance to students from the Caribbean/ African community who are pursuing post-secondary studies in Ontario universities/colleges. **Focus:** Minorities; Philosophy; Sociology. **Qualif.:** Applicant must be Jamaicans enrolled as International students in Ontario universities/colleges.

Funds Avail.: No specific amount. **Contact:** Jamaican Canadian Association, 995 Arrow Rd, Toronto, M9M 2Z5; Phone: 416-746-5772.

6217 ■ Humber College Institute of Technology and Advanced Learning Scholarships (Postgraduate/Scholarship)

Purpose: To provide financial assistance to students enrolled in Humber College. **Focus:** Leadership, Institutional and community. **Qualif.:** Applicants must be first year students of that institution.

Funds Avail.: No specific amount. **Contact:** Jamaican Canadian Association, 995 Arrow Rd, Toronto, M9M 2Z5; Phone: 416-746-5772.

6218 ■ I Have a Dream Scholarships (Undergraduate/Scholarship)

Purpose: To provide financial assistance to students from the Caribbean/ African community who are pursuing dental studies (i.e., dentistry, dental hygiene, dental assistant). **Focus:** General studies/Field of study not specified. **Criteria:** Selection of recipients will be based on the following: demonstrated scholastic ability, in spite of adversity.

Funds Avail.: No specific amount. **Contact:** 220 NW Eighth Avenue, Portland, OR 97209 USA.

6219 ■ Ryerson Scholarships (Undergraduate/Scholarship)

Purpose: To promote the advancement of applied knowledge and research to address societal need, and the provi-

sion of programs of study that provide a balance between theory and application and that prepare students for careers in professional and quasi-professional fields. **Focus:** General studies/Field of study not specified.

Funds Avail.: No specific amount. **Contact:** Jamaican Canadian Association, 995 Arrow Rd, Toronto, M9M 2Z5; Phone: 416-746-5772.

6220 ■ Eva Smith Bursary (Postgraduate/Scholarship)

Purpose: To provide support to African-Canadian youth who are pursuing a post-secondary education. **Focus:** General studies/Field of study not specified. **Qualif.:** Applicant must be an African-Canadian youth (including single parents and those in the justice system), who are pursuing a post-secondary education.

Funds Avail.: No specific amount. **Contact:** Jamaican Canadian Association, 995 Arrow Rd, Toronto, M9M 2Z5; Phone: 416-746-5772.

6221 ■ Barbara Thomas Bursary (Undergraduate/ Award)

Purpose: To provide financial assistance to students from the Caribbean/ African community who are pursuing post-secondary studies in Ontario universities/colleges. **Focus:** General studies/Field of study not specified.

Contact: Jamaican Canadian Association, 995 Arrow Rd, Toronto, M9M 2Z5; Phone: 416-746-5772.

6222 ■ York Regional Police Scholarships (Undergraduate/Scholarship)

Purpose: To provide financial assistance to students from the Caribbean/ African community who are pursuing studies in policing, the justice sector, or a related field. **Focus:** General studies/Field of study not specified. **Qualif.:** Must provide proof of status in Canada; be enrolled as a full-time student at an Ontario university, college or other post-secondary institution; must demonstrate involvement and leadership in campus and/or community activities; must demonstrate financial need; should demonstrate remarkable academic performance or progress in high school, except where otherwise noted. **Criteria:** Preference is given to applicants pursuing studies in policing, the justice sector, or a related field.

Funds Avail.: No specific amount. **To Apply:** Must include an original or copy of the most recent university/college transcript, or report card from the last semester of high school verifying academic performance; must include a two-page double-spaced essay describing the applicant's academic and career goals; this should include how local community/campus activities in which the applicant is involved will enhance these goals; must provide two letters of recommendation as character references and descriptions of the applicant's performance, potential as a student, leader, and employee or volunteer; must provide a digital photograph (JPEG or PNG format) for applications submitted by e-mail; for applications submitted by mail, applicants must provide two passport sized photographs. **Deadline:** July 15. **Contact:** Email: scholarships@jcaontario.org.; Phone: 416-746-5772.

6223 ■ Youth Affairs Committee Rising Star Scholarships (Undergraduate/Scholarship)

Purpose: To provide financial assistance to students from the Caribbean/ African community who are pursuing post-secondary studies in Ontario universities/colleges. **Focus:** General studies/Field of study not specified.

Awards are arranged alphabetically below their administering organizations

Contact: Phone: 416-746-5772 ext. 422.

6224 ■ Jamaican Canadian Association Alberta (JCAA)
PO Box 22264
Bankers Hall
Calgary, AB, Canada T2P 4K1
Ph: (403)775-1235
E-mail: info@jcaalberta.com
URL: www.jcaalberta.com
Social Media: www.facebook.com/jcaalberta
www.instagram.com/jcaalberta
twitter.com/jcaalberta

6225 ■ Jamaican Canadian Association Alberta Scholarship Program *(Undergraduate/Scholarship)*

Purpose: To support the educational pursuits of the association's members, volunteers, and individuals in the community. **Focus:** General studies/Field of study not specified. **Qualif.:** Applicants must be residents of Alberta; Canadian citizens or permanent residents of Canada; enrolled full-time in a post-secondary institution in Canada. **Criteria:** Selection will be based on academic achievement, volunteer activities or community service, personal statement, and availability.

Funds Avail.: No specific amount. **Number Awarded:** Varies. **To Apply:** Applicants must complete the application form available on sponsor's website; must write a statement of no more than 300 words indicating applicant's aspirations and the reasons why they deserve the award. **Deadline:** June 30.

6226 ■ James Madison Memorial Fellowship Foundation
1613 Duke St.
Alexandria, VA 22314
Free: 800-525-6928
URL: www.jamesmadison.com
Social Media: www.facebook.com/
JamesMadisonFoundation
twitter.com/JamesMadisonFdn

6227 ■ James Madison Foundation - Junior Fellowships *(Advanced Professional, Graduate/Fellowship)*

Purpose: To support outstanding college seniors and college graduates without teaching experience who intend to become secondary school teachers of American history, American government, or social studies at the secondary level. **Focus:** Education; History, American; Teaching. **Qualif.:** Applicant must be U.S. citizen; must be teacher, or plan to become a teacher, of American history, American government, or any other social studies class where they will teach topics on the constitution at the secondary school level (grades 7–12). **Criteria:** Selection shall be based on demonstrated commitment to a career teaching American history, American government.

Funds Avail.: $24,000. **Duration:** Annual. **Number Awarded:** Varies.

6228 ■ James Madison Foundation - Senior Fellowships *(Advanced Professional/Fellowship)*

Purpose: To support outstanding current teachers who are required to complete graduate study within 5 calendar years

of part-time study. **Focus:** Education; History, American; Teaching. **Qualif.:** Applicant must be U.S. citizen; must be teacher, or plan to become a teacher, of American history, American government, or any other social studies class where they will teach topics on the constitution at the secondary school level (grades 7–12). **Criteria:** Selection shall be based on demonstrated commitment to a career teaching American history, American government.

Funds Avail.: $24,000. **Duration:** Annual. **Number Awarded:** Varies.

6229 ■ James Madison Graduate Fellowships *(Graduate/Fellowship)*

Purpose: To support individuals desiring to become outstanding teachers of the American Constitution at the secondary school level. **Focus:** General studies/Field of study not specified. **Qualif.:** Applicants must be graduate students, U.S. citizens or U.S. national. **Criteria:** Selection will be based on committee's criteria.

Funds Avail.: $24,000. **Duration:** Annual. **Number Awarded:** 1. **To Apply:** Applicants must complete the application; letters of recommendation; transcripts. **Contact:** James Madison Fellowship Program, One Scholarship Way, Saint Peter, MN, 56082; Phone: 800-525-6928; Email: Madison@scholarshipamerica.org.

6230 ■ Japan-America Society of Hawaii (JASH)
1600 Kapiolani Blvd., Ste. 204
Honolulu, HI 96814
Ph: (808)524-4450
Fax: (808)524-4451
E-mail: admindir@jashawaii.org
URL: www.jashawaii.org
Social Media: www.facebook.com/
JapanAmericaSocietyofHawaii
www.instagram.com/jashawaii

6231 ■ Crown Prince Akihito Scholarship Foundation *(Graduate/Scholarship)*

Purpose: To promote understanding between the U.S. and Japan by offering scholarships for study in Hawaii and Japan. **Focus:** General studies/Field of study not specified.

Funds Avail.: $30,000 for American students plus a $15,000 annual allowance; $25,000 for Japanese students plus a full tuition scholarship. **Duration:** Annual. **To Apply:** Application must be submitted online; letter of recommendation; certificate of Academic Transcript from university admission to application time; copy of the TOEFL or IELTS transcript; outline of research contents. **Remarks:** Established in 1959. **Contact:** Keiji Kimura (Special Adviser, Mitsubishi Estate Corporation), Yoshio Nakamura (Advisor to the Japan Association of Economic Organizations), Secretariat: Keidanren in 1-3-2 Otemachi, Chiyoda-ku, Tokyo, 100-8188; Phone: 03-6741-0161.

6232 ■ Japan Foundation, New York
1700 Broadway, 15th Fl.
New York, NY 10019
Ph: (212)489-0299
Fax: (212)489-0409
E-mail: info@jfny.org
URL: www.jfny.org
Social Media: www.facebook.com/jfny.cgp

Awards are arranged alphabetically below their administering organizations

6233 ■ Japan Foundation, New York Doctoral Candidates *(Doctorate/Fellowship)*

Purpose: To support outstanding scholars in the field of Japanese Studies by offering the opportunity to conduct research in Japan. **Focus:** Japanese studies. **Qualif.:** Applicants must be American citizens; must be doctoral candidates in the humanities or social sciences; and have achieved ABD status by the time the fellowship begins; must be in good health; must be proficient in either Japanese or English; must secure all affiliation arrangements; must be able to stay continuously in Japan for the term of Fellowship.

Funds Avail.: No specific amount. **Duration:** Annual; 4-12 months. **To Apply:** Applications can be submitted online. **Deadline:** November 1. **Contact:** Japanese Studies Fellowship Program, The Japan Foundation, New York: Phone: 212-489-0299; Email: jf_fellowship@jfny.org.

6234 ■ Japan Foundation, New York Scholars and Researchers (Long-Term) *(Professional development/ Fellowship)*

Purpose: To support outstanding scholars in the field of Japanese Studies by offering the opportunity to conduct research in Japan. **Focus:** Japanese studies. **Qualif.:** Applicants must be American citizens; must hold a Ph.D. or equivalent professional experience in research, teaching and writing in the fields of the humanities or social sciences at the time of application; must be in good health; must be proficient in either Japanese or English; must secure all affiliation arrangements; must be able to stay continuously in Japan for the term of Fellowship. **Criteria:** Selection will be based on project's significance to the field and to the applicant's professional development; project's feasibility in terms of time and resources; securing of appropriate affiliation; evidence that residence in Japan is necessary for completion of the project; training, academic history, academic rank or position, professional reputation, and accomplishments are evaluated. priority will be given to relatively junior scholars and researchers, and to those with less research experience in Japan.

Funds Avail.: No specific amount. **Duration:** Annual; 2-12 months. **To Apply:** Applications can be submitted online. **Deadline:** November 1. **Contact:** Japanese Studies Fellowship Program, The Japan Foundation, New York: Phone: 212-489-0299; Email: jf_fellowship@jfny.org.

6235 ■ Japan Foundation, New York Scholars and Researchers (Short-Term) *(Professional development/ Fellowship)*

Purpose: To support outstanding scholars in the field of Japanese Studies by offering the opportunity to conduct research in Japan. **Focus:** Japanese studies. **Qualif.:** Applicants must be American citizens; must hold a Ph.D. or equivalent professional experience in research, teaching and writing in the fields of the humanities or social sciences at the time of application; must be in good health; must be proficient in either Japanese or English; must be able to stay continuously in Japan for the term of Fellowship. **Criteria:** Selection will be based on project's significance to the field and to the applicant's professional development; project's feasibility in terms of time and resources; securing of appropriate affiliation; evidence that residence in Japan is necessary for completion of the project; training, academic history, academic rank or position, professional reputation, and accomplishments are evaluated. priority will be given to relatively experienced scholars and researchers who are expected to publish their research results

shortly after the completion of their Fellowship.

Funds Avail.: No specific amount. **Duration:** Annual; 21-59 days. **To Apply:** Applications can be submitted online. **Deadline:** November 1. **Contact:** Japanese Studies Fellowship Program, The Japan Foundation, New York: Phone: 212-489-0299; Fax: 212-489-0409; Email: jf_fellowship@jfny.org.

6236 ■ Japanese American Bar Association (JABA)
PO Box 71961
Los Angeles, CA 90071
E-mail: info@jabaonline.org
URL: www.jabaonline.org
Social Media: www.facebook.com/jabaonline
www.instagram.com/jabaonline

6237 ■ Justice John F. Aiso Scholarship *(Undergraduate/Scholarship)*

Purpose: To support deserving law students and/or recent law school graduates. **Focus:** Law. **Qualif.:** Applicants must be law students and recent law school graduates with a demonstrated commitment to community service, including but not limited to a commitment to serving the Japanese American community and/or the API community. **Criteria:** Selection will be based on the committee's criteria.

Funds Avail.: $2,000 to $3,000. **Duration:** Annual. **Number Awarded:** 1. **To Apply:** Applicants must submit current resume, an official or unofficial transcript from law school and a personal statement of no more than 500 words addressing demonstrated commitment to community service,ties/involvement with the Japanese American community and/or APIcommunity (past, present and/or future) if any, plans for using your law degree and any other information that is relevant to the application. **Deadline:** January 19, 2020. **Remarks:** The award was established in honor of the first Japanese American California state judge, Justice John F. Aiso. Established in 2006. **Contact:** Email: jefscholarship@gmail.com.

6238 ■ Judge Edward Y. Kakita Memorial Scholarship *(Undergraduate/Scholarship)*

Purpose: To support deserving law students and/or recent law school graduates. **Focus:** Law. **Qualif.:** Applicants must be law students and recent law school graduates with a demonstrated commitment to community service, including but not limited to a commitment to serving the Japanese American community and/or the API community. **Criteria:** Selection will be based on the committee's criteria.

Funds Avail.: $2,000 to $3,000. **Duration:** Annual. **Number Awarded:** 1. **To Apply:** Applicants must submit current resume, an official or unofficial transcript from law school and a personal statement of no more than 500 words addressing demonstrated commitment to community service,ties/involvement with the Japanese American community and/or APIcommunity (past, present and/or future) if any, plans for using your law degree and any other information that is relevant to the application. **Deadline:** January 19, 2020. **Remarks:** The award established in memory of Judge Kakita, a founding member of the Japanese American Bar Association. Established in 2006. **Contact:** Email: jefscholarship@gmail.com.

6239 ■ LimNexus Foundation Scholarship *(Undergraduate/Scholarship)*

Purpose: To support minority law students who are pursuing a more just and equitable society. **Focus:** Law. **Qualif.:**

Awards are arranged alphabetically below their administering organizations

Applicants must be law students and recent law school graduates with a demonstrated commitment to community service, including but not limited to a commitment to serving the Japanese American community and/or the API community. **Criteria:** Selection will be based on the committee's criteria.

Funds Avail.: $2,000 to $3,000. **Duration:** Annual. **Number Awarded:** 1. **To Apply:** Applicants must submit current resume, an official or unofficial transcript from law school and a personal statement of no more than 500 words addressing demonstrated commitment to community service,ties/involvement with the Japanese American community and/or APIcommunity (past, present and/or future) if any, plans for using your law degree and any other information that is relevant to the application. **Deadline:** January 19, 2020. **Remarks:** Established in 2006. **Contact:** Email: jefscholarship@gmail.com.

6240 ■ M. Dick Osumi Civil Rights and Public Interest Scholarship *(Graduate, Undergraduate/Scholarship)*

Purpose: To encourage pursuits in legal education among law students with ethnic backgrounds. **Focus:** Law. **Qualif.:** Applicants must be law students and recent law school graduates with a demonstrated commitment to community service, including but not limited to a commitment to serving the Japanese American community and/or the API community. **Criteria:** Selection will be based on the committee's criteria.

Funds Avail.: $2,000 to $3,000. **Duration:** Annual. **Number Awarded:** 1. **To Apply:** Applicants must submit current resume, an official or unofficial transcript from law school and a personal statement of no more than 500 words addressing demonstrated commitment to community service,ties/involvement with the Japanese American community and/or APIcommunity (past, present and/or future) if any, plans for using your law degree and any other information that is relevant to the application. **Deadline:** January 19, 2020. **Remarks:** The award established in honor of Mr. M. Dick Osumi, prominent civil rights and labor attorney, and through the LimNexus Foundation. Established in 2006. **Contact:** Email: jefscholarship@gmail.com.

6241 ■ Justice Stephen K. Tamura Scholarship *(Undergraduate/Scholarship)*

Purpose: To support deserving law students and/or recent law school graduates. **Focus:** Law. **Qualif.:** Applicants must be law students and recent law school graduates with a demonstrated commitment to community service, including but not limited to a commitment to serving the Japanese American community and/or the API community. **Criteria:** Selection will be based on the committee's criteria.

Funds Avail.: $2,000 to $3,000. **Duration:** Annual. **Number Awarded:** 1. **To Apply:** Applicants must submit current resume, an official or unofficial transcript from law school and a personal statement of no more than 500 words addressing demonstrated commitment to community service,ties/involvement with the Japanese American community and/or APIcommunity (past, present and/or future) if any, plans for using your law degree and any other information that is relevant to the application. **Deadline:** January 19, 2020. **Remarks:** The award was established in honor of Justice Stephen K. Tamura, the first Asian American to sit on the California Court of Appeal. **Contact:** Email: jefscholarship@gmail.com.

6242 ■ Japanese American Citizens League (JACL)

Masao W. Satow Bldg.
1765 Sutter St.
San Francisco, CA 94115
Ph: (415)921-5225
Fax: (415)931-4671
URL: www.jacl.org
Social Media: www.facebook.com/JACLNational
instagram.com/jacl_national
twitter.com/JACL_DC

6243 ■ Kyutaro and Yasuo Abiko Memorial Scholarship *(Undergraduate/Scholarship)*

Purpose: To provide financial assistance to qualified individuals. **Focus:** Agricultural sciences; Journalism. **Qualif.:** Applicant must be active National JACL member; must be planning to attend full-time college, university, or any other institution of higher learning within the United States at the undergraduate level. **Criteria:** Preference will be given to students studying journalism or agriculture.

Funds Avail.: No specific amount. **Duration:** Annual. **To Apply:** Applicants should include JACL membership; personal statement; letter of recommendation; official transcripts including SAT and/or ACT test score verification; work experience; and community involvement. **Deadline:** May 1. **Remarks:** The scholarship was established in honor of the late Kyutaro and Yasuo Abiko. Mr. Yasuo Abiko was a prominent leader of the San Francisco Japanese American community and editor of the Nichi Bei Times newspaper. **Contact:** Mail application to: National JACL Scholarship Committee, c/o JACL Midwest District Council, 10604 Killarney Dr., Union, Kentucky, 41091. For questions contact: JACL Regional Director Patty Wada; Email: pwada@jacl.org, or National Vice President Matthew Farrells; Email: mfarrells@jacl.org.

6244 ■ Grace Andow Memorial Scholarship *(Undergraduate, Graduate/Scholarship)*

Purpose: To support qualified students in pursuing their educational dreams. **Focus:** Law. **Qualif.:** Applicants must be active National JACL member; must be planning to attend full-time college, university, or any other institution of higher learning within the United States at the undergraduate or graduate level. **Criteria:** Selection will be based on JACL involvement, scholastic achievement, extracurricular activities, community involvement, personal statement, and letter of recommendation.

Funds Avail.: No specific amount. **Duration:** Annual. **To Apply:** Applicants should include JACL membership; personal statement; letter of recommendation; official transcripts including SAT and/or ACT test score verification; work experience; and community involvement. **Deadline:** May 1. **Remarks:** The scholarship is given in honor of Grace Andow. **Contact:** Mail application to: National JACL Scholarship Committee, c/o JACL Midwest District Council, 10604 Killarney Dr., Union, Kentucky, 41091. For questions contact: JACL Regional Director Patty Wada; Email: pwada@jacl.org, or National Vice President Matthew Farrells; Email: mfarrells@jacl.org.

6245 ■ Alice Yuriko Endo Memorial Scholarship *(Undergraduate/Scholarship)*

Purpose: To provide financial assistance to qualified individuals. **Focus:** Public service; Social work. **Qualif.:** Applicant must be active National JACL member; must be

Awards are arranged alphabetically below their administering organizations

planning to attend full-time college, university, or any other institution of higher learning within the United States at the undergraduate level. **Criteria:** Preference will be given to students residing in the Eastern District Council and/or students with an interest in public and social service.

Funds Avail.: No specific amount. **Duration:** Annual. **To Apply:** Applicants should include JACL membership; personal statement; letter of recommendation; official transcripts including SAT and/or ACT test score verification; work experience; and community involvement. **Deadline:** May 1. **Remarks:** Established by the Endo family. Mrs. Endo was an active member of the Washington D.C. JACL chapter. An avid supporter of social causes, Mrs. Endo and her son, Todd, proudly marched in the historic Civil Rights March in Washington, D.C. in 1964. **Contact:** JACL Membership Assistant Tomiko Ismail at tismail@jacl.org.

6246 ■ Thomas T. Hayashi Memorial Scholarship (Graduate, Undergraduate/Scholarship)

Purpose: To support individuals who are planning to pursue a legal profession. **Focus:** Law. **Qualif.:** Applicant must be active National JACL member; must be planning to attend full-time college, university, or any other institution of higher learning within the United States at the undergraduate or graduate level in the field of law. **Criteria:** Selection will be based on JACL involvement, scholastic achievement, extracurricular activities, community involvement, personal statement, and letter of recommendation.

Funds Avail.: No specific amount. **Duration:** Annual. **To Apply:** Applicants should include JACL membership; personal statement; letter of recommendation; official transcripts including SAT and/or ACT test score verification; work experience; and community involvement. **Deadline:** May 1. **Remarks:** Established by the Eastern District Council, in memory of Thomas Hayashi, an outstanding Nisei civil rights advocate and attorney in international law. **Contact:** Mail application to: National JACL Scholarship Committee, c/o JACL Midwest District Council, 10604 Killarney Dr., Union, Kentucky, 41091. For questions contact: JACL Regional Director Patty Wada; Email: pwada@jacl.org, or National Vice President Matthew Farrells; Email: mfarrells@jacl.org.

6247 ■ Patricia and Gail Ishimoto Memorial Scholarship (Undergraduate/Scholarship)

Purpose: To help deserving students pursue undergraduate education. **Focus:** General studies/Field of study not specified. **Qualif.:** Applicant must be an active National JACL member; JACL membership is open to everyone of any ethnic background; must be graduating freshmen planning to attend full time at a college, university, trade school, business school, or any other institution of higher learning within the United States at the undergraduate level.

Duration: Annual. **To Apply:** Applicants required to complete a JACL Scholarship Application: JACL Membership; Personal Statement; Letter of Recommendation; Official Transcripts including SAT and/or ACT test score verification; Work Experience; and Community Involvement. **Deadline:** April 2. **Remarks:** Established by Harry K. and Tomoko Ishimoto, in memory of their two daughters who passed away together in an auto accident in January 1969. **Contact:** Freshman applicants may contact JACL Membership Assistant Tomiko Ismail; Phone: 415-921-5225 ext 26; Email: tismail@jacl.org to obtain the mailing address of one's chapter scholarship chair. Please put "Scholarship Chair Info Requested" in the subject line of email.

6248 ■ Henry and Chiyo Kuwahara Creative Arts Award (Graduate/Scholarship)

Purpose: To help qualified students nationwide to achieve their educational dreams in the creative arts. **Focus:** Arts. **Qualif.:** Applicants must be active National JACL member; must be planning to attend full-time college, university, or any other institution of higher learning within the United States at the graduate school level in the field of creative arts. **Criteria:** Selection will be based on JACL involvement, scholastic achievement, extracurricular activities, community involvement, personal statement, and letter of recommendation.

Funds Avail.: No specific amount. **Duration:** Annual. **To Apply:** Applicants must complete and submit application; following is a condensed list of supporting documents required to complete a JACL Scholarship Application: JACL membership, personal statement, letter of recommendation, official transcripts including SAT and/or ACT test score verification, work experience, and JACL and community involvement. **Deadline:** May 1. **Remarks:** Established in honor of Henry and Chiyo Kuwahara. **Contact:** Mail application to: National JACL Scholarship Committee, c/o JACL Midwest District Council, 10604 Killarney Dr., Union, Kentucky, 41091. For questions contact: JACL Regional Director Patty Wada; Email: pwada@jacl.org, or National Vice President Matthew Farrells; Email: mfarrells@jacl.org.

6249 ■ Sam and Florice Kuwahara Memorial Scholarship (Undergraduate/Scholarship)

Purpose: To provide financial support for qualified students intending to pursue their education. **Focus:** General studies/Field of study not specified. **Qualif.:** Applicant must be active National JACL member; must be graduating high school students planning to attend full-time college, university, or any other institution of higher learning within the United States at the undergraduate level.

Funds Avail.: No specific amount. **Duration:** Annual. **To Apply:** Applicants should include JACL membership; personal statement; letter of recommendation; official transcripts including SAT and/or ACT test score verification; work experience; and community involvement. **Deadline:** April 2. **Remarks:** Established to honor Sam & Florice Kuwahara who believed in the importance of education for the young. Established in 2009. **Contact:** Freshman applicants may contact JACL Membership Assistant Tomiko Ismail; Phone: 415-921-5225 ext 26; Email: tismail@jacl.org to obtain the mailing address of one's chapter scholarship chair. Please put "Scholarship Chair Info Requested" in the subject line of email.

6250 ■ Railroad and Mine Workers Memorial Scholarship (Graduate/Scholarship)

Purpose: To help deserving students pursue graduate degrees. **Focus:** General studies/Field of study not specified. **Qualif.:** Applicants must be active National JACL member; must be planning to attend full-time college, university, or any other institution of higher learning within the United States at the graduate school level. **Criteria:** Selection will be based on JACL involvement, scholastic achievement, extracurricular activities, community involvement, personal statement, and letter of recommendation.

Funds Avail.: No specific amount. **Duration:** Annual. **To Apply:** Applicants should include JACL membership; personal statement; letter of recommendation; official transcripts including SAT and/or ACT test score verification; work experience; and community involvement. **Deadline:** May 1. **Remarks:** Established by the families of Japanese

Awards are arranged alphabetically below their administering organizations

American railroad and mine workers to pay tribute to the lives of these Issei and Nisei pioneers and to memorialize the story of these workers, who were fired from their jobs after the outbreak of World War II, and their children's successful fight for recognition and justice decades later. **Contact:** Mail application to: National JACL Scholarship Committee, c/o JACL Midwest District Council, 10604 Killarney Dr., Union, Kentucky, 41091. For questions contact: JACL Regional Director Patty Wada; Email: pwada@jacl.org, or National Vice President Matthew Farrells; Email: mfarrells@ jacl.org.

6251 ■ Sho Sato Memorial Scholarship *(Undergraduate, Graduate/Scholarship)*

Purpose: To support qualified students in pursuing their educational dreams. **Focus:** Law. **Qualif.:** Applicants must be active National JACL member; must be planning to attend full-time college, university, or any other institution of higher learning within the United States at the undergraduate or graduate level in the field of law. **Criteria:** Selection will be based on JACL involvement, scholastic achievement, extracurricular activities, community involvement, personal statement, and letter of recommendation.

Funds Avail.: No specific amount. **Duration:** Annual. **To Apply:** Applicants should include JACL membership; personal statement; letter of recommendation; official transcripts including SAT and/or ACT test score verification; work experience; and community involvement. **Deadline:** May 1. **Remarks:** Established to honor Sho Sato, a professor of law at the University of California at Berkeley, who was one of the nation's most prominent scholars of local governmental law, and who was known as a leading figure in promoting and fostering relations between law schools in Japan and the United States. **Contact:** Mail application to: National JACL Scholarship Committee, c/o JACL Midwest District Council, 10604 Killarney Dr., Union, Kentucky, 41091. For questions contact: JACL Regional Director Patty Wada; Email: pwada@jacl.org, or National Vice President Matthew Farrells; Email: mfarrells@jacl.org.

6252 ■ Chiyoko and Thomas Shimazaki Scholarship *(Graduate/Scholarship)*

Purpose: To help qualified students nationwide to achieve their educational dreams with the scholarship. **Focus:** Medicine. **Qualif.:** Applicants must be active National JACL member; must be planning to attend full-time college, university, trade school, business school or any other institution of higher learning within the United States at the graduate school level in the field of medicine. **Criteria:** Selection is based on JACL involvement, scholastic achievement, extra-curricular activities, community involvement, personal statement, and letter of recommendation.

Funds Avail.: No specific amount. **Duration:** Annual. **To Apply:** Applicants must complete and submit application; following is a condensed list of supporting documents required to complete a JACL Scholarship Application: JACL membership, personal statement, letter of recommendation, official transcripts including SAT and/or ACT test score verification, work experience, and JACL and community involvement. **Deadline:** May 1. **Contact:** Mail application to: National JACL Scholarship Committee, c/o JACL Midwest District Council, 10604 Killarney Dr., Union, Kentucky, 41091. For questions contact: JACL Regional Director Patty Wada; Email: pwada@jacl.org, or National Vice President Matthew Farrells; Email: mfarrells@jacl.org.

6253 ■ Dr. Kiyoshi Sonoda Memorial Scholarship *(Graduate, Master's/Scholarship)*

Purpose: To provide financial assistance to qualified individuals. **Focus:** Dentistry. **Qualif.:** Applicant must be active National JACL member; must be planning to attend full-time college, university, or any other institution of higher learning within the United States at the graduate level in the field of dentistry. **Criteria:** Selection will be based on JACL involvement, scholastic achievement, extracurricular activities, community involvement, personal statement, and letter of recommendation.

Funds Avail.: No specific amount. **Duration:** Annual. **To Apply:** Applicants should include JACL membership; personal statement; letter of recommendation; official transcripts including SAT and/or ACT test score verification; work experience; and community involvement. **Deadline:** May 1. **Remarks:** Established in memory of Dr. Kiyoshi Sonoda, an active member of the JACL beginning in 1945, in which he was one of the first life members of the One Thousand Club and a past president of the West Los Angeles JACL chapter. **Contact:** Mail application to: National JACL Scholarship Committee, c/o JACL Midwest District Council, 10604 Killarney Dr., Union, Kentucky, 41091. For questions contact: JACL Regional Director Patty Wada; Email: pwada@jacl.org, or National Vice President Matthew Farrells; Email: mfarrells@jacl.org.

6254 ■ Reverend H. John and Asako Yamashita Memorial Scholarship *(Graduate/Scholarship)*

Purpose: To help qualified students nationwide to achieve their educational dreams with the scholarship. **Focus:** Civil rights; Education; Social work. **Qualif.:** Applicants must be active National JACL member; must be planning to attend full-time college, university, or any other institution of higher learning within the United States at the graduate level in the fields of education, social justice, and service to their communities. **Criteria:** Selection will be based on JACL involvement, scholastic achievement, extracurricular activities, community involvement, personal statement, and letter of recommendation.

Funds Avail.: No specific amount. **Duration:** Annual. **To Apply:** Applicants should include JACL membership; personal statement; letter of recommendation; official transcripts including SAT and/or ACT test score verification; work experience; and community involvement. **Deadline:** May 1. **Remarks:** Established in the memory of Reverend H. John & Asako Yamashita, who together supported the work of the West Tenth Methodist Church and later the Centenary Methodist Church in Los Angeles. **Contact:** Mail application to: National JACL Scholarship Committee, c/o JACL Midwest District Council, 10604 Killarney Dr., Union, Kentucky, 41091. For questions contact: JACL Regional Director Patty Wada; Email: pwada@jacl.org, or National Vice President Matthew Farrells; Email: mfarrells@jacl.org.

6255 ■ Minoru Yasui Memorial Scholarship *(Graduate/Scholarship)*

Purpose: To provide financial assistance to qualified individuals. **Focus:** Civil rights; Education; Human rights; Law; Sociology. **Qualif.:** Applicant must be active National JACL member; must be planning to attend full-time college, university, or any other institution of higher learning within the United States at the graduate level in the fields of sociology, law, or education. **Criteria:** Preference will be given to students with a strong interest in human rights and civil rights.

Funds Avail.: No specific amount. **Duration:** Annual. **To Apply:** Applicants should include JACL membership;

Awards are arranged alphabetically below their administering organizations

personal statement; letter of recommendation; official transcripts including SAT and/or ACT test score verification; work experience; and community involvement. **Deadline:** May 1. **Remarks:** Establlshed to honor civil rights advocate and attorney, Minoru Yasui, one of the four Nisei who challenged the imprisonment of Japanese Americans during WWII. After the war he practiced law and served as legal counsel for dozens of community organizations and activities. In 1979, Mr. Yasui was appointed chair of the JACL Committee on Redress, in which he traveled extensively around the country advocating for redress and reparations. **Contact:** Mail application to: National JACL Scholarship Committee, c/o JACL Midwest District Council, 10604 Killarney Dr., Union, Kentucky, 41091. For questions contact: JACL Regional Director Patty Wada; Email: pwada@jacl.org, or National Vice President Matthew Farrells; Email: mfarrells@jacl.org.

6256 ■ JCC Association
520 8th Ave.
New York, NY 10018
Ph: (212)532-4949
E-mail: info@jcca.org
URL: jcca.org
Social Media: www.facebook.com/
 JCCAssociationOfNorthAmerica
www.instagram.com/jccassociation/?hl=en
www.linkedin.com/company/jcc-association
www.youtube.com/user/jccAssociation

6257 ■ JCC Association Graduate Education Scholarships (Graduate/Scholarship)

Purpose: To provide exceptionally talented and highly motivated individuals with a scholarship that enables them to pursue a graduate course of study leading to a career in the JCC Movement. **Focus:** Education, Early childhood; Education, Physical; Health education. **Qualif.:** Applicant must be a full-time student pursuing graduate studies that lead to a professional career in the JCC Movement. **Criteria:** Selection is based on the submitted application materials.

Funds Avail.: No specific amount. **To Apply:** Applicants must submit a completed application form together with a two-page personal essay, university transcripts, and 5 letters of reference from individuals who have been listed by the applicant.

6258 ■ JDBNOW
777 Canton Rd.
Akron, OH 44312
Free: 800-233-9293
E-mail: wecare@jdbnow.com
URL: jdbnow.com
Social Media: www.facebook.com/JDBNOW
www.facebook.com/pg/JDBNOW/posts
www.instagram.com/jdbnow
twitter.com/jdb_now
twitter.com/jdb_now?lang=en

6259 ■ JDBNOW Scholarship (Two Year College, Undergraduate, Graduate/Scholarship)

Purpose: To provide financial aid to students pursuing education in Business Administration. **Focus:** Business

administration. **Qualif.:** Applicants must be U.S. citizens accepted to or currently attending a college or university in the United States and pursuing a degree in Business Administration.

Funds Avail.: $1,000. **Duration:** Annual. **Number Awarded:** 1. **To Apply:** Application is available at jdbnow.com/scholarship/. **Deadline:** December 1.

6260 ■ The Jeffcoat Firm
4723-A Sunset Blvd.
Lexington, SC 29072
Ph: (803)373-1302
URL: scinjurylawfirm.com
Social Media: www.facebook.com/South.Carolina.Injury
 .Lawyer
www.instagram.com/thejeffcoatfirm
twitter.com/thejeffcoatfirm
www.youtube.com/channel/UCy66wPeN9bAsX1kfoil-Drw/
 videos

6261 ■ The Jeffcoat Firm Annual Scholarship Essay & Video Competition (College, University, Graduate/Scholarship)

Purpose: To help students pay for higher education. **Focus:** General studies/Field of study not specified. **Qualif.:** Applicant must be a student who is a U.S. resident or an international student who is studying at a U.S. school; a high school junior or senior enrolling in college, a student currently enrolled in a two-year or four-year college or university, or a student currently enrolled in graduate school.

Funds Avail.: $1,500. **Number Awarded:** 2. **To Apply:** Applicant must submit an essay of 600 words or less, a video, a copy of school transcript or other proof of enrollment, and a cover sheet with the following: name, address, photograph, a brief two to three sentence bio, and a parental signature for applicants younger than age 18. All materials should be submitted via email. **Deadline:** May 1. **Contact:** Email: Bradi@thejeffcoatfirm.com; URL: scinjurylawfirm.com/scholarship/.

6262 ■ Jefferson Scholars Foundation
112 Clarke Ct.
Charlottesville, VA 22903
Ph: (434)243-9029
Fax: (434)243-9081
E-mail: info@jeffersonscholars.org
URL: www.jeffersonscholars.org

6263 ■ Jefferson Graduate Fellowship (Doctorate, Graduate/Fellowship)

Purpose: To attract Ph.D. and M.B.A. candidates who demonstrate outstanding achievement and the highest promise as scholars, teachers, public servants, and business leaders in the United States and beyond. **Focus:** General studies/Field of study not specified. **Criteria:** Selection will be based on the committee's criteria.

Funds Avail.: $5,000. **Duration:** Two years. **Remarks:** Established in 2001. **Contact:** Email: selection@jeffersonscholars.org.

6264 ■ Jefferson Science Associates, LLC (JSA)
c/o Southeastern Universities Research Association, Inc.
1201 New York AvenueSuite 430
Washington, DC 20005

Awards are arranged alphabetically below their administering organizations

Ph: (202)408-7872
URL: www.jsallc.org

6265 ■ JSA/Jefferson Lab Graduate Fellowship
(Doctorate, Graduate/Fellowship)

Purpose: To provide the environment and financial resources for graduate students to work alongside Jefferson Lab researchers as they continue their academic studies and pursue research opportunities in this field of science. **Focus:** Science. **Qualif.:** Applicants must be enrolled full-time in a relevant doctoral program at a SURA member university; students may apply at any stage of their graduate careers or while undergraduate seniors; students seeking second-year support must resubmit an application. **Criteria:** Selection is based on the merit and quality of proposed research based on applicant's research plan; utility and relevance of proposed research to the Jefferson Lab, including proposed utilization of lab resources.

Funds Avail.: $11,000. **Duration:** Annual. **To Apply:** Applicants must submit a completed application form including a completed reference form from three individuals for letters of recommendation; academic qualifications from official transcripts; incomplete applications and applications received after the announced deadline will not be considered. **Deadline:** March 13. **Remarks:** Established in 1989. **Contact:** Email: jsaprograms@sura.org.

6266 ■ Jet Insurance Services
9848 Business Park Dr., Ste. H
Sacramento, CA 95827

6267 ■ Jet Business Scholarship *(Graduate/Scholarship)*

Purpose: To help future employees of the business world. **Focus:** Business. **Qualif.:** Applicant must be a U.S. citizen or permanent resident enrolled in a college or university in a business-related field. **Criteria:** Selection will be based on name, mailing address, email address, phone number, projected graduation date, current/planned college, area of study.

Funds Avail.: $500. **Number Awarded:** 1. **To Apply:** Applicant must complete all sections of the application, including a 250- to 500-word essay. Application should be completed and submitted online. **Deadline:** July 31. **Contact:** Email: sadie@jetsurety.com; URL: jetsurety.com/scholarship/.

6268 ■ Jewish Community Federation and Endowment Fund
121 Steuart St.
San Francisco, CA 94105
Ph: (415)777-0411
E-mail: info@sfjcf.org
URL: jewishfed.org
Social Media: www.facebook.com/jewishbayarea
www.instagram.com/jewishbayarea
twitter.com/jewishbayarea
www.youtube.com/user/sfjcf

6269 ■ Marvin Anmuth Scholarship *(Undergraduate, Graduate/Scholarship)*

Purpose: To help Jewish students attend undergraduate or graduate programs in engineering. **Focus:** Engineering. **Qualif.:** Applicants must be Jewish high school seniors or

graduates who are planning to enroll or have already enrolled in a full-time undergraduate or graduate program at an accredited college or university; must be pursuing a degree in engineering; and must have a minimum 3.0 cumulative GPA on a 4.0 scale. Applicants must also reside in the greater San Francisco Bay area, including San Francisco, San Mateo, Santa Clara, Alameda, Contra Costa, Solano, Marin, Napa and Sonoma counties. May reapply for renewal in subsequent years if they continue to meet the eligibility requirements. **Criteria:** Selection is based on financial need, academic merit, and demonstrated leadership in the Jewish and/or larger community.

Funds Avail.: $1,500 to $5,000. **Duration:** Annual. **Number Awarded:** Multiple. **To Apply:** Application must be completed online at jewishfed.org/how-we-help/opportunities-support/scholarships/college-scholarships. **Contact:** Alan Brody, Philanthropy Associate; Phone: 415-512-6222; E-mail: alanb@sfjcf.org.

6270 ■ The Brandenburg Education Scholarship
(College, University, Undergraduate/Scholarship)

Purpose: To provide scholarships for Jewish students to attend undergraduate programs. **Focus:** General studies/Field of study not specified. **Qualif.:** Applicants must be Jewish high school seniors or undergraduate students accepted or currently enrolled in a course of study at an accredited four-year college or university in the United States. Applicants must also be residents of the greater San Francisco Bay area, including San Francisco, San Mateo, Santa Clara, Alameda, Contra Costa, Solano, Marin, Napa, and Sonoma counties. **Criteria:** Selection is based on financial need, academic merit, and demonstrated interest in internships, research, etc. in a specific field of study.

Funds Avail.: $1,000. **Duration:** Annual. **Number Awarded:** 1. **To Apply:** Application must be completed on at jewishfed.org/how-we-help/opportunities-support/scholarships/college-scholarships. **Contact:** Alan Brody, Philanthropy Associate; Phone: 415-512-6222; E-mail: alanb@sfjcf.org.

6271 ■ The Nathan J. and Virginia H. Friedman College Scholarship *(Undergraduate, Four Year College, University/Scholarship)*

Purpose: To help Jewish students afford an undergraduate degree. **Focus:** General studies/Field of study not specified. **Qualif.:** Must be Jewish high school seniors or graduates who are enrolled or will enroll in a four-year undergraduate program at an accredited college or university; must have a cumulative GPA of 3.3 on a 4.0 scale. May reapply for renewal in subsequent years if continue to meet eligibility requirements. Applicant must also reside in the greater San Francisco Bay area, including San Francisco, San Mateo, Santa Clara, Alameda, Contra Costa, Solano, Marin, Napa, and Sonoma counties. **Criteria:** Selection is based on financial need, outstanding academic record, and past participation in the Jewish community.

Funds Avail.: $1,000 to $5,000. **Duration:** Annual. **Number Awarded:** Multiple. **To Apply:** Application must be completed at jewishfed.org/how-we-help/opportunities-support/scholarships/college-scholarships. **Deadline:** August 1. **Contact:** Alan Brody, Philanthropy Associate; Phone: 415-512-6222; E-mail: alanb@sfjcf.org.

6272 ■ The Elaine and Barry Gilbert College Scholarship *(Undergraduate/Scholarship)*

Purpose: To help Jewish students afford an undergraduate degree. **Focus:** General studies/Field of study not specified. **Qualif.:** Applicants must be Jewish high school seniors or past Gilbert Scholarship recipients who are enrolled or plan to enroll in full-time undergraduate courses of study in the University of California (UC) system, California Polytechnic State University in San Luis Obispo, or Hillsdale College in Michigan. New applicants must have a cumulative 3.5 GPA on a 4.0 scale, and renewal applicants must have a 3.0 or higher GPA (except in extenuating circumstances). Applicants must reside in the San Francisco Bay area, including San Francisco, San Mateo, Santa Clara, Alameda, Contra Costa, Solano, Marin, Napa, and Sonoma counties. **Criteria:** Selection is based on financial need, academic merit, and demonstrated involvement in the Jewish community; special consideration will be given to graduates of San Francisco's Lowell or Washington High Schools. **Funds Avail.:** $1,000 to $3,000. **Duration:** Annual. **Number Awarded:** Multiple. **To Apply:** Application must be completed at jewishfed.org/how-we-help/opportunities-support/scholarships/college-scholarships. **Deadline:** August 1. **Contact:** Alan Brody, Philanthropy Associate; Phone: 415-512-6222; E-mail: alanb@sfjcf.org.

6273 ■ Helen B. and Lewis E. Goldstein Scholarship (Undergraduate, Graduate/Scholarship)

Purpose: To help Jewish students afford an undergraduate degree. **Focus:** Business; General studies/Field of study not specified; Law; Library and archival sciences. **Qualif.:** Applicants must be Jewish high school seniors or graduates who are enrolled or plan to enroll in a full-time undergraduate or graduate program at an accredited college or university. Recipients may reapply for renewal in subsequent years if they continue to meet eligibility requirements. **Criteria:** Selection is based on financial need and academic merit. Preference will be given to immigrants and to those enrolled in a professional school such as law school, business, or library/information science. **Funds Avail.:** $10,000. **Duration:** Annual. **Number Awarded:** 1. **To Apply:** Application must be completed at jewishfed.org/how-we-help/opportunities-support/scholarships/college-scholarships. **Deadline:** August 1. **Contact:** Alan Brody, Philanthropy Associate; Phone: 415-512-6222; E-mail: alanb@sfjcf.org.

6274 ■ The Stephanie G. Hoffman Scholarship (Graduate, Undergraduate/Scholarship)

Purpose: To help Jewish students afford an undergraduate degree. **Focus:** Library and archival sciences; Literature. **Qualif.:** Applicants must be Jewish high school seniors, undergraduates, or graduate students accepted to or attending an accredited college or university program in library science, literature, or a related field. Recipients may reapply for renewal in subsequent year if they continue to meet eligibility requirements. Applicants must reside in the greater San Francisco Bay area, including San Francisco, San Mateo, Santa Clara, Alameda, Contra Costa, Solano, Marin, Napa, and Sonoma counties. **Criteria:** Selection is based on financial need and academic merit. **Funds Avail.:** $1,000 to $5,000. **Duration:** Annual. **Number Awarded:** 1 or more. **To Apply:** Application must be completed at jewishfed.org/how-we-help/opportunities-support/scholarships/college-scholarships. **Deadline:** August 1. **Contact:** Alan Brody, Philanthropy Associate; Phone: 415-512-6222; E-mail: alanb@sfjcf.org.

6275 ■ Alexander M. and June L. Maisin Foundation Scholarship (Undergraduate/Scholarship)

Purpose: To help Jewish students afford an undergraduate degree. **Focus:** General studies/Field of study not speci-

fied. **Qualif.:** Must be Jewish high school senior or previous Maisin scholarship recipient who is age 24 or younger as of the application deadline; be enrolled or planning to enroll full-time in an undergraduate program at an accredited college or university; have a minimum 3.0 GPA on a 4.0 scale. Applicant must be a permanent resident of the greater San Francisco Bay Area, including San Francisco, San Mateo, Santa Clara, Alameda, Contra Costa, Solano, Marin, Napa, and Sonoma counties. **Criteria:** Selection is based on financial need, academic merit, and demonstrated leadership. **Funds Avail.:** $1,000 to $3,500. **Duration:** Annual. **Number Awarded:** Multiple. **To Apply:** Application must be completed at jewishfed.org/how-we-help/opportunities-support/scholarships/college-scholarships. **Deadline:** August 1. **Contact:** Alan Brody, Philanthropy Associate; Phone: 415-512-6222; E-mail: alanb@sfjcf.org.

6276 ■ The Gail Karp Orgell Scholarship (Four Year College, University, Undergraduate/Scholarship)

Purpose: To help Jewish students afford an undergraduate degree. **Focus:** General studies/Field of study not specified. **Qualif.:** Applicant must be a Jewish female high school senior or graduate who is beginning the first year of an undergraduate program at a four-year university or college in California, have a minimum 3.5 GPA on a 4.0 scale. Applicant must also be a permanent resident of the greater San Francisco Bay Area, including San Francisco, San Mateo, Santa Clara, Alameda, Contra Costa, Solano, Marin, Napa, and Sonoma counties. Recipient may reapply for renewal in subsequent years if scholarship eligibility requirements are met. **Criteria:** Selection will be based on financial need, academic merit, involvement in athletics, and evidence of consistently practicing the Jewish principles of tzedakah an tikkun olam, defined here as giving of one's time to making the world a better place. **Funds Avail.:** $7,000. **Duration:** Annual. **Number Awarded:** 1. **To Apply:** Application must be completed at jewishfed.org/how-we-help/opportunities-support/scholarships/college-scholarships. **Deadline:** August 1. **Contact:** Alan Brody, Philanthropy Associate; Phone: 415-512-6222; E-mail: alanb@sfjcf.org.

6277 ■ The Shirley and Robert Raymer College Scholarship (Four Year College, University, Undergraduate/Scholarship)

Purpose: To help Jewish students afford an undergraduate degree. **Focus:** General studies/Field of study not specified. **Qualif.:** Applicant must be a Jewish high school senior planning to enroll in an academically selective, four-year college or university. Applicant must be a resident of the greater San Francisco Bay Area, including San Francisco, San Mateo, Santa Clara, Alameda, Contra Costa, Solano, Marin, Napa, and Sonoma counties. **Criteria:** Selection is based on academic excellence, financial need, and demonstrated involvement in the Jewish community. **Funds Avail.:** $10,000. **Duration:** Annual. **Number Awarded:** 2 or 3. **To Apply:** Application must be completed at jewishfed.org/how-we-help/opportunities-support/scholarships/college-scholarships. **Deadline:** August 1. **Contact:** Alan Brody, Philanthropy Associate; Phone: 415-512-6222; E-mail: alanb@sfjcf.org.

6278 ■ The S.F. Humanities, Inc: Leo Hills Scholarship (Undergraduate, Graduate/Scholarship)

Purpose: To help Jewish students afford an undergraduate degree. **Focus:** General studies/Field of study not speci-

Awards are arranged alphabetically below their administering organizations

fied. **Qualif.:** Applicant must be a Jewish high school senior or graduate who is enrolled or planning to enroll in a full-time undergraduate or graduate program at an accredited college, university, or art/music institution. Applicant must have a proven track record of excellence in the area of fine arts. Applicant must also be a permanent resident of the greater San Francisco Bay area, including San Francisco, San Mateo, Santa Clara, Alameda, Contra Costa, Solano, Marin, Napa, and Sonoma counties. **Criteria:** Selection will be based on financial need and a demonstrated excellence in the area of fine arts.

Funds Avail.: $1,000. **Duration:** Annual. **Number Awarded:** 2. **To Apply:** Application must be completed at jewishfed.org/how-we-help/opportunities-support/scholarships/college-scholarships. **Deadline:** August 1. **Contact:** Alan Brody, Philanthropy Associate; Phone: 415-512-6222; E-mail: alanb@sfjcf.org.

6279 ■ Judy Kay Wendland-Young Scholarship
(Undergraduate/Scholarship)

Purpose: To help a woman over the age of 35 afford an undergraduate degree. **Focus:** General studies/Field of study not specified. **Qualif.:** Applicant must be a female over the age of 35 who has not previously attended college at an accredited college or university offering bachelor's degrees, and who will be enrolled in the first year of a four-year college or university program at an accredited college or university in the United States. **Criteria:** Selection is based on financial need.

Funds Avail.: Up to $20,000. **Duration:** Annual. **Number Awarded:** Up to 2. **To Apply:** Application must be completed at jewishfed.org/how-we-help/opportunities-support/scholarships/college-scholarships. **Deadline:** March 31. **Contact:** Alan Brody, Philanthropy Associate; Phone: 415-512-6222; E-mail: alanb@sfjcf.org.

6280 ■ The Ronald P. Wilmot Scholarship
(Undergraduate, Graduate/Scholarship)

Purpose: To help Jewish students afford an undergraduate degree. **Focus:** General studies/Field of study not specified. **Qualif.:** Applicants must be high schools senior or graduates who are children of gay or lesbian parents and who are enrolled, or planning to enroll, in a full-time undergraduate or graduate program at an accredited college or university. Applicants must be residents of the Greater San Francisco Bay Area, including San Francisco, San Mateo, Santa Clara, Alameda, Contra Costa, Solano, Marin, Napa, and Sonoma counties. **Criteria:** Selection is based on academic and artistic excellence, along with financial need.

Funds Avail.: $2,000. **Duration:** Annual. **Number Awarded:** 10. **To Apply:** Application must be completed at jewishfed.org/how-we-help/opportunities-support/scholarships/college-scholarships. **Deadline:** August 1. **Contact:** Alan Brody, Philanthropy Associate; Phone: 415-512-6222; E-mail: alanb@sfjcf.org.

6281 ■ The Jewish Community Foundation of Montreal

1 Qummings Sq., Ste. 510
Montreal, QC, Canada H3W 1M6
Ph: (514)345-6414
Fax: (514)345-6410
E-mail: info@jcfmontreal.org
URL: www.jcfmontreal.org/en/home
Social Media: www.facebook.com/jcfmontreal

www.linkedin.com/company/the-jewish-community-foundation-of-montreal/
twitter.com/jcfmontreal

6282 ■ Evelyn Joy Abramowicz Memorial Scholarship *(Undergraduate/Scholarship)*

Purpose: To support students with disabilities entering CEGEP or enrolled in university programs. **Focus:** General studies/Field of study not specified. **Qualif.:** Applicant must be a student with a disability and good academic standing. **Criteria:** Preference will be given to first time applicants.

To Apply: Applicants must submit the letter of acceptance from a university or proof of enrollment; letter of application outlining disability and reasons for request; transcripts of grades; proof of Quebec residency; social insurance number; Montreal address and telephone number; e-mail address. **Deadline:** May 1.

6283 ■ Jenny Panitch Beckow Memorial Scholarship - Canada *(Graduate/Scholarship)*

Purpose: To provide financial assistance for Israeli students studying in Canada. **Focus:** Art; Culture; Linguistics; Literature; Medicine; Music; Science. **Qualif.:** Applicants must be Israeli students of any age who are entering into or who are currently enrolled in a program of graduate studies at a Canadian university with good academic standing; must be studying in one of the following fields: language, literature, culture, art or music, or in any field of medical, scientific, or industrial, endeavor or research.

To Apply: Applicants must submit the letter of application setting forth area of study and proposed post-graduate plans; transcripts; two letters of reference; proof of Israeli citizenship; letter of acceptance to college or university or proof that studies have commenced at that institution; social insurance number or Israeli equivalent; e-mail address. **Deadline:** May 1.

6284 ■ Jenny Panitch Beckow Memorial Scholarship - Israel *(Graduate/Scholarship)*

Purpose: To assist Canadian students in their graduate study or research at an Israeli university. **Focus:** Art; Culture; Literature; Medicine; Music; Science. **Qualif.:** Applicants must be Canadian students who are entering into or are currently enrolled in a program of graduate studies at an Israeli university in one of the following fields: language, literature, art, music, or any field of medical, scientific, or industrial endeavor or research. **Criteria:** Selection will be based on merit. Preference will be given to first time applicants.

Funds Avail.: 18,000 Canadian dollars. **Duration:** Annual. **To Apply:** Applicants must submit letter of application setting forth area of study and proposed postgraduate plans; transcripts; two letters of reference; proof of Canadian citizenship; letter of acceptance to college or university or proof that studies have commenced at that institution; social insurance number; and email address. Moreover, they must submit progress report within 6 months after commencement of study and a final report within 60 days after completing the academic year. **Deadline:** May 31.

6285 ■ Therese and David Bohbot Scholarship
(Undergraduate/Scholarship)

Purpose: To assist Quebec students pursuing undergraduate degrees. **Focus:** General studies/Field of study not specified. **Qualif.:** Applicants must be resident of Quebec

Awards are arranged alphabetically below their administering organizations

pursuing undergraduate degrees.

Funds Avail.: No specific amount. **Duration:** Annual. **To Apply:** Application form and details are available online on March 1 of each year at: jcfmontreal.org/grants/scholarships/. **Deadline:** May 1.

6286 ■ Stephen Bronfman Scholarship *(Graduate/Scholarship)*

Purpose: To enrich environmental research among graduate level students. **Focus:** Environmental science. **Qualif.:** Applicants must be legal residents of Quebec; must be second year Masters or Ph.D. students in a recognized environmental graduate program anywhere in the world.

Funds Avail.: 7,500 Canadian Dollars (6,000 of such will be received as first payment; 1,500 will be awarded in the final). **Duration:** Annual. **To Apply:** Applicants must submit a maximum two-page letter outlining, in order of importance: how the scholarship will (one or a combination of these): further environmental research and studies; have eventual concrete applications for natural or urban communities; assist in original research; offset travel costs to actively participate in scientific conferences; and, how the scholarship will assist the applicants (financial need) and/or reward their academic excellence and/or exceptional environmental engagement; the letter would need to be completed with the following application requirements: curriculum vitae highlighting personal, academic and professional achievements; official transcript of academic results; social insurance number; email address; two letters of recommendation from professors and/or mentors supervising the students' work that confirms the pertinence of the research being assisted and/or how the scholarship will enrich the student' studies; and proof of full-time status at the time of the request.**Deadline:** May 1.

6287 ■ Bernice & Gordon Brown Scholarship *(Undergraduate/Scholarship)*

Purpose: To support Montreal students in their study and participation in the Jewish community. **Focus:** General studies/Field of study not specified. **Qualif.:** Applicants must be permanent residents of Montreal who have demonstrated academic excellence and agree to return to Montreal and participate in the Jewish community.

Funds Avail.: $5,000 Canadian Dollars. **Duration:** Annual. **To Apply:** Applicants must submit the completed application form; brief letter outlining reasons for wishing to attend university in Israel and career goals; record of involvement in Jewish community; letter of acceptance from an Israeli university; transcript of grades (CEGEP and/or university) and final midterm marks; minimum of 2 letters of recommendation from professors. **Deadline:** May 31.

6288 ■ Hadar J. Chemtob Memorial Scholarship *(Undergraduate/Scholarship)*

Purpose: To support aspiring students wishing to pursue a career in fashion. **Focus:** Fashion design. **Qualif.:** Applicants must be students pursuing a career in fashion.

Duration: Annual. **To Apply:** Application form and details are available online on March 1 of each year at: jcfmontreal.org/grants/scholarships/. **Deadline:** May 1.

6289 ■ Ruth and Victor David Scholarship *(Undergraduate, Graduate/Scholarship)*

Purpose: To help Canadian students studying in Israel. **Focus:** General studies/Field of study not specified. **Qualif.:** Applicants must be Canadian students accepted to a university in Israel.

Duration: Annual. **To Apply:** Application form and details are available online on March 1 of each year at: jcfmontreal.org/grants/scholarships/. **Deadline:** May 1.

6290 ■ Harry Feldman Memorial Scholarship *(Undergraduate/Scholarship)*

Purpose: To support Quebec students in their education. **Focus:** Business. **Qualif.:** Applicants must be undergraduate students who are majoring in business and attending a university in Montreal or in Israel. **Criteria:** Selection will be based on need and merit.

Funds Avail.: No specific amount. **To Apply:** Applicants must submit the letter explaining goals/reasons for request; proof of Quebec residency; grade transcripts; acceptance letter to University (1st yr. students); two letters of reference. **Deadline:** May 1.

6291 ■ Jack Gitlitz Memorial Scholarship - Israel *(Graduate, Undergraduate/Scholarship)*

Purpose: To support Montreal students in their study and participation in the Jewish community. **Focus:** Jewish studies. **Qualif.:** Applicants must be permanent residents of Montreal who have demonstrated academic excellence and agree to return to Montreal and participate in the Jewish community; must be accepted to a university in Israel.

Funds Avail.: 5,000 Canadian Dollars each. **Number Awarded:** 2. **To Apply:** Applicants must submit the completed application form; brief letter outlining reasons for wishing to attend university in Israel and career goals; record of involvement in Jewish community; letter of acceptance from an Israeli university; transcript of grades (CEGEP and/or university) and final midterm marks; minimum of 2 letters of recommendation from professors. **Deadline:** May 31.

6292 ■ Harry Hopmeyer Memorial Scholarship *(Undergraduate/Scholarship)*

Purpose: To support Quebec students in their post-secondary education. **Focus:** General studies/Field of study not specified. **Qualif.:** Applicants must be Quebec students enrolled in undergraduate university studies in Montreal. **Criteria:** Selection will be based on need and merit and Preference will be given to 1st time candidates.

Funds Avail.: No specific amount. **To Apply:** Applicants must submit the letter explaining goals/reasons for request; proof of Quebec residency; grade transcripts; acceptance letter to University (1st yr. students); two letters of recommendation from teachers or employers. **Deadline:** May 1.

6293 ■ Mitchell Karper Memorial Scholarship *(Undergraduate/Scholarship)*

Purpose: To support students in Quebec as they pursue undergraduate degrees. **Focus:** General studies/Field of study not specified. **Qualif.:** Applicants must be permanent residents of Montreal and undergraduate students.

Duration: Annual. **Number Awarded:** 2. **To Apply:** Application form and details are available online on March 1 of each year at: jcfmontreal.org/grants/scholarships/. **Deadline:** May 1.

6294 ■ Joseph Katz Memorial Scholarship *(Undergraduate/Scholarship)*

Purpose: To assist Quebec students in their education. **Focus:** General studies/Field of study not specified. **Qualif.:** Applicants must be university students living and studying in Montreal. **Criteria:** Selection will be based on

Awards are arranged alphabetically below their administering organizations

financial need and academic achievement. Preference will be given to first time applicants under 25 years old.

Funds Avail.: No specific amount. **Duration:** Annual. **To Apply:** Applicants must submit the letter explaining goals/reasons for request; proof of Quebec residency; grade transcripts; acceptance letter to University (if applicable); two letters of recommendation from teachers or employers. **Deadline:** May 1.

6295 ■ Henriette & Marcel Korner Scholarship
(Undergraduate/Scholarship)

Purpose: To support students in their study at Montreal CEGEP. **Focus:** General studies/Field of study not specified. **Qualif.:** Applicants must be permanent residents of Quebec studying at CEGEP. **Criteria:** Selection will be based on the involvement in the Jewish community.

Funds Avail.: $1,000 Canadian Dollars. **Duration:** Annual. **To Apply:** Applicants must submit the letter stating objectives and reasons for request; proof of Quebec residency; letter of university acceptance; transcript of grades; two letters of recommendation from teachers or employers. **Deadline:** May 1.

6296 ■ Liela Klinger Kurztman Memorial Scholarship *(Undergraduate/Scholarship)*

Purpose: To support Quebec students in their education. **Focus:** Education. **Qualif.:** Applicants must be undergraduate students pursuing education studies. **Criteria:** Selection will be based on academic merit. Preference will be given to first time candidates under the age of 25.

Funds Avail.: No specific amount. **To Apply:** Applicants must submit the letter of acceptance to graduate or post graduate studies in Montreal; letter of application outlining need and goals; transcripts of grades; proof of Quebec residency; two letters of recommendation from professors. **Deadline:** May 1.

6297 ■ Karen E. Latt Memorial Scholarship
(Graduate/Scholarship)

Purpose: To support female graduates entering medical school. **Focus:** Medicine. **Qualif.:** Applicants must be female students who have recently graduated, or will be graduating, with an undergraduate degree and have been accepted for admission to medical school.

Funds Avail.: No specific amount. **To Apply:** Applicants must submit the following requirements: letter stating goals; reasons for request; letter of acceptance to medical school for the coming academic year; scholastic performance; two letters of recommendation from professors; involvement in extracurricular activities and athletics; e-mail address. **Deadline:** June 30. **Remarks:** Established in 1993.

6298 ■ Irene Brand Lieberman Memorial Scholarship *(Graduate/Scholarship)*

Purpose: To support graduate students in their studies related to children. **Focus:** Child development; Social work. **Qualif.:** Applicants must be legal residents of Quebec; must be university graduate students enrolled in a course of study related to children. **Criteria:** Selection will be based on academic merit. Preference will be given to the applicants' need and community involvement.

Funds Avail.: No specific amount. **To Apply:** Applicants must submit letter of acceptance to graduate or postgraduate studies in Montreal; letter of application outlining need and goals; transcripts of grades; proof of Quebec residency; two letters of recommendation from professors; Social

Insurance Number; and Montreal address and telephone number and email address. **Deadline:** May 1.

6299 ■ Musia & Leon Schwartz Scholarship
(Graduate/Scholarship)

Purpose: To support students involved in the humanities with a focus on tolerance and historical events, such as the Holocaust, and the resulting consequences. **Focus:** Humanities; Jewish studies. **Qualif.:** Applicants must be Quebec residents pursuing graduate degrees in studies related to the Holocaust. **Criteria:** Preference will be given to first time applicants.

Funds Avail.: No specific amount. **Duration:** Annual. **To Apply:** Application form and details are available online on March 1 of each year at: jcfmontreal.org/grants/scholarships/. **Deadline:** May 1.

6300 ■ Bernard Michael Tarshis Memorial Scholarship *(Undergraduate/Scholarship)*

Purpose: To assist students in their Jewish studies at McGill. **Focus:** Jewish studies. **Qualif.:** Applicants must be permanent residents of Quebec enrolled in Jewish Studies programs. **Criteria:** Selection will be based on the committee's criteria.

Funds Avail.: Up to $4,000 Canadian. **Duration:** Annual. **To Apply:** Application form and details are available online on March 1 of each year at: jcfmontreal.org/grants/scholarships/.

6301 ■ Dr. Steven S. Zalcman Memorial Scholarship *(Graduate, Postgraduate/Scholarship)*

Purpose: To support students in their specialization in behavioral neuroscience, neuroimmunology, psychoneuroimmunology, or a related field. **Focus:** Immunology; Neurology; Neuroscience. **Qualif.:** Applicants must be graduate or medical students who demonstrated interest in pursuing research in behavioral neuroscience, neuroimmunology, psychoneuroimmunology, or a related field.

Funds Avail.: $2,500 (postgraduate). **Duration:** Annual. **To Apply:** Applicants must submit the letter of application describing research intentions and any past or current research the applicants have undertaken; letters of reference from a research supervisor or a professor; university transcripts. **Deadline:** May 1.

6302 ■ Jewish Educators Assembly (JEA)
Broadway & Locust Ave.
Cedarhurst, NY 11516
Ph: (516)569-2537
Fax: (516)295-9039
E-mail: jewisheducators@aol.com
URL: jewisheducators.org
Social Media: twitter.com/JewishEducators

6303 ■ JEA Action Research Initiative *(Postgraduate/Grant)*

Purpose: To provide support for the development and implementation of groundbreaking projects in the field of Jewish education. **Focus:** Education; Jewish studies.

Funds Avail.: up to $1,000. **Duration:** Annual. **Deadline:** June 15. **Contact:** Jewish Educators Assembly; Email: jewisheducators@aol.com.

6304 ■ Jewish Foundation of Manitoba
123 Doncaster St., Ste. C400
Winnipeg, MB, Canada R3N 2B2

Awards are arranged alphabetically below their administering organizations

Ph: (204)477-7520
Fax: (204)477-7525
Free: 855-284-1918
E-mail: info@jewishfoundation.org
URL: www.jewishfoundation.org
Social Media: www.facebook.com/pages/Jewish
  -Foundation-of-Manitoba/395476260596175
instagram.com/jewishfoundationmb
twitter.com/jfm_mb
www.youtube.com/channel/UCO-yYko
  _mkABieBiVL4MbOA

6305 ■ Mark & Dorothy Danzker Scholarship
(Postgraduate/Scholarship)

Purpose: To support students pursuing their educational dreams. **Focus:** Jewish studies. **Qualif.:** Applicants must be full-time Jewish students entering or enrolled in a postgraduate degree program with preference given to persons studying at a Manitoba educational institution; must be residents of Manitoba. **Criteria:** Selection will be based on academic achievement, volunteer work in the Jewish community, volunteer work in the local community, and financial need.

Funds Avail.: $10,000. **Duration:** Annual. **Number Awarded:** 1. **To Apply:** Application must be completed online at www.jewishfoundation.org/scholarships/apply-for-a-scholarship. **Deadline:** February 28. **Contact:** Marla Aronovitch, Grants and Distributions officer; Email: scholarships@jewishfoundation.org.

6306 ■ Mona Gray Creative Arts Scholarship
(Graduate, Undergraduate/Scholarship)

Purpose: To support artist students pursuing undergraduate and graduate studies. **Focus:** Arts; Dance; Filmmaking; Music; Theater arts; Writing. **Qualif.:** Applicants must be Manitoba residents or former Manitobans who have been out of the province for no longer than four years; must be Bachelor's degree graduates or 3rd or 4th year undergraduates who are pursuing university degrees in one of the following areas: creative writing, film, fine arts, music, theatre, or dance. **Criteria:** Selection will based on artist achievement and/or merit, academic excellence, financial need, and community involvement and/or volunteerism.

Funds Avail.: $5,000. **Duration:** Annual. **Number Awarded:** 1. **To Apply:** Application must be completed online at www.jewishfoundation.org/scholarships/apply-for-a-scholarship. **Deadline:** February 28. **Contact:** Marla Aronovitch, Grants and Distributions officer; Email: scholarships@jewishfoundation.org.

6307 ■ Judaic Studies and/or Studies in Israel
(Undergraduate, Postgraduate/Scholarship)

Purpose: To give financial assistance to outstanding students who wish to pursue education in Judaic studies program in a university, college, or any educational institutions in Israel. **Focus:** Jewish studies. **Qualif.:** Applicants must be applying for, have been accepted into, or be continuing studies in a university, college, post-graduate or summer program in Judaic studies and/or an educational institution in Israel; must demonstrate to the selection committee that they are in need of financial assistance in order to pursue the program; and must have a minimum GPA of 2.0 or "C" average; must be a resident of Manitoba. **Criteria:** Selection will be based on financial need, academic achievement, involvement in the local community, volunteer work in the Jewish community, volunteer work in the

general community, and the nature and length of the program to which the applicants have applied or been accepted.

Funds Avail.: No specific amount. **Duration:** Annual. **To Apply:** Application must be completed online at www.jewishfoundation.org/scholarships/apply-for-a-scholarship. **Deadline:** March 31. **Contact:** Marla Aronovitch, Grants and Distributions officer, Phone: 204-480-7557; Toll Free: 855-284-1918; Email: scholarships@jewishfoundation.org.

6308 ■ Joel A. Weinstein Memorial Scholarship
(Postgraduate, Undergraduate/Scholarship)

Purpose: To support outstanding students attending or planning to attend an educational institution in Israel. **Focus:** Jewish studies. **Qualif.:** Applicants must be Jewish and residents of Manitoba applying or have been accepted into or continuing studies at University or College in Israel; must demonstrate to the selection committee a record of volunteer activity in the local community and specific plans for volunteer activity during the year of study in Israel. **Criteria:** Selection will be based on the committee's criteria.

Funds Avail.: $5,000. **Duration:** Annual. **Number Awarded:** 1. **To Apply:** Application must be completed online at www.jewishfoundation.org/scholarships/apply-for-a-scholarship. **Deadline:** February 28. **Contact:** Marla Aronovitch, Grants and Distributions officer, Phone: 204-480-7557; Toll Free: 855-284-1918; Email: scholarships@jewishfoundation.org.

6309 ■ Jewish Vocational Service (JVS)
216 W Jackson Blvd., Ste. 700
Chicago, IL 60606
Free: 855-463-6587
URL: jvschicago.org
Social Media: facebook.com/jvschicago
twitter.com/JVSChicago

6310 ■ Jewish Federation Academic Scholarship
(Graduate, Undergraduate/Scholarship)

Purpose: To support the education of a Jewish college or graduate student. **Focus:** Arts; Education; Law; Medicine; Public health; Social work; Urban affairs/design/planning. **Criteria:** Award will be given based on need.

Duration: Annual. **To Apply:** Applicant must submit a completed Application Data Form; Career Statement Form; Budget Worksheet; and Academic Budget form as an attachment. In addition, applicants must send by mail a Legal Domicility Form; two letter of reference form; IRS Forms; parents' or spouse's IRS; documentation of tuition cost; Release of Information form; and official transcripts. **Deadline:** February 1. **Contact:** Scholarship Administrator, JVS Chicago, 216 W Jackson Blvd., Ste. 700, Chicago, IL, 60606; Email: jvsscholarship@jvschicago.org; Fax: 312-553-5544; Phone: 316-733-444.

6311 ■ JMJ Phillip Group
755 W Big Beaver Rd., Ste. 2100
Troy, MI 48084
Fax: (413)677-6419
Free: 877-500-7762
E-mail: sales@jmjphillip.com
URL: jmjphillip.com
Social Media: www.facebook.com/jmjphillip

Awards are arranged alphabetically below their administering organizations

www.linkedin.com/company/jmj-phillip-group
twitter.com/jmjphillip

6312 ■ JMJ Phillip Group College Scholarships
(Graduate, University, Four Year College, Two Year College/Scholarship)

Purpose: To support students seeking STEM degrees and help to close the skill gap in the current American job market. **Focus:** Engineering; Mathematics and mathematical sciences; Science; Technology. **Qualif.:** Applicant must be an U.S.-based high school student who has been accepted to college or a student who is currently enrolled in a two- or four-year college or university in the United States; and must have a minimum 3.6 GPA. **Criteria:** Quality of essay.

Funds Avail.: $1,000. **Duration:** Quarterly. **Number Awarded:** 1. **To Apply:** Complete application online; submit a 500 to 1,000 word essay written in response to the prompt given on the website, along with a letter of reference from a current or former teacher or employer and transcripts. High school students must also submit a college acceptance letter. Applicants who do not win are eligible to reapply the following year. **Deadline:** January 1; April 1; July 1; September 1. **Contact:** E-mail: webaccts@jmjphillip.com; URL: jmjphillip.com/jmj-phillip-stem-scholarship/.

6313 ■ Jobable
21/F Cityplaza Three
14 Taikoo Wan Rd.
Taikoo
Hong Kong, Hong Kong, China
E-mail: info@aidsmemorial.org
URL: www.jobable.com
Social Media: www.facebook.com/jobableasia
www.instagram.com/jobable/
www.linkedin.com/company/jobable-com/
twitter.com/JobableAsia

6314 ■ Global Entrepreneur's Award *(High School, College/Award)*

Purpose: To help a high school or college student who wants to start their own online business. **Focus:** General studies/Field of study not specified. **Qualif.:** Applicant must be a high school or college student who wants to start their own online business. **Criteria:** Selection of winning submission is entirely at the discretion of Jobable.

Funds Avail.: $1,500. **Duration:** Biennial. **To Apply:** Applications available online at www.jobable.com/resources/scholarship. **Deadline:** December 23; May 10. **Contact:** URL: www.jobable.com/resources/scholarship-international.

6315 ■ Johns Hopkins Medicine - Department of Emergency Medicine
1830 East Monument St., Ste. 6-100
Baltimore, MD 21287
Ph: (410)955-8708
URL: www.hopkinsmedicine.org/emergencymedicine
Social Media: www.facebook.com/Johns.Hopkins.Medicine
www.linkedin.com/company/johns-hopkins-medicine
twitter.com/HopkinsMedicine

6316 ■ Johns Hopkins Department of Emergency Medicine Administration Fellowships *(Advanced Professional, Professional development/Fellowship)*

Purpose: To educate the next generation of business and operational leaders in Emergency Medicine. **Focus:** Emer-

gency and disaster services; Medicine. **Criteria:** Selection will be based on the committee's criteria.

Funds Avail.: No specific amount. **Duration:** Annual; one year. **Number Awarded:** 1. **To Apply:** Applicants must provide a personal statement, curriculum vitae and two letters of recommendation. **Contact:** James Scheulen, PA-C, MBA, Chief Administrative Officer; Email: scheule@jhmi.edu.

6317 ■ Johns Hopkins Medicine Disaster Fellowships *(Professional development/Fellowship)*

Purpose: To train academic and management leaders in disaster preparedness, response, and research. **Focus:** Emergency and disaster services. **Qualif.:** Applicants must be board certified or prepared in emergency medicine; ability to matriculate to the Bloomberg school of public health for a masters in public health degree; ability to obtain medical license in Maryland, USA; ability to obtain a clinical appointment at a Johns Hopkins hospital; fellows will successfully complete two months as teaching attending at the JHU over the two years; fellows will be expected to produce at least 1 peer reviewed research manuscript at completion of fellowship program. **Criteria:** Selection will be based on the committee's criteria.

Funds Avail.: No specific amount. **Duration:** Annual; two years. **Number Awarded:** 1. **To Apply:** Applicants should contact the fellowship director for more information and should provide personal statement and curriculum vitae (CV), and two letters of recommendation. **Contact:** Gabor D. Kelen, M.D., Director, Department of Emergency Medicine at gkelen@jhmi.edu.

6318 ■ Johns Hopkins Medicine Emergency Medical Services Fellowship *(Professional development/Fellowship)*

Purpose: To prepare highly qualified and motivated academic emergency physicians for leadership and medical oversight of pre- and out-of-hospital emergency care systems with advanced competencies in EMS system design, administration, and clinical care. **Focus:** Emergency and disaster services; Medicine. **Qualif.:** Applicants must successfully achieve all established educational milestones as delineated by the fellowship program; successful completion of an ACGME-accredited residency program in emergency medicine; fellows will be expected to complete a publishable research project under the guidance of a designated fellowship faculty mentor; ability to pass a criminal background check commensurate with institutional hiring policies; must have sychomotor skills necessary to function in pre- and out-of-hospital environments. **Criteria:** Selection will be based on the committee's criteria.

Funds Avail.: No specific amount. **Duration:** Annual; one year. **To Apply:** Applicants must contact the department for the application process; must include Curriculum vitae (C.V.); three letters of recommendation with at least one from an EMS faculty member and one from the chair of the department; personal statement discussing interest in EMS and current career goals. **Contact:** Asa Margolis, D.O., M.P.H., M.S., program director at amargol9@jhmi.edu.

6319 ■ Johns Hopkins Medicine International Emergency and Public Health Fellowships *(Graduate, Professional development/Fellowship)*

Purpose: To develop an area of expertise in public health and international emergency medicine for physicians interested in pursuing a career in global health research

Awards are arranged alphabetically below their administering organizations

and practice. **Focus:** Emergency and disaster services; Public health. **Qualif.:** Applicants must have graduate training in Emergency Medicine only; must produce at least 1 peer reviewed research manuscript at completion of fellowship program; must successfully complete an MPH degree at the Bloomberg School of Public Health; must successfully complete the two months as teaching attending at JHU over the two years. **Criteria:** Selection will be based on the committee's criteria.

Funds Avail.: No specific amount. **Duration:** Annual; two years. **To Apply:** Application materials may be submitted to the International Emergency Medicine Fellowship consortium website, however in addition a separate application must also be sent three letters of recommendation, personal statement, and curriculum vitae. **Deadline:** September 15.

6320 ■ Johns Hopkins Medicine Medical Education Fellowships (Professional development/Fellowship)

Purpose: To develop knowledge and expertise in the essential areas of medical education, including administration of Emergency Medicine residency programs and undergraduate medical education programs as well as educational skills and program design. **Focus:** Emergency and disaster services; Medicine. **Qualif.:** Applicants must be board prepared or certified in emergency medicine; understanding RRC and ACGME guidelines for residency. Understanding how to use simulation effectively in education. **Criteria:** Selection will be based on the committee's criteria.

Funds Avail.: No specific amount. **Duration:** Annual; one year. **To Apply:** Applicants should contact the fellowship director for more information and should provide personal statement, curriculum vitae, and two letters of recommendation. **Contact:** Linda Regan, MD, Program Director at lregan@jhmi.edu.

6321 ■ Johns Hopkins Medicine Observation Medicine Fellowships (Professional development/Fellowship)

Purpose: To produce innovative academic leaders of Acute Care Medicine. **Focus:** Medicine. **Qualif.:** Applicants must be board prepared or certified in emergency medicine; fellows will be required to work 800 clinical hours per academic year. **Criteria:** Selection will be based on the committee's criteria.

Funds Avail.: No specific amount. **Duration:** Annual; one year. **Number Awarded:** 1. **To Apply:** Applicants should contact the fellowship director for more information and should provide personal statement and curriculum vitae (CV), and two letters of recommendation. **Contact:** Peter Hill, MSc, MD, Vice Chair of Clinical Affairs at phill@jhmi.edu.

6322 ■ Johns Hopkins Medicine Research Fellowships (Professional development/Fellowship)

Purpose: To train physician scientists to become independent investigators and nationally recognized leaders in emergency medicine research. **Focus:** Emergency and disaster services; Medicine. **Criteria:** Selection will be based on the committee's criteria.

Funds Avail.: No specific amount. **Duration:** Annual; two years. **To Apply:** Applicants must provide a personal statement, curriculum vitae and two letters of recommendation. **Contact:** Richard Rothman, MD, PhD, Fellowship Director at rrothma1@jhmi.edu.

6323 ■ Johns Hopkins Medicine Ultrasound Fellowships (Professional development/Fellowship)

Purpose: To train leaders in Emergency Ultrasound with advanced knowledge and skills in ultrasound, and experience in ultrasound education, research, and administration. **Focus:** Emergency and disaster services; Medical laboratory technology. **Criteria:** Selection will be based on the committee's criteria.

Funds Avail.: No specific amount. **Duration:** Annual; one year or two years. **Number Awarded:** 1. **To Apply:** Applications can be submitted online; must include letter of interest, curriculum vitae, and 3 letters of recommendation. **Deadline:** November 14. **Contact:** Tiffany C. Fong, MD, Fellowship Director at tfong3@jhmi.edu.

6324 ■ Robert Wood Johnson Foundation (RWJF)
50 College Rd. E
Princeton, NJ 08540-6614
Ph: (609)627-6000
Free: 877-843-7953
E-mail: media@rwjf.org
URL: www.rwjf.org
Social Media: www.facebook.com/
  RobertWoodJohnsonFoundation
www.linkedin.com/company/robert-wood-johnson
  -foundation
twitter.com/rwjf
youtube.com/rwjfvideo

6325 ■ Clinical Scholars (Professional development/Scholarship)

Purpose: To integrate scholars' clinical expertise with training in program development and research methods to help them find solutions for the challenges posed by the U.S. health care system and the health of U.S. communities, as well as to augment clinical training of physicians by providing new skills and perspectives necessary to achieving leadership positions within and outside academia. **Focus:** Medical research. **Criteria:** Selected for this program will engage in: Personal, in-depth leadership training in health equity and community engagementCollaborative work across disciplines and professions to tackle problems that emerge from complex systems in communities.

Funds Avail.: $35,000 annually. **Duration:** Annual; Three-year fellowship. **Number Awarded:** up to 35 (in teams of three to five). **Deadline:** March 13. **Remarks:** Established in 1972. **Contact:** Phone: 919-843-3304; Email: clinical.scholars@unc.edu.

6326 ■ Robert Wood Johnson Foundation Health Policy Fellows (Advanced Professional, Professional development/Fellowship)

Purpose: To build and maintain a strong and diverse leadership and workforce in health and health care as well as to develop specific fields. **Focus:** Health care services; Health sciences. **Criteria:** Recipients will be selected based on the professional achievements; potential for leadership in health policy; potential for future growth and career advancement; and interpersonal and communication skills.

Funds Avail.: Amount varies. **Duration:** Annual. **Number Awarded:** Varies. **To Apply:** Applications must be submitted via MyRWJF, the RWJF online system. If the applicants have not already done so, they will be required to register

Awards are arranged alphabetically below their administering organizations

before they begin the application process. To complete and submit an online application, applicants must do the following: enter personal and contact information, including the names, phone numbers, and email addresses of three references who have been asked to comment on the applicants' qualifications for the program; select a preliminary sponsorship track indicating the source of sponsorship (Track 1: provide name of sponsoring institution and name of sponsoring institution's chief executive officer; or Track 2: request for stipend administration by the National Academy of Medicine (NAM); and, prepare in advance the following documents and save them to hard drive: an up-to-date curriculum vitae (no more than 5 pages); one-page biographical sketch (not the form submitted for the National Institutes of Health (NIH) grants, but an essay); and, two separate essays on the following topics: "The reasons you want to be an RWJF Health Policy Fellow, including a discussion of your major strengths and qualifications for the program and how this fellowship experience will fit with your career plans." (300 words); and, a "contemporary health policy topic" (250-500 words). **Remarks:** Established in 1973.

6327 ■ Robert Wood Johnson Health Policy Fellowships (Advanced Professional, Professional development/Fellowship)

Purpose: To develop the capacity of outstanding mid-career health professionals in academic and community-based settings to assume leadership roles in health policy and management. **Focus:** Health care services.

Funds Avail.: $165,000 each. **Duration:** Annual. **Number Awarded:** Up to 6. **To Apply:** Applications for the program must be submitted via the RWJF online system; hence, application is via online; to complete and submit an online application, applicants must do the following enter personal and contact information, as well as three letters of reference; select a preliminary sponsorship track indicating the source of sponsorship; and finally, prepare in advance the following documents and save them to a hard drive, (up-to-date curriculum vitae of no more than five pages); one-page biographical sketch; two essays in which the first is about the reasons why the applicants want to be Fellows (300 words), while the second is a contemporary health policy topic. **Remarks:** Established in 1973.

6328 ■ The Howard and Georgeanna Jones Foundation for Reproductive Medicine

1340 N Great Neck Rd., Ste. 1272-400
Virginia Beach, VA 23454-2268
Ph: (757)961-0222
Fax: (757)961-0223
URL: www.jonesfound.org
Social Media: www.facebook.com/
HowardandGeorgeannaJonesFoundation

6329 ■ Abby and Howard Milstein Innovation Award in Reproductive Medicine (Advanced Professional, Professional development, Graduate/Grant)

Purpose: To support innovative research project dedicated to attempting to identify the human fertilized egg that has pregnancy potential. **Focus:** Biomedical research; Medical research; Medicine. **Qualif.:** Must be working actively in areas related to reproductive medicine at an accredited medical school in the United States. **Criteria:** Selection will be based on the committee's criteria.

Funds Avail.: $200,000. **Duration:** Annual. **To Apply:** Application documents must include the title page including

applicant's name, title of proposal and name of sponsoring institution; letter from the applicants that contains statements asked by the Foundation; curriculum vitae of up to two pages; bibliography listing of peer-reviewed publications; letter of not more than two pages written by the Chair of the Department on behalf of the candidate; a written note from a funded mentor within the Institution; research proposal of no more than two pages; and budget justification. **Deadline:** September 30. **Contact:** Howard and Georgeanna Jones Foundation for Reproductive Medicine, Attn: Mary Davies, at the above address or Email: mary.davies@jonesfound.org.

6330 ■ Abby and Howard Milstein Reproductive Medicine Research Award (Advanced Professional, Professional development/Grant)

Purpose: To facilitate investigation into any aspect of reproductive medicine but preference will be given to investigations designed to improve the efficiency of in vitro fertilization. **Focus:** Biomedical research; Medical research; Medicine. **Qualif.:** Applicants must be working actively in areas related to reproductive medicine at an accredited medical school in the United States. **Criteria:** Selection will be given to those under the age of 45 with a rank of instructor or institutional equivalent up through associate professor.

Funds Avail.: $60,000. **Duration:** Annual. **Number Awarded:** 1. **To Apply:** Application documents must include the title page including name, title of proposal and name of sponsoring institution; letter from the applicants that contains statements asked by the Foundation; curriculum vitae of up to two pages; bibliography listing of peer-reviewed publications; letter of not more than two pages written by the Chair of the Department on behalf of the candidate; a written note from a funded mentor within the Institution; research proposal of no more than two pages; and budget justification. **Contact:** Howard and Georgeanna Jones Foundation for Reproductive Medicine, Attn: Mary Davies; 1340 N. Great Neck Road, Suite 1272-400, Virginia Beach, VA 23454; phone: 757-961-0222; fax: 757-961-0223; Email: mary.davies@jonesfound.org.

6331 ■ Young Investigators Achievement Award (Advanced Professional, Professional development, Graduate/Grant)

Purpose: To foster the career development of a young research investigator working in an approved fellowship program of reproductive medicine. **Focus:** Biomedical research; Medical research; Medicine. **Qualif.:** Applicants must be working actively in areas related to reproductive medicine at an accredited medical school in the United States. **Criteria:** Selection will be given to those under the age of 45 with a rank of instructor or institutional equivalent up through associate professor.

Funds Avail.: $60,000. **Duration:** Annual. **To Apply:** Application documents must include the title page including applicant's name, title of proposal and name of sponsoring institution; letter from the applicants that contains statements asked by the Foundation; curriculum vitae of up to two pages; bibliography listing of peer-reviewed publications; letter of not more than two pages written by the Chair of the Department on behalf of the candidate; a written note from a funded mentor within the Institution; research proposal of no more than two pages; and budget justification. **Deadline:** May 1. **Contact:** Howard and Georgeanna Jones Foundation for Reproductive Medicine, Attn: Mary Davies, 1340 N. Great Neck Road, Suite 1272-400, Virginia

Awards are arranged alphabetically below their administering organizations

Beach, VA 23454; Phone: 757-961-0222; Fax: 757-961-0223; Email: mary.davies@jonesfound.org.

6332 ■ Journalism Association of Community Colleges (JACC)

c/o CNPA Services Inc.
2701 K St.
Sacramento, CA 95816-5131
Fax: (916)288-6002
E-mail: jaccpayment@gmail.com
URL: jacconline.org
Social Media: www.facebook.com/jaccfb
twitter.com/jaccnews

6333 ■ Warren Mack Scholarship *(Undergraduate/Scholarship)*

Purpose: To support the education of journalism students. **Focus:** Journalism. **Qualif.:** Applicants must be either transfer or continuing journalism students. **Criteria:** Selection will be based on the credentials of the applicants and of the applications required.

Funds Avail.: $750 each. **Duration:** Annual. **Number Awarded:** 2. **To Apply:** Applicants must submit the following in one application packet: a cover sheet/form; transcript (may be unofficial); letter of recommendation from the applicants' adviser; a maximum of one page personal statement explaining what the applicants have gained from their journalistic experience, their hopes for a future in journalism, and any special circumstances regarding their background or status; a list of journalism-related experiences other than their community college work (dates and brief descriptions of volunteer or paid work): a list of non-journalism activities and involvements (dates and brief descriptions). **Contact:** Scholarship Chair Erin Hiro, via e-mail at ehiro@palomar.edu.

6334 ■ Art Margosian Scholarship *(Undergraduate/Scholarship)*

Purpose: To support the education of journalism students. **Focus:** Journalism. **Qualif.:** Applicants must be journalism students. **Criteria:** Selection will be based on the credentials of the applicants and of the applications required.

Funds Avail.: $750 each. **Duration:** Annual. **Number Awarded:** 2. **To Apply:** Applicants must complete and submit the application form including all required documents. **Contact:** Scholarship Chair Erin Hiro, via e-mail at ehiro@palomar.edu.

6335 ■ Journalism Education Association (JEA)

105 Kedzie Hall
828 Mid-Campus Dr. S
Manhattan, KS 66506-1505
Ph: (785)532-5532
Free: 866-532-5532
E-mail: staff@jea.org
URL: www.jea.org
Social Media: www.facebook.com/journalismeducation
twitter.com/nationalJEA

6336 ■ JEA Future Journalism Teacher Scholarships *(Undergraduate, Master's/Scholarship)*

Purpose: To support education majors who intend to teach scholastic journalism. **Focus:** Journalism. **Qualif.:** Applicant must be a college junior, senior or master's degree student in a program designed to prepare for secondary-school level teaching; current secondary-school journalism teachers who are in a degree program to improve their journalism teaching skills. **Criteria:** Selection will be based on the committee of teachers and university personnel involved in journalism teacher education.

Funds Avail.: $1,000 each. **Duration:** Annual. **Number Awarded:** 5. **To Apply:** Applicants must complete the application and include the following: 250-word essay explaining their desire to teach high school journalism; answers to the three questions provided at the bottom of the application form; two recommendation letters, preferably from those who have firsthand knowledge of their work with student journalists; and college transcript(s) showing academic standing. **Deadline:** July 15. **Contact:** Candace Perkins Bowen; Phone: 303-672-8297; E-mail: cbowen@kent.edu.

6337 ■ Journalist of the Year Scholarships *(Undergraduate/Monetary, Scholarship)*

Purpose: To recognize some of the top high school journalists in the country. **Focus:** Journalism.

Funds Avail.: $3,000 - 1st place; $850 - runners-up. **Duration:** Annual. **Number Awarded:** 7 (1st place and 6 runners-up). **Deadline:** March 15. **Contact:** Email to rebecca_pollard@lovejoyisd.net.

6338 ■ JPGtoPDF.com

57 4th St., Unit B
Somerville, NJ 08876
Ph: (307)459-1224
Fax: (514)635-6127
URL: www.jpgtopdf.com

6339 ■ JPGtoPDF College Scholarship *(Undergraduate, Graduate/Scholarship)*

Purpose: To support the education of college students. **Focus:** General studies/Field of study not specified. **Qualif.:** Applicant can be any student enrolled at an accredited college or university.

Funds Avail.: $1,000. **Number Awarded:** 1. **To Apply:** Applicant must convert 5 pictures to a single PDF file using JPGtoPDF.com and submit the download link with a note saying that you are giving us permission to publish your pictures on our website; 2) share JPGtoPDF.com on one of your social media and send us a screenshot and link to your profile. **Deadline:** June 30. **Contact:** E-mail: scholarship@jpgtopdf.com.

6340 ■ JuicingBeasts.com

285 -287, Jalan Tuanku Abdul Rahman
50100 Kuala Lumpur, Selangor, Malaysia
Ph: 60 860 506 5173
URL: juicingbeasts.com

6341 ■ JuicingBeasts Staying Healthy Scholarship *(Undergraduate, Graduate/Scholarship)*

Purpose: To promote awareness in the need to stay healthy. **Focus:** General studies/Field of study not specified. **Qualif.:** Open to any undergraduate or postgraduate. **Criteria:** Applicants should have a passion for keeping healthy.

Funds Avail.: $500. **Duration:** Annual. **Number Awarded:** 1. **To Apply:** Applicant must submit an essay (800-1,000

Awards are arranged alphabetically below their administering organizations

words); essays must be 100% original. Each essay will be checked for plagiarism; should only be written in English; submit essay in Microsoft word document; include your contact information in the document. **Deadline:** October 31. **Contact:** E-mail: scholarships@juicingbeasts.com.

6342 ■ Junior Achievement (JA)

1 Education Way
Colorado Springs, CO 80906
Ph: (719)540-8000
E-mail: newmedia@ja.org
URL: jausa.ja.org
Social Media: www.facebook.com/JuniorAchievementUSA
www.instagram.com/juniorachievementusa
www.linkedin.com/company/junior-achievement-usa
www.pinterest.com/juniorachievementusa
twitter.com/JA_USA
www.youtube.com/c/JuniorAchievementUSA

6343 ■ The Joe Francomano Scholarship
(Undergraduate/Scholarship)

Purpose: To allow educational advancements by providing financial assistance. **Focus:** General studies/Field of study not specified.

Deadline: April 11.

6344 ■ Junior Service League of LaGrange, Inc.

PO Box 2195
Lagrange, GA 30241
E-mail: info@jsloflagrange.com
URL: jsloflagrange.com
Social Media: www.facebook.com/jsloflagrange

6345 ■ Mollie Lukken Memorial Scholarship *(Graduate, Other/Scholarship)*

Purpose: To help teachers provide a specialized education for students with learning disabilities. **Focus:** Education, Special. **Qualif.:** Applicants must be qualified teachers in Troup County enrolled in a college/university program pursuing graduate studies in the field of special education interrelated education. **Criteria:** Selection will be based on the evaluation of submitted documents and specific criteria.

Funds Avail.: More than $39,000. **Duration:** Annual. **To Apply:** Applicants must submit a completed application form; evidence of enrollment in a college/university program pursuing a degree in Special Education; evidence of the cost of the program; three recommendation letters; one-page, typed essay detailing interest, experience and plans in the field of special education - interrelated education. **Remarks:** Established in 1984. **Contact:** Junior Service League, Attention: Mollie Lukken Scholarship Committee, at the above address.

6346 ■ Juvenile Diabetes Research Foundation International (JDRF)

26 Broadway, 14th Floor Conference Rooms AB
New York, NY 10004
Fax: (212)785-9595
Free: 800-533-2873
E-mail: info@jdrf.org
URL: www.jdrf.org
Social Media: twitter.com/JDRF

www.youtube.com/c/jdrf?_ga=2.99259158.965345820
.1597720624-1129162128.1597720624

6347 ■ Early-Career Patient-Oriented Diabetes Research Awards *(Professional development/Award)*

Purpose: To provide crucial support to investigators who plan to pursue a career in diabetes-related clinical investigation. **Focus:** Diabetes.

Duration: Five years.

6348 ■ Innovative Grants-Pilot and Research Tool Grants *(Postdoctorate/Grant)*

Purpose: To support proposals for highly innovative research with significant potential to accelerate the mission of JDRF. **Focus:** Diabetes. **Qualif.:** Applicants must hold an MD, DMD, DVM, PhD or equivalent and have a faculty position or equivalent at a college, university, medical school, or other research facility; to assure continued excellence and diversity among applicants and awardees, JDRF welcomes proposals from all qualified individuals and encourages proposals from persons with disabilities, women and member of minority groups underrepresented in the sciences. **Criteria:** Selection will be competitive and performed by an appropriate review panel convened by JDRF; proposals will be evaluated in accordance with the following criteria: innovation, potential impact and relevance to JDRF goals; feasibility of experimental approach and completing in one year; clarity of proposed objectives; qualifications and research experience of the principal investigators and collaborators; availability of resources and facilities necessary for the project; appropriateness of the proposed budget in relation to the proposed research; for the research tool proposals, demonstrable need for the novel reagents/tools.

Funds Avail.: $110,000. **To Apply:** Applicants must visit the website to create a proposalCENTRAL (pC) account; after creating an account, applicants must select the appropriate application from the list of JDRF funding opportunities to gain access to the application template; must complete each of the proposal sections listed in the menu on the left side of the screen and must limit the file size of each uploaded attachment to 3-4 MB.

6349 ■ Advanced Postdoctoral Fellowships *(Postdoctorate, Master's/Fellowship)*

Purpose: To attract qualified, promising scientists to receive full-time research training and to assist these promising individuals in transitioning from a fellowship to an independent (faculty-level) position. **Focus:** Diabetes. **Qualif.:** Applicant must be an MD, DMD, DVM, PhD, or equivalent scholar; must not be simultaneously serving an internship or residency. **Criteria:** Selection will be based on the committee criteria.

Duration: Three years. **Number Awarded:** Varies.

6350 ■ Career Development Awards *(Professional development, Postdoctorate/Grant, Award)*

Purpose: To attract qualified and promising scientists early in their faculty careers and to give them the opportunity to establish themselves in areas that reflect the JDRF research emphasis areas. **Focus:** Diabetes.

Duration: Five years. **Number Awarded:** 1.

6351 ■ JDRF Postdoctoral Fellowships
(Postdoctorate/Fellowship)

Purpose: To support qualified, promising scientists entering their professional career in the T1D research field. **Focus:** Diabetes.

Awards are arranged alphabetically below their administering organizations

Duration: Annual. **Number Awarded:** 1.

6352 ■ JW Surety Bonds

6023A Kellers Church Rd.
Pipersville, PA 18947
Free: 888-592-6631
E-mail: info@jwsuretybonds.com
URL: www.jwsuretybonds.com
Social Media: www.facebook.com/JWSuretyBonds
www.linkedin.com/company/jw-surety-bonds
twitter.com/jw_surety_bonds

6353 ■ JW Surety Bonds Scholarships *(Undergraduate, Graduate/Scholarship)*

Purpose: To aid students and prospective students who demonstrate creativity and talent in their respective fields of study. **Focus:** General studies/Field of study not specified. **Qualif.:** Applicants must be college students, or prospective college students, planning to attend an accredited U.S. institution. **Criteria:** Selection is based on their submitted entries. Entries are judged based on creativity, professionalism, and accuracy.

Funds Avail.: $1,000. **Duration:** Annual. **Number Awarded:** 1. **To Apply:** Applicants must submit their respective entries (in the form of articles, videos, slideshows or infographics) through email. **Deadline:** September 30. **Contact:** scholarship@jwsuretybonds.com.

6354 ■ Kaiser Family Foundation (KFF)

185 Berry St.
San Francisco, CA 94107
Ph: (650)854-9400
Fax: (650)854-4800
URL: kff.org
Social Media: www.facebook.com/pg/
 KaiserFamilyFoundation
twitter.com/KaiserFamFound

6355 ■ Kaiser Media Fellowships in Health Reporting *(Advanced Professional, Professional development/ Fellowship)*

Purpose: To encourage print, broadcast and online journalists to pursue an area of interest in U.S. health policy issues. **Focus:** Editors and editing; Health education; Journalism.

Funds Avail.: No specific amount. **Duration:** Annual. **Remarks:** Established in 2011.

6356 ■ Kaiser Permanente - Division of Research

2000 Broadway
Oakland, CA 94612
Ph: (510)891-3400
URL: www.dor.kaiser.org/external/dorexternal/index.aspx

6357 ■ Kaiser Permanente Northern California Delivery Science Fellowship Program *(Postgraduate/ Fellowship)*

Purpose: To support the ongoing improvement of the Kaiser Permanente health care system, as well as the US health care system; to help highly qualified researchers pursue successful research careers in delivery science. **Focus:** Health care services. **Qualif.:** Applicants must be health professional doctorate degrees (MD, DO, PharmD, Nursing PhD) and/or research doctorate degrees (PhD, ScD, DrPH) in related fields; must be eligible for U.S. employment; women and minority candidates are encouraged to apply.

To Apply: Applicants must submit curriculum vitae; personal statement, limited to two pages, explaining career goals, how the fellowship program would further these goals, and the type of research questions; writing sample of a first-authored publication is strongly recommended; please list 3 persons for reference and their positions and institutions; reference letters should by sent by mail directly to author. **Deadline:** September 17. **Contact:** Karen Estacio; Phone: 510-891-5960; Email: dor-fellowship@kp.org.

6358 ■ Kansas Association of Broadcasters (KAB)

214 SW 6th Ave., Ste. 300
Topeka, KS 66603
Ph: (785)235-1307
E-mail: kent@kab.net
URL: www.kab.net
Social Media: facebook.com/
 KansasAssociationOfBroadcasters

6359 ■ Kansas Association of Broadcasters Scholarships *(Undergraduate/Scholarship)*

Purpose: To support potential and commitment in promising future broadcasters. **Focus:** Broadcasting.

Funds Avail.: Up to $16,000. **Duration:** Annual. **To Apply:** Applicants must submit a completed application form. **Deadline:** May 1. **Contact:** Scholarship Committee, Kansas Association of Broadcasters, 214 SW 6th St., Ste. 300, Topeka, KS, 66603.

6360 ■ Kansas Board of Regents (KBOR)

1000 SW Jackson St., Ste. 520
Topeka, KS 66612-1368
Ph: (785)430-4240
E-mail: scholars@ksbor.org
URL: www.kansasregents.org

6361 ■ James B. Pearson Fellowship *(Graduate/ Scholarship)*

Purpose: To encourage students from Kansas public universities to experience global perspective gained from study abroad. **Focus:** International affairs and relations. **Qualif.:** Applicants must be graduate students from Kansas public universities and whose studies are directly related to foreign affairs. **Criteria:** Applicants whose studies are directly related to foreign affairs.

Funds Avail.: $2,445. **Duration:** Annual. **To Apply:** Application will be submit online. **Deadline:** April 17.

6362 ■ Kansas Dental Education Opportunities Program *(Graduate/Scholarship)*

Purpose: To encourage dentists to establish Kansas practices. **Focus:** Dentistry. **Qualif.:** Applicants must be Kansas residents who are graduate level dentistry students. **Funds Avail.:** No specific amount. **Duration:** Annual.

6363 ■ Kansas Distinguished Scholarship Program *(Graduate/Scholarship)*

Purpose: To encourage students to continue graduate studies at Kansas public universities. **Focus:** General

Awards are arranged alphabetically below their administering organizations

studies/Field of study not specified. **Qualif.:** Applicants must be Kansas residents who are Brasenose, Clevening, Fulbright, Madison, Marshall, Mellon, Rhodes and Truman scholars.

Funds Avail.: No specific amount. **Duration:** Annual. **To Apply:** Interested applicants may contact Kansas Board of Regents for further details. **Contact:** Submissions must be sent to the following Committee Members: Kansas Board of Regents, KS Osteopathic Medical Service Scholarship, 1000 SW Jackson St., Ste. 520, Topeka, KS, 66612-1368; Phone: 785-430-4255; Email: loldhamburns@ksbor.org; Bob Williams, Executive Director, Kansas Association of Osteopathic Medicine, 1260 SW Topeka Blvd., 1260 SW Topeka Blvd., Phone: 785-234-5563; Email: bob@kansasdo.org.

6364 ■ Kansas Nurse Educator Service Scholarship
(Graduate/Scholarship)

Purpose: To encourage students who agree to teach in a nurse education program at a Kansas postsecondary educational institution. **Focus:** Nursing. **Qualif.:** Applicants must be Kansas residents and graduate level nursing students.

Funds Avail.: No specific amount. **Duration:** Annual. **To Apply:** Applicants must complete the online form and mail the State of Kansas Student Aid application.

6365 ■ Kansas Optometry Service Scholarship
(Graduate, Undergraduate/Scholarship)

Purpose: To encourage optometrists to establish a Kansas practice. **Focus:** Optometry. **Qualif.:** Applicants must be designed to encourage optometrists to establish Kansas practices; must Kansas helps to pay the difference between resident and nonresident tuition at eligible out-of-state institutions. **Criteria:** Selection will be based on academic considerations and Kansas residency.

Funds Avail.: No specific amount. **Duration:** Annual. **Number Awarded:** Varies. **To Apply:** Applicants must submit a completed application form. **Deadline:** May 1. **Contact:** Kansas Board of Regents, Kansas Optometry Service Scholarship, 1000 SW Jackson St., Ste. 520, Topeka, KS 66612-1368; Email: loldhamburns@ksbor.org.

6366 ■ Kansas Osteopathic Medical Service Scholarship *(Graduate, Other/Scholarship)*

Purpose: To encourage doctors to establish practices in rural areas of Kansas. **Focus:** Medicine, Osteopathic.

Funds Avail.: $15,000 per year. **Duration:** Annual; up to four years. **Number Awarded:** Varies. **To Apply:** Applicants must submit a completed scholarship application form; one-page statement of purpose; signed copy of Student Aid Report; copy of the most recent federal income tax return. **Deadline:** May 1. **Contact:** Bob Williams, Exec. Dir.; Address: 1260 SW Topeka Blvd., Topeka, KS 66612-1889; Phone: 785-234-5563; Email: bob@kansasdo.org.

6367 ■ Kansas Health Information Management Association (KHIMA)
301 S Estates
Salina, KS 67401
E-mail: annnowlin3@gmail.com
URL: www.khima.com
Social Media: facebook.com/KHIMA-Kansas-Health
  -Information-Management-Association-2005823166354466
www.linkedin.com/company/kansas-health-information
  -management-association

twitter.com/KHIMA_Kansas

6368 ■ Karen Schuvie Scholarship *(Undergraduate/Scholarship, Loan)*

Purpose: To provide financial assistance to students pursuing their potential as Health Information Management professionals. **Focus:** Health education. **Criteria:** Selection is based on submitted application materials.

Funds Avail.: No specific amount. **Duration:** Annual. **Number Awarded:** 1. **To Apply:** Applicants must complete the application form; must submit the verification of enrollment form and references to the Recognition Committee Chairperson; must have two letters of recommendation submitted by an employer, academic counselor, directed practice supervisor or professional contact. **Deadline:** October 31. **Remarks:** Established in 1986.

6369 ■ KHIMA Graduate Scholarship *(Graduate/Scholarship)*

Purpose: To provide financial assistance to students pursuing their education as Health Information Management professionals. **Focus:** Health education.

Funds Avail.: No specific amount. **Duration:** Annual. **Number Awarded:** 1. **To Apply:** Applicants must complete the application form; must submit the verification of enrollment form and references to the Recognition Committee Chairperson; must have two letters of recommendation submitted by an employer, academic counselor, directed practice supervisor or professional contact. **Deadline:** October 31.

6370 ■ Sue A. Malone Scholarship *(Doctorate, Graduate, Professional development/Scholarship)*

Purpose: To provide scholarship funds for professional enhancement of Health Information Management professionals. **Focus:** Health education; Health sciences.

Funds Avail.: No specific amount. **Duration:** Annual. **Number Awarded:** 1. **To Apply:** Applicants must complete the application form; must submit the verification of enrollment form and references to the Recognition Committee chairperson; must have two letters of recommendation submitted by an employer, academic counselor, directed practice supervisor or professional contact. **Deadline:** October 31. **Remarks:** Established in 1995.

6371 ■ Kansas Native Plant Society (KNPS)
University of Kansas
R.L. McGregor Herbarium
2045 Constant Ave.
Lawrence, KS 66047-3729
URL: www.kansasnativeplantsociety.org

6372 ■ Mary A. Bancroft Memorial Scholarship *(Graduate/Scholarship)*

Purpose: To support a graduate student research that enhances the understanding of native plant species or their ecosystems and conservation. **Focus:** Botany. **Qualif.:** Applicants must be graduate students regularly enrolled in a Kansas college or university; proposals must be technically sound and directly applicable to our priorities in Kansas. **Criteria:** Selection was based on KNPS awards committee.

Funds Avail.: $1,000. **Duration:** Annual. **Number Awarded:** Varies. **To Apply:** Applicants should submit project description, budget, time line, career goals, personal statement, two letters of support, college transcript. **Dead-

Awards are arranged alphabetically below their administering organizations

line: March 15. **Remarks:** The scholarship was established in honor of the late Mary A. Bancroft, a long-time member and supporter of the KNPS from Ottawa, Kansas. Established in 1998.

6373 ■ Kansas State University

1800 College Ave.
Manhattan, KS 66502
Ph: (785)532-6011
URL: k-state.edu
Social Media: www.facebook.com/Kstate
twitter.com/Kstate
www.youtube.com/user/Kstate

6374 ■ Kansas State University Cancer Research Award Program *(Undergraduate/Grant)*

Purpose: To provide research opportunities to undergraduates involved in laboratory research. **Focus:** Medical research; Oncology. **Qualif.:** Applicants must be undergraduate students.

Funds Avail.: $1,000. **Duration:** Annual. **Deadline:** October 1.

6375 ■ Kaplan Lawyers PC

6901 Jericho Tpke., Ste. 100
Syosset, NY 11791
Ph: (516)399-2364
E-mail: info@kaplanlawyers.com
URL: www.kaplanlawyers.com
Social Media: www.facebook.com/pages/Kaplan-Lawyers
  -PC/669628723082545
www.linkedin.com/company/kaplan-lawyers-pc
twitter.com/KaplanLawyersPC
www.youtube.com/channel/UCl3s0DT3Oz_JRmqY8IQ5l9Q

6376 ■ Kaplan Lawyers PC Legal Scholarships *(Graduate/Scholarship)*

Purpose: To encourage and award creative authorship. **Focus:** Law. **Qualif.:** Applicants must be U.S. citizens or be authorized to work/attend school in the United States; must be commencing Law School (1L) in fall of the current year. **Criteria:** Selection will be based on the creativity, originality, and ability to relay a message of the published article.

Funds Avail.: $1,000. **To Apply:** Applicants must submit a completed scholarship application form, copy of law school acceptance letter, and essay of their choice.

6377 ■ Kappa Delta Pi (KDP)

3707 Woodview Trace
Indianapolis, IN 46268
Ph: (317)871-4900
Fax: (317)704-2323
Free: 800-284-3167
E-mail: pubs@kdp.org
URL: www.kdp.org
Social Media: www.facebook.com/KDPhome
instagram.com/kappadeltapi
www.linkedin.com/company/779557
pinterest.com/kappadeltapi
twitter.com/kappadeltapi

6378 ■ Louise Berman Fellows Award *(Graduate, Master's, Doctorate/Fellowship)*

Purpose: To advance curriculum, drive creative inquiry into the human condition, collaborate on cross-national education projects and encourage personal growth. **Focus:** Education--Curricula. **Qualif.:** Applicants must be graduate students at the master's and doctorate levels, as well as to practicing educators at all levels. **Criteria:** Selection will be based on the committee's criteria.

Funds Avail.: $1,200 - $1,800. **Duration:** Annual. **To Apply:** Applicants must submit a completely answered application form; submit a current resume or vita; submit an approved program prospectus or course of study. **Deadline:** August 1.

6379 ■ Dr. Stephen J. Fortgang / University of Northern Iowa Chapter Scholarship *(Undergraduate/ Scholarship)*

Purpose: To honor and encourage undergraduate Kadelpians who show signs of mastering pedagogy, but most particularly possess a vital love of knowledge and its centrality to developing educated people and an enlightened democratic citizenry through great teaching. **Focus:** Education; Liberal arts. **Qualif.:** Applicants must be undergraduate students; open to all KDP members. **Criteria:** Selection will be based on the committee's criteria.

Funds Avail.: $2,000. **Duration:** Annual. **Number Awarded:** 1. **To Apply:** Applicants must submit an essay of no more than 750 words, 3, 800 characters, addressing the importance of coherent content planning to ensure excellent teaching in the particular areas of concentration. **Deadline:** May 1.

6380 ■ Donna Gail Scholarship for Chapter Service *(Undergraduate, Graduate, Doctorate/Scholarship)*

Purpose: To support students who demonstrated financial need. **Focus:** Education; Teaching. **Qualif.:** Applicants must be undergraduate, graduate or doctoral students or practicing K-12 educator in the first three years of teaching. **Criteria:** Selection will be based on the committee's criteria.

Funds Avail.: $1,000. **Duration:** Annual. **Number Awarded:** 1. **To Apply:** Applicants are required to write and submit an essay on the topic what is the role of service in becoming a professional educator; essay must contain no more than 750 words limited to 3800 characters; must also provide a description of their service to the chapter, community and profession, and how their service made a difference. **Deadline:** May 1.

6381 ■ Harold D. Drummond Scholarships *(Undergraduate, Graduate/Scholarship)*

Purpose: To support and enhance the professional growth and teaching practices of member educators throughout the phases and levels of their teaching careers. **Focus:** Education, Elementary. **Qualif.:** Applicants must be undergraduate or graduate students in Elementary Education. **Criteria:** Selection will be based on the committee's criteria.

Funds Avail.: $750. **Duration:** Annual. **Number Awarded:** 2. **To Apply:** Applicants must submit an essay of no more than 750 words, 3, 800 characters, on the topic what life experiences have led applicant to study education and how will those experiences influence your role as an elementary educator; Statement of financial need must also be attached. **Deadline:** May 1.

Awards are arranged alphabetically below their administering organizations

6382 ■ J. Everett and Louise Light Scholarships
(Undergraduate, Graduate/Scholarship)

Purpose: To support KDP members who have demonstrated financial need. **Focus:** Education, Special. **Qualif.:** Applicants must be undergraduate, graduate or doctoral students in Special Education. **Criteria:** Selection will be based on the committee's criteria.

Funds Avail.: $750. **Duration:** Annual. **Number Awarded:** 1. **To Apply:** Applicants must complete and submit their application together with the following documents: essay or research paper covering the specific topic required for the scholarship that the applicants applying for; reference letter from the correct individual required by this scholarship program; transcript; program prospectus or course of study; curriculum vitae or resume for doctoral members; explanation of scholarship use; statement of financial need; description of service. **Deadline:** May 1.

6383 ■ J. Jay Hostetler Scholarship *(Undergraduate/ Scholarship)*

Purpose: To support and enhance the professional growth and teaching practices of member educators throughout the phases and levels of their teaching careers. **Focus:** Teaching. **Qualif.:** Applicants must be undergraduate student teachers. **Criteria:** Selection will be based on the committee's criteria.

Funds Avail.: $500. **Duration:** Annual. **Number Awarded:** 2. **To Apply:** Applicants are required to write an essay that portrays their personal vision as educators and how their student teaching experience influenced their future career goals; essay must contain no more than 750 words limited to 3800 characters. **Deadline:** May 1.

6384 ■ KDP Huntington Bank Scholarship
(Undergraduate/Scholarship)

Purpose: To support and enhance the professional growth and teaching practices of member educators throughout the phases and levels of their teaching careers. **Focus:** Education. **Qualif.:** Applicants must be undergraduate students in education major with Pre-K to 12 emphasis and be residents of Indiana or Ohio. **Criteria:** Selection will be based on the committee's criteria.

Funds Avail.: $750. **Duration:** Annual. **Number Awarded:** 1. **To Apply:** Applicants are required to submit an essay that reflects their reasons for wanting to be a teacher and indicate what professional challenges they expect to face upon the completion of their degree. **Deadline:** May 1.

6385 ■ KDP International Scholarship Program - President Scholarship *(Undergraduate, Graduate, Doctorate/Scholarship)*

Purpose: To support students who demonstrated financial needs. **Focus:** Education; Leadership, Institutional and community. **Qualif.:** Applicants must be undergraduate, graduate, doctoral students or practicing educator dedicated to leadership and service in Kappa Delta Pi. **Criteria:** Selection will be based on the committee's criteria.

Funds Avail.: $750. **Duration:** Annual. **Number Awarded:** 1. **To Apply:** Applicants are required to write and submit an essay on the topic what are your professional and personal reasons in seeking leadership and service opportunities in Kappa Delta Pi; how have your academic program and experience prepared you for such an endeavor; essay must contain no more than 750 words limited to 3800 characters. **Deadline:** May 1.

6386 ■ KDP MBNA Scholarships *(Undergraduate, Graduate/Scholarship)*

Purpose: To support students who demonstrated financial need. **Focus:** Education, Special. **Qualif.:** Applicants must be undergraduate or graduate students in special education. **Criteria:** Selection will be based on the committee's criteria.

Funds Avail.: $750. **Duration:** Annual. **Number Awarded:** 1. **To Apply:** Applicants are required to write and submit an essay on the following topic what are the challenges facing teachers working with special needs students; essay must contain no more than 750 words limited to 3800 characters. **Deadline:** May 1.

6387 ■ Dr. Eva Kleinpeter Scholarship
(Undergraduate/Scholarship)

Purpose: To support and enhance the professional growth and teaching practices of member educators throughout the phases and levels of their teaching careers. **Focus:** Education, Elementary. **Qualif.:** Applicants must be undergraduate students in Elementary Education. **Criteria:** Selection will be based on the committee's criteria.

Funds Avail.: $750. **Duration:** Annual. **Number Awarded:** 2. **To Apply:** Applicants must submit a briefly described essay on how they are prepared to address the philosophy, content, principles, goals, objectives and skills of the Common Core Standards and how they plan to implement the standards using the best practices and technology for addressing the learning styles of each student. **Deadline:** May 1.

6388 ■ Louisa Anne Oriente Scholarship *(Graduate, Doctorate/Scholarship)*

Purpose: To support students who demonstrated financial need. **Focus:** Education--Curricula; Teaching. **Qualif.:** Applicants must be graduate students in curriculum and teaching. **Criteria:** Selection will be based on the committee's criteria.

Funds Avail.: $750. **Duration:** Annual. **Number Awarded:** 1. **To Apply:** Applicants are required to write and submit an essay with a topic what challenging demands and opportunities of the 21st century make a graduate degree program in the practices and policies of curriculum and teaching desirable; essay must contain no more than 750 words limited to 3800 characters. **Deadline:** May 1.

6389 ■ Marsh Writing/Research Scholarship Awards *(Undergraduate, Graduate, Doctorate/Scholarship)*

Purpose: To support students who demonstrated financial need. **Focus:** Education. **Qualif.:** Applicants must be undergraduate and graduate students who write research papers based on issues that affect teachers and learning. **Criteria:** Papers will be considered on the basis of the following criteria: significant topic; adequacy and appropriateness of methodology; writing clarity; potential contribution to the field.

Funds Avail.: $750. **Duration:** Annual. **Number Awarded:** 1. **To Apply:** Applicants must submit a completed research paper as part of an undergraduate or graduate program in a recognized school or college of education; Individuals may nominate their own papers, or nominations may be made by advisers, department chairs, Deans, KDP Chapters Counselors or Chapter Presidents; each nomination must include a completed application. **Deadline:** May 1.

6390 ■ Linda and Vincent McGrath Scholarship
(Undergraduate/Scholarship)

Purpose: To support and enhance the professional growth and teaching practices of member educators throughout

Awards are arranged alphabetically below their administering organizations

the phases and levels of their teaching careers. **Focus:** Education, Elementary. **Qualif.:** Applicants must be undergraduate students in Elementary Education. **Criteria:** Selection will be based on the committee's criteria.

Funds Avail.: $500. **Duration:** Annual. **Number Awarded:** 1. **To Apply:** Applicants are required to submit an essay that reflects their reasons for wanting to be elementary teachers; and indicate what professional challenges they expect to face upon the completion of their degree. **Deadline:** May 1.

6391 ■ Nicholas H. Noyes, Jr. Scholarship
(Undergraduate/Scholarship)

Purpose: To support and enhance the professional growth and teaching practices of member educators throughout the phases and levels of their teaching careers. **Focus:** Education. **Qualif.:** Applicants must be undergraduate students in Education residing in Marion County, Indiana and attending a college or university in Indiana. **Criteria:** Selection will be based on the committee's criteria.

Funds Avail.: $500. **Duration:** Annual. **Number Awarded:** 1. **To Apply:** Applicants must provide an essay that reflects their reasons for wanting to be a teacher and indicate what professional challenges they expect to face upon the completion of their degree; essay must contain no more than 750 words limited to 3800 characters. **Deadline:** May 1.

6392 ■ Jerry Robbins Scholarship *(Undergraduate/Scholarship)*

Purpose: To support and enhance the professional growth and teaching practices of member educators throughout the phases and levels of their teaching careers. **Focus:** Education, Music. **Qualif.:** Applicants must be students in instrumental music education. **Criteria:** Selection will be based on the committee's criteria.

Funds Avail.: $1,000. **Duration:** Annual. **Number Awarded:** 1. **To Apply:** Applicants must submit an essay that portrays their personal vision as educators and how they intend to make a difference in the musical and general education of children and youth; essay must contain no more than 750 words limited to 3800 characters. **Deadline:** May 1.

6393 ■ Jack Rosen Scholarship *(Undergraduate/Scholarship)*

Purpose: To support and enhance the professional growth and teaching practices of member educators throughout the phases and levels of their teaching careers. **Focus:** Education, Elementary; Mathematics and mathematical sciences; Science; Technology. **Qualif.:** Applicants must be undergraduate students major in Elementary Education with a science, math or technology focus. **Criteria:** Selection will be based on the committee's criteria.

Funds Avail.: $1,000. **Duration:** Annual. **Number Awarded:** 1. **To Apply:** Applicants must submit an essay that portrays their personal vision as educators and how they intend to make a difference in the general education of children and youth through science, math or technology; essay must contain no more than 750 words limited to 3800 characters. **Deadline:** May 1.

6394 ■ Sandra Jo Hornick Scholarship
(Undergraduate/Scholarship)

Purpose: To support students who have demonstrated financial need. **Focus:** General studies/Field of study not specified. **Qualif.:** Applicants must be undergraduate students; one must be a KDP member and one must be a student at Kent State University. **Criteria:** Selection will be based on the committee's criteria.

Funds Avail.: $1,000. **Duration:** Annual. **Number Awarded:** 3. **To Apply:** Applicants must write an original essay that reflects their reasons for wanting to be a teacher and indicate what professional challenges they expect to face upon the completion of their degree; essay must contain no more than 750 words limited to 3800 characters. **Deadline:** May 1.

6395 ■ William B. Martin East Carolina University Scholarship *(Undergraduate/Scholarship)*

Purpose: To support and enhance the professional growth and teaching practices of member educators throughout the phases and levels of their teaching careers. **Focus:** Education, Special. **Qualif.:** Applicants must be undergraduate students enrolled at East Carolina University in Special Education and Middle Grades Education. **Criteria:** Selection will be based on the committee's criteria.

Funds Avail.: $1,250. **Duration:** Annual. **Number Awarded:** 2. **To Apply:** Applicants must submit an essay that reflects their reasons for wanting to be a special education or middle grades teacher, and indicate what professional challenges they expect to face upon the completion of their degree. **Deadline:** May 1.

6396 ■ Kappa Gamma Pi
1651 Kingsway Ct., Ste. E
Trenton, MI 48183-1959
Ph: (734)393-1222
Fax: (734)571-5954
URL: www.kappagammapi.org
Social Media: www.facebook.com/KappaGammaPi

6397 ■ KGP Cornaro Scholarship *(Graduate/Scholarship)*

Purpose: To provide financial support to individuals as needed for graduate expenses at any accredited college or university. **Focus:** General studies/Field of study not specified. **Qualif.:** Applicants must be a member of the Kappa Gamma Pi and must be already accepted into an accredited graduate or professional program.

Funds Avail.: $7,500. **Duration:** Annual. **To Apply:** Applicants must submit the completed application form along with the required supporting documents via e-mail. **Deadline:** April 20. **Remarks:** Established in 1985. **Contact:** Chair of the Cornaro Scholarship Committee; Email: cornaro@kappagammapi.org.

6398 ■ Kappa Kappa Gamma
6640 Riverside Dr., Ste. 200
Dublin, OH 43017
Ph: (614)228-6515
Fax: (614)228-7809
Free: 866-554-1870
E-mail: kkghq@kkg.org
URL: www.kappakappagamma.org
Social Media: www.facebook.com/kappakappagamma
instagram.com/kappakappagamma
pinterest.com/kappakappagamma
twitter.com/kappakappagamma

Awards are arranged alphabetically below their administering organizations

youtube.com/kappakappagamma

6399 ■ Bette Lou Albert, New Mexico, Memorial Scholarship Fund (Undergraduate, Graduate/Scholarship)

Purpose: To provide financial assistance to members to help them complete their degree program. **Focus:** General studies/Field of study not specified. **Qualif.:** Applicants must be sorority members and full-time undergraduate or graduate students. **Criteria:** Preference given to members of Gamma Beta, New Mexico. Selection will be based on a combination of factors, including academic merit and financial need as well as participation and leadership within Kappa and the community.

Funds Avail.: $3,000. **Duration:** Annual. **To Apply:** Applicants must complete and submit the application form, available at the website. **Deadline:** February 1. **Contact:** Email: scholarships@kappa.org.

6400 ■ Austin Alumnae Association Beta Xi Scholarship in Memory of Katherine Peeres Woolridge (Undergraduate/Scholarship)

Purpose: To provide financial assistance to members to help them complete their degree program. **Focus:** General studies/Field of study not specified. **Qualif.:** Applicants must be full-time undergraduate student member of Beta Xi, Texas. **Criteria:** Selection will be based on a combination of factors, including academic merit and financial need as well as participation and leadership within Kappa and the community.

Funds Avail.: $3,000. **Duration:** Annual. **To Apply:** Applicants must complete and submit the application form, available at the website. **Deadline:** February 1. **Remarks:** The scholarship established in memory of Katherine Peeres Woolridge. **Contact:** Email: scholarships@kappa.org.

6401 ■ Esther Tuttle Bailey Memorial Scholarship (Undergraduate/Scholarship)

Purpose: To provide financial assistance to students to help them complete their degree program. **Focus:** General studies/Field of study not specified. **Qualif.:** Applicants must be full-time undergraduate students and members of KKG. **Criteria:** Selection will be based on a combination of factors, including academic merit and financial need as well as participation and leadership within Kappa and the community.

Funds Avail.: $3,000. **Duration:** Annual. **To Apply:** Applicants must complete and submit the application form, available at the website. **Deadline:** February 1. **Contact:** Email: scholarships@kappa.org.

6402 ■ Marian Sims Baughn Scholarship (Undergraduate/Scholarship)

Purpose: To provide financial assistance to students to help them complete their degree program. **Focus:** General studies/Field of study not specified. **Qualif.:** Applicants should be members of Beta Mu, Colorado. **Criteria:** Selection will be based on a combination of factors, including academic merit and financial need as well as participation and leadership within Kappa and the community.

Funds Avail.: $3,000. **Duration:** Annual. **To Apply:** Applicants must complete and submit the application form, available at the website. **Deadline:** February 1. **Remarks:** The scholarship established in memory of Irene Sims Elofson & Elaine Sims Hawkins. **Contact:** Email: scholarships@kappa.org.

6403 ■ Jean Clark Berry Scholarship (Undergraduate, Graduate/Scholarship)

Purpose: To provide financial assistance to students to complete their degree program. **Focus:** General studies/Field of study not specified. **Qualif.:** Applicants must be full-time undergraduate or graduate students who have a grade average of B (3.0 on a 4.0 scale) or above. **Criteria:** Selection will be based on a combination of factors, including academic merit and financial need as well as participation and leadership within Kappa and the community. First preference is the newly elected President of Delta Sigma, Oklahoma State; second preference, if the Delta Sigma Chapter is not active, the Scholarship Committee may choose to award the scholarship to the newly elected President of Beta Theta, Oklahoma, or may decide to not award the scholarship.

Funds Avail.: $3,000. **Duration:** Annual. **To Apply:** Applicants must complete and submit the application form, available at the website. **Deadline:** February 1. **Contact:** Email: scholarships@kappa.org.

6404 ■ Beta Lambda Project 2000 Scholarship (Undergraduate/Scholarship)

Purpose: To provide financial assistance to students to complete their degree program. **Focus:** General studies/Field of study not specified. **Qualif.:** Applicants must be undergraduate student member of Beta Lambda, Illinois. **Criteria:** Selection will be based on a combination of factors, including academic merit and financial need as well as participation and leadership within Kappa and the community.

Funds Avail.: $3,000. **Duration:** Annual. **To Apply:** Applicants must complete and submit the application form, available at the website. **Deadline:** February 1. **Contact:** Email: scholarships@kappa.org.

6405 ■ Beta Mu Project 2000 Scholarship (Undergraduate/Scholarship)

Purpose: To provide financial assistance to students to complete their degree program. **Focus:** General studies/Field of study not specified. **Qualif.:** Applicants must be full-time undergraduate students and members of Beta Mu, Colorado. **Criteria:** Selection will be based on a combination of factors, including academic merit and financial need as well as participation and leadership within Kappa and the community.

Funds Avail.: $3,000. **Duration:** Annual. **To Apply:** Applicants must complete and submit the application form, available at the website. **Deadline:** February 1. **Contact:** Email: scholarships@kappa.org.

6406 ■ Beta Pi Project 2000 Scholarship in Memory of Kristy LeMond (Undergraduate/Scholarship)

Purpose: To provide financial assistance to students to complete their degree program. **Focus:** General studies/Field of study not specified. **Qualif.:** Applicants must be full-time undergraduate student members of Beta Pi, Washington. **Criteria:** Selection will be based on a combination of factors, including academic merit and financial need as well as participation and leadership within Kappa and the community.

Funds Avail.: $3,000. **Duration:** Annual. **To Apply:** Applicants must complete and submit the application form, available at the website. **Deadline:** February 1. **Remarks:** The scholarship established in Memory of Kristy LeMond. **Contact:** Email: scholarships@kappa.org.

Awards are arranged alphabetically below their administering organizations

6407 ■ Beta Province Project 2000 Scholarship
(Undergraduate/Scholarship)

Purpose: To provide financial assistance to students to complete their degree program. **Focus:** Education. **Qualif.:** Applicants must be undergraduate member from Beta Province, schools included are: Penn State, Bucknell, Dickinson, Lafayette, Villanova, Princeton, Allegheny, Pittsburgh, Carnegie Mellon and Washington and Jefferson. **Criteria:** Selection will be based on a combination of factors, including academic merit and financial need as well as participation and leadership within Kappa and the community.

Funds Avail.: $3,000. **Duration:** Annual. **To Apply:** Applicants must complete and submit the application form, available at the website. **Deadline:** February 1. **Contact:** Email: scholarships@kappa.org.

6408 ■ Beta Tau Scholarship Fund *(Undergraduate/Scholarship)*

Purpose: To provide financial assistance to students to complete their degree program. **Focus:** General studies/Field of study not specified. **Qualif.:** Applicants must be Beta Tau, Syracuse, undergraduate student members or alumni pursuing graduate work. **Criteria:** Selection will be based on a combination of factors, including academic merit and financial need as well as participation and leadership within Kappa and the community.

Funds Avail.: $3,000. **Duration:** Annual. **To Apply:** Applicants must complete and submit the application form, available at the website. **Deadline:** February 1. **Contact:** Email: scholarships@kappa.org.

6409 ■ Beta Theta Memorial Scholarship *(Graduate, Undergraduate/Scholarship)*

Purpose: To provide financial assistance to students to complete their degree program. **Focus:** General studies/Field of study not specified. **Qualif.:** Applicant must be a full-time undergraduate or graduate student member of Beta Theta, Oklahoma. If no qualified Beta Theta member applies, may be awarded to any applicant. **Criteria:** Selection will be based on a combination of factors, including academic merit and financial need as well as participation and leadership within Kappa and the community.

Funds Avail.: $3,000. **Duration:** Annual. **To Apply:** Applicants must complete and submit the application form, available at the website. **Deadline:** February 1. **Contact:** Email: scholarships@kappa.org.

6410 ■ Beta Xi Project 2000 Scholarship
(Undergraduate/Scholarship)

Purpose: To provide financial assistance to students to complete their degree program. **Focus:** General studies/Field of study not specified. **Qualif.:** Applicants must be full-time undergraduate student members of Beta Xi, Texas in good standing. **Criteria:** Selection will be based on a combination of factors, including academic merit and financial need as well as participation and leadership within Kappa and the community.

Funds Avail.: $3,000. **Duration:** Annual. **To Apply:** Applicants must complete and submit the application form, available at the website. **Deadline:** February 1. **Contact:** Email: scholarships@kappa.org.

6411 ■ Beta Zeta Project 2000 Scholarship
(Undergraduate/Scholarship)

Purpose: To provide financial assistance to students to complete their degree program. **Focus:** General studies/Field of study not specified. **Qualif.:** Applicants must be full-time student undergraduate student members of Beta Zeta, Iowa. **Criteria:** Selection will be based on a combination of factors, including academic merit and financial need as well as participation and leadership within Kappa and the community.

Funds Avail.: $3,000. **Duration:** Annual. **To Apply:** Applicants must complete and submit the application form, available at the website. **Deadline:** February 1. **Remarks:** The scholarship established in memory of Emily Wagner. **Contact:** Email: scholarships@kappa.org.

6412 ■ Boston Intercollegiate Alumnae Association Adelphe Scholarship *(Undergraduate/Scholarship)*

Purpose: To provide financial assistance to students to complete their degree program. **Focus:** General studies/Field of study not specified. **Qualif.:** Applicant must be an undergraduate student. **Criteria:** Selection will be based on a combination of factors, including academic merit and financial need as well as participation and leadership within Kappa and the community.

Funds Avail.: $3,000. **Duration:** Annual. **To Apply:** Applicants must complete and submit the application form, available at the website. **Deadline:** February 1. **Remarks:** Established in 1990. **Contact:** Email: scholarships@kappa.org.

6413 ■ Gladys Ross Carlson Adelphe Scholarship Fund *(Undergraduate, Graduate/Scholarship)*

Purpose: To provide financial assistance to students to complete their degree program. **Focus:** General studies/Field of study not specified. **Qualif.:** Applicant must be a member of Gamma Alpha, Kansas State. **Criteria:** Selection will be based on a combination of factors, including academic merit and financial need as well as participation and leadership within Kappa and the community.

Funds Avail.: $3,000. **Duration:** Annual. **To Apply:** Applicants must complete and submit the application form, available on the website. **Deadline:** February 1. **Contact:** Email: scholarships@kappa.org.

6414 ■ Dallas Alumnae Association Adelphe Scholarship in Memory of Janet Jones Buford
(Undergraduate/Scholarship)

Purpose: To provide financial assistance to students to complete their degree program. **Focus:** General studies/Field of study not specified. **Qualif.:** Applicants must be undergraduate sophomore, junior or senior living in Theta Province and attending classes in any of the following schools: SMU, Texas Tech, North Texas, Oklahoma State, Texas, TCU, Texas A&M, and Baylor. **Criteria:** Selection will be based on a combination of factors, including academic merit and financial need as well as participation and leadership within Kappa and the community.

Funds Avail.: $3,000. **Duration:** Annual. **To Apply:** Applicants must complete and submit the application form, available at the website. **Deadline:** February 1. **Remarks:** The scholarship established in memory of Janet Jones Burford. **Contact:** Email: scholarships@kappa.org.

6415 ■ Dallas Alumnae Association Gamma Phi Chapter Scholarship *(Undergraduate/Scholarship)*

Purpose: To provide financial assistance to students to complete their degree program. **Focus:** General studies/Field of study not specified. **Qualif.:** Applicant must be a full-time undergraduate student member of Gamma Phi,

Awards are arranged alphabetically below their administering organizations

SMU. **Criteria:** Selection will be based on a combination of factors, including academic merit and financial need as well as participation and leadership within Kappa and the community.

Funds Avail.: $3,000. **Duration:** Annual. **To Apply:** Applicants must complete and submit the application form, available at the website. **Deadline:** February 1. **Contact:** Email: scholarships@kappa.org.

6416 ■ Lucile Caswell Davids Memorial Adelphe Scholarship *(Undergraduate, Graduate/Scholarship)*

Purpose: To provide financial assistance to students to complete their degree program. **Focus:** General studies/Field of study not specified. **Qualif.:** Applicant must be a full-time undergraduate or graduate student member of Gamma Xi, UCLA. **Criteria:** Selection will be based on a combination of factors, including academic merit and financial need as well as participation and leadership within Kappa and the community.

Funds Avail.: $3,000. **Duration:** Annual. **To Apply:** Applicants must complete and submit the application form, available at the website. **Deadline:** February 1. **Contact:** Email: scholarships@kappa.org.

6417 ■ Delta Kappa Project 2000 Scholarship *(Undergraduate/Scholarship)*

Purpose: To provide financial assistance to students to complete their degree program. **Focus:** General studies/Field of study not specified. **Qualif.:** Applicants must be full-time undergraduate student members of Delta Kappa, Miami. **Criteria:** Selection will be based on a combination of factors, including academic merit and financial need as well as participation and leadership within Kappa and the community.

Funds Avail.: $3,000. **Duration:** Annual. **To Apply:** Applicants must complete and submit the application form, available at the website. **Deadline:** February 1. **Remarks:** The scholarship established in memory of Dorothy Ashe Dunn. **Contact:** Email: scholarships@kappa.org.

6418 ■ Delta Nu Project 2000 Scholarship *(Undergraduate/Scholarship)*

Purpose: To provide financial assistance to students to complete their degree program. **Focus:** General studies/Field of study not specified. **Qualif.:** Applicants must be full-time undergraduate students and members of Delta Nu, Massachusetts. **Criteria:** Selection will be based on a combination of factors, including academic merit and financial need as well as participation and leadership within Kappa and the community.

Funds Avail.: $3,000. **Duration:** Annual. **To Apply:** Applicants must complete and submit the application form, available at the website. **Deadline:** February 1. **Contact:** Email: scholarships@kappa.org.

6419 ■ Delta Project 2000 Scholarship *(Undergraduate/Scholarship)*

Purpose: To provide financial assistance to students to complete their degree program. **Focus:** General studies/Field of study not specified. **Qualif.:** Applicants must be full-time undergraduate student members of Delta, Indiana. **Criteria:** Selection will be based on a combination of factors, including academic merit and financial need as well as participation and leadership within Kappa and the community.

Funds Avail.: $3,000. **Duration:** Annual. **To Apply:** Applicants must complete and submit the application form,

available at the website. **Deadline:** February 1. **Remarks:** The scholarship established in memory of Cecilia Hendricks Wah. **Contact:** Email: scholarships@kappa.org.

6420 ■ Delta Tau Project 2000 Scholarship *(Undergraduate/Scholarship)*

Purpose: To provide financial assistance to students to complete their degree program. **Focus:** General studies/Field of study not specified. **Qualif.:** Applicants must be full-time undergraduate student members of Delta Tau, USC, California in good standing. **Criteria:** Selection will be based on a combination of factors, including academic merit and financial need as well as participation and leadership within Kappa and the community.

Funds Avail.: $3,000. **Duration:** Annual. **To Apply:** Applicants must complete and submit the application form, available at the website. **Deadline:** February 1. **Contact:** Email: scholarships@kappa.org.

6421 ■ Delta Upsilon Project 2000 Nowell Memorial Scholarship *(Undergraduate/Scholarship)*

Purpose: To provide financial assistance to students to complete their degree program. **Focus:** General studies/Field of study not specified. **Qualif.:** Applicants must be full-time undergraduate student members of Delta Upsilon, Georgia. **Criteria:** Selection will be based on a combination of factors, including academic merit and financial need as well as participation and leadership within Kappa and the community.

Funds Avail.: $3,000. **Duration:** Annual. **To Apply:** Applicants must complete and submit the application form, available at the website. **Deadline:** February 1. **Contact:** Email: scholarships@kappa.org.

6422 ■ Helen Cashatt Drais Memorial Adelphe Scholarship *(Undergraduate/Scholarship)*

Purpose: To provide financial assistance to students to complete their degree program. **Focus:** General studies/Field of study not specified. **Qualif.:** Applicants must be full-time undergraduate students and members of KKG. **Criteria:** Selection will be based on a combination of factors, including academic merit and financial need as well as participation and leadership within Kappa and the community.

Funds Avail.: $3,000. **Duration:** Annual. **To Apply:** Applicants must complete and submit the application form, available at the website. **Deadline:** February 1. **Contact:** Email: scholarships@kappa.org.

6423 ■ Epsilon Delta Project 2000 Scholarship *(Undergraduate/Scholarship)*

Purpose: To provide financial assistance to students to complete their degree program. **Focus:** General studies/Field of study not specified. **Qualif.:** Applicants must be full-time undergraduate student members of Epsilon Delta, Arizona State. **Criteria:** Selection will be based on a combination of factors, including academic merit and financial need as well as participation and leadership within Kappa and the community.

Funds Avail.: $3,000. **Duration:** Annual. **To Apply:** Applicants must complete and submit the application form, available at the website. **Deadline:** February 1. **Contact:** Email: scholarships@kappa.org.

6424 ■ Epsilon Mu Scholarship *(Graduate, Undergraduate/Scholarship)*

Purpose: To provide financial assistance to students to complete their degree program. **Focus:** General studies/

Awards are arranged alphabetically below their administering organizations

Field of study not specified. **Qualif.:** Applicants must be undergraduate or graduate members of KKG. **Criteria:** Selection will be based on a combination of factors, including academic merit and financial need as well as participation and leadership within Kappa and the community. First preference is for an undergraduate member of Epsilon Mu, Clemson; second preference is a graduate member of Epsilon Mu; third any qualified applicant.

Funds Avail.: $3,000. **Duration:** Annual. **To Apply:** Applicants must complete and submit the application form, available at the website. **Deadline:** February 1. **Contact:** Email: scholarships@kappa.org.

6425 ■ James R. Favor Risk Management Scholarship Fund *(Undergraduate/Scholarship)*

Purpose: To provide financial assistance to students to complete their degree program. **Focus:** General studies/Field of study not specified. **Qualif.:** Applicants must be full-time undergraduate students. **Criteria:** Selection will be based on a combination of factors, including academic merit and financial need as well as participation and leadership within Kappa and the community.

Funds Avail.: $3,000. **Duration:** Annual. **To Apply:** Applicants must complete and submit the application form, available at the website. **Deadline:** February 1. **Contact:** Email: scholarships@kappa.org.

6426 ■ Diane Ross Fennekohl Endowment Fund for Education *(Undergraduate/Scholarship)*

Purpose: To provide financial assistance to students to complete their degree program. **Focus:** General studies/Field of study not specified. **Qualif.:** Applicants must be full-time undergraduate students and members of KKG. **Criteria:** Selection will be based on a combination of factors, including academic merit and financial need as well as participation and leadership within Kappa and the community.

Funds Avail.: $3,000. **Duration:** Annual. **To Apply:** Applicants must complete and submit the application form, available at the website. **Deadline:** February 1. **Remarks:** Established in 1989. **Contact:** Email: scholarships@kappa.org.

6427 ■ Marjorie Gosselin Fitzgerald, Upsilon, Permanently Restricted Scholarship Fund *(Undergraduate/Scholarship)*

Purpose: To provide financial assistance to qualified students. **Focus:** Education. **Qualif.:** Applicant must be a full-time undergraduate student. **Criteria:** Selection will be based on a combination of factors, including academic merit and financial need as well as participation and leadership within Kappa and the community. Preference order is as follows: first, a member of Upsilon, Northwestern, studying to be a teacher; second, a member of Upsilon; third any qualified member.

Funds Avail.: $3,000. **Duration:** Annual. **To Apply:** Applicants must complete and submit the application form, available at the website. **Deadline:** February 1. **Remarks:** Established in 2011. **Contact:** Email: scholarships@kappa.org.

6428 ■ Mary Metzger Fouse Memorial Scholarship Fund *(Undergraduate/Scholarship)*

Purpose: To provide financial assistance to qualified students. **Focus:** General studies/Field of study not specified. **Qualif.:** Applicants must be full-time undergraduate

students and members of KKG. **Criteria:** Selection will be based on a combination of factors, including academic merit and financial need as well as participation and leadership within Kappa and the community.

Funds Avail.: $3,000. **Duration:** Annual. **To Apply:** Applicants must complete and submit the application form, available at the website. **Deadline:** February 1. **Contact:** Email: scholarships@kappa.org.

6429 ■ Mary Alice Fry Memorial Scholarship *(Undergraduate, Graduate/Scholarship)*

Purpose: To provide financial assistance to members to help them complete their degree program. **Focus:** General studies/Field of study not specified. **Qualif.:** Applicants must be graduate or undergraduate students and members of KKG. **Criteria:** Selection will be based on a combination of factors, including academic merit and financial need as well as participation and leadership within Kappa and the community.

Funds Avail.: $3,000. **Duration:** Annual. **To Apply:** Applicants must complete and submit the application form, available at the website. **Deadline:** February 1. **Remarks:** Established in 1995. **Contact:** Email: scholarships@kappa.org.

6430 ■ Gamma Chi Project 2000 Scholarship *(Undergraduate/Scholarship)*

Purpose: To provide financial assistance to students to complete their degree program. **Focus:** General studies/Field of study not specified. **Qualif.:** Applicants must be full-time undergraduate student members of Gamma Chi, George Washington. **Criteria:** Selection will be based on a combination of factors, including academic merit and financial need as well as participation and leadership within Kappa and the community.

Funds Avail.: $3,000. **Duration:** Annual. **To Apply:** Applicants must complete and submit the application form, available at the website. **Deadline:** February 1. **Contact:** Email: scholarships@kappa.org.

6431 ■ Gamma Mu Project 2000 Scholarship *(Undergraduate/Scholarship)*

Purpose: To provide financial assistance to students to complete their degree program. **Focus:** General studies/Field of study not specified. **Qualif.:** Applicants must be full-time undergraduate student members of Gamma Mu, Oregon State. **Criteria:** Selection will be based on a combination of factors, including academic merit and financial need as well as participation and leadership within Kappa and the community.

Funds Avail.: $3,000. **Duration:** Annual. **To Apply:** Applicants must complete and submit the application form, available at the website. **Deadline:** February 1. **Remarks:** Established in memory of Peggy Blackledge. **Contact:** Email: scholarships@kappa.org.

6432 ■ Gamma Pi Project 2000 Scholarship *(Undergraduate/Scholarship)*

Purpose: To provide financial assistance to students to complete their degree program. **Focus:** General studies/Field of study not specified. **Qualif.:** Applicants must be full-time undergraduate student members of Gamma Pi, Alabama. **Criteria:** Selection will be based on a combination of factors, including academic merit and financial need as well as participation and leadership within Kappa and the community.

Awards are arranged alphabetically below their administering organizations

Funds Avail.: $3,000. **Duration:** Annual. **To Apply:** Applicants must complete and submit the application form, available at the website. **Deadline:** February 1. **Contact:** Email: scholarships@kappa.org.

6433 ■ Gamma Theta Project 2000 Scholarship
(Undergraduate/Scholarship)

Purpose: To provide financial assistance to students to complete their degree program. **Focus:** General studies/Field of study not specified. **Qualif.:** Applicants must be full-time undergraduate student members of Gamma Theta, Drake. **Criteria:** Selection will be based on a combination of factors, including academic merit and financial need as well as participation and leadership within Kappa and the community.

Funds Avail.: $3,000. **Duration:** Annual. **To Apply:** Applicants must complete and submit the application form, available at the website. **Deadline:** February 1. **Contact:** Email: scholarships@kappa.org.

6434 ■ Gamma Zeta Project 2000 Scholarship
(Undergraduate/Scholarship)

Purpose: To provide financial assistance to students to complete their degree program. **Focus:** General studies/Field of study not specified. **Qualif.:** Applicants must be full-time undergraduate student members of Gamma Zeta, Arizona. **Criteria:** Selection will be based on a combination of factors, including academic merit and financial need as well as participation and leadership within Kappa and the community.

Funds Avail.: $3,000. **Duration:** Annual. **To Apply:** Applicants must complete and submit the application form, available at the website. **Deadline:** February 1. **Contact:** Email: scholarships@kappa.org.

6435 ■ Bunny Kline Gerner & Robin Gerner Doty Memorial Adelphe Scholarship *(Undergraduate/Scholarship)*

Purpose: To provide financial assistance to members to help them complete their degree program. **Focus:** General studies/Field of study not specified. **Qualif.:** Applicant must be undergraduate members enrolled full-time in a college or university. **Criteria:** Selection will be based on a combination of factors, including academic merit and financial need as well as participation and leadership within Kappa and the community. Preference order: 1. Undergraduate member of Beta Xi, Texas; 2. An undergraduate who lives in Theta Province or attends school in Theta Province; 3. Any qualified applicant.

Funds Avail.: $3,000. **Duration:** Annual. **To Apply:** Applicants must complete and submit the application form, available at the website. **Deadline:** February 1. **Contact:** Email: scholarships@kappa.org.

6436 ■ Elizabeth Tucker Gessley Scholarship
(Undergraduate/Scholarship)

Purpose: To provide financial assistance to students to complete their degree program. **Focus:** General studies/Field of study not specified. **Qualif.:** Applicant must be an undergraduate student member of KKG. **Criteria:** Selection will be based on a combination of factors, including academic merit and financial need as well as participation and leadership within Kappa and the community.

Funds Avail.: $3,000. **Duration:** Annual. **To Apply:** Applicants must complete and submit the application form, available at the website. **Deadline:** February 1. **Remarks:**

Established in 1988. **Contact:** Email: scholarships@kappa.org.

6437 ■ Sarah "Sally" Ives Gore Gamma Kappa Sapphire Scholarships *(Graduate, Undergraduate/Scholarship)*

Purpose: To provide financial assistance to members to help them complete their degree program. **Focus:** General studies/Field of study not specified. **Qualif.:** Applicant must be a graduate or undergraduate and a member of Gamma Kappa, William and Mary. **Criteria:** Selection will be based on a combination of factors, including academic merit and financial need as well as participation and leadership within Kappa and the community.

Funds Avail.: $3,000. **Duration:** Annual. **To Apply:** Applicants must complete and submit the application form, available at the website. **Deadline:** February 1. **Contact:** Email: scholarships@kappa.org.

6438 ■ Anna Munger Greenwood Memorial Adelphe Scholarship *(Undergraduate/Scholarship)*

Purpose: To provide financial assistance to students to complete their degree program. **Focus:** General studies/Field of study not specified. **Qualif.:** Applicant must be an undergraduate student. and a member of Kappa. **Criteria:** Selection will be based on a combination of factors, including academic merit and financial need as well as participation and leadership within Kappa and the community.

Funds Avail.: $3,000. **Duration:** Annual. **To Apply:** Applicants must complete and submit the application form, available at the website. **Deadline:** February 1. **Remarks:** Established in 1990. **Contact:** Email: scholarships@kappa.org.

6439 ■ Mary Ewing Guthrey/Mary Keller Moyer Memorial Scholarship *(Undergraduate, Graduate/Scholarship)*

Purpose: To provide financial assistance to students to complete their degree program. **Focus:** General studies/Field of study not specified. **Qualif.:** Applicants must be full-time undergraduate or graduate student member of Beta Nu, Ohio State. **Criteria:** Selection will be based on a combination of factors, including academic merit and financial need as well as participation and leadership within Kappa and the community.

Funds Avail.: $3,000. **Duration:** Annual. **To Apply:** Applicants must complete and submit the application form, available at the website. **Deadline:** February 1. **Contact:** Email: scholarships@kappa.org.

6440 ■ Suzanne Lovell Hadsell Memorial Scholarship *(Undergraduate, Graduate/Scholarship)*

Purpose: To provide financial assistance to students to complete their degree program. **Focus:** General studies/Field of study not specified. **Qualif.:** Applicants must be undergraduate or graduate members of Rho Deuteron, Ohio Wesleyan. If no applicants from Rho Deuteron, may go to any qualified applicant. **Criteria:** Selection will be based on a combination of factors, including academic merit and financial need as well as participation and leadership within Kappa and the community.

Funds Avail.: $3,000. **Duration:** Annual. **To Apply:** Applicants must complete and submit the application form, available at the website. **Deadline:** February 1. **Contact:** Email: scholarships@kappa.org.

Awards are arranged alphabetically below their administering organizations

6441 ■ The Caitlin Hammaren Memorial Scholarship
(Undergraduate/Scholarship)

Purpose: To provide financial assistance to students to complete their degree program. **Focus:** General studies/ Field of study not specified. **Qualif.:** Applicants must be full-time undergraduate or graduate students and members of KKG. **Criteria:** Selection will be based on a combination of factors, including academic merit and financial need as well as participation and leadership within Kappa and the community. Preference order is as follows: 1. an undergraduate, out-of-state member of Zeta Mu, Virginia Tech; 2. an undergraduate member of Zeta Mu Chapter; 3. an undergraduate member of Kappa Kappa Gamma.

Funds Avail.: $3,000. **Duration:** Annual. **To Apply:** Applicants must complete and submit the application form, available at the website. **Deadline:** February 1. **Remarks:** Established in 2008. **Contact:** Email: scholarships@kappa.org.

6442 ■ Dolores Ruth Heady Hardy Memorial Scholarship *(Undergraduate/Scholarship)*

Purpose: To provide financial assistance to students to complete their degree program. **Focus:** Home Economics; Mathematics and mathematical sciences; Science. **Qualif.:** Applicants must be member of Gamma Delta, Purdue, preferably a member majoring in science, mathematics, or home economics. **Criteria:** Selection will be based on a combination of factors, including academic merit and financial need as well as participation and leadership within Kappa and the community.

Funds Avail.: $3,000. **Duration:** Annual. **To Apply:** Applicants must complete and submit the application form, available at the website. **Deadline:** February 1. **Contact:** Email: scholarships@kappa.org.

6443 ■ Jessica M. Herron, Epsilon Nu, Memorial Scholarship *(Undergraduate, Graduate/Scholarship)*

Purpose: To provide financial assistance to students to complete their degree program. **Focus:** General studies/ Field of study not specified. **Qualif.:** Applicants must be undergraduate or graduate students who demonstrate need and are pursuing their education at Vanderbilt University. **Criteria:** Selection will be based on a combination of factors, including academic merit and financial need as well as participation and leadership within Kappa and the community. First preference is for an undergraduate student at Vanderbilt; second preference is for a graduate at Vanderbilt; third preference is any deserving applicant.

Funds Avail.: $3,000. **Duration:** Annual. **To Apply:** Applicants must complete and submit the application form, available at the website. **Deadline:** February 1. **Contact:** Email: scholarships@kappa.org.

6444 ■ Houston Alumnae Association Doris Krikham Brokaw Memorial Adelphe Scholarship *(Undergraduate, Graduate/Scholarship)*

Purpose: To provide financial assistance to students to complete their degree program. **Focus:** General studies/ Field of study not specified. **Qualif.:** Applicants must be undergraduate or graduate member who are Texas residents attending colleges and universities in Texas and live in Theta province. **Criteria:** Selection will be based on a combination of factors, including academic merit and financial need as well as participation and leadership within Kappa and the community.

Funds Avail.: $3,000. **Duration:** Annual. **To Apply:** Applicants must complete and submit the application form,

available at the website. **Deadline:** February 1. **Contact:** Email: scholarships@kappa.org.

6445 ■ Houston Alumnae Association, Eunice "Scotty" Scott Siverson Memorial Adelphe Scholarship *(Undergraduate, Graduate/Scholarship)*

Purpose: To provide financial assistance to students to complete their degree program. **Focus:** General studies/ Field of study not specified. **Qualif.:** Applicants must be undergraduate or graduate member who are Texas residents and attending Texas colleges and universities. **Criteria:** Selection will be based on a combination of factors, including academic merit and financial need as well as participation and leadership within Kappa and the community.

Funds Avail.: $3,000. **Duration:** Annual. **To Apply:** Applicants must complete and submit the application form, available at the website. **Deadline:** February 1. **Remarks:** Established in 1991. **Contact:** Email: scholarships@kappa.org.

6446 ■ Betty Jo Creighton Hunkele Adelphe Scholarship *(Undergraduate/Scholarship)*

Purpose: To provide financial assistance to students to complete their degree program. **Focus:** General studies/ Field of study not specified. **Qualif.:** Applicants must be sorority members and full-time undergraduate students. **Criteria:** Selection will be based on a combination of factors, including academic merit and financial need as well as participation and leadership within Kappa and the community. Preference order: 1. Members from Theta, Missouri; 2. Members from Zeta Province, includes: Simpson, Iowa, Drake, Iowa State, Missouri, Washington Univ.(St. Louis), Westminster, Creighton, Wichita State, Kansas State, Kansas and Nebraska.

Funds Avail.: $3,000. **Duration:** Annual. **To Apply:** Applicants must complete and submit the application form, available at the website. **Deadline:** February 1. **Contact:** Email: scholarships@kappa.org.

6447 ■ Iris Scholarship *(Undergraduate/Scholarship)*

Purpose: To provide financial assistance to students to complete their degree program. **Focus:** General studies/ Field of study not specified. **Qualif.:** Applicants must be undergraduate member of Delta Zeta, Colorado College, Epsilon Beta, Colorado State, Gamma Omicron, Wyoming, or any chapters in Colorado and Wyoming that may be established. **Criteria:** Selection will be based on a combination of factors, including academic merit and financial need as well as participation and leadership within Kappa and the community.

Funds Avail.: $3,000. **Duration:** Annual. **To Apply:** Applicants must complete and submit the application form, available at the website. **Deadline:** February 1. **Remarks:** Established in 2006. **Contact:** Email: scholarships@kappa.org.

6448 ■ Wilma Winberg Johnson Adelphe Scholarship for Chapter Consultants *(Undergraduate/Scholarship)*

Purpose: To provide financial assistance to students to complete their degree program. **Focus:** General studies/ Field of study not specified. **Qualif.:** Applicants must be chapter consultants residing in Alpha or Rho provinces or attending a college or university in Alpha or Rho provinces (includes Cornell, Colgate, NYU, St. Lawrence, Toronto,

Awards are arranged alphabetically below their administering organizations

Marist, Waterloo, Syracuse, McGill, Connecticut, Massachusetts, Dartmouth, Harvard, Vermont, Northeastern, Babson, Trinity, and Yale). **Criteria:** Selection will be based on a combination of factors, including academic merit and financial need as well as participation and leadership within Kappa and the community.

Funds Avail.: $3,000. **Duration:** Annual. **To Apply:** Applicants must complete and submit the application form, available at the website. **Deadline:** February 1. **Contact:** Email: scholarships@kappa.org.

6449 ■ Kappa Kappa Gamma Foundation - Mary Maxwell Gates Scholarship (Undergraduate, Graduate/Scholarship)

Purpose: To provide financial assistance to members to help them complete their degree program. **Focus:** General studies/Field of study not specified. **Qualif.:** Applicants must be full-time undergraduate or graduate students and KKG members. **Criteria:** Selection will be based on a combination of factors, including academic merit and financial need as well as participation and leadership within Kappa and the community.

Funds Avail.: $3,000. **Duration:** Annual. **To Apply:** Applicants must complete and submit the application form, available at the website. **Deadline:** February 1. **Remarks:** Established by the William H. Gates Foundation in memory of Mary Maxwell Gates. Established in 1999. **Contact:** Email: scholarships@kappa.org.

6450 ■ Kappa Kappa Gamma Foundation Project 2000 Scholarship (Undergraduate/Scholarship)

Purpose: To provide financial assistance to students to complete their degree program. **Focus:** General studies/Field of study not specified. **Qualif.:** Applicants must be full-time undergraduate student members in good standing from any chapter. **Criteria:** Selection will be based on a combination of factors, including academic merit and financial need as well as participation and leadership within Kappa and the community.

Funds Avail.: $3,000. **Duration:** Annual. **To Apply:** Applicants must complete and submit the application form, available at the website. **Deadline:** February 1. **Contact:** Email: scholarships@kappa.org.

6451 ■ Kappa Project 2000 Scholarship (Undergraduate/Scholarship)

Purpose: To provide financial assistance to students to complete their degree program. **Focus:** General studies/Field of study not specified. **Qualif.:** Applicants must be full-time undergraduate student members of Kappa Chapter, Hillsdale. **Criteria:** Selection will be based on a combination of factors, including academic merit and financial need as well as participation and leadership within Kappa and the community.

Funds Avail.: $3,000. **Duration:** Annual. **To Apply:** Applicants must complete and submit the application form, available at the website. **Deadline:** February 1. **Remarks:** Established in memory of Doris Mauck Friedrichs. **Contact:** Email: scholarships@kappa.org.

6452 ■ Emily Day Koppell Memorial Adelphe Scholarship (Undergraduate, Graduate/Scholarship)

Purpose: To provide financial assistance to Kappa members who are studying music. **Focus:** Music. **Qualif.:** Applicant must be music student and a member of KKG. **Criteria:** Selection will be based on a combination of fac-

tors, including academic merit and financial need as well as participation and leadership within Kappa and the community.

Funds Avail.: $3,000. **Duration:** Annual. **To Apply:** Applicants must complete and submit the application form, available at the website. **Deadline:** February 1. **Remarks:** Established in 1994. **Contact:** Email: scholarships@kappa.org.

6453 ■ Lambda Project 2000 Scholarship (Undergraduate/Scholarship)

Purpose: To provide educational support to undergraduate member of Lambda. **Focus:** General studies/Field of study not specified. **Qualif.:** Applicants must be undergraduate members of Lambda, Akron. **Criteria:** Selection will be based on a combination of factors, including academic merit and financial need as well as participation and leadership within Kappa and the community.

Funds Avail.: $3,000. **Duration:** Annual. **To Apply:** Applicants may contact the Association for the application process and other information. **Deadline:** February 1. **Contact:** Email: scholarships@kappa.org.

6454 ■ Elaine Johnson Lampert Journalism Memorial Adelphe Scholarship (Undergraduate/Award)

Purpose: To provide financial assistance to students to complete their degree program. **Focus:** Journalism. **Qualif.:** Applicants must be Kappa undergraduate student members and journalism majors. **Criteria:** Selection will be based on a combination of factors, including academic merit and financial need as well as participation and leadership within Kappa and the community. First preference is a member of Chi Chapter, Minnesota; second preference is for any qualified applicant.

Funds Avail.: $3,000. **Duration:** Annual. **To Apply:** Applicants must complete and submit the application form, available at the website. **Deadline:** February 1. **Contact:** Email: scholarships@kappa.org.

6455 ■ Katherine Roberts LaPorte Memorial Adelphe Scholarship (Undergraduate/Scholarship)

Purpose: To provide financial assistance to students to complete their degree program. **Focus:** General studies/Field of study not specified. **Qualif.:** Applicant must be a full-time undergraduate students and KGG members. **Criteria:** Selection will be based on a combination of factors, including academic merit and financial need as well as participation and leadership within Kappa and the community.

Funds Avail.: $3,000. **Duration:** Annual. **To Apply:** Applicants must complete and submit the application form, available at the website. **Deadline:** February 1. **Remarks:** Established in 1990. **Contact:** Email: scholarships@kappa.org.

6456 ■ Miriam "Doc" Locke Memorial Adelphe Scholarships (Graduate/Scholarship)

Purpose: To provide financial assistance to students to complete their degree program. **Focus:** General studies/Field of study not specified. **Qualif.:** Applicants must be full-time graduate students and members of KKG. **Criteria:** Selection will be based on a combination of factors, including academic merit and financial need as well as participation and leadership within Kappa and the community.

Funds Avail.: $3,000. **Duration:** Annual. **To Apply:** Applicants must complete and submit the application form,

Awards are arranged alphabetically below their administering organizations

available at the website. **Deadline:** February 1. **Contact:** Email: scholarships@kappa.org.

6457 ■ Louise Loomis Memorial Adelphe Scholarships *(Undergraduate/Scholarship)*

Purpose: To provide financial assistance to students to complete their degree program. **Focus:** General studies/Field of study not specified. **Qualif.:** Applicants must be full-time undergraduate students and KKG members. **Criteria:** Selection will be based on a combination of factors, including academic merit and financial need as well as participation and leadership within Kappa and the community.

Funds Avail.: $3,000. **Duration:** Annual. **To Apply:** Applicants must complete and submit the application form, available at the website. **Deadline:** February 1. **Remarks:** Established in 1991. **Contact:** Email: scholarships@kappa.org.

6458 ■ Shirley Stone Marinkovich Memorial Scholarships *(Undergraduate/Scholarship)*

Purpose: To provide financial assistance to students to complete their degree program. **Focus:** General studies/Field of study not specified. **Qualif.:** Applicant must be a full-time undergraduate student and member of KKG. **Criteria:** Selection will be based on academic merit, financial need, as well as participation and leadership within Kappa and the community. Preference order is as follows: first, member of Beta Pi, Washington; second, member of Iota Province (including Montana, Idaho, Washington State, College of Idaho, Washington, Whitman, Puget Sound, British Columbia, Manitoba, and North Dakota).

Funds Avail.: $3,000. **Duration:** Annual. **To Apply:** Applicants must complete and submit the application form, available at the website. **Deadline:** February 1. **Contact:** Email: scholarships@kappa.org.

6459 ■ Marisol Scholarship *(Undergraduate/Scholarship)*

Purpose: To provide financial assistance to students to complete their degree program. **Focus:** General studies/Field of study not specified. **Qualif.:** Applicant must be a full-time undergraduate student; must have a good scholastic record, a real desire for education, and financial need. **Criteria:** Selection will be based on a combination of factors, including academic merit and financial need as well as participation and leadership within Kappa and the community.

Funds Avail.: Covers 75 percent of college tuition and allowable expenses. **Duration:** Annual. **To Apply:** Applicants must complete and submit the application form, available at the website. Supplemental application is required. **Deadline:** February 1. **Contact:** Email: scholarships@kappa.org.

6460 ■ Margaret Edwards Mason Adelphe Scholarship *(Undergraduate/Scholarship)*

Purpose: To provide financial assistance to students to complete their degree program. **Focus:** General studies/Field of study not specified. **Qualif.:** Applicant must be a full-time undergraduate student and member of KKG. **Criteria:** Selection will be based on a combination of factors, including academic merit and financial need as well as participation and leadership within Kappa and the community.

Funds Avail.: $3,000. **Duration:** Annual. **To Apply:** Applicants must complete and submit the application form,

available at the website. **Deadline:** February 1. **Remarks:** Established in 1990. **Contact:** Email: scholarships@kappa.org.

6461 ■ Mary Bowles McInnis Adelphe Scholarship *(Undergraduate/Scholarship)*

Purpose: To provide financial assistance to students to complete their degree program. **Focus:** General studies/Field of study not specified. **Qualif.:** Applicant must be a full-time undergraduate student and member of KKG. **Criteria:** Selection will be based on a combination of factors, including academic merit and financial need as well as participation and leadership within Kappa and the community.

Funds Avail.: $3,000. **Duration:** Annual. **To Apply:** Applicants must complete and submit the application form, available at the website. **Deadline:** February 1. **Remarks:** Established in 1990. **Contact:** Email: scholarships@kappa.org.

6462 ■ Carol Nelson Scholarship *(Undergraduate/Scholarship)*

Purpose: To provide financial assistance to students to complete their degree program. **Focus:** General studies/Field of study not specified. **Qualif.:** Applicants must be president, officers, outstanding seniors, or member of Beta Xi, Texas. **Criteria:** Selection will be based on a combination of factors, including academic merit and financial need as well as participation and leadership within Kappa and the community.

Funds Avail.: $3,000. **Duration:** Annual. **To Apply:** Applicants must complete and submit the application form, available at the website. **Deadline:** February 1. **Contact:** Email: scholarships@kappa.org.

6463 ■ WillEtta "Willie" Long Oates, Gamma Nu, Memorial Scholarship *(Undergraduate, Graduate/Scholarship)*

Purpose: To provide financial assistance to students to complete their degree program. **Focus:** General studies/Field of study not specified. **Qualif.:** Applicants must be undergraduate or graduate students and members of KKG. **Criteria:** Selection will be based on a combination of factors, including academic merit and financial need as well as participation and leadership within Kappa and the community. Preference order is as follows: 1. undergraduate or graduate member of Gamma Nu, Arkansas; 2. any qualified applicant from the states of Arkansas, Texas, or Kansas; 3. any qualified applicant.

Funds Avail.: $3,000. **Duration:** Annual. **To Apply:** Applicants must complete and submit the application form, available at the website. **Deadline:** February 1. **Contact:** Email: scholarships@kappa.org.

6464 ■ Martha Mitchell Pearson Memorial Scholarship *(Undergraduate, Graduate/Scholarship)*

Purpose: To provide financial assistance to students to complete their degree program. **Focus:** Science; Science technologies; Technology. **Qualif.:** Applicants must be undergraduate or graduate students who are attending school in Kansas or Missouri and studying in a scientific, technological, or related field. If there are no qualified applicants who meet these criteria, then open to any qualified applicant. **Criteria:** Selection will be based on a combination of factors, including academic merit and financial need as well as participation and leadership within Kappa and the community.

Awards are arranged alphabetically below their administering organizations

Funds Avail.: $3,000. **Duration:** Annual. **To Apply:** Applicants must complete and submit the application form, available at the website. **Deadline:** February 1. **Contact:** Email: scholarships@kappa.org.

6465 ■ Pi Project 2000 Tali James Memorial Scholarship *(Undergraduate/Scholarship)*

Purpose: To provide financial assistance to students to complete their degree program. **Focus:** General studies/ Field of study not specified. **Qualif.:** Applicants must be full-time undergraduate student members of Pi Deuteron, UC Berkeley. **Criteria:** Selection will be based on a combination of factors, including academic merit and financial need as well as participation and leadership within Kappa and the community. Scholarship recipients are chosen locally.

Funds Avail.: $3,000. **Duration:** Annual. **To Apply:** Applicants must complete and submit the application form, available at the website. **Deadline:** February 1. **Contact:** Email: scholarships@kappa.org.

6466 ■ Phillis Brinton Pryor Panhellenic Scholarship *(Undergraduate/Scholarship)*

Purpose: To provide financial assistance to students to complete their degree program. **Focus:** General studies/ Field of study not specified. **Qualif.:** Applicants must be undergraduate students who are very active in their campus Panhellenic organization. **Criteria:** Selection will be based on a combination of factors, including academic merit and financial need as well as participation and leadership within Kappa and the community.

Funds Avail.: $3,000. **Duration:** Annual. **To Apply:** Applicants must complete and submit the application form, available at the website. **Deadline:** February 1. **Contact:** Email: scholarships@kappa.org.

6467 ■ Marie Mathew Rask-Gamma Omicron Educational Endowment *(Undergraduate/Scholarship)*

Purpose: To provide financial assistance to students to complete their degree program. **Focus:** General studies/ Field of study not specified. **Qualif.:** Applicants must be undergraduate student member of Gamma Omicron, Wyoming. If no qualified applicant is available from this group, then for a member in the Eta Province (including Colorado, Colorado College, Colorado State, New Mexico, Wyoming, and Utah). **Criteria:** Selection will be based on a combination of factors, including academic merit and financial need as well as participation and leadership within Kappa and the community.

Funds Avail.: $3,000. **Duration:** Annual. **To Apply:** Applicants must complete and submit the application form, available at the website. **Deadline:** February 1. **Contact:** Email: scholarships@kappa.org.

6468 ■ Lois McDonald Rinehart Adelphe Scholarship *(Undergraduate, Graduate/Scholarship)*

Purpose: To provide financial assistance to students to complete their degree program. **Focus:** General studies/ Field of study not specified. **Qualif.:** Applicants must be full-time undergraduate or graduate students and KKG members. **Criteria:** Selection will be based on a combination of factors, including academic merit and financial need as well as participation and leadership within Kappa and the community.

Funds Avail.: $3,000. **Duration:** Annual. **To Apply:** Applicants must complete and submit the application form,

available at the website. **Deadline:** February 1. **Contact:** Email: scholarships@kappa.org.

6469 ■ Sandra Journey Rolf Scholarship Fund *(Undergraduate, Graduate/Scholarship)*

Purpose: To provide financial assistance to students to complete their degree program. **Focus:** General studies/ Field of study not specified. **Qualif.:** Applicants must be full-time undergraduate or graduate students and members of KKG. **Criteria:** Selection will be based on a combination of factors, including academic merit and financial need as well as participation and leadership within Kappa and the community.

Funds Avail.: $3,000. **Duration:** Annual. **To Apply:** Applicants must complete and submit the application form, available at the website. **Deadline:** February 1. **Contact:** Email: scholarships@kappa.org.

6470 ■ Susanna Stover Root Memorial Scholarship *(Undergraduate/Scholarship)*

Purpose: To provide financial assistance to students to complete their degree program. **Focus:** Foreign languages. **Qualif.:** Applicants must be studying a foreign language in the country that language is spoken. France and Germany are listed specifically, but other countries are possible. **Criteria:** Selection will be based on a combination of factors, including academic merit and financial need as well as participation and leadership within Kappa and the community.

Funds Avail.: $3,000. **Duration:** Annual. **To Apply:** Applicants must complete and submit the application form, available at the website. **Deadline:** February 1. **Contact:** Email: scholarships@kappa.org.

6471 ■ A.J. and Lynda Hare Scribante Scholarship Fund *(Undergraduate/Scholarship)*

Purpose: To provide financial assistance to students to complete their degree program. **Focus:** General studies/ Field of study not specified. **Qualif.:** Applicants must be full-time undergraduate student member of Beta Xi, Texas, Epsilon Alpha, TCU, or Gamma Alpha, Kansas State. **Criteria:** Selection will be based on a combination of factors, including academic merit and financial need as well as participation and leadership within Kappa and the community.

Funds Avail.: $3,000. **Duration:** Annual. **To Apply:** Applicants must complete and submit the application form, available at the website. **Deadline:** February 1. **Contact:** Email: scholarships@kappa.org.

6472 ■ Josephine Kerbey Shaw Memorial Undergraduate Scholarship *(Undergraduate/ Scholarship)*

Purpose: To provide financial assistance to students to complete their degree program. **Focus:** General studies/ Field of study not specified. **Qualif.:** Applicants must be full-time undergraduate students and KGG members. **Criteria:** Selection will be based on a combination of factors, including academic merit and financial need as well as participation and leadership within Kappa and the community.

Funds Avail.: $3,000. **Duration:** Annual. **To Apply:** Applicants must complete and submit the application form, available at the website. **Deadline:** February 1. **Contact:** Email: scholarships@kappa.org.

Awards are arranged alphabetically below their administering organizations

6473 ■ Susan Goldsmith Shelley Scholarship
(Undergraduate/Scholarship)

Purpose: To provide financial assistance to students to complete their degree program. **Focus:** General studies/ Field of study not specified. **Qualif.:** Applicants must be full-time undergraduate students and members of KKG. **Criteria:** Selection will be based on a combination of factors, including academic merit and financial need as well as participation and leadership within Kappa and the community. Preference given to members of Delta Kappa, Miami.

Funds Avail.: $3,000. **Duration:** Annual. **To Apply:** Applicants must complete and submit the application form, available at the website. **Deadline:** February 1. **Contact:** Email: scholarships@kappa.org.

6474 ■ Lynn Brower Shonk Memorial Scholarship
(Undergraduate/Scholarship)

Purpose: To provide financial assistance to students to complete their degree program. **Focus:** General studies/ Field of study not specified. **Qualif.:** Applicants must be full-time undergraduate students and members of KKG. **Criteria:** Selection will be based on a combination of factors, including academic merit and financial need as well as participation and leadership within Kappa and the community. First preference is a member of Delta, Indiana; if not qualified Delta member, than any qualified applicant.

Funds Avail.: $3,000. **Duration:** Annual. **To Apply:** Applicants must complete and submit the application form, available at the website. **Deadline:** February 1. **Contact:** Email: scholarships@kappa.org.

6475 ■ Ann Kelsay Small Scholarship
(Undergraduate/Scholarship)

Purpose: To provide financial assistance to students to complete their degree program. **Focus:** Law; Nursing; Pharmacy. **Qualif.:** Applicants must be from Kappa members attending college full-time. **Criteria:** Preference order: 1. Member from Kappa or Eta Provinces includes: UCLA, USC (Calif.), UC Riverside, Chapman, Cal State Northridge, UC Santa Barbera, Pepperdine, Arizona State, Arizona, UC San Diego, Colorado, Colorado College, Colorado State, Utah, New Mexico and Wyoming; 2. member with a major in nursing, pre-law or pharmacy; 3. member from a single parent home; 4. any qualified applicant.

Funds Avail.: $3,000. **Duration:** Annual. **To Apply:** Applicants must complete and submit the application form, available at the website. **Deadline:** February 1. **Contact:** Email: scholarships@kappa.org.

6476 ■ Dell Chenoweth Stifel Scholarship *(Graduate/ Scholarship)*

Purpose: To provide financial assistance to students to complete their degree program. **Focus:** General studies/ Field of study not specified. **Qualif.:** Applicants must be full-time graduate students. **Criteria:** Selection will be based on a combination of factors, including academic merit and financial need as well as participation and leadership within Kappa and the community.

Funds Avail.: $3,000. **Duration:** Annual. **To Apply:** Applicants must complete and submit the application form, available at the website. **Deadline:** February 1. **Remarks:** In honor of Marian Klingbeil Williams. **Contact:** Email: scholarships@kappa.org.

6477 ■ Jane and Gregg Waddill Memorial Adelphe Scholarship *(Undergraduate/Scholarship)*

Purpose: To provide financial assistance to students to complete their degree program. **Focus:** General studies/ Field of study not specified. **Qualif.:** Applicants must be full-time undergraduate student and member of KKG. **Criteria:** Selection will be based on a combination of factors, including academic merit and financial need as well as participation and leadership within Kappa and the community.

Funds Avail.: $3,000. **Duration:** Annual. **To Apply:** Applicants must complete and submit the application form, available at the website. **Deadline:** February 1. **Contact:** Email: scholarships@kappa.org.

6478 ■ Helen Zick Walker Adelphe Scholarship
(Undergraduate/Scholarship)

Purpose: To provide financial assistance to students to complete their degree program. **Focus:** General studies/ Field of study not specified. **Qualif.:** Applicants must be full-time undergraduate student and member of KKG. **Criteria:** Selection will be based on a combination of factors, including academic merit and financial need as well as participation and leadership within Kappa and the community.

Funds Avail.: $3,000. **Duration:** Annual. **To Apply:** Applicants must complete and submit the application form, available at the website. **Deadline:** February 1. **Contact:** Email: scholarships@kappa.org.

6479 ■ Lynn McNabb Walton Adelphe Scholarhship
(Undergraduate/Scholarship)

Purpose: To provide financial assistance to students to complete their degree program. **Focus:** General studies/ Field of study not specified. **Qualif.:** Applicants must be full-time undergraduate students and members of KKG in Oklahoma or Arkansas. **Criteria:** Selection will be based on a combination of factors, including academic merit and financial need as well as participation and leadership within Kappa and the community. Preference order is as follows: first, member of Gamma Nu, Arkansas; second, member of Beta Theta, Oklahoma; third, member of chapters in Oklahoma or Arkansas.

Funds Avail.: $3,000. **Duration:** Annual. **To Apply:** Applicants must complete and submit the application form, available at the website. **Deadline:** February 1. **Contact:** Email: scholarships@kappa.org.

6480 ■ Jean Hess Wells Memorial Adelphe Graduate Scholarship *(Graduate/Scholarship)*

Purpose: To provide financial assistance to students to complete their degree program. **Focus:** General studies/ Field of study not specified. **Qualif.:** Applicants must be full-time graduate students and KKG members. **Criteria:** Selection will be based on a combination of factors, including academic merit and financial need as well as participation and leadership within Kappa and the community.

Funds Avail.: $3,000. **Duration:** Annual. **To Apply:** Applicants must complete and submit the application form, available at the website. **Deadline:** February 1. **Contact:** Email: scholarships@kappa.org.

6481 ■ Jean Hess Wells Memorial Adelphe Scholarship *(Undergraduate/Scholarship)*

Purpose: To provide financial assistance to students to complete their degree program. **Focus:** General studies/

Awards are arranged alphabetically below their administering organizations

Field of study not specified. **Qualif.:** Applicants must be full-time undergraduate students and KGG members. **Criteria:** Selection will be based on a combination of factors, including academic merit and financial need as well as participation and leadership within Kappa and the community.

Funds Avail.: $3,000. **Duration:** Annual. **To Apply:** Applicants must complete and submit the application form, available at the website. **Deadline:** February 1. **Remarks:** Established in 1990. **Contact:** Email: scholarships@ kappa.org.

6482 ■ Mary Elizabeth Westpheling - Long Beach (Calif.) Alumnae Association Memorial Scholarhip
(Undergraduate/Scholarship)

Purpose: To provide financial assistance to students to complete their degree program. **Focus:** General studies/ Field of study not specified. **Qualif.:** Applicants must be full-time undergraduate students and members of KKG. **Criteria:** Selection will be based on a combination of factors, including academic merit and financial need as well as participation and leadership within Kappa and the community. Preference order is as follows: first, undergraduate resident from the Long Beach, California area; second, undergraduate resident from Southern California; third, undergraduate from the State of California; fourth, any qualified applicant.

Funds Avail.: $3,000. **Duration:** Annual. **To Apply:** Applicants must complete and submit the application form, available at the website. **Deadline:** February 1. **Contact:** Email: scholarships@kappa.org.

6483 ■ Nona Hobbs Wolfe Memorial Scholarship
(Undergraduate/Scholarship)

Purpose: To provide financial assistance to students to complete their degree program. **Focus:** General studies/ Field of study not specified. **Qualif.:** Applicants must be full-time undergraduate students and members of KKG. **Criteria:** Selection will be based on a combination of factors, including academic merit and financial need as well as participation and leadership within Kappa and the community.

Funds Avail.: $3,000. **Duration:** Annual. **To Apply:** Applicants must complete and submit the application form, available at the website. **Deadline:** February 1. **Contact:** Email: scholarships@kappa.org.

6484 ■ Zeta Sigma Project 2000 Scholarship
(Undergraduate/Scholarship)

Purpose: To provide financial assistance to students to complete their degree program. **Focus:** General studies/ Field of study not specified. **Qualif.:** Applicants must be full-time undergraduate student members of Zeta Sigma, North Texas. **Criteria:** Selection will be based on a combination of factors, including academic merit and financial need as well as participation and leadership within Kappa and the community.

Funds Avail.: $3,000. **Duration:** Annual. **To Apply:** Applicants must complete and submit the application form, available at the website. **Deadline:** February 1. **Contact:** Email: scholarships@kappa.org.

6485 ■ Kappa Kappa Gamma Foundation of Canada
PO Box 1273
Toronto, ON, Canada M4P 2E0

E-mail: scholarship@kkgfoundationofcanada.org
URL: www.kkgfoundationofcanada.org

6486 ■ Kappa Kappa Gamma Foundation of Canada Graduate Scholarship *(Graduate, Doctorate/ Scholarship)*

Purpose: To support Canadian women in their pursuit of graduate degrees. **Focus:** General studies/Field of study not specified. **Qualif.:** Applicants must be female Canadian citizens who are currently enrolled in or pursuing a Ph.D. program.

To Apply: Applicants must verify the scholarship website and retrieve the provided scholarship application form; additional documents include transcripts and three reference letters sealed separately from their application (letters can be separately sent directly by their referees). **Deadline:** March 16. **Contact:** Scholarship Committee, Kappa Kappa Gamma Foundation of Canada, PO Box 1273, 2708 Yonge St., Toronto ON M4P 2E0; Email: scholarship@ kkgfoundationofcanada.org.

6487 ■ Kappa Omicron Nu (KON)
PO Box 798
Okemos, MI 48805-0798
Ph: (727)940-2658
E-mail: info@kon.org
URL: www.kon.org
Social Media: www.facebook.com/KappaOmicronNu
twitter.com/KappaOmicronNu

6488 ■ Marjorie M. Brown Dissertation Fellowship
(Doctorate/Fellowship)

Purpose: To support research in critical science. **Focus:** Science. **Criteria:** Fellowship will be awarded on a competitive basis.

Funds Avail.: $10,000. **Duration:** Annual. **Number Awarded:** 4. **To Apply:** Interested applicants may contact Kappa Omicron Nu for the application process and other information.

6489 ■ Kappa Omicron Nu National Alumni Fellowships *(Graduate/Fellowship)*

Purpose: To support members with studies and research in family and consumer sciences. **Focus:** Home Economics. **Qualif.:** Applicant must be an active Kappa Omicron Nu member; enrolled in a master's program in home economics or one of the specializations. **Criteria:** Selection is based on applicant's potential for professional leadership and relevance of study or research to significant concerns related to home and family.

Funds Avail.: $2,000. **Duration:** Biennial. **To Apply:** Applicants must submit five (5) copies of the application form, typed or printed together with three letters of recommendations. **Deadline:** April 1. **Remarks:** Awarded biennially by the National Alumni Chapter.

6490 ■ KON/GEICO LeaderShape Undergraduate Scholarship *(Undergraduate/Scholarship)*

Purpose: To provide opportunity for its member to attend The LeaderShape Institute. **Focus:** General studies/Field of study not specified; Leadership, Institutional and community. **Qualif.:** Applicant must be undergraduate student member with at least one more year in the undergraduate program of studies. **Criteria:** Applications are accepted on a first-come first-serve basis.

Awards are arranged alphabetically below their administering organizations

Funds Avail.: $1,025. **Duration:** Annual. **Number Awarded:** Two. **To Apply:** Applicant must submit a short statement of commitment to leadership on campus during the current academic year, and a short description of academic status. **Deadline:** February 15. **Contact:** Dorothy Mitstifer; Email: dmitstifer@kon.org.

6491 ■ KON National Alumni Chapter Grant *(Professional development/Grant)*

Purpose: To support the research agenda of Kappa Omicron Nu in the field of human sciences or in other related specializations. **Focus:** Science. **Qualif.:** Applicants must be active member of Kappa Omicron Nu. **Criteria:** Selection will be based on Kappa Omicron Nu's criteria.

Funds Avail.: $2,000. **Duration:** Annual. **Number Awarded:** 1. **To Apply:** Applicants must submit the application form and all supporting documents electronically to Kappa Omicron Nu; shall be limited to 10 pages including supplementary materials and shall include the following: abstract; cross-specialization and integrative research approach; justification or rationale for project; statement of objective/hypotheses; description of project including methodology or design, subjects or participants, implementation plan, data collection and analysis, and implications; management plan including staff responsibilities/qualifications, and timeline for activities; budget; literature citations; supplementary materials. **Deadline:** April 20.

6492 ■ KON New Initiatives Grant *(Professional development/Grant)*

Purpose: To support the research agenda of Kappa Omicron Nu in the field of human sciences or in other related specializations. **Focus:** Science. **Qualif.:** Applicants must be active member of Kappa Omicron Nu. **Criteria:** Selection will be based on Kappa Omicron Nu's criteria.

Funds Avail.: $3,000. **Duration:** Annual. **To Apply:** Applicants must visit the website for the online application process. **Deadline:** April 1.

6493 ■ Eileen C. Maddex Fellowships *(Graduate/Fellowship)*

Purpose: To support members with studies and research in family and consumer sciences. **Focus:** Home Economics. **Qualif.:** Applicant must be an active Kappa Omicron Nu member; enrolled in a master's program in home economics or one of the specializations. **Criteria:** Selection is based on applicant's potential for professional leadership and relevance of study or research to significant concerns related to home and family.

Funds Avail.: $2,000. **Duration:** Annually. **To Apply:** Applicants must submit five (5) copies of the application form, typed or printed together with three letters of recommendations.

6494 ■ Kappa Omicron Nu Honor Society
4990 Northwind Dr., Ste. 140
East Lansing, MI 48823-5031
Ph: (517)351-8335
E-mail: info@kon.org
URL: www.kon.org
Social Media: www.facebook.com/KappaOmicronNu
www.linkedin.com/groups/1847473/profile
twitter.com/KappaOmicronNu

6495 ■ Hettie M. Anthony Fellowship *(Doctorate/Fellowship)*

Purpose: To provide funding support for a study and research in human sciences or one of its specializations at colleges or universities with strong research programs and supporting disciplines for the chosen major topic. **Focus:** Science. **Qualif.:** Applicants must be active Kappa Omicron Nu member who have demonstrated scholarship, research, and leadership potential. **Criteria:** Fellowships will be awarded on a competitive basis. Selection will be based on the aforesaid qualifications and compliance with the application process.

Funds Avail.: $2,000. **Duration:** Annual. **Number Awarded:** Varies. **To Apply:** Applicants must submit five copies of the application form, type or printed, along with three letters of recommendations from persons that can represent the applicants' scholarship, research, and potential for professional leadership. **Deadline:** January 15.

6496 ■ Marjorie M. Brown Fellowship Program *(Postdoctorate/Fellowship)*

Purpose: To support research projects to continue Brown's Philosophical work using critical social theory, demonstrating understanding of Brown's Philosophical Studies and other recent pieces of work and their ongoing significance for the human sciences profession. **Focus:** Science. **Criteria:** Selection will be based on the aforesaid qualifications and compliance with the application process.

Funds Avail.: $10,000. **Duration:** Annual. **Number Awarded:** 1. **To Apply:** Applicants must submit a cover page, an abstract of 100 words or less; introduction of the research including background, need for the study, and statement of the objectives; review of literature; method including research design, plan of work, approach to analysis; literature citations and supplementary materials; and applicants' five copies of the application form. **Deadline:** April 1. **Contact:** E-mail: info@kon.org.

6497 ■ Omicron Nu Research Fellowship *(Postdoctorate, Graduate/Fellowship)*

Purpose: To provide funding support for a study and research in human sciences or one of its specializations at colleges or universities with strong research programs and supporting disciplines for the chosen major topic. **Focus:** Science. **Qualif.:** Applicants must be Current, active member in good standing (dues paid up) For masters' and doctoral awards, the student must be currently enrolled and demonstrate an ability in graduate student, interest in competence in research. **Criteria:** Fellowships will be awarded The research or project must relate to significant concerns related to individual, family and community development. The student must show potential for professional leadership.

Funds Avail.: $2,000. **Duration:** Annual. **To Apply:** Applicant must submit application form, typed or printed, along with three letters of recommendations from persons that can represent the applicant's scholarship, research, and potential for professional leadership. **Deadline:** April 1. **Contact:** E-mail: info@kon.org.

6498 ■ Kappa Sigma Fraternity
1610 Scottsville Rd.
Charlottesville, VA 22902
Ph: (434)295-3193
E-mail: help@kappasigma.org
URL: www.kappasigma.org
Social Media: www.facebook.com/KappaSigmaHQ
www.instagram.com/kappasigmahq
twitter.com/KappaSigmaHQ
www.youtube.com/user/KappaSigmaHQ

Awards are arranged alphabetically below their administering organizations

6499 ■ Scholarship-Leadership Awards
(Undergraduate/Scholarship)

Purpose: To support undergraduate members who excel in academics, campus involvement and fraternity leadership. **Focus:** General studies/Field of study not specified. **Criteria:** Selection will be based on the committee's criteria.

Funds Avail.: $5,000,000. **Duration:** Annual. **Number Awarded:** 1. **Remarks:** Established in 1947.

6500 ■ Kappa Tau Alpha (KTA)
University of Missouri
School of Journalism
76 Gannett Hall
Columbia, MO 65211-1200
Ph: (573)882-7685
E-mail: umcjourkta@missouri.edu
URL: www.kappataualpha.org

6501 ■ KTA Chapter Adviser Research Grant Award
(Professional development/Grant)

Purpose: To provide research assistance and to recognize and reward KTA advisers for their good work and to support their academic endeavors. **Focus:** General studies/Field of study not specified. **Qualif.:** Applicants must be current KTA Advisors or co-advisers of active chapters who have served for at least two full years at the time of application. **Criteria:** Selection will be based on the committee's criteria.

Funds Avail.: $1,000 each. **Duration:** Annual. **Number Awarded:** Up to 3. **To Apply:** Applicants must complete and submit the application form available online and must provide a one to three-page prospectus/overview of the project. **Deadline:** October 1.

6502 ■ Josephine de Karman Fellowship Trust
PO Box 3389
San Dimas, CA 91773
Ph: (909)592-0607
E-mail: info@dekarman.org
URL: www.dekarman.org

6503 ■ Josephine de Karman Fellowship *(Doctorate/ Fellowship)*

Purpose: To recognize and assist students whose scholastic achievements reflect Professor Von Karman's high standards. **Focus:** General studies/Field of study not specified. **Qualif.:** Applicant must be PhD students in any discipline, including international students, who are currently enrolled in a university located within the united states. **Criteria:** Selection will be given to applicants in the Humanities.

Funds Avail.: $25,000. **Duration:** Annual. **Number Awarded:** 8. **To Apply:** Applicants must submit a completed application form together with official transcripts of graduate and undergraduate studies, and two letters of recommendations (in a sealed envelope with the signature of the writer across the outside flap). **Deadline:** January 31. **Remarks:** The Fellowship was established by the late Dr. Theodore von Karman, world renowned aeronautics expert, teacher and first director of the Guggenheim Aeronautical Laboratory at the California Institute of Technology, in memory of his sister, Josephine. Established in 1954. **Contact:** Judy McClain, Fellowship Secretary,

Josephine de Karman Fellowship Trust, PO Box 3389, San Dimas, CA, 91773; Phone: 909-592-0607; Email: info@dekarman.org.

6504 ■ Ka'u Chamber of Commerce
PO Box 6710
Ocean View, HI 96737
Ph: (808)936-5288
E-mail: kauchamber@gmail.com
URL: www.kauchamber.org

6505 ■ Ka'u Chamber of Commerce Scholarship
(Undergraduate/Scholarship)

Purpose: To provide assistance to be used for all college and vocational training of the students. **Focus:** General studies/Field of study not specified.

Duration: Annual.

6506 ■ Keats-Shelley Association of America (KSAA)
New York Public Library, Rm. 226
476 5th Ave.
New York, NY 10018-2788
E-mail: ksaa.treasurer@gmail.com
URL: k-saa.org

6507 ■ Carl H. Pforzheimer, Jr., Research Grants
(Graduate, Other/Grant)

Purpose: To provide funding for expenses related to research in the field of British Romanticism and literary culture between 1789 and 1832, especially projects involving authors featured in the "Keats-Shelley Journal" bibliography. **Focus:** British studies. **Qualif.:** Applicants must be advanced graduate students, independent scholars and untenured faculty members. **Criteria:** Selection shall be based on the aforementioned qualifications and compliance with the application details. Preference will be given to projects involving authors featured in the bibliography of the "Keats-Shelley Journal", the Association's annual publication.

Funds Avail.: No specific amount. **Duration:** Annual. **To Apply:** Applicants must submit the following: completed application form provided at the program website; curriculum vitae; description of the project (up to 3 pages only); one-page bibliography of publications that treat the topic; and, two letters of reference from people who know the applicants work well and can judge its values. **Deadline:** November 1. **Remarks:** The grants were established to honor the late Carl H. Pforzheimer, Jr., a past President of the Association and among its most vigorous advocates. He also headed The Carl and Lily Pforzheimer Foundation, Inc., long distinguished for funding scholarship centered on early nineteenth-century English literature. Established in 2000. **Contact:** Doucet Fischer, the Administrator of the Grants, Keats-Shelley Association of America, Inc., Rm. 226, The New York Public Library, 476 Fifth Ave., New York, NY 10018-2788; Phone: 212-764-0655; E-mail: doucetfischer@nypl.org.

6508 ■ Donald Keene Center of Japanese Culture (DKC)
507 Kent Hall, MC 3920
Columbia University

Awards are arranged alphabetically below their administering organizations

1140 Amsterdam Ave.
New York, NY 10027
Ph: (212)854-5036
Fax: (212)854-4019
URL: www.keenecenter.org

6509 ■ The Shincho Graduate Fellowship for Study in Japan *(Graduate/Fellowship)*

Purpose: To provide financial support to students pursuing advanced graduate study ore research in Japan. **Focus:** Japanese studies. **Qualif.:** Applicants must be degree candidates in a graduate program at Columbia university in field of Japanese cultural studies.

Funds Avail.: No specific amount. **Duration:** Annual; one year. **Number Awarded:** Up to 2. **To Apply:** Applicants must include the following: four page application form; a five page statement of purpose, which states the objectives, methodology and schedule of the project; official transcript; curriculum vitae. **Deadline:** February 24. **Remarks:** Established in 1992.

6510 ■ Kegler, Brown, Hill, and Ritter Company L.P.A.

65 East State Street, Suite 1800
Columbus, OH 43215
Ph: (614)462-5400
Fax: (614)464-2634
Free: 800-860-7885
URL: www.keglerbrown.com
Social Media: www.facebook.com/KeglerBrownHillRitter
twitter.com/KeglerBrown

6511 ■ Kegler Brown Diversity Scholarship *(Undergraduate/Scholarship)*

Purpose: To assist minority students financially with their legal education. **Focus:** Law. **Qualif.:** Applicants must be first year minority students studying law from all schools. **Criteria:** Selection is based on academic performance, accomplishments, activities and potential contributions to the legal community.

Funds Avail.: $10,000. **Duration:** Annual. **To Apply:** Students may contact the office for more information about the scholarship. **Deadline:** January 13.

6512 ■ Kellogg Community College Foundation

450 North Ave.
Battle Creek, MI 49017
Ph: (269)965-3931
E-mail: kccfoundation@kellogg.edu
URL: www.kellogg.edu
Social Media: www.facebook.com/
  KelloggCommunityCollege
twitter.com/Kellogg_CC
www.youtube.com/user/KelloggCommunityColl

6513 ■ KCC Foundation Gold Key Scholarship *(Undergraduate/Scholarship)*

Purpose: To generate and encourage philanthropic giving and manage funds to enhance the quality of education while building stronger communities. **Focus:** General studies/Field of study not specified. **Qualif.:** Applicants must be students within the KCC district; must have

completed no more than 24 credit hours of college; must have 3.5 cumulative GPA and ACT of 22 or higher. **Criteria:** Recipients are selected based on leadership experience.

Funds Avail.: $9,000($4,500 each year for up to two years). **Duration:** Annual; up to two years. **To Apply:** Applicants must submit a completed application form; an official high school and/or college transcript; three written letters of recommendation; ACT scores; 150 word written essay discussing achievements and future goals; and resume or employment information including activities, leadership, volunteer or school-related positions. **Deadline:** March 2. **Contact:** Bldg. Rm. 301, 450 N Ave. Battle Creek, MI, 49017-3397; Email: kccfoundation@kellogg.edu.

6514 ■ KCC Foundation Scholarship *(Undergraduate/Scholarship)*

Purpose: To generate and encourage philanthropic giving and manage funds to enhance the quality of education while building stronger communities. **Focus:** General studies/Field of study not specified. **Qualif.:** Applicants must have a cumulative GPA of 2.5. Some scholarships require a GPA higher than 2.5. Students with a cumulative GPA below 2.5 may be considered based on a recommendation by a faculty member, advisor or counselor. **Criteria:** Recipients are selected based on financial need, demonstrated academic achievements, number of credit hours and/or special circumstances.

Funds Avail.: No specific amount.

6515 ■ KCC Trustee Scholarship *(Undergraduate/Scholarship)*

Purpose: To generate and encourage philanthropic giving and manage funds to enhance the quality of education while building stronger communities. **Focus:** General studies/Field of study not specified. **Qualif.:** Applicants must be graduating high school seniors within the KCC district; must be in the top 20% of graduating class and have GPA at least a 3.2 or higher. **Criteria:** Recipients are selected based on academic performance and financial need.

Funds Avail.: No specific amount. **Duration:** Annual. **To Apply:** Applicants must submit a completed application form, a 150 word essay, and a copy of high school and college transcripts; private copy of ACT scores; resume; three recommendation letters from teachers, instructors or community members. **Deadline:** March 2. **Contact:** Bldg. Rm. 301, 450 N Ave. Battle Creek, MI, 49017-3397; Email: kccfoundation@kellogg.edu.

6516 ■ Walter and Lucille Harper Transfer Scholarship *(Graduate/Scholarship)*

Purpose: To generate and encourage philanthropic giving and manage funds to enhance the quality of education while building stronger communities. **Focus:** General studies/Field of study not specified. **Qualif.:** Applicants must be second year KCC students graduating with an associate's degree; must have a minimum of 3.0 GPA; must be citizens of the United States. **Criteria:** Recipients are selected based on academic performance and financial need.

Funds Avail.: No specific amount. **To Apply:** Applicants must submit a completed application form; a copy of transcript of records; 150 word personal statement detailing their future aspirations; and three written letters of recommendation from teachers, counselors and employers. **Deadline:** April 14. **Contact:** 450 N Ave. Roll Bldg. Rm. 301

Awards are arranged alphabetically below their administering organizations

Battle Creek, MI, 49017-3397; Email: kccfoundation@kellogg.edu.

6517 ■ Kelly Law Team
1 E Washington St., Ste. 500
Phoenix, AZ 85004
Ph: (602)283-4122
E-mail: mike@jkphoenixpersonalinjuryattorney.com
URL: www.jkphoenixpersonalinjuryattorney.com
Social Media: www.facebook.com/pages/Kelly-Law-Team/616626571702427
instagram.com/kellylawteam
www.linkedin.com/pub/john-kelly/79/131/453
twitter.com/KellyLawTeam

6518 ■ Autism/ASD Scholarship *(Community College, Four Year College, Graduate, Vocational/Occupational, Professional development/Scholarship)*

Purpose: To assist students on the Autism Spectrum in the pursuit of secondary or post-secondary educational opportunities. **Focus:** General studies/Field of study not specified. **Qualif.:** Applicant must be an U.S. citizens who have been diagnosed with autism spectrum disorder (ASD) who would like to continue their education at the trade school, junior college, college, or university level. **Criteria:** Selection will be based on Short statement and optional essay.

Funds Avail.: $1,000. **To Apply:** Applicant must complete online application; submit statement of 100 words or less explaining how the scholarship will assist in achieving your educational goals. Optional: submit essay (1,000 words or less) on how autism has affected your education. **Deadline:** February 5. **Contact:** Email: michael@jkphoenixpersonalinjuryattorney.com.

6519 ■ Disabled Veterans Scholarship *(Vocational/Occupational, Community College, Four Year College, Graduate, Professional development/Scholarship)*

Purpose: To defray the tuition cost at a secondary school, trade or vocational school, junior college, college, or university for a disabled veteran. **Focus:** General studies/Field of study not specified. **Qualif.:** Applicant must be a Veterans of any branch of the U.S. Armed Forces with a disability rating of 30% or higher. **Criteria:** Selection will be based on Short statement and optional essay.

Funds Avail.: $1,000. **To Apply:** Applicants must complete online application; upload statement of up to 100 words setting forth your educational goals. Optional: upload an essay (1,000 words or less) discussing the effect your military service has had on your life. **Deadline:** February 9. **Contact:** Email: michael@jkphoenixpersonalinjuryattorney.com.

6520 ■ Law Student Scholarship *(Graduate/Scholarship)*

Purpose: To defray the cost of law school tuition. **Focus:** Law. **Qualif.:** Applicant must be an U.S. citizen enrolled at or who intend to enroll at a U.S. law school accredited by the American Bar Association.

Funds Avail.: $1,000. **To Apply:** Application must complete online form; upload a statement up to 100 words explaining why you want to pursue a legal education. Optional: essay discussing how you will use your law school degree to make a difference in the world. **Deadline:** February 7.

Contact: Email: michael@jkphoenixpersonalinjuryattorney.com.

6521 ■ The Deana Kendrick Foundation (TDKF)
c/o Kay Litchy
3622 W. Sexton St.
Springfield, MO 65810
URL: tdkf.wordpress.com
Social Media: www.facebook.com/The-Deana-Kendrick-Foundation-123337037738130

6522 ■ Deana Kendrick Foundation Scholarship *(Undergraduate/Scholarship)*

Purpose: To support Morgan County residents who are pursuing a career in health field education. **Focus:** Dentistry; Health care services; Medicine; Nursing. **Qualif.:** Applicants must be admitted into a college or university at the time of your application; scholarship is best suited for community colleges but may be used at a four-year university.

Funds Avail.: No specific amount. **Duration:** Annual. **Number Awarded:** Varies. **To Apply:** Applicants must submit; name, date of birth, address, contact phone number, e-mail address if applicable; highest completed level of education, name of college or university to which you've been admitted, degree you are seeking (may state undecided), semester for which you are applying, current annual income, statement: I have read the frequently asked questions (F.A.Q.) on the website; a 300-word essay on the topic: the Next Stage of My Life; in addition, applicant will need to have two letters of recommendation, each in a sealed envelope. **Contact:** The Deana Kendrick Foundation: c/o Kay Litchy 3622 W. Sexton St. Springfield MO 65810.

6523 ■ Kenhub GmbH
Wurzner Str. 154a
04318 Leipzig, Germany
E-mail: contact@kenhub.com
URL: www.kenhub.com
Social Media: www.facebook.com/kenhubcom
www.pinterest.com/kenhub_official
twitter.com/kenhub

6524 ■ Kenhub Scholarship Program *(Undergraduate, Postgraduate/Scholarship)*

Purpose: To help students seeking degrees in healthcare science. **Focus:** Dentistry; Health sciences; Medicine; Midwifery; Nursing; Optometry. **Qualif.:** Applicant must be currently studying full-time in, or accepted into, an undergraduate or postgraduate program in the field of healthcare science (medicine, nursing, physiotherapy, osteopathy, dentistry, anatomy, midwifery, optometry, or sports science). Applicant must be able to provide proof of course enrollment or acceptance and must have a registered Premium account with the sponsor.

Funds Avail.: $1,250. **Duration:** Annual. **Number Awarded:** 2. **To Apply:** Application from should be completed at the sponsor's website. **Deadline:** October 1. **Contact:** Molly or Declan; E-mail: contact@kenhub.com.

6525 ■ Kennedy Krieger Institute (KKI)
707 N Broadway
Baltimore, MD 21205

Awards are arranged alphabetically below their administering organizations

Ph: (443)923-9200
Free: 800-873-3377
URL: www.kennedykrieger.org
Social Media: www.facebook.com/kennedykrieger
www.instagram.com/kennedykriegerinstitute
www.linkedin.com/company/kennedy-krieger-institute
twitter.com/kennedykrieger
www.youtube.com/user/KennedyKrieger

6526 ■ Dr. James A. Ferguson Emerging Infectious Diseases Research Initiatives for Student Enhancement Fellowship (RISE) *(Graduate/Fellowship)*

Purpose: To provide public health research and professional development in the area of infectious diseases and health disparities with a special focus on increasing knowledge and interest in public health careers among students from under-represented populations. **Focus:** Infectious diseases. **Qualif.:** Applicants must be enrolled as full-time students in a medical, dental, pharmacy, veterinary, or public health graduate program; must have 3.0 GPA or higher on a 4.0 scale; and must be able to commit to the full length of the fellowship. **Criteria:** Selection will be based on the applicant's eligibility and their compliance with the application process.

Funds Avail.: $4,500 stipend for Kennedy Krieger Institute master level graduate and CDC fellows; $5,933 stipend is for pre-doctoral fellows. **To Apply:** Applicant must submit an online application form. **Deadline:** January 31. **Remarks:** The nine-week fellowship program is funded by the Centers for Disease Control and Prevention (CDC). **Contact:** To apply, go to http://kennedykrieger.org/Ferguson. For additional program information, E-mail: Ferguson_Fellowship@kennedykrieger.org; Kennedy Krieger Institute information, visit KennedyKrieger.org; Phone: 888-554-2080.

6527 ■ John F. Kennedy Library Foundation (JFKLF)

Columbia Point
Boston, MA 02125
Ph: (617)514-1550
E-mail: foundation@jfklfoundation.org
URL: www.jfklibrary.org/About-Us/JFK-Library-Foundation.aspx
Social Media: www.facebook.com/JFKLibrary
www.instagram.com/jfklibrary/
twitter.com/jfklibrary
www.youtube.com/user/JFKLF

6528 ■ Ernest Hemingway Research Grants *(Other/ Grant)*

Purpose: To provide funds for scholars and students who are doing research in the Ernest Hemingway Collection. **Focus:** General studies/Field of study not specified. **Qualif.:** Applicant must be a scholar and student interested or doing research in Ernest Hemingway Collection. **Criteria:** Selection will be based on expected utilization of the Hemingway Collection. preference is given to dissertation research by Ph.D. candidates working in newly opened or relatively unused portions of the collection, but all proposals are welcome and will receive careful consideration.

Funds Avail.: Up to $5,000. **Duration:** Annual. **To Apply:** Applicants must submit the online application form and must be accompanied by a brief proposal (three to four

pages) in the form of a letter describing the planned research and its significance; must submit two letters of recommendation from academic or other appropriate references; must provide a sample of applicant's writing, a project budget, and a curriculum vitae. **Deadline:** November 1. **Contact:** Ernest Hemingway Collection John F. Kennedy Presidential Library and Museum, Columbia Point, Boston, MA 02125; Fax: 617-514-1625; E-mail: stephen.plotkin@nara.gov.

6529 ■ John F. Kennedy Presidential Library and Museum

Columbia Point
Boston, MA 02125
Ph: (617)514-1600
Free: 866-JFK-1960
URL: www.jfklibrary.org
Social Media: www.facebook.com/JFKLibrary
www.instagram.com/jfklibrary
twitter.com/jfklibrary
www.youtube.com/user/JFKLF

6530 ■ Abba P. Schwartz Research Fellowship *(Professional development/Fellowship)*

Purpose: To support a scholar in the production of a substantial work in the areas of immigration, naturalization, or refugee policy, subjects of great personal and professional interest to Mr. Schwartz. **Focus:** Immigration. **Qualif.:** Applicants must be conducting research in the area of immigration, naturalization, or refugee policy. **Criteria:** Selection is based on the submitted application and supporting materials; preference is given to projects not supported by large grants from other institutions.

Funds Avail.: Up to $3,100. **Duration:** Annual. **Number Awarded:** 1. **To Apply:** Applicants must submit a completed application form along with brief proposal (3-4 pages) in the form of the letter describing the planned research, its significance, the intended audience, and expected outcome; two letters of recommendation from academic or other appropriate references; a sample of writing; a project budget and a vita. **Deadline:** September 30. **Contact:** Fellowship Coordinator, John F. Kennedy Library Foundation, Columbia Point, Boston, MA, 02125; Phone: 617-514-1629; Fax: 617-514-1625; Email: Kennedy.Fellowships@nara.gov.

6531 ■ Arthur M. Schlesinger Jr. Research Fellowship *(Professional development/Fellowship)*

Purpose: To support scholars in the production of substantial works in either of the following areas: the foreign policy of the Kennedy Presidency, especially in the Western Hemisphere or the Kennedy Administration's domestic policy, particularly with regard to racial justice or the conservation of natural resources. **Focus:** History, American; Latin American studies. **Criteria:** Selection is based on the submitted application and supporting materials; preference is given to projects not supported by large grants from other institutions.

Funds Avail.: Up to $5,000. **Duration:** Annual. **Number Awarded:** 2. **To Apply:** Applicants must submit a completed application form along with brief proposal (3-4 pages) in the form of the letter describing the planned research, its significance, the intended audience, and expected outcome; two letters of recommendation from academic or other appropriate references; a sample of writing; a project budget and a vita. **Deadline:** September 30. **Contact:** Fellowship

Awards are arranged alphabetically below their administering organizations

Coordinator, John F. Kennedy Library Foundation, Columbia Point, Boston, MA, 02125; Phone: 617-514-1629; Fax: 617-514-1625; Email: Kennedy.Fellowships@nara.gov.

6532 ■ Marjorie Kovler Research Fellowship *(Professional development/Fellowship)*

Purpose: To support a student in the production of a substantial work in the area of foreign intelligence and the presidency or a related topic. **Focus:** General studies/Field of study not specified. **Qualif.:** Applicants must be conducting research in the area of foreign intelligence and the presidency or related field. **Criteria:** Selection is based on the submitted application and supporting materials; preference is given to projects not supported by large grants from other institutions.

Funds Avail.: Up to $2,500. **Duration:** Annual. **Number Awarded:** 1. **To Apply:** Applicants must submit a completed application form along with brief proposal (3-4 pages) in the form of the letter describing the planned research, its significance, the intended audience, and expected outcome; two letters of recommendation from academic or other appropriate references; a sample of writing; a project budget and a vita. **Deadline:** September 30. **Contact:** Fellowship Coordinator, John F. Kennedy Library Foundation, Columbia Point, Boston, MA, 02125; Phone: 617-514-1629; Fax: 617-514-1625; Email: Kennedy.Fellowships@nara.gov.

6533 ■ Theodore C. Sorensen Research Fellowship *(Other/Fellowship)*

Purpose: To support a student in the production of a substantial work in the areas of domestic policy, political journalism, polling, press relations or a related topic. **Focus:** Public affairs. **Qualif.:** Applicants must be conducting research in the areas of domestic policy, political journalism, polling, press relations or a related topic. **Criteria:** Selection is based on the submitted application and supporting materials; preference is given to projects not supported by large grants from other institutions.

Funds Avail.: Up to $3,600. **Duration:** Annual. **Number Awarded:** 1. **To Apply:** Applicants must submit a completed application form along with brief proposal (3-4 pages) in the form of the letter describing the planned research, its significance, the intended audience, and expected outcome; two letters of recommendation from academic or other appropriate references; a sample of writing; a project budget and a vita. **Deadline:** September 30. **Contact:** Fellowship Coordinator, John F. Kennedy Library Foundation, Columbia Point, Boston, MA, 02125; Phone: 617-514-1629; Fax: 617-514-1625; Email: Kennedy.Fellowships@nara.gov.

6534 ■ Kentucky Paralegal Association (KPA)
PO Box 2675
Louisville, KY 40201-2675
URL: www.kypa.org
Social Media: www.facebook.com/KYParalegals

6535 ■ Kentucky Paralegal Association Paralegal Student Scholarships *(Undergraduate/Scholarship)*

Purpose: To provide financial assistance to those students who are in need. **Focus:** Paralegal studies.

Funds Avail.: $500. **Duration:** Annual. **To Apply:** Applicant must submit a letter of recommendation; Recommendations may be from a personal, academic or employment reference. **Deadline:** May 18. **Contact:** Education Committee Chair, PO Box 9848, Bowling Green, KY 42102; Email:

skaparalegals@mail.com; contact Nikki L. McKenzie, CKP Email: nmckenzie@elpolaw.com.

6536 ■ Kentucky REALTORS (KAR)
2708 Old Rosebud Rd, Ste. 200
Lexington, KY 40509
Ph: (859)263-7377
Fax: (859)263-7565
Free: 800-264-2185
URL: www.kar.com
Social Media: www.facebook.com/kentuckyrealtors
www.linkedin.com/company/kentuckyrealtors
twitter.com/kyrealtors
www.youtube.com/channel/
  UCY9CZIPWdENvkD8qJghqxrA

6537 ■ Graduate Realtor Institute Scholarships *(Graduate/Scholarship)*

Purpose: To provide quality educational services and programs for the real estate industry and the public. **Focus:** Real estate. **Qualif.:** Applicants must be residents of Kentucky; must be member with good standing with local, state and national association; must complete all GRI courses in the state of Kentucky.

Funds Avail.: Up to $1,000. **Duration:** Annual; up to 36 months. **To Apply:** Applicants must complete the application available on the website; must attach a letter of verification of realtor membership from a local board/association and submit the package to Kentucky Real Estate Education Foundation. **Deadline:** June 1. **Contact:** Kentucky Real Estate Education Foundation, 2708 Old Rosebud Rd., Ste. 200, Lexington, KY, 40509; Phone 859-263-7377; Fax 859-263-7565; Email: ndeboth@kar.com.

6538 ■ Kentucky Society of Certified Public Accountants (KYCPA)
1735 Alliant Ave.
Louisville, KY 40299
Ph: (502)266-5272
Fax: (502)261-9512
Free: 800-292-1754
E-mail: info@kycpa.org
URL: www.kycpa.org
Social Media: www.facebook.com/kycpa.org
www.instagram.com/kycpanews
twitter.com/kycpanews
www.youtube.com/user/kycpas

6539 ■ The Educational Foundation of KyCPA Scholarships *(Undergraduate/Scholarship)*

Purpose: To support students aspiring to become a Certified Public Accountant. **Focus:** Accounting. **Criteria:** Selection awards are based on acceptable academic performance and financial need.

Funds Avail.: up to $2,500. **Duration:** Annual. **Number Awarded:** 1. **To Apply:** Applicants must complete the online application; after such, documents below must be uploaded in the following order: college transcript(s) or unofficial transcripts; one page resume (include info on community service, academic organizations and activities); one page essay stating career goals, reasons for choosing accounting, how applicants are financing their education

Awards are arranged alphabetically below their administering organizations

and why they should receive the scholarship; one recommendations, one must be from an accounting faculty member. **Deadline:** April 1. **Remarks:** Established in 1988. **Contact:** Phone: 502-266-5272; Toll Free: 800-292-1754.

6540 ■ Dr. Arthur Kezian DDS
443 N Larchmont Blvd.
Los Angeles, CA 90004
Ph: (323)467-2777
URL: www.drkezian.com

6541 ■ Dr. Arthur A. Kezian DDS Science Scholarship *(Undergraduate, Graduate, College, University/ Scholarship)*

Purpose: To help deserving science students attend college. **Focus:** Science. **Qualif.:** Applicant must be attending a college or university in the fall semester; must be at least 18 years old and a resident of the United States or Canada; must have a minimum 3.0 GPA. **Criteria:** Selection is based on the 12-page essay submitted on why the applicant deserves this scholarship.

Funds Avail.: $1,200. **Duration:** Annual. **Number Awarded:** 1. **To Apply:** Applicant must submit a application in form; resume or cv; official transcript (gpa needs to be above 3.0); sat score report; dat, gre, or mcat score report; 1 minute video clip introducing yourself (optional but recommended). **Deadline:** March 31. **Contact:** Email: kezian@msn.com.

6542 ■ Kia Motors America Inc.
111 Peters Canyon Rd.
Irvine, CA 92606
Fax: (949)468-4515
URL: www.kia.com/us/en
Social Media: www.facebook.com/kia
www.instagram.com/kiamotorsusa
www.pinterest.com/kiamotorsusa
twitter.com/kia
www.youtube.com/kia

6543 ■ HACU/KIA Motors America, Inc. STEAM Scholarships *(Undergraduate, Graduate/Scholarship)*

Purpose: To assist STEAM students in defraying some of the educational expenditures. **Focus:** Arts; Engineering; Mathematics and mathematical sciences; Science. **Qualif.:** Applicants must be full-time sophomore or junior undergraduate students or graduate students attending a four-year HACU-member institution within the United States or Puerto Rico; must possess a minimum cumulative GPA of 3.0; must be in a STEAM field. **Criteria:** Selection will be based on the committee's criteria.

Funds Avail.: $3,400. **Number Awarded:** 10. **To Apply:** Application is available online. Applicants must fill out the application form and provide the following: documents showing that they are currently enrolled or accepted by a college, university, or institution; resume; scholarship essay; official transcript; enrollment verification form; and letter of recommendation. **Deadline:** May 24. **Contact:** Email: scholarship@hacu.net.

6544 ■ Kidney Foundation of Canada (KFOC)
310-5160 Decarie Blvd.
Montreal, QC, Canada H3X 2H9

Ph: (514)369-4806
Fax: (514)369-2472
Free: 800-361-7494
E-mail: info@kidney.ca
URL: kidney.ca
Social Media: www.facebook.com/kidneyfoundation
twitter.com/kidneycanada

6545 ■ Biomedical Research Grants *(Postdoctorate/ Grant)*

Purpose: To encourage research that may further current knowledge pertaining to the kidney and urinary tract. **Focus:** Biomedical research. **Qualif.:** Applicants must be Canadian citizens or landed immigrants. Eligibility for fellowships will include MDs or postdoctoral PhDs.

Funds Avail.: $50,000 per year. **Duration:** One, Two or three years. **To Apply:** Applicants must submit one complete original copy of the application package (unstapled) and one PDF copy on CD. Application package includes: checklist; Post Doctoral Fellowship Module; letter from proposed supervisor; written proof of offer of permanent position (if applicable); three sponsors' assessment forms; CV Module for Principal applicant; CV Module(s) for supervisor(s); up to five publications from the past five years (relevant to the proposal); and declaration by the applicants and supervisor. **Contact:** Email: chris.marquis@ kidney.ca.

6546 ■ KFOC Allied Health Doctoral Fellowships *(Doctorate/Fellowship)*

Purpose: To promote and enhance the development of nephrology/urology allied health investigators in Canada. **Focus:** Health sciences; Nephrology. **Qualif.:** Applicants must serve as a nephrology nurse or technician, social worker, dietician, transplant coordinator or other allied health professional; must have a demonstrated commitment to the area of nephrology or organ donation; must hold Canadian citizenship of landed immigrant status; must be accepted in proposed course of full-time study; and must have the intention to return to Canada (if studies are outside the country).

Funds Avail.: Up to 31,000 Canadian Dollars/year. **Deadline:** March 15. **Contact:** Email: chris.marquis@kidney.ca.

6547 ■ KFOC Allied Health Scholarships *(Graduate/ Scholarship)*

Purpose: To assist students with a demonstrated interest in nephrology/urology who are pursuing education at the masters or doctoral level. **Focus:** Health sciences; Nephrology; Urology. **Qualif.:** Applicants must serve as a nephrology nurse or technician, social worker, dietician, transplant coordinator or other allied health professional; must have a demonstrated commitment to the area of nephrology or organ donation; must hold Canadian citizenship or landed immigrant status; and must be accepted in proposed course of full-time or part-time study. **Criteria:** Preference will be given to applicants with a minimum of two years full-time equivalent experience in the area of nephrology.

Funds Avail.: No specific amount. **To Apply:** Applications must be submitted via email; Official transcripts must be courier-stamped and forwarded to the KFOC in the original sealed envelope from the institution. **Deadline:** March 15. **Contact:** Email: chris.marquis@kidney.ca.

Awards are arranged alphabetically below their administering organizations

6548 ■ KFOC Biomedical Scholarships *(Doctorate/Scholarship)*

Purpose: To provide salary support of an initial faculty appointment at the rank of assistant professor or its equivalent. **Focus:** Nephrology; Urology. **Qualif.:** Applicants should have an MD and have completed clinical training in nephrology or urology or a PhD and have been appointed to a medical school. Applicants must have demonstrated interest in nephrology or urology and should have completed at least two years of research training at the time of the award. **Criteria:** Selection is based on the research program outlined in the application.

Funds Avail.: $45,000/year. **Duration:** Up to two years. **To Apply:** Applicants must submit one complete original copy of the application package (unstapled) and one PDF copy on CD. Application package includes: the checklist; Biomedical Scholarship Module; letters of collaboration and/or support; list of operating and other grants applied for, or which are planned to apply for; appropriate ethical form(s); CV Module for principal applicant; and up to ten publications in the past five years (relevant to the proposal).

6549 ■ Kids' Chance of Florida, Inc.
PO Box 1648
Sarasota, FL 34230-1648
E-mail: info@kidschancefl.org
URL: kidschancefl.org
Social Media: twitter.com/kidschancefl

6550 ■ The Kids' Chance of Florida Scholarship Program *(All/Scholarship)*

Purpose: To provide financial assistance to students who had a parent severely injured or killed in a work accident in Florida. **Focus:** General studies/Field of study not specified. **Qualif.:** Applicant must be the child of a parent severely injured or killed in a Florida work accident. **Criteria:** Selection consideration will be given to meritorious academic progress and financial need. Demonstration of commitment to family and injured worker is beneficial.

Funds Avail.: $1,000 to $10,000. **Duration:** Annual; Renewable. **To Apply:** Application must be completed online. **Contact:** Email: info@kidschancefl.org; URL: https://kidschancefl.org/scholarship-info/.

6551 ■ Kids and Community
10510 N Springboro Pike
Miamisburg, OH 45342
Ph: (937)434-3095
URL: connorgroup.com/kids-and-community

6552 ■ Kids and Community Scholarship Program *(College, University/Scholarship)*

Purpose: To provide educational opportunities for disadvantaged youth. **Focus:** General studies/Field of study not specified. **Qualif.:** Applicant must be a high school senior or college student attending or planning to attend and accredited college or university in the United States, and must have a combined family income of less than $75,000. **Criteria:** Selection is based on the answers provided on the application. Preference given to students who reside in Atlanta, Austin, Charlotte, Chicago, Cincinnati, Columbus, Dallas, Dayton, Denver, Louisville, Minneapolis, Nashville, Raleigh-Durham, and Tampa.

Funds Avail.: $2,500. **Duration:** Annual. **Number Awarded:** 6. **To Apply:** Submit application, basic demo-

graphic information, evidence of school and community involvement, volunteer work and other activities. **Deadline:** January 15. **Contact:** URL: connorgroup.com/kids-and-community/scholarship/.

6553 ■ Sidney Kimmel Foundation for Cancer Research
Matthew H. Kamens 1650 Market Street, Suite 2800
Philadelphia, PA 19103
Ph: (215)665-2079
URL: www.kimmel.org

6554 ■ Kimmel Scholar Award *(Doctorate/Grant)*

Purpose: To improve the basic understanding of cancer biology and to develop new methods for the prevention and treatment of cancer. **Focus:** Oncology. **Criteria:** Applicants will be judged on the basis of potential impact their research efforts might have in advancing the possibility of a cure for cancer.

Funds Avail.: $200,000. **Duration:** Annual. **Number Awarded:** Up to 15. **Deadline:** December 1. **Remarks:** Established in 1997. **Contact:** Dr. Gary Cohen, c/o Emily Krohn; Email: ekrohn@cozen.com.

6555 ■ King Ice
PO Box 459
Rosemead, CA 91770
Ph: (626)339-3642
E-mail: sales@kingice.com
URL: www.kingice.com
Social Media: www.facebook.com/OfficialKingIce
instagram.com/kingice
twitter.com/OfficialKingIce
youtube.com/kingicedotcom

6556 ■ King Ice Scholarship *(Undergraduate, Graduate/Scholarship)*

Purpose: To alleviate the financial burden of students by providing them educational assistance. **Focus:** General studies/Field of study not specified.

To Apply: Application details available at www.kingice.com/pages/scholarship.

6557 ■ Martin Luther King Jr. Scholarship Association
Seton Hall University
400 S Orange Ave.
South Orange, NJ 07079
Fax: (973)275-2321
Free: 800-843-4255
E-mail: forrest.pritchett@shu.edu
URL: www13.shu.edu/offices/mlk-leadership-index.cfm
Social Media: www.facebook.com/setonhall
www.linkedin.com/school/seton-hall-university
twitter.com/setonhall

6558 ■ Martin Luther King Jr. Scholarships *(Graduate/Scholarship)*

Purpose: To support students in order that they may pursue their education at the post secondary level. **Focus:** Social sciences. **Qualif.:** Applicants must be students of

Awards are arranged alphabetically below their administering organizations

color, preferably african american, who reside and attend school in New London County, in order that they may pursue their education at the post secondary level. **Criteria:** Selection will be based on the submitted application materials; selecting scholars include community service, academic achievement, financial need, and United States citizenship.

Duration: Annual. **To Apply:** Applicant must submit completed application; completed essay(read Letter from a Birmingham Jail and then, in applicant's own words explain how the message in this letter will influence development as an individual and how the applicant will use this education to further Dr. King's Dream); three letters of recommendation (1. school 2. community 3. personal/not related); official transcripts; class standing; SAT and or ACT scores; Release of information form; copy of this application Checklist. **Deadline:** June 30. **Remarks:** Through excellence in academic achievement, distinguished leadership and community service, a commitment to further the legacy of Dr. Martin Luther King, Jr. **Contact:** Dr. Martin Luther King, Jr. Scholarship Trust Fund, Greater New London County - PO Box 1308, New London, Connecticut, 06320; Email: mlktrustfund@gmail.com.

6559 ■ King of Maids, LLC

4524 Oakton St.
Chicago, IL 60634
Free: 800-921-4334
E-mail: info@kingofmaids.com
URL: www.kingofmaids.com
Social Media: www.facebook.com/kingofmaids
twitter.com/KingofMaids

6560 ■ King of Maids Scholarship (Undergraduate, Graduate/Scholarship)

Purpose: To support college students in their studies. **Focus:** General studies/Field of study not specified. **Qualif.:** Open to undergraduate and graduate college students taking at least 12 credit hours per semester.

Funds Avail.: $1,000. **Duration:** Semiannual. **Number Awarded:** 1. **To Apply:** Read the blog posted at www.kingofmaids.com/blog/how-to-clean-your-carpet. Then either leave a unique and thoughtful comment on the blog post, or submit a one-page essay on the topic of why home cleaning is important. **Deadline:** January 30. **Contact:** www.kingofmaids.com/blog/how-to-clean-your-carpet.

6561 ■ Kip Dental and Orthodontics

5021 S Jellison Way, Unit C
Littleton, CO 80123
Ph: (720)608-5557
E-mail: kip@kipdental.com
URL: kipdental.com
Social Media: www.facebook.com/kipdental/reviews

6562 ■ Kip Dental and Orthodontics Scholarship (Undergraduate/Scholarship)

Purpose: To provide educational opportunities to students in the sponsor's community. **Focus:** General studies/Field of study not specified. **Qualif.:** Applicant must be a high school senior living or attending high school in Littleton, Colorado. **Criteria:** Submissions will be evaluated for effort, creativity, accuracy, popularity, and quality.

Funds Avail.: $2,000. **Number Awarded:** 1. **To Apply:** Applicant must create a one- to three-page document one

of the following topics: Why you think Littleton is a great place to live. Why you don't think Littleton is a great place to live. How you would improve Littleton. Entries can be submitted online or by email to the sponsor's address. **Deadline:** April 1. **Contact:** kipdental.com/scholarship-official-rules/.

6563 ■ Kevin Kitchnefsky Foundation

109 German Hill Rd.
Tunkhannock, PA 18657
Ph: (570)836-1240
Fax: (570)836-4584
URL: kitchnefskyfoundation.org
Social Media: www.facebook.com/kevinkitchnefsky

6564 ■ Individual K-Grants (All/Grant)

Purpose: To substantially improve the quality of life for the people affected with spinal cord injuries. **Focus:** Spinal cord injuries and research. **Qualif.:** Applicants must be residents of Pennsylvania who have suffered a spinal cord injury. **Criteria:** Selection will be based on committee's impressions of the materials you submit and your individual circumstances.

Funds Avail.: No specific amount. **Number Awarded:** 1. **To Apply:** Applicants must print and fill out the application, available at the website; use additional paper for the essays, and then attach them to the application. when the grant is awarded, the Foundation pays the monies directly to the organization or individual providing the product or service that the applicants requesting; application must be accompanied by three written estimates, submitted by three different companies, that include an estimate, terms of payment, an outline of work/product. **Deadline:** October 1st. **Contact:** Kevin Kitchnefsky Foundation for spinal cord research, 109 German Hill Rd., Tunkhannock, PA, 18657; Phone: 570-836-1240; Kevin Kitchnefsky; Phone: 570-499-1707; Email:info@KitchnefskyFoundation.org.

6565 ■ Esther A. and Joseph Klingenstein Fund

80 8th Ave., 14th Flr.
New York, NY 10011-7159
E-mail: info@klingfund.org
URL: klingenstein.org

6566 ■ Klingenstein Fellowships in the Neurosciences (Doctorate, Master's/Fellowship)

Purpose: To support young investigators engaged in basic or clinical research that may lead to a better understanding of epilepsy. **Focus:** Neuroscience. **Criteria:** Applications will be reviewed and selections will be made by an Advisory Committee of distinguished neuroscientists.

Duration: Annual. **Number Awarded:** Varies. **To Apply:** Applicants must complete online application form submit one original and ten copies of completed application form, and three letters of recommendation; copies of the abstract; Outline and relevancy of your research plans. **Deadline:** February 15.

6567 ■ Klingenstein Third Generation Foundation (KTGF)

80 8th Ave., 14th Flr.
New York, NY 10011-7159
URL: klingenstein.org

Awards are arranged alphabetically below their administering organizations

6568 ■ ADHD Fellowship *(Postdoctorate/Fellowship)*

Purpose: To support post-doctoral students with their research projects that will help the quality development and outcomes in mental healthcare for children and their families. **Focus:** Child development; Psychiatry. **Qualif.:** Applicants must be post-doctoral investigators with a PhD and/or MD who have completed all critical training; should be planning a career in research related to child and adolescent psychiatry and psychology; and should have demonstrated skills for independent research. **Criteria:** Recipients will be selected based on originality; soundness; contribution to progress within the field; quality of institutional support; mentoring and training program.

Funds Avail.: $30,000. **Duration:** Two years. **To Apply:** Candidates must be nominated by their institutions. **Deadline:** November 15. **Remarks:** Established in 1998.

6569 ■ Klingon Language Institute (KLI)

PO Box 794
Blue Bell, PA 19422
URL: www.kli.org
Social Media: www.facebook.com/klingonlanguageinstitute

6570 ■ Kor Memorial Scholarship *(Undergraduate, Graduate/Scholarship)*

Purpose: To provide financial support to students who are in need. **Focus:** Foreign languages.

6571 ■ John W. Kluge Center at the Library of Congress

101 Independence Ave. SE
Washington, DC 20540-4860
Ph: (202)707-3302
Fax: (202)707-3595
E-mail: scholarly@loc.gov
URL: www.loc.gov/loc/kluge

6572 ■ Kislak Fellowship for the Study of the History and Cultures of the Early Americas *(Undergraduate, Graduate/Fellowship)*

Purpose: To support research that contributes significantly to a greater understanding of the cultures and history of the Americas. **Focus:** United States studies. **Qualif.:** Applicants may be independent scholars, undergraduate or graduate students or a college/university faculty members in any discipline; there is no degree requirement but relevant educational information should be supplied in the application. **Criteria:** Selection is based on the submitted application materials.

Funds Avail.: $4,200 per month. **Duration:** Annual; up to three months. **To Apply:** Applicant must submit: a completed application form, in English; a curriculum vitae (maximum 2 pages; additional pages will be discarded); a single paragraph abstract; a statement of proposed research (maximum 3 pages); an explanation of why the Library of Congress is the required venue for their research (maximum 1 paragraph); a bibliography of works consulted for the proposal (maximum 3 pages); three references with completed reference forms from people who have read the research proposal. **Deadline:** October 15. **Contact:** Email: scholarly@loc.gov.

6573 ■ Kluge Fellowship *(Doctorate, Graduate/Fellowship)*

Purpose: To support students who wish to conduct research at the John W. Kluge Center. **Focus:** Architecture; Humanities; Law; Social sciences. **Qualif.:** Applicants must have received a terminal advanced degree within the past seven years in the humanities, social sciences or in a professional field such as architecture or law. **Criteria:** Selection is based on the submitted application materials.

Funds Avail.: $5,000. **Duration:** Annual; 4- 11 months. **Number Awarded:** Up to 12. **To Apply:** Applicant must submit: a completed application form, in English; a curriculum vitae (maximum 2 pages; additional pages will be discarded); a single paragraph abstract; a statement of proposed research (maximum 3 pages); an explanation of why the Library of Congress is the required venue for their research (maximum 1 paragraph); a bibliography of works consulted for the proposal (maximum 3 pages); three references with completed reference forms from people who have read the research proposal. **Deadline:** July 15. **Remarks:** Established in 2000. **Contact:** The John W. Kluge Center, Library of Congress, 101 Independence Ave SE, Washington, DC, 20540-4860; Email: scholarly@loc.gov.

6574 ■ David B. Larson Fellowships in Health and Spirituality *(Postdoctorate/Fellowship)*

Purpose: To support students who wish to conduct research in the interrelated fields of health and spirituality at the John W. Kluge Center. **Focus:** Health education; Religion. **Qualif.:** Applicants must be U.S. citizens or permanent residents and must possess a doctoral degree (PhD, MD, ScD, DrPH, DSW, PPsy, DST, ThD and JD). **Criteria:** Selection is based on the submitted application materials.

Funds Avail.: $4,200 per month. **Duration:** Annual; 6-12 months. **To Apply:** Applicant must submit: a completed application form, in English; a curriculum vitae (maximum 2 pages; additional pages will be discarded); a single paragraph abstract; a statement of proposed research (maximum 3 pages); an explanation of why the Library of Congress is the required venue for their research (maximum 1 paragraph); a bibliography of works consulted for the proposal (maximum 3 pages); three references with completed reference forms from people who have read the research proposal. **Deadline:** May 1. **Remarks:** The Fellowship was established in honor of Dr. Larson. **Contact:** The John W. Kluge Center; Phone: 202-707-3302; Email: scholarly@loc.gov.

6575 ■ John S. Knight Journalism Fellowships at Stanford (JSK)

450 Jane Stanford Way
Stanford, CA 94305
Ph: (650)723-4937
E-mail: jskfellowships@stanford.edu
URL: jsk.stanford.edu
Social Media: www.facebook.com/jskstanford
www.instagram.com/jskstanford
www.linkedin.com/school/john-s-knight-journalism
 -fellowships-at-stanford
twitter.com/JSKstanford
www.youtube.com/jskstanford

6576 ■ John S. Knight Journalism Fellowships *(Other/Fellowship)*

Purpose: To support diverse journalists from around the world who are deeply engaged in exploring solutions to journalism's biggest problems. **Focus:** Journalism. **Qualif.:** Applicants must already be authorized to work in the United

Awards are arranged alphabetically below their administering organizations

States and have at least three years of full-time professional experience; a college degree is not required. **Funds Avail.:** Varies. **Duration:** Annual. **Number Awarded:** Up to 12. **To Apply:** Applicants must submit a project, which focuses on addressing some aspect of most urgent problems facing journalism, namely Challenging Misinformation and Disinformation; Holding the Powerful Accountable; Eradicating News Deserts and Strengthening Local News; Fighting Bias, Intolerance and Injustice. **Deadline:** July 22. **Contact:** Email: jskfellowships@stanford.edu.

6577 ■ Knights of Columbus (KofC)
1 Columbus Plz.
New Haven, CT 06510
Ph: (203)752-4000
Free: 800-380-9995
E-mail: info@kofc.org
URL: www.kofc.org/en//index.html
Social Media: www.facebook.com/KnightsofColumbus
www.instagram.com/kofc_official
www.linkedin.com/company/knights-of-columbus
twitter.com/kofc

6578 ■ Bishop Charles P. Greco Graduate Fellowships *(Graduate, Master's/Fellowship)*

Purpose: To provide financial assistance to students enrolled in a Master's degree program designed for teachers of people with intellectual disabilities. **Focus:** General studies/Field of study not specified. **Qualif.:** Applicants must be U.S. students enrolled in a full-time master's degree program for teachers of people with intellectual disabilities; must be members in good standing of the Knights of Columbus, or the wife, sons or daughters of such a member or deceased member. **Criteria:** Selection based on the committee's criteria.

Funds Avail.: Up to $2,000; $500 per semester. **Duration:** Annual. **To Apply:** Applications may be obtained by using application order form in the website; official transcript of the applicant's undergraduate academic record to be sent to the Committee on Fellowships through the Department of Scholarships; autobiographical statement which gives evidence of interest in this program; statement should also give reasons for the selection of the graduate school named in this application; Two recommendations from professional people who have observed the applicant's work; certified copy of acceptance as a full time student by a graduate school approved to prepare classroom teachers of people with intellectual disabilities. **Deadline:** May 1. **Remarks:** Established in 1973. **Contact:** Committee on Fellowships, Department of Scholarships, PO Box 1670, New Haven, Connecticut, 06507-0901; Phone: 203-752-4332; Fax: 203-752-4103; Email: scholarships@kofc.org.

6579 ■ Kobe College Corporation-Japan Education Exchange (KCC-JEE)
540 W Frontage Rd., Ste. 3335
Northfield, IL 60093
Ph: (847)386-7661
Fax: (847)386-7662
E-mail: office@kccjee.org
URL: www.kccjee.org
Social Media: www.en-gb.facebook.com/KCCJEE
www.instagram.com/kccjapaneducexchange
twitter.com/kcc_jee

6580 ■ KCC-JEE Graduate Fellowships *(Graduate/Fellowship)*

Purpose: To support future American educators who teach more effectively about Japan. **Focus:** Aesthetics; Japanese studies; Religion. **Qualif.:** Applicants must be support qualified PhD graduate students for research or study in Japan. The purpose of the fellowship is to support future American educators who will teach more effectively about Japan. **Criteria:** Selection will be Selection will be based on scholarly excellence of the applicants.

Funds Avail.: $30,000. **Duration:** Annual. **Number Awarded:** Varies. **To Apply:** Applicants must contact KCC-JEE for the application information. **Deadline:** March 9. **Remarks:** Established in 1996. **Contact:** KCC Japan Education Exchange Graduate Fellowships Program; Email: programs@kccjee.org.

6581 ■ Herb Kohl Educational Foundation
PO Box 877
Sheboygan, WI 53082-0877
Ph: (920)457-1727
E-mail: marggraf@excel.net
URL: www.kohleducation.org

6582 ■ Herb Kohl Educational Foundation Student Excellence Scholarship *(Undergraduate/Scholarship)*

Purpose: To encourage Wisconsin youth to pursue postsecondary education in a public or nonpublic university, college or vocational/technical college. **Focus:** General studies/Field of study not specified. **Qualif.:** Applicants must be graduating high school students who intend to enroll in a post-secondary institution, university, college, or vocational/technical college; must be residents of the State of Wisconsin, are in good standing. **Criteria:** Selection will be based on their leadership, citizenship, school and community involvement, and academic achievement; their ability to clearly articulate goals in each of four areas: future educational goals, personal life goals, community/society service goals, and career goals.

Funds Avail.: $10,000. **Duration:** Annual. **Number Awarded:** 100. **To Apply:** Applicants must submit three letters of recommendation, one from each of the following categories: Teacher; Counselor or Principal; Community member or family friend who is not affiliated with your school district. **Deadline:** December 1.

6583 ■ Herb Kohl Educational Foundation Student Initiative Scholarship *(Undergraduate/Scholarship)*

Purpose: To support and recognize students who have not yet received other academic-based scholarships. **Focus:** General studies/Field of study not specified. **Qualif.:** Applicants should be students who: are unlikely to be eligible for other academic-based scholarships; have overcome personal obstacles or other adversity; have achieved an academic record that represents their maximum effort; show strong promise for succeeding in a postsecondary environment as evidenced by a well-rounded, solid secondary school performance; display other outstanding qualities, demonstrate a high level of motivation to achieve; and are residents of Wisconsin. **Criteria:** Recipients are selected by their teachers and school administrators.

Funds Avail.: $10,000. **Duration:** Annual. **Number Awarded:** Approximately 100. **Deadline:** December 8. **Remarks:** Established in 1997. **Contact:** Mark Mueller, Wisconsin Department of Public Instruction, PO Box 7841,

Awards are arranged alphabetically below their administering organizations

Madison, WI, 53707-7841; Phone: 608-266-3945; Email: mark.mueller@dpi.wi.gov.

6584 ■ Herb Kohl Educational Foundation Teacher Fellowship Program (Professional development/ Fellowship)

Purpose: To support teachers in the pursuit of their unrealized goals for their classrooms or professional development. **Focus:** Teaching. **Qualif.:** Applicants must be Pre-K through Grade 12 Wisconsin teachers who intend to continue teaching for at least the year following the receipt of the fellowship; must be nominated by a parent, teacher, student, community member or administrator. **Criteria:** Selection will be chosen for their superior ability to inspire a love of learning in their students and ability to motivate others through leadership and service within and outside the classroom.

Funds Avail.: $6,000. **Duration:** Annual. **Number Awarded:** Approximately 100. **Deadline:** December 1.

6585 ■ Susan G. Komen
5005 LBJ Freeway, Ste. 250
Dallas, TX 75244
Free: 877-465-6636
E-mail: helpline@komen.org
URL: ww5.komen.org
Social Media: www.facebook.com/SusanGKomen
www.instagram.com/susangkomen
www.linkedin.com/company/susangkomen
www.pinterest.com/susangkomen
twitter.com/SusanGKomen
www.youtube.com/komenforthecure

6586 ■ Susan G. Komen for the Cure College Scholarship Awards (Two Year College/Award, Scholarship)

Purpose: To assist young adults in their academic pursuits. **Focus:** General studies/Field of study not specified. **Qualif.:** Applicants must be U.S. citizens, high school or college graduate students who have lost a parent to breast cancer; planning to attend state-supported college or university in their state where they permanently reside and were never subjected to disciplinary action by any institution; must have 2.8 GPA on a 4.0 scale; and not older than 25 years old. **Criteria:** Applicants will be evaluated based on scholastic achievement, community service, financial need, and demonstrated leadership potential.

Funds Avail.: $5,000. **To Apply:** Applicants must send an email to Susan G. Komen Breast Cancer Foundation to apply for the application. **Deadline:** October 15. **Contact:** For additional information, contact ISTS at contactus@applyists.com.

6587 ■ Susan G. Komen for the Cure Post-doctoral Fellowships - Clinical Research Grants (Postdoctorate/Grant, Fellowship)

Purpose: To support promising scientist and clinician/scientists who are embarking on careers dedicated to breast cancer research. **Focus:** Medical research.

Duration: Annual. **Contact:** Email: kbergman@komen.org.

6588 ■ Koniag Education Foundation (KEF)
4241 B St., Ste. 303 B
Anchorage, AK 99503

Ph: (907)562-9093
Fax: (907)562-9023
E-mail: kef@koniageducation.org
URL: www.koniageducation.org

6589 ■ Glenn Godfrey Sr. Memorial Scholarship (Undergraduate, Graduate/Scholarship)

Purpose: To help our Alutiiq people pursue self-improvement and positive leadership roles in community service and/or civic duty. **Focus:** General studies/Field of study not specified. **Qualif.:** Applicants must be ability to demonstrate continued community service or civic duty; 2.5 GPA or equivalent. **Criteria:** Selection will be based on the committee's criteria.

Funds Avail.: $5,000. **Duration:** Annual. **Number Awarded:** 1. **To Apply:** Applications are completed and submitted online. **Deadline:** June 1. **Remarks:** The scholarship was named in honor of Glenn Godfrey, an Aleut political and social leader who was raised on Kodiak Island. **Contact:** Email: scholarships@koniageducation.org.

6590 ■ KEF General Scholarships (Undergraduate, Graduate/Scholarship)

Purpose: To seek out and honor students who excel academically and who show the potential to succeed in college studies. **Focus:** General studies/Field of study not specified. **Qualif.:** Applicant must be a students with a GPA of 2.5 or higher who are pursuing a degree through an accredited educational institution. **Criteria:** Selection will be based on committee's criteria.

Funds Avail.: Up to $2,500 each. **Duration:** Annual. **Number Awarded:** Varies. **To Apply:** Application must submit online. **Deadline:** March 15 (Funding for Summer, Fall and Spring). **Contact:** Email: scholarships@koniageducation.org.

6591 ■ KEF Vocational Award (Undergraduate/Award)

Purpose: To seek out and honor students who have chosen to further their education through vocational training lasting more than six weeks. **Focus:** General studies/Field of study not specified. **Qualif.:** Applicants must be enrolled in an accredited or state or municipally recognized vocational school and minimum cumulative GPA of 2.00 or equivalent scores and gaining employment or job security and/ or advancement.

Funds Avail.: Up to $2,500. **Duration:** Annual. **Number Awarded:** Multiple. **To Apply:** Application must be submitted by essay, include a description of your personal and family history, community involvement, volunteer activities, as well as your educational and life goals and Recent Resume and one Letter of Recommendation. **Contact:** Email: scholarships@koniageducation.org.

6592 ■ Larry Matfay Cultural Heritage Scholarship (Undergraduate, Graduate/Scholarship)

Purpose: To revitalize and renew heritage and pride of the Alutiiq culture. **Focus:** Anthropology; History; Native American studies. **Qualif.:** Applicants must be majoring in anthropology, history, Alaskan Native or American Indian Studies, or other disciplines which involves research and learning about Alutiiq culture.

Funds Avail.: Up to $1,000. **Duration:** Annual. **Number Awarded:** 1. **Deadline:** June 1. **Remarks:** The Scholarship was named in honor of Larry Matfay, the last chief of Akhiok. **Contact:** Email: scholarships@koniageducation.org.

Awards are arranged alphabetically below their administering organizations

6593 ■ The Korea Society (TKS)

350 Madison, 24th Fl.
New York, NY 10017
Ph: (212)759-7525
Fax: (212)759-7530
URL: www.koreasociety.org
Social Media: www.facebook.com/koreasociety
twitter.com/koreasociety
www.youtube.com/user/TheKoreaSociety

6594 ■ Fall Fellowships in Korean Studies *(Other/ Fellowship)*

Purpose: To provide a general overview of Korea's past and present by covering all the expenses of the participants including round-trip international airfare, accommodations and meals. **Focus:** Korean studies. **Qualif.:** Applicant must be an American educator who is professionally engaged as a textbook writer and editor or an East Asia specialist in higher education who would like to include Korea in teaching, research or writing. **Criteria:** Applicants who are planning to author textbooks on world history or Asian history and are intending to contribute articles to reference works and who will be editors of such works will be given priority.

Funds Avail.: No specific amount. **Duration:** Annual. **To Apply:** Applicants must submit a complete application packet including the application form and supporting documentation. **Deadline:** June 4.

6595 ■ Korean Language Study Awards *(Graduate, Professional development/Scholarship)*

Purpose: To cover student's expenses like tuition fees, round trip airfare to Korea and basic living expenses. **Focus:** Korean studies. **Qualif.:** Applicants must be college graduates, graduate students, educators or other professionals with Korea-related career objectives **Criteria:** Recipients will be selected based on criteria designed by the Scholarship Committee.

Funds Avail.: No specific amount. **Duration:** Annual. **To Apply:** Applicants must submit application form; resume; official college transcripts; and two letters of reference.

6596 ■ Korean American Scholarship Foundation (KASF)

1952 Gallows Rd., Ste. 310
Vienna, VA 22182
E-mail: feedback@kasf.org
URL: www.kasf.org
Social Media: www.facebook.com/
KoreanAmericanScholarshipFoundation
twitter.com/kasf_national?lang=en

6597 ■ KASF scholarships *(Graduate, Undergraduate/Scholarship)*

Purpose: To help meet the financial needs of Korean-American students seeking higher education. **Focus:** General studies/Field of study not specified. **Qualif.:** All applicants must be enrolled in a full time program in the U.S during the scholarship application year in Korean American. **Criteria:** Selection will be based on financial need, scholastic achievement, recommendationsn essay and community service/extracurricular activities.

Funds Avail.: $1,000. **Duration:** Annual. **To Apply:** Applicants must submit a completed scholarship application to

the respective KASF region (each region is designated by the state where school is located). **Contact:** Korean American Scholarship foundation, 1952 Gallows Rd., Ste., 310, Vienna, VA, 22182; Email: feedback@ksea.org.

6598 ■ KASF Designated Scholarships *(Graduate, Undergraduate/Scholarship)*

Purpose: To help meet the financial needs of the students seeking higher education. **Focus:** General studies/Field of study not specified. **Qualif.:** Applicant must be a Korean-American student currently enrolled in a full-time undergraduate or graduate program. Minimum cumulative GPA of 3.0. **Criteria:** Selection will be based on the committee's criteria.

Funds Avail.: $2,000. **Duration:** Annual. **Contact:** Korean American Scholarship foundation, 1952 Gallows Rd., Ste., 310, Vienna, VA, 22182; Email: feedback@ksea.org.

6599 ■ KASF General Scholarships *(Undergraduate, Graduate, Professional development/Scholarship)*

Purpose: To provide educational support for the Korean-American students who are seeking higher education. **Focus:** General studies/Field of study not specified. **Qualif.:** Applicants must be Korean-American high school, college or graduate students, professionals or descendants of Korean War American Veterans. Minimum cumulative GPA of 3.0. **Criteria:** Recipients is selected based on financial need, scholastic achievement, recommendations, essay and community services/extracurricular activities.

Funds Avail.: $500 to $5,000. **Duration:** Annual. **To Apply:** Applicants must submit a completed scholarship application to the respective KASF region (each region is designated by the state where school is located). **Deadline:** Varies with the region. **Contact:** Korean American Scholarship foundation, 1952 Gallows Rd., Ste., 310, Vienna, VA, 22182; Email: feedback@ksea.org.

6600 ■ Kosciuszko Foundation (KF)

15 E 65th St.
New York, NY 10065
Ph: (212)734-2130
URL: www.thekf.org
Social Media: www.linkedin.com/company/the-kosciuszko
  -foundation
twitter.com/KosciuszkoFound

6601 ■ Kosciuszko Foundation Graduate Study and Research in Poland Scholarships *(Graduate, Postgraduate/Scholarship)*

Purpose: To support students and university faculty members in their research at various universities in Poland. **Focus:** General studies/Field of study not specified; Polish studies. **Qualif.:** Applicants must be graduate-level students or university faculty members who are US citizens may apply; Polish citizens are not eligible. **Criteria:** Selection is based on academic excellence, motivation, the need to pursue research in Poland.

Funds Avail.: 1,350 Zloty per month for housing and living expenses and additional funding of $300 per month of approved study. **To Apply:** Applicants must complete the Polish Ministry of National Education application entitled Bureau for Academic Recognition and International Exchange; must provide an abstract of the project proposal; must attach copies of study certificates such as the level of language proficiency; copies of undergraduate and gradu-

Awards are arranged alphabetically below their administering organizations

ate diplomas; must have two letters of recommendation from professor; must submit a letter of invitation from the University/Institute in Poland where research is conducted; must have two passport-size photos with printed name on the reverse. **Deadline:** March 10. **Contact:** Studies & Research in Poland Program, Kosciuszko Foundation, 15 E 65th St., New York, NY 10065; Email: Addy@thekf.org.

6602 ■ Kosciuszko Foundation Tuition Scholarships (Graduate/Scholarship)

Purpose: To support American students of Polish descent for full-time graduate studies in the United States. **Focus:** General studies/Field of study not specified. **Qualif.:** Applicants must be a United States citizens or permanent resident of Polish descent who is in the beginning of or continuing graduate studies in the academic year; must have a minimum GPA of 3.0; and must be a full-time student; Only one member per immediate family may receive a tuition scholarship during a given academic year; Applicants may re-apply for funding, however, scholarship renewals are not guaranteed. Awards are limited to two tuition scholarships per individual during the period of studies. **Criteria:** Selection is based on application completeness, recommendation of teachers and professors, academic excellence and achievements, applicant's interests and motivation, the applicant's essay, interest in Polish subjects or involvement in the Polish American community. Financial need is taken into consideration.

Funds Avail.: $1,000 - $7,000. **Duration:** one academic year. **To Apply:** Applicants must complete the Tuition Scholarship application form and Financial Information page (application may be obtained from the Kosciuszko Foundation); must submit a personal statement about their academic goals, career goals, major they are pursuing and area of specialization; must have two passport photos for publication purposes; must have the official transcript; must prepare two confidential letters of academic reference from professors/teachers submitted on letterhead; must provide proof of Polish ancestry. **Contact:** Grants Department, Kosciuszko Foundation, Inc., 15 E 65th St., New York, NY 10065; Phone: 212-734-2130 ext. 210; E-mail: Addy@thekf.org.

6603 ■ Kosciuszko Foundation Year Abroad Scholarships (Graduate, Undergraduate/Scholarship)

Purpose: To support the deserving students as they continue their Polish language studies in Poland. **Focus:** Polish studies. **Qualif.:** Applicant must be a United States citizen and permanent resident of Polish descent who is an undergraduate sophomore, junior, senior or graduate student; must have a minimum GPA of 3.0. **Criteria:** Selection is based on academic excellence, motivation for pursuing Polish studies, interest in Polish subjects and involvement in the Polish American community. Applications are first reviewed by the Foundation's selection committee; Applications which are reviewed positively are sent to Poland for review by the Polish Ministry.

Funds Avail.: 1,350 Zloty per month for living expenses and additional funding of $900 per semester. **Duration:** one academic year. **To Apply:** Applicants must complete the Polish Ministry of National Education application entitled Bureau for Academic Recognition and International Exchange; must attach copies of transcript of records; must submit two letters of recommendation from professors and must have two passport size photos with printed name on the reverse. **Deadline:** March 30. **Contact:** Year Abroad Program, Kosciuszko Foundation, 15 E 65th St., New York, NY 10065; Email: Addy@thekf.org.

6604 ■ Massachusetts Federation of Polish Women's Clubs Scholarships (Undergraduate/Scholarship)

Purpose: To provide support to those qualified students in pursuing higher education. **Focus:** General studies/Field of study not specified; Polish studies. **Qualif.:** Applicants must be a United States citizens of Polish descent or Polish citizens with permanent residency status in the United States residing in Massachusetts who will engage in a second, third or fourth year of undergraduate studies during the academic year; must have a minimum GPA of 3.0. **Criteria:** Selection will be based on academic excellence, the applicant's academic achievements, interests, motivation, and interest in Polish subjects and involvement in the Polish American community. Financial need is taken into consideration.

Funds Avail.: $1,250. **Duration:** One academic year. **To Apply:** Applicant must complete the scholarship application form and financial information page; must submit a personal statement about their academic goals, career goals and specialization; must have a two passport-sized photos for publication purposes; must submit official transcripts; must have two confidential letters of academic reference from professor and teachers; must provide proof of Polish ancestry. **Contact:** Grants Department, Kosciuszko Foundation, 15 East 65th Street, St., New York, NY 10065; Email: Addy@thekf.org; Phone: 212-734-2130 ext. 210.

6605 ■ Polish American Club of North Jersey Scholarships (Undergraduate/Scholarship)

Purpose: To provide funds to those qualified students in pursuing higher education. **Focus:** General studies/Field of study not specified; Polish studies. **Qualif.:** Applicants must be a United States citizens of Polish descent or Polish citizens with permanent residency status in U.S who are active members of the Polish American Club of North Jersey. **Criteria:** Selection is based on academic excellence, the applicant's academic achievements, interests, motivation, and interest in Polish subjects and involvement in the Polish American community. Financial need is taken into consideration.

Funds Avail.: Amount varies. **Duration:** one academic year. **To Apply:** Applicants must complete the scholarship application form and financial information page; must have a personal statement about their academic goals, career goals and specialization; must have two passport photos for publication purposes; must submit an official transcript; must prepare two confidential letters of academic reference from professor and teachers; must provide proof of Polish ancestry; Curriculum Vitae. **Contact:** Grants Department, Kosciuszko Foundation, 15 East 65th Street, St., New York, NY 10065; Email: Addy@thekf.org; Phone: 212-734-2130 ext. 210.

6606 ■ Polish National Alliance of Brooklyn, USA Scholarships (Undergraduate/Scholarship)

Purpose: To provide financial assistance to all qualified students wanting to pursue their studies in the United States. **Focus:** General studies/Field of study not specified; Polish studies. **Qualif.:** Applicants must be United States citizens of Polish descent or Polish citizens with permanent residency status in the U.S. who are members in good standing of the Polish National Alliance of Brooklyn, USA and the Polish National Alliance of the United States of North America; must have a minimum GPA of 3.0. **Criteria:** Selection is based on the academic excellence, the applicant's academic achievements, interests, motiva-

Awards are arranged alphabetically below their administering organizations

tion, interest in Polish subjects and involvement in the Polish American community. Financial need is taken into consideration; Scholarships are awarded on a competitive basis.

Funds Avail.: $2,000. **Duration:** one academic year. **To Apply:** Applicants must complete the scholarship application form and financial information page; must submit a personal statement about their academic goals, career goals and the major expect to pursue; must have two passport photos for publication purposes; must have two confidential letters of academic reference; must have an official transcript of record; must have two letters of academic reference from professor and teachers; must provide proof of Polish ancestry. **Contact:** Grants Department, Kosciuszko Foundation, Inc., 15 East 65th Street, New York, NY 10065; Email: Addy@thekf.org; Phone: (212) 734-2130 ext. 210.

6607 ■ Dr. Marie E. Zakrzewski Medical Scholarships *(Doctorate/Scholarship)*

Purpose: To provide support for young women of Polish ancestry in their pursuit of medical education. **Focus:** Polish studies. **Qualif.:** Applicants must be U.S. citizens of Polish descent or Polish citizens with permanent residency status in the United States who are entering first, second or third year of M.D. studies in academic year; must have a minimum GPA of 3.0; must be a female. **Criteria:** Selection is based on academic excellence, applicant's academic achievements, and interest, and motivation, interest in Polish subjects and involvement in the Polish American Community; applicant's essay; Interest in Polish subjects or involvement in the Polish American community; Financial need is taken into consideration and preference is given to residents of the state of Massachusetts.

Funds Avail.: $3,500. **Duration:** one academic year. **Number Awarded:** 1. **To Apply:** Applicants must submit a personal statement about the academic goals, career goals and area of specialization; must have a two passport sized photos for publication purposes; must have an official transcript and two confidential letters of academic reference from professors and teachers; must provide proof of Polish ancestry. **Contact:** Grants Department, Kosciuszko Foundation, 15 East 65th Street, St., New York, NY 10065; Email: Addy@thekf.org; Phone: 212-734-2130 ext. 210.

6608 ■ KPMG Foundation

3 Chestnut Ridge Rd.
Montvale, NJ 07645
E-mail: us-kpmgfoundation@kpmg.com
URL: www.kpmgfoundation.org
Social Media: www.linkedin.com/company/kpmg-us
twitter.com/KPMG_Foundation
www.youtube.com/user/KPMGFoundationVideos

6609 ■ KPMG Foundation Minority Accounting Doctoral Scholarships *(Doctorate/Scholarship)*

Purpose: To provide financial assistance to minority students in order to meet the escalating costs of higher education. **Focus:** Accounting. **Qualif.:** Applicants must be African-American, Hispanic-American or Native American doctoral students; must be US citizens or a permanent resident of the United States; must be enrolled, on campus, in a full time AACSB-accredited, Accounting business doctoral program. **Criteria:** Applicants are evaluated based on financial need.

To Apply: Applicants must submit a completed copy of the application Form; a brief cover letter explaining the reason

for pursuing a PhD in accounting; a copy of most recent resume; undergraduate and graduate transcripts; and proof of matriculation status. **Remarks:** Established in 1993. **Contact:** KMPG Foundation, at the above address.

6610 ■ Krell Institute

1609 Golden Aspen Dr., Ste. 101
Ames, IA 50010
Ph: (515)956-3696
Fax: (515)956-3699
URL: www.krellinst.org

6611 ■ DOE Computational Science Graduate Fellowship (DOE CSGF) *(Doctorate, Graduate/ Fellowship)*

Purpose: To provide outstanding benefits and opportunities to students pursuing a PhD in scientific or engineering disciplines with an emphasis in high-performance computing. **Focus:** Aerospace sciences; Astronomy and astronomical sciences; Biology; Chemistry; Computer and information sciences; Engineering, Biomedical; Engineering, Electrical; Engineering, Mechanical; Engineering, Nuclear; Environmental science; Materials research/science; Mathematics and mathematical sciences; Oceanography; Physics. **Criteria:** Selection is based on the application.

Duration: Annual. **To Apply:** Applicants must register and apply online.

6612 ■ Samuel H. Kress Foundation

174 E 80th St.
New York, NY 10075
Ph: (212)861-4993
Fax: (212)628-3146
E-mail: info@kressfoundation.org
URL: www.kressfoundation.org
Social Media: www.instagram.com/kressfdn
twitter.com/KressFdn

6613 ■ History of Art: Institutional Fellowships *(Graduate/Fellowship)*

Purpose: To provide young art historians the opportunities like exposures to the object of the study, prolonged access to key information resources such as libraries and photographic archives, the development of professional relationships with colleagues abroad, and sustained immersion in European cultures. **Focus:** European studies. **Criteria:** Selection of applicant will be based on the fellowship criteria.

Funds Avail.: $30,000 per annum. **Duration:** Annual; two years. **To Apply:** Applicants should include summary of the proposed dissertation research project maximum length five pages; a brief description of any previous research and travel experience abroad; current curriculum vitae; official sealed transcript from the university where you received your MA. **Deadline:** November 30.

6614 ■ Kress Conservation Fellowships *(Postgraduate/Fellowship)*

Purpose: To provide competitive grants to museums and other conservation facilities which sponsor supervised internships in the conservation of specific objects and onsite training. **Focus:** Art conservation. **Qualif.:** Applicants must be an individual who has completed an M.A degree in art

Awards are arranged alphabetically below their administering organizations

conservation; must be a U.S citizen. **Criteria:** Selection of applicant will be based on the fellowship criteria.

Funds Avail.: $32,000. **Duration:** Annual; one year. **Number Awarded:** 6. **To Apply:** Applicants must the Kress Conservation Fellowships are administered by the Foundation for Advancement in Conservation (FAIC). Please visit the FAIC website for detailed application instructions. **Deadline:** January 22.

6615 ■ The Krystal Co.
1455 Lincoln Pkwy, Ste 600
Dunwoody, GA 30346
URL: www.krystal.com
Social Media: www.facebook.com/Krystal
www.instagram.com/krystal
twitter.com/krystal
www.youtube.com/user/krystalloverslounge

6616 ■ The Square Up Scholarship Program *(Two Year College, Undergraduate, Vocational/Occupational, Four Year College/Scholarship)*

Purpose: To support, promote, and encourage the educational pursuits and goals of individual Krystal employees. **Focus:** General studies/Field of study not specified. **Qualif.:** Applicant must be a Krystal Co. employee in good standing with at least 6-months of employment tenure, seeking or planning to seek a 2-year or 4-year degree, trade degree, or technical certification. **Criteria:** Selection is based on academic achievement, leadership, community involvement, brand tenure, unusual family and personal circumstances, and financial need.

Funds Avail.: $2,500. **Number Awarded:** 1. **To Apply:** Application must be completed at www.krystal.com/about-us/. **Deadline:** April 1. **Contact:** Brian Dodgen, Program Manager; Phone: 507-931-0635; Email: bdodgen@scholarshipamerica.org.

6617 ■ Kurz Industrial Solutions
1325 McMahon Dr.
Neenah, WI 54956
Ph: (803)753-1771
Fax: (516)753-1776
URL: kurz.com
Social Media: www.facebook.com/KurzElectric
www.linkedin.com/company/kurz-industrial-solutions

6618 ■ Kurz Industrial Solutions Wind Energy Scholarship Fund *(Graduate/Scholarship)*

Purpose: To assist students studying within the renewable energy field. **Focus:** Energy-related areas; Environmental conservation. **Qualif.:** Applicant must be currently enrolled as a rising sophomore (junior or senior for 2+ year programs), or a graduate student in the renewable energy field and have a minimum 3.0 GPA. Applicant may also be enrolled in specific technical certification programs.

Funds Avail.: $1,000. **Number Awarded:** 2. **To Apply:** Applicant must create and submit a video (up to one minute long) answering the question: What does renewable energy mean to you? Video should be uploaded at kurz.com/wind-scholarship-application. **Deadline:** June 15.

6619 ■ La Fondation pour le journalisme canadien
595 Bay St., Ste. 401
Toronto, ON, Canada M5G 2C2

Ph: (416)955-0394
E-mail: info@cjf-fjc.ca
URL: cjf-fjc.ca
Social Media: www.facebook.com/cjffjc
twitter.com/cjffjc

6620 ■ CJF Canadian Journalism Fellowships *(Graduate, Other, Undergraduate/Fellowship)*

Purpose: To help fellows achieve their future potential as effective and responsible journalists. **Focus:** Journalism. **Qualif.:** Applicants must have at least five years experience and be full-time news or editorial employees with Canadian newspapers, news services, radio, television or magazines. Freelance journalists who have been working consistently in the media over a five-year period will also be considered. Fellows are free to enroll in any graduate or undergraduate courses and use the full facilities of the University of Toronto. **Criteria:** Fellows are selected by a committee appointed by the President of the University of Toronto and the Master of Massey College.

Funds Avail.: 3,000 Canadian Dollars. **Duration:** Annual. **Number Awarded:** 2. **To Apply:** Applicants must include a proposal for a plan of study; statement of the applicant's experience; samples of work; and supporting letters from an employer or references. **Deadline:** March 6.

6621 ■ Greg Clerk Award *(Advanced Professional, Professional development/Award)*

Purpose: To recognize and offer a professional development opportunity to working journalists. **Focus:** Journalism; Media arts; Radio and television. **Qualif.:** Applicants must be Canadian journalists who have been employed for one to five years and are employed by, under contract to, or freelancing on the news and editorial side of regularly published newspapers and periodicals, TV and radio news broadcasters, and online publications. **Criteria:** Applicants will be judged based on the jury will be looking for innovative proposals from journalists interested in expanding their knowledge and understanding of issues rather than their reporting skills.

Funds Avail.: $5,000. **Duration:** Annual. **To Apply:** Applicants must submit a detailed proposal of no more than two pages outlining the use of professional development opportunity; two samples of works; resume; and one letter of recommendation from a relevant employer. **Deadline:** June 8. **Remarks:** The award was created in memory of one of Canada's greatest journalists, Greg Clark - a war correspondent, an avid outdoorsman, a humorist, but above all, a great reporter who excelled at storytelling. **Contact:** Email: programs@cjf-fjc.ca.

6622 ■ Tom Hanson Photojournalism Award *(All/Internship)*

Purpose: To give photographers trying to break into photojournalism the chance to perform on the national stage. **Focus:** Photography, Journalistic. **Qualif.:** Applicants must be Canadian photojournalists who have been in the business less than five years. Applicants can be students, freelance photographers or photographers currently employed at regional or non-daily publications. **Criteria:** Selection committee is made up of Canadian Journalism Foundation board members, photographers and photo editors from The Canadian Press and daily newspapers, and members of Tom's family.

Funds Avail.: $875 weekly salary. **Duration:** Annual; program runs for six weeks. **Number Awarded:** 1. **To Ap-**

Awards are arranged alphabetically below their administering organizations

ply: Applicants must submit the following: a detailed proposal of no more than 1, 000 words on how they would use this internship to expand their experience as a photojournalist; a portfolio of at least 12 and no more than 25 photos. Each photo should be captioned and may include a brief background explanation on how the photo was captured; a multimedia presentation that includes video; resume; and a letter of recommendation from a current employer or teacher, although such is not mandatory. **Deadline:** January 19. **Remarks:** The program was established in memory of Tom Hanson, an award-winning photographer for The Canadian Press who travelled around the world and across the country, shooting some of the most iconic news and sports images of the last 15 years. The Hanson Award is administered by The Canadian Journalism Foundation and offers a six-week paid internship at The Canadian Press head office in Toronto.

6623 ■ La Société Canadienne de Pharmacologie et de Therapeutique (SCPT)

ON, Canada
E-mail: info@pharmacologycanada.org
URL: pharmacologycanada.org
Social Media: www.facebook.com/pharmacologycanada
twitter.com/CSPT_SCPT

6624 ■ Canadian Society for Pharmacology and Therapeutics Clinical Fellowship Award *(Advanced Professional/Fellowship)*

Purpose: To recognize and stimulate research made by a clinical fellow in an accredited Clinical Pharmacology program recognized by the Royal College of Physicians and Surgeons of Canada. **Focus:** Pharmacology. **Qualif.:** Award candidates must be CSPT members in good standing both at the time of nomination and at the time of award presentation. **Criteria:** Applicants are judged on originality and uniqueness of approach to laboratory or clinical research that, in the opinion of the committee, has led to new significant knowledge in Clinical Pharmacology.

Funds Avail.: 1,000 Canadian Dollars. **Duration:** Annual. **Number Awarded:** 1. **To Apply:** Applicants must submit a joint letter of nomination or two individual letters of nomination, prepared by the sponsors; maximum of 2 pages is allowed for the letter(s) of nomination; maximum of two published or in press manuscripts considered pertinent to the nomination; nominee's brief curriculum vitae (maximum 10 pages); two additional letters of support describing the impact of the nominee's research; brief biographical sketch suitable for inclusion in a press release. **Deadline:** February 14. **Contact:** Chair of the Awards Committee - info@pharmacologycanada.org.

6625 ■ LA Tutors 123

9454 Wilshire Blvd., Ste. 600
Beverly Hills, CA 90212
Ph: (424)335-0035
Free: 866-608-8867
E-mail: inquiries@latutors123.com
URL: www.latutors123.com
Social Media: facebook.com/latutors123

6626 ■ LA Tutors 123 Innovation in Education Scholarship *(All/Scholarship)*

Purpose: To commend those outstanding students who have made a difference in the lives of others in some in-

novative or technological fashion. **Focus:** General studies/Field of study not specified. **Qualif.:** Applicants must be currently enrolled as high school or college/university students within the United States or Canada; have a cumulative GPA of at least 3.0 (or the equivalent); be citizens of, permanent residents of, or hold their own valid student visas in the United States or Canada; and have designed an innovative project that makes a difference in the lives of others (such could be a website, series of blogs, an app, fundraising event, etc.). **Criteria:** Selection will be based on the applicants' winning projects. Those projects will be judged on the basis of creativity, innovation, and user experience.

Funds Avail.: $500. **Duration:** Monthly. **Number Awarded:** 1 per month. **To Apply:** Applicants must submit their respective essays (must be of their original work) describing the goal of the particular project (as mentioned in the qualifications) and provide supporting documentation; all entries must be entered using the official LA Tutors 123 Innovation Scholarship submission form which can be accessed at the scholarship website; all essays must be written in English and must be uploaded in either a Microsoft Word or PDF format. **Deadline:** Every 20th of each month.

6627 ■ Labor and Working Class History Association (LAWCHA)

Duke University
226 Carr Bldg.(East Campus)
Durham, NC 27708-0719
Ph: (919)688-5134
Free: 888-651-0122
E-mail: lawcha@duke.edu
URL: lawcha.org
Social Media: www.facebook.com/
  laborandworkingclasshistory
twitter.com/lawcha_org

6628 ■ LAWCHA Graduate Student Travel Grants *(Graduate/Grant)*

Purpose: To support graduate students who are participating in the labor history conferences. **Focus:** General studies/Field of study not specified; History; Labor. **Qualif.:** Applicants must be a graduate student and presenting at the June 6-8 conference. **Criteria:** Selection will be based on the committee's criteria.

Funds Avail.: $250 Each. **Duration:** Annual. **Number Awarded:** 1. **To Apply:** Applicant must submit Curriculum Vitae and a one-page abstract of the paper to be presented; must be submitted through the online application process. **Deadline:** April 15. **Contact:** E-mail: LAWCHA@duke.edu.

6629 ■ Ladah Law Firm P.L.L.C.

517 S 3rd St.
Las Vegas, NV 89101
Ph: (702)570-1264
E-mail: ramzy@ladahlaw.com
URL: www.ladahlaw.com
Social Media: www.facebook.com/pages/Ladah-Law-Firm
  -PLLC/153266228186899
www.instagram.com/ladah_law_firm
twitter.com/LadahLawFirm

6630 ■ Ladah Law Firm, PLLC Injury Scholarships *(Undergraduate, Graduate/Scholarship)*

Purpose: To provide financial assistance to students who want to pursue their dreams in the legal profession. **Focus:**

Awards are arranged alphabetically below their administering organizations

Law. **Qualif.:** Applicants must be attending college or planning to attend law school but will not yet have graduated from law school; must have a minimum GPA of 3.0. **Criteria:** Selection will be based on the committee's criteria.

Funds Avail.: $2,000. **To Apply:** Applicants must submit the complete online application form together with transcript and recommendation letters and/or resumes to substantiate the application; applicants will be required to demonstrate both their merit and their need for the scholarship how an injury or someone close to the applicants' experienced have impacted their lives; how experience with an injury or an accident have contributed the applicants' desire and motivation to become an attorney; and personal commitment to working with, helping or caring for those affected by injuries and accidents; selected finalist must submit an un-opened copy of official transcripts. **Deadline:** May 31.

6631 ■ The LAGRANT Foundation
633 W 5th St. 48th Fl.
Los Angeles, CA 90071
Ph: (323)469-8680
Fax: (323)469-8683
E-mail: tlfinfo@lagrant.com
URL: www.lagrantfoundation.org
Social Media: twitter.com/lagrantfoundatn

6632 ■ The Lagrant Foundation - Graduate Scholarships *(Graduate/Scholarship)*

Purpose: To provide financial support for the education of graduate students who belong to one of the following ethnic groups: African American, Asian Pacific American, Hispanic or Native American or Alaska Native. **Focus:** Advertising; Marketing and distribution; Public relations. **Criteria:** Applicants are evaluated based on scholastic performance.

Funds Avail.: $3,750. **Duration:** Annual. **Number Awarded:** 20. **To Apply:** Applicants must submit completed application form; application must be typed; one reference letter from a college professor or an internship adviser on official letterhead and signed; current resume; unofficial transcripts from college/university; once selected applicant must provide official transcripts; headshot photo; following essay questions should be answered on separate pages: one to two-page essay outlining career goals; explain why it is important to increase the number of ethnic minorities in the fields of advertising, marketing and public relations; can include accomplishments relevant to increasing awareness about diversity in applicants community; brief paragraph explaining community activities of the applicant; brief paragraph describing any honors and awards of the applicant; application and all required documents should be combined as one PDF; submitted via online; applications that are complete and submitted on or before following year January 19 11:59 pm PST will be eligible for an extra 10 points. **Deadline:** February 26. **Contact:** Email: tlfinfo@lagrant.com.

6633 ■ The Lagrant Foundation - Undergraduate Scholarships *(Undergraduate/Scholarship)*

Purpose: To provide financial support for the education of undergraduate students who belong to ethnic groups: African American, Asian Pacific American, Hispanic or Native American or Alaska Native. **Focus:** Advertising; Marketing and distribution; Public relations. **Criteria:** Applicants are evaluated based on scholastic performance.

Funds Avail.: $2,500. **Duration:** Annual. **Number Awarded:** 30. **To Apply:** Applicants must submit completed application form; application must be typed; one reference letter from a college professor or an internship adviser on official letterhead and signed; current resume; unofficial transcripts from college/university; once selected applicant must provide official transcripts; headshot photo; following essay questions should be answered on separate pages: one to two-page essay outlining career goals; explain why it is important to increase the number of ethnic minorities in the fields of advertising, marketing and public relations; can include accomplishments relevant to increasing awareness about diversity in applicants community; brief paragraph explaining community activities of the applicant; brief paragraph describing any honors and awards of the applicant; application and all required documents should be combined as one PDF; submitted via online; applications that are complete and submitted on or before following year January 19 11:59 pm PST will be eligible for an extra 10 points. **Deadline:** February 26. **Contact:** Email: tlfinfo@lagrant.com.

6634 ■ Lakselaget
7001 Golden Valley Rd.
Minneapolis, MN 55427
URL: www.lakselaget.org
Social Media: www.facebook.com/Lakselaget-Minnesota-225823540821207

6635 ■ Lakselaget Foundation Scholarship Fund *(Graduate, Undergraduate/Scholarship)*

Purpose: To promote the international connections between Norway and Minnesota, and learn, teach and share knowledge that will benefit women in their complex roles in today's society. **Focus:** Biology; Mathematics and mathematical sciences; Science.

Funds Avail.: $1,000. **Duration:** Annual. **To Apply:** Applicants must submit a completed application form with official transcripts, two letters or recommendation, a letter from an individual who can assess the applicant's Norwegian language skills (if an American), and a 1000-word essay. **Contact:** Helene MacCallum, Foundation Director; 4744 Garfield Ave South Minneapolis, MN 55419 USA.

6636 ■ Lalor Foundation
c/o GMA Foundations
2 Liberty Sq., Ste. 500
Boston, MA 02109
Ph: (617)391-3088
URL: lalorfound.org

6637 ■ Lalor Foundation Post-Doctoral Fellowships *(Postdoctorate/Fellowship)*

Purpose: To support promising new researchers in establishing scientific and teaching careers. **Focus:** General studies/Field of study not specified. **Qualif.:** Any nonprofit research institution, such as a university or medical research center, may apply. All institutions are required to submit proof of nonprofit status. Applicants do not need to be citizens of the United States. **Criteria:** Recipients will be evaluated based on eligibility and submitted materials.

Funds Avail.: $50,000. **Duration:** Annual. **To Apply:** Applicant's institution may make its nomination of a fellow from among its own personnel or elsewhere, but qualifications being equal, candidates from other than the proposing institution itself may carry modest preference. Must

Awards are arranged alphabetically below their administering organizations

name the institution's nominee for fellowship and include their performance record; must submit project narrative, letters of support, independent expert reviews, and reference. **Deadline:** January 15. **Remarks:** Established in 2006. **Contact:** Emai: fellowshipmanager@gmafoundations.com.

6638 ■ LAM Foundation
4520 Cooper Rd., Ste. 300
Cincinnati, OH 45242
Ph: (513)777-6889
Free: 877-287-3526
E-mail: info@thelamfoundation.org
URL: www.thelamfoundation.org
Social Media: www.facebook.com/TheLAMFoundation
www.instagram.com/thelamfoundation
twitter.com/LAMFoundation

6639 ■ LAM Pilot Project Awards *(Master's, Postdoctorate/Grant)*

Purpose: To provide seed monies to pursue new research directions. **Focus:** Medical research. **Qualif.:** Candidates must have at least two years of experience, an M.D., Ph.D. or equivalent degree, and perform the work in a laboratory with established expertise in smooth muscle biology or the genetics of tuberous sclerosis. **Criteria:** Selection will be based on the committee's criteria.

Funds Avail.: No specific amount. **To Apply:** The Proposed Research section of the online grant application for all LAM awards is limited to 10 pages, including references and figures. Proposals should include: hypotheses and specific aims; literature review, preliminary data; research plan and experimental methods; significance; importance.

6640 ■ Lamaze International
2001 K Street NW, 3rd Floor North
Washington, DC 20006
Ph: (202)367-1128
Fax: (202)367-2128
Free: 800-368-4404
E-mail: info@lamaze.org
URL: www.lamaze.org
Social Media: www.facebook.com/LamazeChildbirth
www.instagram.com/lamazechildbirth
www.pinterest.com/lamaze1
twitter.com/LamazeOnline
www.youtube.com/user/Lamaze1

6641 ■ Childbirth Educator Program Scholarships *(Other/Scholarship)*

Purpose: To provide financial support to cover the cost of enrolling in a Lamaze Accredited Childbirth Educator Program. **Focus:** Motherhood.

To Apply: Applicants must submit a completed Childbirth Educator Program Scholarship application and must include the following information in the statement: circumstances of need, e.g., employment or self-employment status and anticipated gross yearly income (spouse information needed if they file a joint tax return or the equivalent); special medical, educational or unemployment-related circumstances (including disabilities and worker's compensation claims), include number of dependents, students they support in college, and special needs family members; other sources of income (savings, bonds stocks, scholar-

ships, etc.); and how they will finance the remaining fees, lodging, travel, meals and away-from-home expenses, if they receive a scholarship; and a letter describing how they plan to promote the Lamaze International Philosophy of Birth.

6642 ■ Lamaze Childbirth Educator Program Scholarship *(Professional development/Scholarship)*

Purpose: To members enrolled in Lamaze Childbirth Educator Program who demonstrate financial need. **Focus:** Medicine. **Qualif.:** Applicant must have completed all coursework and components and sit as a traditional candidate, or qualify as an experienced educator or as a midwife/midwifery student.

6643 ■ Lance Surety Bond Associates Inc.
4387 Swamp Rd., No. 287
Doylestown, PA 18902
Fax: (267)362-4817
Free: 877-514-5146
E-mail: info@suretybonds.org
URL: www.suretybonds.org
Social Media: www.facebook.com/LanceSurety
www.linkedin.com/company/lance-surety-bond-associates
 -inc-
pinterest.com/LanceSurety
twitter.com/Lance_Surety
youtube.com/channel/UCS8hezyAwoPqbDX2g0IW4gw

6644 ■ Lance Surety College Scholarships *(Undergraduate, Graduate/Scholarship)*

Purpose: To help talented young students reach their educational goals. **Focus:** Business. **Qualif.:** Applicants must be undergraduate or graduate students enrolled at an accredited university, college or trade school in the United States. **Criteria:** Selection is based on relevancy, uniqueness, professionalism and creativity of the submitted essay.

Funds Avail.: $1,500. **Duration:** Non-renewable. **To Apply:** Applicants must write a minimum 500 word essay on one of the following topics "What would be your motivation to start a small business; if you could launch it now?"; "How does the U.S. economy benefit from surety bonds?"; or a topic of their choice about Auto Dealership, Freight Brokerage, Construction or Mortgage Brokerage; applicants must also provide the following information; full name, email address, phone number, accredited institution they are currently attending or are interested in attending and year in school. **Deadline:** December 15.

6645 ■ Landscape Architecture Foundation (LAF)
1129 20th St. NW, Ste. 210
Washington, DC 20036
Ph: (202)331-7070
Fax: (202)331-7079
URL: splash.lafoundation.org
Social Media: www.facebook.com/lafoundation.org
www.instagram.com/lafoundation
www.linkedin.com/company/landscape-architecture
 -foundation
twitter.com/lafoundation

6646 ■ ASLA Council of Fellows Scholarships *(Undergraduate/Scholarship)*

Purpose: To aid outstanding students who would not otherwise have an opportunity to continue a professional

Awards are arranged alphabetically below their administering organizations

degree program due to unmet financial need, increase the interest and participation of economically disadvantaged and under-represented populations in the study of landscape architecture, and enrich the profession of landscape architecture. **Focus:** Landscape architecture and design. **Qualif.:** Applicants must be U.S. citizens or permanent resident aliens who are Student ASLA members and third, fourth, or fifth-year undergraduates in Landscape Architecture Accreditation Board (LAAB) accredited programs of landscape architecture. **Criteria:** Selection will be based on the aforementioned applicant's qualifications and compliance with the application details.

Funds Avail.: $5,000 each. **Duration:** Annual. **Number Awarded:** Up to 4. **To Apply:** Applicants must submit an entry form; a photo; bio for the LAF Website (150 word max), resume; financial aid form; 2 letters of recommendation; essay (2 page max). **Deadline:** February 1. **Remarks:** Established in 2004. **Contact:** E-mail: scholarships@lafoundation.org; Phone: 202-331-7070 x14.

6647 ■ Hawaii Chapter/David T. Woolsey Scholarship (Undergraduate, Graduate, Professional development/Scholarship)

Purpose: To support architecture students in their education. **Focus:** Landscape architecture and design. **Qualif.:** Applicants must be third, fourth, or fifth year undergraduate or graduate students of landscape architecture who are permanent residents of Hawaii. **Criteria:** Recipients will be selected based on the aforesaid qualifications and compliance with the application process.

Funds Avail.: $2,000. **Duration:** Annual. **Number Awarded:** 1. **To Apply:** Applicants must submit all of the following: online general scholarship form; photo; 150-word maximum bio for LAF website; two-page resume; financial aid form; one letter of recommendation; and, two-page maximum originally written essay in PDF format with specific formats provided; additional is the proof of Hawaii residency; three pages of work sample. **Deadline:** February 1. **Remarks:** The scholarship was established in memory of David T. Woolsey, an alumnus of California Polytechnic University and former principal in the firm of Woolsey, Miyabara and Associates. The award provides funds for educational or professional development purposes exclusively. **Contact:** E-mail: scholarships@lafoundation.org; Phone: 202-331-7070 ext. 14.

6648 ■ Steven G. King Play Environments Scholarship (Undergraduate, Master's/Scholarship)

Purpose: To recognize a student who has a high potential in the design of play environments. **Focus:** Landscape architecture and design. **Qualif.:** Applicants must be landscape architecture students with an interest and aptitude in the design of play environments; must be master's students or undergraduates in their final two years of study and enrolled in an LAAB- or LAAC-accredited program at a university in the U.S. or Canada.**Criteria:** Recipients shall be selected on the basis of creativity, openness to innovation and a demonstrated interest in park and playground planning.

Funds Avail.: $5,000. **Duration:** Annual. **To Apply:** Applicants must submit an entry form, a photo (head shot with a plain background; 300 ppi, size 4 x 6 inches in extracurricular activities and financial information); a 300 to 500-word essay describing the applicant's views of the significant social and educational value of play and the value of integrating playgrounds into play and recreation environments; Resume (2 page max); two letters of recommenda-

tion from current professors familiar with the applicant's demonstrated interest in park and playground planning, creativity and openness to innovation; Bio for the LAF Website (150 word max); Work Samples (3 page max); all application materials (with the exception of reference letters) must be sent through email as a single document; each document must be formatted as follows: create one-inch minimum margins; include page number and surname/document name/award name on all pages of all documents prepared by applicant. **Deadline:** February 1. **Remarks:** The Scholarship was created by Steven G. King, FASLA, founder and Chairman of Landscape Structures Inc., and the inventor of the continuous play concept. **Contact:** E-mail: scholarships@lafoundation.org; Phone: 202-331-7070 x14.

6649 ■ Landscape Forms Design for People Scholarship (Undergraduate/Scholarship)

Purpose: To assist students in their study of landscape architecture. **Focus:** Landscape architecture and design. **Qualif.:** Applicants must be landscape architecture students who will be starting their final year of full-time undergraduate study in an LAAB-accredited program U.S. or Canada. **Criteria:** Recipients will be selected on the basis of academic accomplishment and creative ability.

Funds Avail.: $3,000. **Duration:** Annual. **To Apply:** Applicants must submit an entry form; a photo (headshot with a plain background; 300 ppi, size 4 x 6 inches in .jpg format); a personal profile (two-page maximum including education, extracurricular activities and financial information); a 300-word maximum essay describing the qualities essential to the creation of great and successful public spaces; three 8 1/2 x 11 academic or internship work samples in either jpg or PDF format; two letters of recommendation from current professors and/or internship employers; all application materials (with the exception of reference letters) must be sent through email as a single document; each document must be formatted as follows: create one-inch minimum margins; include page number and surname/document name/award name on all pages of all documents prepared by applicant. **Deadline:** February 1. **Contact:** E-mail: scholarships@lafoundation.org; Phone: 202-331-7070 x14.

6650 ■ Courtland P. Paul Scholarships (Undergraduate/Scholarship)

Purpose: To assist students in their study of landscape architecture. **Focus:** Landscape architecture and design. **Qualif.:** Applicants must be United States citizens who are undergraduate students in the final two years of study in Landscape Architecture Accreditation Board (LAAB) accredited schools; must demonstrate financial need and a minimum grade point average of "C". **Criteria:** Selection will be based on the aforementioned applicants' qualifications and compliance with the application details.

Funds Avail.: $5,000. **Duration:** Annual. **To Apply:** Applicants must submit an entry form, a photo (head shot with a plain background; 300 ppi, size 4 x 6 inches in jpg format) and a personal profile (two page maximum including education, extracurricular activities and financial information); 500-word maximum essay describing the applicant's aspirations, ability to surmount obstacles, high level of drive and need for financial assistance; two letters of recommendation from current professors familiar with the applicant's character and goals in pursuing an education in landscape architecture; letters of recommendation should be written on electronic letterhead with an electronic signature from the recommender and must be sent electronically; recom-

Awards are arranged alphabetically below their administering organizations

menders must request a delivery receipt for the e-mail or provide a copy in case of transmittal problem; all application materials (with the exception of reference letters) must be sent through email as a single document; each document must be formatted as follows: create one-inch minimum margins; include page number and surname/ document name/ award name on all pages of all documents prepared by applicant. **Deadline:** February 1. **Remarks:** The scholarship is given in honor of Courtland P. Paul. **Contact:** E-mail: scholarships@lafoundation.org; Phone: 202-331-7070 x14.

6651 ■ Peridian International, Inc./Rae L. Price, FASLA Scholarships (Undergraduate/Scholarship)

Purpose: To support young creative individuals into the profession who may not otherwise have the financial ability to cover all the costs of their educational program. **Focus:** Landscape architecture and design. **Qualif.:** Applicants must be United States citizens; students in the final two years of study in Landscape Architecture at the University of California at Los Angeles Extension Program, or in the case of UCLA's termination of the program, other California accredited schools of programs in Landscape Architecture; must also demonstrate financial need and have a minimum grade point average of B. **Criteria:** Selection will be based on the aforementioned applicants' qualifications and compliance with the application details.

Funds Avail.: $5,000. **Duration:** Annual. **To Apply:** Applicants must submit an entry form; a photo; bio for the LAF Website (150 word max), resume; financial aid form; 2 letters of recommendation; essay (2 page max). **Deadline:** February 1. **Remarks:** The use of funds is restricted to tuition, books and program required supplies within the school year of the award. **Contact:** E-mail: scholarships@lafoundation.org; Phone: 202-331-7070 x14.

6652 ■ Rain Bird Intelligent Use of Water Scholarship (Undergraduate/Scholarship)

Purpose: To support an outstanding landscape architecture, horticulture or irrigation science student. **Focus:** Horticulture; Landscape architecture and design. **Qualif.:** Applicants must be students in the final two years of undergraduate study (third, fourth, or fifth-year students) who have demonstrated commitment to these professions through participation in extracurricular activities and exemplary scholastic achievements. **Criteria:** Selection will be based on the aforementioned applicant's qualifications and compliance with the application details.

Funds Avail.: $2,500. **Duration:** Annual. **To Apply:** Applicants must submit an entry form; a photo; bio for the LAF Website (150 word max), resume; financial aid form; 2 letters of recommendation; essay (2 page max). **Deadline:** February 1. **Contact:** E-mail: scholarships@lafoundation.org; Phone: 202-331-7070 x14.

6653 ■ Lane Powell P.C.

1420 5th Ave., Ste. 4200
Seattle, WA 98101-2375
Ph: (206)223-7000
Fax: (206)223-7107
URL: www.lanepowell.com
Social Media: www.facebook.com/lanepowellpc
www.linkedin.com/companies/lane-powell-pc
twitter.com/lanepowell

6654 ■ George V. Powell Diversity Scholarships (Graduate/Scholarship)

Purpose: To support the education of minority law students. **Focus:** Law. **Qualif.:** Applicants must be second-year students in good standing at an ABA accredited law school and who will be summer associates in the Firm's Seattle or Portland office; students in four-year joint degree programs will be considered after third year.

Funds Avail.: $7,500. **Duration:** Annual. **To Apply:** Applicants must submit a cover letter including a statement indicating eligibility to participate in the program; a resume; current copy of law school transcript; legal writing sample; and a list of two or three professional or academic references. **Contact:** Len Roden; Phone: 206-223-6123; Email: redenl@lanepowell.com.

6655 ■ Lang, Richert & Patch

Fig Garden Financial Ctr.
5200 N Palm Ave., 4th Fl.
Fresno, CA 93704
Ph: (559)228-6700
Fax: (559)228-6727
URL: www.lrplaw.net

6656 ■ Frank H. Lang Merit Scholarships (Undergraduate/Scholarship)

Purpose: To help students defray their law school tuition. **Focus:** Law. **Qualif.:** Applicants must be incoming law students. **Criteria:** Selection will be based on merit.

Funds Avail.: $1,000. **Duration:** Annual. **To Apply:** Interested applicants should complete the online application form. In addition, candidates will be prompted during the online application process to submit the following documentation as PDF attachments: a resume including law school GPA; a law school transcript or copy of last score if incoming 1L; a college transcript; a 1-2 page personal statement explaining why the applicant has chosen to attend law school and their ties to the Central Valley (12 point Times New Roman font, double space with standard margins); list of three references, including names, email addresses and telephone numbers. **Contact:** Questions may be directed to Sydney Smith or via email at scholarship@lrplaw.net.

6657 ■ Lanier Technical College (LTC)

2535 Lanier Tech Drive
Gainesville, GA 30507
Ph: (770)533-7000
Fax: (770)531-6328
URL: www.laniertech.edu
Social Media: www.facebook.com/LanierTechNews
www.instagram.com/lanier_tech
www.pinterest.com/laniertech
twitter.com/LanierTech
www.youtube.com/user/LanierTechCollege

6658 ■ Kenneth H. Breeden Scholarship (Undergraduate/Scholarship)

Purpose: To provide financial support to deserving students who lose HOPE funding prior to the completion of their program of study. **Focus:** General studies/Field of study not specified. **Qualif.:** Applicants must have previously approved for HOPE grant or HOPE Scholarship funding, and be in good academic standing in accordance with

Awards are arranged alphabetically below their administering organizations

college guidelines. **Criteria:** Selection will be based on a first come, first serve.

Funds Avail.: $500. **To Apply:** Applicants must submit a Kenneth H. Breeden Scholarship application (available online) along with a letter of recommendation from an advisor or instructor; application documents must be sent to the Financial Aid Office three weeks prior to registration for the quarter aid is requested.

6659 ■ The Edna A. Noblin Scholarship
(Undergraduate/Scholarship)

Purpose: To provide financial assistance for deserving students who are residents of Dawson or Lumpkin Counties. **Focus:** General studies/Field of study not specified. **Qualif.:** Applicants must be residents of Dawson County or Lumpkin County and in good academic standing in accordance within college guidelines. **Criteria:** Selection will be based upon their normal review procedure to the Edna A. Noblin committee for consideration.

Funds Avail.: No specific amount. **Duration:** Annual. **To Apply:** Applicants must have a completed FAFSA on file with the Lanier Technical College financial aid office for the year scholarship funding is being requested; must submit a Lanier Technical College Foundation Scholarship application and the Edna A. Noblin Budget Worksheet.

6660 ■ United Way Of Forsyth County Scholarship
(Other/Scholarship)

Purpose: To assist the students who are residents of Forsyth County and support them to offset their educational costs, specifically with books and supplies. **Focus:** General studies/Field of study not specified. **Qualif.:** Applicants must be in good academic standing in accordance with college and Financial Aid guidelines and be residents of Forsyth County. **Criteria:** Selection will be made by Lanier Technical College Foundation Scholarship Committee.

To Apply: Applicants must have a completed FAFSA on file with the Lanier Technical College financial aid office for the year scholarship funding is being requested and also complete a Lanier Technical College Foundation Scholarship application.

6661 ■ Lapeer County Community Foundation (LCCF)
235 W Nepessing St.
Lapeer, MI 48446
Ph: (810)664-0691
E-mail: nboxey@lapeercountycf.org
URL: lapeercountycf.org
Social Media: www.facebook.com/
  LapeerCountyCommunityFoundation
www.linkedin.com/company/lapeer-county-community
  -foundation

6662 ■ Clarke Adams Memorial Fund
(Undergraduate/Scholarship)

Purpose: To support the education of Lapeer community students who have lost an immediate family member. **Focus:** General studies/Field of study not specified.

Funds Avail.: $1,000 each. **Duration:** Annual. **Number Awarded:** Varies. **Contact:** General Scholarship Committee, Lapeer County Community Foundation, 235 W. Nepessing St., Lapeer, MI, 48446; Questions: Nancy Boxey, Executive Director; Phone: 810 664-0691; Email: nboxey@lapeercountycf.org.

6663 ■ Irma Gelhausen Scholarship Fund *(Graduate/Scholarship)*

Purpose: To assist Lapeer community students pursuing a career in education. **Focus:** General studies/Field of study not specified. **Qualif.:** Applicants must be in the third year (or higher) of college or university studies; must have a GPA of 3.0 or higher for post-secondary studies and must be residents of Lapeer County. **Criteria:** Preference will be given to graduates of Lapeer Community Schools and those pursuing a career in elementary education studies, although applicants pursuing a career in secondary education will be considered as well.

Funds Avail.: Minimum $1,000. **To Apply:** Applicants must submit a completed application form; academic transcript (including standardized test scores); and two letter of recommendation; current transcript showing credits earned and current GPA; SAT scores if a graduating high school senior; current year FAFSA Student Aid Report (SAR); letter of recommendation (optional); current photo (optional) of yourself to be used for publicity purposes if an award is granted; a 200-word essay discussing the expectations to achieve as an educator. **Deadline:** March 13. **Remarks:** Established in 2005. **Contact:** General Scholarship Committee, Lapeer County Community Foundation, 235 W. Nepessing St., Lapeer, MI, 48446; Questions: Nancy Boxey, Executive Director; Phone: 810 664-0691; Email: nboxey@lapeercountycf.org.

6664 ■ Hazel Simms Nursing Scholarship *(Other/Scholarship)*

Purpose: To provide nursing scholarships for residents of Lapeer County. **Focus:** Nursing. **Criteria:** Recipients are selected based on financial need, scholastic record of the applicants and recommendations from college faculty and official of the college.

Funds Avail.: $500. **Duration:** Annual. **To Apply:** Applicants must submit a completed application form; academic transcript (including standardized test scores); and two letter of recommendation; current transcript showing credits earned and current GPA; SAT scores if a graduating high school senior; current year FAFSA Student Aid Report (SAR); letter of recommendation (optional); current photo (optional) of yourself to be used for publicity purposes if an award is granted; a 200-word essay discussing the expectations to achieve as an educator. **Deadline:** March 13. **Contact:** Executive Director, Nancy Boxey at 810.664.0691 or email to: nboxey@lapeercountycf.org.

6665 ■ Wayne Hildebrant Police Scholarship Fund
(Undergraduate/Scholarship)

Purpose: To support education in the law enforcement fields. **Focus:** Law enforcement. **Qualif.:** Applicants must be residents of Lapeer County accepted into an accredited police academy of college or university law enforcement program, have a cumulative GPA of 3.0 or higher, and show financial need.

Funds Avail.: $500. **To Apply:** Applicants must submit a completed application form; academic transcript (including standardized test scores); and two letter of recommendation; current transcript showing credits earned and current GPA; SAT scores if a graduating high school senior; current year FAFSA Student Aid Report (SAR); letter of recommendation (optional); current photo (optional) of yourself to be used for publicity purposes if an award is granted. **Remarks:** The scholarship is named in memory of Wayne Hildebrant, long-time Metamora police chief. **Contact:** General Scholarship Committee, Lapeer County Community

Awards are arranged alphabetically below their administering organizations

Foundation, 235 W. Nepessing St., Lapeer, MI, 48446; Questions: Nancy Boxey, Executive Director; Phone: 810 664-0691; Email: nboxey@lapeercountycf.org.

6666 ■ Lapeer County Medical Fund (Undergraduate/Scholarship)

Purpose: To support students pursuing medical education and profession. **Focus:** Education, Medical. **Qualif.:** Applicants must be residents of Lapeer County, at least a second year-enrolled college student in a pre-science medical professional career such as medical, dental, nursing, or physician's assistant program; and maintain a 3.2 GPA. **Criteria:** Preference is given to applicants based on financial need.

Funds Avail.: $500. **Duration:** Annual. **Number Awarded:** 2. **To Apply:** Applicants must submit a completed application form; academic transcript (including standardized test scores); and two letter of recommendation; current transcript showing credits earned and current GPA; SAT scores if a graduating high school senior; current year FAFSA Student Aid Report (SAR); letter of recommendation (optional); current photo (optional) of yourself to be used for publicity purposes if an award is granted. **Deadline:** March 13. **Contact:** Executive Director, Nancy Boxey at 810.664.0691 or email to: nboxey@lapeercountycf.org.

6667 ■ Ross P. Broesamle Education Fund (Undergraduate/Scholarship)

Purpose: To support educational assistance to students from Almont Township or the Village of Almont and the Township of Dryden of the Village of Dryden. **Focus:** General studies/Field of study not specified. **Qualif.:** Applicants must be residents of Almont Township, Village of Almont, Dryden Township, or the Village of Dryden. **Criteria:** Selection is based upon financial need and scholastic record.

Funds Avail.: $500. **Duration:** Annual. **To Apply:** Applicants must submit a completed application form; academic transcript (including standardized test scores); and two letter of recommendation; current transcript showing credits earned and current GPA; SAT scores if a graduating high school senior; current year FAFSA Student Aid Report (SAR); letter of recommendation (optional); current photo (optional) of yourself to be used for publicity purposes if an award is granted. **Deadline:** March 13. **Contact:** General Scholarship Committee, Lapeer County Community Foundation, 235 W. Nepessing St., Lapeer, MI, 48446; Questions: Nancy Boxey, Executive Director; Phone: 810 664-0691; Email: nboxey@lapeercountycf.org.

6668 ■ LasikPlus
155 Cranes Roost Blvd.
Altamonte Springs, FL 32701
URL: www.lasikplus.com

6669 ■ The LasikPlus My Vision Essay Scholarship (Undergraduate, Graduate/Scholarship)

Purpose: To help build community through education. **Focus:** General studies/Field of study not specified. **Criteria:** Selection will be based on the following five categories: spelling and grammar; contest theme relevancy; focus on the topic; content logicality and relevancy; and adherence to essay guidelines.

Funds Avail.: $2,500. **Duration:** Quadrennial; Quarterly; Quinquennial. **Number Awarded:** 1 per calendar quarter. **To Apply:** Applicants must submit a 500-700 word essay

showing the entrants desires and ability to bring their vision to life through continuing education and community involvement. Essay should be submitted in a PDF file. Applicants must include contact information including: full name, university or college of enrollment, current major, email address, and phone number. **Deadline:** September 6. **Contact:** Email: scholarship@lasikplus.com.

6670 ■ l'Association Canadienne des Sociétés Elizabeth Fry (ACSEF)
190 Bronson Ave.
Ottawa, ON, Canada K1R 6H4
URL: www.caefs.ca

6671 ■ Elizabeth Fry Memorial Bursary (Undergraduate, Graduate/Scholarship)

Purpose: To assist the educational efforts of criminalized women. **Focus:** Women's studies.

Funds Avail.: 500 Canadian Dollars. **Duration:** Annual. **Number Awarded:** Up to three. **Deadline:** July 16.

6672 ■ Latham & Watkins L.L.P.
12670 High Bluff Dr.
San Diego, CA 92130
Ph: (858)523-5400
Fax: (858)523-5450
E-mail: enquiries@legalombudsman.org.uk
URL: www.lw.com
Social Media: www.facebook.com/lathamwatkins
www.linkedin.com/company/latham-&-watkins
twitter.com/lathamwatkins
www.youtube.com/user/lathamwatkinsglobal

6673 ■ Latham Diversity Scholars - 2L Diversity Scholars (Undergraduate/Scholarship)

Purpose: To increase the number of diverse attorneys who want to pursue careers in global law firms. **Focus:** Law. **Qualif.:** Applicants must be enrolled in an ABA-accredited law school and intend to practice law in a major U.S. city and who has successfully completed the first year of a full-time JD program. **Criteria:** Commitment to promoting inclusion and diversity in the legal profession; academic and leadership achievements.

Funds Avail.: $10,000; $15,000. **Number Awarded:** Varies. **To Apply:** Applicants must submit a completed (signed and dated) application form online along with a resume, unofficial or official law school transcript and a personal statement (maximum of 500 words). **Remarks:** Established in 2005. **Contact:** Email: Recruiting.Global@lw.com.

6674 ■ Latin American Educational Foundation (LAEF)
1035 Osage St, 8th Fl.
Denver, CO 80204
Ph: (303)446-0541
Fax: (303)446-0526
E-mail: info@laef.org
URL: www.laef.org
Social Media: www.facebook.com/laefcolorado
www.instagram.com/laefcolorado
www.linkedin.com/company/laefcolorado
twitter.com/LAEFColorado

Awards are arranged alphabetically below their administering organizations

6675 ■ LAEF Scholarships (Undergraduate/ Scholarship)

Purpose: To provide funds to qualified students who have demonstrated a commitment to the Hispanic community. **Focus:** Hispanic American studies. **Qualif.:** Applicants must be Colorado residents with Hispanic heritage and/or are actively involved in the Hispanic community; and, have at least a 3.0 cumulative grade point average; high school seniors, college undergraduate and graduate students.

Funds Avail.: No specific amount. **Duration:** Annual. **To Apply:** Applicants msut include unofficial transcript; official ACT/SAT scores; current photo; list of extracurricular activities; written statement(s) – not to exceed 1,000 words each, one for first time or two for renewing applicants; two letters of recommendation; one letter must be from a representative at their high school or college - principal, teacher, guidance counselor, etc; one letter must be from another source, personal or professional - employer, mentor, coach, etc; recommender is required to complete a confidential recommendation through the online LAEF application system.**Remarks:** The scholarship funds can be used toward tuition, room and board, books or other qualified educational expenses. **Contact:** Rigo; Email: Rrangel@laef.org.

6676 ■ Latina Leadership Network (LLN)
PO Box 14557
San Luis Obispo, CA 93406
URL: www.latina-leadership-network.org

6677 ■ LLN Student Scholarships (Undergraduate/ Scholarship)

Purpose: To support students who are currently attending California Community Colleges. **Focus:** General studies/ Field of study not specified. **Criteria:** Preference will be given to latino heritage (one parent fully Latino or each parent half Latino).

Funds Avail.: $500 each. **Duration:** Annual. **Number Awarded:** 6. **Deadline:** October 15.

6678 ■ Law Foundation of British Columbia (LFBC)
1340-605 Robson St.
Vancouver, BC, Canada V6B 5J3
Ph: (604)688-2337
Fax: (604)688-4586
E-mail: info@lawfoundationbc.org
URL: www.lawfoundationbc.org

6679 ■ Graduate Fellowships (Graduate/Fellowship)

Purpose: To provide financial assistance to qualified individuals who want to pursue their careers in the legal profession. **Focus:** Law.

Funds Avail.: 15,000 Canadian Dollars each. **Duration:** Annual. **Number Awarded:** 6. **To Apply:** Applications and all supporting documents should be submitted; application can be submitted online with SmartSimple online grant submission and management system accessible through the website; a condition of the Fellowship is that a recipient submit two reports to the Law Foundation: an interim report on the program of study following the first term; and a final report, within three months of the end of the academic year on the program of study undertaken; Process for Re-Applications: letter of request and a signed letter from

academic advisor; summary of program of study; progress report of the work accomplished during the previous year; updated schedule for completing the graduate program. **Deadline:** January 3. **Contact:** Email: fellowshipsandresearch@lawfoundationbc.org.

6680 ■ Law Foundation of Newfoundland and Labrador
55 Elizabeth Ave., Second Fl.
Saint John's, NL, Canada A1A 1W9
Ph: (709)754-4424
Fax: (709)754-4320
E-mail: lfnl@lawfoundationnl.com
URL: www.lawfoundationnl.com

6681 ■ Law Foundation of Newfoundland and Labrador Law School Scholarships (Advanced Professional/Scholarship)

Purpose: To support law students in their legal education. **Focus:** Law. **Qualif.:** Applicants must be residents of newfoundland and Labrador, are tenable for first year studies at any Canadian law school recognized by the scholarships board. **Criteria:** Selection will be made on the basis of academic ability.

Funds Avail.: 5,000 Canadian Dollars. **Duration:** Annual. **To Apply:** Applicants must submit the completed scholarship application form with certified evidence of the courses of study, together with my grades; the copy of LSAT result; a statement of general interests and activities; Sworn Affidavit as to residency. **Deadline:** May 1. **Remarks:** The scholarship was established in honor of the incorporation of the Law Society in 1834. Established in 1984. **Contact:** Email: lfnl@lawfoundationnl.com.

6682 ■ Law Foundation of Ontario (LFO)
20 Queen St. W, Ste. 3002
Toronto, ON, Canada M5H 3R3
Ph: (416)598-1550
Fax: (416)598-1526
E-mail: general@lawfoundation.on.ca
URL: www.lawfoundation.on.ca
Social Media: www.facebook.com/LawFoundationOn
www.linkedin.com/company/law-foundation-of-ontario
twitter.com/LawFoundationOn
www.youtube.com/channel/UCE5mVGFqZUZcZD3Y
-1v98Yg

6683 ■ Community Leadership in Justice Fellowship - The Law Foundation of Ontario (Other/ Fellowship)

Purpose: To provide an opportunity for professional development and renewal for a recognized community leader. **Focus:** Law.

Funds Avail.: 50,000 Canadian Dollars each to cover the fellows' salaries and up to 15,000 Canadian Dollars is available to each academic host. **Duration:** Annual. **Number Awarded:** 2. **To Apply:** Applicants must submit a completed CLJF Application Form via email. **Deadline:** March 23. **Remarks:** Established in 2006. **Contact:** Kirsti Mathers McHenry, Director, Policy and Programs; Phone: 416-598-1550 x 310; Email: kmathersmchenry@lawfoundation.on.ca.

Awards are arranged alphabetically below their administering organizations

6684 ■ Law Office of A. Sam Jubran Scholarship Contest

871 Cassat Ave.
Jacksonville, FL 32205
Ph: (904)360-6100
URL: www.law4jax.com

6685 ■ Law Office of A. Sam Jubran Scholarship Contest *(University, College, Undergraduate/ Scholarship)*

Purpose: To provide financial aid to college students and encourage students to understand their personal motivation for a career in the legal field. **Focus:** Law. **Qualif.:** Applicant must be a high school senior or college freshman in the United States. **Criteria:** Selection is based on submitted video essay or essay.

Funds Avail.: $1,000. **Number Awarded:** 1. **To Apply:** Applicant must create a one- to two-minute video explaining why they want to be a lawyer and publish the video to their YouTube channel, and on their Facebook page and the sponsor's Facebook page; video should be titled Law Office of Sam Jubran Scholarship Contest and should include this link in the description: www.law4jax.com/scholarship-for-college-students. Instead of a video applicant can submit a 1,000 to 1,500 word essay explaining why they want to be a lawyer and submit it to Samjubranscholarship@gmail.com. **Deadline:** August 15.

6686 ■ Law Office of David D. White, PLLC

608 W 12th St.
Austin, TX 78701
Ph: (512)369-3737
URL: wm-attorneys.com
Social Media: www.facebook.com/Law-Office-of-David-D-White-PLLC-122460808445019
twitter.com/austincrimelaw

6687 ■ Law Office of David D. White Annual Traumatic Brain Injury Scholarships *(College, Community College, University, Vocational/Occupational/ Scholarship)*

Purpose: To provide scholarships for those diagnosed with traumatic brain injury. **Focus:** General studies/Field of study not specified. **Qualif.:** Applicants must have been diagnosed with TBI and attending or planning to attend a university, college, community college, secondary school, or trade school. **Criteria:** Selection process is the amount of activity that the applicants' submission receives online; the more compelling a story is the more interest it will tend to generate; all decisions shall be at the discretion of the Law Office of David D. White, PLLC.

Funds Avail.: $1,000. **Duration:** Annual. **Number Awarded:** 2. **To Apply:** Applicants must submit the following information via email: name; phone number; email address; a short statement setting forth their educational goals; an essay, which is optional, telling how TBI has affected their lives. **Deadline:** November 3. **Contact:** Email: michael@wm-attorneys.com.

6688 ■ The Law Office of David E. Gordon

1850 Poplar Crest Cove
Memphis, TN 38119
Ph: (901)479-0323
Fax: (901)667-8305

E-mail: davidg@davidgordonlaw.com
URL: www.davidgordonlaw.com
Social Media: www.facebook.com/davidegordonlaw
twitter.com/davidegordonlaw
www.youtube.com/c/Davidgordonlawoffice
www.youtube.com/channel/UCf4iDRDU-GP1hiVKaM9UTJQ

6689 ■ 2020 The Nuclear Family Scholarship *(College, University, Undergraduate/Scholarship)*

Purpose: To help high school students with college plans as well as current college students who want to achieve their dreams. **Focus:** General studies/Field of study not specified. **Qualif.:** Open to any current high school senior, college student or graduate student who is a legal resident of the United States, and resides in one of the 50 states or the District of Columbia. Must be enrolled in a two to five year post-secondary institution, have a GPA of 3.0 or higher, and be in good overall academic standing. **Criteria:** Quality of essay.

Funds Avail.: $1,000. **Duration:** Annual. **Number Awarded:** 1. **To Apply:** Submit a 750-1000 word essay answering the following question: How has a member of your immediate family, like a parent or a sibling, helped shape the person that you are today?; include resume, transcripts, and proof of acceptance to a college or university. **Deadline:** February 28. **Contact:** Email: info@davidgordonlaw.com; URL: https://www.davidgordonlaw.com/the-nuclear-family-scholarship/.

6690 ■ The Law Office of David P. Shapiro

3500 5th Ave., No. 304
San Diego, CA 92103
Ph: (619)295-3555
URL: www.davidpshapirolaw.com
Social Media: www.facebook.com/davidpshapirolaw
instagram.com/davidpshapirolaw
www.linkedin.com/in/david-p-shapiro-9770985
twitter.com/DPShapiro
www.youtube.com/channel/UCqKSgbTRTPnUlZw7HxoKBTw

6691 ■ Law Office of David P. Shapiro Annual Leukemia Scholarships *(Vocational/Occupational, Community College, University, Undergraduate, College/Scholarship)*

Purpose: To provide scholarships for those diagnosed with leukemia. **Focus:** General studies/Field of study not specified. **Qualif.:** Applicants must be anyone who has been diagnosed with leukemia, and who are interested in pursuing secondary or post-secondary education. **Criteria:** Winners will be chosen, in part, based upon the activity generated online by their application. For example, essays which make interesting reading - based upon style and/or content - may generate more interest. The ultimate decision in all cases will be at the sole discretion of David P. Shapiro.

Funds Avail.: $1,000. **Duration:** Annual. **Number Awarded:** 2. **To Apply:** Applicants must complete the online application form and must submit the following materials: a short statement of not more than 100 words explaining how the applicants intend to further their education goals; an essay (optional) discussing how being diagnosed with and/or treated for leukemia have affected their day to day activities. The essay must be between 650

Awards are arranged alphabetically below their administering organizations

words and 1,000 words. **Deadline:** November 9.

6692 ■ Law Office of John J. Sheehan

10 Tremont St., Ste. 309
Boston, MA 02108
Ph: (617)553-4071
URL: www.attorneysheehan.com
Social Media: www.facebook.com/AttyJohnSheehan
www.linkedin.com/in/attorneysheehan
twitter.com/AttorneySheehan
www.youtube.com/user/attysheehan

6693 ■ Vision Zero Auto Accident Prevention Scholarships *(Postgraduate/Scholarship)*

Purpose: To encourage and support students in their pursuit of legal education. **Focus:** Law. **Qualif.:** Applicants must be U.S. citizens who are currently in their first or second year of law school, or entering law school in the fall of the current year; accepted to or currently attending an ABA accredited law school or program within United States; academic achievement must be reflected by an undergraduate cumulative minimum 3.0 GPA. **Criteria:** Selection will be based on the applicants' eligibility and compliance with the application process.

Funds Avail.: $1,000. **To Apply:** Applicants must submit the proof of Legal Residency in U.S. (i.e. birth certificate, passport, permanent resident card, etc.); a completed scholarship application form; one-page typed essay; an official copy of a law school or undergraduate college transcript; an official copy of a driving record since being eligible to drive; and if entering a law school program or school in the fall of current year, an acceptance letter from an accredited law school. **Deadline:** July 31.

6694 ■ Law Office of Keren Goldenberg

97 Central St., Ste. 403
Lowell, MA 01852
Ph: (978)221-2503
Fax: (978)401-0803
URL: kgdefenselaw.com

6695 ■ Keren Goldenberg Public Defender Scholarship *(College/Scholarship)*

Purpose: To provide an opportunity for a student to go to college. **Focus:** Law. **Qualif.:** Applicant can be any law student, college student, or high school student who is presently or will be interning at a public defender office during the school year or upcoming summer. **Criteria:** Judged primarily on applicant's commitment to indigent defense work and financial need, but does not exclude achievement standards.

Funds Avail.: $1,000. **Number Awarded:** 1. **To Apply:** Application available online at kgdefenselaw.com/scholarship-application/. **Deadline:** April 29. **Contact:** Email: community@kgdefenselaw.com.

6696 ■ Law Office of Manning & Zimmerman PLLC

87 Middle St.
Manchester, NH 03101
Ph: (603)624-7200
Fax: (603)624-7201
Free: 800-984-3151

E-mail: info@manningzimmermanlaw.com
URL: www.manningzimmermanlaw.com

6697 ■ Manning & Zimmerman Distracted Driving Scholarship *(College, University, Undergraduate, Vocational/Occupational/Scholarship)*

Purpose: To administer financial aid to New Hampshire students and to direct attention to the dangers of distracted driving. **Focus:** General studies/Field of study not specified. **Qualif.:** Applicant must be a high school student in New Hampshire planning on attending any type of secondary education in the United States (including vocational-technical education). **Criteria:** Selection is based on submitted video or essay.

Funds Avail.: $1,000. **Number Awarded:** 1. **Contact:** Contact: Daniel Wang.

6698 ■ Law Office of Yuriy Moshes, P.C.

517 Brighton Beach Ave.
Brooklyn, NY 11235
Fax: (646)843-7570
Free: 888-445-0234
E-mail: info@mosheslaw.com
URL: mosheslaw.com
Social Media: www.facebook.com/ymosheslaw
twitter.com/yuriymen
www.youtube.com/channel/UCeZJ0kpMD4ly5cltPSQ5UzQ

6699 ■ Scholarship from Law Office of Yuriy Moshes, P.C. *(Undergraduate/Award, Scholarship)*

Purpose: To promote education and awareness for the victims of sexual harassment. **Focus:** Law. **Qualif.:** Applicants must be currently enrolled in or accepted to an undergraduate law degree program at an accredited university in the United States. **Criteria:** Selection will be based on the applicant's following: responsiveness to the topic; quality of the writing; originality of the argument and proposed solution; ability to think critically about public policy concerns.

Funds Avail.: $1,000. **Duration:** Annual. **Number Awarded:** 1. **To Apply:** Applicant must submit a 500-700 word essay relating to workplace sexual harassment scandals reported in the media, including the Harvey Weinstein and #metoo movement. Essay should include applicant's opinion on these recent events, including: Why did the victims keep silent for so many years before speaking out? Why do the movement begin? Is the movement really a movement or is it simply an avalanche of individual women's stories? And how can we prevent instances of workplace sexual harassment in the future? Essay should identify one public policy problem relating to the issue of workplace sexual harassment, propose a solution to the problem, and explain why the applicant believes the proposal will be effective. Essay should be emailed to scholarship@mosheslaw.com with the word SCHOLARSHIP in the subject line; the body of the email should provide the applicant's full legal name; current mailing address; email; and phone number. **Deadline:** August 31. **Contact:** Email: scholarship@mosheslaw.com.

6700 ■ The Law Offices of David A. Black

40 North Central Ave., Ste. 1400
Phoenix, AZ 85004
Ph: (480)280-8028

Awards are arranged alphabetically below their administering organizations

E-mail: david@dbphoenixcriminallawyer.com
URL: www.dbphoenixcriminallawyer.com

6701 ■ Law Offices of David A. Black Annual Hearing Impaired Scholarships *(All/Scholarship)*

Purpose: To provide scholarships for those who are hearing impaired. **Focus:** General studies/Field of study not specified. **Qualif.:** Applicants must have a 40dB (or greater) bilateral hearing loss, and must be citizens of the United State. **Criteria:** Selection will be based upon the amount of online "activity" related to their submission. For example, if a submission is funny, inspirational, heartfelt, etc., it will often result in higher online appreciation of that submission. However, the final decision for the awarding of the scholarship will be the sole decision of David A. Black.

Funds Avail.: $1,000. **To Apply:** Applicants must submit the following materials: a short statement (no more than 100 words) explaining how they would benefit from the scholarship; an original essay of between 650 and 1,000 words explaining how their hearing loss have affected their education; and proof of hearing loss. **Deadline:** November 8. **Contact:** Law Offices of David A. Black, 40 N Central Ave., Ste. 1850, Phoenix, Arizona, 85004; Phone: 480-280-8028; Phone: michael@dbphoenixcriminallawyer.com.

6702 ■ Scholarship for Disabled Veterans *(High School, Community College, Four Year College, Graduate, Professional development, Vocational/Occupational/Scholarship)*

Purpose: To assist in the payment of tuition. **Focus:** General studies/Field of study not specified. **Qualif.:** Applicants must be a veteran of the U.S. Armed Forces with a 30% or higher disability rating. **Criteria:** Selection will be based on Short statement and optional essay.

To Apply: Applicants must complete and submit online application; upload a statement of 100 words or less indicating what your educational goals are. Optional: upload an essay of not more than 800 words on the topic of how your military service has affected your life. **Deadline:** January 15.

6703 ■ Law Offices of James C. Dezao

322 Route 46 W
Parsippany, NJ 07054
Free: 800-675-2604
URL: dezaolaw.com

6704 ■ Dezao Legal Awards *(Advanced Professional/Scholarship)*

Purpose: To encourage and award individuals for their persuasive writing and communication of thought. **Focus:** Law. **Qualif.:** Applicants must be U.S. citizens or be authorized to work/attend school in the United States; must be entering law school in fall of the current academic year. **Criteria:** Selection will be based on the applicants' respective published articles; such will be judged based on creativity; originality; and the ability to relay a message.

Funds Avail.: $1,000. **Number Awarded:** 1. **To Apply:** Applicants must submit a copy of Law School Acceptance Letter, a completed scholarship application form, and an essay on topic they choose.

6705 ■ Law Offices of Mark E. Salomone

2 Oliver St., Ste. 608
Boston, MA 02109

URL: www.marksalomone.com
Social Media: www.facebook.com/pages/Law-Offices-of-Mark-E-Salomone/104420506263255
www.linkedin.com/in/marksalomonelaw
www.youtube.com/user/marksalomone

6706 ■ Law Offices of Mark E. Salomone Scholarship for Road Safety *(Undergraduate/Scholarship)*

Purpose: To bring attention to the significant and growing problem of drunk driving among all ages, and make young drivers in particular aware of the risks of drunk driving. **Focus:** General studies/Field of study not specified. **Qualif.:** Applicants must be Massachusetts undergraduate students or prospective undergraduate students.

Funds Avail.: First prize: $2,500; second prize: $1,500; third prize: $1,000. **Number Awarded:** 3. **To Apply:** Applicants must submit and an essay of 500 to 1,000 words in Microsoft Word sharing their perspective on drunk driving and answering the following question: How can we prevent drunk driving and promote safe driving among young motorists? Applicants must also submit a digital photo of self, a copy of school transcripts or proof of enrollment, contact information (name, address, phone number), name and address of the school, a two or three sentence bio, and a signed parent waiver for applicants under 18 years old. Applications should be submitted at www.marksalomone.com/scholarship.

6707 ■ Law Offices of Michael A. DeMayo, L.L.P.

1211 E Morehead St.
Charlotte, NC 28204
Ph: (704)333-1000
Fax: (704)333-6677
Free: 877-529-1222
E-mail: info@demayolaw.com
URL: www.demayolaw.com
Social Media: www.facebook.com/DeMayoLaw
www.instagram.com/demayolaw/?hl=en
twitter.com/demayolaw
www.youtube.com/channel/UCPz5ItwNxgrtdv8iBp8FbVA

6708 ■ Law Offices of Michael A. DeMayo Scholarships *(Undergraduate/Scholarship)*

Purpose: To fund high school senior students who wish to continue their education. **Focus:** General studies/Field of study not specified. **Qualif.:** Applicants must be high school seniors in our community.

Funds Avail.: Amount varies. **Duration:** Annual. **Number Awarded:** 15. **Deadline:** March 16. **Remarks:** Established in 2003. **Contact:** Email: DeMayoScholarship@demayolaw.com.

6709 ■ The Law Offices of Scott Henry

17581 Irvine Blvd., Ste. 100
Tustin, CA 92780
Free: 888-542-2811
E-mail: info@duipractice.com
URL: www.duipractice.com
Social Media: www.facebook.com/cacriminallawfirm

6710 ■ The Law Offices of Scott Henry Scholarship Contest *(Undergraduate/Scholarship)*

Purpose: To provide financial aid to a college student, encourage students to understand their personal motivation

Awards are arranged alphabetically below their administering organizations

for a career in the legal field, and inspire students to pursue a career in law. **Focus:** Law. **Qualif.:** Applicant must be a high school senior or college freshman and U.S. resident. **Criteria:** Selection is based on the best video or written essay submitted.

Funds Avail.: $1,000. **Duration:** Annual. **Number Awarded:** 1. **To Apply:** Applicant must record a video (one to two minutes, in English) describing initiatives that could prevent drinking and driving. Applicant must publish the video to their YouTube channel with the title "The Law Offices of Scott Henry Scholarship" and include this link in the description: www.duipractice.com/scholarship-for-college-students. Instead of a video, applicant may submit a 1,000 to 1,500 word essay on the same subject. **Deadline:** June 1. **Contact:** Scott Henry; Email: shenry@duipractice.com; URL: www.duipractice. com/scholarship-for-college-students/.

6711 ■ The Law Offices of Sean M. Cleary
19 W Flagler St., Ste. 618
Miami, FL 33130
Ph: (305)416-9805
URL: www.seanclearypa.com
Social Media: www.facebook.com/Clearypa
www.linkedin.com/company/the-law-offices-of-sean-m
  -cleary-p-a-
twitter.com/Clearypa
www.youtube.com/user/seanclearypa

6712 ■ The Law Offices of Sean M. Cleary Scholarship *(Undergraduate/Scholarship)*

Purpose: To support a student who will help raise awareness on the deadly effects of teen DUI, and to provide financial assistance to students in their pursuit of higher education. **Focus:** General studies/Field of study not specified. **Qualif.:** Applicants must be high school senior or college student; be at least 18 years old; be U.S. citizen.

Funds Avail.: $1,000. **Duration:** Annual. **Number Awarded:** 1. **To Apply:** Compose essay (100-300 words) inspired by a personal story as to "why you shouldn't drink and drive." Submit at www.seanclearypa.com/scholarship, and share it on our Facebook page. **Deadline:** August 31.

6713 ■ Law Offices of Sheryl R. Rentz
326 W Lancaster Ave., No. 100
Ardmore, PA 19003
Ph: (610)645-0100
Fax: (610)645-0111
Free: 866-488-6821
E-mail: sheryl@srrentzlaw.com
URL: www.srrentzlaw.com
Social Media: www.facebook.com/RentzLawOffice
twitter.com/RentzDivorceLaw
www.youtube.com/channel/UCi6RTY1e0LtLdqUbo5Anx8g

6714 ■ Key to a Bright Future Scholarship *(Graduate, College/Scholarship)*

Purpose: To help a promising student pay for college. **Focus:** General studies/Field of study not specified. **Qualif.:** Applicant must be a high school senior on track to graduate or a college student enrolled in an accredited four-year university or college, or currently enrolled in a two-year college and planning to transfer to a four-year

university upon completion; have a minimum 3.0 GPA; and be a U.S. citizen or permanent resident (DACA recipients are welcome to apply).

Funds Avail.: $500. **Number Awarded:** 2. **To Apply:** Application and essay must be submitted online. **Deadline:** April 7. **Contact:** Scholarship Manager; Email: Sheryl@srrentz.com; URL: www.srrentzlaw.com/scholarship/.

6715 ■ The Law Offices of Tad Nelson & Associates
1221 Studewood St., No. 107
Houston, TX 77008
Ph: (713)802-1631
URL: tadnelsonlaw.com

6716 ■ Tad Nelson Law Firm Scholarships *(Undergraduate/Scholarship)*

Purpose: To support students' expenses for their future career in law. **Focus:** Law. **Qualif.:** Applicants must be high school seniors or high school graduates in Texas that seek a future career in law; must have a minimum G.P.A. of 3.0. **Criteria:** Selection will be based on the committee's criteria.

Funds Avail.: $500. **Duration:** Non-renewable. **Number Awarded:** 1. **To Apply:** Applicants must submit the following application materials; student aid report showing income status of their household; have a minimum GPA of 3.0.; and a transcript together with counselor or school representative signature. **Deadline:** May 31.

6717 ■ Law School Admission Council (LSAC)
662 Penn St.
Newtown, PA 18940
Ph: (215)968-1001
URL: www.lsac.org
Social Media: www.facebook.com/
  LawSchoolAdmissionCouncil
www.instagram.com/official_lsac
twitter.com/LSAC_Official

6718 ■ LSAC Diversity Matters Grants *(Graduate/Grant)*

Purpose: To encourage to host events that motivate students who are underrepresented in the legal profession--including racial and ethnic groups, the LGBTQ community, and Indigenous Canadians--to consider law as a career. **Focus:** Law. **Qualif.:** Applicants must be from underrepresented groups pursuing legal education.

Funds Avail.: Up to $3,000. **Duration:** Annual. **Number Awarded:** 1. **To Apply:** The application process is online. **Contact:** Isabelle M. Ramos; Email: iramos@LSAC.org.

6719 ■ LSAC Outreach Grants *(Professional development/Grant)*

Purpose: To encourage law schools to work together to promote legal education. **Focus:** Law. **Criteria:** Selection will be based on the committee's criteria.

Funds Avail.: Up to $10,000. **Deadline:** April 1. **Contact:** Vivian Bowden, Executive Director for Education, Prelaw Programs, and Member Support Services; Phone: 215-968-1297; Email: vbowden@LSAC.org.

6720 ■ Law Society of Alberta
Calgary Courts Ctr.
601 - 5 St. SW, Ste. 501-N

Awards are arranged alphabetically below their administering organizations

Calgary, AB, Canada T2P 5P7
Ph: (403)297-6148
Fax: (403)297-5171
Free: 866-448-6148
E-mail: all.cal@gov.ab.ca
URL: www.lawlibrary.ab.ca
Social Media: twitter.com/ABLawLibraries

6721 ■ Viscount Bennett Scholarship *(Graduate/Scholarship)*

Purpose: To encourage a high standard of legal education, training and excellence. **Focus:** Law. **Qualif.:** Applicants must be law graduates, articling students or lawyers with the Law Society of Alberta, ordinarily resident in or, if not presently resident in, then with an express intention to return to, the province of Alberta. **Criteria:** Selection will be based on academic excellence and Financial need.

Funds Avail.: 20,000 Canadian Dollars each. **Duration:** Annual. **Number Awarded:** Up to 3. **To Apply:** application should include: vitae of personal and professional information, including applicant's past, current and likely future connection to Alberta; official University transcripts (pre-law and law school). **Deadline:** April 12. **Remarks:** Established in 1943.

6722 ■ Law and Society Association (LSA)

417 Machmer Hall, 240 Hicks Way
Amherst, MA 01003-9278
Ph: (413)545-1694
E-mail: lsa@lawandsociety.org
URL: www.lawandsociety.org
Social Media: www.facebook.com/
  LawAndSocietyAssociation
twitter.com/law_soc

6723 ■ John Hope Franklin Prize *(Other/Prize)*

Purpose: To recognize exceptional scholarship in the field of race, racism and the law. **Focus:** Law. **Qualif.:** Applicant must be author of an article published in any scholarly journal, including socio-legal journals, journals in other disciplines, law reviews, or maybe a chapter in a book volume; published in the two calendar years prior to the award year; Only one single-authored work by the same author in a given year will be accepted; Two works by the same author will be accepted if one or both works are jointly authored. **Criteria:** Selection will be based on the committee's criteria.

Funds Avail.: $500. **Duration:** Annual. **To Apply:** Nominations require a support letter from a nominee; supporting documents must be submitted in English and be in DOC, RTF, or PDF format; the full article, including full bibliographic citation. **Remarks:** Established in 2010. **Contact:** Law and Society Association, at the above address.

6724 ■ Law and Society Association Article Prize *(Other/Prize, Award)*

Purpose: To recognize exceptional scholarship in the field of socio-legal studies for an article published in the previous two years. **Focus:** Law. **Criteria:** Selection will be based on the committee's criteria.

Funds Avail.: $500. **Duration:** Annual. **To Apply:** Nominations require a support letter from a nominee; supporting documents must be submitted in English and be in DOC, RTF, or PDF format; the full article, including full biblio-

graphic citation. **Deadline:** January 9.

6725 ■ Law and Society Association Dissertation Prize *(Other/Prize)*

Purpose: To recognize individuals whose dissertation best represents outstanding work in law and society. **Focus:** Law. **Qualif.:** Applicants must be author whose dissertation best represents outstanding work in law and society research. Self-nominations or student-member nominations are not accepted. **Criteria:** Selection will be based on the committee's criteria.

Funds Avail.: $500. **Duration:** Annual. **Number Awarded:** 1. **To Apply:** Applicants should include one letter of nomination from a regular member of the Law and Society Association; full dissertation in English; translations from other languages into English are welcome; an abstract of the dissertation, also in English; supporting documents must be submitted in English and be in DOC, RTF, or PDF format.

6726 ■ Law and Society Association International Prize *(Other/Award, Recognition)*

Purpose: To recognize scholars who have made significant contribution towards advancement of knowledge in the field of law and society. **Focus:** Law. **Qualif.:** Applicants must be a resident outside the United States. **Criteria:** Selection will be based on the committee's criteria.

Funds Avail.: $500. **Duration:** Annual. **Number Awarded:** Varies. **To Apply:** Applicant must submit Curriculum vitae; Letter of support from the nominator; must be submitted in English and be in DOC, RTF, or PDF format.

6727 ■ Law and Society Association Undergraduate Student Paper Prize *(Undergraduate/Prize)*

Purpose: To award students whose nominated papers best represent outstanding law and society research. **Focus:** Law. **Qualif.:** Applicants must be undergraduate matriculated students at any institution of higher education. **Criteria:** Selection will be based on the committee's criteria.

Funds Avail.: $500. **Duration:** Annual. **Number Awarded:** 1. **To Apply:** Applicants must submit a sample of their paper works; nominations can be made by non-student members of the Law and Society Association and through the submission of the recommended paper to the Committee on Student Awards; subject matter of the nominated papers should be in the interdisciplinary tradition of law and society research, and should reflect the style of articles that appear in the Law and Society Review; nominated papers should examine law in culture and society, including interpretative, historical, social scientific and jurisprudential scholarship; all papers entered in the competition must be written by matriculated students at any U.S. or non-U.S. institutions of higher education in the two previous years.

6728 ■ Stan Wheeler Mentorship Awards *(Other/Award)*

Purpose: To recognize a member of the Law and Society community who is regarded as an outstanding mentor for graduate, professional or undergraduate students who are working on issues of law and society. **Focus:** Law. **Qualif.:** Applicants must be members of the Law and Society Association or community who are regarded by their peers and students as outstanding mentors for graduates, professionals or undergraduate students who are working on issues of law and society. **Criteria:** Selection will be based on the committee's criteria.

Awards are arranged alphabetically below their administering organizations

Funds Avail.: $500. **Duration:** Annual. **Number Awarded:** 1. **To Apply:** A letter of support from the nominator; curriculum vitae; 2 to 4 additional letters of support from former students, colleagues, collaborators, or others who have experienced the nominee's skills as a mentor; supporting documents must be submitted in English and be in DOC, RTF, or PDF format. **Remarks:** Established in 2008.

6729 ■ Law Society of British Columbia (LSBC)

845 Cambie St.
Vancouver, BC, Canada V6B 4Z9
Ph: (604)669-2533
Fax: (604)669-5232
Free: 800-903-5300
E-mail: communications@lsbc.org
URL: www.lawsociety.bc.ca
Social Media: www.linkedin.com/company/law-society-of-british-columbia
www.youtube.com/user/lawsocietyofbc

6730 ■ Law Society Scholarship (Graduate/Scholarship)

Purpose: To provide financial assistance for law graduate students intending to complete a full-time program of studies that will benefit students, the province and legal professions in British Columbia. **Focus:** Law.

Funds Avail.: $12,000. **Duration:** Annual. **To Apply:** Applicant must submit applications including all supporting documents; Applicants must submit a letter of application including details of their academic career and proposed plan for graduate study, official transcript of records of all academic institutions attended, and three letters of recommendation (one from the dean and two from professors of the law school). **Deadline:** March 31. **Contact:** Manager, Credentials & Licensing; E-mail: lsmall@lsbc.org.

6731 ■ Law Society of Prince Edward Island (LS-PEI)

49 Water St.
Charlottetown, PE, Canada C1A 1A3
Ph: (902)566-1666
Fax: (902)368-7557
E-mail: lawsociety@lspei.pe.ca
URL: lawsocietypei.ca

6732 ■ Prince Edward Island Law Student Scholarships (Undergraduate/Scholarship)

Purpose: To provide scholarship assistance to three full time law students at an accredited University Law School who have demonstrated financial need and scholastic achievement in the previous year of study. **Focus:** Law. **Criteria:** Recipient will be selected by the Council of Law Society of Prince Edward Island.

Funds Avail.: $2,000. **Duration:** Annual. **Number Awarded:** 3. **To Apply:** Applicant must complete the application form available online; must submit an official transcript of record; Statement as to applicant's financial need or special financial circumstances; curriculum vitae; Proof of CBA membership. **Deadline:** August 31. **Contact:** The Law Society of Prince Edward Island, Attention: Scholarship Committee, 49 Water St., PO Box 128, Charlottetown, PE, C1A 7K2; Email: lawsociety@lspei.pe.ca; Phone: 902- 566-1666; Fax: 902-368-7557.

6733 ■ Lawrence Berkeley National Laboratory

One Cyclotron Rd.
Berkeley, CA 94720
URL: www.lbl.gov
Social Media: www.facebook.com/pg/BerkeleyLab
twitter.com/BerkeleyLab

6734 ■ Advanced Light Source Collaborative Postdoctoral Fellowship Program (Postdoctorate/Fellowship)

Purpose: To identify outstanding individuals in new and emerging scientific and engineering research fields. **Focus:** Engineering; Science. **Qualif.:** Applicants must be legally eligible to work in the United States, regardless of citizenship and have received a doctoral research degree from an accredited academic institution in an appropriate scientific or engineering discipline within three years of the appointment start date doctoral degree candidate, the candidate must present acceptable evidence that all formal academic doctoral degree requirements have been met before starting the fellowship. **Criteria:** Applications will be evaluated based on the qualifications of the applicants, the merits of the proposed collaborative research, and the alignment of the project with ALS strategic priorities.

Funds Avail.: No specific amount. **To Apply:** Applicants must complete and submit the following documents online: an application form; curriculum vitae; publication list; maximum of three pages statement of research to be performed (preferably written in consultation with an ALS Scientific mentor); three references. Applicants must also obtain the commitment of an ALS scientific mentor who will work with them throughout the duration of the proposed fellowship. **Contact:** Andreas Scholl, Email: a_scholl@lbl.gov.

6735 ■ Luis W. Alvarez Postdoctoral Fellowships in Computational Science (Doctorate/Fellowship)

Purpose: To provide recent graduates the opportunities to work on some of the most important research challenges in computing sciences. **Focus:** Clinical laboratory sciences. **Qualif.:** Applicants must be recent graduate with a PhD (or equivalent) within the past three years, and have backgrounds and research interests in any computer and computational science discipline. **Criteria:** Selection is based on the selection committee.

Funds Avail.: No specific amount. **To Apply:** Applicants must apply online and submit in a single attachment the following documents: curriculum vitae; a statement of research interests; and a list of three references.

6736 ■ Lawsuit Legal

401 E Las Olas Blvd.
Fort Lauderdale, FL 33301
Free: 888-713-6653
E-mail: support@lawsuitlegal.com
URL: www.lawsuitlegal.com

6737 ■ Advance Prevention Lawsuit Legal Scholarships (Undergraduate, Graduate/Scholarship)

Purpose: To support students working to build skills and advance their education for use in service of their communities. **Focus:** General studies/Field of study not speci-

Awards are arranged alphabetically below their administering organizations

fied. **Qualif.:** Applicants must be U.S. citizens or permanent residents; must have a GPA of 3.0 or higher; and must be entering freshmen year (or attending first year) in college and plan to declare a major in any field of study. **Criteria:** Selection will be based on the committee's criteria.

Funds Avail.: $1,000. **Duration:** Annual. **To Apply:** Applicants are required to create a video along with a written essay discussing a personal story sharing how reckless, drunk, impaired or distracted driving has impacted their lives, their family, or their community. Entrants are encouraged to provide an analysis on how injuries and fatalities resulting from preventable accidents reach beyond crash victims to those left behind and the community as a whole. Creative ideas for reducing accident rates and reckless/impaired driving in teenage drivers to reduce needless injury and death are welcome. **Deadline:** May 5.

6738 ■ Lawsuit Legal American Nursing Support Scholarships *(Undergraduate, Graduate/Scholarship)*

Purpose: To support individuals who provide excellence in nursing care. **Focus:** Nursing. **Qualif.:** Applicants must be U.S. citizens or permanent residents; must be actively employed registered nurses or nurse practitioners who are entering/enrolled in advanced education in the medical field; and must have an intention to continue employment as healthcare professionals following completion. **Criteria:** Selection will be based on the committee's criteria.

Funds Avail.: $1,500.

6739 ■ Lawyers Committee for Civil Rights Under Law (LCCRUL)
1500 K Street NW Suite 900
Washington, DC 20005
Ph: (202)662-8600
Fax: (202)783-0857
Free: 888-299-5227
URL: www.lawyerscommittee.org
Social Media: www.facebook.com/lawyerscommittee
www.instagram.com/lawyerscomm
www.linkedin.com/company/lawyers'%E2%80%8B
  -committee-for-civil-rights
twitter.com/LawyersComm

6740 ■ George N. Lindsay Fellowship *(Graduate/Fellowship)*

Purpose: To provide an opportunity for recent law school graduates to become familiar with civil rights practice by working with many of the nation's leading civil rights experts. **Focus:** Law. **Criteria:** Preference will be given to those who have been admitted to the bar or are scheduled to take a bar examination.

Funds Avail.: $47,000 supplemented by a loan forgiveness payment of $2,000. **Duration:** Annual. **To Apply:** Applications can be submitted online. **Deadline:** May 22. **Remarks:** Established in 1998. **Contact:** Thomas Silverstein, Co-Chair of the Fellowship Selection Committee Email: tsilverstein@lawyerscommittee.org.

6741 ■ Le Conseil Canadien pour l'Avancement de l'Éducation (CCAE)
The Woolen Mill
4 Cataraqui St., Ste. 310
Kingston, ON, Canada K7K 1Z7
Ph: (613)531-9213

Fax: (613)531-0626
E-mail: admin@ccaecanada.org
URL: www.ccaecanada.org
Social Media: www.linkedin.com/groups/2867119/profile
twitter.com/CCAECanada

6742 ■ CCAE Ontario Regional Chapter Scholarship *(Advanced Professional, Professional development/Scholarship)*

Purpose: To promote professional development within the advancement profession and integration between the different areas of advancement: alumni relations, advancement services, development, public relations, marketing, communications and research. **Focus:** Communications; Marketing and distribution; Public relations. **Qualif.:** Applicant must be employed by a CCAE member institution in Ontario. **Criteria:** Selection will be given to a professional wishing to broaden their understanding in an area outside of their traditional expertise.

Funds Avail.: 500 Canadian Dollars. **Duration:** Annual. **To Apply:** Completed applications can be submitted electronically, date of submission and further information can be obtained from the website. **Deadline:** April 13.

6743 ■ Richard Lim Professional Development Scholarship *(Advanced Professional, Professional development/Scholarship, Recognition)*

Purpose: To help promote cross pollination and integration between the different areas of advancement. **Focus:** Education. **Qualif.:** Applicant must be employed by a CCAE member. **Criteria:** Preference will be given to those planning on attending workshops, seminars and conferences in Ontario.

Funds Avail.: 500 Canadian Dollars. **Duration:** Annual. **Deadline:** April 13.

6744 ■ LEAGUE Foundation
208 S Akard St., Rm. 251012
Dallas, TX 75202
E-mail: info@leaguefoundation.org
Social Media: www.facebook.com/leaguefoundation.org
twitter.com/LEAGUE_ATT_FDN

6745 ■ League Foundation Scholarships *(Undergraduate/Scholarship)*

Purpose: To provide financial assistance for lesbian, gay, bisexual and transgender high school seniors. **Focus:** General studies/Field of study not specified. **Qualif.:** Applicants must be United States citizens; identify as lesbian, gay, bisexual or transgender; be college-bound students; must have a GPA of at least 3.0 on a 4.0 scale; and must be actively and substantially involved in community service. **Criteria:** Selection of scholars will be based on criteria.

Funds Avail.: $1,500 - $2,500. **Duration:** Annual. **Number Awarded:** Up to 13. **To Apply:** Provide two letters of recommendation; detailed list of community involvement, extra-credit is given to those activities and leadership roles relating directly to the Gay, Lesbian, Bisexual and Transgender communities, complete two essays, complete application. **Deadline:** April 30. **Remarks:** All applicants are automatically considered for all LEAGUE Foundation Scholarships. The Laurel Hester and Matthew Shepard Memorial Scholarships are the foundation's highest awards. **Contact:** URL: www.leaguefoundation.org.

Awards are arranged alphabetically below their administering organizations

6746 ■ League of United Latin American Citizens (LULAC)

1133 19th St. NW, Ste. 1000
Washington, DC 20036
Ph: (202)833-6130
Fax: (202)833-6135
Free: 877-585-2201
URL: lulac.org
Social Media: www.facebook.com/lulac.national.dc
twitter.com/lulac
www.youtube.com/lulac

6747 ■ League of Latin American Citizens General Electric Scholarships (Undergraduate/Scholarship)

Purpose: To assist and encourage outstanding minority students in completing their college education. **Focus:** Business; Engineering, Electrical. **Qualif.:** Applicant must be a U.S. citizen or legal resident; must be a minority student pursuing full-time studies leading to a bachelor's degree at a college, university, or graduate school, including two-year colleges, or vocational schools that lead to an associate's degree; must not be related to a scholarship Committee member, the Council President, or an individual contributor to the local funds of the Council; must be a sophomore, junior, or senior student in the field of business or engineering; must have a cumulative GPA of at least 3.25 on a 4.0 scale or the equivalent. **Criteria:** Recipients will be selected based on academic performance; performance in business or engineering-related subjects; likelihood of pursuing a career in business or engineering; writing ability; extracurricular activities; and community involvement.

Funds Avail.: $5,000. **Duration:** One semester. **Number Awarded:** 2. **To Apply:** Applicants must submit a completed application form; college transcript(s); letters of reference from three adults (at least one from professor); and (maximum of 300 words) typed personal statement describing professional and career goals.

6748 ■ LULAC GM Scholarship (Award)

Purpose: To provide high quality educational opportunities to the Hispanic community. **Focus:** Hispanic American studies.

6749 ■ LULAC National Scholarship Fund (LNSF) (Graduate, Undergraduate/Scholarship)

Purpose: To provide youth in underserved communities make the dream of college enrollment a reality in education. **Focus:** Hispanic American studies. **Qualif.:** Applicant GPA of 3.5 or better on a 4.0 scale or equivalent, and if the student is an entering freshman, 29 or higher on the ACT test, or 1350 or higher on the SAT test. **Criteria:** Recipients are chosen through a very rigorous selection process by members of LNESC's scholarship committee.

Funds Avail.: $2,000. **To Apply:** Applications should be mailed directly to the nearest LULAC Council. **Remarks:** Established in 1975. **Contact:** scholarships@lnesc.org.

6750 ■ Leakey Foundation

1003B O'Reilly Ave.
San Francisco, CA 94129-1359
Ph: (415)561-4646
Fax: (415)561-4647
URL: leakeyfoundation.org
Social Media: www.facebook.com/TheLeakeyFoundation

www.instagram.com/theleakeyfoundation
www.pinterest.com/leakeyfndtn
twitter.com/TheLeakeyFndtn
www.youtube.com/user/TheLeakeyFoundation

6751 ■ Franklin Mosher Baldwin Memorial Fellowships (Master's, Doctorate/Fellowship)

Purpose: To support scholars and students who wish to obtain an advanced degree from an institution outside the student's home country. **Focus:** Anthropology. **Qualif.:** Applicants must be Human origins scholars from developing nations seeking advanced degrees (M.A./M.S. or Ph.D.). **Criteria:** Recipients will be chosen based on affiliation and/or employment with an institution in their home country; provisional acceptance to the host institution; demonstrated financial need; and intention to return and work in the home country upon completion of training.

Funds Avail.: $15,000 per year. **Duration:** Annual; up to two years. **To Apply:** Applicants must submit a completed application form and letters from sponsor. **Deadline:** February 15. **Contact:** Paddy Moore, Grant Officer; H. Gregory, Program Engagement Officer; The Leakey Foundation; 1003B O'Reilly Avenue; San Francisco, CA, 94129,USA Phone: (415) 561-4646;Fax: (415) 561-4647; Email: grants@leakeyfoundation.org.

6752 ■ Leakey Foundation Research Grants (Doctorate, Advanced Professional/Grant)

Purpose: To support research related specifically to human origins. **Focus:** Anthropology. **Qualif.:** Applicants must be advanced doctoral students and established scientists. **Criteria:** Recipients will be selected based on submitted research. Priority of funding will be given to applicants whose research project meets the stated purpose of the Foundation.

Funds Avail.: $3,000 to $15,000. **Duration:** Annual. **To Apply:** Applicants must complete the application form; application must be written in English and it should be submitted in PDF format. **Deadline:** January 10; July 15. **Contact:** Paddy Moore, Grants Officer; H. Gregory, Grants Associate; The Leakey Foundation, 1003B O'Reilly Ave., San Francisco, CA, 94129-1359; phone: 415-561-4646; Fax: 415-561-4647; Email: grants@leakeyfoundation.org.

6753 ■ Learning Disabilities Association of Alberta (LDAA)

PO Box 29011, Pleasantview P.O.
Edmonton, AB, Canada T6H 5Z6
Ph: (780)448-0360
E-mail: execdir@ldalberta.ca
URL: ldalberta.ca
Social Media: www.facebook.com/Learning-Disabilities
-Association-of-Alberta-185386404841119

6754 ■ Siobhan Isabella Reid Memorial Scholarships (Graduate, Undergraduate/Scholarship)

Purpose: To provide financial assistance to qualified individuals who want to pursue their studies. **Focus:** Disabilities; Education, Special. **Qualif.:** Applicant must be a full-time student attending an Alberta University; must be enrolled in a program which will be able to assist children and individual with learning disabilities; must have completed two full academic years at either a university or at a junior college at which courses are accepted by a university as applicable toward a university degree; must be an

Awards are arranged alphabetically below their administering organizations

undergraduate or post graduate student enrolled in any faculty at a university in Alberta. **Criteria:** Recipient will be selected based on student's contributions to community and campus life; satisfactory academic record; student's future educational program leading toward assisting children and adults with learning disabilities.

Funds Avail.: $1,000. **Duration:** Annual. **To Apply:** Applicants must submit a completed application form available from the website; and include materials such as official transcript for the last university or college year; three letters of reference from non-relative; outline of contributions to the community and campus life; outline of the program the student wishes to undertake during the scholarship year. **Deadline:** May 15. **Remarks:** Established in 1982.

6755 ■ Learning Disabilities Association of Kingston (LDAK)

817 Division St., Unit 108
Kingston, ON, Canada K7K 4C2
Ph: (613)546-8524
E-mail: ldak@ldakingston.com
URL: www.ldakingston.com
Social Media: www.facebook.com/pages/Learning
-Disabilities-Association-of-Kingston/112500288874783

6756 ■ Tristin Memorial Scholarships *(Undergraduate, Vocational/Occupational/Scholarship)*

Purpose: To encourage Canadian students with learning disabilities to pursue a college, private vocational school or an undergraduate degree at a Canadian university. **Focus:** General studies/Field of study not specified. **Qualif.:** Applicant must have a documented learning disability; a Canadian citizen or permanent resident who has lived in Canada for at least two years as a permanent resident; an Ontario resident living within the city and boundaries of Kingston, towns of Ernestown, Amherst Island, Richmond, Camden, Kaladar, North and South Fredericksburg, Napanee, Lennox and Addington, Townships of Front/Rear Leeds and Lansdown and Front of Yonge, The Town of Gananoque in the county of Leeds and Grenville; and planning to register in a Canadian college, university or vocational school in the next semester or already enrolled in a program. **Criteria:** Selection is based on the submitted application materials.

Funds Avail.: $500. **Duration:** Annual. **To Apply:** Applicant must complete a letter with personal details and submit along with a 200-word outline on: description of learning disability, how it impacts daily life, coping skills and strategies used at school and at home to compensate for the learning disability, extracurricular activities, community involvement and/or employment experience, future goals, and how the scholarship funds will assist them. In addition, applicants must submit a documentation of the learning disability; two letters of recommendation (one from a secondary school teacher); and proof of enrollment as an active student. **Contact:** Phil Perrin; Phone: 613-544-6925.

6757 ■ Learning Disabilities Association of Ontario (LDAO)

365 Evans Ave., Ste. 202
Toronto, ON, Canada M8Z 1K2
Ph: (416)929-4311
Fax: (416)929-3905
E-mail: resource@ldao.ca

URL: www.ldao.ca
Social Media: www.facebook.com/LDAOntario
twitter.com/ldatschool

6758 ■ Roy Cooper Memorial Scholarship *(Undergraduate/Scholarship)*

Purpose: To recognizes an Ontario high school student who has a documented learning disability and who will be attending a post-secondary institution in the upcoming academic year. **Focus:** Engineering; Physical sciences. **Qualif.:** Applicants must be high school students who have a documented learning disability and will be attending a university or college, majoring in an engineering or physical science discipline. **Criteria:** Selection is based on the submitted application materials.

Funds Avail.: $1,000. **Duration:** Annual. **To Apply:** Applicants must contact any of the LDAO's local chapters for the scholarship information and application. **Deadline:** June 14. **Remarks:** The scholarship was established in memory of Roy V. Cooper.

6759 ■ Learning Disabilities Association of Saskatchewan (LDAS)

2221 Hanselman Ct.
Saskatoon, SK, Canada S7L 6A8
Ph: (306)652-4114
Fax: (306)652-3220
E-mail: reception@ldas.org
URL: www.ldas.org
Social Media: www.facebook.com/LDASaskatchewan
twitter.com/LDASaskatchewan

6760 ■ LDAS Scholarship *(Undergraduate/Scholarship)*

Purpose: To recognize the hard work and dedication required of individuals with learning disabilities who succeed in completing their high school education and to encourage those individuals to continue their education in a post-secondary educational institution. **Focus:** General studies/Field of study not specified. **Qualif.:** Applicants must be Canadian citizens or landed immigrants and permanent residents of Saskatchewan who have graduated from a Saskatchewan high school, and who have a written diagnosis of a learning disability. **Criteria:** The selection is made by a committee, appointed by the LDAS Board of Directors, who make their decisions based on the committee criteria.

Funds Avail.: $1,500. **Duration:** Annual. **Number Awarded:** 2. **To Apply:** Completed application form along with three letters of reference one from a teacher who taught the applicant in high school and two from persons who have known the applicant for a minimum of one year, letters from relatives will not be admissible; proof of admission; written documentation of the diagnosis of a learning disability by a registered psychologist; one page explanation how learning disabilities have affected his or her life, how he or she has learned to work with and compensate for those disabilities and what he or she hopes to do in the future must be submitted. **Deadline:** June 30. **Contact:** Learning Disabilities Association of Saskatchewan Scholarship, 2221 Hanselman Crt., Saskatoon, SK, S7L 6A8; Phone: 306-652-4114; Fax: 306-652-3220.

6761 ■ LeClairRyan

2318 Mill Rd., Ste. 1100
Alexandria, VA 22314

Awards are arranged alphabetically below their administering organizations

Ph: (703)684-8007
Fax: (703)684-8075
URL: www.leclairryan.com
Social Media: www.facebook.com/LeClairRyan
www.linkedin.com/company/leclairryan
twitter.com/leclairryan

6762 ■ LeClairRyan 1L Diversity Scholarship
(Undergraduate/Scholarship)

Purpose: To support diversity law students who most exemplifies the late Oliver W. Hill's qualities of legal excellence and selfless dedication to the fight for justice. **Focus:** Law. **Qualif.:** Applicants must be enrolled in good standing at an ABA-accredited US law school in any state in which LeClairRyan has an office; have one semester of law school completed; a law school GPA of at least 3.0; identify as a member of one of the racial/ethnic groups as defined by the Equal Employment Opportunity Commission, or identify as LGBT. **Criteria:** Selection will be based on the committee's criteria.

Funds Avail.: $5,000. **Number Awarded:** 1. **To Apply:** Applicants must submit the completed application along with their resume, law school transcript and two letters of recommendation from a professor or member of the Bar and a maximum of 2,000 words essay on pursuing social justice through the law. **Contact:** Danielle H. Roberts, Recruiting Manager, Riverfront Plz., East Tower, 951 E Byrd St., 8th Fl., Richmond, VA 23219; droberts@ leclairryan.com.

6763 ■ Leesa
3200 Pacific Ave. ste 200
Virginia Beach, VA 23451
Free: 844-335-3372
E-mail: support@leesa.com
URL: www.leesa.com
Social Media: www.facebook.com/LeesaSleep
www.instagram.com/leesasleep
www.pinterest.com/leesasleep
twitter.com/leesasleep
www.youtube.com/user/LeesaSleep

6764 ■ Leesa Social Impact Scholarship (College, University, Undergraduate/Scholarship)

Purpose: To support four exceptional students as they embark on their journey towards social action. **Focus:** General studies/Field of study not specified. **Qualif.:** Applicant must be enrolled in a college or university; must have a minimum cumulative GPA of 3.0; must have demonstrated a commitment to social action. **Criteria:** Selection will be based on submitted video.

Funds Avail.: $1,000 each. **To Apply:** Applicant must submit a video which describes the role social action has had on their life so far, and they role they see it having in the future. Details available at www.leesa.com/scholarship/. **Deadline:** May 15. **Contact:** scholarship@leesa.com.

6765 ■ Legacy, Inc.
4162 A Carmichael Ct.
Montgomery, AL 36106
Ph: (334)270-5921
Fax: (334)270-5527
Free: 800-240-5115

E-mail: info@legacyenved.org
URL: legacyenved.org
Social Media: www.facebook.com/legacyalabama
twitter.com/legacyenved
www.youtube.com/legacyalabama

6766 ■ Legacy Inc. College Undergraduate and Graduate Scholarships (Other/Scholarship)

Purpose: To provide financial assistance to Alabama students who are pursuing environmentally related careers. **Focus:** Environmental science. **Qualif.:** Applicants must be residents of Alabama. **Criteria:** Selection will be based on the committee's criteria.

Funds Avail.: up to $10,000. **Duration:** Annual. **To Apply:** Applicants must submit a completed application form and letters from sponsor. **Deadline:** December 31. **Contact:** Questions concerning eligibility, applicants must contact the Legacy office at 800-240-5115.

6767 ■ Legal Aid of North Carolina Inc. (LANC)
224 S Dawson St.
Raleigh, NC 27601
Free: 866-219-5262
E-mail: acsinfo@legalaidnc.org
URL: www.legalaidnc.org
Social Media: www.facebook.com/legalaidnc
twitter.com/LegalAidNC
www.youtube.com/user/LegalAidNC

6768 ■ Ervin Fellowship (Graduate/Fellowship)

Purpose: To provide free legal assistance in civil matters to low-income persons in Alexander, Burke, Caldwell, Catawba and McDowell Counties of northwest North Carolina. **Focus:** Law. **Qualif.:** Candidates must be licensed to practice law in North Carolina; must have a demonstrated commitment to community service and to be able to relate well to low-income people in a rural setting. **Criteria:** Selected based on their legal abilities and demonstrated commitment to social justice.

Funds Avail.: No specific amount. **Duration:** Annual.

6769 ■ Everett Fellowship (Graduate/Fellowship)

Purpose: To provide excellent opportunities for new law school graduate to gain litigation experience and provide valuable service to low-income, rural communities. **Focus:** Law. **Qualif.:** Applicants must be recently graduated law students; must demonstrate commitment to community service and be able to relate well to low-income people in a rural setting. **Criteria:** Selection will be based on their legal abilities and demonstrated commitment to social justice.

Funds Avail.: No specific amount. **Duration:** Annual. **Remarks:** Established in 1992.

6770 ■ Legalzoom
101 N Brand Blvd.
Glendale, CA 91203
Free: 800-773-0888
URL: www.legalzoom.com

6771 ■ Emerging Entrepreneur Scholarship Grant
(Other/Scholarship, Grant)

Purpose: To help entrepreneurial students who have innovative business ideas. **Focus:** General studies/Field of

Awards are arranged alphabetically below their administering organizations

study not specified. **Qualif.:** Applicant must be a student entrepreneur; must be a U.S. citizen or permanent legal resident and at least 18 years old. **Criteria:** Selection is based on the following: viability of business idea, scalability of business idea, uniqueness of business idea; and local and social benefits of business idea.

Funds Avail.: $5,000. **Duration:** Annual. **Number Awarded:** 1. **To Apply:** Applicant must submit a application in online. **Deadline:** September 10. **Contact:** Email: cneeser@legalzoom.com.

6772 ■ Gilder Lehrman Institute of American History

49 W 45th St., 2nd Fl.
New York, NY 10036
Ph: (646)366-9666
Fax: (646)366-9669
E-mail: info@gilderlehrman.org
URL: www.gilderlehrman.org
Social Media: www.facebook.com/gilderlehrman
www.instagram.com/gilderlehrman
www.pinterest.com/gilderlehrman
twitter.com/Gilder_Lehrman
www.youtube.com/gilderlehrman

6773 ■ Gilder Lehrman Short-Term research Fellowships *(Graduate, Postdoctorate/Fellowship)*

Purpose: To support independent scholars working in the field of American history. **Focus:** History. **Qualif.:** Applicants must be doctoral candidates, college and university faculty at every rank, and independent scholars working in the field of American history.

Funds Avail.: $3,000 each. **Duration:** Annual. **To Apply:** Applicants must submit a project proposal including current contact information, a list of primary sources to be consulted, and an anticipated budget; curriculum vitae; and two letters of recommendation from established scholars. **Remarks:** Established in 1994. **Contact:** The Gilder Lehrman Scholarly Fellowship Program, 49 W 45th St., second Fl., New York, NY, 10036; Phone: 646-366-9666, ext. 29; Fax: 646-366-9669; Email:fellowships@gilderlehrman.org.

6774 ■ Lependorf & Silverstein PC

4365 US Hwy. 1, Ste. 104
Princeton, NJ 08540
Ph: (609)429-5857
Fax: (609)240-0044
URL: www.lependorf.com
Social Media: www.facebook.com/
  NJPersonalInjuryLawyers
www.instagram.com/lependorfsilverstein
twitter.com/Njinjuryfirm
www.youtube.com/channel/UCq5waQ7eqYis04s
  _moHzqYw

6775 ■ Riding Into the Future *(Undergraduate, College, University/Scholarship)*

Purpose: To help students in New Jersey pay for higher education and make a difference in the world. **Focus:** General studies/Field of study not specified. **Qualif.:** Applicant must be a high school student in New Jersey on track to graduate, a college student enrolled in an accredited college or university in New Jersey, or currently

enrolled in a two-year college and planning to transfer to a four-year university; high school students in New Jersey who plan on attending a college outside of New Jersey are also eligible. Applicant must also have a 3.0 or higher cumulative GPA and be a U.S. citizen or permanent resident (DACA recipients are welcome to apply).

Funds Avail.: $500. **Number Awarded:** 1. **To Apply:** Application and essay must be submitted online. **Deadline:** April 8. **Contact:** Scholarship Manager; Email: dsilverstein@lependorf.com; lependorf@gmail.com; URL: www.lependorf.com/scholarship/.

6776 ■ Les Dames d'Escoffier New York (LDNY)

New York, NY
E-mail: info@ldny.org
URL: www.ldny.org
Social Media: www.facebook.com/LesDamesNY
www.pinterest.com/lesdamesnyjc100
twitter.com/LesDamesNY

6777 ■ Les Dames D'Escoffier New York Corporate Scholarship *(Undergraduate/Scholarship)*

Purpose: To provide support for talented women in food and wine-related disciplines; hospitality and table arts. **Focus:** Food service careers; Hotel, institutional, and restaurant management; Nutrition. **Qualif.:** Applicants must be enrolled in a higher education program; must be from the Tri-State area (New York, New Jersey, Connecticut). **Criteria:** Selection will be based on evaluation of submitted documents and specific criteria; the LDNY Scholarship Selection Committee reviews all submissions and selects the winning candidates based on how well they meet or exceed the criteria for consideration.

Funds Avail.: Varies. **Duration:** Annual. **To Apply:** Applicants must submit a completed application form; resume; official transcript from higher education institution; two professional recommendation letters but not from school affiliations; and an essay of less than 500-words. **Deadline:** March 4. **Contact:** E-mail: ldnyscholarship@gmail.com.

6778 ■ LeverEdge

Harvard Innovation Lab
Boston, MA 02163
E-mail: support@leveredge.org
URL: leveredge.org
Social Media: www.facebook.com/harvardinnovationlabs
www.instagram.com/harvardinnovationlabs
twitter.com/innovationlab

6779 ■ LeverEdge Scholarship *(College, Undergraduate, Graduate/Scholarship)*

Purpose: To help students afford college. **Focus:** General studies/Field of study not specified. **Criteria:** Selection is random.

Funds Avail.: $1,000. **Duration:** Monthly. **To Apply:** Application must be completed on the sponsor's website at scholarships.leveredge.org/1000-scholarship. **Deadline:** September 30.

6780 ■ Lewis-Clark State College

500 Eighth Ave.
Lewiston, ID 83501
Ph: (208)792-5272

Awards are arranged alphabetically below their administering organizations

Free: 800-933-5272
URL: www.lcsc.edu
Social Media: www.facebook.com/LewisClarkState
www.instagram.com/lewisclarkstate
twitter.com/lcsc
www.youtube.com/channel/UCneasUNEMEd
_gUaLekhCY0A

6781 ■ The "21" Endowed Scholarships
(Undergraduate/Scholarship)

Purpose: To offset the educationally-related expenses of a Lewis-Clark State College student from the Culdesac-Lapwai area. **Focus:** General studies/Field of study not specified. **Qualif.:** Applicants must be an incoming freshman and must have minimum cumulative GPA of 2.5. **Criteria:** Preference will be given to students from the Culdesac-Lapwai area, as well as those students who demonstrate financial need as determined by the Financial Aid Office.

Duration: Annual. **Number Awarded:** 1. **To Apply:** Applicants must submit information via online and attach typed essay information along with the application. **Deadline:** March 1. **Contact:** Email: scholarships@lcsc.edu.

6782 ■ American Legion Boys/Girls State Scholarship *(High School/Scholarship)*

Purpose: To acknowledge outstanding Idaho high school seniors who have participated in The American Legion of Idaho Boys and Girls State competition and who have selected Lewis-Clark State College as their school of choice. **Focus:** General studies/Field of study not specified. **Qualif.:** Applicants must be outstanding senior students of Idaho High School who have participated the American Legion of Idaho Boys and Girls State competition and have selected Lewis-Clark State College as their school of choice.

Funds Avail.: $200. **Duration:** Annual. **Number Awarded:** 4 (2 Boys state and 2 Girls state). **To Apply:** Applications can be obtained from The American Legion Department of Idaho, must submit information via online and attach typed essay information along with the application. **Deadline:** March 1. **Contact:** The American Legion, Boys State, 901 Warren, Boise, ID 83706, (208) 342-7061, or American Legion Auxiliary, Girls State, 905 Warren St., Boise, ID 83706, (208) 342-7066.

6783 ■ Banner Bank Business Scholarship
(Undergraduate/Scholarship)

Purpose: To provide financial assistance to outstanding junior or senior students in the Business Division. **Focus:** Business. **Qualif.:** Applicants must be students pursuing a degree in the business division; must have a class standing of junior or senior; demonstrate financial need as determined by the Financial Aid Office.

Duration: Annual. **To Apply:** Applicants must submit information via online and attach typed essay information along with the application. **Deadline:** March 1.

6784 ■ Coeur d'Alene Alumni Scholarship
(Undergraduate/Scholarship)

Purpose: To support the educational pursuits among less capable individuals. **Focus:** General studies/Field of study not specified. **Qualif.:** Applicants must have a minimum cumulative GPA of 3.0 with at least half-time, enrolled in 6 or more credits per semester and completed at least one

semester of coursework through LCSC, attending the LCSC-Coeur d'Alene Center. **Criteria:** Preference will be given to students who demonstrate financial need as determined by the Financial Aid Office.

Duration: Annual. **To Apply:** Applicants must submit information via online and attach typed essay information along with the application. **Deadline:** March 1. **Contact:** Email: scholarships@lcsc.edu.

6785 ■ Rob Copeland Memorial Scholarship
(Undergraduate/Scholarship)

Purpose: To provide financial assistance to individuals intending to pursue educational goals. **Focus:** Automotive technology. **Qualif.:** Applicants must be full-time students who are pursuing a degree in Auto Mechanics Technology and enrolled in 12 or more credits per semester; must have a minimum cumulative GPA of 2.5. **Criteria:** Preference will be given to students who demonstrate financial need as determined by the Financial Aid Office.

Duration: Annual. **To Apply:** Applicants must submit information via online and attach typed essay information along with the application. **Deadline:** March 1. **Remarks:** The scholarship was established by Hall-Copeland employees in honor and memory of Rob and Tony Copeland. **Contact:** Lewis-Clark State College, 500 8th Ave., Lewiston, ID, 83501; Phone: 800-377-3529; Email: scholarships@lcsc.edu.

6786 ■ Rick Crane Group Real Estate Scholarship Fund *(Undergraduate/Scholarship)*

Purpose: To offset the educationally-related expenses of Lewis-Clark State College students intending to pursue a career in the field of real estate. **Focus:** Business administration; Real estate. **Qualif.:** Applicants must be individuals seeking a Bachelor's degree in Business, or an Associate of Applied Science degree in Business Management; must be serious about becoming real estate agents or otherwise working in the field of real estate; must have a grade point average of at least 3.5 with strong potential for academic achievement, and be full-time students taking 12 or more credits. **Criteria:** Preference will be given to students who are gainfully employed.

Duration: Annual. **To Apply:** Applicants must complete a general application available on the website. **Deadline:** March 1.

6787 ■ Dean A. Froehlich Endowed Scholarship
(Undergraduate/Scholarship)

Purpose: To provide financial assistance for students and single parents who are in need and are intending to pursue higher education. **Focus:** General studies/Field of study not specified. **Qualif.:** Applicants must be students enrolled full-time in 12 or more credits and have a minimum 2.5 GPA; must answer two discussion topics in order to be considered. **Criteria:** Preference will be given to non-traditional, single parents who are returning to higher education and plan on staying in Idaho, as well as to students who demonstrate financial need as determined by the Financial Aid Office.

Duration: Annual. **To Apply:** Applicants must submit information via online and attach typed essay information along with the application. **Deadline:** March 1. **Remarks:** The scholarship was established by family, friends and colleagues in memory of Dean A. Froehlich. Established in 2004. **Contact:** Lewis-Clark State College, 500 8th Ave., Lewiston, ID, 83501; Phone: 800-377-3529; Email: scholarships@lcsc.edu.

Awards are arranged alphabetically below their administering organizations

6788 ■ Diana Brown Endowed Scholarship
(Undergraduate/Scholarship)

Purpose: To support non-traditional students, who are cancer survivors, in their education. **Focus:** General studies/Field of study not specified. **Qualif.:** Applicants must: have a minimum cumulative GPA of 3.0; be full-time enrolled in 12 or more credits per semester; be non-traditional students and demonstrate financial need as determined by the Financial Aid Office. **Criteria:** Preference will be given to students who are cancer survivors and/or currently battling cancer or have had to deal with cancer in their immediate family.

Duration: Annual. **To Apply:** Applicants must submit information via online and attach typed essay information along with the application. **Contact:** LCSC Financial Aid Office 500 8th Avenue Reid Centennial Hall Room 110 Lewiston, ID 83501 208-792-2224 or 1-800-933-5272 ext. 2224 scholarships@lcsc.edu.

6789 ■ Eleanor Perry Memorial Endowed Scholarship *(Undergraduate/Scholarship)*

Purpose: To offset the educationally-related expenses of Lewis-Clark State College students. **Focus:** General studies/Field of study not specified. **Qualif.:** Applicants must be students in the final year of their program and have full-time enrolled in 12 or more credits per semester; must have a cumulative GPA of 3.0.

Duration: Annual. **To Apply:** Applicants must submit information via online and attach typed essay information along with the application. **Deadline:** March 1. **Contact:** Lewis-Clark State College, 500 8th Ave., Lewiston, ID, 83501; Phone: 800-377-3529; Email: scholarships@lcsc.edu.

6790 ■ Elizabeth McKissick Memorial Scholarship
(Undergraduate/Scholarship)

Purpose: To provide educational support for young people who, for personal, financial, or other reasons discontinued their education, and for those who are in need of retraining who wish to return to school. **Focus:** General studies/Field of study not specified. **Qualif.:** Applicants must be at least 22 years of age at the time of application and must be minimum cumulative GPA of 2.0; at least half-time, enrolled in six or more credits per semester and demonstrate financial need as determined by the Financial Aid Office. **Criteria:** Selection will be based on students who graduated from or attended Lewiston High School.

Duration: Annual. **To Apply:** Applicants must submit information via online and attach typed essay information along with the application. **Deadline:** March 1. **Contact:** Lewis-Clark State College, 500 8th Ave., Lewiston, ID, 83501; Phone: 800-377-3529; Email: scholarships@lcsc.edu.

6791 ■ Eugene Northrup Scholarship
(Undergraduate/Scholarship)

Purpose: To provide financial assistance for individuals intending to pursue their educational goals. **Focus:** General studies/Field of study not specified. **Qualif.:** Applicants must be incoming freshmen coming from an area high school and have a minimum cumulative GPA of 3.0.

Duration: Annual. **To Apply:** Applicants may obtain applications from high school counselors at the following schools: Lewiston, Clarkston, Lapwai, Culdesac, Asotin, and Genesee; must write a 500-word essay on Unionism or the Labor Movement. **Deadline:** April 17. **Contact:**

Scholarship Committee Chairman, Email: usw-712@cableone.net; Chairman/U.S.W. Scholarship, 1618 Idaho St., Ste. 109, Lewiston, ID, 83501; Phone: 208-746-3996; For questions: scholarships@lcsc.edu.

6792 ■ The Fisher-Clark Memorial Endowed Scholarship *(Undergraduate/Scholarship)*

Purpose: To offset the educational expenses of Lewis-Clark State College female students. **Focus:** General studies/Field of study not specified. **Qualif.:** Applicants must be female students who have a cumulative GPA of 2.0 and able to demonstrate financial need as determined by the Financial Aid Office.

Duration: Annual. **Number Awarded:** 1. **To Apply:** Applicants must submit information via online and attach typed essay information along with the application. **Deadline:** March 1. **Remarks:** The scholarship was established by the bequest of Barbara J. Clark in memory of her family and their long history with Lewis-Clark State College. **Contact:** Lewis-Clark State College, 500 8th Ave., Lewiston, ID, 83501; Phone: 800-377-3529; Email: scholarships@lcsc.edu.

6793 ■ Foundation Transfer Scholarship
(Undergraduate/Scholarship)

Purpose: To assist transfer students intending to complete a bachelor's degree at Lewis-Clark State College. **Focus:** General studies/Field of study not specified. **Qualif.:** Applicants must be students who have minimum cumulative GPA of 3.0; must be full-time, enrolled in 12 or more credits per semester; pursuing a bachelor's degree; must have acquired at least 60 credits; must be a new, direct transfer to LCSC; must have a recognized associate degree from an accredited college other than lewis-clark state college. **Criteria:** Preference will be given to transfer students from North Idaho College, Community Colleges of Spokane, College of Southern Idaho, Walla Walla Community College, Treasure Valley Community College and College of Western Idaho.

Duration: Annual. **Number Awarded:** 1. **To Apply:** Applicants must submit a general application on online. **Deadline:** June 15. **Contact:** LCSC Financial Aid Office, 500 8th Ave., Reid Centennial Hall Rm. 110, Lewiston, ID, 83501; Phone: 208-792-2224 or 1-800-933-5272 ext. 2224; Email: scholarships@lcsc.edu.

6794 ■ Glen and Babs Carlson Endowed Scholarship *(Undergraduate/Scholarship)*

Purpose: To offset the educationally-related expenses of Lewis-Clark State College students. **Focus:** General studies/Field of study not specified. **Qualif.:** Applicants must be students who have a minimum cumulative GPA of 2.0.

Funds Avail.: No specific amount. **Duration:** Annual. **To Apply:** Applicants must submit information via online and attach typed essay information along with the application. **Deadline:** March 1. **Contact:** Lewis-Clark State College, 500 8th Ave., Lewiston, ID, 83501; Phone: 800-377-3529; Email: scholarships@lcsc.edu.

6795 ■ Gretchen Dimico Memorial Scholarship
(Undergraduate/Scholarship)

Purpose: To support the educational pursuits of less capable individuals. **Focus:** Nursing. **Qualif.:** Applicants must be current or former member of a professional nursing organization who are pursuing a degree in Nursing at

Awards are arranged alphabetically below their administering organizations

the LCSC-Coeur d'Alene Center; must have at least half-time, enrolled 6 or more credits per semester and a minimum cumulative GPA of 2.5 and have demonstrated financial need as determined by the Financial Aid Office.

Duration: Annual. **To Apply:** Applicants must submit information via online and attach typed essay information along with the application. **Deadline:** March 1. **Contact:** Email: scholarships@lcsc.edu.

6796 ■ Henderson Memorial Endowed Scholarship (Undergraduate/Scholarship)

Purpose: To offset the educational expenses of Lewis-Clark State College students. **Focus:** General studies/Field of study not specified. **Qualif.:** Applicants must have completed at least one semester at LCSC and a cumulative GPA of 3.0. **Criteria:** Preference will be given to students who demonstrate financial need as determined by the Financial Aid Office.

Duration: Annual. **To Apply:** Applicants must submit information via online and attach typed essay information along with the application. **Deadline:** March 1. **Contact:** Lewis-Clark State College, 500 8th Ave., Lewiston, ID, 83501; Phone: 800-377-3529; Email: scholarships@ lcsc.edu.

6797 ■ Hinman-Jensen Endowed Scholarship (Undergraduate/Scholarship)

Purpose: To provide educational assistance for students pursuing either the Bachelor of Arts in Applied Technology or the Bachelor of Arts in Applied Science. **Focus:** Science; Technology. **Qualif.:** Applicants must be full-time students pursuing a Bachelor's of Applied Technology or Applied Science degree; be enrolled in 12 or more credits per semester and have a cumulative GPA of 2.0. **Criteria:** Preference will be given to applicants who have not previously received the scholarship.

Duration: Annual. **To Apply:** Applicants must submit information via online and attach typed essay information along with the application. **Deadline:** March 1. **Contact:** Lewis-Clark State College, 500 8th Ave., Lewiston, ID, 83501; Phone: 800-377-3529; Email: scholarships@ lcsc.edu.

6798 ■ Frank and Gladys Hopkins Endowed Scholarships (Undergraduate/Scholarship)

Purpose: To support varsity players who are also good in academics. **Focus:** General studies/Field of study not specified. **Qualif.:** Applicants must be classified as full-time students who are participating on the LCSC baseball team. They must also have a cumulative GPA consistent with the minimum required for admission and for progress toward their selected major. **Criteria:** Selection will be based on merit.

Duration: Annual. **To Apply:** Applicants must complete a general application available on the website.

6799 ■ Idaho Governor's Cup Scholarship (Undergraduate/Scholarship)

Purpose: To support Idaho high school seniors planning to attend an Idaho college or university. **Focus:** Public service. **Qualif.:** Applicants must be Idaho residents that will graduate from an Idaho high school; academic or Technical students enrolled full-time could be eligible. Students with a 2.8 cumulative GPA and who demonstrate high commitment to public service should apply.

Duration: Annual. **To Apply:** Applicants must submit information via online and attach typed essay information

along with the application. **Contact:** Scholarships Program Manager, Joy Miller; Email: Joy.Miller@osbe.idaho.gov; Phone: 208-332-1595; For Scholarship help, Email: scholarshiphelp@osbe.idaho.gov; Phone: 208-334-2270.

6800 ■ Irene Carlson Gnaedinger Memorial Scholarship (Undergraduate/Scholarship)

Purpose: To provide educational assistance for students from Lapwai High School. **Focus:** General studies/Field of study not specified. **Qualif.:** Applicants must be graduates of Lapwai High School; have a minimum cumulative GPA of 2.5; be enrolled full-time in 12 or more credits per semester and be pursuing a Bachelor's degree. **Criteria:** Preference will be given to students who demonstrate financial need as determined by the Financial Aid Office.

Duration: Annual. **To Apply:** Applicants must submit information via online. **Deadline:** March 1. **Contact:** Lewis-Clark State College, 500 8th Ave., Lewiston, ID, 83501; Phone: 800-377-3529; Email: scholarships@lcsc.edu.

6801 ■ Jack M. & Mary Lou Gruber Scholarship (Undergraduate/Scholarship)

Purpose: To provide financial assistance to those who cannot afford to pursue college education. **Focus:** General studies/Field of study not specified. **Qualif.:** Applicants must have a minimum of 3.0 GPA and be enrolled full-time in 12 or more credits per semester; must be actively involved in both the campus and the community. **Criteria:** Preference will be given to students from the Lewis-Clark Valley.

Duration: Annual. **To Apply:** Applicants must submit information via online and attach typed essay information along with the application. **Remarks:** The scholarship was established by Jack M. and Mary Lou Gruber in memory of their parents. **Contact:** Lewis-Clark State College, 500 8th Ave., Lewiston, ID, 83501; Phone: 800-377-3529; Email: scholarships@lcsc.edu.

6802 ■ Jimmy Guild Memorial Scholarship (Undergraduate/Scholarship)

Purpose: To provide educational assistance to students intending to pursue a career in the area of Computer Science. **Focus:** Computer and information sciences; Mathematics and mathematical sciences. **Qualif.:** Applicants must be full-time students (enrolled in 12 or more credits per semester) who are majoring in mathematics who have interest in Computer science and have a cumulative GPA of 3.0. **Criteria:** Preference will be given by students graduating from local high schools and who are affiliated with a member of the United Steel Workers International Union.

Duration: Annual. **To Apply:** Applicants must submit information via online and attach typed essay information along with the application. **Deadline:** June 30. **Contact:** Lewis-Clark State College, 500 8th Ave., Lewiston, ID, 83501.

6803 ■ John Streiff Memorial Scholarship (Undergraduate/Scholarship)

Purpose: To provide funding for outstanding students who are majoring in social or political science at LCSC. **Focus:** Political science; Social sciences. **Qualif.:** Applicants must: have a minimum cumulative GPA of 3.0; be pursuing a degree in either Social Science or Political Science; have a class standing of junior or above and be actively involved in both the campus and community. **Criteria:** Preference

Awards are arranged alphabetically below their administering organizations

will be given to individuals from LC Valley.

Duration: Annual. **To Apply:** Applicants must submit information via online and attach typed essay information along with the application. **Deadline:** March 1. **Contact:** Lewis-Clark State College, 500 8th Ave., Lewiston, ID, 83501; Phone: 800-377-3529; Email: scholarships@lcsc.edu.

6804 ■ Kaia Lynn Markwalter Endowed Scholarship
(Undergraduate/Scholarship)

Purpose: To encourage educational pursuits among individuals who have experienced congenital heart defects. **Focus:** Business. **Qualif.:** Applicants must: have a minimum cumulative GPA of 3.0; be enrolled full-time in 12 or more credits per semester; be pursuing a degree within the Business Division and they must also be non-traditional students. **Criteria:** Preference will be given to Lewis-Clark State College student who has been directly impacted by congenital heart defects.

Duration: Annual. **To Apply:** Applicants must submit information via online and attach typed essay information along with the application. **Deadline:** March 1. **Remarks:** The scholarship was established in memory of Kaia Lynn Markwalter. **Contact:** Lewis-Clark State College, 500 8th Ave., Lewiston, ID, 83501; Phone: 800-377-3529; Email: scholarships@lcsc.edu.

6805 ■ Kenneth Rogers Memorial Scholarship
(Undergraduate/Scholarship)

Purpose: To provide educational assistance for eligible students who are enrolled full-time in the Auto Body Repair Program at LCSC. **Focus:** Automotive technology. **Qualif.:** Applicants must have a minimum cumulative GPA of 2.0; be full-time, enrolled in 12 or more credits per semester in the Collision Repair Program and able to demonstrate financial need as determined by the Financial Aid Office. **Criteria:** Preference will be given to non-traditional students over the age of 25.

Duration: Annual. **To Apply:** Applicants must submit information via online and attach typed essay information along with the application. **Deadline:** March 1. **Contact:** Lewis-Clark State College, 500 8th Ave., Lewiston, ID, 83501; Phone: 800-377-3529; Email: scholarships@lcsc.edu.

6806 ■ Laura Ann Peck Memorial Endowed Scholarship *(Undergraduate/Scholarship)*

Purpose: To assist Lewis-Clark State College students who are majoring in mathematics. **Focus:** Mathematics and mathematical sciences; Natural sciences. **Qualif.:** Applicants must have a minimum cumulative GPA of 2.5; be enrolled full-time in 12 or more credits per semester; be pursuing a degree in Mathematics and have successfully completed three semesters of calculus.

Funds Avail.: No specific amount. **Duration:** Annual. **To Apply:** Applicants must submit information via online and attach typed essay information along with the application. **Deadline:** March 1. **Contact:** Lewis-Clark State College, 500 8th Ave., Lewiston, ID, 83501; Phone: 800-377-3529; Email: scholarships@lcsc.edu.

6807 ■ Laura Moore Cunningham Foundation General Scholarship *(Undergraduate/Scholarship)*

Purpose: To provide financial assistance to the Idaho youth for them to pursue higher education. **Focus:** General studies/Field of study not specified. **Qualif.:** Applicants

must be students who have minimum cumulative GPA of 3.0; must be full-time, enrolled in 12 or more credits per semester; must be an Idaho resident; must be demonstrate financial need as determined by the Financial Aid Office.

Duration: Annual. **To Apply:** Applicants must submit information via online and attach typed essay information along with the application. **Deadline:** March 1. **Contact:** Lewis-Clark State College, 500 8th Ave., Lewiston, ID, 83501; Phone: 800-377-3529; Email: scholarships@lcsc.edu.

6808 ■ LCSC Presidential Out-of-State Tuition Scholarships *(Undergraduate/Scholarship)*

Purpose: To provide financial assistance to students who have shown improvement in their academic records. **Focus:** General studies/Field of study not specified. **Qualif.:** Applicants must be a new non-resident student; must be minimum cumulative GPA of 3.0 and completing at least 12 credits per semester or a 20 ACT composite or a 1020 SAT critical reading and math combined score.

Duration: Annual; up to four years. **Deadline:** March 1. **Contact:** The Financial Aid Office, LCSC, 500 8th Avenue, Lewiston, ID, 83501; Phone: 800-933-5272 or 208-792-2224.

6809 ■ LCSC Welding Club Scholarship
(Undergraduate/Scholarship)

Purpose: To offset educationally-related expenses of Lewis-Clark State College Welding Technology students. **Focus:** Welding.

Duration: Annual. **Deadline:** March 1. **Contact:** Lewis-Clark State College, 500 8th Ave., Lewiston, ID, 83501; Phone: 800-377-3529; Email: scholarships@lcsc.edu.

6810 ■ Lewis-Clark Coin Club Endowed Scholarship
(Undergraduate/Scholarship)

Purpose: To offset the educationally-related expenses of Lewis-Clark State College students. **Focus:** General studies/Field of study not specified. **Qualif.:** Applicant must have a minimum cumulative GPA of 2.5 Full-time, enrolled in 12 or more credits per semester; shall be awarded in alternate award cycles to an Academic and a Professional-Technical student. **Criteria:** Selection will be based on the committee criteria.

Duration: Annual. **Number Awarded:** 1. **To Apply:** Applicants must submit information via online and attach typed essay information along with the application. **Deadline:** March 1. **Contact:** Email: scholarships@lcsc.edu.

6811 ■ Lewis-Clark State College Foundation Scholars *(Undergraduate/Scholarship)*

Purpose: To support students who have shown consistency and improvement in their scholastic records. **Focus:** General studies/Field of study not specified. **Qualif.:** Applicants must be outstanding Idaho and Asotin County, Washington high school seniors; must be enroll for minimum of 12 credits per semester and maintain 3.5 cumulative GPA.

Funds Avail.: $3,000. **Duration:** Annual; up to 4 years. **Deadline:** March 1. **Remarks:** Established in 1991.

6812 ■ Lewis-Clark State College In-State Non-Traditional Student Scholarship *(Undergraduate/Scholarship)*

Purpose: To assist non-traditional students who have been out of high school for at least 5 years at the time of their

Awards are arranged alphabetically below their administering organizations

initial enrollment at Lewis-Clark State College. **Focus:** General studies/Field of study not specified. **Qualif.:** Applicants must have a cumulative GPA of 3.0; be full-time, enrolled in 12 or more credits per semester; must be new-degree-seeking students to LCSC; be Idaho residents and demonstrate financial need as determined by the Financial Aid Office.

Funds Avail.: $1,500 each. **Duration:** Annual. **To Apply:** Applicants must submit information via online and attach typed essay information along with the application. **Deadline:** March 1. **Contact:** Lewis-Clark State College, 500 8th Ave., Lewiston, ID, 83501; Phone: 800-377-3529; Email: scholarships@lcsc.edu.

6813 ■ Military Order of the Purple Heart
(Undergraduate/Scholarship)

Purpose: To provide educational assistance for students intending to pursue a career in Special Education. **Focus:** Education, Special. **Qualif.:** Applicant must have a minimum cumulative GPA of 3.25; full-time student, enrolled in 12 or more credits per semester; pursuing a degree in Education with a minor in Special Education. **Criteria:** Selection will be based on demonstrate financial need as determined by the Financial Aid Office.

Duration: Annual. **Number Awarded:** 1. **To Apply:** Applicants must submit information via online and attach typed essay information along with the application. **Deadline:** March 1. **Contact:** Email: scholarships@lcsc.edu.

6814 ■ Lewis-Clark State College Provost Scholarship *(Undergraduate/Scholarship)*

Purpose: To recognize promising Idaho High School seniors by providing educational assistance. **Focus:** General studies/Field of study not specified. **Qualif.:** Applicants must be an Idaho resident; must have a minimum cumulative GPA of 3.25-3.74 or a 22 ACT/1100 SAT; be entering college the fall semester directly after high school graduation.

Funds Avail.: $1,500; $500 annual increase. **Duration:** Annual; up to 4 consecutive years. **Number Awarded:** Varies. **To Apply:** Applicants must submit information via online and attach typed essay information along with the application. **Deadline:** March 1. **Contact:** The Financial Aid Office, LCSC, 500 8th Avenue, Lewiston, ID, 83501; Phone: 800-933-5272 or 208-792-2224.

6815 ■ Lewiston Service League Memorial Scholarship *(Undergraduate/Scholarship)*

Purpose: To support family persons returning to school. **Focus:** General studies/Field of study not specified. **Qualif.:** Applicants must have a minimum cumulative GPA of 3.0; be full-time, enrolled in 12 or more credits per semester; be family persons returning to school; show academic promise with intent to continue their education to the completion of a degree and demonstrate financial need as determined by the financial Aid Office.

Duration: Annual. **To Apply:** Applicants must submit information via online and attach typed essay information along with the application. **Contact:** Lewiston Service League, PO Box 1811, Lewiston, ID, 83501; For more information: Lewis-Clark State College, 500 8th Ave., Lewiston, ID, 83501; Phone: 800-377-3529;.

6816 ■ Mamie Adams Memorial Award *(Undergraduate, Four Year College, Two Year College/Scholarship)*

Purpose: To provide educational assistance for students who demonstrate consistency and improvement in their

scholastic records. **Focus:** General studies/Field of study not specified. **Qualif.:** Applicants must be high school seniors who are planning to attend college in the fall or undergraduate college students enrolled at a 2- or 4-year institution with at least a 2.5 GPA. **Criteria:** Preference is given to students who have demonstrated consistency and improvement in their academic records.

Funds Avail.: $1,000. **Duration:** Annual. **Number Awarded:** 1. **To Apply:** Applicants must submit information via online and attach typed essay information along with the application. **Deadline:** April 30. **Contact:** 4126 Pocahontas Dr., Baytown, TX, 77521; Phone, Fax: 713-421-2915; Email: scholarships@lcsc.edu.

6817 ■ Margaret G. Johnson and Marge J. Stout Scholarship *(Undergraduate/Scholarship)*

Purpose: To provide financial assistance to students who are currently enrolled in a vocational program. **Focus:** Business; Education, Vocational-technical. **Qualif.:** Applicants must be Idaho residents who are full-time students pursuing a degree in a two- or four-year Professional-Technical Program and have completed at least 12 credits the previous semester at the LCSC; must have a minimum cumulative GPA of 3.0. **Criteria:** Preference will be given to students who are currently enrolled in a Business Technology and Service program.

Duration: Annual. **To Apply:** Applicants must submit information via online and attach typed essay information along with the application. **Deadline:** March 1. **Contact:** Lewis-Clark State College, 500 8th Ave., Lewiston, ID, 83501; Phone: 800-377-3529; Email: scholarships@lcsc.edu.

6818 ■ Odd Fellows Lodge #8 Endowed Scholarship *(Undergraduate/Scholarship)*

Purpose: To provide financial assistance to individuals who are intending to pursue their educational goals. **Focus:** General studies/Field of study not specified. **Qualif.:** Applicants must be full-time, enrolled students in 12 or more credits per semester; have a minimum cumulative GPA of 3.0 and demonstrate financial need as determined by the Financial Aid Office.

Duration: Annual. **To Apply:** Applicants must submit information via online and attach typed essay information along with the application. **Deadline:** March 1. **Contact:** Lewis-Clark State College, 500 8th Ave., Lewiston, ID, 83501; Phone: 800-377-3529; Email: scholarships@lcsc.edu.

6819 ■ Robbie Miller Memorial Endowed Scholarship *(Undergraduate/Scholarship)*

Purpose: To support students pursuing a degree in a Professional-Technical Program. **Focus:** General studies/Field of study not specified. **Qualif.:** Applicants must be students who have a minimum cumulative GPA of 2.5; must be enrolled in professional technical studies; must have a standing of sophomore or greater; demonstrate financial need as determined by the Financial Aid Office. **Criteria:** Preference will be given to students from Idaho School District 171; non-traditional students from Idaho School District 171.

Duration: Annual. **To Apply:** Applicants must submit information via online and attach typed essay information along with the application. **Deadline:** March 1. **Contact:** Lewis-Clark State College, 500 8th Ave., Lewiston, ID, 83501; Phone: 800-377-3529; Email: scholarships@lcsc.edu.

Awards are arranged alphabetically below their administering organizations

6820 ■ Bill Sawyer Memorial Scholarship
(Undergraduate/Scholarship)

Purpose: To offset the educationally-related expenses of Lewis-Clark State College students. **Focus:** Education, Vocational-technical. **Qualif.:** Applicants must be students pursuing a degree in a Career & Technical Education program and have a cumulative GPA of 2.0; must demonstrate financial need as determined by the Financial Aid Office. **Criteria:** Preference will be given to students from Idaho county; students with special needs (physical handicap, learning disability) or high school underachievers.

Duration: Annual. **To Apply:** Applicants must submit information via online and attach typed essay information along with the application. **Deadline:** March 1. **Remarks:** The scholarship was established by the family and friends of Bill Sawyer to honor his memory. **Contact:** Lewis-Clark State College, 500 8th Ave., Lewiston, ID, 83501; Phone: 800-377-3529; Email: scholarships@lcsc.edu.

6821 ■ Shinn Family Scholarship *(Undergraduate/Scholarship)*

Purpose: To offset the educationally-related expenses of Lewis-Clark State College students. **Focus:** Education, Vocational-technical. **Qualif.:** Applicants must have a minimum cumulative GPA of 2.5; be enrolled full-time in 12 or more credits per semester; be pursuing a degree in professional and technical education program; have completed at least one semester at LCSC and demonstrate financial need as determined by the Financial Aid Office.

Duration: Annual. **To Apply:** Applicants must submit information via online and attach typed essay information along with the application. **Deadline:** March 1. **Remarks:** The scholarship was established in memory of Ethel Shinn by her family and friends. **Contact:** Lewis-Clark State College, 500 8th Ave., Lewiston, ID, 83501; Phone: 800-377-3529; Email: scholarships@lcsc.edu.

6822 ■ Susan P. Schroeder Memorial Scholarship
(Undergraduate/Scholarship)

Purpose: To inspire educational pursuits among less capable individuals by providing financial assistance. **Focus:** English language and literature; Natural sciences. **Qualif.:** Applicants must be have a minimum cumulative GPA of 3.0; be pursuing a degree in either Natural Sciences or English; be graduates of an Idaho high school and have completed at least four upper-division credits in Geology and/or English. **Criteria:** Preference will be given to students who are graduates from Nez Perce County.

Duration: Annual. **To Apply:** Applicants must submit information via online and attach typed essay information along with the application. **Deadline:** March 1. **Remarks:** The scholarship was established by Ned R. Schroeder in memory of his wife, Susan, who devoted her time to education at Lewis-Clark State College. **Contact:** Email: scholarships@lcsc.edu.

6823 ■ Walter & Elsie Carr Endowed Scholarship
(Undergraduate/Scholarship)

Purpose: To provide financial assistance to those graduates of Emmett High School for them to pursue higher education. **Focus:** General studies/Field of study not specified. **Qualif.:** Applicants must be enrolled full-time in 12 or more credits per semester. **Criteria:** Preference will be given to graduates of Emmett High School.

Funds Avail.: No specific amount. **Duration:** Annual. **To Apply:** Applicants must submit information via online and attach typed essay information along with the application. **Deadline:** March 1. **Remarks:** Established in 1928. **Contact:** Lewis-Clark State College, 500 8th Ave., Lewiston, ID, 83501; Phone: 800-377-3529; Email: scholarships@lcsc.edu.

6824 ■ Lewiston Auburn Metropolitan Chamber of Commerce
415 Lisbon St.
Lewiston, ME 04240
Ph: (207)783-2249
URL: lametrochamber.com
Social Media: www.facebook.com/LAMetroChamber
twitter.com/LAMetroChamber

6825 ■ Androscoggin County Chamber of Commerce Adult Scholarships *(Professional development/Scholarship)*

Purpose: To support adults working for LA Metro Chamber member businesses. **Focus:** General studies/Field of study not specified. **Qualif.:** Applicants must be employed 20 or more hours by a member of the Androscoggin County Chamber of Commerce; must begin course within 6 months of receiving award; must be matriculated in college-level coursework applicable toward an associates or bachelor's degree; must be at least 18 years old. **Criteria:** Selection will be based on a scoring rubric.

Funds Avail.: $1,000. **Duration:** Annual; one year. **To Apply:** Applicants must submit a completed application, one-page typewritten essay, completed employer verification form, letter of reference/recommendation from employer. **Deadline:** May 5.

6826 ■ Lexington Community Foundation (LCF)
607 N Washington St.
Lexington, NE 68850
Ph: (308)324-6704
E-mail: office@lexfoundation.org
URL: www.lexfoundation.org
Social Media: www.facebook.com/LexingtonCommunityFoundation
www.instagram.com/lexingtonfoundation
twitter.com/LexFoundation

6827 ■ Lexington Alumni Scholarships
(Undergraduate/Scholarship)

Purpose: To promote community philanthropy by working with individuals, families and organizations to develop tailored giving plans that effectively meet the charitable goals and financial circumstances. **Focus:** General studies/Field of study not specified. **Qualif.:** Applicants must be students who will be enrolled in a post-secondary education with at least a 2.0 GPA. **Criteria:** Selection will be based on the committee criteria.

Funds Avail.: $750. **Duration:** Annual. **Number Awarded:** 3. **To Apply:** Applicants must submit a completed application form; must provide three letters of recommendation and must attach a recent photo; copy of official high school transcript; high school activities resume; statement of financial need; career objectives statement in 250 words or less. **Deadline:** April 1.

6828 ■ Lexington Community Foundation Annual Scholarships *(Undergraduate/Scholarship)*

Purpose: To promote community philanthropy by working with individuals, families and organizations to develop

Awards are arranged alphabetically below their administering organizations

tailored giving plans that effectively meet the charitable goals and financial circumstances. **Focus:** General studies/ Field of study not specified. **Qualif.:** Applicants must be graduating senior students who rank in the upper 1/3 of their class. **Criteria:** Recipients are selected based on qualities of good character and leadership, academic achievement, financial need and participation in extracurriculars and community service.

Funds Avail.: $3,000. **Duration:** Annual. **Number Awarded:** 2. **To Apply:** Applicants must submit a completed application form; must provide three letters of recommendation and must attach a recent photo; copy of official high school transcript; high school activities resume; statement of financial need; career objectives statement in 250 words or less. **Deadline:** April 1.

6829 ■ Lexington Community Foundation/CCC Scholarships *(Undergraduate/Scholarship)*

Purpose: To promote community philanthropy by working with individuals, families and organizations to develop tailored giving plans that effectively meet the charitable goals and financial circumstances. **Focus:** General studies/ Field of study not specified. **Qualif.:** Applicants must be graduating senior students who rank in the upper 1/2 of their class. **Criteria:** Recipients are selected based on qualities of good character and leadership, academic achievement, financial need and participation in extracurriculars and community service.

Duration: Annual. **To Apply:** Applicants must submit a completed application form; must provide three letters of recommendation and must attach a recent photo; copy of official high school transcript; high school activities resume; statement of financial need; career objectives statement in 250 words or less.

6830 ■ Edsel Newman Scholarships *(Undergraduate/ Scholarship)*

Purpose: To promote community philanthropy by working with individuals, families and organizations to develop tailored giving plans that effectively meet the charitable goals and financial circumstances. **Focus:** Computer and information sciences; Engineering. **Qualif.:** Applicants must be graduating seniors who are planning to pursue a career in the field of engineering and/or computer science; must have ranked in the upper 1/3 of their class and must be U.S. citizens. **Criteria:** Recipients are selected based on qualities of good character and leadership, academic achievement, financial need and participation in extracurriculars and community service.

Funds Avail.: $2,000. **Duration:** Annual. **To Apply:** Applicants must submit a completed application form; must provide three letters of recommendation and must attach a recent photo; statement of financial need; copy of transcript; resume listing of memberships and activities.

6831 ■ Norall Scholarship Trust *(Undergraduate, Postdoctorate/Scholarship)*

Purpose: To promote community philanthropy by working with individuals, families and organizations to develop tailored giving plans that effectively meet the charitable goals and financial circumstances. **Focus:** General studies/ Field of study not specified. **Qualif.:** Applicants must be past graduates of high school in Dawson who are enrolled in a US. college. **Criteria:** Recipients are selected based on goal commitment, academic success, recommendations, financial need and programs of study.

Funds Avail.: No specific amount. **Duration:** Annual. **Number Awarded:** 12. **To Apply:** Applicants must complete the application form, a copy of Dawson County High School transcript for first-time applicant, academic transcript for post-secondary education and three personal references. **Deadline:** February 28.

6832 ■ Francelene Skinner Memorial Scholarships *(Undergraduate/Scholarship)*

Purpose: To promote community philanthropy by working with individuals, families and organizations to develop tailored giving plans that effectively meet the charitable goals and financial circumstances. **Focus:** General studies/ Field of study not specified.

Funds Avail.: $500. **Duration:** Annual. **Number Awarded:** 2.

6833 ■ Mark and Vera Turner Memorial Scholarships *(Undergraduate/Scholarship)*

Purpose: To promote community philanthropy by working with individuals, families and organizations to develop tailored giving plans that effectively meet the charitable goals and financial circumstances. **Focus:** General studies/ Field of study not specified. **Qualif.:** Applicants must be to qualifying students who are enrolled in any college, university, community college or trade school at any level with at least a 2.0 GPA. **Criteria:** Selection will be based on the committee's criteria.

Funds Avail.: $500. **Duration:** Annual. **Number Awarded:** 4.

6834 ■ Robert & Barbara Wade Scholarships *(Undergraduate/Scholarship)*

Purpose: To promote community philanthropy by working with individuals, families and organizations to develop tailored giving plans that effectively meet the charitable goals and financial circumstances. **Focus:** General studies/ Field of study not specified.

Funds Avail.: $1,000. **Duration:** Annual. **Number Awarded:** 3. **To Apply:** Applicants must submit a completed application form; must provide three letters of recommendation and must attach a recent photo. **Deadline:** April 1.

6835 ■ Jack G. Lezman
7400 Carmel Executive Park Dr., No. 105
Charlotte, NC 28226
Ph: (704)350-2953
URL: www.jacklezman.com

6836 ■ Jack G. Lezman Scholarship Contest *(College, University, Undergraduate/Scholarship)*

Purpose: To provide financial aid to college students and encourage students to understand why bankruptcy relief is necessary to encourage entrepreneurship and economic development. Also looks to inspire students to pursue a career in any legal field. **Focus:** Law. **Qualif.:** Applicant must be a high school senior or college freshman in the United States. **Criteria:** Selection is based on the video essay.

Funds Avail.: $1,000. **Number Awarded:** 1. **To Apply:** Applicant must create a one- to two-minute video explaining how bankruptcy laws promote entrepreneurship and economic growth and publish the video to their YouTube channel; video should be titled Jack G. Lezman Scholarship contest and should include this link: www.jacklezman.com/scholarship-for-college-students/ in

Awards are arranged alphabetically below their administering organizations

the description. Instead of the video, applicant can submit a 1,000 to 1,500 word essay on How Lawyers Make the World a Safer Place, and submit it to LezmanScholarship@ gmail.com. **Deadline:** August 15.

6837 ■ Library and Information Technology Association (LITA)

50 E Huron St.
Chicago, IL 60611-2795
Fax: (312)280-3257
Free: 800-545-2433
E-mail: lita@ala.org
URL: www.ala.org
Social Media: twitter.com/ALA_LITA

6838 ■ Christian Larew Memorial Scholarship
(Graduate/Scholarship, Monetary)

Purpose: To encourage the entry of qualified persons into the library and information technology field. **Focus:** Information science and technology; Library and archival sciences. **Qualif.:** Candidates must not have earned more than 12 hours towards a Master of Library Science degree from an American Library Association (ALA) Accredited MLS program. **Criteria:** The Christian Larew Scholarship Committee reviews the applications and selects the scholarship winner.

Funds Avail.: $3,000. **Duration:** Annual. **Number Awarded:** 1. **To Apply:** Application forms and instructions are available at ALA/Divisions Scholarship Program. Applicants must submit an application form; a statement indicating the nature of their library experience; letters of reference; transcripts. **Deadline:** March 1. **Remarks:** Established in 1999. **Contact:** E-mail: litaweb@ala.org.

6839 ■ Tom and Roberta Drewes Scholarship
(Graduate/Scholarship, Monetary)

Purpose: To support library support staff worker who is pursuing a master's degree in library and information science. **Focus:** Library and archival sciences. **Qualif.:** Applicant can be a library support-staff member who is a U.S./Canadian citizen or permanent resident and is pursuing an MLS in an ALA-accredited program.

Funds Avail.: $3,000. **Duration:** Annual. **Number Awarded:** 1. **To Apply:** Applicant Completed online application (which includes a personal statement); completed references (only references on the official online form will be accepted). A total of three references must be submitted. You will be prompted to indicate your professional references within the online application; official academic transcripts from institutions where you received your bachelors degree. These can be submitted directly from the institution, or mailed in the unopened envelope as received from the degree-granting institutions along with any other materials you may need to submit. Only official (sealed) copies will be accepted. **Deadline:** March 1. **Remarks:** Established with a donation from the founder of Quality Books. **Contact:** Kimberly L. Redd, Phone: 312-280-4279, Fax: 312-280-3256, American Library Association, 50 E Huron St, Chicago, Illinois, 60611-2788, Email: klredd@ala.org.

6840 ■ Loleta D. Fyan Public Library Research Grant *(Professional development/Grant)*

Purpose: To support a proposal that results in the development and improvement of public libraries and the services they provide and is designed to effect changes in public library services that are innovative and responsive to the future. **Focus:** Library and archival sciences. **Qualif.:** Applicants can include but are not limited to: local, regional or state libraries, associations or organizations, including units of the American Library Association; library schools; or individuals. **Criteria:** Proposals will be judged based upon: the ability to develop and improve public libraries and the services they provide; the potential for broader impact and application beyond meeting a specific local need; design to effect changes in public library services that are innovative and responsive to the future; and capability of completion within one year.

Funds Avail.: $5,000. **Duration:** Annual. **Number Awarded:** 1. **To Apply:** Application cover sheet and details are available online. Send, via email, one completed application cover sheet and proposal with budget to the ALA Staff Liaison, Kelsey Henke. **Deadline:** January 11. **Contact:** Kathy Rosa, Director, Library & Research Center American Library Association Phone: 312-280-4273; Email: krosa@ala.org.

6841 ■ Mary V. Gaver Scholarship *(Master's/ Scholarship, Monetary)*

Purpose: To further the education in the field of library youth services. **Focus:** Library and archival sciences. **Qualif.:** Applicant must be U.S. or Canadian citizen or permanent resident; attend ALA-accredited Master's program; no more than 12 semester hours towards MLS/MLIS/MIS prior to June 1 of the year awarded; personal statement.

Funds Avail.: $3,000. **Duration:** Annual. **Number Awarded:** 1. **To Apply:** Completed applications can be submitted electronically, date of submission and further information can be obtained from the website. **Deadline:** March 1. **Remarks:** Established to honor the memory of a past ALA president and Rutgers University professor. **Contact:** Kimberly L. Redd (Staff Liaison, July 1, 2009, to June 30, 2024) - klredd@ala.org Work Phone: (312) 280-4279 Fax: (312) 280-3256 American Library Association 225 N Michigan Ave Ste 1300 Chicago, IL 60601-7616.

6842 ■ Library Leadership and Management Association (LLAMA)

50 E Huron St.
Chicago, IL 60611-2729
Fax: (312)280-2169
Free: 800-545-2433
E-mail: llama@ala.org
URL: www.ala.org
Social Media: twitter.com/ALALibrary

6843 ■ Diana V. Braddom FRFDS Scholarship
(Professional development/Scholarship)

Purpose: To offer librarians and/or staff members from all types of libraries an opportunity to learn new fundraising skills enabling them to increase funding to their libraries from public, private and corporate sources. **Focus:** Library and archival sciences.

Funds Avail.: $1,000. **Duration:** Annual. **Number Awarded:** 2. **Deadline:** December 5.

6844 ■ Dolores Zohrab Liebmann Fund

PO Box 227237
Dallas, TX 75222-7237

Awards are arranged alphabetically below their administering organizations

URL: foundationcenter.org/grantmaker/liebmann

6845 ■ Dolores Zohrab Liebmann Fund - Graduate School Fellowships (Graduate/Fellowship)

Purpose: To financially support students pursuing graduate studies. **Focus:** Architecture; Engineering; Humanities; Law; Medicine; Natural sciences; Social sciences. **Qualif.:** Applicant must be a graduate student; a U.S. citizen attending an accredited and designated institution of higher education within the United States. **Criteria:** Applicant's selection is based on the application.

Funds Avail.: Cover the cost of tuition and provide an annual $18,000 stipend for living expenses. **Duration:** Annual. **To Apply:** Applications must be submitted through the dean of the university where the student is pursuing graduate studies. **Deadline:** April 15; November 15.

6846 ■ Dolores Zohrab Liebmann Fund - Independent Research/Study Grants (Graduate, Undergraduate/Grant)

Purpose: To financially support graduate students conducting a research. **Focus:** General studies/Field of study not specified. **Qualif.:** Applicants must be based in and conducting research in the United States; have an outstanding undergraduate record; demonstrated financial need; and attending a designated college/university. **Criteria:** Applicants selection is based on the application.

Funds Avail.: Cover the cost of tuition and provide an annual $18,000 stipend for living expenses. **Duration:** Annual. **To Apply:** Applications must be submitted through the dean of the university where the student is pursuing graduate studies. **Deadline:** April 15; November 15.

6847 ■ Dolores Zohrab Liebmann Fund - Publication Grants (Graduate, Undergraduate/Grant)

Purpose: To financially support students pursuing graduate studies. **Focus:** Armenian studies. **Qualif.:** Applicants must have an outstanding undergraduate record, demonstrate financial need and be attending a designated college or university. **Criteria:** Applicant's selection is based on the application.

Funds Avail.: Cover the cost of tuition and provide an annual $18,000 stipend for living expenses. **Duration:** Semi-annual. **Number Awarded:** 1. **To Apply:** Applications must be submitted through the dean of the university where the student is pursuing graduate studies. **Deadline:** April 15; November 15.

6848 ■ Life Happens

1530 Wilson Blvd., Ste. 1060
Arlington, VA 22209
Free: 888-543-3777
E-mail: info@lifehappens.org
URL: www.lifehappens.org
Social Media: www.facebook.com/lifehappens.org
www.linkedin.com/company/lifehappensorg
www.pinterest.com/lifehappensorg
twitter.com/lifehappens
www.youtube.com/user/LIFEfoundation

6849 ■ LIFE Lessons Scholarship Program (Undergraduate/Scholarship)

Purpose: To help deserving young people realize their dream of achieving a college education. **Focus:** General

studies/Field of study not specified.

Funds Avail.: $200,000. **Duration:** Annual. **To Apply:** Applicants must complete the application form available online including an essay of no more than 500 words or video entry of no more than 3 minutes describing the financial and emotional challenges you have experienced as a result of the death of a parent or legal guardian; must explain how the lack of adequate life insurance coverage (or no coverage at all) impacted your family's financial situation. **Contact:** Life Happens, 1530 Wilson Blvd, Ste. 1060, Arlington, VA, 22209.

6850 ■ Life Sciences Research Foundation (LSRF)

PO Box 1482
Baltimore, MD 21218
Ph: (410)467-2597
E-mail: apply@lsrf.org
URL: www.lsrf.org

6851 ■ Life Sciences Research Foundation Postdoctoral Fellowship Program (Postdoctorate/ Fellowship)

Purpose: To provide financial assistance to young scientists towards non-targeted biological research. **Focus:** Biology; Life sciences. **Qualif.:** Applicants must be graduate students in the field of biological sciences holding MD, PhD, DVM or DDS degrees. **Criteria:** Awards will be based solely on the quality of applicants' accomplishment and merit of the proposal.

Duration: Annual; up to three years. **To Apply:** Applicants must submit an abstract, curriculum vitae, research proposal, letter from supervisor and three letters of reference. **Deadline:** October 1. **Contact:** Email: apply@lsrf.org.

6852 ■ Lighthouse Guild International

250 W 64th St.
New York, NY 10023
Ph: (212)769-6200
Free: 800-284-4422
E-mail: info@lighthouseguild.org
URL: www.lighthouseguild.org
Social Media: www.facebook.com/lighthouseguild
www.instagram.com/lighthouseguild
www.linkedin.com/company/lighthouseguild
twitter.com/lighthousegld
www.youtube.com/LighthouseGuild

6853 ■ College-Bound Award (High School/Award, Scholarship)

Purpose: To recognize high school seniors or recent high school graduates for outstanding accomplishments and to provide them with financial assistance to pursue their academic goals. **Focus:** General studies/Field of study not specified. **Qualif.:** Applicants must be a college student; legally blind; a U.S. citizen; not related to Lighthouse employees and not a previous winner of the program. **Criteria:** Awards are given based on academic merit and other achievements.

Funds Avail.: $10,000. **Duration:** Annual. **Number Awarded:** 20. **To Apply:** Applicants must submit a completed application form. **Deadline:** March 31.

Awards are arranged alphabetically below their administering organizations

6854 ■ Graduate Award *(Graduate/Award, Scholarship)*

Purpose: To recognize outstanding college graduates or college seniors planning to pursue a graduate level program, and to provide them with financial assistance to pursue their academic and career goals. **Focus:** Education. **Qualif.:** Applicants should be a student who is pursuing a Master's, PhD or any other post-Baccalaureate degree (MD, JD, MBA, etc.). **Criteria:** Awards are given based on academic merit and other achievements.

Funds Avail.: $10,000. **Duration:** Annual. **To Apply:** Applicants must submit a completed application form. **Deadline:** March 31.

6855 ■ GuildScholar Awards *(Undergraduate/ Scholarship)*

Purpose: To assist blind high school students to pursue college. **Focus:** General studies/Field of study not specified. **Qualif.:** Applicants must be legally blind high school students and be U.S. citizens. **Criteria:** Selection is based on Selection Committee's review of the application materials.

Funds Avail.: $15,000. **Number Awarded:** 12-16. **To Apply:** Applicants must provide proof of legal blindness; proof of U.S. citizenship; documentation of academic achievement; three letters of recommendation and two personal statements. **Deadline:** September 15. **Remarks:** Chosen school must be accredited by the Council of Higher Education Accreditation. **Contact:** Gordon Rovins, 212-769-7801 or guildscholar@jgb.org.

6856 ■ Lighthouse International Scholarships - College-bound Awards *(High School, Undergraduate/ Scholarship)*

Purpose: To provide support to visually impaired students to continue their education to college. **Focus:** General studies/Field of study not specified. **Qualif.:** Applicants must be a senior or high school graduate; legally blind; a U.S. citizen; not related to any Lighthouse employees and not a previous winner of program. **Criteria:** Awards are given based on academic merit and other achievements.

Funds Avail.: $10,000. **Duration:** Annual. **Number Awarded:** 20. **To Apply:** Applicants must send an application form (can be downloaded at the website); an essay; proof of the applicant's visual condition; transcripts; and two letters of recommendation. **Deadline:** March 31. **Contact:** Melissa Shorey at mshorey@lighthouse.org.

6857 ■ Lighthouse International Scholarships - Graduate Awards *(Graduate, Postgraduate/ Scholarship)*

Purpose: To provide support to visually impaired who wants to pursue a graduate -level program. **Focus:** General studies/Field of study not specified. **Qualif.:** Applicants must be a college senior or college graduate; must be legally blind; a U.S. citizen; not related to any Lighthouse employees and not a previous winner of the program. **Criteria:** Awards are given based on academic merit and other achievements.

Funds Avail.: $10,000. **Duration:** Annual. **To Apply:** Applicants must send an application form (can be downloaded at the website); an essay; proof of the applicant's visual condition; transcripts; and two letters of recommendation. **Deadline:** March 31. **Contact:** sca@ligthouse.org.

6858 ■ Lighthouse International Scholarships - Undergraduate Awards *(Undergraduate/Scholarship)*

Purpose: To provide support to visually impaired students to continue their education. **Focus:** General studies/Field of study not specified. **Qualif.:** Applicants must be a college student; legally blind; a U.S. citizen; not related to Lighthouse employees and not a previous winner of the program. **Criteria:** Awards are given based on academic merit and other achievements.

Funds Avail.: $10,000. **Duration:** Annual. **To Apply:** Applicants must send an application form (can be downloaded at the website); an essay; proof of the applicant's visual condition; transcripts; and two letters of recommendation. **Deadline:** March 31. **Contact:** Melissa Shorey at mshorey@lighthouse.org.

6859 ■ Lime Connect, Inc.
590 Madison Ave., 21st Fl.
New York, NY 10022
URL: www.limeconnect.com
Social Media: www.facebook.com/limeconnect
twitter.com/limeconnect

6860 ■ BMO Capital Markets Lime Connect Equity through Education Scholarships *(Undergraduate, Graduate/Scholarship)*

Purpose: To provide scholarships for students with disabilities to achieve their dreams and to develop themselves through education. **Focus:** Disabilities. **Qualif.:** Applicants must be current undergraduate or graduate students at a four-year university in the United States or Canada pursuing a degree in business/commerce, engineering, math, physics, statistics or a related discipline; with visible or invisible disabilities are eligible to apply. **Criteria:** Preference will be given to the applicants interested in a career in Financial Services with a focus on Capital Markets.

Funds Avail.: $5,000; $10,000. **Duration:** Annual. **To Apply:** Applicants must submit the following requirements: Contact and education information; Current copy of resume/ CV; Copy of current university transcripts; Answer to an essay question related to the applicant's career goals and an explanation of the applicant on why they deserve to be selected as a BMO Capital Markets Lime Connect Equity through Education Scholar; and one letter of reference from a professor, advisor, supervisor, etc. **Deadline:** September 30. **Remarks:** In partnership with BMO Capital Markets. Established in 2005.

6861 ■ BMO Financial Group Lime Connect Canada Scholarship Program for Students with Disabilities *(Undergraduate, Graduate/Scholarship)*

Purpose: To support the education of the students with disabilities. **Focus:** Disabilities. **Qualif.:** Applicants must be current undergraduate or graduate students enrolled at a four-year university or recognized college in Canada with strong interest and passion for pursuing a career in retail banking and must be Canadian residents eligible to legally work in Canada; with visible or invisible disabilities are eligible to apply. **Criteria:** Selection will be based on the committee's criteria.

Funds Avail.: 2,500 Canadian dollars. **Duration:** Annual. **To Apply:** Applicants must submit the following requirements: contact and education information; current resume/ CV; copy of current university/college transcripts; answer to an essay question (250 words or less) related to how the applicant has overcome adversity or a challenge in life; and one letter of reference from a professor, adviser or supervisor.

Awards are arranged alphabetically below their administering organizations

6862 ■ Google Lime Scholarship (*Undergraduate, Graduate, Doctorate/Scholarship*)

Purpose: To help innovators make the most of their talents by providing scholarships and networking retreats. **Focus:** Disabilities. **Qualif.:** Applicants must be undergraduate, graduate or Ph.D. students currently enrolled at a university in the United States or Canada; must have plan to enroll in or accepted as a full time student at a university in the United States or Canada; must be pursuing a Computer Science or Computer Engineering degree, or a degree in a closely related technical field (such as software engineering or electrical engineering with a heavy computer science course load); must have a strong academic performance; and must exemplify leadership and demonstrate a commitment to and passion for computer science and technology. **Funds Avail.:** $5,000; $10,000. **Duration:** Annual. **To Apply:** Applicants must submit the requirements such as contact, education and experience information; current resume and unofficial transcripts; three essays regarding computer science; and two recommendation letters from a professor, adviser or supervisor. **Remarks:** Established in 2008.

6863 ■ Lime Connect Pathways Scholarship for High School Seniors with Disabilities (*Undergraduate/Scholarship*)

Purpose: To help a disabled student reach their potential in college. **Focus:** General studies/Field of study not specified. **Qualif.:** Applicants must have, or consider themselves to have, a visible or invisible disability; be graduating high school seniors in the U.S. or Canada who are accepted to, or applied and awaiting acceptance, to a four-year college or university in the U.S. or Canada; and intending to be enrolled in the upcoming fall semester. **Funds Avail.:** $1,000. **Number Awarded:** 3. **To Apply:** Applicants must join or log into The Lime Network (which is free) at www.limeconnect.com/pathwaysscholarship. Application form and information is also available at this website. **Deadline:** May 25.

6864 ■ Abraham Lincoln Brigade Archives (ALBA)
799 Broadway, Ste. 341
New York, NY 10003
Ph: (212)674-5398
Fax: (212)674-2101
E-mail: info@alba-valb.org
URL: www.alba-valb.org
Social Media: www.facebook.com/
AbrahamLincolnBrigadeArchives
twitter.com/LincolnBrigade

6865 ■ George Watt Prize (*Undergraduate, Graduate/Prize*)

Purpose: To recognize the best essay made by students to to honor Lincoln vet George Watt, a writer and lifelong activist central to the creation of ALBA. **Focus:** Human rights. **Qualif.:** Applicants must be undergraduate or graduate students from the united states and elsewhere. **Criteria:** Selection will be based on the committee's criteria. **Funds Avail.:** Three $250 pre-collegiate; One $500 undergraduate; One $1,000 graduate. **Duration:** Annual. **Number Awarded:** 5. **To Apply:** Applicants must submit an essay or thesis chapter about any aspect of the Spanish Civil War, the global political or cultural struggles against fascism in the 1920s and 1930s, or the lifetime histories and contributions of the Americans who fought in support of the Spanish Republic from 1936 to 1938; for graduate submissions must be between 3,500 and 12,500 words; must be in Spanish or English; Applicant must currently be registered as a graduate student and work must be related to graduate studies; For undergraduate Essays must be between 2,000 and 10,500 words. **Deadline:** July 1. **Remarks:** Established in 1998.

6866 ■ Lincoln Forum
125 W. Vine St.
Redlands, CA 92373
Ph: (909)798-7632
URL: www.thelincolnforum.org
Social Media: www.facebook.com/The-Lincoln-Forum
-176655849602921
twitter.com/TheLincolnForum

6867 ■ Platt Family Scholarship Prize Essay Contest (*Undergraduate/Scholarship, Monetary*)

Purpose: To enhance the understanding and preserve the memory of Abraham Lincoln and the Civil War. **Focus:** History, American. **Qualif.:** Applicants must be full-time undergraduate students in an American college or university. **Criteria:** Selection will be made by the essay committee of The Lincoln Forum. **Funds Avail.:** $1,500 (1st Prize); $750 (2nd Prize); $500 (3rd Prize). **Duration:** Annual. **Number Awarded:** Varies. **To Apply:** Applicants must submit an essay on a given topic (1, 500-5, 000 words); essay must be typed and include a works cited page or bibliography as well as the name and contact information of the applicant's college or university; must include the name of their college or university with their entire and all contact information (regular and email address) must be put on the essay proper. **Contact:** Don McCue, Curator, Lincoln Memorial Shrine, 125 W Vine St. Redlands, CA 92373; Phone: 909-798-7632; E-mail: archives@akspl.org.

6868 ■ Charles A. and Anne Morrow Lindbergh Foundation
PO Box 10883
Chicago, IL 60610
E-mail: info@lindberghfoundation.org
URL: lindberghfoundation.org
Social Media: www.facebook.com/AirShepherd
twitter.com/AirShepherd

6869 ■ Lindbergh Grants (*Professional development/Grant*)

Purpose: To support individuals around the world who are conducting research projects dedicated to finding innovative solutions to our global environmental challenges. **Focus:** Environmental conservation; Technology.

6870 ■ Lineups.com, Inc.
6789 Quail hill Pkwy., No. 701
Irvine, CA 92603
Ph: (310)906-0648
E-mail: info@lineups.com
URL: www.lineups.com

Awards are arranged alphabetically below their administering organizations

Social Media: www.facebook.com/lineups
twitter.com/lineups
www.youtube.com/c/Lineups

6871 ■ Lineups.com Future of Sports Scholarship Program *(Undergraduate, Graduate/Scholarship)*

Purpose: To provide financial aid to future and current students with an interest in sports. **Focus:** Sports studies. **Qualif.:** Applicant must be a high schooler, undergraduate, or graduate student over the age of 16 and be a resident of the U.S. or Canada; be attending or have a letter of acceptance from a college or university in the U.S. or Canada; and have an interest in sports. **Criteria:** Selection is based on passion, motivation, and need of aid.

Funds Avail.: $1,000. **Duration:** Annual. **Number Awarded:** 2. **To Apply:** Application must be completed online at www.lineups.com/articles/scholarship-application/. **Deadline:** May 31.

6872 ■ Richard Linn American Inn of Court
Chicago, IL 60654
URL: www.linninn.org
Social Media: www.facebook.com/LinnInnofCourt

6873 ■ Mark T. Banner Scholarships for Law Students *(Postdoctorate/Scholarship)*

Purpose: To foster the development of intellectual property lawyers of high ethics, civility and professionalism, and especially those from diverse backgrounds. **Focus:** Law. **Qualif.:** Applicants must be law students who have entered into a JD program at an ABA-accredited law school in the United States. **Criteria:** Academic merit, written and oral communication skills determined in part through a telephone interview for finalists, demonstrate leadership qualities and community involvement, preference given to a member of a historically underrepresented group in IP law (including race, sex, ethnicity, sexual orientation and disability).

Funds Avail.: $10,000. **Duration:** Annual. **To Apply:** Applicants must complete and submit the application form including the following documents for consideration such as resume; academic transcripts; three-page statement describing how ethics, civility and professionalism have been a focus of the candidate, how diversity has impacted the candidate, the commitment to the pursuit of a career in IP law; contact information for three references. **Deadline:** December 4.

6874 ■ Lionsdeal.com
27 Chestnut St.
Suffern, NY 10901
Free: 877-747-0111
E-mail: contactus@lionsdeal.com
URL: www.lionsdeal.com
Social Media: www.facebook.com/lionsdeal
twitter.com/lionsdeal

6875 ■ LionsDeal.com Scholarships *(Undergraduate/Scholarship)*

Purpose: To help students achieve their dreams of a career in the food service and hospitality industry. **Focus:** Food science and technology. **Qualif.:** Applicants must be legal residents of the United States and Canada; must be at least 18 years of age; must be current students in an ac-

credited U.S. or Canadian college or university; must be pursuing a career in the food service and hospitality industry, including, but not limited to marketing, nutrition, and business management **Criteria:** Selection will be on the applicants' demonstrated leadership ability in their field, outstanding creativity and/or entrepreneurial skills.

Funds Avail.: $1,200 each. **Duration:** Biennial. **Number Awarded:** 2 per year. **To Apply:** Applicants must submit a 550-650 word essay describing why they decided to pursue a culinary career and what they plan on contributing to this field upon completion of their degree; please feel free to include graphics and visual presentations as part of the submitted written essay; should include a separate, brief personal biography, including origin of birth, marital status, if they have children, interests, hobbies and etc. Must also submit proof of enrollment at an accredited college or university; one of the following proofs are acceptable: scanned copy of transcripts (winner must mail an unopened copy of official transcripts); enrollment verification form; acceptance letter to college; letter from admissions office confirming registration; in addition, they must submit a clear headshot 300 px or larger along with their submission. **Deadline:** July 15; January 15. **Contact:** Email: scholarship-program@lionsdeal.com; URL: www.lionsdeal.com/scholarships.php.

6876 ■ Literary Arts
925 SW Washington St.
Portland, OR 97205
Ph: (503)227-2583
Fax: (503)241-4256
E-mail: la@literary-arts.org
URL: www.literary-arts.org
Social Media: www.facebook.com/LiteraryArts
www.instagram.com/literaryarts
twitter.com/literaryarts

6877 ■ Oregon Literary Fellowships *(Advanced Professional/Fellowship)*

Purpose: To help Oregon writers initiate, develop or complete literary projects in poetry, fiction, literary nonfiction, drama and young readers literature. **Focus:** Literature. **Qualif.:** Applicants must be current, full-time Oregon residents, both at the time of application and at receipt of award; those who have received an Oregon Literary Fellowship in the last five (5) years are ineligible.

Funds Avail.: $3,500. **Duration:** Annual. **Number Awarded:** Varies. **To Apply:** Applicants may download and review the Fellowship Guidelines as PDF or MS Word documents at the website. **Deadline:** August 2. **Remarks:** Established in 1987. **Contact:** Oregon Literary Fellowships, 925 SW Washington St., Portland, OR, 97205.

6878 ■ Litner + Deganian
1776 Briarcliff Rd. NE
Atlanta, GA 30306
Ph: (678)956-8500
Fax: (678)809-1775
E-mail: info@litnerlaw.com
URL: www.litnerlaw.com
Social Media: www.facebook.com/litnerlaw
www.linkedin.com/company/litner-deganian
twitter.com/litnerdeganian

Awards are arranged alphabetically below their administering organizations

6879 ■ Litner + Deganian College Scholarship Program *(College, University/Scholarship)*

Purpose: To help the next generation of students realize their educational and professional goals. **Focus:** General studies/Field of study not specified. **Qualif.:** Applicant must be a full-time student and a U.S. citizen. **Criteria:** Selection is based on the most creative video on the theme of the scholarship.

Funds Avail.: $2,500. **Number Awarded:** 1. **To Apply:** Application must be completed online. **Deadline:** March 31. **Contact:** Email: marketing@litnerlaw.com; URL: www.litnerlaw.com/scholarship/.

6880 ■ Livestock Publications Council (LPC)

200 W Exchange Ave.
Fort Worth, TX 76164
Ph: (785)614-5371
URL: livestockpublications.com

6881 ■ Forrest Bassford Student Award *(Undergraduate/Award)*

Purpose: To recognize and reward excellence, leadership, and encourage professionalism among students. **Focus:** Agricultural sciences. **Qualif.:** Applicant must be junior or senior at the start of the year; must have at least one semester before graduation.

Funds Avail.: $2,000 and $750 travel scholarships. **Duration:** Annual. **Deadline:** February 15. **Remarks:** Established in 1992.

6882 ■ Lochmueller Group Inc.

6200 Vogel Rd.
Evansville, IN 47715
Ph: (812)479-6200
Free: 800-423-7411
E-mail: info@lochgroup.com
URL: lochgroup.com
Social Media: www.facebook.com/lochgroup
www.instagram.com/lochgroup
www.linkedin.com/company/lochmueller-group
twitter.com/lochgroup

6883 ■ Marian Norby Scholarships *(Other/ Scholarship)*

Purpose: To assist U.S. federal government employees interested in obtaining training in technical communication to improve their employment opportunities. **Focus:** Technical communications. **Qualif.:** Applicants must be female; working full- or part-time for the federal government as a secretary or administrative assistant; and interested in enrolling in a training or academic class related to technical communication. **Criteria:** Selection is based on applicants' expressed interest in technical communication, experience with technical communication and potential for contributing to the profession of technical communication. Consideration will also be given to financial need.

To Apply: Applicants must submit a completed application form along with an essay on interests and achievements, and letters of recommendation from two co-workers (such as a supervisor and a peer). **Contact:** Society for Technical Communication, at the above address.

6884 ■ STC Scholarships *(Graduate, Undergraduate/ Scholarship)*

Purpose: To assist students who are pursuing established degree programs in some area of technical communication.

Focus: Technical communications. **Criteria:** Selection is based on applicants academic records, experience with technical communication, and applicants potential for contributing to theprofession of technical communication.

Funds Avail.: $500. **Duration:** Annual. **To Apply:** Applicants must submit a completed online application form together with an essay on interests and achievements; a certified copy of the latest transcript from the school currently or last attended; and letters of recommendation from two faculty members in the field of technical communication. **Deadline:** November 30. **Contact:** Email: scholarship@cac-stc.org.

6885 ■ London Goodenough Association of Canada (LGAC)

PO Box 5896
Toronto, ON, Canada M5W 1P3
E-mail: lgac@lgac.ca
URL: www.lgac.ca
Social Media: www.facebook.com/
LondonGoodenoughAssociationofCanada
www.linkedin.com/company/london-goodenough
-association-of-canada
twitter.com/lgacalumni

6886 ■ London Goodenough Association of Canada Scholarships *(Graduate/Scholarship)*

Purpose: To support the study of graduate students in London, England. **Focus:** General studies/Field of study not specified. **Criteria:** Recipients will be selected based on academic excellence and extracurricular contributions at Goodenough College.

Funds Avail.: $5,500. **Duration:** Annual. **Number Awarded:** 6. **To Apply:** Applicants must submit a completed application form; must attach all post-secondary transcripts; and three letters of recommendation. **Deadline:** January 25. **Contact:** The London Goodenough Association of Canada, Paul Zed, Chair; PO Box 5896, STN A, Toronto, ON, M5W 1P3, Canada; Email: admin@lgac.ca.

6887 ■ Looka Inc.

116 Spadina Ave.
Toronto, ON, Canada M5V2K6
Free: 888-966-0917
E-mail: support@looka.com
URL: looka.com/logo-maker
Social Media: www.facebook.com/lookadesign
www.instagram.com/lookadesign
www.linkedin.com/company/looka
twitter.com/lookadesign

6888 ■ Logojoy Student Entrepreneur Scholarship *(Undergraduate, Graduate/Scholarship)*

Purpose: To help a student entrepreneur in the fields of business and design. **Focus:** Business; Design. **Qualif.:** Applicant must be currently enrolled in a full-time business, marketing, or design program at a postsecondary institution; must be a small business owner; must have a minimum 2.5 GPA. **Criteria:** Selection will be based on the essay submission, GPA, and business plan.

Funds Avail.: $1,000. **To Apply:** Applicant must submit a short (500 to 750 word) essay on one of the following topics: 1. What changes do you predict the design industry will

Awards are arranged alphabetically below their administering organizations

face in the next decade? How do you intend to react to these changes and contribute to the industry?; 2. What challenges have you faced while running your business and going to school? What role does technology play in your chosen industry and how will you use if after you graduate? Applicant must submit essay, copy of transcript, and business plan to Jordan Smith at scholarship@logojoy.com. **Deadline:** July 31.

6889 ■ Michael Lorenzen Foundation

21 Partridge Dr.
Exeter, RI 02822
E-mail: michaellorenzenfoundation@gmail.com
URL: michaellorenzenfoundation.com
Social Media: www.facebook.com/buglorenzen

6890 ■ Michael Lorenzen Foundation Scholarship
(Undergraduate, Graduate/Scholarship)

Purpose: To provide financial assistance to college students with autism. **Focus:** General studies/Field of study not specified. **Qualif.:** Applicant must be diagnosed with Autism Spectrum Disorder, a U.S. citizen, a recent high school graduate or current undergraduate, and accepted or enrolled in an accredited school in the United States. **Criteria:** Board will be looking for an articulate and clear essay that shows the applicant's unique personality and special experiences.

Funds Avail.: Up to $2,500 (may change from year to year). **To Apply:** Applicants must complete the application and submit with the following: a letter of recommendation from a teacher or therapist; a letter from a doctor or therapist confirming diagnosis of Autism; a copy of high school transcript; and a 600-word essay. The essay should answer one of the following questions: What does it mean to you to be going to college?; What was your biggest accomplishment in school?; What do you see yourself doing in 10 years? Application and other materials should be mailed to address above. **Deadline:** January 31. **Contact:** URL:michaellorenzenfoundation.com/how-to-apply/.

6891 ■ Los Abogados Hispanic Bar Association

PO Box 813
Phoenix, AZ 85001
URL: www.losabogados.org
Social Media: www.facebook.com/AZHispanicBar
twitter.com/AZHispanicBar

6892 ■ Los Abogados LSAT Pipeline Fellowship
(Graduate/Fellowship)

Purpose: To provide fellowships to students in Arizona law schools with a demonstrated commitment to the Hispanic community. **Focus:** Law. **Qualif.:** Applicant must be an Arizona law student preparing for the LSAT.

Funds Avail.: 12-week, in-person LSAT preparation course taught by Kaplan instructors. **Number Awarded:** 10. **To Apply:** Application must be completed online on sponsor's website.

6893 ■ Louis August Jonas Foundation (LAJF)

77 Bleecker St., Ste. C2-13
New York, NY 10012
Ph: (212)686-1930
Fax: (212)981-3722

E-mail: contact@lajf.org
URL: www.lajf.org
Social Media: www.facebook.com/crs.lajf
www.instagram.com/crs_lajf
twitter.com/CRS_LAJF
www.youtube.com/user/RisingSunAlumni

6894 ■ George E. Jonas Scholarships *(Graduate, Undergraduate/Scholarship)*

Purpose: To provide financial assistance to Camp Rising Sun alumni. **Focus:** General studies/Field of study not specified. **Criteria:** Applicants will be judged based on intellectual ability, character, financial need, evaluation of experiences and future promise for fostering the values of Camp Rising Sun.

Funds Avail.: $1,000-$5,000. **Duration:** Annual. **Contact:** Email: alumni@lajf.org.

6895 ■ Louisiana Agricultural Consultants Association (LACA)

11137 Highway 71 S
Cheneyville, LA 71325
E-mail: denise@laca1.org
URL: laca1.org

6896 ■ Louisiana Agricultural Consultants Association Scholarship *(Graduate, Undergraduate/Scholarship)*

Purpose: To support students financially who are in the field of agriculture. **Focus:** Agribusiness; Botany; Entomology; Horticulture. **Criteria:** Selection will be based on application materials; extracurricular activities will be considered.

Funds Avail.: $2,000 each. **Duration:** Annual. **Number Awarded:** 2. **To Apply:** Applicants must submit a completed application form along with two current letters of recommendation and one-page statement (about 200 words) explaining why they deserve the award. **Deadline:** November 5. **Contact:** Ashley Peters, Chairman,LACA Scholarship Committee, 1335 Ward 3 School Rd, Winnsboro, LA, 71295; Phone: 318-282-8803; Email: edpeters1@aol.com.

6897 ■ Louisiana Association of Criminal Defense Lawyers

PO Box 82531
Baton Rouge, LA 70884
Ph: (225)767-7640
Fax: (225)767-7648
E-mail: lacdl@tatmangroup.com
URL: lacdl.org
Social Media: www.facebook.com/louisianacdl
www.linkedin.com/company/louisiana-association-of
 -criminal-defense-lawyers
twitter.com/LouisianaCDL

6898 ■ Camille F. Gravel, Jr. Scholarship *(Professional development/Scholarship)*

Purpose: To support students by covering their tuition and housing expenses. **Focus:** Law. **Qualif.:** Applicants must be Louisiana lawyers who regularly represent indigent defendants. **Criteria:** Selection preference will be given to

Awards are arranged alphabetically below their administering organizations

those who regularly represent indigent defendants and who have practiced more than two, but less than 15 years.

Funds Avail.: No specific amount. **Duration:** Annual. **Number Awarded:** 1. **To Apply:** Applicants must complete and submit the application form on or before the deadline; application forms can be obtained on the website; applicants do not need to fill out the NCDC application unless they awarded the LACDL Camille gravel scholarship; recipient of the scholarship must agree to perform indigent defense service for at least one year from the conclusion of the NCDC session attended. **Deadline:** March 30. **Remarks:** Established in 2003.

6899 ■ Louisiana Environmental Health Association (LEHA)
PO Box 2661
Baton Rouge, LA 70821
E-mail: info@leha.net
URL: leha.net

6900 ■ Frank L. Dautriel Memorial Scholarships for Graduates *(Graduate/Scholarship)*
Purpose: To encourage an outstanding graduate student to pursue their education. **Focus:** Engineering; Environmental science; Environmental technology; Public health. **Criteria:** Selection will be reviewed by the LEHA Awards Committee.

Funds Avail.: $1,000. **Duration:** Annual. **Number Awarded:** 1. **To Apply:** Application forms are available online and must be sent to Louisiana Environmental Health Association. Nominee must submit two letters of recommendation from a faculty of said accredited college or from any LEHA member in good standing; college transcripts must be submitted with the letters of recommendation. **Deadline:** February 1. **Remarks:** Established in 1947.

6901 ■ Frank L. Dautriel Memorial Scholarships for Undergraduates *(Undergraduate/Scholarship)*
Purpose: To encourage an outstanding undergraduate student to pursue their education. **Focus:** Engineering; Environmental science; Environmental technology; Public health. **Criteria:** Selection will be based on the criteria of LEHA awards Committee.

Funds Avail.: $1,000. **Duration:** Annual. **Number Awarded:** 1. **To Apply:** Application forms are available online and must be sent to Louisiana Environmental Health Association. Nominee must submit two letters of recommendation, along with college transcript. **Deadline:** February 1. **Contact:** Jeff Jackson at 337-262-5582 or jeff.jackson@la.gov; Sara Krupa at 225-342-8917 or sara krupa@la.gov.

6902 ■ Louisiana Library Association (LLA)
1190 Meramec Station Rd,207 Ste .
Ballwin, MO 63021
Free: 800-969-6562
E-mail: lla@amigos.org
URL: www.llaonline.org
Social Media: www.facebook.com/
LouisianaLibraryAssociation

6903 ■ LLA Scholarships (LLA) *(Graduate/Scholarship)*
Purpose: To provide financial support to Louisiana students during their full-time study towards the Master's Degree in

Library Science. **Focus:** Library and archival sciences. **Qualif.:** Applicants must be born in Louisiana or have lived in Louisiana for at least one year exclusive of any period of full-time enrollment in post-secondary education; or with a parent who has lived in Louisiana for a period of five years exclusive of any period of full-time enrollment in post-secondary education. **Criteria:** Preference will be given to applicants having a composite undergraduate GPA of at least 3.2; graduate degree with a grade point average of at least 3.5 from that degree on a 4.0 scale; and a combined score on the verbal and quantitative portions of the G.R.E. of at least 1050.

Funds Avail.: $3,000. **Duration:** Annual; An academic year of three consecutive semesters. **To Apply:** Applicants must submit a completed application form along with a letter of recommendation from a librarian, professor, or employer who can speak knowledgeably of the applicants' talents and skills in addition to recommendations required for entry into the Louisiana State University School of Library and Information Science. **Deadline:** May 1. **Contact:** Scholarship Committee Chair, Louisiana Library Association, 8550 United Plaza Blvd., Ste. 1001, Baton Rouge, LA, 70809.

6904 ■ Mary Moore Mitchell Scholarship *(Graduate/Scholarship)*
Purpose: To support Louisiana students during their part-time study toward the Master's Degree in Library Science at Louisiana State University SLIS. **Focus:** Library and archival sciences. **Qualif.:** Applicants must be born in Louisiana or have lived in Louisiana for at least one year exclusive of any period of full-time enrollment in post-secondary education; or with a parent who has lived in Louisiana for a period of five years exclusive of any period of full-time enrollment in post-secondary education; Applicants must be enrolled in part-time study at LSU's SLIS during at least two of those three semesters. **Criteria:** Preference will be given to applicants having a composite undergraduate GPA of at least 3.2 or a graduate degree with a grade point average of at least 3.5 from that degree on a four point scale, and a combined score on the verbal and quantitative portions of the G.R.E. of at least 1050.

Funds Avail.: $1,000. **Duration:** Annual; An academic year of three consecutive semesters. **To Apply:** Applicants must submit a completed application form along with a letter of recommendation from a librarian, professor, or employer who can speak knowledgeably of the applicant's talents and skills in addition to recommendations required for entry into the Louisiana State University School of Library and Information Science. **Deadline:** May 1. **Contact:** Scholarship Committee Chair, Louisiana Library Association, 8550 United Plaza Blvd., Ste. 1001, Baton Rouge, LA, 70809.

6905 ■ Louisiana Public Health Association (LPHA)
7515 Jefferson Hwy. 161
Baton Rouge, LA 70806
Ph: (225)324-6989
E-mail: busmgr.lpha@yahoo.com
URL: www.lpha.org
Social Media: twitter.com/lahealthfan

6906 ■ LPHA Scholarships *(Graduate, Undergraduate/Scholarship)*
Purpose: To provide financial assistance to qualified individuals who want to pursue their education. **Focus:** Public health. **Criteria:** Applicants will be selected by the

Awards are arranged alphabetically below their administering organizations

Scholarship Committee Chair.
Funds Avail.: No specific amount. **Duration:** Annual. **Number Awarded:** 1. **To Apply:** Applicants must complete the application form available on the website; must submit two personal references. **Contact:** LPHA Scholarship Committee, 7515 Jefferson Hwy., Box 161, Baton Rouge, LA 70806; Email: busmgr.lpha@yahoo.com.

6907 ■ Louisiana State Paralegal Association (LSPA)
PO Box 51690
Lafayette, LA 70505
E-mail: education@la-paralegals.org
URL: www.la-paralegals.org

6908 ■ Rochelle Scholarship *(College/Scholarship)*
Purpose: To promote paralegal studies in Louisiana. **Focus:** Paralegal studies. **Qualif.:** Applicants must be paralegal students currently enrolled in an institutionally accredited paralegal program in Louisiana which offers a curriculum of at least sixty (60) semester hours; must have an overall grade point average of at least a 3.0; must be enrolled in a minimum of six hours of paralegal studies; must be planning on a future career as a paralegal.
Funds Avail.: $500. **Duration:** Annual. **To Apply:** Application and supporting documentation details are available at www.la-paralegals.org/scholarships/rochellescholarship.html. **Deadline:** February 15. **Remarks:** In honor of Carol Rochelle, a founding member of LSPA. **Contact:** Email: Scholarship@la-paralegals.org.

6909 ■ Louisiana State University Health Sciences Center New Orleans - School of Medicine - Department of Ophthalmology - Eye Center
3700 St. Charles Ave., 6th Fl.
New Orleans, LA 70115
Ph: (504)412-1200
Fax: (504)568-2866
URL: www.medschool.lsuhsc.edu/Ophthalmology

6910 ■ LSU Eye Center Clinical Retina Fellowships *(Undergraduate/Fellowship)*
Purpose: To foster students in all aspects of the eye and to enhance their skills by hands-on training and examinations. **Focus:** Ophthalmology. **Qualif.:** Applicants must be graduates of ACGME-accredited ophthalmology residency program and eligible for Louisiana State Licensure; foreign applicants must acquire J1 visa through ECFMG and must be certified by the said organization. **Criteria:** Selection will be based on the committees' criteria.
Funds Avail.: No specific amount. **To Apply:** Applicants may accept their applications through SF Match only. **Contact:** Josh Butrick, 504-568-2242.

6911 ■ Louisville Institute
1044 Alta Vista Rd.
Louisville, KY 40205
Ph: (502)992-5432
Fax: (502)894-2286
URL: www.louisville-institute.org
Social Media: www.facebook.com/LouisvilleInstitute
twitter.com/louinst

6912 ■ Louisville Institute Dissertation Fellowships (DF) *(Doctorate/Fellowship)*
Purpose: To support the final year PhD or ThD dissertation of students engaged in research pertaining to North American Christianity. **Focus:** Christian education. **Criteria:** Selection must be based on a committee to review proposals and award Dissertation Fellowships; committee membership and deliberations remain confidential.
Funds Avail.: $25,000. **Duration:** Annual. **To Apply:** Applicants must: complete the online Information and Project Summary form project in approximately 200-words; fill-out the downloadable Dissertation Fellowship Program; and submit two to three-pages, double-spaced selective bibliography, as well as a dissertation adviser's letter of recommendation, Curriculum Vitae or resume; dissertation prospectus; two Letters of Recommendation; dissertation Advisor's Letter of Recommendation Your dissertation advisor will be asked to provide a letter that assesses your doctoral work, dissertation topic and research to date, and your promise for a vocation of teaching and scholarly research; must be submitted Transcripts copy. **Deadline:** February 1. **Contact:** contact Pamala Collins; Email: info@louisville-institute.org.

6913 ■ Louisville Institute Project Grant for Researchers (PGR) *(Doctorate/Grant)*
Purpose: To support projects that can contribute to enhance understanding of important issues concerning Christian faith and life, pastoral leadership and/or religious institutions. **Focus:** Christian education. **Qualif.:** Applicants must be academic and pastoral leaders; must have earned Ph.D. or The degree must demonstrate a capacity to complete the proposed project in a timely fashion. **Criteria:** Selection will be based on submitted project.
Funds Avail.: $30,000. **Duration:** Annual. **To Apply:** Applicants must include Information and Project Summary form; submit a narrative statement (five to seven pages), selective bibliography (two to three-page, double-spaced), detailed budget and budget narrative, copy of current curriculum vitae or resume and one letter of recommendation. **Deadline:** October 1. **Contact:** Keri Liechty, Email: kliechty@louisville-institute.org.

6914 ■ Louisville Institute Sabbatical Grants for Researchers (SGR) *(Doctorate/Grant)*
Purpose: To support pastoral and religious leaders whose research projects can contribute to enhance understanding of issues concerning Christian faith and life, pastoral leadership and/or religious institutions. **Focus:** Christian education. **Qualif.:** Applicants must be both academic and pastoral leaders who are based in the United States or Canada. **Criteria:** Selection will be evaluated based on submitted research project.
Funds Avail.: $40,000. **Duration:** Annual. **Number Awarded:** Varies. **To Apply:** Applicants must include Information and Project Summary form; submit a narrative statement (five to seven pages), selective bibliography (two to three-page, double-spaced), detailed budget and budget narrative, copy of current curriculum vitae or resume and one letter of recommendation. **Deadline:** November 1. **Contact:** Jessica Bowman; Email: jbowman@louisville-institute.org.

6915 ■ Louisville Institute's First Book Grant Program for Minority Scholars (FBM) *(Doctorate/Grant)*
Purpose: To assist junior, non-tenured religion scholars to complete their major research and book project pertaining

to American Christianity. **Focus:** Christian education.

Funds Avail.: $40,000. **Duration:** Annual. **To Apply:** Applicants must include Information and Project Summary form; submit a narrative statement (five to seven pages), selective bibliography (two to three-page, double-spaced), detailed budget and budget narrative, copy of current curriculum vitae or resume and one letter of recommendation. **Deadline:** January 15. **Contact:** Email: info@louisville-institute.org.

6916 ■ Lounge Lizard Worldwide Inc.
18th Fl,112 W 34th St.
New York, NY 10120
Ph: (646)661-7828
Fax: (888)308-8990
Free: 888-444-0110
E-mail: info@loungelizard.com
URL: www.loungelizard.com
Social Media: www.facebook.com/pages/Lounge-Lizard
  -Worldwide-Inc/43528043595
www.instagram.com/loungelizardww
www.linkedin.com/company/lounge-lizard-worldwide-inc.
www.pinterest.com/loungelizardpin
twitter.com/LoungeLizardWW

6917 ■ Web Design Scholarship (College, University, Undergraduate, Vocational/Occupational, Graduate/ Scholarship, Award)

Purpose: To provide students who are designers the opportunity to win a scholarship and a design critique with expert Ken Braun. **Focus:** General studies/Field of study not specified. **Qualif.:** Applicant must be attending school in the United States; must be a student at an accredited school, or be accepted to begin school at an accredited school. **Criteria:** Selection will be based on the submitted web designs.

Funds Avail.: $1,000. **Duration:** Semiannual. **Number Awarded:** 2. **To Apply:** Applicant must submit design with online application form. **Deadline:** October 4, February 20. **Contact:** Email: mac.fox@lizardlounge.com.

6918 ■ Louthian Law Firm, P.A.
1116 Blanding St., Ste. 300
Columbia, SC 29201
Ph: (803)454-1200
Free: 888-662-9820
URL: www.louthianlaw.com
Social Media: www.facebook.com/SouthCarolinaLawyers
www.linkedin.com/pub/bert-louthian/16/8a4/490
www.pinterest.com/scattorney/
twitter.com/SCInjuryLawyers
www.youtube.com/user/SCInjuryLawyer

6919 ■ Louthian Law School Scholarships (Advanced Professional/Scholarship)

Purpose: To encourage and award creative authorship. **Focus:** Law. **Qualif.:** Applicants must be U.S. citizens or authorized to work in the United States; must be commencing law school (1L) in August of the current year; must have a written article which has been published (in print or digital media). **Criteria:** Selection will be based on creativity, originality and ability to clearly convey a complex message of the submitted article.

Funds Avail.: $1,000. **Duration:** Annual; non-renewable. **Number Awarded:** 1. **To Apply:** Applicants must include completed scholarship application form; copy of law school acceptance letter; copy of previously published article or link to its online location. **Deadline:** December 31;January 15.

6920 ■ The Whistleblower Lawyer-Louthian Law Legal Scholarship Award (Graduate/Scholarship)

Purpose: To encourage and award creative authorship by members of the legal profession. **Focus:** Law. **Qualif.:** Applicants must be commencing law school in August; have written an article that has been published in print or digital media; be U.S. citizen or authorized to work in the U.S. **Criteria:** Creativity, originality, and the ability to clearly convey a complex message--a critical skill for legal professionals, whether addressing a client, a judge, or a jury.

Funds Avail.: $1,000. **Number Awarded:** 1. **To Apply:** Submit application form at www.thewhistleblowerlawyer.com/legal-award. **Deadline:** May 1. **Contact:** www.thewhistleblowerlawyer.com/legal-award.

6921 ■ Loveland Archaeological Society, Inc. (LAS)
3317 E. 115th Drive
Thornton, CO 80233
E-mail: stoneagefair@gmail.com
URL: www.stoneagefair.com

6922 ■ Dorothy Mountain Memorial Scholarship (Graduate/Scholarship)

Purpose: To provide support to students with their studies in archeology. **Focus:** Archeology. **Qualif.:** Applicants must be graduate students in Anthropology at the University of Wyoming with emphasis towards archaeology; must have maintained 3.0 GPA in all courses. **Criteria:** Selection will be an emphasis on Colorado or Wyoming for areas of study, both for thesis and career goals.

Funds Avail.: $250. **Duration:** Annual. **To Apply:** Application must include the following: application form, filled out completely; short vita; two letters of recommendation; unofficial transcript from the University of Wyoming or Colorado State University. **Deadline:** May 15. **Contact:** Keith Kanbe; Email: Kanbe@uwyo.edu.

6923 ■ Harry Walts Memorial Graduate Scholarship (Graduate/Scholarship)

Purpose: To provide assistance to graduate students with their studies in archaeology. **Focus:** Archeology. **Qualif.:** Applicants must be graduate students in Anthropology at the University of Wyoming with emphasis towards archaeology; must have maintained 3.0 GPA in all courses. **Criteria:** Selection will be an emphasis on Colorado or Wyoming for areas of study, both for thesis and career goals.

Funds Avail.: $500. **Duration:** Annual. **To Apply:** Applicants must submit a completed application form together with a short vita; two letters of recommendation, one of which must be from a professional Anthropologist/ Archaeologist; and a verification of GPA by submitting an unofficial transcript from the University of Wyoming. **Deadline:** May 15. **Contact:** Keith Kanbe; Email: Kanbe@uwyo.edu.

6924 ■ Lozano Law Firm
5718 University Heights Blvd., Ste. 104
San Antonio, TX 78249

Awards are arranged alphabetically below their administering organizations

Ph: (210)507-3348
Fax: (210)932-3601
URL: www.abogadolozano.com
Social Media: www.facebook.com/TheLozanoLawFirm

6925 ■ The Lozano Law Firm Scholarship Contest
(College, University, Undergraduate/Scholarship)

Purpose: To provide financial aid to college students and encourage students to understand their personal motivation for a career in the legal field. Also seeks to inspire students to purse a career in law and to highlight the positive impact immigration has on communities and career paths. **Focus:** Law. **Qualif.:** Applicant must be a high school senior or a college freshman in the United States. **Criteria:** Selection is based on the submitted video essay or essay.

Funds Avail.: $1,000. **Number Awarded:** 1. **To Apply:** Applicant must create a one- to two-minute video explaining why they want to be a lawyer or how their career path reflects or highlights the positive impact of immigration in the community; video should be published to applicant's YouTube channel with the title "The Loranzo Law Firm Scholarship Contest" and should include this link www.abogadolozano.com/scholarship-for-college-students/ in the description. Instead of a video, applicant can submit a 1,000 to 1,500 word essay on the same subject and submit it to scholarship@abogadolozano.com. **Deadline:** August 1.

6926 ■ Lucid Software Inc.
10355 S Jordan Gateway, Ste. 150
South Jordan, UT 84095
Ph: (801)948-4577
URL: www.golucid.co
Social Media: www.facebook.com/lucidpress
instagram.com/lucidchart
www.linkedin.com/company/lucidsoftware
twitter.com/lucidpress

6927 ■ Lucidchart Scholarship *(Undergraduate, Graduate/Scholarship)*

Purpose: To provide financial support to creative college students. **Focus:** General studies/Field of study not specified. **Qualif.:** Current and incoming freshmen, sophomores, juniors, seniors, and graduate students. **Criteria:** Creativity - make your submission stand out.

Funds Avail.: $1,000. **Number Awarded:** 1. **To Apply:** Use Lucidchart flowchart maker to craft a creative diagram in response to one of the three prompts provided at www.lucidchart.com/pages/scholarship. **Deadline:** June 17. **Contact:** www.lucidchart.com/pages/scholarship; E-mail: scholarships@lucidchart.com.

6928 ■ Lucidpress Scholarship *(Undergraduate, Graduate/Scholarship)*

Purpose: To provide financial support to creative college students. **Focus:** General studies/Field of study not specified. **Qualif.:** Current and incoming freshmen, sophomores, juniors, seniors, and graduate students. **Criteria:** Creativity - make your submission stand out.

Funds Avail.: $1,000. **Number Awarded:** 1. **To Apply:** Use Lucidpress to design creative answers to one of the three prompts provided at www.lucidpress.com/pages/scholarship. **Deadline:** June 17. **Contact:** www.lucidpress.com/pages/scholarship; E-mail:

scholarships@lucidpress.com.

6929 ■ Lunenfeld-Tanenbaum Research Institute - Research Training Centre
Mount Sinai Hospital
Toronto, ON, Canada M5G 1X5
Ph: (416)586-4800
Fax: (416)586-8857
URL: research.lunenfeld.ca

6930 ■ Norm Hollend Fellowships In Oncology
(Postdoctorate/Fellowship)

Purpose: To provide support for individuals conducting research in the area of cancer. **Focus:** Oncology. **Qualif.:** Applicants must be at the post-PhD or post-health professional degree who is conducting a research at the Samuel Lunenfeld Research Institute in the area of cancer. **Criteria:** Selection is based on the submitted application materials.

To Apply: Applicants must submit an up-to-date CV and a one-page summary of the research project to Dr. Cindy Todoroff.

6931 ■ Gail Posluns Fellowships in Hematology
(Postdoctorate/Fellowship)

Purpose: To provide support for individuals conducting research in the area of hematology. **Focus:** Hemophilia. **Qualif.:** Applicant must be at the post-PhD or post-health professional degree who is conducting a research at the Samuel Lunenfeld Research Institute in the area of hematology. **Criteria:** Selection is based on the submitted application materials.

Funds Avail.: No specific amount. **To Apply:** Applicants must submit an up-to-date CV and a one-page summary of the research project.

6932 ■ Lung Cancer Research Foundation
155 E 55 St., Ste. 6H
New York, NY 10022
Free: 844-835-4325
E-mail: info@lcrf.org
URL: www.lungcancerresearchfoundation.org
Social Media: www.facebook.com/
  LungCancerResearchFoundation
www.instagram.com/lungcancerresearchfoundation
twitter.com/lcrf_org

6933 ■ LCRF Grant *(Advanced Professional, Professional development/Grant)*

Purpose: To support projects focused on lung cancer research. **Focus:** Medical research; Oncology. **Criteria:** Selection will be based on the applicants' qualifications and research projects.

Funds Avail.: Disbursed at $75,000 per year. **Duration:** For 2 years. **To Apply:** Applicants must include curriculum vitae (CV) or NIH biosketch of the primary investigator; must include at least one letter of support from the applicant's program director/advisor affirming the applicants will be affiliated with the institution/organization during the grant period; adequate institutional space and equipment to accomplish the proposed project; program director/advisor confirms commitment to and provision of institutional space and equipment for the grantee. **Contact:** Phone: 212-588-1580; Email: grants@lcrf.org.

Awards are arranged alphabetically below their administering organizations

6934 ■ Luso-American Education Foundation (LAEF)

7080 Donlon Way, Ste. 200
Dublin, CA 94568
Ph: (925)828-3883
Fax: (925)828-4554
Free: 877-525-5876
E-mail: education@luso-american.org
URL: www.luso-american.org

6935 ■ A-2 Joaquim Pereira Memorial Scholarship
(Undergraduate/Scholarship)

Purpose: To support students achieve their educational goals. **Focus:** General studies/Field of study not specified. **Qualif.:** Applicants must be high school graduating seniors or enrolled in a four-year college or university; must have a GPA of 3.5 or higher; and be member of the Luso-American Fraternal Federation - Luso-American Life Insurance Society and policy holders in good standing for a minimum of two years. **Criteria:** Selection will be based on the Commitee's criteria.

Funds Avail.: $1,000. **Duration:** Annual. **Number Awarded:** 1. **To Apply:** Applicants must request for the application form; must submit the completed application form together with an official transcript and a letter of recommendation be submitted directly from two individuals who can speak of your character and/or financial needs. If a student, one letter must be from your Advisor; if an educator, one letter must be from either your Supervisor or from your Principal; each letter of recommendation must be submitted with a Letter of Recommendation Cover Sheet; a recent wallet-size photo of yourself (no photo copies). **Deadline:** February 15. **Contact:** Luso-American Education Foundation, 7080 Donlon Way, Ste. 200, Dublin, CA, 94568; Phone: 925-828-4884; Fax: 925-828-4554; Toll Free: 877-525-5876.

6936 ■ A-4 António Mattos Memorial Scholarship
(Undergraduate/Scholarship)

Purpose: To provide financial assistance to qualified students to further their education. **Focus:** General studies/Field of study not specified. **Qualif.:** Applicants must be high school graduating seniors or enrolled in a four-year college or university; must have GPA of 3.0 or higher; Sacramento or East Bay area (CA) resident; and member of the Luso-American Fraternal Federation Luso-American Life Insurance Society and policy holder in good standing for a minimum of two years; excel in a sport during the four high school years; and active in Fraternal Community. **Criteria:** Selection will be based on the Commitee's criteria.

Funds Avail.: $1,000. **Duration:** Annual. **Number Awarded:** 1. **To Apply:** Applicants must request for the application form; must submit the completed application form together with an official transcript and a letter of recommendation be submitted directly from two individuals who can speak of your character and/or financial needs. If a student, one letter must be from your Advisor; if an educator, one letter must be from either your Supervisor or from your Principal; each letter of recommendation must be submitted with a Letter of Recommendation Cover Sheet; a recent wallet-size photo of yourself (no photo copies). **Deadline:** February 15. **Contact:** Luso-American Education Foundation, 7080 Donlon Way, Ste. 200, Dublin, CA, 94568; Phone: 925-828-4884; Fax: 925-828-4554; Toll Free: 877-525-5876.

6937 ■ B-2 LAFF 20-30's Financial Aid Scholarship
(Postgraduate/Scholarship)

Purpose: To provide financial support to students to continue or re-enter a post-graduate program. **Focus:** General studies/Field of study not specified. **Qualif.:** Applicants must be Luso-American Fraternal Federation Luso-American Insurance Society's 20-30s associate member in good standing; must be 18-39 years old. **Criteria:** Selection will be based on the Commitee's criteria.

Funds Avail.: $750. **Duration:** Annual. **Number Awarded:** 1. **To Apply:** Applicants must request for the application form; must submit the completed application form together with an official transcript and a letter of recommendation be submitted directly from two individuals who can speak of your character and/or financial needs. If a student, one letter must be from your Advisor; if an educator, one letter must be from either your Supervisor or from your Principal; each letter of recommendation must be submitted with a Letter of Recommendation Cover Sheet; a recent wallet-size photo of yourself (no photo copies). **Deadline:** April 1. **Contact:** Luso American Education Foundation, 7080 Donlon Way, Ste. 200, Dublin, CA, 94568.

6938 ■ B-3 LAFF 20-30's Financial Aid Scholarship
(Professional development/Scholarship)

Purpose: To assist students to attend a vocational school program or specialty job training. **Focus:** General studies/Field of study not specified. **Qualif.:** Applicants must be Luso-American Fraternal Federation Luso-American Insurance Society's 20-30s associate member in good standing; must be 18-39 years old; must be in need of financial assistance to attend a vocational school program or a specialty job training program. **Criteria:** Selection will be based on the Commitee's criteria.

Funds Avail.: $500. **Duration:** Annual. **Number Awarded:** 1. **To Apply:** Applicants must request for the application form; must submit the completed application form together with an official transcript and a letter of recommendation be submitted directly from two individuals who can speak of your character and/or financial needs. If a student, one letter must be from your Advisor; if an educator, one letter must be from either your Supervisor or from your Principal; each letter of recommendation must be submitted with a Letter of Recommendation Cover Sheet; a recent wallet-size photo of yourself (no photo copies). **Deadline:** April 1. **Contact:** Luso American Education Foundation, 7080 Donlon Way, Ste. 200, Dublin, CA, 94568.

6939 ■ B-4 Albert S. Vieira Memorial Scholarship
(Professional development/Scholarship)

Purpose: To support individuals to make a career change. **Focus:** General studies/Field of study not specified. **Qualif.:** Applicants must be Luso-American Fraternal Federation Luso-American Insurance Society's 20-30s associate member in good standing; must be 18-39 years old; must have minimum GPA of 2.5. **Criteria:** Selection will be based on the Commitee's criteria.

Funds Avail.: $1,000. **Duration:** Annual. **Number Awarded:** 1. **To Apply:** Applicants must request for the application form; must submit the completed application form together with an official transcript and a letter of recommendation be submitted directly from two individuals who can speak of your character and/or financial needs. If a student, one letter must be from your Advisor; if an educator, one letter must be from either your Supervisor or from your Principal; each letter of recommendation must be submitted with a Letter of Recommendation Cover Sheet; a

Awards are arranged alphabetically below their administering organizations

recent wallet-size photo of yourself (no photo copies). **Deadline:** April 1. **Contact:** Luso American Education Foundation, 7080 Donlon Way, Ste. 200, Dublin, CA, 94568.

6940 ■ C-1 General Youth Scholarship
(Undergraduate/Scholarship)

Purpose: To support students to further their education. **Focus:** Business. **Qualif.:** Applicants must be currently a high school graduating senior; enrolled to begin classes at a Community or four year College/University; must be official resident of the United States of America. **Criteria:** Selection will be based on the Commitee's criteria.

Funds Avail.: $4,000. **Duration:** Annual. **Number Awarded:** 1. **To Apply:** Applicants must submit a letter of recommendation be submitted directly from two individuals who can speak of their character and/or financial need; must submit letter of recommendation; must be submitted with a Letter of Recommendation Cover Sheet.forms). **Deadline:** February 15. **Contact:** Luso American Education Foundation, 7080 Donlon Way, Ste. 200, Dublin, CA, 94568.

6941 ■ G-1 Research Project Grants *(Undergraduate/Grant)*

Purpose: To promote and support the Portuguese language and culture. **Focus:** Portuguese studies. **Qualif.:** Applicant must be a Community or four-year College/University student and a U.S. citizen. **Criteria:** Selection will be based on the Commitee's criteria.

Funds Avail.: Up to $2,000. **Number Awarded:** varies. **To Apply:** Applicants must request for the application form; must submit the completed application form together with an official transcript and a letter of recommendation be submitted directly from two individuals who can speak of your character and/or financial needs. If a student, one letter must be from your Advisor; if an educator, one letter must be from either your Supervisor or from your Principal; each letter of recommendation must be submitted with a Letter of Recommendation Cover Sheet; a recent wallet-size photo of yourself (no photo copies). **Deadline:** February 15. **Contact:** Luso American Education Foundation, 7080 Donlon Way, Ste. 200, Dublin, CA, 94568.

6942 ■ G-2 Summer Portuguese Language Program
(Undergraduate/Grant)

Purpose: To support students who wants to pursue the study of Portuguese language and culture. **Focus:** Portuguese studies. **Qualif.:** Applicants enrolled at a Community or four year College/University; official resident of the United States of America; must be of Portuguese descent or working in an educational setting with Portuguese adults or children; enrolled in a college or university not offering Portuguese language or literature. **Criteria:** Selection will be based on the Commitee's criteria.

Funds Avail.: Up to $2,000. **Number Awarded:** Varies. **To Apply:** Applicants must request for the application form; must submit the completed application form together with an official transcript and a letter of recommendation be submitted directly from two individuals who can speak of your character and/or financial needs. If a student, one letter must be from your Advisor; if an educator, one letter must be from either your Supervisor or from your Principal; each letter of recommendation must be submitted with a Letter of Recommendation Cover Sheet; a recent wallet-size photo of yourself (no photo copies). **Deadline:** February 15. **Contact:** Luso American Education Foundation, 7080 Donlon Way, Ste. 200, Dublin, CA, 94568.

6943 ■ G-3 Summer Program in Portugal
(Postgraduate/Grant)

Purpose: To improve the professional career of Portuguese teachers. **Focus:** Portuguese studies. **Qualif.:** Applicants must be official resident of the United States of America; must be of Portuguese descent; enrolled in an accredited College/ University not offering any Portuguese language or literature courses. **Criteria:** Selection will be based on the Commitee's criteria.

Funds Avail.: Up to $3,000. **Number Awarded:** 1. **To Apply:** Applicants must request for the application form; must submit the completed application form together with an official transcript and a letter of recommendation be submitted directly from two individuals who can speak of your character and/or financial needs. If a student, one letter must be from your Advisor; if an educator, one letter must be from either your Supervisor or from your Principal; each letter of recommendation must be submitted with a Letter of Recommendation Cover Sheet; a recent wallet-size photo of yourself (no photo copies). **Deadline:** February 15. **Contact:** Luso American Education Foundation, 7080 Donlon Way, Ste. 200, Dublin, CA, 94568.

6944 ■ Ryan "Munchie" Taylor Memorial Scholarships *(Undergraduate/Scholarship)*

Purpose: To provide financial assistance to qualified students who wish to further their education. **Focus:** General studies/Field of study not specified. **Qualif.:** Applicants must be Society member and policy holder in good standing for a minimum of 2 years; currently a high school graduating senior; enrolled as a full time student at a community or four year College/University; must be active Fraternal member and must be a northern California resident. **Criteria:** Selection will be based on the Commitee's criteria.

Funds Avail.: $1,000. **Duration:** Annual. **Number Awarded:** 1. **To Apply:** Applicants must request for the application form; must submit the completed application form together with an official transcript and a letter of recommendation be submitted directly from two individuals who can speak of your character and/or financial needs. If a student, one letter must be from your Advisor; if an educator, one letter must be from either your Supervisor or from your Principal; each letter of recommendation must be submitted with a Letter of Recommendation Cover Sheet; a recent wallet-size photo of yourself (no photo copies). **Deadline:** February 15. **Contact:** Luso-American Education Foundation, 7080 Donlon Way, Ste. 200, Dublin, CA 94568.

6945 ■ Lymphoma Research Foundation (LRF)
Wall Street Plz., 88 Pine St., Ste. 2400
New York, NY 10005
Ph: (212)349-2910
Free: 800-500-9976
E-mail: lrf@lymphoma.org
URL: www.lymphoma.org
Social Media: www.facebook.com/lymphomacommunity
www.instagram.com/lymphomacommunity
www.linkedin.com/company/lymphoma-research
 -foundation
twitter.com/lymphoma
www.youtube.com/lymphomaresearch

Awards are arranged alphabetically below their administering organizations

6946 ■ Adolescent/Young Adult Lymphoma Correlative Studies Grant (Advanced Professional/Grant)

Purpose: To support adjunct studies that compliment and synergize with ongoing lymphoma clinical trials within the National Cancer Institute Cancer Cooperative Groups. **Focus:** Hematology; Oncology. **Qualif.:** Open to investigators in different disciplines (e.g. pathology and medical oncology, basic science research and clinical investigators) and/or different institutions. **Criteria:** Selection will be based on the committee's criteria.

Funds Avail.: No specific amount. **Duration:** Occasionally; Two years. **To Apply:** Applications can be submitted online.

6947 ■ Chronic Lymphocytic Leukemia Grant (Advanced Professional/Grant)

Purpose: To fund high quality research studies in Chronic Lymphocytic Leukemia (CLL) including the study of primary CLL patient samples to assure relevance to the human disease. **Focus:** Hematology; Oncology. **Qualif.:** Open to investigators in different disciplines (e.g. pathology and medical oncology, basic science research and clinical investigators) or different institutions. **Criteria:** Selection will be based on the committee's criteria.

Funds Avail.: No specific amount. **Duration:** Two years. **To Apply:** Applicants may contact the Foundation for the application process and other information.

6948 ■ Diffuse Large B-Cell Lymphoma Grant (Advanced Professional/Grant)

Purpose: To fund studies that are clinically relevant to the improvement of outcomes for patients with Diffuse Large B-Cell Lymphoma (DLBCL). **Focus:** Hematology; Oncology. **Qualif.:** Open to investigators in different disciplines (e.g. pathology and medical oncology, basic science research and clinical investigators) or different institutions. **Criteria:** Selection will be based on the committee's criteria.

Funds Avail.: No specific amount. **Duration:** Two years. **To Apply:** Applicants may contact the Foundation for the application process and other information.

6949 ■ Follicular Lymphoma Pathways Grant (Advanced Professional/Grant)

Purpose: To fund follicular lymphoma research that includes the study of primary FL patient samples and incorporates collaborative interactions between/among investigators in different disciplines and/or different institutions. **Focus:** Hematology; Oncology. **Qualif.:** Open to investigators in different disciplines (e.g. pathology and medical oncology, basic science research and clinical investigators) and/or different institutions. **Criteria:** Selection will be based on the committee's criteria.

Funds Avail.: No specific amount. **Duration:** Two years. **To Apply:** Applicants may contact the Foundation for the application process and other information. **Deadline:** September 2.

6950 ■ Mantle Cell Lymphoma Therapeutic Studies Grant (Advanced Professional/Grant)

Purpose: To accelerate the pace of research in mantle cell lymphoma (MCL). **Focus:** Hematology; Oncology.

Funds Avail.: No specific amount. **To Apply:** Applications can be submitted online.**Contact:** Email: researchgrants@lymphoma.org. For technical assistance or questions on the application process, Proposal Central helpline Phone: 703-964-5840 or Toll-free: 800-875-2562; email: pcsupport@altum.com.

6951 ■ Boyd Lyon Sea Turtle Fund (BLSTF)

1320 19th St. NW, Ste. 500
Washington, DC 20001
Ph: (202)887-8992
E-mail: boydlyonseaturtlefund@gmail.org
URL: www.boydlyonseaturtlefund.org
Social Media: www.facebook.com/boydlyonseaturtlefund
twitter.com/blstf

6952 ■ Boyd Lyon Sea Turtle Fund Scholars (Doctorate, Graduate, Postgraduate/Scholarship)

Purpose: To support field research projects that further knowledge on sea turtle behavior and habitat use in the marine environment as well as promotion of management and conservation in coastal ecosystems. **Focus:** Biology, Marine; Oceanography.

6953 ■ MacArthur Foundation

140 S Dearborn St.
Chicago, IL 60603-5285
Ph: (312)726-8000
Fax: (312)579-3457
E-mail: 4answers@macfound.org
URL: www.macfound.org
Social Media: www.facebook.com/macarthurfdn
www.instagram.com/macfound
www.linkedin.com/company/macarthur-foundation
twitter.com/macfound
www.youtube.com/user/macfound

6954 ■ MacArthur Fellows Program (Professional development/Fellowship)

Purpose: To award unrestricted fellowships to talented individuals who have shown extraordinary originality and dedication in their creative pursuits and a marked capacity for self-direction. **Focus:** General studies/Field of study not specified. **Criteria:** Selection will be based on exceptional creativity,promise for important future advances based on a track record of significant accomplishments,potential for the fellowship to facilitate subsequent creative work.

Funds Avail.: $625,000. **Duration:** Annual; Five years. **Number Awarded:** 20 to 30. **To Apply:** Nominators will be invited by the Foundation to nominate individuals who demonstrate exceptional creativity and promise; fellows program does not accept applications or unsolicited nominations. **Remarks:** Established in 1981. **Contact:** MacArthur Communications; Phone: 312-917-3690; Andy Solomon; Email: asolomon@macfound.org; Cecilia Conrad, Managing Director.

6955 ■ Robert Mack Scholarship Foundation (RMSF)

c/o Marty Schoonderwoerd
9367 Angwin Pl.
San Diego, CA 92123
Ph: (858)268-3262
E-mail: info@robertmacksf.org
URL: robertmacksf.org

6956 ■ Robert Mack Scholarships (Graduate, Undergraduate/Scholarship)

Purpose: To support qualified students who wish to pursue studies in healthcare engineering. **Focus:** Engineering;

Awards are arranged alphabetically below their administering organizations

Health care services. **Qualif.:** Applicant must be a student pursuing undergraduate, graduate or vocational courses in the field of healthcare engineering. **Criteria:** Selection will be based on the committee's criteria.

Funds Avail.: No specific amount. **To Apply:** Applicants must complete the application form available online together with a grade transcript from the most recent school; SAT reasoning score; community service must be detailed; essays, entitled "What does education mean to me?" and "What are my goals in the field of healthcare engineering?"; references, a minimum of three, one of each must be related to school activities; grade transcripts from most recent school (GPA) should be from the ninth grade through the first semester (or first two quarters of the twelfth grade) or the most current for persons enrolled in courses of study beyond the twelfth grade. **Remarks:** Established in 1986. **Contact:** The Robert Mack Scholarship Foundation, c/o Marty Schoonderwoerd, 9367 Angwin Place, San Diego, CA, 92123.

6957 ■ Mackenzie Municipal Services Agency (MMSA)
5109-51 St.
Berwyn, AB, Canada T0H 0E0
Ph: (780)338-3862
Fax: (780)338-3811
E-mail: info@mmsa.ca
URL: mmsa.ca
Social Media: www.facebook.com/official.mmsa
www.linkedin.com/company/mackenzie-municipal-services
  -agency
twitter.com/MMSA_Official

6958 ■ Robert E. Walter Memorial Scholarship
(Undergraduate/Scholarship)

Purpose: To financially assist students from the Mackenzie Region. **Focus:** General studies/Field of study not specified. **Criteria:** Preference will be given to students enrolled in studies leading towards working in local government.

Funds Avail.: $500. **Duration:** Annual. **Number Awarded:** 1. **To Apply:** Applicants must provide a cover letter indicating the intentions for the R. E. Walter Memorial Scholarship funds, future goals, resume and why they deserve the scholarship funds; must also include two recommendation letters (one must be from teachers or staff from the school they have attended or employers they currently work for and the other one from a member of the community); a copy of grades and list of academic achievements and community involvement must also be included. **Remarks:** The Scholarship was established in honor of Robert E. Walter, one of the Mackenzie Region's leader. **Contact:** Mackenzie Municipal Services Agency, PO Box 450, Berwyn, AB, T0H 0E0.

6959 ■ Macomb County Bar Foundation (MCBF)
40 N Main St., Ste. 435
Mount Clemens, MI 48043
Ph: (586)468-2940
Fax: (586)468-6926
E-mail: mcbf@macombbar.org
URL: macombcountybarfoundation.weebly.com

6960 ■ Philip F. Greco Memorial Scholarship
(Undergraduate/Scholarship)

Purpose: To provide financial assistance for second or third year law students enrolled in evening classes at any

accredited Michigan law school. **Focus:** Law. **Criteria:** Selection will be based on the committee's criteria.

Funds Avail.: $3,000. **Duration:** Annual. **To Apply:** Application form can be downloaded online and must include: completed application form; most recent law school transcript; resume; three letters of recommendation; a personal statement in which the candidate discusses their interest in law, reason for applying for scholarship, career goals, and any other pertinent information for the Scholarship Committee to consider. **Contact:** Macomb County Bar Foundation; Macomb County Bar Foundation, 40, North Main, Ste., 435, Mount Clemens, MI, 48043; Email: RTroy@ macombbar.org.

6961 ■ Trustees College Scholarships
(Undergraduate/Scholarship)

Purpose: To award scholarships for students enrolled in Macomb County Community College who have been affected by Michigan's economic circumstances. **Focus:** Law. **Qualif.:** Applicants for the Macomb County Bar Foundation Trustees Scholarship must be enrolled or accepted for enrollment at Macomb Community College at least part-time (six credit hours). **Criteria:** Preference is given to students who are returning to school due to job loss resulting from downsizing, restructuring, lay-off or corporate buyout. Preference is also given to students who seek to adjust skills by enrolling in a law-related education program.

Funds Avail.: No specific amount. **To Apply:** Applicants may download application online. The application packet must include: completed application; brief summary of applicant's educational and career goals; resume; three letters of recommendation; a personal statement in which the candidate discuss their interest in law, reason for applying for scholarship, career goals, and any other pertinent information for the Scholarship Committee to consider.

6962 ■ Trustees Law School Scholarship
(Undergraduate/Scholarship)

Purpose: To provide financial assistance to law students who are in need. **Focus:** Law. **Criteria:** Selection will be based on the committee's criteria.

Funds Avail.: $3,000. **Duration:** Annual. **To Apply:** Application form can be downloaded online; must include: completed application form; most recent law school transcript; resume; three letters of recommendation; a personal statement in which the candidate discusses their interest in law, reason for applying for scholarship, career goals, and any other pertinent information for the Scholarship Committee to consider. **Contact:** Macomb County Bar Foundation at RTroy@macombbar.org.

6963 ■ MAES: Latinos in Science and Engineering
2437 Bay Area Blvd., No. 100
Houston, TX 77058
Ph: (281)557-3677
Fax: (281)715-5100
E-mail: questions@mymaes.org
URL: mymaes.org

6964 ■ MAES Founders Scholarship *(Graduate, Undergraduate/Scholarship)*

Purpose: To increase the number of Hispanic students completing their higher education goals. **Focus:** Engineering; Mathematics and mathematical sciences; Science;

Awards are arranged alphabetically below their administering organizations

Technology. **Qualif.:** Applicants must enrolled full-time at an Austin area university or college; studying in a STEM related field; beginning their freshman or Sophomore year; with 2.0 GPA or higher. **Criteria:** Selection is based on academic achievement, financial need, leadership, community service, personal qualities, and completeness of application.

Duration: Annual. **To Apply:** Applicants must submit a complete scholarship application packet. **Contact:** Raul Munoz at rmunoz@mymaes.org; Phone: 925-209-3693.

6965 ■ MAES General Scholarships *(Graduate, Undergraduate/Scholarship)*

Purpose: To increase the number of Hispanic students completing their higher education goals. **Focus:** Engineering; Mathematics and mathematical sciences; Science; Technology. **Qualif.:** Applicant must be an MAES student member in the field of science, technology, engineering, and mathematics. **Criteria:** Applicant selection is based on academic achievement, financial need, leadership, community service, personal qualities, and completeness of application.

Funds Avail.: $1,000; $2,000. **Duration:** Annual. **Number Awarded:** Varies. **To Apply:** Applicants must submit a complete scholarship application packet. **Contact:** Scholarship Program, MAES, Inc., 2437 Bay Area Blvd., Ste. 100, Houston, TX 77058.

6966 ■ MAES Padrino/Madrina Scholarships *(Graduate, Undergraduate/Scholarship)*

Purpose: To increase the number of Hispanic students completing their higher education goals. **Focus:** Engineering; Mathematics and mathematical sciences; Science; Technology. **Qualif.:** Applicants must be MAES student members in the field of science, technology, engineering, and mathematics. **Criteria:** Selection is based on academic achievement, financial need, leadership, community service, personal qualities, and completeness of application.

To Apply: Applicants must submit a complete scholarship application packet. **Deadline:** October 18.

6967 ■ MAES Pipeline Scholarship *(Graduate, Undergraduate/Scholarship)*

Purpose: To increase the number of Hispanic students completing their higher education goals. **Focus:** Engineering; Mathematics and mathematical sciences; Science; Technology. **Qualif.:** Applicant must be a MAES student member in the field of science, technology, engineering, and mathematics. **Criteria:** Selection is based on academic achievement, financial need, leadership, community service, personal qualities, and completeness of application.

Funds Avail.: $1,000. **Duration:** Annual. **To Apply:** Applicants must submit a complete scholarship application packet. **Contact:** Scholarship Program, MAES, Inc., 2437 Bay Area Blvd., Ste. 100, Houston, TX 77058.

6968 ■ MAES Presidential Scholarship *(Graduate, Undergraduate/Scholarship)*

Purpose: To increase the number of Hispanic students completing their higher education goals. **Focus:** Engineering; Mathematics and mathematical sciences; Science; Technology. **Qualif.:** Applicants must be an MAES student member in the field of science, technology, engineering, and mathematics.**Criteria:** Applicants selection is based on

academic achievement, financial need, leadership, community service, personal qualities, and completeness of application.

Duration: Annual. **To Apply:** Applicants must submit a complete scholarship application packet. **Contact:** Scholarship Program, MAES, Inc., 2437 Bay Area Blvd., Ste. 100, Houston, TX 77058.

6969 ■ MAES Scholarships *(Graduate/Scholarship)*

Purpose: To increase the number of Hispanic students completing their higher education goals. **Focus:** Engineering; Mathematics and mathematical sciences; Science; Technology.

Funds Avail.: $1,500. **Number Awarded:** Varies. **Deadline:** October 16.

6970 ■ Brandon Magalassi Memorial Scholarship Foundation
13800 E 106th St. N
Owasso, OK 74055
Ph: (918)519-2077
E-mail: secretary@magalassifoundation.org
URL: www.magalassifoundation.org

6971 ■ Brandon Magalassi Memorial Scholarship Foundation Scholarship Awards *(Undergraduate/Scholarship)*

Purpose: To provide support to students pursuing higher education. **Focus:** General studies/Field of study not specified. **Qualif.:** Applicants must be graduating seniors in Owasso High School / Collinsville area.

Duration: Annual. **Remarks:** Established in 2004.

6972 ■ Maine Association of Physician Assistants (MEAPA)
PO Box 10143
Portland, ME 04101
Ph: (207)620-7577
Fax: (207)622-3332
E-mail: info@mainepa.com
URL: www.mainepa.com
Social Media: www.facebook.com/meapa4me
www.instagram.com/meapa_/
www.linkedin.com/company/maine-association-of-physician
 -assistants/

6973 ■ Susan Vincent Memorial Scholarship *(Undergraduate/Scholarship)*

Purpose: To support a Maine resident with desire to become a physician assistant in Maine. **Focus:** Medical assisting. **Qualif.:** Applicants must be students residing in Maine at the time of acceptance into a PA program and share a desire to work and serve in Maine upon graduation.

Funds Avail.: $1,000. **Duration:** Annual. **To Apply:** Applicants must submit a letter of acceptance from an accredited Physician Assistant Program together with the following requirements: a brief statement detailing why they deserve and need this scholarship (maximum length - 2 single-typed pages); applicants should exemplify those qualities that Susan Vincent modeled during her life - against the odds, achieving goals set forth educationally

Awards are arranged alphabetically below their administering organizations

and career-wise, while serving their community. **Deadline:** June 9. **Contact:** URL: mainepa.mypanetwork.com/page/616-susan-vincent-memorial-scholarship.

6974 ■ Maine Community Foundation

245 Main St.
Ellsworth, ME 04605-1613
Ph: (207)667-9735
Fax: (207)667-0447
Free: 877-700-6800
E-mail: info@mainecf.org
URL: www.mainecf.org
Social Media: www.facebook.com/mainecf
www.instagram.com/mainecf
www.linkedin.com/company/maine-community-foundation
twitter.com/MaineCF
www.youtube.com/user/mainecommunityfdn

6975 ■ Daniel Cardillo Charitable Fund (Professional development/Scholarship)

Purpose: To encourage young people to achieve their personal best and reach their goals. **Focus:** General studies/Field of study not specified. **Qualif.:** Applicants must have a demonstrated need for financial assistance along with compassion for others (e.g. through school and community involvement). **Criteria:** Selection will be based on the committee's criteria.

Funds Avail.: No specific amount. **Duration:** Annual. **To Apply:** Applicants must submit most recent transcript or grade report, two letters of recommendation, college's financial aid offer and student aid report from the FAFSA. **Deadline:** May 1. **Remarks:** Established in 1999. **Contact:** The Daniel Cardillo Charitable Fund, Maine Community Foundation, 245 Main St., Ellsworth, ME, 04605-1613.

6976 ■ Catharine Wilder Guiles Scholarship (Graduate/Scholarship)

Purpose: To provide financial assistance to undergraduates pursuing higher education. **Focus:** Mental health. **Qualif.:** Applicants must be Maine residents with demonstrated financial need who are pursuing graduate education in the mental health field at the University of Maine (Orono) or the University of Southern Maine. **Criteria:** Selection will be given to second-year graduate students with demonstrated commitment and potential; students who plan to work in the public sector rather than the private sector in Maine; and to students participating in classroom setting rather than distance learning.

Funds Avail.: No specific amount. **To Apply:** Applicants must submit most recent transcript or grade report, two letters of recommendation, college's financial aid offer and student aid report from the FAFSA. **Contact:** UMaine or USM financial aid offices.

6977 ■ Brent R. Churchill Memorial Scholarship (Undergraduate/Scholarship)

Purpose: To provide financial assistance to students seeking higher education. **Focus:** Education, Music. **Qualif.:** Applicants must be graduating seniors from Mt. Blue High School, including those who attend classes at Foster Applied Technology Center, who are pursuing post-secondary education at a university, community college or business school with a curriculum of at least one year; must also be in good academic standing with a 2.5 to 3.5 GPA. **Criteria:**

Selection will be based on the committee's criteria.
Funds Avail.: No specific amount. **Duration:** Annual. **Number Awarded:** 1. **To Apply:** Applicants must submit most recent transcript or grade report, two letters of recommendation, college's financial aid offer and student aid report from the FAFSA. **Deadline:** April 15. **Remarks:** The scholarship was established in honor of Brent Churchill's deep commitment to community service. Established in 2000. **Contact:** Mt. Blue High School, 129 Seamon Rd., Farmington, ME, 04938.

6978 ■ Downeast Feline Fund (Graduate/Scholarship)

Purpose: To provide financial assistance to undergraduates pursuing higher education. **Focus:** Veterinary science and medicine. **Qualif.:** Applicants must be graduates of Maine high schools who are attending a veterinary school of medicine. **Criteria:** Preference is for students in their third or fourth year.

Funds Avail.: No specific amount. **To Apply:** Applicants must submit an application form, 500 word personal statement, and letter of recommendation from a teacher, employer or friend. **Deadline:** June 15. **Remarks:** Established in 1995. **Contact:** contact Principal Derek Pierce at (207) 874-8160 or piercd@portlandschools.org.

6979 ■ Gary Merrill Memorial Scholarship Fund (Undergraduate/Scholarship)

Purpose: To provide financial assistance to undergraduates pursuing higher education. **Focus:** Government. **Qualif.:** Applicants must be Bowdoin undergraduates demonstrating financial need. **Criteria:** Selection will be Government majors who have distinguished themselves in their studies.

Funds Avail.: No specific amount. **To Apply:** Applicants must submit most recent transcript or grade report, two letters of recommendation, college's financial aid offer and student aid report from the FAFSA. **Remarks:** Established in 1990. **Contact:** Department of Government and Legal Studies at Bowdoin College, Lynne Atkinson, Department Coordinator; Phone: 207-725-3295; Fax: 207-725-3168; Email: latkinso@bowdoin.edu.

6980 ■ Ronald P. Guerrette FFA Scholarship Fund (Undergraduate/Scholarship)

Purpose: To provide financial assistance to people seeking higher education. **Focus:** Agricultural sciences. **Qualif.:** Applicants are graduating seniors at Maine high schools who are FFA members and have a demonstrated interest and motivation to pursue a career in farming and agriculture/natural. **Criteria:** Preference is for applicants pursuing post-secondary studies in farming or agriculture.

Funds Avail.: $1,000. **Duration:** Annual. **To Apply:** Applicants must submit most recent transcript or grade report, two letters of recommendation, college's financial aid offer and student aid report from the FAFSA. **Deadline:** March 1. **Remarks:** The Scholarship was established to honor the life and work of Ronald P. Guerrette of Caribou. Established in 1998.

6981 ■ Guy P. Gannett Scholarship Fund (Undergraduate/Scholarship)

Purpose: To provide financial assistance to people seeking higher education. **Focus:** Journalism. **Qualif.:** Applicants must be graduates of Maine high schools, public or private, or be schooled at home in a Maine community during their last year of secondary education; attend either an under-

Awards are arranged alphabetically below their administering organizations

graduate program, including a trade school or technical institute program, or a graduate program at an accredited post-secondary educational institution in the United States; and major in print or broadcast journalism or a reasonably related field. **Criteria:** Selection will be evidence of excellence in academic performance; evidence of a student's serious commitment to journalism, as demonstrated by work on campus publications/media, area broadcast stations, summer jobs/internships in journalism or other significantjournalistic endeavors, paid or unpaid; and evidence of financial need.

Funds Avail.: No specific amount. **Duration:** Annual. **To Apply:** Applicants must submit most recent transcript or grade report, two letters of recommendation, college's financial aid offer and student aid report from the FAFSA. **Deadline:** June 1. **Remarks:** Established in 2000. **Contact:** Liz Fickett, MaineCF; Phone: 207-412-2015; Toll-free: 877-700-6800, ext. 2015; Email: efickett@mainecf.org.

6982 ■ Henry L.P. Schmelzer College Transitions Scholarship Fund (Undergraduate/Scholarship)

Purpose: To provide financial assistance to undergraduates pursuing higher education. **Focus:** General studies/Field of study not specified. **Criteria:** Selection will be given to residents of Hancock County, Washington County, and statewide.

Funds Avail.: Minimum award is $2,000. **Duration:** Annual. **To Apply:** Applicants must Applicants must have completed at least one successful semester of part-time enrollment (at least two, three-credit courses). **Remarks:** The scholarship was established to recognize Hank's leadership. **Contact:** University College of Ellsworth.

6983 ■ Hugh and Elizabeth Montgomery Scholarship Fund (Undergraduate/Scholarship)

Purpose: To support students for whom a scholarship would make a significant difference in their ability to attend school. **Focus:** General studies/Field of study not specified. **Qualif.:** Applicants must be adult learners from Franklin County who are returning to school to continue their education at the post-secondary level.

Funds Avail.: No specific amount. **Duration:** Annual. **To Apply:** Applicants must submit an application form, 500 word personal statement, and letter of recommendation from a teacher, employer or friend. **Deadline:** August 14; December 11. **Contact:** Tania Dawson; Phone Number 207-779-2554; Email: tsdawson@fchn.org.

6984 ■ Iberdrola USA Scholarships (Undergraduate/Scholarship)

Purpose: To provide financial assistance to undergraduates pursuing higher education. **Focus:** General studies/Field of study not specified. **Qualif.:** Applicants must be dependents of employees or recent retirees of Central Maine Power Company or its subsidiaries who are graduating from a Maine high school, residents of towns within CMP's service area, and enrolled in an accredited two- or four-year undergraduate college or university. **Criteria:** Selection will be based on personal aspirations, academic achievement, financial need, and the student's contribution to school or community activities.

Funds Avail.: No specific amount. **To Apply:** Applicants must submit most recent transcript or grade report, two letters of recommendation, college's financial aid offer and student aid report from the FAFSA. **Deadline:** May 1. **Contact:** Liz Fickett at (207) 667-9735; Email: efickett@mainecf.org.

6985 ■ Ella R. Ifill Fund (Undergraduate/Scholarship)

Purpose: To provide financial assistance to people seeking higher education. **Focus:** General studies/Field of study not specified. **Qualif.:** Applicants must be a member of the International Order of the Rainbow Girls in Maine to pursue post-secondary education. **Criteria:** Selection will be based on the committee's criteria.

Funds Avail.: No specific amount. **Duration:** Annual. **To Apply:** Applicants must submit most recent transcript or grade report, two letters of recommendation, college's financial aid offer and student aid report from the FAFSA. **Remarks:** The Scholarship was established by Ella R. Ifill. **Contact:** International Order of Rainbow Girls in Maine.

6986 ■ James and Marilyn Rockefeller Scholarship Fund (Undergraduate/Scholarship)

Purpose: To provide financial assistance to undergraduates pursuing higher education. **Focus:** General studies/Field of study not specified. **Criteria:** Selection will be based on the committee's criteria.

Funds Avail.: No specific amount. **Duration:** Annual. **To Apply:** Applicants must submit most recent transcript or grade report, two letters of recommendation, college's financial aid offer and student aid report from the FAFSA. **Deadline:** June 15; November 15. **Contact:** James and Marilyn Rockefeller Scholarship Fund, Maine Community Foundation, 245 Main St., Ellsworth, ME, 04605.

6987 ■ Jerome Peters Family Fund (Undergraduate/Scholarship)

Purpose: To provide financial assistance to undergraduates pursuing higher education. **Focus:** General studies/Field of study not specified. **Qualif.:** Applicant must be a Maine resident who is a second, third or fourth year student at Bentley College. **Criteria:** Preference is given to residents of Aroostook County.

Funds Avail.: No specific amount. **To Apply:** Applicants must submit most recent transcript or grade report, two letters of recommendation, college's financial aid offer and student aid report from the FAFSA. **Remarks:** The scholarship was established in the memory of Michael K. Peters.

6988 ■ John S. and Marjoria R. Cunningham Camp Scholarship (Other/Scholarship)

Purpose: To provide scholarships for week-long residential summer camp experiences. **Focus:** General studies/Field of study not specified. **Qualif.:** Applicants must be Maine residents, ages 10-15, whose financial need would otherwise prevent them from affording such experiences. **Criteria:** Recipients will be chosen from the pool of eligible campers attending each camp.

Funds Avail.: No specific amount. **Duration:** Annual. **Contact:** Maine Community Foundation; Email: efickett@mainecf.org.

6989 ■ Joseph W. Mayo ALS Scholarship Fund (Graduate/Scholarship)

Purpose: To recognize his contributions as a father, friend and public servant, who are attending a post-secondary educational institution, including both four-year colleges and two-year associate programs. **Focus:** General studies/Field of study not specified. **Qualif.:** Applicants must be students attending a post-secondary educational institution, including both four-year colleges and two-year associate programs and must be graduates of a Maine high school or

Awards are arranged alphabetically below their administering organizations

GED program. **Criteria:** Selection will be based on the committee's criteria.

Funds Avail.: No specific amount. **Duration:** Annual; one year. **To Apply:** Applicants must submit most recent transcript or grade report, two letters of recommendation, college's financial aid offer and student aid report from the FAFSA. **Deadline:** May 1. **Remarks:** The scholarship was established to recognize Joseph W. Mayo's contributions as a father, friend and public servant by his Friends. **Contact:** Joseph W. Mayo ALS Scholarship Committee c/o Joseph Pietroski 37 Sherwood Forest Dr. Winthrop, ME 04364, joepietroski@gmail.com.

6990 ■ Keepers Preservation Education Fund
(Undergraduate/Award)

Purpose: To provide financial support to aspiring professionals in the United States to increase their professional knowledge or enhance their career potential in historic preservation-related subjects. **Focus:** General studies/Field of study not specified. **Criteria:** Selection will be given to applicants who have not received an award in the past 24 months.

Funds Avail.: No specific amount. **Number Awarded:** Varies. **To Apply:** Applicants must submit most recent transcript or grade report, two letters of recommendation, college's financial aid offer and student aid report from the FAFSA. **Remarks:** The fund was established by William J. Murtagh. Established in 1988. **Contact:** Keepers Preservation Education Fund, Maine Community Foundation, 245 Main St., Ellsworth, ME, 04605; Email: efickett@mainecf.org.

6991 ■ Lawrence and Louise Robbins Scholarship Fund *(Undergraduate/Scholarship)*

Purpose: To provide financial assistance to undergraduates pursuing higher education. **Focus:** General studies/Field of study not specified. **Qualif.:** Applicants must be employees or retirees of the Robbins Lumber company of Searsmont, or their children or grandchildren, looking to pursue post-secondary education. **Criteria:** Recipients will be selected on the basis of academic achievement, personal aspirations, and contributions to school and the community.

Funds Avail.: No specific amount. **To Apply:** Applicants must submit most recent transcript or grade report, two letters of recommendation, college's financial aid offer and student aid report from the FAFSA. **Contact:** Catherine Robbins-Halsted, Robbins Lumber Inc; Phone: 207-342-5221.

6992 ■ Maine Community Foundation - Rice Scholarships *(Undergraduate/Scholarship)*

Purpose: To support students who have resided a substantial part of their formative years. **Focus:** General studies/Field of study not specified. **Criteria:** Selection will focus on financial need and applicant's ongoing demonstrated commitment to community service.

Funds Avail.: No specific amount. **Number Awarded:** 1. **To Apply:** Applicants must submit online. **Deadline:** May 1. **Remarks:** Established in 1996. **Contact:** Liz Fickett, MaineCF; Phone: 207-412-2015; Toll-free: 877-700-6800, ext. 2015; Email: efickett@mainecf.org.

6993 ■ Maine Vietnam Veterans Scholarship
(Advanced Professional/Scholarship)

Purpose: To support Maine veterans of the United States Armed Services who served in the Vietnam Theater and their descendants. **Focus:** General studies/Field of study not specified. **Qualif.:** Applicants must be Maine veterans of the United States Armed Services who served in the Vietnam Theater and their descendants or children of veterans of the United States Armed Services. **Criteria:** Selection will be based on the committee's criteria.

Funds Avail.: No specific amount. **To Apply:** Applicants must submit an application form, 500 word personal statement, and letter of recommendation from a teacher, employer or friend. **Deadline:** May 1. **Remarks:** Established in 1985. **Contact:** Maine Vietnam Veterans' Scholarship Fund, Maine Community Foundation, 245 Main St., Ellsworth, ME, 04605.

6994 ■ Patriot Education Scholarship Fund
(Undergraduate/Scholarship)

Purpose: To provide financial assistance to undergraduates pursuing higher education. **Focus:** Business; Insurance and insurance-related fields. **Qualif.:** Applicants must be graduates of Maine high schools pursuing a degree in business/insurance at a college or university in Maine; pursuing a degree in business as a full- or part-time student; part-time students must be carrying a minimum of nine credit hours to apply. **Criteria:** Selection will be based on the committee's criteria.

Duration: Annual. **To Apply:** Applicants must submit most recent transcript or grade report, two letters of recommendation, college's financial aid offer and student aid report from the FAFSA. **Deadline:** June 1. **Contact:** Liz Fickett, MaineCF; Phone: 207-412-2015; Toll-free: 877-700-6800, ext. 2015; Email: efickett@mainecf.org.

6995 ■ Ruth Milan-Altrusa Scholarship Fund
(Undergraduate/Scholarship)

Purpose: To support students who are pursuing a B.S. in nursing in the Husson/EMMC Nursing Program. **Focus:** Nursing. **Qualif.:** Applicants must be students pursuing a B.S. in nursing and enrolled in the EMMC/Husson University Nursing Program. **Criteria:** Selection will be based on the committee's criteria.

Duration: Annual. **To Apply:** Applicants must submit most recent transcript or grade report, two letters of recommendation, college's financial aid offer and student aid report from the FAFSA. **Deadline:** April 30. **Remarks:** The scholarship was established in memory of Ruth Milan. Established in 1993. **Contact:** Susan M. Hawes; Altrusa Scholarship Committee, 213 Buck St., Bangor, ME, 04401.

6996 ■ Maine Graphic Arts Association
PO Box 265
Sanford, ME 04073-0265

6997 ■ Maine Graphic Arts Association Scholarships *(Undergraduate/Scholarship)*

Purpose: To reward deserving students who desire to continue their education in the field of graphic arts printing technology. **Focus:** Graphic art and design. **Qualif.:** Applicants must have completed or will complete their secondary education in Maine with at least a C average; must be a member of the MGAA and have been accepted into a post-secondary Graphic Arts program.

Funds Avail.: No specific amount. **Duration:** Annual. **Contact:** The MGAA Educational Needs Committee, PO Box 265, Sanford, Maine, 04073.

Awards are arranged alphabetically below their administering organizations

6998 ■ Maine Landscape and Nursery Association (MeLNA)

PO Box 4666
Augusta, ME 04330
Ph: (207)623-6430
Fax: (207)623-6431
E-mail: mngmtplus@aol.com
URL: www.melna.org

6999 ■ MELNA Scholarship *(Undergraduate, Graduate/Scholarship)*

Purpose: To promote post-secondary horticultural education. **Focus:** Horticulture. **Qualif.:** Applicants must be members of MELNA. **Criteria:** Selection will be based on the committee's criteria.

Funds Avail.: Amount not specified. **Duration:** Annual.

7000 ■ Maine Nutrition Council (MNC)

PO Box 246
Augusta, ME 04330
E-mail: info@mainenutritioncouncil.org
URL: www.mainenutritioncouncil.org
Social Media: www.facebook.com/MaineNutritionCouncil

7001 ■ Maine Nutrition Council Scholarships *(Undergraduate/Scholarship)*

Purpose: To provide financial assistance to the students enrolled at the University of Maine. **Focus:** Food science and technology; Nutrition.

Funds Avail.: $500. **Duration:** Annual. **To Apply:** Applicants must submit one letter of recommendation from a faculty member together with their application form. **Deadline:** February 15. **Contact:** Andrea LaFlamme, 189 Norfolk St., Bangor, ME 04401.

7002 ■ Maine Space Grant Consortium (MSGC)

87 Winthrop St., Ste. 200
Augusta, ME 04330-5509
Free: 877-397-7223
URL: www.msgc.org
Social Media: www.facebook.com/Mainespacegrant
twitter.com/mainespacegrant

7003 ■ MSGC Internships *(Undergraduate/Internship)*

Purpose: To provide an education and research experience for students so that they consider career opportunities related to NASA. **Focus:** Aerospace sciences. **Qualif.:** Applicants must be U.S. citizens.

Funds Avail.: $6,500. **Duration:** Annual. **Deadline:** January 15.

7004 ■ Maine State Employees Association (MSEA)

65 State St.
Augusta, ME 04330-5126
Ph: (207)622-3151
URL: www.mseaseiu.org
Social Media: www.facebook.com/MSEASEIU1989
twitter.com/MSEASEIU1989

7005 ■ Dr. Howard L. Bowen Scholarship *(Undergraduate/Scholarship)*

Purpose: To support students who have relationships with a dues-paying MSEA/SEIU member. **Focus:** General studies/Field of study not specified. **Qualif.:** Applicants must be entering full-time post-secondary educational or vocational programs for the first time as freshmen; must be an MSEA/SEIU member or child of an MSEA member. **Criteria:** Applicants are judged upon the committee's criteria.

Funds Avail.: $1,000. **Duration:** Annual. **To Apply:** Applicants should submit high school transcript; essay; one reference letter. **Deadline:** April 15.

7006 ■ Murray L. Brown Scholarships *(Undergraduate/Scholarship)*

Purpose: To support students who have relationships with a dues-paying MSEA/SEIU member. **Focus:** General studies/Field of study not specified. **Qualif.:** Applicant must be entering full-time post-secondary educational or vocational programs for the first time; must be an MSEA/SEIU member or the child of an MSEA member. **Criteria:** Applicants are judged upon the committee's criteria.

Funds Avail.: $1,000. **Duration:** Annual. **Number Awarded:** 1. **To Apply:** Applicants should submit high school transcript; essay; one reference letter. **Deadline:** April 17.

7007 ■ George A. Davala Scholarship *(Undergraduate, Vocational/Occupational/Scholarship)*

Purpose: To support students who have relationships with a dues-paying MSEA/SEIU member. **Focus:** General studies/Field of study not specified. **Qualif.:** Applicant must be an MSEA/SEIU Member; must be a full-time, first-year student in a post-secondary educational or vocational program. **Criteria:** Applicants are judged upon the committee's criteria.

Funds Avail.: $1,000. **Duration:** Annual. **To Apply:** Applicants should submit high school transcript; essay; one reference letter.

7008 ■ Maine Community College Scholarships (MCCS) *(Undergraduate, Vocational/Occupational/Scholarship)*

Purpose: To provide assistance to Maine students who lack financial aid for education. **Focus:** General studies/Field of study not specified. **Qualif.:** Applicants must be: children of MSEA member; students who are under legal guardianship of MSEA member; grandchildren of MSEA member who resides with the grandparents; students entering full-time at any post-secondary educational or vocational institutions for the first time. **Criteria:** Selection will be based on the following criteria: character, leadership, service to others, financial need, and scholastic ability.

Funds Avail.: $750. **Duration:** Annual. **Number Awarded:** 3. **To Apply:** Applicants must submit the following materials with the application: high school transcript; essay on how the union affected the applicant's family or parents/guardians' financial resources and outstanding obligations; Federal Income Tax Return including all statements and schedules; description of extracurricular activities; scholastic and non-scholastic reference letter.

7009 ■ Richard J. McDonough Scholarship *(Undergraduate/Scholarship)*

Purpose: To support students pursuing higher education who have a connection to an MSEA/SEIU member. **Focus:** General studies/Field of study not specified. **Qualif.:** Applicant must be a MSEA member, child/stepchild of a MSEA members, child of a MSEA member's significant other who

Awards are arranged alphabetically below their administering organizations

reside with the MSEA member, or under legal guardianship of an MSEA member, who is attending post-secondary education for the first time on a full-time basis. **Criteria:** Applicants are judged upon the committee's criteria.

Funds Avail.: $1,500. **Duration:** Annual. **To Apply:** Applicants should submit high school transcript; essay; one reference letter.

7010 ■ MSEA/SEIU Part-time Student Members Scholarships *(Undergraduate/Scholarship)*

Purpose: To provide financial assistance to students who want to pursue higher education. **Focus:** General studies/Field of study not specified. **Qualif.:** Applicants must be MSEA members who are furthering their education either on a part-time basis while employed, or on a full time basis after obtaining an educational leave of absence. **Criteria:** Applicants must be MSEA member who are furthering their education either on a part-time basis while employed, or on a full time basis after obtaining an educational leave of absence.

Funds Avail.: $500. **Duration:** Annual. **Number Awarded:** 1. **To Apply:** Applicants must submit the following materials along with the application: high school transcript; essay on how the union affected the applicant's family or parents/guardians' financial resources and outstanding obligations; Federal Income Tax Return including all statements and schedules; description of extracurricular activities; scholastic and non-scholastic reference letter.

7011 ■ Malayalee Engineers Association (MEA)
8303 SW Fwy., Ste. 335
Houston, TX 77074
E-mail: meahouston@gmail.com
URL: meahouston.org
Social Media: www.facebook.com/meahouston

7012 ■ Malayalee Engineers Association Scholarships *(Undergraduate/Scholarship)*

Purpose: To encourage young professionals to pursue their engineering, technology, computer science, or naval architecture studies towards a Bachelor's Degree. **Focus:** Architecture; Architecture, Naval; Computer and information sciences; Engineering; Technology. **Qualif.:** Applicants must be first year students of Kerala origin, enrolled for at least a four-year degree course in Engineering, Technology, Computer Science, Architecture, or Naval Architecture, in a nationally accredited engineering college or university in India. **Criteria:** Selection will be based on the academic merit and financial hardship of the applicant.

Funds Avail.: No specific amount. **Duration:** Annual; 4 years. **To Apply:** Online application and details are available at: meahouston.org/scholarship/applyforscholarship/. **Deadline:** October 15. **Remarks:** Established in 2000.

7013 ■ Mangum & Associates PC
Brownstone Milano Bldg., 25511 Budde Rd., No. 1802
The Woodlands, TX 77380
Free: 877-343-3103
E-mail: info@mangumlaw.net
URL: mangumlaw.net

7014 ■ Mangum & Associates PC Scholarship Contest *(Undergraduate/Scholarship)*

Purpose: To provide financial aid to students, encourage students to understand their personal motivation for a career in the legal field, and inspire students to pursue a career in law. **Focus:** Law. **Qualif.:** Applicant must be a high school senior or college freshman in the U.S. who is studying, or plans to study, in the field of law. **Criteria:** Selection is based on the best video essay or written essay submitted.

Funds Avail.: $1,000. **Number Awarded:** 1. **To Apply:** Applicant must record a video (one to two minutes long, in plain English) explaining how lawyers help businesses. Video must be published on the applicant's YouTube channel with the title "Magnum and Associates PC Scholarship Contest" and this link in the description: magnumlaw.net/scholarship-for-college-students. Applicant must also share the video on their Facebook page and the sponsor's Facebook page. Instead of a video, applicant may submit a 1,000 to 1,500 word essay on the same subject via email. **Deadline:** August 15. **Contact:** Darin Mangum; Email: darin@mangumlaw.net; URL: mangumlaw.net/scholarship-for-college-students/.

7015 ■ Manhattan Street Capital, LLC
5694 Mission Center Rd., Ste. 602-468
Las Vegas, NV 89120-1183
Ph: (858)848-9566
E-mail: support@manhattanstreetcapital.com
URL: www.manhattanstreetcapital.com
Social Media: www.facebook.com/ManhattanStreetCapital-?fref=ts
www.instagram.com/manhattanstcapital/
www.pinterest.com/manhattanstcap/
twitter.com/ManhattanStCap

7016 ■ Manhattan Street Capital National Scholarship *(Undergraduate/Scholarship)*

Purpose: To give back to students and learn about Regulation A+ crowd funding. **Focus:** General studies/Field of study not specified. **Qualif.:** Applicants must be U.S. or Canadian residents who are currently enrolled in college or plan to attend in the next 12 months; must have a minimum 3.0 GPA.

Funds Avail.: $2,000. **Duration:** Annual. **Number Awarded:** 1. **To Apply:** Applicants must submit a 500 to 1,000 word essay via email. **Deadline:** October 31. **Contact:** Email: scholarship@manhattanstreetcapital.com; URL: www.manhattanstreetcapital.com/national-scholarship.

7017 ■ David Mann Law Office
130 N Crest Blvd.
Macon, GA 31210
Ph: (478)742-3381
Fax: (478)746-3354
Free: 855-507-7598
URL: www.manninjurylaw.com
Social Media: www.facebook.com/georgialawfirm
www.linkedin.com/company/mann-law-firm
twitter.com/GeorgiaLawFirm

7018 ■ Mann Law Firm Scholarships *(Advanced Professional/Scholarship)*

Purpose: To reward clear and concise communication which conveys a message to the target audience. **Focus:** Law. **Qualif.:** Applicants must be U.S. citizens or authorized

Awards are arranged alphabetically below their administering organizations

to work/go to school in the United States. **Criteria:** Selection will be based on creativity, originally and ability to clearly convey a complex message of the submitted article.

Funds Avail.: $1,000. **Number Awarded:** 1. **To Apply:** Applicants must visit the website for the online application process; must submit a copy of law school acceptance letter and published article in print or digital. **Deadline:** May 1.

7019 ■ Mansfield Soccer Association (MSA)
2363 Highway 287 N, Ste. 206
Mansfield, TX 76063
Ph: (817)473-1177
Fax: (817)473-7786
E-mail: registrar@mansfieldsoccer.org
URL: www.mansfieldsoccer.org

7020 ■ Mansfield Soccer Association Scholarship
(Undergraduate/Scholarship)

Purpose: To help individuals pursue their post-secondary education. **Focus:** General studies/Field of study not specified. **Qualif.:** Applicants must live within the MISD boundaries; must have plans to attend an institution of higher education for the upcoming year; and must have been players, coaches or referees in MSA within the last five years. **Criteria:** Selection will be based on academic record, school and community involvement, financial need, work experience and completeness of the application.

Funds Avail.: $1,000. **Duration:** Annual. **Number Awarded:** 2. **To Apply:** The application process is online; application must include PERSONAL PROFILE;HIGH SCHOOL TRANSCRIPT;LETTERS OF RECOMMENDATION. **Deadline:** May 12. **Contact:** Mansfield Soccer Association, Attn: Scholarship Committee, 2363 Hwy 287 N, Ste. 206, Mansfield, TX 76063; Phone: 817-473-1177; E-mail: registrar@mansfieldsoccer.org.

7021 ■ ManTech International Corporation
2251 Corporate Park Dr.
Herndon, VA 20171
Ph: (703)218-6000
E-mail: gwac@mantech.com
URL: www.mantech.com
Social Media: www.facebook.com/
  mantechinternationalcorporation
www.linkedin.com/company/mantech
twitter.com/mantech

7022 ■ AFCEA STEM Teacher Graduate Scholarships *(Graduate/Scholarship)*

Purpose: To promote science, mathematics or information technology education at the US Secondary School, and support graduate students to become STEM teachers. **Focus:** Education; Engineering; Mathematics and mathematical sciences; Science; Technology. **Qualif.:** Applicants must be U.S. citizens who are graduate students attending an accredited U.S. college or university on-campus and majoring in secondary education for the purpose of teaching STEM (science, technology, engineering or math) subjects in a U.S. middle/intermediate and high schools; graduate-level candidates must currently be in their second semester with current overall GPA of 3.5 or higher on a 4.0 scale and taking at least two semester-equivalent classes at an accredited U.S. college or university at the time of applica-

tion; current credential and licensure students must have completed a bachelor's of science degree or graduate degree in a STEM major; undergraduate students are ineligible.

Funds Avail.: $2,500. **Duration:** Annual. **Number Awarded:** 1. **To Apply:** Completed application along with current official transcript issued by the school Registrar's Office; minimum of two letters of recommendation required from faculty in the major of study; current resume and undergrad transcript - either official or unofficial (through email); one additional letter from the school principal for currently employed teacher must be submitted. **Deadline:** April 10. **Contact:** Email: edfoundation@afcea.org; URL: www.afcea.org/site/foundation/scholarships.

7023 ■ Manufacturing Jewelers and Suppliers of America (MJSA)
8 Hayward St.
Attleboro, MA 02703
Free: 800-444-6572
E-mail: info@mjsa.org
URL: www.mjsa.org
Social Media: www.facebook.com/theMJSA
www.instagram.com/mjsa_jewelrymaking
twitter.com/MJSAtweets

7024 ■ MJSA Education Foundation Scholarship
(Undergraduate/Scholarship)

Purpose: To financially support students enrolled in jewelry-related field. **Focus:** Design. **Qualif.:** Applicant must be enrolled in a jewelry program, who intends to pursue a career in the jewelry industry and can demonstrate financial need, is eligible to apply. Applicants are assessed on the basis of course of study, academics, career plans, recommendations, and industry experience. Students must be U.S. citizens. **Criteria:** Selection is based on the course of study, academics, career plans, recommendations, and industry experience.

Funds Avail.: No specific amount. **Duration:** Annual. **To Apply:** Applicants must complete the application form available at the website; must submit a copy of financial aid award letter; official transcript; an essay; and a letter of recommendation. Forward completed application and supporting documents in one envelope. **Deadline:** May 15. **Contact:** For application eligibility and content inquiries, Kelly Riley Donor Services Administrator; Phone: 401-427-4028; E-mail: kriley@rifoundation.org.

7025 ■ March of Dimes Foundation
1275 Mamaroneck Ave.
White Plains, NY 10605
Ph: (914)997-4488
URL: www.marchofdimes.org
Social Media: www.facebook.com/marchofdimes
instagram.com/marchofdimes
www.linkedin.com/company/march-of-dimes
twitter.com/marchofdimes

7026 ■ March of Dimes General Research Grants
(Professional development/Grant)

Purpose: To support research on basic biological processes of development, genetics, clinical studies, studies of reproductive health, environmental toxicology, and stud-

Awards are arranged alphabetically below their administering organizations

ies in social and behavioral sciences that focus on factors contributing to adverse pregnancy outcomes, and on consequences of birth defects and prematurity. **Focus:** Biological and clinical sciences.

Duration: Annual. **To Apply:** Applicants must have previously submitted a full proposal that was reviewed but not funded, a response to the critique is not necessary in the LOI; however, relevant remarks may be included, but mustbe incorporated within the 3 pages. **Contact:** Email: researchgrantssupport@marchofdimes.org.

7027 ■ March of Dimes Graduate Nursing Scholarships *(Graduate/Scholarship)*

Purpose: To provide financial assistance to registered nurses in a graduate program. **Focus:** Nursing. **Qualif.:** Applicants must be registered nurses, currently enrolled in a graduate program in maternal-child nursing at the master's or doctoral level; must have at least one academic term to complete after August of the year in which the scholarship is awarded; must be member of at least one of the following professional organizations: Association of Women's Health, Obstetric and Neonatal Nurses, American College of Nurse-Midwives or National Association of Neonatal Nurses.

Funds Avail.: $5,000. **Duration:** Annual. **Deadline:** January 13. **Remarks:** Established in 2016.

7028 ■ Basil O'Connor Starter Scholar Research Awards (BOC) *(Professional development/Grant)*

Purpose: To support young scientists just embarking on their independent research careers. **Focus:** Biological and clinical sciences. **Qualif.:** Applicant must have a Ph.D. and be no more than eight years past earning their degree; successful applicants have traditionally completed four to six years of postdoctoral training or other faculty-mentored work, but not more than eight years, and have been hired as faculty member at their respective current institutions; for M.D. or M.D./Ph.D. the same 4-8 year timeline applies, but begins upon completion of the last year of clinical training required for medical specialty board certification; requests for exceptions (e.g., pregnancy and maternity leave) should be directed to the Senior Vice President for Research & Global Programs.

Funds Avail.: $150,000. **Duration:** Annual; up to two years. **To Apply:** Application is through online nomination; the entire process must be completed online. The following information is required from the candidates: title of the proposed research project; candidate's name, academic appointment, mailing address, telephone and fax numbers and e-mail address; candidate's biosketch. Must also provide a letter of intent (template provided) for the proposed research, which includes the following information in this order: title of proposal, hypothesis, preliminary data, precis of specific aims and methods of procedure; and finally, current financial support (list all current financial support; if there is no current support, state "none"); those mentioned items should not exceed 3 pages. Pieces of information required from the nominators are the following: deans, chairs of departments, or directors of institutes/centers may submit nominations for this award, addressed to the senior vice president for research and global programs (included should be the nominator's name, academic appointment, mailing address, telephone and fax number and e-mail address). The nominators should submit the letter of nomination through the online system. **Deadline:** March 15. **Remarks:** Named for the first March of Dimes chairman and president the Basil O'Connor. **Con-**

tact: Email: researchgrantssupport@marchofdimes.org.

7029 ■ Stephen T. Marchello Scholarship Foundation
1170 E Long Pl.
Centennial, CO 80122
Ph: (303)886-5018
E-mail: stmfoundation@hotmail.com
URL: www.stmfoundation.org

7030 ■ Stephen T. Marchello Scholarship *(Graduate/Scholarship)*

Purpose: To support the education of students who have a history of childhood cancer. **Focus:** General studies/Field of study not specified. **Qualif.:** Applicants must be current year high school graduates and are residents of Colorado and Montana; must have survived childhood cancer. **Criteria:** Selection will be based on high school grade point average and how the applicant answers the two questions given in the application.

Funds Avail.: No specific amount. **To Apply:** Applicants must submit a completed scholarship application along with a copy of transcript (with GPA); SAT or ACT test scores; a confirmation of the treatment by the doctor or by the hospital or clinic; and a reference letter provided by two other people (from someone other than a family member). **Deadline:** March 16. **Contact:** Stephen T. Marchello Foundation Scholarship; 1170 E Long Place, Centennial, CO, 80122; Phone: 303-886-5018.

7031 ■ The Margarian Law Firm
801 N Brand Blvd., Ste. 210
Glendale, CA 91203
Ph: (818)553-1000
URL: www.lemonlawcourt.com
Social Media: www.facebook.com/LemonLawCourt
www.linkedin.com/company/margarian-law
twitter.com/LemonLawCourt

7032 ■ Margarian Scholarship *(Undergraduate, Graduate/Scholarship)*

Purpose: To reward a select number of deserving students for their academic and personal achievements. **Focus:** General studies/Field of study not specified. **Qualif.:** Applicants must be high school juniors or seniors, college/university students, or graduate school students. **Criteria:** Applicants will be selected in the basis of who have demonstrated a commitment to their heritage, community, and society through persistence, dedication, success, and humility; the selection does not only determine recipients solely on GPA. basis or economic hardship;

Funds Avail.: $1,000 each. **Duration:** Annual. **Number Awarded:** 5. **To Apply:** Application and letter of recommendation template are available online at margarianlaw.com/scholarship/; submit application, one letter of recommendation, resume, personal statement, and transcripts. **Deadline:** August 1. **Contact:** Shushanik Margarian, Scholarship Fund Director; Email: scholarship@margarianlaw.com.

7033 ■ Maricopa County Community College District
2411 W 14th St.
Tempe, AZ 85281

Awards are arranged alphabetically below their administering organizations

Ph: (480)731-8000
E-mail: contact.us@domail.maricopa.edu
URL: www.maricopa.edu

7034 ■ Maricopa County Community College District Scholarships (MCCCD) *(Undergraduate/ Scholarship)*

Purpose: To provide financial assistance to qualified individuals who want to pursue their career. **Focus:** Accounting; Economics; Education; Education, Vocational-technical; Engineering, Chemical; Engineering, Civil; Engineering, Electrical; Engineering, Mechanical; Finance; Health care services; Information science and technology; Management; Marketing and distribution. **Qualif.:** Applicants must complete a Free Application for Federal Student Aid (FAFSA); must verify applicant lawful presence within the U.S.

To Apply: Applicant must complete the application form available online.

7035 ■ Marine Aquarium Societies of North America (MASNA)

PO Box 105603
Atlanta, GA 30348-5603
URL: masna.org
Social Media: www.facebook.com/MASNA-159858221132
www.instagram.com/macnaconference
www.linkedin.com/groups/6956856
twitter.com/MASNA

7036 ■ MASNA Student Scholarships *(Undergraduate, Graduate/Scholarship)*

Purpose: To support those undergraduate and graduate students from the various colleges and universities in U.S. as well as to assist each of the chosen applicants in attending MACNA. **Focus:** Biology, Marine. **Qualif.:** Applicants must be current/entering undergraduate or graduate students at an accredited college or university; have declared a major/focus or intent to declare a major/focus in one of the marine science disciplines; has a GPA above 2.5 / 4.0. **Criteria:** Selection will be based upon the students' academic history and the contributions and demonstrated commitment to the marine aquarium hobby.

Funds Avail.: $4,000 each. **Duration:** Annual. **Number Awarded:** 2. **To Apply:** Applications can be submitted online. **Deadline:** June 5. **Contact:** Email: Scholarship@MASNA.org.

7037 ■ Marine Biological Laboratory (MBL)

7 MBL St.
Woods Hole, MA 02543
Ph: (508)548-3705
E-mail: comm@mbl.edu
URL: www.mbl.edu
Social Media: www.facebook.com/mblscience
instagram.com/mblwoodshole
twitter.com/mblscience
youtube.com/user/mblwoodshole

7038 ■ Benjamin Kaminer Endowed Scholarship in Physiology *(Graduate, Doctorate, Master's/ Scholarship)*

Purpose: To provide financial support for students studying in any Marine Biological Laboratory summer courses in

Physiology. **Focus:** Physiology. **Qualif.:** Applicants must demonstrate the need for financial aid to attend MBL courses; will be considered for all sources of financial assistance; fund supports students in the Physiology course. **Criteria:** Selection will be selected based on academic standing and financial need.

Duration: Annual. **To Apply:** Applicants who apply for financial aid to attend MBL courses are automatically considered; see the requirements for Embryology Summer Course program.

7039 ■ Bruce and Betty Alberts Endowed Scholarship in Physiology *(Undergraduate/Scholarship)*

Purpose: To provide educational support for Physiology students. **Focus:** Physiology. **Qualif.:** Applicants must demonstrate the need for financial aid to attend MBL; they will be considered for all sources of financial assistance; fund provides support for students participating in the physiology course. **Criteria:** Selection will be selected based on academic standing and financial need.

Duration: Annual. **To Apply:** Applicants who apply for financial aid to attend MBL courses are automatically considered; see the requirements for Embryology Summer Course program.

7040 ■ C. Lalor Burdick Scholarship *(Graduate, Master's, Doctorate/Scholarship)*

Purpose: To provide financial support for students attending the Embryology and Frontiers in Reproduction courses. **Focus:** Biological and clinical sciences; Life sciences. **Qualif.:** Applicants must demonstrate the need for financial aid to attend MBL courses; will be considered for all sources of financial assistance; fund supports students in the Embryology and Frontiers in Reproduction courses. **Criteria:** Selection will be selected based on academic standing and financial need.

Duration: Annual. **To Apply:** Applicants who apply for financial aid to attend MBL courses are automatically considered; see the requirements for Embryology Summer Course program.

7041 ■ Caswell Grave Scholarship *(Undergraduate, Graduate/Scholarship)*

Purpose: To provide financial support for students studying in any Marine Biological Laboratory summer courses. **Focus:** Biology, Marine. **Qualif.:** Applicants must demonstrate the need for financial aid to attend MBL courses; will be considered for all sources of financial assistance; fund supports students in any of the MBL summer courses. **Criteria:** Selection will be selected based on academic standing and financial need.

Duration: Annual. **To Apply:** Applicants who apply for financial aid to attend MBL courses are automatically considered; see the requirements for Embryology Summer Course program.

7042 ■ Florence C. Rose and S. Meryl Rose Endowed Scholarship *(Master's, Graduate, Doctorate/ Scholarship)*

Purpose: To provide financial support for students at the Marine Biological Laboratory Embryology Summer Course Program. **Focus:** Biology; Life sciences. **Qualif.:** Applicants must demonstrate the need for financial aid to attend MBL courses; will be considered for all sources of financial assistance; fund supports students in any of the Embryology course. **Criteria:** Selection will be selected based on

Awards are arranged alphabetically below their administering organizations

academic standing and financial need.

Duration: Annual. **To Apply:** Applicants who apply for financial aid to attend MBL courses are automatically considered; see the requirements for Embryology Summer Course program.

7043 ■ Frank Morrell Endowed Memorial Scholarship *(Graduate, Master's, Doctorate/Scholarship)*

Purpose: To provide financial support for students attending a neurobiology course. **Focus:** Biology, Marine. **Qualif.:** Applicants must demonstrate the need for financial aid to attend MBL courses; will be considered for all sources of financial assistance; fund supports students in the Neurobiology course. **Criteria:** Selection will be selected based on academic standing and financial need.

Duration: Annual. **To Apply:** Applicants who apply for financial aid to attend MBL courses are automatically considered.

7044 ■ Frank R. Lillie Fellowship and Scholarship *(Undergraduate, Graduate/Scholarship)*

Purpose: To support students in their courses and for research fellows working independently in laboratories. **Focus:** Biology. **Qualif.:** Applicants must be financial aid to attend MBL courses are considered for ALL sources of financial assistance; must fund provides support for students in the courses and for research fellows working independently in laboratories. **Criteria:** Selection will be selected based on academic standing and financial need.

Duration: Annual. **To Apply:** Applicants who apply for financial aid to attend MBL courses are automatically considered.

7045 ■ Herbert W. Rand Fellowship and Scholarship *(Undergraduate, Graduate/Scholarship)*

Purpose: To provide financial support for students in their courses and for research fellows working independently in laboratories. **Focus:** Biology, Marine. **Qualif.:** Applicants must demonstrate the need for financial aid to attend MBL courses; will be considered for all sources of financial assistance; fund supports students in the courses and for research fellows working independently in laboratories. **Criteria:** Selection will be selected based on academic standing and financial need.

Duration: Annual. **To Apply:** Applicants who apply for financial aid to attend MBL courses are automatically considered; see the requirements for Embryology Summer Course program.

7046 ■ Horace W. Stunkard Scholarship *(Undergraduate, Graduate/Scholarship)*

Purpose: To provide financial support for students in any of the Marine Biological Laboratory summer courses. **Focus:** Biology, Marine. **Qualif.:** Applicants must demonstrate the need for financial aid to attend MBL courses; will be considered for all sources of financial assistance; fund supports students in any of the MBL summer courses. **Criteria:** Selection will be selected based on academic standing and financial need.

Duration: Annual. **To Apply:** Applicants who apply for financial aid to attend MBL courses are automatically considered.

7047 ■ John and Elisabeth Buck Endowed Scholarship *(Graduate, Postdoctorate/Scholarship)*

Purpose: To provide financial support for a graduate or postdoctoral student taking a summer course in fundamen-

tal biological science. **Focus:** Biology. **Qualif.:** Applicants must be graduate or postdoctoral students attending a summer course at Marine Biological Laboratory. **Criteria:** Selection will be selected based on academic standing and financial need.

Duration: Annual. **To Apply:** Students who apply for financial aid to attend MBL courses are automatically considered. See the requirements for the Summer Course program.

7048 ■ J.P. and Madeline Trinkaus Endowed Scholarship in Embryology *(Graduate, Doctorate, Master's/Scholarship)*

Purpose: To provide financial support for students studying at the Marine Biological Laboratory in the embryology course. **Focus:** Biology; Life sciences. **Qualif.:** Applicants must demonstrate the need for financial aid to attend MBL courses; will be considered for all sources of financial assistance; fund supports students in the Embryology course. **Criteria:** Selection will be selected based on academic standing and financial need.

Duration: Annual. **To Apply:** Applicants who apply for financial aid to attend MBL courses are automatically considered; see the requirements for Embryology Summer Course program.

7049 ■ Arthur Klorfein Scholarship and Fellowship Fund *(Undergraduate, Graduate/Scholarship)*

Purpose: To provide financial support for students in their courses and for research fellows working independently in laboratories. **Focus:** Biology, Marine. **Qualif.:** Applicants must demonstrate the need for financial aid to attend MBL courses; will be considered for all sources of financial assistance; fund supports students in the courses and for research fellows working independently in laboratories. **Criteria:** Selection will be selected based on academic standing and financial need.

Duration: Annual. **To Apply:** Students who apply for financial aid to attend MBL courses are automatically considered. See the requirements for the Summer Course program.

7050 ■ Lola Ellis Robertson Scholarship *(Graduate, Master's, Doctorate/Scholarship)*

Purpose: To provide financial support for students studying at the Marine Biological Laboratory. **Focus:** Biological and clinical sciences; Life sciences. **Qualif.:** Applicants must demonstrate the need for financial aid to attend MBL courses; will be considered for all sources of financial assistance; fund supports students in any of the MBL summer courses. **Criteria:** Selection will be selected based on academic standing and financial need.

Duration: Annual. **To Apply:** Applicants who apply for financial aid to attend MBL courses are automatically considered; see the requirements for Embryology Summer Course program.

7051 ■ Max M. Burger Endowed Scholarship in Embryology *(Graduate, Master's, Doctorate/Scholarship)*

Purpose: To provide financial support for students attending the Embryology course. **Focus:** Biological and clinical sciences; Life sciences. **Qualif.:** Applicants must demonstrate the need for financial aid to attend MBL courses; will be considered for all sources of financial assistance; fund supports students in the Embryology course. **Criteria:** Se-

Awards are arranged alphabetically below their administering organizations

lection will be selected based on academic standing and financial need.

Duration: Annual. **To Apply:** Students who apply for financial aid to attend MBL courses are automatically considered. See the requirements for Embryology Summer Course program.

7052 ■ MBL Pioneers Fund *(Undergraduate, Graduate/Scholarship)*

Purpose: To provide financial support for students attending a Marine Biological Laboratory. **Focus:** Biology, Marine. **Qualif.:** Applicants must demonstrate the need for financial aid to attend MBL courses; will be considered for all sources of financial assistance; fund supports students in any of the MBL summer courses. **Criteria:** Selection will be selected based on academic standing and financial need.

Duration: Annual. **To Apply:** Applicants must complete the application form. See the requirements for the Summer Course program.

7053 ■ Milton L. Shifman Endowed Scholarship *(Graduate, Undergraduate/Scholarship)*

Purpose: To provide financial support for students to attend Marine Biological Laboratory courses. **Focus:** Biology, Marine. **Qualif.:** Applicants must be students from Dartmouth College or Dartmouth Medical School or students working in a lab of MBL summer investigator. **Criteria:** Selection will be selected based on academic standing and financial need.

Duration: Annual. **To Apply:** Applicants who apply for financial aid to attend MBL courses are automatically considered; see the requirements for Embryology Summer Course program.

7054 ■ Mountain Memorial Fund *(Undergraduate/Award)*

Purpose: To provide financial support for students who are accepted in the physiology course. **Focus:** Physiology.

7055 ■ Pfizer Scholarship Fund *(Undergraduate, Graduate/Scholarship)*

Purpose: To provide financial support to underwrite tuition, room and board expenses for students participating in the MBL's research intensive courses in the life sciences. **Focus:** Biology, Marine. **Qualif.:** Applicants must demonstrate a need for financial aid to attend MBL courses; will be considered for all sources of financial assistance; fund provides support to underwrite tuition, room and board expenses for two students participating in the MBL's research-intensive courses in the life sciences. **Criteria:** Selection will be selected based on academic standing and financial need.

Duration: Annual. **To Apply:** Students who apply for financial aid to attend MBL courses are automatically considered. See the requirements for the Summer Course program.

7056 ■ Ruth Sager Scholarship *(Undergraduate, Graduate/Scholarship)*

Purpose: To provide financial support for women students studying in any of the MBL summer courses. **Focus:** Biology, Marine. **Qualif.:** Applicants must demonstrate the need for financial aid to attend MBL courses; will be considered for all sources of financial assistance; fund supports students in any of the MBL summer courses. **Criteria:**

Selection will be selected based on academic standing and financial need.

Duration: Annual. **To Apply:** Applicants must complete the application form. See the requirements for the Summer Course program.

7057 ■ S. O. Mast Founders' Scholarship *(Undergraduate/Scholarship)*

Purpose: To support students attending a Marine Biological Laboratory Summer Courses. **Focus:** Biology, Marine. **Qualif.:** Applicants must demonstrate financial need to attend MBL courses; they will be considered for all sources of financial assistance; fund supports students in any of the MBL summer courses.

7058 ■ Selman A. Waksman Endowed Scholarship in Microbial Diversity *(Graduate, Master's, Doctorate/Scholarship)*

Purpose: To provide financial support for students participating in the microbial diversity course. **Focus:** Life sciences; Microbiology. **Qualif.:** Applicants must demonstrate the need for financial aid to attend MBL courses; will be considered for all sources of financial assistance; fund supports students participating in the Microbial Diversity course. **Criteria:** Selection will be selected based on academic standing and financial need.

Duration: Annual. **To Apply:** Students who apply for financial aid to attend MBL courses are automatically considered. See the requirements for Microbial Diversity Summer Course program.

7059 ■ Thomas B. Grave and Elizabeth F. Grave Scholarship *(Undergraduate, Graduate/Scholarship)*

Purpose: To provide financial support for students studying in any Marine Biological Laboratory summer courses. **Focus:** Biology, Marine. **Qualif.:** Applicants must demonstrate the need for financial aid to attend MBL courses; will be considered for all sources of financial assistance; fund supports students in any of the MBL summer courses. **Criteria:** Selection will be selected based on academic standing and financial need.

Duration: Annual. **To Apply:** Students who apply for financial aid to attend MBL courses are automatically considered. See the requirements for the Summer Course program.

7060 ■ William Randolph Hearst Educational Endowment *(Undergraduate, Graduate/Scholarship)*

Purpose: To provide financial support for students studying in any Marine Biological Laboratory summer courses. **Focus:** Biology, Marine. **Qualif.:** Applicants must demonstrate the need for financial aid to attend MBL courses; will be considered for all sources of financial assistance; fund supports students in any of the MBL summer courses. **Criteria:** Selection will be selected based on academic standing and financial need.

Duration: Annual. **To Apply:** Students who apply for financial aid to attend MBL courses are automatically considered. See the requirements for the Summer Course program.

7061 ■ Marine Corps Engineer Association (MCEA)

6998 Hwy-64E
Wartrace, TN 37183

Awards are arranged alphabetically below their administering organizations

Ph: (512)394-9333
E-mail: treasurer@marcorengasn.org
URL: www.marcorengasn.org

7062 ■ MCEA Financial Assistance Award
(Undergraduate/Scholarship)

Purpose: To provide financial assistance for the education of the members of the United States Marine Corp's engineer and explosive ordinance disposal communities and their families or for members of the United States Armed Forces who have served with or been attached to Marine Corps Air Ground Task Force engineer or EOD units. **Focus:** Engineering. **Qualif.:** Applicants must be citizens of the United States seeking for financial assistance to further education beyond high school at an accredited college, university or higher technical trade school up to a maximum of four years; they can also be individuals who are already enrolled in a post-secondary curriculum; neither graduate study request nor applications at the high school or prep school level are acceptable. **Criteria:** Selection will be evaluated by the Scholarship Selection Committee.

Funds Avail.: No specific amount. **To Apply:** Applicants must complete and submit the application form and enclose all items requested in the application; name and address; and have the application and attachment notarized. **Remarks:** Established in 2006. **Contact:** Chairman, MCEA Assistance Fund, 269 Creedmoor Rd., Jacksonville, NC 28546.

7063 ■ Marine Corps League Foundation
PO Box 3070
Merrifield, VA 22116-3070
Ph: (828)342-2024
E-mail: president@mclfoundation.org
URL: www.mclfoundation.org
Social Media: www.facebook.com/
  MarineCorpsLeagueFoundation

7064 ■ Marine Corps League National Scholarship
(Undergraduate/Scholarship)

Purpose: To grant scholarship to qualified applicants pursuing full-time undergraduate or technical training at a recognized institution. **Focus:** General studies/Field of study not specified. **Criteria:** Selection will based on the Marine Corps League Scholarship Committee's criteria.

Funds Avail.: No specific amount. **Duration:** Annual. **Contact:** Jerry Holt, Chairman, Scholarship Committee; Email: jerryholt813@gmail.com; Phone: 973-897-9251.

7065 ■ Marine Corps Scholarship Foundation
909 N Washington St., Ste. 400
Alexandria, VA 22314
Free: 866-496-5462
URL: www.mcsf.org
Social Media: linkedin.com/company/marine-corps
  -scholarship-foundation
youtube.com/user/mcsf1962

7066 ■ Marine Corp Scholarship Foundation
Scholarship *(Vocational/Occupational, Community College, Undergraduate/Scholarship)*

Purpose: To honor Marines by educating their children. **Focus:** General studies/Field of study not specified. **Qua-**

lif.: Applicant must be a child of one of the following: active duty or reserve U.S. Marine; veteran U.S. Marine who has received an honorable discharge, or was killed while serving in the U.S. Marine Corps; active duty or reserve U.S. Navy Corpsman who is serving, or has served, with a U.S. Marine unit; veteran U.S. Navy Corpsman who served with a U.S. Marine unit and has received an honorable discharge, or was killed while serving in the U.S. Navy as a Corpsman attached to a Marine unit. Applicant must maintain a minimum 2.0 GPA; must meet financial requirements; must attend or plan to attend a college or career-training school listed in the National Education Statistic's College Navigator website in the upcoming academic year. **Criteria:** All applicants who qualify and submit an application will be awarded a scholarship.

Funds Avail.: Varies from $1,500-$10,000. **To Apply:** Applicant should submit to online. **Deadline:** March 3.

7067 ■ Marine Technology Society (MTS)
1100 H St. NW, Ste. LL-100.
Washington, DC 20005
Ph: (202)717-8705
Fax: (202)347-4302
E-mail: membership@mtsociety.org
URL: www.mtsociety.org
Social Media: www.facebook.com/Marine-Technology
  -Society-1458821247682406
www.linkedin.com/groups/1859481
twitter.com/MTSociety

7068 ■ Charles H. Bussmann Graduate Scholarship
(Graduate, Undergraduate/Scholarship)

Purpose: To provide scholarships to students focused on studying marine technology, marine engineering and marine science. **Focus:** Biology, Marine; Engineering, Marine. **Qualif.:** Applicants must be MTS members who are either high school seniors or full-time college students currently enrolled or have been accepted in a 2-year or 4-year academic program; college undergraduate students currently enrolled full time in a marine-related field. **Criteria:** Selection will be based on the committee's criteria.

Funds Avail.: $2,500. **Duration:** Annual. **To Apply:** Applicants must complete and submit the following requirements; one letter of recommendation from a teacher, counselor or professor in a marine-related field that they have studied with or received advice from within the past two years; for high school seniors, the recommendation must be from a current science teacher or counselor in any field; the letter must be on official letterhead, no colored paper, dated, no more than one page, and state that it is a letter of recommendation, signed and addressed to the scholarship committee; one reference letter from someone they know who is not a teacher or counselor or advisor; this letter is to show the qualities, characteristics and capabilities of the person applying for the scholarship; the letter must be dated, not more than one page, no colored paper, and state that it is a letter of reference, signed and addressed to the scholarship committee. **Deadline:** April 18. **Contact:** Marine Technology Society Scholarships, 1100 H St. NW, Ste. LL-100, Washington, DC, 20005; Email: scholarships@mtsociety.org.

7069 ■ Marine Technology Society ROV Scholarship
(MTS ROV) *(Undergraduate, Graduate/Scholarship)*

Purpose: To provide scholarships to students focused on studying marine technology, marine engineering or marine

Awards are arranged alphabetically below their administering organizations

science. **Focus:** Biology, Marine; Engineering, Marine. **Qualif.:** Applicants must be MTS student members who are interested in remotely operated vehicles (ROVs) or underwater work that furthers the use of ROVs; must be graduate, undergraduate or high school students. **Criteria:** Recipients will be selected based on academic standing.

Funds Avail.: Up to $8,000. **Duration:** Annual. **Number Awarded:** Varies. **To Apply:** Applicants must submit a written recommendation from a current teacher or counselor in a marine-related field; a written letter of reference from someone who is not a teacher or counselor; an official sealed transcript; For high school seniors, proof of acceptance to a two-year or four-year academic program must be submitted; must submit a biographical sketch including academic, personal and professional goals; and a one-page essay about interest in ROVs or underwater work that furthers the use of Rovs. **Deadline:** April 18. **Contact:** E-mail: rovscholarships@mtsociety.org.

7070 ■ The MTS Student Scholarship for Graduate Students *(Graduate/Scholarship)*

Purpose: To provide scholarships to students focused on studying marine technology, marine engineering or marine science. **Focus:** Biology, Marine. **Qualif.:** Applicants must be MTS members who are currently enrolled in or have been accepted to graduate school in a marine-related field. **Criteria:** Recipients will be selected based on academic standing.

Funds Avail.: $2,000. **Duration:** Annual. **Number Awarded:** Varies. **To Apply:** Applicants must apply online, then print and mail or email the application; submit also the other required documents prescribed by the organization; One Reference Form; One Recommendation Form; transcripts. **Deadline:** April 18. **Contact:** Marine Technology Society Scholarships, 1100 H St. NW, Ste. LL-100, Washington, DC 20005; E-mail: scholarships@mtsociety.org.

7071 ■ The MTS Student Scholarship for Graduating High School Seniors *(Undergraduate/Scholarship)*

Purpose: To provide scholarships to students focused on studying marine technology, marine engineering or marine science. **Focus:** Biology, Marine. **Qualif.:** Applicants must be MTS members and high school seniors who have been accepted into a full-time undergraduate program. **Criteria:** Recipients will be selected based on academic standing.

Funds Avail.: $2,000. **Duration:** Annual. **Number Awarded:** Varies. **To Apply:** Applicants must apply online, then print and mail or email the application; submit also the other required documents prescribed by the organization; One Reference Form; One Recommendation Form; transcripts. **Deadline:** April 18. **Contact:** Marine Technology Society Scholarships, 1100 H St. NW, Ste. LL-100, Washington, DC 20005; Phone: 202-717-8705; E-mail: scholarships@mtsociety.org.

7072 ■ The MTS Student Scholarship for Two-Year, Technical, Engineering and Community College Students *(Undergraduate/Scholarship)*

Purpose: To provide scholarships to students focused on studying marine technology marine engineering or marine science. **Focus:** Biology, Marine; Engineering, Marine. **Qualif.:** Applicants must be MTS members who are enrolled in a two-year technical, engineering or community college in a marine-related field. **Criteria:** Recipients will be selected based on academic standing.

Funds Avail.: $3,000. **Duration:** Annual. **Number Awarded:** Varies. **To Apply:** Applicants must apply online,

then print and mail or email the application; submit also the other required documents prescribed by the organization; One Reference Form; One Recommendation Form; transcripts. **Deadline:** April 18. **Contact:** Marine Technology Society Scholarships, 1100 H St. NW, Ste. LL-100, Washington, DC 20005; Phone: 202-717-8705; E-mail: scholarships@mtsociety.org.

7073 ■ The Paros-Digiquartz Scholarship *(Graduate, Undergraduate/Scholarship)*

Purpose: To provide scholarships to students focused on studying marine technology, marine engineering or marine science. **Focus:** Biology, Marine. **Qualif.:** Applicants must be MTS members; high school seniors who have been accepted into a full-time undergraduate program, or graduate studies; must have interests in marine instrumentation. **Criteria:** Selection will be selected based on academic standing.

Funds Avail.: $2,000. **Duration:** Annual. **Number Awarded:** Varies. **To Apply:** Applicants must apply online, then print and mail or email the application; submit also the other required documents prescribed by the organization; One Reference Form; One Recommendation Form; transcripts. **Deadline:** April 18. **Contact:** Marine Technology Society Scholarships, 1100 H St. NW, Ste. LL-100, Washington, DC 20005; Phone: 202-717-8705; E-mail: scholarships@mtsociety.org.

7074 ■ Marines Memorial Association
Marines Memorial Club & Hotel
609 Sutter St.
San Francisco, CA 94102
Ph: (415)673-6672
Fax: (415)441-3649
Free: 800-562-7463
URL: www.marineclub.com
Social Media: www.facebook.com/MarinesMemorial
www.instagram.com/marinesmemorial
www.pinterest.com/marinesmemorial

7075 ■ Bechtel Engineering and Science Scholarship *(Undergraduate/Scholarship)*

Purpose: To provide support to students pursuing their educational goals. **Focus:** Engineering; Science. **Qualif.:** Applicants must be members, dependents, or grandchildren of members; must have plans to attend an engineering program accredited by the Engineering Accreditation Commission of the Accreditation Board for Engineering and Technology (ABET-EAC); and must be full-time high school students who are attending a qualified institution of higher education.

Funds Avail.: $5,000. **Duration:** Annual. **Number Awarded:** 5. **To Apply:** Applicants must complete an application form; a copy of most recent transcript; typewritten (250 words) essay; and three letters of reference; high school senior applicants are required to submit a copy of SAT and/or ACT scores. **Deadline:** April. **Contact:** 609 Sutter St., CA, 94102; Phone: 415-673-6672 ext. 293; Email: scholarship@marineclub.com.

7076 ■ Marion Community Foundation
504 S State St.
Marion, OH 43302
Ph: (740)387-9704

Awards are arranged alphabetically below their administering organizations

E-mail: info@marioncommunityfoundation.org
URL: www.marioncommunityfoundation.org

7077 ■ Alex Family Scholarship *(Undergraduate/ Scholarship)*

Purpose: To help students further their education and career goals. **Focus:** General studies/Field of study not specified. **Qualif.:** Applicants must be seniors at the Harding High School who attended the high school all four years; must be in the upper 25th percentile of HS class. **Criteria:** Special consideration will be given to those who demonstrated excellence in the study of history or who will be pursuing a college major in history.

Funds Avail.: No specific amount. **Duration:** Annual. **To Apply:** Application details available by contacting sponsoring organization. **Deadline:** February 28.

7078 ■ A. B. and Hazel Augenstein Scholarship *(Undergraduate/Scholarship)*

Purpose: To help students further their education and career goals. **Focus:** General studies/Field of study not specified. **Qualif.:** Applicants must be senior students from the River Valley High School who attended the high school all four years; must be in the upper 25th percentile of class, but not in the upper class 10th percentile. **Criteria:** Priority will be given to those who best meet the criteria.

Funds Avail.: No specific amount. **Duration:** Annual. **To Apply:** Application details available by contacting sponsoring organization. **Deadline:** February 28. **Remarks:** Established in 1988.

7079 ■ Irene Ballinger Memorial Scholarship *(Undergraduate/Scholarship)*

Purpose: To help students pursue post-secondary studies, especially in health care or elementary education. **Focus:** General studies/Field of study not specified. **Qualif.:** Applicants must be graduates of or graduating seniors from Elgin High School and must have attended Elgin High School for at least 2 years; must have a minimum 2.9 GPA (high school or college). **Criteria:** Special consideration will be given to those pursuing careers in health care or elementary education, and to previous recipients. Class ranking, GPA, financial need, and relative difficulty of courses will also be considered.

Duration: Annual. **To Apply:** Application details available by contacting sponsoring organization. **Deadline:** May 28.

7080 ■ Bergmann Family Scholarship *(Undergraduate/Scholarship)*

Purpose: To help students further their education and career goals. **Focus:** General studies/Field of study not specified. **Qualif.:** Applicants must be graduating high school seniors or graduates of Marion Community High School who attended the high school all four years; must be in the 25th percentile of HS class; must have a minimum 3.0 GPA. **Criteria:** Preference given to those studying engineering or computer science.

Funds Avail.: No specific amount. **Duration:** Annual. **To Apply:** Application details available by contacting sponsoring organization. **Deadline:** February 28.

7081 ■ Helen & Bob Bintz Scholarship *(Undergraduate/Scholarship)*

Purpose: To help students further their education and career goals. **Focus:** General studies/Field of study not specified. **Qualif.:** Applicants must be Marion County residents for 18 months prior to application; must be registered to attend the University of Dayton or a Catholic university; must be in the upper 25th percentile of ACT/SAT and high school class; must have a minimum 3.0 college GPA.

Funds Avail.: No specific amount. **Duration:** Annual. **To Apply:** Application details available by contacting sponsoring organization. **Deadline:** February 28.

7082 ■ Catherine Amelia Thew Brown Memorial Scholarship *(Undergraduate/Scholarship)*

Purpose: To help students further their education and career goals. **Focus:** General studies/Field of study not specified. **Qualif.:** Applicants must be high school seniors or graduates of Marion County High School who attended the high school all four years; must be in the 25th percentile of high school class.

Funds Avail.: No specific amount. **To Apply:** Application details available by contacting sponsoring organization. **Deadline:** February 28.

7083 ■ William & Martha Buckingham Scholarship *(Undergraduate/Scholarship)*

Purpose: To help students pursue undergraduate degrees. **Focus:** General studies/Field of study not specified. **Qualif.:** Applicants must be graduating seniors or previous graduates of Harding High School; must have a minimum 2.5 high school or college GPA; must not be a relative of William or Martha Buckingham. **Criteria:** Special consideration for the following factors: attend Ohio State University, especially Marion campus; participate in Harding High School varsity sports for at least one season; previous recipients of this scholarship (for 2nd, 3rd, or 4th year students); financial need; held full-time or part-time job during high school.

Duration: Annual. **To Apply:** Application details available by contacting sponsoring organization. **Deadline:** February 28.

7084 ■ Stephen J. Byrnes & Mary "Sally" Byrnes Scholarship *(Undergraduate, Two Year College, Four Year College/Scholarship)*

Purpose: To help students pursue degrees in nursing. **Focus:** Nursing. **Qualif.:** Applicants must be graduating seniors or previous graduates of Marion County High School; must have either a 3.0 GPA for college, or be in the upper 25th percentile of class for high school; must be attending or enrolled in a two or four-year nursing program or bachelor's program in nursing; must not be a relative of Mary M. Byrnes.

Duration: Annual. **To Apply:** Application details available by contacting sponsoring organization. **Deadline:** February 28.

7085 ■ Caledonia Alumni Association Scholarship *(Graduate/Scholarship)*

Purpose: To help students further their education and career goals. **Focus:** General studies/Field of study not specified. **Qualif.:** Applicants must be high school seniors or graduates of River Valley High School; must have a minimum 2.5 high school or college GPA. **Criteria:** Preference will be given to applicants whose parents or grandparents attended Caledonia school.

Funds Avail.: No specific amount. **To Apply:** Application details available by contacting sponsoring organization. **Deadline:** February 28.

Awards are arranged alphabetically below their administering organizations

7086 ■ Carey Family Scholarship *(Undergraduate/ Scholarship)*

Purpose: To help students pursue degrees in agriculture, business, and education. **Focus:** Agricultural sciences; Business; Education. **Qualif.:** Applicants must be graduating seniors or previous graduates of Marion County High School, or have at least two years of residency in Marion County and be a senior or candidate for graduation/ completion from a home school, eSchool, digital/online school, virtual academy, community school, or other state-recognized non public school; must have a minimum 2.5 GPA (high school or college); must intend to major in agriculture, business, or education; must not be a relative of Max G. and Luanne Carey.

Duration: Annual. **To Apply:** Application details available by contacting sponsoring organization. **Deadline:** February 28.

7087 ■ Joe & Peggy Casey Memorial Scholarship *(Undergraduate/Scholarship)*

Purpose: To help students from Marion County High School pursue post-secondary education. **Focus:** General studies/Field of study not specified. **Qualif.:** Applicants must be high school seniors graduating from Marion County High School who have attended the high school all four years; must have participated in high school golf for at least one year; must be in the upper 25th percentile of class; must not be related to Joseph H. Casey, Margaret H. (Peggy) Casey, or Joseph H. Casey, Jr.

Duration: Annual. **To Apply:** Application details available by contacting sponsoring organization. **Deadline:** February 28.

7088 ■ Collier Scholarship *(Undergraduate, College, University/Scholarship)*

Purpose: To help students pay for college. **Focus:** General studies/Field of study not specified. **Qualif.:** Applicants must be graduating high school seniors or previous graduates from one of these high schools: Buckeye Central, Bucyrus, Colonel Crawford, Wynford, or Bellevue Senior; if high school senior must be in top 25th percentile but not top 5th percentile of class, if college must have a minimum 2.5 GPA; must not be a relative of Dr. Wayne Collier. **Criteria:** Special consideration will be given to those who participated in music (band, orchestra, choir) throughout high school or college.

Duration: Annual. **Number Awarded:** Up to 6. **To Apply:** Applicants must submit a letter of recommendation from a Crawford, Erie, Huron, or Sandusky County teacher or community member. Application details available by contacting the sponsoring organization. **Deadline:** February 28.

7089 ■ Community's Memorial Scholarship *(Undergraduate, College, University/Scholarship)*

Purpose: To help graduates of Marion County High School pursue college degrees. **Focus:** General studies/Field of study not specified. **Qualif.:** Applicants must be graduating seniors or previous graduates of Marion County High School who attended the school all four years; must be in the upper 50th percentile of class; must not be a relative of Mary H. Hollaway or Ronald D. Cramer.

Duration: Annual. **To Apply:** Application details available by contacting the sponsoring organization. **Deadline:** February 28.

7090 ■ Bill & Joan Cones Scholarship *(Undergraduate, College, University/Scholarship)*

Purpose: To help students from River Valley High School pursue college degrees, especially in the field of education.

Focus: Education; General studies/Field of study not specified. **Qualif.:** Applicants must be graduating high school seniors or previous graduates who attended River Valley High School for a minimum of two years; must have a minimum 2.5 GPA (high school or college); must not be a relative of Robert Cones or Douglas Cones. **Criteria:** Special consideration will be given to applicants pursuing degrees in the field of education.

Duration: Annual. **To Apply:** Application details available by contacting the sponsoring organization. **Deadline:** February 28.

7091 ■ Clare Cooke Performing Arts Scholarship *(Undergraduate, College, University/Scholarship)*

Purpose: To help students from Marion County High School pursue post-secondary education in performing arts. **Focus:** Performing arts. **Qualif.:** Applicants must be graduating high school seniors or previous graduates of Marion County High School who attended the school all four years; must be in the upper 50th percentile of class for high school, or have a minimum 2.5 GPA for college; must be intending to major in performing arts; must not be a relative of Clare Cooke.

Duration: Annual. **To Apply:** Application details available by contacting the sponsoring organization. **Deadline:** February 28.

7092 ■ Alex Cooper Memorial Scholarship *(Undergraduate, College, University/Scholarship)*

Purpose: To help students pursue post-secondary education. **Focus:** General studies/Field of study not specified. **Qualif.:** Applicants must be graduating seniors or previous graduates of River Valley High School, including those who attended Tri-Rivers Career Center; applicants may also be seniors and candidates for graduation/completion from a home school, eSchool, digital/online school, virtual academy, community school, or other state-recognized charter non-public school provided applicants are River Valley School District residents at time of application; must have a minimum 2.5 GPA (high school or college); must not be a relative of Jonathan Culler or Andrea Ault. **Criteria:** Special consideration will be given to applicants for the following: active in River Valley athletics (football or baseball) or River Valley music (band or orchestra); personally diagnosed with cancer or immediate family member with cancer; financial need affected by treatment of cancer.

Duration: Annual. **To Apply:** Application details available by contacting the sponsoring organization. **Deadline:** February 28.

7093 ■ Cornell/Goodman Scholarship *(Undergraduate, College, University, Vocational/Occupational/ Scholarship)*

Purpose: To help students from Marion County pursue college or trade school educations. **Focus:** Business; General studies/Field of study not specified. **Qualif.:** Applicants must be residents of Marion County and graduating high school seniors or previous graduates of Marion County High School who attended the high school for a minimum of two years; must be attending or planning to attend college or trade school; must be in the upper 25th percentile of ACT/SAT or upper 25th percentile of class for high school, or a minimum 3.0 GPA for college; must not be a relative of Adam or Gina Goodman. **Criteria:** Special consideration will be given to applicants for the following: Harding senior or graduate; pursuing a business-oriented field of study (accounting, economics, finance, marketing)

Awards are arranged alphabetically below their administering organizations

with a demonstrated interest in business.
Duration: Annual. **To Apply:** Application details available by contacting the sponsoring organization. **Deadline:** February 28.

7094 ■ Craig Scholarship *(Undergraduate, College, University/Scholarship)*

Purpose: To help students from Ridgedale High School pursue post-secondary education, especially in the fields of science, medicine, health, engineering, or education. **Focus:** General studies/Field of study not specified. **Qualif.:** Applicants must be graduating seniors from Ridgedale High School; must have a minimum 3.25 GPA; must not be a relative of Diane Craig. **Criteria:** Special consideration will be given to applicants for the following: demonstrated commitment to their education; intended major of sciences, medicine, health, engineering, or education; good character, service, citizenship; attended Ridgedale all four years.

Duration: Annual. **To Apply:** Application details available by contacting the sponsoring organization. **Deadline:** February. 28.

7095 ■ Stormy Ray Cushing Scholarship *(Undergraduate, College, University/Scholarship)*

Purpose: To help students from Marion County pursue post-secondary education. **Focus:** General studies/Field of study not specified. **Qualif.:** Applicants must be graduating seniors or previous graduates of Marion County High School and a resident of Marion County for a minimum of two years during high school; if in college must have a minimum 2.5 GPA; must not be a relative of Stormy Ray, Robert R., Marsha, or Misty Cushing, or Amanda Burns.

Duration: Annual. **To Apply:** Application details available by contacting the sponsoring organization. **Deadline:** February 28.

7096 ■ Marge Sorreles Davies Memorial Scholarship *(Undergraduate, College, University/Scholarship)*

Purpose: To help Marion County students pursue nursing degrees. **Focus:** Nursing. **Qualif.:** Applicants must be graduating high school seniors or previous graduates of Marion County High School and must have attended one of these schools for all four years; must be in upper 25th percentile of their class for high school, or minimum 3.0 GPA for college; must intend to major in nursing; must not be a relative of Marge Sorreles Davies or Bobb L. Davies. **Criteria:** Special consideration will be given to those who graduated from Elgin High School and past recipients.

Duration: Annual. **To Apply:** Application details available by contacting the sponsoring organization. **Deadline:** February 28.

7097 ■ Dr. Kathy Dixon Memorial Scholarship *(Undergraduate, University, College/Scholarship)*

Purpose: To help students in pursue college degrees, especially in the fields of science and health care. **Focus:** General studies/Field of study not specified; Health care services; Science. **Qualif.:** Applicants must be graduating seniors or previous graduates who attended high school in any of the following counties: Marion, Hardin, Wyandot, Crawford, Morrow, Deleware, or Union; must have been a resident of one of these counties throughout high school years; must be attending Ohio State University or Marion Technical College; must have a 3.0 GPA (high school or college); must not be a relative of Mark E. Davis. **Criteria:** Special consideration will be given to applicants in their

2nd, 3rd, or 4th years of college and majoring in science or health care.
Duration: Annual. **To Apply:** Application details available by contacting the sponsoring organization. **Deadline:** February 28.

7098 ■ Brenda Dye Music Boosters Scholarship *(Undergraduate, University, College/Scholarship)*

Purpose: To help students pursue post-secondary education. **Focus:** General studies/Field of study not specified. **Qualif.:** Applicants must be high school seniors from River Valley High School; must be members of River Valley music program for one or more years in grades 9-12; must not be a relative of River Valley Education Foundation members.

Duration: Annual. **To Apply:** Application details available by contacting the sponsoring organization. **Deadline:** February 28.

7099 ■ Elgin Alumni Association Scholarship *(Undergraduate, University, College/Scholarship)*

Purpose: To help students from Elgin High School pursue college degrees. **Focus:** General studies/Field of study not specified. **Qualif.:** Applicants must be graduating high school seniors or previous graduates of Elgin High School; must have a minimum 3.0 GPA; high school applicants must have participated in at least one school-sanctioned extracurricular activity during previous 12 months.

Duration: Annual. **To Apply:** Application details available by contacting the sponsoring organization. **Deadline:** February 28.

7100 ■ Helen E. Evans Scholarship *(Undergraduate, College, University/Scholarship)*

Purpose: To assist Elgin High School students in pursuing post-secondary education. **Focus:** Education. **Qualif.:** Applicants must be high school seniors at Harding High School; must be in the 50th percentile of class and intend to major in education; must not be a relative of Lydia Roebuck.

Duration: Annual. **To Apply:** Application details available by contacting the sponsoring organization. **Deadline:** February 28.

7101 ■ Everett Family Scholarship *(Undergraduate, College, University/Scholarship)*

Purpose: To help students from Elgin High School pursue college degrees in agriculture. **Focus:** Agricultural sciences. **Qualif.:** Applicants must be graduating seniors from Elgin High School who attended the school all four years; must be in the upper 50th percentile of class and intend to major in agriculture; must not be a relative of Robert E. Everett, Gertrude E. Everett, Nancy Everett Hafer, or Beverly Everett Roby.

Duration: Annual. **To Apply:** Application details available by contacting the sponsoring organization. **Deadline:** February 28.

7102 ■ Marketing EDGE
500 Seventh Ave., 8th Fl.
New York, NY 10018
Ph: (212)790-1512
E-mail: admin@marketingedge.org
URL: marketingedge.org
Social Media: www.facebook.com/marketingedgeorg
twitter.com/mktgEDGEorg

Awards are arranged alphabetically below their administering organizations

7103 ■ Mike Buoncristiano Memorial Scholarship Fund (Undergraduate/Scholarship)

Purpose: To support students further their education in the field of direct and interactive marketing. **Focus:** Marketing and distribution. **Qualif.:** Applicants must be U.S. citizens or permanent residents; must be enrolled in an accredited four-year undergraduate institution; must have a minimum GPA of 3.0 on a 4.0 scale in major and have 3.0 overall; must show a commitment to pursue a career in direct/interactive marketing. **Criteria:** Selection is based on evaluation of submitted documents and specific criteria.

Funds Avail.: No specific amount. **Duration:** Annual. **To Apply:** Applicants must submit a completed application form; official transcripts and resume.

7104 ■ Mark Duda Scholarship Fund (Graduate, Undergraduate/Scholarship)

Purpose: To provide financial support to the students who are studying data and targeting strategies in direct and interactive marketing. **Focus:** Marketing and distribution. **Qualif.:** Applicants must be U.S. citizens or permanent residents; must be enrolled in an accredited four-year undergraduate institution or be graduate students; must have a minimum GPA of 3.0 on a 4.0 scale in major and have 3.0 overall; must show a commitment to pursue a career in direct/interactive marketing. **Criteria:** Selection is based on evaluation of submitted documents and specific criteria.

Funds Avail.: No specific amount. **Duration:** Annual. **To Apply:** Applicants should submit a completed application form, official transcripts and resume. **Remarks:** Established in 2011.

7105 ■ Dave Florence Scholarship Fund (Undergraduate/Scholarship)

Purpose: To support students further their education in the field of direct and interactive marketing. **Focus:** Marketing and distribution. **Qualif.:** Applicants must be U.S. citizens or permanent residents; must be enrolled in an accredited four-year undergraduate institution; must have a minimum GPA of 3.0 on a 4.0 scale in major and have 3.0 overall; must show a commitment to pursue a career in direct/interactive marketing. **Criteria:** Selection is based on evaluation of submitted documents and specific criteria.

Funds Avail.: No specific amount. **Duration:** Annual. **To Apply:** Applicants must submit a completed application form, official transcripts and resume. **Remarks:** Established in 1967.

7106 ■ Don Kuhn Memorial Scholarship Fund (Graduate/Scholarship)

Purpose: To provide financial support to those students who have demonstrated commitment to pursue a career in non-profit direct/interactive marketing. **Focus:** Marketing and distribution. **Qualif.:** Applicant must have participated in at least one Marketing EDGE program; must maintain a minimum overall GPA of 3.0 or higher; must have a related major and demonstrate an interest in marketing.

Funds Avail.: No specific amount. **Duration:** Annual. **Remarks:** The Scholarship was established in honor of the late, direct-response fundraising pioneer, Don Kuhn, to commemorate his contributions to the practice of charitable fundraising. Established in 2006.

7107 ■ Lee Epstein Fund Scholarship (Graduate, Undergraduate/Scholarship)

Purpose: To provide support to students in the field of direct and interactive marketing. **Focus:** Marketing and distribution. **Qualif.:** Applicants must participated in at least one Marketing EDGE program; Maintain a minimum overall GPA of 3.0 or higher; Demonstrate an interest in marketing; have a related major (marketing, advertising, analytics, business, communications, economics, graphic design, psychology, mathematics, sociology). **Criteria:** Selection is based on a combination of academic performance and demonstrated interest in the marketing field.

Funds Avail.: $1,000-$7,000. **Duration:** Annual. **Remarks:** Established in 1980.

7108 ■ Willa Yeck Memorial Scholarship Fund (Undergraduate/Scholarship)

Purpose: To support students further their education in the field of direct and interactive marketing. **Focus:** Marketing and distribution. **Qualif.:** Applicants must be U.S. citizens or permanent residents; must be enrolled in an accredited four-year undergraduate institution; must have a minimum GPA of 3.0 on a 4.0 scale in major and have 3.0 overall; must show a commitment to pursue a career in direct/interactive marketing. **Criteria:** Selection is based on evaluation of submitted documents and specific criteria.

Funds Avail.: No specific amount. **Duration:** Annual. **To Apply:** Applicants must submit a completed application form, official transcripts and resume.

7109 ■ Lorraine Zitone Memorial Scholarship Fund (Undergraduate/Scholarship)

Purpose: To support students further their education in the field of direct and interactive marketing. **Focus:** Marketing and distribution. **Qualif.:** Applicant must have participated in at least one Marketing EDGE program; must maintain a minimum overall GPA of 3.0 or higher; must have a related major and demonstrate an interest in marketing.

Funds Avail.: No specific amount. **Duration:** Annual. **Remarks:** Established in memory of Lorraine Zitone, a 21-year loyal employee of the DMA. Established in 2003.

7110 ■ George C. Marshall Foundation (GCMF)
1600 VMI Parade
Lexington, VA 24450-1600
Ph: (540)463-7103
Fax: (540)464-5229
E-mail: marshallfoundation@marshallfoundation.org
URL: www.marshallfoundation.org
Social Media: www.facebook.com/georgecmarshallmuseum
www.instagram.com/georgecmarshallmuseum/?hl=en
www.linkedin.com/company/george-c-marshall-foundation
www.pinterest.com/georgecmarshall
twitter.com/georgecmarshall
www.youtube.com/channel/UC7pRzBWT9yznrKlGc-GWKqg

7111 ■ Marshall-Baruch Fellowships (Doctorate/Fellowship)

Purpose: To encourage doctoral or postdoctoral research in US military or diplomatic history and related fields. **Focus:** History, Military; United States studies. **Qualif.:** Applicants must be currently enrolled in an accredited academic program leading to a doctoral degree; must be engaged in postdoctoral research; and be independent scholars who already received their PhD. **Criteria:** Selection of applicant will be based on the application and other supporting documents.

Awards are arranged alphabetically below their administering organizations

Funds Avail.: No specific amount. **Number Awarded:** Varies. **To Apply:** Applicants must submit a recommendation letter; application instruction and forms are available at the website.

7112 ■ Marshall Foundation Scholars Program
(Undergraduate/Scholarship)

Purpose: To promote primary research and study as the cornerstone of the library, archives, and educational programs. **Focus:** General studies/Field of study not specified. **Qualif.:** Applicant must be undergraduate students studying history at select institutions. **Criteria:** Selection is based on submission of documents.

Funds Avail.: No specific amount. **To Apply:** Applications can be submitted online. **Deadline:** Spring semester: May 15. **Contact:** Phone: 540-463-7103 ext. 122; Email: mdavis@marshallfoundation.org.

7113 ■ Maryland Association of Certified Public Accountants (MACPA)
901 Dulaney Valley Rd., Ste. 800
Towson, MD 21204
Ph: (410)296-6250
Free: 800-782-2036
E-mail: team@macpa.org
URL: www.macpa.org
Social Media: www.facebook.com/macpa
www.linkedin.com/company/maryland-association-of-cpas
twitter.com/macpa
www.youtube.com/user/macpapro

7114 ■ MACPA Scholarships *(Undergraduate, Graduate/Scholarship)*

Purpose: To provide scholarship money to accounting majors at maryland colleges and universities. **Focus:** Accounting. **Criteria:** Selection will be based on the committee's criteria.

Funds Avail.: No specific amount. **Duration:** Annual. **To Apply:** Applicants are required to submit complete copy of the four-page student aid report (sar) which is generated upon completion of the free application for federal student aid (fafsa); official, sealed transcript from the previous semester which shows cumulative gpa, total credit hours completed and hours completed during the previous semester; a completed application form; signed statement; and, paperworks to be submitted, together with the enumerated application requirements to the contact provided. **Deadline:** May 15. **Contact:** MACPA Educational Foundation, 901 Dulaney Valley Rd, Ste. 800, Towson, MD, 21204.

7115 ■ Maryland Poison Center (MPC)
220 Arch St., Office Level 1
Baltimore, MD 21201
Ph: (410)706-7604
Fax: (410)706-7184
Free: 800-222-1222
E-mail: mpcadmin@rx.umaryland.edu
URL: www.mdpoison.com
Social Media: www.facebook.com/MarylandPoisonCenter
twitter.com/MDPoisonCtr

7116 ■ Maryland Poison Center Clinical Toxicology Fellowship *(Doctorate, Graduate/Fellowship)*

Purpose: To train a Doctor of Pharmacy graduate to function in a professional, administrative and research capacity in a regional poison center, clinical toxicology service and/or academic environment. **Focus:** Pharmacy. **Qualif.:** Applicants must possess a PharmD degree from an accredited School of College of Pharmacy. **Criteria:** Selection is based on the application.

Funds Avail.: No specific amount. **Duration:** Annual. **To Apply:** Applicants should submit application form; official transcripts; letter of intent; letters of recommendation.

7117 ■ Maryland Speech-Language-Hearing Association (MSHA)
PO Box 31
Manchester, MD 21102
Ph: (410)239-7770
E-mail: office@mdslha.org
URL: www.mdslha.org
Social Media: www.facebook.com/mdslha

7118 ■ Maryland Speech Language Hearing Association Graduate Scholarships *(Graduate/Scholarship)*

Purpose: To financially support qualified graduate students who want to pursue their studies in speech language pathology at a university in the state of Maryland. **Focus:** Speech and language pathology/Audiology.

Funds Avail.: $500 to $1,000. **Duration:** Annual. **Remarks:** Established in 2011. **Contact:** Paul Evitts, Ph.D., CCC-SLP, Department of Audiology, Speech-Language Pathology and Deaf Studies, Towson University, 8000 York Rd, Towson, MD, 21252; Email: pevitts@towson.edu.

7119 ■ Jorge Mas Canosa Freedom Foundation
PO Box 141898
Coral Gables, FL 33114-1898
Ph: (305)507-7323
E-mail: jmcff@jmcff.org
URL: jmcff.org
Social Media: www.facebook.com/people/Jmcff-Jmcff/100010056900325
twitter.com/JMCFF1

7120 ■ Mas Family Scholarship *(Graduate, Undergraduate/Scholarship)*

Purpose: To further the education of students with leadership potential. **Focus:** Business; Communications; Economics; Engineering; International affairs and relations; Journalism. **Qualif.:** Applicant must be a Cuban-American undergraduate or graduate student in the field of engineering, business, international relations, economics, communications or journalism who intends to pursue an academic or professional career, and who has demonstrated a leadership potential to excel in these fields; must have a minimum GPA of 3.5 on a 4.0 scale. **Criteria:** Selection is based on an applicant's academic performance, leadership qualities, potential to contribute to the advancement of a free society and likelihood of success in chosen career.

To Apply: Applicants must submit a completed and signed application form (plus two copies) together with an official school transcript; admissions test scores; three evaluation forms; essays (three copies, typed, double-spaced, minimum of 1, 000 words); proof of Cuban descent; proof of admission; tuition cost information; and statement of

Awards are arranged alphabetically below their administering organizations

need. **Deadline:** November 4. **Remarks:** Established in 1996. **Contact:** Jorge Mas Canosa Freedom Foundation P.O. Box 14-1898 Coral Gables, FL 33114-1898 call 305.507.7323.

7121 ■ Massachusetts Association of Land Surveyors and Civil Engineers (MALSCE)
1 Walnut St.
Boston, MA 02108-3616
Ph: (617)227-5551
Fax: (617)227-6783
E-mail: malsce@engineers.org
URL: www.malsce.org

7122 ■ MALSCE Memorial Scholarship
(Undergraduate/Scholarship)

Purpose: To provide educational support to the residents of Massachusetts who are studying surveying, civil engineering or environmental engineering programs. **Focus:** Cartography/Surveying; Engineering, Civil. **Criteria:** Selection of applicants will be based on the scholarship application criteria.

Funds Avail.: $500, $1,000 or $2,000. **Duration:** Annual. **Number Awarded:** Varies. **To Apply:** Applicants must write/call the chairman for an application; must complete the application form available online; must have a letter of recommendation; and must submit a transcript of grades. **Deadline:** October 31. **Contact:** Mary Ann Corcoran, PLS, MALSCE Education Trust Chair, c/o The Engineering Center, One Walnut St., Boston, MA 02108; Phone: 413-841-0355.

7123 ■ Massachusetts Association of Women Lawyers (MAWL)
The College Club Commonwealth
Boston, MA 02116
E-mail: info@mawl.org
URL: maassociationofwomenlawyers.wordpress.com

7124 ■ Carol DiMaiti Scholarship *(Undergraduate/Scholarship)*

Purpose: To award scholarships to law students in Massachusetts. **Focus:** Law. **Qualif.:** Application must be a students entering their second and third year of law school. **Criteria:** Selection is based on financial need and academic achievements.

Funds Avail.: $1,000. **Duration:** Annual. **Number Awarded:** Varies. **To Apply:** Applicants must submit a completed application form and must check the available website for details; Applications should be mailed to Office address. **Deadline:** April. **Remarks:** The scholarship honors the Honorable Sheila B. McGovern and Carol DiMaiti.

7125 ■ Massachusetts Bar Foundation (MBF)
20 West St.
Boston, MA 02111
Ph: (617)338-0500
E-mail: foundation@massbar.org
URL: www.massbarfoundation.org
Social Media: www.facebook.com/MassBarFdn/
www.instagram.com/massbarfdn/

twitter.com/MassBarFdn

7126 ■ Massachusetts Bar Foundation Legal Intern Fellowship Program (LIFP) *(Graduate/Fellowship)*

Purpose: To assist law students in gaining practical experience in the public sector. **Focus:** Law. **Qualif.:** Applicants must have secured a volunteer internship with a qualified nonprofit organization in Massachusetts; currently be enrolled in a United States law school; and must demonstrate a commitment to public interest law, including experience working with low-income clients or issues that affect this population. **Criteria:** Preference will be given to permanent/future residents of Massachusetts

Funds Avail.: $6,000 each. **Duration:** Annual. **Number Awarded:** 3. **To Apply:** Applicants must submit a complete application package which includes: information form, essay, organization supporting statement form, resume, unofficial law student transcript, unofficial undergraduate transcript, and one letter of reference from a supervisor, professor, or similar professional contact. **Deadline:** March 12. **Remarks:** Established in 1996. **Contact:** MBF Legal Intern Fellowship Program, 20 W St., Boston, MA, 02111; Phone: 617-338-0534; Email: foundation@massbar.org.

7127 ■ Massachusetts Chapter of the International Association of Arson Investigators, Inc. (MAIAAI)
PO Box 1874
Lowell, MA 01853
E-mail: secretary.maiaai@gmail.com
URL: maiaai.com
Social Media: www.facebook.com/Massachusetts-Chapter-IAAI-228865470492099

7128 ■ Sgt. Cherven Scholarship *(Undergraduate/Scholarship)*

Purpose: To support the relatives of IAAI Massachusetts Chapter members in their education. **Focus:** General studies/Field of study not specified. **Qualif.:** Applicants must be members, immediate family members or grandchildren of a Massachusetts IAAI Chapter member in good standing, and graduating high school seniors or entering or currently enrolled at a college or university. **Criteria:** Selection will be based on demonstrated commitment to public service or desire to enter public service.

Funds Avail.: $500. **Duration:** Annual. **Number Awarded:** 2. **To Apply:** Applicants must submit the following a completed application form provided at the website, along with the required supporting documents such as essay as to why they believe they should be awarded the scholarship; three recommendation letters from individuals over 21 years old; and an official transcript from their current school. **Deadline:** May 19. **Contact:** MAIAAI, c/o Scholarship Committee, PO Box1874, Lowell, MA, 01853.

7129 ■ Massachusetts Educational Financing Authority (MEFA)
160 Federal St., 4th Fl.
Boston, MA 02110
E-mail: info@mefa.org
URL: www.mefa.org
Social Media: www.facebook.com/mefaMA
www.linkedin.com/company/44754
twitter.com/mefatweets

Awards are arranged alphabetically below their administering organizations

www.youtube.com/user/mefacounselor

7130 ■ MEFA Graduate Loans (Graduate/Loan)

Purpose: To help students pay for graduate school. **Focus:** General studies/Field of study not specified. **Qualif.:** Applicants must be students enrolled at least half-time in an accredited degree-granting graduate program at an eligible nonprofit college or university; primary borrower and/or applicants' co-borrower must live in Massachusetts, or the student must live in Massachusetts or attend a Massachusetts college or university; must maintain satisfactory academic progress as defined by their college or university; must be either US citizens or permanent residents. **Criteria:** Selection will be based on MEFA's current credit approval standards.

Funds Avail.: Minimum of $2,000 for a private school; $1,500 for a public school. **Duration:** Annual. **To Apply:** Applications and required documents can be submitted online. Applicants may apply for a loan for one academic year; if they need a loan for more than one year, they must reapply each year. **Contact:** Creditor, MEFA, 60 State St., Ste. 900, Boston, MA, 02109; Phone: 800-266-0243.

7131 ■ Massachusetts General Hospital - Center for Engineering in Medicine (CEM)

114 16th St., Rm. 1402
Charlestown, MA 02129-4404
Ph: (617)726-3474
Fax: (617)573-9471
E-mail: ireis@sbi.org
URL: www.massgeneral.org
Social Media: facebook.com/massgeneral
instagram.com/massgeneral
youtube.com/user/MassGeneralHospital

7132 ■ Center for Engineering in Medicine Predoctoral Fellows Program (Postdoctorate/Fellowship)

Purpose: To support individuals who wish to devote their careers to developing innovative diagnostic and therapeutic approaches find rich educational opportunities while conducting research at the CEM under the direct supervision of outstanding faculty. **Focus:** Engineering; Medicine. **Qualif.:** Applicants must be pre-doctoral students who want to complete their PhD dissertation at the CEM. **Criteria:** Selection will be based on the committees' criteria.

Funds Avail.: No specific amount. **To Apply:** Applicants may contact the Center for application process and other information.

7133 ■ Massachusetts General Hospital Department of Psychiatry

55 Fruit St.
Boston, MA 02114
Ph: (617)724-5600
URL: www.massgeneral.org
Social Media: facebook.com/massgeneral
instagram.com/massgeneral
youtube.com/user/MassGeneralHospital

7134 ■ Clinical Translational Fellowship at Pfizer (Advanced Professional/Fellowship)

Purpose: To provide a unique opportunity for a board-certified or board-eligible physician-scientist trained in psychiatry to spend working with the Pfizer Neuroscience Research Unit (NSRU) in Cambridge, Massachusetts and performing clinical activities at Massachusetts General Hospital in Boston. **Focus:** Neurology; Neuroscience; Psychiatry. **Qualif.:** Applicants must be physician scientists who are BS/BE Psychiatrists by July 1st of the previous year; must be fellows or junior faculties in Psychiatry; must be able to commit 75% of time to NSRU and 25% of time to MGH; must be demonstrating excellence in the field of neuroscience. **Criteria:** Selection will be based on the applicants' eligibility and submitted applications.

Funds Avail.: $75,000 per year. **Duration:** Annual; Up to 2 years. **Number Awarded:** 1. **To Apply:** Applicants must submit the following: letter of intent (2 pages maximum) describing the relevance of the program to previous experience, research interests, and career goals; current curriculum vitae; letter of support from the local Psychiatry Chair; two additional letters of support; and NIH other support (current and pending grants). **Deadline:** November 1. **Contact:** Carol Quian, Email:bo.qian@mgh.harvard.edu.

7135 ■ Massachusetts General Hospital/Harvard Medical School Internship (Doctorate/Internship)

Purpose: To support matriculated doctoral students enrolled in clinical or counseling psychology programs. **Focus:** Psychology. **Qualif.:** Applicants must have three years of full-time graduate study in a doctoral program (preferably APA -approved programs in Clinical Psychology but will accept applicants from other programs); and must have two years of clinical experience, at least one of which must be supervised practicum experience.

Funds Avail.: $30,000. **Duration:** Annual. **Number Awarded:** 13. **To Apply:** Applicants must submit the required AAPI Online application by midnight on the deadline. Indicate the elective track for which they would like to be considered and preferred interview date according to elective track in the cover letter accompanying their application. **Deadline:** November 1. **Contact:** Sherry Brooks; 15 Parkman St., ACC 812 Boston, MA, 2114; Phone: 617-726-3648; Email: asbrooks@partners.org.

7136 ■ MGH Department of Psychiatry Behavioral Neurology and Neuropsychiatry Fellowship Program (Advanced Professional, Professional development/Fellowship)

Purpose: To help train the next generations of outstanding neuropsychiatrists and behavioral neurologists. **Focus:** Mental health; Neurology; Psychiatry. **Qualif.:** Applicants must be those within the field of behavioral neurology and neuropsychiatry. **Criteria:** Selection will be based on the committee's criteria.

Funds Avail.: No specific amount. **To Apply:** Applicants must include the following requirements in their application: curriculum vitae; personal statement; and, three (3) letters of recommendations. **Contact:** Zeina Chemali, M.D., M.P.H.; Departments of Psychiatry and Neurology; Massachusetts General Hospital; 15 Parkman St., WACC 815, Boston, Massachusetts 02114.

7137 ■ Eating Disorders Summer Research Fellowship (Advanced Professional, Professional development/Fellowship)

Purpose: To stimulate interest in eating disorders research and train young investigators in the field. **Focus:** Psychiatry. **Qualif.:** Applicants must be young investigators in the eating disorder field. **Criteria:** Selection will be based on the

Awards are arranged alphabetically below their administering organizations

candidates' submitted research proposals.

Funds Avail.: No specific amount. **Duration:** Annual. **To Apply:** Applicants must include the following requirements in their application: completed copy of downloaded application form; curriculum vitae; two-page abstract or proposal; and two (2) letters of reference. **Deadline:** January 15. **Remarks:** Established in 1997. **Contact:** Ani Keshishian, Eating Disorders Clinical and Research Program; Massachusetts General Hospital, 2 Longfellow Place, Ste. 200, Boston, MA, 02114; Email: akeshishian@mgh.harvard.edu.

7138 ■ MGH Department of Psychiatry Forensic Psychiatry Fellowship (Professional development/ Fellowship)

Purpose: To develop proficiency in all aspects of forensic psychiatric practice: evaluation, report writing, courtroom testimony and treatment in correctional facilities. **Focus:** Psychiatry. **Qualif.:** Applicants must have completed an ACGME-accredited general psychiatry residency program at the time the fellows begin the program, they must have a Massachusetts medical license. **Criteria:** Selection will be based on the aforesaid qualifications and compliance with the application process.

Funds Avail.: No specific amount. **Duration:** Annual; one year. **To Apply:** Applicants must download and fill out the provided application form; required application materials are application form; curriculum vitae; one-page personal statement; copy of professional licensure; two writing samples; written statement if there are any interruptions in the medical education or training to date (for academic disciplinary reasons, please provide a separate written of explanation); and three letters of reference (one should be from the director of the applicant's psychiatry residence program). The additional two should be from supervisors and attending staff with whom the applicants have worked directly. **Deadline:** April 15. **Contact:** Patricia L. Kneeland Forensic Psychiatry Fellowship Coordinator Law & Psychiatry Service Massachusetts General Hospital 55 Fruit Street, Bulfinch 360 Boston, MA 02114 Phone: 617-724-3119 Email: pkneeland1@mgh.harvard.edu.

7139 ■ MGH Department of Psychiatry Global Psychiatric Clinical Research Training Program (Advanced Professional/Fellowship)

Purpose: To develop independent and productive clinical scientists committed to addressing the rising burden of mental illness, including schizophrenia, in global settings. **Focus:** Biological and clinical sciences; Neurology; Psychiatry. **Qualif.:** Applicants must be outstanding psychiatrists, clinical psychologists, and Ph.D. candidates from an accredited School of Public Health; must have the motivation and potential for an independent research career in academic medicine. **Criteria:** Selection will be based on the applicants' eligibility and submitted applications.

Funds Avail.: No specific amount. **To Apply:** Applicants must submit the following: application form; curriculum vitae; personal statement (2-5 pages) that contains description of the substantive areas of interest, the type of project to undertake, and the particular methods/approaches in which applicants want additional training; copy of passport and/or green card; proof of a full medical license or of completion of Ph.D. in public health or of completion of Ph.D. in psychology and internship (psychology licensure not required); and three letters of reference. Please submit also medical and/or graduate school transcript(s), which should be sent in a sealed envelope, from the university and has/have the official institutional seal. **Contact:** Chester

M. Pierce, MD Division of Global Psychiatry; 151 Merrimac St., 4th Fl., Boston, MA, 02114; For more information Email: MGHGlobalpsychiatry@partners.org.

7140 ■ Partners HealthCare Geriatric Psychiatry Fellowship (Professional development/Fellowship)

Purpose: To fulfill the specialized post-residency training requirement necessary for ABPN certification in the subspecialty of geriatric psychiatry. **Focus:** Gerontology; Psychiatry. **Qualif.:** Applicants must be U.S. Citizens or have a permanent resident visa; Massachusetts medical license required; must have completed approved residency in psychiatry by time of starting fellowship. **Criteria:** Selection will be based on the applicants' eligibility and submitted applications.

Funds Avail.: No specific amount. **Duration:** Annual. **To Apply:** Applicants must download the provided application form and fill out the required fields. Required application materials are application form; curriculum vitae; one-page personal statement; copy of professional licensure; two writing samples; written statement if there are any interruptions in the medical education or training to date (for academic disciplinary reasons, please provide a separate written of explanation); and three letters of reference (one should be from the director of the applicant's psychiatry residence program. The additional two should be from supervisors and attending staff with whom the applicants have worked directly. **Deadline:** May 1. **Contact:** Feyza E. Marouf, MD, Program Director; Massachusetts General Hospital; Phone: 617-724-5600; Email: fmarouf@mgh.harvard.edu; Patricia Kneeland, Fellowship Coordinator; Massachusetts General Hospital; 55 Fruit St., Bulfinch Bldg., Ste. 360, Boston, MA, 02114; Phone: 617-724-3119; Email: pkneeland1@mgh.harvard.edu.

7141 ■ Massachusetts Historical Society (MHS)
1154 Boylston St.
Boston, MA 02215-3695
Ph: (617)536-1608
Fax: (617)859-0074
URL: www.masshist.org
Social Media: www.facebook.com/
MassachusettsHistoricalSociety
www.instagram.com/mhs1791
twitter.com/MHS1791

7142 ■ W.B.H. Dowse Fellowships (Graduate/ Fellowship)

Purpose: To provide support for scholars studying the history of colonial New England. **Focus:** History, American. **Qualif.:** Applicants must be independent scholars, advanced graduate students, and holders of the Ph.D. or the equivalent; they must be US citizens or already hold the J-1 visa or equivalent documents that will allow them to accept the stipend. **Criteria:** Selection will be given to candidates who live fifty or more miles from Boston.

Funds Avail.: $2,000. **Duration:** Annual; up to four weeks. **Number Awarded:** 1. **To Apply:** Applicants must submit the following materials online: a cover letter; current curriculum vitae; a project proposal approximately 1,000 words in length; for the applicants who do not hold a PhD, a letter of recommendation from a faculty member familiar with applicants' work and with the project being proposed; a project proposal should include: a description of the project; a statement explaining the historiographical significance of

Awards are arranged alphabetically below their administering organizations

the project; an indication of the specific MHS collections the applicants wishes to consult. **Deadline:** March 1. **Remarks:** Established in 1996. **Contact:** Phone: 617-646-0577; Email: fellowships@masshist.org.

7143 ■ Malcolm and Mildred Freiberg Fellowships
(Professional development/Fellowship)

Purpose: To support research relating to reading and publishing. **Focus:** Publishing; Reading. **Qualif.:** Applicants must be independent scholars, advanced graduate students, and holders of the Ph.D. or the equivalent; they must be US citizens or already hold the J-1 visa or equivalent documents that will allow them to accept the stipend. **Criteria:** Selection will be based on the committee's criteria.

Funds Avail.: $2,000. **Duration:** Annual; up to four weeks. **Number Awarded:** 1. **To Apply:** Applicants must submit the following materials online: a cover letter; current curriculum vitae; a project proposal approximately 1,000 words in length; for the applicants who do not hold a PhD, a letter of recommendation from a faculty member familiar with applicants' work and with the project being proposed; a project proposal should include: a description of the project; a statement explaining the historiographical significance of the project; an indication of the specific MHS collections the applicants wishes to consult. **Deadline:** March 1. **Contact:** Phone: 617-646-0577; Email: fellowships@masshist.org.

7144 ■ MHS Marc Friedlaender Fellowships *(Professional development/Fellowship)*

Purpose: To support documentary editing projects and research on the Adams family. **Focus:** History, American. **Qualif.:** Applicants must be independent scholars, advanced graduate students, and holders of the Ph.D. or the equivalent; they must be US citizens or already hold the J-1 visa or equivalent documents that will allow them to accept the stipend. **Criteria:** Selection will be based on the committee's criteria.

Funds Avail.: $2,000. **Duration:** Annual; up to four weeks. **Number Awarded:** 1. **To Apply:** Applicants must submit the following materials online: a cover letter; current curriculum vitae; a project proposal approximately 1,000 words in length; for the applicants who do not hold a PhD, a letter of recommendation from a faculty member familiar with applicants' work and with the project being proposed; a project proposal should include: a description of the project; a statement explaining the historiographical significance of the project; an indication of the specific MHS collections the applicants wishes to consult. **Deadline:** March 1. **Remarks:** Established in 1999. **Contact:** Phone: 617-646-0577; Email: fellowships@masshist.org.

7145 ■ Suzanne and Caleb Loring Research Fellowships *(Professional development/Fellowship)*

Purpose: To support individuals who will conduct a research on the civil war, its origins and consequences. **Focus:** History, American. **Qualif.:** Applicants must be U.S. citizens or already hold the J-1 visa or equivalent documents that will allow them to accept the stipend. Foreign nationals must consult with MHS staff about their eligibility to receive a stipend before submitting an application. **Criteria:** Selection will be based on the committee's criteria.

Funds Avail.: $4,000. **Duration:** Annual; at least four weeks. **To Apply:** Applicants must submit the following materials online: a cover letter; current curriculum vitae; a project proposal approximately 1,000 words in length; for

the applicants who do not hold a PhD, a letter of recommendation from a faculty member familiar with applicants' work and with the project being proposed; A project proposal should include: a description of the project; a statement explaining the historiographical significance of the project; an indication of the specific Massachusetts Historical Society and Boston Athenaeum collections the applicants wishes to consult. **Deadline:** February 15. **Contact:** Phone: 617-646-0577; Email: fellowships@masshist.org.

7146 ■ MHS Andrew W. Mellon Fellowships *(Professional development, Doctorate/Fellowship)*

Purpose: To support any project for which the Society's collection are appropriate. **Focus:** History, American. **Qualif.:** Applicants must be independent scholars, advanced graduate students, and holders of the Ph.D. or the equivalent; they must be US citizens or already hold the J-1 visa or equivalent documents that will allow them to accept the stipend. **Criteria:** Selection will be given to candidates who live fifty or more miles from Boston.

Funds Avail.: $2,000. **Duration:** Annual; up to four weeks. **Number Awarded:** Approximately 9. **To Apply:** Applicants must submit the following materials online: a cover letter; current curriculum vitae; a project proposal approximately 1,000 words in length; for the applicants who do not hold a PhD, a letter of recommendation from a faculty member familiar with applicants' work and with the project being proposed; a project proposal should include: a description of the project; a statement explaining the historiographical significance of the project; an indication of the specific MHS collections the applicants wishes to consult. **Deadline:** March 1. **Remarks:** Established in 1996. **Contact:** Phone: 617-646-0577; Email: fellowships@masshist.org.

7147 ■ MHS African American Studies Fellowships *(Professional development/Fellowship)*

Purpose: To support research at the Massachusetts Historical Society in African American History. **Focus:** African-American studies. **Qualif.:** Applicants must be independent scholars, advanced graduate students, and holders of the Ph.D. or the equivalent; they must be US citizens or already hold the J-1 visa or equivalent documents that will allow them to accept the stipend. **Criteria:** Selection will be given to candidates who live fifty or more miles from Boston.

Funds Avail.: $2,000. **Duration:** Annual; up to four weeks. **To Apply:** Applicants must submit the following materials online: a cover letter; current curriculum vitae; a project proposal approximately 1,000 words in length; for the applicants who do not hold a PhD, a letter of recommendation from a faculty member familiar with applicants' work and with the project being proposed; a project proposal should include: a description of the project; a statement explaining the historiographical significance of the project; an indication of the specific MHS collections the applicants wishes to consult. **Deadline:** March 1. **Remarks:** Established in 1999. **Contact:** Phone: 617-646-0577; Email: fellowships@masshist.org.

7148 ■ MHS/Cushing Academy Fellowships on Environmental History *(Professional development/Fellowship)*

Purpose: To support research on any aspect of environmental history. **Focus:** Environmental science. **Qualif.:** Applicants must be independent scholars, advanced graduate students and holders of the PhD or the equivalent. They

Awards are arranged alphabetically below their administering organizations

must be US citizens or already hold the J-1 visa or equivalent documents that will allow them to accept the stipend. **Criteria:** Selection will be based on the committee's criteria.

Funds Avail.: $2,500. **Duration:** Annual; up to four weeks of research. **To Apply:** Applicants must submit the following materials online: a cover letter; current curriculum vitae; a project proposal approximately 1,000 words in length; for the applicants who do not hold a PhD, a letter of recommendation from a faculty member familiar with applicants' work and with the project being proposed; a project proposal should include: a description of the project; a statement explaining the historiographical significance of the project; an indication of the specific MHS collections the applicants wishes to consult. **Deadline:** March 1. **Remarks:** Established in 2012. **Contact:** Email at fellowships@masshist.org; or call via phone: 617-646-0568.

7149 ■ MHS Long-Term Research Fellowships
(Professional development/Fellowship)

Purpose: To support individuals who will conduct a long-term research at the Massachusetts Historical Society. **Focus:** History, American. **Qualif.:** Applicants must be US citizens and foreign nationals who have lived in the United States for at least three years; must have completed their professional training, ordinarily including an earned doctorate. **Criteria:** Selection will be based on the quality of proposed projects and to their relationship to the Society's collections.

Funds Avail.: $4,200 per month. **Duration:** Annual; from 4 to 12 months. **To Apply:** Applicants must submit the following materials online: a cover letter; current curriculum vitae; a project proposal approximately 1,000 words in length; a Certification for Participants form; two letters of recommendation. A project proposal should include a description of the project; a statement explaining the historiographical significance of the project; an indication of the specific MHS collections the applicants wishes to consult. Applicants must specify the number of months for which they are applying. **Deadline:** January 15. **Contact:** Phone: 617-646-0577; Email: fellowships@masshist.org.

7150 ■ MHS/Massachusetts Society of the Cincinnati Fellowships *(Professional development/ Fellowship)*

Purpose: To support research projects pertaining to the era of the American Revolution. **Focus:** History, American. **Qualif.:** Applicants must be independent scholars, advanced graduate students, and holders of the Ph.D. or the equivalent; they must be US citizens or already hold the J-1 visa or equivalent documents that will allow them to accept the stipend. **Criteria:** Selection will be based on the committee's criteria.

Funds Avail.: $2,000. **Duration:** Annual; up to four weeks. **Number Awarded:** 1. **To Apply:** Applicants must submit the following materials online: a cover letter; current curriculum vitae; a project proposal approximately 1,000 words in length; for the applicants who do not hold a PhD, a letter of recommendation from a faculty member familiar with applicants' work and with the project being proposed; a project proposal should include: a description of the project; a statement explaining the historiographical significance of the project; an indication of the specific MHS collections the applicants wishes to consult. **Deadline:** March 1. **Remarks:** Established in 1997. **Contact:** Phone: 617-646-0577; Email: fellowships@masshist.org.

7151 ■ Ruth R. and Alyson R. Miller Fellowships
(Professional development/Fellowship)

Purpose: To encourage research in women's history. **Focus:** Women's studies. **Qualif.:** Applicants must be independent scholars, advanced graduate students, and holders of the Ph.D. or the equivalent; they must be US citizens or already hold the J-1 visa or equivalent documents that will allow them to accept the stipend. **Criteria:** Selection will be based on the committee's criteria.

Funds Avail.: $2,000. **Duration:** Annual; up to four weeks. **Number Awarded:** 2. **To Apply:** Applicants must submit the following materials online: a cover letter; current curriculum vitae; a project proposal approximately 1,000 words in length; for the applicants who do not hold a PhD, a letter of recommendation from a faculty member familiar with applicants' work and with the project being proposed; a project proposal should include: a description of the project; a statement explaining the historiographical significance of the project; an indication of the specific MHS collections the applicants wishes to consult. **Deadline:** March 1. **Remarks:** Established in 1998. **Contact:** Phone: 617-646-0577; Email: fellowships@masshist.org.

7152 ■ MHS Andrew Oliver Research Fellowships
(Professional development/Fellowship)

Purpose: To support research in the Society's collections of portraits, engravings, silhouettes and other graphic materials. **Focus:** Graphic art and design. **Qualif.:** Applicants must be independent scholars, advanced graduate students, and holders of the Ph.D. or the equivalent; they must be US citizens or already hold the J-1 visa or equivalent documents that will allow them to accept the stipend. **Criteria:** Selection will be given to candidates who live fifty or more miles from Boston.

Funds Avail.: $2,000. **Duration:** Annual; up to four weeks. **Number Awarded:** 1. **To Apply:** Applicants must submit the following materials online: a cover letter; current curriculum vitae; a project proposal approximately 1,000 words in length; for the applicants who do not hold a PhD, a letter of recommendation from a faculty member familiar with applicants' work and with the project being proposed; a project proposal should include: a description of the project; a statement explaining the historiographical significance of the project; an indication of the specific MHS collections the applicants wishes to consult. **Deadline:** March 1. **Remarks:** Established in 1996. **Contact:** Phone: 617-646-0577; Email: fellowships@masshist.org.

7153 ■ Benjamin F. Stevens Fellowships *(Professional development/Fellowship)*

Purpose: To support research on any aspect of the history of New England. **Focus:** History, American. **Qualif.:** Applicants must be independent scholars, advanced graduate students, and holders of the Ph.D. or the equivalent; they must be US citizens or already hold the J-1 visa or equivalent documents that will allow them to accept the stipend. **Criteria:** Selection will be given to candidates who live fifty or more miles from Boston.

Funds Avail.: $2,000. **Duration:** Annual; up to four weeks. **Number Awarded:** 1. **To Apply:** Applicants must submit the following materials online: a cover letter; current curriculum vitae; a project proposal approximately 1,000 words in length; for the applicants who do not hold a PhD, a letter of recommendation from a faculty member familiar with applicants' work and with the project being proposed; a project proposal should include: a description of the project; a statement explaining the historiographical significance of

Awards are arranged alphabetically below their administering organizations

the project; an indication of the specific MHS collections the applicants wishes to consult. **Deadline:** March 1. **Remarks:** Established in 1996. **Contact:** Phone: 617-646-0577; Email: fellowships@masshist.org.

7154 ■ Swensrud Teacher Fellowships at MHS (Massachusetts Historical Society) *(Professional development/Fellowship)*

Purpose: To support the public and/or parochial school teachers and library media specialists. **Focus:** English language and literature; History, American. **Qualif.:** Applicants must be any K-12 teachers with a serious interest in using the collections at the MHS to prepare primary-source-based curricula, supported by documents and visual aids, in the fields of American history, world history or English/language arts. **Criteria:** Selection will be based on the strength of project design; the plan for using MHS collections; the creativity of the proposed classroom activities; usability in other classrooms; recommendations.

Funds Avail.: $4,000. **Duration:** Annual; up to four weeks. **To Apply:** Applicants must provide the following materials: a current resume; a letter of intent (no longer than two pages, single-spaced) outlining the topic of interest, as well as the scope and goals of the proposed curriculum project; a list of potential primary source materials to be used; a letter of support from the school principal or department head. **Deadline:** January 15. **Contact:** Center for the Teaching of History, Massachusetts Historical Society, 1154 Boylston St., Boston, MA, 02215; Phone: 617-646-0588; Email: education@masshist.org.

7155 ■ Massachusetts LGBTQ Bar Association (MLGBA)
c/o Boston Bar Association
16 Beacon St.
Boston, MA 02108
URL: www.masslgbtqbar.org

7156 ■ Alexander G. Gray, Jr., Scholarship Award *(Graduate/Scholarship)*

Purpose: To help a second year or third year law student who demonstrates a commitment to and involvement in the LGBTQ community. **Focus:** Law. **Qualif.:** Applicant must be a second or third year law student who demonstrates a commitment to and involvement in the LGBT community, as well as leadership, maturity, and responsibility. **Criteria:** Recipient must attend the Mass. LGBTQ Bar Annual Dinner to accept the Scholarship award in person.

Funds Avail.: $3,500. **Duration:** Annual. **Number Awarded:** 1. **To Apply:** Submit completed application, one letter of recommendation, law school transcript, resume. **Deadline:** February 18. **Contact:** KG Gasseling, Email: kgasseling@choate.com; Brian Huber, Email:bhuber@gunder.com.

7157 ■ Massachusetts Office of Student Financial Assistance
75 Pleasant St.
Malden, MA 02148
Ph: (617)391-6070
E-mail: osfa@osfa.mass.edu
URL: www.osfa.mass.edu
Social Media: www.facebook.com/MassDHE
twitter.com/MassDHE

7158 ■ Early Childhood Educators Scholarship Program *(Undergraduate/Scholarship)*

Purpose: To provide financial assistance for currently employed early childhood and out of school time educators and providers who enroll in an associate's or bachelor's degree program in Early Childhood Education or related programs. **Focus:** Education, Early childhood; Psychology; Sociology. **Qualif.:** Applicants must be permanent legal residents of Massachusetts; must be United States citizens or eligible non-citizens under Title IV Regulations and not in default of a state or federal education loan or grant; must be enrolled as matriculated students without a bachelor's degree, in an undergraduate degree program (full- or part-time) in early childhood education or a related field (i.e., elementary education, sociology, psychology); employed as early childhood educators or licensed family child care providers in Massachusetts for at least one year; and must continue employment while enrolled in the required degree program. **Criteria:** Selection will be based on the committee's criteria.

Duration: Annual. **Contact:** Phone: 617-391-6070.

7159 ■ Massachusetts State Automobile Dealers Association (MSADA)
1 McKinley Sq., 6th Fl.
Boston, MA 02109
Ph: (617)451-1051
Fax: (617)451-9309
URL: www.msada.org
Social Media: twitter.com/MassAutoDealers

7160 ■ Automotive Technician Scholarship Program *(Undergraduate/Scholarship)*

Purpose: To enrich the lives of auto tech students through scholarships. **Focus:** Automotive technology. **Qualif.:** Applicants must be retraining for a career change or a recent high school graduate; must be enrolled in an automotive program at an accredited college. **Criteria:** Recipients will be selected based on academic standing and financial need.

Funds Avail.: $6,000 - $13,000. **Duration:** Annual; 2 years. **Number Awarded:** Varies. **To Apply:** Applicants must complete the provided application form which can be downloaded from the program website; such must be submitted together with the other prescribed requirements; other procedures must also be followed and complied with. **Remarks:** Established in 2003. **Contact:** Auto Tech Scholarship; Massachusetts State Automobile Dealers Association, One McKinley Square, 6th Fl., Boston, MA 02109 USA; Fax: 617-451-9309; Attention: Jean Fabrizio; Phone: 617-451-1051; Email: jfabrizio@msada.org.

7161 ■ Edmund F. Maxwell Foundation
PO Box 55548
Seattle, WA 98155-0548
E-mail: support@maxwell.org
URL: www.maxwell.org

7162 ■ Edmund F. Maxwell Scholarships *(Undergraduate/Scholarship)*

Purpose: To provide assistance to those who have demonstrated financial need and have shown ability, aptitude and a promise of useful citizenship. **Focus:** General studies/Field of study not specified.

Awards are arranged alphabetically below their administering organizations

Funds Avail.: Up to $5,000. **Duration:** Annual; Up to 4 years. **To Apply:** Applicants must submit a completed scholarship application along with the 500-word essay; official, certified high school transcript; certification of SAT/ACT scores; and financial aid worksheet (to be completed by each College/University); applicants must also submit a Free Application for Student Aid form (FAFSA) to the institution that they are planning to attend. **Deadline:** May 15.

7163 ■ The May Firm
8050 N Pal Ave., Ste. 300
Fresno, CA 93711
Ph: (805)980-7758
E-mail: info@mayfirm.com
URL: www.mayfirm.com
Social Media: www.facebook.com/
  TheMayFirmInjuryLawyers
www.linkedin.com/company/the-may-firm
twitter.com/themayfirm

7164 ■ Injury Scholarship *(Undergraduate/Scholarship)*

Purpose: To help students obtain a higher education. **Focus:** General studies/Field of study not specified. **Qualif.:** Must be currently enrolled or accepted into a community college, college, or university in the U.S.

Funds Avail.: $1,000. **Duration:** Biennial. **To Apply:** Submit a 300-word essay in response to the question: "What would really make drivers stop texting and driving?". **Deadline:** January 15; September 15.

7165 ■ McDonough Scholarship Foundation
61 North St.
Manchester, NH 03104
Ph: (603)315-7913
E-mail: mcdonoughscholarship@gmail.com
URL: mcdonough.nhgolf.com

7166 ■ The Dr. George T. Bottomley Scholarship
(Undergraduate/Scholarship)

Purpose: To support outstanding young men and women employed at New Hampshire golf courses in pursuing higher education. **Focus:** General studies/Field of study not specified. **Qualif.:** Applicants must be a graduate of an accredited high school or enrolled in a bachelor or associate degree college program, a minimum academic GPA of 2.5 on a 4.0 scale; must have a minimum of two summers of successful work at a NH golf course as a caddie, in the Pro Shop, on the grounds crew, or in the clubhouse; must be of proven character, integrity, and citizenship; must be a qualified Abenaqui scholar or to a young man or woman from the Seacoast area.

Duration: Annual. **To Apply:** Completed application along with an official copy of your transcript (through Fall of previous year); copy of Free Application for Student Aid (FAFSA) report (the 5 page report, not the application); letter from the club or course where you have completed the employment requirement, certifying you have worked at least 2 seasons (for new applicant); copy of the acceptance letter from the school, college or university, applicant going to attend and confidential school report completed by high school principal or guidance counselor (for high school senior) must be submitted. **Deadline:** May 15. **Remarks:** The Scholarship established in memory by The Fuller

Foundation, and his family in recognition of his lifelong support of golf at Abenaqui Country Club and in New Hampshire. **Contact:** McDonough Scholarship Foundation; c/o Kerri Coughlin; 61 N St., Manchester, NH, 03104; Email: mcDonoughapplication@comcast.net.

7167 ■ The Dr. Robert Elliott Memorial Scholarship
(Undergraduate/Scholarship)

Purpose: To support outstanding young men and women employed at New Hampshire golf courses in pursuing higher education. **Focus:** General studies/Field of study not specified.

Funds Avail.: No specific amount. **Duration:** Annual. **Number Awarded:** 1. **To Apply:** Completed application along with an official copy of your transcript (through Fall of previous year); copy of Free Application for Student Aid (FAFSA) report (the 5 page report, not the application); letter from the club or course where you have completed the employment requirement, certifying you have worked at least 2 seasons (for new applicant); copy of the acceptance letter from the school, college or university, applicant going to attend and confidential school report completed by high school principal or guidance counselor (for high school senior) must be submitted. **Deadline:** May 15. **Remarks:** The Scholarship established in Memory of Dr. Robert Elliott was president of the NHGA for many years, president of The McDonough Foundation. **Contact:** McDonough Scholarship Foundation; c/o Kerri Coughlin; 61 N St., Manchester, NH, 03104; Email: mcDonoughapplication@comcast.net.

7168 ■ The Pauline Elliott Scholarship
(Undergraduate/Scholarship)

Purpose: To support outstanding young men and women employed at New Hampshire golf courses in pursuing higher education. **Focus:** General studies/Field of study not specified. **Qualif.:** Applicants must be a graduate of an accredited high school or enrolled in a bachelor or associate degree college program, a minimum academic GPA of 2.5 on a 4.0 scale; must have a minimum of two summers of successful work at a NH golf course as a caddie, in the Pro Shop, on the grounds crew, or in the clubhouse; must be of proven character, integrity, and citizenship.

Funds Avail.: No specific amount. **Duration:** Annual. **To Apply:** Completed application along with an official copy of your transcript (through Fall of previous year); copy of Free Application for Student Aid (FAFSA) report (the 5 page report, not the application); letter from the club or course where you have completed the employment requirement, certifying you have worked at least 2 seasons (for new applicant); copy of the acceptance letter from the school, college or university, applicant going to attend and confidential school report completed by high school principal or guidance counselor (for high school senior) must be submitted. **Deadline:** May 15. **Remarks:** The Scholarship established in honor of Pauline Elliott on behalf of the NHGA and New Hampshire golf in general. **Contact:** McDonough Scholarship Foundation; c/o Kerri Coughlin; 61 N St., Manchester, NH, 03104; Email: mcDonoughapplication@comcast.net.

7169 ■ The Robert C. Erb Sr. Scholarship
(Undergraduate/Scholarship)

Purpose: To support outstanding young men and women employed at New Hampshire golf courses in pursuing higher education. **Focus:** General studies/Field of study not specified. **Qualif.:** Applicants must be a graduate of an accredited high school or enrolled in a bachelor or associ-

Awards are arranged alphabetically below their administering organizations

ate degree college program, a minimum academic GPA of 2.5 on a 4.0 scale; must have a minimum of two summers of successful work at a NH golf course as a caddie, in the Pro Shop, on the grounds crew, or in the clubhouse; must be of proven character, integrity, and citizenship.

Duration: Annual. **To Apply:** Completed application along with an official copy of your transcript (through Fall of previous year); copy of Free Application for Student Aid (FAFSA) report (the 5 page report, not the application); letter from the club or course where you have completed the employment requirement, certifying you have worked at least 2 seasons (for new applicant); copy of the acceptance letter from the school, college or university, applicant going to attend and confidential school report completed by high school principal or guidance counselor (for high school senior) must be submitted. **Deadline:** May 15. **Remarks:** The Scholarship Established in memory by his wife. Elizabeth P. Erb, and his son, Bob Erb Jr., in recognition of his longtime support of the education of New Hampshire youths and their involvement in golf. **Contact:** McDonough Scholarship Foundation; c/o Kerri Coughlin; 61 N St., Manchester, NH, 03104; Email: mcDonoughapplication@comcast.net.

7170 ■ The Phil Friel Scholarship (Undergraduate/ Scholarship)

Purpose: To support outstanding young men and women employed at New Hampshire golf courses in pursuing higher education. **Focus:** General studies/Field of study not specified. **Qualif.:** Applicant must have e any student employee, male or female, of a New Hampshire golf course or club. Candidates should demonstrate promise of academic success, as well as require financial assistance. Once awarded, a McDonough Scholarship may be renewed each year for a total of four years. **Criteria:** Selection will be based on the committee criteria.

Funds Avail.: No specific amount. **Duration:** Annual. **To Apply:** Completed application along with an official copy of your transcript (through Fall of previous year); copy of Free Application for Student Aid (FAFSA) report (the 5 page report, not the application); letter from the club or course where you have completed the employment requirement, certifying you have worked at least 2 seasons (for new applicant); copy of the acceptance letter from the school, college or university, applicant going to attend and confidential school report completed by high school principal or guidance counselor (for high school senior) must be submitted. **Deadline:** May 30. **Remarks:** The Scholarship established in honor and say thank you to one of the great gentlemen of New Hampshire golf and one of the McDonough Foundation founders. **Contact:** McDonough Scholarship Foundation; c/o Kerri Coughlin; 61 N St., Manchester, NH, 03104; Email: mcDonoughapplication@comcast.net.

7171 ■ The Alex Gissler Memorial Scholarship (Undergraduate/Scholarship)

Purpose: To support outstanding young men and women employed at New Hampshire golf courses in pursuing higher education. **Focus:** General studies/Field of study not specified. **Qualif.:** Applicants must be remembered as an outstanding young man and a loyal employee. deserving young man or woman employed at Baker Hill Golf Club.

Funds Avail.: No specific amount. **Duration:** Annual. **To Apply:** Completed application along with an official copy of your transcript (through Fall of previous year); copy of Free Application for Student Aid (FAFSA) report (the 5 page report, not the application); letter from the club or course where you have completed the employment requirement, certifying you have worked at least 2 seasons (for new applicant); copy of the acceptance letter from the school, college or university, applicant going to attend and confidential school report completed by high school principal or guidance counselor (for high school senior) must be submitted. **Remarks:** The scholarship was established by Baker Hill Golf Club membership in his memory. Alex is remembered as an outstanding young man and a loyal employee. **Contact:** McDonough Scholarship Foundation; c/o Kerri Coughlin; 61 N St., Manchester, NH, 03104; Email: mcDonoughapplication@comcast.net.

7172 ■ The Stan Lencki Scholarship (Undergraduate/ Scholarship)

Purpose: To support outstanding young men and women employed at New Hampshire golf courses in pursuing higher education. **Focus:** General studies/Field of study not specified. **Qualif.:** Applicants must be a graduate of an accredited high school or enrolled in a bachelor or associate degree college program, a minimum academic GPA of 2.5 on a 4.0 scale; must have a minimum of two summers of successful work at a NH golf course as a caddie, in the Pro Shop, on the grounds crew, or in the clubhouse; must be of proven character, integrity, and citizenship. **Criteria:** Selection will be based on the critical need for financial aid determined by the scholarship committee.

Funds Avail.: No specific amount. **Duration:** Annual. **To Apply:** Completed application along with an official copy of your transcript (through Fall of previous year); copy of Free Application for Student Aid (FAFSA) report (the 5 page report, not the application); letter from the club or course where you have completed the employment requirement, certifying you have worked at least 2 seasons (for new applicant); copy of the acceptance letter from the school, college or university, applicant going to attend and confidential school report completed by high school principal or guidance counselor (for high school senior) must be submitted. **Deadline:** May 15. **Remarks:** The Scholarship Established in honor of Mr. Lencki's 50 years of service to MCC. **Contact:** McDonough Scholarship Foundation; c/o Kerri Coughlin; 61 N St., Manchester, NH, 03104; Email: mcDonoughapplication@comcast.net.

7173 ■ The Rick Mahoney Scholarship (Undergraduate/Scholarship)

Purpose: To support outstanding young men and women employed at New Hampshire golf courses in pursuing higher education. **Focus:** General studies/Field of study not specified. **Qualif.:** Applicants must be a graduate of an accredited high school or enrolled in a bachelor or associate degree college program, a minimum academic GPA of 2.5 on a 4.0 scale; must have a minimum of two summers of successful work at a NH golf course as a caddie, in the Pro Shop, on the grounds crew, or in the clubhouse; must be of proven character, integrity, and citizenship; must be resident of Nashua, NH.

Funds Avail.: No specific amount. **Duration:** Annual. **To Apply:** Completed application along with an official copy of your transcript (through Fall of previous year); copy of Free Application for Student Aid (FAFSA) report (the 5 page report, not the application); letter from the club or course where you have completed the employment requirement, certifying you have worked at least 2 seasons (for new applicant); copy of the acceptance letter from the school, college or university, applicant going to attend and confidential school report completed by high school principal or guidance counselor (for high school senior) must be submitted.

Awards are arranged alphabetically below their administering organizations

Deadline: May 15. **Remarks:** The Scholarship Established in honor of Mr. Mahoney's 25 plus years of service as a Director and Chairman of the Scholarship Committee. **Contact:** McDonough Scholarship Foundation; c/o Kerri Coughlin; 61 N St., Manchester, NH, 03104; Email: mcDonoughapplication@comcast.net.

7174 ■ The NHPGA Apprentice Scholarship
(Undergraduate/Scholarship)

Purpose: To support outstanding young men and women employed at New Hampshire golf courses in pursuing higher education. **Focus:** General studies/Field of study not specified. **Qualif.:** Applicants must be a graduate of an accredited high school or enrolled in a bachelor or associate degree college program, a minimum academic GPA of 2.5 on a 4.0 scale; must have a minimum of two summers of successful work at a NH golf course as a caddie, in the Pro Shop, on the grounds crew, or in the clubhouse; must be of proven character, integrity, and citizenship.

Duration: Annual. **To Apply:** Completed application along with an official copy of your transcript (through Fall of previous year); copy of Free Application for Student Aid (FAFSA) report (the 5 page report, not the application); letter from the club or course where you have completed the employment requirement, certifying you have worked at least 2 seasons (for new applicant); copy of the acceptance letter from the school, college or university, applicant going to attend and confidential school report completed by high school principal or guidance counselor (for high school senior) must be submitted. **Deadline:** May 15. **Contact:** McDonough Scholarship Foundation; c/o Kerri Coughlin; 61 N St., Manchester, NH, 03104; Email: mcDonoughapplication@comcast.net.

7175 ■ The Walter T. Philippy Scholarship
(Undergraduate/Scholarship)

Purpose: To support outstanding young men and women employed at New Hampshire golf courses in pursuing higher education. **Focus:** General studies/Field of study not specified. **Qualif.:** Applicants must be a graduate of an accredited high school or enrolled in a bachelor or associate degree college program, a minimum academic GPA of 2.5 on a 4.0 scale; must have a minimum of two summers of successful work at a NH golf course as a caddie, in the Pro Shop, on the grounds crew, or in the clubhouse; must be of proven character, integrity, and citizenship; must be employed at Derryfield Country Club or a Manchester, NH, golf course.

Duration: Annual. **To Apply:** Completed application along with an official copy of your transcript (through Fall of previous year); copy of Free Application for Student Aid (FAFSA) report (the 5 page report, not the application); letter from the club or course where you have completed the employment requirement, certifying you have worked at least 2 seasons (for new applicant); copy of the acceptance letter from the school, college or university, applicant going to attend and confidential school report completed by high school principal or guidance counselor (for high school senior) must be submitted. **Deadline:** May 15. **Remarks:** The scholarship was established memory by Matilda Philippy and her family. An avid golfer, Walter was a 48-year veteran of Derryfield Country Club, an advocate of young people's involvement in the game, and for many years a member of the New Hampshire Golf Association. **Contact:** McDonough Scholarship Foundation; c/o Kerri Coughlin; 61 N St., Manchester, NH, 03104; Email: mcDonoughapplication@comcast.net.

7176 ■ The David J. Pollini Scholarship
(Undergraduate/Scholarship)

Purpose: To support outstanding young men and women employed at New Hampshire golf courses in pursuing higher education. **Focus:** General studies/Field of study not specified. **Qualif.:** Applicants must be a graduate of an accredited high school or enrolled in a bachelor or associate degree college program, a minimum academic GPA of 2.5 on a 4.0 scale; must have a minimum of two summers of successful work at a NH golf course as a caddie, in the Pro Shop, on the grounds crew, or in the clubhouse; must be of proven character, integrity, and citizenship; must be an employee of Kingswood Golf Club or to an employee of a Lakes Region golf course if Kingswood does not have an eligible candidate.

Duration: Annual. **To Apply:** Completed application along with an official copy of your transcript (through Fall of previous year); copy of Free Application for Student Aid (FAFSA) report (the 5 page report, not the application); letter from the club or course where you have completed the employment requirement, certifying you have worked at least 2 seasons (for new applicant); copy of the acceptance letter from the school, college or university, applicant going to attend and confidential school report completed by high school principal or guidance counselor (for high school senior) must be submitted. **Deadline:** May 15. **Remarks:** The scholarship was established in honor, upon his retirement, of his 39 of service as head golf a professional at Kingswood Golf Club. **Contact:** McDonough Scholarship Foundation; c/o Kerri Coughlin; 61 N St., Manchester, NH, 03104; Email: mcDonoughapplication@comcast.net.

7177 ■ The Pope Scholarship Award *(Undergraduate/Scholarship)*

Purpose: To support outstanding young men and women employed at New Hampshire golf courses in pursuing higher education. **Focus:** General studies/Field of study not specified. **Qualif.:** Applicants must be a graduate of an accredited high school or enrolled in a bachelor or associate degree college program, a minimum academic GPA of 2.5 on a 4.0 scale; must have a minimum of two summers of successful work at a NH golf course as a caddie, in the Pro Shop, on the grounds crew, or in the clubhouse; must be of proven character, integrity, and citizenship.

Duration: Annual. **To Apply:** Completed application along with an official copy of your transcript (through Fall of previous year); copy of Free Application for Student Aid (FAFSA) report (the 5 page report, not the application); letter from the club or course where you have completed the employment requirement, certifying you have worked at least 2 seasons (for new applicant); copy of the acceptance letter from the school, college or university, applicant going to attend and confidential school report completed by high school principal or guidance counselor (for high school senior) must be submitted. **Deadline:** May 15. **Remarks:** The Scholarship established in Memory of Ken Pope former the University of New Hampshire golf coach and Concord Country Club member. **Contact:** McDonough Scholarship Foundation; c/o Kerri Coughlin; 61 N St., Manchester, NH, 03104; Email: mcDonoughapplication@comcast.net.

7178 ■ The Jim Sheerin Scholarship *(Undergraduate/Scholarship)*

Purpose: To support outstanding young men and women employed at New Hampshire golf courses in pursuing higher education. **Focus:** General studies/Field of study not specified. **Qualif.:** Applicants must be a graduate of an

Awards are arranged alphabetically below their administering organizations

accredited high school or enrolled in a bachelor or associate degree college program, a minimum academic GPA of 2.5 on a 4.0 scale; must have a minimum of two summers of successful work at a NH golf course as a caddie, in the Pro Shop, on the grounds crew, or in the clubhouse; must be of proven character, integrity, and citizenship; must be employed at Abenaqui Country Club or at a seacoast-area golf course.

Funds Avail.: No specific amount. **Duration:** Annual. **To Apply:** Completed application along with an official copy of your transcript (through Fall of previous year); copy of Free Application for Student Aid (FAFSA) report (the 5 page report, not the application); letter from the club or course where you have completed the employment requirement, certifying you have worked at least 2 seasons (for new applicant); copy of the acceptance letter from the school, college or university, applicant going to attend and confidential school report completed by high school principal or guidance counselor (for high school senior) must be submitted. **Deadline:** May 15. **Remarks:** The Scholarship Established in honor of his many years of service as head golf professional and director of golf. **Contact:** McDonough Scholarship Foundation; c/o Kerri Coughlin; 61 N St., Manchester, NH, 03104; Email: mcDonoughapplication@comcast.net.

7179 ■ The William H. McGannon Foundation
c/o Joseph Restoule, President
6093 Signal Ridge Hts. SW
Calgary, AB, Canada T3H 2P1
Ph: (403)242-7939
URL: www.mcgannonfoundation.ca
Social Media: www.facebook.com/mcgannonfoundation
www.instagram.com/mcgannonfoundation
www.linkedin.com/company/william-h-mcgannon
  -foundation

7180 ■ William H. McGannon Foundation Scholarships (Graduate, Undergraduate/Scholarship)

Purpose: To provide financial assistance to students enrolled in risk management or other insurance disciplines. **Focus:** Insurance and insurance-related fields; Risk management. **Qualif.:** Applicant must be a full-time student at a university (undergraduate or postgraduate) or college; must be enrolled in a risk management or insurance discipline; must be a Canadian citizen or permanent resident of Canada.

Funds Avail.: No specific amount. **Number Awarded:** 1. **To Apply:** Applicants must submit a completed scholarship application form. **Deadline:** November 30. **Contact:** Joe Restoule, President; 6093 Signal Ridge Hts. S.W., Calgary, Alberta, T3H 2P1; Phone: 403-242-7939; Email: jrestoule@shaw.ca.

7181 ■ McGill University
James Administration Bldg., 845 Sherbrooke St. W
Montreal, QC, Canada H3A 0G4
Ph: (514)398-4455
E-mail: info.communications@mcgill.ca
URL: www.mcgill.ca
Social Media: www.facebook.com/McGillUniversity
www.instagram.com/mcgillu
www.linkedin.com/school/mcgill-university
twitter.com/mcgillu
www.youtube.com/mcgilluniversity

7182 ■ Mackenzie King Open Scholarship (Graduate, Postgraduate, Undergraduate/Scholarship)

Purpose: To defray the student's educational expenses in pursuing their goals. **Focus:** General studies/Field of study not specified. **Qualif.:** Applicants must be graduates of Canadian university who engaged in graduate study in any field, in Canada or elsewhere.

Funds Avail.: $8,500 (subject to change). **Duration:** Annual. **Deadline:** February 1. **Contact:** For submission, James Administration Bldg., Rm. 400 or by mail to 845 Sherbrooke St., Rm. 400 Montreal, QC, H3A 0G4.

7183 ■ Mackenzie King Travelling Scholarship (Graduate/Scholarship, Monetary)

Purpose: To defray the student's educational expenses in pursuing their goals. **Focus:** Industrial and labor relations; International affairs and relations. **Criteria:** Awards will be based on high academic achievements; personal qualities; and demonstrated aptitudes. Consideration will also be given to the applicant's proposed program of study.

Funds Avail.: $10,500. **Duration:** Annual. **Deadline:** February 1. **Contact:** For submission, James Administration Bldg., Rm. 400 or by mail to 845 Sherbrooke St., Rm. 400 Montreal, QC, H3A 0G4.

7184 ■ Philip F. Vineberg Travelling Fellowship in the Humanities (Undergraduate/Scholarship, Monetary)

Purpose: To support students in furthering their studies in such discipline at another university. **Focus:** Art; Education; Education, Religious; Law; Library and archival sciences; Music; Social work. **Qualif.:** Applicant must be a registered student at McGill in a degree program in Arts, Education, Law, Library Science, Music, Religious Studies or Social Work. **Criteria:** Selection of applicant will be based on academic achievements and personal qualities.

Funds Avail.: $14,500. **Duration:** Annual; one academic year. **Deadline:** February 3. **Remarks:** Established in 1988.

7185 ■ McGill University - Centre for Host-Parasite Interactions
Institute of Parasitology 21,111 Lakeshore Road
Sainte Anne de Bellevue, QC, Canada H9X 3V9
URL: www.mcgill.ca

7186 ■ CHPI Travel Fellowships (Undergraduate/Fellowship)

Purpose: To provide travel and accommodation support for trainees to attend national or international meetings to present Centre research and as a way to foster interactions with other researchers at national or international institutions. **Focus:** Microbiology. **Qualif.:** Applicants must be students registered in Quebec.

Funds Avail.: $20,000 per year. **Duration:** Annual. **To Apply:** Applicants must include original receipts/invoices; copy of the front page of the conference booklet (showing date and location); copy of the page where their presentation or poster is indicated (showing time and date).

7187 ■ McGill University - Institute and Centre of Air and Space Law (IASL)
3690 Peel St.
Montreal, QC, Canada H3A 1W9
URL: www.mcgill.ca/iasl

Awards are arranged alphabetically below their administering organizations

7188 ■ Erin J.C. Arsenault Fellowships in Space Governance (Graduate/Fellowship)

Purpose: To aid graduate students engaged in research on the pursuit of peace and security in outer space through law, policy and global governance. **Focus:** Aerospace sciences; Public administration. **Qualif.:** Applicants must hold a postgraduate doctoral degree in law obtained within the last five years; must have a solid track record of original research, a high level of proficiency in English and must propose a research project.

Funds Avail.: Up to 20,000 Canadian Dollars (for Master of Laws (LL.M.) students); up to 30,000 Canadian Dollars (for Doctor of Civil Law (D.C.L.) students at the Institute of Air and Space Law, at McGill's Faculty of Law). **Duration:** Annual. **Number Awarded:** Varies. **Remarks:** The Arsenault Fellowships are supported by the Erin J. C. Arsenault Trust. Established in 2008. **Contact:** Professor Ram Jakhu; Email: ram.jakhu@mcgill.ca.

7189 ■ McGill University - Montreal Neurological Institute and Hospital
3801 University St.
Montreal, QC, Canada H3A 2B4
Ph: (514)398-6644
URL: www.mcgill.ca
Social Media: www.facebook.com/NeuroMontreal
www.instagram.com/mcgillu/
www.linkedin.com/company/the-montreal-neurological
 -institute
twitter.com/mcgillu
twitter.com/TheNeuro_MNI
www.youtube.com/mcgilluniversity
www.youtube.com/user/MontrealNeuro

7190 ■ Jeanne Timmins Costello Fellowships (JTC) (Professional development/Fellowship)

Purpose: To support research and study in clinical and basic neuroscience. **Focus:** Neurology.

Funds Avail.: $10,000. **Duration:** Annual. **To Apply:** Applicants must submit the information via online. **Deadline:** October 31.

7191 ■ The Preston Robb Fellowship (Professional development, College, Master's/Fellowship)

Purpose: To support the training of a clinical fellow to work jointly with the basic and clinician scientists. **Focus:** Neurology. **Qualif.:** Applicant must support the training of a clinical fellow to work jointly with basic and clinician scientists and must have an M.D. degree with clinical studies in neurology or neurosurgery.

Funds Avail.: $40,000. **Duration:** Annual. **Deadline:** October 31.

7192 ■ McKelvey Foundation
PO Box 1195
Greenwich, CT 06830
Ph: (212)847-7236
E-mail: info@mckelveyfoundation.org
URL: www.mckelveyfoundation.org

7193 ■ The McKelvey Scholarship (Undergraduate/Scholarship)

Purpose: To provide first-generation scholarship to high school students whose resources may be limited, but whose ambitions are not. **Focus:** General studies/Field of study not specified. **Qualif.:** Applicants must be first in the family to pursue a college education; must be high school seniors to attend any four-year college in their home state. **Criteria:** Selection will be based on high school seniors who'd be the first in their families to attend college.

Funds Avail.: $12,000.

7194 ■ McMaster University - Ontario Public Interest Research Group-McMaster (OPIRG)
McMaster University 1280 Main St. W.
Hamilton, ON, Canada L8S 4S4
URL: www.opirgmcmaster.org

7195 ■ OPIRG McMaster Public Interest Research Grant (PIG) (Undergraduate, Graduate/Grant)

Purpose: To facilitate and encourage students to develop their research and advocacy skills in order to become active and informed citizens. **Focus:** Environmental conservation; Human rights; Social work.

Funds Avail.: $1,000. **Duration:** Annual. **To Apply:** Proposals should include: description of the project; description of how the project achieves OPIRG McMaster's objective(s); outline of the individual/group's history, objectives, and current activities; and preliminary budget (including specification of all other possible funders).Timeline of activities **Deadline:** March 20. **Contact:** E-mail: opirg@mcmaster.ca.

7196 ■ McMurray Stern
15511 Carmenita Rd.
Santa Fe Springs, CA 90670
Ph: (562)623-3000
Fax: (562)623-3039
Free: 800-342-8994
E-mail: info@mcstern.com
URL: www.mcmurraystern.com
Social Media: www.facebook.com/McMurrayStern
www.linkedin.com/company/mcmurray-stern
twitter.com/McMurrayStern

7197 ■ McMurray Stern - Scholarship Opportunity (Undergraduate, College, University/Scholarship)

Purpose: To help a student gain an education in an industrial engineering field. **Focus:** Engineering, Industrial. **Qualif.:** Applicant must be legal U.S. resident and either currently enrolled or planning to enroll in an industrial engineering program at an accredited U.S. college or university; full academic scholarships are not eligible to enter this contest. **Criteria:** Selection will be based on demonstration of a genuine desire and goal to use the scholarship to advance in the industrial engineering field and an overall passion for knowledge.

Funds Avail.: $500. **Number Awarded:** 1. **To Apply:** Applicant must submit a brief narrative (500 words or more) describing the most applicable and meaningful takeaways from their industrial engineering education so far; applicant should also discuss their future career goals. **Deadline:** September 10. **Contact:** Email: mmurray@mcstern.com.

7198 ■ McNeely Stephenson Attorneys at Law
2150 Intelliplex Dr., Ste. 200
Shelbyville, IN 46176

Awards are arranged alphabetically below their administering organizations

Ph: (317)680-2011
Free: 888-991-7921
URL: www.indianapilaw.com
Social Media: www.facebook.com/Stephenson-Rife
-381991155253448
www.linkedin.com/company/stephenson-rife-llp

7199 ■ Mike Stephenson Legal Scholarships
(Graduate/Scholarship)

Purpose: To support law students who have made an outstanding creative and persuasive writing. **Focus:** Law. **Qualif.:** Applicants must meet the following criteria: be a U.S. Citizen or be authorized to work/attend school in the United States; commencing University in August 2020. **Criteria:** selection will be based on length of community service history;depth of dedication to the community;ability to clearly convey a complex message.

Funds Avail.: $1,000. **Duration:** Annual. **Number Awarded:** 2. **To Apply:** Applicants must submit a completed Scholarship Application Form; copy of University acceptance letter; essay outlining the description of past community service efforts and how award will enhance education and future service opportunities. **Deadline:** May 1.

7200 ■ MCRD Museum Foundation
PO Box 400085
San Diego, CA 92140-0085
Ph: (619)524-4426
Fax: (619)524-0076
URL: mcrdmuseumfoundation.org
Social Media: www.facebook.com/pages/MCRD-Museum
-Foundation/350778671700007
www.instagram.com/mcrdmuseum
twitter.com/mcrdmf

7201 ■ Colonel Nate Smith Scholarship *(Graduate, Undergraduate/Scholarship)*

Purpose: To provide educational assistance for MCRD San Diego enlisted marines or sailors and their dependents that are enrolled in an accredited graduate or undergraduate college program. **Focus:** Military science and education. **Qualif.:** Applicants must be enlisted active duty marines or sailors currently assigned to MCRD San Diego/Western Recruiting Region or their dependents; must be high school graduates and must provide a proof of enrollment in a undergraduate or graduate program. **Criteria:** Selection will be based on academic performance, extracurricular activities and future potentials.

Funds Avail.: $1,000. **Duration:** Annual. **Number Awarded:** 3. **To Apply:** Applicant must submit an application form along with personal information; must fill eligibility category information; high school academic status; college enrollment status; police records check; significant military accomplishments (maximum of 20 lines); high school and college achievements (maximum of 15 lines); church and community achievement, activities, service and participation (maximum of 15 lines); career goals (maximum of 10 lines) and an essay (maximum of 20 lines). **Deadline:** July 31. **Contact:** Christina Curtin, MCRD Museum Foundation Director of Donor relations; Email:christina@mcrdmhs.org.

7202 ■ The Medalist Club
PO Box 71996
Tuscaloosa, AL 35407

Ph: (205)348-3830
E-mail: Info@bamagymnastics.org
URL: bamagymnastics.org
Social Media: www.facebook.com/UAmedalistclub
www.instagram.com/BamaGymnastics
twitter.com/uamedalistclub
www.youtube.com/user/MedalistClub

7203 ■ The Medalist Club Post Graduate Scholarship *(Postgraduate/Scholarship)*

Purpose: To support former student athletes in their educational pursuits. **Focus:** General studies/Field of study not specified. **Qualif.:** Applicants must be former University of Alabama athletes who have contributed to the success of the Alabama gymnastics program; must hold a Bachelor's Degree from the University of Alabama; must be accepted to, or be currently enrolled in, a graduate degree program at the University of Alabama; must have a minimum undergraduate GPA of 3.0. **Criteria:** Scholarship Committee will do the final award decisions via a majority vote.

Funds Avail.: $1,000 minimum in $500 increments. **Number Awarded:** 2. **To Apply:** Applicants must complete and submit the application form available online together with two letters of recommendation; current resume; copy of letter of acceptance to graduate degree program; and University of Alabama undergraduate transcripts. **Deadline:** June 1; November 1.

7204 ■ Meded Media LLC
300 Center Dr., Ste. G265
Superior, CO 80027
URL: medicalschoolhq.net
Social Media: www.instagram.com/medicalschoolhq
twitter.com/medicalschoolhq
www.youtube.com/user/MedicalSchoolHQ

7205 ■ MSHQ Premed Scholarship *(Undergraduate, Graduate, Postgraduate/Scholarship)*

Purpose: To help students pay for medical school. **Focus:** Medicine. **Qualif.:** Applicant must be enrolling in medical school, an undergraduate, a post-baccalaureate, taking more classes, or applying to medical school.

Funds Avail.: $4,000; $1,500; $500. **Number Awarded:** 3. **To Apply:** Applicant must follow the guidelines on the scholarship page and submit all materials at premedscholarship.com/submit. **Deadline:** December 31. **Contact:** Email: team@medicalschoolhq.net; URL: medicalschoolhq.net/mshq-premed-scholarship/.

7206 ■ Medex Biocare Pharmacy L.L.C.
8024 Stage Hills Blvd., Ste. 107
Bartlett, TN 38133
Free: 800-962-6339
URL: www.medexbiocare.com

7207 ■ Education Factor Scholarships *(Graduate, Undergraduate/Scholarship)*

Purpose: To provide financial assistance to students living with hemophilia or other bleeding disorder. **Focus:** General studies/Field of study not specified. **Qualif.:** Applicants must have plan to attend an accredited college, private preparatory, graduate or vo-tech school; applicants must have minimum 2.0 GPA on a 4.0 scale; must be U.S.

Awards are arranged alphabetically below their administering organizations

citizens with hemophilia (Factor VII, VIII or IX) or von Wille-brand disease (verified by physician) and their immediate family members; must have verified ACT/SAT score (if available). **Criteria:** Selection will be based on application, essay, reference letters and community service.

Funds Avail.: $500 to $1,500. **Duration:** Annual. **To Apply:** Applicants must submit a completed application form; copy of school records to confirm a cumulative GPA of 2.0 or above on a 4.0 scale; 500-word typed essay on "My Academic Field of Study and Why I Chose It"; explanation of financial need in a maximum 100-word typed amplification separate from the required essay; two recommendation letters from teachers/employer; evidence of ongoing community service.

7208 ■ Medford Rogue Rotary Club
PO Box 4002
Medford, OR 97501
URL: www.medfordrogue.org

7209 ■ Medford Rogue Rotary Scholarship
(Undergraduate/Scholarship)

Purpose: To financially support those students who are planning to attend Hillsdale College in Hillsdale, Michigan. **Focus:** General studies/Field of study not specified. **Qualif.:** Applicants must be college-bound high school seniors.

7210 ■ Media Mister Inc.
3696 Woodrow Way
Houston, TX 77006
Ph: (484)968-5453
URL: www.mediamister.com
Social Media: facebook.com/mediamister
pinterest.com/mediamister
twitter.com/MediaMr

7211 ■ MediaMister $1000 Student Scholarship
(Undergraduate, Graduate/Scholarship)

Purpose: To support the college education of U.S. and Canadian students. **Focus:** Engineering; Health care services. **Qualif.:** College student in such disciplines as health care, engineering, and related academic programs; minimum GPA of 3.0; older than 18 years at time of scholarship distribution; at least 70% in attendance; U.S. or Canadian citizen; living in the U.S. or Canada; regular graduate from an affiliated university and shouldn't have a gap of more than two consecutive years. **Criteria:** Creativity, grammar, way of explanation and clarity.

Funds Avail.: $1,000. **Duration:** Semiannual. **To Apply:** Write an essay of 350 to 500 words on a topic related to the social media and social media promotion, along with a simple video containing the details of your previous projects and achievements as well as a video with details of faculty who are recommending you for this scholarship. **Deadline:** June 30 (Fall); November 30 (Spring).

7212 ■ Medical Group Management Association (MGMA)
104 Inverness Ter. E
Englewood, CO 80112-5306
Free: 877-275-6462
E-mail: service@mgma.com
URL: www.mgma.com

Social Media: www.facebook.com/mgmaorg
www.instagram.com/mgma_
www.linkedin.com/company/mgma
twitter.com/mgma

7213 ■ ACMPE Scholarship Fund Program (SFI)
(Graduate, Undergraduate/Scholarship)

Purpose: To support and promote healthcare leaders' personal and professional growth toward advancement of the profession. **Focus:** Health care services. **Qualif.:** Applicants must be students enrolled in an undergraduate or graduate degree program relevant to medical practice management, including public health, business administration, healthcare administration and other related areas. **Criteria:** Applicants will be evaluated by the ACMPE Scholarship Fund Program Committee.

Duration: Annual. **To Apply:** Applications can be submitted by online which includes submission resume; Two reference letters that pertain to your application and signed by the referee; Board Certified through ACMPE; Enrolled or seeking enrollment in the FACMPE. **Contact:** Email: scholarship@mgma.org.

7214 ■ Medical Library Association (MLA)
65 E Wacker Pl., Ste. 1900
Chicago, IL 60601-7246
Ph: (312)419-9094
Fax: (312)419-8950
URL: www.mlanet.org
Social Media: www.facebook.com/MedicalLibraryAssn
www.linkedin.com/groups/127723/profile
twitter.com/MedLibAssn

7215 ■ Clarivate Analytics/MLA Doctoral Fellowship
(Doctorate, Graduate/Fellowship)

Purpose: To foster and encourage superior students to conduct doctoral work in health sciences librarianship or information science by providing support to individuals who have been admitted to candidacy. **Focus:** Health sciences; Information science and technology; Library and archival sciences. **Qualif.:** Applicant must be a graduate of an ALA-accredited school of library science; a candidate in a Ph.D. program focusing on biomedical and health-related information science and a U.S. or Canadian citizen of permanent residence status; must be a member of MLA. **Criteria:** Preference is given to those applicants who have completed at least 75 percent of their coursework and dissertation prospectus either approved or in the approval process.

Funds Avail.: $2,000. **Duration:** Biennial; in even-numbered years. **To Apply:** Applicants must complete online application form; must submit two letters of reference (submitted directly to MLA); informative summary and detailed budget; transcript or proof of enrollment in the graduate program and list of completed courses (mailed directly to MLA); and the name, title, address, phone and email of doctoral advisor; an informative summary; statement of career objectives; current photo. **Deadline:** December 1. **Remarks:** Established in 1986. **Contact:** Email: lopez@mail.mlahq.org.

7216 ■ David A. Kronick Travelling Fellowship
(Doctorate, Graduate/Fellowship)

Purpose: To cover the expenses involved in traveling to three or more medical libraries in the United States or

Awards are arranged alphabetically below their administering organizations

Canada. **Focus:** Health care services; Management. **Qualif.:** Applicant must be a U.S. or Canadian citizen or have permanent residence status; member of the Medical Library Association; must have a graduate degree in library science; must be a practicing health sciences librarian with at least five years of professional experience. **Criteria:** Selection will be based on merits and quality of materials submitted including originality and relevance.

Funds Avail.: $2,000. **Duration:** Annual. **Number Awarded:** 1. **To Apply:** Application form are available at the website; must prepare a resume/curriculum vitae; names of three references not related to the applicant; and a proposal containing: title, goals, objectives, methodology, significance and budget of project. Nine copies of completed application and supporting documents should be provided. **Deadline:** December 1. **Remarks:** Established in 2002. **Contact:** Email: lopez@mail.mlahq.org.

7217 ■ Donald A. B. Lindberg Research Fellowship
(Doctorate, Graduate/Fellowship)

Purpose: To fund a research aimed at expanding the knowledge base used by librarians in improving health care and advances in biomedical research. **Focus:** Biomedical research; Health care services. **Qualif.:** Applicants must be sponsored by an institution or an organization; must be citizens of the United States or Canada; must have a bachelor's, master's, or doctor's degree or is enrolled in a degree program; must be committed to the health sciences; must be members of MLA. **Criteria:** Selection will be based on academic, scientific and technical specifications.

Funds Avail.: $10,000. **Duration:** Annual. **To Apply:** Applicants must submit an application electronically together with a curriculum vitae or biographical sketch; research proposal (5-10 pages) including background and rationale, research aims, budget, research design and methodology, timeline, and plans for disseminating the results; letters of support from the applicant's home institution or from sponsoring institutions or organizations. **Deadline:** November 15. **Remarks:** The Donald A. B. Lindberg Research Fellow is named in honor of Donald A. B. Lindberg, MD, former director of the National Library of Medicine (NLM). Established in 2003. **Contact:** Email: lopez@mail.mlahq.org.

7218 ■ HLS/MLA Professional Development Grants
(Other/Grant)

Purpose: To provide librarians working in hospitals and similar clinical settings with the support needed for educational or research activities. **Focus:** Health sciences; Library and archival sciences. **Qualif.:** Applicants must have been employed as a health sciences librarian within the last year in either a hospital or other clinical care institution; must not have previously received an HLS/MLA Professional Development Award or any MLA grant, scholarship or other awards within the past year; must be a member of the Hospital Libraries Sections/MLA. **Criteria:** Selection will be based on the submitted application and supporting documents.

Funds Avail.: Up to $800 each. **Duration:** Annual. **Number Awarded:** 2. **To Apply:** Applicants must submit an application form and signed statement of terms and condition; Nine copies of the completed application and other documents should be provided. **Deadline:** December 1. **Remarks:** Established in 1996. **Contact:** Email: lopez@mail.mlahq.org.

7219 ■ MLA Continuing Education Grants (CE)
(Graduate/Grant)

Purpose: To support students in developing their knowledge of theoretical, administrative, or technical aspects of librarianship. **Focus:** Library and archival sciences. **Qualif.:** Applicants must hold a graduate degree in library science; must be practicing health science librarians with at least two years of professional experience; must be a member of the MLA who is U.S. or Canadian citizens or has permanent residence status; must clearly identify a continuing education program within the United States or Canada. **Criteria:** Selection will be based on library experience and their professional activities are given consideration.

Funds Avail.: $100-$500. **Duration:** Annual. **Number Awarded:** Varies. **To Apply:** Application forms are available at the website; must submit additional documentation and names of three references not related to the applicant; current photo. **Deadline:** December 1. **Contact:** Email: lopez@mail.mlahq.org.

7220 ■ MLA/NLM Spectrum Scholarship
(Undergraduate/Scholarship)

Purpose: To support students in their goals to become health sciences information professionals. **Focus:** Health sciences. **Qualif.:** Applicants must be of African American, Hispanic, Asian, Native American or Pacific Islander heritage attending an ALA-accredited library school. **Criteria:** Recipients are selected based on merit.

Funds Avail.: $6,500. **Duration:** Annual. **Number Awarded:** 2. **To Apply:** Applicants must contact ALA Spectrum program for scholarship information. **Deadline:** March 1. **Contact:** ALA Spectrum program; Phone: 800-545-2433; Email: spectrum@ala.org.

7221 ■ MLA Research, Development, and Demonstration Project Grant *(Graduate/Grant)*

Purpose: To fund a research or project that promotes excellence in the field of health sciences librarianship. **Focus:** Health sciences; Library and archival sciences. **Qualif.:** Applicants must have a graduate degree in library science; should be a practicing health sciences librarian with at least two years of professional experience; an individual member of the Medical Library Association; a U.S. or Canadian citizen or has permanent residence status. **Criteria:** Recipients of the awards will be evaluated based on applicant's ability to meet the proposal criteria set by the Awards committee.

Funds Avail.: $100-$1,000. **Duration:** Annual. **Number Awarded:** Varies. **To Apply:** Applicants must submit a completed application form; names of three references; and project proposal; proposals must contain title, goals, objectives, methodology, significance and budget. Nine copies of the completed application form and all related documents should be submitted provided. **Deadline:** December 1. **Contact:** Email: lopez@mail.mlahq.org.

7222 ■ MLA Scholarship *(Graduate, Master's/Scholarship)*

Purpose: To support a student who shows excellence in scholarship and potential for accomplishment in health sciences librarianship. **Focus:** Library and archival sciences. **Qualif.:** Applicant must be entering a Master's program at an ALA-accredited graduate library school or, at the time of the granting of the scholarship (February); must have completed no more than one-half of the academic require-

Awards are arranged alphabetically below their administering organizations

ments of the graduate program and be citizens of or have permanent residence in U.S. or Canada. **Criteria:** Selection will be based on the committee's criteria.

Funds Avail.: $5,000. **Duration:** Annual. **To Apply:** Applicants must submit a completed nomination form including two letters of reference; official transcript; current photo; copy of library school's catalog or web page. **Deadline:** December 1. **Remarks:** Established in 1973. **Contact:** Email: lopez@mail.mlahq.org.

7223 ■ MLA Scholarship for Minority Students (Graduate/Scholarship)

Purpose: To support minority students who are pursuing to enter a Masters program. **Focus:** Health sciences; Library and archival sciences. **Qualif.:** Applicant must be a U.S. or Canadian citizen or have permanent residence status; a member of a minority group (African-American, Hispanic, Asian, Native American, Alaskan Native or Pacific Islander); entering an ALA-accredited graduate library school; must have completed no more than half of the graduate program. **Criteria:** Preference will be given to those who have not been a recipient of the award and based on their qualifications.

Funds Avail.: Up to $5,000. **Duration:** Annual. **To Apply:** Applicants must submit an application form available at the website; two letters of reference from persons not related to the applicant and an official transcript (sent directly by the respective institution to the MLA office); copy of library school's catalog or web page; current photo. **Deadline:** December 1. **Contact:** Email: lopez@mail.mlahq.org.

7224 ■ Medical Scrubs Collection LLC
1665 Corporate Rd. W
Lakewood, NJ 08701
Ph: (732)719-8600
E-mail: customerservice@medicalscrubscollection.com
URL: medicalscrubscollection.com
Social Media: www.facebook.com/pages/Medical-Scrubs
-Collection/228180727226606
www.instagram.com/medicalscrubscollection
www.pinterest.com/medicalscrubsco/
twitter.com/medicalscrubsco

7225 ■ Medical Scrubs Collection Scholarship (Undergraduate, Graduate/Scholarship)

Purpose: To recognize individuals who go above and beyond to help others every day by providing financial assistance to those pursuing a degree in the medical or health field. **Focus:** Health sciences; Medicine; Nursing. **Qualif.:** Applicants should be pursuing a degree in the medical field such as therapy, nursing, medicine, nutrition, laboratory science, or dentistry; high school senior or enrolled in an accredited U.S. college or university; citizen or legal resident of the U.S.; minimum cumulative GPA of 3.0.**Criteria:** Combination of judges' scores and the number of votes garnered on social media. Five to 10 finalists will be selected by judges and posted on the Medical Scrubs Collection's website, where voting will be open to the public.

Funds Avail.: $1,000. **Duration:** Annual. **To Apply:** Submit a transcript along with either 1) an image up to 8.5 x 11 inches, along with a short description, or 2) an essay up to 500 words that explains what inspired you to pursue a degree in the medical field. **Deadline:** December 15. **Contact:** Medical Scrubs Collection, Attn: Scholarship Department, 1665 Corporate Rd., West Lakewood, NJ, 08701;

Email: scholarships@medicalscrubscollection.com.

7226 ■ MedicalFieldCareers.com
1940 Thibodo Rd., No. 203
Vista, CA 92081
Ph: (760)855-8499
URL: medicalfieldcareers.com

7227 ■ MedicalFieldCareers.com Healthcare Scholarship (Professional development/Scholarship)

Purpose: To support aspiring healthcare support professionals and technicians. **Focus:** Health care services. **Qualif.:** Applicant must be enrolled in a nationally-accredited healthcare career training program for the upcoming term; must be a U.S. citizen or current resident; must be at least 18 years old and have a high school diploma or GED. **Criteria:** Selection is based on the best submitted essay.

Funds Avail.: $1,500. **Duration:** Annual. **Number Awarded:** 1. **To Apply:** Applicant must submit an essay of at least 1,000 to 1,500 words explaining why they want to pursue a career in healthcare. Applicant can fill out application and submit essay online at medicalfieldcareers.com/healthcare-scholarship/. **Contact:** jlowman@medicalfieldcareers.com.

7228 ■ Medieval Academy of America (MAA)
17 Dunster St., Ste. 202
Cambridge, MA 02138
Ph: (617)491-1622
Fax: (617)492-3303
E-mail: info@themedievalacademy.org
URL: www.medievalacademy.org
Social Media: twitter.com/MedievalAcademy

7229 ■ Birgit Baldwin Fellowship (Graduate/Fellowship)

Purpose: To help defray research and living expenses for the equivalent of an academic year of study. **Focus:** Medieval studies.

Funds Avail.: $20,000. **Duration:** Annual. **To Apply:** Applicants should upload a PDF file explaining what part of your dissertation research and/or writing you expect to accomplish during the tenure of your fellowship: essay of not more than 1000 words: Explain how your dissertation research requires study in France. Detail where you propose to live and work in France; Describe previous funding you have received to support your dissertation research and how it was used. Explain the need for the Baldwin fellowship to complete the dissertation successfully; a letter of recommendation from your dissertation director and a second graduate professor. **Deadline:** November 15. **Remarks:** The fellowship was established in memory of their daughter Birgit. It is endowed through the generosity of her family. Established in 2004. **Contact:** Lisa Fagin Davis, Medieval Academy of America, 17 Dunster St., Ste. 202, Cambridge, MA, 02138; .E-mail: LFD@TheMedievalAcademy.org.

7230 ■ Medieval Academy Dissertation Grants (Graduate/Grant)

Purpose: To support advanced graduate students who are writing doctoral dissertations on medieval topics. **Focus:** Medieval studies. **Qualif.:** Applicants must be graduate

Awards are arranged alphabetically below their administering organizations

students whose primary research focuses on an aspect of medieval studies; must have received approval from their dissertation committee for their projects by the application date; must be members of the Medieval Academy. **Criteria:** Selection will be based on the following criteria: originality of the dissertation project, the clarity of its methodology, and its likelihood to contribute to medieval studies; the cogency of the writing and organization of the dissertation project description; the dissertation director's statement regarding the excellence of the project and the applicant's preparation to complete the project; the applicant's demonstrated need for the grant to complete the dissertation successfully.

Funds Avail.: $2,000. **To Apply:** Along with the completed application form, applicants must provide a letter of recommendation from the dissertation director certifying that the applicant has passed the qualifying exams and received an approval for the dissertation project and discussing the merits of the project and the applicant's preparation to complete it successfully. The letter of recommendation should be submitted in a sealed envelope signed on the back across the seal or may be sent directly to the Academy office. **Deadline:** February 15. **Contact:** Dissertation Grants, Medieval Academy, 17 Dunster St., Ste. 202. Cambridge, MA, 02138; Executive Director (LFD@ TheMedievalAcademy.org).

7231 ■ Schallek Award (Graduate/Award)

Purpose: To support advanced graduate students who are writing doctoral dissertations on medieval topics. **Focus:** Medieval studies. **Qualif.:** Applicants must be graduate students conducting doctoral research in any relevant discipline dealing with late-medieval Britain (ca. 1350-1500); must be member of the Medieval Academy as of January 15 of the year in which they apply; must be citizens or permanent residents of the United States or Canada. **Criteria:** Selection will be based on the following criteria: The originality of the dissertation project, the clarity of its methodology, and the significance of the subject to be studied for understanding French medieval history; cogency of the writing and organization of the dissertation proposal; the graduate professor's statement regarding the excellence of the project and the applicant's preparation to complete the dissertation; demonstrated need for the grant to complete the dissertation successfully.

Funds Avail.: $2,000. **Duration:** Annual. **Number Awarded:** Varies. **To Apply:** Applicants should upload a PDF file with the following: Describe your research project, rationale, methodology, and significance. What will you accomplish? Why is your project important? How will it contribute to medieval studies?; If the award will support research for a thesis or dissertation, briefly outline its chapters; Detail research expenses for which you request financial support. If you must travel, explain why; Describe previous funding you have received to support your research and how it was used. List other sources you will apply to for financial support; Along with the completed application form, applicants must provide a letter of recommendation from a graduate program professor discussing the merits of the dissertation project and the applicant's preparation to complete it successfully. The letter of recommendation may be submitted by mail or may be sent by email as a signed PDF on letterhead to Executive Director. **Deadline:** February 15. **Contact:** Schallek Award, Medieval Academy, 17 Dunster St., Site. 202, Cambridge, MA 02138.

7232 ■ Schallek Fellowship (Graduate/Fellowship)

Purpose: To support a graduate student who is writing a PhD dissertation in any relevant discipline. **Focus:** Medieval studies.

Funds Avail.: $30,000. **Duration:** Annual. **To Apply:** Along with the completed application form, applicants must submit the following: a dissertation proposal that has been approved by the applicant's dissertation committee; a letter of recommendation from the applicant's dissertation director certifying that the applicant has passed the qualifying exams and received approval for the dissertation project and discussing the merits of the project and the applicant's preparation to complete it successfully; a second letter of recommendation from a graduate professor discussing the merits of the dissertation project and the applicant's preparation to complete it successfully. Completed application consists of six copies of the application form and the dissertation proposal and the two letters of recommendation. **Deadline:** October 15. **Remarks:** The fellowship was established in memory of William B. and Maryloo Spooner Schallek. **Contact:** Schallek Fellowship, Medieval Academy, 17 Dunster St., Ste. 202, Cambridge, MA, 02138.

7233 ■ MEDIGO
Rosenthaler St. 13
10119 Berlin, Germany
E-mail: contact@medigo.com
URL: medigo.com

7234 ■ The MEDIGO Scholarship Program (Undergraduate, Graduate/Scholarship)

Purpose: To support students' with values of diversity and inclusion. **Focus:** General studies/Field of study not specified. **Qualif.:** Applicant must be enrolled, or have been offered a place, at a university or college in the U.S.; must be a student whose university/college has approved the MEDIGO Scholarship Program. **Criteria:** Selection will be based on the essay (creativity, ability to craft an essay, relevance) and how well the applicant aligns with MEDIGO's values of diversity and inclusion.

Funds Avail.: $2,000. **To Apply:** Applicant must submit an essay of 800-1,200 words on the following question: How should a company ensure that all nationalities, races, and cultures are celebrated and integrated into the office environment? Essay should be in Word or PDF. Applicant should submit the essay, along with any questions about the scholarship, to scholarship@medigo.com. Email should also include the student's name, email, date of birth, and the name of the college/university the student is enrolled in or plans to attend. **Deadline:** September 1. **Contact:** URL: www.medigo.com/blog/scholarship/.

7235 ■ Medina County Retired Teachers Association
c/o Nancy McNeal
1044 Brimfield Dr.
Medina, OH 44256
Ph: (330)722-1948
E-mail: greglincrane@roadrunner.com
URL: medinacrta.weebly.com

7236 ■ Medina County Retired Teachers Association Scholarship (Graduate/Scholarship)

Purpose: To support students who have committed themselves to careers in education. **Focus:** General studies/Field of study not specified. **Qualif.:** Applicants must be graduates of any Medina County high school, majoring in education who will be juniors or seniors in college. **Criteria:** Selection will be based on the committee's criteria.

Funds Avail.: Amount varies. **Duration:** Annual. **To Apply:** Applicant must submit an online application form along with recommendation letters. Application should be submitted on sponsor's website. **Deadline:** May 31. **Contact:** Amy Panchumarti; Phone: 330-635-1106; Email: Amy4Ohio@gmail.com.

7237 ■ Meeting Professionals International Connecticut River Valley Chapter (MPI CRV)

701 Hebron Ave., 3rd Fl.
Glastonbury, CT 06033
Ph: (860)541-6438
E-mail: mpicrv@gmail.com
URL: www.mpicrv.org
Social Media: www.facebook.com/MPICRV
www.instagram.com/meetingprofessionalsintl

7238 ■ MPI CRV Membership Scholarships *(Other/Scholarship)*

Purpose: To promote members' professional development and encourage their active participation in the chapter. **Focus:** General studies/Field of study not specified. **Qualif.:** Applicants must be current MPI CRV members in good standing; cost of a Preferred MPI membership for one (1) year. **Criteria:** Selection will be based on an on-going basis for most programs; preference is given to members that have been an MPI member for at least 1 year for most conference and professional development scholarships.

Funds Avail.: No specific amount. **Duration:** Annual. **Contact:** Annamarie Grise, President-Elect, CMP; Phone: 413-577-8232; E-mail: grise@umass.edu.

7239 ■ Meeting Professionals International - Wisconsin Chapter (MPIWI)

2820 Walton Commons, Ste. 103
Madison, WI 53718
Ph: (608)204-9816
Fax: (608)204-9818
URL: www.mpiwi.org
Social Media: www.facebook.com/mpiwi
instagram.com/mpi_wi_chapter
twitter.com/MPIWisconsin

7240 ■ Kristin Bjurstrom Krueger Student Scholarship Program *(Undergraduate/Scholarship)*

Purpose: To provide financial support to students pursuing higher education. **Focus:** General studies/Field of study not specified. **Qualif.:** Applicants must be any person currently enrolled in a course of study in the meetings field at an accredited college; must carry a minimum of six credits per semester and maintain a minimum grade point average of 3.25; this scholarship is available to any student attending a Wisconsin college. **Criteria:** Selection will be based on the committee's criteria.

Funds Avail.: $500. **Duration:** Annual. **To Apply:** Applicants must complete the online Student Scholarship Application form; create an essay on the topic "Why I Want to Work in the meetings Industry." The essay must be typed,

double-spaced and not exceed 500 words; provide one letter of reference from a teacher or an employer; and a transcript that identifies courses of study and grade point average. **Deadline:** May 25. **Contact:** Scholarship Program, MPI Wisconsin Headquarters, 2820 Walton Commons, Ste. 103, Madison, WI 53718.

7241 ■ MPI-WI Founders Grant Program *(Professional development/Grant)*

Purpose: To support individuals to access new ideas, new information, further grow their knowledge within the industry and to help them financially fund their new endeavor. **Focus:** Business. **Qualif.:** Applicants can be any individuals who are current members of MPI-Wisconsin and have been members for at least one year at the date of the application; previous year's winner is not eligible to apply. **Criteria:** Selection will be based on the committee's criteria.

Funds Avail.: $500. **Duration:** Annual. **To Apply:** Applicants must submit the complete application package consists of the online Founders Grant Application form and; a narrative describing the contribution to MPI-Wisconsin, why the applicants deserve the grant and how the grant will benefit the member and MPI-Wisconsin; narrative must be typed, double-spaced, and not to exceed 500 words. **Deadline:** September 8. **Contact:** Scholarship Program, MPI Wisconsin Headquarters, 2820 Walton Commons, Ste. 103, Madison, WI 53718.

7242 ■ Megan Meier Foundation

515 Jefferson St., Ste. A
Saint Charles, MO 63301
Ph: (636)757-3501
E-mail: info@meganmeierfoundation.org
URL: www.meganmeierfoundation.org
Social Media: www.facebook.com/meganmeierfoundation
www.instagram.com/meganmeierfoundation
www.linkedin.com/in/tinameier
www.pinterest.ph/meganmeierfndn
twitter.com/MeganMeierFndn

7243 ■ Megan Meier Memorial Scholarships *(Undergraduate/Scholarship)*

Purpose: To acknowledge high school seniors that have made a positive impact in regards to issues of bullying and cyberbullying in their own school environment and community. **Focus:** General studies/Field of study not specified. **Qualif.:** Applicants must be currently enrolled as a full-time student, in high school or through an approved college correspondence program; must reside in St. Louis City, St. Louis County, or St. Charles County to be eligible; currently possess senior status for the academic year; possess a minimum cumulative GPA 3.0 on most recent report card; passionately pursue bullying and cyberbullying prevention in their school and community. **Criteria:** Priority will be given to students pursuing degrees aimed at helping others (i.e. psychology, social work, nursing)

Funds Avail.: $1,000. **Duration:** Annual. **To Apply:** Applicants must complete the online personal information form and submit the following materials: copy of applicants' most recent report card or transcript; faculty/staff letter of recommendation; any applicable pictures or videos; one to two-page essay including description on how the applicants' accomplishments relate to the mission of the Megan Meier Foundation; must describe ways they have proactively helped to lessen all forms of bullying within your school

Awards are arranged alphabetically below their administering organizations

community; professional goals after graduation, specifically the degree you plan to pursue and the ways in which you plan to use your degree to continue helping others. **Deadline:** January 31. **Contact:** Kate Bolhofner, Director of Community Outreach, Phone: 636-757-3501; Email: kate@meganmeierfoundation.org.

7244 ■ Melanoma Foundation of New England

490 Virginia Rd., Ste. 11
Concord, MA 01742
Ph: (978)371-5613
Fax: (978)371-0109
Free: 800-557-6352
E-mail: info@impactmelanoma.org
URL: mfne.org
Social Media: www.facebook.com/IMPACTMelanoma
twitter.com/IMPACTMelanoma

7245 ■ Your Skin Is In College Ambassador Scholarships *(Undergraduate/Scholarship)*

Purpose: To help spread awareness of melanoma and melanoma prevention. **Focus:** General studies/Field of study not specified. **Qualif.:** Applicants must be college students and must be registered for Your Skin Is In. **Criteria:** Selection will be based on committee's criteria.

Funds Avail.: $1,000. **To Apply:** Applicants must do the following: Take the eLearning lesson to become an educated Your Skin Is In Ambassador! Be sure to play the Trivia Game, watch the 3 video scenarios, and check out the "how are you exposed?" and "take action" sections!; Take the Your Skin Is In Pledge themselves. Then, share their unique referral link with their classmates, friends and family so they can take the Pledge too!. Applicants should educate others and spread the word at their campus with the ideas in the Ambassador Toolkit; submit an application explaining what they did at their campus as an Ambassador. We'll ask them about how they used the program at their school, how many pledges they collected, what they learned with the eLearning program, and any results they saw because of their efforts. **Deadline:** April 13.

7246 ■ The Melissa Institute for Violence Prevention and Treatment

1507 Levante Ave. Ste. 331
Coral Gables, FL 33146
Ph: (305)284-2930
E-mail: info@melissainstitute.org
URL: www.melissainstitute.org
Social Media: www.facebook.com/melissainstitute
twitter.com/melissainstitut

7247 ■ Belfer-Aptman Dissertation Research Awards *(Doctorate/Award)*

Purpose: To provide financial assistance to support expenses that are directly related to violence prevention research. **Focus:** Aggression and violence. **Qualif.:** Applicants must be students in an accredited doctoral dissertation program; may be from any academic discipline; must have their dissertation proposal approved by their dissertation committee prior to their application to the Melissa Institute. **Criteria:** Selection will be based on the committee's criteria.

Funds Avail.: $3,500. **Duration:** Annual. **Number Awarded:** 3. **To Apply:** Applicants must submit the title of

the proposed thesis; a brief 300 - 500 word abstract of proposed study; hypotheses to be tested and research design; description of subjects number and how selected; list of proposed measures; proposed data analyses; budget justification (not counted as part of the abstract word count); proposed timeline for completion; a curriculum vitae, including any scientific publications and presentations with a brief description of their career plan; a letter of recommendation from their dissertation advisor. **Deadline:** April 25. **Remarks:** The award was established to honor the memory of Melissa Aptman, a Miami native. **Contact:** The Melissa Institute Belfer-Aptman Scholars Award for Dissertation Research, Donald Meichenbaum, Ph.D, 1507 Levante Ave., Ste. 331, Coral Gables, FL, 33146; Phone: 305-284-2930; Fax: 305-284-2960; Email: Info@melissainstitute.org.

7248 ■ Memorial Foundation for Jewish Culture (MFJC)

50 Broadway, 34th Fl.
New York, NY 10004
Ph: (212)425-6606
Fax: (212)425-6602
E-mail: info@mfjc.org
URL: www.mfjc.org

7249 ■ International Scholarship Programs for Community Service *(Undergraduate/Scholarship)*

Purpose: To assist well-qualified individuals to train for careers in the rabbinate, Jewish education, social work and as religious functionaries. **Focus:** Education, Religious; Jewish studies; Social work. **Qualif.:** Applicants must be undergoing (or planning to undergo) training in a recognized yeshiva, teacher training seminary, school of social work, university or other educational institution; must commit to serve in a community of need for a minimum of two to three years and must be knowledgeable in the language and culture. **Criteria:** Selection of recipients will be done by outside experts and appropriate committees of the foundation.

Duration: Annual. **To Apply:** Applications may be obtained through individual written requests with a brief description of the project from the Memorial Foundation for Jewish Culture. **Deadline:** November 30.

7250 ■ MFJC Doctoral Scholarships *(Doctorate/Scholarship)*

Purpose: To help train qualified individuals for careers in Jewish scholarship and research. **Focus:** Jewish studies. **Qualif.:** Applicant must be any graduate student specializing in a Jewish field who is officially enrolled or registered in a doctoral program at a recognized university with an approved dissertation. **Criteria:** Applications and references are evaluated by outside experts and then considered by appropriate committees of the foundation.

Funds Avail.: $10,000. **Duration:** Annual; one academic year. **To Apply:** Application is available online on sponsor's website. **Deadline:** November 16.

7251 ■ MFJC Fellowship Grants *(Professional development/Fellowship)*

Purpose: To assist individuals in carrying out an independent scholarly, literary or art project, in a field of Jewish specialization, which makes a significant contribution to the understanding, preservation, enhancement, or transmission of Jewish culture. **Focus:** Jewish studies. **Qualif.:** Ap-

---

Awards are arranged alphabetically below their administering organizations

plicants must be qualified scholars, researchers, or artists who possess the knowledge and experience to formulate and implement a project in a field of Jewish studies.

Funds Avail.: Up to $10,000. **Duration:** Annual; one academic year. **To Apply:** Application information is available on sponsor's website. **Deadline:** November 16.

7252 ■ Ephraim E. Urbach Post-Doctoral Fellowship
(Postdoctorate/Fellowship)

Purpose: To assist well-qualified individuals in carrying out an independent scholarly, literary or art project, in a field of Jewish specialization, which makes a significant contribution to the understanding, preservation, enhancement, or transmission of Jewish culture. **Focus:** Jewish studies. **Qualif.:** Applicants must be graduates of a Ph.D. program in a field of Jewish Studies who is interested in publishing their first book, launching their scholarly career, and/or furthering research in their area of special interest.

To Apply: Applicants must be nominated by their university/department or dissertation supervisor in a letter to the MFJC indicating that the PhD was granted with distinction; two additional letters of reference supporting the applicant's candidacy are also required. Links for these reference letters are provided with the application.

7253 ■ Mennonite Central Committee (MCCC)
134 Plaza Dr.
Winnipeg, MB, Canada R3T 5K9
Ph: (204)261-6381
Fax: (204)269-9875
Free: 888-622-6337
E-mail: canada@mcccanada.ca
URL: mcccanada.ca
Social Media: www.facebook.com/MCCpeace
www.instagram.com/mccpeace
twitter.com/mccorg?lang=en

7254 ■ Canadian Japanese-Mennonite Scholarship
(Undergraduate/Scholarship)

Purpose: To assist the protection of minority and human rights in Canada and to reduce the potential for abuse of cultural minorities. **Focus:** Human rights. **Qualif.:** Applicants must be enrolled in a graduate degree program; must be a Canadian citizen studying at a University in Canada; must be engaged in research that will assist the protection of minority or human rights in Canada. **Criteria:** Selection will be based on the committee's criteria.

Funds Avail.: $2,000. **Duration:** Annual. **To Apply:** Applicants must complete the application form available on the website and include a one page description of how the academic work will contribute to the objectives of the scholarship; must provide a reference letter and information page. **Remarks:** Established in 1984. **Contact:** MCC Canada, Attn: CJM Scholarship; 134 Plaza Dr., Winnipeg, MBR3T 5K9; Email: canada@mennonitecc.ca.

7255 ■ The Menominee Indian Tribe of Wisconsin (MITW)
W2908 Tribal Office Loop Rd.
Keshena, WI 54135
Ph: (715)799-5100
Free: 877-209-5866
URL: menominee-nsn.gov

7256 ■ Menominee Tribal Scholarships *(Undergraduate, Graduate, High School/Scholarship)*

Purpose: To provide assistance and support to Menominees and Community Residents who are in need of preparation to advance in the workforce and to pursue higher educational opportunities. **Focus:** General studies/Field of study not specified. **Qualif.:** Applicants must be Menominee tribe members and Wisconsin residents pursuing higher education; undergraduate 4-year college students; vocational/technical/tribal college students. **Criteria:** Selection will be based on the aforementioned applicants qualifications and compliance with the application details.

Funds Avail.: $1,000. **Duration:** Annual. **Number Awarded:** 4. **To Apply:** Applicants must provide and submit the letter of acceptance; grade report/transcript; letter of recommendation/support; personal essay; and proof of tribal enrollment.

7257 ■ Mensa Canada
1 Eglinton Ave. E., Suite 705
Toronto, ON, Canada M4P 3A1
Free: 844-202-6761
E-mail: info@mensacanada.org
URL: www.mensacanada.org
Social Media: www.facebook.com/MensaCanada
twitter.com/MensaCanada

7258 ■ Edgar Kerstan Memorial Scholarship
(Undergraduate/Scholarship)

Purpose: To help students pursue their post-secondary education. **Focus:** General studies/Field of study not specified. **Qualif.:** Applicants must be enrolled full-time in a full-time program at a Canadian post-secondary institution; must be Canadian citizens or landed immigrants; must be 18 years old on January 31 of the current year.

Funds Avail.: 3,000 Canadian Dollars. **Duration:** Annual. **To Apply:** Applicants must submit a 250-word essay describing plans for achieving their goals. It should be written either in English or French; must provide proof of citizenship and two letters of reference. **Deadline:** January 31. **Remarks:** The scholarship was established in honor of Edgar Kerstan's commitment to Mensa Canada. Established in 2011.

7259 ■ Mensa Canada Scholarship Programme
(Undergraduate/Scholarship)

Purpose: To help students pursue their post-secondary education. **Focus:** General studies/Field of study not specified. **Qualif.:** Applicants must be enrolled full-time in a full-time program at a Canadian post-secondary institution; must be Canadian citizens or landed immigrants; must be 18 years old on January 31 of the current year. **Criteria:** Selection will be evaluated based on submitted essay.

Funds Avail.: $2,000. **Duration:** Annual. **Number Awarded:** Varies. **To Apply:** Applicants submit a 250-word essay describing their career goals and their efforts on the path to achieve those goals. **Deadline:** January 31.

7260 ■ The Frank & Betty Woodhams Memorial Scholarship *(Undergraduate/Scholarship)*

Purpose: To help students pursue their post-secondary education. **Focus:** Computer and information sciences; Mathematics and mathematical sciences. **Qualif.:** Ap-

Awards are arranged alphabetically below their administering organizations

plicants must be enrolled full-time in either a Computer Science or Mathematics program at a Canadian university; must be Canadian citizens or landed immigrants. **Criteria:** Selection will be evaluated based on submitted essay.

Funds Avail.: 2,700 Canadian Dollars. **Duration:** Annual. **Number Awarded:** Varies. **To Apply:** Applicants must submit a 250-word essay describing plans for achieving their goals. It should be written either in English or French; must provide proof of citizenship and two letters of reference. **Remarks:** The scholarship was established in a memory of Mr. Woodhams' 20-years with Mensa Canada, and his commitment to providing a stimulating intellectual and social environment for its members. **Contact:** Email: essay@mensacanada.ca with "Essay Competition" as the subject.

7261 ■ Mensa Education and Research Foundation

1200 E Copeland Rd. Ste. 550
Arlington, TX 76011
Ph: (817)607-5577
Fax: (817)649-5232
E-mail: info@mensafoundation.org
URL: www.mensafoundation.org

7262 ■ Mensa Education and Research Foundation U.S. Scholarship *(Undergraduate/Scholarship)*

Purpose: To support students in their educational pursuits. **Focus:** General studies/Field of study not specified. **Qualif.:** Applicants must be U.S. citizens or permanent residents enrolled in a degree program in an accredited U.S. institution of higher learning during the academic year following the application date. **Criteria:** Selection will be based on committee's criteria.

Funds Avail.: $100,000. **Duration:** Annual. **Number Awarded:** Varies. **To Apply:** Applicants must submit an application and essay explaining his or her career, academic or vocational goals. **Deadline:** January 15. **Contact:** Email: director@mensafoundation.org.

7263 ■ Mental Health Research Canada

180 Bloor St. W, UC 101
Toronto, ON, Canada M5S 2V6
URL: www.mhrc.ca
Social Media: facebook.com/MHRCanada
twitter.com/MHRCanada

7264 ■ OMHF Postdoctoral Fellowships *(Postdoctorate/Fellowship)*

Purpose: To provide an opportunity for a person with a PhD to obtain further training. **Focus:** Mental health. **Qualif.:** Applicants must hold a professional qualification in a field relevant to mental health. **Criteria:** Preference will be given to applicants who have not yet previously held a postdoctoral position.

To Apply: Applicants must submit a complete application consisting of applicant's letter (plans for a long-term career and details of any support anticipated or sought from other sources); factsheet (page A); resubmission sheet (page B); project summary sheet (page C); administration of funds (page G); plain language statement; project description (background, hypothesis/research question, methods, originality, timetable, references); consent forms; curriculum vitae and recent publications; department head's ac-

ceptance letter; supervisor's letter; transcripts; and references (in signed, sealed envelopes). Applicants are required to submit applications both online and in a paper format.

7265 ■ Merchants Exchange Scholarship Fund

200 SW Market St., Ste. 190
Portland, OR 97201
Ph: (503)228-4361
Fax: (503)295-3660
URL: pdxmex.com
Social Media: www.linkedin.com/company/merchants
-exchange-of-portland
twitter.com/TheExchangePDX

7266 ■ Merchants Exchange Scholarship *(Undergraduate, Vocational/Occupational, Graduate, Professional development/Scholarship)*

Purpose: To strengthen the maritime industry by supporting students seeking or advancing careers in the industry. **Focus:** International trade; Maritime studies; Oceanography. **Qualif.:** Applicant must be a student in a four-year college or university (junior or senior year), a student in a two-year degree program (any year), a graduate student (any year), or a student in the US Coast Guard-approved training program (any year); have a minimum 2.5 GPA in a program of study focused on the maritime industry and/or related fields; and be pursuing or advancing a career in the maritime industry. **Criteria:** Selection is based the recipients of the Merchants Exchange Scholarship will be selected by the Merchants Exchange Scholarship Fund Board of Directors and rewarded to outstanding individuals who meet the following criteria

Funds Avail.: $500 to $2,500. **Number Awarded:** 1-10. **To Apply:** Application must be completed online (short answers and essay questions). Applicant must also provide a certified copy of their academic transcripts and submit one letter of recommendation from a professor or direct supervisor. **Deadline:** May 31. **Contact:** Email: scholarship@pdxmex.com; URL: www.pdxmex.com/scholarship.

7267 ■ Merck Company Foundation

2000 Galloping Hill Rd.
Kenilworth, NJ 07033-1310
Ph: (908)740-4000
URL: www.msdresponsibility.com

7268 ■ UNCF Merck Graduate Science Research Dissertation Fellowships *(Graduate/Fellowship)*

Purpose: To increase the number of African Americans in the pipeline of biomedical science education and research in the fields of biological and physical sciences. **Focus:** Engineering; Life sciences; Physical sciences. **Qualif.:** Candidates must be African-American; must be citizens or permanent residents of the United States; must be enrolled full-time in a PhD or equivalent doctoral degree program majoring in a life science, physical science or engineering; must be engaged in and within 1-3 years of completing dissertation research; and must successfully complete all qualifying exams. **Criteria:** Selection will be based on academic ability and record of accomplishment of the Applicants and the soundness of the proposed doctoral research plan.

Awards are arranged alphabetically below their administering organizations

Funds Avail.: Up to $53,500. **Duration:** Annual. **Number Awarded:** 10. **To Apply:** Applicants may contact the UNCF or the Merck Company Foundation for the application process and other information. **Contact:** United Negro College Fund, 8260 Willow Oaks Corporate Dr., Ste 510, Fairfax, VA 22031-8044; Phone: 800-331-2244, E-mail: uncfmerck@uncf.org.

7269 ■ UNCF/Merck Postdoctoral Science Research Fellowships *(Postdoctorate/Scholarship)*

Purpose: To support post-graduate students to obtain postdoctoral training and to prepare for a career in biomedical research. **Focus:** Engineering; Life sciences; Physical sciences. **Qualif.:** Applicants must be African-Americans; must be citizens or permanent residents of the United States; must be PhD or equivalent doctoral degree recipients in a life or physical science by the end of the current academic year; must be appointed as new or continuing postdoctoral fellows at an academic or on-academic research institution in the USA (private industrial laboratories are excluded). **Criteria:** Selection will be based on academic ability and record of accomplishment of the Applicants and the soundness of the proposed doctoral research plan.

Funds Avail.: Up to $92,000. **Duration:** Annual. **Number Awarded:** 10. **To Apply:** Applicants may contact the UNCF or the Merck Company Foundation for the application process and other information.

7270 ■ George Cedric Metcalf Charitable Foundation
38 Madison Ave.
Toronto, ON, Canada M5R 2S1
URL: metcalffoundation.com

7271 ■ Metcalf Innovation Fellowship program
(Advanced Professional, Professional development/ Fellowship)

Purpose: To support individuals who have vision, passion for their issue, intellectual rigour and willingness to ask hard questions and propose novel solutions. **Focus:** Medical research. **Qualif.:** Applicants must be policymakers, managers, academicians, or entrepreneurs; must have a significant record of achievement and be recognized within their field; and must have worked in an area related to their proposed exploration for a minimum of ten years. **Criteria:** Selection will be based on the applicants' respective research proposals.

Funds Avail.: Maximum of 30,000 Canadian Dollars; Typical awards - $15,000-$25,000. **To Apply:** Applicants can review all information on the website regarding the Innovation Fellowship program. Interested individuals are encouraged to contact the Program Director in the field most closely aligned with their work. **Remarks:** Established in 2005. **Contact:** Metcalf Foundation, 38 Madison Ave., Toronto, Ontario, Canada, M5R 2S1; Fax: 416-926-0370; Email: info@metcalffoundation.com; Heather Dunford, Grants Manager; Email: hdunford@metcalffoundation.com; Phone: 416-926-0366 x 233.

7272 ■ Metropolitan Museum of Art
1000 5th Ave.
New York, NY 10028
Ph: (212)535-7710
Fax: (212)472-2764

URL: www.metmuseum.org
Social Media: www.facebook.com/metmuseum
www.instagram.com/metmuseum
www.pinterest.com/metmuseum
twitter.com/metmuseum
www.youtube.com/user/metmuseum

7273 ■ The Bothmer Fellowship *(Doctorate, Graduate/Fellowship)*

Purpose: To provide an opportunity for fellows to present short papers on their work in progress to university colleagues and Museum staff. **Focus:** Art history. **Qualif.:** Applicants must be outstanding graduate students who have been admitted to the doctoral program of a university in the United States and who have submitted outlines of their theses dealing with either Greek or Roman art. **Criteria:** Preference will be given to the applicant who, in the opinion of the Grants Committee, will profit most from utilizing the resources of the Department of Greek and Roman Art: its collections, library, and photographic and other archives, and the guidance of its curatorial staff.

Funds Avail.: No specific amount.

7274 ■ Conservation and Scientific Research Fellowships *(Graduate/Fellowship)*

Purpose: To provide an opportunity for fellows to present short papers on their work in progress to university colleagues and Museum staff. **Focus:** Museum science.

Funds Avail.: $42,000 for junior fellows and $52,000 for senior fellows, with up to an additional $6,000 for travel. **Duration:** Annual; 6 weeks. **To Apply:** Applicant must submit full curriculum vitae of education, professional experience, honors, awards, and publications; statement of interest and intent, not to exceed one thousand words, describing why The Metropolitan Museum of Art in uniquely suited to applicant's fellowship objectives, and how they will utilize the Museum's resources to achieve their goals; official undergraduate and graduate transcripts; contact information for three recommendations; Paper Conservation applicant only: two treatment reports and associated documentation with explanations justifying the reason for treatment and decision entering each stage of treatment (not to exceed 750 words per project). **Contact:** Email: academic.programs@metmuseum.org.

7275 ■ Chester Dale Fellowships *(Doctorate/ Fellowship)*

Purpose: To provide an opportunity for fellows to present short papers on their work in progress to university colleagues and Museum staff. **Focus:** Art. **Qualif.:** Applicants whose fields of study are related to the fine arts of the Western world and who are preferably American citizens under the age of 40.

Funds Avail.: No specific amount. **Duration:** Three months to one year.

7276 ■ The Douglass Foundation Fellowship in American Art *(Graduate/Fellowship)*

Purpose: To provide an opportunity for fellows to present short papers on their work in progress to university colleagues and Museum staff. **Focus:** Arts. **Qualif.:** Applicants must be enrolled for at least one year in an advanced degree program in the field of American art or culture.

Funds Avail.: No specific amount. **Remarks:** The Scholarship Fund was established in honor of John K. Howat.

Awards are arranged alphabetically below their administering organizations

7277 ■ Annette Kade Fellowships *(Graduate/Fellowship)*

Purpose: To provide an opportunity for fellows to present short papers on their work in progress to university colleagues and Museum staff. **Focus:** Art history. **Qualif.:** Applicants must be French or German pre-doctoral art history students who would not otherwise have the opportunity to study in the United States. **Criteria:** Selection will be based on the committee's criteria.

Funds Avail.: No specific amount. **To Apply:** Applicants need not specify the name of a particular fellowship. Fellowship applications must be submitted in English. Three letters of recommendation are required, none of which may be from current Metropolitan Museum of Art staff. The submission of the required letters of recommendation in English is encouraged. Applicants must submit a typed application in triplicate including the following, in the order listed: Name, home and present address, and telephone number; full resume of education and employment; two-part statement, not to exceed 1,000 words, specifying what the applicant wishes to accomplish during the fellowship period and detailing how the Museum's resources can be utilized to accomplish the applicant's goals; tentative schedule of work to be accomplished during the fellowship period; tentative schedule of travel required during the fellowship period; three letters of recommendation (at least one academic and one professional); list of other applications for fellowships or grants applied for in same period; official undergraduate and graduate transcripts (for pre-doctoral applicants).

7278 ■ J. Clawson Mills Scholarships *(Doctorate/Fellowship)*

Purpose: To provide an opportunity for fellows to present short papers on their work in progress to university colleagues and Museum staff. **Focus:** Art. **Qualif.:** Applicants must be conducting research at the Museum or abroad in any branch of fine arts relating to the Metropolitan Museum's collection.

Funds Avail.: No specific amount.

7279 ■ Polaire Weissman Fund Fellowship *(Graduate/Fellowship)*

Purpose: To provide an opportunity for fellows to present short papers on their work in progress to university colleagues and Museum staff. **Focus:** Architecture; Arts; Design. **Qualif.:** Applicants must be graduate students interested in pursuing an academic or museum career in the history of conservation of dress; must be enrolled for at least one year in an advanced degree program in the field of art, architecture, cultural studies, design, or costume history.

Funds Avail.: No specific amount.

7280 ■ Research Scholarship in Photograph Conservation *(Graduate/Scholarship)*

Purpose: To provide an opportunity for fellows to present short papers on their work in progress to university colleagues and Museum staff. **Focus:** Museum science. **Qualif.:** Applicants must have a graduate degree in conservation or equivalent experience and should be completely committed to the conservation of photographs as their area of specialization.

Funds Avail.: $52,000 per year, plus a $6,000 travel allowance. **Duration:** 6 weeks. **To Apply:** Applicants must submit full curriculum vitae of education, professional experience, honors, awards, and publications; project proposals; contact information for three recommenders (at least one academic and one professional); once you have submitted your recommenders' names, titles, and email addresses, they will automatically be emailed instructions for uploading their letters online; we encourage recommenders to submit letters in English. **Contact:** Email: academic.programs@metmuseum.org.

7281 ■ Theodore Rousseau Fellowships *(Graduate/Fellowship)*

Purpose: To provide an opportunity for fellows to present short papers on their work in progress to university colleagues and Museum staff. **Focus:** Painting.

Funds Avail.: No specific amount.

7282 ■ The Slifka Foundation Interdisciplinary Fellowship *(Doctorate, Master's/Fellowship)*

Purpose: To provide an opportunity for fellows to present short papers on their work in progress to university colleagues and Museum staff. **Focus:** Painting. **Qualif.:** Applicants must be in the Ph.D. level for training in an interdisciplinary approach or joining art historical research with technical investigation of the Museum's Northern Renaissance and German paintings. **Criteria:** Recipient of this fellowship will conduct research with the curator for the collection catalogue of early Netherlandish paintings.

Funds Avail.: No specific amount.

7283 ■ The Hanns Swarzenski and Brigitte Horney Swarzenski Fellowship *(Graduate/Fellowship)*

Purpose: To provide an opportunity for fellows to present short papers on their work in progress to university colleagues and Museum staff. **Focus:** Art history. **Qualif.:** Applicants must be promising young scholars who wish to study and research at the Museum. **Criteria:** Preference will be given to applicants with a proven interest in museum work or those planning to pursue a museum career in the field of Medieval Art.

Funds Avail.: No specific amount.

7284 ■ Jane and Morgan Whitney Fellowships *(Graduate/Fellowship)*

Purpose: To provide an opportunity for fellows to present short papers on their work in progress to university colleagues and Museum staff. **Focus:** Art. **Qualif.:** Applicants must be students of the fine arts whose fields are related to the Museum's collections. **Criteria:** Preference will be given to students in the decorative arts who are under 40 years of age.

Funds Avail.: No specific amount.

7285 ■ Mexican American Bar Foundation
6100 Center Dr., Ste. 1130
Los Angeles, CA 90045
Ph: (424)675-1810
URL: www.themabf.org
Social Media: www.facebook.com/themabf

7286 ■ MABF Scholarships *(Professional development/Scholarship)*

Purpose: To support Latino students in their pursuit of legal education. **Focus:** Law. **Criteria:** Selection will be based on the applicants' financial need, academic achieve-

Awards are arranged alphabetically below their administering organizations

ment, community service, leadership experience and any hardship experienced in pursuing an education.

Funds Avail.: Range from $7,500 to $15,000. **Duration:** Annual. **Number Awarded:** 25. **To Apply:** Applications can be submitted online. **Deadline:** March 10. **Remarks:** Established in 1991.

7287 ■ Mexican American Catholic College (MACC)

3115 W Ashby Pl.
San Antonio, TX 78228-5104
Ph: (210)732-2156
E-mail: macc@maccsa.org
URL: maccsa.org

7288 ■ MACC Scholarships (Other/Scholarship)

Purpose: To support an individual's spiritual and educational journey. **Focus:** Education, Religious; Foreign languages. **Qualif.:** Applicants must be a member of any religious community. **Criteria:** Priority will be given to applicants ministering in the United States with possible exceptions based on individual requests and based on need.

Funds Avail.: No specific amount. **To Apply:** Applicant must have the registration form and fee; must have two letters of recommendation from the applicant's superior, bishop, chancellor, pastor, or supervisor; must have one letter from the organization's executive director; must have 2-3 typed pages of autobiography (pastoral program only); must have a questionnaire and placement (language program only).

7289 ■ Mexican American Legal Defense and Educational Fund (MALDEF)

634 S Spring St.,11th Fl.
Los Angeles, CA 90014
Ph: (213)629-2512
E-mail: info@maldef.org
URL: www.maldef.org
Social Media: www.facebook.com/MALDEF
instagram.com/maldefian
twitter.com/MALDEF
www.youtube.com/user/maldef

7290 ■ MALDEF Dream Act Student Activist Scholarships (Undergraduate, Graduate/Scholarship)

Purpose: To support the nation's college and graduate student leaders who have been outstanding advocates for the DREAM Act and all immigrants rights. **Focus:** Civil rights; Law. **Qualif.:** Applicants must be enrolled undergraduate or graduate students with a record of activism around immigrant rights and/or active in the Dreamer movement. **Criteria:** Selection will be based on both demonstrated academic merit and potential for academic success, as well as financial need.

Duration: Annual. **To Apply:** Applicants must submit a completed application form; current resume; a 500-word each essay, responses to: applicants' background and financial need; an activism that the applicants engaged in around the DREAM Act and in support of immigrant rights; and applicants' future plans. **Deadline:** February 15.

7291 ■ MALDEF Law School Scholarship Program (Undergraduate, Graduate/Scholarship)

Purpose: To increase the number of Latinos in the legal profession; to provide financial assistance to qualified individuals in pursuit of higher education. **Focus:** Law. **Qualif.:** Applicants must be students who are enrolled full-time at an accredited United States law school and are completing their first law degree; must seek to advance the civil rights of the Latino community in the United States. **Criteria:** Selection will be awarded to candidates who have outstanding academic record including participation and leadership in extracurricular activities, and financial need.

Funds Avail.: $2,000. **Duration:** Annual. **Number Awarded:** 5-10. **To Apply:** Applicants must complete and send the following materials; a completed and signed MALDEF Scholarship form; current resume; a typed personal statement of 750 words or less, double-spaced, detailing professional objectives, plans after school, and describing their past involvement in activities for which they believed would served or benefited the Latino community and how these activities affect their decision to pursue a career in the legal profession; an official undergraduate transcript or photocopy of an official transcript; for law students who have already completed one year or more of law school, please, also provide; an official law school transcript or photocopy of an official transcript; a letter of recommendation describing their involvement in the Latino community from a person familiar with that involvement; a letter of recommendation from a college, or law school professor; and enclosed statement from the financial aid office of the school currently attending which indicates the financial assistance provided. **Deadline:** December 31. **Contact:** Email: lawscholarships@maldef.org.

7292 ■ MHI

8720 Red Oak Blvd., Ste. 201
Charlotte, NC 28217
Ph: (704)676-1190
Fax: (704)676-1199
Free: 800-345-1815
URL: www.mhi.org
Social Media: www.facebook.com/poweredbymhi
www.linkedin.com/company/mhi---the-industry-that-makes
 -supply-chains-work

7293 ■ Material Handling Education Foundation Scholarships (Doctorate, Graduate, Undergraduate/Scholarship)

Purpose: To promote the study of material handling and to expose as many students as possible to the material handling industry, including the vast array of equipment, systems and technologies represented by the industry; the role material handling in a productive enterprise; and career paths available within the supplier, distributor and end-user (applications) sides of the industry. **Focus:** Education, Industrial.

Funds Avail.: Varies. **Remarks:** Established in 1976. **Contact:** Donna Varner at dvarner@mhi.org or 704-676-1190.

7294 ■ Miami County Retired Teachers Association

c/o Barbara Miller, Membership Chair
6644 Roberta Dr.
Tipp City, OH 45371

Awards are arranged alphabetically below their administering organizations

Ph: (937)667-1563
URL: miamicountyrta.weebly.com

7295 ■ MCRTA Book Scholarships *(Undergraduate/ Scholarship)*

Purpose: To support students with their studies. **Focus:** General studies/Field of study not specified. **Qualif.:** Applicants must be high school seniors in Miami County in Ohio. **Criteria:** Selection will be based on the committee's criteria.

Funds Avail.: $250. **Duration:** Annual. **Number Awarded:** 4. **To Apply:** Applicants may contact the Scholarship Chair for the application process and other information. **Contact:** Scholarship Chair, Alice Fae Detert, 164 Kiser Dr., Tipp City, OH, 45371.

7296 ■ The Miami Foundation

40 NW 3rd Street Suite, 305
Miami, FL 33128
Ph: (305)371-2711
Fax: (305)371-5342
E-mail: info@miamifoundation.org
URL: www.miamifoundation.org
Social Media: www.facebook.com/themiamifoundation
www.instagram.com/miamifoundation
twitter.com/miamifoundation
www.youtube.com/user/TheMiamiFoundation

7297 ■ Alan R. Epstein "Reach for the Stars" Scholarships *(College/Scholarship)*

Purpose: To honor the life of an outstanding young man who was tragically killed in an automobile accident. **Focus:** General studies/Field of study not specified. **Qualif.:** Applicants must be high school seniors graduating in May or June 2019; must be accepted to a college or university. **Criteria:** Selection are evaluated based on financial need, Recommendation, Official Transcript, Personal Statement-Essay.

Funds Avail.: $1,000 to $5,000. **Duration:** One year. **To Apply:** Applicants must submit completed application form; high school official transcript; college acceptance letters; two letters of recommendation; volunteer/work experience and school activities; personal statement; one or two paragraphs describing the importance of scholarship. **Deadline:** April 15.

7298 ■ Judge Sidney M. Aronovitz Memorial Scholarship Fund *(Undergraduate/Scholarship)*

Purpose: To provide financial assistance to Miami-Dade County minority students planning to continue their education at the university level and pursue a career in South Florida. **Focus:** General studies/Field of study not specified. **Qualif.:** Applicants must be minority high school seniors or GED recipients no older than 19 years of age attending a Miami Dade County public school with a minimum high school grade point average of 3.0. **Criteria:** Selection will be based on Career and educational aspirations; recommendations; academic achievement; financial need; and volunteer/work experience.

Funds Avail.: $1,000 to $3,000. **Duration:** Annual. **To Apply:** Applications can be submitted online. **Deadline:** April 15.

7299 ■ Jacki Tuckfield Memorial Graduate Business Scholarship Fund *(Doctorate, Graduate, Master's/ Scholarship)*

Purpose: To provide financial assistance to African-American students to pursue their professional careers.

Focus: Business. **Qualif.:** Applicant must be African American United States citizen, resident of South Florida, enrolled in a graduate business degree program (master's or doctoral), at Florida University; must be planning to pursue professional career in South Florida. **Criteria:** Recipients are selected based on merit.

To Apply: Applicants must submit the completed application form; essay; transcripts; color passport photo; letter of recommendation; and resume.

7300 ■ Michigan Association of Certified Public Accountants

888 West Big Beaver Rd.Suite 550
Troy, MI 48084
Ph: (248)267-3700
URL: micpa.org
Social Media: www.facebook.com/MichiganCPAs
www.linkedin.com/company/micpa
twitter.com/MichiganCPAs
www.youtube.com/user/MichiganCPAs

7301 ■ Michigan Accountancy Foundation Final Year Accounting Scholarship *(Graduate/Scholarship)*

Purpose: To encourage students to become certified public accountants in Michigan. **Focus:** Accounting. **Qualif.:** Applicants must be accounting students attending Michigan colleges; have passed the Michigan CPA Exam; United State citizen or eligible for permanent employment in the United States. **Criteria:** Selection shall be based on the aforementioned applicants' qualifications and compliance with the application details.

Funds Avail.: No specific amount. **Duration:** Annual. **Number Awarded:** Varies. **To Apply:** Applicants must submit official transcripts with university/college seal for all college level coursework's, including all courses completed in the term prior to the fixed application deadline (course grades for fall term just prior to deadline may be submitted separately); two essays (500 words or less); two letters of recommendation, including one from a faculty member; Current resume. **Deadline:** January 31. **Contact:** Michigan Accountancy Foundation, Attn: Rachel Lombardo, 5480 Corporate Dr., Ste. 200, Troy, MI 48098; Email: rlombardo@micpa.org.

7302 ■ Michigan Association of Fire Fighters (MAFF)

667 E. Big Beaver Rd. Suite 109
Troy, MI 48083
Ph: (248)509-7160
Fax: (248)509-7176
Free: 800-509-7176
URL: www.maff.org

7303 ■ Carl Parsell Scholarship Fund *(Undergraduate/Scholarship)*

Purpose: To assist members and their families to pursue a college education. **Focus:** General studies/Field of study not specified. **Qualif.:** Applicants must be residents of Michigan; be members or relatives of employees of one of the following organizations: Michigan Association of Police, Michigan Association of Fire Fighters, or Michigan Association of Public Employees. Must have not been convicted of any misdemeanors or felonies; and must be enrolled full-

Awards are arranged alphabetically below their administering organizations

time at an accredited educational institution. **Criteria:** Selection will be based on academic achievement and potential, character, leadership, social awareness, career goals, financial need, will to succeed, and public service/community involvement.

Funds Avail.: $2,500. **Duration:** Annual. **To Apply:** Applicants must submit an original application form; should submit applications on the forms available (or photocopies of these forms). **Deadline:** March 1. **Remarks:** The scholarship was established to continue the legacy of Parsell, a law enforcement union movement pioneer. Established in 1991. **Contact:** 667 E Big Beaver Rd., Ste. 109, Troy, MI, 48083; Phone: 248-509-7160; Fax: 248-509-7176; Email: jpalmquist@mapmapemaff.com.

7304 ■ Michigan Auto Law

30101 Northwestern Hwy.
Farmington Hills, MI 48334
Free: 866-886-9668
E-mail: help@michiganautolaw.com
URL: www.michiganautolaw.com
Social Media: www.facebook.com/MichiganAutoLaw/
www.instagram.com/official_miautolaw/
www.linkedin.com/company/michiganautolaw
twitter.com/MichiganAutoLaw/
www.youtube.com/michiganautolaw/

7305 ■ Kelsey's Law Distracted Driving Awareness Scholarship *(High School, Undergraduate/Scholarship)*

Purpose: To inspire change in teens who drive distracted and help prevent car accidents. **Focus:** General studies/Field of study not specified. **Qualif.:** Applicants must be a junior or senior attending any public or private Michigan high school; must be a resident of Michigan with a valid Michigan driver's license; if under 18, parental consent form must be signed by parent or guardian. **Criteria:** Entries will be judged and critiqued on the quality, creativity, and persuasiveness of submission.

Funds Avail.: $2,000 (Overall Best Submission); $1,500 (Best Video Submission); $1,000 (Best Graphic Submission); $500 (Best Tweet Submission). **Duration:** Annual. **Number Awarded:** 4. **To Apply:** All applicants are required to submit a message in the form of a video, graphic or Tweet that resonates with teens and influences their driving behavior; limit one type of submission per student; must read and sign submission form found on website agreeing to terms and conditions, privacy policy, and terms of use. **Deadline:** August 31. **Remarks:** Established in memory of Kelsey Raffaele, 17, of Sault Ste. Marie, tragically died in a cell phone-related automobile crash in 2010. **Contact:** URL: michiganautolaw.com/scholarships/kelseys-law; Email: scholarships@michiganautolaw.com.

7306 ■ Michigan Auto Law Student Diversity Scholarships *(Undergraduate/Scholarship)*

Purpose: To provide financial support to students who contribute to the diversity of the law school student body as they pursue their legal career. **Focus:** Law. **Qualif.:** Applicants must be students currently in their first or second year of law school; must be members of an ethnic or racial minority or demonstrate a defined commitment to issues of diversity within their academic career; must be U.S. citizens and currently enrolled in an accredited law school within the United States, or entering law school in the fall; must have a cumulative minimum of 3.0 GPA.

Funds Avail.: $2,000. **Duration:** Annual. **To Apply:** Applicants must submit the following items; a completed application (available at the website); a current academic transcript; a one page essay describing their efforts to encourage greater racial or ethnic diversity within the student body of their law school and/or undergraduate program. **Deadline:** June 1. **Contact:** Beth; Phone: 248-353-4504; Email: scholarships@michiganautolaw.com.

7307 ■ Michigan Competing Band Association (MCBA)

10237 Seymour Rd.
Montrose, MI 48457-9014
Ph: (810)639-2442
Fax: (810)639-3786
E-mail: mcba@mac.com
URL: www.themcba.org/theMCBA.org/Welcome.html

7308 ■ MCBA Scholarship (MCBA) *(Undergraduate/Scholarship)*

Purpose: To grant scholarships to deserving students from Michigan high schools that are members of MCBA. **Focus:** Music. **Qualif.:** Applicants must be high school seniors who are members of an MCBA marching band and plan to enter a college or university with a major in music or related field. **Criteria:** Selection will be made by MCBA judging committee.

Funds Avail.: $2,000. **Duration:** Annual. **Number Awarded:** up to four. **To Apply:** The applicants are asked to write a paragraph stating why they should be considered for the scholarship award. **Contact:** MCBA, 1583 Lake Breeze Ct, Muskegon, MI 49445; Phone: 231-750-9207.

7309 ■ Michigan Council of Women in Technology (MCWT)

24800 Denso Dr., Suite 150
Southfield, MI 48033
Ph: (248)218-2578
URL: www.mcwt.org
Social Media: www.facebook.com/MCWTFoundation
www.instagram.com/mcwtfoundation
www.linkedin.com/company/michigan-council-of-women-in
  -technology-foundation
twitter.com/MCWT

7310 ■ Michigan Council of Women in Technology High School Scholarship Program *(High School/Scholarship)*

Purpose: To support those women who are pursuing a career in technology. **Focus:** Technology. **Qualif.:** Applicants must be Michigan-based women who are currently or will be enrolled in college or university-level courses; must be U.S. citizens; and must have 3.0 GPA.

Funds Avail.: $5,000 per annum. **Duration:** Annual; up to three years.

7311 ■ Michigan Council of Women in Technology Undergraduate Scholarship Program *(Undergraduate, Graduate/Scholarship)*

Purpose: To provides scholarships to women who have the interest, aptitude and potential for a successful career in computer science. **Focus:** Technology. **Qualif.:** Ap-

Awards are arranged alphabetically below their administering organizations

plicants must be Michigan-based women who are currently or will be enrolled in college or university-level courses; must be U.S. citizens; and must have 3.0 GPA.

Funds Avail.: $5,000 per annum. **Duration:** Annual; up to two years. **Number Awarded:** 28. **To Apply:** Applicant must be able to provide documentation showing she meets these requirements.

7312 ■ Michigan Education Association (MEA)

1216 Kendale Blvd.
East Lansing, MI 48823
Free: 800-292-1934
URL: www.mea.org
Social Media: www.facebook.com/
 MichiganEducationAssociation
www.instagram.com/meaonline
www.pinterest.com/michiganeducationassociation
twitter.com/meaonline
www.youtube.com/channel/UCgXXU5SVb0dqXWxw5b
 -gW6w

7313 ■ Michigan Education Association Scholarships *(Undergraduate/Scholarship)*

Purpose: To provide education, advancement of quality education and security of the rights of education employees. **Focus:** General studies/Field of study not specified. **Criteria:** Recipients will be selected based on academic achievement; extra-curricular activities; school and community service; first consideration will be given to children of MEA members and students from lower income households.

Funds Avail.: No specific amount. **Duration:** Annual. **Number Awarded:** Varies. **To Apply:** Applicants must submit completed application form. **Deadline:** February 20. **Remarks:** Established in 1852. **Contact:** Human Resources, MEA Scholarship Fund, Michigan Education Association, 1350 Kendale Blvd, East Lansing, MI, 48823.

7314 ■ Michigan League for Nursing (MLN)

503 Frandor Mall Ct Ste. 321
Lansing, MI 48912
E-mail: info@michleaguenursing.org
URL: www.michleaguenursing.org

7315 ■ Michigan League for Nursing Student Scholarships *(Undergraduate/Scholarship)*

Purpose: To provide funds and numerous programs addressing complex issues of nursing education and clinical practice for Michigan nursing students. **Focus:** Nursing. **Funds Avail.:** $1,000. **Deadline:** April 15.

7316 ■ Michigan Nursery and Landscape Association (MNLA)

2149 Commons Pky.
Okemos, MI 48864
Ph: (517)381-0437
Fax: (517)381-0638
URL: www.mnla.org
Social Media: www.facebook.com/MichiganNLA
twitter.com/mnlamembers
twitter.com/MichiganNLA

7317 ■ MNLA Academic Scholarship *(Undergraduate/Scholarship)*

Purpose: To further the education of those students who are pursuing careers in green industry. **Focus:** Landscape architecture and design. **Qualif.:** Applicants must be students pursuing a degree in the area of landscaping. **Criteria:** Recipients are selected based on academic performance and financial need.

Funds Avail.: No specific amount. **Duration:** Annual. **To Apply:** Applicants must submit a completed application form, a cover letter, resume, two letters of recommendation and photos or information on industry work completed. **Deadline:** November 1. **Contact:** Emily Huening, MNLA's Education/Certification Director; Phone: 517-381-0437; Email: emily@mnla.org.

7318 ■ Michigan Nurses Foundation (MNF)

2310 Jolly Oak Rd.
Okemos, MI 48864
Ph: (517)349-5640
E-mail: contact@minursesfoundation.org
URL: www.michigannursesfoundation.org

7319 ■ Conduct and Utilization of Research in Nursing (CURN) Awards *(Professional development, Doctorate, Master's/Prize)*

Purpose: To fund research or utilization of research in practice. **Focus:** Nursing. **Qualif.:** Principal investigators must be a regular MNA member in good standing and a registered nurse who is licensed to practice in Michigan and living in the state, and possess or be working on a masters or doctoral degree. **Criteria:** Selection will be based on the committee's criteria.

Funds Avail.: $5,000. **To Apply:** Applicants must submit the following materials: four copies of the completed grant application; research support and abstract; detailed budget for proposed research; project narrative, must not exceed 10 single spaced pages, excluding appendices. Recipients will be known as CURN Scholars. All publications and publicity must reflect such title and acknowledge the Michigan Nurses Foundation. CURN Scholars will be asked to present their research at the MNA Convention or to write an article for publication in Michigan Nurse describing their research and its implications for nursing practice.

7320 ■ MNF Scholarships *(Undergraduate, Graduate/Scholarship)*

Purpose: To promote nursing and nursing education by awarding scholarships and research grants and by providing financial aid for the treatment of recovering nurses. **Focus:** Nursing. **Criteria:** Selection will be based on influential criteria including MNA Membership and community involvement.

Funds Avail.: $1,000. **Duration:** Annual. **Number Awarded:** 4. **To Apply:** Applicant must submit application form along with: a one-page personal vision of future nursing practice;currecnt transcript; letter of reference from a nursing faculty member. **Deadline:** May 1.

7321 ■ Michigan Parkinson Foundation (MPF)

30400 Telegraph Rd., Ste. 150
Bingham Farms, MI 48025
Ph: (248)433-1011
Fax: (248)433-1150
Free: 800-852-9781
E-mail: info@parkinsonsmi.org
URL: www.parkinsonsmi.org
Social Media: www.facebook.com/ParkinsonsMI.org

Awards are arranged alphabetically below their administering organizations

www.instagram.com/miparkinsonfoundation/?hl=en
www.pinterest.com/parkinsonsmiorg
twitter.com/ParkinsonsMiOrg
www.youtube.com/michiganparkinsonfoundation

7322 ■ Raymond B. Bauer Research Award (Professional development/Award, Grant)

Purpose: To help support research and to foster the study of Parkinson's disease among individuals with career interests in neurological disorders. **Focus:** Biological and clinical sciences; Epidemiology; Medical research; Nursing; Psychology; Rehabilitation, Physical/Psychological; Social sciences. **Qualif.:** Applicants must be researchers in Michigan colleges, universities and not-for-profit organizations who work with students and trainees.

Funds Avail.: Up to $20,000. **Duration:** Annual; up to two years. **To Apply:** Applicants must submit a project proposal (maximum of 6 pages in length) outlining their topic and relevant background, method of study, collaborative or supervisory arrangements and further plans once the project is completed; a letter of support from a chairman or supervisor; a copy of the institutional review board approval prior to the distribution of funds; a current cv, a budget for their studies and a list of other current financial support (include sponsor, title, dates of support, total direct costs funded and pi). **Deadline:** December 31. **Contact:** Michigan Parkinson Foundation, Professional Advisory Board, 30400 Telegraph, Ste. 150, Bingham Farms, MI, 48025; Phone: 800-852-9781 or 248-433-1011; Fax: 248-433-1150; Email: info@parkinsonsmi.org.

7323 ■ Michigan Realtors

720 N Washington Ave.
Lansing, MI 48906
Fax: (517)334-5568
Free: 800-454-7842
URL: www.mirealtors.com
Social Media: www.facebook.com/mirealtors
www.instagram.com/michiganrealtors
twitter.com/intent/follow?source=followbutton&variant=1
  .0&screen_name=michREALTORS
www.youtube.com/user/MICHREALTORS?sub_confirmation=1

7324 ■ Michigan Realtors Scholarship Trust (Graduate, Undergraduate/Scholarship)

Purpose: To encourage and support outstanding, highly-motivated students to specialize in the study of real estate. **Focus:** Real estate. **Qualif.:** Applicants must have an average grade point of 2.0 on a 4.0 scale or equivalent of a "C" average and show evidence of academic achievement; must exemplify character, including demonstrated evidence of good citizenship; must agree to take courses which are related to the real estate field; must be full-time students, entering junior or senior year or post-graduate work at a university or college. **Criteria:** Applicants are selected based on the committee's review of the application materials.

Funds Avail.: Up to $3,000. **Duration:** Annual. **Number Awarded:** Varies. **To Apply:** Applicants must complete and submit the application before the deadline; form can be downloaded at the Michigan Association of Realtors web site; must also provide a copy of ACT or SAT test scores and a copy of their college transcript. **Deadline:** May 31. **Contact:** E-mail: marst@mirealtors.com; Phone: 517-372-8890.

7325 ■ Michigan Society of Fellows

0540 Rackham Bldg.
915 E Washington St.
Ann Arbor, MI 48109-1070
Ph: (734)763-1259
E-mail: society.of.fellows@umich.edu
URL: societyoffellows.umich.edu

7326 ■ Michigan Society of Fellows Three-Year Fellowships (Postdoctorate/Fellowship)

Purpose: To assist qualified candidates who are at the beginning of their academic careers, having received the ph.D. Or comparable professional or artistic degree. **Focus:** Life sciences; Physical sciences; Social sciences. **Qualif.:** Applicants must have received their Ph.D. degree at the beginning of their academic careers; must be involved in social, physical, life sciences and in the professional schools. **Criteria:** Selection will be based on the committee's criteria.

Funds Avail.: $60,000. **Duration:** Annual; up to three years. **To Apply:** Applicants must complete the online application; must submit a curriculum vitae, writing sample and research proposal; $35 application fee; confidential letters of reference from no more than two referees; letterhead is preferred. **Deadline:** September 15. **Contact:** 0540 Rackham Bldg, 915 E. Washington St., Ann Arbor, MI, 48109-1070; Phone: 734- 763-1259; Email: society.of.fellows@umich.edu.

7327 ■ Michigan Society of Professional Engineers (MSPE)

PO Box 160
Parma, MI 49269
Ph: (517)487-9388
E-mail: mspe@michiganspe.org
URL: www.michiganspe.org
Social Media: www.facebook.com/Michigan-Society-of-Professional-Engineers-120217141389019

7328 ■ Michigan Society of Professional Engineers Scholarships (Undergraduate/Scholarship)

Purpose: To support high school students who have talent and commitment in pursuing engineering degree. **Focus:** Engineering. **Criteria:** Selection will be based on high school record, participation in extracurricular activities, evidence of leadership, character and self-reliance.

Funds Avail.: No specific amount. **Duration:** Annual. **Number Awarded:** 1. **To Apply:** Applicants must submit a completed application form which can be obtained from a guidance counselor, local chapters or the MSPE Headquarters; a list of senior classes being taken; and a documented high school transcript and SAT test scores. **Deadline:** February 5. **Contact:** MSPE Office, 215 N. Walnut Street, Lansing, MI; Phone: 517-487-9388; Email: mspe@michiganspe.org.

7329 ■ Michigan Space Grant Consortium (MSGC)

1049 FXB Bldg.
University of Michigan
1320 Beal Ave.
Ann Arbor, MI 48109-2140
Ph: (734)764-9508
Fax: (734)763-6904

Awards are arranged alphabetically below their administering organizations

URL: www.mi.spacegrant.org

7330 ■ Michigan Space Grant Consortium Research Seed Grant Program *(Professional development/ Grant)*

Purpose: To support junior faculty members, and senior faculty members interested in initiating a new area of research. **Focus:** Aerospace sciences. **Qualif.:** Applicant must be a junior or senior faculty at MSBC or a research scientist at an affiliated institution. **Criteria:** Selection will be based on the committee's criteria.

Funds Avail.: Up to $5,000. **Duration:** Annual. **To Apply:** Applications must include: approval from the affiliate representative on your campus; a six-page research description; a one-page detailed budget and budget justification; one-page of biographical information on the PI; a one-page listing of significant publications; up to a two-page list of grants; and a letter from the designated signer of the Research Office at the home institution of the investigator verifying the non-federal match. Use 12 point font and convert to a single PDF. application materials must be submitted online. **Deadline:** November 14.

7331 ■ MSGC Undergraduate-Under-Represented Minority Fellowship Program *(Undergraduate/ Fellowship)*

Purpose: To support students' education and research who exemplifies interest in aerospace, space science, Earth system science and other related science, engineering or mathematics fields. **Focus:** Aerospace sciences. **Qualif.:** Applicants must be underrepresented minority undergraduates who are U.S. citizens and currently enrolled at MSGC Affiliate Institutions; those with a GPA below 3.0, but who have strong mentorship, do qualify for the award; mentors must have up to two underrepresented minority students on their team. **Criteria:** Selection will be based on the committee's criteria.

Funds Avail.: Up to $14,000. **To Apply:** Applicants must submit the following requirements; approval from the affiliate representative on the campus; completed online application form; abstract; a three-page essay; a scanned copy of the applicants' most recent transcript and; two letters of recommendation. **Deadline:** November 14.

7332 ■ Michigan State Horticultural Society (MSHS)
7087 East Napier Ave.
Benton Harbor, MI 49022
Ph: (269)252-5461
E-mail: ben@mihortsociety.com
URL: www.mihortsociety.org

7333 ■ Fruits and Vegetable Industries Scholarships *(Undergraduate/Scholarship)*

Purpose: To support students who intend to pursue careers in the Midwest fruit and vegetable industries. **Focus:** Horticulture. **Qualif.:** Applicants must be students who intend to pursue a career in the Midwest fruit industry or vegetable industry. **Criteria:** Recipients are selected based on financial need and academic performance.

Funds Avail.: $1,500. **Duration:** Annual. **To Apply:** Applicants must complete the application form. **Deadline:** September 30. **Contact:** Michigan Vegetable Council, P.O. Box 367 Mason, MI, 48854, Phone: 517-663-6725; Email: gbird@michiganvegetablecouncil.org.

7334 ■ Jordan B. Tatter Scholarship *(Undergraduate, Graduate/Scholarship)*

Purpose: To encourage among the people a greater love for choice fruit products; to awaken a larger interest in Michigan's horticultural possibilities; to offer practical suggestions along modern cultural and marketing methods; and to encourage the improved methods in the production, harvest, handling, storage, marketing and utilization of fruit and vegetable crops as well as a full farm marketers program. **Focus:** Horticulture. **Criteria:** Recipients are selected based on financial need.

Duration: Annual. **Number Awarded:** 2. **To Apply:** Applicants must complete the application form. **Deadline:** October. **Contact:** Jim Flore, MSU Dept. of Horticulture; Email: flore@msu.edu.

7335 ■ Michigan State University - Gender, Development and Globalization Program (GDG)
427 N Shaw Ln., Rm. 206
East Lansing, MI 48824
Ph: (517)353-5040
E-mail: gencen@msu.edu
URL: gencen.isp.msu.edu/features/gender-resources/
  gender-and-environment
Social Media: www.facebook.com/MSUGenCen
www.linkedin.com/company/msugencen
twitter.com/MSUGenCen

7336 ■ GJEC Dissertation Completion Fellowship *(Postdoctorate/Fellowship)*

Purpose: To provide funds to dissertations that focus on gender dimensions of environmental and/or agricultural change, and give opportunities to outstanding students for their career and personal development. **Focus:** Sexuality.

Funds Avail.: $8,500. **To Apply:** Applicants must submit the completed application form; five-page (double-spaced) summary of the dissertation research; letter of recommendation from dissertation committee chair and curriculum vitae (CV).

7337 ■ Michigan Stormwater-Floodplain Association (MSFA)
PO Box 14265
Lansing, MI 48901-4265
URL: mifloods.org

7338 ■ Michigan Stormwater-Floodplain Association Scholarships *(Graduate, Undergraduate/Scholarship)*

Purpose: To mitigate the losses, costs and human suffering caused by flooding and to promote wise use of the natural and beneficial functions of floodplains. **Focus:** Water supply industry. **Criteria:** Recipients are selected based on academic performance and financial need.

Funds Avail.: $2,500. **Duration:** Annual. **Number Awarded:** Varies. **To Apply:** Applicants must submit a completed application form; a copy of their program of study showing courses remaining and photocopy of their transcript; a current resume that includes a statement of their career objectives and graduation date; a one page, typed essay highlighting their academic achievements, extracurricular activities, past and present work experiences, future occupation and commitment to the mission and goals of the MSFA; must submit a letter of recommendation from a

Awards are arranged alphabetically below their administering organizations

faculty member of their department. **Deadline:** November 2. **Contact:** MSFA, PO Box 14265, Lansing, MI, 48901-4265.

7339 ■ Michigan Sugar Co.
2600 S Euclid Ave.
Bay City, MI 48706
Ph: (989)686-0161
URL: www.michigansugar.com
Social Media: www.facebook.com/michigansugar
www.instagram.com/michigansugarco
www.linkedin.com/company/michigan-sugar-co
twitter.com/michigansugarco
www.youtube.com/user/michigansugarcompany/featured

7340 ■ Albert Flegenheimer Memorial Scholarship
(Undergraduate/Scholarship)

Purpose: To provide academic support to high school seniors who have completed a documented Youth Sugarbeet Project. **Focus:** General studies/Field of study not specified. **Qualif.:** Applicants must be residents of a county where sugar beets are grown; must be high school graduating seniors; must have participated in the Michigan Sugar Youth Sugar beet Program at one time and have completed a Sugar beet Project. **Criteria:** Applicants are selected based on the committee's review of the application materials.

Funds Avail.: $2,500. **To Apply:** Applicants must submit a completed application form available at the Michigan Sugar Company web site along with three letters of reference. **Deadline:** March 31. **Remarks:** Established in 1974. **Contact:** Email: scholarships@MichiganSugar.com.

7341 ■ Michigan Sugar Company Hotel Restaurant/ Resort Management Scholarship *(Undergraduate/ Scholarship)*

Purpose: To provide financial support to deserving students enrolled in the Hotel Restaurant/Resort Management program of study. **Focus:** Hotel, institutional, and restaurant management. **Qualif.:** Applicants must be enrolled full-time in the Hotel Restaurant/Resort Management program in any college or university. **Criteria:** Applicants are selected based on the committee's review of the application materials; demonstrated financial need and academic merit.

Funds Avail.: $1,000. **Duration:** Annual. **To Apply:** Applicants are required to apply online. **Contact:** Northwood University Financial Aid Office, 4000 Whiting Drive, Midland, MI, 48640; Phone: 989- 837-4230.

7342 ■ Michigan Sugar Queen Scholarship
(Undergraduate/Scholarship)

Purpose: To provide academic support to high school seniors who have completed a document at the Michigan Sugar Festival. **Focus:** General studies/Field of study not specified. **Criteria:** Applicants are selected based on the committee's review of the application materials.

Funds Avail.: $1,000-$2,000. **Duration:** Annual. **Number Awarded:** 3. **To Apply:** Interested applicants need to complete an application and a current picture; two written recommendations. **Deadline:** April 24. **Contact:** Rob Clark, Queen Coordinator; Michigan Sugar Company, 122 Uptown Dr., Ste., 300 Bay City, MI, 48708, Phone: 989-686-0161; Email: rob.clark@michigansugar.com.

7343 ■ Michigan Turfgrass Foundation (MTF)
PO Box 27156
Lansing, MI 48909
Ph: (517)392-5003
E-mail: miturfgrass@gmail.com
URL: www.michiganturfgrass.org
Social Media: www.facebook.com/MiTurfgrass
twitter.com/miturfgrass
www.youtube.com/channel/UCNhUQG40Y7pNliUHLU_4xag

7344 ■ Kenyon T. Payne Outstanding Student Award *(Undergraduate/Award, Monetary)*

Purpose: To support the ongoing research, education and extension in the area of professional turfgrass management that will benefit all individuals who manage turfgrasses or derive pleasure from the results of such management. **Focus:** Management. **Qualif.:** Applicants must be senior undergraduates in the four-year Turfgrass Management Program and must have a 3.0 GPA or higher.

Funds Avail.: $2,000. **Duration:** Annual. **Number Awarded:** 1. **To Apply:** Applicants must complete the application form and submit along with a cover letter, resume, and at least two letters of recommendation from instructors, employers, or the like. **Contact:** Send application form by email to Michigan State University, College of Agriculture and Natural Resources, Department of Plant, Soil and Microbial Sciences, Plant and Soil Sciences Bldg., 1066 Bogue St., Rm. A284 East Lansing, MI 48824-1039.

7345 ■ Norman W. Kramer Outstanding Scholar Award *(Undergraduate/Scholarship)*

Purpose: To support the ongoing research, education and extension in the area of professional turfgrass management that will benefit all individuals who manage turfgrasses or derive pleasure from the results of such management. **Focus:** General studies/Field of study not specified. **Qualif.:** Applicants must be students with a minimum of 42 credits completed and who have a 3.0 GPA or higher; active service in Turfgrass Programs at MSU.

Funds Avail.: $2,500. **Duration:** Annual. **Number Awarded:** 1. **To Apply:** Applicants must complete the application form and submit along with a cover letter, resume, and at least two letters of recommendation from instructors, employers, or the like. **Remarks:** The award is dedicated to the memory of Norm Kramer. Established in 1972. **Contact:** Send application form by email to Michigan State University, College of Agriculture and Natural Resources, Department of Plant, Soil and Microbial Sciences, Plant and Soil Sciences Bldg., 1066 Bogue St., Rm. A284 East Lansing, MI 48824-1039.

7346 ■ Robert Hancock Memorial Scholarship Award *(Undergraduate/Scholarship)*

Purpose: To support the ongoing research, education and extension in the area of professional turfgrass management that will benefit all individuals who manage turfgrasses or derive pleasure from the results of such management. **Focus:** Management. **Qualif.:** Applicants must be senior undergraduates in the four-year Turfgrass Management Program and must have a 3.0 GPA or higher.

Funds Avail.: $2,000. **Duration:** Annual. **Number Awarded:** 1. **To Apply:** Applicants must complete the application form and submit along with a cover letter, resume, and at least two letters of recommendation from instructors,

Awards are arranged alphabetically below their administering organizations

employers, or the like. **Contact:** Dan Lucas, MTF BOD at akcsuptdfl@yahoo.com.

7347 ■ Michigan Water Environment Association

5815 Clark Rd., Ste. F
Bath, MI 48808
Social Media: facebook.com/
 MichiganWaterEnvironmentAssociation
linkedin.com/company/michigan-water-environment
 -association

7348 ■ Antenore C. "Butch" Davanzo Scholarships
(Graduate, Undergraduate/Scholarship)

Purpose: To support a student that has excelled at a Michigan college or university. **Focus:** Environmental conservation. **Criteria:** Recipients are selected based on academic performance and adherence to the requirements by panel of judges.

Funds Avail.: $1,000. **Duration:** Annual. **To Apply:** Applicants must submit a paper of between 500 and 600 words reflecting on their career interests and objectives and how they envision using their education to enhance water quality; must submit a current copy of their college or university transcript; resume with all full and part-time employment, education history and extracurricular activities; a letter of recommendation from their academic advisor or other appropriate official attesting to their course of study and other aspects of their application. **Deadline:** March 1.

7349 ■ John P. Hennessey Scholarship *(Graduate, Undergraduate/Scholarship)*

Purpose: To support a student that has excelled at a Michigan college or university. **Focus:** Environmental conservation. **Criteria:** Selection will be judged by a panel representing the diverse membership of the Michigan Water Environment Association.

Funds Avail.: $2,000. **Duration:** Annual. **Number Awarded:** 1. **To Apply:** Applicants must submit a paper of between 500 and 600 words reflecting on their career interests and objectives and how they envision using their education to enhance water quality; must submit a current copy of their college or university transcript; resume with all full and part-time employment, education history and extracurricular activities; a letter of recommendation from their academic advisor or other appropriate official attesting to their course of study and other aspects of their application. **Deadline:** March 1.

7350 ■ Jack H. Wagner Scholarship *(Graduate, Undergraduate/Scholarship)*

Purpose: To support a student that has excelled at a Michigan college or university. **Focus:** Environmental conservation. **Criteria:** Recipients are selected based on academic performance and adherence to the requirements by panel of judges.

Funds Avail.: $2,000. **Duration:** Annual. **Number Awarded:** 2. **To Apply:** Applicants must submit a paper of between 500 and 600 words reflecting on their career interests and objectives and how they envision using their education to enhance water quality; a current copy of their college or university transcript; a resume with all full and part-time employment, education history and extracurricular activities; letter of recommendation from their academic advisor or other appropriate official attesting to their course of study and other aspects of their application. **Deadline:** March 1.

7351 ■ The Micklin Law Group LLC

187 Washington Ave., Ste. 2F
Nutley, NJ 07110
Ph: (973)562-0100
Fax: (973)556-1732
E-mail: brad@micklinlawgroup.com
URL: www.micklinlawgroup.com
Social Media: www.facebook.com/BradM.MicklinEsq

7352 ■ Micklin Law Group Scholarship *(College, University/Scholarship)*

Purpose: To help members of the next generation afford college and make their mark on society. **Focus:** General studies/Field of study not specified. **Qualif.:** Applicant must be accepted into an accredited college in the United States and demonstrate financial need. **Criteria:** Selection is based online application.

Funds Avail.: $1,000. **Duration:** Annual. **Number Awarded:** 2. **To Apply:** Application must be completed online. **Deadline:** July 31.

7353 ■ Microscopy Society of America (MSA)

11130 Sunrise Valley Dr.Ste 350
Reston, VA 20191
Ph: (703)234-4115
Fax: (703)435-4390
Free: 800-538-3672
E-mail: associationmanagement@microscopy.org
URL: www.microscopy.org
Social Media: www.facebook.com/Microscopy-Society-of
 -America-Official-113120678747959
www.instagram.com/microscopy_soc
www.linkedin.com/company/microscopy-society-of-america
 -official-/?trk=top_nav_home
twitter.com/MicroscopySoc

7354 ■ MSA Presidential Student Awards (PSA)
(Graduate, Undergraduate/Scholarship)

Purpose: To provide financial support to those college/university students who are attending Microscopy & Microanalysis meeting. **Focus:** Science. **Qualif.:** Applicants must be bonfire students at a recognized college or university at the time of the meeting; must be the first author of the submitted paper; the paper must be submitted for platform presentation. **Criteria:** Selection based on the quality of the paper submitted for presentation at the meeting.

Funds Avail.: Up to $1,000 for travel plus lodging stipend of up to $100/day for up to 5 days. **To Apply:** Applicants must submit their respective papers and support letters on or before the deadline. **Deadline:** February 22.

7355 ■ Microsoft Research

1 Microsoft Way
Redmond, WA 98052
URL: research.microsoft.com
Social Media: www.facebook.com/microsoftresearch
www.instagram.com/msft_research

Awards are arranged alphabetically below their administering organizations

twitter.com/MSFTResearch
www.youtube.com/user/MicrosoftResearch

7356 ■ Microsoft Research Graduate Women's Scholarships (Graduate/Scholarship)

Purpose: To support women who are pursuing a PhD. **Focus:** Computer and information sciences; Engineering, Electrical; Mathematics and mathematical sciences. **Qualif.:** Applicant must be a full-time student who is enrolled in PhD-level studies at one of the participating universities during the academic year of the award, or forfeit the fellowship. **Criteria:** Selection will be based on the committee's criteria.

Funds Avail.: $20,000. **Duration:** Annual. **To Apply:** Applicants must submit a completed application form available on the website. **Contact:** Microsoft Research, at the above address, or Email: msrsch@microsoft.com.

7357 ■ Microsoft Research PhD Fellowships (Doctorate/Fellowship)

Purpose: To support individuals who are in their third and fourth years of PhD graduate studies. **Focus:** Computer and information sciences; Engineering, Electrical; Mathematics and mathematical sciences.

Duration: Annual. **To Apply:** Applications must include: nominee's thesis proposal, nominee's curriculum vitae and three letters of reference from established researchers familiar with the nominee's research; applications must be submitted online via the application tool in any of the following formats: word documents, text-only file or PDF; all application materials must be submitted by the person designated as the application contact by the departmental chair's office and must not be the applicant. **Deadline:** August 14. **Contact:** Email: msfellow@microsoft.com.

7358 ■ Mid-Ohio District Nurses Association (MODNA)

1520 Old Henderson Rd., Ste. 100
Columbus, OH 43220
Ph: (614)326-1630
Fax: (614)326-1633
E-mail: modna@modna.org
URL: www.modna.org
Social Media: www.facebook.com/WeAreONA
www.linkedin.com/company/mid-ohio-district-nurses
  -association

7359 ■ MODNA Nursing Education Scholarship (Doctorate, Graduate/Scholarship)

Purpose: To provide financial assistance to qualified MODNA members who want to pursue their nursing profession. **Focus:** Nursing. **Criteria:** Selection are based upon committee criteria.

Funds Avail.: No specific amount. **Duration:** Annual. **To Apply:** Applicants not awarded a scholarship may re-apply during future application periods; proof of acceptance to the nursing program OR, if a freshman or first year level, proof showing application has been received and is being processed by the nursing education program; tentative plan that outlines the course work to complete your degree. **Contact:** Mid-Ohio District Nurses Association, 1520 Old Henderson Rd., Ste. 100, Columbus, OH, 43220; Phone: 614-326-1630; Email: modna@modna.org.

7360 ■ Middle East Studies Association of North America (MESA)

3542 N Geronimo Ave.
Tucson, AZ 85705
Ph: (520)333-2577
Fax: (520)207-3166
URL: mesana.org
Social Media: www.facebook.com/MiddleEastStudiesAssoc
twitter.com/MESA_1966

7361 ■ Student Travel Grant (Undergraduate/Grant)

Purpose: To help subsidize travel expenses for students who are presenting papers at the MESA Annual Meeting. **Focus:** General studies/Field of study not specified. **Criteria:** Recipients will be selected based on submitted application materials.

Funds Avail.: $250. **Duration:** Annual. **Number Awarded:** Varies. **To Apply:** Applicants must submit a letter of application by e-mail or mail outlining their eligibility and have their academic department chair submit to MESA a letter of confirming that they are not receiving departmental support to attend the meeting. **Deadline:** September 15. **Contact:** Omar Sirri, Graduate Student Member of the Board, Email: omar.sirri@utoronto.ca.

7362 ■ Midlothian Rotary Club

224 S 11th St.
Midlothian, TX 76065
E-mail: midlorotary@gmail.com
URL: www.midlothianrotary.com
Social Media: www.facebook.com/MidlothianRotary

7363 ■ Midlothian Rotary Club "Service Above Self" Scholarships (Undergraduate/Scholarship)

Purpose: To encourage and promote community service and leadership among Midlothian students, and reward the achievements of those students who have exemplified these ideals. **Focus:** General studies/Field of study not specified. **Qualif.:** Applicants must have a permanent address in the Midlothian Independent school district; however, the applying student may attend a public, private, or home school within the Midlothian Independent School District; must be classified as a senior and have met all the State of Texas education requirements to graduate on; must plan on attending a qualified college, university and/ or vocational institution. **Criteria:** Selection will be based on the committee's criteria.

Funds Avail.: $1,500. **Duration:** Annual. **Number Awarded:** 4. **To Apply:** Applicant must complete and submit the application form along with all questions answered; student's parent/guardian, and the adult supervisor of the service activity must sign documentation; letter of recommendation turned into MISD High School Guidance Center; applicant must submit a essay on Service Above Self. In a 150 words or less, tell what "Service Above Self" means to you. Please type your essay and staple it to your application. **Contact:** MISD: MHS - Becky Oliver - College / Career Liaison; Email: becky_oliver@misd.gs; MISD: MHHS - Christi Ramirez - College / Career Liaison, Email: christi_ramirez@misd.gs.

7364 ■ Midwest Archives Conference (MAC)

2598 E. Sunrise Blvd, Ste. 2104
Fort Lauderdale, FL 33304

Awards are arranged alphabetically below their administering organizations

E-mail: membership@midwestarchives.org
URL: www.midwestarchives.org

7365 ■ Louisa Bowen Memorial Scholarship for Graduate Students in Archival Administration
(Graduate/Scholarship)

Purpose: To encourage the study in the field of archival administration. **Focus:** Library and archival sciences. **Qualif.:** Applicant must be a resident or full-time student residing in one of the following states: Illinois, Indiana, Iowa, Kansas, Kentucky, Michigan, Minnesota, Missouri, Nebraska, North Dakota, Ohio, South Dakota, and Wisconsin; must be currently enrolled or accepted into a graduate, multi-course program in archival administration; must be a grade point average of at least 3.0 (based on 4.0 scale) in their most recent academic year. **Criteria:** Selection is based on merit.

Funds Avail.: $750. **Duration:** Annual. **Number Awarded:** 1. **To Apply:** Applicants must submit a completed application form available on the website; current resume including: education; relevant (archives related) employment/volunteer/internship experience; honors, scholarships or awards received; campus and community activities you are involved in; memberships in professional organizations; transcript; essay of no more than 500 words outlining the applicant's interests and future goals in archival administration; two letters of recommendation. **Deadline:** April 20. **Remarks:** Established in 1997. **Contact:** Lynn Smith, Chair; Email:lynn.smith@nara.gov.

7366 ■ MAC Emeritus Membership Award *(Professional development/Award)*

Purpose: To recognize those who have contributed to the success, growth, and visibility of MAC through committee work, programming, outreach, and governance. The award intends to recognize those who work behind the scenes for MAC, as well as those who have been honored by election to office. **Focus:** General studies/Field of study not specified. **Qualif.:** Applicants must be an individual member of MAC for a minimum of 10 years, retired from paid archival work, and have made a significant and substantial contribution to MAC during their course of membership. **Criteria:** MAC membership committee solicits nominations from members.

Funds Avail.: One Scholarship of $500 or two scholarships of $250. **Duration:** Annual. **Number Awarded:** Varies. **To Apply:** Applicants must submit a completed application form available on the website. **Deadline:** January 31. **Contact:** Completed applications to: Matthew Gorzalski University Archivist, Southern Illinois University Carbondale Library Affairs, 605 Agriculture Drive, Mailcode 6632 Carbondale, IL 62901; Email: mgorzalski@lib.siu.edu.

7367 ■ Archie Motley Memorial Scholarships for Minority Students *(Graduate/Scholarship)*

Purpose: To provide financial assistance to minority students pursuing graduate education. **Focus:** Library and archival sciences. **Qualif.:** Applicant must be a student of African, American Indian, Asian or Pacific Islander, or Latin descent and currently enrolled in a graduate, multi-course program in archival administration or accepted into such a program for the next academic year. The applicant must also have a grade point average of at least 3.0 (based on a 4.0 scale) in their most recent academic year. **Criteria:** Recipients are selected based on their merits.

Funds Avail.: $750 and one-year membership to MAC. **Duration:** One year. **Number Awarded:** 2. **To Apply:** Applicants must submit a completed application form available on the website; transcript of recent academic program; essay (maximum of 500 words) on the applicant's interests and future goals in archival administration; and two letters of recommendation. Applicant completed applications (in hard-copy) should be sent to: Rachel Howard. **Deadline:** March 1. **Contact:** Mail completed application and related materials to: Lara Friedman-Shedlov; Description and Access Archivist; Kautz Family YMCA Archives; University of Minnesota Libraries; 318 Elmer L. Andersen Library; 222 2st Ave S; Minneapolis, MN 55455; Telephone: 61.

7368 ■ Midwest Dairy Association (MDA)
2015 Rice St.
Saint Paul, MN 55113
Free: 800-642-3895
URL: www.midwestdairy.com
Social Media: www.facebook.com/midwestdairy
www.instagram.com/midwestdairy
www.linkedin.com/company/midwest-dairy
twitter.com/midwestdairy

7369 ■ Illinois Division of Midwest Dairy Educational Award *(Undergraduate/Scholarship)*

Purpose: To provide financial assistance to college students within the Illinois Division. **Focus:** General studies/Field of study not specified. **Qualif.:** Applicants must be enrolled in an accredited college; must be immediate family member of dairy farmers. **Criteria:** Selection is based on involvement in the dairy industry, leadership, career plans, academic standing.

Funds Avail.: $1,000. **Duration:** Annual. **Number Awarded:** 3. **To Apply:** Applicants must submit a completed application form including High Resolution Photograph, Newspaper Information Form, Publicity Consent Form, W9 Form. **Deadline:** March 15. **Contact:** Email: kanderson@midwestdairy.com.

7370 ■ Iowa Division of Midwest Dairy Educational Award *(Undergraduate/Scholarship)*

Purpose: To provide financial assistance to Iowa students. **Focus:** General studies/Field of study not specified. **Qualif.:** Applicants must be enrolled full-time in an accredited college; and must be immediate family member of dairy farmers. **Criteria:** Selection is based on involvement in the dairy industry, leadership, career plans, academic standing.

Funds Avail.: $1,000. **Duration:** Annual. **Number Awarded:** 11. **To Apply:** Applicants must submit a completed application form including High Resolution Photograph, Newspaper Information Form, Publicity Consent Form, W9 Form. **Deadline:** March 13. **Contact:** Email: mschulte@midwestdairy.com.

7371 ■ Minnesota Division Scholarships
(Undergraduate/Scholarship)

Purpose: To provide financial assistance to University of Minnesota students who are in need. **Focus:** General studies/Field of study not specified. **Qualif.:** Applicants must be enrolled students at the University of Minnesota CFANS in St. Paul or in Crookston.

Funds Avail.: $1,200 - $3,000. **Duration:** Annual. **To Apply:** Applicants must check the available website for the required materials.

7372 ■ MoKan Division of Midwest Dairy Educational Award *(Undergraduate/Scholarship)*

Purpose: To provide financial assistance to students who are in need. **Focus:** General studies/Field of study not

Awards are arranged alphabetically below their administering organizations

specified. **Qualif.:** Applicants must be enrolled in an accredited college; must be immediate family member of dairy farmers in Kansas and northern Missouri. **Criteria:** Selection is based on involvement in the dairy industry, leadership, career plans, academic standing.

Funds Avail.: $500 - $1,000. **Duration:** Annual. **Number Awarded:** 10. **To Apply:** Applicants must submit a completed application form including High Resolution Photograph, Newspaper Information Form, Publicity Consent Form, W9 Form. **Deadline:** March 30. **Contact:** Ron Grusenmeyer; Phone: 816-873-0351.

7373 ■ North Dakota Division Scholarships
(Undergraduate, Graduate/Scholarship)

Purpose: To provide financial assistance to deserving students of North Dakota State University. **Focus:** Education; Nutrition. **Qualif.:** Undergraduates must be juniors or non-graduating seniors majoring in food nutrition, family and consumer science education or education. Applicants seeking a graduate degree must reside in the Midwest Dairy Council region which includes North Dakota, South Dakota, Minnesota, Iowa, Nebraska, Kansas, Missouri, Arkansas and Illinois. **Criteria:** Recipients will be chosen by the University.

Funds Avail.: $1,000. **Duration:** Annual. **Number Awarded:** 1. **To Apply:** Applicants must check the available website for the required materials. **Deadline:** March 1.

7374 ■ Ozarks Division of Midwest Dairy Educational Award *(Undergraduate/Scholarship)*

Purpose: To provide financial support to students who are in need. **Focus:** General studies/Field of study not specified. **Qualif.:** Applicants must be enrolled students in an accredited college; must be immediate family member of dairy farmers in the Ozarks Division territory, including Arkansas, Southern Missouri or Eastern Oklahoma. **Criteria:** Selection is based on involvement in the dairy industry, leadership, career plans, academic standing.

Funds Avail.: $750. **Duration:** Annual. **Number Awarded:** 4. **To Apply:** Applicants must submit a completed application form including High Resolution Photograph, Newspaper Information Form, Publicity Consent Form, W9 Form. **Deadline:** March 30. **Contact:** Email: sdohle@midwestdairy.com.

7375 ■ South Dakota Division Scholarships
(Undergraduate/Scholarship)

Purpose: To provide financial support to students who are in need. **Focus:** Dairy science. **Qualif.:** Applicants must be incoming freshmen majoring in Dairy Science who are admitted at Dakota State University in Brookings. **Criteria:** Recipients will be chosen by the SDSU selection committee. Preference will be given to students who are from South Dakota.

Funds Avail.: $1,000 - $3,500. **Duration:** Annual. **Number Awarded:** 5. **To Apply:** Applicants must check the available website for the required materials. **Contact:** Phone: 605-688-4117.

7376 ■ Midwest Food Processors Association, Inc.
4600 American Pky., Ste. 210
Madison, WI 53718-8334
Social Media: www.facebook.com/MWFPA
twitter.com/MWFPA
www.youtube.com/channel/UCxi4LLf93yD0Ch85ISQwgQw

7377 ■ Carleton A. Friday Scholarship
(Undergraduate/Scholarship)

Purpose: To support those who are studying agriculture or food science. **Focus:** Agricultural sciences; Food science and technology. **Qualif.:** Applicants must be undergraduate students who are majoring in agriculture or food science within the University of Wisconsin system (currently Madison, Platteville and River Falls). **Criteria:** Recipients are selected based on financial need.

Funds Avail.: Up to $1,500. **Duration:** Annual. **Number Awarded:** 3. **To Apply:** Applicants must submit completed application form indicating GPA; a letter of recommendation from advisor or other faculty member; a letter of interest; letter of recommendation from past employer; document/s indicating financial need; and contact information. **Deadline:** April 24.

7378 ■ Kenneth G. Weckel Scholarship
(Undergraduate/Scholarship)

Purpose: To support those who are studying agriculture or food science. **Focus:** Agricultural sciences; Food science and technology. **Qualif.:** Applicants must be undergraduate students who are majoring in agriculture or food science within the University of Wisconsin system (currently Madison, Platteville and River Falls). **Criteria:** Recipients are selected based on financial need.

Funds Avail.: Up to $1,500. **Duration:** Annual. **Number Awarded:** 3. **To Apply:** Applicants must submit completed application form indicating GPA; a letter of recommendation from advisor or other faculty member; a letter of interest from students; letter of recommendation from past employer; documents indicating financial need; and contact information. **Deadline:** April 24.

7379 ■ Midwest Modern Language Association (M/MLA)
Dept. of English
1032 W Sheridan Rd.
Chicago, IL 60660
Ph: (773)508-6083
Fax: (773)508-8696
E-mail: mmla@luc.edu
URL: www.luc.edu
Social Media: www.facebook.com/MidwestMLA
twitter.com/MidwestMLA

7380 ■ Midwest Modern Language Association Fellowship *(Doctorate, Postdoctorate/Fellowship)*

Purpose: To provide assistance to researchers who wish to use the Newberry Library's collections. **Focus:** General studies/Field of study not specified. **Qualif.:** Applicants must be members of the Midwest Modern Language Association. **Criteria:** Selection will be based on the committee's criteria.

Funds Avail.: $2,500. **To Apply:** Applicants must submit the following Cover Sheet; Project Abstract of no more than 300 words; Project Description of no more than 1500 words; Curriculum Vitae; Three letters of reference.

7381 ■ MIE Solutions
13252 Garden Grove Blvd., No. 123
Garden Grove, CA 92843
Ph: (714)786-6230
E-mail: info@mie-solutions.com

Awards are arranged alphabetically below their administering organizations

URL: www.mie-solutions.com
Social Media: www.facebook.com/MIESolutionsUS
www.instagram.com/miesolutions
www.linkedin.com/in/miesolutions
twitter.com/MIESolutions
www.youtube.com/channel/UCF-1Il5RPpjwvex09Nu2zbA

7382 ■ MIE Solutions Scholarship Opportunity
(Undergraduate/Scholarship)

Purpose: To support students in the fields of computer engineering and/or computer science. **Focus:** Computer and information sciences. **Qualif.:** Applicant must be a legal US resident, and either a current (1) student at an accredited U.S. College or University, or (2) an undergraduate student who has applied (or will apply) to a U.S. College or University. Students with full academic scholarships are not eligible to enter this contest. **Criteria:** Selection will be based on the applicant's essay.

Funds Avail.: $500. **To Apply:** Applicant must submit a 300-500 word essay about their college experience so far, their future career, and their educational objectives (or a Prezi/PowerPoint Presentation, graphic, or creative presentation would also be acceptable) with a focus on computer science or computer engineering. Applicant should also tell their story in a brief narrative, telling about themselves and their interests. Application should be emailed to scholarship@miesolutions.com. **Deadline:** November 30. **Contact:** Scholarships@mie-solutions.com (714) 786-6230 ext. 105 MIE Solutions, Inc. 13252 Garden Grove Blvd Ste 215 Garden Grove, CA 92843.

7383 ■ mikeroweWORKS Foundation
1207 4th St., PH1
Santa Monica, CA 90401
Ph: (310)393-5522
URL: www.mikeroweworks.org

7384 ■ Work Ethic Scholarship *(Vocational/Occupational, Two Year College/Scholarship)*

Purpose: To help students attain degrees in trade programs that are in demand. **Focus:** Agricultural sciences; Automotive technology; Aviation; Construction; Education, Vocational-technical; Electronics; Fires and fire prevention; Heating, air conditioning, and refrigeration; Welding. **Qualif.:** Applicant must be a high school senior, high school graduate, or have a GED; must be enrolled in an approved trade program at an accredited two-year college, vocational school, technical school, or other approved technical institute in the United States. Acceptable trade programs include: automotive or aviation technology, carpentry, commercial driving, construction, diesel technology, electrical technology, emergency medical technology, farming and agriculture, fire science and technology, heavy equipment operation, HVAC, machinery, manufacturing, marine technology, pipefitting, plumbing, and welding. **Criteria:** Selection committee will consider the following: approved program and school, strength of recommendations, video content, short answer responses, financial need, completeness of application, overall ability to demonstrate a solid work ethic, and extra recommendation, if applicable.

Funds Avail.: Varies. **Duration:** Annual. **Number Awarded:** Varies. **To Apply:** Send at least 2 recommendations from eligible references, provide high school/college transcript, answer four short essay questions, make a short video. **Deadline:** March 31. **Contact:** Email:

mikeroweWORKS@applyISTS.com;   URL: www.mikeroweWORKS.org/scholarship.

7385 ■ Military Intelligence Corps Association (MICA)
500 N. Garden Ave, S1A Ste. 105
Sierra Vista, AZ 85635
Ph: (520)458-1221
URL: www.mica-national.org
Social Media: www.facebook.com/MICANational
twitter.com/MICANational

7386 ■ MICA Scholarships *(Undergraduate/Scholarship)*

Purpose: To provide scholarships for individuals pursuing undergraduate degrees or technical certifications. **Focus:** General studies/Field of study not specified. **Criteria:** Selection will be based Notification & Announcement among students inviting applications.

Funds Avail.: $1,000. **Duration:** Annual. **Contact:** MICA, Attn: MICA Scholarship Chairman, P.O. Box 13020, Fort Huachuca, Arizona 85670-3020.

7387 ■ Military Officers Association of America (MOAA)
201 N Washington St.
Alexandria, VA 22314
Ph: (703)549-2311
Free: 800-234-6622
E-mail: msc@moaa.org
URL: www.moaa.org
Social Media: www.facebook.com/moaa
www.instagram.com/moaaofficial
twitter.com/MilitaryOfficer
www.youtube.com/user/TheMOAAChannel

7388 ■ American Patriot Scholarship *(Undergraduate/Scholarship, Monetary)*

Purpose: To help children of Uniformed Services members who died or were severely disabled while in active service as members of the Regular, Guard or Reserve Forces. **Focus:** General studies/Field of study not specified. **Criteria:** Awards are given based on scholastic ability, activities and financial need.

Funds Avail.: $5,000. **Duration:** Annual. **Deadline:** March 1.

7389 ■ General John Paul Ratay Educational Fund Grants *(Undergraduate/Grant)*

Purpose: To help children of Uniformed Services members. **Focus:** General studies/Field of study not specified. **Qualif.:** Applicant must be the child, military, parent retired officer. Students who believe they are eligible for these grants and who do not receive a request for supporting documentation. **Criteria:** Applicants must apply for a loan in order to be considered.

7390 ■ MILK Tailor Made Books Ltd.
150 Karangahape Rd., Ste. 404
Auckland 1010, New Zealand
Ph: 64 9 889-7170
E-mail: contact@milkbooks.com

Awards are arranged alphabetically below their administering organizations

URL: www.milkbooks.com
Social Media: www.facebook.com/milkbooks
www.instagram.com/milkbooks
www.pinterest.com/milkbooks
twitter.com/milkbooks
www.youtube.com/user/MILKBooks

7391 ■ The MILK Scholarship *(University/Scholarship)*

Purpose: To encourage creativity and fresh ideas in making the world a better place. **Focus:** General studies/Field of study not specified. **Qualif.:** Applicant must be a U.S.-based student.

To Apply: Applicant must share what being creative means to them (up to 150 words, or an image, or both). Application form is available online at www.milkbooks.com/scholarship/united-states/. **Contact:** Email: scholarship@milkbooks.com.

7392 ■ Mill Creek Chamber of Commerce (MCBA)
13300 Bothell-Everett Hwy.
Mill Creek, WA 98012
Ph: (360)513-0615
E-mail: Jeff@MillCreekChamber.com
URL: millcreekchamber.com
Social Media: www.facebook.com/millcreekbiz
www.instagram.com/millcreekchamber

7393 ■ Mill Creek Chamber of Commerce Scholarship *(Undergraduate/Scholarship)*

Purpose: To encourage and assist local high school students in their pursuit of higher learning in business or fine arts. **Focus:** Art; Business. **Qualif.:** Must live in Mill Creek and/or attend school at either Cascade High School, Jackson High School, or Archbishop Murphy, and be a senior in good standing at the time of application; be accepted to attend a full-time accredited college, university, or fine arts school; plan to pursue a career in business. **Criteria:** Selection will be based on the committee's criteria.

Funds Avail.: $2,000. **Number Awarded:** 4. **To Apply:** Submit the application; two letters of reference and recommendation from teachers, advisors or local business people (cannot be a relative); a copy of the letter of acceptance from the institution they plan to attend; provide a 200 word, typed essay stating their academic and career plans. **Deadline:** May 8. **Contact:** Dr. Michael LaMarche, Phone: 425-357-1818.

7394 ■ Glenn Miller Birthplace Society (GMBS)
122 W Clark St.
Clarinda, IA 51632
Ph: (712)542-2461
URL: glennmiller.org

7395 ■ Glenn Miller Scholarship *(Undergraduate/Scholarship)*

Purpose: To assist promising young talents in any field of applied music who may be musical leaders of tomorrow. **Focus:** Music. **Qualif.:** Applicants must be graduating high school seniors or first year college students intending to make music a central part of their future life and high school seniors, unless they have been previous first place winners. **Criteria:** Recipients will be selected based on questions of eligibility, conformance to the rules and their intent.

Funds Avail.: $1,000; $2,000; $3,000. **Duration:** Annual. **To Apply:** Applicants must submit a clear high-quality audio CD or tape; completed application; and statement of musical intentions. **Remarks:** The award was named in honor of Glenn Miller. **Contact:** Shari Greenwood, Executive Director, Glenn Miller Birthplace Museum, 122 W. Clark St., Clarinda, Iowa, 51632; Phone: 712-542-2461; Email: shari@glennmiller.org.

7396 ■ Mineralogical Society of America (MSA)
3635 Concorde Pky., Ste. 500
Chantilly, VA 20151-1110
Ph: (703)652-9950
Fax: (703)652-9951
E-mail: business@minsocam.org
URL: www.minsocam.org

7397 ■ MSA Grant for Research in Crystallography *(Professional development/Grant)*

Purpose: To support research in the field of mineralogical crystallography. **Focus:** Mineralogy. **Qualif.:** Applicants must not be an MSA Councilor; cannot submit proposals for both this and Mineralogy/Petrology grant in the same year. **Criteria:** Selection will be based on the following: applicants' qualifications; the quality, innovativeness, and scientific significance of the research; and the likelihood success of the project.

Funds Avail.: Up to $5,000. **Duration:** Annual. **To Apply:** Applicants may not apply for both this and the MSA Grant in Student Research In Mineralogy and Petrology in the same year; proposal submissions for the grant are to be made online. **Contact:** Dr. J. Alex Speer, Mineralogical Society of America, 3635 Concorde Pkwy., Ste. 500, Chantilly VA 20151-1110 USA; Phone: 703-652-9950; Fax: 703-652-9951; Email: jaspeer@minsocam.org.

7398 ■ MSA Grant for Student Research in Mineralogy and Petrology *(Undergraduate, Graduate/Grant)*

Purpose: To encourage research in the fields of either mineralogy or petrology. **Focus:** Mineralogy. **Qualif.:** Applicants must be an MSA member, more than one year from completing a degree, cannot submit proposals for both this and Crystallography grant in the same year, and is not an MSA Councilor. **Criteria:** Selection will be based on the following: applicants' qualifications; the quality, innovativeness, and scientific significance of the research; and the likelihood success of the project.

Funds Avail.: Up to $5,000 each. **Duration:** Annual. **Number Awarded:** 2. **To Apply:** Proposal submissions for the grant are to be made online and comprise the following parts: a short, descriptive title of the research proposal; name and contact information; a brief description of the proposed research project. Be sure to include the motivation and importance of the study, its specific objectives, approach to the problem, research methods, and the location where the research will be done; an explicit budget and budget justification on no more than one additional page. Indicate briefly and specially how the funds will be used and what other support for the proposed research is available and/or has been sought. **Deadline:** March 1. **Remarks:** Established in 1981. **Contact:** Dr. Ann E. Benbow Mineralogical Society of America 3635 Concorde Pkwy Ste 500 Chantilly VA 20151-1110 USA Tel: +1 (703) 652-9950 Fax: +1 (703) 652-9951 e-mail:abenbow@minsocam.org.

7399 ■ Minneapolis Jewish Federation
111 Cheshire Ln, Ste.50
Minnetonka, MN 55305

Awards are arranged alphabetically below their administering organizations

Ph: (952)593-2600
URL: jewishminneapolis.org
Social Media: www.facebook.com/jewishminneapolis
www.linkedin.com/company/minneapolis-jewish-federation
twitter.com/jewishmpls

7400 ■ Minneapolis Jewish Federation Camp Scholarships *(Undergraduate, Other/Scholarship)*

Purpose: To provide financial assistance to children for Jewish summer day and overnight camp programs. **Focus:** General studies/Field of study not specified. **Qualif.:** Applicant must be children in the greater Minneapolis metropolitan area for the Jewish summer day and overnight camp programs. **Criteria:** Selection will be based on their financial need.

Funds Avail.: No specific amount. **Duration:** Annual. **To Apply:** Applicants must submit a completed application form to the Minneapolis Jewish Federation office. **Deadline:** February 24. **Contact:** Laura Tilsner, Administrative Professional-Community; Phone: 952-417-2348; Email: ltilsner@jewishminneapolis.org.

7401 ■ Minnesota Association of County Probation Officers (MACPO)

Goodhue County Court Services
454 W. 6th St.
Red Wing, MN 55066
URL: www.macpo.net

7402 ■ Minnesota Association County Probation Officers Scholarships *(Undergraduate/Scholarship)*

Purpose: To promote and attract quality students to consider Corrections as a career. **Focus:** Criminal justice. **Criteria:** Selection is based on Applicant's qualification and selection committee.

Funds Avail.: $750. **Duration:** Annual. **Number Awarded:** 1. **To Apply:** Applications can be submitted online. **Contact:** Emily Ostlund, Goodhue County Court Services, 454 W. 6th St., Red Wing, MN, 55066; E-mail: emily.ostlund@co.goodhue.mn.us.

7403 ■ Minnesota Association of Public Accountants

PO BOX 301
Saint Paul, MN 55101
Ph: (612)366-1983
Fax: (763)263-8020
E-mail: enebben@vividmanagementllc.com
URL: mapa-mn.com

7404 ■ Minnesota Association of Public Accountant Scholarship *(Undergraduate/Scholarship)*

Purpose: To further the knowledge of the practitioner and offer a source of current information and interplay of ideas among professionals. **Focus:** Accounting.

Duration: Annual. **To Apply:** Applicants must submit a completed application form; official transcript; and letters of recommendation from advisors or professors. **Deadline:** April 15. **Contact:** MAPA, PO Box 301, Big Lake, MN, 55309.

7405 ■ Minnesota Association of Townships (MAT)

805 Central Ave E
Saint Michael, MN 55376

Ph: (763)497-2330
Fax: (763)497-3361
Free: 800-228-0296
E-mail: info@mntownships.org
URL: mntownships.org
Social Media: www.facebook.com/
    MNAssociationofTownships
twitter.com/MNTownships

7406 ■ MAT Scholarship *(Undergraduate, Vocational/Occupational/Scholarship)*

Purpose: To foster efficient, effective and economical town governmental services and to further awareness and education about the township government. **Focus:** Government. **Qualif.:** Applicants must be currently enrolled in the 11th grade and attending a Minnesota public, private, or parochial high school or a home study program and plan to further their education at a college, university, or vocational school. **Criteria:** Recipients are selected based on the written essay; originality; knowledge of the subject matter in relationship to the title; supporting statements; correct spelling and punctuation.

Funds Avail.: $1,000. **Duration:** Annual. **Number Awarded:** 6. **To Apply:** Applicants must complete an application form; a 450-500-word, typed, double-spaced written essay; a current high school transcript and a letter of recommendation from a high school teacher or counselor. **Deadline:** May 1. **Contact:** Minnesota Association of Townships Scholarship Program, PO Box 267, St. Michael, MN, 55376.

7407 ■ Minnesota Health Information Management Association (MHIMA)

233 N Michigan Ave., 21st Flr.
Chicago, IL 60601-5809
URL: www.mnhima.org
Social Media: www.facebook.com/MNHealthInfo
www.linkedin.com/company/mnhima--mn-health
    -information-management
twitter.com/MNHIMA

7408 ■ Minnesota Health Information Management Association Scholarships *(Undergraduate/Scholarship)*

Purpose: To promote high quality health information and benefit the public, healthcare providers and other clinical data users. **Focus:** Health education. **Criteria:** Selection will be made by the Scholarship Committee; will be based on submitted application components and rated on a score sheet with a five (5) point scale.

Funds Avail.: No specific amount. **Duration:** Annual. **To Apply:** Applicants must submit an application form; one letter of recommendation from faculty advisor, faculty member or mentor; a verification program; an essay with 500 words; and an official transcript of grades indicating cumulative grades. **Deadline:** March 11. **Contact:** MHIMA Executive Director; PO Box 16246, Duluth, Minnesota, 55816-0246; Phone: 218-340-6735; Email: executivedirector@mnhima.org.

7409 ■ Minnesota State Archery Association (MSAA)

33266 County Hwy. 4
Sanborn, MN 56083

Awards are arranged alphabetically below their administering organizations

URL: www.mnarchery.org
Social Media: www.facebook.com/
MNStateArcheryAssociation

7410 ■ MSAA Scholarship Program *(Graduate/ Scholarship)*

Purpose: To encourage outstanding students to prepare for worthwhile careers at the college of their choice and to promote the sport of archery. **Focus:** General studies/Field of study not specified. **Qualif.:** Applicants must be graduating high school students who are academically successful and who can also demonstrate a sincere interest in the sport of archery.

Funds Avail.: $500. **Duration:** Annual. **Number Awarded:** 2. **To Apply:** Applicants must submit a completed application form and a resume. **Deadline:** June 15. **Remarks:** Established in 1971. **Contact:** MSAA Secretary, c/o Stephanie Wiseman, 302 Champagne Ave SW, Red Lake Falls, MN, 56750.

7411 ■ Minority Corporate Counsel Association (MCCA)

1111 Pennsylvania Ave. NW
Washington, DC 20004
Ph: (202)739-5901
Fax: (202)739-5999
E-mail: education@mcca.com
URL: www.mcca.com
Social Media: www.facebook.com/MCCA.law
www.instagram.com/mcca.law
www.linkedin.com/company/minority-corporate-counsel
 -association
twitter.com/mccalaw

7412 ■ MCCA Lloyd M. Johnson, Jr. Scholarships *(Graduate/Scholarship)*

Purpose: To provide scholarship support for newly entering first year law students pursuing a Juris Doctor degree. **Focus:** Law. **Criteria:** An independent selection committee will evaluate the Complete applications and select recipients considering:financial need;community involvement;essay content;academic achievements and records.

Funds Avail.: $10,000. **Duration:** Annual. **Number Awarded:** Up to 6. **To Apply:** Application must be submitted online and must include the following uploaded application materials: undergraduate and graduate transcripts, resume, provision of contract information for two recommenders and response to a two-part essay question. **Deadline:** July 2. **Remarks:** Established in 2004.

7413 ■ Miss America Organization

PO Box 1919
Atlantic City, NJ 08404-1919
Ph: (609)344-1800
E-mail: info@missamerica.org
URL: missamerica.org
Social Media: www.facebook.com/missamerica
www.instagram.com/missamerica/
www.pinterest.com/missamericaorg/
twitter.com/MissAmericaOrg
www.youtube.com/user/MissAmericaOrg

7414 ■ Dr. and Mrs. David B. Allman Medical Scholarship *(Undergraduate/Scholarship)*

Purpose: To assist women who competed in Miss America Pageant to commence their education in the medical field.

Focus: Medicine. **Qualif.:** Applicants must be former contestants who have competed within the system on the State, Local or National level from 2008 to present regardless of whether a title was won and who are currently study or aspire to enter the field of medicine. **Criteria:** Recipients will be chosen by the committee based on several factors - grade point average (high school and college/university), class rank, MCAT score, extra-curricular activities, financial aid requirements, household income and level of participation within the system.

Funds Avail.: No specific amount. **Duration:** Annual. **To Apply:** Complete online application. **Deadline:** June 30. **Remarks:** Funded by Dr. & Mrs. David B. Allman.

7415 ■ The Jean Bartel Military Scholarship *(Undergraduate/Scholarship)*

Purpose: To support the individuals who have gone above and beyond in their dedication to community service and improving the lives of others. **Focus:** General studies/Field of study not specified. **Qualif.:** Applicants must be women who have competed on the local, state, or national level from 2008 to present, regardless of whether a title was won. **Criteria:** The Scholarship Committee will review all applications for this scholarship, and will consider the following (among other things): grade point average (high school & college/university), class rank, extracurricular activities, financial aid requirements, household income, level of participation within the MAO system, and an essay describing how the applicant has fulfilled a legitimate need in their community through the creation, development, and/or participation in a community-based project or event to support and raise awareness of the brave men and women who dedicate their lives to protect our freedom.

Funds Avail.: $3,000. **To Apply:** Application form and details available on the sponsor's website. **Deadline:** October 15.

7416 ■ Eugenia Vellner Fischer Award for the Performing Arts *(Undergraduate/Scholarship)*

Purpose: To assist women who competed in Miss America Pageant in pursuing a degree in the performing arts. **Focus:** Performing arts. **Qualif.:** Applicants must be contestants in Miss America Pageant local or national level from 1998 to present.

Funds Avail.: No specific amount. **To Apply:** Applicants may contact the Association for the application process and other information.

7417 ■ Miss America Social Impact Initiative Scholarship *(Undergraduate/Scholarship)*

Purpose: To support outstanding individuals who compete in the state competitions to achieve their personal and professional goals and demonstrate exemplary community service initiatives. **Focus:** General studies/Field of study not specified. **Qualif.:** Applicants must be contestants competing at the state level.

Funds Avail.: $6,000 (first place); $4,000 (second place); $2,000 (third place). **To Apply:** Applicants may contact the Association for application process and other information.

7418 ■ Mission Aviation Fellowship of Canada (MAF)

264 Woodlawn Rd. W
Guelph, ON, Canada N1H 1B6
Free: 877-351-9344
E-mail: info@mafc.org

Awards are arranged alphabetically below their administering organizations

URL: www.mafc.org
Social Media: www.facebook.com/MAFCanada
www.instagram.com/mafcanada
www.pinterest.com/mafcanada
twitter.com/mafcanada
www.youtube.com/user/mafcanada

7419 ■ MAF Canada Scholarship Fund
(Undergraduate/Scholarship)

Purpose: To support students preparing for a full-time career in mission aviation who have plans to use their skills overseas. **Focus:** Aviation. **Qualif.:** Applicants must be post-secondary students; must be Canadian citizens or landed immigrants; and must have successfully completed at least one year of Bible school; must possess either (Pilot) private license or (AME) all required courses completed. **Criteria:** Preference will be given to applicants who have demonstrated financial need.

To Apply: Applicants must prepare a minimum two-page essay describing their goals and objectives with regards to a vocation in mission aviation; essay should include all information required to assess the Christian life and Ministry. It should be accompanied by a transcript of recent grades, copy of their vocational certification; and a reference letter from a pastor or senior church official to whom they reported while participating in church ministry or community outreach. **Remarks:** Established in 2004. **Contact:** Scholarship Fund Committee, Mission Aviation Fellowship of Canada, 264 Woodlawn Rd. W, Guelph, ON, N1H 1B6.

7420 ■ Mississippi Society of Certified Public Accountants (MSCPA)
306 Southampton Row
Ridgeland, MS 39157
Ph: (601)856-4244
Fax: (601)856-8255
Free: 800-772-1099
E-mail: mscpa@ms-cpa.org
URL: www.ms-cpa.org
Social Media: www.facebook.com/mssocietyofcpas
www.linkedin.com/company/mississippi-society-of-cpas

7421 ■ MSCPA Undergraduate Scholarship
(Undergraduate/Scholarship)

Purpose: To support undergraduate students majoring in accounting. **Focus:** Accounting. **Criteria:** Selection is based on academic excellence, campus involvement, faculty recommendations, written essay and financial need.

Duration: Annual. **To Apply:** Applicants must submit a completed undergraduate student application signed and dated; a recent photograph, one-page essay and official transcript of all college work to the chair of the accounting department or designee of the applicant's institution. **Deadline:** June 1. **Contact:** MSCPA Awards, Education and Scholarship Committee, 306 Southampton Row, Ridgeland, MS, 39157, Email: kmoody@ms-cpa.org.

7422 ■ Ross/Nickey Scholarships *(Graduate/Scholarship)*

Purpose: To financially support students enrolled at a graduate accounting program. **Focus:** Accounting. **Qualif.:** Applicants must be enrolled in or admitted to a graduate accounting program in Mississippi; must be Mississippi residents; must demonstrate special merit and exceptional

promise in the field of accounting. **Criteria:** Selection is based on academic excellence, campus involvement, faculty recommendations, written essay and financial need.

Funds Avail.: $1,000. **Duration:** Annual. **To Apply:** Applicants must submit a completed graduate student application form (5 pages) signed and dated; a recent photograph; a one-page essay; GMAT score; acceptance letter from the college/university chosen for graduate study; and official transcript of all college undergraduate and graduate work to the chair of the accounting department or designee of the applicant's institution. **Contact:** Mississippi Society of Certified Public Accountants, at the above address.

7423 ■ Missouri Department of Health and Senior Services
912 Wildwood Dr.
Jefferson City, MO 65102
Ph: (573)751-6400
Fax: (573)751-6010
Free: 800-235-5503
E-mail: info@health.mo.gov
URL: health.mo.gov
Social Media: www.facebook.com/HealthyLivingMo
twitter.com/HealthyLivingMo
www.youtube.com/user/MODHSS

7424 ■ Health Professional Nursing Student Loans
(Undergraduate, Graduate, Community College, Doctorate/Loan)

Purpose: To address the needs of Missouri students pursuing degrees in nursing. **Focus:** Nursing. **Qualif.:** Applicants must be Missouri residents attending a Missouri institution; must have been accepted by or currently attending an eligible nursing program in a Missouri institution leading to one of the following degrees/licensures: Licensed Practical Nurse (LPN); Registered Nurse (RN); Diploma in Nursing (DN); Associate Degree in Nursing (ADN); Bachelor of Science in Nursing (BSN); Master of Science Degree in Nursing (MSN) leading to advanced practice licensure; or, Doctorate Students seeking a Doctor of Philosophy (PhD), Doctor of Nursing Practice (DNP), or a student with a master of science in nursing seeking Doctor of Education (EdD), or leading to the completion of educational requirements for a licensed practical nurse. Doctoral applicants may be part-time students.

Funds Avail.: $2,500 for LPN students; $5,000 for professional nursing students. **Duration:** Annual. **To Apply:** Application and details are available at: health.mo.gov/living/families/primarycare/healthprofloans/. **Deadline:** March 1. **Contact:** Nurse Student Loan (NSL) Program, Email: DHSS.LoanRepayment@health.mo.gov.

7425 ■ Modern Language Association of America (MLA)
85 Broad St., Ste. 500
New York, NY 10004-2434
Ph: (646)576-5000
Fax: (646)458-0030
URL: www.mla.org
Social Media: www.facebook.com/
  modernlanguageassociation
www.linkedin.com/company/modern-language-association
twitter.com/mlanews

Awards are arranged alphabetically below their administering organizations

7426 ■ MLA Financial Assistance (Graduate, Advanced Professional/Grant)

Purpose: To provide partial travel assistance to the members of the MLA who shall attend preconvention workshops, sessions in their areas of scholarly interest, meetings with job counselors, or interviews. **Focus:** Modern languages. **Qualif.:** Applicants must be MLA members; graduate students, non-tenure track faculty members, and unemployed members along with regular and life members residing outside the United States and Canada are eligible. **Criteria:** Selection will be based on the committee's criteria.

Funds Avail.: $400. **Duration:** Annual. **Number Awarded:** 3. **To Apply:** Applicants may apply online (through MLA website) or via mail as an alternative. each letter should include complete contact information and a brief statement by students indicating whether they are receiving external support for travel to the convention. all letters required should be mailed to the Travel Grant Program of MLA. **Deadline:** December 1. **Contact:** MLA; Phone: 646-576-5141; E-mail: awards@mla.org.

7427 ■ Molded Dimensions Inc.

701 W Sunset Rd.
Port Washington, WI 53074-2165
Ph: (262)284-9455
Fax: (262)284-0696
E-mail: sales@moldeddimensions.com
URL: www.moldeddimensions.com
Social Media: www.facebook.com/moldeddimensionsllc
www.linkedin.com/company/molded-dimensions

7428 ■ Molded Dimensions, LLC Scholarship (College, University/Scholarship)

Purpose: To help students pursue a degree in STEM fields. **Focus:** Engineering; Mathematics and mathematical sciences; Science. **Qualif.:** Applicant must be a U.S. citizen in the process of pursuing a STEM degree at a college or university in the United States. **Criteria:** Selection is based on online.

Funds Avail.: $500. **To Apply:** Provide proof of acceptance to a college or university, or college transcripts; submit a one page essay on past accomplishments, education, and career goals in the field of STEM, along with a description of extra-curricular activities; application must be filled out on the sponsor's website at www.moldeddimensions.com/scholarship.php. **Deadline:** November 30.

7429 ■ Moline Foundation

1601 River Drive, Suite 210
Moline, IL 61265
Ph: (309)736-3800
E-mail: info@molinefoundation.org
URL: www.molinefoundation.org

7430 ■ Clement T. Hanson Scholarship (Undergraduate/Scholarship)

Purpose: To provide grants to health, human services, education, community development, the arts and other charitable organizations which benefit the citizens of Moline Foundations. **Focus:** General studies/Field of study not specified. **Qualif.:** Applicant must be live within Moline School District No. 40 boundaries; must be graduate from Class of 2018 or Community College student; must have

minimum 2.5 grade point. **Criteria:** Recipients are selected based on financial need; finalists will be evaluated based on personal interview and letters of reference.

Funds Avail.: $1,500. **Duration:** Annual. **To Apply:** Applicants must complete the application form; must submit transcripts, two letters of reference, and brief personal essay (200 words or less).

7431 ■ Lee Womack Scholarship (Undergraduate/Scholarship)

Purpose: To support students with their educational expenses in obtaining a college degree in education. **Focus:** Education.

Funds Avail.: No specific amount. **To Apply:** Applicants must complete and submit the application form together with their transcript, two letters of reference and a statement of the following questions: Why you want to obtain an Education degree and your goals? How your feel this would be an asset to your community? two letters of reference. **Deadline:** February 20.

7432 ■ Monadnock Folklore Society (MFS)

c/o Bruce Myrick, Director
54 Brook St.
Keene, NH 03431-3281
Ph: (401)526-4731
E-mail: info@monadnockfolk.org
URL: www.monadnockfolk.org

7433 ■ Johnny Trombly Memorial Scholarship (Undergraduate/Scholarship)

Purpose: To provide financial assistance to musicians. **Focus:** Music. **Qualif.:** Applicants must be residents of Cheshire, Sullivan or Hillsborough counties (NH); upper Connecticut river valley and windham county (VT) residents are welcome to apply. **Criteria:** Preference will be given to Monadnock area residents.

Funds Avail.: Up to $500. **Duration:** Quarterly; Quarterly scholarships will be awarded until the annual scholarship fund is exhausted. **Number Awarded:** 1. **To Apply:** Application must be accompanied by at least one recommendation letter from someone who is knowledgeable about the applicants and music. Selected applicants are required to provide a photo and report describing the prospective benefits to be acquired from the funding. **Deadline:** April 1, July 1, October 1, and January 1. **Remarks:** The award was established in honor of Bob McQuillen. Established in 2001. **Contact:** Monadnock Folklore Society c/o Bruce Myrick, 54 Brook Street, Keene, NH, 03431; Phone: 603-352-8616; Email: info@monadnockfolk.org.

7434 ■ Money Metals Exchange (MME)

PO Box 2599
Eagle, ID 83616
Fax: (866)861-5174
Free: 800-800-1865
E-mail: inquiry@moneymetals.com
URL: www.moneymetals.com
Social Media: www.facebook.com/MoneyMetals
www.instagram.com/moneymetals
www.linkedin.com/company/money-metals
www.pinterest.com/moneymetals
twitter.com/MoneyMetals

Awards are arranged alphabetically below their administering organizations

7435 ■ Money Metals Exchange & Sound Money Defense League Scholarship *(Undergraduate, Graduate/Scholarship)*

Purpose: To help qualified students pay for the ever-rising costs of higher education. **Focus:** General studies/Field of study not specified. **Qualif.:** Applicants must be high school seniors, undergraduate students, or graduate students with an interest in economics, specifically the tradition of the Austrian school; not necessary to be an economics major. **Criteria:** Quality of essay, with the People's Choice winner chosen based on number of "shares" or "retweets" on social media.

Funds Avail.: $2,000 for undergraduate and graduate first places; $1,000 for undergraduate and graduate runners-up; $500 for People's Choice. **Duration:** Annual. **To Apply:** Application and details available at www.moneymetals.com/scholarship. **Deadline:** September 30. **Contact:** Email: scholarship@moneymetals.com.

7436 ■ MoneySolver
9000 Southside Blvd., Ste. 11000
Jacksonville, FL 32256
Free: 888-613-4396
URL: www.moneysolver.org

7437 ■ Back to School Scholarship *(All/Scholarship)*

Purpose: To help students or previous students pay tuition, fees, or student loan debt. **Focus:** General studies/Field of study not specified. **Qualif.:** Applicant must be at least 18 years old, a legal U.S. resident, and enrolled, previously enrolled, or planning to enroll (for next semester) in an accredited post-secondary institution (college, university, or trade school). **Criteria:** Selection is based on written response submitted: writing ability, creativity, originality, and overall excellence will be weighted equally.

Funds Avail.: $1,000. **Number Awarded:** 1. **To Apply:** Application must be completed on the sponsor's website and must include: name and contact information, background details, and a short, original, previously unpublished written response to the question, "If you could go back to high school for one day, what would you do?" (250 words or less, in English). **Deadline:** September 30. **Contact:** Tamara Krause; Email: tamara.krause@moneysolver.org; Phone No: 904-404-3531; URL: www.moneysolver.org/scholarships/scholarship-faqs/.

7438 ■ Easter Scholarship *(All/Scholarship)*

Purpose: To help a student or previous student with tuition, fees, or student loan debt. **Focus:** General studies/Field of study not specified. **Qualif.:** Applicant must be at least 18 years old, a legal U.S. resident, and enrolled, previously enrolled, or planning to enroll (for next semester) in an accredited post-secondary institution (college, university, or trade school). **Criteria:** Selection is based on written response submitted: writing ability, creativity, originality, and overall excellence will be weighted equally.

Funds Avail.: $1,000. **Number Awarded:** 1. **To Apply:** Application must be completed on sponsor's website and must include: name and contact information, background details, and a short, original, previously unpublished written response to the question, "What Easter scholarship would you create and why?" (250 words or less, in English). **Deadline:** April 30. **Contact:** Tamara Krause; Email: tamara.krause@moneysolver.org; Phone No: 904-404-3531; URL: www.moneysolver.org/scholarships/scholarship-faqs/.

7439 ■ Emoji Scholarship *(All/Scholarship)*

Purpose: To help a student or previous student pay for tuition, fees, or student loan debt. **Focus:** General studies/Field of study not specified. **Qualif.:** Applicant must be at least 18 years old, a legal U.S. resident, and enrolled, previously enrolled, or planning to enroll (for next semester) in an accredited post-secondary institution (college, university, or trade school). **Criteria:** Selection is based on the written response submitted: writing ability, creativity, originality, and overall excellence will be equally weighted.

Funds Avail.: $1,000. **Number Awarded:** 1. **To Apply:** Application must be completed on the sponsor's website and must include: name and contact information, background details, and a short, original, previously unpublished written response to the question, "What emoji describes your life, and why?" (250 words or less, in English). **Deadline:** August 31. **Contact:** Tamara Krause; Email: tamara.krause@moneysolver.org; Phone No: 904-404-3531; URL: www.moneysolver.org/scholarships/scholarship-faqs/.

7440 ■ Father's Day Scholarship *(All/Scholarship)*

Purpose: To help a student or previous student pay for tuition, fees, or student loan debt. **Focus:** General studies/Field of study not specified. **Qualif.:** Applicant must be at least 18 years old, a legal U.S. resident, and enrolled, previously enrolled, or planning to enroll (for next semester) in an accredited post-secondary institution (college, university, or trade school). **Criteria:** Selection is based on written response submitted: writing ability, creativity, originality, and overall excellence will be weighted equally.

Funds Avail.: $1,000. **Number Awarded:** 1. **To Apply:** Application must be completed on sponsor's website and must include: name and contact information, background details, and a short, original, previously unpublished written response to the question, "How does your dad make a difference in your life?" (250 words or less, in English). **Deadline:** June 30. **Contact:** Tamara Krause; Email: tamara.krause@moneysolver.org; Phone No: 904-404-3531; URL: www.moneysolver.org/scholarships/scholarship-faqs/.

7441 ■ Halloween Costume Scholarship *(All/Scholarship)*

Purpose: To help students or previous students pay for tuition, fees, and student loan debt. **Focus:** General studies/Field of study not specified. **Qualif.:** Applicant must be at least 18 years old, a legal U.S. resident, and enrolled, previously enrolled, or planning to enroll (for next semester) in an accredited post-secondary institution (college, university, or trade school). **Criteria:** Selection will be based on the written response submitted: writing ability, creativity, originality, and overall excellence will be weighted equally.

Funds Avail.: $1,000. **Number Awarded:** 1. **To Apply:** Application must be completed on sponsor's website and must include: name and contact information, background details, and a short, original, previously unpublished written response to the question, "What was your favorite costume (worn by either you or your pet)?" (250 words, in English). **Deadline:** October 31. **Contact:** Tamara Krause; Email: tamara.krause@moneysolver.org; Phone No: 904-404-3531; URL: www.moneysolver.org/scholarships/scholarship-faqs/.

7442 ■ Holiday Celebration Scholarship *(All/Scholarship)*

Purpose: To help students or previous students pay for tuition, fees, or student loan debt. **Focus:** General studies/

Awards are arranged alphabetically below their administering organizations

Field of study not specified. **Qualif.:** Applicant must be at least 18 years old, a legal U.S. resident, and enrolled, previously enrolled, or planning to enroll (for next semester) in an accredited post-secondary institution (college, university, or trade school). **Criteria:** Selection will be based on the written response submitted: writing ability, creativity, originality, and overall excellence will be weighted equally.

Funds Avail.: $1,000. **Number Awarded:** 1. **To Apply:** Application must be completed on sponsor's website and must include: name and contact information, background details, and a short, original, previously unpublished written response to the question, "What is your favorite way to celebrate the holidays with the people you love?" (250 words or less, in English). **Deadline:** December 31. **Contact:** Tamara Krause; Email: tamara.krause@moneysolver.org; Phone No: 904-404-3531; URL: www.moneysolver.org/scholarships/scholarship-faqs/.

7443 ■ Mother's Day Scholarship *(All/Scholarship)*

Purpose: To help students or previous students pay for tuition, fees, or student loan debt. **Focus:** General studies/Field of study not specified. **Qualif.:** Applicant must be at least 18 years old, a legal U.S. resident, and enrolled, previously enrolled, or planning to enroll (for next semester) in an accredited post-secondary institution (college, university, or trade school). **Criteria:** Selection is based on written response: writing ability, creativity, originality, and overall excellence will be weighted equally.

Funds Avail.: $1,000. **Number Awarded:** 1. **To Apply:** Application must be completed on sponsor's website and must include: name and contact information, background details, and a short, original, previously unpublished written response to the question, "If you could create a Mother's Day card, what would it say?" (250 words or less, in English). **Deadline:** May 31. **Contact:** Tamara Krause; Email: tamara.krause@moneysolver.org; Phone No: 904-404-3531; URL: www.moneysolver.org/scholarships/scholarship-faqs/.

7444 ■ St. Patrick's Day Scholarship *(All/Scholarship)*

Purpose: To help a student or previous student pay for tuition, fees, or student loan debt. **Focus:** General studies/Field of study not specified. **Qualif.:** Applicant must be at least 18 years old, a legal U.S. resident, and enrolled, previously enrolled, or planning to enroll (for next semester) in an accredited post-secondary institution (college, university, or trade school). **Criteria:** Selection is based on the written response submitted: writing ability, creativity, originality, and overall excellence will be given equal weight.

Funds Avail.: $1,000. **Number Awarded:** 1. **To Apply:** Application must be completed on sponsor's website and must include: name and contact information, background details, and a short, original, previously unpublished written response to the topic, "Are you creative? Spin your best St. Patrick's Day tale for a chance to win a $1,000 scholarship (250 words or less, in English). **Deadline:** March 31. **Contact:** Tamara Krause; Email: tamara.krause@moneysolver.org; Phone No: 904-404-3531; URL: www.moneysolver.org/scholarships/scholarship-faqs/.

7445 ■ Student Loan Relief Scholarship *(All/Scholarship)*

Purpose: To help students or previous students pay down student loan debt. **Focus:** General studies/Field of study not specified. **Qualif.:** Applicant must be at least 18 years old, a legal U.S. resident, and enrolled, previously enrolled,

or planning to enroll (for next semester) in an accredited post-secondary institution (college, university, or trade school). **Criteria:** Selection will be based on the written response: writing ability, creativity, originality, and overall excellence will each be given equal weight.

Funds Avail.: $2,500. **Number Awarded:** 1. **To Apply:** Application must be completed online at sponsor's website and must include: name and contact information; background details; and a short, original, and previously unpublished written response to the question "What wish would you request if you found a genie in a bottle? (250 words or less, in English). **Deadline:** June 30. **Contact:** Tamara Krause; Email: tamara.krause@moneysolver.org; Phone No: 904-404-3531; URL: www.moneysolver.org/scholarships/scholarship-faqs/.

7446 ■ Summer Scholarship *(All/Scholarship)*

Purpose: To help students or previous students pay for tuition, fees, and student loan debt. **Focus:** General studies/Field of study not specified. **Qualif.:** Applicant must be at least 18 years old, a legal U.S. resident, and enrolled, previously enrolled, or planning to enroll (for next semester) in an accredited post-secondary institution (college, university, or trade school). **Criteria:** Selection is based on written response submitted: writing ability, creativity, originality, and overall excellence will be weighted equally.

Funds Avail.: $1,000. **Number Awarded:** 1. **To Apply:** Application must be completed on sponsor's website and must include: name and contact information, background details, and a short, original, previously unpublished written response to the question, "If money wasn't an issue, where would you go and why?" (250 words or less, in English). **Deadline:** July 31. **Contact:** Tamara Krause; Email: tamara.krause@moneysolver.org; Phone No: 904-404-3531; URL: www.moneysolver.org/scholarships/scholarship-faqs/.

7447 ■ Valentine's Day Scholarship *(All/Scholarship)*

Purpose: To help a student or previous student with college tuition or fees or to pay down loan debt. **Focus:** General studies/Field of study not specified. **Qualif.:** Applicant must be at least 18 years old, a legal U.S. resident, and enrolled, previously enrolled, or planning to enroll (for next semester) in an accredited post-secondary institution (college, university, or trade school). **Criteria:** Selection is based on the written response: writing ability, creativity, originality, and overall excellence will be given equal weight.

Funds Avail.: $1,000. **Duration:** Annual. **Number Awarded:** 1. **To Apply:** Application must be completed at sponsor's website and must include: name and contact information, background details, and a short, original, previously unpublished written response to the question, "For Valentine's Day, would you prefer a $1,000 college scholarship or some gift of equal value?" (250 words or less, in English). **Deadline:** February 29. **Contact:** Tamara Krause; Email: tamara.krause@moneysolver.org; Phone No: 904-404-3531; URL: www.moneysolver.org/scholarships/scholarship-faqs/.

7448 ■ Monsanto Co.
800 N Lindbergh Blvd.
Saint Louis, MO 63167
Ph: (314)694-1000
Free: 888-725-9529
URL: www.monsanto.com
Social Media: www.facebook.com/monsantoco

Awards are arranged alphabetically below their administering organizations

www.instagram.com/bayer4crops
www.youtube.com/c/bayercrosciencegblobal

7449 ■ Monsanto Commitment To Agriculture Scholarships *(Undergraduate/Scholarship)*

Purpose: To support the education of students who have long-term career interest in agriculture. **Focus:** Agricultural sciences. **Qualif.:** Applicants must be high school seniors who come from a farm family, plan to enroll as a full-time student in an agriculture-related academic major in an accredited school and be committed to pursuing a career in agriculture. **Criteria:** Applicants will be evaluated on their academic record, leadership, extracurricular activities and personal essays submitted as a part of the application process.

Funds Avail.: $1,500 each. **Number Awarded:** 100. **To Apply:** Applicants may contact the Program Administrator for the application. **Remarks:** The scholarship is in association with the National Association of Farm Broadcasters (NAFB). Established in 1999.

7450 ■ Montana Broadcasters Association (MBA)
18 Ruby Mountain Rd.
Clancy, MT 59634
Ph: (406)431-2139
URL: www.mtbroadcasters.org

7451 ■ Joe Durso, Jr. Memorial Scholarship
(Undergraduate/Scholarship)

Purpose: To support students attending any accredited Montana state college, university or college of technology in the aforementioned disciplines. **Focus:** Broadcasting. **Qualif.:** Applicants must be students entering their senior year, majoring in Radio-TV or Broadcast Journalism.

Funds Avail.: No specific amount. **Duration:** Annual. **Deadline:** February 28. **Remarks:** The award was established to honor Joe Durso, former MBA board member and chair of the Radio-Television Department at UM.

7452 ■ Great Falls Broadcasters Association Scholarships *(Undergraduate/Scholarship)*

Purpose: To promote the values of local, free over-the-air broadcasting to the business community, governmental bodies and the general public in Montana; and to support the Montana broadcasting industry by providing services, information, continuing education, recruitment and a strong unified voice. **Focus:** Broadcasting.

Funds Avail.: No specific amount. **Duration:** Annual. **To Apply:** Applicants must complete an application form; must include a one-page statement summarizing their professional abilities, career goals and extra-curricular activities; and two letters of recommendation from an instructor. **Deadline:** February 28. **Contact:** Montana Broadcasters Association; 18 Ruby Mountain Road Clancy, MT 59634; e-mail: dbruce@mtbroadcasters.org.

7453 ■ Montana Broadcasters Association Broadcast Engineering Scholarships
(Undergraduate/Scholarship)

Purpose: To promote the values of local, free over-the-air broadcasting to the business community, governmental bodies and the general public in Montana; and to support the Montana broadcasting industry by providing services, information, continuing education, recruitment and a strong

unified voice. **Focus:** Broadcasting; Engineering. **Qualif.:** Applicants must be Montana students interested in pursuing a career in Broadcast Engineering. **Criteria:** Recipients are selected based on academic performance.

Funds Avail.: No specific amount. **Duration:** Annual. **To Apply:** Applicants must complete an application form; must include a one-page statement summarizing their professional abilities, career goals and extra-curricular activities; and two letters of recommendation from an instructor. **Deadline:** February 28. **Contact:** Montana Broadcasters Association; e-mail: dbruce@mtbroadcasters.org.

7454 ■ Montana Health Care Association (MHCA)
c/o Rose M. Hughes, Executive Director
36 S Last Chance Gulch, Ste. A
Helena, MT 59601
Ph: (406)443-2876
Fax: (406)443-4614
URL: www.montanahealthcareassociation.org

7455 ■ Donald E. Pizzini Memorial Nurse Scholarship *(Undergraduate, Professional development/ Scholarship)*

Purpose: To facilitate the development of an educated long-term care nursing workforce to meet current and future demands. **Focus:** Nursing. **Criteria:** Preference shall be given to those individuals currently working in or demonstrating an interestin pursuing a career in long term care.

Funds Avail.: Up to $1,000. **Duration:** Annual. **Number Awarded:** Varies. **To Apply:** Applicant must submit a completed application form; official transcripts from all attended educational institutions; statement of nursing career intentions; two recommendations from individuals who are familiar with the applicant; proof of acceptance or proof of enrollment. **Deadline:** February. **Contact:** Montana Health Care Association Scholarship Foundation, 36 S Last Chance Gulch, Ste. A, Helena, MT 59601; Phone: 406 443 2876; Fax: 406 443 4614.

7456 ■ Montana Society of Certified Public Accountants Helena Chapter
46 N Last Chance Gulch, Ste. 2D
Helena, MT 59624-0861
Ph: (406)442-7301
Free: 800-272-0307
E-mail: mscpa@mscpa.org
URL: www.mscpa.org/about/chapter/HE-helena
Social Media: www.facebook.com/MontanaCPA
www.linkedin.com/in/montanasocietyofcpas
twitter.com/MTCPASociety

7457 ■ Anthony Gerharz Scholarship *(Undergraduate, Graduate/Scholarship)*

Purpose: To reward individuals who have made excellence in accounting. **Focus:** Accounting. **Qualif.:** Applicants must be Montana residents who have graduated from a Montana high school; must be currently enrolled at the MSU Billings with at least a junior standing and one semester of coursework remaining; must be accounting major; must have a minimum GPA of 3.0. Graduate students are also eligible. **Criteria:** Preference will be given to student members of the MSCPA.

Funds Avail.: No specific amount. **Duration:** Annual. **Deadline:** March 18.

Awards are arranged alphabetically below their administering organizations

---

7458 ■ Eldon E. and JoAnn C. Kuhns Family Scholarship *(Undergraduate, Graduate/Scholarship)*

Purpose: To recognize the tremendous talents and potential of Montana accounting students. **Focus:** Accounting. **Qualif.:** Applicants must be Montana residents who have graduated from a Montana high school; must be currently enrolled in an accounting program with at least a junior standing and one semester of coursework remaining; must have a minimum GPA of 3.0. Graduate students are also available. **Criteria:** Preference will be given to student members of the MSCPA.

Funds Avail.: No specific amount. **Duration:** Annual. **Deadline:** March 18.

7459 ■ MSCPA Scholarship - Montana Tech *(Undergraduate, Graduate/Scholarship)*

Purpose: To reward individuals who have made excellence in accounting. **Focus:** Accounting. **Qualif.:** Applicants must be Montana residents who have graduated from a Montana high school; must be currently enrolled at the Montana Tech with at least a junior standing and one semester of coursework remaining; must be accounting major; must have a minimum GPA of 3.0. Graduate students are also available. **Criteria:** Preference will be given to student members of the MSCPA.

Funds Avail.: No specific amount. **Duration:** Annual. **Deadline:** March 18.

7460 ■ MSCPA Scholarship - MSU Bozeman *(Undergraduate, Graduate/Scholarship)*

Purpose: To reward individuals who have made excellence in accounting. **Focus:** Accounting. **Qualif.:** Applicants must be Montana residents who have graduated from a Montana high school; must be currently enrolled at the MSU Bozeman with at least a junior standing and one semester of coursework remaining; must be accounting major; must have a minimum GPA of 3.0. Graduate students are also available. **Criteria:** Preference will be given to student members of the MSCPA.

Funds Avail.: No specific amount. **Duration:** Annual. **Deadline:** March 18.

7461 ■ MSCPA Scholarship - University of Montana *(Undergraduate, Graduate/Scholarship)*

Purpose: To reward individuals who have made excellence in accounting. **Focus:** Accounting. **Qualif.:** Applicants must be Montana residents who have graduated from a Montana high school; must be currently enrolled at the University of Montana with at least a junior standing and one semester of coursework remaining; must be accounting major; must have a minimum GPA of 3.0. Graduate students are also available. **Criteria:** Preference will be given to student members of the MSCPA.

Funds Avail.: No specific amount. **Duration:** Annual. **Deadline:** March 18.

7462 ■ Scott Brownlee Memorial Scholarship *(Undergraduate, Graduate/Scholarship)*

Purpose: To reward individuals who have made excellence in accounting. **Focus:** Accounting. **Qualif.:** Applicants must be Montana residents who have graduated from a Montana high school; must be currently enrolled at the Carroll College with at least a junior standing and one semester of coursework remaining; must be accounting major; must have a minimum GPA of 3.0. Graduate students are also

available. **Criteria:** Preference will be given to student members of the MSCPA.

Funds Avail.: No specific amount. **Duration:** Annual. **Deadline:** March 18.

7463 ■ Michael Moody Fitness
900 N North Branch St.
Chicago, IL 60642
Ph: (773)484-8094
E-mail: michael@michaelmoodyfitness.com
URL: www.michaelmoodyfitness.com
Social Media: www.facebook.com/pages/Michael-Moody
  -Fitness/128901700448
www.instagram.com/michaelmoodyfitness
www.linkedin.com/in/michaelmoodyfitness
twitter.com/MichaelMoodyFit

7464 ■ Michael Moody Fitness Scholarship *(Undergraduate, Graduate/Scholarship)*

Purpose: To provide financial support to an individual pursuing a career in the health and fitness related fields. **Focus:** Education, Physical; Health sciences; Physical therapy; Sports studies. **Qualif.:** Applicant must be United States citizens or legal residents living or claiming residency in one of the 50 united states, Washington, D.C. or Puerto Rico; current high school senior, undergraduate, or graduate students who plan to enroll full-time in an accredited two-year or four-year college or university in the United States for the current academic year; demonstrate ambition and self-drive as evidenced by outstanding achievement in school, and participation and leadership in school activities and work experience. **Criteria:** Demonstrated interest in pursuing a career in the health and fitness related fields; possessing ambition and self-drive as evidenced by outstanding achievement in school, and participation and leadership in school activities and work experience.

Funds Avail.: $1,500. **Deadline:** July 15. **Contact:** Email: michael@michaelmoodyfitness.com.

7465 ■ Morgan, Lewis & Bockius LLP
1701 Market St.
Philadelphia, PA 19103-2921
Ph: (215)963-4831
Fax: (215)963-6001
E-mail: info@morganlewis.com
URL: www.morganlewis.com
Social Media: www.facebook.com/morganlewislaw
www.instagram.com/morganlewis_law
www.linkedin.com/company/morgan-lewis-&-bockius-llp
twitter.com/morganlewislaw

7466 ■ Diversity Fellowship Program (DFP) *(Undergraduate/Fellowship)*

Purpose: To promote diversity in the legal profession and to attract future leaders who are committed to the importance of diversity. **Focus:** Law. **Qualif.:** Applicants must be second year law students who have successfully completed one year of law school; have demonstrated excellence; have outstanding leadership skills; and have a demonstrated interest in promoting diversity. **Criteria:** Selection is based on merit.

Funds Avail.: $15,000. **To Apply:** Applicants must sign up for an on-campus interview at the participating law schools

Awards are arranged alphabetically below their administering organizations

and submit a completed application form along with a resume, transcript, and a brief personal statement.

7467 ■ Morgan Library & Museum
225 Madison Ave.
New York, NY 10016
Ph: (212)685-0008
Fax: (212)481-3484
E-mail: visitorservices@themorgan.org
URL: www.themorgan.org
Social Media: www.facebook.com/morganlibrary
www.instagram.com/themorganlibrary
www.pinterest.com/morganlibrary
twitter.com/morganlibrary
www.youtube.com/user/morganlibrary

7468 ■ Sherman Fairchild Post-Graduate Fellowship in Conservation *(Graduate/Fellowship)*

Purpose: To provide a junior professional with the opportunity to apply the principles of paper and book conservation acquired through an accredited graduate program in museum/library conservation or equivalent work/life experience. **Focus:** Library and archival sciences. **Qualif.:** Applicants must be a graduate of a recognized graduate-level program in conservation or be able to demonstrate the acquisition of equivalent skills and knowledge through life/work work/life experience; should possess strong public speaking oral and written communications skills; and have a demonstrated commitment to the profession of conservation and scholarly advancement. **Criteria:** Selection is based on the application materials.

Funds Avail.: $30,000. **Duration:** Annual. **To Apply:** Applicants must submit a cover letter addressing their interest in the fellowships, including a statement of career goals and areas of particular interest; curricula vitae; and three letters of recommendation. **Deadline:** February 19. **Contact:** Maria Fredericks, Acting Director, Thaw Conservation Center Email: tcc@themorgan.org.

7469 ■ Morphisec
11 Beacon St, Ste 735
Boston, MA 02108
Ph: (617)826-1212
E-mail: info@morphisec.com
URL: www.morphisec.com
Social Media: www.facebook.com/Morphisec
www.instagram.com/morphisec
www.linkedin.com/company/9434365
twitter.com/morphisec
www.youtube.com/channel/UCe48cR5xTxPJSYMjG
  -So7Rw

7470 ■ Morphisec's Women in Cybersecurity Scholarships *(Undergraduate, Graduate/Scholarship)*

Purpose: To increase the number of women employed in cybersecurity and related fields. **Focus:** Computer and information sciences; Security. **Qualif.:** Applicant must be female undergraduate and graduate students currently studying for degrees in:cybersecurity;information Assurance; information Security; information Systems security; computer Science; other cybersecurity-related STEM disciplines; applicants must be enrolled in a Bachelor's or

Master's degree program at an accredited college or university; applicants must also be Citizens or Permanent Legal Residents of the United States, Israel or a European Union member country. **Criteria:** Selection will be based on the submitted essay, with a focus on creativity, thoughtfulness, and insight.

Funds Avail.: $2,500; $1,500; $1,000. **To Apply:** Applications are providing our essay entry and other information to Morphisec and not to any other party. **Deadline:** June 15.

7471 ■ The Morris Law Firm
400 W 11th St., Ste. A
Panama City, FL 32401
Ph: (850)257-5680
Fax: (850)640-3061
URL: www.dmorrislaw.com
Social Media: www.facebook.com/danamorrislaw
twitter.com/danamorrislaw

7472 ■ Robby Strong Cancer Survivor Scholarships *(Graduate/Scholarship)*

Purpose: To support law students whose life have been affected by cancer. **Focus:** Law. **Qualif.:** Applicants must be students planning to attend law school or not yet graduated from law school but with a minimum GPA of 3.0.

7473 ■ James B. Morris Scholarship Fund
PO Box 12145
Des Moines, IA 50312
Ph: (515)864-0922
Fax: (515)864-0922
URL: www.morrisscholarship.org

7474 ■ James B. Morris Scholarship *(Undergraduate/Scholarship)*

Purpose: To provide assistance, motivation and internship opportunities for minority students pursuing post-secondary and graduate degrees. **Focus:** General studies/Field of study not specified. **Criteria:** Applicants will be selected based on financial need and selection criteria.

Duration: Annual. **Deadline:** February 29. **Remarks:** The scholarship was established in memory of James B. Morris. **Contact:** Email:vbuie@morrisscholarship.org.

7475 ■ Mortar Board National College Senior Honor Society
1200 Chambers Rd., Ste. 201
Columbus, OH 43212
Ph: (614)488-4094
Fax: (614)488-4095
Free: 800-989-6266
E-mail: mortarboard@mortarboard.org
URL: www.mortarboard.org
Social Media: www.facebook.com/MortarBoard
www.instagram.com/mortar_board
twitter.com/MortarBoard
www.youtube.com/nationalmortarboard

7476 ■ Mortar Board National Foundation Fellowship *(Postdoctorate/Fellowship, Award)*

Purpose: To provide financial support for members who want to pursue a post-graduate education. **Focus:** General

Awards are arranged alphabetically below their administering organizations

studies/Field of study not specified. **Qualif.:** Applicants can be a member of any age may apply for a Mortar Board Fellowship for postbaccalaureate degree study in any field. **Criteria:** Selection will be based on their academic record, recommendations, goals and objectives, need and contribution/commitment to mortar board.

Funds Avail.: $3,000 - $5,000. **Duration:** Annual. **To Apply:** Applicants must complete online application. **Deadline:** March 1. **Remarks:** Established in 1941.

7477 ■ The Mortgage Reports
c/o Full Beaker
200 112th Ave. NE, Ste. 310
Bellevue, WA 98004
Free: 866-240-7180
URL: themortgagereports.com
Social Media: www.facebook.com/MortgageReports
www.instagram.com/mortgagereports/
twitter.com/mortgagereports

7478 ■ Business Leaders of Tomorrow (Community College, Four Year College, Graduate/Scholarship)

Purpose: To financially support students entering or currently pursuing an educational program related to business or finance. **Focus:** Business; Economics; Finance. **Qualif.:** Applicants must be students entering or currently pursuing an educational program related to business or finance. Students must be at least 17 years of age and have a GPA of 3.0 or higher. **Criteria:** Selection based on the criteria set forth in the requirements section of this document and reviewed by a panel.

Funds Avail.: $1,000. **To Apply:** Applicant should submit a 600 to 1, 000-word essay explaining what they hope to accomplish during their career in a business or finance field; must provide proof of enrollment, letters of acceptance, transcripts before the scholarship recipient is selected. **Deadline:** January 29.

7479 ■ Morton Cure Paralysis Fund
5021 Vernon Ave., Ste. 145
Minneapolis, MN 55436
Ph: (612)904-1420
E-mail: info@mcpf.org
URL: www.mcpf.org

7480 ■ Morton Cure Paralysis Fund Research Grants (Professional development, Postdoctorate/Grant)

Purpose: To develop effective therapies for paralysis associated with spinal cord injury and other disorders of the central nervous system. **Focus:** Spinal cord injuries and research.

Duration: Biennial.

7481 ■ John R. Mott Scholarship Foundation
1860 19th St. NW
Washington, DC 20009
Ph: (320)577-5578
E-mail: info@mottscholarship.org
URL: www.mottscholarship.org
Social Media: www.facebook.com/pg/MottScholarships/
  about

7482 ■ John R. Mott Scholarships (Undergraduate, Graduate/Scholarship)

Purpose: To provide scholarship for higher education to students who are natives of Calabria. **Focus:** General studies/Field of study not specified. **Qualif.:** Applicants must be natives to the region of Calabria, Italy who are enrolled at any university or graduate school in the fall of current year and seeking an education leading to a degree or professional certificate. **Criteria:** Recipients will be selected based on academic achievement and financial need, consideration is also given to the candidate's past and intended future contributions to the region.

Funds Avail.: $10,000. **Duration:** Annual. **To Apply:** Applicants must complete the application form available online. **Deadline:** April 15.

7483 ■ Mount Desert Island Biological Laboratory (MDIBL)
159 Old Bar Harbor Rd.
Bar Harbor, ME 04609
Ph: (207)288-3605
Fax: (207)288-2130
URL: mdibl.org
Social Media: www.facebook.com/MDIBL
www.linkedin.com/company/mount-desert-island-biological
  -laboratory
twitter.com/mdibl

7484 ■ MDI Biological Laboratory High school Student Summer Research Fellowship (High School/Fellowship)

Purpose: To help students develop professional skills sets and foster connections within the scientific research community. **Focus:** Biological and clinical sciences. **Qualif.:** Applicants must be 16 years old during relevant year; if nominees are under 18 they must have parental/guardian consent before applying; must have successfully completed high school biology with laboratory, high school chemistry with laboratory, and high school mathematics (at least Algebra 1); high school students from in-state (Maine) and out-of-state are eligible; international students must be enrolled in a US High School and have a valid visa throughout the program; must commit to the full 7-week program.

Duration: Annual. **To Apply:** Application form and details available at mdibl.org/education/high-school-opportunities/hs-applications/.

7485 ■ MDI Biological Laboratory Undergraduate Summer Research Fellowships (Undergraduate/Fellowship)

Purpose: To provide students the opportunity to have hands-on, research training experience within an advanced laboratory that complements current resident research programs. **Focus:** Biological and clinical sciences. **Qualif.:** Applicant must be at least 16 years old in order to work in a laboratory; demonstrate successful completion of 1 semester of college biology with laboratory, 1 semester of college mathematics; must have a cumulative GPA of 3.0 or equivalent; must be a U.S. Citizen or permanent resident, or have the appropriate immigration status to be able to receive a work stipend; different funding sources have different citizenship requirements; undergraduate fellows must commit to the entire duration of the program. **Criteria:**

Awards are arranged alphabetically below their administering organizations

Selection will be based on the committee's criteria.

Duration: Annual. **To Apply:** Application and details available at mdibl.org/education/undergraduate-opportunities/undergraduate-applications/.

7486 ■ Mountain Plains Adult Education Association (MPAEA)
840 E. 400 S.
Smithfield, UT 84335
Ph: (480)517-8806
URL: mpaea.wildapricot.org

7487 ■ Larry B. Wickham Memorial Scholarship for Graduate Studies *(Graduate/Scholarship)*

Purpose: To provide financial assistance for students' tuition, books and school-related expenses. **Focus:** Adult education. **Qualif.:** Applicants must be students enrolled in a graduate degree program in an MPAEA member state; must be pursuing a graduate degree in adult education or closely related field, or graduate students who have not previously received the scholarship; must be active members of MPAEA. **Criteria:** Applicant will be evaluated based on financial need.

Funds Avail.: $1,000. **Duration:** Annual. **Number Awarded:** 1. **To Apply:** Applicants must review the criteria for eligibility before applying for the scholarship; they are advised to contact state MPAEA Board member for a copy of the application or download it from the MPAEA website; www.mpaea.org. **Deadline:** December 31. **Contact:** Diane White, MPAEA Scholarship Chair, Adult Education/Family Literacy Coordinator, dwhite@uintaeducation.org.

7488 ■ MPOWER Financing
1101 Connecticut Ave NW Ste. 900
Washington, DC 20036
URL: www.mpowerfinancing.com
Social Media: www.facebook.com/mpowerfinancing
linkedin.com/company/mpower-financing
twitter.com/mpowerfinancing

7489 ■ MPOWER Financing's Global Citizen Scholarship *(College, University, Undergraduate/Scholarship)*

Purpose: To provide financial aid to international and DACA students studying in the United States. **Focus:** General studies/Field of study not specified. **Qualif.:** Applicant must have been accepted to a full-time program at a U.S. college or university or must be currently enrolled full-time in a U.S. college or university; be an international student with F1 visa status or a DACA recipient; and must be at least 18 years old. **Criteria:** Unbiased committee of MPOWER employees will judge essays based on grammar and vocabulary, organization, creativity, and overall effect and coherence.

Funds Avail.: $1,000. **Number Awarded:** 3. **To Apply:** Applicant must write an essay and complete the online application form. **Deadline:** December 31.

7490 ■ Mrs Prindables
6300 Gross Point Rd.
Niles, IL 60714
Ph: (847)588-2900
Fax: (847)588-0392

Free: 888-215-1100
E-mail: customerservice@mrsprindables.com
URL: www.mrsprindables.com
Social Media: www.facebook.com/mrsprindables
www.instagram.com/mrsprindables
www.pinterest.com/mrsprindables
twitter.com/mrsprindables

7491 ■ Future Educators Scholarship *(College, University/Scholarship)*

Purpose: To help students in the education field afford higher education as the sponsor believes they have the power to spark positive developments in students lives and futures. **Focus:** Education. **Qualif.:** Applicant must be a U.S. citizen accepted to or currently enrolled in a college or university in the United States in an education-related field. **Criteria:** Recipient will be randomly selected.

Funds Avail.: $1,000. **Number Awarded:** 1. **To Apply:** Applicant must fill out form on sponsor's website and upload transcripts or college acceptance letter. **Deadline:** August 19. **Contact:** Kevin Brown; URL: www.mrsprindables.com/news/education-scholarship/.

7492 ■ Mu Alpha Theta
c/o University of Oklahoma
3200 Marshall Ave., Ste. 190
Norman, OK 73019
Ph: (405)325-0144
E-mail: info@mualphatheta.org
URL: www.mualphatheta.org
Social Media: www.facebook.com/MATNatlOffice
twitter.com/MATNatlOffice

7493 ■ Mu Alpha Theta Summer Grants *(Undergraduate, Graduate/Grant)*

Purpose: To support students enrolled in a summer program to pay their tuition or fees for a summer math program at, or sponsored by, an accredited school or university. **Focus:** Mathematics and mathematical sciences. **Qualif.:** Applicants must be Mu Alpha Theta members. **Criteria:** Selection will be based on the committee's criteria.

Funds Avail.: Up to $2,000. **Duration:** Annual. **To Apply:** Applicants must submit the application form with sponsor's signature, student essay, resume, description of summer program and acceptance letter, two letters of recommendation, itemized list of funds being requested, official high school transcript. **Contact:** University of Oklahoma, 3200 Marshall Ave, Ste 190, Norman, OK, 73019; Email: info@mualphatheta.org.

7494 ■ Multiple Myeloma Research Foundation (MMRF)
383 Main Ave., 5th Fl.
Norwalk, CT 06851
Ph: (203)229-0464
URL: www.themmrf.org
Social Media: www.facebook.com/theMMRF
www.instagram.com/themmrf/
www.linkedin.com/company/multiple-myeloma-research-foundation
twitter.com/theMMRF

Awards are arranged alphabetically below their administering organizations

www.youtube.com/user/TheMMRF

7495 ■ MMRF Research Fellow Awards *(Postdoctorate, Professional development/Grant)*

Purpose: To help support young investigators to begin their studies in the field of multiple myeloma while advancing the understanding of myeloma disease biology, treatment and drug resistance. **Focus:** Medical research. **Qualif.:** Applicants must be researchers who hold a Ph.D., M.D. or equivalent degree at the post-doctorate, clinical fellow, or junior faculty level; must have obtained their highest degreewithin the last 5 years and may not hold a position higher than Assistant Professor. **Criteria:** Research Fellow applications are reviewed by an external group of scientists who have the appropriate area of scientific expertise.

Funds Avail.: Up to $75,000. **Duration:** Annual. **To Apply:** Applications must be in English using single-spaced text, half inch margins, using either Arial or Times New Roman 11 or 12 pt font. Pagelimitations must be observed for each section as described below; currently in good standing with the MMRF. **Deadline:** August 28. **Contact:** Mark Hamilton, PhD, Multiple Myeloma Research Foundation, 383 Main Ave., 5th Fl., Norwalk, CT, 06851; Phone: 203-652-0233; Email: hamiltonm@themmrf.org.

7496 ■ Multiple Sclerosis Society of Canada
250 Dundas St. W, Ste. 500
Toronto, ON, Canada M5T 2Z5
Ph: (416)922-6065
E-mail: info@mssociety.ca
URL: mssociety.ca
Social Media: www.facebook.com/MSSocietyCanada
www.instagram.com/mssocietycanada
twitter.com/mssocietycanada
www.youtube.com/user/MSSocietyCanada

7497 ■ endMS Doctoral Studentship Awards
(Doctorate/Internship)

Purpose: To support training students in studies related to Multiple Sclerosis and to provide them the opportunity to gain research experience in the field of MS. **Focus:** Multiple sclerosis. **Criteria:** Selection will be based on the committee's criteria.

Funds Avail.: $22,000 - $50,500. **Duration:** Annual. **To Apply:** Applicants are required to use the website for the completion of their proposal and must submit their studentship applications through online system only. **Deadline:** October 1. **Contact:** Email: msresearchgrants@mssociety.ca.

7498 ■ endMS Master's Studentship Awards
(Master's/Internship)

Purpose: To support training students in studies related to Multiple Sclerosis and to provide them the opportunity to gain research experience in the field of MS. **Focus:** Multiple sclerosis. **Qualif.:** Applicant must any working towards a Master's degree pertaining to research in MS; enrolled in graduate training at a Canadian institution; or those interested in studying abroad must be a Canadian citizen or permanent resident of Canada; studentships must be held in a recognized institution; and responsible to an appropriate supervisor who is in a field relevant to MS. **Criteria:** Selection will be based on the committee's criteria.

Funds Avail.: $20,000. **Duration:** Biennial. **Number Awarded:** 2. **To Apply:** Applicants are required to use the website for the completion of their proposal and must submit their studentship applications through online system only. **Deadline:** October 1. **Contact:** Email: msresearchgrants@mssociety.ca.

7499 ■ endMS Postdoctoral Fellowships
(Postdoctorate/Fellowship)

Purpose: To support training students in studies related to Multiple Sclerosis and to provide them the opportunity to gain research experience in the field of MS. **Focus:** Multiple sclerosis. **Criteria:** Selection will be based on the committee's criteria.

Funds Avail.: $41,000-$50,500. **Duration:** Annual. **Number Awarded:** 1. **To Apply:** Applicants are required to use the website for the completion of their proposal and must submit their studentship applications through online system only. **Deadline:** October 1. **Contact:** Email: msresearchgrants@mssociety.ca.

7500 ■ Anthony Munoz Foundation (AMF)
8919 Rossash Rd.
Cincinnati, OH 45236
Ph: (513)772-4900
Fax: (513)772-4911
E-mail: info@munozfoundation.org
URL: www.munozfoundation.org
Social Media: www.facebook.com/munozfoundation
www.instagram.com/munozfoundation
twitter.com/MunozFoundation

7501 ■ Anthony Munoz Scholarship Fund
(Undergraduate/Scholarship)

Purpose: To support Tri-State youth in achieving their dreams of attending a local college or university. **Focus:** General studies/Field of study not specified. **Qualif.:** Applicants must be graduating high school senior with a minimum 3.0 grade point average or a minimum composite ACT score of 18; must attend a high school in the Tri-State region(Kentucky, Indiana, Ohio); must be a student entering an accredited Tri-State college or university. Must maintain full-time student status and cumulative grade point average above 2.5.**Criteria:** Recipients will be chosen by the Munoz Family based on the submitted application.

Funds Avail.: $20,000. **Number Awarded:** Varies. **To Apply:** Applicants must submit a completed scholarship application form; personal statement of adversity or intent to overcome; a high school transcript for the entirety of high school career up to date ofapplication submission. **Deadline:** May 1. **Contact:** Anthony Munoz Foundation, 8919 Rossash Rd., Cincinnati, Ohio, 45236; Fax: 513-772-4911, Caleigh Willis; Email: cwillis@munozfoundation.org or impact@munozfoundation.org.

7502 ■ Daniel Murphy Scholarship Fund (DMSF)
309 W Washington, Ste. 700
Chicago, IL 60606
Ph: (312)455-7800
Fax: (312)455-7801
E-mail: info@dmsf.org
URL: www.dmsf.org

Awards are arranged alphabetically below their administering organizations

Social Media: www.facebook.com/MurphyScholars
www.instagram.com/murphyscholars
www.linkedin.com/company/daniel-murphy-scholarship
 -foundation
www.linkedin.com/company/daniel-murphy-scholarship
 -fund
www.pinterest.com/pin/367887863282833310
twitter.com/murphyscholars
www.youtube.com/channel/UCQ_Te_fC
 -dQLiFZM4cM4lbQ/videos

7503 ■ DMSF Scholarship *(High School/Scholarship)*

Purpose: To provide financial assistance to those families who also qualify for financial assistance; DMSF will cover part of the tuition, the partner school provides significant financial aid, and families are also responsible for contributing to the tuition. **Focus:** General studies/Field of study not specified. **Qualif.:** Applicants must be an 8th grade student; applicant should get recommendations from 7th grade English/language arts teacher, maths teacher, and principal or school counselor. **Criteria:** Selection is based on academic potential, strong character and financial need.

Funds Avail.: No specific amount. **Duration:** Annual. **To Apply:** Applicants must submit a completed application form together with a response to two essay questions; provide financial information; recommendation forms, standardized test result and report cards from teachers, principals and/or counselors.

7504 ■ Murrietta Circuits

5000 E Landon Dr.
Anaheim, CA 92807
Ph: (714)970-2430
Fax: (714)970-2406
E-mail: sales@murrietta.com
URL: www.murrietta.com
Social Media: www.facebook.com/MurriettaCircuits
www.linkedin.com/company/murrietta-circuits

7505 ■ Murrietta Circuits Scholarship Opportunity *(Undergraduate, College, University/Scholarship)*

Purpose: To help a veteran student to advance their Studies in STEM related fields. **Focus:** Engineering; Mathematics and mathematical sciences; Science; Technology. **Qualif.:** Applicant must be a legal U.S. resident and either currently enrolling or planning to enroll in an undergraduate program based in STEM field at accredited U.S college or university; must be a veteran or the child of a veteran. **Criteria:** Selection will be based on a demonstrated genuine desire to use the scholarship to advance in a STEM field and an overall passion for knowledge.

Funds Avail.: $500. **Number Awarded:** 1. **To Apply:** Applicant must submit an essay of 300 to 500 words about their college experience so far via email. **Deadline:** September 10. **Contact:** Email: brett@mabventures.com.

7506 ■ Murse World

1665 Corporate Rd. W
Lakewood, NJ 08701
E-mail: info@murseworld.com
URL: www.murseworld.com
Social Media: www.facebook.com/murseworld
twitter.com/murseworld

7507 ■ Murse World Scholarship *(Undergraduate, Graduate, Postdoctorate/Scholarship)*

Purpose: To support college students who are studying in an field of medicine or health. **Focus:** Dentistry; Medicine; Nursing; Nutrition. **Qualif.:** Applicant must be a high school senior enrolling in an accredited U.S. college or university, or a student currently enrolled; have a minimum cumulative GPA of 3.0; be a U.S. citizen or permanent resident; and be pursuing a degree in a medical field, such as therapy, nursing, medicine, nutrition, laboratory science, dentistry, etc. **Criteria:** Murse World judges will choose the finalists based on the essays submitted. Final essays will then be opened up for public voting to select recipient.

Funds Avail.: $1,000. **Number Awarded:** 1. **To Apply:** Applicant must write a 500 word or less explaining how they plan on making the world a better place through their career in the medical field. **Deadline:** January 15. **Contact:** Email: scholarships@murseworld.com.

7508 ■ Muscular Dystrophy Association (MDA)

161 N Clark, Ste. 3550
Chicago, IL 60601
Free: 800-572-1717
E-mail: resourcecenter@mdausa.org
URL: www.mda.org
Social Media: www.facebook.com/MDANational
instagram.com/mdaorg
twitter.com/MDAnews
youtube.com/mda

7509 ■ MDA Development Grants *(Doctorate/Grant)*

Purpose: To provide financial assistance for promising new neuromuscular disease researchers in launching their scientific programs. **Focus:** Muscular dystrophy. **Qualif.:** Applicants must: hold an MD, PhD, DSc or equivalent degree; be members of a research team at an appropriate institution; be qualified to conduct a program of original research under the supervision of a principal investigator; have an acceptable research plan for a specific disease in MDA's program; have access to institutional resources necessary to conduct the proposed research project; have 18 months of post-doctoral research laboratory training at the time of application; be no more than 60 months from receiving their most recent advanced degree; and, not have been funded under the MDA development grant program in the past.

Funds Avail.: $60,000 per year. **Number Awarded:** Varies. **To Apply:** Applicants must send a completed pre-proposal form to formally request an application form. **Contact:** Email: grants@mdausa.org.

7510 ■ MDA Research Grants *(Advanced Professional/Grant)*

Purpose: To provide the best clinical care and support to families living with muscle disease by funding the most promising and innovative research in neuromuscular disease. **Focus:** Muscular dystrophy. **Qualif.:** Applicants must: hold an MD, PhD, DSc or equivalent degree; be professional or faculty members (professors, associate professors or assistant professors) at an appropriate educational, medical or research institution; be qualified to conduct and mentor a program of original research; assume both administrative and financial responsibility for the grant; and, have access to institutional resources necessary to conduct the proposed research project.

Awards are arranged alphabetically below their administering organizations

Number Awarded: Varies. **To Apply:** Applicant must send a completed pre-proposal form to formally request an application form.

7511 ■ Music Library Association (MLA)

1600 Aspen Commons, Ste. 100
Middleton, WI 53562
Ph: (608)836-5825
Fax: (608)831-8200
E-mail: mla@areditions.com
URL: www.musiclibraryassoc.org
Social Media: www.facebook.com/Music.Library.Association
twitter.com/musiclibassoc

7512 ■ Carol June Bradley Award for Historical Research in Music Librarianship *(Professional development/Grant, Award)*

Purpose: To promote education involving the history of music libraries or special collections. **Focus:** Library and archival sciences; Music. **Qualif.:** Applicants must be studying musical librarianship; applicants will be considered regardless of age, nationality, profession or institutional affiliation. **Criteria:** Selection will be reviewed on the basis of merit.

Duration: Annual. **Number Awarded:** Varies. **To Apply:** Applicants must submit Summary of the project, including plans for disseminating the findings; preliminary budget with justification for expenses; current vita; names of three references with complete contact information for each. **Remarks:** Established in 2003.

7513 ■ Dena Epstein Award for Archival and Library Research in American Music *(Professional development/Award)*

Purpose: To support research in archives or libraries internationally on any aspect of American music. **Focus:** Library and archival sciences; Music. **Qualif.:** Applicants must be in the library research and archival fields; applicants are considered regardless of age, nationality, profession, or institutional affiliation. **Criteria:** Selection will be reviewed based on merit.

Funds Avail.: $4,850. **Duration:** Annual. **Number Awarded:** Varies. **To Apply:** Applicants must submit a brief research proposal (under 5 pages) which includes description, detailed budget indicating the amount, justification, and additional sources of funding; curriculum vitae and two letters of support from librarians and/or scholars; submissions made electronically must be in Microsoft word or pdf format and sent as email attachments. **Deadline:** June 29. **Remarks:** The award was established through a generous gift from Morton and Dena Epstein to the Music Library Association. Established in 1995. **Contact:** Rahni Kennedy, Chair of the Dena Epstein Award Committee; Email: rbkennedy@smu.edu.

7514 ■ Kevin Freeman Travel Grant *(Graduate, Other/Grant)*

Purpose: To support travel and accommodation expenses for attendees of the MLA annual meeting. **Focus:** Library and archival sciences; Music. **Qualif.:** Applicants must be regular, paraprofessional, or student member of MLA; must be a graduate library school student aspiring to become a music librarian; recent graduate (within one year of degree) of a graduate program in librarianship.

Funds Avail.: $750. **Duration:** Annual. **Number Awarded:** Varies. **To Apply:** Applicants must submit an application form; two letters of support; file formats must be pdf, word, or plain email text. **Deadline:** September 27;September 29. **Remarks:** The award was established in the honor of Kevin Freeman, endowed by contributions of members of the Northern and Southern California chapters as well as colleagues and friends of Kevin's across the country. **Contact:** Kyra Folk-Farber, Chair, Kevin Freeman Travel Grant Committee, Music Librarian, University of California, Santa Barbara; Email: kfolkfarber@ucsb.edu.

7515 ■ Walter Gerboth Award *(Other/Award, Monetary)*

Purpose: To assist research-in-progress in music or music librarianship. **Focus:** Library and archival sciences; Music. **Qualif.:** Applicants must be a member of MLA who is in the first five years of their professional library careers. **Criteria:** Preference will be given to newer MLA members (within your first decade), as well as to MLA members regardless of the length of service who are new to research.

Funds Avail.: $1,650. **Duration:** Annual. **Number Awarded:** Varies. **To Apply:** Applicants must submit a summary of the project including a statement about its significance; a detailed total budget; two recommendation letters (one for the applicant and one for the project) and a curriculum vitae; name and contact information for two additional references. **Deadline:** July 19. **Remarks:** The award was established in the honor of Past-President Walter Gerboth, librarian, teacher, mentor, leader in the Music Library Association, and pathmaker in music librarianship. Established in 1984.

7516 ■ Muslim Public Affairs Council (MPAC)

3010 Wilshire Blvd., No. 217
Los Angeles, CA 90010
Ph: (323)258-6722
Fax: (323)258-5879
E-mail: hello@mpac.org
URL: www.mpac.org
Social Media: twitter.com/mpac_national
www.youtube.com/user/mpacnational

7517 ■ MPAC-DC Graduate Policy Fellowships *(Graduate/Fellowship)*

Purpose: To identify and develop graduate students in international relations, economics, political science, or public policy to engage in faith-based policy research and advocacy in the heart of the nation's capital. **Focus:** Economics; International affairs and relations; Political science; Public affairs. **Qualif.:** Applicant must be committed to the organizational philosophy and civic approach of the Muslim Public Affairs Council; have completed at least one year (or recently matriculated within one year) of a graduate program in International Relations, Political Science, Economics or Public Policy; and with minimum requirements for overall GPA: 3.0, in specialization coursework: 3.3. **Criteria:** Selection is based on the application materials.

Funds Avail.: No specific amount. **To Apply:** Applicant must submit a resume; cover letter addressing how the applicant believes the Fellowship will advance both their career goals as well as MPAC's work on Capitol Hill; list of three references with contact information (at least two must be academic, the third may be professional or academic);

Awards are arranged alphabetically below their administering organizations

unofficial academic transcript from most recently graduated university/college; and a three-page writing sample relevant to the topic of the incoming Fellow's research topic at the DC office (information about the topic can be found in the "Graduate Policy Fellowship Research Topic" document). **Deadline:** February 26. **Contact:** Muslim Public Affairs Council, at the above address.

7518 ■ Mustard Seed Foundation

7115 Leesburg Pke., Ste. 304
Falls Church, VA 22043
URL: www.msfdn.org

7519 ■ Harvey Fellows Program *(Graduate/ Fellowship)*

Purpose: To provide scholarships to Christian students who are pursuing graduate studies at premier universities. **Focus:** Business; Economics; Filmmaking; Finance; Journalism; Teaching.

Duration: Annual. **Deadline:** November 1.

7520 ■ My Home Improvement Solutions

2389 Joes Rd.
Millerton, NY 12546
Ph: (218)663-0295
URL: www.myhomeimprovementsolutions.com
Social Media: www.facebook.com/Homeimprovement222
linkedin.com/in/myhomeimprovement-solutions-736b77176
twitter.com/homesolutons

7521 ■ Home Improvement Scholarship *(High School, Undergraduate, Graduate, Vocational/ Occupational/Scholarship)*

Purpose: To support the education of students. **Focus:** General studies/Field of study not specified. **Qualif.:** Applicant All the undergraduate and postgraduate students can apply for this scholarship.

Funds Avail.: $500. **To Apply:** Submit an essay (1,000 to 1,500 words) on a topic provided at www.myhomeimprovementsolutions.com/scholarship. **Deadline:** December 15. **Contact:** Email: scholarship@ homeimprovementsolutions.com.

7522 ■ My Pool Vacuum

4518 Werninger St.
Houston, TX 77026
Ph: (832)681-4107
E-mail: mypoolvacuum1@gmail.com
URL: mypoolvacuum.com
Social Media: www.facebook.com/mypoolvacuum
www.pinterest.com/mypoolvacuum

7523 ■ Annual Pool Cleaner Scholarship *(Undergraduate, Postgraduate/Scholarship)*

Purpose: To help needy but skilled students with their education. **Focus:** General studies/Field of study not specified. **Qualif.:** Applicant must be an undergraduate or postgraduate student; must be able to write creative and imposing content. **Criteria:** selection will be based on creativity and imagination power; ability of expression; writing skills; organizing skills; consistency and strong logic ability.

Funds Avail.: $500. **Duration:** Annual. **Number Awarded:** 1. **To Apply:** Applicants have to submit all the required information including full name, Email, ID proof that reflects their college identity along with the content. **Deadline:** January 30. **Contact:** Email: scholarship@ mypoolvacuum.com.

7524 ■ My Weather Analyser

4638 Stoneybrook Rd.
Maitland, FL 32751
URL: myweatheranalyser.net

7525 ■ Scholarship Program By My Weather Analyser *(Postgraduate, Undergraduate/Scholarship)*

Purpose: To help students further their studies and encourage them to enhance their writing skills. **Focus:** General studies/Field of study not specified. **Qualif.:** Applicant must be an undergraduate or post-graduate student with excellent writing skills. **Criteria:** Selection will be based on creative and unique content, powerful logic, no plagiarism, no grammar errors, impressive and engaging article.

Funds Avail.: $1,000. **Duration:** Annual. **Number Awarded:** 1. **To Apply:** Candidates need to pick one topic from our given topics and write the content of 1500 words; only PDF or DOC files will be acceptable; full name, Email ID, school/college name and ID proof. **Deadline:** January 30. **Contact:** Email: scholarship@myweatheranalyser.net.

7526 ■ MyApartmentMap

c/o Reardon, Ian
190 Locke Rd.
Rye, NH 03870
URL: www.myapartmentmap.com

7527 ■ MyApartmentMap Housing Fall Scholarship *(Undergraduate/Scholarship)*

Purpose: To support students who wants to pursue their educational career. **Focus:** General studies/Field of study not specified. **Qualif.:** Applicant must be a legal U.S. resident who is 18 years or older and is attending or will attend an accredited college, university. **Criteria:** Selection will be based on the committee's criteria.

Funds Avail.: $1,000. **Number Awarded:** 1. **To Apply:** Applicants must write an essay of 500-1000 words or less that describes how the MyApartmentMap housing scholarship would make their semester better and send Facebook and Twitter.

7528 ■ Myasthenia Gravis Foundation of America (MGFA)

355 Lexington Ave., 15th Fl.
New York, NY 10017
Ph: (212)297-2156
Fax: (212)370-9047
Free: 800-541-5454
E-mail: mgfa@myasthenia.org
URL: www.myasthenia.org
Social Media: www.facebook.com/
MyastheniaGravisFoundation
www.instagram.com/myastheniaorg
twitter.com/myastheniaorg

7529 ■ Myasthenia Gravis Foundation of America Nursing Research Fellowships *(Undergraduate/ Fellowship)*

Purpose: To provide financial assistance to nurses or nursing students interested in studying problems encountered

Awards are arranged alphabetically below their administering organizations

by patients with myasthenia gravis or related neuromuscular conditions. **Focus:** Myasthenia Gravis. **Qualif.:** Applicants must be professional nurses or nursing students. **Criteria:** Selection will be evaluated based on criteria designed by the Fellowship Committee.

Funds Avail.: $5,000. **Duration:** Annual. **To Apply:** Applicants must submit four copies of a cover letter and the completed application form to the Chief Executive of the MGFA national office. **Deadline:** October 15.

7530 ■ Student Fellowship *(Graduate, Undergraduate/Fellowship)*

Purpose: To support students with their research projects in myasthenia gravis or related neuromuscular conditions. **Focus:** Myasthenia Gravis. **Qualif.:** Applicants must be medical or graduate students. **Criteria:** Applicants will be evaluated based on criteria designed by the Fellowship Committee.

Funds Avail.: Up to $5,000. **Duration:** Annual. **To Apply:** Applicants must submit one hardcopy or one PDF file of the letter of interest, summary of the research and its significance to myasthenia gravis or related neuromuscular conditions, proposed budget, curriculum vitae of applicant and sponsoring preceptor and letter of recommendation from preceptor that indicates acceptance of the candidate and outlines the proposed work plan for the research study. **Deadline:** March 15.

7531 ■ Mycological Society of America (MSA)
PO Box 1897
Lawrence, KS 66044-8897
Ph: (785)865-9402
Fax: (785)843-6153
Free: 800-627-0326
E-mail: msa@allenpress.com
URL: www.msafungi.org
Social Media: www.facebook.com/msafungi
twitter.com/msafungi

7532 ■ MSA Graduate Fellowship *(Graduate/Fellowship)*

Purpose: To recognize and support outstanding student research in mycology. **Focus:** Biology. **Qualif.:** Applicants must be student members of MSA or must have applied for membership at the time of the award application.Ph.D. candidates Student resident during the tenure of the fellowship in a university in Canada or the United States. **Criteria:** Applicants are evaluated on the basis of their scholastic merit, research ability, and promise shown as a mycologist.

Funds Avail.: $2,000 each. **Duration:** Annual. **Number Awarded:** 2. **To Apply:** Applicants must submit the following: Application Form including a statement that you have passed your qualifying exams; curriculum vitae; detailed plan of study; one letter of recommendation from your supervisor or thesis advisor. **Deadline:** February 15. **Contact:** Email:msafungi@reesgroupinc.com.

7533 ■ The Myositis Association (TMA)
2000 Duke Street Suite 300
Alexandria, VA 22314
Ph: (703)553-2632
Free: 800-821-7356
E-mail: tma@myositis.org
URL: www.myositis.org

Social Media: www.facebook.com/myositis
twitter.com/TheMyositisAssoc
www.youtube.com/user/MyositisAssociation

7534 ■ Mentored Research Fellowship *(Postdoctorate/Fellowship)*

Purpose: To support promising post-doctoral investigators who wish to improve and advance their career in myositis research. **Focus:** Health sciences; Medical assisting. **Qualif.:** Applicants must have completed residency training or have received a PhD within the past three years; must have devoted a major portion of their time to research, but may include some study and clinical experience in allied health. **Criteria:** Applicants will be selected by the TMA board of directors based on evaluation and recommendation from its medical advisory board.

Funds Avail.: $50,000. **Duration:** Annual; two years. **To Apply:** Applicant must submit completed application form, applicant and mentor's bio sketch in NIH format, an outline of the research project (up to six pages), a letter from mentor, personal statement and career development plan. **Deadline:** June 30. **Contact:** Bob Goldberg, TMA Executive Director; Email: goldberg@myositis.org.

7535 ■ Myotonic Dystrophy Foundation (MDF)
663 Thirteenth St., Ste.100
Oakland, CA 94612
Free: 866-968-6642
E-mail: info@myotonic.org
URL: www.myotonic.org
Social Media: www.facebook.com/MyotonicStrong
twitter.com/myotonicstrong
www.youtube.com/c/myotonicstrong

7536 ■ MDF Postdoctoral Fellowship *(Postdoctorate/Fellowship)*

Purpose: To support innovative research on myotonic dystrophy. **Focus:** Muscular dystrophy.

Funds Avail.: $105,000. **Duration:** Annual; up to two years. **To Apply:** Selection will be based on the following criteria: The impact the proposed research could have on the quality of life of people living with DM. Foundation staff will rank proposals based on the case for impact made by the applicant in the "Lay Summary" component of the application (approximately 20% of total Score); The strength of the **Deadline:** September 6. **Contact:** Email: info@myotonic.org.

7537 ■ NAACP Legal Defense and Educational Fund (LDF)
40 Rector St., 5th Fl.
New York, NY 10006
Ph: (212)965-2200
Fax: (212)226-7592
URL: www.naacpldf.org
Social Media: www.facebook.com/naacpldf
instagram.com/naacp_ldf
twitter.com/naacp_ldf

7538 ■ Earl Warren Civil Rights Training Scholarships *(Graduate/Scholarship)*

Purpose: To support the careers of law students dedicated to advancing the cause of racial justice. **Focus:** Law. **Qua-**

Awards are arranged alphabetically below their administering organizations

lif.: Applicant must be a U.S. citizen; must be entering the first year of full-time study; must be a college graduate with good academic records, outstanding community service, and strong recommendations. **Criteria:** Preference is given to applicants who have a well-defined interest in civil rights and community service.

Duration: Annual. **To Apply:** Requests for applications should be from the applicant and should include information about the applicant's undergraduate background, expected graduation date, law school plans and career goals.

7539 ■ Earl Warren Scholarship (Graduate/Scholarship)

Purpose: To support rising law students whose commitment to social justice reveals outstanding potential for training as civil rights and public interest attorneys. **Focus:** Law. **Qualif.:** Applicants must be college U.S. citizens enrolled in its final year of college/university or first year law students with record of academic achievement; must have demonstrated an ongoing commitment to racial justice and civil rights. **Criteria:** Selection will be based on the committee's criteria.

Funds Avail.: $10,000. **Duration:** Annual. **To Apply:** Applicants must submit the following nine items: completed scholarship application form; copy of acceptance letter to law school; two recommendation letters; resume; copy of transcript from current college/university (finalist will be required to submit an official transcript); one essay; one personal statement; copy of LSAT score; and copy of Student Aid Report (FAFSA). Finalists will be required to submit a head and shoulder photograph (Passport Size) when notified. All nine items must be attached in PDF format to one email with the heading: Earl Warren Scholarship - Last name, First name. **Deadline:** May 1.

7540 ■ The Herbert Lehman Education Fund Scholarship (Undergraduate/Scholarship)

Purpose: To help transform the promise of racial equality into a social, economic, and political reality for all people by supporting talented undergraduate students who need financial help to stay in school and successfully complete their bachelor's degree. **Focus:** General studies/Field of study not specified. **Qualif.:** Applicants must be African-American students entering a four-year college as full-time for the first time; be U.S. citizens; be of excellent character with recommendations from teachers, community representatives or employers; and have an exceptional leadership potential with an ability to work well in diverse settings. **Criteria:** Selection will be based on candidate with an outstanding potential as evidenced by high school academic records, test scores and personal essays.

Funds Avail.: $2,000 per year. **Duration:** Annual. **To Apply:** Applications may be requested by writing to The Herbert Lehman Education Fund; must submit three letters of recommendation, one of which must be from a professor, teacher, principal or school counselor; application materials must be typed or neatly printed in ink and must conform to program guidelines. **Deadline:** April 1. **Remarks:** Established in 1964.

7541 ■ NALS of Arizona

PO Box 1851
Tucson, AZ 85702
Ph: (520)325-2000
E-mail: nalsoftucson@gmail.com

URL: www.nalsoftucson.org
Social Media: www.facebook.com/nalsoftucson
twitter.com/nalstucson

7542 ■ Gail Goodell Folsom Memorial Scholarships (Undergraduate/Scholarship)

Purpose: To enhance the education of NOA members and the legal community. **Focus:** Paralegal studies. **Qualif.:** Applicants must be Arizona students who are currently working in the legal field, or are pursuing or plan to pursue a career as legal support professionals. **Criteria:** Selection will be based on the committee's criteria.

Funds Avail.: $250. **Duration:** Annual. **To Apply:** Applicants must submit a completed application and must include the following attachment: autobiographical statement or personal letter; current transcript of grades (if currently attending school); and letter of recommendation. **Deadline:** March 15. **Contact:** wbirk@fclaw.com.

7543 ■ NALS of Detroit

Harrison Township, MI
URL: www.nalsofdetroit.org
Social Media: www.facebook.com/NALSofDetroit

7544 ■ NALS of Detroit Scholarships (Undergraduate/Scholarship)

Purpose: To award scholarship to an individual entering the legal field. **Focus:** Law; Paralegal studies. **Qualif.:** Applicants must be high school senior or enrolled in a school of advanced education (including current school year) or NALS members; have at least a B average, or if percentile system is used, not below 90%; be in need of financial assistance. **Criteria:** Scholarship will be awarded on the basis of scholastic or legal career achievements, future career goals, demonstration of financial need and leadership ability.

Funds Avail.: $500. **Number Awarded:** 2. **To Apply:** Applicants must submit a completed application and must attach an official transcript of grades; a one-page letter of recommendation from the applicant's current major teacher or counselor, addressed to NALS of Detroit Scholarship Fund, stating applicant's activity and leadership record; description of applicant's personal traits, character, drive, home background and brief statement of financial need; the reasons why the applicant should be awarded this scholarship; must also submit a one-page autobiographical statement, showing the date of birth, school attended, employment, school and outside activities, accomplishments, family background, hobbies and a brief description of goals and desires.**Contact:** Return completed applications to: Mary E. Tortomose, Scholarship Chair, 29635 Greater Mack, Saint Clair Shores, MI 48082.

7545 ■ NALS of Michigan

c/o Becky Quimby
Warner Norcross & Judd LLP
111 Lyon St., Ste. 900
Grand Rapids, MI 49503
URL: www.nalsofmichigan.org
Social Media: facebook.com/groups/NALSofMichigan
instagram.com/nalsofmichigan

7546 ■ NALS of Michigan Scholarship (Undergraduate/Scholarship)

Purpose: To support individuals pursuing their education in the legal field. **Focus:** Law; Paralegal studies. **Qualif.:** Ap-

Awards are arranged alphabetically below their administering organizations

plicants must be high school seniors or enrolled in a school of advanced education (including the current school year); must be residents of Michigan and be enrolling in a Michigan school of advanced education in the legal field; have at least a B average, or if percentile system is used, not below 90%; be a resident of Michigan and be enrolling in a Michigan school of advanced education in the legal field; have at least a B average, or if percentile system is used, not below 90 percent; be in need of financial assistance; be able to enroll in the fall term.**Criteria:** Selection will be awarded on the basis of scholastic or legal career achievements, future career goals, demonstration of financial need and leadership ability.

Funds Avail.: $1,000 each. **Duration:** Annual. **To Apply:** Applicant must submit an official transcript of grades; one-page letter of recommendation from the applicant's current major teacher or counselor, addressed to NALS of Michigan Scholarship Fund; description of applicant's personal traits, character, drive, home background and brief statement of financial need; reasons the applicant should be awarded this scholarship; one additional letter of recommendation from someone other than a member of the applicant's family, such as an employer, teacher, pastor or friend; a one-page autobiographical statement prepared by the applicant, showing the date of birth, school attended, employment, school and outside activities, accomplishments, family background, hobbies and a brief description of applicant's goals and desires, including the name of the college the applicant will be attending and their major.**Contact:** Cynthia A. Taylor, PP, PLS NALS of Michigan Scholarship Co-Chair 1703 Bear River Rd., Petoskey, MI, 49770; Phone: 231-838-3147; Email: cataylor989@yahoo.com.

7547 ■ NAON Foundation

390 N Main St.
Alpharetta, GA 30009
Ph: (678)341-0809
E-mail: info@naonfoundation.org
URL: www.naonfoundation.org
Social Media: www.facebook.com/naonfoundation.org

7548 ■ Bachelor of Science in Nursing Academic Scholarships *(Graduate/Scholarship)*

Purpose: To provide scholarship assistance to nursing students who want to pursue their baccalaureate degree. **Focus:** Nursing. **Qualif.:** Applicant must be a current NAON member; must hold current licensure as a registered nurse; must currently spend at least 50% of time devoted to the specialty of orthopedic nursing; must be enrolled full or part time in a nationally accredited school of a nursing baccalaureate program. **Criteria:** Selection of applicants will be based on the application form and materials.

Funds Avail.: $2,000. **Number Awarded:** 3. **To Apply:** Applicants must submit a completed application form available online along with the following requirements: (1) proof of current licensure as a registered nurse, NAON membership, and college BSN enrollment status; (2) statement of chosen NAON contribution; (3) signed scholarship agreement form; (4) narrative of 500 words or less, doubled-spaced, one inch margins in 12 point font addressing the applicant's professional goals (as they pertain to the academic activity and orthopedic nursing) and the impact of a nursing education on the applicant's career in orthopedic nursing; (5) two letters of recommendation, one must be from an orthopedic health care professional; (6) one digital photo, head or head-shoulder shot; (7) one self-

addressed, stamped postcard for acknowledging receipt of application if submitted by mail. **Contact:** NAON Foundation, at the above address or Email: info@ naonfoundation.org.

7549 ■ Master's Degree with a Major in Nursing Academic Scholarships *(Graduate/Scholarship)*

Purpose: To provide scholarship assistance to nursing students who want to pursue their Master's degree. **Focus:** Nursing. **Qualif.:** Applicant must be a current NAON member; must hold current licensure as a registered nurse; must currently spend at least 50% of time devoted to the specialty of orthopedic nursing; must be currently enrolled full- or part-time in a nationally accredited Master's degree program in nursing. **Criteria:** Awards are given based on the application materials.

Duration: Annual. **Number Awarded:** 1. **To Apply:** Applicants must submit a completed application form available online together with proof of current licensure as a registered nurse, NAON membership, and college master's enrollment status; must provide a statement of chosen NAON contribution, signed scholarship agreement form, and narrative of 500 words or less, doubled-spaced, one inch margins in 12 point font addressing the applicant's professional goals (as they pertain to the academic activity and orthopedic nursing) and the impact of a nursing education on the applicant's career in orthopedic nursing; must submit two letters of recommendation, one must be from an orthopedic health care professional; one digital photo (head or head-shoulder shot in professional attire); and one self-addressed (stamped postcard for acknowledging receipt of application if submitted by mail). **Contact:** NAON Foundation, at the above address or Email: info@ naonfoundation.org.

7550 ■ NARAL Pro-Choice America

1725 Eye St., NW, Ste. 900
Washington, DC 20006
Ph: (202)973-3000
Fax: (202)973-3096
E-mail: can@prochoiceamerica.org
URL: www.prochoiceamerica.org
Social Media: www.facebook.com/naralprochoiceamerica
www.instagram.com/prochoiceamerica/
www.linkedin.com/company/naral-pro-choice-america
twitter.com/naral
www.youtube.com/prochoiceamerica

7551 ■ NARAL Pro-Choice America Development Internships *(Undergraduate, Graduate, Professional development/Internship)*

Purpose: To support the training of aspiring interns for the benefit of their career training in development policy. **Focus:** Civil rights. **Qualif.:** Applicants must be currently enrolled in or recently completed an accredited undergraduate or graduate degree program; have demonstrated commitment to protecting a woman's right to choose; have strong interest in the political process; have strong research and analytical skills; have the ability to work in a fast-paced collaborative environment; have excellent attention to detail; have experience with Microsoft Office and Google Drive; and have general computer proficiency.

Duration: Semiannual. **To Apply:** Applicants must send a one-page letter of interest and current resume. **Deadline:** July 15. **Contact:** Email: internship@prochoiceamerica.org.

Awards are arranged alphabetically below their administering organizations

7552 ■ NARAL Summer Intership Program
(Undergraduate, Graduate, Professional development/ Internship)

Purpose: To support the training of aspiring interns for the benefit of their career development in political campaigns and related matters. **Focus:** Civil rights; Political science. **Qualif.:** Applicants must be currently enrolled in or recently completed an accredited undergraduate or graduate degree program; have demonstrated commitment to protecting a woman's right to choose; have strong interest in the political process; have strong research and analytical skills; have the ability to work in a fast-paced collaborative environment; have excellent attention to detail; have experience with Microsoft Office and Google Drive; and have general computer proficiency.

Duration: Annual. **To Apply:** Applicants must submit a one-page letter of interest, resume and 1-2 page writing sample. Details are available at www.prochoiceamerica.org/ about/jobs/internships/. **Contact:** Email: internship@ prochoiceamerica.org.

7553 ■ Elizabeth Nash Foundation (ENF)
PO Box 590883
San Francisco, CA 94159
E-mail: info@elizabethnashfoundation.org
URL: www.elizabethnashfoundation.org

7554 ■ Elizabeth Nash Foundation Scholarship
(Undergraduate, Graduate/Scholarship)

Purpose: To assist persons with cystic fibrosis (CF) to pursue undergraduate and graduate degrees. **Focus:** General studies/Field of study not specified. **Qualif.:** Applicants must be individuals with CF who are in-going or current undergraduate or graduate students at an accredited US-based college or university; given limited resources, the program is currently only open to US citizens. **Criteria:** Selection shall be based on the applicants' scholastic record, character, demonstrated leadership, service to CF-related causes and the broader community, and need for financial assistance.

Funds Avail.: $1,000-$2,500. **Duration:** Annual. **To Apply:** Applicants must submit a completed scholarship application form (there is a separate application for undergraduate and graduate students), attach a one page essay, letter of recommendation from a teacher, a letter confirming CF diagnosis, an academic transcript, a copy of FAFSA, and the specific details of fees and tuition cost from the academic institution. **Deadline:** April 7. **Remarks:** Established in 2005. **Contact:** Email: scholarships@ elizabethnashfoundation.org.

7555 ■ Nashville Catholic Business Women's League (NCBWL)
PO Box 50994
Nashville, TN 37205-0994
E-mail: info@ncbwl.org
URL: www.ncbwl.org
Social Media: www.facebook.com/NCBWL

7556 ■ Aurelia Varallo Mariani Scholarship Program
(Graduate/Scholarship)

Purpose: To provide financial support to those students who are in need. **Focus:** General studies/Field of study not specified.

7557 ■ NCBWL Scholarships *(Graduate/Scholarship)*

Purpose: To provide scholarship assistance to deserving female students. **Focus:** General studies/Field of study not specified. **Qualif.:** Applicants must be female students; must be enrolled at St. Cecilia Academy, Father Ryan High School or Pope John Paul II High School for their full four years of matriculation. **Criteria:** Preference will be given to those students who meet the criteria.

Funds Avail.: No specific amount. **Duration:** Annual. **Number Awarded:** 3. **To Apply:** Applicants must submit a completed application form.

7558 ■ NASIG
1902 Ridge Rd.
PMB 305
West Seneca, NY 14224-3312
E-mail: info@nasig.org
URL: www.nasig.org
Social Media: www.facebook.com/groups/2399345882
twitter.com/nasig?lang=en
www.youtube.com/channel/UCVvnh_CzXS8YgftuvIypTiQ

7559 ■ John Riddick Student Grant *(Graduate/Grant)*

Purpose: To encourage participation in the serials information chain. **Focus:** Computer and information sciences. **Qualif.:** Applicants must be full or part-time students in any NASIG member country (defined for this purpose as the United States, Canada, Mexico, and Greenland); must not be employed in a position requiring an ALA-accredited degree or on leave from such a position at the time of acceptance of the grant. **Criteria:** Preference will be given to those earning their degrees the year of the conference.

Funds Avail.: No specific amount. **To Apply:** Applicants must submit a completed application form and a reference questionnaire electronically either in Microsoft Word or plain text (.txt) format. **Deadline:** February 20. **Remarks:** In honor of John F. Riddick, co-founder and first elected president of NASIG in 1986. Established in 1988. **Contact:** Jamie Carlstone, Email: jamie.carlstone@ northwestern.edu.

7560 ■ Fritz Schwartz Serials Education Scholarship *(Graduate/Scholarship)*

Purpose: To advance the serials profession by providing educational opportunities for students with prior serials experience. **Focus:** Library and archival sciences. **Qualif.:** Applicants must be students in any NASIG member country (defined for this purpose as the United States, Canada, Mexico, and Greenland); must be entering an ALA-accredited graduate library program (or Mexican equivalent) or must have completed no more than 12 hours of academic requirements towards the graduate degree at the time of enrollment.

Funds Avail.: $3,000. **Duration:** Annual. **Number Awarded:** 1. **To Apply:** Applicants must submit a completed application form along with the Reference Questionnaire from two information professionals; a current resume; a personal statement; and a copy of current Library/ Information Science Graduate transcript or proof of admission in Microsoft word or plain text, electronically only; applicant's current Library Science Graduate transcript or proof of admission to an ALA-accredited program may be faxed. **Deadline:** February 20. **Remarks:** The scholarship is named in honor of Fritz Schwartz, who was a well-known and highly respected authority on Electronic Data Inter-

Awards are arranged alphabetically below their administering organizations

change (EDI), the Internet, and library standards. Established in 1985. **Contact:** Jamie Carlstone, Email: jamie.carlstone@northwestern.edu.

7561 ■ NASSCO
2470 Longstone Ln., Ste. M
Marriottsville, MD 21104
Ph: (410)442-7473
Fax: (410)442-7788
E-mail: info@nassco.org
URL: nassco.org
Social Media: www.facebook.com/sewersavvy
www.linkedin.com/company/national-association-of-sewer
  -service-companies
www.youtube.com/user/nassco111

7562 ■ Jeffrey D. Ralston Memorial Scholarship
(Undergraduate/Scholarship)

Purpose: To improve the To improve industry and is sponsored by an active NASSCO member. **Focus:** General studies/Field of study not specified. **Qualif.:** Applicant must be a currently enrolled college student who is a relative or dependent of an active member of NASSCO or has worked actively in the industry and is sponsored by an active NASSCO member. **Criteria:** Recipients are selected based on ethics, high integrity, work experience, community service and leadership.

Funds Avail.: $2,000 or more. **Duration:** Annual. **Number Awarded:** 1. **To Apply:** Applicants must submit a completed application form. **Deadline:** March 1.

7563 ■ National 4-H Council (N4-HC)
7100 Connecticut Ave.
Chevy Chase, MD 20815
Ph: (301)961-2800
E-mail: 4hmarketing@4-h.org
URL: www.4-h.org
Social Media: www.facebook.com/4-h
www.linkedin.com/company/national-4-h-council
www.pinterest.com/national4h
twitter.com/4H
www.youtube.com/user/national4h

7564 ■ 4-H Youth in Action Awards *(Graduate, Undergraduate, Vocational/Occupational, High School, College, University/Scholarship)*

Purpose: To share the stories of 4-H members who make a difference in their communities. **Focus:** General studies/Field of study not specified. **Qualif.:** Applicant must be unique perspectives in our core pillar areas: agriculture, civic engagement, healthy living and STEM.

Funds Avail.: $5,000. **Duration:** Annual. **Number Awarded:** 4. **To Apply:** Must complete the online application, answer two short answer questions, submit a 60-second video, share three photos, and submit a reference form.

7565 ■ National 4th Infantry Ivy Division Association
PO Box 1914
Saint Peters, MO 63376-0035
Ph: (678)480-4422

URL: www.4thinfantry.org
Social Media: twitter.com/4thInfDiv

7566 ■ Annual Educational Scholarships
(Undergraduate/Scholarship)

Purpose: To provide educational assistance to association members, the children, step-children, or legally adopted children of those soldiers who died while serving with the Fourth Infantry. **Focus:** General studies/Field of study not specified. **Qualif.:** Applicants must be child, children or step-children, legally adopted child or children and/or grandchild, grandchildren or step-grandchildren of regular member of the association; regular member of the Association in good standing. **Criteria:** Selection based on the committee's criteria.

Duration: Annual. **To Apply:** Interested applicants may download the Memorial Scholarship Request form at the website. **Deadline:** June 15. **Remarks:** The scholarship is named in honor of Platoon Sergeant Elmenlindo R. Smith. Established in 1968. **Contact:** Philip Menendez, 27110 Jones Loop Rd., No.17, Punta Gorda, FL 33982.

7567 ■ National Academic Advising Association (NACADA)
Kansas State University
2323 Anderson Ave., Ste. 225
Manhattan, KS 66502-2912
Ph: (785)532-5717
Fax: (785)532-7732
E-mail: nacada@ksu.edu
URL: www.nacada.ksu.edu
Social Media: www.facebook.com/NACADA
twitter.com/nacada

7568 ■ NACADA Scholarships *(Graduate, Postdoctorate/Scholarship)*

Purpose: To support the promotion of professional training of advisors. **Focus:** General studies/Field of study not specified. **Qualif.:** Applicant must be a current member of NACADA and have been a NACADA member for two years; be currently enrolled in either a master's or doctoral program; must have worked as an academic advisor for two years with a minimum of a half-time appointment. **Criteria:** Selection will be based on documents provided by applicants.

Funds Avail.: One $1,000; four $500. **Duration:** Annual. **To Apply:** Applicants must submit the following documents: Online NACADA Scholarship Application Form, including financial assessment; Career Goals Statement; resume/vitae; faculty Recommendation Letter; employer Recommendation Letter. **Deadline:** March 10. **Contact:** Email: nacada@ksu.edu.

7569 ■ Wesley R. Habley Summer Institute Scholarships *(Professional development/Scholarship)*

Purpose: To assist selected NACADA members who demonstrate involvement in national, regional, state, and/or local advising organizations and exhibit the potential for national leadership roles. **Focus:** General studies/Field of study not specified. **Qualif.:** Applicant must be a current member at the time of scholarship application; demonstrate involvement in professional activities and institutional organizations (including NACADA); this includes conferences attended, presentations, committees, commissions, etc.

Awards are arranged alphabetically below their administering organizations

Funds Avail.: No specific amount. **Duration:** Annual. **To Apply:** Applicants must submit the following documents: completed Online Application Form; resume/vita (curriculum vitae); current job position description or list of job responsibilities; professional development summary; summer institute participation description; and, letters of recommendation. **Contact:** Email: nacada@ksu.edu.

7570 ■ The National Academies of Sciences, Engineering, and Medicine
500 5th St. NW
Washington, DC 20001
Ph: (202)334-2000
E-mail: research@nas.edu
URL: www.nationalacademies.org
Social Media: www.facebook.com/NationalAcademies
www.linkedin.com/company/the-national-academies
twitter.com/TheNASEM

7571 ■ The Christine Mirzayan Science & Technology Policy Graduate Fellowship Program *(Graduate, Postdoctorate, High School/Fellowship)*

Purpose: To engage early career professionals in the analytical processes that informs US science and technology policy. **Focus:** Behavioral sciences; Biological and clinical sciences; Business; Engineering; Law; Physical sciences; Public administration; Social sciences. **Qualif.:** Applicants must be graduate and professional school students; must have completed graduate studies within the last five years; areas of study may include social/behavioral sciences, health and medicine, physical or biological sciences, engineering, law/business/public administration, or relevant interdisciplinary fields. **Criteria:** Selection will be based on the committee's criteria.

Funds Avail.: $9,000. **Duration:** Annual; 12 weeks. **To Apply:** Applicants must submit two references which must pertain to the applicant's academic, professional or other work-related experiences. **Deadline:** September 6.

7572 ■ Ford Foundation Dissertation Fellowship *(Postdoctorate/Fellowship)*

Purpose: To provide support for individuals working to complete a dissertation leading to a Doctor of Philosophy or Doctor of Science degree. **Focus:** Area and ethnic studies; Interdisciplinary studies; Peace studies.

Funds Avail.: $25,000. **Duration:** Annual. **Number Awarded:** 36. **To Apply:** Applicants must complete the online application form including personal and contact information; personal statement describing the applicant's background and experience and commitment to the goals of the Ford Foundation Fellowship Programs; statement of previous research and scholarly productivity including a list of publications and presentations; proposed plan of graduate study and research and the applicant's long-range career goals; names and contact information of a minimum of three individuals who will upload a letter of recommendation on the applicant's behalf (four letters are highly recommended; five letters maximum); and also must include supplementary materials: baccalaureate degree transcript; graduate transcript; letters of recommendation (maximum 4 MB); fewer than three letters of recommendation; prepare essays in advance and save each in a separate pdf file (maximum 4 MB) so that you are ready to upload these documents. **Deadline:** December 17 for online application; January 7 for supplementary materials. **Contact:** Email: fordapplications@nas.edu.

7573 ■ Ford Foundation Diversity Fellowships *(Graduate, Doctorate, Postdoctorate, Postgraduate/Fellowship)*

Purpose: To increase the diversity of the nation's college and university faculties by increasing their ethnic and racial diversity; to maximize educational benefits of diversity; and to increase the number of professors who can and will use diversity as a resource for enriching the education of all students. **Focus:** Area and ethnic studies; Interdisciplinary studies; Peace studies. **Criteria:** Recipients are selected based on the evidence of superior academic achievement; degree of promise of continuing achievement as scholars and teachers; capacity to respond in pedagogically productive ways to the learning needs of students from diverse backgrounds; sustained personal engagement with communities that are underrepresented in the academy and an ability to bring this asset to learning, teaching, and scholarship at the college or university level; and likelihood of using the diversity of human experience as an educational resource in teaching and scholarship; recipients are also selected based on the academic records, essays, letters of recommendation, the application itself, and other appropriate materials that meet the eligibility requirements and the selection criteria.

Funds Avail.: No specific amount. **Duration:** Annual. **Number Awarded:** Varies. **To Apply:** Applicants must complete the online application form including personal and contact information; a two-page, double-spaced statement of previous research; an essay describing proposed plan of graduate study or research and the applicant's long-range career goals; transcript showing baccalaureate degree or undergraduate work; Graduate School Transcript; letters of reference; Verification of Predoctoral Status form; and GRE General Test Scores. **Deadline:** December 14.

7574 ■ Ford Foundation Postdoctoral Fellowship *(Postdoctorate/Fellowship)*

Purpose: To provide support for individuals engaged in postdoctoral study after the attainment of the Doctor of Philosophy or Doctor of Science degree. **Focus:** Area and ethnic studies; Interdisciplinary studies; Peace studies.

Funds Avail.: $45,000. **Duration:** Annual. **Number Awarded:** 24. **To Apply:** Applicants must complete the online application form including personal and contact information; personal statement describing the applicant's background and experience and commitment to the goals of the Ford Foundation Fellowship Programs; statement of previous research and scholarly productivity including a list of publications and presentations; proposed plan of graduate study and research and the applicant's long-range career goals; names and contact information of a minimum of three individuals who will upload a letter of recommendation on the applicant's behalf (four letters are highly recommended; five letters maximum); and also must include supplementary materials: baccalaureate degree transcript; graduate transcript; letters of recommendation (maximum 4 MB); fewer than three letters of recommendation; prepare essays in advance and save each in a separate pdf file (maximum 4 MB) so that you are ready to upload these documents. **Deadline:** December 17 for online application; January 7 for supplementary materials.

7575 ■ Ford Foundation Predoctoral Fellowship *(Graduate, Doctorate/Fellowship)*

Purpose: To provide support for individuals engaged in graduate study leading to a Doctor of Philosophy or Doctor of Science degree. **Focus:** Area and ethnic studies;

Awards are arranged alphabetically below their administering organizations

Interdisciplinary studies; Peace studies.

Funds Avail.: $24,000. **Duration:** Annual; up to 3 years. **To Apply:** Applicants must complete the online application form including personal and contact information; personal statement describing the applicant's background and experience and commitment to the goals of the Ford Foundation Fellowship Programs; statement of previous research and scholarly productivity including a list of publications and presentations; proposed plan of graduate study and research and the applicant's long-range career goals; names and contact information of a minimum of three individuals who will upload a letter of recommendation on the applicant's behalf (four letters are highly recommended; five letters maximum); and also must include supplementary materials: baccalaureate degree transcript; graduate transcript; letters of recommendation (maximum 4 MB); fewer than three letters of recommendation; prepare essays in advance and save each in a separate pdf file (maximum 4 MB) so that you are ready to upload these documents. **Deadline:** December 17 for online application; January 8 for supplementary materials.

7576 ■ National Academy of Education (NAEd)
500 5th St. NW
Washington, DC 20001
E-mail: info@naeducation.org
URL: naeducation.org
Social Media: linkedin.com/company/national-academy-of -education
twitter.com/NAEduc

7577 ■ NAED/Spencer Dissertation Fellowship Program *(Graduate, Doctorate/Fellowship)*

Purpose: To encourage a new generation of scholars from a wide range of disciplines and professional fields to undertake research relevant to the improvement of education. **Focus:** Education. **Qualif.:** Applicants must be non-US citizens; must be candidates for the doctoral degree at a graduate school within the United States.**Criteria:** Applications will be judged on the applicant's past research record, career trajectory in education research, and the quality of the project described in the application.

Funds Avail.: $27,500. **Duration:** Annual. **Number Awarded:** 35. **To Apply:** Applications must submit an abstract of proposed research project; project description; Graduate transcripts; curriculum vitae/resume; two reference letters. **Deadline:** October 8. **Contact:** E-mail: info@ naeducation.org.

7578 ■ National Academy of Public Administration (NAPA)
1600 K Street, NW, Suite 400
Washington, DC 20006
Ph: (202)347-3190
URL: www.napawash.org
Social Media: www.facebook.com/napawash
twitter.com/napawash
www.youtube.com/channel/UCrBcegZJjqMZmhum2oi8RoQ

7579 ■ Herbert Roback Scholarship *(Graduate, Master's/Scholarship)*

Purpose: To encourage college students to pursue careers in public service. **Focus:** International affairs and relations; Public administration. **Criteria:** Selection will be based on

the potential for excellence in a career of public administration.

Funds Avail.: Up to $7,500. **Duration:** Annual. **Number Awarded:** 1. **To Apply:** Applicants must submit undergraduate and graduate transcripts; biographical resume or curriculum vitae; two letters of recommendation from professors; and a 500-word statement describing applicant's professional interest. **Deadline:** June 12. **Remarks:** Established in honor of late Herbert Roback, a highly respected public servant. **Contact:** Herbert Roback Scholarship Coordinator, Cyntethia Brown, E-mail: cbrown@napawash.org.

7580 ■ National Action Council for Minorities in Engineering (NACME)
1 N Broadway, Ste. 601
White Plains, NY 10601-2318
Ph: (914)539-4010
Fax: (914)539-4032
URL: www.nacme.org
Social Media: www.facebook.com/Nacme.org
www.linkedin.com/company/national-action-council-for -minorities-in-engineering
twitter.com/nacme
www.youtube.com/nacmetv

7581 ■ Alfred P. Sloan Foundation Graduate Scholarships - Sloan Indigenous Graduate Partnership (SIGP) *(Master's, Doctorate/Scholarship)*

Purpose: To assist students in acquiring graduate study in mathematics, natural sciences, and engineering. **Focus:** Engineering; Mathematics and mathematical sciences; Natural sciences. **Qualif.:** Applicants must be American Indian/Alaska Native master's and doctoral students at the University of Alaska, Anchorage and Fairbanks, The University of Arizona, The University of Montana-Missoula, Montana Tech of The University of Montana-Butte, Montana State University, or Purdue University. **Criteria:** Selection will be based on the committee's criteria.

Funds Avail.: No specific amount. **Duration:** Annual. **To Apply:** Applicants may contact National Action Council for Minorities in Engineering for further details.

7582 ■ Alfred P. Sloan Foundation Graduate Scholarships - Sloan Minority Ph.D. Program (MPHD) *(Doctorate/Scholarship)*

Purpose: To support underrepresented minority students of America interested in sciences, technology, engineering and mathematics. **Focus:** Engineering; Mathematics and mathematical sciences; Natural sciences; Physical sciences. **Qualif.:** Applicants must be U.S. citizens enrolled in a doctoral degree in engineering, physical and natural sciences, or mathematics at a limited number of partner universities; must self-identify as African-American, Hispanic, or American Indian/Alaska Native. **Criteria:** Recipients will be selected based on the merits of the application.

Funds Avail.: No specific amount. **Duration:** Annual.

7583 ■ National Active and Retired Federal Employees Association (NARFE)
606 N Washington St.
Alexandria, VA 22314
Ph: (703)838-7760

Awards are arranged alphabetically below their administering organizations

Fax: (703)838-7785
URL: www.narfe.org
Social Media: www.facebook.com/NARFEHQ

7584 ■ NARFE-FEEA Scholarship Awards Program
(Undergraduate/Scholarship)

Purpose: To provide financial assistance for the education of children and grandchildren of federal employees. **Focus:** General studies/Field of study not specified.

Duration: Annual. **Remarks:** Established in 1987. **Contact:** NARFE-FEEA Fund, c/o FEEA, 1641 Prince St., Alexandria, VA, 22314; Email: scholarship@narfe.org.

7585 ■ National Administrative Law Judiciary Foundation (NALJF)
c/o National Association of Administrative Law Judiciary 1 Ridge Court,
Placitas, NM 87043
Fax: (855)787-2225
Free: 855-756-2255
E-mail: naalj@naalj.org
URL: www.naalj.org

7586 ■ Neil Alexander Scholarships *(Undergraduate/ Scholarship)*

Purpose: To provide scholarship to young NAALJ members who wish to study administrative law. **Focus:** Law. **Qualif.:** Applicants must be NAAJL members and must demonstrate outstanding academic and other qualifications.

Funds Avail.: $500. **Duration:** Annual. **Number Awarded:** 2. **To Apply:** Applicants must complete the application form available online and send the forms to NAAJL. **Contact:** NAALJ, 1001 Office Park Rd., Ste. 105, West Des Moines, IA 50265; Email: naalj@naalj.org.

7587 ■ National AIDS Memorial Grove
870 Market St., Ste. 965
San Francisco, CA 94102
Ph: (415)765-0446
Fax: (415)707-6150
E-mail: info@aidsmemorial.org
URL: www.aidsmemorial.org
Social Media: www.facebook.com/nationalaidsmemorial
twitter.com/aids_memorial

7588 ■ Pedro Zamora Young Leaders Scholarship
(Undergraduate, Graduate/Scholarship)

Purpose: To support the academic efforts of emerging young leaders who share Pedro Zamora's passionate commitment to ending the HIV/AIDS pandemic. **Focus:** General studies/Field of study not specified. **Qualif.:** Applicants must demonstrate an active commitment to fighting HIV/AIDS; must be open to all current high school seniors, and college freshman, sophomores and juniors. **Criteria:** Preferred applicants have taken on roles of public service and leadership, and intend to continue to find ways to make a difference in the epidemic through their careers or public service opportunities.

To Apply: Applicant must complete the application; must submit written essay, not to exceed 1,500 words, in which, Reflect on the ways in which your life has been impacted by HIV/AIDS; Explore and describe the ways in which you

are providing public service or leadership that makes a difference in the lives of people with HIV/AIDS, or people at risk; Detail how the scholarship will help you in your career path and how that career will allow you to continue to fight HIV/AIDS in a way that makes a difference. **Remarks:** The scholarship was named in memory of AIDS educator and activist, Pedro Zamora. **Contact:** Matt Kennedy; Email: mkennedy@aidsmemorial.org.

7589 ■ National Air Filtration Association (NAFA)
PO Box 68639
Virginia Beach, VA 23471
Ph: (757)313-7400
Fax: (757)313-7401
E-mail: nafa@nafahq.org
URL: www.nafahq.org
Social Media: www.facebook.com/NAFAHQ
www.linkedin.com/company/national-air-filtration
  -association
twitter.com/nafahq

7590 ■ NAFA Scholarship Program *(Undergraduate/ Scholarship)*

Purpose: To honor and aid students who demonstrate outstanding personal and academic characteristics. **Focus:** General studies/Field of study not specified. **Qualif.:** Applicants must be immediate family members of NAFA members in good standing, or family members of employees of NAFA member firms; grandchildren of NAFA members are also qualified. Incoming freshmen must have a minimum ACT score of 22 or SAT score of 900 and rank in the top 35% of the graduating class; transfer students must have a cumulative GPA of 2.75 on a 4.0 scale. **Criteria:** Applicants are selected based on the NAFA Past Presidents' review of the application materials.

Funds Avail.: $1,000 each. **Duration:** Annual. **Number Awarded:** 3. **To Apply:** Applicants must submit a recent photo for press release purposes; a written essay of 1-2 typewritten pages that gives a brief biographical sketch of the individual along with reasons why they feel they should receive the scholarship; and two letters of recommendation, one of which must be from a recent teacher; neither recommendation should be from a family member; must also submit a recent photo attached to the application for press release purposes. **Deadline:** September 1. **Contact:** Phone: 608-310-7542; E-mail: nafa@nafahq.org.

7591 ■ National Aircraft Finance Association (NAFA)
PO Box 1570
Edgewater, MD 21037
Ph: (410)571-1740
E-mail: info@nafa.aero
URL: www.nafa.aero/cpages/home
Social Media: www.facebook.com/NAFAaircraft
www.linkedin.com/groups/3053135
twitter.com/NAFAaviation

7592 ■ NAFA Corporate Aviation Business Scholarship *(Undergraduate, Graduate/Scholarship)*

Purpose: To support students seeking a business career in Corporate Aviation and, specifically, within the corporate aircraft Finance, Legal and Insurance community. **Focus:** Accounting; Aviation; Business; Economics; Finance. **Qua-**

Awards are arranged alphabetically below their administering organizations

lif.: Applicants must be full-time undergraduate or graduate students; must have a 3.0 minimum cumulative GPA on a 4.0 grade scale (High School GPA or equivalent for Freshman applicants); must be U.S. citizens or permanent residents. **Criteria:** Selection will be based on the committee's criteria.

Funds Avail.: $1,000 to $5,000. **Duration:** Annual. **To Apply:** Eligible students should apply through their school's Financial Aid office. **Deadline:** October 31. **Contact:** National Aircraft Finance Association, Attn: Scholarship Award Selection Committee; PO Box 1570, Edgewater, MD, 21037; Karen Griggs; E-mail: karengriggs@nafa.aero; Phone: 410-571-1740.

7593 ■ National Alliance of Preservation Commissions (NAPC)

PO Box 1011
Virginia Beach, VA 23451
Ph: (757)802-4141
E-mail: stephanie@napcommissions.org
URL: napcommissions.org
Social Media: twitter.com/napc

7594 ■ NAPC Forum Student Scholarships
(Undergraduate, Graduate/Scholarship)

Purpose: To provide financial assistance to the students in historic preservation. **Focus:** Historic preservation. **Qualif.:** Applicants must be undergraduate and graduate students in historic preservation or related fields who want to participate in the national commission forum. **Criteria:** Recipients will be selected based on their academic standing.

Funds Avail.: Up to $400. **Duration:** Annual. **To Apply:** Application must include a cover letter stating name, address, telephone numbers, e-mail address, academic institution, area of study, degree and date of graduation, statement describing interest in FORUM and what they hope to gain from the experience (statement limited to one page); indicate if applicant has attended FORUM previously; estimate expenses to attend FORUM and applicant's anticipated financial contribution if any; proof of current student status: signed and dated letter from applicant's program or academic institution's registrar certifying student status; resume; two academic and /or professional references. **Deadline:** March 2. **Contact:** Patricia Blick, NAPC Board Chair Elect; E-mail: patricia.blick@quapaw.com.

7595 ■ National American Arab Nurses Association (NAANA)

18000 W 9 Mile Rd., Ste. 360
Southfield, MI 48075
Ph: (313)680-5049
URL: www.n-aana.org

7596 ■ National American Arab Nurses Association Scholarships for Nursing Study *(Undergraduate, Master's/Scholarship)*

Purpose: To provide financial assistance to applicants who are engaged in studying nursing at the associate degree, bachelor's degree, and master's degree or RN-BSN levels. **Focus:** Nursing. **Qualif.:** Applicants must be enrolled in an accredited nursing program at the time of application, and should be pursuing a nursing program during the year for which the award is made; demonstrated leadership, academic, professional, or through student organizations;

must be of Arab heritage, citizens or permanent residents of the United States, and must reside within the US or its territories; further, applicants must be members of NAANA; average GPA of 3.0 is required. **Criteria:** Recipients will be evaluated on the basis of demonstrated academic excellence; leadership; academic; professional; applications will be reviewed by a selection committee comprised of members of the Board of Directors.

Funds Avail.: $500 - $1,000. **Duration:** Annual. **To Apply:** Application must be submitted electronically as email. **Deadline:** June 30. **Contact:** E-mail: scholarship@n-aana.org.

7597 ■ National Arab American Medical Association (NAAMA)

2265 Livernois Rd., Ste. 720
Troy, MI 48083
Ph: (248)646-3661
Fax: (248)457-5036
E-mail: naama@naama.com
URL: www.naama.com
Social Media: www.facebook.com/
   NAAMANATIONALOFFICIAL
twitter.com/NAAMA_NTL

7598 ■ NAAMA Scholarships *(Undergraduate/ Scholarship)*

Purpose: To provide financial assistance to Arabic students who are studying in a medical, osteopathic, or dental school. **Focus:** Dentistry; Medicine, Osteopathic. **Qualif.:** Applicants must be Arabic students enrolled in a U.S. or Canadian medical, osteopathic, or dental school. **Criteria:** Awards are given based on academic excellence and financial need.

Funds Avail.: $1,000. **Duration:** Annual.

7599 ■ National Asian Pacific American Bar Association (NAPABA)

1612 K St. NW, Ste. 510
Washington, DC 20006
Ph: (202)775-9555
Fax: (202)775-9333
URL: www.napaba.org
Social Media: www.facebook.com/NAPABANational
instagram.com/napabanational
linkedin.com/company/napaba
twitter.com/NAPABA

7600 ■ 1L SUMMER INTERNSHIP PROGRAM
Prudential Financial, Inc. *(Postgraduate/Internship)*

Purpose: To provide a summer internship opportunity for a highly-motivated first-year law students. **Focus:** Law. **Qualif.:** Applicants must be members of NAPABA; must be enrolled at an ABA-accredited law school; must have successfully completed the first year of law school with a minimum 3.0 GPA on a 4.0 scales (or equivalent) and be scheduled for graduation; must have financial or business-related experience or interest. **Criteria:** Selection will be based on the committee's criteria.

Funds Avail.: Approximately $10,000.

7601 ■ Anheuser-Busch NAPABA Law Foundation Presidential Scholarships *(Undergraduate/ Scholarship)*

Purpose: To support law students who demonstrate an outstanding leadership potential to serve the Asian Pacific

Awards are arranged alphabetically below their administering organizations

American community. **Focus:** Law. **Qualif.:** Applicants must be students enrolled as law degree candidates in an accredited law school in the United States at least half time as determined by the school. **Criteria:** Applicants will be selected based on consultation with the president of NA-PABA.

Funds Avail.: $7,500 each. **Duration:** Annual. **Remarks:** Established in 1995.

7602 ■ Lim, Ruger & Kim Scholarships
(Undergraduate/Scholarship)

Purpose: To provide financial aid for law students who demonstrate a commitment to serve or contribute to the Asian Pacific American community as future leaders. **Focus:** Law. **Qualif.:** Applicant must be a student enrolled as a law degree part- or full-time at an ABA-accredited law school in the US. **Criteria:** Selection will be based on the committee's criteria.

Funds Avail.: $2,500. **Duration:** Annual. **To Apply:** Applicant must submit resume and an essay with application. **Remarks:** Established in 2004.

7603 ■ NLF Scholarships *(Undergraduate/Scholarship)*

Purpose: To support law students who demonstrate a commitment to serve or contribute to the Asian Pacific American community as future leaders. **Focus:** Law.

Funds Avail.: $2,000. **Duration:** Annual. **Number Awarded:** Varies.

7604 ■ National Association of Abandoned Mine Land Programs (NAAMLP)
c/o Dustin Morin, AML Supervisor
Alabama Dept. of Labor., 4351 Crescent Rd.
Irondale, AL 35210
Ph: (205)945-8671
Fax: (205)945-8685
URL: naamlp.net

7605 ■ National Association of Abandoned Mine Land Programs Scholarship *(Undergraduate/Scholarship)*

Purpose: To assist students who intend to work as scientists or technicians in the field of mine land reclamation. **Focus:** Mining. **Criteria:** Recipients will be selected based on submitted application.

Funds Avail.: $2,500. **Duration:** Annual. **Number Awarded:** 4. **To Apply:** Applicants must complete an application form; must submit a (one-page) essay addressing the following criteria: 1) commitment to the reclamation and restoration of lands affected by the abandoned mining; 2) statement of intended career; 3) declared area of study; 4) educational history and level of education; 5) coursework, employment, and/or volunteer activities; 6) transcript of last year's course work; 7) statement of intent; and 8) personal statement of financial need. **Deadline:** June 15.

7606 ■ National Association for the Advancement of Colored People (NAACP)
4805 Mt. Hope Dr.
Baltimore, MD 21215
Ph: (410)580-5777
Free: 877-622-2798
E-mail: actso@naacpnet.org

URL: www.naacp.org
Social Media: www.facebook.com/naacp
instagram.com/naacp
twitter.com/NAACP
youtube.com/user/naacpvideos/videos

7607 ■ Law Fellows Program *(Undergraduate/Fellowship)*

Purpose: To develop future generations of civil rights attorneys. **Focus:** Law. **Qualif.:** Applicants must be completed at least one year of law school; must be have Resume, Cover Letter, Transcript, Writing Sample and two (2) Letters of Recommendation via email. **Criteria:** Applicant Interest in civil rights law and commitment to public interest law.

Funds Avail.: No specific amount. **Duration:** Annual. **To Apply:** Applicants may contact Anson Asaka for the application process and further inquiries. **Deadline:** January 31. **Remarks:** Established in 2003. **Contact:** Anson Asaka, Email: legal@naacpnet.org.

7608 ■ National Association of Agricultural Educators (NAAE)
2525 Harrodsburg Road, Suite 200
Lexington, KY 40504-3358
Ph: (859)967-2892
Free: 800-509-0204
URL: www.naae.org
Social Media: www.pinterest.com/natassnageducat
twitter.com/naae
www.youtube.com/user/NatlAgEducators

7609 ■ NAAE Upper Division Scholarship
(Undergraduate/Scholarship)

Purpose: To support students who are majoring in agricultural education. **Focus:** Agricultural sciences; Education. **Qualif.:** Applicants must be agricultural education majors who want to be agricultural teachers; and, be members of NAAE; majoring in agricultural education with intentions to become an agriculture teacher; one of a maximum of three applicants selected to apply for this scholarship from the institution – the teacher education faculty at the respective institution must certify accordingly. **Criteria:** Awards are given based on academics, character and perseverance to the field of teaching in agricultural education.

Funds Avail.: $1,500. **Duration:** Annual. **To Apply:** Applicants must submit original copy and eight copies of application form; description of applicants' leadership and service activities; (400 words) essay entitled "Why I Want to Teach Agriculture"; a letter of recommendation from an agricultural education teacher in the applicant's college or university or from an agricultural education teacher at the local, state or national level; official transcript; and a photograph in a CD. **Deadline:** May 15. **Remarks:** Sponsored by National Geographic Learning and Delmar Cengage Learning. **Contact:** For assistance or verification, Phone: 800-509-0204.

7610 ■ National Association of Biology Teachers (NABT)
PO Box 3363
Warrenton, VA 20188
Ph: (703)264-9696
Fax: (202)962-3939

Awards are arranged alphabetically below their administering organizations

Free: 888-501-6228
E-mail: office@nabt.org
URL: nabt.org
Social Media: www.facebook.com/NABTAdmin
twitter.com/nabt_news?lang=en

7611 ■ National Association of Biology Teachers BioClub Student Award (Undergraduate/Scholarship)

Purpose: To support exceptional students who are inspired to be even better biology teachers. **Focus:** Biology. **Qualif.:** Applicants must be NABTA BioClub student members who are graduating high school seniors and have been accepted to a two or four year college/university. **Criteria:** Selection will be based on the committee's criteria.

Funds Avail.: Amount varies. **Duration:** Annual. **Number Awarded:** 2. **To Apply:** Applicants can nominate themselves or a colleague for one or more of the following NABT awards by filling out the online nomination form. Nominees can also send a letter stating why the candidate should be selected for an award. The nominee will be sent all the information, application materials and cover sheet that he or she needs to complete to be considered for the award. **Deadline:** March 31.

7612 ■ National Association of Black Accountants, Inc. (NABA)

7474 Greenway Center Dr., Ste. 1120
Greenbelt, MD 20770
Ph: (301)474-6222
Free: 888-571-2939
E-mail: customerservice@nabainc.org
URL: www.nabainc.org
Social Media: www.facebook.com/NABAInc/timeline
www.linkedin.com/company/national-association-of-black
 -accountants-naba-
twitter.com/nabainc
www.youtube.com/user/NABAInc

7613 ■ NABA National Scholarship Program (Graduate, Undergraduate/Scholarship, Award, Monetary)

Purpose: To support students who are deserving students preparing to enter various accounting, finance and business professions. **Focus:** Accounting; Business; Finance. **Qualif.:** Applicants must be Black, includes African, African-American, Caribbean, etc., must be an ACTIVE NABA student member, Must be currently enrolled at a four-year United States college or university as a full-time (12 semester hours or equivalent) undergraduate student (freshman, sophomore, junior, or first-year senior) majoring in accounting, finance, or business major, or they may be a full-time graduate student. Must meet the minimum required grade point average* of 3.5 in your major and 3.3 overall. **Criteria:** Selection will be made by the selection committee.

Funds Avail.: $1,500. **Duration:** Annual. **Number Awarded:** 50. **To Apply:** Applicants must submit a completed National Scholarship Application (NSA) available on the website; an official current Academic Transcript (through the current fall semester); official transcripts must be uploaded to the online application; we will not accept student copies or other unofficial transcripts; a clear copy of Student/Permanent Resident Visa (only if applicant IS NOT a United States citizen); a Current Resume. Resumes are to be uploaded in the online application; one Letter of

Recommendation; a Personal Biography of 75 words or less (copy and paste in webform); a Professional Headshot; an Essay Response of 500 words or less (copy and paste in webform). **Deadline:** December 31. **Contact:** NABA Member Service Center; Phone: 240-542-5000 or 888-571 2939; Email: memberservices@nabainc.org.

7614 ■ National Association of Black Journalists (NABJ)

1100 Knight Hall, Ste. 3101
College Park, MD 20742
Ph: (301)405-0248
Fax: (301)314-1714
E-mail: press@nabj.org
URL: www.nabj.org
Social Media: www.instagram.com/nabjofficial
twitter.com/nabj

7615 ■ Allison E. Fisher Scholarship (Undergraduate, Graduate/Scholarship)

Purpose: To provide financial assistance to students who are attending an accredited four-year university. **Focus:** Journalism; Photography; Radio and television.

Funds Avail.: $2,500. **Duration:** Annual. **Number Awarded:** 1. **To Apply:** Application must includes Resume Cover Letter Official College Transcript Five, Work Samples Three, References. **Deadline:** February 13. **Remarks:** The scholarship established in memory of their daughter Allison, who lost her battle with breast cancer at the age of 28.

7616 ■ National Association of Black Social Workers (NABSW)

2305 Martin Luther King, Jr. Ave. SE
Washington, DC 20020-5813
Ph: (202)678-4570
Fax: (202)678-4572
URL: nabsw.site-ym.com
Social Media: www.facebook.com/nabswincorporated
twitter.com/NABSWLive

7617 ■ Cenie Jomo Williams Tuition Scholarship (Graduate, Undergraduate/Scholarship)

Purpose: To provide financial assistance for African-American students who are active in community service. **Focus:** Social work. **Qualif.:** Applicants must be African-American students enrolled in full-time study at an accredited United States social work program in the semester that the award will be granted, and have a GPA of 3.0 on a 4.0 scale. **Criteria:** Applicants are evaluated based on academic achievement; community service; and financial need.

Funds Avail.: $2,500. **Number Awarded:** 2. **To Apply:** Applicants must submit the completed application form along with the following: statement of purpose letter; two recommendation letters; official school registrar letter; and official academic transcript. **Deadline:** June 28.

7618 ■ Dr. Joyce Beckett Scholarship (Graduate, Undergraduate/Scholarship)

Purpose: To help students complete graduate work and develop professional skills and talents to work in the African American community. **Focus:** Social work. **Qualif.:** Ap-

Awards are arranged alphabetically below their administering organizations

plicants must be African-American students enrolled in full-time study at an accredited United States social work program in the semester that the award will be granted, and have a GPA of 2.5 on a 4.0 scale; they must also express a research interest in the black community. **Criteria:** Applicants are evaluated based on academic achievement; community service; and financial need.

Funds Avail.: $1,000. **Duration:** Annual. **Number Awarded:** 1. **To Apply:** Applicants must submit the completed application form along with the following: statement of purpose letter; two recommendation letters; official school registrar letter; and official academic transcript.

7619 ■ Emma and Meloid Algood Tuition Scholarship (Graduate, Undergraduate/Scholarship)

Purpose: To provide financial assistance for African-American students who are active in community service and planning to work in the field of social work. **Focus:** Social work. **Qualif.:** Applicants must be African-American students enrolled in full-time study at an accredited United States social work program in the semester that the award will be granted, and have a GPA of 2.5 on a 4.0 scale; they must also express a research interest in the black community. **Criteria:** Applicants are evaluated based on academic achievement; community service; and financial need.

Funds Avail.: $1,000. **Duration:** Annual. **Number Awarded:** 1. **To Apply:** Applicants must submit the completed application form along with the following: statement of purpose letter; two recommendation letters; official school registrar letter; and official academic transcript.

7620 ■ Selena Danette Brown Book Scholarship (Graduate, Undergraduate/Scholarship)

Purpose: To provide financial assistance for African-American students who are active in community service. **Focus:** Social work. **Qualif.:** Applicants must be African-American students enrolled for full-time study at an accredited United States social work program in the semester that the award will be granted, and have a GPA of 2.5 on a 4.0 scale; they must also express a research interest in the black community. **Criteria:** Applicants are evaluated based on academic achievement; community service; and financial need.

Funds Avail.: $2,500. **Number Awarded:** 4. **To Apply:** Applicants must submit the completed application form along with the following: statement of purpose letter; two recommendation letters; official school registrar letter; and official academic transcript.

7621 ■ National Association for Campus Activities (NACA)

13 Harbison Way
Columbia, SC 29212-3401
Ph: (803)732-6222
URL: www.naca.org
Social Media: www.facebook.com/TheNACA
instagram.com/TheNACA
twitter.com/thenaca
youtube.com/naca50

7622 ■ Tese Caldarelli Memorial Scholarship (Graduate, Undergraduate/Scholarship)

Purpose: To provide educational support to students enrolled in colleges and universities in the NACA Mid Atlantic and Mid America Regions. **Focus:** Education, Secondary; Educational administration. **Qualif.:** Applicants must be current undergraduate or graduate students within the NACA Mid Atlantic & Mid America Regions; must be U.S. citizens; must have demonstrated significant leadership skills and ability and made significant contributions via volunteer involvement, either on or off campus. **Criteria:** Recipients are selected based on the following criteria: demonstrate significant leadership skills and abilities; hold significant leadership position on campus; make significant contributions via volunteer involvement, either on or off campus.

Funds Avail.: No specific amount. **Duration:** Annual. **To Apply:** Applicants must complete the online application and submit with the following: two letters of recommendation from administrators or faculty members who are well acquainted with the applicant as a student leader (should specify the applicant's leadership positions, responsibilities, skills and ability, training and accomplishments); resume or description of the applicant's leadership activities, skills and ability, training and accomplishments; official verification of the applicant's current enrollment status from the college/university registrar. All materials must be submitted online; only the first 75 qualified applications will be considered. **Deadline:** November 30. **Contact:** Email: scholarships@naca.org.

7623 ■ Markley Scholarship (Undergraduate, Graduate/Scholarship)

Purpose: To recognize and honor involved students who have made significant contributions to the NACA Central Region. **Focus:** General studies/Field of study not specified. **Qualif.:** Applicants must have a minimum of a 2.5 cumulative GPA; be juniors, seniors, or graduate students at a four-year school in in the NACA Central region or be sophomores at a two-year school in the NACA Central region; and must be U.S. citizens. **Criteria:** Recipients are selected based on the involvement and contribution to NACA Central; demonstrated potential in the field of student activities; contribution to the field of student activities and/or student activities employment; involvement in and contribution to other organizations.

Funds Avail.: No specific amount. **Duration:** Annual. **Number Awarded:** Up to 2. **To Apply:** Applicants must submit the following: completed online application form; at least two letters of recommendation; resume; official verification of the applicant's current enrollment status. All materials must be submitted online; only the first 75 qualified applications will be considered. **Deadline:** September 30. **Remarks:** Established in 1983. **Contact:** Email: scholarships@naca.org.

7624 ■ NACA Foundation Graduate Scholarships (Graduate, Master's, Doctorate/Scholarship)

Purpose: To promote the development of professionals in the field of campus activities. **Focus:** Education, Secondary; Educational administration. **Qualif.:** Applicants must be enrolled in a graduate or doctoral degree program in student personnel services or a related area; must have demonstrated experience and involvement in campus activities and be committed to pursue a career as a campus activities professional; and must be U.S. citizens. NACA offers five graduate scholarships for students within the regions shown: D.L. McCullough Memorial Scholarship (All Regions); McCullough Memorial Scholarship (Northeast); William E. Brattain Graduate Scholarship (Mid America/Central/Mid Atlantic); Hayward M. "Skip" Daugherty, Jr. Graduate Scholarship (Mid America/Central/Mid Atlantic);

Awards are arranged alphabetically below their administering organizations

Mid Atlantic Graduate Scholarship (Mid Atlantic).**Criteria:** Recipients are selected based on the demonstrated leadership, academic record and financial need.

Funds Avail.: No specific amount. **Duration:** Annual. **To Apply:** Applicants must complete the online application and submit with the following: copy of the applicant's undergraduate and graduate academic transcript (if a graduate transcript is not yet available, please upload proof of acceptance or enrollment into a graduate program); summary (resume or vitae) of applicant's volunteer (campus, community or organization) and employment activities related to campus activities; two letters of reference from professors, advisers or employers who are familiar with the applicant's experience related to campus activities; summary of professional goals in which the applicant hopes to accomplish in one year, five years and 10 years AND a summary describing how receiving an NACA Foundation Graduate Scholarship will better enable applicant to achieve these goals. All materials must be submitted online; only the first 75 qualified applications will be considered.**Deadline:** April 15. **Remarks:** Established in 1995. **Contact:** Email: scholarships@naca.org.

7625 ■ NACA Mid Atlantic Higher Education Research Scholarships *(Master's/Scholarship)*

Purpose: To assist students pursuing a career in student activities or a related student services field. **Focus:** Education, Secondary; Educational administration. **Qualif.:** Applicants must show that their research will add to the college student personnel knowledge base, particularly campus activities, or address issues challenging student affairs practitioners or higher education as they relate to campus activities. Applicants must be pursuing a master's degree; must be a U.S. Citizen. **Criteria:** Recipients are selected based on the demonstrated leadership, academic record, and financial need. All scholarship recipients will be selected by an anonymous Scholarship Committee appointed by the Chair of the Board of Trustees.

Funds Avail.: Up to $500. **Duration:** Annual. **To Apply:** Applicants must submit the following: completed online application form; at least two letters of recommendation; resume; official verification of the applicant's current enrollment status. All materials must be submitted online. **Deadline:** June 30. **Remarks:** Established in 1995.

7626 ■ NACA Mid Atlantic Undergraduate Scholarship *(Undergraduate/Scholarship)*

Purpose: To assist undergraduate students in pursuing degrees. **Focus:** General studies/Field of study not specified. **Qualif.:** Applicants must be undergraduate students enrolled in a college or university within the NACA Mid Atlantic region; must have a minimum 2.5 GPA on a 4.0 scale; must demonstrate significant leadership skills and ability, hold a significant leadership position on campus or in the community, and have made significant contributions via volunteer involvement, either on or off campus; must be U.S. citizens. **Criteria:** Recipients are selected based on the demonstrated leadership, academic record, and financial need. All scholarship recipients will be selected by an anonymous Scholarship Committee appointed by the Chair of the Board of Trustees.

Duration: Annual. **Number Awarded:** Up to 2. **To Apply:** Applicant must complete the online application and submit with the following: two letters of recommendation from administrators or faculty members who are well acquainted with the applicant as a student leader (should specify the applicant's leadership positions, responsibilities, skills and

ability, training and accomplishments); resume or description of the applicant's leadership activities, skills and ability, training and accomplishments; official verification of the applicant's current enrollment status from the college/ university registrar. All materials must be submitted online; only the first 75 qualified applications will be considered. **Deadline:** November 30. **Contact:** Email: scholarships@ naca.org.

7627 ■ NACA Multicultural Professional Development Grant *(Undergraduate, Graduate, Professional development/Grant)*

Purpose: To increase the participation of ethnic minority individuals in the field of campus activities. **Focus:** Education, Secondary; Educational administration. **Qualif.:** Applicants must be members of the African-American, Latina/ Latino, Native American, Asian-American or Pacific Islander ethic minorities; must be a U.S. Citizen; must be current undergraduate students, graduate students, or school staff members.

Funds Avail.: No specific amount. **Duration:** Annual. **Number Awarded:** 4. **To Apply:** Applicant must complete the online application and submit with one letter of recommendation from someone well acquainted with the applicant (letter should address applicant's involvement in student activities and potential in the field, and also affirm applicant's ethnic minority status, financial need, and that applicant will be in the campus activities field at least one year following the program for which a scholarship is being sought). All materials must be submitted online; only the first 75 qualified applicants will be considered. **Deadline:** June 30. **Contact:** Email: scholarships@naca.org.

7628 ■ NACA Scholarship for Student Leaders in the Central & Northern Plains Regions *(Undergraduate/Scholarship)*

Purpose: To assist students undergraduate studies leading to careers in student activities or a related student services field. **Focus:** Education, Secondary; Educational administration. **Qualif.:** Applicants must be matriculated undergraduates in good standing at the time of their application and during the semester in which the award is received; have a GPA of 2.5 on a 4.0 scale; have demonstrated significant leadership skills and ability; have made significant contributions via volunteer involvement, either on or off campus; be enrolled in a college or university within the NACA Central & Northern Plains regions; must be U.S. citizens. **Criteria:** Recipients are selected based on the undergraduate record of academic achievement; involvement in and contributions to NACA Northern Plains by a student from a Wisconsin or Upper Peninsula of Michigan school; potential for success in the field of campus activities. All scholarship recipients will be selected by an anonymous Scholarship Committee appointed by the Chair of the Board of Trustees.

Funds Avail.: No specific amount. **Duration:** Annual. **Number Awarded:** 1. **To Apply:** Applicants must complete the online application and submit with the following: two letters of recommendation from administrators or faculty members who are well acquainted with the applicant as a student leader (should specify the applicant's leadership positions, responsibilities, skills and ability, training and accomplishments); resume or description of the applicant's leadership activities, skills and ability, training and accomplishments; official verification of the applicant's current enrollment status from the college/university registrar. All materials must be submitted online; only the first 75 qualified applica-

Awards are arranged alphabetically below their administering organizations

tions will be considered. **Deadline:** November 30.

7629 ■ NACA Scholarship for Student Leaders in the Mid America & Central Regions *(Undergraduate/Scholarship)*

Purpose: To assist students pursuing undergraduate studies leading to a career in student activities or a related student services field. **Focus:** Education, Secondary; Educational administration. **Qualif.:** Applicants must be matriculated undergraduates in good standing at the time of their application and during the semester in which the award is received; have a GPA of 2.5 on a 4.0 scale; have demonstrated significant leadership skills and ability; have made significant contributions via volunteer involvement, either on or off campus; be enrolled in a college or university within the NACA Mid Atlantic or Central regions; must be a U.S. Citizen. **Criteria:** Recipients will be selected based on demonstrated leadership, academic record, and financial need.

Duration: Annual. **To Apply:** Applicants must complete the online application and submit with the following: two letters of recommendation from administrators or faculty members who are well acquainted with the applicant as a student leader (should specify the applicant's leadership positions, responsibilities, skills and ability, training and accomplishments); resume or description of the applicant's leadership activities, skills and ability, training and accomplishments; official verification of the applicant's current enrollment status from the college/university registrar. All materials must be submitted online; only the first 75 qualified applications will be considered. **Deadline:** November 30. **Remarks:** Established in 1995. **Contact:** Email: scholarships@naca.org.

7630 ■ NACA Silver Anniversary Scholarship for Student Leaders *(Undergraduate/Scholarship)*

Purpose: To provide financial assistance to undergraduate student leaders enrolled and new professionals employed in colleges and universities. **Focus:** Education, Secondary; Educational administration. **Qualif.:** Applicants must be undergraduate students in good standing at the time of the application and during the semester in which the award is received; must hold significant leadership positions on their campuses and to their communities; must have demonstrated leadership skills and ability; must be US citizens. **Criteria:** Recipients are selected based on the demonstrated leadership skills and abilities and significant contributions to their campus communities: all scholarship recipients will be selected by an anonymous Scholarship Committee appointed by the Chair of the Board of Trustees.

Funds Avail.: No specific amount. **Duration:** Annual. **To Apply:** Applicants must complete the online application and submit with the following: two letters of recommendation from administrators or faculty members who are well acquainted with the applicant as a student leader (should specify the applicant's leadership positions, responsibilities, skills and ability, training and accomplishments); resume or description of the applicant's leadership activities, skills and ability, training and accomplishments; official verification of the applicant's current enrollment status from the college/university registrar. All materials must be submitted online; only the first 75 qualified applications will be considered. **Deadline:** November 30. **Remarks:** Established in 1985. **Contact:** Email: scholarships@naca.org.

7631 ■ NACA South Student Leadership Scholarships *(Undergraduate/Scholarship)*

Purpose: To support undergraduate students enrolled at colleges and universities within the NACA Southern

regions. **Focus:** Education, Secondary; Educational administration. **Qualif.:** Applicants must be matriculated undergraduates in good standing at the time of their application and during the semester in which the award is received; have demonstrated significant leadership skills and ability; hold a significant leadership position on campus or in the community; have made significant contributions via volunteer involvement, either on or off the campus; be enrolled in a college or university within the former NACA South Region; must be a U.S. Citizen.

Funds Avail.: No specific amount. **Duration:** Annual. **Number Awarded:** Up to 4. **To Apply:** Applicants must complete the online application and submit with the following: two letters of recommendation from administrators or faculty members who are well acquainted with the applicant as a student leader (should specify the applicant's leadership positions, responsibilities, skills and ability, training and accomplishments); resume or description of the applicant's leadership activities, skills and ability, training and accomplishments; official verification of the applicant's current enrollment status from the college/university registrar. All materials must be submitted online; only the first 75 qualified applications will be considered. **Deadline:** November 30. **Remarks:** Established in 1994. **Contact:** Email: scholarships@naca.org.

7632 ■ Lori Rhett Memorial Scholarships *(Graduate, Undergraduate/Scholarship)*

Purpose: To recognize the achievements of undergraduate or graduate student leaders enrolled in colleges and universities located in the former NACA Pacific Northwest Region. **Focus:** General studies/Field of study not specified. **Qualif.:** Applicants must be matriculated undergraduate or graduate students with a cumulative GPA of 2.5 or better at the time of application and during the semester in which the award is received; must be students within the NACA West Region; must demonstrate significant leadership skills and abilities; must hold a significant leadership position on campus; must have made significant contributions via volunteer involvement, either on or off campus; must be enrolled in a college or university within the former NACA Pacific Northwest Region; must be a U.S. Citizen. **Criteria:** Recipients are selected based on financial need and academic record; all scholarship recipients will be selected by an anonymous Scholarship Committee appointed by the Chair of the Board of Trustees.

Funds Avail.: No specific amount. **Duration:** Annual. **Number Awarded:** 1. **To Apply:** Applicants must complete the application form (online); at least two letters of recommendation; a resume; official verification of the applicant's current enrollment status and a copy of academic transcripts from the college or university. All materials must be submitted online; only the first 75 qualified applications will be considered. **Deadline:** November 30. **Remarks:** Established in 1996. **Contact:** Email: scholarships@naca.org.

7633 ■ Zagunis Student Leader Scholarship *(Graduate, Undergraduate/Scholarship)*

Purpose: To provide financial assistance to undergraduate or graduate student leaders enrolled in the NACA Mid Atlantic & Mid America Regions. **Focus:** Education, Secondary; Educational administration. **Qualif.:** Applicants must be current undergraduate or graduate students who are enrolled in a college or university within the NACA Mid America and Mid Atlantic regions; must be U.S. citizens. **Criteria:** Recipients are selected based on the demonstrated leadership skills and abilities and significant contributions to their campus communities. All scholarship

Awards are arranged alphabetically below their administering organizations

recipients will be selected by an anonymous Scholarship Committee appointed by the Chair of the Board of Trustees.

Funds Avail.: No specific amount. **Duration:** Annual. **To Apply:** Applicants must complete the online application and submit with the following: two letters of recommendation from administrators or faculty members who are well acquainted with the applicant as a student leader (should specify the applicant's leadership positions, responsibilities, skills and ability, training and accomplishments); resume or description of the applicant's leadership activities, skills and ability, training and accomplishments; official verification of the applicant's current enrollment status from the college/university registrar. All materials must be submitted online; only the first 75 qualified applications will be considered. **Deadline:** November 30. **Contact:** Email: scholarships@naca.org.

7634 ■ National Association of Chain Drug Stores Foundation
1776 Wilson Blvd., Ste. 200
Arlington, VA 22209
Ph: (703)549-3001
URL: www.nacdsfoundation.org

7635 ■ NACDS Foundation Merit-Based Scholarship Awards (All/Scholarship, Award)

Purpose: To support educational programs holding promise to: 1) meaningfully improve community health outcomes and patient care through innovation; and/or 2) elevate and innovate pharmacy school curricula to reflect contemporary clinical practice. **Focus:** Pharmaceutical sciences; Pharmacy. **Criteria:** Selection will be based on Relevance, Innovation, Scope, Feasibility.

Funds Avail.: $20,000. **Duration:** Annual. **To Apply:** Applicants must upload a summary of their proposed project, three to five pages in length, highlighting its purpose, timeline, and budget. **Remarks:** Established in 1996.

7636 ■ National Association of Clinical Nurse Specialists (NACNS)
11130 Sunrise Valley Drive, Suite 350
Reston, VA 20191
Ph: (703)436-0092
Fax: (703)435-4390
E-mail: info@nacns.org
URL: nacns.org
Social Media: www.facebook.com/clinicalnursespecialists
www.linkedin.com/company/nacns
twitter.com/NACNS

7637 ■ Katie Brush Memorial Scholarships (Master's, Doctorate/Scholarship)

Purpose: To increase the number of CNSs who are educated and prepared and thus, address the shortage of CNSs in the United States. **Focus:** Nursing. **Qualif.:** Applicants must be students who are pursuing a master's degree in an accredited CNS program or Clinical Nurse Specialists pursuing a research or practice doctorate. **Criteria:** Scholarship is competitive and is based on academic performance, clinical excellence, and demonstrated leadership.

To Apply: Applicants must complete and submit their application and must attach the following documents: docu-

mentation of admission as a student in a CNS master's or DNP program, or a CNS DNP or PhD program; documentation of current active student status by registrar, faculty member or dean; a current official transcript provided by a Registrar or by an academic advisor that confirms their current minimum cumulative GPA of 3.0 or higher; evidence of study in the field of acute or critical care nursing specialty by recommendation of two program faculty; evidence of clinical competence in the area of critical care; evidence of leadership abilities/activity in the area of critical care.

7638 ■ National Association of Collegiate Directors of Athletics (NACDA)
24651 Detroit Rd.
Westlake, OH 44145
Ph: (440)892-4000
Fax: (440)892-4007
URL: www.nacda.com
Social Media: www.facebook.com/NACDA
twitter.com/nacda

7639 ■ John McLendon Minority Postgraduate Scholarship (Postdoctorate/Scholarship)

Purpose: To support minority students pursuing graduate degrees in athletics administration. **Focus:** Sports studies. **Qualif.:** Applicants must be full-time senior or an undergraduate degree with two years work experience, preferably in athletics administration; have a minimum GPA of 3.2 (on a 4.0 scale); official classification as a minority as defined by federal guidelines; intention to attend graduate school to earn a degree in athletics administration; and involvement on the college/university or community level; must submit a 500-word personal essay explaining why they are deserving of a McLendon Postgraduate Scholarship.

Funds Avail.: $10,000. **Number Awarded:** 8. **To Apply:** Submit application form, 500 word essay, a completed nomination form, and a one-page letter of recommendation from the applicant's advisor. Forms must be signed and approved by the student's academic advisor.

7640 ■ National Association of Container Distributors (NACD)
3400 W Stonegate Blvd, Suite 2315
Arlington Heights, IL 60005
Ph: (630)942-6585
Fax: (630)790-3095
E-mail: info@nacd.net
URL: www.nacd.net

7641 ■ Henry Hoffman Memorial Scholarship (Undergraduate/Scholarship)

Purpose: To provide higher education assistance to children of employees of NACD member companies. **Focus:** General studies/Field of study not specified. **Qualif.:** Applicants must be students who have completed their junior year in high school and are children of employees of member companies of NACD; must have a 3.0 GPA in high school and 2.5 GPA in college; as a pre-requisite for eligibility, a NACD member company must employ one of the applicant's parents at the time the application is made. **Criteria:** Scholarship recipients will be selected based on past academic performance, performance on tests designated to measure ability and aptitude for higher education, and

Awards are arranged alphabetically below their administering organizations

the applicant's rank in school; recommendations by instructors or other persons unrelated to the candidate, extracurricular activities and leadership contributions will also be considered.

Funds Avail.: No specific amount. **Duration:** Annual. **Number Awarded:** Varies. **To Apply:** Applicants must submit a completed application form; current photo; two letters of recommendation from teachers; counselor's report; school transcript; SAT and/or ACT scores. **Deadline:** February 10. **Contact:** NACD; 3400 W. Stonegate Blvd., Ste. 2315, Arlington Heights, IL 60005; Phone: 630-942-6585; Email: info@nacd.net.

7642 ■ National Association for County Community and Economic Development (NACCED)

2001 K St., N.W., 3rd Fl., N.
Washington, DC 20036-3309
Ph: (202)367-1149
E-mail: info@nacced.org
URL: www.nacced.org
Social Media: www.facebook.com/NACCEDnews
twitter.com/naccednews
www.youtube.com/channel/UCKMVWsGtrzdYQV
_hdoXf9BQ?reload=9

7643 ■ NACCED Annual John C. Murphy Scholarships *(Graduate, Undergraduate/Scholarship)*

Purpose: To provide financial assistance for undergraduate and graduate students. **Focus:** Housing. **Qualif.:** Applicants must be currently attending an American college or university with a chosen field of study including course work in the areas of affordable housing and/or community and economic development. Applicants must also exhibit financial need. **Criteria:** Recipients will be selected based on the quality of their personal statement, financial need, grade point average and content of the letter of recommendation.

Funds Avail.: $1,500. **Duration:** Annual. **To Apply:** Applicants must be nominated by a NACCED member in good standing. Candidates must submit a completed scholarship application; official school transcript with official grade point average; certification of financial need - with an attached Financial Aide Award letter from the university; collegiate letter of acceptance stating the date of enrollment; personal statement of approximately 500 words introducing the applicant; letter of recommendation from a teacher, faculty or civic leader; support letter from a NACCED member in good standing.

7644 ■ National Association of Fellowships Advisors (NAFA)

191 Core Campus, 511 D Fort Hill St. Clemson University
Clemson, SC 29634
E-mail: info@nafadvisors.org
URL: www.nafadvisors.org

7645 ■ The Hertz Graduate Fellowship Award *(Graduate, Master's, Doctorate/Fellowship)*

Purpose: To build America's capacity for innovation by nurturing remarkable applied scientists and engineers who show the most promise to change the world. **Focus:** Engineering; Science. **Qualif.:** Applicants must be students of the applied physical, biological and engineering sciences who are citizens or permanent residents of the United

States of America, and who are willing to morally commit to make their skills available to the United States in time of national emergency. **Criteria:** Award is based on merit, not need; the bestowing organization screens the applicants and has the criteria set such as exceptional creativity and intelligence, excellent technical education, orientation and commitment, extraordinary accomplishment in technical or related professional studies, features of temperament and character conducive to high attainment as a technical professional, appropriate moral and ethical values, and leverage.

Funds Avail.: No specific amount. **Duration:** Annual. **To Apply:** Application is via online. Applicants must visit the program website for the other application details. **Deadline:** October 24. **Contact:** Hertz Foundation Graduate Fellowships: www.hertzfoundation.org.

7646 ■ George J. Mitchell Postgraduate Scholarships *(Postgraduate/Scholarship)*

Purpose: To introduce and connect generations of future American leaders to the island of Ireland while recognizing and fostering intellectual achievement, leadership, and a commitment to public service and community. **Focus:** General studies/Field of study not specified. **Qualif.:** Applicants must be U.S. citizens ages between 18 and 30 years; High academic achievement and intellectual distinction; no GPA minimum is stipulated; usually have a 3.8 or higher. **Criteria:** Criteria for the selection of awardees are the following: academic excellence, leadership, and commitment to community and public service.

Funds Avail.: No specific amount. **Duration:** Annual. **To Apply:** Applicants must submit a passport-style picture (PDF); all transcripts scanned into a single PDF; 1, 000-word personal statement; scan of signature. Information required are: GPA; contact information for 4 Recommenders including email, mailing address and phone number; contact information for Institutional Endorser (for full time undergraduate students only); complete mailing address of the university; university choice and field of study option; other awards, achievements. All information and supporting documents including recommendations and institutional endorsements must be submitted through the online application on the program website. **Remarks:** The scholarship was named in the honor of George J. Mitchell.

7647 ■ NAFA International Dissertation Research Fellowships *(Graduate, Doctorate/Fellowship)*

Purpose: To support distinguished graduate students in the humanities and social sciences who are writing their respective dissertations and conducting on-site researches outside the United States. **Focus:** Humanities; Social sciences. **Qualif.:** Applicants must be graduate students in the Humanities and Social Sciences who are enrolled in a doctoral program in the United States and conducting a research outside the country; and must have completed all Ph.D. requirements except on-site dissertation research by the time the fellowship begins. **Criteria:** Prospected awardees shall be selected based on their proposals or on-site researches.

Funds Avail.: No specific amount. **Duration:** Annual. **To Apply:** Applicants must complete and submit online application downloaded from the program's website. Other requirements shall be determined by the bestowing organization. **Contact:** IDRF, idrf@ssrc.org.

Awards are arranged alphabetically below their administering organizations

7648 ■ National Association of FSA County Office Employees (NASCOE)

c/o Mark Van Hoose, President
6155 Nichols Ln.
Johnstown, OH 43031
Ph: (740)670-5340
URL: www.nascoe.org

7649 ■ NASCOE Traditional Scholarships
(Undergraduate/Scholarship)

Purpose: To provide financial assistance to members who wish to enroll in adult education courses aimed at enhancing their careers with FSA. **Focus:** Adult education. **Qualif.:** Applicants must be graduating high school senior or first-year college freshman enrolled as a full time student with a minimum of 12 hours at an accredited college, university or trade school; must be a NASCOE member's child, or a member's legal dependent. **Criteria:** Selection will be evaluated based on their abilities, incentive assistance and other personal characteristics.

Funds Avail.: $1,500. **Duration:** Annual. **To Apply:** Applicants must submit an application together with official high school and/or college transcript, recommendation letter and all required signatures. **Deadline:** January 15. **Contact:** E-mail nascoescholarships@gmail.com.

7650 ■ National Association of Graduate Admissions Professionals (NAGAP)

4400 College Blvd., Ste. 220
Overland Park, KS 66211
Ph: (913)895-4616
Fax: (913)895-4652
E-mail: info@nagap.org
URL: www.nagap.org
Social Media: www.facebook.com/NAGAPorg
www.instagram.com/nagaporg
twitter.com/NAGAPorg
www.youtube.com/user/NAGAPvideo

7651 ■ NAGAP Graduate Student Enrollment Management Research Grants *(Graduate/Grant)*

Purpose: To encourage emerging knowledge and understanding of the complexities of graduate enrollment management including all aspects of admissions and recruitment, enrollment, retention and graduation in higher education. **Focus:** Management. **Qualif.:** Applicants must be individuals who are enrolled in graduate school and desire to conduct research in any aspect of graduate enrollment management activities and programs. **Criteria:** Selection will be based on demonstrated record and knowledge of research experience relevant to higher education and their respective research proposals.

Duration: Annual. **Number Awarded:** Up to 2. **To Apply:** Applicants must submit application; abstract of proposed research project; curriculum vitae or resume; list of graduate coursework; personal statement addressing interest in research topic and future career goals; letters of support from major professor and from a graduate enrollment management office at their institution; proposal (there is no set length; previous proposals have varied from 5-20 pages); and any other supporting material deemed appropriate by the applicants. **Deadline:** November 12.

7652 ■ National Association of Health Services Executives (NAHSE)

1050 Connecticut Ave. NW, 5th Fl.
Washington, DC 20036
Ph: (202)772-1030
Fax: (202)772-1072
E-mail: nahsehq@nahse.org
URL: www.nahse.org
Social Media: www.facebook.com/headquarters.nahse
www.instagram.com/nahse1968
www.linkedin.com/nahse-conference-41110479
twitter.com/NAHSEConference
twitter.com/NAHSEhq

7653 ■ The Ellis Bonner Award *(Graduate/Scholarship)*

Purpose: To support students attending universities and colleges to help defer the tuition costs. **Focus:** Health care services; Health services administration. **Qualif.:** Applicants must be graduate students and NAHSE member enrolled in an accredited college or university program, pursuing a Master or Doctorate Degree, and majoring in healthcare administration or a related field. They must also have a minimum grade point average (GPA) of 2.5 for undergraduate and 3.0 for the graduate on a scale or four (4.00). **Criteria:** Selection shall be based on academic merit and financial need.

Funds Avail.: $2,500. **To Apply:** Applicants must submit completed application along with cover letter; resume; application portfolio checklist; transcripts (if applicable); three letters of reference; (maximum of three pages); personal statement; personal photo (3 x 5); NAHSE student membership application. **Contact:** NAHSE Educational Assistance Program, 1050 Connecticut Ave., NW, 5th Fl., Washington, DC, 20036; Email: NAHSEawards@gmail.com.

7654 ■ The Florence Gaynor Award *(Graduate/Scholarship)*

Purpose: To recognize outstanding achievements among, and support female graduate students who are striving to become future leaders in Healthcare Management and NAHSE. **Focus:** Health care services; Health services administration. **Qualif.:** Applicants must be graduate students and NAHSE member enrolled in an accredited college or university program, pursuing a Master or Doctorate Degree, and majoring in healthcare administration or a related field. They must also have a minimum grade point average (GPA) of 2.5 for undergraduate and 3.0 for the graduate on a scale or four (4.00). **Criteria:** Selection shall be based on academic merit and financial need.

Funds Avail.: $2,500. **Duration:** Annual. **Deadline:** May 29. **Remarks:** The scholarship was established in memory of Florence Gaynor. **Contact:** NAHSE Educational Assistance Program, 1050 Connecticut Ave., NW, 5th Fl., Washington, DC, 20036; Email: NAHSEawards@gmail.com.

7655 ■ The Haynes Rice Award *(Graduate/Scholarship)*

Purpose: To support and encourage African American students to pursue a career in healthcare management. **Focus:** Health care services; Health services administration. **Qualif.:** Applicants must be graduate students and NAHSE member enrolled in an accredited college or university program, pursuing a Master or Doctorate Degree,

Awards are arranged alphabetically below their administering organizations

and majoring in healthcare administration or a related field. They must also have a minimum grade point average (GPA) of 3.0 for the graduate on a scale or four (4.00). **Criteria:** Selection shall be based on academic merit and financial need.

Funds Avail.: $2,500. **Duration:** Annual. **To Apply:** Applicants must submit completed application along with cover letter; resume; application portfolio checklist; transcripts (if applicable); three letters of reference; (maximum of three pages); personal statement; personal photo (3 x 5); NAHSE student membership application. **Remarks:** The scholarship was established in memory of Mr. Haynes Rice. **Contact:** NAHSE Educational Assistance Program, 1050 Connecticut Ave., NW, 5th Fl., Washington, DC, 20036; Email: NAHSEawards@gmail.com. nahsehq@nahse.org.

7656 ■ National Association for Healthcare Quality (NAHQ)
8600 W. Bryn Mawr Avenue, Suite 710 N.
Chicago, IL 60631
Ph: (847)375-4720
Fax: (847)375-6320
Free: 800-966-9392
E-mail: info@nahq.org
URL: www.nahq.org
Social Media: www.facebook.com/mynahq
www.instagram.com/mynahq
twitter.com/mynahq

7657 ■ HQF New Quality Professional Grant *(Professional development/Award, Grant)*
Purpose: To support NAHQ members in enhancing their professional skills and nurture their leadership potential. **Focus:** Health care services.

Duration: Annual. **Number Awarded:** 1.

7658 ■ National Association of Hispanic Nurses (NAHN)
1500 Sunday Drive, Suite 102
Raleigh, NC 27607
Ph: (919)573-5443
Fax: (919)787-4916
E-mail: info@thehispanicnurses.org
URL: nahnnet.org
Social Media: www.facebook.com/nahnnursing
www.linkedin.com/in/national-association-of-hispanic
  -nurses-36a67416
twitter.com/nahnnursing
www.youtube.com/channel/UCS0-I8rc-vZ9xbgreCmCztQ

7659 ■ United Health Foundation National Association of Hispanic Nurses Scholarships *(High School/ Scholarship)*
Purpose: To provide financial support to those Hispanic students who want to pursue their nursing profession. **Focus:** Nursing. **Qualif.:** Applicants must be NAHN members who are currently enrolled in an accredited school of nursing and be U.S. citizens or legal residents of the United States; must have academic standing and a minimum GPA of 3.0. **Criteria:** Preference is given to students who are rising sophomores and above.

Duration: Annual. **To Apply:** Applicants must complete the application form available on the website; must provide the

following supporting documents: one letter of recommendation from a faculty member outlining the applicant's future professional contribution to the nursing profession and potential to act as a role model for other aspiring nursing students; an essay (300 words or less) written by the student that reflects the qualifications and potential for leadership in nursing in the Hispanic community; a resume which includes earned certificates, awards and special honors; official transcript from applicant's college, university, or nursing program.

7660 ■ National Association of Intercollegiate Athletics (NAIA)
120 W. 12th St., Ste.700
Kansas City, MO 64105
Ph: (816)595-8000
E-mail: ecinfo@naia.org
URL: www.naia.org
Social Media: www.facebook.com/PlayNAIA
www.instagram.com/playnaia
www.linkedin.com/company/naia
twitter.com/NAIA
www.youtube.com/user/PlayNAIA

7661 ■ A. O. Duer Scholarship Award
(Undergraduate/Scholarship)
Purpose: To support a male and female junior student-athlete in any sport who has excelled in scholarship, character, and citizenship. **Focus:** General studies/Field of study not specified. **Qualif.:** Applicant must be an outstanding junior student of any NAIA intercollegiate athletic team with a minimum 3.75 GPA. **Criteria:** Selection is based on scholarship, character, citizenship and playing ability.

Funds Avail.: $1,000. **Duration:** Annual. **Deadline:** June 15. **Remarks:** Established in 1967.

7662 ■ Emil S. Liston Award *(Other/Scholarship)*
Purpose: To honor and recognize a player who has shown high athletic and scholastic achievement. **Focus:** General studies/Field of study not specified. **Qualif.:** Applicant must have an overall GPA of at least 3.50 (on a 4.00 scale) and must have attained junior standing academically. **Criteria:** Selection shall be based on athletic and academic achievement.

Funds Avail.: $1,000. **Duration:** Annual. **Number Awarded:** 2(one male,one female). **To Apply:** Applicant must submit an official nomination form; current high-resolution photo; an official transcript, signed by the registrar, must accompany the nomination along with a statement of the total hours required for graduation; a letter from the athlete's coach attesting to the athlete's playing ability and value to the team. **Deadline:** June 15. **Remarks:** Named in honor of the NAIA's first executive secretary. Established in 1950. **Contact:** Kelli Briscoe; Email: kbriscoe@naia.org.

7663 ■ National Association of Junior Auxiliaries, Inc. (NAJA)
845 S Main St.
Greenville, MS 38701
Ph: (662)332-3000
Fax: (662)332-3076
E-mail: najanet@bellsouth.net
URL: www.najanet.org

Awards are arranged alphabetically below their administering organizations

Social Media: www.facebook.com/NAJAinc
www.instagram.com/naja_inc
www.pinterest.com/najainc
twitter.com/najainc
www.youtube.com/channel/UCnMwIve6oP5SZBjN
_aU9IQA

7664 ■ NAJA Scholarship *(Graduate/Scholarship)*

Purpose: To support graduate study in fields which address the special needs of children and youth. **Focus:** Counseling/Guidance; Education, Special; Hearing and deafness; Mental health; Psychology; Speech and language pathology/Audiology. **Criteria:** Selection shall be based on the aforementioned applicant's qualifications and compliance with the application details.

Funds Avail.: Unspecified. **Duration:** Annual. **Deadline:** February 15. **Remarks:** Established in 1962. **Contact:** NAJA Headquarters, 845 S Main St., PO Box 1873, Greenville, Mississippi, 38701 / 38702; E-mail: najanet@bellsouth.net.

7665 ■ National Association of Music Merchants (NAMM)

5790 Armada Dr.
Carlsbad, CA 92008
Ph: (760)438-8001
Fax: (760)438-7327
Free: 800-767-6266
E-mail: info@namm.org
URL: www.namm.org
Social Media: www.facebook.com/nammorg
www.instagram.com/thenammshow
twitter.com/NAMM

7666 ■ William R. Gard Memorial Scholarships *(Graduate/Scholarship)*

Purpose: To enhance education and careers in the music product industry. **Focus:** Education, Music; Music. **Qualif.:** Applicants continues to be employed by a NAMM member and maintains an overall 3.0 grade point average or higher. Must have completed at least 400 hours of employment at the NAMM member company. Must be enrolled as a full-time college student for the upcoming fall term. **Criteria:** Applicants will be evaluated based on career intent; academic record; financial need; honors, awards and community involvement.

Funds Avail.: $2,000. **Duration:** Annual. **To Apply:** Application form is available at the website. Applicants must submit letters of reference (including one from the NAMM member employer, grade transcripts, awards and community involvement). Upload employer information completed by employer; Upload official college transcripts. list all high school(s) and college(s) attended, graduation date(s) and diploma(s) received. Describe any special recognition, honors or prizes received during the past five years. Describe your leisure interests or hobbies, noting any accomplishments in the area of music. Submit an essay of no more than 500 words demonstrating your unique interest in pursuing a career in the music products industry and what you expect from the education that the scholarship will provide. Upload a file that lists jobs (including summer employment) you have held in the past three years or attach your resume. **Deadline:** July 31.

7667 ■ National Association of Negro Business and Professional Women's Clubs, Inc. (NANBPWC)

1806 New Hampshire Ave. NW
Washington, DC 20009
Ph: (202)483-4206
Fax: (202)462-7253
URL: www.nanbpwc.org
Social Media: www.instagram.com/nanbpwc
www.linkedin.com/groups/4603132/profile
twitter.com/NANBPWC

7668 ■ Dr. Julianne Malveaux Scholarship *(Undergraduate/Scholarship)*

Purpose: To provide financial assistance for African-American students pursuing their college education. **Focus:** Creative writing; Economics; Journalism; Public administration.

Funds Avail.: No specific amount. **Duration:** Annual. **To Apply:** Applicants must complete the scholarship application online and submit a 1, 000-word essay on their career plans and their relevance to the Dr. Julianne Malveaux Program Theme "Black Women's Hands Can Rock the World". **Deadline:** March 1. **Contact:** Cheryl McKay, National Director of Education; Email: education@nanbpwc.org.

7669 ■ The Dr. Blanca Moore-Velez Woman of Substance Scholarship *(Undergraduate/Scholarship)*

Purpose: To provide financial assistance for African American students pursuing their college education. **Focus:** General studies/Field of study not specified.

Funds Avail.: No specific amount. **Duration:** Annual. **Number Awarded:** 1. **To Apply:** Applicants must submit a typed essay of no less than 500 words on the topic: "Challenges to the mature student and how I overcame them"; Complete the scholarship Application Form Online. **Deadline:** February 1 to April 15. **Contact:** Cheryl McKay, Technology Team Leader; Email: education@nanbpwc.org.

7670 ■ NANBPWC National Scholarship *(Graduate/Scholarship)*

Purpose: To provide financial assistance for African-American students pursuing their college education. **Focus:** General studies/Field of study not specified. **Qualif.:** Applicants must be graduating African-American high school seniors who have a cumulative grade point average of 3.0 or above on a 4.0 scale by February 1st in the year of graduation; must be a United States citizen.

Funds Avail.: No specific amount. **Duration:** Annual. **To Apply:** Applicants must complete the scholarship application form online and submit a typed essay of no less than 300 words on the topic "Explain the Benefits You Have Gained through the Contributions of Two (2) Trailblazers ofAfrican Descent (past and/or contemporary) and How It Has Benefited You as a Person". **Deadline:** April 1. **Contact:** Dr. June M. Johnson, National Director of Education education@nanbpwc.org.

7671 ■ National Association of Oil and Energy Service Professionals (OESP)

312 N Ave. E, Ste. 5
Cranford, NJ 07016
Fax: (908)967-5044

Awards are arranged alphabetically below their administering organizations

Free: 888-552-0900
URL: thinkoesp.org
Social Media: www.facebook.com/ThinkOESP
www.linkedin.com/in/thinkoesp
twitter.com/OESP1

7672 ■ Dave Nelsen Scholarships *(Undergraduate/ Scholarship)*

Purpose: To support students interested in pursuing their careers in the energy service industry. **Focus:** Heating, air conditioning, and refrigeration. **Criteria:** Recipients are selected based on the submitted application form and evaluation committee.

Funds Avail.: $5,000. **Duration:** Annual. **Number Awarded:** 3. **To Apply:** Applicants must submit completed application form and a 500-word essay stating their goals towards the heating industry; must also include a letter of recommendation from their HVAC or plumbing instructor. **Deadline:** March 13. **Remarks:** Established in 1999. **Contact:** OESP, 312 N Ave. E, Ste. 5, Cranford, NJ, 07016; E-mail: lstrug@thinkoesp.org; Phone: 888-552-0900.

7673 ■ National Association of Pastoral Musicians (NPM)

962 Wayne Ave., Ste. 210
Silver Spring, MD 20910-4461
Ph: (240)247-3000
Fax: (240)247-3001
Free: 855-207-0293
E-mail: npmsing@npm.org
URL: www.npm.org

7674 ■ NPM Academic Scholarship *(Graduate, Undergraduate/Scholarship)*

Purpose: To assist with the cost of education formation for pastoral musicians. **Focus:** Music. **Qualif.:** Applicants must be NPM members; part-time or full-time in an undergraduate or graduate degree program of studies related to the field of pastoral music during the current year; and must intend to work at least two years in the field of pastoral music following graduation/program completion. **Criteria:** Applicants must demonstrate financial need.

Funds Avail.: No specific amount. **Duration:** One year. **Number Awarded:** Varies. **To Apply:** Applicants must submit letter or short essay containing the following information: name and contact information including address, home, work phone and email; definition of the term "pastoral musician"; description of talents; previous experience as pastoral musician; educational background, educational program enrolled; recording (cassette or CD format) demonstrating solo performance skills or those of an ensemble under applicants' direction; two letters of recommendation, including one written by pastor; and completed financial need statement. **Deadline:** April 27. **Contact:** U.S. Mail/UPS/FedEx: NPM Academic Scholarship, National Association of Pastoral Musicians, 962 Wayne Ave., Ste. 210, Silver Spring, MD 20910-4461; Email: NPMSing@npm.org.

7675 ■ NPM Program Scholarship *(Graduate, Undergraduate/Scholarship)*

Purpose: To assist pastoral musicians with limited financial resources in taking advantage of opportunities for continuing formation at NPM conventions and institutes. **Focus:**

Music. **Qualif.:** Applicant must be NPM member and should be from economically disadvantaged parishes. **Criteria:** Recipient will be selected based on financial need.

Funds Avail.: No amount mentioned. **Duration:** 1 year. **To Apply:** Must submit completed application form; an audio or video recording of approximately 5 minutes demonstrating solo performance; two letters of recommendation, one completed by applicant's pastor or pastoral administrator; and financial need statement. **Deadline:** April 7.

7676 ■ National Association of Pediatric Nurse Practitioners (NAPNAP)

5 Hanover Sq., Ste. 1401
New York, NY 10004
Ph: (917)746-8300
Fax: (212)785-1713
Free: 877-662-7627
E-mail: info@napnap.org
URL: www.napnap.org
Social Media: www.facebook.com/NAPNAP1973
www.instagram.com/napnap_73
twitter.com/NAPNAP

7677 ■ Reckitt Benckiser Student Scholarships *(Graduate/Scholarship)*

Purpose: To provide financial assistance to Pediatric Nurse Practitioner Student to allow for attendance at the NAPNAP Annual Meeting. **Focus:** Nursing. **Qualif.:** Applicant must be a NAPNAP member, registered nurse and a graduate student who has completed at least 1 semester of graduate studies in a Pediatric Nurse Practitioner Program; must be enrolled in a recognized program of study (associated with an academic institution authorized to award a master's degree or DNP in nursing), leading to completion of qualifications for education and practice as a PNP (a program defined as one which primarily prepares an individual to deliver child health care services, either in primary care, specialty care or acute care settings). **Criteria:** Recipient will be selected by the NAPNAP Foundation Scholarship Committee.

Funds Avail.: No specific amount. **Duration:** Annual. **To Apply:** Applicants must submit original plus four copies (total 5) of the completed application with all the support documents.

7678 ■ Elaine Gelman Scholarship *(Undergraduate/ Scholarship)*

Purpose: To support the education of nurse practitioner students who are demonstrating their ability to articulate and follow through an innovative solution. **Focus:** Nursing. **Qualif.:** Applicants must be full or part-time Nurse Practitioner (NP) students enrolled in an accredited NP program with an expected graduation date of two years or less. **Criteria:** Applicants will be judged based on clinical competence, academic achievement, and involvement in political activism relating to health care issues. Preference will be given to those applicants who are in a PNP program or those with interest or experience in health policy or advocacy.

Duration: Annual. **To Apply:** Applicants must submit completed Elaine Gelman Scholarship Award Application Form; a personal statement (200 words or less) describing why the individual is competing for this award and specifically what goals would be accomplished if the award is

Awards are arranged alphabetically below their administering organizations

received; two letters of reference from a faculty member and professional colleague. Applicants must provide four copies each to be submitted.

7679 ■ National Association of Pediatric Nurse Practitioners McNeil Annual Scholarships
(Undergraduate/Scholarship)

Purpose: To provide financial assistance to students enrolled in pediatric nurse practitioner programs. **Focus:** Nursing. **Qualif.:** Applicant must be a registered nursing student who has completed at least two semesters or quarters as defined by the university; enrolled at a recognized PNP program and have no previous formal pediatric nurse practitioner education; must be a full-time student while enrolled in PNP program; must have a GPA of 3.0 or higher. **Criteria:** Applicants will be judged based on academic performance and financial need status.

Funds Avail.: $2,500. **To Apply:** Applicants must submit five copies of the application and accompanying needed materials to the NAPNAP Foundation.

7680 ■ National Association of Pediatric Nurse Practitioners McNeil Rural and Underserved Scholarships *(Graduate/Scholarship)*

Purpose: To provide financial support to PNP students who plan on practicing in a rural or underserved geographical region for the first two years after they complete their PNP education. **Focus:** Medicine, Pediatric; Nursing. **Qualif.:** Applicants must be planning on practicing in a rural or undeserved geographical region for the first two years after PNP education completed; must be registered nurses who have completed at least two semesters or quarters as defined by the university; enrolled at a recognized Master's degree program; have no previous formal pediatric nurse practitioner education; and demonstrated financial need. In addition, applicants must be in full-time status (nine or more credit hours/semester) while in PNP program; have GPA of 3.0 or higher; be member of NAPNAP providing with ongoing accounts regarding students. **Criteria:** Recipients will be selected based on academic performance and financial status.

Funds Avail.: No specific amount. **To Apply:** Applicants must submit five copies of the completed application form; documentation of RN license; documentation of acceptance into a PNP program signed by Faculty coordinating the program; PNP program brochure with designated plan of study highlighted; documentation of the length of clinical coursework; and documentation of tuition fees. **Deadline:** June 30.

7681 ■ National Association of Puerto Rican Hispanic Social Workers (NAPRHSW)
PO Box 651
Brentwood, NY 11717
URL: www.naprhsw.org

7682 ■ NAPRHSW Scholarships *(Undergraduate, Graduate/Scholarship)*

Purpose: To provide educational support to Hispanic students in the Schools of Social Welfare. **Focus:** Social sciences. **Qualif.:** Applicants must be undergraduate or graduate students. **Criteria:** Selection will be based on the committee's criteria.

Funds Avail.: No specific amount. **Duration:** Annual. **To Apply:** Applicants may contact the NAPRHSW for the ap-

plication details and other information. **Deadline:** February 9. **Contact:** Vilma E. Matos; Email: vmatos39@yahoo.com, Phone: 631-807-2822; Packet to be addressed to Ms. Vilma E. Matos, LCSW-R, 39, Georgia St., East Northport, NY,11731.

7683 ■ National Association for Pupil Transportation (NAPT)
1840 Western Ave.
Albany, NY 12203-4624
Ph: (518)452-3611
Fax: (518)218-0867
Free: 800-989-6278
E-mail: info@napt.org
URL: www.napt.org
Social Media: www.facebook.com/NAPTHQ
www.linkedin.com/company/national-association-for-pupil
  -transportation-napt
twitter.com/NAPTHQ
www.youtube.com/channel/UC
  _oRBuGHuCN6k4V4cJQzWNg

7684 ■ NAPT Continuing Education Award
(Undergraduate/Award)

Purpose: To provide financial support to NAPT members in the field of public transportation. **Focus:** Transportation. **Qualif.:** Applicant must be a NAPT member for three or more consecutive years; and who has not been recipient of the award for the four preceding years. **Criteria:** Recipient will be selected based on merit.

Funds Avail.: Up to $500. **Duration:** Annual. **Number Awarded:** Up to 3. **To Apply:** Applicants must submit the online application form. **Deadline:** July 30. **Remarks:** Established in 1987.

7685 ■ National Association of School Psychologists (NASP)
4340 E West Hwy., Ste. 402
Bethesda, MD 20814
Ph: (301)657-0270
Fax: (301)657-0275
Free: 866-331-6277
URL: www.nasponline.org
Social Media: www.facebook.com/nasponline
www.instagram.com/nasponline
www.pinterest.com/nasponline
twitter.com/nasponline

7686 ■ NASP-ERT Minority Scholarship Program
(Graduate/Scholarship)

Purpose: To ease the financial burden of minority graduate students enrolled in a psychology program. **Focus:** Psychology. **Criteria:** Selection is based on the submitted application materials.

Funds Avail.: $5,000. **Duration:** Annual. **Number Awarded:** Varies. **To Apply:** Applicants must submit a completed application form along with the required materials. **Remarks:** Established in 1995. **Contact:** Katie Britton; Email: kbritton@naspweb.org.

7687 ■ National Association of School Safety and Law Enforcement Officials (NASSLEO)
Lotus, CA 95651
Ph: (760)472-3389

Awards are arranged alphabetically below their administering organizations

E-mail: nassleo@nassleo.org
URL: www.nassleo.org
Social Media: www.facebook.com/NASSLEO
twitter.com/NASSLEO1

7688 ■ NASSLEO Scholarships - Region I
(Undergraduate/Scholarship)

Purpose: To provide financial assistance to students who have chosen to further their education and are considering a career in school security and/or law enforcement. **Focus:** Law enforcement. **Qualif.:** Applicants must be currently enrolled in their graduating year of a high school and will be enrolled full-time in a degree or diploma program at a university or college that is accredited by the appropriate accrediting agency for the fall academic term; present a minimum cumulative average of 85%; have not received a full scholarship; and, have been outstanding in the area of citizenship and community service. **Criteria:** Selection will be based on the aforesaid qualifications and compliance with the application process.

Funds Avail.: $2,000. **Duration:** Annual. **To Apply:** Applicants must submit the complete nomination form, which can be downloaded at the NASSLEO website. Faculty members must list the individual's accomplishments in the area of citizenship and community service, what they have done to improve safety in the school, the contributions the students have made to their school, and any recognition received from their peers and/or faculty of the school for personal or academic achievement during the past school year. The narrative report must be limited to a single page. **Deadline:** April 15. **Contact:** E-mail: nassleo@nassleo.org.

7689 ■ National Association of Secondary School Principals (NASSP)
1904 Association Dr.
Reston, VA 20191-1537
Ph: (703)860-0200
Free: 800-253-7746
E-mail: nassp@nassp.org
URL: www.nassp.org

7690 ■ NASSP/Herff Jones Principal's Leadership Award *(Undergraduate/Scholarship)*

Purpose: To recognize and support the education of student leaders from the senior class. **Focus:** General studies/Field of study not specified. **Qualif.:** Applicants must be college-bound high school seniors. **Criteria:** Nominees are selected on the basis of their leadership skills, participation in service organizations and clubs, achievements in the arts and sciences, employment experience, and academic record.

Funds Avail.: $100,000. **Duration:** Annual.

7691 ■ National Association for the Self-Employed (NASE)
PO Box 241
Annapolis Junction, MD 20701-0241
Fax: (800)678-4605
Free: 800-232-6273
URL: www.nase.org
Social Media: www.facebook.com/NASEonFB
www.instagram.com/NASEonIG
www.linkedin.com/company/national-association-for-the
  -self-employed-nase-

twitter.com/NASEtweets
www.youtube.com/user/NASEview

7692 ■ NASE Future Entrepreneur *(Undergraduate/ Scholarship)*

Purpose: To promote entrepreneurial philosophy to promising young business owners. **Focus:** Business. **Qualif.:** Applicants must be dependents of NASE member. **Criteria:** Applicants who demonstrate the characteristics of a future micro-business owner will be given preference.

Funds Avail.: Amount varies. **Number Awarded:** 1. **To Apply:** Applicants must submit a completed application form and original copies of transcripts and test scores.

7693 ■ National Association for the Self-Employed Scholarships *(Undergraduate, High School/ Scholarship)*

Purpose: To assist members in sending their children to college. **Focus:** General studies/Field of study not specified. **Qualif.:** Applicants must be a legal dependent of a NASE member, aged 16-24; must be a high school student or college undergraduate. **Criteria:** Applicants will be selected based on leadership ability; academic performance; teacher recommendations; career and educational background; and school and community participation.

Funds Avail.: No specific amount. **Duration:** Annual. **Number Awarded:** 4. **To Apply:** Applicants must submit a completed application form and original copies of transcripts and test scores.

7694 ■ National Association of Social Workers (NASW)
750 1st St. NE, Ste. 800
Washington, DC 20002
Ph: (202)408-8600
Fax: (202)336-8313
Free: 800-742-4089
E-mail: membership@naswdc.org
URL: www.socialworkers.org
Social Media: www.facebook.com/socialworkers
twitter.com/nasw
www.youtube.com/user/socialworkers

7695 ■ Jane B. Aron Doctoral Fellowship *(Doctorate/ Fellowship)*

Purpose: To provide graduate students the financial assistance who are pursuing research in health care policy and practice. **Focus:** Health education. **Qualif.:** Applicant must be an NASW member and enrolled in an accredited social work/social welfare doctoral program.

Funds Avail.: $15,500($2,400 will be earmarked for conference attendance and participation and leadership development). **Duration:** Annual. **Number Awarded:** 1. **Remarks:** The fellowship was established in honor of Jane B. Aron. Established in 1987. **Contact:** E-mail: naswfoundation@ naswdc.org.

7696 ■ Eileen Blackey Doctoral Fellowship *(Doctorate/Fellowship)*

Purpose: To financially assist students who want to pursue their research in welfare policy and practice. **Focus:** Social work. **Qualif.:** Applicant must be an NASW member and enrolled in an accredited social work/social welfare doctoral

Awards are arranged alphabetically below their administering organizations

program. **Criteria:** Selection is based on need in the field; quality of project design; potential for completion.

Funds Avail.: $4,000 to $6,500. **Duration:** Annual. **Number Awarded:** 1. **To Apply:** Applicants must provide a biographical essay (two typed, doubled-spaced pages); must provide two letters of support from professional references; must submit an official copy of a transcript from their most recent academic work; must have a letter from the candidate's academic advisor. **Remarks:** The fellowship was established in honor of Dr. Eileen Blackey. Established in 1987. **Contact:** E-mail: naswfoundation@naswdc.org.

7697 ■ Consuelo W. Gosnell Memorial MSW Scholarship (Graduate/Fellowship)

Purpose: To provide financial assistance to graduate students who want to pursue their education in social work. **Focus:** Social work. **Qualif.:** Applicant must be a NASW member and have applied to or have been accepted into an accredited MSW program; have a grade point average (GPA) of 3.0 or above. **Criteria:** Selection of applicants will be based on the projected annual earnings to the fund and contributions.

Funds Avail.: Up to $4,000 each. **Duration:** Annual. **Number Awarded:** Up to 10. **To Apply:** Applicants must complete the application form available on the website; must provide a biographical essay (two typed, doubled-spaced pages); must provide an optional statement of merit and need for the award; must have two letters of support from professional references; must have an official copy of a transcript from their most recent academic work; must have a letter from the candidate's academic advisor. **Contact:** E-mail: naswfoundation@naswdc.org.

7698 ■ Verne LaMarr Lyons Memorial MSW Scholarship (Graduate, Master's/Fellowship)

Purpose: To provide financial assistance to graduate students who want to pursue their education in social work. **Focus:** Social work. **Qualif.:** Applicants must be a Master of Social Work student who has interest and/or demonstrated ability in health/mental health practice and a commitment to working in African American communities; must be an NASW member and have applied to or have been accepted into an accredited MSW Program; must have potential for completing a MSW Program and have a GPA of 3.0 or above; must be enrolled in a MSW program for more than one year. **Criteria:** Selection of applicants will be based on the projected annual earnings to the fund and contributions.

Funds Avail.: $5,500 each. **Duration:** Annual. **Number Awarded:** 4. **To Apply:** Applicants must complete the application form available on the website; must provide a biographical essay (two typed, doubled-spaced pages); must provide an optional statement of merit and need for the award; must have two letters of support from professional references; must have an official copy of a transcript from their most recent academic work; must have a letter from the candidate's academic advisor. **Remarks:** The fellowship was established in honor of Verne LaMarr Lyons. **Contact:** E-mail: naswfoundation@naswdc.org.

7699 ■ National Association of State Land Reclamationists (NASLR)

c/o Jeff Meitrott 186 Enterprise Dr.
Philipsburg, PA 16866
Ph: (814)342-8116
Fax: (814)342-8216
E-mail: jmeitrott@pa.gov
URL: naslr.org
Social Media: www.facebook.com/NationalASLR
twitter.com/NASLR72

7700 ■ NASLR Mined Land Reclamation Educational Grant (Undergraduate/Grant)

Purpose: To provide deserving individuals with a financial grant that will cover costs associated with education and research regarding mined land reclamation. **Focus:** Land management. **Criteria:** Applicants will be evaluated based on the following: college grades; quality and relevance of course work or research; proposed special project or research budget; information obtained from references and other related considerations.

Funds Avail.: $2,000. **Duration:** Annual. **To Apply:** Applicants must submit completed application form. **Deadline:** July 1. **Contact:** Jeff Meitrott; Email: jmeitrott@pa.gov.

7701 ■ National Association of Student Anthropologists (NASA)

2300 Clarendon Blvd., Ste. 1301
Arlington, VA 22201
URL: www.studentanthropologists.org
Social Media: www.facebook.com/groups/46461027296
twitter.com/NAStudentAnthro

7702 ■ Carrie Hunter-Tate Award (Undergraduate, Graduate/Award)

Purpose: To honor student anthropologists who demonstrate enthusiasm, passion, and service to anthropology. **Focus:** Anthropology. **Qualif.:** Applicants must be anthropology students and members of the National Association of Student Anthropologists. **Criteria:** Selection will be based on the academic and professional achievements of applicants.

Funds Avail.: $500. **Duration:** Annual. **To Apply:** Applicants must be nominated with an official nomination form submitted with their completed application; all nominated students will become potential applicants who need to send the following specific materials required for the application: name; Social Security Number (if US applicant); address; school and school year; research interests; geographical area of interest; transcripts of universities attended (unofficial copies are acceptable); one to three page essay explaining significance of anthropology; where the applicants see the direction of the field and how the applicants feel qualified for the award; curriculum vitae for graduate students. **Remarks:** The award was established to honor the memory of former officer of the National Association of Student Anthropologists, Carrie Hunter-Tate who dedicated herself to the profession of anthropology. **Contact:** Email: students.anthropology@gmail.com.

7703 ■ National Association for Surface Finishing (NASF)

1800 M St., Ste. 400 S
Washington, DC 20036
Ph: (202)457-8404
Fax: (202)530-0659
E-mail: info@nasf.org
URL: www.nasf.org
Social Media: www.facebook.com/SurfaceFinishers

Awards are arranged alphabetically below their administering organizations

www.linkedin.com/company/nasf-the-national-association
-for-surface-finishing

7704 ■ AESF Foundation Scholarships *(Undergraduate, Graduate/Scholarship)*

Purpose: To enable students to further their studies and future careers in the field of surface finishing. **Focus:** Chemistry; Engineering, Chemical; Engineering, Mechanical; Engineering, Metallurgical; Environmental technology; Materials research/science. **Criteria:** Selection shall be based on academic record; personal statement; working experience and extracurricular activities.

Funds Avail.: $1,500. **Duration:** Annual. **To Apply:** Applicants must submit a completed application form along with a statement on career objective and an intended plan of study and/or research in plating and surface finishing science and engineering (2 pages); resume detailing academic achievements (2 pages); three recommendation letters (one must be from an academic advisor); and an official copy of recent undergraduate or graduate transcript (to be sealed by the academic institution where the applicants attends). **Deadline:** February 28. **Contact:** The AESF Foundation Scholarship; 1800 M St, Ste 400 S Washington, D.C, 20036.

7705 ■ National Association of Teacher Educators for Family and Consumer Sciences (NATE-FACS)

PO Box 6050
Fargo, ND 58108-6050
Ph: (701)231-7968
E-mail: mari.borr@ndsu.edu
URL: www.natefacs.org

7706 ■ FACS Graduate Fellowships *(Graduate, Undergraduate/Fellowship)*

Purpose: To provide financial support to students for the study of family and consumer sciences. **Focus:** Home Economics. **Qualif.:** Applicants must be U.S. citizens; and a family and consumer sciences education graduate student. **Criteria:** Selection will be rated in consideration of the likelihood of completing the degree and the contribution to family and consumer science education; academic work; professional association involvement; professional experience and scholarly work; and references.

Funds Avail.: $2,000-$4,000. **To Apply:** Application form along with one official scanned copy of transcripts from all institutions you attended-both undergraduate and graduate; brief (no more than three single-spaced pages) autobiographical sketch; three letters of recommendation from three persons whom can attest to your: professional and academic qualifications, potential for graduate work and contributions to the profession. **Deadline:** October 1. **Contact:** Debra Price; E-mail: debraprice81@gmail.com.

7707 ■ National Association of Women in Construction (NAWIC)

327 S Adams St.
Fort Worth, TX 76104
Ph: (817)877-5551
Fax: (817)877-0324
Free: 800-552-3506
E-mail: nawic@nawic.org
URL: www.nawic.org

Social Media: www.facebook.com/nawicnational
www.instagram.com/nawicnational
www.linkedin.com/in/nawicnational
twitter.com/nawicnational

7708 ■ National Association of Women in Construction Construction Trades Scholarship *(Undergraduate/Scholarship)*

Purpose: To support women in a field of construction-related career. **Focus:** Construction. **Qualif.:** Applicants must be currently enrolled in a construction-related training program which is approved by the Bureau of Apprenticeship Training or their home state's Post Secondary Education Commission; must be obtaining training in a construction-related craft or trade. Only students attending school in the United States will be considered for awards.**Criteria:** Application will be reviewed and selected by the NAWIC Founders' Scholarship Foundation Awards Committee.

Funds Avail.: No specific amount. **Duration:** Annual. **To Apply:** Applicants must have the following: Complete and signed application form; extracurricular activities and Employment history. **Deadline:** February 28. **Contact:** Email: nfsf@nawic.org.

7709 ■ National Association of Women in Construction Founders Undergraduate Scholarship *(Undergraduate/Scholarship)*

Purpose: To support women in a field of construction-related career. **Focus:** Construction. **Qualif.:** Applicants must be currently enrolled in a construction-related degree program at a school in the United States; must have at least one term remaining in course of study leading to a degree or an associate degree in a construction-related field; desires a career in a construction related field; must be enrolled full-time; must have current cumulative GPA of 3.0 or higher to be considered for awards.**Criteria:** Applications will be reviewed and selected by the NAWIC Founders' Scholarship Foundation Awards Committee. Preference will be given to the applicant's interest in construction, grades, extracurricular activities, employment experience and financial need.

Funds Avail.: No specific amount. **Duration:** Annual. **To Apply:** Applicants must have the following: Complete and signed application form; must have the transcript of grades of three most of the most recent semesters; extracurricular activities and employment history. **Deadline:** February 28. **Contact:** Email: nfsf@nawic.org.

7710 ■ National Ataxia Foundation (NAF)

600 Hwy. 169 S, Ste. 1725
Minneapolis, MN 55426
Ph: (763)553-0020
Fax: (763)553-0167
E-mail: naf@ataxia.org
URL: www.ataxia.org
Social Media: www.facebook.com/ataxiafoundation
www.linkedin.com/company/nationalataxiafoundation
twitter.com/NAF_Ataxia
www.youtube.com/user/NatlAtaxiaFound

7711 ■ National Ataxia Foundation Postdoctoral Fellowship Award *(Postdoctorate/Fellowship, Award)*

Purpose: To serve as a bridge from post-doctoral positions to junior faculty positions. **Focus:** Medicine. **Qualif.:** Ap-

Awards are arranged alphabetically below their administering organizations

plicants must have at least completed one year of post-doctoral training but not more than two at the time of application; and must have commitment to research in the field of ataxia. **Criteria:** Applicants will be selected by a Committee appointed by NAF's Director; priority will be given to those who have high scores on the relevance of research to ataxia.

Funds Avail.: Up to $35,000. **Duration:** Annual. **To Apply:** Applicants must submit a completed applications and letters of support as single PDF file attachment with the last name of the researcher in the subject line of the email. **Deadline:** October 5.

7712 ■ National Ataxia Foundation Research Grants (Other/Grant)

Purpose: To support new and innovative studies that are relevant to the cause, pathogenesis or treatment of the hereditary or sporadic ataxias. **Focus:** Medicine. **Qualif.:** Applicants must be National Ataxia Foundation members; non U.S. citizens are eligible to apply for a research grant from NAF. **Criteria:** Selection of applicants will be evaluated by a Committee appointed by NAF's Research Director. Consideration will be based on the score of applicant's recommendation.

Funds Avail.: $15,000-$30,000. **Duration:** Annual. **To Apply:** For the pre-submission of application, applicants must always include the last name of the principle investigator as the first word in the subject line of any email. Submit email with applicants' intentions to apply for NAF funding, including a full title and a one-page abstract of a proposal. Complete application must be sent as a single PDF file attachment with the last name of the researcher in the subject line of the email. Electronic signatures will be accepted.

7713 ■ National Beta Club

151 Beta Club Way
Spartanburg, SC 29306
Fax: (864)542-9300
Free: 800-845-8281
URL: www.betaclub.org
Social Media: www.facebook.com/nationalbetaclub
www.instagram.com/nationalbetaclub
twitter.com/betaclub
www.youtube.com/betaclubspotlight

7714 ■ National Beta Club Scholarships (Undergraduate/Scholarship, Monetary)

Purpose: To provide financial assistance to Beta Club members in their senior year. **Focus:** General studies/Field of study not specified. **Criteria:** Candidate Evaluations Assess character and leadership, as well as service activities and academic prowess.

Funds Avail.: $1,000 - $15,000. **Duration:** Annual. **Number Awarded:** 5. **To Apply:** Applicant Complete the application online; submit your high school transcript; copies of these documents must be uploaded directly into your application. **Deadline:** January 21. **Remarks:** Established in 1991.

7715 ■ National Biosafety and Biocontainment Training Program (NBBTP)

3000 S Hulen St. Ste. 124-199 Ft.
Fort Worth, TX 76109
Ph: (301)451-3290

E-mail: info@nbbtp.org
URL: www.nbbtp.org
Social Media: www.facebook.com/National-Biosafety
-Biocontainment-Training-Program-195754560535345
twitter.com/nbbtp

7716 ■ National Biosafety and Biocontainment Training Program Fellowships (Graduate, Postgraduate/Fellowship)

Purpose: To provide extraordinary environment and rigorous program including academic training, experimental learning, mentorship, development assignments, and applied occupational safety and health research opportunities. **Focus:** Health sciences; Medicine; Microbiology; Public health.

Funds Avail.: No specific amount. **Duration:** Annual. **To Apply:** Applicants must submit a completed application form along with the essay; references; additional materials (should be paper-clipped together and labeled with last name on each piece turned in); and transcripts. **Contact:** NBBTP Admissions, CDIC, Inc 3000 S Hulen St., Ste. 124-199, Ft. Worth, TX, 76109; Phone: 301-451-3290; Email: info@nbbtp.org.

7717 ■ National Black Coalition of Federal Aviation Employees (NBCFAE)

PO Box 87216
Atlanta, GA 30337
E-mail: info@nbcfae.org
URL: nbcfae.org
Social Media: www.facebook.com/NBCFAEofficial
www.instagram.com/official_nbcfae
twitter.com/NbcfaeOfficial

7718 ■ NBCFAE Mamie W. Mallory National Scholarship Program (Undergraduate/Scholarship)

Purpose: To support students who want to pursue higher education for prospective college, university, vocational or technical school. **Focus:** Aviation. **Qualif.:** Applicants must be dependents of NBCFAE members; must be high school or returning to college students, and have a 2.5 GPA or higher. **Criteria:** Recipients will be selected based on academic merits.

Funds Avail.: No specific amount. **Duration:** Annual. **Number Awarded:** 24. **To Apply:** Applicants must submit completed application with signature, transcript, letter of recommendation, digital photograph and college acceptance letter.

7719 ■ National Black Deaf Advocates (NBDA)

2028 E. Ben White Blvd, Ste 240-1982
Austin, TX 78741
E-mail: info@nbda.org
URL: www.nbda.org
Social Media: www.facebook.com/NBDAdvocates
twitter.com/NBDAdvocates
www.youtube.com/NBDAdvocates

7720 ■ Andrew Foster Scholarship (Undergraduate/Scholarship)

Purpose: To strengthen the educational and economic advancement of deaf and hard of hearing African-Americans. **Focus:** General studies/Field of study not

Awards are arranged alphabetically below their administering organizations

specified. **Qualif.:** Applicants must be Black deaf students at Gallaudet University with at least 3.0 GPA. **Criteria:** Selection will be based on financial need and academic performance.

Funds Avail.: No specific amount. **Duration:** Annual. **To Apply:** Applicants must complete the scholarship application supplement. **Deadline:** May 31.

7721 ■ Glenn B. Anderson Scholarship *(Graduate, Undergraduate/Scholarship)*

Purpose: To strengthen the educational and economic advancement of Black Deaf and hard of hearing people. **Focus:** General studies/Field of study not specified. **Qualif.:** Applicant must be a Black deaf or hard of hearing undergraduate or graduate student who is also a member of NBDA. **Funds Avail.:** No specific amount. **Number Awarded:** 3. **To Apply:** Applicants must complete and submit the application form together with two letters of reference, photocopy of official transcript, and photocopy of a valid student ID. **Deadline:** April 10.

7722 ■ Youth Empowerment Summit Scholarships *(Undergraduate/Scholarship)*

Purpose: To strengthen the educational and economic advancement of deaf and hard of hearing African-Americans. **Focus:** General studies/Field of study not specified. **Qualif.:** Applicants must be former or current Youth Empowerment Summit participants; must be deaf or hard of hearing; must be high school seniors or college students; must be or have been in a leadership position; and must have at least B grade average. **Criteria:** Selection will be based on the committee's criteria.

Funds Avail.: No specific amount. **Duration:** Biennial. **To Apply:** Applicants must fill out an application form and submit together with two letters of recommendation, one from a teacher. **Contact:** Y.E.S.; Email: youth@nbda.org.

7723 ■ National Black MBA Association (NBM-BAA)
PO Box 8513
Chicago, IL 60680
Ph: (312)458-9161
E-mail: chicago.chapter@nbmbaa.org
URL: nbmbaa.org
Social Media: www.facebook.com/groups/51537118260
www.instagram.com/theblackmba
www.linkedin.com/company/theblackmba
twitter.com/chicagoblackmba

7724 ■ CEIBS scholarship *(Graduate/Scholarship)*

Purpose: To financially assist qualified business students who have the potential to make great contributions in the field of business. **Focus:** Business. **Qualif.:** Applicants must meet CEIBS admissions requirements in order to be considered for the scholarship.

Funds Avail.: $15,000. **Duration:** Annual. **To Apply:** Applications can be submitted online. Once submitted, you will receive a follow up email with a link to the CEIBS application. **Deadline:** March 31.

7725 ■ National Black Nurses Association (NBNA)
8630 Fenton Street, Ste. 910
Silver Spring, MD 20910

Ph: (301)589-3200
Fax: (301)589-3223
E-mail: info@nbna.org
URL: www.nbna.org
Social Media: www.facebook.com/NBNAORG
www.instagram.com/nbna_insta/
twitter.com/nbnainc

7726 ■ National Black Nurses Association Scholarships *(Undergraduate/Scholarship)*

Purpose: To provide funding for continuing education. **Focus:** Nursing. **Qualif.:** Applicants must be members of NBNA and a local chapter; currently enrolled in a nursing program (B.S.N., A.D., Diploma or L.P.N./L.V.N.); in good scholastic standing at the time of application and must have at least one full year of school remaining. **Criteria:** Selection is made by the NBNA Scholarship Committee.

Funds Avail.: $1,000-$6,000. **Duration:** Annual. **To Apply:** Applicants must submit an official transcript from an accredited school of nursing; a two-page written essay; two letters of recommendation (one from applicant's school of nursing and one from the local chapter, or a nurse in the area if a local chapter does not exist); and additional items that will support the applicants' eligibility and desirability. **Deadline:** April 15.

7727 ■ National Black Police Association (NBPA)
1725 I Street, NW, Ste 300
Washington, DC 20006
Free: 855-879-6272
E-mail: nationaloffice@blackpolice.org
URL: www.blackpolice.org

7728 ■ Alphonso Deal Scholarship Award *(Undergraduate/Scholarship)*

Purpose: To provide financial support for students to have higher educational training in the academics of law enforcement or other related areas, for the betterment of the Criminal Justice system. **Focus:** Law enforcement.

Funds Avail.: No specific amount. **Deadline:** August 1.

7729 ■ National Board of Boiler and Pressure Vessel Inspectors (NBBI)
1055 Crupper Ave.
Columbus, OH 43229-1183
Ph: (614)888-8320
Fax: (614)888-0750
E-mail: information@nationalboard.org
URL: www.nationalboard.org
Social Media: www.facebook.com/NBBI.org
www.linkedin.com/company/nbbidotorg
twitter.com/NBBIdotorg

7730 ■ National Board Technical Scholarship *(College, Four Year College, University/Scholarship)*

Purpose: To provide financial assistance to children, step-children, grandchildren or great-grandchildren of past and present staff and members of the National Board and the past or present Commissioned Inspectors employed by a member jurisdiction. **Focus:** Engineering. **Criteria:** Selection will be based on a competitive basis.

Funds Avail.: $12,000. **Duration:** Annual. **Number Awarded:** Upto 2. **To Apply:** Applicants must include a

Awards are arranged alphabetically below their administering organizations

personal statement of 500-750 words expressing how college experiences-academics, extracurricular activities, outside activities and work/internship experiences are shaping their educational and career goals; why they should be considered for this scholarship award and other information that may be of importance to the selection committee in its review of the application; must also submit two letters of recommendation from appropriate college instructors or other college representatives on official school letterhead; a letter of recommendation from a current National Board member, that is the Chief Boiler inspector in a jurisdiction; a listing of current National Board members, including contact information, is shown on National Board's website; names and contact information of two persons (not family members) that the applicants have known for at least one year, to be used as personal references; an official college transcript including the most recent course work. **Deadline:** February 28. **Contact:** Mr. David A. Douin, National Board, 1055 Crupper Ave., Columbus, OH, 43229; Phone: 614-888-8320; Fax: 614-888-0750; Email: ddouin@nationalboard.org.

7731 ■ National Business Aviation Association (NBAA)

1200 G St. NW, Ste. 1100
Washington, DC 20005
Ph: (202)783-9000
Fax: (202)331-8364
Free: 800-394-6222
E-mail: info@nbaa.org
URL: www.nbaa.org
Social Media: www.facebook.com/NBAAfans
www.instagram.com/nbaaphotos
www.linkedin.com/company/national-business-aviation
 -association
twitter.com/nbaa
www.youtube.com/user/NBAAvideo

7732 ■ Al Conklin and Bill de Decker Business Aviation Management Scholarship (Undergraduate/ Scholarship)

Purpose: To promote professional development and business aviation careers. **Focus:** Aviation. **Qualif.:** Applicants must be full-time undergraduate sophomores, juniors, or senior students; officially enrolled or accepted for enrollment in an aviation management program; U.S. citizens; and must have grade point average of 3.0 or above on a 4.0 scale. **Criteria:** Recipients are selected based on academic performance and financial need.

Funds Avail.: $5,000. **Duration:** Annual. **Number Awarded:** 1. **To Apply:** Applicants must submit essay; resume; unofficial transcript and one signed letter of recommendation. **Deadline:** July 26. **Remarks:** Established in 2007. **Contact:** NBAA's Tyler Austin; Phone: 202-783-9267; Email: scholarships@nbaa.org.

7733 ■ Donald A. Baldwin Sr. Business Aviation Management Scholarship (Professional development/ Scholarship)

Purpose: To promote professional development and business aviation careers and to benefit individuals seeking to become NBAA Certified Aviation Managers (CAMs). **Focus:** Aviation. **Qualif.:** Applicants must be eligible to take the CAM Exam within two years of the date of the scholarship award; must meet the minimum qualifications to take the CAM Exam; must be U.S. citizens; and must score greater than 100 points on CAM application; must be business aviation professionals. **Criteria:** Recipients are selected based on academic performance and financial need.

Funds Avail.: $1,225. **Duration:** Annual. **Number Awarded:** 1. **To Apply:** Applicant must submit application; current resume; essay and two signed letters of recommendation; If pursuing CAM certification, NBAA must have applicant's completed CAM application; Applicants may also submit their CAM application along with the scholarship application. **Deadline:** November 30. **Remarks:** The Scholarship is given in Honor of Donald A. Baldwin Sr. Established in 2007. **Contact:** NBAA's Molly Hitch; Phone: 202-783-9353; Email: scholarships@nbaa.org.

7734 ■ UAA Janice K. Barden Aviation Scholarship (Undergraduate/Scholarship)

Purpose: To promote professional development and business aviation careers. **Focus:** Aviation. **Qualif.:** Applicants must be undergraduate sophomores, juniors, or seniors enrolled in an aviation-related two-year, four-year, or postgraduate degree program; must have GPA of at least 3.0; must be U.S. citizens; must be officially enrolled at NBAA and University Aviation Association member institutions. **Criteria:** Recipients are selected based on academic performance and financial need.

Funds Avail.: $1,000 each. **Duration:** Annual. **Number Awarded:** 5. **To Apply:** Applicants must submit completed application form; a typed essay of 500-words or less; two professional letters of recommendation; and a current resume. **Deadline:** January 10. **Remarks:** The Scholarship is given in Honor of Janice K. Barden. **Contact:** NBAA's Tyler Austin; Phone: 202-783-9267; Email: scholarships@nbaa.org.

7735 ■ Flight Attendants/Flight Technician Scholarship (Other/Scholarship)

Purpose: To promote education and training as a means for business aviation flight attendants and flight technicians to enhance their professional careers. **Focus:** Aviation. **Qualif.:** Applicants must be flight attendants or flight technicians. **Criteria:** Recipients are selected based on academic performance and financial need.

Funds Avail.: No specific amount. **Duration:** Annual. **Number Awarded:** 1. **To Apply:** Applicants be at least 18 years old, completed application. a current one-page resume, essay, two signed letters of recommendation specifically relating to scholarship qualifications (dated within the last calendar year). **Deadline:** February 29. **Contact:** NBAA's Tyler Austin; Phone: 202-783-9267; Email: scholarships@nbaa.org.

7736 ■ Lawrence Ginocchio Aviation Scholarships (Undergraduate/Scholarship)

Purpose: To support students who have demonstrated honesty, integrity, and selflessness in their dealings with others. **Focus:** Aviation. **Criteria:** Recipients are selected based on academic performance and financial need.

Funds Avail.: $4,500. **Duration:** Annual. **Number Awarded:** 5. **To Apply:** Application must be completed essay, resume, official transcript and two signed letters of recommendation. **Deadline:** July 26. **Remarks:** The Scholarship is given in Honor of Lawrence Ginocchio. Established in 2001. **Contact:** NBAA's Tyler Austin; Phone: 202-783-9267; Email: scholarships@nbaa.org.

Awards are arranged alphabetically below their administering organizations

7737 ■ International Operators Scholarship *(Professional development/Scholarship)*

Purpose: To promote the education and training of individuals to increase the safety and professionalism of their positions. **Focus:** Aviation. **Qualif.:** Applicants must be aviation professionals engaged in international operations. **Criteria:** Recipients are selected based on academic performance and financial need.

Funds Avail.: Up to $9,000. **Duration:** Annual. **Number Awarded:** 1. **To Apply:** Applicant must submit essay, resume and one signed letters of recommendation. **Deadline:** December 20. **Contact:** NBAA's Molly Hitch; Phone: 202-783-9353; Email: scholarships@nbaa.org.

7738 ■ Leadership Conference Scholarship *(Other/Scholarship)*

Purpose: To promote professional development and business aviation careers and to benefit individuals seeking to become NBAA Certified Aviation Managers (CAMs). **Focus:** Aviation. **Qualif.:** Applicants must be currently working in the business aviation industry or attending a university-level aviation program; and must be U.S. citizens. **Criteria:** Recipients are selected based on academic performance, financial need, career planning and progress of the individual toward a career in business aviation.

Funds Avail.: Up to $850. **Duration:** Annual. **To Apply:** Applicant must submit essay, resume, official transcript or acceptance letter and one signed letters of recommendation. **Deadline:** November 30. **Contact:** NBAA's Tyler Austin; Phone: 202-783-9267; Email: scholarships@nbaa.org.

7739 ■ Maintenance Technical Reward and Career Scholarship *(Undergraduate/Scholarship)*

Purpose: To promote technical education and professional development as a means for business aviation maintenance technicians to enhance their careers. **Focus:** Aviation. **Qualif.:** Applicant must be Current or aspiring business aviation maintenance technicians; Military aviation personnel transitioning to business aviation can also apply. **Criteria:** Recipients are selected based on academic performance and financial need; to U.S. citizens or nonresident aliens on a student visa without regards to sex, race, religion or national origin.

Funds Avail.: No specific amount. **Duration:** Annual. **To Apply:** Applicant must submit completed essay; resume and one signed letter of recommendation; submit a transcript; also submit a copy of license. **Deadline:** February 28. **Contact:** Molly Hitch 202-783-9353, E-mail:scholarships@nbaa.org.

7740 ■ Schedulers and Dispatchers Monetary Scholarship *(Other/Scholarship)*

Purpose: To promote education and training of individuals to increase the safety and professionalism of their positions. **Focus:** Aviation. **Qualif.:** Applicants must have completed all professional/educational training. **Criteria:** Recipients are selected based on academic performance and financial need.

Funds Avail.: Up to $10,000. **Duration:** Annual. **To Apply:** Applicants must submit completed application form; a typed essay of 500-words or less; two professional letters of recommendation; and a current resume. **Deadline:** October 18. **Contact:** Molly Hitch at 202-783-9353 or scholarships@nbaa.org.

7741 ■ U.S. Aircraft Insurance Group Professional Development Program (USAIG PDP) Scholarships *(Undergraduate/Scholarship)*

Purpose: To promote professional development and business aviation careers. **Focus:** Aviation. **Qualif.:** Applicants must be full-time undergraduate sophomores, juniors, or senior students in academic year enrolled in an aviation-related two-year, four-year, or postgraduate degree program that incorporates the NBAA PDP; must be U.S. citizens; and must have a grade point average of 3.0 or above on a 4.0 scale. **Criteria:** Recipients are selected based on academic performance and financial need.

Funds Avail.: No specific amount. **To Apply:** Applicants must submit a completed application form; an official transcript of record; a 250-word, typed, double-spaced essay describing the applicant's interest in and goals for a career in business aviation flight department; two letters of recommendation from a member of aviation department faculty at the institution where the applicant is currently enrolled; and current resume. **Contact:** Tyler Austin at 202-783-9267 or scholarships@nbaa.org.

7742 ■ William M. Fanning Maintenance Scholarship *(Undergraduate/Scholarship)*

Purpose: To promote professional development and business aviation careers. **Focus:** Aviation. **Qualif.:** Applicants must be students who are currently enrolled in an accredited airframe and powerplant program at an approved FAR Part 147 school or individuals who are not currently enrolled but have been accepted for enrollment in an A&P program; must be U.S. citizens; and must have a grade point average of 3.0 or above on a 4.0 scale; must be a Business aviation maintenance technician. **Criteria:** Recipients are selected based on academic performance and financial need.

Funds Avail.: $2,500. **Duration:** Annual. **Number Awarded:** 2. **To Apply:** Applicant must submit essay, resume, official transcript or acceptance letter and one signed letters of recommendation. **Deadline:** July 26. **Contact:** NBAA's Tyler Austin; Phone: 202-783-9267; Email: scholarships@nbaa.org.

7743 ■ National Cattlemen's Foundation (NCF)
9110 E Nichols Ave., Ste. 300
Centennial, CO 80112
URL: www.nationalcattlemensfoundation.org

7744 ■ CME Beef Industry Scholarship *(Undergraduate/Scholarship)*

Purpose: To identify and encourage talented and thoughtful students who will emerge as industry leaders. **Focus:** Agricultural sciences.

Funds Avail.: $1,500. **Duration:** Annual. **Number Awarded:** 10. **To Apply:** Applicants must submit letter of Intent explaining future career goals related to the beef industry; original Essay--750 words or less describing an issue confronting the beef industry and offering a solution; two Letters of Recommendation. **Remarks:** Established in 1989.

7745 ■ W.D. Farr Scholarship *(Graduate/Scholarship)*

Purpose: To support and promote education in the animal industry. **Focus:** Animal science and behavior. **Criteria:** Applicants will be evaluated on the components of the application requirements through effective communication

Awards are arranged alphabetically below their administering organizations

skills, clarity of expression, originality and interest/passion for the cattle industry.

Funds Avail.: $15,000. **Duration:** Annual. **Number Awarded:** 2. **Deadline:** September 11. **Remarks:** The foundation honoring the successful career of the late W.D. Farr of Greeley, Colorado.

7746 ■ National Center for American Indian Enterprise Development (NCAIED)

953 E Juanita Ave.
Mesa, AZ 85204
Ph: (480)545-1298
E-mail: info@ncaied.org
URL: www.ncaied.org
Social Media: www.facebook.com/NCAIED
twitter.com/ncaied
www.youtube.com/channel/UC4ZAGk-GMn
_1PFKwahezH6A/videos

7747 ■ NCAIED American Indian Business Scholarship Program *(Graduate, Master's, Undergraduate/ Scholarship)*

Purpose: To financially support American Indian college or graduate students majoring in business. **Focus:** Business. **Criteria:** Selection is based on grades, community involvement, personal challenges, business experiences and on the essay.

Funds Avail.: No specific amount. **To Apply:** Applicants must submit a completed application form together with a letter (stating the reasons for pursuing higher education; plans following completion of degree program; activities and commitment to community they wish to have considered); essays on community involvement, personal challenges, business experience (250-word each); transcript; letter of Admission/Enrollment and documentation of tribal enrollment; copy of class schedule for fall semester. **Deadline:** May 15. **Contact:** Application should be sent at The National Center for American Indian Enterprise Development; Attn: 2013 Scholarship Committee, 953 E Juanita Ave., Mesa, AZ 85204; Phone: 800-462-2433; Fax: 480-545-4208; E-mail: scholarships@ncaied.org.

7748 ■ National Center for Farmworker Health (NCFH)

1770 FM 967
Buda, TX 78610
Ph: (512)312-2700
Fax: (512)312-2600
Free: 800-531-5120
URL: www.ncfh.org
Social Media: www.facebook.com/NCFHTX/?fref=ts
www.linkedin.com/company/national-center-for-farmworker
-health-ncfh-/
twitter.com/NCFHTX

7749 ■ Migrant Health Scholarships *(Other/ Scholarship)*

Purpose: To support health center staff to pursue their educational goals in health care and to contribute to the development of the community health center workforce. **Focus:** Health education. **Qualif.:** Applicants must be interested in pursuing or continuing a career in the migrant health field, and must be employees at a community/

migrant health center. **Criteria:** Selection awards are given based on demonstrated commitment to working in migrant health, choice of career path, and personal experience, with special recognition of those who have a family history as farm workers.

Funds Avail.: $1,000 to $1,500. **Number Awarded:** 3. **Remarks:** Established in 1984.

7750 ■ National Center for Law and Economic Justice (NCLEJ)

275 7th Ave., Ste. 1506
New York, NY 10001-6860
Ph: (212)633-6967
Fax: (212)633-6371
E-mail: info@nclej.org
URL: www.nclej.org
Social Media: www.facebook.com/NCLEJ
www.linkedin.com/company/national-center-for-law-and
-economic-justice/?trk=top_nav_home
twitter.com/NCLEJustice

7751 ■ NCLEJ Law School Graduate Fellows and Volunteers *(Graduate, Advanced Professional/ Fellowship)*

Purpose: To protect the legal rights of low-income families and individuals to public benefits and to hold governmental agencies accountable for their administration of these vital programs. **Focus:** Law. **Qualif.:** Applicants must be recent law graduates who have post graduate public interest fellowships from their schools or who wish to volunteer. **Criteria:** Applications are considered on a rolling basis.

Funds Avail.: No specific amount. **To Apply:** Applicants must provide a cover letter describing their interests; resume; writing sample; and three references. **Contact:** National Center For Law and Economic Justice, Inc. 275 Seventh Avenue, Suite 1506 New York, NY 10001-6860 Phone: (212) 633-6967 Email: info@nclej.org.

7752 ■ National Center for Learning Disabilities (NCLD)

32 Laight St., 2nd Fl.
New York, NY 10013-2152
E-mail: help@ncld.org
URL: www.ncld.org
Social Media: twitter.com/ncldorg
youtube.com/user/NCLD1401

7753 ■ Anne Ford Scholarships *(High School/ Scholarship)*

Purpose: To assist students who are facing the challenges of living with a learning disability. **Focus:** General studies/ Field of study not specified. **Qualif.:** Applicants must have a high school senior and pursuing a four-year undergraduate degree. **Criteria:** Selection will be based on the committee's criteria.

Funds Avail.: $10,000. **Duration:** 4 years. **Number Awarded:** 1. **To Apply:** Applicants must submit a completed application form; a personal statement; a high school transcript; three letters of recommendation; a financial statement; copies of SAT/ACT scores; and a current documentation of a learning disability that includes evaluation reports. **Remarks:** Established in 2002.

7754 ■ National Chapter of Canada IODE

40 Orchard View Blvd., Ste. 219
Toronto, ON, Canada M4R 1B9

Awards are arranged alphabetically below their administering organizations

Ph: (416)487-4416
Free: 866-827-7428
E-mail: iodecanada@bellnet.ca
URL: www.iode.ca
Social Media: www.facebook.com/IODECanada
twitter.com/iodecanada

7755 ■ Joan Butler Award in Perinatal Intensive Care Nursing *(Advanced Professional/Award)*

Purpose: To promote the study of Perinatal Intensive Care Nursing. **Focus:** Nursing. **Qualif.:** Applicants must be Canadian graduate nurses enrolled in the certificate program in Perinatal Intensive Care Nursing at George Brown College, Toronto. **Criteria:** Selection will be based on the committee's criteria.

Funds Avail.: No specific amount. **Duration:** Annual. **To Apply:** Interested applicants may contact the IODE Canada for the application process and other information. **Remarks:** Established in 1988.

7756 ■ Shirley Cheshire Memorial Scholarship Awards *(Undergraduate/Scholarship)*

Purpose: To nurture the Inuit culture and language as well as to prepare students for the future. **Focus:** Culture. **Qualif.:** Recipients must be in at least second year of the degree-granting program and are bilingual candidates. **Criteria:** Selection will be based on the committee's criteria.

Funds Avail.: $2,500. **To Apply:** Interested applicants may contact the IODE Canada for the application process and other information.

7757 ■ Wilhelmina Gordon Foundation Scholarships *(Undergraduate/Scholarship)*

Purpose: To support students who qualifies for a first-class Bachelor of Arts in English. **Focus:** English language and literature. **Qualif.:** Applicants must be undergraduate Canadian students who ranks first in the graduating group in English. **Criteria:** Selection will be based on the committee's criteria.

Funds Avail.: No specific amount. **Duration:** Annual. **To Apply:** Interested applicants may contact the IODE Canada for the application process and other information.

7758 ■ IODE 100th Anniversary Grant *(Other/Grant)*

Purpose: To support programs that prevent, treat and alleviate abuse and neglect in children and youth. **Focus:** Child care; Youth. **Qualif.:** Applications are available for individuals or groups working as professionals, to research, develop or implement ways to alleviate child abuse and neglect. **Criteria:** Candidates will be selected by seven member committee, 4 IODE member and three professional advisors.

Funds Avail.: $25,000. **Duration:** Biennial; in odd-numbered years. **Deadline:** October 31. **Remarks:** Established in 2000. **Contact:** IODEinfo@bellnet.ca.

7759 ■ IODE Labrador Bursary *(Undergraduate/Scholarship)*

Purpose: To grant bursaries to eager, bright coastal high school students accepted at community college, university, technical or vocational schools. **Focus:** General studies/Field of study not specified. **Qualif.:** Applicants must be graduating Labrador students from coastal high schools. **Criteria:** Selection will be based on the scholarship committee's criteria.

Funds Avail.: No specific amount. **Duration:** Annual. **To Apply:** Applications can be submitted online. **Deadline:** February 15. **Remarks:** Established in 1982.

7760 ■ War Memorial Doctoral Scholarships *(Postgraduate/Scholarship)*

Purpose: To provide bursaries for university studies in Canada to children of men killed or permanently disabled in the Great War. **Focus:** General studies/Field of study not specified. **Qualif.:** Applicants must be Canadian citizens and at least in the second year of their doctoral program; must be graduates of Canadian university and must have done or be doing post-graduate work. **Criteria:** Selection will be evaluated by the National Selection Committee; and will be based on their academic attainments; commitment; personal character; and career goals.

Funds Avail.: $15,000. **Number Awarded:** 3. **To Apply:** Applicants must submit certified copy of academic transcripts; three letters of reference; copy of birth or baptismal certificate; and proof of Canadian citizenship if not born in Canada; must also provide an original and seven photocopies of the following; completed signed application form; (maximum of 250 words) statement of research topic, reasons of choosing the school including graduate work completed, plans and career goals; list of secondary awards received; bibliographic list of publications or research; involvement in activities; and list of scholarships that have been applied for. **Deadline:** October 1; November 1. **Remarks:** Established in 1918. **Contact:** IODE War Memorial Officer at iodewarmemorial@gmail.com.

7761 ■ National Chief Petty Officers' Association (NCPOA)
c/o Richard A. Oubre, Treasurer
5730 Misty Glen
San Antonio, TX 78247-1373
URL: www.ncpoa.club

7762 ■ Bart Longo Memorial Scholarship Program *(Undergraduate, Graduate/Scholarship)*

Purpose: To provide financial assistance to a high school graduate and to an upper classman or graduate student. **Focus:** General studies/Field of study not specified. **Qualif.:** Applicants must be family members of NCPOA members in good standing (living or deceased); or current members of the NCPOA.

Funds Avail.: $1,000. **Duration:** Annual. **Number Awarded:** 2. **Deadline:** May 15.

7763 ■ National Child Support Enforcement Association (NCSEA)
7918 Jones Branch Dr., Ste. 300
McLean, VA 22102
Ph: (703)506-2880
Fax: (703)506-3266
E-mail: customerservice@ncsea.org
URL: www.ncsea.org
Social Media: www.facebook.com/ncsea1
www.linkedin.com/company/national-child-support
-enforcement-association
twitter.com/NCSEA1

7764 ■ Judge Ross Leadership Scholarship *(Professional development/Scholarship)*

Purpose: To assist those who are able to demonstrate outstanding potential in improving their team's performance

Awards are arranged alphabetically below their administering organizations

in child support. **Focus:** Leadership, Institutional and community. **Qualif.:** Applicant must be an individual in the child support community from the state of Pennsylvania.

Funds Avail.: No specific amount. **To Apply:** Applicants must provide a brief statement (150 words) on how they will utilize information and networking gained in the course of attending the Leadership Symposium and how they would then share that information upon return to the agency; in addition to the statement, the applicants' respective managers need to submit a letter of recommendation as well as a statement that if chosen, the applicants will be able to travel to the Leadership Symposium. **Deadline:** June 15. **Contact:** Ann Marie Ruskin, NCSEA Executive Director; Email: AnnMarieRuskin@ncsea.org.

7765 ■ NCSEA New Leader Scholarship (Professional development/Scholarship)

Purpose: To assist those who are able to demonstrate outstanding potential in improving their team's performance in child support. **Focus:** Leadership, Institutional and community. **Qualif.:** Applicants must have been managers for two years or less and demonstrating outstanding potential to improve their team's performance.

Funds Avail.: Upto $500. **To Apply:** Applicants must provide a brief statement (150 words) on how they will utilize information and networking gained in the course of attending the Leadership Symposium and how they would then share that information upon return to the agency; in addition to the statement, the applicants' respective managers need to submit a letter of recommendation as well as a statement that if chosen, the applicants will be able to travel to the Leadership Symposium. **Contact:** Ann Marie Ruskin, NCSEA Executive Director; Email: AnnMarieRuskin@ncsea.org.

7766 ■ National Children's Cancer Society (NCCS)
500 N Broadway, Ste. 1850
Saint Louis, MO 63102
Ph: (314)241-1600
Fax: (314)241-1996
E-mail: kschuermann@thenccs.org
URL: www.thenccs.org
Social Media: www.facebook.com/thenccs
twitter.com/The_NCCS

7767 ■ Beyond the Cure Ambassador Scholarship Program (Community College, College, Undergraduate, Graduate, Vocational/Occupational/Scholarship)

Purpose: To support survivors who have demonstrated the ability to overcome the difficult challenges of cancer with determination and motivation. **Focus:** General studies/Field of study not specified. **Qualif.:** Applicant must be a childhood cancer survivor under the age of 25 and diagnosed before the age of 18 with cancer or a high grade or anaplastic brain tumor; must be a U.S. citizen living with the country and attending school in the United States; must be accepted into a post-secondary college/university for the upcoming school year; must have a minimum 2.5 GPA. **Criteria:** Selection is made by the NCCS staff and board members.

Funds Avail.: $2,500. **Duration:** Annual; Renewable up to four years upon reapplication. **Number Awarded:** 58. **To Apply:** Application is available online at www.thenccs.org/scholarship. Applicant must submit two recommendation

letters, a one to two page essay, high school or college transcripts, acceptance letter, written documentation from treating physician confirming cancer diagnosis, and brief summary of community service. **Deadline:** March 31. **Contact:** Stephanie Diekemper, Beyond the Cure Assistant; Email: sdiekemper@thenccs.org.

7768 ■ National Collegiate Athletic Association (NCAA)
700 W Washington St.
Indianapolis, IN 46206-6222
Ph: (317)917-6222
Fax: (317)917-6888
URL: www.ncaa.org
Social Media: www.facebook.com/ncaa1906
www.instagram.com/ncaa
twitter.com/NCAA
www.youtube.com/user/ncaa

7769 ■ Walter Byers Postgraduate Scholarships (Graduate, Postgraduate/Scholarship)

Purpose: To promote and encourage postgraduate education for student-athletes. **Focus:** Sports studies. **Qualif.:** Applicants must be student-athletes must have overall undergraduate cumulative GPA of 3.50 or better (based on a maximum 4.0), or the equivalent; have competed in intercollegiate athletics as a member of a varsity team at an NCAA member institution; be graduating seniors or enrolled in graduate studies at an NCAA member institution; have intentions of applying for admission into a graduate degree program at a properly accredited, nonprofit educational institution or into a post baccalaureate professional degree program at a professionally accredited law school, medical school, or the equivalent, without restriction as to the national site of the institution; committed to work on a full-time basis toward a graduate degree or toward a post baccalaureate professional degree; have evidenced superior character and leadership; have demonstrated that participation in athletics has been a positive influence in personal and intellectual development; and enrolled in a graduate degree program within five years of being named a Byer's Scholar. **Criteria:** Selection is based on financial need.

Funds Avail.: $24,000. **Duration:** One academic year. **Number Awarded:** One male and one female. **To Apply:** Applicants must be nominated by the Institution's Faculty Athletics Representative (FAR) or a FAR designee (an individual in academics); must complete the application form; must submit personal essay outlining the nominees long and short-term goals; separate factual lists of principal activities while in college; honors received; and principal involvement in community activities; four recommendation letters; and official transcript of records. **Deadline:** January 17. **Remarks:** Established in 1988. **Contact:** Contact Lori Thomas at the NCAA national office at 317/917-6222 or by e-mail at lthomas@ncaa.org.

7770 ■ Ethnic Minority and Women's Enhancement Postgraduate Scholarships (Graduate, Postgraduate/Scholarship)

Purpose: To increase the pool of opportunities for qualified minority and female candidates in intercollegiate athletics. **Focus:** Sports studies. **Qualif.:** Applicants must be seeking admission or have been accepted into a sports administration or sports-related program that will assist in

Awards are arranged alphabetically below their administering organizations

obtaining a career in intercollegiate athletics (athletics administrator, coach, athletic trainer or other careers that provide a direct service to intercollegiate athletics); must have not yet begun any initial postgraduate studies; must be U.S. citizens; and have performed with distinction as student body members at their respective undergraduate institution. **Criteria:** Selection is made by a subcommittee from the NCAA Committee on Women's Athletics which will select 13 award recipients, and a subcommittee from the NCAA Minorities Opportunities and Interests Committee will select 13 award recipients.

Funds Avail.: $7,500. **Number Awarded:** 26. **To Apply:** Applicants must complete the application form along with three letters of recommendation. **Deadline:** February 18. **Contact:** Lori Thomas; E-mail: lthomas@ncaa.org; Phone: 317-917-6683.

7771 ■ National Collegiate Athletic Association Postgraduate Scholarships *(Postgraduate/Scholarship)*

Purpose: To promote and encourage postgraduate education for student-athletes. **Focus:** General studies/Field of study not specified. **Qualif.:** Applicants must be a student-athlete at an active NCAA member institution and in the final season of NCAA athletics eligibility or will not be using any remaining athletics eligibility; have an overall undergraduate minimum cumulative GPA of 3.200 (based on a 4.000 scale) or its equivalent; have performed with distinction as a member of the varsity team in the sport in which the student-athlete is being nominated; intend to continue academic work beyond the baccalaureate degree and enroll in a graduate degree program on a part- or full-time basis at an accredited graduate or degree-granting professional school; and an outstanding citizen and excellent role model for the institution and intercollegiate athletics as a whole; must be in final year of intercollegiate athletics competition. **Criteria:** Selections are reviewed by seven regional selection committees.

Funds Avail.: $7,500. **Duration:** Annual. **Number Awarded:** 21 men; 21 women. **To Apply:** Applicants must be nominated by the institution's Faculty Athletics Representative (FAR) or a FAR designee (an individual in academics). **Deadline:** January 15; April 1; June 5. **Remarks:** Established in 1964.

7772 ■ National Collegiate Cancer Foundation (NCCF)
8334 North Brook Lane
Bethesda, MD 20814
Ph: (240)515-6262
E-mail: info@collegiatecancer.org
URL: collegiatecancer.org

7773 ■ NCCF Survivor Scholarship *(Undergraduate/Scholarship)*

Purpose: To provide financial support for college students who have a personal diagnosis with cancer and are seeking to continue their higher education. **Focus:** General studies/Field of study not specified. **Criteria:** Awards will be based on four criteria: financial need, quality of essay and recommendations, displaying a "Will Win" attitude, overall story of cancer survivorship, and displaying a "Will Win" attitude with respect to the cancer experience.

Funds Avail.: $1,000. **Duration:** Annual. **Number Awarded:** 1. **To Apply:** Application must be submitted

along with copy of college transcript or course registration if you are an incoming Freshman; resume or summary of any awards, honors or special recognition received; essays describing impact of cancer diagnosis and treatments in applicant life and pursuit of a higher education, describing experience with cancer on winning attitude note, providing advice to young adult who has recently been diagnosed, short explanation of current financial situation. **Deadline:** May 15. **Contact:** Send application in single PDF to info@collegiatecancer.org.

7774 ■ National Community Pharmacists Association (NCPA)
100 Daingerfield Rd.
Alexandria, VA 22314
Ph: (703)683-8200
Fax: (703)683-3619
Free: 800-544-7447
URL: www.ncpanet.org
Social Media: www.facebook.com/commpharmacy
www.instagram.com/commpharmacy
www.linkedin.com/company/ncpa
twitter.com/NCPA
twitter.com/commpharmacy
www.youtube.com/user/NCPAvids

7775 ■ J.C. and Rheba Cobb Memorial Scholarships *(Undergraduate/Scholarship)*

Purpose: To promote the continuing growth and prosperity of independent community pharmacy in the United States. **Focus:** Pharmacy. **Qualif.:** Applicants must be full-time pharmacy students in an accredited United States college of pharmacy and must be student member of NCPA. **Criteria:** Recipients are selected based on leadership qualities, academic achievement and demonstrated interest in government affairs.

Funds Avail.: $2,000 and $300 travel stipend. **Duration:** Annual. **Number Awarded:** 1. **To Apply:** Applicants must submit a copy of the most recent official transcript of record; must submit a letter from school official familiar with the students activities; a letter from a pharmacy owner or manager, preferably an NCPA member; a letter from the applicants to the NCPA Foundation Scholarships Award Committee outlining his or her school and civic accomplishments and objectives for the future; a resume or curriculum vitae describing the student's work and professional experience. **Contact:** NCPA Foundation Scholarship Committee, at the above address.

7776 ■ NCPA Foundation Presidential Scholarships *(Undergraduate/Scholarship)*

Purpose: To promote the continuing growth and prosperity of independent community pharmacy in the United States. **Focus:** Pharmacy. **Qualif.:** All pharmacy students who are NCPA student members are eligible. **Criteria:** Recipients are selected based on leadership qualities and academic achievement.

Funds Avail.: $2,000 and $300 travel stipend. **To Apply:** Applicants must submit a copy of the most recent official transcript of record; must submit a letter from school official familiar with the students activities; a letter from a pharmacy owner or manager, preferably an NCPA member; a letter from the applicants to the NCPA Foundation Scholarships Award Committee outlining his or her school and civic accomplishments and objectives for the future; a resume or

Awards are arranged alphabetically below their administering organizations

curriculum vitae describing the student's work and professional experience. **Contact:** NCPA Foundation Scholarship Committee; 100 Daingerfield Rd. Alexandria, VA, 22314. Email: ncpaf@ncpa.org.

7777 ■ NCPA Summer Internship Program
(Undergraduate/Internship)

Purpose: To provide undergraduate pharmacy students with an opportunity to become more aware of the vast opportunities that exist in independent pharmacy practice. To provide an experience that demonstrates the importance of a national pharmacy association to the profession. **Focus:** Pharmacy. **Criteria:** Recipients are selected based on academic standing.

Funds Avail.: No specific amount. **Deadline:** December 31. **Contact:** National Community Pharmacists Association; Attn: Student Affairs, 100 Daingerfield Rd. Alexandria, VA, 22314, Email: studentaffairs@ncpanet.org.

7778 ■ Neil Pruitt, Sr. Memorial Scholarships
(Undergraduate/Scholarship)

Purpose: To promote the continuing growth and prosperity of independent community pharmacy in the United States. **Focus:** Pharmacy. **Qualif.:** Applicants must be full-time pharmacy students at an accredited U.S. college of pharmacy and member of NCPA. **Criteria:** Recipients are selected based on leadership qualities, academic achievement and demonstrated interest in entrepreneurism.

Funds Avail.: $2,000 plus $300 travel stipend. **Number Awarded:** 1. **To Apply:** Applicants must submit a copy of the most recent official transcript of record; must submit a letter from school official familiar with the students activities; a letter from a pharmacy owner or manager, preferably an NCPA member; a letter from the applicants to the NCPA Foundation Scholarships Award Committee outlining his or her school and civic accomplishments and objectives for the future; a resume or curriculum vitae describing the student's work and professional experience. **Contact:** NCPA Foundation Scholarship Committee, at the above address.

7779 ■ Willard B. Simmons Sr. Memorial Scholarships *(Undergraduate/Scholarship)*

Purpose: To promote the continuing growth and prosperity of independent community pharmacy in the United States. **Focus:** Pharmacy. **Qualif.:** Applicants must be full-time pharmacy students at an accredited United States college of pharmacy and must be student member of NCPA. **Criteria:** Recipients are selected based on leadership qualities, academic achievement and demonstrated interest in independent pharmacy management.

Funds Avail.: $2,000 plust $300 travel stipend. **Number Awarded:** 1. **To Apply:** Applicants must submit a copy of the most recent official transcript of record; must submit a letter from school official familiar with the students activities; a letter from a pharmacy owner or manager, preferably an NCPA member; a letter from the applicants to the NCPA Foundation Scholarships Award Committee outlining his or her school and civic accomplishments and objectives for the future; a resume or curriculum vitae describing the student's work and professional experience. **Deadline:** March 15. **Contact:** NCPA Foundation Scholarship Committee, at the above address.

7780 ■ National Conference of Bar Examiners (NCBE)
302 S Bedford St.
Madison, WI 53703-3622

Ph: (608)280-8550
Fax: (608)280-8552
E-mail: contact@ncbex.org
URL: www.ncbex.org
Social Media: www.facebook.com/ncbexaminers
www.instagram.com/ncbexaminers/
www.linkedin.com/company/national-conference-of-bar-examiners/
www.linkedin.com/company/ncbex
twitter.com/NCBEX

7781 ■ Covington Award *(Doctorate, Graduate/Award)*

Purpose: To provide support for graduate students in any discipline doing research germane to bar admissions. **Focus:** General studies/Field of study not specified. **Qualif.:** Applicant must be a student conducting a research and is enrolled in a doctoral program and has completed a minimum of one year of study towards a Ph.D. degree or just completing a Ph.D. degree. **Criteria:** Selection is made by the Award Committee.

Funds Avail.: $6,000; $1,000 for the advisor. **Duration:** Annual. **To Apply:** Applicants must submit an application which includes a curriculum vitae; a letter of intent from the student's project advisor; a brief research proposal of up to four pages; a cover letter; recent scholarly writing sample. **Deadline:** March 1. **Remarks:** The award was established in honor of Joe E. Covington, a former dean of the University of Missouri-Columbia School of Law who was the first Director of Testing for NCBE. **Contact:** Dr. Mark A. Albanese, Director of Testing and Research, National Conference of Bar Examiners, 302 S Bedford St., Madison, WI, 53703-3622; Phone: 608-316-3051; Fax: 608-442-7974; E-mail: malbanese@ncbex.org.

7782 ■ National Conservation District Employees Association (NCDEA)
c/o Rich Duesterhaus, Executive Director
509 Capitol Ct. NE
Washington, DC 20002-4937
URL: ncdea.us
Social Media: www.facebook.com/MYNCDEA
twitter.com/myncdea

7783 ■ Don Aron Scholarship *(Undergraduate/Scholarship)*

Purpose: To provide financial support to district employees or members of their immediate families who are participating in a resource conservation curriculum while enrolled in an accredited college or university. **Focus:** Agriculture, Economic aspects. **Criteria:** Selection will be judged by the NCDEA scholarship committee at the NCDEA mid-year meeting.

Funds Avail.: $1,000. **Duration:** Annual. **To Apply:** Applicants must fill out the application form and provide proof that they are currently enrolled. **Remarks:** The scholarships have been established in memory of Don Aron, who worked to organize the National Conservation District Employees Association. He also helped to establish the by-laws and served as the first President of our organization from 1992-1993. **Contact:** E-mail: myncdea@gmail.com.

7784 ■ National Costumers Association (NCA)
cø Ed Avis Associates
Chicago, IL 60613

Awards are arranged alphabetically below their administering organizations

E-mail: office@costumers.org
URL: www.costumers.org
Social Media: www.facebook.com/NATLCostumers

7785 ■ Memorial Fund Scholarship (Undergraduate/Scholarship)

Purpose: To promote the costume industry through education. **Focus:** General studies/Field of study not specified. **Qualif.:** Applicants must be 17 years old and above, with a GPA of 2.75 or higher and enrolled in an accredited university or school. **Criteria:** Awards are given based on academic merit.

Funds Avail.: No specific amount. **Duration:** Annual. **To Apply:** Applicants must submit a completed and signed application form; proof of GPA; copy of online transcript; and one photo - preferably a headshot; must also submit a 100-word (max) biography and a 500-word (min) essay of the candidate's field of study and how it applies to the costume industry. **Deadline:** April 1. **Contact:** Linda Adams Foat, Immediate Past President; Email: ipp@costumers.org.

7786 ■ National Council on Education for the Ceramic Arts (NCECA)

4845 Pearl East Cir., Ste. 101
Boulder, CO 80301
Ph: (303)828-2811
Fax: (303)828-0911
Free: 866-266-2322
E-mail: joberman.nceca@gmail.com
URL: nceca.net
Social Media: www.facebook.com/
   NationalCouncilOnEducationForTheCeramicArts
instagram.com/nceca
www.linkedin.com/company/nceca
pinterest.com/nceca
twitter.com/NCECA
youtube.com/user/WatchNCECA

7787 ■ NCECA Graduate Student Fellowships (Graduate/Fellowship)

Purpose: To promote and improve the ceramic arts through education, research and creative practice. **Focus:** Arts. **Qualif.:** Applicant must be a NCECA member, and a full-time graduate student matriculated in a degree program at an accredited college, university or art institute in the U.S; must have at least one complete semester or two quarters remaining in Master's program AFTER receipt of the award at the NCECA Pittsburgh conference. **Criteria:** Selected is based on the creativity of the project, the impact the award will have on the student's work and development, the quality of work presented, and the nature of the recommendation letters.

Funds Avail.: $2,000. **Duration:** Annual. **Number Awarded:** 3. **To Apply:** Applicants should include Proposed Research Project description (3000 character limit); Project Abstract(600 character limit with spaces); Budget Excel spreadsheet; Cumulative Undergraduate and Graduate GPAs; Transcripts; Recommenders' information to include: Name, Institution, best phone, email and relation to student; Two (2) Letters of Recommendation - One from a current instructor and one from another instructor or professional ceramist; Exactly 10 images. **Deadline:** October 25. **Remarks:** Established in 2005. **Contact:** Steve Hilton, Board Steward steve.hilton@mwsu.edu.

7788 ■ Regina Brown Undergraduate Student Fellowship (Undergraduate/Fellowship)

Purpose: To promote and improve the ceramic arts through education, research and creative practice. **Focus:** Arts. **Qualif.:** Applicant must be a NCECA member; a full-time undergraduate student matriculated in a degree program at an accredited college, university or art institute in the U.S.; and must have attained the classification of at least a junior or its equivalent. **Criteria:** Selected is based on the creativity of the project, the impact the award will have on the student's work and development, the quality of work presented, and the nature of the recommendation letters.

Funds Avail.: $1,800. **Duration:** Annual. **Number Awarded:** 3. **To Apply:** Applicants should include Proposed Research Project description (3000 character limit); Project Abstract(600 character limit with spaces); Budget Excel spreadsheet; Cumulative Undergraduate and Graduate GPAs; Transcripts; Recommenders' information to include: Name, Institution, best phone, email and relation to student; Two (2) Letters of Recommendation - One from a current instructor and one from another instructor or professional ceramist; Exactly 10 images. **Deadline:** October 25. **Contact:** Steve Hilton, Board Steward; E-mail: steve.hilton@mwsu.edu; For technical assistance, e-mail: kate@nceca.net or candice@nceca.net.

7789 ■ National Council of Jewish Women, Greater Houston Section

PO Box 3011
Bellaire, TX 77401
Ph: (281)974-6364
E-mail: info@ncjwhouston.org
URL: ncjwhouston.org

7790 ■ Lee K. Feine Scholarship (Undergraduate, Graduate/Scholarship)

Purpose: To advance the values of NCJW, a volunteer organization inspired by Jewish values, and focused on improving the quality of life for women, children, and families, and ensuring individual rights and freedoms for all. **Focus:** Education; Health care services; Jewish studies; Medicine; Social work. **Qualif.:** Applicants must be entering their junior or senior year of undergraduate studies, or be graduate students, in the fall semester of application year; must be permanent residents of the greater Houston metropolitan area, including Harris, Galveston. Fort Bend, Montgomery, Austin, Brazoria, Chambers, Liberty, San Jacinto, and Waller counties; and must be preparing for careers in the health professions, education, community or social services, or Jewish Studies. **Criteria:** Selection based on academics, financial need, and course of study.

Funds Avail.: $1,500. **Duration:** Annual. **Number Awarded:** 1. **To Apply:** Applicants should download the application form the website or by mail and completed application should be mailed to the respective email address. **Deadline:** March 4. **Remarks:** The scholarship was named in memory of Dr. Lee K. Feine, community activist, professional woman, and devoted wife and mother. **Contact:** Email: scholarship@ncjwhouston.org.

7791 ■ National Council on Public History (NCPH)

127 Cavanaugh Hall
425 University Blvd.
Indianapolis, IN 46202-5140

Awards are arranged alphabetically below their administering organizations

Ph: (317)274-2716
Fax: (317)278-5230
E-mail: ncph@iupui.edu
URL: ncph.org

7792 ■ National Council on Public History Graduate Student Travel Awards (Doctorate, Graduate, Master's/Grant)

Purpose: To provide assistance with conference travel costs for graduate student members who have a paper, poster, or other presentation accepted for inclusion in the program of the NCPH annual meeting. **Focus:** History. **Qualif.:** Applicants must be currently enrolled MA or PhD students doing research and/or practice that is recognizably public history; must have had a paper, poster or other presentation accepted for inclusion in the program of the NCPH annual meeting for which they seek a travel award; the paper, poster, or presentation abstract must be of exceptional quality; applicants must be current members of NCPH. **Criteria:** Selection will be based primarily on the merit of the planned presentation.

Funds Avail.: Up to $300 each. **Duration:** Annual. **Number Awarded:** 5. **To Apply:** Applications must be sent in ONE complete document (Word or PDF) to each of the committee members and to the NCPH Executive Office. A complete application consists of signed and completed application form; copy of the abstract submitted for the annual meeting regular session or poster session; copy of applicant's curriculum vitae./resume, which should include education, honors/awards, publications, and public history research and/or experience; a brief description of financial need. Applicant must also provide a narrative of no more than 500 words that addresses/clarifies one of the following: the original contribution the applicants will make to the session or poster; the specific argument the applicants will be posing in the session or poster; the significance of the applicant's original contribution to the field of public history. **Deadline:** December 1.

7793 ■ National Council on Public History Student Project Awards (Undergraduate/Grant)

Purpose: To support and recognize students who have the most outstanding work to the field of public history. **Focus:** History. **Qualif.:** Applicants must meet the following criteria: the project must be the work of one or more students in a public history program, and have been completed within the two academic years preceding the date of submission; the project must have been initiated as academic coursework, then subsequently recognized beyond the classroom as a contribution to public history; and, the sponsoring faculty members or academic institutions must be members of NCPH. **Criteria:** Selection will be based on the committee's criteria.

Funds Avail.: $500 travel grant. **Duration:** Annual. **Number Awarded:** 1. **To Apply:** Applicants must submit a cover sheet and a two-page written description of the project explaining its methods, conclusions and significance to public history. Include appropriate supporting materials such as written text, graphics, photographs, audio/video tapes and printed materials. Endorsements must include the following: a letter from the project's faculty sponsor explaining the relationship of the project to the coursework, evaluating the project as a contribution to public history and verifying the applicant's status as a full-time student at the time the project was undertaken; a letter from the institution which accepted the project, explaining the relationship between the institution and the student(s) and how the project helped

advance the institution's public history mission. Send endorsement letters directly to the NCPH Executive Offices. **Deadline:** December 1. **Contact:** NCPH, 127 Cavanaugh Hall - IUPUI, 425 University Blvd., Indianapolis, IN 46202; Email: ncph@iupui.edu.

7794 ■ National Council for the Social Studies (NCSS)

8555 16th St., Ste. 500
Silver Spring, MD 20910
Ph: (301)588-1800
Fax: (301)588-2049
Free: 800-683-0812
E-mail: registration@ncss.org
URL: www.socialstudies.org

7795 ■ FASSE-International Assembly International Understanding Grants (Professional development/Grant)

Purpose: To support collaborative projects that demonstrate potential to enhance international relationships and global perspectives in social studies education. **Focus:** Education; Social sciences.

Funds Avail.: $5,000. **Duration:** Annual. **Number Awarded:** 3. **Deadline:** May 31. **Remarks:** Established in 1984.

7796 ■ NCSS Grant for Geographic Literacy (Other/Grant)

Purpose: To promote geography education in the schools, enhance the geographic literacy of students at the classroom, district, or statewide level, and encourage the integration of geography into the social studies curriculum/classroom. **Focus:** Geography; Social sciences. **Qualif.:** Recipients may be individuals or groups in school districts, or public institutions looking to improve geographic literacy; may be individuals or groups in school districts, public institutions, or universities; individuals having already received this grant may be considered after three-years from the last time they received this grant. **Criteria:** Selection is based on sound rationale and appropriate methods for incorporating the study of geography into the social studies curricula; specific plans for enhancing geographic literacy; feasibility of program implementation; and number of teachers and students served.

Funds Avail.: $2,500. **Duration:** Annual. **Number Awarded:** Varies. **To Apply:** Applicant must complete the online application; program description that highlights; 200 word biographical sketch. **Deadline:** May 31. **Contact:** Email: awards@ncss.org.

7797 ■ National Council of Teachers of English (NCTE)

340 N. Neil St., Ste. 104
Champaign, IL 61820
Ph: (217)328-3870
Fax: (217)328-9645
Free: 877-369-6283
E-mail: customerservice@ncte.org
URL: www.ncte.org
Social Media: www.facebook.com/ncte.org
www.instagram.com/nctegram
www.linkedin.com/company/national-council-of-teachers-of-english-ncte-

Awards are arranged alphabetically below their administering organizations

www.pinterest.com/nctedotorg
twitter.com/ncte
www.youtube.com/user/NCTEEnglish

7798 ■ CEE Cultural Diversity Grant *(Professional development/Grant)*

Purpose: To increase participation in CEE on the part of teachers and teacher educators (including graduate students and student teachers) from historically under-represented groups whose presence and whose contributions are central to the full realization of our professional goals. **Focus:** Education; English language and literature. **Qualif.:** Applicants should be member of NCTE and CEE. **Criteria:** Selection will be based on Program Proposal and past accomplishments indicate the greatest potential for contributing to the mission of CEE.

Funds Avail.: $500. **Duration:** Annual. **Number Awarded:** Up to 2. **To Apply:** Applicants should submit a brief letter of application explaining how you anticipate your presentation (include your accepted proposal title) benefiting your colleagues; A brief letter (no more than one page) describing your professional or pre-professional background; A brief letter of support from a senior colleague or mentor commenting on your accomplishments or promise as a teacher or teacher educator. **Deadline:** May 20. **Remarks:** Established in 1996. **Contact:** Submit the following to elate@ncte.org.

7799 ■ Edwyna Wheadon Postgraduate Training Scholarship *(Postgraduate/Scholarship)*

Purpose: To support postgraduate training to enhance teaching skills and/or career development in teaching. **Focus:** English language and literature; Teaching. **Qualif.:** Applicants must be teachers of English/Language Arts in a publicly funded institution; must also be a member of NCTE. **Criteria:** Recipients are selected based on submitted requirements.

Funds Avail.: $500. **Duration:** Annual. **Number Awarded:** 1. **To Apply:** Applicants must also indicate the professional development experience for which they seeks support (separate piece of paper, less than 500 words). **Deadline:** January 31. **Contact:** Email: college@ncte.org.

7800 ■ NCTE Research Foundation Grants *(Other/ Grant)*

Purpose: To support research projects about the teaching and learning of language and literacies. **Focus:** English language and literature. **Qualif.:** Applicants must be member of NCTE in good standing conducting a research related to teaching and learning of language and literacies; applicant can be teachers, teacher researchers, teacher educators, and scholars of language, literacy, and cultural studies. **Criteria:** Preference will be given to an applicant who will best meet the requirements.

Funds Avail.: Up to $5,000. **Duration:** Biennial; odd numbered years. **Number Awarded:** 2. **To Apply:** Applicants must submitted electronically also submit application cover sheet; Grant Proposal; One-page Resume. **Deadline:** March 15. **Remarks:** Established in 1960. **Contact:** Email: researchfoundation@ncte.org.

7801 ■ National Council of Teachers of Mathematics (NCTM)

1906 Association Dr.
Reston, VA 20191-1502
Ph: (703)620-9840

Fax: (703)476-2970
Free: 800-235-7566
E-mail: nctm@nctm.org
URL: www.nctm.org
Social Media: www.instagram.com/nctm.math
www.linkedin.com/company/national-council-of-teachers-of
  -mathematics---nctm?trk=NUS_CMPY_TWIT
www.pinterest.com/nctmpins
twitter.com/nctm
www.youtube.com/profile?user=NCTMChannel

7802 ■ Clarence Olander School In-Service Training Grants for Grades Prek-5 *(High School/Grant)*

Purpose: To provide financial assistance to secondary schools for in-service education in mathematics. **Focus:** Mathematics and mathematical sciences; Teaching. **Qualif.:** NCTM Pre-K-8 schools with a membership are eligible to apply for this grant.

Funds Avail.: Up to $4,000 each. **Duration:** Annual. **Number Awarded:** 1. **To Apply:** Applicants must submit Proposal Cover Form; a proposal describing the design of the action research, including sources of information about teaching and/or learning and methodology to be used to collect the information; budget; letter of support from principal. **Deadline:** December 1.

7803 ■ Ernest Duncan - Pre-K-8 Preservice Teacher Action Research Grants *(Professional development/ Grant)*

Purpose: To provide financial support for action research conducted as a collaborative by university faculty, pre-service teacher(s) and classroom teacher(s) seeking to improve their understanding of mathematics in Pre-K-8 classroom(s). **Focus:** Teaching.

Funds Avail.: $3,000. **Duration:** Annual. **To Apply:** Applicants must submit Proposal Cover Form; a proposal describing the design of the action research, including sources of information about teaching and/or learning and methodology to be used to collect the information; budget; background and experience; letter of support from principal. **Deadline:** May 1.

7804 ■ Future Leader Initial NCTM Annual Meeting Attendance Awards *(Advanced Professional/Award, Monetary)*

Purpose: To provide financial assistance to first-time attendees at an NCTM annual meeting and exposition. **Focus:** Mathematics and mathematical sciences; Teaching. **Criteria:** Selection will be based on the credentials of the qualified applicants. Special consideration will be given to teachers of underserved and rural students.

Funds Avail.: Up to $1,500. **Duration:** Annual. **Number Awarded:** Varies. **To Apply:** Applicants must submit a Proposal cover form; a proposal describing plan and lesson plan (Two pages maximum); Budget (No direct cost); letter of Support from Principal. **Deadline:** November 2. **Contact:** The Mathematics Education Trust, NCTM, 1906 Association Dr., Reston, VA, 20191-1502.

7805 ■ Mathematics Graduate Course Work Scholarships for Grades 6-8 Teachers *(Graduate/ Scholarship)*

Purpose: To provide financial support for improving teachers' understanding of mathematics by completing course work in mathematics. **Focus:** Teaching.

Awards are arranged alphabetically below their administering organizations

Funds Avail.: $3,200 each. **Duration:** Annual. **To Apply:** Applicants must submit Proposal Cover Form; a proposal describing the design of the action research, including sources of information about teaching and/or learning and methodology to be used to collect the information; budget; background and experience; letter of recommendation from principal. **Deadline:** November 1. **Contact:** The Mathematics Education Trust, NCTM, 1906 Association Dr., Reston, VA, 20191-1502.

7806 ■ NCTM Emerging Teacher-Leaders in Elementary School Mathematics Grants for Grades PreK-5 *(Other/Grant)*

Purpose: To increase the breadth and depth of the mathematics content knowledge of one elementary school teacher who has a demonstrated commitment to mathematics teaching and learning. **Focus:** Mathematics and mathematical sciences. **Qualif.:** Applicants must have the support of the school principal in becoming mathematics teacher-leaders within their respective schools or districts; be current full individuals or E-member of NCTM; and, be full-time elementary school teachers with at least three years of experience; having mathematics as their regular teaching responsibility. **Criteria:** Selection shall be based on the aforementioned qualifications and compliance with the application details.

Funds Avail.: $6,000 each. **Duration:** Annual. **To Apply:** Applicants must submit a proposal; must be completed and serve as the top page of each copy of the proposal; must be typewritten, double-spaced and single-sided (please organize as outlined below), with margins of at least one inch on 8.5" x 11" paper and font size must be no smaller than 10-point, and width between characters should be normal (100%); five copies (one original and four copies) of the proposal should be included in a single packet addressed to the Mathematics Education Trust; and a principal's letter of support. **Deadline:** November 1. **Contact:** The Mathematics Education Trust, NCTM, 1906 Association Dr., Reston, VA, 20191-1502.

7807 ■ NCTM Prospective 7-12 Secondary Teacher Course Work Scholarships *(Professional development/Scholarship)*

Purpose: To provide financial support to college students preparing for teaching secondary school mathematics. **Focus:** Mathematics and mathematical sciences. **Qualif.:** Applicants must be persons currently completing their sophomore year of college, scheduling for full-time study at a four- or five-year college or university in the next academic year, and pursuing a career goal of becoming a certified teacher of secondary school mathematics.

Funds Avail.: Maximum of $10,000. **Duration:** Annual. **To Apply:** Applicants must submit a proposal; must be completed and serve as the top page of each copy of the proposal; must be typewritten, double-spaced and single-sided (please organize as outlined below), with margins of at least one inch on 8.5" x 11" paper and font size must be no smaller than 10-point, and width between characters should be normal (100%); five copies (one original and four copies) of the proposal should be included in a single packet addressed to the Mathematics Education Trust; and a principal's letter of support. **Deadline:** May 1. **Contact:** The Mathematics Education Trust, NCTM, 1906 Association Dr., Reston, VA, 20191-1502.

7808 ■ NCTM School In-Service Training Grants for Grades 6-8 *(Undergraduate/Grant)*

Purpose: To provide financial assistance to middle schools for in-service education in mathematics. **Focus:** Mathematics and mathematical sciences. **Qualif.:** Applicants must be schools with a current NCTM K-8 school membership.

Funds Avail.: Maximum of $4,000 each. **To Apply:** Applicants must submit a proposal; must be completed and serve as the top page of each copy of the proposal; must be typewritten, double-spaced and single-sided (please organize as outlined below), with margins of at least one inch on 8.5" x 11" paper and font size must be no smaller than 10-point, and width between characters should be normal (100%); five copies (one original and four copies) of the proposal should be included in a single packet addressed to the Mathematics Education Trust; and a principal's letter of support. **Deadline:** May 1. **Contact:** The Mathematics Education Trust, NCTM, 1906 Association Dr., Reston, VA, 20191-1502.

7809 ■ NCTM School In-Service Training Grants for Grades 9-12 *(Undergraduate/Grant)*

Purpose: To provide financial assistance to secondary schools for in-service education in mathematics. **Focus:** Mathematics and mathematical sciences. **Qualif.:** Candidates must be schools with at least one current Full Individual or E-member of NCTM.

Funds Avail.: Maximum of $4,000 each. **To Apply:** Applicants must submit a proposal; must be completed and serve as the top page of each copy of the proposal; must be typewritten, double-spaced and single-sided (please organize as outlined below), with margins of at least one inch on 8.5" x 11" paper and font size must be no smaller than 10-point, and width between characters should be normal (100%); five copies (one original and four copies) of the proposal should be included in a single packet addressed to the Mathematics Education Trust; and a principal's letter of support. **Deadline:** May 1. **Contact:** The Mathematics Education Trust, NCTM, 1906 Association Dr., Reston, VA, 20191-1502.

7810 ■ NCTM School In-Service Training Grants for Grades PreK-5 *(Undergraduate/Grant)*

Purpose: To provide financial assistance to elementary schools for in-service education in mathematics. **Focus:** Mathematics and mathematical sciences. **Qualif.:** Applicants must be schools with a current NCTM K-8 school membership.

Funds Avail.: Maximum of $4,000 each. **To Apply:** Applicants must submit a proposal; must be completed and serve as the top page of each copy of the proposal; must be typewritten, double-spaced and single-sided (please organize as outlined below), with margins of at least one inch on 8.5" x 11" paper and font size must be no smaller than 10-point, and width between characters should be normal (100%); five copies (one original and four copies) of the proposal should be included in a single packet addressed to the Mathematics Education Trust; and a principal's letter of support. **Deadline:** May 1. **Contact:** The Mathematics Education Trust, NCTM, 1906 Association Dr., Reston, VA, 20191-1502.

7811 ■ National Council on U.S.-Arab Relations (NCUSAR)

1730 M St. NW, Ste. 503
Washington, DC 20036
Ph: (202)293-6466
Fax: (202)293-7770
URL: www.ncusar.org
Social Media: www.facebook.com/NCUSAR

Awards are arranged alphabetically below their administering organizations

www.instagram.com/ncusar
www.linkedin.com/company/national-council-on-u-s---arab -relations
twitter.com/NCUSAR
www.youtube.com/user/ncusar

7812 ■ Joseph J. Malone Fellowship in Arab and Islamic Studies *(Professional development/Fellowship)*

Purpose: To provide American professionals in academia, government, and business unparalleled educational experiences in the Arab world. **Focus:** General studies/Field of study not specified. **Qualif.:** Applicants must be U.S. citizens and qualified American professionals in academia, government, and business; students are not eligible.

Funds Avail.: No specific amount. **Duration:** Annual. **To Apply:** Completed application along with a CV; a double-spaced essay (no more than 3-pages in length) on the topic: U.S.-Arab relations: challenges for American leaders; description, with relevant details, of the number and kinds of public affairs outreach programs, applicant has addressed in the last 10 years; names of the two most widely read local newspapers in applicant community, along with contact information (fax number or e-mail address) for each publication must be submitted. **Remarks:** Established in 1984. **Contact:** Completed applications should be sent to: National Council on U.S. Arab Relations, ATTN: Malone Fellowship Program, 1730 M St. NW, Ste. 503, Washington, DC, 20036; Phone: 202-293-6466.

7813 ■ National Council of University Research Administrators New England Region I (NCURA Region 1)
Denise Rouleau, Chairman
Tufts University
419 Boston Ave.
Medford, MA 02155
URL: ncuraregioni.org
Social Media: www.facebook.com/ncuraregioni
twitter.com/NCURA_Reg_I

7814 ■ Region I Travel Grants *(Professional development/Grant)*

Purpose: To defray the costs associated with attending regional and national NCURA meetings. **Focus:** Educational administration. **Qualif.:** Applicant must be a research administrator from the Region I geographical area (New England); must be members of NCURA at the time of nomination; Region 1 Spring Meeting are not required to be members of NCURA at the time of nomination. **Criteria:** Preference will be given to research administrators with 6-18 months experience in the field of research administration and who can demonstrate financial need. Individuals must not have received a travel award within the last 3 years.

Funds Avail.: $500 each. **Duration:** Semiannual. **Number Awarded:** 3. **To Apply:** Applicant must complete an online application form. **Deadline:** March 8. **Contact:** Email: awards@ncuraregioni.org.

7815 ■ National Council of Women of Canada (NCWC)
PO Box 67099
Ottawa, ON, Canada K2A 4E4
Ph: (613)712-4419

E-mail: presncwc@gmail.com
URL: www.ncwcanada.com
Social Media: www.facebook.com/thencwc

7816 ■ The Alison Hardy Tea and Bursary *(Undergraduate/Recognition)*

Purpose: To support and help students who are studying journalism. **Focus:** Journalism. **Qualif.:** Applicants must be students, in the third or fourth year of the journalism program, school of journalism and communication, Carleton University.

Duration: Annual. **Remarks:** The award was established in the memory of OCW member Alison Taylor Hardy, a career journalist and WREN during WWII who also worked for the Department of External Affairs Press Information and Finance Division for 30 years.

7817 ■ National Court Reporters Association (NCRA)
12030 Sunrise Valley Dr., Ste. 400
Reston, VA 20191
Ph: (703)556-6272
Fax: (703)391-0629
Free: 800-272-6272
URL: www.ncra.org
Social Media: www.facebook.com/NCRAfb
www.linkedin.com/company/ nationalcourtreportersassociation
twitter.com/NCRA
www.youtube.com/user/NCRAonline

7818 ■ National Court Reporters Association Student Intern Scholarship *(Undergraduate/ Scholarship)*

Purpose: To provide scholarships to NCRA students. **Focus:** General studies/Field of study not specified. **Qualif.:** Applicants must be current NCRA student members and be interns in any of the three career paths: judicial, CART, and captioning; must also be enrolled in an NCRA-certified Court Reporter Training Program; nominees in a judicial court reporting program must have passed at least one of the program's Q and A tests at a minimum of 190 words per minute. Nominees in a CART or captioning program must have passed at least one of the program's literary tests at a minimum of 160 words per minute; must have a GPA of at least 3.5 overall, based on a 4.0 standard or equivalent; must possess all the qualities exemplified by a professional court reporter, including professional attitude, demeanor, dress, and motivation. **Criteria:** Selection will be based on the committee's criteria.

Funds Avail.: $1,000. **Duration:** Annual. **Number Awarded:** 2. **Contact:** Email: ncrfoundation@ncra.org.

7819 ■ NCRF New Professional Reporter Grant *(Other/Grant)*

Purpose: To help support start-up expenses for new employees in their first year out of school. **Focus:** General studies/Field of study not specified. **Qualif.:** Applicants must be current NCRA student members and be enrolled in an NCRA-certified court reporting program; must have passed at least one of the court reporting program's Q and A tests at a minimum of 200 words per minute; must have a GPA of at least 3.5 overall, based on a 4.0 standard; must have a demonstrated a need for financial assistance;

Awards are arranged alphabetically below their administering organizations

must also possess all the qualities exemplified by a professional court reporter, including professional attitude, demeanor, dress and motivation. All criteria must be confirmed and verified by the submitting court reporting program.

Funds Avail.: $2,000. **Duration:** Annual. **Number Awarded:** 1. **To Apply:** Applicant must submit an application form along with a copy of official transcript; a letter of recommendation from an employer or contracting agency attesting to the applicant's professional demeanor, attitude, and motivation. **Contact:** Email: ncrfoundation@ncra.org.

7820 ■ Frank Sarli Memorial Scholarship
(Undergraduate/Scholarship)

Purpose: To support deserving, qualified NCRA student members at an NCRA-certified program. **Focus:** General studies/Field of study not specified. **Qualif.:** Nominees must be current NCRA student member and be enrolled in an NCRA-certified court reporting program; must have passed at least one of the court reporting program's Q and A tests at a minimum of 200 words per minute; must have a grade point average of at least a 3.5 overall, based on a 4.0 standard; must have a demonstrated need for financial assistance; must possess all the qualities exemplified by professional court reporters, including professional attitude, demeanor, dress, motivation. All criteria must be confirmed and verified by the submitting court reporting program. **Criteria:** Selection will be based on the committee criteria.

Funds Avail.: $2,000. **Duration:** Annual. **Number Awarded:** 1. **To Apply:** Application must submit online. **Deadline:** December 1. **Remarks:** The scholarship honors the late Frank Sarli, a court reporter who was committed to supporting students through years of service on NCRA's committees and boards that guide the education of court reporting students. **Contact:** April Weiner, Foundation Manager; Phone: 800-272-6272, ext. 152; Email: aweiner@ncra.org.

7821 ■ National Cowboy & Western Heritage Museum
1700 NE 63rd St.
Oklahoma City, OK 73111
Ph: (405)478-2250
E-mail: info@nationalcowboymuseum.org
URL: www.nationalcowboymuseum.org

7822 ■ Stacey Scholarship Fund *(All/Scholarship)*

Purpose: To support the education of young men and women who aim to make art their profession. **Focus:** Art. **Qualif.:** Applicants must be U.S. citizens and be 18 to 35 years old. **Criteria:** Selection is based on the applications and the submitted work examples.

Funds Avail.: $500 - $5,000. **Duration:** Annual. **Number Awarded:** Varies. **To Apply:** Applicants must submit a brief quarterly report together with digital images on a disk of their work and a more complete report at the termination of the scholarship. **Deadline:** February 1. **Remarks:** In accordance with the will of the late Anna Lee Stacey, a trust fund has been created for the education of young men and women who aim to make art their profession. **Contact:** E-mail: scholarship@nationalcowboymuseum.org.

7823 ■ National Dairy Herd Improvement Association (NDHIA)
5940 Seminole Centre Ct., Ste. 200
Fitchburg, WI 53711

Ph: (608)848-6455
Fax: (608)260-7772
URL: www.dhia.org

7824 ■ National Dairy Herd Information Association Scholarship Program *(Undergraduate/Scholarship)*

Purpose: To provide financial assistance for the education of incoming and continuing students at technical and two-year and four-year institutions. **Focus:** Education, Vocational-technical. **Qualif.:** Applicants must be family members or employees of a herd on DHIA testing, or family members of an employee or employees of a DHIA affiliate. **Criteria:** Selection is based on scholastic achievements and leadership in school and community activities.

Funds Avail.: $1,000. **Duration:** Annual. **To Apply:** Applicants must submit all the required application information. **Deadline:** November 30. **Contact:** JoDee Sattler, National DHIA scholarship coordinator; Phone: 608-848-6455 ext. 112; Email: jdsattler@dhia.org.

7825 ■ National Dairy Shrine
PO Box 68
Fort Atkinson, WI 53538
Ph: (920)542-1003
E-mail: info@dairyshrine.org
URL: www.dairyshrine.org
Social Media: www.facebook.com/DairyShrine

7826 ■ Progressive Dairy Producer Awards *(All/Grant)*

Purpose: To achieve a more profitable dairy business. **Focus:** Agribusiness; Agricultural sciences; Business; Dairy science. **Qualif.:** Applicants must be an individual, couple, family or multiple partner operation dairy producer between 21-45 years of age at the time of the application due date. **Criteria:** Priority will be given to nominees who own or manage operations.

Funds Avail.: $2,000. **Duration:** Annual. **Number Awarded:** 2. **To Apply:** Applicants must submit the following: two letters of support; Six copies of nomination and supporting information; two letters of reference. Applicant's references must submit their letters directly to National Dairy Shrine. **Deadline:** April 15.

7827 ■ National Debt Relief
180 Maiden Ln., 30th Fl.
New York, NY 10038
Free: 800-300-9550
E-mail: service@nationaldebtrelief.com
URL: www.nationaldebtrelief.com
Social Media: www.facebook.com/NationalDebtRelief
www.instagram.com/nationaldebtrelief
www.pinterest.com/NationalRelief
twitter.com/NationalRelief_

7828 ■ National Debt Relief Scholarship *(University, Four Year College, Undergraduate/Scholarship)*

Purpose: To support a student going to a four-year college or university in a STEM field. **Focus:** Engineering; Mathematics and mathematical sciences; Science; Technology. **Qualif.:** Applicant must be a U.S. citizen enrolled in an accredited graduate or undergraduate four-year college/university program in the United States, or a high school

Awards are arranged alphabetically below their administering organizations

senior with a minimum 3.0 GPA; must be pursuing or planning to pursue a bachelor's degree in a STEM (science, technology, engineering, and math) field. **Criteria:** Selection will be based on committee criteria

Funds Avail.: $1,000. **Duration:** Annual. **Number Awarded:** 5. **To Apply:** Applicant must provide a solution to the following issue: Come up with a unique way to solve the $1+ trillion dollar student loan crisis. This can be via YouTube video, an essay, or an infographic. Applicant must submit this solution along with a cover letter, name, college, college year, graduating year, and intended major. Cover letter should include how applicant intends to use the scholarship and why they should be selected. Scholarship application should be submitted via email to Scholarships@nationaldebtrelief.com. **Deadline:** December 31.

7829 ■ National Defense Industrial Association - Iowa-Illinois Chapter
29925 150th Ave.
Long Grove, IA 52756
Ph: (563)650-3252
E-mail: admin@ndia-ia-il.org
URL: www.ndia-ia-il.org

7830 ■ Sergeant Paul Fisher Scholarship
(Undergraduate/Scholarship)

Purpose: To provide opportunities for higher education for students who are interested in achieving a place of leadership in their chosen fields. **Focus:** General studies/Field of study not specified.

Duration: Annual. **Number Awarded:** Varies. **Remarks:** The award is established in honor of Sergeant Paul Fishe. Established in 2005.

7831 ■ National Defense Industrial Association - Picatinny Chapter
PO Box 528
Wharton, NJ 07885
Ph: (973)442-8200
URL: www.ndiapicatinny.com

7832 ■ NDIA Picatinny Chapter Scholarships
(Undergraduate/Scholarship)

Purpose: To provide financial assistance to students in pursuit of higher technology educational programs. **Focus:** Technology. **Qualif.:** Applicants must be graduating high school seniors. **Criteria:** Election shall be based on ability as demonstrated.

Funds Avail.: $5,000 each. **Number Awarded:** Up to 7. **To Apply:** Applicants must submit a completed scholarship application form provided at the scholarship website. **Deadline:** April 29. **Contact:** NDIA, Scholarship Fund Corporation, PO Box 528, Wharton, NJ, 07885.

7833 ■ National Defense Science and Engineering Graduate Fellowship (NDSEG)
3152 Presidential Drive
Fairborn, OH 45324
Ph: (937)412-5075
E-mail: ndsegf@sti-tec.com
URL: www.ndsegfellowships.org

7834 ■ NDSEG Fellowship *(Graduate/Fellowship)*

Purpose: To increase the number and quality of scientists and engineers. **Focus:** Architecture, Naval; Behavioral sciences; Biology; Chemistry; Computer and information sciences; Engineering, Aerospace/Aeronautical/Astronautical; Engineering, Chemical; Engineering, Civil; Engineering, Electrical; Engineering, Materials; Engineering, Ocean; Geosciences; Oceanography; Physics. **Qualif.:** Applicants must be citizens or nationals of the U.S. who have received or be on track to receive a bachelor's degree; and, at or near the beginning of doctoral studies in science or engineering. **Criteria:** Selection will be Aeronautical and Astronautical Engineering Biosciences (includes toxicology) Chemical Engineering Chemistry Civil Engineering Cognitive, Neural, and Behavioral Sciences.

Funds Avail.: $1,000 medical insurance (excluding dental and vision insurance). **Duration:** Annual; up to three years.

7835 ■ National Defense Transportation Association (NDTA)
50 S. Pickett St., Suite 220
Alexandria, VA 22304-7296
Ph: (703)751-5011
Fax: (703)823-8761
Free: 844-620-2715
URL: www.ndtahq.com
Social Media: www.facebook.com/
  NationalDefenseTransportationAssociation
www.linkedin.com/in/ndtahq
twitter.com/ndtahq

7836 ■ NDTA Academic Scholarship Program A
(Undergraduate/Scholarship)

Purpose: To encourage good college students to study the fields of logistics, transportation, supply chain, physical distribution, and passenger travel services. **Focus:** Logistics; Transportation.

Funds Avail.: No specific amount. **Duration:** Annual. **To Apply:** Applicants must attach a brief statement from a responsible administrator stating that the proposed courses will constitute acceptable work toward a degree; must provide a brief 300-500 word essay outlining how the course of studies will assist in meeting the applicant's career goals; must be accompanied by at least one but no more than three letters of recommendation from mentors, professors, pastors, or other people, who are not related to the applicant and can attest to the applicant's character, work habits, and accomplishments. **Deadline:** June 1. **Contact:** Leah Ashe; Email: leah@ndtahq.com.

7837 ■ NDTA Academic Scholarship Program B
(Undergraduate/Scholarship)

Purpose: To assist high school graduates to achieve their academic goals in the fields of business/ management, logistics, transportation, supply chain, physical distribution, and passenger travel services. **Focus:** Logistics; Transportation. **Criteria:** Selection will be based upon the merit of each applicant as attested to by academic performance and extracurricular involvement in school and community life.

Funds Avail.: No specific amount. **Duration:** Annual. **To Apply:** Applicant must submit an online application form along with one page summary of work, scholastic and extracurricular activities, honors and awards; brief (500

Awards are arranged alphabetically below their administering organizations

word maximum) essay outlining your career goals and methods of attaining those goals; high school transcript; at least one or not more than three signed letter of recommendation form guidance counselors. **Deadline:** April 15. **Contact:** NDTA Scholarship Committee, Attention: Email: NDTAHQ@ndtahq.com.

7838 ■ National Dental Hygienists' Association (NDHA)

c/o LaVerna Wilson, Treasurer
366 E Gorgas Ln.
Philadelphia, PA 19119
Ph: (202)670-3467
URL: ndhaonline.org
Social Media: www.instagram.com/Ndhaonline
twitter.com/ndhaonline

7839 ■ National Dental Hygienists' Association Scholarships *(Undergraduate/Scholarship)*

Purpose: To increase interest in dental hygiene particularly among African American students by providing financial assistance. **Focus:** Dental hygiene. **Qualif.:** Applicant must be a current member of the NDHA; must be a U.S. citizen particularly African American; must have minimum of 2.5 GPA or greater. **Criteria:** Awards are given based on merit.

Funds Avail.: No specific amount. **To Apply:** Applicants must send completed application form (downloadable from the website); NDHA student membership of $35; a copy of official sealed transcript; a print verification of enrollment form signed by Registrar/Office of Dean of Students; a passport type photo; two recommendation letters (one from a dental hygiene director and the other one from dental hygiene teacher or employer); proof of financial need; statement of leadership skills; and stated ideas on how to promote the profession of dental hygiene and the NDHA Organization. **Deadline:** March 15. **Contact:** Applications should be submitted to Linda Hart Lewis, Scholarship Committee Chair, 1613 W Ormsby Ave., Louisville, KY 40210.

7840 ■ National Driving and Traffic School

64 Shattuck Sq., Ste. 285
Berkeley, CA 94704
Ph: (510)848-5508
Fax: (510)848-5585
Free: 877-786-5969
E-mail: info@dmvedu.org
URL: www.dmvedu.org
Social Media: www.facebook.com/dmvedu

7841 ■ Youth Forward Scholarship Opportunity *(High School, College, University/Scholarship)*

Purpose: To help students with their financial aid. **Focus:** General studies/Field of study not specified. **Qualif.:** Applicant must be a full-time student, currently enrolled in high school as a junior or senior, or in college as a freshman, for the current school year.

Funds Avail.: $500 each. **To Apply:** Applicant must answer the following questions in an essay: What is the importance of driver education in reducing the number of deaths as a result of driving? What steps can be taken to reduce the number of deaths related to driving? Have you ever had an experience of being in a car accident or have seen your friends or family members driving irresponsibly? What steps

can you take to be a better and safer driver? **Deadline:** March 31; August 1; November 30.

7842 ■ National Eagle Scout Association (NESA)

1325 W Walnut Hill Lane
Irving, TX 75015
Ph: (972)580-2489
Fax: (972)580-7870
E-mail: nesa@scouting.org
URL: www.nesa.org
Social Media: www.facebook.com/NESABSA
twitter.com/nesabsa
www.youtube.com/channel/UCWm1A2BiXdJl8jR9YV_2idw?

7843 ■ American Legion Eagle Scout of the Year *(Undergraduate/Scholarship)*

Purpose: To support students who demonstrates practical citizenship in church, school, Scouting, and in community. **Focus:** General studies/Field of study not specified. **Qualif.:** Applicants must have received the Eagle Scout Award and the religious emblem awarded by his religious institution; have demonstrated practical citizenship in church, school, Scouting, and the community; son or grandson of an American Legion or American Legion Auxiliary member; or must be a member of a Scouting unit chartered to a Legion post, an Auxiliary unit, or a Sons of the American Legion squadron. **Criteria:** Selection is based on the committee's review on the applications.

Funds Avail.: One $10,000 & three $2,500. **Number Awarded:** 4. **To Apply:** Applicants must complete and file the nomination form. **Deadline:** March 1. **Contact:** American Legion department headquarters in their state.

7844 ■ Arthur M. & Berdena King Eagle Scout Scholarship *(Undergraduate/Scholarship)*

Purpose: To provide financial support to Eagle Scout students who are in need. **Focus:** General studies/Field of study not specified. **Qualif.:** Applicants must be Eagle Scouts currently registered in Scouting and have not reached their 19th birthday. **Criteria:** Selection is based on the application.

Funds Avail.: $4,000 - $10,000.

7845 ■ Birmingham-Southern College Eagle Scout Scholarships *(Undergraduate/Scholarship)*

Purpose: To provide financial support to Eagle Scout students who are in need. **Focus:** General studies/Field of study not specified. **Qualif.:** Applicants must be incoming freshmen at the Birmingham Southern College; and must be Eagle Scout member. **Criteria:** Selection will be based on the committee's criteria.

Funds Avail.: $2,500. **Duration:** Annual. **Number Awarded:** Varies. **To Apply:** Applicants must forward letter of interest and student resume to the BSC Admission Office. **Deadline:** January 15. **Contact:** Admission Office, Birmingham-Southern College Box 549008 Birmingham, AL 35254; Phone: 800-523-5793.

7846 ■ Emmett J. Doerr Memorial Distinguished Scout Scholarship *(High School/Scholarship)*

Purpose: To support the education of high school seniors who are currently registered and active in Boy Scouting, Varsity Scouting, or Venturing. **Focus:** General studies/

Awards are arranged alphabetically below their administering organizations

Field of study not specified. **Qualif.:** Applicants must be outstanding Catholic high-school seniors currently registered and active in Boy Scouting, Varsity Scouting, or Venturing; have earned the Eagle Scout Award or the Silver Award; have earned the Ad Altare Dei or Pope Pius XII religious emblem; have held a Scouting leadership position; and have served in parish; earned the Eagle Scout, Silver Award or Quartermaster Award. **Criteria:** Selection is based on the committee's review on the applications.

Funds Avail.: $2,000. **Duration:** Annual. **Number Awarded:** 7. **To Apply:** Applicants must submit a complete application; four (4) letters of recommendations. One letter each must come from a religious institution, Scouting Unit, School, and Community; official high school transcript; an acceptance letter from an accredited institution of higher learning, if selected as a Scholarship recipient; a 3 X 5 picture with the application. **Deadline:** March 1. **Remarks:** The scholarship was established in honor of Mr. Emmett J. Doerr. **Contact:** nccs@scouting.org.

7847 ■ Dofflemyer Scholarship *(Undergraduate/Scholarship)*

Purpose: To support the education of an Eagle Scout student. **Focus:** General studies/Field of study not specified. **Qualif.:** Applicants must be an Eagle Scout entering Stanford University. **Criteria:** Selection is based on a family's demonstrated need.

Funds Avail.: Varies. **Duration:** Annual. **To Apply:** Applicants must follow the university's standard application process. **Deadline:** February 1. **Contact:** Financial Aid Office, Stanford University, Montag Hall, 355 Galvez St., Stanford, CA 94305-6106; Phone: 888-326-3773; E-mail: financialaid@stanford.edu.

7848 ■ Eastern Orthodox Scouting Scholarships *(Undergraduate/Scholarship)*

Purpose: To support the education of a student active in Scouting, Varsity Scouting, or Venturing. **Focus:** General studies/Field of study not specified. **Qualif.:** Applicants must be registered and active in Boy Scouting must have earned the Eagle Scout Award (Boy Scouts); active in an Eastern Orthodox church; and have earned the Alpha Omega religious emblem. **Criteria:** Selection is based on merit.

Funds Avail.: $500 - $1,000. **Duration:** Annual. **Deadline:** May 1. **Contact:** Dr. M. E. Kotsonis mekotsonis@gmail.com 908.672.0001.

7849 ■ Epsilon Tau Pi's Soaring Eagle Scholarship *(Undergraduate/Scholarship)*

Purpose: To assist the education of an Eagle Scout student. **Focus:** General studies/Field of study not specified. **Qualif.:** Applicants must be Eagle Scout entering as freshmen; must have demonstrated leadership ability in Scouting, and have a strong record of community participation beyond Scouting; must have a SAT score of at least 1600 or an ACT score of at least 25; Locations include: Appalachian State University, Augustana College, Robert Morris University, University of Dayton, Western Carolina University, West Virginia University. **Criteria:** Selection is based on the committee's review on the applications.

Funds Avail.: $500. **Number Awarded:** Varies. **To Apply:** Applicants must visit the Epsilon Tau Pi Alpha Chapter's website for the application process and other details. **Deadline:** June 7. **Contact:** scholarship@etp-foundation.org.

7850 ■ Frank L. Weil Memorial Eagle Scout Scholarship *(Undergraduate/Scholarship)*

Purpose: To support the education of students who are active in Boy Scouting, Varsity Scouting or Venturing. **Focus:** General studies/Field of study not specified. **Qualif.:** Applicants must be currently registered and active in Boy Scouting, Varsity Scouting, or Venturing; must have earned the Eagle Scout Award, the Ner Tamid or Etz Chaim religious emblem; must be active in a synagogue; must demonstrate practical citizenship in the synagogue, school, Scouting unit, and community. **Criteria:** Selection is based on the committee's review on the applications.

Funds Avail.: $500 - $1,000. **Number Awarded:** 1 winner and 2 runners-up. **To Apply:** Applicants must submit a completed application. **Deadline:** January 31. **Contact:** National Jewish Committee on Scouting, Boy Scout of America, 1325 W Walnut Hill Ln., Irving, TX, 75015-2079; Phone: 972-580-2000.

7851 ■ Gaebe Eagle Scout Award *(Undergraduate/Scholarship)*

Purpose: To assist the education of an Eagle Scout student. **Focus:** General studies/Field of study not specified. **Qualif.:** Applicants must be entering as freshman at Johnson and Wales University and must be an Eagle Scout. **Criteria:** Selection will be based on the submitted application.

Funds Avail.: $1,000. **Duration:** Annual. **Deadline:** February 1. **Contact:** National Student Organizations, Johnson and Wales University, 8 Abbott Park Pl., Providence, RI, 02903; Phone: 800-342-5598, ext-2345.

7852 ■ Lamar University College of Engineering Scholarships *(Undergraduate/Scholarship)*

Purpose: To assist the education of an Eagle Scout student. **Focus:** Engineering. **Qualif.:** Applicant must be a Lamar University undergraduate student, scholarships are a minimum GPA of 3.0 and must be an undergraduate student. **Criteria:** Selection is based on the committee's review of the applications.

Funds Avail.: $5,000 per year. **Duration:** Annual. **To Apply:** Applicants must submit a completed Scholarship application form. **Deadline:** February 1.

7853 ■ Lindenwood University Scouting Scholarships *(Undergraduate/Scholarship)*

Purpose: To assist the education of an Eagle Scout student. **Focus:** General studies/Field of study not specified. **Qualif.:** Applicants must be undergraduate residential students who have been Boy Scouts. **Criteria:** Selection is based on the committee's review of the applications.

Funds Avail.: $6,000 - $12,000 per year. **Duration:** Annual. **Number Awarded:** 2. **To Apply:** Applicants must visit the Lindenwood University website for the details of application. **Contact:** Office of Undergraduate Admissions, Lindenwood University, 209 S Kings Hwy., Saint Charles, MO, 63301-1695; Phone: 636-949-4949; E-mail: admissions@lindenwood.edu.

7854 ■ McDaniel College Eagle Scout Scholarship *(Undergraduate/Scholarship)*

Purpose: To assist the education of an Eagle Scout student. **Focus:** General studies/Field of study not specified. **Qualif.:** Applicants must be enrolled full-time and have a minimum 2.50 cumulative GPA and a minimum SAT-I combined score of 1000. **Criteria:** Selection is based on

Awards are arranged alphabetically below their administering organizations

the Committee's review on the applications.

Funds Avail.: $2,000 per year. **Duration:** Annual. **To Apply:** Applicants must visit the McDaniel College website for the details of application. **Deadline:** February 1. **Contact:** McDaniel College, 2 College Hill Westminster, MD 21157; Phone: 410-848-7000.

7855 ■ Newman University Scouting Scholarships
(Undergraduate/Scholarship)

Purpose: To assist the education of a boy and a girl scout student. **Focus:** General studies/Field of study not specified. **Qualif.:** Applicants must be an Eagle Scout or a Girl Scout (Gold Award winners) with a high school GPA of 2.5 or higher on a 4.0 scale; a first-time freshman at Newman University; full-time student and maintains a cumulative GPA of at least 2.25; and active in one or more campus organization each year. **Criteria:** Selection is based on the Committee's review of the applications.

Funds Avail.: $1,500 per year. **Duration:** Annual; four years. **To Apply:** Applicants must visit the Newman University website for the details of application. **Contact:** Newman University, 3100 McCormick Ave. Wichita, KS 67213; Phone: 877-639-6268.

7856 ■ Rick Arkans Eagle Scout Scholarship
(Undergraduate/Scholarship)

Purpose: To support the education of a student active in Boy Scouting, Varsity Scouting, or Venturing. **Focus:** General studies/Field of study not specified. **Qualif.:** Applicants must be currently registered and active in Boy Scouting, Varsity Scouting, or Venturing; have earned the Eagle Scout Award; have earned the Ner Tamid or Etz Chaim religious emblem; active in a synagogue; have demonstrated practical citizenship in the synagogue, school, Scouting unit, and community; must demonstrate financial need; and be enrolled in an accredited high school and in his final year. **Criteria:** Selection is based on the committee's review on the applications.

Funds Avail.: $1,000. **Number Awarded:** 1. **To Apply:** Applicants must submit a complete application. **Deadline:** January 31. **Contact:** National Jewish Committee on Scouting, Boy Scout of America, 1325 W Walnut Hill Ln., Irving, TX, 75015-2079; Phone: 972-580-2000.

7857 ■ University of Louisville Eagle Scout Scholarships *(Undergraduate/Scholarship, Award)*

Purpose: To assist the education of an Eagle Scout student. **Focus:** General studies/Field of study not specified. **Qualif.:** Applicants must be an incoming freshman; a resident of Kentucky or Indiana; achieved the rank of Eagle Scout in the Lincoln Heritage Council, Blue Grass Council, Shawnee Trails Council, Dan Beard Council, or Tri-State Area Council; have a minimum high-school GPA of 3.35 on a 4.0 scale and a minimum score of 24 on the ACT or 1090 on the SAT-I. **Criteria:** Selection is based on the committee's review on the applications.

Funds Avail.: Varies. **Duration:** Annual. **To Apply:** Applicants must visit the University of Louisville website for the details of application. **Deadline:** January 15. **Contact:** Student Financial Aid Office, University of Louisville, Louisville, KY 40292; Phone: 502-852-5511; E-mail: finaid@louisville.edu.

7858 ■ University of Southern Mississippi Eagle Scout Scholarship *(Undergraduate/Scholarship)*

Purpose: To assist the education of scout students. **Focus:** General studies/Field of study not specified. **Qualif.:** Ap-

plicants must have received the Eagle Scout Award or Girl Scout Gold Award designation earned no later than date of high school graduation. **Criteria:** Selection is based on the committee's review of the applications.

Funds Avail.: No specific amount. **Duration:** Annual. **To Apply:** Applicants must submit copy of award certificate or letter from council leader. **Deadline:** July 1. **Contact:** scholars@usm.edu.

7859 ■ Chester M. Vernon Memorial Eagle Scout Scholarships *(Undergraduate/Scholarship)*

Purpose: To support the education of a student active in Boy Scouting, Varsity Scouting, or Venturing. **Focus:** General studies/Field of study not specified. **Qualif.:** Applicants must be currently registered and active in Boy Scouting, Varsity Scouting, or Venturing; have earned the Eagle Scout Award; have earned the Ner Tamid or Etz Chaim religious emblem; active in a synagogue; have demonstrated practical citizenship in the synagogue, school, Scouting unit, and community; have demonstrated financial need; and be enrolled in an accredited high school and in his final year. **Criteria:** Selection is based on the committee's review on the applications.

Funds Avail.: $1,000 per year. **Duration:** Annual; four years. **Number Awarded:** 1. **To Apply:** Applicants must submit a completed application and other required materials. **Deadline:** January 31. **Contact:** National Jewish Committee on Scouting, Boy Scout of America, 1325 W Walnut Hill Ln., Irving, TX, 75015-2079; Phone: 972-580-2000.

7860 ■ Veterans of Foreign Wars Scout of the Year
(Undergraduate/Scholarship)

Purpose: To provide financial support to Eagle Scout students who are in need. **Focus:** General studies/Field of study not specified. **Qualif.:** Applicants must be active member of Boy Scout troops, Venturing crews, and Sea Scout ships; must have received the Eagle Scout Award, the Venturing Silver Award, or the Sea Quartermaster; and must have demonstrated practical citizenship in school, Scouting, and the community. **Criteria:** Selection is based on the committee's review on the applications.

Funds Avail.: $1,000 to $5,000. **Number Awarded:** 3. **To Apply:** Application must be submitted through a single, local VFW post. **Deadline:** March 1.

7861 ■ Zenon C. R. Hansen Leadership Scholarship
(Undergraduate/Scholarship)

Purpose: To assist the education of an Eagle Scout student. **Focus:** General studies/Field of study not specified. **Qualif.:** Applicants must be a full-time Doane College student who is an Eagle Scout; active in the Boy Scouts of America, and planning to remain active in Scouting and leadership activities. **Criteria:** Selection is based on the committee's review on the applications.

Funds Avail.: Varies. **Duration:** Annual. **To Apply:** Applicants may contact the Doane College for the application process and other information. **Deadline:** March 10. **Contact:** Financial Aid Office, Doane College, 1014 Boswell Avenue Crete, NE, 68333; Phone: 800-333-6263.

7862 ■ National Eating Disorders Association (NEDA)
1500 Broadway Suite 1101
New York, NY 10036
Ph: (212)575-6200
Fax: (212)575-1650

Awards are arranged alphabetically below their administering organizations

Free: 800-931-2237
E-mail: info@nationaleatingdisorders.org
URL: www.nationaleatingdisorders.org
Social Media: www.facebook.com/
  NationalEatingDisordersAssociation
www.instagram.com/neda
www.linkedin.com/company/national-eating-disorders
  -association
www.pinterest.com/nedastaff
twitter.com/NEDAstaff
www.youtube.com/user/NEDANETWORK

7863 ■ The Eating Recovery Center Foundation Early Career Investigator Grants *(Professional development/Grant)*

Purpose: To support research projects that cover a range of research domains relevant to the treatment and prevention of eating disorders, including anorexia nervosa, bulimia nervosa and binge eating disorder. **Focus:** Health sciences.

Duration: Annual; up to 2 years.

7864 ■ Feeding Hope Fund for Clinical Research Grants *(Professional development/Grant)*

Purpose: To support research projects that cover a range of research domains relevant to the treatment and prevention of eating disorders, including anorexia nervosa, bulimia nervosa and binge eating disorder. **Focus:** Health sciences. **Criteria:** Selection will be based on the candidates' research track record and other sources of funding. Review of the submitted applications will also be made.

Funds Avail.: $100,000 each ($50,000 per year). **Duration:** Annual; up to 2 years. **Number Awarded:** 2. **To Apply:** Applicants must complete and submit the application form, available at the website, together with biosketches for all key personnel; project description (maximum 4 pages); budget for each year of proposed project. **Deadline:** December 15. **Remarks:** Established in 2013.

7865 ■ National Electrical Manufacturers Representatives Association (NEMRA)

1905 South New Market St.
Carmel, IN 46032
Ph: (914)524-8650
Free: 800-446-3672
E-mail: nemra@nemra.org
URL: www.nemra.org
Social Media: www.linkedin.com/groups/2497384/profile
twitter.com/nemra_and_nmg
www.youtube.com/channel/
  UCHgySxJ49dHQtCPxtwQeZ2g

7866 ■ NEMRA Educational Scholarship Foundation *(Undergraduate, Vocational/Occupational/Scholarship)*

Purpose: To reward the academic excellence of the sons and daughters of NEMRA members and their employees. **Focus:** General studies/Field of study not specified. **Qualif.:** Applicants must be dependent children, age 25 and under, of members of National Electrical Manufacturers Representatives Association (NEMRA) and their employees; high school seniors or graduates or be current postsecondary undergraduates or graduate level students; plan to enroll in full-time undergraduate, graduate or doctoral study at an accredited two-year or four-year college, university, or vocational-technical school for the entire academic year. **Criteria:** Selection based on academic record, as well as participation in school and community activities, work experience, and unusual personal or family circumstances with preference given to applicants demonstrating interest in club membership or majoring in Business administration, marketing and sales or electrical engineering-related fields.

Funds Avail.: No specific amount. **Duration:** Annual. **Number Awarded:** Up to 17. **To Apply:** Applicants must submit a completed and signed application form; a current official transcript; a recommendation from an individual who can give an honest assessment of the applicant's academic and personal abilities such as a teacher, pastor or college advisor; application materials must be placed in a stamped No. 10 business size envelope; two first class stamps are required. **Contact:** Phone: 507-931-1682; E-mail: nemra@nemra.org.

7867 ■ National Endowment for the Arts (NEA)

400 7th St. SW
Washington, DC 20506-0001
Ph: (202)682-5400
URL: www.arts.gov
Social Media: www.facebook.com/
  NationalEndowmentfortheArts
www.instagram.com/neaarts
twitter.com/NEAarts
www.youtube.com/user/NEAarts

7868 ■ NEA/TCG Career Development Program for Designers *(Professional development/Grant)*

Purpose: To provide financial support and creative opportunities to exceptional early-career scenic-lighting, costume and sound designers who seek a career in America's not-for-profit professional theatre. **Focus:** Theater arts. **Qualif.:** Applicants must be early-career theater designers.

Funds Avail.: $25,000. **Duration:** Annual. **Number Awarded:** 6. **Contact:** Jessica Lewis, Artistic Programs Project Coordinator; Email: jlewis@tcg.org.

7869 ■ NEA/TCG Career Development Program *(Professional development/Grant)*

Purpose: To provide financial support and creative opportunities to exceptional early-career stage directors who seek a career in America's not-for-profit professional theatre. **Focus:** Theater arts. **Qualif.:** Applicants must be early-career theatre directors. **Criteria:** Selection will be based on the committee criteria.

Funds Avail.: $25,000. **Duration:** Annual; up to two years. **Number Awarded:** 6. **Contact:** Email:webmgr@arts.gov.

7870 ■ National Endowment for the Humanities (NEH)

400 7th St. SW
Washington, DC 20506
Ph: (202)606-8400
Free: 800-634-1121
E-mail: questions@neh.gov
URL: www.neh.gov
Social Media: www.facebook.com/nehgov
www.instagram.com/nehgov
twitter.com/NEHgov

Awards are arranged alphabetically below their administering organizations

www.youtube.com/channel/UCPQ3xb0ky2WsNM
_U1FKjrNQ

7871 ■ National Endowment for the Humanities Advanced Fellowships for Research in Turkey
(Postdoctorate/Fellowship)

Purpose: To promote American and Turkish research and exchange related to Turkey. **Focus:** Archeology; Art; History; Humanities; Linguistics; Literature; Social sciences. **Qualif.:** Applicants may be U.S. citizens or three-year residents of the U.S. (they may consult ARIT headquarters on questions of eligibility); scholars who have completed all formal training by the application deadline and plan to carry out research in Turkey for four months or longer are eligible.

Funds Avail.: $4,200. **To Apply:** Applicants must provide complete application information. Application materials and three letters of recommendation; download, save, and complete the application form appended here (.pdf); letters of reference sent directly to ARIT by mail or e-mail. Letters should support the proposed research and your capacity to carry out the project and supporting documents in paper form. **Deadline:** November 1.

7872 ■ National Environmental Health Association (NEHA)
720 S Colorado Blvd., Ste. 1000-N
Denver, CO 80246-1926
Ph: (303)756-9090
Fax: (303)691-9490
Free: 866-956-2258
E-mail: staff@neha.org
URL: www.neha.org
Social Media: www.facebook.com/NEHA.org
www.linkedin.com/company/390375
www.linkedin.com/company/national-environmental-health
  -association

7873 ■ NEHA/AAS Scholarship *(Graduate, Undergraduate/Scholarship)*

Purpose: To encourage and support early commitment by students to a career in environmental health. **Focus:** Environmental science. **Qualif.:** Applicants pursuing a Bachelor's Degree in Environmental Health or Postgraduate Degree in Environmental Health Sciences. **Criteria:** Applicants are selected based on the committee's review of the application materials.

Funds Avail.: No specific amount. **Number Awarded:** 3. **To Apply:** Applicants must complete the online application form; provide an official academic transcript from the school in which the applicant is currently enrolled; submit one faculty letter of recommendation from the school in which the applicant is currently enrolled; incomplete applications will not be considered. **Contact:** Jonna Ashley; E-mail: jashley@neha.org.

7874 ■ National Estuarine Research Reserve System (NERRS)
Estuarine Reserves Division, N/ORM5
Office of Ocean and Coastal Resource Management
NOAA Ocean Service
1305 E West Hwy.
Silver Spring, MD 20910
URL: coast.noaa.gov/nerrs

7875 ■ NERRS Graduate Research Fellowship
(Graduate/Fellowship)

Purpose: To support management-related research projects that will enhance scientific understanding of the reserve ecosystem, provide information needed by reserve management and coastal management decision-makers and improve public awareness and understanding of estuarine ecosystems and estuarine management issues. **Focus:** Ecology. **Qualif.:** Applicants must be admitted to or enrolled in a full-time master's or doctoral program at a U.S. accredited university; have completed a majority of the graduate course work at the beginning of the fellowship; and have an approved thesis research program.

Funds Avail.: $20,000. **Duration:** Annual; up to three years. **Number Awarded:** 2. **Deadline:** November 1. **Contact:** Dr. Ken Moore; Phone: 804-684-7384; Email: moore@vims.edu.

7876 ■ National Federation of the Blind (NFB)
200 E Wells St. at Jernigan Pl.
Baltimore, MD 21230
Ph: (410)659-9314
Fax: (410)685-5653
E-mail: nfb@nfb.org
URL: nfb.org
Social Media: www.facebook.com/
  NationalFederationoftheBlind
twitter.com/nfb_voice
www.youtube.com/user/NationsBlind

7877 ■ Kenneth Jernigan Scholarships
(Undergraduate/Scholarship, Monetary)

Purpose: To support and create opportunities for all blind people. **Focus:** General studies/Field of study not specified. **Qualif.:** Applicant must be active NFB member, blind or sighted, who has not yet attended an NFB national convention. **Criteria:** Committee of Scholarship Program will evaluate the application based on the academic excellence, community service, and financial need.

Funds Avail.: $400 - $500 each. **To Apply:** Applications can be submitted online and further details can be obtained from the website. **Deadline:** March 31. **Contact:** Allen Harris; E-mail: kjscholarships@nfb.org; Phone: 410-659-9314, ext. 2415.

7878 ■ National Federation of the Blind Scholarship Program *(Undergraduate/Scholarship, Monetary)*

Purpose: To support outstanding achievement by blind scholars. **Focus:** Architecture; Engineering, Civil; General studies/Field of study not specified; History; Law; Medicine; Religion; Science; Visual impairment. **Qualif.:** Applicant must be legally blind; pursuing or planning to pursue a full-time post secondary course of study, and reside in one of the 50 U.S. States, Puerto Rico, or the District of Columbia. **Criteria:** Selection is based on academic excellence, community service, and leadership.

Funds Avail.: $3,000-$12,000. **Duration:** Annual. **Number Awarded:** 30. **To Apply:** Applications can be submitted online and further details can be obtained from the website. **Deadline:** March 31. **Contact:** National Federation of the Blind 200 East Wells Street at Jernigan Place Baltimore, MD 21230; Cayte Mendez, Chairperson; Phone: 410-659-9314, extension 2415; Email: scholarships@nfb.org.

Awards are arranged alphabetically below their administering organizations

7879 ■ Charles and Melva T. Owen Memorial Scholarships *(Undergraduate/Scholarship, Monetary)*

Purpose: To support and create opportunities for all blind people. **Focus:** General studies/Field of study not specified.

Funds Avail.: $10,000. **To Apply:** Applications can be submitted online and further details can be obtained from the website. **Deadline:** March 31.

7880 ■ E.U. and Gene Parker Scholarships *(Undergraduate/Scholarship, Monetary)*

Purpose: To support and create opportunities for all blind people. **Focus:** General studies/Field of study not specified. **Qualif.:** All applicants must be legally blind; pursuing or planning to pursue a full-time, postsecondary course of study in a degree program at a United States institution; must be participants in the NFB national convention and in all scheduled scholarship program activities. **Criteria:** Committee of Scholarship Program will evaluate the application based on the academic excellence, community service, and financial need.

Funds Avail.: $3,000. **To Apply:** Applications can be submitted online and further details can be obtained from the website. **Deadline:** March 31.

7881 ■ National Federation of Paralegal Associations (NFPA)
400 S 4th St., Ste. 754E
Minneapolis, MN 55415
Ph: (317)454-8312
Fax: (980)444-2269
E-mail: info@paralegals.org
URL: www.paralegals.org
Social Media: www.facebook.com/NFPAparalegals
www.linkedin.com/groups/1072727

7882 ■ NFPA PCCE Scholarship *(Other, Professional development/Scholarship)*

Purpose: To help paralegal students pay for the PCCE exam. **Focus:** Paralegal studies. **Qualif.:** Applicants must be NFPA member; must be eligible to take the PCCE exam. **Criteria:** Recipients are selected based on the quality of the essay and financial needs.

Funds Avail.: Covers the costs of a review manual, an online review course, and the exam fee for the Paralegal CORE Competency Exam. **Duration:** Annual. **To Apply:** Applicants must complete the application form on sponsor's website.

7883 ■ NFPA/Thomson Reuters Scholarships *(Undergraduate, Two Year College/Scholarship)*

Purpose: To support students who pursue paralegal education. **Focus:** Paralegal studies. **Qualif.:** Applicants must be paralegal students in United States; willing to travel to attend the NFPA Annual Convention, $1,000 travel stipend provided to winners.

Funds Avail.: $3,000 first place; $2,000 second place. **Duration:** Annual. **Number Awarded:** 2. **To Apply:** Applicants should submit a letter of recommendation from the director of the paralegal education program, instructor from the paralegal education program, or employer; current official transcript from the paralegal program they are attending, showing at least a B average; statement of financial

need; two references; essay. **Deadline:** July 1.

7884 ■ National Federation of Republican Women (NFRW)
124 N Alfred St.
Alexandria, VA 22314
Ph: (703)548-9688
Fax: (703)548-9836
E-mail: mail@nfrw.org
URL: www.nfrw.org
Social Media: www.facebook.com/nationalfederationofrepublicanwomen
www.instagram.com/republicanwomen
www.linkedin.com/company/national-federation-of-republican-women
twitter.com/NFRW
www.youtube.com/user/NFRW1

7885 ■ National Pathfinder Scholarship *(Graduate, Master's, Undergraduate/Scholarship)*

Purpose: To support students with their education. **Focus:** General studies/Field of study not specified. **Qualif.:** Applicant must be a college undergraduate sophomore, junior or senior, or student enrolled in a master's degree program; must be a U.S. citizen. **Criteria:** State Federation President and will choose applications to be submitted to NFRW. Only completed applications will be considered.

Funds Avail.: $2,500. **Duration:** Annual. **Number Awarded:** 3. **To Apply:** Applicants must submit a completed application form together with three letters of recommendation (include contact numbers of the authors); an official copy of recent college transcript; a (one-page, typed) essay stating why the applicants deserves the scholarship; another (one-page, typed) essay on career goals; a photograph (optional); and State Federation President Certification. **Deadline:** June 1. **Remarks:** Founded in honor of First Lady Nancy Reagan. Established in 1985.

7886 ■ Betty Rendel Scholarships *(Undergraduate/Scholarship)*

Purpose: To support students with their education. **Focus:** Economics; Government; Political science. **Qualif.:** Applicants must be college undergraduate students majoring in political science, government or economics; and have completed at least two years of college coursework. **Criteria:** Applications must be received by applicant's State Federation President who will choose an application to submit to NFRW.

Funds Avail.: $1,000. **Duration:** Annual. **Number Awarded:** 3. **To Apply:** Applicants must submit a completed application form together with three letters of recommendation (include contact numbers of the authors); an official copy of recent college transcript; a 1-page typed essay stating why the applicants deserves the scholarship; another 1-page typed essay on career goals; a photograph (optional); and State Federation President Certification. **Deadline:** June 1. **Remarks:** Founded in honor of NFRW Past President Betty Rendel's extraordinary leadership skills and dedication to the Republican Party in her home state of Indiana. Established in 1995.

7887 ■ National Forum for Black Public Administrators (NFBPA)
777 N Capitol St. NE, Ste. 550
Washington, DC 20002

Awards are arranged alphabetically below their administering organizations

Ph: (202)408-9300
Free: 844-235-6154
URL: www.nfbpa.org
Social Media: www.facebook.com/BPA83
twitter.com/NFBPA1
www.youtube.com/user/NFBPA2011

7888 ■ CIGNA Healthcare Graduate Scholarships
(Graduate/Scholarship)

Purpose: To support the education and development of African-American students to prepare them for careers in public administration. **Focus:** Political science; Public administration; Urban affairs/design/planning. **Qualif.:** Applicants must be full-time students, working towards a graduate degree in public administration, political science, urban affairs, public policy, or a related field preferably at an HBCU with excellent interpersonal and analytical abilities, strong oral and written communication skills and a 3.0 or better GPA for at least 1 remaining full-time semester. **Criteria:** Applicants will be evaluated based on some criteria designed by the Scholarship Selection Committee.

Funds Avail.: $5,000. **Duration:** Annual. **Number Awarded:** 2. **To Apply:** Applicants must submit cover letter describing status as a student and other relevant information that might be used in evaluating application (extra-curricular activities, volunteer activities, etc.); official copies of all graduate (if applicable) and undergraduate transcripts; two reference letters, at least one of which should be from a faculty member; three-page essay, detailing autobiography and career goals and objectives; and a current resume. **Contact:** Application package should be sent to, NFBPA, ATTN: Scholarships 777 N Capitol St. NE, Ste. 550, Washington, DC, 20002; Marcia L. Conner; Email: mconner@nfbpa.org; Phone: 202-408-9300 ext. 114.

7889 ■ CIGNA Undergraduate Scholarships
(Undergraduate/Scholarship)

Purpose: To support the education and development of African-American students to prepare them for careers in public administration. **Focus:** Political science; Public administration; Urban affairs/design/planning. **Qualif.:** Applicants must be full-time students working towards an undergraduate degree in public administration, political science, urban affairs, public policy, or a related field preferably at an HBCU with excellent interpersonal and analytical abilities, strong oral and written communication skills and a 3.5 or better grade point average for completed 1 full-time college semester and at least 1 full-time academic year. **Criteria:** Recipients will be selected based on financial need.

Funds Avail.: $10,000. **Duration:** Annual. **Number Awarded:** 1. **To Apply:** Applicants must submit a cover letter describing their current student status and other relevant information to support in evaluating the application; must also submit the following materials: official copies of all graduate and undergraduate transcripts; two reference letters (at least one of which should be from a faculty member); three-page essay detailing autobiography and career goals and objectives; a current resume; three-page essay answering the question, "In your opinion, what are the five most critical skills public administrators ought to possess, and why?". **Deadline:** February 28. **Contact:** Application package should be sent to, NFBPA, ATTN: Scholarships 777 N Capitol St. NE, Ste. 550, Washington, DC, 20002; Marcia L. Conner; Email: mconner@nfbpa.org; Phone: 202-408-9300 ext. 114.

7890 ■ Johnnie L. Cochran, Jr./MWH Scholarships
(Graduate, Undergraduate/Scholarship)

Purpose: To help NFBPA further achieve its mission of attracting the best and brightest African Americans to careers in public service. **Focus:** Public service. **Qualif.:** Applicants must be full-time students working towards an undergraduate or graduate degree in public administration, political science, urban affairs, public policy, or a related field who have excellent interpersonal and analytical abilities, strong oral and written communication skills and have 3.0 or better GPA for at least 1 full time semester remaining. **Criteria:** Evaluation will be made by the Scholarship Selection Committee.

Funds Avail.: $5,000. **Duration:** Annual. **To Apply:** Applicants must submit a cover letter describing their current student status and other relevant information to support in evaluating the application. Applicants must also submit the following materials: official copies of all graduate and undergraduate transcripts; two reference letters (at least one of which should be from a faculty member); three-page essay detailing autobiography and career goals and objectives; and current resume.

7891 ■ NFBPA Future Colleagues Scholarships
(Undergraduate/Scholarship)

Purpose: To provide financial assistance for the education of undergraduate students pursuing a career in public service. **Focus:** Public service.

Funds Avail.: $1,000. **Duration:** Annual.

7892 ■ NFBPA Land-Use Planning Scholarships
(Master's, Doctorate/Scholarship)

Purpose: To support the education and development of post-secondary African American students. **Focus:** Public service. **Qualif.:** Applicants must be full-time students working towards a graduate degree (master's or doctoral) in urban planning or a related field (such as transportation engineering, landscape architecture, environmental planning, etc.); must be enrolled in an accredited college or university and either have a home domicile in the state of Maryland or attend a college or university located in Maryland; should have excellent interpersonal and analytical abilities, strong oral and written communication skills; should have a 3.0 or better grade point average and at least 1 full-time semester remaining. **Criteria:** Evaluation will be made by the Scholarship Selection Committee.

Funds Avail.: $3,000. **Duration:** Annual. **To Apply:** Applicants must submit a cover letter describing their current student status and other relevant information to support in evaluating the application. Applicants must also submit the following materials: official copies of all graduate and undergraduate transcripts; two reference letters (at least one of which should be from a faculty member); three-page essay detailing autobiography and career goals and objectives; and current resume.

7893 ■ RA Consulting Service/Maria Riley Scholarships
(Graduate, Undergraduate/Scholarship)

Purpose: To provide financial assistance for the education and development of public administrators serving in the engineering and information technology field. **Focus:** Engineering. **Qualif.:** Applicants must be full-time students, working towards an undergraduate or graduate degree in engineering or information technology with excellent interpersonal and analytical abilities, strong oral and written communication skills and a 3.0 or better grade point aver-

Awards are arranged alphabetically below their administering organizations

age for at least 1 remaining full-time semester. **Criteria:** Evaluation will be made by the Scholarship Selection Committee.

Funds Avail.: $2,500. **Duration:** Annual. **To Apply:** Applicants must submit a cover letter describing their current student status and other relevant information to support in evaluating the application. Applicants must also submit the following materials: official copies of all graduate and undergraduate transcripts; two reference letters (at least one of which should be from a faculty member); three-page essay detailing autobiography and career goals and objectives; and current resume.

7894 ■ Willie T. Loud scholarship (Undergraduate, Graduate/Scholarship)

Purpose: To assist African Americans in their pursuit of careers in public service. **Focus:** Public service. **Qualif.:** Applicants must be full-time students with 3.0 or better GPA who are at least 1 full-time semester remaining or working towards a Bachelor's or Master's degree in Public Administration or a related field and should have strong interpersonal skills, excellent writing, analytical, and oral communication abilities. **Criteria:** Applicants will be evaluated based on criteria designed by the Scholarship Committee.

Funds Avail.: $5,000. **Duration:** Annual. **To Apply:** Applicants must submit a cover letter describing current student status and other relevant information that might be used in evaluating application; official copies of all graduate and undergraduate transcripts; two reference letters (at least one of which should be from a faculty member); three-page essay detailing their autobiography and career goals and objectives; and current resume. **Remarks:** Established in 1997.

7895 ■ National Foster Parent Association (NFPA)

14508 Owen-Tech Boulevard, Ste. 129
Austin, TX 78728
Free: 800-557-5238
E-mail: info@nfpaonline.org
URL: nfpaonline.org
Social Media: www.linkedin.com/company/nfpaonlinw
twitter.com/NFPAOnline
www.youtube.com/channel/UCi-jmOBA4EsddO77-Cl4bTw

7896 ■ NFPA Youth Scholarships (Undergraduate/Scholarship)

Purpose: To support foster parents in achieving safety, permanence and well-being for the children and youth in their care. **Focus:** General studies/Field of study not specified. **Qualif.:** Applicant must be a birth, foster, kinship, and youth adopted through foster care wishing to further their education beyond high school, and member of NFPA. **Criteria:** Applicants are selected based on the academic performance.

Funds Avail.: $500 each. **Duration:** Annual. **To Apply:** Applicants must submit a completed online application form; have a parent or adult that is a member of NFPA; a minimum of two (2) letters of recommendation from: foster parents, social workers, residential center, principal/teacher/guidance counselor, employer, etc.; and an essay in 300-500 words on "How my foster care experience has shaped my future goals". Applicants must also provide a copy of high school transcript (planning to attend College or

University); return unused portion or appropriate percentage if withdrawing from college/university or course/program or unable to maintain grade point average required by the college/university or course/program. **Deadline:** April 5.

7897 ■ National Gallery of Art (NGA)

2000B S Club Dr.
Landover, MD 20785
Ph: (202)737-4215
URL: www.nga.gov
Social Media: www.facebook.com/nationalgalleryofart
www.instagram.com/ngadc
www.pinterest.com/ngadc
twitter.com/ngadc
www.youtube.com/user/NationalGalleryArtDC

7898 ■ NGA Conservation Fellowships (Graduate/Fellowship)

Purpose: To enable graduates of conservation programs to participate in the Gallery's mission to care for the collections. **Focus:** Art conservation. **Qualif.:** Applicants should be graduates of a recognized training program or have equivalent training; should have no more than five years of work experience and a proven record of research and writing ability; and must possess English-language skills.

Funds Avail.: Amount not specified. **Duration:** 3/year. **To Apply:** Applicants must prepare the transcripts of both undergraduate and graduate courses of academic study; a curriculum vitae with basic biographical information; current addresses and telephone numbers; a brief statement of interest and intent for the fellowship; offprints of any publications or lectures; two supporting letters of recommendation; and one letter of personal reference. **Deadline:** Mid-February. **Remarks:** Established in 1983. **Contact:** Michael Skalka, Conservation Administrator, Conservation Division, National Gallery of Art, 2000B South Club Dr., Landover, MD, 20785; Email: dcl@nga.gov.

7899 ■ National Garden Clubs (NGC)

4401 Magnolia Ave.
Saint Louis, MO 63110
Ph: (314)776-7574
E-mail: headquarters@gardenclub.org
URL: www.gardenclub.org
Social Media: www.facebook.com/NGCSOCIALMEDIA
www.instagram.com/nationalgarden/?hl=en
www.pinterest.com/natlgardenclubs
www.youtube.com/channel/UCUnNSWjpNIff8QuqH534bMA

7900 ■ NGC College Scholarships (Graduate, Undergraduate/Scholarship)

Purpose: To support career of students majoring in fields of study related to horticulture and the environment. **Focus:** Agricultural sciences; Biology; Botany; Ecology; Economics; Environmental conservation; Floriculture; Forestry; Horticulture; Land management; Landscape architecture and design; Wildlife conservation, management, and science.

Funds Avail.: $4,000 for each. **Duration:** Annual. **Number Awarded:** Up to forty-one (41). **To Apply:** Applicants must submit a completed application form together with official

Awards are arranged alphabetically below their administering organizations

academic transcript(s); a letter discussing goals, background, financial need and commitment to chosen field of study (limited to 2 typed pages); a list of extracurricular activities, honors and recognitions received; signed financial aid Form; and three letters of recommendation (each limited to 1 typed page). **Deadline:** February 1. **Contact:** Lisa Robinson.

7901 ■ National GEM Consortium
1430 Duke St.
Alexandria, VA 22314
Ph: (703)562-3646
Fax: (202)207-3518
E-mail: info@gemfellowship.org
URL: www.gemfellowship.org
Social Media: www.facebook.com/gem.consortium
twitter.com/gemfellowship
www.youtube.com/channel/UCsklM7CmIThdEwy-DCkjnUQ

7902 ■ National GEM Consortium - MS Engineering Fellowships *(Master's/Fellowship)*
Purpose: To support highly qualified but underrepresented students who wish to pursue graduate studies in engineering or science. **Focus:** Engineering; Science.

Funds Avail.: $4,000 living stipend per full-time semester up to 4 semesters ($8K per academic year -3 quarters). **Duration:** 3 semesters or 4 quarters. **To Apply:** Applicants must submit copy of official GRE scores.

7903 ■ National GEM Consortium - PhD Engineering Fellowships *(Master's, Graduate/Fellowship)*
Purpose: To offer funding to underrepresented minority students who have either completed or are currently enrolled in a master's in engineering program. **Focus:** Engineering.

Funds Avail.: $16,000. **Duration:** Five years. **To Apply:** Applicants must submit copy of official GRE scores. **Deadline:** November 13.

7904 ■ National GEM Consortium - PhD Science Fellowships *(Doctorate, Graduate/Fellowship)*
Purpose: To increase the number of minority students who pursue doctoral degrees in the natural science disciplines. **Focus:** Biological and clinical sciences; Chemistry; Computer and information sciences; Earth sciences; Mathematics and mathematical sciences; Physics.

Funds Avail.: $16,000. **Duration:** Five years. **To Apply:** Applicants must submit copy of official GRE scores.

7905 ■ National Geographic Society (NGS)
1145 17th St. NW
Washington, DC 20036
Ph: (202)857-7000
Free: 800-373-1717
E-mail: legacy@ngs.org
URL: www.nationalgeographic.org
Social Media: www.facebook.com/InsideNatGeo
twitter.com/InsideNatGeo

7906 ■ National Geographic Conservation Trust Grants *(Doctorate, Advanced Professional/Grant)*
Purpose: To support conservation activities around the world as they fit within the mission of the National Geographic Society. **Focus:** Environmental conservation. **Qualif.:** Applicants are not expected to have a PhD or other advanced degrees; however, applicants must provide a record of prior research or conservation action as it pertains to the proposed project. **Criteria:** Selection will be based on the committee's criteria.

Duration: Annual. **Contact:** conservationtrust@ngs.org.

7907 ■ National Geographic Expedition Council Grants *(Advanced Professional/Grant)*
Purpose: To support exploration and adventure worldwide. **Focus:** Environmental conservation. **Qualif.:** Applicants are expected to have qualifications and experience pertinent to the expedition or project they propose; advanced academic degrees may be required, depending on the nature of the project. International applicants are encouraged. **Criteria:** Selection will be based on the committee's criteria.

Funds Avail.: $15,000. **Duration:** Annual. **Contact:** ecouncil@ngs.org.

7908 ■ National Geographic Society/Waitt Grants *(Advanced Professional/Grant, Award)*
Purpose: To fund projects that require venture capital, supporting exceptional projects while foregoing a time-consuming peer-review process. **Focus:** Environmental conservation. **Qualif.:** Applicants are not required to have advanced degrees to be eligible for funding, though they will be required to show a commensurate level of expertise and experience; must have an affiliation with an educational organization or other institution. **Criteria:** Selection will be based on scientific merit.

Funds Avail.: $5,000 - $15,000. **Duration:** Annual. **Contact:** waitt@ngs.org.

7909 ■ National Geographic Young Explorers Grants *(Advanced Professional/Grant)*
Purpose: To offer opportunities to individuals to pursue research, conservation, and exploration-related projects consistent with National Geographic's existing grant programs, including: the Committee for Research and Exploration (CRE), the Expeditions Council (EC), and the Conservation Trust (CT). **Focus:** Conservation of natural resources; Environmental conservation. **Qualif.:** Applicants must be US citizens or foreign nationals. Researchers planning to work in countries abroad should make great effort to include at least one local collaborator as part of their team; they are not required to have advanced degrees; however, a record of prior experience in the fields of research, conservation, or exploration should be submitted as it pertains to the proposed project. **Criteria:** Selection will be based on the submitted application.

Funds Avail.: $2,000 to $5,000. **Duration:** Annual. **To Apply:** Applicants may visit the website for the online application process. **Contact:** cre@ngs.org; conservationtrust@ngs.org; council@ngs.org.

7910 ■ National Ground Water Association (NGWA)
601 Dempsey Rd.
Westerville, OH 43081
Ph: (614)898-7791
Fax: (614)898-7786
Free: 800-551-7379
E-mail: ngwa@ngwa.org

Awards are arranged alphabetically below their administering organizations

URL: www.ngwa.org
Social Media: www.facebook.com/NGWAFB
www.instagram.com/nationalgroundwater
twitter.com/ngwatweets
www.youtube.com/user/NGWATUBE

7911 ■ Len Assante Scholarship Program
(Undergraduate/Scholarship)

Purpose: To assist those studying groundwater-related fields. **Focus:** Water supply industry. **Qualif.:** Applicant must be a full-time students only (including high school seniors who are applying for scholarships to be used in their first quarter or semester of post-secondary study). **Criteria:** Recipients are selected based on academic performance and financial need. Incomplete applications will not be evaluated; an independent panel decides how to distribute the funds and the number of scholarships to be awarded from the pool of scholarship applicants.

Funds Avail.: Up to $5,000. **Duration:** Annual. **Number Awarded:** Varies. **To Apply:** Applicants must complete the application form. **Deadline:** Varies.

7912 ■ National Guard Association of Rhode Island (NGARI)
645 New London Ave.
Cranston, RI 02920-3003
E-mail: ngarinews@gmail.com
URL: ngari.org
Social Media: www.facebook.com/ngarhodeisland

7913 ■ National Guard Association of Rhode Island Scholarship *(Undergraduate/Scholarship)*

Purpose: To support members and their families by providing them with a scholarship. **Focus:** General studies/Field of study not specified. **Criteria:** Selection will be based on the committee's criteria.

Funds Avail.: No specific amount. **Duration:** Annual. **To Apply:** Applicants must furnish copies of College Board exam scores (PSAT, SAT, etc.) and high school or college transcripts with the fully completed application; they are strongly encouraged to provide any additional information that may be helpful to the selection committee. **Deadline:** May 31. **Contact:** NGARI Scholarship Committee, Command Readiness Center, 645 New London Ave., Cranston, RI, 02920.

7914 ■ National Guard Association of Texas (NGAT)
3706 Crawford Ave.
Austin, TX 78731
Ph: (512)454-7300
Fax: (512)467-6803
Free: 800-252-6428
E-mail: membership@ngat.org
URL: www.ngat.org
Social Media: www.facebook.com/national-guard
-association-of-texas-ngat/354269962037
www.pinterest.com/ngatx
twitter.com/NGATX

7915 ■ NGAT Educational Foundation Scholarship
(Graduate, Undergraduate/Scholarship)

Purpose: To provide educational assistance for deserving students and dependents of the texas military forces who want to pursue their education. **Focus:** General studies/Field of study not specified. **Qualif.:** Applicants must be current annual or life member of NGAT or the spouse or dependent son or daughter of a current annual or life member. **Criteria:** Applicants will be selected based on the criteria of the scholarship committee.

Funds Avail.: $500 - $5,000. **Duration:** Annual. **To Apply:** Applicants must submit a completed application form available online along with an essay stating their specific facts about their desire to continue their education; for high school applicants must have a recent educational transcript and should reflect class rank; must include the first semester of the 12th grade transcript; for college freshmen: must include their high school transcript with their application; for undergraduate and graduate: must have a copy of their latest college transcript; must have a letter of recommendation from commanders, teachers, ministers, or others not related to them; photocopies of all of the above and keep it for your files. **Contact:** Theresa Billeck-Zuniga, NGAT Education Committee, 3706 Crawford Ave., Austin, Tx 78731-6803; Phone: 512-454-7300; Email: rlindner@ngat.org.

7916 ■ National Hartford Centers of Gerontological Nursing Excellence
11130 Sunrise Valley Dr., Ste. 350
Reston, VA 20191
Ph: (703)885-3500
Fax: (703)234-4147
E-mail: info@nhcgne.org
URL: www.nhcgne.org
Social Media: www.facebook.com/NHCGNE
www.linkedin.com/company/national-harford-center-of
-gerontological-nursing-excellence
twitter.com/NHCGNE

7917 ■ Claire M. Fagin Fellow Award *(Doctorate/Scholarship)*

Purpose: To assist doctorally prepared nurses committed to academic careers in gerontological nursing. **Focus:** Medicine, Geriatric.

Number Awarded: 1. **Contact:** Email: info@nhcgne.org.

7918 ■ NHCGNE Patricia G. Archbold Scholar Award *(Doctorate/Scholarship)*

Purpose: To support doctoral work for nurses committed to careers in academic gerontological nursing. **Focus:** Medicine, Geriatric.

Contact: Email: info@nhcgne.org.

7919 ■ National Hemophilia Foundation (NHF)
7 Penn Plaza Ste. 1204
New York, NY 10001
Ph: (212)328-3700
Fax: (212)328-3777
E-mail: mrice@hemophilia.org
URL: www.hemophilia.org
Social Media: www.facebook.com/
NationalHemophiliaFoundation
instagram.com/nhf_hemophilia
twitter.com/NHF_Hemophilia
youtube.com/NHFvideo

7920 ■ Beth Carew Memorial Scholarship Program
(Undergraduate/Scholarship)

Purpose: To provide assistance and support to individual and families affected by chronic illness and help these

Awards are arranged alphabetically below their administering organizations

students obtain a higher education degree. **Focus:** General studies/Field of study not specified. **Qualif.:** Applicant must be an individual diagnosed with hemophilia, von Willebrand disease or other inherited bleeding disorder; either entering or attending an accredited 2- or 4-year undergraduate institution in the US.; may be high school seniors, undergrad freshmen, sophomores or juniors.

Funds Avail.: $3,000-$6,000. **Duration:** Annual. **Number Awarded:** Up to 10. **Deadline:** February 19. **Contact:** Colburn-Keenan Foundation, Inc, PO Box 811, Enfield, CT, 6083; Phone: 800-966-2431; Email: admin@colkeen.org.

7921 ■ Kevin Child Scholarship (Undergraduate/ Scholarship)

Purpose: To encourage aspirations of higher education among individuals with bleeding disorders by supporting their education. **Focus:** General studies/Field of study not specified. **Qualif.:** Applicant must have hemophilia A or B, and be a high school senior with aspirations of attending an institute of higher education (college, university or vocational-technical school); a college student already pursuing a post-secondary education. **Criteria:** Recipients will be selected based on academic performance, participation in school or community activities and an essay detailing educational and career goals.

Funds Avail.: $1,000. **Duration:** Annual. **Number Awarded:** 1. **To Apply:** Applicants must complete the application form and should include personal essay; a letter of recommendation; and an official school transcript. **Deadline:** June 21. **Remarks:** The Scholarship was established in honor of Kevin Child. **Contact:** NHF/HANDI, 7 Penn Plz., 370 Seventh Ave., Ste. 1204, New York, NY, 10001; Phone: 800-424-2634, ext. 2; Email: handi@hemophilia.org.

7922 ■ Pfizer Soozie Courter Hemophilia Scholarship Program (Undergraduate/Scholarship)

Purpose: To provide educational assistance to people with hemophilia and their families. **Focus:** General studies/Field of study not specified. **Qualif.:** Applicants must have been diagnosed with hemophilia A or B; be U.S. residents attending a school in the U.S. and meet one of the following educational criteria: high school seniors or graduates, or have completed high school or an equivalent, or currently accepted to (or enrolled in) a junior college, college (undergraduate or graduate), or vocational school. **Criteria:** Recipients are selected based on the best combination of a creative and persuasive essay, excellent recommendations, and superior academic standing.

Funds Avail.: $4,000 each (graduates); $2,500 each (undergraduates). **Duration:** Annual. **Number Awarded:** 5 graduates; 10 undergraduates. **To Apply:** Applicants should include essay, completed release form, two personal recommendations, one healthcare provider recommendation, and all original transcript documents. **Deadline:** May 4. **Remarks:** Established in 1997. **Contact:** Pfizer Scholarship Program, 120 Albany St., Twr. 1, Ste. 503, New Brunswick, NJ, 08901; Email: Pfizerscholarship@Soundhc.com.

7923 ■ "Education is Power" Scholarships (Undergraduate/Scholarship)

Purpose: To inspire attainment of higher education among individuals with hemophilia and von Willebrand Disease by providing educational funds. **Focus:** General studies/Field of study not specified. **Qualif.:** Applicants must be U.S. residents living with hemophilia or von Willebrand disease and attending a community college, junior college, four-

year college, university, or vocational school. **Criteria:** Selection shall be based on the aforementioned qualifications and compliance with the application details.

Funds Avail.: $500 to 2,500. **Duration:** Annual. **Number Awarded:** 20. **To Apply:** Applicants must submit the completed application form available from the website (www.medprorx.com); documentation from a physician/nurse of the applicant's bleeding disorder; copy of diploma or graduate equivalency diploma (GED); most recent transcript; proof of admission to the school; proof of school tuition; a separate document outlining the applicant's community involvement and/or volunteer work; an essay (no less than 250 words); and one letter of recommendation or character reference. **Contact:** MedPro Rx, Inc., 140 Northway Court, Raleigh, North Carolina 27615-4916; Att'n: Kathy Robinette-Stoneberg, Scholarship Coordinator; Phone: 866-528-4963; Email: educationispower@medprorx.com.

7924 ■ Joshua Gomes Memorial Scholarship Fund (Graduate/Scholarship)

Purpose: To provide academic scholarships for young adults with HIV/AIDS. **Focus:** General studies/Field of study not specified. **Qualif.:** Applicants must be HIV positive or have AIDS; must be accepted into or enrolled in a US college, university, institute or technical college; must be accepted into or enrolled in full-time undergraduate or graduate study.

Funds Avail.: $1,000. **Duration:** Annual. **Number Awarded:** 1. **To Apply:** Applicants must submit the completed application form available from the website; letter from a doctor certifying that the applicant is HIV positive or has AIDS; official transcripts from high school showing the applicant's cumulative GPA; letter of acceptance from a U.S. college or university; three letters of recommendation; and an attached 500-word essay; recent photograph of the applicant. **Deadline:** July 15. **Contact:** Joshua Gomes Memorial Scholarship Fund, 45767 McKenzie Hwy., Vida, OR, 97488.

7925 ■ Lawrence Madeiros Scholarship (Undergraduate/Scholarship)

Purpose: To inspire educational pursuits among individuals with bleeding disorders by providing financial aid. **Focus:** General studies/Field of study not specified. **Qualif.:** Applicants must be students graduating from high school with inherited bleeding disorder or other chronic disorder attending an accredited college or universe.

Funds Avail.: $1,000. **Duration:** Annual. **Number Awarded:** 1. **To Apply:** Applicants must submit the completed application form available from the website along with a copy of current transcript and a statement of recommendation; recent photo; copy of SAT scores. **Deadline:** May 1. **Contact:** The Lawrence Madeiros Scholarship, PO Box 11 Mayfield, New York 12117; Phone: 518-863-8998.

7926 ■ Doreen McMullan McCarthy Memorial Academic Scholarship for Women with Bleeding Disorders (Undergraduate/Scholarship)

Purpose: To assist women with bleeding disorders in their pursuit of post high school studies. **Focus:** Hemophilia. **Qualif.:** Applicants must be female residents of the U.S. and have a bleeding or clotting disorder diagnosed by a hematologist, including those with a diagnosis of von Willebrand disease, hemophilia, platelet disorder, or other factor deficiency, carrier status or clotting disorder. **Criteria:** Selection will be based on the submitted application, essay,

Awards are arranged alphabetically below their administering organizations

achievements, and community service to the bleeding disorders community.

Funds Avail.: $2,500. **To Apply:** Applicants must submit the following: application form; essay; and, personal reference. **Contact:** Sonia Roger at sroger@hemophilia.org.

7927 ■ National Hispanic Coalition of Federal Aviation Employees (NHCFAE)

PO Box 23276
Washington, DC 20026-3276
E-mail: dopa@nhcfae.org
URL: nhcfae.org

7928 ■ Rene Matos Memorial Scholarship Program
(Undergraduate, Vocational/Occupational/Scholarship)

Purpose: To assist dependents of NHCFAE members, students of minority and women complete their higher education efforts by recognizing and rewarding academically superior performance and achievements, leadership and community involvement. **Focus:** General studies/Field of study not specified. **Qualif.:** Applicants must be accepted to or attending an accredited college, university, or vocational/ trade school at the time the scholarship is awarded; must be US citizens or residing in the United states or Puerto Rico.

Funds Avail.: No specific amount. **To Apply:** Applicants must complete the online application and submit the following: completed application form; financial need statement; official transcript; must have school compute and annotate GPA on official transcript based on 4.0 (unweighted; letter of recommendation; letter of Recommendation (dated within past year) is to be submitted from a school official who can verify your academic honors and/or awards; student activities; and community involvement; faxed applications will not be accepted. **Deadline:** May 1. **Remarks:** The scholarship was named in the honor of Rene Matos. **Contact:** NHCFAE Scholarship Selection Committee, PO Box 23276, Washington, DC, 20026-3276; E-mail: doe@nhcfae.org.

7929 ■ National Hispanic Foundation for the Arts (NHFA)

1050 Connecticut Ave. NW, 5th Fl.
Washington, DC 20036
Ph: (202)293-8330
Fax: (202)772-3101
E-mail: info@hispanicarts.org
URL: www.hispanicarts.org
Social Media: www.facebook.com/hispanicarts
twitter.com/felix_sanchez

7930 ■ NHFA Scholarships *(Graduate/Scholarship)*

Purpose: To support the education of Hispanic youth in the media, arts, and communications industry. **Focus:** Arts; Communications; Media arts. **Criteria:** Selection shall be based on academic record, academic plans and career goals, financial need (for educational purposes), community service, compelling essay responses, letter of recommendation, and portfolio submission.

Funds Avail.: No specific amount. **To Apply:** Applicants must complete the scholarship application online; must provide transcripts; letter of recommendation and financial information documentation. **Deadline:** July 31. **Contact:** NHFA Scholarship selection committee, 1050 Connecticut

Ave., N.W. 5th Floor, Washington, DC 20036; Phone: 202-293-8330; Fax: 202-772-3101.

7931 ■ National Honor Society (NHS)

1904 Association Dr.
Reston, VA 20191-1537
Ph: (703)860-0200
Fax: (703)476-5432
Free: 866-647-7253
E-mail: nhs@nhs.us
URL: www.nhs.us
Social Media: www.facebook.com/NHSandNJHS
www.instagram.com/nhs_njhs
twitter.com/nhs_njhs

7932 ■ NHS Scholarships *(Undergraduate/ Scholarship)*

Purpose: To provide educational assistance to NHS members. **Focus:** General studies/Field of study not specified. **Qualif.:** Candidate must be an active NHS member in good standing, a senior enrolled at a high school with an active NHS chapter.**Criteria:** Selection is based on scholarship, service, leadership, character, and financial need is also a consideration.

Funds Avail.: Varies. **Duration:** Annual. **To Apply:** Interested applicants may contact the Society for the application process and other details. **Deadline:** December 7. **Remarks:** Established in 1946. **Contact:** Email: scholarship@nhs.us; URL: www.nhs.us/scholarship.

7933 ■ National Housing Endowment

1201 15th St. NW
Washington, DC 20005
Free: 800-368-5242
E-mail: nhe@nahb.org
URL: www.nationalhousingendowment.org
Social Media: www.facebook.com/
 NationalHousingEndowment

7934 ■ Lee S. Evans/National Housing Endowment Scholarships *(Undergraduate, Graduate/Scholarship)*

Purpose: To assist promising students entering the field of residential construction management. **Focus:** Construction. **Qualif.:** Applicants must be registered as full-time undergraduate or graduate students; have at least one full academic year of course work remaining after the scholarship is awarded; be majoring in construction management, mortgage finance, or a construction related field in an accredited four-year institution; and, demonstrate an interest in obtaining employment in the construction industry, mortgage finance, or a construction related field upon graduation. **Criteria:** Selection is based on preference will be given to students who are current members (or will be a member in the upcoming semester) of a student chapter of the National Association of Home Builders (NAHB) with both A) elected officers and B) a demonstrated program of activities.

Funds Avail.: No specific amount. **Duration:** Annual. **To Apply:** Applicants should include at least one semester of completed course work at a college or university on their official transcript. **Deadline:** March 15. **Remarks:** Established in 1990.

7935 ■ Herman J. Smith Scholarship *(Undergraduate, Graduate/Scholarship)*

Purpose: To address the pressing need for educating and training construction managers in the residential building

Awards are arranged alphabetically below their administering organizations

industry. **Focus:** Construction. **Qualif.:** Applicants must be registered as full-time undergraduate or graduate students; have at least one full academic year of course work remaining after the scholarship is awarded; be majoring in construction management, mortgage finance, or a construction related field in an accredited four-year institution; and, demonstrate an interest in obtaining employment in the construction industry, mortgage finance, or a construction related field upon graduation. **Criteria:** Selection will be based on financial need (for educational purposes); career goals; academic achievement; employment history; extracurricular activities; recommendations; preference will be given to applicants who are legal residents of Texas or attend an academic institution in Texas.

Funds Avail.: No specific amount. **Duration:** Annual. **To Apply:** Applicants should includes application form; transcript; three letters of recommendation; and an essay. **Deadline:** March 15. **Remarks:** The scholarship was established in honor of Herman J. Smith for his lifelong commitment to both the housing industry and to the education of future generations of home builders. Established in 1987. **Contact:** NHE Scholarship; Phone: 202-266-8069; Email: Scholarships@nahb.org.

7936 ■ National Huguenot Society (NHS)
7340 Blanco Rd., Ste. 104
San Antonio, TX 78216
URL: huguenot.netnation.com

7937 ■ National Huguenot Society College and Postgraduate Student Scholarships *(Undergraduate, Postgraduate/Scholarship)*

Purpose: To provide financial aid for higher education of students who are members of the National Huguenot Society. **Focus:** General studies/Field of study not specified. **Criteria:** Recipients will be selected based on academic standing and financial need.

Funds Avail.: $5,000. **Duration:** Annual. **Number Awarded:** Varies. **To Apply:** Applicants must complete the application form; attach proof of enrollment at an accredited college or graduate school; attach a transcript of college grades for last two years showing a 3.0 or better GPA; attach proof of membership in the National Huguenot Society. **Deadline:** February 1. **Contact:** Chairman of the Scholarship Committee via e-mail at scholarship@huguenot.netnation.com.

7938 ■ National Humanities Center (NHC)
7 TW Alexander Dr.
Research Triangle Park, NC 27709-2256
Ph: (919)549-0661
Fax: (919)990-8535
E-mail: info@nationalhumanitiescenter.org
URL: nationalhumanitiescenter.org

7939 ■ National Humanities Center Fellowships *(Doctorate, Postdoctorate/Fellowship)*

Purpose: To promote and encourage advanced study and research on humanities. **Focus:** Humanities. **Criteria:** Selection shall be based on the aforementioned applicants' qualifications and compliance with the application details.

Funds Avail.: $65,000. **Duration:** Annual. **Number Awarded:** Up to 40. **To Apply:** Applicants must submit the completed application form together with a curriculum vitae

(maximum of 4 pages); a project description (1, 000-word); a one-page tentative outline of chapters; and a short bibliography. Submit application materials in five copies via regular mail (materials must not be stapled); short bibliography (up to 2 pages). **Deadline:** October 8.

7940 ■ National Industrial Belting Association (NIBA)
1818 Parmenter St, Ste 30
Middleton, WI 53562
Ph: (608)310-7549
E-mail: staff@niba.org
URL: www.niba.org
Social Media: www.facebook.com/NIBABeltingAssn
twitter.com/NIBABeltingAssn

7941 ■ NIBA Presidential Scholarships *(Undergraduate/Scholarship)*

Purpose: To provide financial assistance to an individual pursuing a minimum two-year course at an accredited college, university or technical school. **Focus:** General studies/Field of study not specified. **Qualif.:** Applicants must be children of NIBA Distributor/ Fabricator Member Company employees and must attend a two-year or more accredited college, university or technical school. **Criteria:** Candidates will be evaluated based on academic achievement, community service/activities, demonstration of leadership and written thesis.

Funds Avail.: $4,000. **Duration:** Annual. **To Apply:** Applicants must submit resume including contact information, work experience, leadership roles, community and volunteer activities; and (one-page) thesis explaining: goals, objectives and personal influences. **Deadline:** May 1. **Contact:** NIBA office; Phone: 608-310-7549; Email: staff@niba.org.

7942 ■ National Institute of Justice (NIJ)
810 7th St. NW
Washington, DC 20531
Ph: (202)307-0703
Social Media: www.facebook.com/OJPNIJ
twitter.com/OJPNIJ
youtube.com/user/OJPOCOM

7943 ■ NIJ Visiting Fellows Program *(Other/Fellowship)*

Purpose: To encourage researchers from a broad range of disciplines related to crime and justice. **Focus:** Criminal justice. **Qualif.:** Applicants must be researchers in all areas of criminal justice scholarship pertinent to NIJ's broad research mission including the social sciences, forensic sciences and criminal justice technology. **Criteria:** Selection will be based on the committee's criteria.

Funds Avail.: No specific amount. **Duration:** Annual.

7944 ■ W.E.B. Du Bois Program *(Doctorate/Fellowship)*

Purpose: To provide talented researchers with an opportunity, early in their career, to elevate independently generated research and ideas to the level of national discussion. **Focus:** Criminal justice. **Qualif.:** Applicants must have a terminal degree in any academic discipline and not yet have been awarded tenure.

Duration: Annual. **Number Awarded:** Varies. **Remarks:** The Fellowship was established in memory of W.E.B. Du

Awards are arranged alphabetically below their administering organizations

Bois was an early leader in the struggle for racial equality in the United States.

7945 ■ National Institute of Mental Health (NIMH)
6001 Executive Blvd.
Rockville, MD 20852
Ph: (301)443-4536
Fax: (301)443-4279
Free: 866-615-6464
URL: www.nimh.nih.gov
Social Media: www.facebook.com/nimhgov
twitter.com/nimhgov
www.youtube.com/nimhgov

7946 ■ NIMH Postbaccalaureate Intramural Research Awards *(Graduate/Award)*

Purpose: To introduce recent college graduates to biomedical research, as well as provide additional time to pursue successful application to a doctoral degree program. **Focus:** Medical research. **Qualif.:** Candidates must be U.S. Citizens or permanent residents who have graduated from an accredited college or university more than three years prior to arriving at the NIH. **Criteria:** Applications are reviewed on a rolling basis year round by scientists in the Institutes and Centers of the NIH.

Funds Avail.: $2,000. **Duration:** Annual. **To Apply:** Applicants must curriculum vitae or resume, a list of coursework and grades, a cover letter describing the applicant's research interests and career goals, and the names and contact information for three references.

7947 ■ National Institute of Nursing Research (NINR)
31 Center Dr., Rm. 5B10
Bethesda, MD
Ph: (301)496-0207
E-mail: info@ninr.nih.gov
URL: www.ninr.nih.gov
Social Media: www.linkedin.com/company/ninr
twitter.com/NINR
www.youtube.com/user/NINRnews

7948 ■ NINR Mentored Patient-Oriented Research Career Development Award *(Doctorate/Award)*

Purpose: To support the career development of clinically trained professionals carrying out patient oriented research. **Focus:** Medical research. **Criteria:** Selection will be made by NINR Scientific Review Branch.

Funds Avail.: No specific amount. **To Apply:** Applicants must submit the completed nomination form and associated documents including reference letters. **Deadline:** January 12.

7949 ■ NINR Midcareer Investigator Award in Patient-Oriented Research *(Doctorate/Award)*

Purpose: To support mid-career clinicians and provides protected time for patient-oriented research and for mentoring beginning clinical investigators. **Focus:** Medical research. **Qualif.:** Applicants must be clinicians and investigators. **Criteria:** Selection will be made by NINR Scientific Review Branch.

Funds Avail.: No specific amount. **To Apply:** Applicants must submit the completed nomination form and associated documents including reference letters.

7950 ■ NINR Pathway to Independence Award *(Doctorate, Postdoctorate/Award)*

Purpose: To support promising postdoctoral scientists to receive both mentored (K99) and independent (R00) phases or research support for up to five years. **Focus:** Medical research. **Qualif.:** Applicants must be postdoctoral researchers. **Criteria:** Selection will be made by NINR Scientific Review Branch.

Funds Avail.: No specific amount. **To Apply:** Applicants must submit the completed nomination form and associated documents including reference letters.

7951 ■ National Investment Company Service Association (NICSA)
225 Franklin St., 26th fl.
Boston, MA 02110
Ph: (508)485-1500
Fax: (508)485-1560
E-mail: info@nicsa.org
URL: www.nicsa.org
Social Media: www.facebook.com/pages/Nicsa/
155284844485438
www.instagram.com/nicsa_news
www.linkedin.com/company/nicsa
twitter.com/NICSAnews

7952 ■ NICSA/William T. Blackwell Scholarship Fund *(Undergraduate/Scholarship)*

Purpose: To financially support dependents of NICSA member company employees in their education. **Focus:** General studies/Field of study not specified. **Qualif.:** Applicants must be dependents of full-time employees of NICSA member companies; be enrolled or planning to enroll in a full-time degree seeking course at an accredited four-year college or university. **Criteria:** Recipients are selected based on academic record; leadership; and participation in school and community activities, honors, work experience, statement of goals and aspirations, unusual personal or family circumstances and an outside appraisal.

Funds Avail.: $3,000-$5,000. **Duration:** One year. **To Apply:** Applicants can download the application form from the website; must prepare a current transcript of grades and an appraisal provided by the school (sent in a sealed envelope). **Deadline:** May 10. **Remarks:** The program is administered by Scholarship America. **Contact:** Fund Administration, The Boston Foundation, 75 Arlington St., 3rd Floor, Boston, MA 02116.

7953 ■ National Iranian American Council (NIAC)
1629 K St NW, Ste. 503
Washington, DC 20006
Ph: (202)386-6325
URL: www.niacouncil.org
Social Media: www.facebook.com/NIACouncil
www.instagram.com/niacouncil
twitter.com/niacouncil
www.youtube.com/user/NIACouncil

7954 ■ Iranian-American Scholarship Fund *(Undergraduate, Graduate/Scholarship)*

Purpose: To provide scholarships to students of Iranian descent. **Focus:** General studies/Field of study not speci-

Awards are arranged alphabetically below their administering organizations

fied. **Criteria:** Selection will be based on financial need and commitment to community service.

Funds Avail.: No specific amount. **Duration:** Annual. **Number Awarded:** Varies. **To Apply:** Applicants must submit the completed application form; must submit Student Aid Report (SAR); two essays; two letters of recommendation and two Standard Recommendation Forms; official transcript; and GPA certification form for non-GPA schools (only required for applicants whose transcripts are unable to display GPA on a 4.0 scale). **Remarks:** The Iranian-American Scholarship fund was created by Iranian-Americans in San Diego, California. Established in 1998. **Contact:** Phone: 202-386-6325.

7955 ■ Momeni Foundation Scholastic Achievement Scholarships *(Undergraduate/Scholarship)*

Purpose: To provide scholarships to students of Iranian descent. **Focus:** General studies/Field of study not specified. **Criteria:** Selection will be based on merit.

Funds Avail.: $1,000 each. **Duration:** Annual. **Number Awarded:** 3. **To Apply:** Applicant should include resume or list of extracurricular activities, community leadership or volunteerism, membership in clubs or organizations and any other evidence of outstanding achievement; a short narrative (less than 500 words) describing applicant's goals and plans and what has motivated them to follow those goals and plans. **Deadline:** June 30. **Remarks:** Established in 2001. **Contact:** Momeni Foundation, PO Box 322, Clearwater, FL, 33757; Phone: 727-433-2133; E-mail: momenifoundation@aol.com.

7956 ■ National Iranian American Council Fellowships *(Graduate, Undergraduate/Fellowship)*

Purpose: To provide outstanding Iranian-American college students with internships in political and media organizations. **Focus:** Economics; International affairs and relations; Journalism; Political science. **Qualif.:** Applicants must be college junior, senior and graduate students who are U.S. citizens or a legal permanent residents of Iranian descent. A background in public policy, political science, economics, international affairs, or journalism is preferred. **Criteria:** Selection process is highly competitive. Applicants are judged on the basis of their academic credentials; demonstrated interest in community and public service; and the ability to fulfill the needs and expectations of the congressional office they will be placed in.

To Apply: Applicants must submit the following requirements: a completed application form; three letters of recommendation (two academic and one from an employment supervisor); resume; current college transcript; a 500-word essay answering the question: "How has being Iranian-American influenced your decision to pursue a career in public service or journalism?".

7957 ■ National Italian American Bar Association (NIABA)

2020 Pennsylvania Ave. NW
Washington, DC 20006-1846
Ph: (203)859-1018
E-mail: niabagroup@gmail.com
URL: www.niaba.org
Social Media: www.facebook.com/NIABA.org

7958 ■ NIABA/NIAF Scholarships *(Graduate/Scholarship)*

Purpose: To assist deserving and qualified students who wish to further their legal education at a law school. **Focus:**

Law. **Qualif.:** Applicants must be enrolled at a Law School member of the National Italian American Bar Association. **Criteria:** Major criteria for selection are financial need, but academic and leadership potential are also important considerations.

Funds Avail.: Amount varies. **Duration:** Annual. **Number Awarded:** Varies. **To Apply:** Applicants must submit an official law school grade transcript for the most recent academic year; (two-page, double-spaced) personal letter in support of the application; and two letters of reference.

7959 ■ National Italian American Foundation (NIAF)

1860 19th St. NW
Washington, DC 20009
Ph: (202)387-0600
Fax: (202)387-0800
E-mail: information@niaf.org
URL: www.niaf.org
Social Media: www.facebook.com/niaf.org
www.instagram.com/niafitalianamerican
www.pinterest.com/theniaf
twitter.com/niaforg
www.youtube.com/user/NIAFITALY

7960 ■ Agnes E. Vaghi Scholarship *(Undergraduate/Scholarship)*

Purpose: To promote the study of Italian American studies or a related field. **Focus:** Italian studies.

Funds Avail.: $2,500-$12,000. **Duration:** Annual. **To Apply:** Applicant must submit the completed application and all required documents through online only; must submit Recent transcript(s) (either official or unofficial); recent resume outlining academic achievement, awards received, extra-curricular involvement and work experience; 1 Letter of Recommendation; FAFSA Student Aid Report (SAR).

7961 ■ A. Lucchetti Martino Scholarship *(Undergraduate/Scholarship)*

Purpose: To financially support the education of Italian American students. **Focus:** General studies/Field of study not specified. **Criteria:** Selection wii be mabe by the selection committee.

Funds Avail.: $2,500-$12,000. **Duration:** Annual. **To Apply:** Applicant must submit the completed application and all required documents through online only; must submit Recent transcript(s) (either official or unofficial); recent resume outlining academic achievement, awards received, extra-curricular involvement and work experience; 1 Letter of Recommendation; FAFSA Student Aid Report (SAR). **Deadline:** March 1.

7962 ■ National Judges Association (NJA)

PO Box 325
Glendale, OR 97442
Fax: (541)832-2647
E-mail: njaoffice@yahoo.com
URL: www.nationaljudgesassociation.org

7963 ■ National Judges Association Scholarships *(Other/Scholarship)*

Purpose: To engage in education and research concerning the procedures, powers and practices of non-attorneys.

Awards are arranged alphabetically below their administering organizations

Focus: Law. **Qualif.:** Applicants must be non-attorney judges and be members of National Judges Association (NJA). **Criteria:** Selection is based on financial need.

Funds Avail.: No specific amount. **To Apply:** Applicants must complete the application form and provide evidence that they are members of the American judiciary.

7964 ■ National Junior Angus Association (NJAA)
3201 Frederick Ave.
Saint Joseph, MO 64506
Ph: (816)383-5100
E-mail: info@njaa.info
URL: www.angus.org
Social Media: www.facebook.com/jrangusassoc
twitter.com/jrangusassoc

7965 ■ Angus Foundation Scholarships
(Undergraduate, Graduate/Scholarship)

Purpose: To support young men and women who are active in the Angus breed pursuing higher education. **Focus:** General studies/Field of study not specified. **Qualif.:** Applicants must be National Junior Angus Association members, regular or life members of American Angus Association graduating high school seniors or must be enrolled in junior college, four-year college/university or other accredited institution of higher education for the fall term, and must have a minimum 2.0 GPA.

Funds Avail.: $213,000. **Duration:** Annual. **Number Awarded:** Varies. **To Apply:** Applicants must submit an online application form along with a copy of high school transcript (for freshmen) or college/university transcript and three (3) letters of recommendation which should be mailed to the Angus Foundation, postmarked by the U.S. Postal Service by May 1 of the application year. **Deadline:** May 1. **Contact:** Clint Mefford, Director of Communications; E-mail: cmefford@angus.org; Phone: 816-383-5143.

7966 ■ National Junior Horticultural Association (NJHA)
c/o Carole Carney, Executive Secretary
15 Railroad Ave.
Homer City, PA 15748-1378
Ph: (724)479-3254
E-mail: carole@njha.org
URL: www.njha.org
Social Media: www.facebook.com/njha.org
twitter.com/NJHA_org

7967 ■ Stan and Mary Stark Alumni Scholarship
(Other/Scholarship)

Purpose: To help young people develop their skills and obtain an understanding of horticulture. **Focus:** Horticulture. **Qualif.:** Applicants must have already attended one convention and are planning on returning to the convention to expand their knowledge within NJHA. **Criteria:** Selection will be based on the committee's criteria.

Funds Avail.: No specific amount. **Number Awarded:** 3. **To Apply:** Resume along with letter of recommendation from a NJHA leader that is not from your state consisting of NJHA Involvement, involvement in 4-H, FFA or anything related to agriculture, Financial needs, one paragraph about yourself must be submitted electronically. **Deadline:** Sep-

tember 15. **Remarks:** The scholarship was started by Stan and Mary Stark. Established in 2005. **Contact:** Stan and Mary Stark, N 1196 Rich Rd., Watertown, WI, 53098; Phone: 920-261-7355; E-mail: grandparents1196@yahoo.com.

7968 ■ National Junior Swine Association (NJSA)
2639 Yeager Rd.
West Lafayette, IN 47906
Ph: (765)463-3594
E-mail: cassie@nationalswine.com
Social Media: www.facebook.com/nationaljuniorswine

7969 ■ Claude Robinson Memorial Scholarship
(Undergraduate/Scholarship)

Purpose: To support students who have an interest in livestock or swine industry. **Focus:** Agriculture, Economic aspects. **Qualif.:** Applicants must be a sophomore, junior or senior as of the upcoming fall semester enrolled in a collegiate (junior college or senior college) livestock judging program. **Criteria:** Selection will be based on demonstrated leadership activities; livestock judging experience; livestock industry interest and community service.

Funds Avail.: $1,000. **Duration:** Annual. **Number Awarded:** 1. **To Apply:** Applicants should include one letter of recommendation from a 4-H, FFA, or person unrelated to the applicant who has knowledge of the livestock industry involvement; one letter of recommendation from their college livestock judging coach. **Contact:** National Swine Registry, Attn: Director of Development, 2639 Yeager Rd., West Lafayette, IN, 47906.

7970 ■ Gregory D. Johnson Memorial Scholarships
(Doctorate, Graduate, Master's/Scholarship)

Purpose: To support individuals who are pursuing an advanced degree in swine genetics, swine reproduction or swine nutrition. **Focus:** Agriculture, Economic aspects. **Qualif.:** Applicants must be spring college graduates with a bachelor's degree in an agricultural field; or current graduate students pursuing a master's; or doctorate degree in swine genetics, swine reproduction or swine nutrition. **Criteria:** Selection will be based on academics; goals for future and collegiate involvement; swine industry experience and honors; NJSA experience and honors.

Funds Avail.: $1,000. **Duration:** Annual. **Number Awarded:** 1. **To Apply:** Applicants must enclose one letter of recommendation from a college advisor who can verify participants' graduate school acceptance or enrollment, in addition to their college activities and involvement; must submit a graduate school acceptance letter or proof of graduate school enrollment. **Deadline:** March 1. **Contact:** National Swine Registry, Attn: Director of Development, 2639 Yeager Rd., West Lafayette, IN, 47906.

7971 ■ The Maschhoffs Pork Production Scholarships
(Undergraduate/Scholarship)

Purpose: To provide support to youth who are interested in swine industry who wants to nurture and inspire the passion for pork production through the experiences offered. **Focus:** Agriculture, Economic aspects. **Qualif.:** Applicant must be a member of the National Junior Swine Association (NJSA); must be 18-21 years of age and enrolled in an agricultural program at a recognized college/university. **Criteria:** Selection will be based on overall thought process and merit.

Awards are arranged alphabetically below their administering organizations

Funds Avail.: $1,000. **Duration:** Annual. **Number Awarded:** 5. **To Apply:** Applicants must submit two letters of recommendation from a non-related industry professional, 4-H leaders, FFA adviser or school teacher; must fill out the scholarship application and complete 4 questions with a 300-word maximum essay. **Deadline:** May 1. **Contact:** National Swine Registry, Attn: Director of Development, 2639 Yeager Rd., West Lafayette, IN, 47906.

7972 ■ National Junior Swine Association Outstanding Member Scholarships (Graduate/Scholarship)

Purpose: To support students who have an interest in livestock or swine industry. **Focus:** Agriculture, Economic aspects. **Qualif.:** Applicants must be member of the National Junior Swine Association; must be under the age 17-21. **Criteria:** Selection will be based on demonstrated NJSA or livestock industry leadership, scholastic excellence, youth leadership activities and interest in the swine industry.

Funds Avail.: $1,000 (senior). **Duration:** Annual. **To Apply:** Applicants may submit their application to the office together with the other requirements. **Deadline:** March 1. **Contact:** National Swine Registry, Attn: Director of Development, 2639 Yeager Rd., West Lafayette, IN, 47906.

7973 ■ NJSA Visionary Leader Scholarships (Graduate/Scholarship)

Purpose: To recognize and support an individual for outstanding contribution and service to the members of the NJSA. **Focus:** Agriculture, Economic aspects. **Qualif.:** Applicants must be member of the NJSA Board of Directors and must be signed by a parent or guardian who has knowledge of the applicant's involvement in the NJSA. **Criteria:** Application will be scored by a committee that will independently review and score each application received.

Funds Avail.: No amount mentioned. **Duration:** Annual. **Number Awarded:** 1. **To Apply:** Applications should be typed extra pages may be used as necessary; must be signed by a parent or guardian who has knowledge of the involvement in the NJSA. **Deadline:** March 1. **Contact:** National Swine Registry, Attn: Director of Development, 2639 Yeager Rd., West Lafayette, IN, 47906.

7974 ■ Jason Shipley Memorial Scholarships (Undergraduate/Scholarship)

Purpose: To support students who have an interest in livestock or swine industry. **Focus:** Agriculture, Economic aspects. **Qualif.:** Applicants must be incoming freshmen, sophomores or juniors enrolled in an agriculturally related field. **Criteria:** Selection will be based on demonstrated athletics experience and honors; swine industry experience and honors; academics and future goals.

Funds Avail.: $1,000. **Number Awarded:** 1. **To Apply:** Applicants must send two letters of reference; one letter should be written by an athletic coach, and the second letter should be written by a non-family member who has knowledge of the applicants involvement in the swine industry. **Deadline:** March 1.

7975 ■ National Kidney Foundation (NKF)
30 E 33rd St.
New York, NY 10016
Fax: (212)689-9261
Free: 800-622-9010
E-mail: info@kidney.org

URL: www.kidney.org
Social Media: Instagram.com/nationalkidneyfoundation
www.linkedin.com/company/national-kidney-foundation
twitter.com/nkf

7976 ■ American Diabetes Association and Boehringer Ingelheim Research Award: Chronic Kidney Disease and Renal Insufficiency in the Setting of Diabetes (Doctorate, Professional development/Award)

Purpose: To funds research aimed at improving the care of people with diabetes and chronic kidney disease. **Focus:** Medical research. **Qualif.:** Applicants must hold a PhD, MD, PharmD, DO or DPM degree, or other science-related degree; must possess the necessary skills and training to carry out proposed work; and must agree to devote sufficient time and effort to research. **Criteria:** Preference will be given on evaluated applications that has original study design with applicability to the scope of study, its potential impact, and its treatment and prevention to kidney disease and diabetes.

Duration: Annual.

7977 ■ National Kindergarten Alliance (NKA)
c/o Penny Pillack, President
PO Box 309
Agua Dulce, TX 78330
E-mail: ppillack@aol.com
URL: www.nkateach.org
Social Media: www.facebook.com/NKAteach

7978 ■ NKA Dr. Violet B. Robinson Memorial Graduate Scholarship (Advanced Professional/Scholarship)

Purpose: To assist a classroom teacher pursuing an advanced degree in Early Childhood Education or a closely related field. **Focus:** Education, Early childhood. **Qualif.:** Applicants must be NKA members in good standing for at least one year and be classroom teachers pursuing an advanced degree in Early Childhood Education or related field.

Funds Avail.: $250. **To Apply:** Applicants must submit a completed application form; a narrative (two or three pages) of professional work experience, extracurricular activities responsibilities, leadership, citizenship activities, and awards and honors; reasons for choosing Early Childhood Education as a career; post graduation plans; a copy of transcripts; and two professional letters of recommendation. **Deadline:** March 1.

7979 ■ National Laser Institute
16601 N 90th St.
Scottsdale, AZ 85260
Free: 800-982-6817
E-mail: info@nationallaserinstitute.com
URL: nationallaserinstitute.com
Social Media: www.facebook.com/nationallaserinstitute
www.instagram.com/nationallaserinst
twitter.com/NatLaserSchool
www.youtube.com/user/nlionline

7980 ■ Cosmetic Laser Technician Scholarship (Vocational/Occupational, Professional development/Scholarship)

Purpose: To support who demonstrate a financial need and have a passion as well as the drive to continue to

Awards are arranged alphabetically below their administering organizations

expand their education in the medical aesthetics field. **Focus:** Cosmetology. **Qualif.:** Applicant must have financial need and must be pursuing education in the laser technician field. Applicant must study in Scottsdale, AZ; Boston, MA; or Chicago, IL. **Criteria:** Selection is based on financial need.

Funds Avail.: $4,000. **Number Awarded:** 2. **To Apply:** Application is available at nationallaserinstitute.com/laser-training-scholarships/. **Deadline:** December 1. **Contact:** Email: Scholarship@NationalLaserInstitute.com.

7981 ■ National Law Enforcement and Firefighters Children's Foundation (NLEAFCF)
38 East 32nd Street, Suite 602
New York, NY 10016-5566
Ph: (646)822-4236
E-mail: info@1strcf.org
URL: www.1strcf.org
Social Media: www.facebook.com/1strcf
www.instagram.com/1strcf
twitter.com/1strcf
www.youtube.com/user/nleafcf

7982 ■ Victoria Ovis Memorial Scholarship
(Undergraduate/Scholarship)

Purpose: To provide financial assistance for qualified individuals. **Focus:** General studies/Field of study not specified.

Funds Avail.: No specific amount. **Duration:** Annual. **Number Awarded:** 1. **To Apply:** Applicants must submit a completed application form; personal essay not exceeding 500 words that summarizes their personal accomplishments, chosen course of study and personal and professional goals; documentation verifying connection to law enforcement and firefighter decent (the statement may come from an agency representative); copy of tuition bill or statement from school or degree program; proof of US citizenship (birth certificate, naturalization papers or US passport); documentation of academic record and current school status. Include the most recent transcripts and letter of acceptance into chosen school and study program; letters of recommendation from two individuals other than family members, including one academic and one personal reference. **Remarks:** The scholarship was established in Victoria Ovis who had over 30 years of law enforcement experience with the United States Customs Service and the Department of Homeland Security.

7983 ■ National Legal Aid and Defender Association (NLADA)
1901 Pennsylvania Ave. NW, Ste. 500
Washington, DC 20006
Ph: (202)452-0620
Fax: (202)872-1031
URL: www.nlada.org
Social Media: www.facebook.com/nlada.org/timeline
www.instagram.com/explore/locations/63943348/national-legal-aid-defender-association/?hl=en
www.linkedin.com/company/national-legal-aid-&-defender-association_2
www.pinterest.com/pin/545287467378634268
twitter.com/nlada

7984 ■ The C. Lyons Fellowship Program *(Advanced Professional/Fellowship)*

Purpose: To support emerging leaders in the equal justice community. **Focus:** Law.

Funds Avail.: No specific amount. **Duration:** Annual. **Remarks:** The fellowship was established to honor the hard work and significant achievements of Clinton Lyons, by the board of directors of NLADA.

7985 ■ National Lesbian, Gay, Bisexual and Transgender Bar Association (NLGLA)
1701 Rhode Island Ave. NW
Washington, DC 20036
Ph: (202)637-7661
E-mail: info@lgbtbar.org
URL: lgbtbar.org
Social Media: www.facebook.com/natllgbtbar
www.instagram.com/lgbtbar
www.linkedin.com/company/national-lgbt-bar-association
twitter.com/LGBTBar
www.youtube.com/user/LGBTbar

7986 ■ Michael Greenberg Student Writing Competition *(Graduate/Monetary, Scholarship)*

Purpose: To encourage outstanding law student scholarship on the legal issues affecting lesbian, gay, bisexual and transgender (LGBT) persons. **Focus:** Law. **Qualif.:** Applicants must be students enrolled in an ABA-accredited law school during the given academic year. **Criteria:** Selection shall be based on the essays submitted.

Funds Avail.: $1,000. **Duration:** Annual. **Number Awarded:** Varies. **To Apply:** Applicants may visit the website to verify the application process and other pieces of information. **Deadline:** April 1. **Remarks:** Established in 1998. **Contact:** All entries must be submitted to the Email: writingcompetition@lgbtbar.org.

7987 ■ National Lesbian and Gay Journalists Association (NLGJA)
2120 L St. NW, Ste. 850
Washington, DC 20037
Ph: (202)588-9888
E-mail: info@nlgja.org
URL: www.nlgja.org
Social Media: www.facebook.com/nlgja
twitter.com/nlgja

7988 ■ Leroy F. Aarons Scholarship Award *(Graduate, Undergraduate/Scholarship)*

Purpose: To support LGBTQ students who plan to have a career in journalism and is committed to furthering NLGJA's mission of fair and accurate coverage of the LGBTQ community. **Focus:** Journalism. **Qualif.:** Applicants must be planning to pursue a career in journalism; demonstrate an awareness of the issues facing the LGBTQ community and the importance of fair and accurate news coverage. **Criteria:** Selection is based on an applicant's journalistic and scholastic ability.

Funds Avail.: Up to $5,000. **Duration:** Annual. **Number Awarded:** 1. **To Apply:** Applicants must submit a completed application form along with a one page resume; five work samples; official transcript provided in a sealed

Awards are arranged alphabetically below their administering organizations

envelope; a copy of a letter of acceptance to a community college or four-year university (high school seniors); three letters of recommendation (from a teacher or professor - high school students may obtain letters from counselors and/or the principal); and an autobiography in the third person and written as a news story, describing the commitment and passion for journalism and career goals (maximum of 1, 000 words in 11-point typed and double spaced). **Deadline:** June 5. **Remarks:** The scholarship award was established to honor Aarons' memory and to continue the work he began when he founded NLGJA in 1990. **Contact:** Aarons Scholarship – NLGJA, 2120 L St NW, Ste. 850, Washington, DC 20037; Email: awards@nlgja.org.

7989 ■ Facebook Journalism Project Scholarship
(Graduate, Undergraduate/Scholarship)

Purpose: To offer assistance to a journalism students serving underrepresented communities. **Focus:** General studies/Field of study not specified. **Qualif.:** Must be enrolled juniors, seniors or graduate students at an accredited university in the United States; applicants from all disciplines, departments and majors are eligible. **Criteria:** Selection is based on an applicant's journalistic and scholastic ability.

Funds Avail.: $10,000. **Duration:** Annual. **Number Awarded:** 5. **To Apply:** Completed application, One page resume, a letter of acceptance or a letter of enrollment from a U.S. community college or four-year university, official transcripts, two letters of recommendation, personal statement demonstrating commitment to NLGJA's mission and the field of journalism, and three to five work samples. **Deadline:** June 5. **Contact:** Email: awards@nlgja.org.

7990 ■ Kay Longcope Scholarship Award *(Graduate, Undergraduate/Scholarship)*

Purpose: To support LGBTQ students who plan to have a career in journalism and is committed to furthering NLGJA's mission of fair and accurate coverage of the LGBTQ community. **Focus:** Journalism. **Qualif.:** Applicants must be an LGBTQ individual of color planning to pursue a career in journalism; demonstrate an awareness of the issues facing the LGBTQ community and the importance of fair and accurate news coverage. **Criteria:** Selection is based on an applicant's journalistic and scholastic ability.

Funds Avail.: Up to $3,000. **Duration:** Annual. **To Apply:** Applicants must submit a completed application form along with a one page resume; five work samples; official transcript provided in a sealed envelope; a copy of a letter of acceptance to a community college or four-year university (high school seniors); three letters of recommendation (from a teacher or professor - high school students may obtain letters from counselors and/or the principal); and an autobiography in the third person and written as a news story, describing the commitment and passion for journalism and career goals (maximum of 1, 000 words in 11-point typed and double spaced). **Deadline:** June 5. **Remarks:** The award was established in 2008 through a gift from Longcope's estate and with the guidance of Longcope's partner Barbara Wohlgemuth. Established in 2008. **Contact:** Longcope Scholarship - NLGJA, 2120 L St NW, Ste., 850, Washington, DC 20037; Email: awards@nlgja.org.

7991 ■ Steve Mason Sports Media Scholarship
(Graduate, Undergraduate/Scholarship)

Purpose: To provide funding to an LGBTQ student who plans to pursue a career in sports journalism. **Focus:** Communications; Journalism. **Qualif.:** Applicants must be as-

sociation members in good standing; incoming undergrad students enrolled in a U.S. community college or four-year university; or incoming graduate students enrolled in an accredited journalism or mass communications field; demonstrated commitment to journalism. **Criteria:** Selection is based on an applicant's journalistic and scholastic ability.

Funds Avail.: $2,500. **Duration:** Annual. **Number Awarded:** 1. **To Apply:** Completed application, one page resume, three to five work samples; submit a vlog or podcast/audio clip that demonstrates journalistic approach. **Deadline:** June 5. **Contact:** Email: awards@nlgja.org.

7992 ■ National Little Britches Rodeo Association (NLBRA)
5050 Edison Ave., Ste. 105
Colorado Springs, CO 80915
Ph: (719)389-0333
Fax: (719)578-1367
Free: 800-763-3694
E-mail: info@nlbra.com
URL: nlbra.com
Social Media: www.facebook.com/NLBRA
instagram.com/n.l.b.r.a

7993 ■ NLBRA Age-Out Scholarship *(Undergraduate/Scholarship)*

Purpose: To support age-out members of the Association to further their education. **Focus:** General studies/Field of study not specified. **Qualif.:** Applicants must be members of NLBRA. **Criteria:** All scholarship requests are brought to the upcoming Executive Board Meeting and are voted on to be approved.

Funds Avail.: $500. **Duration:** Annual. **To Apply:** Applicant must complete the back of the scholarship certificate and then send it to the NLBRA National Office. **Deadline:** May 31. **Remarks:** Established in 2014.

7994 ■ NLBRA National Royalty Scholarship *(Other/Scholarship)*

Purpose: To support youth members in their pursuit of higher education. **Focus:** General studies/Field of study not specified. **Qualif.:** Applicants must be an member of NLBRA and Queen, Princess, or Little Wrangler Princess.

Funds Avail.: $500. **Duration:** Annual. **To Apply:** Applicants must complete a year's service promoting the NLBRA and returning to present the crown to the newly selected representatives.

7995 ■ NLBRA Rainwater Scholarships
(Undergraduate/Scholarship)

Purpose: To support youth members in their pursuit of higher education. **Focus:** General studies/Field of study not specified. **Qualif.:** Applicants must be an member of NLBRA. **Criteria:** Selection will be based on committee criteria.

Funds Avail.: $500 each. **Duration:** Annual. **Number Awarded:** 4. **To Apply:** Applicants must complete the provided scholarship certificate along with high school transcripts.

7996 ■ NLBRA World All Around Scholarships
(Undergraduate/Scholarship)

Purpose: To support youth members in their pursuit of higher education. **Focus:** General studies/Field of study

Awards are arranged alphabetically below their administering organizations

not specified. **Qualif.:** Applicants must be a member of NLBRA. **Criteria:** All scholarship requests are brought to the upcoming Executive Board Meeting and are voted on to be approved.

Funds Avail.: $500 to $1,000. **Duration:** Annual. **To Apply:** Applicants must complete the provided scholarship certificate and then send it to the NLBRA National Office.

7997 ■ NLBRA World Event Scholarships
(Undergraduate/Scholarship)

Purpose: To support youth members in their pursuit of higher education. **Focus:** General studies/Field of study not specified. **Qualif.:** Applicants must be a member of NLBRA. Includes the World Champions, Reserve Champions, and Third in the World Scholarships. **Criteria:** All scholarship requests are brought to the upcoming Executive Board Meeting and are voted on to be approved.

Funds Avail.: $700 to $1,000. **Duration:** Annual. **To Apply:** Applicants must complete the provided scholarship certificate and then send it to the NLBRA National Office.

7998 ■ NLBRA/Wrangler Academic Scholarships
(Undergraduate/Scholarship)

Purpose: To support student members in their education. **Focus:** General studies/Field of study not specified. **Qualif.:** Applicants must be high school seniors; must be members of NLBRA. These scholarships are awarded during an awards ceremony at the National Little Britches Finals Rodeo; all recipients must be present in Wrangler attire and have met all of the criteria or the award is handed to the next highest scored application. **Criteria:** Selection is based on academic excellence. All scholarship requests are brought to the upcoming Executive Board Meeting and are voted on to be approved.

Funds Avail.: $2,000 (top boy and girl); $1,000 (next four). **Duration:** Annual. **To Apply:** Applicants must complete the provided scholarship certificate; submit transcripts and then send it to the NLBRA National Office.

7999 ■ NLBRA Youth Board Officer Scholarships
(Undergraduate/Scholarship)

Purpose: To support youth members in their pursuit of higher education. **Focus:** General studies/Field of study not specified. **Qualif.:** Applicants must serve the membership by attending and being actively involved at four annual board meetings. **Criteria:** All scholarship requests are brought to the upcoming Executive Board Meeting and are voted on to be approved.

Funds Avail.: $500. **Duration:** Annual. **To Apply:** Applicants must complete the back of the scholarship certificate and then send it to the NLBRA National Office.

8000 ■ National Medical Fellowships (NMF)
12 East 46th Street, Suite 5E
New York, NY 10017
Ph: (212)483-8880
Fax: (212)483-8897
E-mail: info@nmfonline.org
URL: nmfonline.org
Social Media: www.facebook.com/nmfonline
www.instagram.com/nmfonline
www.linkedin.com/company/national-medical-fellowships
 -inc-
twitter.com/NMFonline

8001 ■ National Medical Fellowships Need-Based Scholarships *(Undergraduate/Scholarship)*

Purpose: To support medical students in educational pursuits. **Focus:** Medicine. **Qualif.:** Applicants must be first or second year medical students; must be African-American, Mexican-American, Native American, Alaska Native, Native Hawaiian, or mainland Puerto Ricans who permanently reside within the 50 U.S. states; must be accepted to AAMC or AOA-accredited U.S. medical schools for study leading to M.D. or D.O. degrees. **Criteria:** Selection is based on financial need.

Funds Avail.: $2,000-$7,500. **Duration:** Annual. **Number Awarded:** Varies. **To Apply:** Applicants must complete the application form.

8002 ■ National Merit Scholarship Corporation (NMSC)
1560 Sherman Ave., Ste. 200
Evanston, IL 60201-4897
Ph: (847)866-5100
Fax: (847)866-5115
URL: www.nationalmerit.org

8003 ■ National Merit Scholarship Program
(Undergraduate/Scholarship)

Purpose: To support the education of undergraduate students. **Focus:** General studies/Field of study not specified. **Qualif.:** Applicants must be high school students; have taken the Preliminary SAT/National Merit Scholarship Qualifying Test (PSAT/NMSQT); and must be U.S. citizens or have applied for permanent residence; must have consistent high academic records. **Criteria:** Recipients will be selected based on abilities, skills and accomplishments.

Funds Avail.: $2,500. **Duration:** Annual. **To Apply:** Applicants must send their application forms to their school principal. To be considered as finalists, applicants must request an official transcript right after the current term ends. **Remarks:** Established in 1955.

8004 ■ NMSC College and University Sponsorship of Merit Scholarship Awards *(Undergraduate/ Scholarship)*

Purpose: To support the education of undergraduate students. **Focus:** General studies/Field of study not specified. **Qualif.:** Applicants must be U.S. citizens or have applied for permanent residence; have taken the Preliminary SAT/National Merit Scholarship Qualifying Test (PSAT/ NMSQT); must have been admitted to a college or university. **Criteria:** Recipients will be selected based on abilities, skills and accomplishments.

Duration: Annual; renewable up to four years. **To Apply:** Applicants must complete the NMSC application form; must submit a copy of their Permanent Resident Card (Green Card); or a copy of Form I-797 receipt from U.S. Citizenship and Immigration Services (CIS). Applicants must send their SAT scores to NMSC.

8005 ■ NMSC Corporate-Sponsored merit Scholarship Awards *(Undergraduate/Scholarship)*

Purpose: To financially assist students who have plans to pursue a college education. **Focus:** General studies/Field of study not specified. **Criteria:** Recipients will be selected based on abilities, skills and accomplishments.

Duration: Annual; renewable up to four years. **To Apply:** Applicants must submit a filled-out application form.

Awards are arranged alphabetically below their administering organizations

8006 ■ NMSC National Achievement Scholarship Program *(Undergraduate/Scholarship)*

Purpose: To support the education of undergraduate students. **Focus:** General studies/Field of study not specified. **Qualif.:** Applicants must be high school students; have taken the Preliminary SAT/National Merit Scholarship Qualifying Test (PSAT/NMSQT); and must be U.S. citizens or have applied for permanent residence; must have consistent high academic records. **Criteria:** Recipients will be selected based on abilities, skills and accomplishments.

Duration: Annual. **To Apply:** Applicants must submit a filled-out application form. **Remarks:** Established in 1964.

8007 ■ NMSC Special Scholarships *(Undergraduate/Scholarship)*

Purpose: To support the education of undergraduate students. **Focus:** General studies/Field of study not specified.

Funds Avail.: No specific amount. **Duration:** Annual; renewable up to four years. **Deadline:** January 31.

8008 ■ National Military Family Association (NMFA)
2800 Eisenhower Ave., Ste. 250
Alexandria, VA 22314
Ph: (703)931-6632
E-mail: info@militaryfamily.org
URL: www.militaryfamily.org
Social Media: www.facebook.com/militaryfamily
www.instagram.com/militaryfamilyorg
twitter.com/military_family

8009 ■ Joanne Holbrook Patton Military Spouse Scholarships *(Graduate, Undergraduate/Scholarship)*

Purpose: To support the spouses of Uniformed Services members to obtain professional certification or to attend post secondary or graduate school. **Focus:** General studies/Field of study not specified. **Qualif.:** Applicant must be a military ID-carrying Uniformed Services' spouse (active duty, retiree, Reserve, National Guard and/or survivor). **Criteria:** Selection is based on the application materials submitted.

Funds Avail.: Varies. **Duration:** Annual. **To Apply:** Applicants must complete the application online. **Remarks:** Established in 2004.

8010 ■ National Military Intelligence Foundation (NMIF)
PO Box 683
Charlotte Court House, VA 23923
Fax: (703)738-7487
URL: nmif.org
Social Media: www.facebook.com/National-Military
 -Intelligence-Foundation-NMIF-2100385243608444
www.linkedin.com/company/nmif

8011 ■ National Military Intelligence Foundation Scholarship *(Undergraduate, Graduate/Scholarship)*

Purpose: To support the growth of professional studies in the field of military intelligence and to recognize and reward excellence in the development and transfer of knowledge about military and associated intelligence disciplines. **Fo-**

cus: Military science and education. **Qualif.:** Applicants must be full time students pursuing courses of study and formal degrees in intelligence studies and related disciplines.

Funds Avail.: $1,000. **Duration:** Annual. **Number Awarded:** 4.

8012 ■ National Milk Producers Federation (NMPF)
2107 Wilson Blvd., Suite 600
Arlington, VA 22201
Ph: (703)243-6111
Fax: (703)841-9328
E-mail: info@nmpf.org
URL: www.nmpf.org
Social Media: www.facebook.com/nationalmilk
www.linkedin.com/company/national-milk
twitter.com/nmpf
www.youtube.com/user/NationalMilk

8013 ■ NMPF National Dairy Leadership Scholarship Program *(Graduate, Master's, Doctorate/Scholarship)*

Purpose: To support graduate students of dairy-related fields in their education. **Focus:** Agriculture, Economic aspects; Dairy science; Economics; Environmental science; Food science and technology; Nutrition. **Criteria:** Selection will be made by NMPF Board of Directors.

Funds Avail.: No specific amount. **Duration:** Annual. **Number Awarded:** 1. **To Apply:** Applicants must complete the application package, which consists of the following three items submitted as a single pdf file: the attached, completed, information form; research summary; and current resume. Applicants must also provide two letters of recommendation (should come directly from the reference). **Remarks:** Established in 1916. **Contact:** NMPF Scholarship Program; 2107 Wilson Blvd., Suite 600; Arlington, VA 22201; Nicole Ayache; Email: nayache@nmpf.org.

8014 ■ National Multiple Sclerosis Society - New Jersey Metro Chapter
1480 US Highway 9-N, Ste. 301
Woodbridge, NJ 07095
Ph: (732)660-1005
Fax: (732)855-6984
Free: 800-344-4867
E-mail: njminfo@nmss.org
URL: www.nationalmssociety.org/Chapters/NJM
Social Media: www.facebook.com/NMSSnjm
www.linkedin.com/company/national-ms-society
twitter.com/NMSSnjm
www.youtube.com/user/NationalMSSociety

8015 ■ National MS Society New Jersey Metro Chapter Scholarship Program *(Undergraduate/Scholarship)*

Purpose: To assist students who are affected by multiple sclerosis, either by having MS themselves or having a parent with MS. **Focus:** General studies/Field of study not specified. **Qualif.:** Applicants must be individuals who live with multiple sclerosis, or have a parent with multiple sclerosis, and will be attending an accredited postsecond-

Awards are arranged alphabetically below their administering organizations

ary school; must be enrolled in at least six credit hours per semester in course work leading to a degree, license, or certificate; must be United States citizens or legal residents living in the U.S., Puerto Rico, U.S. Virgin Islands, Guam or any other U.S. territory and plan to enroll in an undergraduate course of study at an accredited two-or four-year college, university, or vocational-technical school located in the U.S., Puerto Rico, Virgin Islands, Guam or any other U.S. territory. **Criteria:** Selection is on the basis of demonstrated financial need, academic record, leadership and participation in school or community activities, work experience, an outside appraisal, goals and aspirations special circumstances, and an essay (written by the applicant) regarding the impact of multiple sclerosis on their life.

Funds Avail.: No specific amount. **Duration:** Annual. **To Apply:** Applicants must fill out the online application and mail supporting documents on or before the deadline. **Deadline:** January 18.

8016 ■ National Oceanic and Atmospheric Administration - NOAA Center for Atmospheric Sciences (NCAS)
1840 Seventh St, NW Rm 305
Washington, DC 20001
Ph: (202)865-8678
E-mail: noaa-cas@howard.edu
URL: ncas.howard.edu
Social Media: www.facebook.com/
NoaaCenterForAtmosphericSciences
instagram.com/ncasnews/
www.instagram.com/ncasnews
www.linkedin.com/pub/ncas-news/ba/aa2/727
www.linkedin.com/in/ncas-news-727aa2ba
twitter.com/NCASNews
www.youtube.com/channel/UCmyzf9COsW9Bp_ES-AwDBFrg

8017 ■ Dr. Nancy Foster Scholarship Program
(Doctorate/Scholarship)

Purpose: To support students for independent graduate-level studies in oceanography, marine biology, or maritime archeology and all other science, engineering, social science and resource management disciplines involving ocean and coastal areas particularly by women and members of minority groups. **Focus:** Biology, Marine; Maritime studies; Oceanography.

Funds Avail.: $42,000(a 12-month stipend of $30,000 in addition to an education allowance of up to $12,000). **Duration:** Annual. **To Apply:** Applicants may reach NOAA for the application process and other details. **Deadline:** December 6.

8018 ■ National Organization of Gay and Lesbian Scientists and Technical Professionals (NOGL-STP)
PO Box 91803
Pasadena, CA 91109
Ph: (626)791-7689
URL: www.noglstp.org
Social Media: www.facebook.com/NOGLSTP
twitter.com/stemforequality

8019 ■ Out to Innovate Scholarship (Graduate, Undergraduate, Community College/Scholarship)
Purpose: For undergraduate and graduate students pursuing degrees in science, technology, engineering, or mathematics (STEM) who are either lesbian, gay, bisexual, transgender, queer or an active ally of the LGBTQ+ community. **Focus:** Engineering; Mathematics and mathematical sciences; Science; Technology. **Qualif.:** Successful completion of a minimum of two years of post-high school education at an accredited U.S. college or university; cumulative grade point average (GPA) of 3.0 on 4.0 point scale; a declared major in an accredited STEM or STEM-related teaching field; be an active supporter of and participant in programs or organizations that promote LGBTQ+ inclusion and visibility. **Criteria:** Academic excellence.

Funds Avail.: Varies. **Duration:** Annual. **Number Awarded:** Varies. **To Apply:** Applications must be submitted online. Applications submitted via email will not be evaluated. Incomplete or late application submissions will not be evaluated. **Deadline:** June 5. **Remarks:** Established in 2011. **Contact:** David Crombecque, Ph.D., NOGLSTP Scholarship Program Coordinator, Email: scholarships@noglstp.org; URL: www.noglstp.org/programs-projects/scholarships/.

8020 ■ National Organization for Human Services (NOHS)
147 SE 102nd Ave.
Portland, OR 97216
Ph: (503)595-2736
Fax: (503)253-9172
E-mail: info@nationalhumanservices.org
URL: www.nationalhumanservices.org
Social Media: www.facebook.com/groups/
nationalhumanservices
www.linkedin.com/company/national-organization-for-human-services

8021 ■ David C. Maloney Scholarship
(Undergraduate/Scholarship)
Purpose: To support the education of a student in a human service program. **Focus:** Human relations; Humanities. **Qualif.:** Applicants must be Associate, Baccalaureate, or Master's students who are members of NOHS; have a GPA of 3.2 and above on a 4.0 scale and be enrolled in a Human Services studies program. **Criteria:** Selection will be given to applicants with special established needs or minority status.

Funds Avail.: No specific amount. **Number Awarded:** 1. **To Apply:** Applicants must submit an official transcript (sent by the university in a sealed envelope); a resume; an essay (500 words) about the applicant's commitment to the field of helping and quality of Human Service Education; copy of current NOHS membership card; and two reference letters. **Deadline:** July 31. **Contact:** Application E-mail: scholar@nationalhumanservices.org; Transcripts (only) Mail: Dr. Radha Horton-Parker, Counseling and Human Services, Darden College of Education, Old Dominion University, Norfolk, VA, 23529.

8022 ■ National Organization of Industrial Trade Unions (NOITU)
148-06 Hillside Ave.
Jamaica, NY 11435

Awards are arranged alphabetically below their administering organizations

Ph: (718)291-3434
URL: www.noitu.org

8023 ■ Daniel Lasky Scholarship Fund
(Undergraduate/Scholarship, Award)

Purpose: To provide financial support to students who are in need. **Focus:** Education, Industrial. **Qualif.:** Applicants must be sons or daughters of a NOITU member who will graduate from high school this year and plan to attend an accredited college in the coming fall term. **Criteria:** Selection of applicants will be judged by the scholarship committee.

Funds Avail.: No specific amount. **Number Awarded:** Up to 5. **To Apply:** Applicants must submit the (SAT I) scores; verification of acceptance by a college or university approved by the federation of regional accrediting commission of higher education; letters of recommendation from two faculty members in the high school they are attending; high school transcript (showing final grades of the graduating year); and the name and address of the college applicants will be attending. **Deadline:** May 31. **Contact:** Daniel Lasky, Scholarship Committee, 148-06 Hillside Ave., Jamaica, NY, 11435.

8024 ■ National Organization of Italian-American Women (NOIAW)
25 W 43rd St., Ste. 1010
New York, NY 10036
Ph: (212)642-2003
Fax: (212)642-2006
E-mail: noiaw@noiaw.org
URL: www.noiaw.org
Social Media: www.facebook.com/NOIAW
instagram.com/noiaw
www.pinterest.com/noiaw/
twitter.com/noiaw

8025 ■ National Organization of Italian-American Women Scholarships *(Undergraduate, Graduate/ Scholarship)*

Purpose: To give Italian American women the opportunity to achieve their dreams of higher education. **Focus:** General studies/Field of study not specified. **Qualif.:** Applicants must be female undergraduate or graduate students; must be currently enrolled in an undergraduate or graduate program at an accredited US academic institution; must be enrolled at a four-year college or university; must be citizens of the United States; must have at least one ancestor of Italian descent; must have minimum GPA of 3.5 and demonstrated financial need. **Criteria:** Preference will be given to applicants who have demonstrated excellence in fields of study of Italian language and/or culture as well as current students of CUNY.

Funds Avail.: No specific amount. **Duration:** Annual. **To Apply:** Applicants must submit completed application form; official college transcript; student aid report; curriculum vitae or resume; two (2) letters of recommendation (academic and professional); a $25 non-refundable processing fee and a two-page essay (double spaced) that addresses the question "How has being an Italian American impacted you, personally and professionally?" **Deadline:** March 2. **Remarks:** Established in 1980.

8026 ■ National Organization for the Professional Advancement of Black Chemists and Chemical Engineers (NOBCCHE)
PO Box 255
Blue Bell, PA 19422
E-mail: answers@nobcche.org
URL: www.nobcche.org
Social Media: www.facebook.com/NOBCChE
www.instagram.com/nobcche_official
twitter.com/NOBCChE
www.youtube.com/channel/UCpPVZIUJBmoKhUZyfzyL-oQ

8027 ■ Dow Chemical Company Fellowships
(Graduate/Fellowship)

Purpose: To support outstanding minority graduate students who have made significant contributions to science and/or engineering research. **Focus:** Biology; Chemistry; Engineering, Chemical; Life sciences. **Qualif.:** Applicants must be a candidate in a PhD program for Chemistry, Chemical Engineering, Biology, or Life Sciences; be in at least second year of graduate study; and be enrolled in the PhD program for the Fall/Spring academic year. **Criteria:** Selection is based on the application.

Funds Avail.: No specific amount. **To Apply:** Applicants must submit a completed application with official transcripts from undergraduate and graduate schools; a resume; research description (one page); career objective (one page); title and Abstract for presentation at the meeting; and two completed recommendation forms (at least 1 must be from thesis advisor); application materials must be submitted electronically.

8028 ■ E.I. DuPont Graduate Fellowship *(Graduate/ Fellowship)*

Purpose: To support outstanding minority graduate students who have made significant contributions to science and/or engineering research. **Focus:** Biology; Chemistry; Engineering, Chemical; Life sciences. **Qualif.:** Applicant must be a candidate in a PhD program for Chemistry, Chemical Engineering, Biology, or Life Sciences; be in at least second year of graduate study; and be enrolled in the PhD program for the Fall/Spring academic year. **Criteria:** Selection is based on the application.

Duration: Annual. **To Apply:** Applicants must include resume; official transcripts; two letters of recommendation (letters must be sent from recommender); complete curriculum vitae.

8029 ■ Dolphus E. Milligan Graduate Fellowships
(Graduate/Fellowship)

Purpose: To support outstanding minority graduate students who have made significant contributions to science and/or engineering research. **Focus:** Biology; Chemistry; Engineering, Chemical; Life sciences. **Qualif.:** Applicant must be a U.S. citizen and will have completed undergraduate degrees in chemistry, chemical engineering, or a related discipline. **Criteria:** Fellowship winner will be selected after consideration of the finalists' records and presentations.

Funds Avail.: No specific amount. **To Apply:** Applicants must submit a completed application with official transcripts from undergraduate and graduate schools; a resume; research description (one page); career objective (one page); title and Abstract for presentation at the meeting; and two completed recommendation forms (at least 1 must

Awards are arranged alphabetically below their administering organizations

be from thesis advisor); application materials must be submitted electronically.

8030 ■ NOBCChE Procter and Gamble Fellowships
(Graduate/Fellowship)

Purpose: To support outstanding minority graduate students who have made significant contributions to science and/or engineering research. **Focus:** Biology; Chemistry; Engineering, Chemical; Life sciences. **Qualif.:** Applicants must be a candidate in a PhD program for Chemistry, Chemical Engineering, Biology, or Life Sciences; be in at least second year of graduate study; and be enrolled in the PhD program for the Fall/Spring academic year. **Criteria:** Selection is based on the application.

Funds Avail.: No specific amount. **To Apply:** Applicants must submit a completed application with official transcripts from undergraduate and graduate schools; a resume; research description (one page); career objective (one page); title and Abstract for presentation at the meeting; and two completed recommendation forms (at least 1 must be from thesis advisor); application materials must be submitted electronically.

8031 ■ Lendon N. Pridgen, GlaxoSmithKline - NOBCChE Fellowships *(Graduate/Fellowship)*

Purpose: To support outstanding minority graduate students who have made significant contributions to science and/or engineering research. **Focus:** Chemistry. **Qualif.:** Applicants must be in the third or fourth year of graduate study and majoring in Synthetic Organic Chemistry. **Criteria:** Selection is based on the application.

Funds Avail.: No specific amount. **To Apply:** Applicants must submit a completed application with official transcripts from undergraduate and graduate schools; a resume; research description (one page); career objective (one page); title and Abstract for presentation at the meeting; and two completed recommendation forms (at least 1 must be from thesis advisor); application materials must be submitted electronically.

8032 ■ Eastman Kodak Dr. Theophilus Sorrell Fellowships *(Graduate/Fellowship)*

Purpose: To support outstanding minority graduate students who have made significant contributions to science and/or engineering research. **Focus:** Biology; Chemistry; Engineering, Chemical; Life sciences.

Funds Avail.: No specific amount. **Number Awarded:** 1. **To Apply:** Applicants must submit a completed application with official transcripts from undergraduate and graduate schools; a resume; research description (one page); career objective (one page); title and Abstract for presentation at the meeting; and two completed recommendation forms (at least 1 must be from thesis advisor); application materials must be submitted electronically.

8033 ■ National Orientation Directors Association (NODA)
1200 S Washington Ave., Ste. 215
Minneapolis, MN 55415
Ph: (612)301-6632
Free: 866-521-6632
E-mail: noda@umn.edu
URL: www.nodaweb.org

8034 ■ Norman K. Russell Scholarship *(Graduate, Doctorate/Scholarship)*

Purpose: To recognize and assist graduate or doctoral students who have demonstrated a strong commitment to orientation, retention and transition, who will contribute to the enhancement of the orientation field, and who are currently enrolled as graduate students in orientation-related fields. **Focus:** General studies/Field of study not specified. **Qualif.:** Applicants must be graduate or doctoral students with a strong commitment to orientation, retention and transition, who will contribute to the enhancement of the orientation field; must be enrolled in a graduate program in orientation-related fields. **Criteria:** Selection shall be based on the aforementioned qualifications and compliance with the application details.

Funds Avail.: $1,000 each. **Duration:** Annual. **To Apply:** Applicants must submit a Norman K. Russell Scholarship application form; a statement (double-spaced, three pages); a resume; an official transcript (must state enrollment in a graduate program, or graduation from a graduate program); official verification of present enrollment; and two letters of recommendations.

8035 ■ National Parking Association (NPA)
1112 16th St. NW, Ste. 840
Washington, DC 20036
Ph: (202)296-4336
Fax: (202)296-3102
Free: 800-647-7275
E-mail: info@weareparking.org
URL: weareparking.org
Social Media: www.facebook.com/nationalparkingassociation
www.linkedin.com/company/national-parking-association
twitter.com/WeAreParking
www.youtube.com/channel/UChCvzcdYqlG2RizK_ZbfCJA/featured

8036 ■ Parking Industry Institute Scholarship Program *(Undergraduate/Scholarship)*

Purpose: To provide financial aid to support the association's commitment to advance educational opportunities. **Focus:** General studies/Field of study not specified. **Qualif.:** Applicants must be undergraduate students enrolled at an accredited two or four year college/university; a child or spouse of a full-time employee of a firm which is a member of the National Parking Association; a full-time or part-time employee of a firm which is a member of the National Parking Association. **Criteria:** Selection will be based on merits, scholastic and extracurricular achievement, charter, meritorious service and application criteria such as transcripts, recommendations, etc.

Funds Avail.: $500-$3,000. **Duration:** One year. **To Apply:** Applicants must submit (four pages) application form; statement outlining goals, accomplishments and community involvement; official transcripts; and three letters of recommendation; copy of acceptance letter is required for those freshmen and transferee applicants; Appraisal Forms; certification. **Deadline:** June 1. **Contact:** Trustees of The Parking Industry Institute, 1112 16th St, N.W. Ste. 840, Washington, DC 20036.

8037 ■ National Pest Management Association (NPMA)
10460 North St.
Fairfax, VA 22030
Ph: (703)352-6762
Fax: (703)352-3031

Awards are arranged alphabetically below their administering organizations

Free: 800-678-6722
E-mail: npma@pestworld.org
URL: npmapestworld.org
Social Media: www.facebook.com/
  NationalPestManagementAssn
www.instagram.com/NationalPestMgt
www.linkedin.com/company/nationalpestmgt
twitter.com/NationalPestMgt

8038 ■ PWIPM Professional Empowerment Grant
(Graduate/Grant)

Purpose: To support a female interested in advancing or securing a career in the pest management industry. **Focus:** Pesticide science. **Qualif.:** Applicants must be women who are currently employed in the pest management industry and have a minimum of two years experience in the industry. **Criteria:** Selection shall be based on the afore-mentioned applicants' qualifications and compliance with the application details.

Funds Avail.: Minimum of $1,000 plus $1,000 travel expenses. **Duration:** Annual. **Number Awarded:** Varies. **To Apply:** Applicants must submit a resume with work experience; essay (to be no more than 3 pages long (500-1500-words); itemized budget detailing the use of the $1,000 grant to help meet career goals and two letters of recommendation (sealed and signed by author). **Deadline:** August 15. **Contact:** Allison Allen Professional Women in Pest Management c/o NPMA 10460 North Street Fairfax, VA 22030; Email: aallen@pestworld.org.

8039 ■ National Potato Council (NPC)
1300 L St. NW, Ste. 910
Washington, DC 20005
Ph: (202)682-9456
Fax: (202)682-0333
E-mail: info@nationalpotatocouncil.org
URL: nationalpotatocouncil.org
Social Media: www.facebook.com/nationalpotatocouncil
twitter.com/thisspudsforyou
www.youtube.com/user/NatlPotatoCouncil

8040 ■ NPC Scholarship *(Graduate/Scholarship)*

Purpose: To assist a student conducting research for the benefit of the potato industry. **Focus:** Agribusiness; Engineering, Agricultural. **Qualif.:** Applicant must be a graduate student (Master's degree or higher) working to improve the future of the U.S. potato industry. **Criteria:** Selection is based on academic achievement, leadership abilities and potato-related areas of graduate study.

Funds Avail.: $10,000. **Duration:** Annual. **Number Awarded:** 1. **To Apply:** Applicants must submit a completed scholarship application form along with an essay on goals, ambitions and research benefits(maximum of 200 words), undergraduate and graduate transcripts with cumulative GPA; resume; a list of activities (if applicable), and a list of names and contact information for the references. **Contact:** National Potato Council, Scholarship Program, 1300 L St. NW, Ste. 910, Washington, DC, 20005.

8041 ■ National Poultry and Food Distributors Association (NPFDA)
2014 Osborne Rd.
Saint Marys, GA 31558

Ph: (912)439-3603
URL: www.npfda.org
Social Media: www.facebook.com/NPFDA-Scholarship
  -Foundation-56890499963
www.instagram.com/npfda1/
www.linkedin.com/company/national-food-&-poultry
  -distributors-association-npfda-
twitter.com/NPFDA1

8042 ■ National Poultry and Food Distributors Association Scholarships *(Undergraduate/Scholarship)*

Purpose: To help build "people resources" for the poultry and food industries. **Focus:** Agribusiness; Agricultural sciences; Agriculture, Economic aspects; Food science and technology; Poultry science. **Qualif.:** Applicants must be a college junior or senior during the upcoming school year; be enrolled as a full-time student; pursuing a poultry or related agricultural degree, i.e. Agricultural Business, Poultry Science, Food Science, Animal Science, Food Marketing, Ag. Econ, and other related business and agricultural degrees. **Criteria:** Recipients are selected based on the committee's review of their application; the scholarship winners are chosen based on their aspirations, extra-curricular activities, as well as their academic progress. Provide a 500 word essay describing candidate's goals and aspirations.

Funds Avail.: $20,000. **Duration:** Entire length of study. **Number Awarded:** 5. **To Apply:** Applicants must submit an application form; official transcript; letter of recommendation from Dean; and a one-page letter describing goals and aspirations. Submission may be typed in the online form or uploaded as an attachment. **Remarks:** Established in 1979. **Contact:** NPFDA Scholarship Foundation, Inc., 2014 Osborne Rd., Saint Marys, GA, 31558; Phone: 770-535-9901; E-mail: Cece@npfda.org.

8043 ■ National Preservation Institute (NPI)
PO Box 1702
Alexandria, VA 22313
Ph: (703)765-0100
E-mail: info@npi.org
URL: www.npi.org
Social Media: www.facebook.com/National-Preservation
  -Institute-273102762795

8044 ■ National Preservation Institute Scholarships
(Undergraduate/Scholarship)

Purpose: To provide financial assistance to individuals who wish to attend the NPI seminars. **Focus:** General studies/Field of study not specified. **Qualif.:** Applicants must work at least 20 hours a week (paid or volunteer) at the organization that they will represent; must be full-time students; must have a commitment to improving their own performance, as well as their staff, and wish to impact the field at large; must agree to attend the entire seminar. **Criteria:** Recipients will be selected based on the eligibility criteria; preference will be given to applicants from nonprofit institutions or from diverse ethnic or racial backgrounds or representing ethnic-specific institutions, or to full-time students.

Funds Avail.: No specific amount. **To Apply:** Applicants must complete and submit online application. **Contact:** Phone: 703-765-0100; Email: info@npi.org.

Awards are arranged alphabetically below their administering organizations

8045 ■ National Press Photographers Association (NPPA)
120 Hooper St.
Athens, GA 30602
URL: nppa.org
Social Media: www.facebook.com/NPPA.Visual.Journalists
twitter.com/nppa

8046 ■ Bob Baxter Scholarship (Graduate, Undergraduate/Scholarship)
Purpose: To encourage those with the talent and dedication to photojournalism and who need financial help to continue their studies. Focus: Journalism; Photography. Qualif.: Applicants must be undergraduate and graduate students studying full-time.
Funds Avail.: $2,000. Number Awarded: 1.

8047 ■ Bob East Scholarship (Graduate, Undergraduate/Scholarship)
Purpose: To encourage those with the talent and dedication to photojournalism and who need financial help to continue their studies. Focus: Journalism; Photography. Qualif.: Applicants must be undergraduate and graduate students.
Funds Avail.: $2,000. Duration: Annual. Number Awarded: 1. Remarks: Established in 1986.

8048 ■ Kit C. King Graduate Scholarships (Graduate/Scholarship)
Purpose: To encourage those with the talent and dedication to photojournalism and who need financial help to continue their studies. Focus: Journalism; Photography. Qualif.: Open only to graduate students.
Funds Avail.: $2,000. Duration: Annual. Number Awarded: 1.

8049 ■ NPPF Still & Multimedia Scholarship (Undergraduate/Scholarship)
Purpose: To encourage those with the talent and dedication to photojournalism and who need financial help to continue their studies. Focus: Journalism; Photography. Qualif.: Applicants must be undergraduate students.
Funds Avail.: $2,000. Duration: Annual. Number Awarded: 1.

8050 ■ NPPF TV News Scholarship (Undergraduate/Scholarship)
Purpose: To encourage those with the talent and dedication to photojournalism and who need financial help to continue their studies. Focus: Journalism; Photography. Qualif.: Applicants must be undergraduate students.
Funds Avail.: $2,000. Number Awarded: 1.

8051 ■ Reid Blackburn Scholarship (Undergraduate/Scholarship)
Purpose: To encourage those with the talent and dedication to photojournalism and who need financial help to continue their studies. Focus: Journalism; Photography. Qualif.: Applicants must be graduate students studying full-time.
Funds Avail.: $2,000. Number Awarded: 1.

8052 ■ National Private Truck Council (NPTC)
950 N Glebe Rd., Ste. 530
Arlington, VA 22203-4183
Ph: (703)683-1300
Fax: (703)683-1217
E-mail: info@nptc.org
URL: www.nptc.org

8053 ■ CTP Scholarship Program (Other/Scholarship)
Purpose: To promote continuous learning and professional development by providing financial aid for individuals lacking the necessary corporate funding to pursue the CTP designation. Focus: Management; Transportation. Qualif.: Applicants must be members in good standing of the National Private Truck Council; be currently employed in a fleet management position; have at least five years of fleet management experience; and, be able to fully participate in all offerings included in the CTP Scholarship. Criteria: Recipients who will get the highest score on the following: letters of recommendation; community involvement; work and professional activities; and originality of essay will be selected.
Funds Avail.: No specific amount. Duration: Annual. To Apply: Applicants must submit a resume which indicates the candidate's history of accomplishments, active participation in transportation/logistics organizations, a continuing pursuit of knowledge and learning and participation in community service or volunteer organizations; two letters of recommendation from a member of the NPTC or from a management personnel within the candidate's company who is familiar with the candidate's job performance; an original essay (not less than 300 words) on "Why I Want a Certified Transportation Professional (CTP) Scholarship." Deadline: September 1. Contact: Mail complete application to: Institute for Truck Transportation Management, 2200 Mill Rd., Ste. 350, Alexandria, VA 22314.

8054 ■ National PTA
1250 N Pitt St.
Alexandria, VA 22314
Ph: (703)518-1200
Fax: (703)836-0942
Free: 800-307-4782
E-mail: info@pta.org
URL: www.pta.org
Social Media: www.instagram.com/nationalpta/
www.linkedin.com/company/42718
www.pinterest.com/nationalpta/
twitter.com/NationalPTA
www.youtube.com/user/nationalpta

8055 ■ National PTA Reflections - Outstanding Interpretation Awards (Undergraduate/Award, Medal, Scholarship)
Purpose: To recognize students who excel in the field of arts. Focus: Arts. Criteria: Selection will be based on personal interpretations on the program theme that best exemplify creativity and technical skill.
Funds Avail.: $200; $800. Duration: Annual. To Apply: Applicants should contact their local/state PTAs for official program rules and deadlines.

8056 ■ National Public Employer Labor Relations Association (NPELRA)
10951 Sorrento Valley Rd., Ste. 2K
San Diego, CA 92121

Awards are arranged alphabetically below their administering organizations

Ph: (858)299-3150
Fax: (858)299-3156
Free: 877-673-5721
E-mail: info@npelra.org
URL: www.npelra.org
Social Media: www.facebook.com/NationalPELRA
www.linkedin.com/company/npelra
twitter.com/npelra

8057 ■ NPELRA Foundation - Anthony C. Russo Scholarships *(Graduate/Scholarship)*

Purpose: To provide worthy graduate students interested in a career in public sector labor and employee relations with financial assistance. **Focus:** Industrial and labor relations; Personnel administration/human resources. **Qualif.:** Applicant must U.S. citizen; must be a graduate student currently enrolled and seeking a graduate degree in human resources, labor and industrial relations, public administration or political science with a strong and documented interest in the public sector; National PELRA members are encouraged to apply. **Criteria:** Preference will be given to students currently working for a state, local, county or special district governments.

Funds Avail.: $3,000. **Duration:** Annual. **Number Awarded:** 1. **To Apply:** Completed application form along with a resume and recommendations from at least two faculty members (must not be less than two) who know the applicant must be submitted by email (subject line NPELRA Foundation Scholarship Application, Last name, First Name). **Deadline:** January 31. **Remarks:** Established in 1996. **Contact:** Email: contact: sean@npelra.org.

8058 ■ National Recreation and Park Association (NRPA)

22377 Belmont Ridge Road
Ashburn, VA 20148-4501
Ph: (703)858-0784
Free: 800-626-6772
E-mail: customerservice@nrpa.org
URL: www.nrpa.org
Social Media: www.facebook.com/
  NationalRecreationandParkAssociation
www.instagram.com/nrpa
www.linkedin.com/company/national-recreation-and-park
  -association
www.pinterest.com/nrpa
twitter.com/NRPA_news
www.youtube.com/user/NRPA1

8059 ■ National Recreation and Park Association Diversity Scholarships *(Undergraduate/Scholarship)*

Purpose: To support individuals from historically under-represented groups in the parks as well as those that demonstrate outstanding contributions serving diverse communities with hopes of engaging their interest in future leadership roles. **Focus:** Parks and recreation. **Qualif.:** Applicants Current members of NRPA from an underrepresented group in the park and recreation community and/or demonstrate outstanding contributions serving diverse communities specifically related to park and recreation programs and services. **Criteria:** Selection will be based on the applicant's compliance with basic eligibility requirements set by the National Recreation and Park Association.

Duration: Annual. **Number Awarded:** 2. **Contact:** E-mail: awards@nrpa.org.

8060 ■ National Restaurant Association Educational Foundation (NRAEF)

2055 L St. NW
Washington, DC 20036
Free: 800-424-5156
E-mail: comms@nraef.org
URL: chooserestaurants.org
Social Media: www.facebook.com/nraefoundation
twitter.com/nraef

8061 ■ Al Schuman/Ecolab Undergraduate Entrepreneurial Scholarship *(Undergraduate/Scholarship)*

Purpose: To support students pursuing an education in a restaurant, food service, or hospitality related major. **Focus:** Food service careers. **Qualif.:** Applicants must be citizens or permanent residents of the United States of America planning to attend full-time or substantial part-time in a foodservice related program and accepted or enrolled in the following schools California State Polytechnic University Pomona, Cornell University, Culinary Institute of America, Johnson and Wales University, Kendall College, Lynn University, Michigan State University, New York University, Pennsylvania State University, Purdue University, University of Denver, University of Houston, University of Nevada (Las Vegas) or University of Massachusetts-Amherst; must also have a minimum grade point average of 3.0.

Funds Avail.: No specific amount. **Duration:** Annual. **Number Awarded:** Varies.

8062 ■ National Roofing Contractors Association (NRCA)

10255 W Higgins Rd., Ste. 600
Rosemont, IL 60018-5607
Ph: (847)299-9070
Fax: (847)299-1183
E-mail: info@nrca.net
URL: www.nrca.net
Social Media: www.facebook.com/nrcainfo
www.instagram.com/NRCAnews
www.linkedin.com/company/national-roofing-contractors
  -association
twitter.com/NRCAnews
www.youtube.com/user/nrcanews?sub_confirmation=1

8063 ■ Melvin Kruger Endowed Scholarship Program *(Graduate, Undergraduate/Scholarship)*

Purpose: To help employees and their families who plan to pursue post-secondary education in college and vocational programs. **Focus:** General studies/Field of study not specified.

Remarks: The scholarship was established in memory of Melvin Kruger. **Contact:** Bennett Judson, Executive Director; Toll: 800-323-9545 ext. 7513; Email: bjudson@roofingalliance.net.

8064 ■ National Science Foundation (NSF)

2415 Eisenhower Ave.
Alexandria, VA 22314
Ph: (703)292-5111
Free: 800-877-8339
E-mail: info@nsf.gov

Awards are arranged alphabetically below their administering organizations

URL: www.nsf.gov
Social Media: instagram.com/nsfgov
www.linkedin.com/company/national-science-foundation
twitter.com/NSF
youtube.com/user/VideosatNSF

8065 ■ ASA/NSF/BLS Fellowships *(Graduate/ Fellowship, Recognition, Grant)*

Purpose: To improve the collaboration between government and academic research. **Focus:** Government; Statistics. **Qualif.:** Applicants should have academically recognized research records and considerable expertise in their areas of proposed research. Moreover, applicants must be affiliated with a U.S. institution. **Criteria:** Recipients will be selected based on the proposed research project; preference will be given to those who meet the criteria.

Funds Avail.: No specific amount. **Duration:** Annual. **Number Awarded:** Varies. **To Apply:** Applicants must submit the following information via email: a curriculum vitae; names and addresses of three references; a detailed research proposal that includes background information about research topic, significance of expected results; advantages of conducting research at the bls; and detailed budget estimate (salary, relocation, travel expenses, research support). all of these must be compiled in one pdf file. **Deadline:** January 3. **Contact:** Email: joyce@ amstat.org.

8066 ■ ASEE/NSF Small Business Postdoctoral Research Diversity Fellowship (SBPRDF) *(Postdoctorate/Fellowship)*

Purpose: To encourage creative and highly-trained recipients of doctoral degrees in NSF-supported science, technology, engineering and mathematical disciplines to engage in hands-on research projects in their areas of expertise at the kind of small innovative businesses that historically have fueled the nation's economic regime. **Focus:** Business; Economics. **Qualif.:** Applicants must be U.S. citizens, U.S. nationals or U.S. permanent residents, and must have received a Ph.D. degree in a NSF-supported science, technology, engineering or mathematical (STEM) discipline in the seven years prior to the application date; must not have received a prior postdoctoral fellowship in a corporate laboratory for a term of more than six months. **Criteria:** Selection will be based on the committee's criteria.

Funds Avail.: $75,000. **To Apply:** Applicants must submit online. **Deadline:** February 1;July 31. **Contact:** E-mail: nsfsbir@asee.org.

8067 ■ EAPSI Fellowships *(Doctorate, Graduate/ Fellowship, Award)*

Purpose: To provide educational opportunities for graduate students in science, education, and engineering. **Focus:** Behavioral sciences; Biological and clinical sciences; Computer and information sciences; Education; Engineering; Geosciences; Mathematics and mathematical sciences; Social sciences. **Qualif.:** Applicants must be U.S. citizens or permanent residents enrolled in a research-oriented master's PhD degree program at a U.S. institution; and pursuing studies in fields of sciences and engineering research and education supported by the NSF; must propose a location, host scientist, and research project that is appropriate for the host site and duration of the international visit. **Criteria:** Selection shall be based on the aforementioned applicants' qualifications and compliance with the application details.

Funds Avail.: Amount varies. **Duration:** Annual. **Contact:** National Science Foundation, at the above address.

8068 ■ National Science Foundation Graduate Research Fellowship Program (GRFP) *(Graduate/ Fellowship)*

Purpose: To help ensure the vitality and diversity of the scientific and engineering workforce of the United States; and to support also the graduate level students pursuing their own degrees. **Focus:** Engineering; Science; Technology. **Qualif.:** Applicants must be graduate students in NSF-supported science, technology, engineering, and mathematics disciplines who are pursuing research-based master's and doctoral degrees at accredited United States institutions. **Criteria:** Selection will be based on the committee's criteria.

Funds Avail.: Stipend of $34,000 along with a $12,000 cost of education allowance for tuition and fees. **Duration:** Annual. **Remarks:** Established in 1952. **Contact:** GRF Operations Center; Email: info@nsfgrfp.org.

8069 ■ National Science Teachers Association (NSTA)
1840 Wilson Blvd.
Arlington, VA 22201
Ph: (703)243-7100
Fax: (703)243-7177
Free: 800-277-5300
E-mail: executive@nsta.org
URL: www.nsta.org

8070 ■ Toyota Tapestry Grants for Science Teachers *(Other/Grant)*

Purpose: To encourage the development of science projects that can be implemented in a school district over a one-year period. **Focus:** Science.

Funds Avail.: Up to $10,000. **Duration:** Annual.

8071 ■ National Sculpture Society (NSS)
6 E 39th St., Ste. 903
New York, NY 10016
Ph: (212)764-5645
URL: www.nationalsculpture.org

8072 ■ Alex J. Ettl Grants *(Other/Grant)*

Purpose: To honor sculptors who demonstrate commitment and exceptional ability in their work. **Focus:** Sculpture. **Qualif.:** Applicants must be U.S. citizens; and must be figurative or realist sculptors who are not elected member of the National Sculpture Society (NSA). **Criteria:** Selection will be consist of three prominent sculptors.

Funds Avail.: Up to $7,695. **Duration:** Annual. **To Apply:** Applicants must submit biography or resume in PDF or Word format; and images of six to twelve works of sculpture (up to twenty-four images total); must be JPEG (.jpg) format; must be roughly 72-150 dpi and 8 inches to 11 inches on its longest side. **Deadline:** October 5.

8073 ■ National Sculpture Society Participation Scholarships *(Undergraduate/Scholarship)*

Purpose: To provide financial assistance to individuals studying figurative or representational sculpture. **Focus:** Sculpture. **Qualif.:** Applicants must have been born

---

Awards are arranged alphabetically below their administering organizations

between 1984-1999. All applicants must be citizens of or residents in the United States with a social security number. **Criteria:** Selection will be consist of three sculptors and an NSS member.

Funds Avail.: $150. **Duration:** Annual. **Number Awarded:** Up to 4. **To Apply:** Applicants must submit Images of six to twelve works of sculpture (up to twenty-four images total). Images should be in JPEG (.jpg) format. The longest side of the image should be at least 1500 pixels long. A list stating the title, medium and dimensions of the sculpture in PDF (.pdf) or Word (.docx) format. A biography or resume in PDF (.pdf) or Word (.docx) format. Applications can be shared with competition@nationalsculpture.org through file sharing programs such as Dropbox, Google Drive, send this file, Hightail, WeTransfer, etc. **Deadline:** March 16.

8074 ■ National Sheriffs' Association (NSA)
1450 Duke St.
Alexandria, VA 22314
Fax: (703)838-5349
Free: 800-424-7827
E-mail: nsamail@sheriffs.org
URL: www.sheriffs.org
Social Media: www.facebook.com/
 Nationalsheriffsassociation
www.linkedin.com/groups/3400924/profile
twitter.com/nationalsheriff
www.youtube.com/channel/UCzQh_oUkrEYGZC0R8f-ziFw

8075 ■ Triple Crown Award *(Other/Recognition, Award)*
Purpose: To provide educational assistance to employees of a sheriff's office or their dependents. **Focus:** Criminal justice; Law.

Funds Avail.: No specific amount. **Duration:** Annual. **To Apply:** Applicant must provide a completed Official NSA scholarship application form available at the website; and an essay (minimum of 500 words) stating the applicant deserves the scholarship and describing the greatest challenge sheriffs faces today. Materials must be photocopied and forwarded to the NSA Awards and Scholarship Committee together with the application form. **Contact:** National Sheriffs' Association, Awards Committee, 1450 Duke St., Alexandria, VA, 22314-3490; Ross Mirmelstein, Director of Meeting; Phone: 571-237-3292; Email: rossmir@sheriffs.org.

8076 ■ National Slovak Society of the United States of America (NSS)
351 Valley Brook Rd.
McMurray, PA 15317-3337
Ph: (724)731-0094
Fax: (724)731-0145
Free: 800-488-1890
E-mail: info@nsslife.org
URL: nsslife.org
Social Media: www.facebook.com/NSSLife
www.linkedin.com/company/nss-life-national-slovak-society
 -of-the-usa-?trk=company_logo
www.youtube.com/user/NSSLifeTV

8077 ■ Senior Scholarships *(Undergraduate, Vocational/Occupational/Scholarship)*
Purpose: To support elder members who are interested in continuing their intellectual growth and making fuller use of their leisure time. **Focus:** Education, Vocational-technical; Nursing. **Qualif.:** Applicants must be members of the National Slovak Society; must be 55 years and above; must be enrolled and successfully completed a continuing education or adult education course; continuing education classes for the attainment or maintenance of a degree or certification are not qualified.

Funds Avail.: $200. **Duration:** Annual. **To Apply:** Applicants can submit up to two applications in one calendar year; Applicants must enroll and pay for the course of their choice, after the applicants have finished the class, they must submit an application, along with the verification that the class was successfully completed. **Remarks:** Established in 1966.

8078 ■ National Society of Accountants (NSA)
1330 Braddock Pl., Ste. 540
Alexandria, VA 22314
Ph: (703)549-6400
Fax: (703)549-2984
Free: 800-966-6679
E-mail: members@nsacct.org
URL: www.nsacct.org
Social Media: www.facebook.com/nsacct
www.linkedin.com/company/national-society-of
 -accountants
twitter.com/NSAtax

8079 ■ NSA Scholarship Foundation *(Undergraduate/ Scholarship)*
Purpose: To helps accounting students with the increasing costs of higher education. **Focus:** Accounting. **Qualif.:** Applicant must be a United States or Canadian citizen; be majoring in accounting, having maintained a 3.0 cumulative GPA or higher (on a 4.0 scale); be an undergraduate enrolled part- or full-time at an accredited two-year or four-year college or university in the United States. **Criteria:** Recipients are selected on the basis of academic record, demonstrated leadership and participation in school and community activities, honors, work experience, statement of goals and aspirations, unusual personal or family circumstances and an outside appraisal. Financial need is also considered.

Duration: Annual. **Number Awarded:** 45. **To Apply:** Applicants must complete the application form (available on the website) and mail it with a transcript of records. **Deadline:** April 1. **Contact:** For additional information regarding the scholarship program call toll free (855) 670-ISTS (4787).

8080 ■ The Stanley H. Stearman Awards *(Undergraduate/Scholarship)*
Purpose: To provide financial assistance for students majoring in accounting. **Focus:** Accounting. **Qualif.:** Applicant must be a United States or Canadian citizen; be majoring in accounting, having maintained a 3.0 cumulative GPA or higher (on a 4.0 scale); be an undergraduate enrolled part- or full-time at an accredited two-year or four-year college or university in the United States. **Criteria:** Recipients are selected on the basis of academic record, demonstrated leadership and participation in school and community activities, honors, work experience, statement of goals and aspirations, unusual personal or family circumstances and an outside appraisal. Financial need is also considered.

Funds Avail.: $2,000. **Duration:** Annual. **Number Awarded:** 2. **To Apply:** Applicants must complete the ap-

Awards are arranged alphabetically below their administering organizations

plication form (available on the website) and mail it with a transcript of records. **Deadline:** April 1. **Contact:** For additional information regarding the scholarship program call toll free (855) 670-ISTS (4787).

8081 ■ National Society of Black Physicists (NSBP)

3303 Wilson Blvd., Ste. 700
Arlington, VA 22201
Ph: (703)617-4176
E-mail: headquarters@nsbp.org
URL: www.nsbp.org
Social Media: www.facebook.com/pages/National-Society
 -of-Black-Physicists-Inc/356311781194959?fref=ts
www.instagram.com/nsbpinc
www.linkedin.com/in/nsbpinc
twitter.com/nsbpinc

8082 ■ Michael P. Anderson Scholarships in Space Science *(Undergraduate/Scholarship)*

Purpose: To support interest in physics by providing educational assistance for skilled physics majors. **Focus:** Physics. **Qualif.:** Applicants must be physics majors in their junior or senior year. **Criteria:** Recipient is selected based on merit and evaluation of the applicant's scientific abilities and potential which includes versatility, ability to make sound judgments, major academic strengths and weaknesses (if any) and performance in an independent study (if any) as manifested through documents submitted.

Funds Avail.: $1,000. **To Apply:** Applicant must send the complete application package along with official transcripts and a stamped envelope. **Deadline:** December.

8083 ■ Arthur B.C. Walker II Scholarship *(Undergraduate/Scholarship)*

Purpose: To support interest in physics by providing educational assistance for skilled physics majors. **Focus:** Physics. **Qualif.:** Applicants must be physics majors in their junior or senior year. **Criteria:** Recipient is selected based on merit and evaluation of the applicant's scientific abilities and potential which includes versatility, ability to make sound judgments, major academic strengths and weaknesses (if any) and performance in an independent study (if any) as manifested through documents submitted.

Funds Avail.: $1,000. **To Apply:** Applicant must send the complete application package along with official transcripts and a stamped envelope. **Deadline:** December.

8084 ■ Charles S. Brown Scholarships in Physics *(Graduate, Undergraduate/Scholarship)*

Purpose: To inspire the next generation of physicians by providing financial assistance for individuals pursuing further studies in the field of physics. **Focus:** Physics. **Qualif.:** Applicants must be graduate students and undergraduate students with a declared major in physics are eligible for this scholarship. **Criteria:** Recipient is selected based on merit and evaluation of the applicant's scientific abilities and potential which includes versatility, ability to make sound judgments, major academic strengths and weaknesses (if any) and performance in an independent study (if any) as manifested through documents submitted.

Funds Avail.: Not specific amount. **To Apply:** Applicant must send complete application package available in the website with official transcript and supply a stamped envelope.

8085 ■ Robert A. Ellis Scholarships in Physics *(Undergraduate/Scholarship)*

Purpose: To support interest in physics by providing educational assistance for skilled physics majors. **Focus:** Physics. **Qualif.:** Applicants must be physics majors in their junior or senior year. **Criteria:** Recipient is selected based on merit and evaluation of the applicant's scientific abilities and potential which includes versatility, ability to make sound judgments, major academic strengths and weaknesses (if any) and performance in an independent study (if any) as manifested through documents submitted.

To Apply: Applicant must send the complete application package along with official transcripts and a stamped envelope. **Deadline:** December.

8086 ■ Harvey Washington Banks Scholarship in Astronomy *(Undergraduate/Scholarship)*

Purpose: To support interest in physics by providing educational assistance for skilled physics majors. **Focus:** Physics. **Qualif.:** Applicants must be physics majors in their junior or senior year.

Funds Avail.: $1,000 for one academic year. **Number Awarded:** 1. **Contact:** Scholarship Committee Chair, National Society of Black Physicists, 6704G Lee Highway, Arlington, VA 22205; E-mail: scholarship@nsbp.org; Phone: 703-536-4207; Fax: 703-536-4203.Phone: 703-536-4207.

8087 ■ Elmer S. Imes Scholarships in Physics *(Undergraduate/Scholarship)*

Purpose: To support interest in physics by providing educational assistance for skilled physics majors. **Focus:** Physics. **Qualif.:** Applicants must be physics majors in their junior or senior year. **Criteria:** Recipient is selected based on merit and evaluation of the applicant's scientific abilities and potential which includes versatility, ability to make sound judgments, major academic strengths and weaknesses (if any) and performance in an independent study (if any) as manifested through documents submitted.

To Apply: Applicant must send the complete application package along with official transcripts and a stamped envelope.

8088 ■ Walter Samuel McAfee Scholarships in Space Physics *(Undergraduate/Scholarship)*

Purpose: To support interest in physics by providing educational assistance for skilled physics majors. **Focus:** Physics. **Qualif.:** Applicants must be physics majors in their junior or senior year. **Criteria:** Recipient is selected based on merit and evaluation of the applicant's scientific abilities and potential which includes versatility, ability to make sound judgments, major academic strengths and weaknesses (if any) and performance in an independent study (if any) as manifested through documents submitted.

To Apply: Applicant must send the complete application package along with official transcripts and a stamped envelope.

8089 ■ Ronald E. McNair Scholarships in Space and Optical Physics *(Undergraduate/Scholarship)*

Purpose: To support interest in physics by providing educational assistance for skilled physics majors. **Focus:** Physics. **Qualif.:** Applicants must be physics majors in their junior or senior year. **Criteria:** Recipient is selected based on merit and evaluation of the applicant's scientific abilities and potential which includes versatility, ability to make sound judgments, major academic strengths and

Awards are arranged alphabetically below their administering organizations

weaknesses (if any) and performance in an independent study (if any) as manifested through documents submitted.

Funds Avail.: $1,000. **To Apply:** Applicant must send the complete application package along with official transcripts and a stamped envelope. **Deadline:** December.

8090 ■ Willie Hobbs Moore Scholarships
(Undergraduate/Scholarship)

Purpose: To support interest in physics by providing educational assistance for skilled physics majors. **Focus:** Physics. **Qualif.:** Applicants must be physics majors in their junior or senior year. **Criteria:** Recipient is selected based on merit and evaluation of the applicant's scientific abilities and potential which includes versatility, ability to make sound judgments, major academic strengths and weaknesses (if any) and performance in an independent study (if any) as manifested through documents submitted.

Funds Avail.: $1,000. **To Apply:** Applicant must send the complete application package along with official transcripts and a stamped envelope.

8091 ■ Harry L. Morrison Scholarships
(Undergraduate/Scholarship)

Purpose: To support interest in physics by providing educational assistance for skilled physics majors. **Focus:** Physics. **Qualif.:** Applicants must be physics majors in their junior or senior year. **Criteria:** Recipient is selected based on merit and evaluation of the applicant's scientific abilities and potential which includes versatility, ability to make sound judgments, major academic strengths and weaknesses (if any) and performance in an independent study (if any) as manifested through documents submitted.

Funds Avail.: $1,000. **To Apply:** Applicant must send the complete application package along with official transcripts and a stamped envelope.

8092 ■ National Society, Daughters of the American Revolution (DAR)
1776 D St. NW
Washington, DC 20006
Ph: (202)628-1776
URL: www.dar.org/national-society
Social Media: www.facebook.com/TodaysDAR
twitter.com/TodaysDAR
youtube.com/TodaysDAR

8093 ■ Arthur Lockwood Beneventi Law Scholarship *(Undergraduate/Scholarship, Award, Monetary)*

Purpose: To award scholarship to students showing dedication to the pursuit of degrees in diverse disciplines including law. **Focus:** Law. **Qualif.:** Applicants must be students who are either enrolled in or attend an accredited law school and have a minimum GPA of 3.25. **Criteria:** Selection will be based on the committee's criteria.

Funds Avail.: $2,000. **Duration:** Annual. **To Apply:** Applications must complete and arranged the following in order: scholarship application; statement of 1, 000 words or less setting forth career objectives; original transcript of high school or college grades. major must be indicated on original transcript where specific major is required. home schooled students must include transcripts for grade 9 through the current year; at least two but not to exceed four letters of recommendation from high school or college they are currently attending. letter should cover applicant's abil-

ity, work habits, integrity, character, potential and volunteer activities. a letter from a sponsoring chapter is optional; list of extracurricular activities, honors received and scholastic achievements; photocopy of united states citizenship, such as birth certificate, naturalization papers or information page of us passport. cover the applicant's photograph if they are submitting a copy of naturalization or passport pages; typed or computer generated financial needs form; self-addressed, stamped postcard. **Deadline:** February 15. **Contact:** Email; ALBeneventiLawScholarship@ NSDAR.org.

8094 ■ DAR Centennial Scholarship *(Undergraduate/ Scholarship, Award, Monetary)*

Purpose: To support outstanding students pursuing a course of graduate study in the field of historic preservation at a college or university in the United States. **Focus:** Historic preservation. **Qualif.:** Applicants must be students who plan to pursue their course of graduate study in the field of historic preservation. **Criteria:** Selection shall be based on the aforementioned qualifications and compliance with the application details.

Funds Avail.: $2,500. **Duration:** Annual. **To Apply:** Applicants must obtain a letter of sponsorship from their local DAR chapter; forms and other supporting documents must be completed correctly and submitted in one package. **Deadline:** February 15. **Remarks:** The scholarship was established from a portion of the proceeds from the sale of the Centennial Pin. **Contact:** Email: DARCentennialScholarship@NSDAR.org.

8095 ■ Dr. Aura-Lee A. and James Hobbs Pittenger American History Scholarship *(Undergraduate/ Scholarship, Award, Monetary)*

Purpose: To support graduating high school students who will pursue an undergraduate degree in American History and American Government. **Focus:** History, American. **Qualif.:** Applicants must be graduating high school students who will pursue an undergraduate degree with a concentrated study of a minimum of 24 credit hours in American History and American Government. **Criteria:** Selection shall be based on the aforementioned qualifications and compliance with the application details.

Funds Avail.: $2,000 per year. **Duration:** Annual; up to four years. **To Apply:** Applicants must obtain a letter of sponsorship from their local DAR chapter; forms and other supporting documents must be completed correctly and submitted in one package. **Deadline:** February 15. **Contact:** Email: PittengerAmerHistoryScholarship@ NSDAR.org.

8096 ■ Enid Hall Griswold Memorial Scholarship
(Undergraduate/Scholarship, Award, Monetary)

Purpose: To encourage students to pursue an undergraduate degree. **Focus:** Economics; Government; History; Political science. **Qualif.:** Applicants must be juniors or seniors enrolled in an accredited college or university in the United States pursuing a major in political science, history, government, or economics. **Criteria:** Selection shall be based on the aforementioned qualifications and compliance with the application details.

Funds Avail.: $5,000. **Duration:** Annual. **To Apply:** Applicants must obtain a letter of sponsorship from their local DAR chapter; forms and other supporting documents must be completed correctly and submitted in one package. **Deadline:** February 15. **Contact:** Email: EnidHallMemorialScholarship@NSDAR.org.

Awards are arranged alphabetically below their administering organizations

8097 ■ William Robert Findley Graduate Chemistry Scholarship (Graduate/Scholarship, Award, Monetary)

Purpose: To support students showing dedication to the pursuit of degree in chemistry. **Focus:** Chemistry. **Qualif.:** Applicants must be U.S. citizens; must be students attending graduate school full time in any accredited college or university and majoring in chemistry; must have a minimum GPA of 3.25. **Criteria:** Selection will be based on the committee's criteria.

Funds Avail.: $2,000. **Duration:** Annual. **To Apply:** Applicants must obtain a letter of sponsorship from their local DAR chapter; forms and other supporting documents must be completed correctly and submitted in one package. **Deadline:** February 15. **Contact:** Email: WRFindleyChemistryScholarship@nsdar.org.

8098 ■ Mary Elizabeth Lockwood Beneventi MBA Scholarship (Graduate/Scholarship, Award, Monetary)

Purpose: To support students attending graduate school in any accredited college or university. **Focus:** Business administration. **Qualif.:** Applicants must be U.S. citizens; must be full-time students attending graduate school in any accredited college or university and majoring in business administration; must have a minimum GPA of 3.25. **Criteria:** Selection will be based on the committee's criteria.

Funds Avail.: $2,000. **Duration:** Annual. **To Apply:** Applicants must complete both DAR Scholarship Application Form and the Financial Need Form available at the website. The application packet must be completed and arranged in the following order: application form; statement of 1, 000 words or less setting forth their career objectives; original transcript of high school (must indicate class rank, size and test scores) or college grades; all scholarships with a minimum GPA are based on a 4. 0 scale or the equivalent GPA on the scale used by the applicable educational institution; letters of recommendation; list of extracurricular activities, honors received and scholastic achievements; photocopy of us citizenship (birth certificate, naturalization papers or information page of us passport); financial need form; self-address, stamped postcard. **Deadline:** February 15. **Contact:** Email: MELBeneventiMBAScholarship@NSDAR.org.

8099 ■ National Society of Genetic Counselors (NSGC)

330 N Wabash Ave., Ste. 2000
Chicago, IL 60611
Ph: (312)321-6834
Fax: (312)673-6972
E-mail: nsgc@nsgc.org
URL: www.nsgc.org
Social Media: www.facebook.com/GeneticCounselors
www.linkedin.com/groups/3394310
twitter.com/GeneticCouns
www.youtube.com/channel/UCS3GPAJ
_dXmFAh1BzyVvrSA

8100 ■ Jane Engelberg Memorial Fellowship (JEMF) (Professional development/Fellowship)

Purpose: To encourage and fund initiatives by board-certified genetic counselors who are members in good standing of the National Society of Genetic Counselors (NSGC) and by genetic counseling students enrolled in ACGC accredited training programs. **Focus:** Counseling/Guidance; Genetics.

Duration: Annual. **Deadline:** May 1. **Remarks:** Established in 1991.

8101 ■ National Society of High School Scholars (NSHSS)

1936 N Druid Hills Rd.
Atlanta, GA 30319
Ph: (404)235-5500
Free: 866-343-1800
URL: www.nshss.org
Social Media: www.facebook.com/nshss
www.instagram.com/nshss
www.linkedin.com/company/national-society-of-high-school
 -scholars
twitter.com/nshss
youtube.com/user/NSHSS

8102 ■ Abercrombie and Fitch Global Diversity and Leadership Scholar Awards (Undergraduate/Scholarship)

Purpose: To support members to attain higher education. **Focus:** General studies/Field of study not specified. **Qualif.:** Applicants must be members of the NSHSS. **Criteria:** Selection is based on the submitted essay, and will be judged on ingenuity and quality; exploring their perspectives on the theme of diversity and inclusion.

Funds Avail.: No amount mentioned. **Duration:** Annual. **Number Awarded:** 10. **To Apply:** Applicants must submit a completed application form and required materials. **Deadline:** April 30.

8103 ■ Claes Nobel Academic Scholarships for Members (High School, College/Scholarship)

Purpose: To support the education of student members. **Focus:** General studies/Field of study not specified. **Qualif.:** Applicants must be high school junior and senior students members. **Criteria:** Selection is based on academic performance; demonstrated leadership; school and extracurricular activities; and community service.

Funds Avail.: Varies. **Duration:** Annual. **To Apply:** Applications can submitted by online going to the member log in page. Must submit a personal statement; resume of honors, awards, leadership activities, extracurricular activities, and community service; educator recommendation; transcripts; and photo. **Deadline:** June 30.

8104 ■ NSHSS Academic Paper Awards (High School/Scholarship)

Purpose: To support the education of student members. **Focus:** General studies/Field of study not specified. **Qualif.:** Applicants must be a NSHSS member. **Criteria:** Selection is based on the submitted materials such as a research paper, an original essay, or an analytical paper.

Funds Avail.: $250. **Duration:** One year. **Number Awarded:** 25. **To Apply:** Applicants must submit their written high school academic paper (research paper, original essay or analytical paper); title of the paper; brief description of the assignment. **Deadline:** May 1.

8105 ■ NSHSS National Scholar Awards (High School, College/Scholarship)

Purpose: To support the education of student members. **Focus:** General studies/Field of study not specified. **Qualif.:** Applicant must be a high school junior and senior

---

Awards are arranged alphabetically below their administering organizations

student member.**Criteria:** Selection is based on academic performance; demonstrated leadership; school and extra-curricular activities; and community service.

Funds Avail.: $1,000. **Duration:** Annually. **To Apply:** Applicant must submit personal statement of 500 words; resume; transcript; educator Recommendation; color head-shot suitable for website posting. **Deadline:** June 30. **Remarks:** Award will be given to selected finalist for the Class Nobel Academic Scholarships.

8106 ■ Robert P. Sheppard Leadership Awards
(High School, College/Scholarship)

Purpose: To support the education of student members. **Focus:** General studies/Field of study not specified. **Qualif.:** Applicants must be high school sophomore, junior, and senior NSHSS members. **Criteria:** Selection will be demonstrate an outstanding commitment to community service and initiative in volunteer activities.

Funds Avail.: $2,500 for the winner; $1,000 for the top 4 finalists. **Number Awarded:** 5. **To Apply:** Applicants must submit a completed application form together with a personal statement; resume of honors, awards, leadership activities, extracurricular activities, and community service; educator recommendation; transcript, and photo. **Deadline:** June 30.

8107 ■ National Society for HistoTechnology (NSH)
3545 Ellicott Mills Dr.
Ellicott City, MD 21043
Ph: (443)535-4060
Fax: (443)535-4055
E-mail: histo@nsh.org
URL: www.nsh.org
Social Media: www.facebook.com/NS4Histotech
www.linkedin.com/groups/1987903/profile
twitter.com/NS4Histotech

8108 ■ Irwin S. Lerner Student Scholarship
(Undergraduate/Scholarship)

Purpose: To promote the study of histotechnology. **Focus:** General studies/Field of study not specified. **Qualif.:** Applicants must be students from approved histotechnology schools. **Criteria:** Selection will be according to their academic ability and financial need.

Funds Avail.: $500. **Duration:** Annual. **To Apply:** Applicants must complete online application and submit with supporting documentation. **Deadline:** March 2. **Remarks:** Established in 1983.

8109 ■ Lee G. Luna Foreign Travel Scholarship
(Professional development/Scholarship)

Purpose: To support costs for study and/or obtaining histo-technological education abroad of a member seeking continuing education. **Focus:** Medical technology. **Qualif.:** Applicant must be an NSH member for a minimum of 2 consecutive years.

Funds Avail.: Up to $6,000. **Duration:** Annual. **To Apply:** Applicant must submit at least one letter of recommendation that outlines the commitment to the profession; must include a curriculum vitae; resume. **Deadline:** June 1.

8110 ■ Newcomer Supply Student Scholarship
(Undergraduate/Scholarship)

Purpose: To promote the study of histotechnology. **Focus:** General studies/Field of study not specified. **Qualif.:** Ap-

plicants must be students from approved histotechnology schools. **Criteria:** Selection will be according to their academic ability and financial need.

Funds Avail.: $500. **Duration:** Annual. **To Apply:** Applicants must complete online application and submit with supporting documentation. **Deadline:** March 2.

8111 ■ Leonard Noble Educational Scholarships
(Professional development/Scholarship)

Purpose: To promote the study of histotechnology. **Focus:** Histology. **Qualif.:** Applicant must be an NSH member. **Criteria:** Recipients will be selected based on their sincere efforts and not necessarily upon academic merit.

Funds Avail.: $1,000. **Duration:** Annual. **To Apply:** Applicants should be submitted electronically using the applicant portal, or to natalie@nsh.org. One-page letter of recommendation from the applicant's supervisor, mentor, advisor, etc. that outlines why the applicant is uniquely qualified for an NSH scholarship. **Deadline:** June 1. **Remarks:** Established in 1995.

8112 ■ Robert A. Clark Memorial Educational Scholarship *(Professional development/Scholarship)*

Purpose: To promote the study of histotechnology. **Focus:** Histology. **Qualif.:** Applicants must be pursuing advanced education and knowledge within the profession of histo-technology. **Criteria:** Recipients will be selected based on their sincere efforts and not necessarily upon academic merit.

Funds Avail.: No specific amount. **Duration:** Annual. **To Apply:** Applicants must submit the completed application form; must have at least one letter of recommendation on the candidate's behalf and CV/Resume. **Deadline:** June 1.

8113 ■ Sakura Finetek Student Scholarship
(Undergraduate/Scholarship)

Purpose: To promote the study of histotechnology. **Focus:** General studies/Field of study not specified. **Qualif.:** Applicants must be students from approved histotechnology schools. **Criteria:** Selection will be according to their academic ability and financial need.

Funds Avail.: $500. **Duration:** Annual. **To Apply:** Applicants must complete online application and submit with supporting documentation. **Deadline:** March 2. **Remarks:** Established in 1988.

8114 ■ Sigma Diagnostics Student Scholarships
(Undergraduate/Scholarship)

Purpose: To provide educational scholarships and student scholarships for recipients on a reimbursement basis. **Focus:** General studies/Field of study not specified. **Qualif.:** The applicants must be students from approved histotech-nology schools. **Criteria:** Recipients will be selected according to their academic ability and financial need.

Funds Avail.: $500. **To Apply:** Applicants must complete online application and submit together with supporting documentation.

8115 ■ Thermo Scientific Educational Scholarships
(Professional development/Scholarship)

Purpose: To promote the study of histotechnology. **Focus:** Histology. **Qualif.:** Applicants must be pursuing advanced education and knowledge within the profession of histo-technology. **Criteria:** Recipients will be selected based on their sincere efforts and not necessarily upon academic merit.

Awards are arranged alphabetically below their administering organizations

Funds Avail.: $1,000. **Duration:** Annual. **To Apply:** Applicants must complete the online application and submit plans for utilization of a scholarship, up-to-date curriculum vitae and written evaluation of the applicant's supervisor, pathologist or director for the suitability of the candidates. **Deadline:** June 1. **Remarks:** Established in 1996.

8116 ■ Ventana Medical Systems In Situ Hybridization Awards (Other/Award)

Purpose: To provide educational scholarships on a reimbursement basis. **Focus:** Histology. **Qualif.:** Applicants must be pursuing an advanced education within the profession of histotechnology. **Criteria:** Recipient will be selected based on working achievement and/or academic merit.

Funds Avail.: $3,000. **Duration:** Annual. **To Apply:** Applicants must submit a proof of required certification for at least two members of the laboratory staff; up-to-date curriculum vitae for the same members; written evaluation by the laboratory director and/or pathologist as to the laboratory's suitability as the recipient of this award and educational value to the institution; and plans for the utilization which includes identification of educational event. Plans must be utilized within two years after the award is presented. **Deadline:** June 1.

8117 ■ National Society of Professional Surveyors (NSPS)

5119 Pegasus Ct., Ste. Q
Frederick, MD 21704
Ph: (240)439-4615
Fax: (240)439-4952
E-mail: info@nsps.us.com
URL: www.nsps.us.com
Social Media: www.facebook.com/nspsinc
www.instagram.com/nsps.us
www.linkedin.com/company/national-society-of
 -professional-surveyors
twitter.com/NSPSINC
www.youtube.com/channel/
 UCSWFUr5kRwt1FhRHxi6gLDw

8118 ■ NSPS Berntsen International Scholarship in Surveying Technology (Undergraduate/Scholarship)

Purpose: To support the continuing education of students enrolled in two-year degree programs in surveying technology. **Focus:** Engineering, Civil. **Qualif.:** Applicants must be students enrolled in two-year degree programs in surveying technology; must be a member of NSPS. **Criteria:** Selection will be based on academic achievement, applicant's statement, letters of recommendation, professional activities and financial need.

Funds Avail.: $2,000. **Duration:** Biennial. **Number Awarded:** 1. **To Apply:** Applicants must include completed application form; proof of student membership; brief, yet complete, statement indicating educational objectives, future plans of study or research, professional activities, and financial need; three letters of recommendation. **Deadline:** January 17. **Contact:** Scholarships, 5119 Pegasus Ct., Ste. Q, Frederick, MD, 21704; Phone: 240-439-4615; Email: trisha.milburn@nsps.us.com.

8119 ■ NSPS and AAGS Scholarships (Undergraduate/Scholarship)

Purpose: To provide an opportunity to students in surveying, mapping, geographic information system, and geodetic science programs. **Focus:** Cartography/Surveying. **Criteria:** Selection will be based on their level of academic achievements, desire to pursue a career in surveying and mapping, and the quality and neatness of their essay.

Funds Avail.: $2,000. **Duration:** Annual. **Number Awarded:** Varies. **To Apply:** Applicants must include completed application form; proof of student membership; brief, yet complete, statement indicating educational objectives, future plans of study or research, professional activities, and financial need; three letters of recommendation. **Deadline:** June 30. **Contact:** National Society of Professional Surveyors ATTN: Trig-Star Scholarship 5119 Pegasus Court, Suite Q Frederick, MD 21704 Phone (240) 439-4615 Fax (240) 439-4952.

8120 ■ National Space Biomedical Research Institute

6500 Main St., Ste. 910
Houston, TX 77030-1402
Ph: (713)798-7412
Fax: (713)798-7413
E-mail: info@nsbri.org
URL: nsbri.org

8121 ■ NSBRI First Award Fellowships (Postdoctorate/Fellowship)

Purpose: To support talented scientists in conducting space-related biomedical or biotechnological research. **Focus:** Biomedical research. **Qualif.:** Applicants must be U.S. citizens, permanent residents or with pre-existing visas obtained through their sponsoring institutions that permit postdoctoral training for the project's duration. **Criteria:** Selection will be based on merit, need and includes allocation for health insurance.

Funds Avail.: No specific amount. **Duration:** Annual; two years. **To Apply:** Applicants must prepare a proposal with the support of a mentor. **Contact:** NSBRI's Postdoctoral Fellowship Program, at the above address.

8122 ■ National Space Club and Foundation

515 2nd St. NE
Washington, DC 20002
Ph: (202)547-0060
E-mail: info@spaceclub.org
URL: www.spaceclub.org
Social Media: www.facebook.com/NationalSpaceClub
www.instagram.com/nationalspaceclub
twitter.com/SpaceClubNews
www.youtube.com/user/NationalSpaceClub

8123 ■ The Dr. Robert H. Goddard Memorial Scholarship (Graduate, Undergraduate/Scholarship)

Purpose: To stimulate the interest of students in the opportunity to advance scientific knowledge through space research and exploration. **Focus:** Engineering; Science. **Qualif.:** Applicants must be U.S. citizens, at least junior years of an accredited university, and have the intention of pursuing undergraduate or graduate studies in science or engineering during the interval of the scholarship.

Funds Avail.: $10,000. **Remarks:** The scholarship was established in memory of Dr. Robert H. Goddard, America's rocket pioneer.

8124 ■ National Speleological Society (NSS)

6001 Pulaski Pke.
Huntsville, AL 35810-1122

Awards are arranged alphabetically below their administering organizations

Ph: (256)852-1300
E-mail: nss@caves.org
URL: www.caves.org
Social Media: www.facebook.com/
  NationalSpeleologicalSociety
instagram.com/nsscaves
www.linkedin.com/groups/106900
pinterest.com/nsscaves
twitter.com/NSScaves

8125 ■ NSS Sara Corrie Memorial Grants (Professional development/Grant)

Purpose: To support cave exploration in the U.S territories. **Focus:** Cave studies. **Qualif.:** Applicants must be NSS member at the time of application. **Criteria:** Selection will be made by committee.

Funds Avail.: Maximum amount of $1,000. **Duration:** Annual. **Number Awarded:** Up to 6. **To Apply:** Applicants must send a letter to the Chairman of the U.S Exploration Committee explaining the importance and usage of the grant as well as the amount needed. **Contact:** Thomas Shifflett, Committee Chairman, 224 Barker Ln., Bluemont, VA, 20135; Phone: 703-404-6323 (W); 540-535-8389 (C); E-mail: tommyshifflett@gmail.com.

8126 ■ NSS Conservation Grants (Advanced Professional/Grant)

Purpose: To support NSS members for specific projects that involve cave or karst conservation, restoration, or cleanup. **Focus:** Cave studies. **Qualif.:** Applicants must be individuals conducting cave conservation-linked research, including student projects.

Funds Avail.: Up to $5,000. **Duration:** Annual. **To Apply:** Applicants must include adequate description of one or more of the following: scientific investigation of cave or karst conservation problems; speleological research that will directly contribute to cave or karst conservation; the remediation of ecological problems in cave, karst, or pseudokarst areas; hands-on, in-cave efforts to restore cave passages to a former ecological state; equipment and supplies for conservation or restoration projects that include hands-on participation from cavers; public outreach to inform and raise awareness of cave and karst values. **Contact:** Val Hildreth-Werker, PO Box 207, Hillsboro, New Mexico, 88042; Phone: 575-895-5050; E-mail: werks@cunacueva.com.

8127 ■ NSS Education Grants (Undergraduate/Grant)

Purpose: To promote cave and karst education programs for primary and secondary students. **Focus:** Cave studies. **Qualif.:** Applicants must be individuals or from private organizations. **Criteria:** Selection will be based on merit.

Funds Avail.: No specific amount. **Duration:** Biennial. **To Apply:** Applicants must submit the online application form and send it electronically in MS Word or PDF file. **Deadline:** March; September. **Contact:** Education Division Chief, Pam Tegelman Malabad, 231 Price St., Blacksburg, VA 24060; E-mail: pam.teg.mal@gmail.com; education@caves.org.

8128 ■ Ralph W. Stone Graduate Fellowship in Cave and Karst Studies (Graduate/Fellowship)

Purpose: To recognize a graduate student on cave-related thesis research. **Focus:** Geology. **Qualif.:** National Speleological Society members currently pursuing graduate studies anywhere in the world are eligible to apply. **Criteria:** Selection will be based on the merit of the applicant.

Funds Avail.: $2,000. **Duration:** Annual. **To Apply:** Applicants should submit a proposal package including: a project description; a resume, including NSS number; a detailed academic record, such as a grade transcript (unofficial copies are acceptable); at least two letters of recommendation, including one from your thesis advisor; a budget and budget justification, including a list of other organizations to which this (or a similar) proposal has been or will be submitted. **Deadline:** March 15. **Remarks:** Established in 1989. **Contact:** Dr. Donald A. McFarlane, WM.Keck Science Center, The Claremont Colleges, 925 N Mills Ave., Claremont, CA, 91711-5916, USA; E-mail: dmcfarla@jsd.claremont.edu.

8129 ■ Ralph W. Stone Graduate Fellowships (Graduate/Fellowship)

Purpose: To support cave-related thesis research. **Focus:** Cave studies. **Qualif.:** Applicants must be NSS members currently pursuing graduate studies. **Criteria:** Applicants are selected based on the committee's review of submitted proposals.

Funds Avail.: $2,000 each. **Duration:** One year. **Number Awarded:** Two. **To Apply:** Applicants must send a proposal which includes a project description; a resume with NSS number; a detailed academic record transcript; two letters of recommendation (one from the thesis advisor); a budget and its justification. **Deadline:** March 15. **Contact:** Dr. Donald A. McFarlane, WM.Keck Science Center, The Claremont Colleges, 925 N Mills Ave., Claremont, CA, 91711-5916, USA; E-mail: dmcfarla@jsd.claremont.edu.

8130 ■ National Sporting Clays Association (NSCA)
5931 Roft Rd.
San Antonio, TX 78253
Ph: (210)688-3371
Fax: (210)688-3014
Free: 800-877-5338
E-mail: nscrv@nssa-nsca.com
URL: www.nssa-nsca.org
Social Media: www.facebook.com/MyNSCA
www.instagram.com/nationalshootingcomplex

8131 ■ NSSA/NSCA Collegiate High School Senior Scholarships (Undergraduate/Scholarship)

Purpose: To support active students in sporting clays who are pursuing their educational career. **Focus:** General studies/Field of study not specified. **Qualif.:** Applicants must be graduating high school seniors; NSCA/NSSA members; pursuing a 4-year degree program and active NSCA registered sporting clays participants. **Criteria:** Selection is based on scholarship, citizenship and participation in NSCA activities.

Funds Avail.: $2,500. **Duration:** Four years. **To Apply:** Applicants must submit a completed scholarship application; an essay (100 words or less) explaining the need of financial assistance; a letter of personal recommendation; copy of class rank/high school grades from the school registrar; and a copy of past shooting history and accomplishments. **Deadline:** March 15. **Contact:** Stephanie Haga, NSSA Scholarship Program, 5931 Roft Rd., San Antonio, TX, 78253-9261; Phone: 210-688-3371 ext. 962.

Awards are arranged alphabetically below their administering organizations

8132 ■ National Stone, Sand and Gravel Association (NSSGA)

66 Canal Center Plz., Ste. 300
Alexandria, VA 22314
Ph: (703)525-8788
Fax: (800)342-1415
URL: www.nssga.org
Social Media: www.facebook.com/nssga
twitter.com/nssga
www.youtube.com/nssga
www.youtube.com/c/NssgaOrg

8133 ■ Jennifer Curtis Byler Scholarship
(Undergraduate/Scholarship)

Purpose: To support a child of an aggregates industry employee who wishes to pursue collegiate studies in public policy, government affairs or related fields. **Focus:** Public affairs. **Qualif.:** Applicants must be graduating high school seniors or students already majoring in public policy, government affairs or related fields in college; must be sons or daughters of an aggregates company employee. **Criteria:** Selection is based upon applications being reviewed and judged by a panel including the current NSSGA chairman of the Government Affairs Committee, a representative of the industry trade press, and a senior NSSGA staff member.

Funds Avail.: $5,000. **To Apply:** Applicant must complete the application form at the program website and include a letter of recommendation from the faculty advisor; if the applicant has work experience as a summer employee, intern or through a cooperative work program, they should include a letter of recommendation from the employer(s). **Deadline:** June 24.

8134 ■ National Swimming Pool Foundation (NSPF)

4775 Granby Cir.
Colorado Springs, CO 80919
Ph: (719)540-9119
Fax: (719)540-2787
E-mail: service@nspf.org
URL: www.nspf.org
Social Media: twitter.com/nspf

8135 ■ NSPF Ray B. Essick Scholarship Awards
(Other/Scholarship)

Purpose: To encourage healthier living through aquatic education and research. **Focus:** Health education. **Qualif.:** Applicant must be a Certified Pool/Spa Operator; a Certified Pool/Spa Operator Instructor; or have an immediate family member possessing CPO certification. **Criteria:** Selection is based on the applications and supporting materials.

Funds Avail.: $2,000. **Duration:** Annual. **Number Awarded:** 1. **To Apply:** Application form is available at the website. Applicant must prepare a biographical sketch (maximum of 300 words); a resume; a 2″ x 3″ photograph; an essay of no more than five double-spaced, 12 font size, type-written pages; official academic transcripts; a copy of recent SAT or ACT scores; and two letters of recommendation from teachers or college professors. **Deadline:** June 1.

8136 ■ National Swimming Pool Foundation Scholarship Award *(Other/Scholarship)*

Purpose: To encourage healthier living through aquatic education and research. **Focus:** Health education. **Qualif.:**

Applicants must be certified Pool/Spa operators; be certified Pool/Spa operator instructors; or have an immediate family member possessing CPO certification.

Funds Avail.: $1,000. **Duration:** Annual. **Number Awarded:** Up to 12. **To Apply:** Applications can be submitted online; must prepare a biographical sketch (maximum of 300 words); a resume; a photograph; an essay of no more than five double-spaced, 12 font size, type-written pages; official academic transcripts; a copy of recent SAT or ACT scores; two letters of recommendation from teachers or college professors. **Deadline:** June 1. **Contact:** Application Package Submission: NSPF Scholarship Program, National Swimming Pool Foundation, 4775 Granby Circle, Colorado Springs, CO 80919-3131; Email: dolores.malocsay@nspf.org.

8137 ■ National Taxidermists Association (NTA)

1615 Montana St.
Missoula, MT 59801
URL: www.nationaltaxidermists.com

8138 ■ Charlie Fleming Scholarship Fund (CFEF)
(Undergraduate/Scholarship)

Purpose: To provide cash scholarships for qualified NTA members or their dependents to further their education in Taxidermy; to attain higher education. **Focus:** Taxonomy. **Qualif.:** Applicants must be NTA members and/or their children under the age of twenty one; member must be in the third year of continuous NTA membership. **Criteria:** Selection is based on the scholarship committee's review of all applications.

Funds Avail.: $1,500 each. **Duration:** Annual. **Number Awarded:** 2. **To Apply:** Applicants must submit an 250 word essay on why you are pursuing an education in taxidermy, wildlife conservation or related field and what the art of taxidermy and/or wildlife conservation means to you. **Contact:** 1615 Montana St., Missoula, MT, 59801; Email: nationaltaxidermistassoc@gmail.com.

8139 ■ National Technical Honor Society (NTHS)

PO Box 1336
Flat Rock, NC 28731
Fax: (828)698-8564
Free: 800-801-7090
E-mail: info@nths.org
URL: www.nths.org
Social Media: www.facebook.com/
   NationalTechnicalHonorSociety
www.instagram.com/nths_hq
www.linkedin.com/company/national-technical-honor
   -society
twitter.com/nths1

8140 ■ NTHS/HOSA Scholarships *(Undergraduate/Scholarship)*

Purpose: To provide students the countless educational opportunities in the field of health care industry. **Focus:** Health care services. **Qualif.:** Applicants must be HOSA members who are also NTHS members in good standing; must be a dues-paying member of both organizations and the requirements and criteria are decided by HOSA.

Funds Avail.: $1,000. **Duration:** Annual. **Number Awarded:** 7. **Deadline:** March 15. **Contact:** NTHS Scholar-

Awards are arranged alphabetically below their administering organizations

ship, Coordinator; Phone: 800-801-7090; E-mail: aupchurch@nths.org.

8141 ■ National Trust for Canada
190 Bronson Ave.
Ottawa, ON, Canada K1R 6H4
Ph: (613)237-1066
Fax: (613)237-5987
Free: 866-964-1066
E-mail: nationaltrust@nationaltrustcanada.ca
URL: www.nationaltrustcanada.ca
Social Media: www.facebook.com/NationalTrustCanada
www.instagram.com/nationaltrustca/
www.linkedin.com/company/heritage-canada-foundation
twitter.com/nationaltrustca
www.youtube.com/user/HeritageCanadaFdn

8142 ■ Herb Stovel Scholarship - National Trust Conference Bursaries *(Undergraduate, Graduate, Professional development/Scholarship)*

Purpose: To cover the cost of travel, conference accommodation and registration for candidates to attend the National Trust's annual conference. **Focus:** Historic preservation. **Qualif.:** Applicants must be Canadian students or young professionals (age 20-35) pursuing post-secondary or graduate studies in built heritage conservation, or working in the field of built heritage conservation.

Funds Avail.: Approximately 1,000 Canadian dollars. **Duration:** Annual. **To Apply:** Applicant must submit a written proposal (1,000 words maximum); a Curriculum Vitae (CV), including references; proof of student status (if applicable); and proof of Canadian citizenship. **Deadline:** April 1. **Contact:** Email: eboulet@nationaltrustcanada.ca.

8143 ■ Herb Stovel Scholarship - Project Research Bursaries *(Undergraduate, Graduate, Professional development/Scholarship)*

Purpose: To support individuals who propose special projects, results-oriented travel and participation at conferences and events that continue Herb's passion for community innovation and/or international dialogue in built heritage conservation theory and practice. **Focus:** Historic preservation. **Qualif.:** Applicants must be Canadian students or young professionals (age 20-35) pursuing post-secondary or graduate studies in built heritage conservation, or working in the field of built heritage conservation.

Funds Avail.: Up to 2,500 Canadian dollars. **To Apply:** Applicant must submit a written proposal (1,000 words maximum); a Curriculum Vitae (CV), including references; proof of student status (if applicable); and proof of Canadian citizenship. **Deadline:** April 1. **Contact:** Email: eboulet@nationaltrustcanada.ca.

8144 ■ National Trust for Historic Preservation
2600 Virginia Ave. NW, Ste. 1100
Washington, DC 20037
Ph: (202)588-6000
Fax: (202)588-6038
Free: 800-315-6847
E-mail: info@savingplaces.org
URL: savingplaces.org
Social Media: www.facebook.com/
 NationalTrustforHistoricPreservation

instagram.com/savingplaces
twitter.com/SavingPlaces
www.youtube.com/nationaltrustforhistoricpreservation

8145 ■ Mildred Colodny Diversity Scholarships for Graduate Program in Historic Preservation *(Graduate/Scholarship, Award, Monetary)*

Purpose: To increase the diversity of people pursuing degrees and careers in historic preservation in the United States. **Focus:** Historic preservation. **Qualif.:** Applicants must be in their final year of undergraduate study intending to enroll in a graduate program in historic preservation or must be graduate students enrolled in or intending to enroll in historic preservation programs; program of study must be at a U.S. university, college or institution; must be eligible to work in the United States. **Criteria:** Selection will be based partly on financial need; partly on application materials; academic performance; promise shown for future achievement; commitment to working in preservation in the United States following graduation; potential to help increase diversity within Selection will be based partly on financial need; partly on application materials; academic performance; promise shown for future achievement; commitment to working in preservation in the United States following graduation; potential to help increase diversity within the preservation movement.

Funds Avail.: Up to $15,000. **Duration:** Annual. **To Apply:** Applicants must submit a completed application form; resume; two recommendation letters; appropriate academic transcripts. **Deadline:** February 28. **Contact:** David Field, Colodny Scholarship Coordinator, Phone: 800-944-NTHP x 6124, Email: dfield@savingplaces.org.

8146 ■ National Union of Public and General Employees (NUPGE)
15 Auriga Dr.
Nepean, ON, Canada K2E 1B7
Ph: (613)228-9800
Fax: (613)228-9801
E-mail: national@nupge.ca
URL: www.nupge.ca

8147 ■ Terry Fox Memorial Scholarship *(Undergraduate/Scholarship)*

Purpose: To support individuals who are pursuing to enhance the quality of life of people with disabilities. **Focus:** General studies/Field of study not specified. **Qualif.:** Applicants must be minority Canadian citizens; applicants must be students with a disability and who are children/grandchildren (including foster children/grandchildren) of a current or retired member of a Component or affiliate of the National Union of Public and General Employees and are planning to enter the 1st year of a Canadian public, post-secondary education institution. **Criteria:** Selection will be based on the essay.

Funds Avail.: 2,500 Canadian Dollars. **Duration:** Annual. **To Apply:** Submit a 750 to 1,000 word essay with completed application. **Deadline:** August 24. **Contact:** Terry Fox Memorial Scholarship, National Union of Public and General Employees, 15 Auriga Dr., Nepean, Ontario, K2E 1B7; Phone: 613-228-9800; Fax: 613-228-9801; Email: dsonego@nupge.ca.

8148 ■ Scholarship for Indigenous Students *(Undergraduate/Scholarship)*

Purpose: To support students who are planning to enter the first year of a Canadian public post-secondary educa-

Awards are arranged alphabetically below their administering organizations

tion. **Focus:** General studies/Field of study not specified. **Qualif.:** Applicants must be minority Canadian citizens who plan to enter as full-time first-year students at any Canadian public post-secondary educational institutions; must be children, grandchildren or foster children of a NUPGE member. **Criteria:** Selection will be based on the essay.

Funds Avail.: 2,500 Canadian Dollars. **Duration:** Annual. **To Apply:** Submit a 750 to 1,000 word essay and completed application. **Deadline:** August 24. **Contact:** Scholarship for Indigenous Students, National Union of Public and General Employees, 15 Auriga Dr., Nepean, Ontario, K2E 1B7; Fax: 613-228-9801; Email: dsonego@nupge.ca; URL: https://nupge.ca/content/national-unions-scholarship-program-2020-extended-deadline.

8149 ■ Scholarship for Students of Colour
(Undergraduate/Scholarship)

Purpose: To assist and support Canadian citizens of color with the cost of public post-secondary education. **Focus:** General studies/Field of study not specified. **Qualif.:** Applicants must be Canadian citizens of color who plan to enter as full-time first-year students at any Canadian public post-secondary educational institutions; must be children, grandchildren or foster children of a NUPGE member. **Criteria:** Selection will be based on the essay.

Funds Avail.: 2,500 Canadian Dollars. **Duration:** Annual. **To Apply:** Submit 750 to 1,000 word essay with completed application. **Deadline:** July 6. **Contact:** Scholarship for Students of Colour, National Union of Public and General Employees, 15 Auriga Dr., Nepean, Ontario, K2E 1B7; Phone: 613-228-9800; Fax: 613-228-9801; Email: dsonego@nupge.ca; URL: https://nupge.ca/content/national-unions-scholarship-program-2020.

8150 ■ Tommy Douglas Scholarship *(Undergraduate/Scholarship)*

Purpose: To support and assist students who plan to enter the first year of a Canadian public post-secondary education. **Focus:** General studies/Field of study not specified. **Qualif.:** Applicants must be Canadian citizens who are children/grandchildren (including foster children/grandchildren) of a current or retired member of a Component or affiliate of the National Union of Public and General Employees and are planning to enter the 1st year of a Canadian public, post-secondary education institution. **Criteria:** Selection will be based on the essay.

Funds Avail.: 2,500 Canadian Dollars. **Duration:** Annual. **To Apply:** Submit a 750 to 1,000 word essay with completed application. **Deadline:** August 24. **Contact:** National Union Tommy Douglas Scholarship, 15 Auriga Dr., Nepean, Ontario, K2E 1B7; Phone: 613-228-9800; Fax: 613-228-9801; Email: dsonego@nupge.ca.

8151 ■ National Urban Fellows (NUF)
1120 Ave. of the Americas, 4th Fl.
New York, NY 10036
Ph: (212)730-1700
E-mail: info@nuf.org
URL: www.nuf.org
Social Media: www.facebook.com/nationalurbanfellows
www.instagram.com/nationalurbanfellows
twitter.com/NUFlead

8152 ■ Master of Public Administratation Fellowship *(Graduate, Postgraduate, Other/Fellowship)*

Purpose: To counter the under-representation of people of color and women in leadership positions. **Focus:** Public

service. **Qualif.:** Applicants must: be U.S. citizens; have a bachelor's degree; have a minimum of 5 -7 years administrative or managerial employment; meet the admission requirements of Baruch College; possess self-discipline and interpersonal and problem-solving skills; have a high standard of integrity and work ethic; and be committed to the solution of urban problems. **Criteria:** Selection is based on a combination of criteria including strong personal character, the highest standard of work ethic and integrity, self-discipline, and a positive attitude with a passion for equity and social justice.

Funds Avail.: $25,000. **Duration:** Annual; 14 months. **Number Awarded:** Varies. **To Apply:** Applicants must submit a completed scholarship application form together with an updated resume and bio; career goal statements; official transcripts; and a non-refundable $150 application fee. Applicants must request three letters from academic and professional evaluators (typewritten on company or personal letterhead).

8153 ■ National Volunteer Fire Council (NVFC)
7852 Walker Dr., Ste. 375
Greenbelt, MD 20770
Ph: (202)887-5700
Fax: (202)887-5291
Free: 888-275-6832
E-mail: nvfcoffice@nvfc.org
URL: www.nvfc.org
Social Media: www.facebook.com/nvfc1
twitter.com/NVFC
www.youtube.com/user/NVFCCommunications

8154 ■ The Junior Firefighter of the Year Award
(Undergraduate/Scholarship)

Purpose: To provide resources on how to establish a program, a network for connecting with other programs and to increase recruitment and retention to junior firefighters. **Focus:** Fires and fire prevention. **Qualif.:** Applicants must have been a junior firefighter for at least one year and have gone above and beyond in their participation at the station.

Funds Avail.: $500. **Duration:** Annual. **To Apply:** Applicant must complete nomination form; 500-word essay describing the nominee's contribution to their fire department, including specific examples of how they have exemplified the spirit of youth community involvement and why they should be chosen for this award; Two (2) letters of recommendation, including one from department chief of program advisor; Up to three (3) additional supporting documents. **Contact:** National Volunteer Fire Council, 7852 Walker Dr., Ste. 375, Greenbelt, MD, 20770; Phone: 888-275-6832; Fax: 202-887-5291; Email: nvfcoffice@nvfc.org.

8155 ■ National Walking Horse Association (NWHA)
PO Box 7111
Jacksonville, NC 28540
Ph: (859)252-6942
E-mail: office@nwha.com
URL: nwha.com
Social Media: www.facebook.com/NWHAofficial
twitter.com/NWHA1998
www.youtube.com/channel/UCbq57r3OdpcOKhaBDc-9jDw

8156 ■ Neil Clark Memorial Scholarship
(Undergraduate/Scholarship)

Purpose: To encourage youth participation in equestrian sport, at NWHA events, and at the NWHA National Cham-

Awards are arranged alphabetically below their administering organizations

pionship Show. Funds are to be used for educational purposes or towards the advancement of the winners' equestrian experience. **Focus:** Equine studies; General studies/Field of study not specified. **Qualif.:** Applicant must be a member of NWHA (either as an individual Youth Member or as a youth whose parents or guardians hold a Family Membership); must be aged 17 or under on January 1 of the current year.

Funds Avail.: $500. **Duration:** Annual. **Number Awarded:** 2. **To Apply:** Applications can be submitted online; should submit an essay; art or poetry; and photography. **Contact:** National Walking Horse Association, PO Box 7111, Jacksonville, NC, 28540.

8157 ■ National Water Research Institute (NWRI)
18700 Ward St.
Fountain Valley, CA 92708
Ph: (714)378-3278
Fax: (714)378-3375
E-mail: bcaskey@nwri-usa.org
URL: www.nwri-usa.org
Social Media: www.facebook.com/NWRIwater
twitter.com/NWRIwater

8158 ■ NWRI Fellowship *(Graduate, Doctorate/Fellowship)*

Purpose: To support graduate students conducting water-related research. **Focus:** Water resources. **Qualif.:** Applicants must be students at US universities who are currently enrolled fulltime in a master's or doctoral graduate program in the area of water resources and treatment.

Funds Avail.: $5,000 per year. **Duration:** Two years. **To Apply:** Applicants must submit the application in PDF format via email; items to be emailed include: application cover sheet, letter of inquiry describing research goals, current resume, Short, original research proposal; letter from the endorsement from faculty advisor; official verification of enrollment as a full-time graduate student and Official school transcripts. **Deadline:** July 1. **Contact:** Email: fellow@nwri-usa.org.

8159 ■ Ronald B. Linsky Fellowship for Outstanding Water Research *(Graduate, Master's, Doctorate/Fellowship)*

Purpose: To support and encourage graduate students to investigate and develop the innovative procedures, technologies, and policies crucial to resolving these critical water needs. **Focus:** Water resources. **Qualif.:** Applicants must be master's or doctoral graduate students in a US university whose research pertains to water, including water supply, water resources, water quality, and technologies and treatment.

Funds Avail.: $10,000 per year. **Duration:** Annual; Two years. **Number Awarded:** 2. **To Apply:** Applicants must prepare an application package, available at the website, following the NWRI's fellowship application procedures. As part of the application process, applicants are asked to prepare a 1-page, single-spaced essay detailing why they should receive the fellowship. The essay must address their technical capabilities, their interest in other fields beside the one they are studying, their career goals, and where they hope to take their technical expertise and vision in the future. Applicants' research must pertain to NWRI's mission statement, which is to create new sources of water through research and technology and to protect the

freshwater and marine environments. NWRI' specific research interests include, but are not limited to: water treatment technologies; water quality; water environmental chemistry; water policy and economics; public health and risk assessment; water resources management. **Deadline:** March 1. **Contact:** Email: fellow@nwri-usa.org.

8160 ■ National Wildlife Federation (NWF)
11100 Wildlife Center Dr.
Reston, VA 20190
Ph: (703)438-6000
Free: 800-822-9919
URL: www.nwf.org
Social Media: www.facebook.com/NationalWildlife
www.instagram.com/nationalwildlife/?hl=en
www.pinterest.com/nwfpins
twitter.com/nwf
www.youtube.com/user/NationalWildlife

8161 ■ NWF Campus Ecology Fellowships *(Graduate, Undergraduate/Fellowship)*

Purpose: To assist students who are working on projects ranging from campus-wide energy audits to implementing sustainable forestry practices. **Focus:** Earth sciences. **Qualif.:** Applicants must be graduate students from any college or university within the U.S. **Criteria:** Project proposals will be evaluated based on: how prospect will measurably contribute to campus climate leadership; demonstrated interest in and experience working within or with diverse constituencies; engagement with students, faculty, community organizations, and businesses; plans for outreach to local and campus newspapers; innovative approaches or models for the national climate action movement; arrangement of academic credit for successful completion of the project, as an independent study or integration of the fellowship project into course curricula; matching funds or other financial support from the campus or another source; securing appropriate project advisor and verifier; nomination of the applicant by a formal environmental or sustainability group or committee on campus; and host campus that is currently enrolled with NWF's Campus Ecology Program and especially those that have applied to earn the designation of NWF Climate Champion.

Funds Avail.: $3,000. **Duration:** 4-6 months. **Number Awarded:** Varies. **To Apply:** Applicants must submit a proposal. Proposals must be 3-5 pages and must include: date, header, summary, purpose, short-term results, long-term results, participation and support, nomination process, education and documentation, timeline, evaluation, qualifications and interests, project budget, and a confirmation of the applicant's availability in attending and to participate in the fellowship meeting (refer to the fellowship guidelines for the format). **Deadline:** May 21. **Remarks:** Established in 2000. **Contact:** National Wildlife Federation, at the above address.

8162 ■ National Wildlife Rehabilitators Association (NWRA)
8400 Normandale Lake Dr., Ste. 920
Bloomington, MN 55437
Ph: (320)230-9920
URL: www.nwrawildlife.org
Social Media: www.facebook.com/NWRAWildlife
twitter.com/nwrawildlife

Awards are arranged alphabetically below their administering organizations

8163 ■ NWRA Research Grants *(Professional development/Grant)*

Purpose: To support research projects in the field of wildlife rehabilitation. **Focus:** Wildlife conservation, management, and science. **Qualif.:** Research should focus on improving animal care; assessing wildlife health; developing new technology for wildlife care in captivity; or develop new, or evaluating current, techniques used in wildlife education.

Funds Avail.: up to $6,000. **Duration:** Annual. **Number Awarded:** Varies. **To Apply:** Prepoposals should include: title of the preproposal; applicant's information. including name, affiliation, mailing address, phone number, and email address for principle investigator, name and affiliation for all coinvestigators; and hypothesis and objectives document in which the hypothesis is explicitly stated and specific aims are given (less than three pages). **Deadline:** October 1. **Remarks:** Established in 1984.

8164 ■ National Women's Studies Association (NWSA)
1720 W. Division St.
Chicago, IL 60622
Ph: (312)761-5491
Fax: (773)701-5828
E-mail: nwsaoffice@nwsa.org
URL: www.nwsa.org
Social Media: twitter.com/nwsa

8165 ■ National Women's Studies Association Lesbian Caucus Award *(Master's, Doctorate/Award, Grant)*

Purpose: To recognize and support a Master's Thesis or Doctoral Dissertation research project in areas of Lesbian, Queer, and LGBT Studies that resonates with the mission of NWSA. **Focus:** Sociology; Women's studies. **Qualif.:** Applicants must be master's and/or doctoral students who are members of NWSA.

Funds Avail.: $500. **Duration:** Annual. **Number Awarded:** 1. **To Apply:** Applications can be submitted online; one letter of recommendation, preferably from dissertation or thesis adviser is required (although DGS letters will be accepted); will automatically send a notification to letter writer so they may directly upload their recommendation. **Deadline:** June 7.

8166 ■ NWSA Graduate Scholarship *(Master's, Doctorate/Scholarship)*

Purpose: To encourage the participation in NWSA of individuals whose presence enrich the diversity of and increase participation by underrepresented constituencies in the NWSA. **Focus:** General studies/Field of study not specified.

Funds Avail.: $1,000. **To Apply:** Applications can be submitted online; must provide PDF of one-page curriculum vitae and Letter of recommendation from Program Director. **Deadline:** June 22.

8167 ■ Native Women's Association of Canada (NWAC)
85 Albert St., 12th Fl.
Ottawa, ON, Canada K1P 6A4
Ph: (613)722-3033
Fax: (613)722-7687

Free: 800-461-4043
E-mail: reception@nwac.ca
URL: www.nwac.ca
Social Media: www.facebook.com/NWAC.AFAC
www.instagram.com/nwac_ca/
twitter.com/NWAC_CA
www.youtube.com/channel/UCe_rjq2FleC4XN3qmF5tT2A

8168 ■ NWAC Helen Bassett Commemorative Student Award *(Undergraduate, Graduate/Scholarship)*

Purpose: To provide financial support to students intending to pursue their law careers. **Focus:** Law. **Qualif.:** Applicants must be Indigenous woman, gender-diverse, or Two-Spirit person under 31 years of age; must be post-secondary students pursuing a law career; and, demonstrate financial need and commitment to improving the situation of Aboriginal women and youth in Canada politically, culturally, economically, or otherwise. **Criteria:** Selection will be based on financial need and academic standing; priority will be given to those studying in law or justice related fields.

Funds Avail.: $1,000 each. **Duration:** Annual. **Number Awarded:** 4. **To Apply:** Applicants must submit application form (available online), proof of age, and proof of Aboriginal descent; must have a proof of attending post-secondary studies: acceptance letter from a post-secondary institution; must have the most recent official transcript, proof of community involvement/interest and dedication in working on Aboriginal women's issues; one reference letter of support from a local community organization, or school, or any relevant organization/person; must provide a short 1-2-page essay and statement of financial need in a letter, plus monthly or yearly budget and a list of other funding sources and scholarships. **Deadline:** July 17. **Remarks:** Established by the generous donation of Helen Bassett who was an Ontario artist and an amazing woman who tried to make a difference as an individual and engage the government into fair solutions to Aboriginal land claim issues. **Contact:** URL: www.nwac.ca/helen-bassett-commemorative-student-award/.

8169 ■ Naval Helicopter Association Scholarship Fund (NHASF)
PO Box 180578
Coronado, CA 92178-0578
Ph: (619)435-7139
E-mail: info@nhascholarshipfund.org
URL: www.nhascholarshipfund.org
Social Media: www.facebook.com/nhascholarshipfund

8170 ■ Naval Helicopter Association Scholarship *(Graduate, Undergraduate/Scholarship)*

Purpose: To assist persons who desire to pursue their educational goals and expand their knowledge. **Focus:** General studies/Field of study not specified. **Qualif.:** Applicants must be prospective or current high school graduates, high school equivalents, or college undergraduate or graduate students; Marine Corps, or Coast Guard rotary-wing aviators. **Criteria:** Selection will be based on the committee's criteria.

Funds Avail.: $3,000. **Duration:** Annual. **Number Awarded:** Varies. **To Apply:** Applicants must submit an application that includes four parts: online form submission; teacher/counselor recommendation (minimum one recommendation per application); for active duty applicants, a let-

Awards are arranged alphabetically below their administering organizations

ter of recommendation from their commanding officer; high school and/or undergraduate/graduate transcript; and, documents establishing eligibility (i.e. any correspondence that shows connection with the naval helicopter community: DD-214, awards, certifications, history of assignment, etc.). All applications (including transcripts/letters of recommendations) must be submitted or postmarked by date identified under Selection Process. **Deadline:** January 31.

8171 ■ Navy League of the United States (NLUS)

2300 Wilson Blvd., Suite 200
Arlington, VA 22201
Ph: (703)528-1775
Fax: (703)528-2333
Free: 800-356-5760
E-mail: communications@navyleague.org
URL: navyleague.org
Social Media: www.facebook.com/NavyLeagueUS
www.instagram.com/navyleague_us
twitter.com/NavyLeagueUS

8172 ■ CAPT Winifred Quick Collins, USN (Ret.) Scholarship *(Undergraduate/Scholarship)*

Purpose: To assist in the college or university expenses of the dependents of sea service personnel. **Focus:** General studies/Field of study not specified. **Qualif.:** Applicants must be child or grandchild of a member of the sea services, to include the United States Navy, United States Marine Corps, United States CoastGuard, and U.S.-flag Merchant Marine; properly enrolled in any curriculum at an accredited institution of higher education.

Funds Avail.: $10,000. **Duration:** Annual.

8173 ■ John G. Brokaw Scholarship *(Undergraduate/Scholarship)*

Purpose: To assist in the college or university expenses of the dependents of sea service personnel. **Focus:** General studies/Field of study not specified. **Qualif.:** Applicants must be child or grandchild of a member of the sea services, to include the United States Navy, United States Marine Corps, United States CoastGuard, and U.S.-flag Merchant Marine; properly enrolled in any curriculum at an accredited institution of higher education.

Funds Avail.: $10,000. **Duration:** Annual.

8174 ■ RADM William A. Sullivan, USN (Ret.) Scholarship *(Undergraduate/Scholarship)*

Purpose: To assist in the college or university expenses of the dependents of sea service personnel. **Focus:** General studies/Field of study not specified. **Qualif.:** Applicants must be child or grandchild of a member of the sea services, to include the United States Navy, United States Marine Corps, United States CoastGuard, and U.S.-flag Merchant Marine; properly enrolled in any curriculum at an accredited institution of higher education.

Funds Avail.: $10,000. **Duration:** Annual.

8175 ■ Gladys Ann Smith Greater Los Angeles Women's Council Scholarship *(Undergraduate/Scholarship)*

Purpose: To financially assist the dependents of sea service personnel for college/university expenses. **Focus:** General studies/Field of study not specified. **Qualif.:** Applicants must be child or grandchild of a member of the sea

services, to include the United States Navy, United States Marine Corps, United States CoastGuard, and U.S.-flag Merchant Marine; properly enrolled in any curriculum at an accredited institution of higher education.

Funds Avail.: $10,000. **Duration:** Annual.

8176 ■ Subic Bay-Cubi Point Scholarships *(Undergraduate/Scholarship)*

Purpose: To assist in the college or university expenses of the dependents of sea service personnel. **Focus:** General studies/Field of study not specified. **Qualif.:** Applicants must be child or grandchild of a member of the sea services, to include the United States Navy, United States Marine Corps, United States CoastGuard, and U.S.-flag Merchant Marine; properly enrolled in any curriculum at an accredited institution of higher education.

Funds Avail.: $10,000. **Duration:** Annual.

8177 ■ Wesley C. Cameron Scholarship *(Undergraduate/Scholarship)*

Purpose: To assist in the college or university expenses of the dependents of sea service personnel. **Focus:** General studies/Field of study not specified. **Qualif.:** Applicants must be child or grandchild of a member of the sea services, to include the United States Navy, United States Marine Corps, United States CoastGuard, and U.S.-flag Merchant Marine; properly enrolled in any curriculum at an accredited institution of higher education. **Criteria:** Preference will be given to applicants who have demonstrated an interest in and an intention to continue their education in mathematics or the sciences.

Funds Avail.: $10,000. **Duration:** Annual.

8178 ■ Navy-Marine Corps Relief Society (NM-CRS)

875 N Randolph St., Ste. 225
Arlington, VA 22203
Ph: (703)696-4904
Fax: (703)696-0144
Free: 800-654-8364
E-mail: education@nmcrs.org
URL: www.nmcrs.org
Social Media: facebook.com/NMCRS
twitter.com/NMCRS1
www.youtube.com/user/TheNMCRS

8179 ■ Admiral Mike Boorda Loan Program *(Undergraduate/Loan)*

Purpose: To help eligible Navy and Marine Corps families pursue their academic goals by providing education grants and interest-free loans. **Focus:** General studies/Field of study not specified. **Qualif.:** Applicants must be Sailor or Marine service member participating in one of the following: Marine Enlisted Commissioning Education Program (MECEP), or Medical Enlisted Commissioning Program (MECP); must be full-time students, enrolled for the entire academic year, and pursuing a first undergraduate degree at a qualifying school and also maintain 2.0 or better GPA on a 4.0 grade scale. **Criteria:** Selection shall be based on the demonstrated financial need for assistance.

Funds Avail.: $500-$3,000. **Number Awarded:** Varies. **To Apply:** Applicants must submit the following: completed application form (PDF); official high school or current college transcript; copy of transfer orders to the MECEP or

Awards are arranged alphabetically below their administering organizations

MECP program; and, Student Aid Report (SAR) from completed FAFSA. **Deadline:** June 1; November 1.

8180 ■ NMCRS Gold Star Scholarship Program
(Undergraduate/Scholarship)

Purpose: To provide educational assistance to spouses and children of members of the Society. **Focus:** General studies/Field of study not specified. **Qualif.:** Applicants must be either of the following: children (under age 23) of Sailors or Marines who died while serving on active duty or after retirement, or unmarried spouses of Navy or Marine Corps service member who died as a result of the attack on the USS STARK or the Pentagon, or during service in Operation Iraqi Freedom (OIF), Operation Enduring Freedom (OEF), or Operation New Dawn (OND); generally, scholarship must be full-time students, enrolled for the entire academic year, and pursuing a first undergraduate degree at a qualifying school and must also maintain 2.0 or better GPA on a 4.0 grade scale. **Criteria:** Selection shall be based on the demonstrated financial need for assistance.

Funds Avail.: $500-$2,500. **Number Awarded:** Varies. **To Apply:** Applicants must submit the following: completed application form (PDF); official high school or current college transcript; copy of DD 1300 or a death certificate; and, Student Aid Report (SAR) from completed FAFSA. **Deadline:** May 1; November 1.

8181 ■ Spouse Tuition Aid Loan Program (STAP)
(Undergraduate, Graduate/Loan)

Purpose: To help eligible Navy and Marine Corps families pursue their academic goals by providing education grants and interest-free loans. **Focus:** General studies/Field of study not specified. **Qualif.:** Applicants must: be spouses of active duty Navy or Marine Corps service member stationed outside the 50 United States; be part-time or full-time undergraduate or graduate students and be enrolled at an institution accredited by a regional/national accrediting agency recognized by the U.S. Secretary of Education. **Criteria:** Selection shall be based on the aforementioned qualifications and compliance with the application details.

Funds Avail.: Up to $3,000. **To Apply:** Application form and instructions are available from the website.

8182 ■ Nazareth Association
3901 Emerald Dr, Ste N
Kalamazoo, MI 49001-7923
Ph: (269)342-1191
E-mail: associationoffice@nazarethassociation.org
URL: www.nazarethassociation.org

8183 ■ The Nazareth Scholarships - Sr. Kevin Whelan Scholarship *(Undergraduate/Scholarship)*

Purpose: To provide financial support to students wishing to complete their degree at approved Catholic colleges in Michigan. **Focus:** General studies/Field of study not specified. **Criteria:** Selection is based on good academic standing with their school, federal, state and institutional financial aid procedures, extra-curricular volunteer activities and/or community services.

Funds Avail.: $2,000. **Duration:** Annual. **Number Awarded:** Varies. **To Apply:** Applicants must complete the application form and submit along with transcript of records, a 500-word essay and three letters of recommendation. **Remarks:** Established in 1994. **Contact:** Nazareth As-

sociation Office; Phone: 269-342-1191; Email: office@nazarethassociation.org.

8184 ■ The NEA Foundation
1201 16th St. NW
Washington, DC 20036
Ph: (202)822-7840
Fax: (202)822-7779
E-mail: neafoundation@nea.org
URL: www.neafoundation.org
Social Media: www.facebook.com/theneafoundation
twitter.com/neafoundation
www.youtube.com/user/neafoundation

8185 ■ NEA Foundation Learning and Leadership Grants *(Professional development/Grant)*

Purpose: To provide opportunities for teachers, education support professionals, and higher education faculty and staff to engage in high-quality professional development and to lead their colleagues in professional growth. **Focus:** Education. **Qualif.:** Applicants must be current members of the National Education Association (NEA). All professional development must improve practice, curriculum, and student achievement.

Funds Avail.: $2,000 (individuals); $5,000 (groups). **Duration:** Annual. **To Apply:** Applicant must submit summary of proposed project in 100 words or fewer in the NEA foundation website. Applications missing lead applicant data and partner data will not be considered. **Deadline:** February 1. **Contact:** E-mail: neafoundation@nea.org.

8186 ■ Nebraska Farm Bureau (NFB)
5225 S 16th St.
Lincoln, NE 68512
Ph: (402)421-4400
Fax: (402)421-4439
Free: 800-742-4016
E-mail: information@nefb.org
URL: www.nefb.org
Social Media: www.facebook.com/NEFarmBureau
www.instagram.com/nebraskafarmbureau
twitter.com/NEFarmBureau
www.youtube.com/nebraskafarmbureau

8187 ■ Nebraska Farm Bureau Greater Horizon Scholarship *(Undergraduate/Scholarship)*

Purpose: To encourage and assist young people to meet their personal goals of higher education. **Focus:** Agricultural sciences; Agriculture, Economic aspects. **Qualif.:** Applicants must be students, age 18-35, university's agricultural field of study and that plan on returning to farming or ranching.

Funds Avail.: $1,000 each. **Duration:** Annual. **Number Awarded:** 1. **Deadline:** October 1. **Contact:** Nebraska Farm Bureau Foundation, P.O. Box 80299, Lincoln, NE, 68501-0299, Phone: 402-471-4747, Email: FoundationForAg@nefb.org.

8188 ■ Nebraska High School Rodeo Association (NHSRA)
c/o Brandi Pokorny, Secretary
83940 493 Ave.
Bartlett, NE 68622

Awards are arranged alphabetically below their administering organizations

Ph: (308)654-3413
E-mail: pokornyrope@gmail.com
URL: www.hsrodeo-nebraska.com
Social Media: www.facebook.com/groups/
142610082444101

8189 ■ Sharon Kreikemeier Memorial Scholarships
(Undergraduate/Scholarship)

Purpose: To provide financial assistance to students in continuing their education. **Focus:** General studies/Field of study not specified. **Qualif.:** Applicants must be enrolled in Nebraska High School. **Criteria:** Selection will be based on academic performance.

Funds Avail.: $500. **To Apply:** Applicants must complete the application form. **Deadline:** June 15.

8190 ■ Swede Swanson Memorial Scholarships
(Undergraduate/Scholarship)

Purpose: To assist a graduating student who participates in Steer Wrestling at Nebraska High School. **Focus:** Medicine, Sports. **Qualif.:** Applicants must be graduating senior boys who participate in the Steer Wrestling event in the Nebraska High School Rodeo Association. **Criteria:** Selection will be based on academic performance.

Funds Avail.: $500. **Duration:** Annual. **To Apply:** Applicants must submit a cover sheet, including name, and address; personal essay with career goals; the essay should include the number of years in High School Rodeo, events participated in, future goals, anticipated major of study in school, and school, church, and community activities; the essay needs to be at least one to two pages in length; must provide two letters of recommendation and cumulative High School Grade Point Average. **Deadline:** June 1.

8191 ■ Nebraska Library Association (NLA)
PO Box 21756
Lincoln, NE 68542-1756
URL: www.nebraskalibraries.org
Social Media: www.facebook.com/NebLibraries

8192 ■ Louise A. Nixon Scholarship *(Graduate/Scholarship)*

Purpose: To support students who pursue graduate level library education. **Focus:** Library and archival sciences. **Criteria:** Preference will be given to applicants who can demonstrate the best potential for employment in Nebraska libraries after graduation.

Funds Avail.: No specific amount. **Duration:** Annual. **Number Awarded:** 1. **Deadline:** April 15. **Remarks:** The award was established to honor Louise A. Nixon (1897-1989), who worked constantly to enlighten the legislature about Nebraska's libraries' needs. She served as Assistant Director of the Nebraska Legislative Reference Bureau and as Legislative Council Librarian. **Contact:** Joe Pittman; E-mail: executivedirector@nebraskalibraries.org.

8193 ■ Nebraska Paralegal Association (NEPA)
PO Box 24943
Omaha, NE 68124
E-mail: info@nebraskaparalegal.org
URL: nebraskaparalegal.org

8194 ■ Nebraska Paralegal Association Student Scholarships *(Undergraduate/Scholarship)*

Purpose: To support students who are in pursuit of training for careers as legal assistants. **Focus:** Law. **Qualif.:** Applicants must be Nebraska residents or a member of NePA admitted to an accredited paralegal program at a University, College, Community College or Business College; must have completed one academic term, and be currently enrolled as a paralegal student. **Criteria:** Selection of award recipients shall be made without regard to race, color, creed, sex, age, national origin or marital status.

Funds Avail.: $500. **Duration:** Annual. **Number Awarded:** Up to 2. **To Apply:** Applicants must submit a resume with current contact information; must submit proof of acceptance to a Nebraska paralegal program, and an official transcript of grades; an essay of at least one page in length; one letter of recommendation. **Deadline:** March 1. **Contact:** NePA, Student Scholarship Committee, P.O. Box 24943, Omaha, NE, 68124; Email: nepastudentscholarship@yahoo.com.

8195 ■ Nebraska Section American Water Works Association
PO Box 94791
Lincoln, NE 68509-4791
Ph: (402)957-2482
E-mail: chair@awwaneb.org
URL: www.awwaneb.org
Social Media: www.facebook.com/awwaneb
twitter.com/awwaneb

8196 ■ Colonel Theodore A. Leisen Memorial and Training Endowment Fund *(Graduate/Grant)*

Purpose: To encourage water industry professionals to obtain additional training and encourage graduate students to choose the water industry as their field of work. **Focus:** Water resources; Water supply industry. **Qualif.:** Applicants must be graduate students and water industry professionals seeking additional training and knowledge in the said field.

Funds Avail.: $500 each. **Duration:** Annual. **Deadline:** September 1. **Remarks:** The Fund was established in memory of the Colonel Theodore A. Leisen, he as one of the incorporators of AWWA and served as president from 1917-1918 and also chaired several national committees on public health and pollution. Established in 1993. **Contact:** Dr. Xu Li. N117 SEC Link, Civil Engineering, University of Nebraska, Lincoln, NE, 68583-6105; Email: xuli@unl.edu.

8197 ■ Nebraska Society of Certified Public Accountants (NSCPA)
7435 O Street, Suite 100
Lincoln, NE 68510
Ph: (402)476-8482
Fax: (402)476-8731
Free: 800-642-6178
E-mail: society@nescpa.org
URL: www.nescpa.org
Social Media: www.facebook.com/NebraskaCPAs
www.linkedin.com/company/nebraska-society-of-cpas
twitter.com/NebraskaCPAs

8198 ■ NESCPA Fifth-year (150 hour) scholarships
(Graduate/Scholarship)

Purpose: To financially support accounting students. **Focus:** Accounting. **Criteria:** Selections are made by the Ac-

---

Awards are arranged alphabetically below their administering organizations

counting Department faculty members and approved by an Accounting Department Committee (or equivalent). Selection is based on the applicant's personality, leadership and character.

Duration: Annual. **Number Awarded:** 16. **Deadline:** April 1.

8199 ■ NESCPA General Scholarship (Graduate, Undergraduate/Scholarship)

Purpose: To financially support accounting students. **Focus:** Accounting. **Qualif.:** Applicant must be an accounting major who has completed their junior year; planning to sit for the CPA exam; and who has an interest and is capable of becoming a successful accountant and is considering an accounting career in Nebraska. **Criteria:** Selection are to be made by the Accounting Department faculty members and approved by an Accounting Department Committee (or equivalent). Selection is based on an applicant's personality, leadership and character.

Duration: Annual. **Number Awarded:** varies. **Deadline:** August 1.

8200 ■ Craig H. Neilsen Foundation

16830 Ventura Blvd., Ste. 352
Encino, CA 91436
Ph: (818)925-1245
E-mail: contact@chnfoundation.org
URL: chnfoundation.org
Social Media: www.facebook.com/NeilsenFoundation
twitter.com/NeilsenFndn

8201 ■ Psychosocial Research Pilot Grants (Professional development/Grant)

Purpose: To support psychosocial research projects that lay the groundwork to inform future studies, that test the feasibility of novel methods, and/or that collect psychosocial data that can enhance larger scale studies. **Focus:** Spinal cord injuries and research. **Qualif.:** Applicants must have a doctoral degree or other equivalent terminal professional degree and demonstrate appropriate experience to serve as an independent PI. **Criteria:** Selection will be based on scientific merit of the project, the innovative nature of the proposed psychosocial research and the likelihood that success will move the SCI field forward.

Funds Avail.: $200,000. **Duration:** Two years. **To Apply:** Applicants should include a research plan; a biosketch for the fellow; a biosketch for the mentors; a training plan; a letter of recommendation from the mentor and two additional recommendation letters. **Deadline:** October 14. **Contact:** Kim Cerise, Director ofGrants Management; Email: kim@chnfoundation.org.

8202 ■ Psychosocial Research - Postdoctoral Psychosocial Fellowships (Postdoctorate/Fellowship)

Purpose: To increase professional interest in the SCI field and to specifically encourage researcher from related health disciplines, to undertake training in psychosocial research to benefit the SCI field. **Focus:** Spinal cord injuries and research.

Funds Avail.: $75,000 per year, for up to two years; $150,000. **Duration:** Two years. **To Apply:** Applicants should include a research plan; a biosketch for the fellow; a biosketch for the mentors; a training plan; a letter of recommendation from the mentor and two additional recom-

mendation letters. **Contact:** Kim Cerise, Director ofGrants Management; Email: kim@chnfoundation.org.

8203 ■ Psychosocial Research Studies and Demonstration Projects (Professional development/Grant)

Purpose: To encourage critical and/or innovative research on psychosocial interventions or related research topics that will lead to improved outcomes for people living with SCI. **Focus:** Spinal cord injuries and research. **Qualif.:** Applicants must have a doctoral degree or other equivalent terminal professional degree and demonstrate appropriate experience to serve as an independent PI. **Criteria:** Selection will be based on the innovative nature of the proposed psychosocial research, the likelihood that success will move the field forward, and a history of productivity and significant contributions by the investigator.

Funds Avail.: $400,000. **Duration:** Annual; Three years. **To Apply:** Applicants should include a research plan; a biosketch for the fellow; a biosketch for the mentors; a training plan; a letter of recommendation from the mentor and two additional recommendation letters. **Deadline:** July 29. **Contact:** Kim Cerise, Director ofGrants Management; Email: kim@chnfoundation.org.

8204 ■ SCIRTS (Spinal Cord Injury Research on the Translational Spectrum) Pilot Research Grants (Professional development/Grant)

Purpose: To support basic and clinical research aimed at developing a cure for spinal cord injury. **Focus:** Spinal cord injuries and research. **Qualif.:** Applicants must have a doctoral degree or other equivalent terminal professional degree, be beyond the postdoctoral level (i.e., Instructor, Assistant Professor or equivalent research position) at the time of the FGA submission and demonstrate appropriate experience to serve as an independent PI. **Criteria:** Selection will be based on scientific merit of the project, the innovative nature of theproposed research.

Funds Avail.: $150,000 per year, for up to two years; $300,000. **Duration:** Annual; Two years. **To Apply:** Applicants should include a research plan; a biosketch for the fellow; a biosketch for the mentors; a training plan; a letter of recommendation from the mentor and two additional recommendation letters. **Contact:** Kim Cerise, Director ofGrants Management; Email: kim@chnfoundation.org.

8205 ■ SCIRTS (Spinal Cord Injury Research on the Translational Spectrum) Postdoctoral Fellowships (Postdoctorate/Fellowship)

Purpose: To support scientist who are wishing to specialize or train in the field of spinal cord injury research. **Focus:** Spinal cord injuries and research.

Funds Avail.: $75,000 per year, for up to two years; $150,000. **Duration:** Two years. **To Apply:** Applicants should include a research plan; a biosketch for the fellow; a biosketch for the mentors; a training plan; a letter of recommendation from the mentor and two additional recommendation letters. **Contact:** Kim Cerise, Director ofGrants Management; Email: kim@chnfoundation.org.

8206 ■ SCIRTS (Spinal Cord Injury Research on the Translational Spectrum) Senior Research Grants (Professional development/Grant)

Purpose: To support spinal cord injury research and rehabilitation. **Focus:** Spinal cord injuries and research. **Qualif.:** Applicants must be individuals who are senior,

Awards are arranged alphabetically below their administering organizations

independent investigators (equivalent to Associate Professor or above), employed at the grantee institution, at the time of the FGA submission. **Criteria:** Selection based on the innovative nature of the proposed research, the likelihood that success will move the field forward, and a history of productivity and significant contributions by the Investigator.

Funds Avail.: $200,000 per year, for up to three years, $600,000. **Duration:** Three years. **To Apply:** Applicants should include a research plan; a biosketch for the fellow; a biosketch for the mentors; a training plan; a letter of recommendation from the mentor and two additional recommendation letters. **Contact:** Kim Cerise, Director ofGrants Management; Email: kim@chnfoundation.org.

8207 ■ Netfloor USA Access Flooring

374 Crompton St., Ste. B
Charlotte, NC 28273
Free: 844-638-3566
E-mail: information@netfloorusa.com
URL: www.netfloorusa.com
Social Media: www.facebook.com/netfloorusa
www.pinterest.com/netfloorusa
twitter.com/NetfloorUSA
www.youtube.com/c/netfloorusa

8208 ■ Netfloor USA Access Flooring College Scholarships *(Undergraduate/Scholarship)*

Purpose: To give back to the next generation of business and technology leaders. **Focus:** General studies/Field of study not specified. **Qualif.:** Applicants must be U.S. citizens or permanent residents who are enrolled at an accredited college or university, or high school students who will be attending an accredited university or college in the next academic year. Must have a cumulative GPA of at least 3.0 (or equivalent).

Funds Avail.: $1,000. **To Apply:** Application form and details available at www.netfloorusa.com/scholarship/netfloor-usa-access-flooring-college-scholarship. **Deadline:** March 1; September 1.

8209 ■ Nevada Organization of Nurse Leaders

3983 S McCarran Blvd., No. 257
Reno, NV 89502
Ph: (775)848-9595
E-mail: stevielynn@nonl.org
URL: nonl.org
Social Media: www.facebook.com/NONL-Nevada
-Organization-of-Nurse-Leaders-260758313490
twitter.com/tweetNONL

8210 ■ Dan Mordecai Educational Scholarship Award *(Graduate, Undergraduate/Scholarship)*

Purpose: To provide financial assistance to students taking up nursing education. **Focus:** Nursing. **Qualif.:** Applicants must be graduate and undergraduate nursing students in Nevada; Nevada residency. **Criteria:** Selection will be based on the committee's criteria.

Funds Avail.: $1,000. **Duration:** Annual. **Remarks:** Established in 2002.

8211 ■ New Brunswick Health Research Foundation

100 - 30 Knowledge Park Dr.
Fredericton, NB, Canada E3C 2R2

Ph: (506)455-8886
E-mail: info@nbhrf.com
URL: www.nbhrf.com
Social Media: www.facebook.com/NBHRF
www.linkedin.com/company/new-brunswick-health
-research-foundation-la-fondation-de-la-recherche-en
-sant-du-nouveau-brunswick
twitter.com/nbhrf
www.youtube.com/channel/
UCGflrYSFMmzNMmOxMr7df3w

8212 ■ NBHRF/ASRP Doctoral Training Awards *(Doctorate/Award)*

Purpose: To encourage doctoral degree students to pursue research related to Alzheimer's Disease. **Focus:** Alzheimer's disease; Medical research. **Qualif.:** Applicants must be enrolled in a Canadian university-based program leading to a PhD degree; at the time of application they have been enrolled in a PhD program for 18 months or less. **Criteria:** Selection is based on top-ranked applicants and will work with institutions in New Brunswick to administer awards.

Funds Avail.: $22,000/year; ($500/year) research allowance. **Duration:** Up to 3 years. **To Apply:** Candidates must apply to the ASRP regular research grants competition. They must also notify NBHRF of their ASRP application by email and attach to it all documents and materials submitted to the regular ASRP competition. The ASRP/NBHRF will make awards to the top-ranked applicants and will work with institutions in New Brunswick to administer awards. **Remarks:** The awards are co-sponsored by the New Brunswick Health Research Foundation and Alzheimer Society of Canada.

8213 ■ NBHRF Bridge Grants *(Professional development/Grant)*

Purpose: To provide continuous support for health researchers in New Brunswick that have not obtained funding at any national level competition but have scored at the fundable level. **Focus:** Health sciences. **Qualif.:** Applicants must be affiliated with a New Brunswick university, research institution, health service organization, voluntary health agency or non-profit research organization; must be New Brunswick residents, applying through a New Brunswick Institution; must have obtained peer review comments and scored equivalent 3.75 or above prior to submit the application. **Criteria:** Selection will be based on the submitted application materials.

Funds Avail.: $35,000. **Duration:** Annual; 12 to 18 months. **To Apply:** Applicants must complete an updated online Common curriculum vitae using the template entitled "NBHRF Template" and the online application form; must prepare and submit all required attachment documents including a scanned completed signature page.

8214 ■ NBHRF Doctoral Studentship *(Doctorate/Grant)*

Purpose: To reward excellence and assist students undertaking their own research project or program as part of their thesis based degree studies at Doctorate program at a New Brunswick University. **Focus:** Medical research. **Criteria:** Selection will be based on the committee's criteria.

Funds Avail.: 24,500 Canadian Dollars per annum. **Duration:** Annual; up to 3 years. **To Apply:** Applicants must complete and submit online application through the New Brunswick Health Research Foundation website the

Awards are arranged alphabetically below their administering organizations

electronic signature page document (obtained by scanning the paper copy after signatures have been obtained) must be uploaded as an attachment and an electronic signature page document (obtained by scanning the paper copy after signatures have been obtained) must be uploaded as an attachment using the "Browse" button on the application form; there is no need to submit the paper copy of the signature page; the electronic scanned version will be sufficient. **Deadline:** May 1.

8215 ■ NBHRF Establishment Grants (Professional development/Grant)

Purpose: To assist in the establishment of new outstanding health researchers by providing funds to establish their independent health research program within the province. **Focus:** Health sciences. **Qualif.:** Applicants must be health researchers at a New Brunswick Institution; must be Canadian residents, permanent residents or actively pursuing such status; must be able to commit a minimum of 50% of their time to conduct research; be sponsored by the appropriate Department Head, Dean and Vice-President-academic/research, of a New Brunswick Institution; must have obtained peer-review comments and scored the equivalent of 3.75 or above to be granted.

Funds Avail.: $60,000. **Duration:** Annual; up to 2 years. **To Apply:** Applicants must complete an updated online Common curriculum vitae using the template entitled "NBHRF Template" and the online application form; must prepare and submit all required attachment documents including a scanned fully completed signature page. **Contact:** Email: grants@nbhrf.

8216 ■ NBHRF Health Research Strategic Initiative Grants (Professional development/Grant)

Purpose: To provide support to members of the health research enterprise and the healthcare system in New Brunswick. **Focus:** Health sciences. **Qualif.:** Applicant must be affiliated with a New Brunswick based University, college, medical training program, regional health authority or research institution. Students will not be funded as principal investigators. **Criteria:** Selection based on fit within a field of human health research defines/categorizes these fields by four pillars: 1 – biomedical, 2 – clinical, 3 – health system services and 4 – population health; and meet the required leveraging ratio.

Funds Avail.: Varies. **To Apply:** Applicant must complete the NBHRF online application form (all fields with an asterisk (*) are mandatory). Attach all documents in the appropriate section of the form (either CCV Attachments or Application Details Attachments). Attachments are detailed: Plain Language Project/Program Summary, Budget justification, Letter(s) of support/commitment from the private sector partner, Upload under the section "Application Details Attachments, Canadian Common CV, Signatures.

8217 ■ NBHRF Master's Studentship (Master's/Grant)

Purpose: To reward excellence and assist students undertaking their own research project or program as part of their thesis based degree studies at Master's program at a New Brunswick University college or research institution. **Focus:** Medical research.

Funds Avail.: 17,000 Canadian Dollars per annum. **Duration:** Annual; up to 2 years. **To Apply:** Applications must be submitted online on or before the given deadline; must include project Information, funding sources, student supervisor(s), required Additional Documents and Signatures; completion and submission of a Canadian Common

curriculum vitae using the template entitled "NBHRF Template" for applicants and supervisors is required. Such must be downloaded from the Common curriculum vitae website and then uploaded as an attachment to the NBHRF application using the "Browse" button on the online application form; the electronic signature page document (obtained by scanning the paper copy after signatures have been obtained) must be uploaded as an attachment using the "Browse" button on the application form; there is no need to submit the paper copy of the signature page; the electronic scanned version will be sufficient. **Deadline:** May 1.

8218 ■ NBHRF Postdoctoral Fellowships (Postdoctorate/Fellowship)

Purpose: To reward excellence and assist students undertaking their own research project or program as part of their thesis based degree studies at postdoctorate program at a New Brunswick University. **Focus:** Medical research. **Qualif.:** Applicants must be propose original research which is directly relevant to the health of New Brunswickers and the mandate of the Maritime SPOR SUPPORT Unit; at the time of application, be in the process of applying to, or be accepted into, a thesis-based full-time Master's or PhD graduate university program offered in New Brunswick or in the process of applying, being accepted or registered as a postdoctoral fellow and be under the supervision of a researcher (i.e. supervisor) conducting research in New Brunswick, in a New Brunswick university or institution. (e.g. medical training programs, regional health authorities' hospitals);not hold any remunerated academic appointment or any other fellowship/studentship funding; for PhD applicants, be registered at a university offering PhD graduate training in New Brunswick and reside in New Brunswick for the tenure of the award; if students are working full time, they must demonstrate that they have a reasonable work plan for their proposed research activities.

Funds Avail.: 40,000 Canadian Dollars per annum. **Duration:** Annual; Up to 2 years. **To Apply:** Applicants must complete and submit online application through the New Brunswick Health Research Foundation website the electronic signature page document (obtained by scanning the paper copy after signatures have been obtained) must be uploaded as an attachment and an electronic signature page document (obtained by scanning the paper copy after signatures have been obtained) must be uploaded as an attachment using the "Browse" button on the application form; there is no need to submit the paper copy of the signature page; the electronic scanned version will be sufficient. **Deadline:** May 1.

8219 ■ New Brunswick Institute of Agrologists (NBIA)
PO Box 6000
Fredericton, NB, Canada E3B 5H1
URL: www.ianbia.com

8220 ■ NBIA Scholarship (Undergraduate/Scholarship)

Purpose: To support NB students entering the third year of a degree program in Agriculture. **Focus:** Agricultural sciences.

Funds Avail.: $1,000.

Awards are arranged alphabetically below their administering organizations

8221 ■ New Brunswick Medical Education Foundation, Inc. (NBMEFI)

70C Hampton Rd
Rothesay, NB, Canada E2E-5L5
Ph: (506)848-0036
URL: nbmeded.ca

8222 ■ Astra Zeneca Medical Scholarship *(Advanced Professional/Scholarship)*

Purpose: To encourage students to study or practice medicine in New Brunswick. **Focus:** Health education. **Qualif.:** Applicants must be New Brunswick residents accepted for studies at an accredited medical school; must be committed to establishing their medical practice in the province. **Criteria:** Selection will be grant committee makes a decision based on information provided on the application and criteria identified by the donor.

Funds Avail.: $12,000. **Duration:** Annual; renewable for four years. **Number Awarded:** 1. **To Apply:** Applicants must fill the online application form and upload the following documents: Latest Curriculum Vitae; Proof of acceptance or current enrollment in an Accredited Medical School, Transcript of most recent academic record, Photo (headshot), Letter of intent/motivation. **Deadline:** May 31. **Contact:** N.B. Medical Education Foundation Grants Committee, c/o New Brunswick Medical Education Foundation, 70C Hampton Road, Rothesay, NB, E2E – 5L5 Phone:(506) 848-0036.

8223 ■ Bell Aliant Medical Education Scholarship *(Advanced Professional/Scholarship)*

Purpose: To encourage students to study or practice medicine in New Brunswick. **Focus:** Mental health. **Qualif.:** Applicants must be residents of New Brunswick; must be accepted to any accredited medical school; must have demonstrated interest in mental illness or have demonstrated desire to work with patients who suffer from mental illnesses or have experiences with mental illness and wishes to translate that into their medical practice. **Criteria:** Selection will be grant committee makes a decision based on information provided on the application and criteria identified by the donor.

Funds Avail.: $10,000. **Duration:** Annual; renewable for four years. **Number Awarded:** 1. **To Apply:** Applicants must fill the online application form and upload the following documents: Latest Curriculum Vitae; Proof of acceptance or current enrollment in an Accredited Medical School, Transcript of most recent academic record, Photo (headshot), Letter of intent/motivation. **Deadline:** May 31. **Contact:** N.B. Medical Education Foundation Grants Committee, c/o New Brunswick Medical Education Foundation, 70C Hampton Road, Rothesay, NB, E2E – 5L5 Phone:(506) 848-0036.

8224 ■ Berton W. Huestis Memorial Scholarship *(Advanced Professional/Scholarship)*

Purpose: To encourage students to study or practice medicine in New Brunswick. **Focus:** Health education. **Qualif.:** Applicants must be New Brunswick residents accepted for studies at an accredited medical school who are committed to establishing their medical practice in the province. **Criteria:** Selection will be grant committee makes a decision based on information provided on the application and criteria identified by the donor.

Funds Avail.: No specific amount. **Duration:** Annual. **Number Awarded:** 1. **To Apply:** Applicants must fill the online application form and upload the following documents: Latest Curriculum Vitae; Proof of acceptance or current enrollment in an Accredited Medical School, Transcript of most recent academic record, Photo (headshot), Letter of intent/motivation. **Deadline:** May 31. **Contact:** N.B. Medical Education Foundation Grants Committee, c/o New Brunswick Medical Education Foundation, 70C Hampton Road, Rothesay, NB, E2E – 5L5 Phone:(506) 848-0036.

8225 ■ BMO Medical Education Scholarship *(Advanced Professional/Scholarship)*

Purpose: To encourage students to study or practice medicine in New Brunswick. **Focus:** Health education. **Qualif.:** Applicants must be New Brunswick residents accepted for studies at an accredited medical school who are committed to establishing their medical practice in the province. **Criteria:** Selection will be grant committee makes a decision based on information provided on the application and criteria identified by the donor.

Funds Avail.: $10,000. **Duration:** Annual; renewable for four years. **To Apply:** Applicants must fill the online application form and upload the following documents: resume, cover letter, and proof of acceptance. **Deadline:** May 31. **Contact:** For Submittion: NB Medical Education Grants Committee, PO Box 22061, Saint John, N.B., E2K 4T7; For Questions: Phone: 506-648-7073.

8226 ■ CIBC Medical Education Scholarships *(Advanced Professional/Scholarship)*

Purpose: To encourage students to study or practice medicine in New Brunswick. **Focus:** Health education. **Qualif.:** Applicants must be New Brunswick residents accepted for studies at any accredited medical school; must be committed to establishing their medical practice in the province.

Funds Avail.: $5,000. **Duration:** Annual; renewable for four years. **Number Awarded:** 1. **To Apply:** Applicants must fill out the online application form and upload the following documents: resume; cover letter and; proof of acceptance. **Deadline:** April 30.

8227 ■ Dr. Frank and Audrey Wanamaker Medical Scholarship *(Advanced Professional/Scholarship)*

Purpose: To encourage students to study or practice medicine in New Brunswick. **Focus:** Health education. **Qualif.:** Applicants must be New Brunswick residents accepted to the Dalhousie Medicine New Brunswick program; must be committed to establishing their medical practice in the province. **Criteria:** Selection will be grant committee makes a decision based on information provided on the application and criteria identified by the donor.

Funds Avail.: No specific amount. **Duration:** Annual. **Number Awarded:** 1. **To Apply:** Applicants must fill the online application form and upload the following documents: Latest Curriculum Vitae; Proof of acceptance or current enrollment in an Accredited Medical School, Transcript of most recent academic record, Photo (headshot), Letter of intent/motivation. **Deadline:** May 31. **Contact:** N.B. Medical Education Foundation Grants Committee, c/o New Brunswick Medical Education Foundation, 70C Hampton Road, Rothesay, NB, E2E – 5L5 Phone:(506) 848-0036.

8228 ■ Dr. Henrik and Wanda Tonning Memorial Scholarship *(Advanced Professional/Scholarship)*

Purpose: To encourage students to study or practice medicine in New Brunswick. **Focus:** Health education. **Qualif.:** Applicants must be New Brunswick residents accepted

Awards are arranged alphabetically below their administering organizations

to the Dalhousie Medicine New Brunswick program; must be committed to establishing their medical practice in the province. **Criteria:** Selection will be grant committee makes a decision based on information provided on the application and criteria identified by the donor.

Funds Avail.: No specific amount. **Duration:** Annual. **Number Awarded:** 1. **To Apply:** Applicants must fill the online application form and upload the following documents: Latest Curriculum Vitae; Proof of acceptance or current enrollment in an Accredited Medical School, Transcript of most recent academic record, Photo (headshot), Letter of intent/motivation. **Deadline:** May 31. **Contact:** N.B. Medical Education Foundation Grants Committee, c/o New Brunswick Medical Education Foundation, 70C Hampton Road, Rothesay, NB, E2E – 5L5 Phone:(506) 848-0036.

8229 ■ Dr. Isaac Keillor Farrer, Advanced Medical Education Scholarship *(Advanced Professional/Scholarship)*

Purpose: To encourage students to study or practice medicine in New Brunswick. **Focus:** Health education. **Qualif.:** Applicants must be 4th year undergraduate students and residents of New Brunswick studying at any accredited medical school who have declared interest in specialty residency postgraduate training identified by the Officers of the New Brunswick Medical Education Trust in consultation with the Dean of Dalhousie Medicine N.B. **Criteria:** Selection will be grant committee makes a decision based on information provided on the application and criteria identified by the donor.

Funds Avail.: No specific amount. **Duration:** Annual. **Number Awarded:** 1. **To Apply:** Applicants must fill the online application form and upload the following documents: Latest Curriculum Vitae; Proof of acceptance or current enrollment in an Accredited Medical School, Transcript of most recent academic record, Photo (headshot), Letter of intent/motivation. **Deadline:** May 31. **Contact:** N.B. Medical Education Foundation Grants Committee, c/o New Brunswick Medical Education Foundation, 70C Hampton Road, Rothesay, NB, E2E – 5L5 Phone:(506) 848-0036.

8230 ■ Dr. Paul and Gayle Sohi Medical Education Scholarship *(Advanced Professional/Scholarship)*

Purpose: To encourage students to study or practice medicine in New Brunswick. **Focus:** Health education. **Qualif.:** Applicants must be 4th year undergraduate students studying at program located in Saint John, New Brunswick; must have interest in internal medicine and/or Nephrology. **Criteria:** Selection will be grant committee makes a decision based on information provided on the application and criteria identified by the donor.

Funds Avail.: No specific amount. **Duration:** Annual. **Number Awarded:** 1. **To Apply:** Applicants must fill the online application form and upload the following documents: Latest Curriculum Vitae; Proof of acceptance or current enrollment in an Accredited Medical School, Transcript of most recent academic record, Photo (headshot), Letter of intent/motivation. **Deadline:** May 31. **Contact:** N.B. Medical Education Foundation Grants Committee, c/o New Brunswick Medical Education Foundation, 70C Hampton Road, Rothesay, NB, E2E – 5L5 Phone:(506) 848-0036.

8231 ■ Friends of the Christofor Foundation Scholarship *(Advanced Professional/Scholarship)*

Purpose: To encourage students to study or practice medicine in New Brunswick. **Focus:** Health education. **Qualif.:** Applicants must be scholarship is awarded preferably

to a resident from Charlotte County, New Brunswick accepted to the Dalhousie Medicine New Brunswick program; if a qualifying student is not available from Charlotte County, the Scholarship(s) will be awarded to another New Brunswick resident. **Criteria:** Selection will be based on the committee's criteria.

Funds Avail.: $12,000. **Duration:** Annual; one or more every year and renewable for four years. **Number Awarded:** Varies. **To Apply:** Applicants must fill the online application form and upload the following documents: Latest Curriculum Vitae; Proof of acceptance or current enrollment in an Accredited Medical School, Transcript of most recent academic record, Photo (headshot), Letter of intent/motivation. **Deadline:** May 31. **Contact:** N.B. Medical Education Foundation Grants Committee, c/o New Brunswick Medical Education Foundation, 70C Hampton Road, Rothesay, NB, E2E – 5L5 Phone:(506) 848-0036.

8232 ■ Horizon Health Network Scholarship *(Advanced Professional/Scholarship)*

Purpose: To encourage students to study or practice medicine in New Brunswick. **Focus:** Health education. **Qualif.:** Applicants must be New Brunswick residents accepted for studies at an accredited medical school; must be committed to establishing their medical practice in the province. **Criteria:** Selection will be grant committee makes a decision based on information provided on the application and criteria identified by the donor.

Funds Avail.: No specific amount. **Duration:** Annual. **Number Awarded:** 2. **To Apply:** Applicants must fill the online application form and upload the following documents: Latest Curriculum Vitae; Proof of acceptance or current enrollment in an Accredited Medical School, Transcript of most recent academic record, Photo (headshot), Letter of intent/motivation. **Deadline:** May 31. **Contact:** N.B. Medical Education Foundation Grants Committee, c/o New Brunswick Medical Education Foundation, 70C Hampton Road, Rothesay, NB, E2E – 5L5 Phone:(506) 848-0036.

8233 ■ G. William McQuade Memorial Scholarships *(Advanced Professional/Scholarship)*

Purpose: To encourage students to study or practice medicine in New Brunswick. **Focus:** Health education. **Qualif.:** Applicants must be New Brunswick residents accepted to the Dalhousie Medicine New Brunswick program; must be committed to establishing their medical practice in the province. **Criteria:** Selection will be grant committee makes a decision based on information provided on the application and criteria identified by the donor.

Duration: Annual. **Number Awarded:** 1. **To Apply:** Applicants must fill the online application form and upload the following documents: Latest Curriculum Vitae; Proof of acceptance or current enrollment in an Accredited Medical School, Transcript of most recent academic record, Photo (headshot), Letter of intent/motivation. **Deadline:** May 31. **Remarks:** Endowed by Dr. Richard Currie. **Contact:** N.B. Medical Education Foundation Grants Committee, c/o New Brunswick Medical Education Foundation, 70C Hampton Road, Rothesay, NB, E2E – 5L5 Phone:(506) 848-0036.

8234 ■ NB College of Physicians and Surgeons Medical Education Scholarship *(Advanced Professional/Scholarship)*

Purpose: To encourage students to study or practice medicine in New Brunswick. **Focus:** Health education. **Qualif.:** Applicants must be New Brunswick residents accepted to the Dalhousie Medicine New Brunswick program; must

Awards are arranged alphabetically below their administering organizations

be committed to establishing their medical practice in the province. **Criteria:** Selection will be grant committee makes a decision based on information provided on the application and criteria identified by the donor.

Funds Avail.: No specific amount. **Duration:** Annual. **To Apply:** Applicants must fill the online application form and upload the following documents: Latest Curriculum Vitae; Proof of acceptance or current enrollment in an Accredited Medical School, Transcript of most recent academic record, Photo (headshot), Letter of intent/motivation. **Deadline:** May 31. **Contact:** N.B. Medical Education Foundation Grants Committee, c/o New Brunswick Medical Education Foundation, 70C Hampton Road, Rothesay, NB, E2E – 5L5 Phone:(506) 848-0036.

8235 ■ RBC Medical Education Scholarship
(Advanced Professional/Scholarship)

Purpose: To encourage students to study or practice medicine in New Brunswick. **Focus:** Health education. **Qualif.:** Applicants must be New Brunswick residents accepted to any accredited medical school; must have an interest in Adolescent Mental Health or in Mental Health. **Criteria:** Selection will be grant committee makes a decision based on information provided on the application and criteria identified by the donor.

Funds Avail.: $10,000. **Duration:** Annual; renewable for four years. **Number Awarded:** 2. **To Apply:** Applicants must fill the online application form and upload the following documents: Latest Curriculum Vitae; Proof of acceptance or current enrollment in an Accredited Medical School, Transcript of most recent academic record, Photo (headshot), Letter of intent/motivation. **Deadline:** May 31. **Contact:** N.B. Medical Education Foundation Grants Committee, c/o New Brunswick Medical Education Foundation, 70C Hampton Road, Rothesay, NB, E2E – 5L5 Phone:(506) 848-0036.

8236 ■ Regional Development Corporation Scholarship *(Advanced Professional/Scholarship)*

Purpose: To encourage students to study or practice medicine in New Brunswick. **Focus:** Health education. **Qualif.:** Applicants must be New Brunswick residents accepted for studies at an accredited medical school who are committed to establishing their medical practice in the province. **Criteria:** Selection will be grant committee makes a decision based on information provided on the application and criteria identified by the donor.

Funds Avail.: No specific amount. **Duration:** Annual. **Number Awarded:** 2. **To Apply:** Applicants must fill the online application form and upload the following documents: Latest Curriculum Vitae; Proof of acceptance or current enrollment in an Accredited Medical School, Transcript of most recent academic record, Photo (headshot), Letter of intent/motivation. **Deadline:** May 31. **Contact:** N.B. Medical Education Foundation Grants Committee, c/o New Brunswick Medical Education Foundation, 70C Hampton Road, Rothesay, NB, E2E – 5L5 Phone:(506) 848-0036.

8237 ■ Robert R. McCain Memorial Scholarship
(Advanced Professional/Scholarship)

Purpose: To encourage students to study or practice medicine in New Brunswick. **Focus:** Health education. **Qualif.:** Applicant must be a resident of the Upper Saint John River Valley, New Brunswick accepted to any New Brunswick medical school program; if a qualifying student is not found in the Upper Saint John River Valley area, the scholarship can be given to a any resident of New Bruns-

wick. **Criteria:** Selection will be grant committee makes a decision based on information provided on the application and criteria identified by the donor.

Funds Avail.: No specific amount. **Duration:** Annual. **Number Awarded:** 1. **To Apply:** Applicants must fill the online application form and upload the following documents: Latest Curriculum Vitae; Proof of acceptance or current enrollment in an Accredited Medical School, Transcript of most recent academic record, Photo (headshot), Letter of intent/motivation. **Deadline:** May 31. **Contact:** N.B. Medical Education Foundation Grants Committee, c/o New Brunswick Medical Education Foundation, 70C Hampton Road, Rothesay, NB, E2E – 5L5 Phone:(506) 848-0036.

8238 ■ Scotiabank Medical Education Scholarship
(Advanced Professional/Scholarship)

Purpose: To encourage students to study or practice medicine in New Brunswick. **Focus:** Health education. **Qualif.:** Applicants must be New Brunswick residents accepted for studies at any accredited medical school; must be committed to establishing their medical practice in the province. **Criteria:** Selection will be grant committee makes a decision based on information provided on the application and criteria identified by the donor.

Funds Avail.: $10,000. **Duration:** Annual; renewable for four years. **Number Awarded:** 1. **To Apply:** Applicants must fill the online application form and upload the following documents: Latest Curriculum Vitae; Proof of acceptance or current enrollment in an Accredited Medical School, Transcript of most recent academic record, Photo (headshot), Letter of intent/motivation. **Deadline:** May 31. **Contact:** N.B. Medical Education Foundation Grants Committee, c/o New Brunswick Medical Education Foundation, 70C Hampton Road, Rothesay, NB, E2E – 5L5 Phone:(506) 848-0036.

8239 ■ TD Bank Medical Education Scholarship
(Advanced Professional/Scholarship)

Purpose: To encourage students to study or practice medicine in New Brunswick. **Focus:** Health education. **Qualif.:** Applicants must be New Brunswick residents accepted for studies at any accredited medical school; must be committed to establishing their medical practice in the province. **Criteria:** Selection is based on the grant committee making decisions based on information provided on the application and criteria identified by the donor.

Funds Avail.: $10,000. **Duration:** Annual; renewable for four years. **Number Awarded:** 2. **To Apply:** Applicants must fill the online application form and upload the following documents: resume; cover letter and; proof of acceptance. **Deadline:** May 31. **Contact:** For Submittion: NB Medical Education Grants Committee, PO Box 22061, Saint John, N.B., E2K 4T7; For Questions: Phone: 506-648-7073.

8240 ■ New England Club Managers Association (NECMA)
William F. Connell Golf House and Museum
300 Arnold Palmer Blvd., Ste. 227
Norton, MA 02766-1365
Ph: (774)430-9050
Fax: (774)430-9051
E-mail: necma@necma.org
URL: www.necma.org
Social Media: www.facebook.com/CMAANEWENGLAND
twitter.com/NECMA
www.youtube.com/user/NECMA1914

Awards are arranged alphabetically below their administering organizations

8241 ■ David Meador Foundation - Hospitality-Food Service Scholarships (Undergraduate/Scholarship)

Purpose: To support students interested in pursuing a career in the club management profession. **Focus:** Food service careers. **Criteria:** Selection will be based on the committee's criteria.

Funds Avail.: No specific amount. **Duration:** Annual. **Number Awarded:** 2. **To Apply:** Applicants must complete and submit the application including all the required attachments, transcripts, two letters of reference and essay; must be typed with correct grammar and spelling. **Deadline:** October 1.

8242 ■ David Meador Foundation - Club Management Student Scholarships (Undergraduate/Scholarship)

Purpose: To support students of hospitality studies and those interested in the club management profession. **Focus:** General studies/Field of study not specified. **Qualif.:** Applicants must be full-time students enrolled in a hospitality degree program; must have completed at least two semesters of college with a minimum GPA of 3.0; must be active student member of CMAA; must have worked at least one season at a private club and can demonstrate an interest in pursuing Private Club Management as a career; must have attended at least one NECMA Meeting each year. **Criteria:** Recipients are selected based on achievement; only single and completed applications will be considered.

Funds Avail.: No specific amount. **Duration:** Annual. **Number Awarded:** 2. **To Apply:** Applicants must complete and submit the application including all the required attachments, transcripts, two letters of reference and essay. Applications must be typed with correct grammar and spelling. **Contact:** New England Club Managers Association, Attn: Scholarship Chairman, PO Box 832, Hampstead, NH, 03841. Email: managing.director@necmafoundation.org.

8243 ■ New England Employee Benefits Council (NEEBC)

561 Virginia Rd, Ste 217
Concord, MA 01742
Ph: (781)684-8700
Fax: (781)684-9200
E-mail: info@neebc.org
URL: www.neebc.org
Social Media: www.facebook.com/Neebc
www.linkedin.com/company/
  newenglandemployeebenefitscouncil
twitter.com/neebc
www.youtube.com/channel/UCpXNP7If1-Mh5lbvlA_7Nxg

8244 ■ NEEBC Scholarship Award (Undergraduate, Graduate/Scholarship)

Purpose: To further the aims of the Council, which is to advance the knowledge and education of individuals in the employee benefits field, or those aspiring to careers in employee benefits. **Focus:** Employment. **Qualif.:** Applicant must be a college student (undergraduate or graduate) studying in an accredited academic program leading to a degree; residing either in New England, or enrolled in a college in New England.

Funds Avail.: Up to $5,000. **Duration:** Annual. **To Apply:** Applicants must submit college transcripts; a minimum of

two references from college professors, NEEBC members, or other benefits professionals. **Contact:** New England Employee Benefits Council, 240 Bear Hill Rd., Ste. 102, Waltham, MA 02451; Fax: 781-684-9200.

8245 ■ New England Library Association (NELA)

55 N Main St., Unit 49
Belchertown, MA 01007
Ph: (413)323-5925
E-mail: info@nelib.org
URL: www.nelib.org
Social Media: www.facebook.com/nelibraries
www.instagram.com/newenglandlib

8246 ■ NELA Conference Scholarships (All/Scholarship)

Purpose: To provide financial assistance to attend the annual conference of NELA. **Focus:** Library and archival sciences. **Criteria:** Applicants will be selected by the committee members.

Duration: Annual. **To Apply:** Application must be submitted at least eight weeks prior to the program and is available online. **Deadline:** June 30.

8247 ■ New England Water Works Association (NEWWA)

125 Hopping Brook Rd.
Holliston, MA 01746
Ph: (508)893-7979
Fax: (508)893-9898
URL: www.newwa.org
Social Media: www.facebook.com/newaterworks
www.instagram.com/newaterworks
www.linkedin.com/company/new-england-water-works
 -assn
twitter.com/newaterworks
www.youtube.com/user/NEWaterWorks

8248 ■ Francis X. Crowley Scholarship (Undergraduate/Scholarship)

Purpose: To help and support worthy students pursuing their undergraduate studies. **Focus:** Business; Engineering, Civil; Water resources. **Qualif.:** Applicants must be Civil engineering, environmental engineering, or business management students at a 4-year college or university.

Funds Avail.: $3,000. **Duration:** Annual. **To Apply:** Applicants must submit official student application form; a two-page (maximum) resume (that includes educational history); official transcripts of all university education (if applicant has not started higher education, official transcript from high school is required); two letters of recommendation (one must be from a teacher/professor; the second may be from a teacher/professor or professional reference such as an employer); a one-page (maximum) statement of educational plans and career objectives demonstrating how these plans are beneficial to water works practice in New England; copy of FAFSA (Free Applications for Federal Student Aid) confirmation. **Deadline:** April 1. **Contact:** NEWWA at 508-893-7979; Stephen Donovan, Scholarship Committee Chair; Phone: (508) 248-2893; Email: sdonovan@rhwhite.com.

8249 ■ Elson T. Killam Memorial Scholarship (Undergraduate, Graduate/Scholarship)

Purpose: To provide a scholarship to students of civil engineering or environmental engineering seeking under-

Awards are arranged alphabetically below their administering organizations

graduate or graduate degrees. **Focus:** Engineering, Civil; Water resources. **Qualif.:** Applicant must be a student enrolled in a civil or environmental engineering program at a 4-year college or university; must be members of NEWWA and reside in New England or attend a college/ university in New England to qualify. **Criteria:** Selection will be based on merit, character and need to members and student members of the New England Water Works Association, with preference given to applicants whose programs are considered by the Scholarship Committee as beneficial to water works practice in New England.

Funds Avail.: $1,500. **Duration:** Annual. **Number Awarded:** 1. **To Apply:** Applicants must submit official student application form; a two-page (maximum) resume (that includes educational history); official transcripts of all university education (if applicant has not started higher education, official transcript from high school is required); two letters of recommendation (one must be from a teacher/ professor; the second may be from a teacher/professor or professional reference such as an employer); a one-page (maximum) statement of educational plans and career objectives demonstrating how these plans are beneficial to water works practice in New England; copy of FAFSA (Free Applications for Federal Student Aid) confirmation. **Deadline:** April 1. **Contact:** Official transcripts and reference letters should be included in the full application package in a signed/sealed envelope to Stephen B. Donovan, WhiteWater, Inc., 253 B Worcester Rd., Charlton, MA, 01507.

8250 ■ New Hampshire Association of Educational Office Professionals (NHAEOP)
150 Wakefield St., Ste. 8
Rochester, NH 03867
E-mail: info@nhaeop.org
URL: www.nhaeop.org
Social Media: facebook.com/NHAEOP

8251 ■ NHAEOP Member Scholarships
(Undergraduate/Scholarship)

Purpose: To help defray the expenses of NHAEOP student members. **Focus:** General studies/Field of study not specified. **Qualif.:** Applicants must be NHAEOP members who are taking college credits. **Criteria:** Selection will be given to students who are dues-paying members and who are in financial need.

Funds Avail.: $500. **Duration:** Annual. **To Apply:** Applicants must submit an application form and proof of registration for the desired course. **Deadline:** April 18. **Contact:** Pam Patnode, NHAEOP President, Charlestown Middle School, Email: ppatnode@sau60.org; Phone: (603)-826-7711.

8252 ■ Julia T. Pingree Student Scholarship
(Undergraduate/Scholarship)

Purpose: To help students further their education. **Focus:** Business. **Criteria:** Selection will be selected based on submitted application materials.

Funds Avail.: No specific amount. **To Apply:** Applicants must submit a filled-out application form, biographical information, essay and an official transcript of records; must provide one original and two copies of the application packet in order (no folders, binders, etc.). **Deadline:** April 1. **Remarks:** Established in 1997. **Contact:** Patti Kallander, NHAEOP Scholarship Committee Chair; HDHS 12 Hillcat Drive Hillsboro, NH 03244; Email: pkallander@hdsd.org.

8253 ■ New Hampshire Automobile Dealers Association (NHADA)
507 South St. Bow
Concord, NH 03302-2337
Free: 800-852-3372
E-mail: cives@nhada.com
URL: www.nhada.com
Social Media: www.facebook.com/NHAutoDealers
twitter.com/nhautodealers

8254 ■ The Medallion Fund Scholarship
(Undergraduate/Scholarship)

Purpose: To encourage students applying for a scholarship to the new hampshire automobile dealers association's education foundation **Focus:** Automotive technology. **Qualif.:** Applicants student is attending school in new hampshire; must have a minimum grade point average (gpa) of 2.5; must possess a valid driver's license. Scholarships may be denied if applicant is 19 y/o or under has two or more points or if 20 y/o or older has three or more points.; are insurable and employed, this will be taken into consideration; high school students must be enrolled in an auto program, or been enrolled in 4 years of mathematics, or be currently employed in the automobile industry; college students must be currently employed in the automobile industry; be enrolled and in good standing in an automotive technology, auto body or heavy equipment/diesel program within the community college system of new hampshire for the upcoming academic school year.

Funds Avail.: No specific amount. **Duration:** Annual. **To Apply:** Applicants high school students letter of recommendation from automotive instructor; if applicant does not have an automotive instructor, then a letter of recommendation from the applicant's 4-year mathematics teacher or current automotive industry employer/supervisor may be substituted high school transcript; college students letter of recommendation from a ccsnh automotive, heavy equipment/diesel or auto body instructor; letter of recommendation from applicant's automotive industry employerlk;/ supervisor; college transcript. **Deadline:** April 1. **Contact:** Nicole Havey, NHAEF, PO Box 2337, Concord, NH, 03302-2337; Phone: 800-852-3372, Email: foundation@ nhada.com.

8255 ■ New Hampshire Charitable Foundation (NHCF)
37 Pleasant St.
Concord, NH 03301-4005
Ph: (603)225-6641
Free: 800-464-6641
E-mail: info@nhcf.org
URL: www.nhcf.org
Social Media: www.facebook.com/nhcfoundation
www.linkedin.com/company/new-hampshire-charitable
 -foundation
twitter.com/nhcfoundation
www.youtube.com/user/NHCFoundation

8256 ■ Caroline and Martin Gross Fellowship
(Professional development/Fellowship)

Purpose: To honor individuals for their extraordinary work in public service. **Focus:** Public service. **Qualif.:** Applicants who hold an elected or appointed position in a state, country, or municipal government within New Hampshire

Awards are arranged alphabetically below their administering organizations

and also demonstrate the highest standards of performance in public service will be considered for this fellowship. **Criteria:** The selection committee looks for candidates requirements such as experience in public service; capacity to benefit from the program; desire to enhance and improve the public decision-making process in New Hampshire.

Funds Avail.: No specific amount. **Duration:** Annual. **To Apply:** Applicants are asked to download a nomination form and fill it out; if there are others who support the nomination, their comments and contact information may be sent along with the primary nomination form; once nominated, candidates are notified and sent an application. Nomination and application forms must be sent via email, fax, or mail. **Deadline:** March 13. **Remarks:** The award was established in honor of Caroline and Martin Gross, whose dedication to public service will live on through the work of the fellowship recipients. **Contact:** Mail to: Caroline and Martin Gross Fellowship, New Hampshire Charitable Foundation, 37 Pleasant St., Concord, NH, 03301-4005; Jessica Kierstead, Student Aid Officer, Phone: 603-225-6641, Email: Jessica.Kierstead@nhcf.org.

8257 ■ Louise Tillotson Teaching Fellowship
(Professional development/Fellowship)

Purpose: To raise public awareness about the value of excellence in education and to retain good teachers in the North Country schools of New Hampshire. **Focus:** General studies/Field of study not specified. **Qualif.:** Applicants must be kindergarten through twelfth-grade public school teachers who work in New Hampshire's North Country region; teachers in Coos County public schools are given preference. **Criteria:** Selection will be based on the following criteria such as the applicants' commitment to serve public education in their school and community; the extent and nature of the applicants past and present public education service and commitment to continued professional learning; applicants' ability to implement a creative and imaginative educational atmosphere for North Country students; applicants ability to bring ideas and inspire proactive solutions to resolve educational challenges; applicants' ability to articulate their educational vision, knowledge of content, and teaching methodology with passion; applicants' ability to inspire and challenge the current and next generation of educators and students in the North Country.

Duration: Annual. **Number Awarded:** 3. **To Apply:** Applicants are asked to download an application form and fill it out, including all contact information for the applicants. **Deadline:** April 24. **Remarks:** Established in 2006. **Contact:** Jean Clarke, Senior Tillotson Program Associate, Phone: 603-225-6641, Email: Jean.Clarke@nhcf.org.

8258 ■ Louise Tillotson Teaching Professional Development Scholarship *(Professional development/Scholarship)*

Purpose: To assists educators in meeting their continuing education and professional development goals. **Focus:** General studies/Field of study not specified. **Qualif.:** Applicants must be kindergarten through twelfth-grade public school teachers who work in New Hampshire's North Country region; teachers in Coos County public schools are given preference. **Criteria:** Selection will be based on the following criteria such as the applicants' commitment to serve public education in their school and community; the extent and nature of the applicants past and present public education service and commitment to continued professional learning; applicants' ability to implement a creative

and imaginative educational atmosphere for North Country students; applicants ability to bring ideas and inspire proactive solutions to resolve educational challenges; applicants' ability to articulate their educational vision, knowledge of content, and teaching methodology with passion; applicants' ability to inspire and challenge the current and next generation of educators and students in the North Country.

Duration: Annual. **To Apply:** Applicants are asked to download an application form and fill it out, including all contact information for the applicants. **Deadline:** April 27. **Remarks:** Established in 2006. **Contact:** Jean Clarke, Senior Tillotson Program Associate, Phone: 603-225-6641, Email: Jean.Clarke@nhcf.org.

8259 ■ Piscataqua Region Artist Advancement Grant *(Professional development/Grant)*

Purpose: To provide financial support to individual visual artists and craftspeople in the Piscataqua Region to promote their artistic growth. **Focus:** Crafts; Visual arts. **Qualif.:** Applicants must be over 18 years of age at the time of application; must be visual artists and craftspeople whose resume and body of work demonstrate a strong commitment to an artistic discipline; collaborating visual artists and craftspeople are also eligible; eligible art disciplines includes Crafts, which includes work in clay, leather, plastic, fiber, metal, wood, glass, paper and mixed media; 2-Dimensional work, which includes drawing, painting, works on paper, printmaking, book arts, collage, assemblage, mixed media; 3-Dimensional work, which includes sculpture, installation art; experimental visual arts, which includes conceptual, new media; photography; must have been permanent residents within New Hampshire Charitable Foundation's Piscataqua Region for at least two full years prior to applying and must plan to maintain permanent residence in the region during the entire grant period. **Criteria:** Selection will be based on the following criteria's as the artists' body of work, as evidenced by work samples, shows high artistic quality and a strong artistic vision; the artists' body of work and resume demonstrate perseverance and a commitment to their artistic career; the artists' proposed advancement plan is clear and well-reasoned and is likely to make a significant impact on the artists' work and future direction; the proposed amount and use of funds supports the advancement plan and will make a significant impact on the artists' development and that impact will be sustained beyond the grant period.

Duration: Annual. **Number Awarded:** 1. **To Apply:** Applicants must go to www.nhcf.slideroom.com to create an account and must submit the following: resume/CV; must list their accomplishments and endeavors that have been most important to them and to their work; a timeline of applicants' artistic development; an advancement plan, maximum of two pages, describing how this grant would advance their artistic growth in the short term and the long term; must include the direction they plan to pursue and/or any activities they intend to undertake during the grant period; budget describing specifically how the applicants plan to use the grant funds and discuss how the use of the grant funds are related to their advancement plan; five digital images of work samples and additional five images to show details of 3-D work. **Deadline:** April 30. **Contact:** Maria Sillari, Consultant, Phone: 603-430-2129, Email: msillari14@gmail.com; Simon Delekta, Senior Program Officer, Piscataqua Region, Phone: 603-430-9182, Email: Simon.Delekta@nhcf.org.

Awards are arranged alphabetically below their administering organizations

8260 ■ New Hampshire Council on Developmental Disabilities

2 1/2 Beacon St.
Concord, NH 03301
Ph: (603)271-3236
Fax: (603)271-1156
URL: www.nhcdd.org
Social Media: www.facebook.com/NHCDD
instagram.com/nhcddcouncil

8261 ■ Community Project Grants *(Other/Grant)*

Purpose: to provide individuals with developmental disabilities with opportunities to be a part of community life. **Focus:** Public service.

Funds Avail.: $1,000. **Duration:** Annual.

8262 ■ Small Grants for Community Projects and Educational Programs *(Other/Grant)*

Purpose: To educate people with developmental disabilities and their families about specific disabilities and develop their leadership skills and ability to advocate for themselves and others. **Focus:** Disabilities; Leadership, Institutional and community.

Funds Avail.: Up to $1,000. **Duration:** Annual. **Deadline:** September 30. **Contact:** Small Grants, NH Council on Developmental Disabilities, 2 1/2 Beacon St., Ste. 10, Concord, NH, 03301-4447; Phone: 603-271-3236; Fax: 603-271-1156; Executive Director; Phone: 603-271-1157; Administrative Assistant; Phone: 603-271-7039.

8263 ■ New Hampshire Golf Association (NHGA)

56 S State St.
Concord, NH 03301
Ph: (603)219-0371
E-mail: membership@nhgolf.com
URL: www.nhgolfassociation.org
Social Media: www.facebook.com/NewHampshireGA
twitter.com/NewHampshireGA

8264 ■ The Dr. Robert Elliott Memorial Scholarship *(Undergraduate/Scholarship)*

Purpose: To support outstanding young men and women employed at New Hampshire golf courses in pursuing higher education. **Focus:** General studies/Field of study not specified.

Funds Avail.: No specific amount. **Duration:** Annual. **Number Awarded:** 1. **To Apply:** Completed application along with an official copy of your transcript (through Fall of previous year); copy of Free Application for Student Aid (FAFSA) report (the 5 page report, not the application); letter from the club or course where you have completed the employment requirement, certifying you have worked at least 2 seasons (for new applicant); copy of the acceptance letter from the school, college or university, applicant going to attend and confidential school report completed by high school principal or guidance counselor (for high school senior) must be submitted. **Deadline:** May 15. **Remarks:** The Scholarship established in Memory of Dr. Robert Elliott was president of the NHGA for many years, president of The McDonough Foundation. **Contact:** McDonough Scholarship Foundation; c/o Kerri Coughlin; 61 N St., Manchester, NH, 03104; Email: mcDonoughapplication@comcast.net.

8265 ■ The Pauline Elliott Scholarship *(Undergraduate/Scholarship)*

Purpose: To support outstanding young men and women employed at New Hampshire golf courses in pursuing higher education. **Focus:** General studies/Field of study not specified. **Qualif.:** Applicants must be a graduate of an accredited high school or enrolled in a bachelor or associate degree college program, a minimum academic GPA of 2.5 on a 4.0 scale; must have a minimum of two summers of successful work at a NH golf course as a caddie, in the Pro Shop, on the grounds crew, or in the clubhouse; must be of proven character, integrity, and citizenship.

Funds Avail.: No specific amount. **Duration:** Annual. **To Apply:** Completed application along with an official copy of your transcript (through Fall of previous year); copy of Free Application for Student Aid (FAFSA) report (the 5 page report, not the application); letter from the club or course where you have completed the employment requirement, certifying you have worked at least 2 seasons (for new applicant); copy of the acceptance letter from the school, college or university, applicant going to attend and confidential school report completed by high school principal or guidance counselor (for high school senior) must be submitted. **Deadline:** May 15. **Remarks:** The Scholarship established in honor of Pauline Elliott on behalf of the NHGA and New Hampshire golf in general. **Contact:** McDonough Scholarship Foundation; c/o Kerri Coughlin; 61 N St., Manchester, NH, 03104; Email: mcDonoughapplication@comcast.net.

8266 ■ New Hampshire Sheep and Wool Growers Association (NHSWGA)

220 Loudon Rd.
Concord, NH 03301
URL: nhswga.org

8267 ■ The Bruce Clement Post-Secondary Education Scholarship *(Undergraduate/Scholarship)*

Purpose: To financially assist students who are pursuing an education related to the sheep industry. **Focus:** Industry and trade. **Qualif.:** Applicants must be NH residents who have completed at least one year at a post-secondary institution; and must be majoring in a field that will benefit the sheep industry. **Criteria:** Applicants will be selected based on past involvement and/or future plans in the sheep industry; volunteer services including youth involvement in agricultural programs; and review of transcript and letters of recommendation.

Funds Avail.: Up to $1,000 each. **To Apply:** Applicants must submit a filled-out application form, transcript of records and three letters of recommendation. **Deadline:** August 1. **Remarks:** Interview will be held at the NH Farm Bureau Office, 295 Sheep Davis Rd., Concord with the New Hampshire Sheep and Wool Growers' Scholarship Committee.

8268 ■ New Hampshire Snowmobile Association (NHSA)

600 Laconia Rd., Ste. 2
Tilton, NH 03276
Ph: (603)273-0220
Fax: (603)273-0218
E-mail: nhsaoffice@nhsa.com
URL: www.nhsa.com
Social Media: www.facebook.com/

Awards are arranged alphabetically below their administering organizations

NewHampshireSnowmobileAssociation
twitter.com/SnowmobileNH
www.youtube.com/channel/UC0i0gwAaureVTgE5rzpVAlw

8269 ■ New Hampshire Snowmobile Association Book Scholarships (Undergraduate/Scholarship)

Purpose: To assist the education of dependents of NHSA members. **Focus:** General studies/Field of study not specified. **Qualif.:** Applicants must be graduating high school seniors who have been accepted at a college, junior college, or vocational school or to a college students already enrolled; student's parents or guardians must already be members in good standing of the New Hampshire Snowmobile Association. **Criteria:** The scholarship committee will review applications and will select based on academic achievement, extracurricular involvement, community service and the quality of the original essay.

Funds Avail.: $1,000; $500; $250. **Duration:** Annual. **Number Awarded:** 3. **To Apply:** Applicant must submit an official high school or college transcript, whichever applies; current written recommendations by at least two teachers, dated and signed; current written recommendations by one or two friends, employers or clergy, dated and signed; proof of acceptance at the listed college, university or vocational school; a 500-word or less essay about snowmobiling in their state. (Economy, trails, environment, or what snowmobiling means the applicant); an overview of applicant's extracurricular activities and any snowmobile associated volunteerism within the last year. **Deadline:** March 1. **Contact:** NHSA, 614 Laconia Rd., Ste. 4, Tilton, NH 03276; E-mail: execdir@nhsa.com.

8270 ■ New Jersey Association of Osteopathic Physicians and Surgeons (NJAOPS)

666 Plainsboro Rd, Ste. 356
Plainsboro, NJ 08536
Ph: (732)940-9000
Fax: (732)940-8899
URL: www.njosteo.com

8271 ■ Osteopathic Medical School Scholarship (Undergraduate/Scholarship)

Purpose: To support deserving New Jersey residents who have been accepted into the fall first-year class of an approved osteopathic medical school. **Focus:** Medicine, Osteopathic. **Qualif.:** Applicants must be first year medical student enrolled in any osteopathic medical school in united states.

Funds Avail.: No specific amount. **Duration:** Annual. **To Apply:** Applicants must submit A copy of Your Acceptance Letter From an Osteopathic Medical School; A Current Curriculum Vitae (CV); A headshot photograph; Notorized and completed NJOEF application (found below) submitted to NJAOPS before the May 31st deadline; Academic records to be submitted directly from your college/testing institution(s); Use the AA.MC TI-Ix System to Print and Mail Your Official MCAT Score Report to NJOEF. Official MCAT Score Report Includes a validation Code at the Top Along with Specific Identification Information. **Contact:** New Jersey Osteopathic Education Foundation, 666 Plainsboro Rd, Ste. 356, Plainsboro, NJ, 08536.

8272 ■ New Jersey Broadcasters Association (NJBA)

7 Centre Dr., Ste. 12
Monroe Township, NJ 08831
Fax: (888)652-2329
Free: 888-657-2346
E-mail: njba@njba.com
URL: www.njba.com

8273 ■ Howard L. Green Scholarships (Undergraduate/Scholarship)

Purpose: To support students enrolled full-time at any colleges or universities in New Jersey. **Focus:** Broadcasting; Communications; Journalism. **Qualif.:** Applicants must be undergraduate students studying broadcasting, journalism or communications at any colleges or universities in New Jersey. **Criteria:** Selection will be based on the committee's criteria.

Funds Avail.: $1,000. **Duration:** Annual. **To Apply:** Applicants must complete and submit a biographical sketch,letter of recommendation,academic evaluation, work sample and a brief statement explaining their interest in broadcasting, how they expect to develop this interest and experience they have had so far in this field in high school, college or professionally; a brief biography; a letter of recommendation from a person qualified to judge their performance and/or aptitude for a career in broadcasting; a short note from their instructor or advisor evaluating their overall academic ability; some representative sample (tape, disc, written) of their work in the field for evaluation.

8274 ■ New Jersey Hospital Association (NJHA)

760 Alexander Rd.
Princeton, NJ 08543-0001
Ph: (609)275-4000
URL: www.njha.com

8275 ■ HRET Health Career Scholarships (Postgraduate, Undergraduate/Scholarship)

Purpose: To encourage and enable New Jersey residents to pursue health careers. **Focus:** Health care services; Health sciences; Nursing. **Qualif.:** Applicants must be a New Jersey resident; accepted into a graduate or undergraduate (junior and seniors only) program in hospital or healthcare administration or a graduate or undergraduate (junior or senior only) program in Nursing or Allied Health Profession; have maintained a GPA of at least 3.0 (on a 4 point system or equivalent); demonstrated financial need with a FAFSA document and financial aid application and/or federal tax return from the previous year. **Criteria:** Selection is based on the application.

Funds Avail.: $2,500. **Duration:** Annual. **To Apply:** Applicants must provide a two-page essay letter detailing academic plans for the future and substantiating that the eligibility requirements have been met (essays will be 50% of the judging criteria); one letter of recommendation from the head of the program in which the student is enrolled or from a current supervisor; official transcript (online transcript copies are not accepted); FAFSA, Financial aid application and/or federal tax return from the previous year; and provide a current address, phone number and e-mail address. **Deadline:** September 7. **Contact:** HRET Scholarship Program, PO Box 1, Princeton, NJ, 08543-0001; Debbie Furchak; Phone: 609-275-4072.

8276 ■ New Jersey Library Association (NJLA)

PO Box 1534
Trenton, NJ 08607
Ph: (609)394-8032

Awards are arranged alphabetically below their administering organizations

Fax: (609)394-8164
E-mail: njla_office@njla.org
URL: www.njla.org
Social Media: www.facebook.com/njlibraryassociation/
 posts/10156452118997766
www.facebook.com/njlibraryassociation
twitter.com/NJLA
www.youtube.com/user/NJLibraryAssociation

8277 ■ NJLA Scholarships (Graduate, Postgraduate/ Scholarship)

Purpose: To support students for their study leading to a graduate or postgraduate degree in librarianship. **Focus:** Library and archival sciences. **Qualif.:** Applicants must live or work in the state of New Jersey and recognize library students who demonstrate academic achievement, innovation, and the potential for leadership. **Criteria:** Selection will be based on merit.

Funds Avail.: No specific amount. **Duration:** Annual. **To Apply:** Applicants must provide and submit completed application form, A 150-250 word essay explaining your choice of librarianship as a profession, resume or CV, sealed official transcripts, and two letters of recommendation. **Deadline:** March 13. **Contact:** Timur A. Davis MS(ILS) MA Professor/Librarian, Dr. Martin Luther King, Jr Library, Essex County College, 303 University Ave., Newark, NJ 07103; Email: ScholarshipNJLA@gmail.com.

8278 ■ New Jersey Performing Arts Center (NJPAC)

1 Center St.
Newark, NJ 07102
Ph: (973)642-8989
Free: 888-466-5722
E-mail: artseducation@njpac.org
URL: www.njpac.org
Social Media: www.facebook.com/NJPAC
twitter.com/njpac

8279 ■ Jeffrey Carollo Music Scholarship (Undergraduate/Scholarship)

Purpose: To provide financial assistance to advanced students who study classical vocal and instrumental music. **Focus:** Music. **Qualif.:** Applicants must be enrolled in the music program at the Newark Community School of the Arts and must be 18 years old and below.

Funds Avail.: No specific amount. **Duration:** Annual. **To Apply:** Applicant must include letter of recommendation. **Contact:** New Jersey Performing Arts Center, c/o The NJPAC Jeffrey Carollo Music Scholarship, Attn: Rebecca Hinkle, Director, Arts Education One Center Street Newark, NJ, 07102.

8280 ■ Star-Ledger Scholarships for the Performing Arts (Undergraduate/Scholarship)

Purpose: To provide higher education opportunities for the young people of Newark; to provide an opportunity to gain practical experience at the New Jersey Performing Arts Center through internships. **Focus:** Performing arts. **Criteria:** Recipients are selected based on merit and demonstrated potential to become leading arts professionals.

To Apply: Applicants must submit a completed application form; high school transcript; three letters of recommenda-

tion: one from an arts teacher, one from a non-arts teacher, and one from a principal or guidance counselor; SAT scores; personal essay describing how this scholarship will help them achieve their goals; resume; list of pieces that will be performed for the audition.

8281 ■ New Jersey Press Foundation (NJPF)

810 Bear Tavern Rd., Ste. 307
West Trenton, NJ 08628-1022
Ph: (609)406-0600
Fax: (609)406-0300
URL: www.njpa.org

8282 ■ Bernard Kilgore Memorial Scholarship (Undergraduate/Scholarship)

Purpose: To promote journalism career and newspaper readership among New Jersey residents. **Focus:** Journalism. **Qualif.:** Applicants must be graduating high sohool seniors; must be planning to study journalism in college and to pursue a journalism career; must have at least a 3.0 GPA on a 4.0 scale and have participated in high school journalism for at least two years.

Funds Avail.: $5,000. **Duration:** Annual. **To Apply:** Applicants must submit an official entry form; a self-analytical evaluation of the journalistic life using a creative form; and one action photo of themselves in a journalistic role; and an official copy of their transcript; should secure three to four letters of recommendation from advisers, teachers familiar with their leadership and journalistic abilities or practitioners with whom they have worked. **Deadline:** February 7. **Remarks:** The scholarship was named in the honor of Bernard Kilgore. **Contact:** New Jersey Press Foundation, P.O. Box 358, Titusville, NJ, 08560.

8283 ■ Richard Drukker Memorial Scholarships (Undergraduate/Scholarship)

Purpose: To promote journalism careers and newspaper readership among New Jersey residents. **Focus:** Journalism. **Qualif.:** Applicants must be journalism minors and staff member of the Montclarion.

Funds Avail.: $2,000. **To Apply:** Applicants must complete the application form and submit an academic transcript for all college work completed; three samples of journalistic writing that has appeared in any newspaper or was done for class assignments; a statement of interest in a newspaper career, written as an autobiographical sketch describing their journalistic skills and achievements (no more than 500 words). **Deadline:** August 3. **Remarks:** The scholarship was named in the honor of Richard Drukker.

8284 ■ New Jersey Psychological Association (NJPA)

354 Eisenhower Pwy., Plz I, Ste. 1150,
Livingston, NJ 07039
Ph: (973)243-9800
Fax: (973)243-9818
E-mail: njpa@psychologynj.org
URL: www.psychologynj.org
Social Media: www.facebook.com/
 newjerseypsychologicalassociation
www.instagram.com/njpsychassn
www.linkedin.com/company/new-jersey-psychological
 -association
twitter.com/NJPsychAssn

Awards are arranged alphabetically below their administering organizations

8285 ■ NJPA Foundation Scholarship for Research on Diversity Issues *(Graduate/Scholarship)*

Purpose: To support graduate students in psychology who promote scientific understanding of the role of diversity in psychology and Foster the development of sensitive models for delivery of psychological services to diverse populations. **Focus:** Psychology.

Funds Avail.: $2,000. **Duration:** Annual. **To Apply:** Applicant must submit an online application form.

8286 ■ New Jersey Society of Certified Public Accountants (NJCPA)

105 Eisenhower Parkway, Ste. 300
Roseland, NJ 07068
Ph: (973)226-4494
E-mail: njcpa@njcpa.org
URL: njcpa.org
Social Media: www.facebook.com/njscpa
www.instagram.com/thenjcpa
www.pinterest.ca/njscpa
twitter.com/njcpa
www.youtube.com/njcpa

8287 ■ NJSCPA College Scholarships *(Graduate, Undergraduate/Scholarship)*

Purpose: To support college students currently in junior year or seniors who will be entering an accounting-related graduate program. **Focus:** Accounting. **Qualif.:** Applicants must be a resident of New Jersey attending a New Jersey college/university; an accounting major or with a concentration in accounting with at least 12 credits in accounting completed; currently at junior-year status or above in an undergraduate program or enrolled in, or entering, an accounting related program. **Criteria:** Selection is based on the application materials submitted.

Funds Avail.: No specific amount. **Duration:** Annual. **To Apply:** Applicants must submit a completed application together with a letter of recommendation from an accounting professor; an official transcript showing a minimum overall GPA of 3.2; and a resume. **Contact:** Theresa Hinton; Email: thinton@njcpa.org; Phone: 973-226-4494 x 212.

8288 ■ NJSCPA High School Seniors *(Undergraduate/Scholarship)*

Purpose: To support New Jersey high school seniors who plan to major in accounting. **Focus:** Accounting. **Qualif.:** Applicants must intend to begin the study of accounting as a major; a U.S. citizen or lawfully admitted for permanent residence; a New Jersey resident attending, or just recently graduated from, a New Jersey high school; a high school senior planning to enter college; and has a GPA of 3.5 or above, or a minimum combined verbal, math and essay SAT score of 1260, or a minimum average ACT score of 26. **Criteria:** Selection is based on academic performance, an essay and a personal interview.

Funds Avail.: $7,000. **Duration:** Annual; four years. **To Apply:** Applicant must submit Application via online with all required fields completed; essay 500-word about the Topic: Why did you choose accounting and what do you think being a CPA will mean to your career; Guidance Department Form including student grade point average, standardized test score, guidance counselor name and signature; Copy of SAT or ACT score results. **Contact:** Pam Isenburg; Email: pisenburg@njcpa.org; Email: scholarship@njcpa.org.

8289 ■ New Jersey State Bar Foundation (NJSBF)

New Jersey Law Ctr., 1 Constitution Sq.
New Brunswick, NJ 08901
Ph: (732)249-5000
Fax: (732)828-0034
Free: 800-373-3529
E-mail: meetingsdepartment@njsba.com
URL: www.njsbf.org
Social Media: www.facebook.com/NJStateBarFdn
www.instagram.com/njstatebarfdn
www.linkedin.com/company/njstatebar
twitter.com/NJStateBarFdn
www.youtube.com/channel/UCKgFx55IKTLm_mUrUH
  -GgTg

8290 ■ Abram D. and Maxine H. Londa Scholarship *(Undergraduate/Scholarship)*

Purpose: To support students who are pursuing the legal education. **Focus:** Law. **Qualif.:** Applicants must be students entering their second or third year at a New Jersey law school. **Criteria:** Preference will be given to students from Union County.

Funds Avail.: No specific amount. **Duration:** Annual. **To Apply:** Scholarship applications are available at the beginning of the second semester at the financial aid offices of the New Jersey law schools. **Remarks:** Established in 1996. **Contact:** NJSBF, Director of Grant Programs and Administration, Cynthia Pellegrino; Phone: 732-937-7507 or E-mail: cpellegrino@njsbf.org.

8291 ■ NJSBF Labor Law Scholarship *(Undergraduate/Scholarship)*

Purpose: To support students who are pursuing the legal education. **Focus:** Law. **Qualif.:** Applicants must be students wishing to enter the field of labor law, and are in the second or third year at a New Jersey law school. **Criteria:** Selection will be based on academic achievement in the area of labor law.

Funds Avail.: No specific amount. **Duration:** Annual. **To Apply:** Scholarship applications are available at the beginning of the second semester at the financial aid offices of the New Jersey law schools. **Deadline:** June 26. **Contact:** NJSBF, Director of Grant Programs and Administration, Cynthia Pellegrino; Phone: 732-937-7507 or E-mail: cpellegrino@njsbf.org.

8292 ■ Sonia Morgan Scholarship *(Undergraduate/Scholarship)*

Purpose: To support female students who are pursuing legal education. **Focus:** Law. **Qualif.:** Applicants must be female students entering their second or third year at a New Jersey law school. **Criteria:** The criteria for the selection of candidates include academic excellence (GPA and class standing), participation in extracurricular activities, financial need and community service.

Funds Avail.: No specific amount. **Duration:** Annual. **To Apply:** Scholarship applications are available at the beginning of the second semester at the financial aid offices of the New Jersey law schools. **Contact:** Florence Nathan, NJSBF Director of Special Programs; Email: fnathan@njsbf.org.

8293 ■ Wallace Vail Scholarship *(Undergraduate/Scholarship)*

Purpose: To support students who are pursuing the legal education. **Focus:** Law. **Qualif.:** Applicants must be

Awards are arranged alphabetically below their administering organizations

students entering their second or third year at a New Jersey law school. **Criteria:** Selection will be based on the academic excellence (grade-point average and class standing), participation in extracurricular activities, financial need and community service.

Funds Avail.: No specific amount. **Duration:** Annual. **Number Awarded:** 9. **Contact:** Mary Jean Barnes at mjbarnes@njsbf.org.

8294 ■ New Mexico Association for Bilingual Education (NMABE)
PO Box 6578
Albuquerque, NM 87197
Ph: (505)803-7120
URL: www.nmabe.net
Social Media: www.facebook.com/987539914723102
twitter.com/NM_ABE

8295 ■ New Mexico Association for Bilingual Education Scholarships (NMABE) *(Undergraduate/Scholarship)*

Purpose: To provide financial support for deserving students intending to pursue studies in the field of bilingual education. **Focus:** Education, Bilingual and cross-cultural. **Qualif.:** Applicants must be juniors or seniors in a New Mexico university bilingual education teacher preparation program; must have a GPA of 3.0 or better for initial consideration and for renewal; must reapply by the appropriate deadline for consideration each semester. **Criteria:** Preference will be given to those students who meet the criteria.

Funds Avail.: $500. **Duration:** Annual. **To Apply:** Applicants must submit the completed application form; two letters of recommendation; a written essay in Spanish or a Native American language outlining their reasons for entering the field of Bilingual Education; and current university transcripts. **Deadline:** May 1; July 1; October 1.

8296 ■ New Orleans Ghost Tours
625 St. Philip St.
New Orleans, LA 70116
Ph: (504)434-7314
URL: nolaghosts.com
Social Media: www.facebook.com/neworleansghosts

8297 ■ New Orleans Ghost Tours Scholarships *(Undergraduate/Scholarship)*

Purpose: To support students in their educational pursuits. **Focus:** General studies/Field of study not specified. **Qualif.:** Applicants must be students enrolled in an accredited college.

Funds Avail.: $250. **Duration:** Annual. **To Apply:** Applicants must fill out the online form and submit the essay via the scholarship link; they must include an essay (1,000 word minimum) explaining their education goals and plans after graduating college; explain why they deserve to win and what the scholarship means to them. **Deadline:** December 15.

8298 ■ New York City Bar Association (NYCB)
42 W 44th St.
New York, NY 10036
Ph: (212)382-6600

Fax: (212)398-6634
E-mail: cdunne@nycbar.org
URL: www.nycbar.org
Social Media: twitter.com/NYCBARCom
twitter.com/NYCBarDiversity

8299 ■ C. Bainbridge Smith Scholarship *(Undergraduate/Scholarship)*

Purpose: To provide scholarships to second and third year inner-city law students who have spent a significant portion of their lives in New York City, demonstrate character, intelligence and promising aptitude for the law, and face a special economic disadvantage (including lack of funds, or physical or cultural handicaps). **Focus:** Law. **Qualif.:** Applicants must be second or third year inner-city law students who have spent a significant portion of their lives in New York City and demonstrate character, intelligence and promising aptitude for the law and face special economic disadvantages. **Criteria:** Selection will be based on the committee's criteria.

Funds Avail.: No specific amount.

8300 ■ City Bar Diversity Fellowship Program *(Undergraduate/Fellowship)*

Purpose: To offer first-year students from underrepresented populations a unique summer employment opportunity in outstanding law firms and corporate law departments. **Focus:** Law. **Qualif.:** Candidates must be first year students from underrepresented populations. **Criteria:** Selection will be based on the committee's criteria.

Funds Avail.: No specific amount. **To Apply:** Applicant must submit undergraduate and law school transcripts, resume, personal statement and legal writing sample. **Remarks:** Established in 1991. **Contact:** Chair of the Committee, Steven Seltzer; Email: sseltzer@metlife.com.

8301 ■ Thurgood Marshall Fellowships Program *(Undergraduate/Fellowship)*

Purpose: To provide internship experience in public service or civil rights to talented minority law students. **Focus:** Law. **Qualif.:** Applicants must be minority law students. **Criteria:** Selection will be based on the committee's criteria.

Funds Avail.: No specific amount. **To Apply:** Applicants may contact the Association for the application process and other information. **Remarks:** Established in 1993.

8302 ■ The New York Community Trust
909 3rd Ave., 22nd Fl.
New York, NY 10022
Ph: (212)686-0010
Fax: (212)532-8528
URL: www.nycommunitytrust.org
Social Media: www.facebook.com/nycommtrust
twitter.com/nycommtrust

8303 ■ Fahs-Beck Fund for Research and Experimentation - Doctoral Dissertation Grants *(Doctorate/Grant)*

Purpose: To help support dissertation expenses of doctoral students in the United States and Canada whose studies have the potential for adding significantly to knowledge about problems in the functioning or well being of children, adults, couples, families, or communities, or about interventions designed to prevent or alleviate such problems. **Fo-**

Awards are arranged alphabetically below their administering organizations

cus: Public health. **Qualif.:** Applicant must be enrolled in an accredited doctoral program in the United States or Canada; must have a sponsoring organization that agrees to accept administrative responsibility for the project and submit required financial forms and reports to the fund. **Criteria:** Selection will be based on the applicants' project proposals; the committee considers four criteria in evaluating proposals; the compatibility of the proposed work with the areas of funding supported by the fund; the significance, impact, and expected benefit of the study; conceptual and technical merit of the proposed study; and the likelihood of successful and timely completion of the proposed work.

Funds Avail.: Up to $5,000. **Duration:** Semiannual. **To Apply:** Applicants must submit the following requirements: research proposals (to be submitted electronically as a PDF format with the applicants' name in the subject line); two copies of the completed application form); ten copies of a project summary statement with a completed project summary cover sheet stapled to the top of each (cover sheet is page 4 of the application form); evidence that the dissertation proposals have received official faculty approval; evidence that the dissertation proposals have received official final approval from the IRB of the sponsoring institution; curriculum vitae; a time schedule showing probable dates for completion of data collection, data analysis, and the dissertation; proposed budget; letter of agreement from the applicants (stating that they will: make all reasonable efforts to complete the dissertation on a timely basis; agree to send the Fahs-Beck Fund a brief progress report and an interim accounting of expenditures from the fund one year after the awarding of the grant; notify the fund of the date of acceptance of the dissertation by the sponsoring institution and submit at that time an abstract of the final dissertation (not the complete dissertation); and, submit a final financial report to the fund on all expenditures from the grant award and return any unused portion of the grant to the fund); letter from sponsoring organization indicating whether or not charges (maximum 10%) will be assessed for administering the grant; letter from sponsoring organization affirming tax-exempt status, relevant accreditation or certification; and a confidential letter from the applicants' primary faculty dissertation sponsors; the letter should include the faculty sponsors judgment of the competence of the applicants to produce a quality product, the likelihood that the students will complete the dissertation in a timely manner, and the potential contribution of the dissertation; the letter must be written on official letterhead and have an original signature. **Deadline:** April 1; November 1. **Contact:** Email dissertations at dissertation@fahsbeckfund.org.

8304 ■ Fahs-Beck Fund for Research and Experimentation - Postdoctoral Grants
(Postdoctorate/Grant)

Purpose: To help support the research of faculty members or post-doctoral researchers affiliated with non-profit human service organizations in the United States and Canada. **Focus:** Public health. **Qualif.:** Applicants must be faculty members of accredited colleges or universities or individuals affiliated with accredited non-profit human service organizations in the United States or Canada.

Funds Avail.: $20,000. **Duration:** Semiannual. **To Apply:** Applicants must submit the following requirements; 10-page project description (to be sent as PDF formats using the name of the primary investigators in the subject line); two copies of the completed application form with original signatures; printed copy of the project description (no longer than 10 pages, typed in 11-point Tahoma typeface, double

spaced including the following; statement of the problem/purpose of the study; brief review of literature; description of intervention and setting, if applicable; description of the research plan, including measures to be used; and the significance, expected benefits); copies of measures to be used; ten copies of a project summary statement with a project summary cover sheet stapled to the top of each (the cover sheet is p. 5 of the application form); evidence of official and final IRB approval; letters of agreement from organizations that will be providing services that are part of the study or access to subjects; curriculum vitae of the principal investigators and other relevant personnel on the project; a chart of the tasks and subtasks necessary for the conduct of the study, indication of the responsible parties, and time line for accomplishment; a proposed budget listing the individual items for which funding is requested, the amount requested for each item, and a budget narrative justifying each item; letter from sponsoring organization indicating whether or not administrative charges (maximum 10%) will be assessed for administering the grant; and, letter from sponsoring organization affirming tax-exempt status, relevant accreditation or certification. **Contact:** Email project proposals at postdoc@fahsbeckfund.org.

8305 ■ NYCT Paid Graduate Student Philanthropy Fellowships - Arts and Historic Preservation
(Graduate/Fellowship)

Purpose: To promote diversity in the arts, as well as to support preservation in low-income and minority communities and the boroughs outside of Manhattan. **Focus:** Arts; Historic preservation. **Qualif.:** Applicants must be students who are entering their last year of a full-time graduate program; and must be able to commit to the entire period of the fellowship; must have authorization to work in the United States. **Criteria:** Selection will be based on the Trust's criteria.

Funds Avail.: $21 per hour. **To Apply:** Applicant should email their resume, a cover letter, and a short writing sample (500-1500 words); in the subject line please put first name, last name, and fellowship for which applicant is submitting the application; may only apply for one position. **Deadline:** February 16. **Contact:** Email: jem@nyct-cfi.org.

8306 ■ NYCT Paid Graduate Student Philanthropy Fellowships - Children, Youth, Families, Education, Human Justice and Workforce *(Graduate/Fellowship)*

Purpose: To support individuals in improving the sectors of children, youth, families, education, human justice and workforce. **Focus:** Education; Family planning; Human rights; Youth. **Qualif.:** Applicants must be students who are entering their last year of a full-time graduate program; and must be able to commit to the entire period of the fellowship; must have authorization to work in the United States. **Criteria:** Selection will be based on the Trust's criteria.

Funds Avail.: $21 per hour. **To Apply:** Applicant should email their resume, a cover letter, and a short writing sample (500-1500 words); in the subject line please put first name, last name, and fellowship for which applicant is submitting the application; may only apply for one position. **Deadline:** March 24. **Contact:** Email Beth Mirarchi at em@nyct-cfi.org.

8307 ■ NYCT Paid Graduate Student Philanthropy Fellowships - Community Development and the Environment *(Graduate/Fellowship)*

Purpose: To promote the community development and protect the environment in the New York community. **Focus:**

Awards are arranged alphabetically below their administering organizations

Environmental conservation; Social work. **Qualif.:** Applicants must be students who are entering their last year of a full-time graduate program; and must be able to commit to the entire period of the fellowship; must have authorization to work in the United States. **Criteria:** Selection will be based on the Trust's criteria.

Funds Avail.: $21 per hour. **To Apply:** Applicant should email their resume, a cover letter, and a short writing sample (500-1500 words); in the subject line please put first name, last name, and fellowship for which applicant is submitting the application; may only apply for one position. **Deadline:** March 24. **Contact:** Email Phoebe Scarborough at ps@nyct-cfi.org.

8308 ■ NYCT Paid Graduate Student Philanthropy Fellowships - Health and People with Special Needs (Graduate/Fellowship)

Purpose: To support individuals in improving services for children and youth with disabilities, the elderly, and for people with AIDS, mental illness and mental retardation, and/or visual disabilities. **Focus:** AIDS; Disabilities; Health care services; Mental retardation. **Qualif.:** Applicants must be students who are entering their last year of a full-time graduate program; and must be able to commit to the entire period of the fellowship; must have authorization to work in the United States. **Criteria:** Selection will be based on the Trust's criteria.

Funds Avail.: $21 per hour. **To Apply:** Applicant should email their resume, a cover letter, and a short writing sample (500-1500 words); in the subject line please put first name, last name, and fellowship for which applicant is submitting the application; may only apply for one position. **Deadline:** March 24. **Contact:** Email Phoebe Scarborough at ps@nyct-cfi.org.

8309 ■ Hazaros Tabakoglu Scholarship Fund (Undergraduate/Scholarship)

Purpose: To provide financial assistance to students of Armenian descent from New York, Connecticut, and New Jersey. **Focus:** General studies/Field of study not specified. **Qualif.:** Applicants must be full-time undergraduates of Armenian descent who are or will be enrolled at colleges in the United States; must be residents of New York, New Jersey or Connecticut. **Criteria:** Selection will be based on the demonstrated financial need, academic ability, and commitment to the Armenian community and culture.

Funds Avail.: $1,000-$6,000. **To Apply:** Application information available at www.nycommunitytrust.org/about/armenian/. **Deadline:** July 2. **Contact:** Shaneshia Rivers; Email: sr@nyct-cfi.org.

8310 ■ New York Financial Writers' Association (NYFWA)
PO Box 338
Ridgewood, NJ 07451-0338
Ph: (201)612-0100
Fax: (201)256-4115
E-mail: contact@nyfwa.org
URL: www.nyfwa.org

8311 ■ New York Financial Writers' Associations Scholarships (Graduate, Undergraduate/Scholarship)

Purpose: To provide financial assistance to those studying business, finance, and journalism. **Focus:** Business; Finance; Journalism. **Qualif.:** Applicants must be under-

graduate or graduate journalism students in the New York area who are seriously interested in pursuing a career in business and financial journalism.

Funds Avail.: No specific amount. **Duration:** Annual. **To Apply:** Applicants must submit the following requirements; school, division, major and expected graduation date; present address and permanent home address (if different), telephone number; any other relevant personal information; essay explaining why the applicants are pursuing a career in business and financial journalism; current resume, including other scholarships received; samples of financial writing (3 to 5 pieces) including links to online work and print clippings in PDF format. **Deadline:** April 15. **Contact:** Email: scholarships@nyfwa.org.

8312 ■ NYFWA Scholarships (Undergraduate, Graduate/Scholarship)

Purpose: To support students who are seriously interested in pursuing a career in business and financial journalism. **Focus:** Business; Finance; Journalism. **Qualif.:** Applicants must be undergraduate or graduate journalism students in the tri-state New York area. **Criteria:** Selection will be based on the committee's criteria.

Funds Avail.: $3,000. **Duration:** Annual. **Number Awarded:** Varies. **To Apply:** Applicants must submit the following requirements: school, division, major and expected graduation date; present address and permanent home address (if different), telephone number; any other relevant personal information; essay explaining why the applicants are pursuing careers in business and financial journalism; current resume, including other scholarships received; samples of financial writing (3 to 5 pieces) including links to online work and print clippings in PDF format. **Deadline:** April 15. **Contact:** Applications should be sent to scholarships@nyfwa.org.

8313 ■ New York Library Association (NYLA)
6021 State Farm Rd.
Guilderland, NY 12084
Ph: (518)432-6952
Fax: (518)427-1697
E-mail: info@nyla.org
URL: www.nyla.org
Social Media: www.facebook.com/pages/New-York-Library
  -Association-NYLA/48043315840
www.facebook.com/NYLA1890
twitter.com/NYLA_1890

8314 ■ NYLA-Dewey Fellowship Award (Graduate/Award, Fellowship)

Purpose: To recognize a librarian with five or more years of experience with accomplishments in the library profession and involvement in activities that advance the library community. **Focus:** Library and archival sciences. **Qualif.:** Applicants must be NYLA members; five or more years of experience as a librarian; record of accomplishment in the library profession; involvement in activities to advance the library community.

Funds Avail.: Up to $1,000. **Duration:** Annual. **Number Awarded:** 3 or 4. **Deadline:** July 15.

8315 ■ NYLA-Dewey Scholarship (Master's, Undergraduate/Award, Scholarship)

Purpose: To provide financial assistance to deserving student to pursue a Masters Degree in Library Science at

Awards are arranged alphabetically below their administering organizations

an ALA-accredited library school in New York State. **Focus:** Library and archival sciences. **Qualif.:** Applicants must be full- or part-time students; must have maintained at least a B average during the semester; must both the students and the library school must be members of the New York Library Association; the successful candidates are expected to work in a library or library system in New York State for at least two years upon graduation. **Criteria:** Selection will be based on the following criteria: evidence of a commitment to a career in librarianship; demonstrated leadership ability, and scholarly excellence.

Funds Avail.: $1,000. **Duration:** Annual. **To Apply:** Applications form can be downloaded online and must be submitted to the Dean of the Library School or Information Sciences at the ALA accredited institution. **Deadline:** September 30.

8316 ■ New York School Nutrition Association (NYSNA)
2900 South Quincy St, Ste 700
Arlington, VA 22206
Ph: (518)446-9061
Fax: (518)446-0113
Free: 800-697-7372
E-mail: servicecenter@schoolnutrition.org
URL: www.nyschoolnutrition.org
Social Media: www.facebook.com/nyschoolnutrition
www.instagram.com/newyorksna
twitter.com/NewYorkSNA

8317 ■ Jeff Siegel Memorial Scholarships
(Undergraduate/Scholarship)

Purpose: To help defray the cost of food service education for students; to provide means of recognition for the school food service department. **Focus:** Food service careers.

Funds Avail.: $1,000. **Duration:** Annual. **To Apply:** Applicants must attach a letter of recommendation from the NYSNA member who submitted their name for the award; must attach a 200 word essay on how/why they chose food service as their future career; must attach a letter of recommendation from a school official, guidance counselor, principal etc.; must attach a copy of letter of acceptance from college; must submit a copy of high school transcript, including first semester of the senior year; must attach any additional comments or information that will be helpful. **Deadline:** May 1. **Remarks:** Established in 2003. **Contact:** NY School Nutrition Association, 125 Wolf Rd., Ste., 312,Albany, NY 12205.

8318 ■ New York State Association of Agricultural Fairs (NYSAAF)
PO Box G
Elma, NY 14059
Ph: (716)655-1958
E-mail: nysaaf@gmail.com
URL: www.nyfairs.org
Social Media: www.no.pinterest.com/pin/
397161260878735571

8319 ■ New York State Association of Agricultural Fairs Scholarship *(Undergraduate/Scholarship)*

Purpose: To provide financial assistance to those high school and college students who have been active in their local fairs and who intend to pursue higher education in an agricultural or fair management related field. **Focus:** Agriculture, Economic aspects. **Qualif.:** Applicants must be in their senior year of high school in New York State or New York residents planning to pursue or already attending college in an agricultural or fair management-related field at an accredited institution of higher education. **Criteria:** Selection will be based on the quality of the essay, citizenship and leadership, fair participation, field of study, presentation of the application and academic achievements.

Funds Avail.: $1,000. **Duration:** Annual. **Number Awarded:** 10. **To Apply:** Applications submitted through the NYSSA should be submitted to: Sarah McAndrew, Secretary NYSSA, 7194 Rosewood Circle, North Syracuse, NY 13212. Applicants may submit only one application. **Deadline:** April 24.

8320 ■ New York State Government Finance Officers' Association (NYSGFOA)
126 State St., 5th Fl.
Albany, NY 12207
Ph: (518)465-1512
Fax: (518)434-4640
E-mail: info@nysgfoa.org
URL: www.nysgfoa.org

8321 ■ Stanley M. Schoenfeld Memorial Scholarship *(Postgraduate/Scholarship)*

Purpose: To provide scholarships to outstanding students who have demonstrated a commitment to public service. **Focus:** Management; Public affairs. **Criteria:** Selection will be based on academic records, demonstrated promise of completing a graduate level program at a high level performance and evidence of intention to enter the field of public administration.

Funds Avail.: $750 up to $3,000. **Duration:** Annual. **To Apply:** Applicants must complete the application form available on the website; must provide a letter of recommendation from either their undergraduate program dean or a professor from the program, a mentor/supervisor they worked for/within the field of public affairs/ management and/or the dean of the graduate program; must provide a statement of proposed plan of graduate study and their career plans; must include an undergraduate grade transcript, GRE scores and resume. **Deadline:** December 20. **Contact:** NYGFOA Stanley M. Schoenfeld Memorial Scholarship Committee, 126 State St., 5th Fl., Albany, New York 12207; Phone: 518-465-1512; Email: scholarship@nysgfoa.org.

8322 ■ New York State Higher Education Services Corporation
99 Washington Ave.
Albany, NY 12255
E-mail: customerservice@firstmarkservices.com
URL: www.hesc.ny.gov
Social Media: www.facebook.com/
NewYorkStudentFinancialAid
twitter.com/NYStudentFinAid

8323 ■ Senator Patricia K. McGee Nursing Faculty Scholarship *(Doctorate, Graduate/Scholarship)*

Purpose: To provide financial assistance to faculty nurses providing clinical nursing education in New York state. **Focus:** Nursing.

Awards are arranged alphabetically below their administering organizations

Funds Avail.: Up to $20,000. **Duration:** Annual; up to three years. **Deadline:** May 31. **Contact:** Email: scholarships@hesc.ny.gov; Phone: 888-697-4372.

8324 ■ New York State Senate

Room 506, LOB
Albany, NY 12247
Ph: (518)455-3511
URL: www.nysenate.gov
Social Media: www.facebook.com/NYsenate
twitter.com/nysenate
www.youtube.com/user/NYSenate

8325 ■ James L. Biggane Fellowship in Finance
(Graduate/Fellowship)

Purpose: To give students the opportunity to experience fields of communications, journalism, and/or public relations. **Focus:** General studies/Field of study not specified. **Qualif.:** Applicant must be a full-time matriculated graduate student in an accredited university during the immediately previous spring and fall semesters. **Criteria:** Selection is based on the application.

Duration: Annual. **Number Awarded:** 1. **To Apply:** Applicants must submit a complete application including course work-in-progress list signed by campus official (if not on transcript); Policy Proposal; Rebuttal of Policy Proposal; Statement of Purpose; resume or CV; all official transcripts (graduate and undergraduate, to be mailed directly to the Office of Student Programs); and three letters of reference from persons familiar with the applicant's character, academic and/or professional abilities (at least two from faculty members). **Deadline:** April 27. **Contact:** Nicholas J. Parrella, Director, Office of Student Programs, Legislative Office Bldg., Ste. 1426, Albany, NY, 12247; For questions: Phone: 518-455-2611; Fax: 518-426-6827; Email: students@nysenate.gov.

8326 ■ New York State Senate - Legislative Fellowship *(Graduate, Postgraduate/Fellowship)*

Purpose: To provide talented and skilled graduate/postgraduate students with intimate knowledge of New York State government, fostering an understanding of our governmental system, and to attract those able students to public service careers from a variety of academic disciplines. **Focus:** General studies/Field of study not specified. **Qualif.:** Applicants must be a full-time matriculated graduate student in an accredited university during the immediately previous spring and fall semesters. **Criteria:** Selection is based on the application.

Funds Avail.: No specific amount. **Duration:** Annual. **Number Awarded:** 13. **To Apply:** Applicants must submit a complete application including course work-in-progress list signed by campus official (if not on transcript); policy proposal; rebuttal of policy proposal; statement of purpose; resume or CV; all official transcripts (graduate and undergraduate, to be mailed directly to the Office of Student Programs); and three letters of reference from persons familiar with the character, academic and/or professional abilities (at least two from faculty members). **Contact:** Nicholas J. Parrella, Director, Office of Student Programs, Legislative Office Bldg., Ste. 1426, Albany, NY, 12247; For questions: Phone: 518-455-2611; Fax: 518-426-6827; Email: students@nysenate.gov.

8327 ■ Richard A. Wiebe Public Service Fellowship
(Graduate/Fellowship)

Purpose: Fellow serves in the Majority Counsel/Program Services Office. **Focus:** Public service. **Qualif.:** Applicant must be a full-time matriculated graduate student in an accredited university during the immediately previous spring and fall semesters. **Criteria:** Selection is based on the application. Typically, students with a legal background are selected.

Duration: Annual. **Number Awarded:** 1. **To Apply:** Applicants must submit a complete application including course work-in-progress list signed by campus official (if not on transcript); policy proposal; rebuttal of policy proposal; statement of purpose; resume or CV; all official transcripts (graduate and undergraduate, to be mailed directly to the Office of Student Programs); and three letters of reference from persons familiar with the character, academic and/or professional abilities (at least two from faculty members). **Contact:** Senate Office of Student Programs; Tel: 518-455-2611; FAX: 518-426-6827; Email: students@nysenate.gov; URL: nysenate.gov/student-programs.

8328 ■ Richard J. Roth Journalism Fellowship
(Graduate/Fellowship)

Purpose: To give students experience in the fields of communications, journalism, and/or public relations. **Focus:** Communications; Journalism; Public relations. **Qualif.:** Applicant must be a full-time matriculated graduate student in an accredited university during the immediately previous spring and fall semesters. **Criteria:** Selection is based on the application.

Duration: Annual. **Number Awarded:** 1. **To Apply:** Applicants must submit a complete application including course work-in-progress list signed by campus official (if not on transcript); policy proposal; rebuttal of policy proposal; statement of purpose; resume or CV; all official transcripts (graduate and undergraduate, to be mailed directly to the Office of Student Programs); and three letters of reference from persons familiar with the character, academic and/or professional abilities (at least two from faculty members). **Contact:** Senate Office of Student Programs; Tel: 518-455-2611; FAX: 518-426-6827; Email: students@nysenate.gov; URL: nysenate.gov/student-programs.

8329 ■ Undergraduate Session Assistants Program
(Undergraduate/Other)

Purpose: To provide talented students with firsthand experience in New York State government at the legislative level. **Focus:** Public service. **Criteria:** Selection is based on the application.

Funds Avail.: $5,850. **To Apply:** Applicants must submit a completed application form along with official transcripts of all collegiate work; special areas of skill or honors; a resume (1 page); preferred area of policy interest; three confidential letters of reference from persons familiar with the academic abilities and professional aptitude; two policy memoranda; a statement of purpose; a certification by the CLO or other authorized campus official for each applicants stating that the applicants has been interviewed and/or the individual academic record reviewed to ensure applicants is eligible and meets all program and institutional requirements; certification of the present coursework-in-progress; and a signed Student Statement.

8330 ■ New York State Society of Certified Public Accountants (NYSSCPA)

14 Wall St., 19th Fl.
New York, NY 10005
Ph: (212)719-8300

Awards are arranged alphabetically below their administering organizations

Fax: (212)719-3364
Free: 800-537-3635
URL: www.nysscpa.org
Social Media: www.facebook.com/NYSSCPA
www.instagram.com/nysscpa
www.linkedin.com/company/nysscpa
twitter.com/nysscpa
www.youtube.com/user/thenysscpa/videos

8331 ■ David J. Moynihan Scholarships
(Undergraduate, Graduate/Scholarship)

Purpose: To provide financial assistance to encourage and aid deserving candidates to enter the accounting profession. **Focus:** Accounting. **Criteria:** Selection will be based on financial need and academic achievement.

Funds Avail.: $2,500 for full-time study and $1,250 for part-time study. **Duration:** Annual. **To Apply:** Complete and file a FAFSA application and be approved for financial aid; letter of recommendation from FAE Campus Liaison or Department Chair or letter of accounting related recommendation (can be an employer). **Contact:** Lauren Biggers, Manager of Outreach; E-mail: lbiggers@nysscpa.org.

8332 ■ New York Theological Seminary (NYTS)
475 Riverside Dr., Ste. 500
New York, NY 10115
Ph: (212)870-1211
URL: www.nyts.edu
Social Media: www.facebook.com/nytsem
www.instagram.com/newyorktheologicalseminary/
www.linkedin.com/company/new-york-theological-seminary
twitter.com/nytsem
www.youtube.com/user/NewYorkTheoSem

8333 ■ Ellen Blodgett Memorial Scholarship
(Master's/Scholarship)

Purpose: To support current students with scholarship assistance. **Focus:** Theology. **Qualif.:** Applicants must be students from underrepresented communities in the Seminary with strong commitment to the ministry in the real world.

Funds Avail.: No specific amount. **Duration:** Annual. **To Apply:** Application form and details are available on the sponsor's website at www.nyts.edu/financial-aid. **Remarks:** The Scholarship was established in memory of Ellen Blodgett by the Rev. Agnes C. Saffoury. Established in 2005.

8334 ■ William L. Bradley Memorial Scholarship
(Master's/Scholarship)

Purpose: To support current students with scholarship assistance. **Focus:** Theology. **Qualif.:** Applicants must be students from Southeast Asia, Indonesia, or in the Philippines with strong commitment to the ministry in the real world.

Funds Avail.: No specific amount. **Duration:** Annual. **To Apply:** Application form and details are available on the sponsor's website at www.nyts.edu/financial-aid. **Remarks:** The Scholarship was established in memory of William L. Bradley by the family and friends including Paul W. Bradley.

8335 ■ Paul W. Bradley Scholarship *(Master's/Scholarship)*

Purpose: To support current students with scholarship assistance. **Focus:** Theology. **Qualif.:** Applicants must be students at NYTS who are lesbian, gay, bisexual, or transgendered.

Funds Avail.: No specific amount. **Duration:** Annual. **To Apply:** Application form and details are available on the sponsor's website at www.nyts.edu/financial-aid. **Remarks:** Established in memory of Rev. Dr. Paul W. Bradley, who served first as Vice President for Development and Institutional Advancement, and then as a Trustee of New York Theological Seminary until his death in 2014.

8336 ■ Esther Cummings Memorial Scholarship
(Master's/Scholarship)

Purpose: To support current students with scholarship assistance. **Focus:** Theology. **Qualif.:** Applicants must be students interested to study theology with strong commitment to the ministry in the real world.

Funds Avail.: No specific amount. **Duration:** Annual. **To Apply:** Application form and details are available on the sponsor's website at www.nyts.edu/financial-aid. **Remarks:** The Scholarship was established by the Seminary to commemorate the life and ministry of Esther Cummings who served as Professor of Missionary Linguistics and Public Speaking at the Biblical Seminary in New York.

8337 ■ Margaret Eddy Scholarship *(Graduate, Master's/Scholarship)*

Purpose: To support current students with scholarship assistance. **Focus:** Theology. **Qualif.:** Applicants must be graduate students in the Master of Divinity Program.

Funds Avail.: No specific amount. **Duration:** Annual. **To Apply:** Application form and details are available on the sponsor's website at www.nyts.edu/financial-aid. **Remarks:** Established in memory of Margaret Eddy, a graduate of the Seminary and a member of the Board of Trustees.

8338 ■ Ethel Mae Gaston Memorial Scholarship
(Master's/Scholarship)

Purpose: To support current students with scholarship assistance. **Focus:** Theology. **Qualif.:** Applicants must be Baptist students with strong commitment to the ministry in the real world.

Funds Avail.: No specific amount. **Duration:** Annual. **To Apply:** Application form and details are available on the sponsor's website at www.nyts.edu/financial-aid. **Remarks:** Established in honor of Ethel Mae Gaston by her family and friends.

8339 ■ Emily V. Gibbes Scholarship *(Master's/Scholarship)*

Purpose: To support current students with scholarship assistance. **Focus:** Theology. **Qualif.:** Applicants must be black female students who demonstrate unusual leadership potential.

Funds Avail.: No specific amount. **Duration:** Annual. **To Apply:** Application form and details are available on the sponsor's website at www.nyts.edu/financial-aid. **Remarks:** The scholarship was established by friends of Emily Gibbes to honor Dr. Gibbes' courageous leadership and role-modeling for Black Christian women.

8340 ■ The William Randolph Hearst Endowed Scholarship *(Master's/Scholarship)*

Purpose: To promote excellence in ministry and to assist those who are financially challenged in obtaining quality accredited theological education. **Focus:** Theology. **Qualif.:**

Awards are arranged alphabetically below their administering organizations

Applicants must be NYST students who have financial need.

Funds Avail.: No specific amount. **Duration:** Annual. **To Apply:** Application form and details are available on the sponsor's website at www.nyts.edu/financial-aid. **Remarks:** Established in memory of William Randolph Hearst.

8341 ■ The Melvyn F. Hester Scholarship (Master's/Scholarship)

Purpose: To support current students with scholarship assistance. **Focus:** Theology. **Qualif.:** Applicants must be students in the Master's Program with strong commitment to the ministry in the real world. **Criteria:** Preference will be given to applicants employed in public service.

Funds Avail.: No specific amount. **Duration:** Annual. **To Apply:** Application form and details are available on the sponsor's website at www.nyts.edu/financial-aid. **Remarks:** Established by Dr. Laura J. Pires-Hester in memory of Dr. Melvyn F. Hester.

8342 ■ The Barbara J. and M. William Howard Jr. Scholarship (Master's/Scholarship)

Purpose: To support current students with scholarship assistance. **Focus:** Theology. **Qualif.:** Applicants must be students who have a strong denominational identity, who are deeply involved in a local congregation and demonstrate a discernible ecumenical commitment. Applicants must also demonstrate a call to a ministry of social justice and social transformation.

Funds Avail.: No specific amount. **Duration:** Annual. **To Apply:** Application form and details are available on the sponsor's website at www.nyts.edu/financial-aid. **Remarks:** The scholarship was established to honor the work and ministry of the Rev. Dr. M. William Howard, Jr., president of NYTS from 1992-2000, and his wife, Barbara.

8343 ■ The Sang Ok Hur Scholarships (Master's/Scholarship)

Purpose: To support current students with scholarship assistance. **Focus:** Theology. **Qualif.:** Applicants must be women enrolled at New York Theological Seminary who are called to the ministry.

Funds Avail.: No specific amount. **Duration:** Annual. **To Apply:** Application form and details are available on the sponsor's website at www.nyts.edu/financial-aid. **Remarks:** Established by the Rev. Dr. Young S. Kim in memory of his mother, Mrs. Sang Ok Hur. Established in 1994.

8344 ■ The Hwain Chang Lee scholarship (Master's/Scholarship)

Purpose: To support current students with scholarship assistance. **Focus:** Theology. **Qualif.:** Applicants must be female international NYTS students.

Funds Avail.: No specific amount. **Duration:** Annual. **Number Awarded:** 1 or more. **To Apply:** Application form and details are available on the sponsor's website at www.nyts.edu/financial-aid. **Remarks:** Established in honor of the life and service of Dr. Hwain Chang Lee.

8345 ■ The William K. Lee Scholarship (Master's/Scholarship)

Purpose: To support current students with scholarship assistance. **Focus:** Theology. **Qualif.:** Applicants must be NYST students. **Criteria:** Preference is given to international students who demonstrate academic excellence and a commitment to ministry.

Funds Avail.: No specific amount. **Duration:** Annual. **Number Awarded:** 1 or more. **To Apply:** Application form and details are available on the sponsor's website at www.nyts.edu/financial-aid. **Remarks:** Established in honor of Dr. William K. Lee, Chair of the Board of Trustees. **Contact:** New York Theological Seminary, 475 Riverside Dr., Ste. 500, New York, NY, 10115; Phone: 212-870-1236; Email: Twhite@nyts.edu.

8346 ■ The Margaret Smith Maase Scholarships (Master's/Scholarship)

Purpose: To support current students with scholarship assistance. **Focus:** Theology. **Qualif.:** Applicants must be students of New York Theological Seminary, preferably affiliated with the Baptist tradition, who either comes from Southeast Asia, or is planning to do missionary work, or is planning to enter the ordained ministry and exhibits financial need.

Funds Avail.: No specific amount. **Duration:** Annual. **To Apply:** Application form and details are available on the sponsor's website at www.nyts.edu/financial-aid. **Remarks:** Established to honor the life and missionary zeal of Margaret Smith Maase. Established in 2001. **Contact:** New York Theological Seminary, 475 Riverside Dr., Ste. 500, New York, NY, 10115; Phone: 212-870-1236; Email: Twhite@nyts.edu.

8347 ■ The Ann M. Mallouk Scholarships (Master's/Scholarship)

Purpose: To support current students with scholarship assistance. **Focus:** Theology. **Qualif.:** Applicants must be students pursuing Master's degrees at the Seminary.

Funds Avail.: No specific amount. **Duration:** Annual. **Number Awarded:** 1 or more. **To Apply:** Application form and details are available on the sponsor's website at www.nyts.edu/financial-aid.

8348 ■ The Rev. Richard S. McCarroll and Mrs. E. Allison McCarroll Scholarship (Master's/Scholarship)

Purpose: To support current students with scholarship assistance. **Focus:** Theology. **Qualif.:** Applicants must be students of Master of Divinity.

Funds Avail.: No specific amount. **Duration:** Annual. **To Apply:** Application form and details are available on the sponsor's website at www.nyts.edu/financial-aid. **Remarks:** Established by the Board of Trustees on the 50th anniversary of Reverend McCarroll's graduation (class of 1929) from The Biblical Seminary in New York.

8349 ■ The Ella and Harold Midtbo Scholarship (Master's/Scholarship)

Purpose: To support current students with scholarship assistance. **Focus:** Theology. **Qualif.:** Applicants must be deserving students who are financially challenged.

Funds Avail.: No specific amount. **Duration:** Annual. **To Apply:** Application form and details are available on the sponsor's website at www.nyts.edu/financial-aid.

8350 ■ The William Howard Morton Scholarship (Master's/Scholarship)

Purpose: To support current students with scholarship assistance. **Focus:** Theology. **Qualif.:** Applicants must be NYST students in the Master of Divinity Program.

Funds Avail.: No specific amount. **Duration:** Annual. **To Apply:** Application form and details are available on the

Awards are arranged alphabetically below their administering organizations

sponsor's website at www.nyts.edu/financial-aid. **Remarks:** Established by the parents of William Howard Morton in memory of their son, whose untimely death cut short a promising career of great potential in Christian ministry. **Contact:** New York Theological Seminary, 475 Riverside Dr., Ste. 500, New York, NY, 10115; Phone: 212-870-1236; Email: Twhite@nyts.edu.

8351 ■ Abraham A. Oyedeji Scholarship *(Master's/Scholarship)*

Purpose: To support current students with scholarship assistance. **Focus:** Theology. **Qualif.:** Applicants must be students of Christ Apostolic Church or from African Instituted churches who intend to serve in ministry within an African Instituted Church anywhere in the world.

Funds Avail.: No specific amount. **Duration:** Annual. **To Apply:** Application form and details are available on the sponsor's website at www.nyts.edu/financial-aid. **Remarks:** The Scholarship was established by members of Christ Apostolic Church to honor founding pastor, Reverend Doctor Abraham A. Oyedeji.

8352 ■ The George D. Younger Scholarship *(Graduate/Scholarship)*

Purpose: To support current students with scholarship assistance. **Focus:** Theology. **Qualif.:** Applicants must be students who demonstrate courage, integrity, and commitment to urban ministry. **Criteria:** Preference will be given to students who are members of the Riverside Church in New York City.

Funds Avail.: No specific amount. **Duration:** Annual. **To Apply:** Application form and details are available on the sponsor's website at www.nyts.edu/financial-aid. **Remarks:** Established in memory of Rev. Dr. George S. Younger, by his family and friends.

8353 ■ The New York Times Co.

620 Eighth Ave.
New York, NY 10018
Ph: (212)556-1234
Free: 800-591-9233
E-mail: help@nytimes.com
URL: investors.nytco.com/investors/default.aspx
Social Media: www.facebook.com/nytimes
www.linkedin.com/company/the-new-york-times
twitter.com/nytimes

8354 ■ The New York Times College Scholarship *(Undergraduate/Scholarship, Internship)*

Purpose: To recognize students who have achieved academic excellence while overcoming hardship or other difficult circumstances. **Focus:** General studies/Field of study not specified. **Qualif.:** Applicants must be high school seniors attending public, parochial or private high schools in New York City; must have demonstrated academic achievement, commitment to learning-especially in the face of financial and other obstacles and community service; Applicants must be citizens or permanent residents of the United States. **Criteria:** Preference will be given to students whose parents have not graduated from accredited American four-year colleges or universities.

Funds Avail.: $15,000. **Duration:** Annual. **Number Awarded:** 10. **Remarks:** Established in 1999.

8355 ■ New York University - Clinical and Translational Science Institute - Clinical Research Center (CRC)

227 E 30th St., 8th Fl.
New York, NY 10016
Ph: (212)263-7900
URL: med.nyu.edu
Social Media: www.linkedin.com/company/nyu-medical -center
twitter.com/nyuschoolofmed

8356 ■ CTSI Collaborative Translational Pilot Project Program *(Professional development/Grant)*

Purpose: To support collaborative scientific studies to enable the development of preliminary data that will serve as the foundation for submission of translational research grant applications. **Focus:** Health care services; Medical research. **Criteria:** Selection will be based on impact of the proposed research on the health of New York City or other populations with particular emphasis on special populations and quality of the science proposed.

Funds Avail.: Up to $50,000. **Duration:** Annual. **To Apply:** Applications can be submitted through online; along with Departmental Approval Letter; Brief Description of the Project, including departments/divisions/schools participating in the collaboration, Performance Sites and Key Personnel; Budget; NIH Biographical Sketch for all key personnel on the project; Other Support; Research Methodology (up to 5 pages: single spaced, no less than 0.5 inch margins, 11 point Arial font, including project title, background and rationale, specific aims, hypothesis, research design, methods) (can be plain paper or PHS 398 Continuation Format Page); References not included in Research Methodology page count (please limit to 2 pages). **Contact:** Keith Brown, Project Coordinator- Early Translational Research; Email: Keith.Brown@nyumc.org; Phone: 212-263-2652.

8357 ■ New York University School of Law - Center for Human Rights and Global Justice (CHRGJ)

139 MacDougal St., 5th Fl.
New York, NY 10012
E-mail: lauren.stackpoole@nyu.edu
URL: chrgj.org
Social Media: www.facebook.com/CHRGJ.NYU
www.linkedin.com/in/chrgj-center-for-human-rights-global -justice-58797195
twitter.com/humanrightsnyu

8358 ■ CHRGJ Emerging Human Rights Scholarship Conference *(Graduate/Scholarship)*

Purpose: To encourage the development of human rights research and scholarship by giving students an opportunity to present papers and works-in-progress in a constructive and collaborative environment. **Focus:** Human rights; Law. **Qualif.:** Applicants must be current NYU School of Law JD, LLM, and JSD students. **Criteria:** Selection shall be based on the submitted papers of the applicants.

Funds Avail.: No specific amount. **Duration:** Annual. **To Apply:** Applicants must submit their papers or works-in-progress in all areas of international law and/or human rights. Although there is no strict page limit for submissions, selected papers should ideally not exceed 30 double-

Awards are arranged alphabetically below their administering organizations

spaced pages. **Remarks:** Established in 2003. **Contact:** Angelina Fisher, Email: fishera@exchange.law.nyu.edu; URL: chrgj.org/for-students/emerging-scholarship-conference/.

8359 ■ CHRGJ International Human Rights Fellowships (Doctorate, Professional development/Fellowship)

Purpose: To provide opportunity to complete a specialized training program in international law, undertake a summer internship at an elite institution, and complete a substantial research paper growing out of that work experience. **Focus:** Human rights; Law. **Qualif.:** Applicants must be full-time first-year JD, second-year JD, LLM and JSD students at NYU School of Law.

Funds Avail.: Amount varies. **Duration:** Annual. **To Apply:** Application details are available online at: chrgj.org/for-students/international-law-and-human-rights-fellowship-program/. **Remarks:** Established in 2002. **Contact:** ILHR Fellowship Program: Tish Armstrong, CHRGJ Fellowship Coordinator, tish.armstrong@nyu.edu.

8360 ■ CHRGJ Students Human Rights Scholars Program (Graduate, Advanced Professional, Professional development/Scholarship)

Purpose: To encourage and facilitate independent student academic research, writing and publications related to the Center's theme. **Focus:** Human rights; Law. **Qualif.:** Applicants must be current NYU law students who are interested in developing writing in the human rights field for publication. The Center particularly encourages former Global Justice Clinic or International Human Rights Clinic students and former Center Summer Fellowship recipients who wish to develop academic writing about their clinic or fellowship human rights work. **Criteria:** Selection shall be based on applicants' proven academic merit, commitment to human rights practice and to furthering human rights scholarship, and demonstrated potential for engaged and rigorous scholarship.

Funds Avail.: No specific amount. **Duration:** Annual. **To Apply:** Applicants must submit a current curriculum vitae and statement of interest specifying their research/scholarship goals, the timeframe of their commitment and applicants' general interest in being a CHRGJ Human Rights Scholar. **Contact:** For Question: Brianne Cuffe; Email: cuffeb@mercury.law.nyu.edu; URL: chrgj.org/for-students/human-rights-scholars-program/.

8361 ■ Arthur Helton Global Rights Fellowships (Graduate/Fellowship)

Purpose: To support students who have demonstrated a commitment to pursuing careers in international human rights law. **Focus:** Human rights; Law. **Qualif.:** Applicants must be graduate students of NYU School of Law who have demonstrated a commitment to pursuing a career in international human rights law and who have designed sound proposals for work at a host organization that they have chosen.

Duration: Annual. **To Apply:** Application details are available online at www.law.nyu.edu/publicinterestlawcenter/forstudents/post-graduate-fellowships/arthur-helton-global-human-rights-fellowship. **Remarks:** Established in 2008.

8362 ■ New York Water Environment Association Inc. (NYWEA)

525 Plum St., Ste. 102
Syracuse, NY 13204

Ph: (315)422-7811
Fax: (315)422-3851
Free: 877-556-9932
E-mail: pcr@nywea.org
URL: nywea.org
Social Media: www.facebook.com/nywea
www.instagram.com/nywea
www.linkedin.com/in/nywea
twitter.com/NYwaterEnviro
www.youtube.com/embed/nla1OUOQ7dQ

8363 ■ Jim Anderson Memorial Scholarship (Undergraduate/Scholarship)

Purpose: To help lead the way toward existing state and national clean water programs. **Focus:** Environmental science. **Qualif.:** Applicants must be students enrolled at a college or university where there is a NYWEA student chapter or high school students who will be enrolled in an environmentally related program in a four year college or university. **Criteria:** Recipients are selected based on academic performance.

Funds Avail.: $1,250. **Duration:** Annual. **Number Awarded:** Varies. **To Apply:** Applicants must complete the application form; must submit a requested essay; official school transcript; and a minimum of two letters of recommendation, from which one must come from a teacher and the other from someone not related to the applicant. **Deadline:** February 28. **Remarks:** Established with a bequest from the late Jim Anderson, was a Senior Vice President and the Director of Technology at Metcalf & Eddy | AECOM.

8364 ■ N.G. Kaul Memorial Scholarship (Doctorate, Graduate/Scholarship)

Purpose: To support students pursuing graduate or doctoral degrees in environmental/civil engineering or environmental science concentrating on water quality who show a commitment to government service. **Focus:** Environmental science. **Qualif.:** Applicants must be students pursuing graduate or doctoral degrees in environmental/civil engineering or environmental science, concentrating on water quality; must show commitment to government service. **Criteria:** Recipients are selected based on demonstrated interest in or commitment to pursue government service, relevance of career objective to the environmental field related to water quality, academic potential, character and other activities.

Funds Avail.: Up to $5,000. **Duration:** Annual. **Number Awarded:** varies. **To Apply:** Applicants must complete the application form; must provide letter verifying enrollment or acceptance in a college environmental program on college stationary; must attach transcripts, and two requested essays. **Deadline:** February 26. **Remarks:** Established with a bequest from the late N.G. Kaul, was a highly respected engineer, an immigrant from India who fulfilled the American dream of opportunity realized.

8365 ■ New York Women in Communications Foundation (NYWICI)

355 Lexington Ave., 15th Fl.
New York, NY 10017
Ph: (212)297-2133
E-mail: info@nywici.org
URL: www.nywici.org
Social Media: www.facebook.com/nywici

Awards are arranged alphabetically below their administering organizations

www.instagram.com/nywici
www.linkedin.com/company/new-york-women-in
 -communications
twitter.com/NYWICI
www.youtube.com/user/nywici

8366 ■ Ann Liguori Foundation Sports Media Scholarship *(Graduate, Undergraduate/Scholarship)*

Purpose: To provide financial assistance for the education of the residents of New York, New Jersey, Connecticut, or Pennsylvania. **Focus:** Advertising; Broadcasting; Communications; Journalism; Marketing and distribution; Media arts; Public relations. **Qualif.:** Applicants must be at least a rising junior. **Criteria:** Recipients are selected based on academic achievement, financial need and involvement in the field of communications.

Duration: Annual. **To Apply:** Applicants must submit completed application form; resume including extracurricular activities, significant achievements, academic awards, community service work; 300-500 word essay; two recommendation letters; official high school or college transcripts; other supporting documents.

8367 ■ Newberry Library
60 W Walton St.
Chicago, IL 60610
Ph: (312)943-9090
URL: www.newberry.org

8368 ■ The Frances C. Allen Fellowship *(Graduate/ Fellowship)*

Purpose: To encourage American Indian women in their studies of any field related to the Newberry Library's collections. **Focus:** General studies/Field of study not specified. **Qualif.:** Applicants must be American Indian women's who are pursuing studies of any field related to the Newberry's collection. **Criteria:** Preference for this award is given to non-tenured women working in any graduate or preprofessional field.

Funds Avail.: $2,500 per month. **Duration:** Monthly. **To Apply:** Applicants must submit the following Cover Sheet; Project Abstract of no more than 300 words; Project Description of no more than 1500 words; Curriculum Vitae; Three letters of reference. **Deadline:** December 15.

8369 ■ Audrey Lumsden-Kouvel Fellowship *(Postdoctorate/Fellowship)*

Purpose: To provide assistance to researchers who wish to use the Newberry Library's collections. **Focus:** Culture. **Qualif.:** Applicants must be post-doctoral scholars who wish to use the Newberry's extensive holdings in late medieval and early modern history and literature. **Criteria:** Preference will be given to projects focusing on the colonial Americas and Romance cultures, especially translations and topics focusing on Portuguese, Spanish, and Latin American Studies.

Funds Avail.: $4,200 per month. **To Apply:** Applicants must submit the following Cover Sheet; Project Abstract of no more than 300 words; Project Description of no more than 1500 words; Curriculum Vitae; Three letters of reference. **Deadline:** November 1. **Contact:** Email: research@ newberry.org.

8370 ■ The Lester J. Cappon Fellowship in Documentary Editing *(Postdoctorate/Fellowship)*

Purpose: To support post doctoral scholars in historical editing projects based on Newberry sources, and to support residential research in the Newberry's collections in preparation of the edition, and helps defray other costs related to its preparation. **Focus:** General studies/Field of study not specified. **Qualif.:** Applicants must be postdoctoral scholars; must be within Chicago metropolitan area. **Criteria:** Selection will be based on the committee's criteria.

Funds Avail.: $2,500. **Duration:** up to 2 months. **To Apply:** Applicants must submit the following Cover Sheet; Project Abstract of no more than 300 words; Project Description of no more than 1500 words; Curriculum Vitae; Three letters of reference.

8371 ■ The École Nationale des Chartes Exchange Fellowship *(Postdoctorate/Fellowship)*

Purpose: To provide assistance to researchers who wish to use the Newberry Library's collections. **Focus:** General studies/Field of study not specified. **Qualif.:** Applicants must be PhD candidates from a U.S. or Canadian university who have achieved ABD status. **Criteria:** Selection will be given to students attending institutions that are members of the Center for Renaissance Studies Consortium.

Funds Avail.: $2,500. **Duration:** Annual; 3 months. **To Apply:** Applicants must submit the following Cover Sheet; Project Abstract of no more than 300 words; Project Description of no more than 1500 words; Curriculum Vitae; Three letters of reference; should provide specific information about their need for the training available at the Ecole des Chartes and how it will contribute to their dissertation or future projects and also required to submit a fourth letter from their university certifying French language fluency. **Deadline:** December 15. **Contact:** École Nationale des Chartes at the following address: Relations internationales et Stages, International relations, École nationale des chartes, 65 Rue de Richelieu, 75002 Paris, France.

8372 ■ Herzog August Bibliothek Wolfenbüttel Fellowships *(Postdoctorate/Fellowship)*

Purpose: To provide assistance to researchers who wish to use the Newberry Library's collections. **Focus:** General studies/Field of study not specified. **Qualif.:** Applicants for long and short-term fellowships at the Newberry may also ask to be considered for this joint fellowship providing an additional two-month fellowship in Wolfenbuttel, Germany. The proposed project should link the collections of both libraries. Applicants should plan to hold both fellowships sequentially to ensure continuity of research. **Criteria:** Selection will be based on the committee's criteria.

Funds Avail.: 1,050 Euros plus up to 600 Euros for travel expenses. **To Apply:** Applicants must submit the following Cover Sheet; Project Abstract of no more than 300 words; Project Description of no more than 1500 words; Curriculum Vitae; Three letters of reference. **Deadline:** December 15. **Contact:** Email: research@newberry.org.

8373 ■ The Arthur and Janet Holzheimer Fellowship in the History of Cartography *(Postdoctorate, Doctorate/Fellowship)*

Purpose: To support work in residence at the Newberry on projects related to the history of cartography which focus on cartographic materials in the Library's collection. **Focus:** Cartography/Surveying. **Qualif.:** Applicants should be PhD candidates or postdoctoral scholars supports work on projects related to the history of cartography. **Criteria:** Selection will be based on the committee's criteria.

Funds Avail.: $2,500. **To Apply:** Applicants must submit the following Cover Sheet; Project Abstract of no more than

Awards are arranged alphabetically below their administering organizations

300 words; Project Description of no more than 1500 words; Curriculum Vitae; Three letters of reference. **Deadline:** December 15.

8374 ■ Institute for the International Education of Students Faculty Fellowships *(Postdoctorate/ Fellowship)*

Purpose: To provide assistance to researchers who wish to use the Newberry Library's collections. **Focus:** General studies/Field of study not specified. **Qualif.:** Applicants must be a faculty members from any IES Center; must be an postdoctoral scholars. **Criteria:** Selection will be based on the committee's criteria.

Funds Avail.: $1,200 each. **Duration:** up to 1 month. **Number Awarded:** 2. **To Apply:** Applicants must submit the following Cover Sheet; Project Abstract of no more than 300 words; Project Description of no more than 1500 words; Curriculum Vitae; Three letters of reference. **Deadline:** December 15.

8375 ■ Lloyd Lewis Fellowships in American History *(Postdoctorate/Fellowship)*

Purpose: To provide assistance to researchers who wish to use the Newberry Library's collections. **Focus:** History, American. **Qualif.:** Applicants must be post-doctoral scholars pursuing projects in any area of American history appropriate to the Newberry's collection.

Funds Avail.: $4,200 per month. **To Apply:** Applicants must submit the following Cover Sheet; Project Abstract of no more than 300 words; Project Description of no more than 1500 words; Curriculum Vitae; Three letters of reference. **Deadline:** November 1. **Contact:** E-mail: research@ newberry.org.

8376 ■ The Lawrence Lipking Fellowship *(Postdoctorate/Fellowship)*

Purpose: To provide assistance to researchers who wish to use the Newberry Library's collections. **Focus:** General studies/Field of study not specified. **Qualif.:** Applicants must be Northwestern PhD students in English. **Criteria:** Selection will be based on the committee's criteria.

Funds Avail.: $2,500. **To Apply:** Applicants must submit the following Cover Sheet; Project Abstract of no more than 300 words; Project Description of no more than 1500 words; Curriculum Vitae; Three letters of reference; one letter of recommendation is required to apply. **Deadline:** December 15. **Contact:** Email: research@newberry.org.

8377 ■ Midwest Modern Language Association Fellowship *(Doctorate, Postdoctorate/Fellowship)*

Purpose: To provide assistance to researchers who wish to use the Newberry Library's collections. **Focus:** General studies/Field of study not specified. **Qualif.:** Applicants must be members of the Midwest Modern Language Association. **Criteria:** Selection will be based on the committee's criteria.

Funds Avail.: $2,500. **To Apply:** Applicants must submit the following Cover Sheet; Project Abstract of no more than 300 words; Project Description of no more than 1500 words; Curriculum Vitae; Three letters of reference.

8378 ■ Newberry Consortium on American Indian Studies Faculty Fellowships *(Professional development/Fellowship)*

Purpose: To support faculty members at institutions participating in the Newberry Consortium in American

Indian Studies. **Focus:** Native American studies. **Qualif.:** Applicants must be working on a project in American Indian studies requiring research in the Newberry's collections. **Criteria:** Preference is given to scholars at an early career stage. There are long- and short-term opportunities available.

Funds Avail.: $5,000. **To Apply:** Applicants must submit the following Cover Sheet; Project Abstract of no more than 300 words; Project Description of no more than 1500 words; Curriculum Vitae; Three letters of reference. **Deadline:** November 1(long-term fellowship), December 15(short-term fellowship). **Contact:** Email: research@newberry.org.

8379 ■ The Newberry Consortium in American Indian Studies Graduate Student Fellowships *(Graduate/Fellowship)*

Purpose: To provide assistance to researchers who wish to use the Newberry Library's collections. **Focus:** General studies/Field of study not specified. **Qualif.:** Applicants must be graduate students from an institution participating in the Newberry Consortium in American Indian Studies; must be within the Chicago metropolitan area. **Criteria:** Selection will be based on the committee's criteria.

Funds Avail.: $2,500. **Duration:** Monthly; up to 2 months. **To Apply:** Applicants must submit the following Cover Sheet; Project Abstract of no more than 300 words; Project Description of no more than 1500 words; Curriculum Vitae; Three letters of reference. **Deadline:** December 15. **Contact:** Email: research@newberry.org.

8380 ■ Newberry Library ACM/GLCA Faculty Fellowships *(Other/Fellowship)*

Purpose: To provide assistance to researchers who wish to use the Newberry Library's collections. **Focus:** General studies/Field of study not specified.

Funds Avail.: $4,200 per month. **Duration:** Annual.

8381 ■ Newberry Library National Endowment for the Humanities Fellowships *(Postdoctorate/ Fellowship)*

Purpose: To support postdoctoral scholars in any field appropriate to Newberry's collection. **Focus:** Humanities. **Qualif.:** Applicants must be post-doctoral scholars; must be U.S. citizens or foreign nationals with three continuous years' residence.

Funds Avail.: $4,200 per month. **Duration:** Annual; from 4 to 12 months. **To Apply:** Applicants must submit the following Cover Sheet; Project Abstract of no more than 300 words; Project Description of no more than 1500 words; Curriculum Vitae; Three letters of reference. **Deadline:** November 1.

8382 ■ The Newberry Library Short-Term Residential Fellowships for Individual Research *(Postdoctorate, Doctorate/Fellowship)*

Purpose: To provide assistance to researchers who wish to use the Newberry Library's collections. **Focus:** General studies/Field of study not specified. **Qualif.:** Applicants must be post-doctoral scholars who demonstrate a specific need for the Newberry's collection and work outside the Chicago area. **Criteria:** Selection will be based on the committee's criteria.

Funds Avail.: $2,500. **Duration:** Monthly. **To Apply:** Applicants must submit the following Cover Sheet; Project Abstract of no more than 300 words; Project Description of

Awards are arranged alphabetically below their administering organizations

no more than 1500 words; Curriculum Vitae; Three letters of reference. **Deadline:** December 15. **Contact:** Email: research@newberry.org.

8383 ■ South Central Modern Language Association Fellowships *(Doctorate, Postdoctorate/Fellowship)*

Purpose: To provide assistance to researchers who wish to use the Newberry Library's collections. **Focus:** General studies/Field of study not specified. **Qualif.:** Applicants must be PhD candidates or post-doctoral scholars who are members of the South Central Modern Language Association.

Funds Avail.: No specific amount. **To Apply:** Applicants must submit the following: cover sheet; project abstract of no more than 300 words; project description of no more than 1500 words; curriculum vitae; and three letters of reference. Applicants should compile their applications electronically and submit them as email attachments not larger than 10 MB. Application forms may be downloaded online. **Deadline:** February 28. **Contact:** 780 Van Vleet Oval, Kaufman Hall 203, Norman, OK, 73019; Phone: 405-325-6011; Email: scmla@ou.edu.

8384 ■ The Susan Kelly Power and Helen Hornbeck Tanner Fellowship *(Doctorate, Postdoctorate/Fellowship)*

Purpose: To provide assistance to researchers who wish to use the Newberry Library's collections. **Focus:** General studies/Field of study not specified. **Qualif.:** Applicants must be scholars of American Indian heritage. This fellowship is open to all fields of study. Applicants within the Chicago metropolitan area are eligible. **Criteria:** Selection will be based on the committee's criteria.

Funds Avail.: $2,500. **Duration:** Monthly. **To Apply:** Applicants must submit the following Cover Sheet; Project Abstract of no more than 300 words; Project Description of no more than 1500 words; Curriculum Vitae; Three letters of reference. **Deadline:** December 15. **Contact:** Email: research@newberry.org.

8385 ■ The Arthur and Lila Weinberg Fellowship for Independent Researchers *(Other, Graduate/Fellowship)*

Purpose: To provide assistance to researchers who wish to use the Newberry Library's collections. **Focus:** General studies/Field of study not specified. **Qualif.:** Applicants must be individuals writers, journalists, filmmakers, visual and performing artists, and other humanists who wish to use the Newberry's collection to further their creative work. **Criteria:** Preference is given to individuals working on projects that focus on social justice or reform. Applicants must be individuals working outside of traditional academic settings, who are not employed as, or seeking employment as, full-time academic faculty.

Funds Avail.: $2,500. **To Apply:** Applicants must submit the following Cover Sheet; Project Abstract of no more than 300 words; Project Description of no more than 1500 words; Curriculum Vitae; Three letters of reference. **Deadline:** December 15. **Contact:** Email: research@newberry.org.

8386 ■ The Charlotte W. Newcombe Foundation
35 Park Pl.
Princeton, NJ 08542-6918
Ph: (609)924-7022
E-mail: info@newcombefoundation.org
URL: www.newcombefoundation.org

8387 ■ Charlotte W. Newcombe Doctoral Dissertation Fellowship *(Graduate/Fellowship)*

Purpose: To support students in the final stages of doctoral study whose work offers significant potential for advancing academic scholarship related to ethics or religion. **Focus:** Ethics and bioethics; Religion. **Criteria:** Selection will be based on the committee's criteria.

Funds Avail.: $25,000. **Duration:** Annual. **Remarks:** Established in 1981. **Contact:** Newcombe Doctoral Dissertation Fellowships: The Woodrow Wilson National Fellowship Foundation, P.O. Box, 5281, Princeton, NJ, 08543-5281 Phone: (609) 452-7007 Email: www.woodrow.org/newcombe.

8388 ■ Newfangled Networks
20801 Miles Pkwy.
Warrensville Heights, OH 44128
Ph: (216)400-8006
URL: www.newfanglednetworks.com

8389 ■ Newfangled Networks $1,000 Scholarship *(Undergraduate, Graduate/Scholarship)*

Purpose: To celebrate and support outstanding students who strive for excellence. **Focus:** General studies/Field of study not specified. **Qualif.:** Applicants must be legal residents of the U.S. or hold valid student visas; be currently enrolled in or accepted to full-time undergraduate or graduate programs; and be at least 18 years old. **Criteria:** Selection is based on the submitted essays.

Funds Avail.: $1,000. **Duration:** Annual. **Number Awarded:** 1. **To Apply:** Applicant must write a 300-word essay on the topic: Live Online Classes vs Offline Classes. Essay must be emailed to as an attached Word document, along with applicant's full name, address, phone number, school name, and date of birth. **Deadline:** June 20. **Contact:** Email: scholarships@newfanglednetworks.com; URL: www.newfanglednetworks.com/blogs/news/newfangled-networks-1000-scholarship.

8390 ■ Newkirk Center for Science and Society
5544 Social and Behavioral Sciences Gateway (SBSG)
University of California, Irvine
Irvine, CA 92697-7090
Ph: (949)824-3119
E-mail: newkirk@uci.edu
URL: www.newkirkcenter.uci.edu
Social Media: www.facebook.com/newkirkcenter
twitter.com/NewkirkCenter
www.youtube.com/watch?v=pp-uHFPcy-k

8391 ■ Newkirk Graduate Student Fellow Awards *(Doctorate, Graduate/Fellowship)*

Purpose: To promote effective uses of research in natural and social sciences fields and to financially assist graduate students. **Focus:** Natural sciences; Social sciences. **Qualif.:** Applicants must be UCI graduate students; projects that engage the community with scientific knowledge and research; projects that analyze the production of scientific knowledge or technological artifacts and systems.

Funds Avail.: $10,000. **Duration:** Annual. **To Apply:** Applicants must submit a curriculum vitae be no more than 1500 words; include name, department, advisor's name and year in graduate school; include a simple budget

Awards are arranged alphabetically below their administering organizations

indicating how the awards will be used; indicate the goals of your research activity and methods that will be used; indicate the research fulfills the mission of the newkirk center; list any other support you have; have your cv attached (this is in addition to the application) and indicate your gpa. **Deadline:** May 15. **Contact:** Email: newkirk@uci.edu.

8392 ■ The Newswomen's Club of New York (NCNY)

15 Gramercy Park S
New York, NY 10003-1705
E-mail: newswomen@newswomensclubnewyork.com
URL: www.newswomensclubnewyork.com
Social Media: www.facebook.com/NYNewswomen
twitter.com/NYNewswomen

8393 ■ Anne O'Hare McCormick Memorial Scholarship *(Graduate/Scholarship)*

Purpose: To provide financial assistance to cover aspiring journalism student's education. **Focus:** Journalism. **Qualif.:** Applicants must be women journalists attending Columbia University's Graduate School of Journalism.

Funds Avail.: No specific amount. **Duration:** Annual. **Number Awarded:** Up to 3. **Remarks:** Established in 1954.

8394 ■ Nigerian Women Association of Georgia (NWAG)

PO Box 244132
Atlanta, GA 30324
Ph: (770)496-4380
E-mail: info@nwag.org
URL: www.nwag.org
Social Media: www.facebook.com/groups/nigerianwomenga
twitter.com/NWAG1

8395 ■ NWAG Georgia Students Scholarship *(Undergraduate/Scholarship)*

Purpose: To assist Nigerian male or female students to study in Georgia high school. **Focus:** General studies/Field of study not specified. **Qualif.:** Applicants must be of Nigerian descent; must be high school seniors and be residents of Georgia. **Criteria:** Selection will be based on submitted materials.

Funds Avail.: $500 each. **Duration:** Annual. **Number Awarded:** 4. **To Apply:** Applicants must submit Proof of State of Residence; two letters of recommendation from any two of the following; church pastor/mosque imam, principal, teacher or counselor; one letter of recommendation from the principal of their school; photocopy of their current high school student identification card; and a current photograph; proof of 10 Hours of community service. **Deadline:** May 15. **Contact:** E-mail: nwagscholarship@yahoo.com.

8396 ■ NWAG Nigeria Scholarships *(Undergraduate/Scholarship)*

Purpose: To help Nigerian female students pursue their education. **Focus:** General studies/Field of study not specified. **Qualif.:** Applicants must be Nigerian female, undergraduate students in a Nigerian university. **Criteria:** Selection will be chosen based on submitted materials.

Funds Avail.: $1,000. **Duration:** Annual. **Number Awarded:** 37. **To Apply:** Applicants must complete the application form; must submit a proof of state of origin, two letters of recommendation from any two of the following: Pastor/Imam, village head, local government chairperson or one of the lecturers; must also submit one letter of recommendation from either the Dean of the Faculty or Head of the Department, photocopy of current university student identification card, a current photo; must provide an explanation on why applicants deserves the award and an essay on the topic given by the scholarship committee. **Deadline:** May 30. **Contact:** E-mail: nwagscholarship@yahoo.com.

8397 ■ Nikko Cosmetic Surgery Center

1001 West Loop S Fwy., Ste. 813
Houston, TX 77027
Ph: (832)906-2904
URL: www.drnikko.com
Social Media: www.facebook.com/drnikko
twitter.com/nikkomd

8398 ■ Nikko Cosmetic Surgery Center Annual Breast Cancer Survivor Scholarships *(All/Scholarship)*

Purpose: To provide scholarships for breast cancer survivors. **Focus:** General studies/Field of study not specified. **Qualif.:** Applicants must be U.S. citizens who have been diagnosed with breast cancer. **Criteria:** Winners will be chosen, at least in part, based upon online activity generated by their application. That activity may, for example, be increased by the submission of a humorous or particularly heartfelt statement or essay. The decision in all cased will be made by Dr. Anthony Nikko at his sole discretion.

Funds Avail.: $1,000. **Duration:** Annual. **Number Awarded:** 2. **To Apply:** Applicants must submit the following materials: a brief statement (100 words or less) about their educational goals; an original essay of 650 to 1,000 words on the subject of how being diagnosed with breast cancer has affected their lives; documentation that they have been diagnosed with or treated for breast cancer. **Deadline:** September 30.

8399 ■ Ninety Nines, Inc. International Organization of Women Pilots

4300 Amelia Earhart Dr., Ste. A
Oklahoma City, OK 73159
Ph: (405)685-7969
Fax: (405)685-7985
Free: 844-994-1929
E-mail: friendsof99s@ninety-nines.org
URL: www.ninety-nines.org
Social Media: www.facebook.com/99sinc
twitter.com/TheNinetyNines

8400 ■ AE Flight Training Scholarship *(Other/Scholarship)*

Purpose: To assist licensed pilot members who wish to complete an additional pilot certificate and pilot training course. **Focus:** Aviation. **Qualif.:** Applicant must be a women pilot with an appropriate medical certificate and a member of The Ninety-Nines Inc.; must have sufficient flight time experience to meet or exceed the flight time require-

Awards are arranged alphabetically below their administering organizations

---

ment for the certificate; must demonstrate financial need.

Funds Avail.: No specific amount. **Duration:** Annual. **Contact:** Email: AEApps@Ninety-Nines.org.

8401 ■ AE Jet Type Rating Scholarships *(Other/Scholarship)*

Purpose: To assist licensed pilot members who wish to complete type rating certification in any jet aircraft. **Focus:** Aviation. **Qualif.:** Applicant must be a woman pilot and a member of The Ninety-Nines Inc.; a current Airline Transport Pilot with first-class medical certificate; must have a minimum of 100 hours multi-engine flight time or combined multi-engine and turbine time. **Criteria:** Awards are given based on credentials and financial need.

Funds Avail.: No specific amount. **Duration:** Annual. **To Apply:** Applicants must complete the application form (please visit website) on an 8 1/2x11 paper (clipped or stapled) and submit it to the Section AE Scholarship Chairman or to Section Governor.

8402 ■ AE Technical Training Scholarship *(Other/Scholarship)*

Purpose: To assist licensed pilot members to complete an aerospace technical training or certification course. **Focus:** Aviation.

Funds Avail.: No specific amount. **Duration:** Annual.

8403 ■ Vicki Cruse Memorial Emergency Maneuver Training Scholarship *(Undergraduate/Scholarship)*

Purpose: To assist licensed pilot members who wish to complete type rating certification in any jet aircraft. **Focus:** Aviation. **Qualif.:** Applicant must be a licensed pilot member of The 99s.

Funds Avail.: No specific amount. **Duration:** Annual. **To Apply:** Applicants must visit the website to download an appropriate application form.

8404 ■ Ning Interactive Inc.

2850 Horizon Ridge Pkwy., Ste. 200
Henderson, NV 89052
URL: www.ning.com
Social Media: www.facebook.com/ningnetworkplatform
www.linkedin.com/company/ning
twitter.com/ning

8405 ■ NING Scholarship *(Undergraduate, Graduate/Scholarship)*

Purpose: To reward students for opinions and creative thinking. **Focus:** General studies/Field of study not specified. **Qualif.:** Applicant must be at least 18 years old and currently enrolled in a bachelors or masters degree program at any accredited university, college, or school with the United States; and be a U.S. citizen or permanent resident. **Criteria:** Entries will be judged on originality and uniqueness, grammatical correctness, and skillful use of language.

Funds Avail.: $500 (1st); $300 (2nd); $200 (3rd). **Number Awarded:** 3. **To Apply:** Applicant must write a convincing essay and submit the essay via email. **Deadline:** September 30. **Contact:** Email: scholarships@ning.com.

8406 ■ Nitro College

1105 N Market St., Ste. 1600
Wilmington, DE 19801
E-mail: support@nitrocollege.com

URL: www.nitrocollege.com
Social Media: www.facebook.com/NitroCollege
www.instagram.com/Nitrocollege/
www.pinterest.com/nitrocollege/
twitter.com/nitrocollege

8407 ■ $2,000 Nitro College Scholarship *(Community College, University, Undergraduate, Graduate/Scholarship)*

Purpose: To provide financial support to students pursuing a college degree. **Focus:** General studies/Field of study not specified. **Qualif.:** Applicants must be legal residents of the 50 United States or the District of Columbia, age 17 or older at the time of entry, and who meet one of the five following eligibility requirements at the time of entry: be a parent who currently has a child enrolled in an accredited college or university located within the United States; be a student who is currently enrolled in an accredited college or university located within the United States; be a parent who currently has a child enrolled as a high school senior located within the United States; be a student who is currently enrolled as a high school senior located with the United States; or be a student or a parent whose child has graduated from an accredited undergraduate school is currently paying back a student or parent loan for his/her/child's educational expenses.

Funds Avail.: $5,000. **Duration:** Semimonthly. **To Apply:** Application must be completed online on the sponsor's website. **Deadline:** August 31; September 30; October 31; November 30; December 31.

8408 ■ Non Commissioned Officers Association of the United States of America (NCOA)

9330 Corporate Drive Suite 708
Selma, TX 78154
Ph: (210)653-6161
E-mail: tkish@ncoausa.org
URL: www.ncoausa.org
Social Media: www.facebook.com/NCOAUSA

8409 ■ Non Commissioned Officers Association Scholarships *(Undergraduate/Scholarship)*

Purpose: To assist the children and spouses of NCOA members who wish to pursue their education. **Focus:** General studies/Field of study not specified. **Qualif.:** Applicants must be children and spouses of current members of the Non Commissioned Officers Association; awards not limited by race, color, creed, national origin, or sex; for undergraduate study only at accredited colleges and universities; children of members must be under age 25 to receive initial grant. **Criteria:** Recipients will be selected by the committee of educators.

Funds Avail.: $900. **To Apply:** Applicants must submit a completed application form; two letters of recommendation; a handwritten autobiography; personal letter of recommendation; transcripts; copy of ACT/SAT scores; and a composition (maximum of 200 words) about Americanism; spouses of NCOA members must submit a completed application form; a copy of high school diploma or GED; transcript of completed college courses (if any); a certificate of completion for other training courses; a brief biography; and a letter of intent on: degree course of study, plans for completion of a degree program, and a paragraph about, "What a College Degree Means to Me." Mail all documents in one complete package. **Deadline:** March 31. **Remarks:**

Awards are arranged alphabetically below their administering organizations

Students must maintain a B average to be considered for renewal. Established in 1970.

8410 ■ Nonstop Signs and Graphics

2010 Hancock St.
San Diego, CA 92110
Free: 800-971-3021
URL: www.nonstopsigns.com
Social Media: facebook.com/nonstopsigns
linkedin.com/company/nonstop-signs
twitter.com/nonstopsigns

8411 ■ Graphic Design Scholarships *(Undergraduate, Graduate/Scholarship)*

Purpose: To help a graphic design student gain an education. **Focus:** Graphic art and design. **Qualif.:** Applicant must be attending college or planning to attend college in the field of graphic design.

Funds Avail.: $2,500. **Duration:** Annual. **Number Awarded:** 1. **To Apply:** Applicant must submit the following information: first and last name, link to graphic design portfolio, email address, their story, the reason why they think they should win, and their dream career. Application available online at www.nonstopsigns.com/graphic-design-scholarship/. **Deadline:** July 31. **Contact:** Email: vlad.kushneryk@nonstopsigns.com.

8412 ■ Noorali Bharwani Professional Corp.

439 6 Ave. SW
Medicine Hat, AB, Canada T1A 5A9
Ph: (403)487-5151
URL: nbharwani.com

8413 ■ Dr. Noorali and Sabiya Bharwani Endowment *(Undergraduate/Scholarship)*

Purpose: To provide financial assistance to qualified individuals who want to pursue their studies. **Focus:** Nursing. **Qualif.:** Applicants must be first year nursing students with a minimum GPA of B, equivalent of 3.0. **Criteria:** Preference will be given to students with financial need.

Funds Avail.: No specific amount. **Duration:** Annual. **Number Awarded:** 1. **To Apply:** Applicants for further information about the scholarship and application form, applicants are advice to contact Noorali Bharwani Professional Corporation.

8414 ■ Hussein Jina Bharwani Memorial Endowment *(Undergraduate/Scholarship)*

Purpose: To provide financial assistance to qualified individuals who want to pursue their studies. **Focus:** Nursing. **Criteria:** Recipients will be selected based on the committee's review of the application materials.

Funds Avail.: No specific amount. **Duration:** Annual. **Number Awarded:** 1. **To Apply:** Applicants should contact the Noorali Bharwani Professional Corporation or visit the website for application details.

8415 ■ Noplag

31-00 47th Ave.
Long Island City, NY 11101
Ph: (646)712-9895
E-mail: support@noplag.com

URL: noplag.com
Social Media: www.facebook.com/noplag
linkedin.com/company/noplag
twitter.com/NoPlag

8416 ■ Noplag Scholarship Essay Contest *(High School, Undergraduate, Graduate/Scholarship)*

Purpose: To support students in their education. **Focus:** General studies/Field of study not specified. **Qualif.:** Applicants must be high school/college/university students at least 16 years old. **Criteria:** Quality of the submitted essay.

Funds Avail.: $2,500 for first place; $700 for second place; $300 for third place. **Number Awarded:** 3. **To Apply:** Submit an essay of at least 700 words on a multitude of suggested topics, such as student life, educational technology, plagiarism intelligence. See full list of topics and specifications regarding essay style/composition at noplag.com/students-scholarship. **Deadline:** August 31.

8417 ■ North American Bancard Holdings, LLC (NABH)

250 Stephenson Hwy.
Troy, MI 48083
E-mail: custservice@nabancard.com
URL: www.nabancard.com
Social Media: www.facebook.com/nabholdings

8418 ■ NAB Dollars for Scholars $1,000 College Scholarship *(Undergraduate, Graduate/Scholarship)*

Purpose: To provide financial support to a business student who demonstrates thoughtful ideas about the future of payments. **Focus:** Business. **Qualif.:** Must be currently enrolled in high school with the intent of attending a university in the following semester, or must be currently enrolled in college; minimum GPA of 2.8; 18 years or older. **Criteria:** Creativity and reasoning of essay response.

Funds Avail.: $1,000. **To Apply:** Submit essay (500-750 words) expressing your thoughts on how the payments landscape will change in the next five years and what you think the future of payments is. **Deadline:** March 31. **Contact:** Cherilyn Zorrilla; Email: czorrilla@nabancard.com.

8419 ■ North American Conference on British Studies (NACBS)

c/o Elizabeth Prevost, Executive Secretary
Grinnell College Department of History
1213 6th Ave.
Grinnell, IA 50112
URL: www.nacbs.org

8420 ■ NACBS Dissertation Fellowship *(Graduate, Doctorate/Fellowship)*

Purpose: To support dissertation research in the British Isles on any topic of British history or British studies. **Focus:** History. **Qualif.:** Applicants must be a citizen or permanent resident of the United States or Canada; enrolled in a PhD program in a U.S. or Canadian institution; has completed all degree requirements for dissertation; must be nominated by a dissertation advisor; must need to travel to the British Isles for the purpose of dissertation research and must conduct full-time research in the British Isles for a period of at least three months. **Criteria:** Selection is based on merit and importance of research.

Awards are arranged alphabetically below their administering organizations

Funds Avail.: $10,000; $5,000 for runner-up. **Duration:** Annual. **Number Awarded:** 1. **To Apply:** Nomination must be supported by a letter of recommendation; application consists of the two letters of nomination and recommendation, (one-page) curriculum vitae, a (1000-word) research proposal which should explain the importance of the topic to the field of British history. **Deadline:** June 1.

8421 ■ NACBS-Dissertation Year Fellowship
(Postdoctorate/Fellowship)

Purpose: To support dissertation research In the British Isles on any topic of British (including Irish, Scottish, and Imperial) history. **Focus:** History. **Qualif.:** Applicants must enroll in a Ph.D. program in a U.S. or Canadian institution. **Criteria:** Applicants are judged upon the committee's criteria.

Funds Avail.: $10,000 stipend; $5,000 (two runners-up). **Duration:** Annual. **To Apply:** Applicants must include the two letters of nomination and recommendation; a one-page curriculum vitae; and a 1000-word research proposal written; must send an electronic copy (via e-mail) of the application package (as a single document-either WORD or PDF) to each member of the dissertation awards. **Deadline:** June 1. **Remarks:** Established in 1997.

8422 ■ NACBS-Huntington Library Fellowship
(Doctorate, Postdoctorate/Fellowship)

Purpose: To aid in dissertation research in British studies using the collections of the library. **Focus:** History. **Qualif.:** Applicants must be U.S. or Canadian citizens or permanent residents; must be enrolled in a PhD program in a U.S. or Canadian institution; the time of fellowship tenure must be spent in residence at the Huntington Library. **Criteria:** Selection is based on merit and importance of research.

Funds Avail.: $3,000. **Duration:** Annually. **To Apply:** Applications should consist of a curriculum vitae; two supporting letters (one from applicant's dissertation advisor); and a description of the research project. A copy of the application package must be sent to each member of the Huntington Library Fellowship Committee. Letters should be placed in sealed envelopes with signature across the flap. **Deadline:** November 15.

8423 ■ North American Van Lines Inc.
5001 US Hwy 30 W
Fort Wayne, IN 46818
Ph: (800)348-3746
Fax: (260)429-1802
URL: www.navl.com
Social Media: facebook.com/northAmericanVL
linkedin.com/company/northamerican-van-lines
twitter.com/northAmericanVL

8424 ■ North American Van Lines Military Scholarship Competition *(Undergraduate/Scholarship)*

Purpose: To support the education of those in the military services, as well as their relatives. **Focus:** Business; Logistics; Management. **Qualif.:** Applicants must be either U.S. citizens or permanent residents who are enrolled, or planning to enroll, as full time students at an accredited college/university within the United States for completion of an undergraduate degree in Logistics or equivalent field; or honorably discharged veterans or current members of the active military (including National Guard and Reserves); or spouses of current military service members or honorably

discharged veterans; or children (under the age of 21 or full-time students under age 23) of current military service members or honorably discharged veterans. **Criteria:** Selection will be based on the committee's criteria.

Funds Avail.: $1,000 each. **Number Awarded:** 2. **To Apply:** Applicants must submit a brief essay of between 400 and 800 words, detailing why a career in logistics/supply chain management is their college major of choice. Personalized tones, referencing sincere firsthand experiences and sentiments, are best and no need to be too formal. Additional requirements include current transcript and verification of enrollment. **Deadline:** September 1. **Contact:** Call Ryan Cox via phone at 630-570-3612.

8425 ■ North Carolina Association of Certified Public Accountants (NCACPA)
3100 Gateway Centre Blvd.
Morrisville, NC 27560
E-mail: memberservicecenter@ncacpa.org
URL: www.ncacpa.org
Social Media: www.facebook.com/NCACPA
www.instagram.com/ncacpa
twitter.com/NCACPA
www.youtube.com/user/NCACPAtv

8426 ■ NCACPA Outstanding Minority Accounting Student Scholarships *(Undergraduate/Scholarship)*

Purpose: To further the development of accounting education and the accounting profession in North Carolina. **Focus:** Accounting.

Funds Avail.: $1,000-$2,000. **Duration:** Annual. **To Apply:** Applicants must submit a completed application form together with the essay (maximum of 500 words) and transcript of all course work completed (official, sealed and may be sent directly from the Registrar's office to the NC CPA Foundation).

8427 ■ North Carolina CPA Foundation Scholarships *(Undergraduate/Scholarship)*

Purpose: To further the development of accounting education and the accounting profession in North Carolina. **Focus:** Accounting. **Qualif.:** Applicant must be a citizen of North Carolina. **Criteria:** Selection will be based on the committee's criteria.

Duration: Annual. **Number Awarded:** Varies. **Contact:** NC CPA Foundation Inc, PO Box 80188, Raleigh, NC, 27623.

8428 ■ North Carolina Association of Health Care Recruitment (NCAHCR)
c/o Ms. Terry Bynum, Treasurer
494 May Farm Rd.
Pittsboro, NC 27312
Ph: (984)214-2137
URL: www.ncahcr.org
Social Media: twitter.com/ncahcr

8429 ■ North Carolina Association of Health Care Recruiters Scholarship *(Undergraduate/Scholarship)*

Purpose: To assist, encourage and enable deserving students currently enrolled in an accredited program for health professions. **Focus:** Health care services. **Qualif.:** Applicants must be full-time students in North Carolina who have been accepted into an accredited ADN, BSN or allied

Awards are arranged alphabetically below their administering organizations

health program; preference will be given to students pursuing their degree in a North Carolina program. **Criteria:** Selection will be based on the committee's criteria.

Funds Avail.: $1,500. **Duration:** Annual. **To Apply:** Applicants must complete the Scholarship Application Program; all parts of the completed application must be submitted electronically; Proof of acceptance into the program in the form of a formal letter of acceptance; letter of verification from the Program Chairman; least two (2) appropriate recommendations; college instructors for students enrolled in a degree program; reference from friends or family are not sufficient; copy of the applicant's most recent official high school/college transcript. **Deadline:** October 13.

8430 ■ North Carolina Council of Epsilon Sigma Alpha
5512 Tangelo Dr.
Wilmington, NC 28412
E-mail: esanorthcarolina@gmail.com
URL: northcarolinaesa.wixsite.com/ncesa

8431 ■ North Carolina Council of Epsilon Sigma Alpha Scholarships *(Graduate/Scholarship)*

Purpose: To support individuals training for work with exceptional children. **Focus:** Teaching. **Criteria:** Selection is based on financial need, desire and academics.

Funds Avail.: Up to $2,500. **Duration:** Annual. **Number Awarded:** Varies. **To Apply:** Applicants must submit a completed application form together with a letter of recommendation, brief essay and financial aid statement filled out by the college Financial Aid Director. **Remarks:** Established in 1952. **Contact:** Email:esanorthcarolina@gmail.com.

8432 ■ North Carolina Economic Development Association (NCEDA)
PO Box 30934
Raleigh, NC 27622
Free: 888-246-2332
URL: www.nceda.org
Social Media: www.facebook.com/groups/
820416788301405

8433 ■ Dan Stewart Scholarship *(Other/Scholarship)*

Purpose: To support the advancement of outstanding practitioners by paying tuition to the one-week basic economic development course at UNC-Chapel Hill. **Focus:** Economics. **Qualif.:** Applicants must be residing and working in North Carolina; member of NCEDA for the duration of the program; and willing to complete all coursework. **Criteria:** Recipients are selected based primarily on financial need, followed by demonstrated professional development and presentation of the application itself.

Funds Avail.: $575. **Duration:** Annual. **To Apply:** Application package must include documents demonstrating need for financial assistance as well as documents demonstrating chosen career path in the profession (past, present and future) and how the program fits into those plans; letters of recommendation and supporting documentation are suggested. **Deadline:** February 23.

8434 ■ Governor James E. Holshouser Professional Development Scholarship *(Other/Scholarship)*

Purpose: To provide general support toward the cost of Economic Development Institute. **Focus:** Economics. **Crite-**

ria: Recipients are selected based on financial need.

Funds Avail.: $1,000 per year. **Duration:** Annual; three years. **To Apply:** Application package must include documents demonstrating need for financial assistance as well as documents demonstrating chosen career path in the profession (past, present and future) and how the program fits into those plans; letters of recommendation and supporting documentation are suggested. **Deadline:** May 15. **Contact:** Email: liz@nceda.org; randall_johnson@ncbiotech.org.

8435 ■ Jack Ervin Economic Development Institute Scholarship *(Other/Scholarship)*

Purpose: To provide tuition to the Economic Development Institute (EDI), the premier continuing education program for economic development professionals. **Focus:** Economics. **Criteria:** Recipients are selected based on financial need and professional development.

Funds Avail.: $650. **Duration:** Annual; three years. **To Apply:** Application package must include documents demonstrating need for financial assistance as well as documents demonstrating chosen career path in the profession (past, present and future) and how the program fits into those plans; letters of recommendation and supporting documentation are suggested. **Deadline:** May 15. **Contact:** Email: liz@nceda.org; randall_johnson@ncbiotech.org.

8436 ■ North Carolina Federation of Republican Women (NCFRW)
c/o Celeste Stanley, Coordinator
2941 St. Claire Rd.
Winston Salem, NC 27106
Ph: (336)659-9254
E-mail: ncfrepublicanwomen@gmail.com
URL: www.ncfederationofrepublicanwomen.org

8437 ■ Dottie Martin Teacher Scholarship *(Graduate, Undergraduate/Scholarship)*

Purpose: To assist aspiring teachers who are interested in child guidance and counseling and who want to make a difference in the lives of North Carolina's children. **Focus:** Counseling/Guidance; Education. **Qualif.:** Applicants must be enrolled and studying in the field of education. **Criteria:** Selection is based on the applicant's submitted application.

Funds Avail.: $500. **Duration:** Annual. **To Apply:** Applicants must submit a completed application form along with three letters of recommendation (including telephone number of authors); most recent copy of college or university transcript; and a typed essay. **Deadline:** June 1. **Remarks:** Established in 1991. **Contact:** Joyce Glass, 4413 Driftwood Dr., Clemmons, NC, 27012; Phone: 336-766-0067.

8438 ■ North Carolina Heroes Fund
PO Box 652
Pineville, NC 28134
Free: 888-777-0955
E-mail: info@ncheroes.org
URL: www.ncheroes.org
Social Media: www.facebook.com/ncheroesfund
www.linkedin.com/groups/1800432/profile
twitter.com/ncheroesfund

8439 ■ North Carolina Heroes Financial Hardship Grant *(Other/Grant)*

Purpose: To provide financial support to military men and women who were returning from active duty and facing

Awards are arranged alphabetically below their administering organizations

very difficult transitions as well as financial hardships. **Focus:** General studies/Field of study not specified. **Qualif.:** Applicant must be a military veteran with a financial hardship who is a native of North Carolina, or currently a permanent resident of North Carolina, or is associated with a North Carolina Guard or Reservist unit, or is Active Duty and stationed in North Carolina.

Funds Avail.: No specific amount. **To Apply:** Applicant must provide all requested information with their application, including forms, copies of bills, and photos; Incomplete information may lead to denial of application. Applicant must also provide email and phone numbers and be available to answer questions.

8440 ■ North Carolina Nursery and Landscape Association (NCNLA)

968 Trinity Rd.
Raleigh, NC 27607
Ph: (919)816-9119
Fax: (919)816-9118
E-mail: info@ncnla.com
URL: www.ncnla.com
Social Media: www.facebook.com/
  NCNurseryandLandscapeAssociation
www.instagram.com/ncnla
www.linkedin.com/company/north-carolina-nursery-&
  -landscape-association
twitter.com/ncnlacom

8441 ■ North Carolina Nursery and Landscape Association Horticulture Scholarships *(Undergraduate/Scholarship)*

Purpose: To identify and reward horticulture students who exemplify scholastic aptitude, positive attitude and industry potential. **Focus:** Horticulture. **Qualif.:** Applicants must be full-time students who are enrolled in a two-to-four year ornamental horticulture or landscape program in North Carolina. **Criteria:** Recipients are selected based on academic performance, attitude and leadership potential.

Funds Avail.: $1,000. **To Apply:** Applicants must complete the application form; must submit a resume, transcripts and a wallet size black and white photograph. **Deadline:** August 26.

8442 ■ North Carolina Restaurant and Lodging Association (NCRLA)

222 N Person St., Ste. 210
Raleigh, NC 27601
Ph: (919)844-0098
E-mail: info@ncrla.org
URL: www.ncrla.org
Social Media: www.facebook.com/NCRLA
www.instagram.com/ncrla
www.linkedin.com/company/n-c--restaurant-and-lodging
  -association-ncrla-
www.pinterest.com/ncrla
twitter.com/NCRLA

8443 ■ William F. Carl Scholarships *(Undergraduate/Scholarship)*

Purpose: To support the education of children of hourly employees in the restaurant industry. **Focus:** General

studies/Field of study not specified. **Qualif.:** Applicants must be a children of hourly employees in the restaurant industry. **Criteria:** Selection is based on the applicant's academic success, community involvement and recommendations. Preference will be given to students majoring in a hospitality related field.

Funds Avail.: $3,500. **Duration:** Annual. **To Apply:** Applicant must submit a completed application form together with the letters of recommendation and transcripts. **Remarks:** The Scholarship was established to honor William F. Carl. **Contact:** Mandy Hines; E-mail: mhines@ncrla.org; Phone: 919-277-8587.

8444 ■ Vickie Clark-Flaherty Scholarships *(Undergraduate/Scholarship)*

Purpose: To support female students who wish to continue their education in the restaurant industry. **Focus:** Culinary arts; Hotel, institutional, and restaurant management. **Qualif.:** Applicant must be a female high school senior, high school graduate or current undergraduate college student enrolled in a full-time undergraduate course of study at an accredited two- or four-year college, university or vocational-technical school in the U.S. **Criteria:** Selection will be based on the committee's criteria.

Funds Avail.: $2,000. **Duration:** Annual. **To Apply:** Applicants must submit a completed application form along with letters of recommendation. **Deadline:** June 24. **Remarks:** The scholarship was established in memory of Vickie Clark-Flaherty. **Contact:** Mandy Hines; E-mail: mhines@ncrla.org; Phone: 919-277-8587.

8445 ■ Davidson and Jones Hotel Corporation Scholarship *(Undergraduate/Scholarship)*

Purpose: To support a college junior student enrolled in a four-year culinary or hospitality program in North Carolina. **Focus:** Culinary arts; Hotel, institutional, and restaurant management. **Qualif.:** Applicant must be a permanent North Carolina resident and a college junior enrolled in a four-year culinary or hospital program in North Carolina. **Criteria:** Selection is based on the submitted application materials.

Funds Avail.: $1,000. **Duration:** Annual. **To Apply:** Applicants must submit a completed application form together with a current complete official transcript of grades. All materials must be sent to NC Hospitality Education Foundation Scholarships. **Contact:** Phone: 800-582-8750.

8446 ■ North Carolina Hospitality Education Foundation Scholarship *(Undergraduate/Scholarship)*

Purpose: To support students pursuing a career in culinary arts, hospitality management or tourism. **Focus:** Culinary arts; Hotel, institutional, and restaurant management; Travel and tourism. **Qualif.:** Applicant must be a student enrolled in a full-time undergraduate course of study at an accredited four-year college, university or culinary program in NC and a permanent NC resident. **Criteria:** Selection is based on the submitted application materials.

Funds Avail.: Minimum of $750. **Duration:** Annual. **To Apply:** Applicants must submit a completed application form together with current complete official transcript(s) of grades. All materials must be mailed to NC Hospitality Education Foundation Scholarships. **Contact:** Mandy Hines; E-mail: mhines@ncrla.org; Phone: 919-277-8587.

8447 ■ NC Hospitality Education Foundation Scholarships - Graduate *(Graduate/Scholarship)*

Purpose: To support graduate students pursuing a graduate course in a hospitality related field, or MBA, in NC.

Awards are arranged alphabetically below their administering organizations

Focus: Culinary arts; Hotel, institutional, and restaurant management. **Qualif.:** Applicant must be a graduate of a four-year program with a hospitality or culinary degree; planning to enroll (or is already enrolled) in a full-time graduate course of study in a hospitality related field, or MBA, in NC and a permanent NC resident. **Criteria:** Selection is based on the submitted application materials.

Funds Avail.: No specific amount. **Duration:** Annual. **Number Awarded:** Varies. **To Apply:** Applicants must submit a completed application form together with current complete official transcript(s) of grades. All materials must be mailed to NC Hospitality Education Foundation Scholarships.

8448 ■ NC Hospitality Education Foundation Scholarships - High School (Undergraduate/Scholarship)

Purpose: To support students pursuing a career in culinary arts, hospitality management or tourism. **Focus:** Culinary arts; Hotel, institutional, and restaurant management; Travel and tourism.

Funds Avail.: $750-$1,500. **Duration:** Annual. **To Apply:** Applicants must submit a completed application form together with current complete official transcript(s) of grades. All materials must be mailed to NC Hospitality Education Foundation Scholarships. **Deadline:** March 15.

8449 ■ NC Hospitality Education Foundation Scholarships - Two Year Community or Junior College (Undergraduate/Scholarship)

Purpose: To support students pursuing a career in culinary arts, hospitality management or tourism. **Focus:** Culinary arts; Hotel, institutional, and restaurant management; Travel and tourism. **Qualif.:** Applicant must be a student enrolled in a full-time undergraduate course of study at an accredited two-year college or culinary program in NC; pursuing a degree in culinary arts, hospitality management or tourism; and a permanent NC resident. **Criteria:** Selection is based on the submitted application materials.

Funds Avail.: No specific amount. **Duration:** Annual. **To Apply:** Applicants must submit a completed application form together with current complete official transcript(s) of grades. All materials must be mailed to NC Hospitality Education Foundation Scholarships.

8450 ■ NCRLA Golden Corral Scholarship (Undergraduate/Scholarship)

Purpose: To support a college junior student enrolled in a four-year culinary or hospitality program in North Carolina. **Focus:** Culinary arts; Hotel, institutional, and restaurant management. **Qualif.:** Applicant must be a permanent North Carolina resident and a college junior enrolled in a four-year culinary or hospitality program in North Carolina. **Criteria:** Selection is based on the submitted application materials.

Funds Avail.: $4,000. **Duration:** Annual. **Number Awarded:** 1. **To Apply:** Applicants must submit a completed application form together with a current complete official transcript of grades. All materials must be sent to NC Hospitality Education Foundation Scholarships. **Contact:** Mandy Hines; E-mail: mhines@ncrla.org; Phone: 919-277-8587.

8451 ■ North Carolina Section of the American Water Works Association (NC AWWA-WEA)
2841 Plaza Place, Ste.130
Raleigh, NC 27612

Ph: (919)784-9030
Fax: (919)784-9032
URL: www.ncsafewater.org
Social Media: www.facebook.com/pages/NC-AWWA-WEA/130678316967490
www.linkedin.com/company/nc-awwa-wea
twitter.com/ncawwawea

8452 ■ Carol Bond Fund Community College Students Scholarship (Undergraduate/Scholarship)

Purpose: To encourage interest in environmental education. **Focus:** Environmental science. **Qualif.:** Applicants must be pursuing a degree in environmental sciences or environmental education at a community college in North Carolina during the 2020 - 2021 academic year. must have a minimum GPA of 2.75. must have a minimum GPA of 2.75. **Criteria:** Recipients are selected based on potential to provide leadership in the environmental sciences and environmental engineering fields and potential to positively impact the fields.

Funds Avail.: $2,000. **To Apply:** Applicants must submit a completed application form; recommendations from at least two college instructors in envelopes signed by the instructors; essay discussing reasons for studying in a curriculum with a focus on water environment and what contributions the applicant hopes to make that will improve the water environment. (maximum 800 words); official college transcript with community college seal; academic advisor certification. **Deadline:** March 22.

8453 ■ Carol Bond Scholarship (Undergraduate/Scholarship)

Purpose: To encourage interest in environmental education. **Focus:** Environmental science. **Qualif.:** Applicants may be pursuing a degree in a curriculum that emphasizes; Student must be a United States citizen; Student must maintain a GPA of 3.0. **Criteria:** Recipients are selected based on academic records and potential to provide leadership in the environmental sciences and environmental engineering fields.

Funds Avail.: $2,500. **To Apply:** Applicants must submit a completed application form; recommendations from at least two college instructors in envelopes signed by the instructors; essay discussing reasons for studying in a curriculum with a focus on water environment and what contributions the applicant hopes to make that will improve the water environment. (maximum 800 words); official college transcript with community college seal; academic advisor certification.

8454 ■ North Carolina Simmental Association
c/o Jennie Rucker, Secretary
1341 Hwy. 21
Hamptonville, NC 27020
Ph: (336)468-1679
E-mail: ncsa@yadtel.net
URL: simmental.org
Social Media: www.facebook.com/NC-Simmental-Association-268944489793077

8455 ■ Jim Graham Scholarship (Undergraduate/Scholarship)

Purpose: To provide educational support to students planning to pursue a career in an agricultural-related field of

Awards are arranged alphabetically below their administering organizations

study. **Focus:** Agricultural sciences. **Qualif.:** Applicants must be high school or college students planning to pursue or pursuing a career in an agricultural-related field of study; must maintain a grade point average of 2.0 must be maintained to qualify if presently enrolled in college. **Criteria:** Applicants are selected based on the need for financial assistance, satisfactory scholastic record, leadership potential and character.

Funds Avail.: $500. **To Apply:** Applicants must complete the application form; attach a photo; submit a transcript of high school grades or college grades with SAT scores; two character reference letter. **Deadline:** July 15. **Contact:** Shirley Maxwell at max1994@bellsouth.net.

8456 ■ North Carolina Space Grant Consortium (NCSGC)

CB 7515
Raleigh, NC 27695-7515
Ph: (919)515-4240
E-mail: ncspacegrant@ncsu.edu
URL: www.ncspacegrant.org
Social Media: www.facebook.com/NCSpaceGrant
instagram.com/ncspacegrant/
twitter.com/ncspacegrant

8457 ■ NCSGC Undergraduate Research Scholarships (Undergraduate/Scholarship)

Purpose: To support students who are pursuing careers in science, technology, engineering and mathematics (STEM) fields that support NASA's mission. **Focus:** Aerospace sciences. **Qualif.:** Applicants must be students pursuing bachelor's degree in science, engineering, technology or mathematics (STEM) discipline of interest to NASA or aerospace industry, they must be enrolled as full-time students at a NC Space Grant member university during the academic year and in good academic standing with a GPA of 3.0 (out of 4.0). Applicants must be conducting specific faculty-mentored research project that has NASA or aerospace relevance. Students enrolled in an accredited Dual Engineering Degree program are also eligible to apply. **Criteria:** Selection will be based on the committee's criteria.

Funds Avail.: $6,000. **Duration:** Annual. **To Apply:** Applicants must complete an online application and must submit complete following requirements description of proposed research project; faculty recommendation provided by the applicants mentor and university transcripts. **Contact:** Jobi Cook, Associate Director; NC Space Grant, 850 Main Campus Dr., Toxicology Building, Ste. 105, NC State University, Campus Box 7515, Raleigh, NC, 27695-7515; Phone: 919-515-5933; E-mail: jobi_cook@ncsu.edu.

8458 ■ NCSGC Undergraduate Scholarships (Undergraduate/Scholarship)

Purpose: To support students who are pursuing careers in science, technology, engineering and mathematics (STEM) fields that support NASA's mission. **Focus:** Aerospace sciences. **Qualif.:** Applicants must be permanent United States citizens, pursuing a bachelor's degree in science, technology, engineering or mathematics (STEM) discipline of interest to NASA or aerospace industry. Applicants must be enrolled as full-time students and classified as sophomore at a NC Space Grant member university during the academic year in good academic standing with a GPA of 3.0 (out of 4.0). Students transferring from Community Col-

leges are encouraged to apply. **Criteria:** Selection will be based on the committee's criteria.

Funds Avail.: $1,000. **Duration:** Annual. **To Apply:** Applicants must complete an online application and must submit the following requirements: statement of the applicants' academic and career goals; letter of recommendations and; university transcripts.

8459 ■ North Dakota Farmers Union (NDFU)

1415 12th Ave. SE
Jamestown, ND 58401
Ph: (701)252-2341
Fax: (701)252-6584
Free: 800-366-8331
E-mail: ndfu@ndfu.org
URL: ndfu.org
Social Media: www.facebook.com/NorthDakotaFarmersUnion
www.instagram.com/ndfarmersunion
twitter.com/ndfarmersunion

8460 ■ Bergman Scholarship (Undergraduate/Scholarship)

Purpose: To provide scholarship to Farmers Union Torchbearers. **Focus:** General studies/Field of study not specified. **Qualif.:** Applicants must be receiving Torchbearer award at the upcoming Farmers Union State Convention and have at least 2.50 grade point average. **Criteria:** Selection will be based on the committee's criteria.

Funds Avail.: No specific amount. **Duration:** Annual. **To Apply:** Application and personal recommendations must be returned by application deadline indicated on the application. **Contact:** Bergman Scholarship, North Dakota Farmers Union, PO Box 2136, Jamestown, ND, 58402-2136; For questions: Phone: 800-366-8331;.

8461 ■ Hubert K. and JoAnn Seymour Scholarship (Undergraduate/Scholarship)

Purpose: To provide financial assistance for students who deserve to pursue college but are financially constrained. **Focus:** General studies/Field of study not specified. **Qualif.:** Applicants must be Farmers' Union members, graduating high school seniors enrolled in an accredited two- or four-year college or university. **Criteria:** Applicants are evaluated based on academic record; social and community activities; written essay; and final phone interview.

Funds Avail.: $1,000 to $2,000. **Duration:** Annual. **Number Awarded:** 1 or 2. **To Apply:** Applicants must submit a completed application form; copy of high school transcript; two letters of recommendation - one from a Farmers Union leader and one from a school counselor or teacher; an essay, identifying and discussing the significance of rural values in America and on their life. **Deadline:** April 1. **Contact:** Return application materials to: NFU Attn: Melissa Miller, 20 F St. NW, Ste. 300, Washington, DC, 20001; For questions: Melissa Miller, Education Director, Phone: 202-554-1600; Email: Melissamiller@nfudc.org.

8462 ■ NDFU Scholarship (Undergraduate/Scholarship)

Purpose: To support first-year or undergraduate students enrolled in a secondary educational facility. **Focus:** Agribusiness; Agricultural sciences; Agriculture, Economic aspects. **Criteria:** Selection will be based on the committee criteria.

Awards are arranged alphabetically below their administering organizations

Funds Avail.: $500. **Duration:** Annual. **Number Awarded:** 1. **To Apply:** Applicants must submit a completed application; financial information; letters of recommendation; and grade transcript. **Deadline:** January 31. **Contact:** NDFU Scholarship North Dakota Farmers Union PO Box 2136 Jamestown ND 58402-2136.

8463 ■ North Dakota Farmers Union Co-op House Scholarship *(Undergraduate/Scholarship)*

Purpose: To support students who are financially in need for their education. **Focus:** General studies/Field of study not specified. **Criteria:** Applicants are evaluated based on academic performance and financial need.

Funds Avail.: No specific amount. **Duration:** Annual. **To Apply:** Applicants must submit a completed application form along with transcripts and ACT scores. **Deadline:** March 15. **Contact:** Scholarship should be returned to: Co-op House Scholarship, North Dakota Farmers Union, PO Box 2136, Jamestown, ND, 58402-2136; Phone: 800-366-6338; For questions; Phone: 800-366-8331; Brenda, Email: bthoms@ndfu.org; Pam, Email: pmusland@ndfu.org.

8464 ■ Stanley Moore FUI Foundation Regional Scholarships *(Four Year College, High School, Two Year College/Scholarship)*

Purpose: To provide financial assistance for deserving students to further their college education. **Focus:** General studies/Field of study not specified. **Criteria:** Applicants are evaluated based on academic record; social and community activities; essay or oral speech (video); and, final interview.

Funds Avail.: $1,500 each. **Duration:** Annual. **Number Awarded:** Varies. **To Apply:** Applicants must submit a completed application form; copy of high school/college transcripts; letters of recommendation from a Farmer Union leader and from a teacher or professor; a three-page written essay. **Deadline:** May 30. **Contact:** David G. Velde, FUI Foundation, 220 Ponderosa Road PO Box 319 Redwood Falls, MN 56283.

8465 ■ Stanley Moore National Scholarships *(Undergraduate/Scholarship)*

Purpose: To provide financial assistance for students who deserve to pursue college but financially constrained. **Focus:** General studies/Field of study not specified. **Qualif.:** Applicants must be Farmers Union members, high school seniors, college students or nontraditional students seeking funding to attend a two- or four-year accredited college, university or technical school for any area of study. **Criteria:** Recipients are selected based on academic achievement; social and community involvement; an essay; and phone interview.

Funds Avail.: $1,000 each. **Duration:** Annual. **Number Awarded:** Varies. **To Apply:** Applicants must submit completed application; essay; grade transcripts and letters of recommendation. **Deadline:** April 1. **Contact:** Return application materials to: NFU Attn: Melissa Miller, 20 F St. NW, Ste. 300, Washington, DC, 20001; For questions: Melissa Miller, Education Director, Phone: 202-554-1600; Email: Melissamiller@nfudc.org.

8466 ■ North Dakota Space Grant Consortium (NDSGC)
Clifford Hall, Rm. 512
4149 University Ave., Stop 9008
Grand Forks, ND 58202-9008

E-mail: casler@space.edu
URL: ndspacegrant.und.edu
Social Media: www.facebook.com/UofNorthDakota
www.instagram.com/nd_space_grant/
twitter.com/UofNorthDakota

8467 ■ NDSGC American Indian Scholarships *(Undergraduate/Scholarship)*

Purpose: To encourage and support Native American students who are interested to pursue STEM degrees and continue their education beyond their current enrollment in community college. **Focus:** Aeronautics. **Qualif.:** Applicants must be students committed to attend UND or NDSU after the applicants' graduation and pursue a STEM degree at UND/NDSU. **Criteria:** Selection will be based on the committees' criteria.

Funds Avail.: $2,500. **To Apply:** Applicants must contact the Financial Aid office for their respective Institution, and fill out the application form together with applicants' one letter or recommendation from a faculty member. **Deadline:** November 14. **Contact:** Marissa Saad, Phone: 701-777-4161; Email: msaad@space.edu.

8468 ■ NDSGC Graduate Fellowships *(Graduate, Master's, Doctorate/Scholarship, Fellowship)*

Purpose: To provide financial assistance for outstanding students of North Dakota University to complete research fellowships at both the undergraduate and graduate levels. **Focus:** Aeronautics. **Qualif.:** Applicants must be citizens of the United States who are, or will be, enrolled as on-campus students as one of the DSGC affiliate colleges and applicants' degree programs should be in the areas of science, technology, engineering, or mathematics (STEM). **Criteria:** Selection will be based on the following criteria: academic excellence - a minimum grade of point of 3.00 is required and; relevance of the students' discipline and interests to STEM fields. Preference will be given to those students not receiving graduate research assistantship (GRA) or graduate teaching assistantship (GTA) funding. Partial fellowships may be rewarded to those students receiving a 1/4th time GRA or GTA appointment.

Funds Avail.: $4,500 (each semester of Fall and Spring); $2,850 each (Summer). **To Apply:** Applicants will be required to submit a 1-2 page summary of their research to the NDSGC at the end of the semester during which they conducted their research. **Deadline:** August 6; December 2; April 15. **Contact:** Caitlin Nolby; Phone: 701-777-4856; Email:cnolby@space.edu.

8469 ■ NDSGC Summer Faculty Fellowship *(Professional development/Scholarship, Fellowship)*

Purpose: To assist faculty in creating or revising a college-level course that is in a science, technology, education, or mathematics (STEM) field and is NASA-relevant and to increase the exposure of college students to NASA and NASA research. **Focus:** Aeronautics. **Qualif.:** Applicants must be faculty member in college level course related to science, technology, engineering or mathematics (STEM) fields or NASA-relevant. **Criteria:** Selection will be based on the committees' criteria. Preference will be given to North Dakota faculty in four year and two year colleges, and faculty who have not received a faculty fellowship the previous summer.

Funds Avail.: $4,500. **To Apply:** Applicants may apply through online and contact the Association for the application process and other information. **Deadline:** April 15.

Awards are arranged alphabetically below their administering organizations

Contact: Caitlin Nolby; Phone: 701-777-4856; Email:cnolby@space.edu.

8470 ■ NDSGC Undergraduate Fellowships
(Undergraduate/Scholarship, Fellowship)

Purpose: To provide financial assistance for outstanding students of North Dakota University to complete research fellowships at both the undergraduate and graduate levels. **Focus:** Aeronautics. **Qualif.:** Applicants must be citizens of the United States who are, or will be, enrolled as on-campus students as one of the DSGC affiliate colleges and applicants' degree programs should be in the areas of science, technology, engineering, or mathematics (STEM). **Criteria:** Selection will be based on the following criteria: academic excellence - a minimum grade of point of 3.00 is required and; relevance of the students' discipline and interests to STEM fields.

Funds Avail.: $2,250; $3,600. **To Apply:** Applicants will be required to submit a 1-2 page summary of their research to the NDSGC at the end of the semester during which they conducted their research. **Deadline:** August 6; December 2; April 15. **Contact:** Caitlin Nolby; Phone: 701-777-4856; Email:cnolby@space.edu.

8471 ■ NDSGC Undergraduate Scholarship
(Undergraduate/Scholarship)

Purpose: To provide financial assistance for outstanding students at North Dakota's public two-and-four year colleges and universities. **Focus:** Aeronautics. **Qualif.:** Applicants must be students pursuing STEM degrees that support NASA research and technology needs. **Criteria:** Selection will be based on the committees' criteria.

Funds Avail.: No specific amount. **To Apply:** Applicants must contact the Financial Aid office for their respective Institution, and fill out the application form together with applicants' one letter or recommendation from a faculty member. **Deadline:** November 14. **Contact:** Marissa Saad, Phone: 701-777-4161; Email: msaad@space.edu.

8472 ■ Pearl I. Young Scholarship *(Undergraduate/Scholarship)*

Purpose: To recognize outstanding female student major in Science, Technology, Engineering or Mathematics field at University of North Dakota and ideally be involved in a research project of NASA relevance. **Focus:** Aeronautics. **Qualif.:** Applicants must be female American citizens, minimum of 3.5 GPA and on-campus students majoring in a STEM (Science, Technology, Engineering or Mathematics) fields at the University of North Dakota. **Criteria:** Selection will be based on the committees' criteria.

Funds Avail.: No specific amount. **Duration:** Annual. **To Apply:** Applicants may contact the Association for the application process and other information. **Deadline:** March 1. **Contact:** Marissa Saad, Phone: 701-777-4161; Email: msaad@space.edu.

8473 ■ North Dakota Veterinary Medical Association (NDVMA)

PO Box 1231
Bismarck, ND 58502-1231
Ph: (701)221-7740
Fax: (701)751-4451
E-mail: execdir@ndvma.com
URL: www.ndvma.com

8474 ■ Dr. Roger E. Meisner Veterinary Medicine Educational Scholarship Fund *(Undergraduate, Graduate/Scholarship)*

Purpose: To promote veterinary medicine and quality animal care through communication, fellowship and professional growth. **Focus:** Veterinary science and medicine. **Qualif.:** Applicants must be students who have graduated from North Dakota High School and have been accepted in a college of veterinary medicine in North America. **Criteria:** Recipients are selected based on need and motivation.

Funds Avail.: No specific amount. **Duration:** Annual. **To Apply:** Applicants must submit a completed application form and a statement of less than one page of their reasons for choosing veterinary medicine as a career, plans and extracurricular activities. **Deadline:** June 15. **Contact:** North Dakota Community Foundation, 711 Riverwood Dr., Ste 2, PO Box 387, Bismarck, ND, 58502-0387.

8475 ■ North Dakota Veterinary Medical Association Scholarships *(Undergraduate/Scholarship)*

Purpose: To promote veterinary medicine and quality animal care through communication, fellowship and professional growth. **Focus:** Veterinary science and medicine. **Criteria:** Recipients are selected based on financial need and an expressed interest in returning to North Dakota to practice veterinary medicine.

Funds Avail.: No specific amount. **To Apply:** Applicants must submit a completed application form; an autobiography; college transcripts; verification of graduation from North Dakota High School or proof of two years residency; verification of acceptance to veterinary school; and must send references and residency verification for those applicants who have not applied before for the NDVMA scholarship. **Deadline:** May 1. **Remarks:** Established in 1997. **Contact:** NDVMA: PO Box 123, Bismarck, ND 58502-1231; Email: execdir@ndvma.com.

8476 ■ Dr. William "Tim" Whalen Memorial Scholarships *(Undergraduate/Scholarship)*

Purpose: To promote veterinary medicine and quality animal care through communication, fellowship and professional growth. **Focus:** Veterinary science and medicine.

Funds Avail.: $5,000. **To Apply:** Applicants must submit completed application form; a typed and short autobiography including educational objectives, veterinary-related work experiences, career plans and other activities, awards, honors and special interests; college transcript; three references; verification of one-year residency; and verification of acceptance to veterinary school. **Contact:** Dr. Mike Harvey; Phone: 701-293-8888.

8477 ■ North Texas Relocation Professionals (NTRP)

2909 Winterberry Dr.
Carrollton, TX 75007
E-mail: admin@northtexasrelocationprofessionals.org
URL: www.northtexasrelocationprofessionals.org
Social Media: facebook.com/
  NorthTexasRelocationProfessionals
linkedin.com/company/ntrp
twitter.com/northtxrelo

8478 ■ North Texas Relocation Professionals Scholarship *(Undergraduate/Scholarship)*

Purpose: To support students enrolled in a Dallas/Fort Worth area accredited high school in pursuing post-

Awards are arranged alphabetically below their administering organizations

secondary education. **Focus:** General studies/Field of study not specified. **Qualif.:** Applicants must currently be seniors who are in good standing in a Dallas/Fort Worth area accredited high school; must have relocated between grades 9 and 12; must have relocated more than 50 miles and changed schools due to their family's relocation; currently have a cumulative grade point average of 3.0 on a scale of 4.0 (or equivalent achievement on a different scale). **Criteria:** Selection will be based on the submitted application.

Funds Avail.: $1,000-$3,000. **Duration:** Annual. **Number Awarded:** 2. **To Apply:** Application form and details are available at: northtexasrelocationprofessionals.org/Scholarships. **Deadline:** January 31. **Contact:** Patience Hawley; Email: phawey@ighr.com; or Amber Gibson; Email: agibson@alexanders.net.

8479 ■ Northampton County Medical Society Alliance (NCMSA)

PO Box 21012
Lehigh Valley, PA 18002
E-mail: medsocietyalliance@gmail.com
URL: www.ncmsa.org

8480 ■ Northampton County Medical Society Alliance Scholarships *(Undergraduate/Scholarship)*

Purpose: To provide financial assistance to eligible medical, nursing and physician assistant students. **Focus:** Medical assisting; Nursing; Physics. **Qualif.:** Applications must be United State citizens whose permanent residence is within Northampton County, Pennsylvania, or have a Bethlehem mailing address; must be accepted or currently enrolled in a fully accredited institute of medicine. **Criteria:** Selection is based on academic, and financial and community service criteria.

Funds Avail.: $1,000. **To Apply:** Applicants must submit the following a completed application form; two letters of reference; personal statement about why you have chosen your career; official school transcript; signed certification or authorization form; entering students: a copy of your letter of acceptance. **Deadline:** March 15. **Contact:** Northampton County Medical Society Alliance, PO Box 21012, Lehigh Valley, PA, 18002-1012; Email: ncmsascholarship@gmail.com.

8481 ■ Northeast Conference on the Teaching of Foreign Languages (NECTFL)

2400 Main St.
Buffalo, NY 14214
E-mail: info@nectfl.org
URL: www.nectfl.org
Social Media: www.facebook.com/nectfl

8482 ■ Mead Leadership Fellowships *(Professional development/Fellowship)*

Purpose: To support an individual in the development of a project that contributes to the foreign language teaching profession and advances quality language instruction. **Focus:** Education, Bilingual and cross-cultural; Foreign languages. **Qualif.:** Applicants must be foreign language teachers who demonstrate leadership potential at their schools, colleges or universities and/or professional organizations at the local, state, or regional or national level; must teach in one of the thirteen NECTFL states or

the District of Columbia (CT, DC, DE, MA, MD, ME, NH, NJ, NY, PA, RI, VA, VT, WV). **Criteria:** Selection is based on work experience and merits.

Funds Avail.: No amount specified. **Number Awarded:** 3. **To Apply:** Applicants must submit a completed application form; a resume or curriculum vitae (maximum of two pages); a letter of nomination (maximum of two pages) from the nominating body declaring the leadership potential of the candidate; and a written commitment containing a draft of specific plan of action; a letter of support from the state organization; a signed commitment form. **Deadline:** November 1. **Contact:** E-mail: info@nectfl.org.

8483 ■ Northeast Modern Language Association (NEMLA)

University at Buffalo
306 Clemens Hall
Buffalo, NY 14260-4610
Ph: (716)645-6342
Fax: (716)645-5980
E-mail: support@nemla.org
URL: www.buffalo.edu
Social Media: www.facebook.com/Northeast-Modern -Language-Association-NeMLA-776430012416295
www.instagram.com/northeastmla
twitter.com/northeastMLA

8484 ■ NEMLA Summer Fellowships *(Graduate/Fellowship)*

Purpose: To defray the cost of traveling incurred by researchers who are pursuing their work-in-progress over the summer. **Focus:** General studies/Field of study not specified. **Qualif.:** Applicants must be untenured junior faculties, graduate students and independent scholars; must be NEMLA members. **Criteria:** Recipients will be selected based on submitted research.

Funds Avail.: Up to $1,200. **Duration:** Annual. **Number Awarded:** Varies. **To Apply:** Applicants must A two-page (single-spaced) application that describes the summer project and includes a timeline; two letters from colleagues in the field supporting the proposed project. **Deadline:** December 31. **Contact:** Email: fellowship@nemla.org.

8485 ■ NeMLA-University at Buffalo Special Collections Fellowship *(Undergraduate, Graduate/Fellowship)*

Purpose: To support the University at Buffalo Poetry Collection, or the University at Buffalo Rare and Special Books Collection. **Focus:** History, American. **Criteria:** Selected on the basis of the applicant's scholarly qualifications, the scholarly significance or importance of the project, and the appropriateness of the proposed study to the UB Library's collections.

Funds Avail.: $1,400 for one month. **Duration:** Annual. **To Apply:** Applicant must submit the following via email in one PDF: cover letter, two- to three-page, single-spaced research proposal that identifies collections and materials to be used and includes length and approximate timing of proposed visit; current two- to three-page CV that indicates in detail previous and upcoming research support (grants, fellowships, leaves, etc.); budget for use of Fellowship funds; letter of support from department chair (this can be sent separately). **Deadline:** April 14. **Remarks:** Supported jointly by The University at Buffalo Library and the Northeast

Awards are arranged alphabetically below their administering organizations

Modern Language Association. Established in 1937. **Contact:** Email: ublibraryfellow@nemla.org; URL: http://www.buffalo.edu/nemla/awards/fellowships/ub-library.html.

8486 ■ Northern Illinois University - Center for Southeast Asian Studies
1425 W. Lincoln Hwy
DeKalb, IL
Ph: (815)753-1771
Fax: (815)753-1776
E-mail: cseas@niu.edu
URL: www.cseas.niu.edu/cseas/index.shtml

8487 ■ NIU-CSEAS Foreign Language and Area Studies (FLAS) Graduate Fellowship (Undergraduate, Graduate/Fellowship)

Purpose: To assist students with the study of Southeast Asian languages at any educational institution. **Focus:** Linguistics; South Asian studies. **Qualif.:** Applicants must have enrolled as full-time students or accepted at NIU and must be a citizen, national or permanent resident of the U.S.

Funds Avail.: $15,000 ($1,500.00/month for 10 months). **Duration:** Annual; Ten-months. **To Apply:** Applicant must submit the application and these additional materials: transcripts showing degree(s) granted and/or in process (PDF for NIU; PDF and hard copy for non-NIU); curriculum vitae (PDF); statement of purpose explaining applicant's need for one of the offered Southeast Asian languages as part of your academic program, previous language learning experiences both formal and informal, and commitment and plans more broadly for the study of Southeast Asia; other materials where applicable (e.g., graduate test scores, copy of green card for Permanent Residents); must also solicit two letters of recommendation from those in a position to evaluate your academic credentials. **Deadline:** January 15. **Contact:** E-mail: cseas@niu.edu.

8488 ■ Northern Indiana Community Foundation, Inc. (NICF)
227 E 9th St.
Rochester, IN 46975
Ph: (574)223-2227
Fax: (574)224-3709
Free: 877-432-6423
URL: www.nicf.org
Social Media: www.facebook.com/Northern-Indiana
  -Community-Foundation/207271679290731
www.instagram.com/NICF_fulton_miami_starke/
twitter.com/intent/tweet
www.youtube.com/channel/UCe7mb5fe5o1znaAK8WIp_Xg

8489 ■ Frederick Rakestraw Law Scholarship
(Graduate/Scholarship)

Purpose: To help students of Fulton County pursue law degrees. **Focus:** Law. **Qualif.:** Applicants must be residents of Fulton County Indiana for at least three years during their high school career; must be graduate students pursuing a Degree in Law enrolled in any school in United States, current recipients must maintain a 2.25 Cumulative GPA or higher during graduate school program. **Criteria:** Selection of recipients will be based on merit.

Funds Avail.: $1,000. **Duration:** Annual. **To Apply:** Applicants must submit a completed scholarship form; first-

year recipients must attach a copy of acceptance letter or other proof of enrollment from any School of Law in the United States; current Transcript (College/University/Graduate School); three (3) Letters of Recommendation (1-Community Leader, 2-College Professor or Employer).

8490 ■ Eric E. Smoker Memorial Scholarship
(Undergraduate, Two Year College, Four Year College/Scholarship)

Purpose: To help students from Fulton County pursue post-secondary education. **Focus:** Art history; Arts. **Qualif.:** Applicants must residents of Fulton County who are accepted into and attend accredited two- or four-year public or private institutions of higher learning and in particular to such students who are pursuing a degree in an art-related field. **Criteria:** Special consideration will be made to handicapped students.

Duration: Annual. **To Apply:** Application can be completed on sponsor's website. **Remarks:** Established in 2001.

8491 ■ Northern Lights Library Network
1104 7th Ave. S
Moorhead, MN 56563
Ph: (218)477-2934
URL: nlln.org
Social Media: www.facebook.com/nllnmn
twitter.com/NLLN_MN

8492 ■ NLLN Continuing Education Scholarship
(Professional development/Scholarship)

Purpose: To provide supplemental funds to library staff and library board members, for continuing education programs and events. **Focus:** Library and archival sciences. **Qualif.:** Applicants must be employees of NLLN member libraries. **Criteria:** Selection will be based on the committee's criteria.

Funds Avail.: $500; $1,000. **Duration:** Annual. **Number Awarded:** 3. **To Apply:** Applicants must fill out completely the application form provided at the website. **Contact:** Northern Lights Library Network, P.O. Box 136, 1104 7th Ave S, Moorhead, MN, 56563; Fax: 218-477-2937; Email: Deb.Keena@nlln.org.

8493 ■ Northern Ohio Chapter of Healthcare Information Management Systems Society (NO-HIMSS)
c/o Dr. Christine Hudak
Case Western Reserve University
Cleveland, OH 44106
URL: northernohio.himsschapter.org
Social Media: linkedin.com/groups/Northern-Ohio-Chapter
  -HIMSS-NOHIMSS-2052538/about
twitter.com/hashtag/nohimss

8494 ■ NOHIMSS Student Scholarship Program
(Undergraduate, Master's, Doctorate/Scholarship)

Purpose: To assist HIMSS student members who exhibit excellence and future leadership potential in healthcare information and management systems industry and whose intention is to practice in the North Eastern Ohio area. **Focus:** Health care services. **Qualif.:** Applicants must be Baccalaureate, Master's or PhD students enrolled in an accredited academic program related to healthcare informa-

Awards are arranged alphabetically below their administering organizations

tion and management systems; must be members in good standing of both HIMSS and NOHIMSS; must be attending an accredited educational program in Ohio at least half-time as determined by the educational institution; undergraduate applicants must be first time juniors when the scholarship is awarded. **Criteria:** Selection will be given to applicants whose program includes a strong research component.

Funds Avail.: $2,000. **Duration:** Annual. **To Apply:** Applicants must submit a personal statement each relating to healthcare information management, involvement to date in HIMSS and NOHIMSS, professional achievement and academic society activity; must include three letters of recommendation, an official transcript of records; and must attach a technical paper or essay (no more than eight pages) relating to healthcare information management. **Deadline:** July 15. **Contact:** Email questions or problems to: mike.canfield@firelands.com.

8495 ■ Northern Tier Hardwood Association (NTHA)
PO Box 7
Tunkhannock, PA 18657
Ph: (570)265-7753
URL: www.nthardwoods.org
Social Media: www.facebook.com/nthardwoods

8496 ■ NTHA Forest Resources Scholarships for College Students *(Undergraduate/Scholarship)*

Purpose: To help students pursue their education in forest management, forest products or closely related field. **Focus:** Forestry. **Qualif.:** Applicants must be current students at a two or four year college or university majoring in forest management, forest products, or a closely related field; must also need to have graduated from a high school or lived in one of the following counties in pennsylvania; bradford, sullivan, susquehanna, tioga, wyoming, pike, wayne, lackawanna, and luzerne.

Funds Avail.: $1,500. **Duration:** Annual. **To Apply:** Applicants must complete the provided scholarship application form. **Deadline:** April 30. **Contact:** Northern Tier Hardwood Association, College Scholarship, PO Box 7, Tunkhannock, PA, 18657; Phone: 570-265-7753; Email: nthapa@nthardwoods.org.

8497 ■ Northrop Grumman Corporation
2980 Fairview Park Dr.
Falls Church, VA 22042
Ph: (703)280-2900
URL: www.northropgrumman.com
Social Media: www.facebook.com/NorthropGrumman
www.linkedin.com/company/northrop-grumman-corporation
twitter.com/northropgrumman

8498 ■ Northrop Grumman Engineering Scholars Program *(Undergraduate/Scholarship)*

Purpose: To support promising high school seniors who intend to pursue a career in an approved engineering, computer science, mathematics or physics program and who live in communities where Northrop Grumman Electronic Systems has a major presence. **Focus:** Computer and information sciences; Engineering; Mathematics and mathematical sciences; Physics. **Qualif.:** Applicants must be U.S. citizens and residents in one of Maryland's coun-

ties or communities; must be graduate seniors of a public or accredited private high school in sponsoring location; must plan to attend an accredited college or university as full-time students in an approved engineering, computer science, mathematics, or physics program; must have a minimum composite SAT score of 1150 or ACT score of 27; must have a minimum GPA of 3.5 (un-weighted) 9-12.

Funds Avail.: $2,000 each. **Duration:** Annual. **Number Awarded:** 4. **To Apply:** Application available online at scholarshipamerica.org/scholarship/northrop-grumman-engineering-scholars-program/. **Contact:** E-mail: scholars@ngc.com.

8499 ■ Northwest-Shoals Community College Foundation (NW-SCC)
800 George Wallace Blvd.
Muscle Shoals, AL 35661
Ph: (256)331-5200
Fax: (256)331-5222
E-mail: nwscc@nwscc.edu
URL: www.nwscc.edu
Social Media: www.facebook.com/officialnwscc
www.instagram.com/nwscc
twitter.com/NWSCC

8500 ■ Alabama Power Scholarships *(Undergraduate/Scholarship)*

Purpose: To support NW-SCC students in their educational pursuit. **Focus:** General studies/Field of study not specified. **Qualif.:** Applicants must be high school students entering Northwest-Shoals Community College. **Criteria:** Students will be selected by high school counselors or by the NW-SCC Foundation Scholarship Committee.

Funds Avail.: No specific amount. **Duration:** Annual. **To Apply:** Applicants must submit a completed application form together with the required materials and information. **Deadline:** March 2.

8501 ■ American Legion Florence/Lauderdale Post 11 Scholarship *(Undergraduate, Community College/Scholarship)*

Purpose: To help students pay for college. **Focus:** General studies/Field of study not specified. **Qualif.:** Applicants must be a U.S. citizen with no criminal record; must be a high school graduate, GED or home-school graduate; must be the child or grandchild of a member of the Florence/Lauderdale Post 11 American Legion; must reside in Lauderdale County; must be a full-time student at NW-SCC with continuous enrollment and a minimum 2.5 GPA.

Duration: Annual. **To Apply:** Application can be completed online at www.nwscc.edu/about-nw-scc/foundation, and submitted along with recommendations and a 300 to 500 word essay answering the question: Why is this scholarship important to you? **Deadline:** March 2.

8502 ■ Diana Ashe-Clayton Memorial Scholarship *(Undergraduate/Scholarship)*

Purpose: To help NW-SCC second-year students pay for college. **Focus:** General studies/Field of study not specified. **Qualif.:** Applicants must be second-year students at Northwest-Shoals Community college; must be single parents; must have full-time, continuous enrollment and financial need.

Funds Avail.: Tuition, fees, books, and childcare for one child for one academic year. **Duration:** Annual. **To Apply:**

Awards are arranged alphabetically below their administering organizations

Application can be completed online at www.nwscc.edu/about-nw-scc/foundation, and submitted along with recommendations and a 300 to 500 word essay answering the question: Why is this scholarship important to you? **Deadline:** March 2.

8503 ■ Barry "Tyler" Rhea Memorial Scholarship
(Undergraduate/Scholarship)

Purpose: To support NW-SCC students in their educational pursuit. **Focus:** General studies/Field of study not specified.

Funds Avail.: $1,000 per year or $500 per semester. **Duration:** Annual. **Contact:** Adriana Wuotto, Northwest-Shoals Community College Foundation, Inc., PO Box 2390, Muscle Shoals, AL, 35662-2390.

8504 ■ Billy Bowling Memorial Scholarship
(Undergraduate/Scholarship)

Purpose: To support NW-SCC students in their educational pursuit. **Focus:** General studies/Field of study not specified. **Qualif.:** Applicants must be high school students entering Northwest-Shoals Community College. **Criteria:** Students will be selected by the NW-SCC Foundation Scholarship Committee.

Funds Avail.: No specific amount. **To Apply:** Applicant must submit a completed application form along with the required materials and information; must attach a copy of high school or college transcript; essay should be 300-500 words; any letters of recommendation can be mailed with a transcript. **Contact:** Adriana Wuotto, Northwest-Shoals Community College Foundation, Inc., PO Box 2390, Muscle Shoals, AL, 35662-2390.

8505 ■ Cecil Earl Clapp, Sr. Memorial Scholarship
(Undergraduate/Scholarship)

Purpose: To support NW-SCC students in their educational pursuit. **Focus:** Forestry. **Qualif.:** Applicants must be high school students entering Northwest-Shoals Community College planning to enter the field of Forestry or Agriculture. **Criteria:** Students will be selected by the NW-SCC Foundation Scholarship Committee.

Funds Avail.: No specific amount. **To Apply:** Applicant must submit a completed application form along with the required materials and information; must attach a copy of high school or college transcript; essay should be 300-500 words; any letters of recommendation can be mailed with a transcript. **Contact:** Adriana Wuotto, Northwest-Shoals Community College Foundation, Inc., PO Box 2390, Muscle Shoals, AL, 35662-2390.

8506 ■ Marvin E. Daly Memorial Scholarship
(Undergraduate/Scholarship)

Purpose: To support NW-SCC students in their educational pursuit. **Focus:** General studies/Field of study not specified. **Qualif.:** Applicants must be Lauderdale County senior students entering Northwest-Shoals Community College. **Criteria:** Students will be selected by the NW-SCC Foundation Scholarship Committee.

Funds Avail.: No specific amount. **Duration:** Annual. **To Apply:** Applicant must submit a completed application form along with the required materials and information; must attach a copy of high school or college transcript; essay should be 300-500 words; any letters of recommendation can be mailed with a transcript. **Contact:** Adriana Wuotto, Northwest-Shoals Community College Foundation, Inc., PO Box 2390, Muscle Shoals, AL, 35662-2390.

8507 ■ Ashley Darby Memorial Scholarship *(Community College, Undergraduate/Scholarship)*

Purpose: To help second-year students at NS-CC pay for college. **Focus:** Nursing; Science. **Qualif.:** Applicants must be second-year students at Northwest-Shoals Community College with a desire to further their education as a science major or are applying for the Nursing Program and who may not qualify for other financial assistance; must have continuous enrollment, full-time status, and a minimum 2.5 GPA.

Funds Avail.: $1,000 per year ($500 per semester). **Duration:** Annual. **To Apply:** Application can be completed online at www.nwscc.edu/about-nw-scc/foundation, and submitted along with recommendations and a 300- to 500-word essay answering the question: Why is this scholarship important to you? **Deadline:** March 2.

8508 ■ Bobby Michael Denton Memorial Scholarship *(High School/Scholarship)*

Purpose: To support NW-SCC students in their educational pursuit. **Focus:** General studies/Field of study not specified. **Qualif.:** Applicants must be selected Colbert Heights High School senior students entering Northwest-Shoals Community College. **Criteria:** Students will be selected by the NW-SCC Foundation Scholarship Committee.

Funds Avail.: No specific amount. **To Apply:** Applicant must submit a completed application form along with the required materials and information; must attach a copy of high school or college transcript; essay should be 300-500 words; any letters of recommendation can be mailed with a transcript. **Contact:** Adriana Wuotto, Northwest-Shoals Community College Foundation, Inc., PO Box 2390, Muscle Shoals, AL, 35662-2390.

8509 ■ Edward Fennel Mauldin Endowed Scholarship *(Undergraduate, Community College/Scholarship)*

Purpose: To help local first-generation high school seniors pay for college. **Focus:** General studies/Field of study not specified. **Qualif.:** Applicants must be first generation high school seniors from high schools in Colbert, Lauderdale, Lawrence, or Franklin counties attending NW-SCC; must have full-time status, continuous enrollment, and a minimum 2.0 GPA. Renewable for one additional year.

Funds Avail.: $5,000. **Duration:** Annual. **To Apply:** Application can be completed online at www.nwscc.edu/about-nw-scc/foundation, and submitted along with recommendations and a 300- to 500-word essay answering the question: Why is this scholarship important to you? **Deadline:** March 2.

8510 ■ GIST - Mattie Lou Gist Memoral Scholarship Endowment *(Undergraduate, Community College/Scholarship)*

Purpose: To help students from Franklin County pursue a nursing degree. **Focus:** Nursing. **Qualif.:** Applicants must be students from Franklin County seeking a nursing degree from NW-SCC, or who plan to complete the basic preparations at NW-SCC to pursue a four-year nursing degree; must have full-time status, continuous enrollment, and a minimum 2.75 GPA; must have expressed financial need and remain in good standing with the college. **Criteria:** Preference will be given to employees or families of employees of G&G/FMI, regardless of their place of residence.

Funds Avail.: $1,000. **Duration:** Annual. **To Apply:** Application can be completed online at www.nwscc.edu/about-

Awards are arranged alphabetically below their administering organizations

nw-scc/foundation, and submitted along with recommendations and a 300 to 500 word essay answering the question: Why is this scholarship important to you? **Deadline:** March 2.

8511 ■ GIST - Orben F. Gist Memorial Scholarship Endowment *(Undergraduate, Community College/ Scholarship)*

Purpose: To help local students pursue degrees in technology or engineering. **Focus:** Engineering; Technology. **Qualif.:** Applicants must be students from Franklin County seeking technical degrees from NW-SCC, or who plan to complete the basic preparations at NW-SCC and then pursue four-year engineering or technology degrees; must have full-time status, continuous enrollment, and a minimum 2.75 GPA. **Criteria:** Preference will be given to the employees or the families of employees of G&G/FMI, regardless of their place of residence.

Funds Avail.: $1,000. **Duration:** Annual. **To Apply:** Application can be completed online at www.nwscc.edu/about-nw-scc/foundation, and submitted along with recommendations and a 300 to 500 word essay answering the question: Why is this scholarship important to you? **Deadline:** March 2.

8512 ■ Joshua "Josh" Green Memorial Scholarship Endowment *(Undergraduate, Community College/ Scholarship)*

Purpose: To help Russellville High School seniors pay for college. **Focus:** General studies/Field of study not specified. **Qualif.:** Applicants must be Russellville High School graduating seniors attending NW-SCC; must have full-time status, continuous enrollment, and a minimum 2.5 GPA.

Duration: Annual. **To Apply:** Application can be completed online at www.nwscc.edu/about-nw-scc/foundation, and submitted along with recommendations and a 300 to 500 word essay answering the question: Why is this scholarship important to you? **Deadline:** March 2.

8513 ■ Homajean Grisham Memorial Scholarship *(Undergraduate/Scholarship)*

Purpose: To support NW-SCC students in their educational pursuit. **Focus:** General studies/Field of study not specified. **Qualif.:** Applicants must be Cherokee High School Senior students entering Northwest-Shoals Community College. **Criteria:** Students will be selected by the NW-SCC Foundation Scholarship Committee.

Funds Avail.: No specific amount. **To Apply:** Applicant must submit a completed application form along with the required materials and information; must attach a copy of high school or college transcript; essay should be 300-500 words; any letters of recommendation can be mailed with a transcript. **Contact:** Adriana Wuotto, Northwest-Shoals Community College Foundation, Inc., PO Box 2390, Muscle Shoals, AL, 35662-2390.

8514 ■ Shelby Grissom Memorial Scholarship *(Undergraduate, Community College/Scholarship)*

Purpose: To help Phil Campbell High School seniors pay for college. **Focus:** General studies/Field of study not specified. **Qualif.:** Applicants must be Phil Campbell High School seniors attending NW-SCC; must have full-time status, continuous enrollment, and a minimum 2.5 GPA.

Funds Avail.: $1,000. **Duration:** Annual. **To Apply:** Application can be completed online at www.nwscc.edu/about-nw-scc/foundation, and submitted along with recommenda-

tions and a 300 to 500 word essay answering the question: Why is this scholarship important to you? **Deadline:** March 2.

8515 ■ Howell Heflin Memorial Scholarship *(Undergraduate/Scholarship)*

Purpose: To support NW-SCC students in their educational pursuit. **Focus:** General studies/Field of study not specified. **Qualif.:** Applicants must be Individuals in the college-service area with a desire to further education at NW-SCC and who may not qualify for financial assistance otherwise provided. **Criteria:** Students will be selected by the NW-SCC Foundation Scholarship Committee.

Funds Avail.: $1,500 per school year, $750 per semester. **To Apply:** Applicant must submit a completed application form along with the required materials and information; must attach a copy of high school or college transcript; essay should be 300-500 words; any letters of recommendation can be mailed with a transcript. **Deadline:** March 2. **Contact:** Adriana Wuotto, Northwest-Shoals Community College Foundation, Inc., PO Box 2390, Muscle Shoals, AL, 35662-2390.

8516 ■ Walston and Jewel Hester Memorial Scholarship Endowment *(Undergraduate, Community College/Scholarship)*

Purpose: To help local high school seniors pay for college. **Focus:** General studies/Field of study not specified. **Qualif.:** Applicants must be graduating high school seniors attending NW-SCC; must have full-time status, continuous enrollment, and a minimum 2.5 GPA.

Duration: Annual. **To Apply:** Application can be completed online at www.nwscc.edu/about-nw-scc/foundation, and submitted along with recommendations and a 300 to 500 word essay answering the question: Why is this scholarship important to you? **Deadline:** March 2.

8517 ■ Esther McAfee Flippo Hunt Memorial Scholarship *(Undergraduate/Scholarship)*

Purpose: To help second-year NW-SCC students in the nursing program pay for college. **Focus:** Nursing. **Qualif.:** Applicants must be second-year students at Northwest-Shoals Community College applying for the Nursing Program (LPN preferred but RN acceptable); must have full-time status and continuous enrollment; must have a minimum 2.5 GPA.

Duration: Annual. **To Apply:** Application can be completed online at www.nwscc.edu/about-nw-scc/foundation, and submitted along with recommendations and a 300 to 500 word essay answering the question: Why is this scholarship important to you? **Deadline:** March 2.

8518 ■ ICS Scholarship *(Undergraduate/Scholarship)*

Purpose: To help second-year NW-SCC students studying computer information systems pay for college. **Focus:** Computer and information sciences. **Qualif.:** Applicants must be second-year, full-time students with continuous enrollment; must be majoring in computer information systems; must have a minimum 2.5 GPA.

Funds Avail.: $1,500. **Duration:** Annual. **To Apply:** Application can be completed online at www.nwscc.edu/about-nw-scc/foundation, and submitted along with recommendations and a 300 to 500 word essay answering the question: Why is this scholarship important to you? **Deadline:** March 2.

Awards are arranged alphabetically below their administering organizations

8519 ■ Broughton Isom Memorial Scholarship
(Undergraduate/Scholarship)

Purpose: To support NW-SCC students in their educational pursuit. **Focus:** General studies/Field of study not specified. **Qualif.:** Applicants must be Phil Campbell High School senior high school students entering Northwest-Shoals Community College. **Criteria:** Students will be selected by the NW-SCC Foundation Scholarship Committee.

Funds Avail.: No specific amount. **To Apply:** Applicant must submit a completed application form along with the required materials and information; must attach a copy of high school or college transcript; essay should be 300-500 words; any letters of recommendation can be mailed with a transcript. **Contact:** Adriana Wuotto, Northwest-Shoals Community College Foundation, Inc., PO Box 2390, Muscle Shoals, AL, 35662-2390.

8520 ■ Franklin A. Lenfesty Memorial Scholarship
(Undergraduate/Scholarship)

Purpose: To support NW-SCC students in their educational pursuit. **Focus:** General studies/Field of study not specified. **Qualif.:** Applicant must be a senior in a high school, a high school graduate or equivalent and have a desire to further their education with a major in Chemical Laboratory Technician (AAS) at NW-SCC; must remain good standing with the College; must be of a high moral character and remain in good standing with the community. **Criteria:** Students will be selected by the NW-SCC Foundation Scholarship Committee.

Funds Avail.: No specific amount. **To Apply:** Applicant must submit a completed application form along with the required materials and information; must attach a copy of high school or college transcript; essay should be 300-500 words; any letters of recommendation can be mailed with a transcript. **Deadline:** March 11. **Contact:** Adriana Wuotto, Northwest-Shoals Community College Foundation, Inc., PO Box 2390, Muscle Shoals, AL, 35662-2390.

8521 ■ Lockheed Martin Scholarship
(Undergraduate/Scholarship)

Purpose: To help veterans pay for college at NW-SCC. **Focus:** General studies/Field of study not specified. **Qualif.:** Applicants must be veterans who are beginning or completing their education at NW-SCC; must have full-time status, continuous enrollment, and a minimum 2.0 GPA.

Duration: Annual. **To Apply:** Application can be completed online at www.nwscc.edu/about-nw-scc/foundation, and submitted along with recommendations and a 300 to 500 word essay answering the question: Why is this scholarship important to you? **Deadline:** March 2.

8522 ■ Bill Lucas Memorial Scholarship Endowment
(Undergraduate, Community College/Scholarship)

Purpose: To help students graduating from Russellville High School pay for college. **Focus:** General studies/Field of study not specified. **Qualif.:** Applicants must be graduating seniors from Russellville High School planning to attend NW-SCC; must have full-time status, continuous enrollment, and a minimum 2.0 GPA.

Duration: Annual. **To Apply:** Application can be completed online at www.nwscc.edu/about-nw-scc/foundation, and submitted along with recommendations and a 300- to 500-word essay answering the question: Why is this scholarship important to you? **Deadline:** March 2.

8523 ■ Muscle Shoals Kiwanis Club/Wal-mart
(Undergraduate/Scholarship)

Purpose: To support NW-SCC students in their educational pursuit. **Focus:** General studies/Field of study not specified.

Funds Avail.: No specific amount.

8524 ■ Northwest-Shoals Community College Academic Scholarship *(Undergraduate/Scholarship)*

Purpose: To support students in their educational pursuit. **Focus:** General studies/Field of study not specified. **Criteria:** Students will be selected by the NW-SCC Foundation Scholarship Committee.

To Apply: Applicant must submit a completed application form along with the required materials and information; must attach a copy of high school or college transcript; essay should be 300-500 words; any letters of recommendation can be mailed with a transcript. **Deadline:** February 1. **Contact:** Adriana Wuotto, Northwest-Shoals Community College Foundation, Inc., PO Box 2390, Muscle Shoals, AL, 35662-2390.

8525 ■ Northwest-Shoals Community College Applied Technology Scholarship *(Undergraduate/Scholarship)*

Purpose: To support students in their educational pursuit. **Focus:** Education, Vocational-technical. **Qualif.:** Applicants must enter NW-SCC with at least a 2.5 overall GPA or its numerical equivalent; Maintain a 2.5 cumulative GPA at NW-SCC; Applicants must have a technical or occupational program as their declared major. **Criteria:** Students will be selected by the NW-SCC Foundation Scholarship Committee.

Funds Avail.: No specific amount. **Deadline:** February 1. **Contact:** Adriana Wuotto, Northwest-Shoals Community College Foundation, Inc., PO Box 2390, Muscle Shoals, AL, 35662-2390.

8526 ■ Northwest-Shoals Community College Athletic Scholarships *(Undergraduate/Scholarship)*

Purpose: To support NW-SCC students in their educational pursuit. **Focus:** Athletics. **Qualif.:** Applicants must be entering full-time freshmen or currently enrolled full-time students with an overall GPA of 2.0 in basketball, baseball, softball, volleyball, cheerleaders or managers. **Criteria:** Selection will be based on the result of the tryouts.

Funds Avail.: No specific amount. **Duration:** Annual. **To Apply:** Applicants must file a Northwest-Shoals Community College Application for Admission, and submit a high school or previous college transcript; and portfolio. **Deadline:** March 1.

8527 ■ Northwest-Shoals Community College Fine Arts Scholarships - Art *(Undergraduate/Scholarship)*

Purpose: To support NW-SCC students in their educational pursuit. **Focus:** Art. **Qualif.:** Applicants must be entering full-time college freshmen or currently enrolled full-time students, and have an overall GPA of 2.25. **Criteria:** Selection will be based on the submitted portfolio and other requirements.

Funds Avail.: No specific amount. **Duration:** Annual. **Number Awarded:** 20. **To Apply:** To qualify, students must file a Northwest-Shoals Community College Application for Admission; and must submit a completed scholarship application form together with the portfolio. **Deadline:** June 1.

Awards are arranged alphabetically below their administering organizations

8528 ■ **Northwest-Shoals Community College Fine Arts Scholarships - Drama** *(Undergraduate/Scholarship)*

Purpose: To support NW-SCC students in their educational pursuit. **Focus:** Criticism (Art, Drama, Literary). **Qualif.:** Applicants must be entering full-time freshmen or currently enrolled full-time students, and have an overall GPA of 2.5. **Criteria:** Selection will be based on the result of the audition.

To Apply: To qualify, students must file a Northwest-Shoals Community College Application for Admission. Applicants must submit a completed scholarship application form along with the required materials.

8529 ■ **Northwest-Shoals Community College Fine Arts Scholarships - Music** *(Undergraduate/Scholarship)*

Purpose: To support NW-SCC students in their educational pursuit. **Focus:** Music. **Qualif.:** Applicants must be entering full-time college freshmen or currently enrolled full-time students and have an overall GPA of 2.0. **Criteria:** Selection will be based on the results of the auditions.

To Apply: To qualify, students must file a Northwest-Shoals Community College Application for Admission, and submit a completed scholarship application form together with the required materials.

8530 ■ **Northwest-Shoals Community College High School Academic Scholarships** *(Undergraduate/Scholarship)*

Purpose: To support students with their educational pursuit. **Focus:** General studies/Field of study not specified. **Qualif.:** Applicant must be a graduating high school senior; have an overall GPA of 3.25; and enrolled full-time. **Criteria:** Selection is based on merit.

Funds Avail.: $1,300. **To Apply:** To qualify, students must file a Northwest-Shoals Community College Application for Admission; and must submit a completed scholarship application form together with the required materials and information. **Deadline:** February 1.

8531 ■ **Northwest-Shoals Community College Independent Computer Scholarships** *(Undergraduate/Scholarship)*

Purpose: To support NW-SCC students in their educational pursuit. **Focus:** General studies/Field of study not specified. **Qualif.:** Applicants must be high school students entering Northwest-Shoals Community College. **Criteria:** Students will be selected by high school counselors or by the NW-SCC Foundation Scholarship Committee.

Funds Avail.: No specific amount. **Duration:** Annual. **To Apply:** Applicants must submit a completed application form together with the required materials and information. **Deadline:** March 2.

8532 ■ **Northwest-Shoals Community College Student Activities Scholarships** *(Undergraduate/Scholarship)*

Purpose: To support NW-SCC students in their educational pursuit. **Focus:** General studies/Field of study not specified. **Qualif.:** Applicants must: be entering full-time freshmen or currently enrolled full-time students; have an overall GPA of 2.5; and, have successfully completed tryouts, interviews, or have been elected/appointed to positions (SGA President, Vice President or Secretary/Treasurer;

Ambassadors; College Bowl). **Criteria:** Selection will be based on merit.

Funds Avail.: No specific amount. **Duration:** Annual. **To Apply:** Interested students must file a Northwest-Shoals Community College Application for Admission; and must submit a completed scholarship application form together with the required materials and information. **Deadline:** March 2.

8533 ■ **NW-SCC Faculty and Staff Scholarship** *(Undergraduate/Scholarship)*

Purpose: To help second-year NW-SCC students pay for college. **Focus:** General studies/Field of study not specified. **Qualif.:** Applicants must be second-year NW-SCC students with full-time status and continuous enrollment; must have a minimum 3.0 GPA.

Funds Avail.: $1,700. **Duration:** Annual. **To Apply:** Application can be completed online at www.nwscc.edu/about-nw-scc/foundation, and submitted along with recommendations and a 300 to 500 word essay answering the question: Why is this scholarship important to you? **Deadline:** March 2.

8534 ■ **NW-SCC General Foundation Scholarship** *(Undergraduate/Scholarship)*

Purpose: To help second-year NW-SCC students pay for college. **Focus:** General studies/Field of study not specified. **Qualif.:** Applicants must be second-year, full-time NW-SCC students with continuous enrollment and a minimum 3.0 GPA.

Funds Avail.: $1,700. **Duration:** Annual. **To Apply:** Application can be completed online at www.nwscc.edu/about-nw-scc/foundation, and submitted along with recommendations and a 300 to 500 word essay answering the question: Why is this scholarship important to you? **Deadline:** March 2.

8535 ■ **Barry "Tyler" Rhea Memorial Scholarship** *(Undergraduate, Community College/Scholarship)*

Purpose: To help students from Phil Campbell High School pay for college. **Focus:** General studies/Field of study not specified. **Qualif.:** Applicants must be graduating seniors at Phil Campbell High School planning to attend NW-SCC; must have full-time status, continuous enrollment, and a minimum 2.5 GPA.

Funds Avail.: $1,000. **Duration:** Annual. **To Apply:** Application can be completed online at www.nwscc.edu/about-nw-scc/foundation, and submitted along with recommendations and a 300 to 500 word essay answering the question: Why is this scholarship important to you? **Deadline:** March 2.

8536 ■ **D. Mitchell Self Memorial Scholarship** *(Undergraduate/Scholarship)*

Purpose: To support scholarship to full-time students. **Focus:** General studies/Field of study not specified. **Qualif.:** Applicants must be full-time students with a GPA of at least 2.00. **Criteria:** Students will be selected by the Department Office of Student Financial Services Scholarship Committee.

Funds Avail.: No specific amount. **To Apply:** Applicant must submit a completed application form along with the required materials and information. **Deadline:** February 15.

8537 ■ **Simms Scholarship** *(Undergraduate, Community College/Scholarship)*

Purpose: To help local high school seniors pay for college. **Focus:** General studies/Field of study not specified. **Qua-**

Awards are arranged alphabetically below their administering organizations

lif.: Applicants must be Hatton High School, East Lawrence High School, Lawrence County High School, or Lawrence County Center for Technology High School seniors attending NW-SCC; must have full-time statues, continuous enrollment, and a minimum 2.5 GPA.

Funds Avail.: $1,500. **Duration:** Annual. **To Apply:** Application can be completed online at www.nwscc.edu/about-nw-scc/foundation, and submitted along with recommendations and a 300 to 500 word essay answering the question: Why is this scholarship important to you? **Deadline:** March 2.

8538 ■ Aaron B. Singleton Memorial Scholarship
(Undergraduate/Scholarship)

Purpose: To support NW-SCC students in their educational pursuit. **Focus:** General studies/Field of study not specified. **Qualif.:** Applicant must be graduating seniors with a desire to further their education at NW-SCC who may not qualify for financial assistance otherwise provide; PA 2.0 Full-time status and continuous enrollment. **Criteria:** Students will be selected by the NW-SCC Foundation Scholarship Committee.

Funds Avail.: No specific amount. **Duration:** Annual. **To Apply:** The application process is online. **Deadline:** March 2. **Contact:** Adriana Wuotto, Northwest-Shoals Community College Foundation, Inc., PO Box 2390, Muscle Shoals, AL, 35662-2390.

8539 ■ Karen Thompson Memorial Scholarship
(Undergraduate, Community College/Scholarship)

Purpose: To help Florence High School students pay for college. **Focus:** General studies/Field of study not specified. **Qualif.:** Applicants must be Florence High School graduating seniors in Talent Search Program attending NW-SCC; must have full-time status, continuous enrollment, and a minimum 2.5 GPA.

Funds Avail.: $1,000. **Duration:** Annual. **To Apply:** Application can be completed online at www.nwscc.edu/about-nw-scc/foundation, and submitted along with recommendations and a 300 to 500 word essay answering the question: Why is this scholarship important to you? **Deadline:** March 2.

8540 ■ Tuscumbia Kiwanis Club Scholarship
(Undergraduate/Scholarship)

Purpose: To support NW-SCC students in their educational pursuit. **Focus:** General studies/Field of study not specified. **Criteria:** Students will be selected by the NW-SCC Foundation Scholarship Committee.

Duration: Annual. **To Apply:** Applicant must submit a completed application form along with the required materials and information; must attach a copy of high school or college transcript; essay should be 300-500 words; any letters of recommendation can be mailed with a transcript.

8541 ■ VFW Post 5140/Paul W. Shockley Sr. Memorial Scholarship *(Undergraduate/Scholarship)*

Purpose: To help students with a relative who is presently serving or has served in the Armed Forces of the United States pay for college. **Focus:** General studies/Field of study not specified. **Qualif.:** Applicants must be U.S. citizens with no criminal record; must be high school seniors, GED graduates, home-schooled, or second-year students enrolled full- or part-time at NW-SCC; must have a relative who has served or is presently serving in the Armed Forces of the United States; must have a minimum 2.5 GPA.

Funds Avail.: $1,000. **Duration:** Annual. **To Apply:** Application can be completed online at www.nwscc.edu/about-nw-scc/foundation, and submitted along with recommendations and a 300 to 500 word essay answering the question: Why is this scholarship important to you? Applicant must mail in a copy of the document certifying relationship and proof of relative serving in the military. **Deadline:** March 2.

8542 ■ Joseph W. Wade Memorial Scholarship Endowment *(Undergraduate, Community College/ Scholarship)*

Purpose: To help NW-SCC students pay for college. **Focus:** General studies/Field of study not specified. **Qualif.:** Applicant must be second-year, full-time students at NW-SCC with continuous enrollment and a minimum 2.5 GPA.

Duration: Annual. **To Apply:** Application can be completed online at www.nwscc.edu/about-nw-scc/foundation, and submitted along with recommendations and a 300 to 500 word essay answering the question: Why is this scholarship important to you? **Deadline:** March 2.

8543 ■ Wayne County Bank Scholarship
(Undergraduate/Scholarship)

Purpose: To support NW-SCC students in their educational pursuit. **Focus:** General studies/Field of study not specified. **Qualif.:** Applicants must be Wayne County graduating seniors entering Northwest-Shoals Community College. **Criteria:** Students will be selected by the NW-SCC Foundation Scholarship Committee.

Funds Avail.: $1,000. **Duration:** Annual. **To Apply:** Applicant must submit a completed application form along with the required materials and information; must attach a copy of high school or college transcript; essay should be 300-500 words; any letters of recommendation can be mailed with a transcript. **Contact:** Adriana Wuotto, Northwest-Shoals Community College Foundation, Inc., PO Box 2390, Muscle Shoals, AL, 35662-2390.

8544 ■ Northwest Territories Law Foundation
PO Box 1298
Yellowknife, NT, Canada X1A 2P9
URL: nwtlawfoundation.ca

8545 ■ NWT Law Foundation/Graeme Garson Scholarships *(Advanced Professional/Scholarship)*

Purpose: To assist those students with debt reduction or supplement their income when they return to the NWT to work during articles and to continue to practice in the NWT. **Focus:** Law. **Qualif.:** Applicants should be those who are able to demonstrate some distinct and valuable commitment or dedication to the NWT and its people; this may be accomplished by any one or more of residency in the NWT for at least 3 years; attendance at a secondary school in the NWT; intention to return to the NWT after their education is complete; involvement in community activities; leadership qualities; and academic standing. **Criteria:** Selection will be based on the aforesaid qualifications and compliance with the application process.

Funds Avail.: Total of 20,000 Canadian Dollars. **To Apply:** Applicants must use the fillable PDF form (the Scholarship Application Form) and contact the Executive Manager to discuss the application. **Deadline:** May 15. **Contact:** NWT Law Foundation, PO Box 1298, Yellowknife, NT, X1A 2P9; Phone: 867-873-3828; Fax: 867-873-6344.

8546 ■ NortonLifeLock Inc.
60 E Rio Salado Pkwy., Ste. 100
Tempe, AZ 85281

Awards are arranged alphabetically below their administering organizations

Ph: (650)527-8000
URL: www.nortonlifelock.com
Social Media: www.facebook.com/NortonLifeLock
www.instagram.com/nortonlifelock
www.linkedin.com/company/nortonlifelock
twitter.com/NortonLifeLock
www.youtube.com/channel/
   UCa3h96az7881wsRH5uoTxuQ

8547 ■ Symantec Research Labs Graduate Fellowships *(Doctorate, Graduate/Fellowship)*

Purpose: To fund innovative research that has real-world value, in areas of Symantec's business interests in privacy and identity, security, machine learning and data mining and human factors. **Focus:** Information science and technology. **Qualif.:** Applicants must be a student who enrolled in a Ph.D. program. **Criteria:** Recipients will be selected based on their overall potential for research excellence and their academic progress to date as evidenced by publications; preference will be given to students with a desire to work in an industrial research lab and those working on innovative research projects in areas related to Symantec's businesses and interests.

Funds Avail.: Up to $20,000. **Duration:** Annual. **To Apply:** Applicants must submit a application form along with the following: resume or curriculum vitae; a personal statement of research interests not to exceed 750 words; applicants are strongly encouraged to articulate the practical value to customers of their proposed research areas; two letters of recommendation from professors or industry researchers who can evaluate the applicant's scientific aptitude and potential for research. **Deadline:** December 5. **Contact:** E-mail: srlfellowship@symantec.com.

8548 ■ NotMP3

29 Harley St.
London W1G 9QR, United Kingdom
URL: notmp3.com
Social Media: www.facebook.com/Notmp3
twitter.com/NotMP3

8549 ■ NotMP3 Scholarship Program *(College, University, Undergraduate/Scholarship)*

Purpose: To support young, creative minds during their study period and inspire them to share their ideas. **Focus:** General studies/Field of study not specified. **Qualif.:** Applicant must be a current full- or part-time student at an accredited institute. **Criteria:** Selection is based on creativity, argumentation, and originality of the submitted essay.

Funds Avail.: $1,000. **Number Awarded:** 1. **To Apply:** Applicant must write an essay or article (at least 1,000 words) on the following topic: Downloading internet content, what is and isn't legal? Essay must be submitted via email as a Word document. Email must include full name, contact information, and school applicant is attending. Upon submission of all required materials, entrant will receive a confirmation indicating their application has been received. **Deadline:** May 1. **Contact:** Email: scholarship@notmp3.com.

8550 ■ Novik & Stanley, A Professional Law Corporation

16830 Venture Blvd., Ste. 508
Encino, CA 91436

Ph: (818)305-6041
Fax: (818)305-6042
URL: www.novikstanley.com

8551 ■ Road to Success Scholarship *(Undergraduate/Scholarship)*

Purpose: To recognize students who have overcome obstacles on the way to achieving their goals. **Focus:** General studies/Field of study not specified.

Funds Avail.: $1,000. **Number Awarded:** 1. **Deadline:** June 6. **Contact:** Subject line should read: Attention: Scholarship Manager; Phone No:(888) 846-4771.

8552 ■ Novus Biologicals L.L.C.

8100 Southpark Way, A-8
Littleton, CO 80120
Social Media: www.facebook.com/NovusBiologicals
www.linkedin.com/company/novus-biologicals-llc
www.youtube.com/user/novusbiologicals

8553 ■ Novus Biologicals Scholarship Program *(All/ Scholarship)*

Purpose: To further scientific achievement by helping students who are interested in developing a career in science **Focus:** Science. **Qualif.:** Applicants must have a major declared in a science related field; enrolled or accepted for enrollment (baccalaureate, graduate, associate degree, or diploma); open in the US, UK, and Canada only. **Criteria:** Selection will be Open for Schools/Colleges/ Institutes within the US, Canada, and European countries only; No GPA requirement

Funds Avail.: $1,500. **Duration:** Semiannual. **Number Awarded:** 1, twice a year. **To Apply:** Applicants must submit the completed application form with the required documents. **Deadline:** July 29; December 10. **Contact:** Email: scholarship@bio-techne.com.

8554 ■ Nuffield Canada

Box 20800 Whitehorse,
Yukon Territory, YT, Canada Y1A 6N7
Ph: (780)646-2161
URL: nuffield.ca/wp
Social Media: facebook.com/NuffieldCanada
instagram.com/nuffieldcanada
twitter.com/nuffieldcanada

8555 ■ Nuffield Canada Farming Scholarships *(Undergraduate/Scholarship)*

Purpose: To help students develop their leadership within Canada's rural industries, communities and practices of agriculture. **Focus:** Agriculture, Economic aspects. **Qualif.:** Applicants must be Canadian citizens between ages 25 to 45 who are working in the field of agriculture. **Criteria:** Selection will be based on contributions and innovations within their respective fields of study upon return to Canada.

Funds Avail.: $15,000. **Duration:** Annual. **To Apply:** Applicants must submit a filled-out application form with attached resume. **Contact:** Shannon McArton, Nuffield Canada, Executive Director; Phone: 306-731-7610; Email: shannon@nuffield.ca; Ian McPhadden, Nuffield Canada, Chair; Phone: 306-493-7890; Email: imcphadden@gmail.com.

8556 ■ Number 1 Auto Transport

1745 Merrick Ave., Ste. 22
Merrick, NY 11566

Awards are arranged alphabetically below their administering organizations

Fax: (516)203-4231
Free: 855-422-4141
E-mail: info@number1autotransport.com
URL: number1autotransport.com
Social Media: www.facebook.com/Number1AutoTransport
www.instagram.com/number1autotransport
www.linkedin.com/company/number-1-auto-transport
twitter.com/Number1AutoTran
www.youtube.com/channel/UC7UTSu7YDnI77jAcD_0DIxQ

8557 ■ Number 1 Auto Transport Annual Scholarship *(Undergraduate, Graduate/Scholarship)*

Purpose: To help undergraduate and graduate students pay for a college education. **Focus:** General studies/Field of study not specified. **Qualif.:** Applicant must be enrolled in an accredited undergraduate or graduate program and currently have at least a 3.0 GPA. **Criteria:** Selection is based on the most creative essay.

Funds Avail.: $500. **Duration:** Annual. **Number Awarded:** 2 (1 for fall and 1 for spring). **To Apply:** Applicant must write an essay and submit via email. Application details are available online at number1autotransport.com/number-1-auto-transport-annual-scholarship/. **Deadline:** August 1. **Contact:** E-mail: scholarships@number1autotransport.com.

8558 ■ Nurses Organization of Veterans Affairs (NOVA)
47595 Watkins Island Sq.
Sterling, VA 20165
Ph: (703)444-5587
Fax: (703)444-5597
E-mail: nova@vanurse.org
URL: www.vanurse.org
Social Media: www.facebook.com/VAnurse.org
instagram.com/NOVANurses
www.linkedin.com/in/nova-nurses-organization-of-veterans
 -affairs-b7a918117
twitter.com/novanurses

8559 ■ NOVA Foundation Scholarships *(Doctorate, Master's/Scholarship)*

Purpose: To help students further their education in a graduate degree program. **Focus:** Nursing. **Criteria:** Selection will be based on the following criteria: Completion of three essay questions on application. Academic performance (Copy of transcript) Most recent proficiency/performance appraisal or ECF.

Funds Avail.: $1,500 to $3,000 each. **Duration:** Annual. **To Apply:** Applicants must submit an official transcript record, letter of acceptance from the academic program for which they are receiving the scholarship; letter of endorsement from their current VA Nurse Executive/Designee confirming that they are not on restricted or light duty, LWOP, or FMLA. **Deadline:** August 21.

8560 ■ NursingProcess.org
Buffalo, NY
E-mail: editor@nursingprocess.org
URL: www.nursingprocess.org
Social Media: www.facebook.com/nursingprocess.org
twitter.com/nursing_process

8561 ■ Health is a Right Not a Privilege Scholarship *(Advanced Professional, Master's, Graduate/Scholarship)*

Purpose: To encourage a deserving nurse to go into advanced practice nursing either to become a nurse practitioner or a nurse anesthetist. **Focus:** Anesthesiology; Nursing. **Qualif.:** Applicant must be a citizen or permanent resident of the United States who has completed an ACEN or CCNE accredited BSN or MSN degree program with a cumulative 3.5 GPA on a 4.0 scale; must be holding an active RN license; must be enrolled full-time or part-time in one of the following academic disciplines: ACEN or CCNE accredited Nurse Practitioner program at either the MSN or DNP degree level, or COA accredited Nurse Anesthesia program at either the MSN or DNP degree level. **Criteria:** The scholarship committee will review all applications received and elect the winner through a competitive and nondiscriminatory process. Applicants will be judged on the following: essay, academic performance, personal and professional goals statement, letter of recommendation, and resume/CV.

Funds Avail.: $1,500. **Duration:** Annual. **Number Awarded:** 1. **To Apply:** Must submit an essay of 1000 - 1500 words, topic available online; resume/CV that includes all relevant information such as education history, awards, honors, work/practical experience, service & volunteer actions, and professional activities; letter of recommendation; completed application. **Deadline:** December 31. **Contact:** Email: scholarship@nursingprocess.org; URL: www.nursingprocess.org/scholarships/aprn-students/.

8562 ■ Nuts, Bolts & Thingamajigs (NBT)
2135 Point Blvd.
Elgin, IL 60120
Ph: (815)399-8700
Free: 888-394-4362
E-mail: foundation@fmanet.org
URL: www.nutsandboltsfoundation.org
Social Media: www.facebook.com/nutsandboltsfoundation
www.linkedin.com/company/nuts-bolts-&-thingamajigs
www.pinterest.com/nbtfoundation
twitter.com/NBThingamajigs
www.youtube.com/playlist?list=PLT
 _lv5Z5FZEgWI4kggH0pLy2rNNvtg5XO

8563 ■ NBT Trade School, Community/Technical College, or University Scholarships *(Undergraduate/Scholarship)*

Purpose: To provide financial support to students in courses of study that may lead to careers in manufacturing. **Focus:** Engineering; Manufacturing.

Funds Avail.: $1,500 to $2,500. **Duration:** Annual. **To Apply:** Applications can be submitted online; must submit an official high school or college transcripts from the school last attended for a complete semester; must submit the signed photo release form. **Contact:** 2135 Point Boulevard, Elgin, IL 60123.

8564 ■ Nuttall Ornithological Club
65 Bare Hill Rd.
Bolton, MA 01740
URL: www.nuttallclub.org

8565 ■ Blake-Nuttall Fund Grants *(Other/Grant)*
Purpose: To support ornithological research, conservation, and education, with particular emphasis on the birds of

Awards are arranged alphabetically below their administering organizations

New England and the Northeast. **Focus:** Ornithology. **Qualif.:** Organizations must be tax-exempt under section 501(c)(3) of the Internal Revenue Code and must not be private foundations under section 509(a). Applications from individuals cannot be considered.

Funds Avail.: $1,000 - $5,000. **Duration:** Annual. **To Apply:** Send an electronic copy of the proposal to the Blake-Nuttall Fund Committee Chair in the following format: (1) Title page: project title and brief abstract; name, address and phone number; proposed starting and completion dates; total amount requested from the Blake-Nuttall Fund; (2) Narrative of up to 5 pages including a) objectives, b) brief review of what is already known or has already been done, c) project methods, d) value of the project to ornithology, e) project timetable, including a submission date for the final report, f) specific address to which a check should be mailed if the project is funded, g) detailed budget, including funds applied for or expected from other sources; (3) Brief statement of investigator qualifications and a resume; (4) Documentary evidence of section 501(c)(3) tax-exempt status. **Deadline:** September 1. **Contact:** Dr. Michael Reed Vice President, Nuttall Ornithological Club Chair, Blake-Nuttall Fund Committee; E-mail: blake@nuttallclub.org.

8566 ■ NVIDIA Corporation
2788 San Tomas Expy.
Santa Clara, CA 95051
Ph: (408)486-2000
E-mail: info@nvidia.com
URL: www.nvidia.com
Social Media: www.facebook.com/NVIDIA
www.instagram.com/nvidia/
www.linkedin.com/company/nvidia
twitter.com/nvidia
www.youtube.com/user/nvidia

8567 ■ NVIDIA Graduate Fellowships *(Postdoctorate/ Fellowship)*

Purpose: To provide funding to PhD students who are researching topics that will lead to major advances in the graphics and high-performance computing industries. **Focus:** Computer and information sciences; Engineering, Computer; Engineering, Electrical. **Qualif.:** Applicant must have already completed the first year of PhD level; majoring in Computer Science, Computer Engineering, System Architecture, Electrical Engineering, or a related area; must be engaged in active research as part of their PhD thesis; enrolled as a full-time active PhD student during the academic year of the award. **Criteria:** Selection will be based on Student quality, research quality and relevance to NVIDIA.

Funds Avail.: Up to $50,000. **Duration:** Annual. **Number Awarded:** Up to 10. **To Apply:** Applicants must complete the application online. In addition, applicants must provide 1-2 page research summary/thesis proposals; resume/ curriculum vitae including contact information; confirmation of availability for summer internship; and Professor Nomination Form (1 letter minimum from thesis advisor, up to 3 letters maximum) including nomination letter. **Deadline:** September 13.

8568 ■ NYCTutoring.com
New York, NY
E-mail: info@nyctutoring.com
URL: www.nyctutoring.com

Social Media: www.facebook.com/TopNYCTutors

8569 ■ The NYCTutoring.com Scholarship *(Undergraduate/Scholarship)*

Purpose: To help talented students pay for college. **Focus:** General studies/Field of study not specified. **Qualif.:** Applicant must be a graduating high school senior or undergraduate student in the United States who has maintained a minimum 3.0 GPA over the previous school year.

Funds Avail.: $500. **Duration:** Annual. **Number Awarded:** 1. **To Apply:** Submit application and a 500 to 750 word essay on the following prompt: At NYCTutoring.com we understand the value of education, so our goal is to help students of all ages achieve their learning goals. What are your learning goals, and how will achieving these goals improve your life or the lives of others? **Deadline:** August 1. **Contact:** Email: scholarship@NYCTutoring.com; URL: www.nyctutoring.com/scholarship.

8570 ■ The O'Brien Foundation
215 Kings College Rd
Fredericton, NB, Canada E3B 2E6
URL: www.obrienfoundation.ca

8571 ■ O'Brien Foundation Fellowships *(Professional development/Fellowship)*

Purpose: To pursue advanced study or research in any academic, artistic, or professional field at any recognized university or research establishment. **Focus:** Education. **Criteria:** Applicants will be selected based on their application requirements.

Duration: Annual; 12 months. **To Apply:** Applicants must complete the online application form and submit three letters of support and official transcripts. **Deadline:** November 1. **Remarks:** Established in 1975.

8572 ■ Oceanic Research Group (ORG)
PO Box 94
North Reading, MA 01864
Ph: (978)664-9091
URL: www.oceanicresearch.org
Social Media: www.facebook.com/Oceanic-Research -Group-121010587793

8573 ■ Oceanic Research Group Scholarships *(Graduate, Undergraduate/Scholarship)*

Purpose: To provide assistance to deserving students pursuing marine-related undergraduate or graduate studies. **Focus:** Biology, Marine. **Criteria:** Selection will be based on submitted documents and demonstrated financial need.

Funds Avail.: $1,000. **Duration:** Annual. **To Apply:** Applicants should submit a completed application form and transcript for each college or university attended. **Deadline:** October 1. **Contact:** Oceanic Research Group, at the above address, or E-mail at scholarship@ oceanicresearch.org.

8574 ■ Ohio Association of Broadcasters
17 S High St., Ste. 1010
Columbus, OH 43215
Ph: (614)228-4052
URL: business.oab.org

Awards are arranged alphabetically below their administering organizations

Social Media: www.linkedin.com/company/ohio-association
-of-broadcasters

8575 ■ OAB Kids Scholarships *(Undergraduate/Scholarship)*

Purpose: To further the broadcasting industry by supporting family members of employees in the industry. **Focus:** Broadcasting. **Qualif.:** Applicants must be high school seniors who are children of a full-time employee of an OAB member station; must plan to enroll in a postsecondary institution. **Criteria:** Recipients are selected based on academic performance.

Funds Avail.: $1,500. **Duration:** Annual. **Number Awarded:** 1. **To Apply:** Applicants must submit a completed application form. **Deadline:** March 6. **Remarks:** Established in 2004. **Contact:** Carrie Newton; E-mail: cnewton@oab.org; Phone: 614-228-4052.

8576 ■ OAB Kids Scholarship *(Undergraduate/Scholarship)*

Purpose: To support students who are pursuing career in broadcasting. **Focus:** Broadcasting; Communications. **Criteria:** Recipients are selected based on academic performance.

Funds Avail.: $3,000. **Number Awarded:** 2. **To Apply:** Application packets must include the following items: a completed application form; the essay requested under the section titled "Essay"; a copy of your high school transcript; one letter of recommendation. **Deadline:** March 6.

8577 ■ Ohio Farm Bureau Federation (OFBF)
280 N High St., 6th Fl.
Columbus, OH 43215
Ph: (614)249-2400
Fax: (614)249-2200
E-mail: info@ofbf.org
URL: ofbf.org
Social Media: www.facebook.com/OhioFarmBureau
www.pinterest.com/ourohio
twitter.com/ohiofarmbureau
www.youtube.com/user/OhioFarmBureau

8578 ■ Women's Leadership in Agriculture Scholarship *(Undergraduate/Scholarship)*

Purpose: To provide financial support to deserving women who must explain how their chosen career field will benefit a field related to agriculture or community development, such as food production, scientific research, education/outreach, marketing, policymaking, advocacy, or leadership development. **Focus:** Agricultural sciences.

Duration: Annual. **To Apply:** Application Three (3) letters from adult leaders, mentors and/or educators describing the applicant's academic, community service and/or leadership experiences, and 500 words or less. High School and/or College/Technical School transcripts. **Deadline:** February 28.

8579 ■ Ohio News Media Association (ONMA)
1335 Dublin Rd., Ste. 216B
Columbus, OH 43215
Ph: (614)486-6677
Fax: (614)486-6373
URL: www.ohionews.org/aws/ONA/pt/sp/home_page

Social Media: www.facebook.com/pages/Ohio-Newspaper
-Association/161981200509447
twitter.com/ONAnews

8580 ■ The Harold K. Douthit Scholarship *(Undergraduate/Scholarship)*

Purpose: To provide educational assistance to students from Northern Ohio. **Focus:** Advertising; Communications; Journalism; Marketing and distribution. **Qualif.:** Applicants must be enrolled as a sophomore, junior or senior at an Ohio college or university of school year; a minimum grade point average of 3.0 (B) is required. **Criteria:** Selection will be based on the committee's criteria.

Funds Avail.: $1,500. **Duration:** Annual. **To Apply:** Applicants must submit a completed, typed or printed legibly, application form; official university or college transcript; an autobiography of 750 to 1,000 words describing academic and career interests, awards, extracurricular activities and any journalism-related activities; and two letters of recommendation from college or university faculty members familiar with the student's work and career interests, with special emphasis on the student's financial need. Students are encouraged to provide writing samples or articles that have been published. **Deadline:** April 30. **Remarks:** The scholarship is named for Harold K. Douthit, founder of Douthit Communications, Inc., Sandusky, and a former president of The Ohio Newspaper Association. **Contact:** Submit the application and all other material required to: The Ohio News Media Foundation Douthit Scholarship, 1335 Dublin Rd., Ste. 216-B, Columbus, Ohio 43215. Or submit your completed application and attachments in PDF format to mwidner@ohionews.org.

8581 ■ Ohio Newspaper Association Minority Scholarship *(Undergraduate/Scholarship)*

Purpose: To provide educational assistance to those minority high school seniors in Ohio intending to pursue a newspaper journalism career. **Focus:** Advertising; Communications; Journalism; Marketing and distribution. **Qualif.:** Applicants must be graduating seniors at any Ohio high school; must be enrolled as college freshmen at any Ohio college or university; have a minimum high school GPA of 2.5 (C+); clearly demonstrate the ability to read and write; must be African American, Hispanic, Asian American or American Indian. **Criteria:** Selection will be based on the committee's criteria.

Funds Avail.: $1,500. **Duration:** Annual. **To Apply:** Applicants must submit completed application form typed or printed legibly by the applicant; an autobiography of 750 to 1,000 words describing academic and career interest awards; extracurricular activities and any journalism-related activities; and two letters of recommendation from high school faculty members familiar with the student's work and career interests; Students may provide additional information such as samples or articles that have been published. **Deadline:** March 31. **Contact:** Submit the application and all other material required to The Ohio News Media Foundation Minority Scholarship, 1335 Dublin Rd., Ste. 216-B, Columbus, Ohio 43215. Or submit your completed application and attachments in PDF format too.

8582 ■ ONWA Annual Scholarship *(Undergraduate/Scholarship)*

Purpose: To provide educational assistance to students enrolled at any Ohio college or university. **Focus:** Advertising; Communications; Journalism; Marketing and distribution. **Qualif.:** Applicants must be students currently enrolled

Awards are arranged alphabetically below their administering organizations

as juniors or seniors at an Ohio college or university and majoring in a field relevant to the industry, particularly journalism, advertising, marketing or communications degree program. **Criteria:** Selection will be based on the committee's criteria.

Funds Avail.: $2,000. **Duration:** Annual. **To Apply:** Applicants must submit a completed application form together with official college or university transcript; two letters of recommendation; three to four news clippings; statements answering the following questions; Who or what was your inspiration to get involved in the field of journalism, advertising; marketing or communications and why did you select your chosen field as your area of interest; Why do you need a scholarship; What do you think qualifies you for a scholarship; What do you hope to accomplish during your career as a newspaper industry professional. **Deadline:** April 30. **Remarks:** After the ONWA disbanded, the group graciously donated the group's assets to the Ohio News Media Foundation to continue a scholarship endowed by Ruth Neely France, one of Cincinnati's first female journalists and certainly one of the most courageous and colorful reporters of the early 20th Century. **Contact:** Submit the application and all other material required to The Ohio News Media Foundation ONWA Annual Scholarship, 1335 Dublin Rd., Ste. 216-B, Columbus, Ohio 43215. Or submit your completed application and attachments in PDF format too.

8583 ■ University Journalism Scholarships
(Undergraduate/Scholarship)

Purpose: To provide educational assistance for students who are demonstrating a career commitment to newspaper journalism. **Focus:** Journalism. **Qualif.:** Applicants must: be enrolled as sophomores, juniors or seniors at an Ohio college or university; have a minimum grade point average of 2.5 (C+); and, clearly demonstrate ability to write. **Criteria:** Preference will be given to students demonstrating a career commitment to newspaper journalism.

Funds Avail.: $2,000. **Duration:** Annual. **To Apply:** Applicants must submit a completed, typed or printed legibly, application form; official college or university transcript; an autobiography of 750 to 1, 000 words describing academic and career interests, awards, extracurricular activities and any journalism-related activities (emphasis should be given to newspaper or print journalism); two letters of recommendation from college or university faculty members familiar with the students' work and career interests; and writing samples or articles that have been published. **Deadline:** April 30. **Contact:** Ohio News Media Foundation University Journalism Scholarship, 1335 Dublin Rd., Ste. 216-B, Columbus, Ohio 43215; Email: mwidner@ohionews.org.

8584 ■ Ohio Nursery and Landscape Association (ONLA)
72 Dorchester Sq.
Westerville, OH 43081
Ph: (614)899-1195
Fax: (614)899-9489
Free: 800-825-5062
E-mail: info@onla.org
URL: www.onla.org
Social Media: www.facebook.com/onlaconnect
instagram.com/onlaconnect
www.linkedin.com/company/onlaconnect
twitter.com/onlaconnect

Awards are arranged alphabetically below their administering organizations

8585 ■ The Artist in Landscape Design Scholarship
(Undergraduate/Scholarship)

Purpose: To provide financial support to students who aim to achieve higher education in horticultural field. **Focus:** Horticulture. **Qualif.:** Applicants must be students studying in the horticultural field and attending school in the Tri-State area of Ohio, Indiana, or Kentucky. **Criteria:** Selection will be based on the committee's criteria.

Funds Avail.: $2,000. **Number Awarded:** 1. **To Apply:** Applicants must submit a completed application form along with their statement of purpose, college transcripts, recommendation letter on school letterhead, and a resume. To be submitted by the student directly to the ONLA office.

8586 ■ FFA Scholarship *(Undergraduate/Scholarship)*

Purpose: To provide financial support to students who aim to achieve higher education in horticulture and related fields. **Focus:** Horticulture. **Qualif.:** Applicants must be horticulture students enrolled full- or part-time in programs at the following schools only: The Ohio State University, The Ohio State University Agricultural Technical Institute, Kent State University-Salem, Clark State Community College, Owens Community College, Columbus State Community College, Cuyahoga Community College, Cincinnati State Technical and Community College, and the University of Cincinnati. **Criteria:** Selection will be based on the committee's criteria.

Funds Avail.: $1,500. **To Apply:** Applicants must submit completed application form along with their statement of purpose, college transcripts, recommendation letter on school letterhead, and a resume. To be submitted by the student directly to the ONLA office.

8587 ■ Southwest Ohio Environmental Horticulture Association (SOEHA) Lloyd W. Kennedy Scholarship *(Graduate/Scholarship)*

Purpose: To provide financial support to students who aim to achieve higher education in horticulture and related fields. **Focus:** General studies/Field of study not specified. **Qualif.:** Applicants must be enrolled full- or part-time in programs at the following schools: The Ohio State University, The Ohio State University Agricultural Technical Institute, Kent State University-Salem, Clark State Community College, Owens Community College, Columbus State Community College, Cuyahoga Community College, Cincinnati State Technical & Community College, and the University of Cincinnati. **Criteria:** Selection will be based on the committee's criteria.

Funds Avail.: $500. **Duration:** Annual. **To Apply:** Applicants must submit a completed application form along with their statement of purpose, college transcripts, recommendation letter on school letterhead, and a resume. To be submitted by the student directly to the ONLA office.

8588 ■ Phil Kozel Memorial Scholarship
(Undergraduate/Scholarship)

Purpose: To provide financial support to students who aim to achieve higher education in horticulture. **Focus:** Horticulture. **Qualif.:** Applicants must be horticulture students enrolled full- or part-time in programs at the following schools: The Ohio State University, The Ohio State University Agricultural Technical Institute, Kent State University-Salem, Clark State Community College, Owens Community College, Columbus State Community College, Cuyahoga Community College, Cincinnati State Technical & Community College, and the University of Cincinnati.

Criteria: Selection will be based on the committee's criteria.

Funds Avail.: Amount not specified. **To Apply:** Applicants must submit a completed application form along with their statement of purpose, college transcripts, recommendation letter on school letterhead, and a resume. To be submitted by the student directly to the ONLA office.

8589 ■ ONLA President's Scholarship
(Undergraduate/Scholarship)

Purpose: To provide financial support to students who aim to achieve higher education in horticulture and related fields. **Focus:** Horticulture. **Qualif.:** Applicants must be current ONLA member; horticulture students enrolled full- or part-time in programs at the following schools: The Ohio State University, The Ohio State University Agricultural Technical Institute, Kent State University-Salem, Clark State Community College, Owens Community College, Columbus State Community College, Cuyahoga Community College, Cincinnati State Technical & Community College, and the University of Cincinnati. **Criteria:** Selection will be based on financial need, noteworthy participation in outside activities, successful submission of all requested materials on time.

Funds Avail.: $3,000. **To Apply:** Applicants must submit a completed application form along with their statement of purpose, college transcripts, recommendation letter on school letterhead, and a resume. To be submitted by the student directly to the ONLA office.

8590 ■ ONLA Scholarships *(Undergraduate, Two Year College, College/Scholarship)*

Purpose: To support students from in Ohio pursuing degrees in horticulture. **Focus:** Horticulture. **Qualif.:** Applicants must be students enrolled full- or part-time in programs at the following schools: The Ohio State University, The Ohio State University Agricultural Technical Institute, Kent State University-Salem, Clark State Community College, Owens Community College, Columbus State Community College, Cuyahoga Community College, Cincinnati State Technical & Community College, Hocking College and the University of Cincinnati. **Criteria:** Selection will be based on academic achievement, school involvement, extracurricular activities, and interest in horticulture.

Funds Avail.: $2,000. **Duration:** Annual. **To Apply:** Applicants must submit a copy of their college acceptance letter, along with information detailing their school's financial office and student account identification numbers, prior to receiving the scholarship funds.

8591 ■ Ohio Rural Electric Cooperatives Inc.
6677 Busch Blvd.
Columbus, OH 43229
Ph: (614)846-5757
Free: 800-282-6962
E-mail: communications@ohioec.org
URL: ohioec.org
Social Media: www.facebook.com/OhioEC
twitter.com/ohelectriccoops
www.youtube.com/c/OhiosElectricCooperatives

8592 ■ Technical Scholarship *(Undergraduate/Scholarship)*

Purpose: To support high school seniors who are pursuing their education at a college, vocational or technical school. **Focus:** General studies/Field of study not specified. **Qua-

lif.: Applicants must be graduating high school senior students whose parents or guardians are electric members of an Ohio rural electric cooperative.

Funds Avail.: $1,400 to $3,800. **Duration:** Annual. **Number Awarded:** Up to 24. **To Apply:** Applicants must submit a completed scholarship application to Ohio Rural Electric Cooperative (OREC). **Deadline:** April 30.

8593 ■ Ohio School Counselor Association (OSCA)
PO Box 1445
Dublin, OH 43017-6445
Ph: (614)401-4642
Fax: (614)401-4642
E-mail: osca@ohioschoolcounselor.org
URL: www.ohioschoolcounselor.org
Social Media: www.facebook.com/ohioschoolcounselor
twitter.com/OSCA_tweets

8594 ■ OSCA Graduate Student Scholarship Program *(Graduate/Scholarship)*

Purpose: To help quality school counseling graduate students fulfill their educational goals. **Focus:** Counseling/Guidance. **Criteria:** Selection will be based on application.

Funds Avail.: $1,000. **Duration:** Annual. **Number Awarded:** 2. **To Apply:** Applicants must submit four complete copies of completed scholarship application form; a typewritten essay of no more than one double-spaced page; copy of official graduate school transcripts showing a minimum of six completed credit hours (may submit one original and three photocopies); professional letter of support written by a current academic adviser or professor. **Deadline:** April 30. **Contact:** Ohio School Counselor Association; E-mail: debgray@ohioschoolcounselor.org.

8595 ■ Ohio Space Grant Consortium (OSGC)
22800 Cedar Point Rd.
Cleveland, OH 44142
Ph: (440)962-3032
Free: 800-828-6742
E-mail: webmaster@osgc.org
URL: www.osgc.org
Social Media: facebook.com/#!/pages/Ohio-Space-Grant-Consortium/142208655827669
www.linkedin.com/in/osgc-ohio-space-grant-consortium-91764754
twitter.com/SpaceGrant_Ohio

8596 ■ Kenneth J. De Witt NASA/OSGC Scholarship at The University of Toledo *(Undergraduate/Scholarship)*

Purpose: To support students who are pursuing careers in the field of Chemical Engineering. **Focus:** Aerospace sciences. **Qualif.:** Applicants must be sophomore undergraduate students majoring in Chemical Engineering at The University of Toledo. **Criteria:** Selection will be based on the committee's criteria.

Funds Avail.: No specific amount. **Duration:** Annual. **To Apply:** Applicants may contact the Center for application process and other information. **Remarks:** Established in 2007. **Contact:** Phone: 419-530-8080.

8597 ■ Paul C. K. Lam Memorial Scholarship at The University of Akron *(Undergraduate/Scholarship)*

Purpose: To support students who are pursuing careers in the field of Mechanical Engineering. **Focus:** Engineering,

Awards are arranged alphabetically below their administering organizations

Mechanical. **Qualif.:** Applicants must be underrepresented undergraduate students majoring in Mechanical Engineering at The University of Akron. **Criteria:** Selection will be based on the committee's criteria.

Funds Avail.: No specific amount. **Duration:** Annual. **To Apply:** Applicants may contact the Center for application process and other information. **Remarks:** Established in 2009. **Contact:** Phone: 330-972-2823.

8598 ■ Ohio Space Grant Consortium Graduate Fellowships *(Graduate, Doctorate, Master's/Fellowship)*

Purpose: To provide financial support through competitively awarded fellowships to Master's and Doctoral students. **Focus:** Engineering; Mathematics and mathematical sciences; Science; Technology. **Qualif.:** Applicants must be Master's and Doctoral students pursuing degrees in one of the STEM disciplines (science, technology, engineering, or mathematics) at OSGC universities. **Criteria:** Selection will be based on the committee's criteria.

Funds Avail.: $16,000. **To Apply:** Applicants must submit a completed application form (available from the website); a resume (maximum of two pages); undergraduate and previous graduate official transcript(s); two completed recommendation forms (in sealed envelopes). Completed application form must be sent or delivered to the Ohio Space Grant Consortium Campus Representative at the member university where you intend to pursue your studies. **Deadline:** February 1.

8599 ■ Ohio Space Grant Consortium Special Minority Fellowships *(Doctorate, Graduate, Master's/ Fellowship)*

Purpose: To provide financial support through competitively awarded fellowships to Master's and Doctoral students. **Focus:** Engineering; Mathematics and mathematical sciences; Science; Technology. **Qualif.:** Applicants must be underrepresented-underserved minority seniors who are holders of undergraduate OSGC scholarships at any of the OSGC universities. **Criteria:** Selection will be based on the committee's criteria.

Funds Avail.: No specific amount. **Duration:** Annual. **Number Awarded:** 1. **To Apply:** Applicants must submit a completed application form (available from the website); a resume (maximum of two pages); undergraduate and previous graduate official transcript(s); two completed recommendation forms (in sealed envelopes). Completed application form must be sent or delivered to the Ohio Space Grant Consortium Campus Representative at the member university where you intend to pursue your studies. **Deadline:** February 1. **Remarks:** Established in 2008.

8600 ■ OSGC Community College Scholarships *(Undergraduate/Scholarship)*

Purpose: To support students who are pursuing careers in science, technology, engineering and mathematics (STEM) fields. **Focus:** Aerospace sciences. **Qualif.:** Applicants must be sophomore students who are United States' citizens and currently enrolled in a program of study at one of the member community colleges, studying in Science, Technology, Engineering and Mathematics (STEM) related discipline. Underrepresented students including women, minorities and persons with disabilities are encouraged to apply. **Criteria:** Selection is competitive and will be based upon the applicants' academic record, written letters of recommendation and the applicants' personal statement and project proposal.

Funds Avail.: $1,000. **To Apply:** Applicants must submit a completed application package that includes a personal objective statement discussing educational and career goals, and the benefits derived from a Space Grant scholarship; one recommendation form (from the Student's Advisor or Campus Representative); official college transcript(s) and; proposed research project. **Deadline:** October 31.

8601 ■ OSGC Education Scholarships *(Undergraduate/Scholarship)*

Purpose: To provide financial support to students pursuing certification and licensure in a Science- or Mathematics-related discipline. **Focus:** Aerospace sciences. **Qualif.:** Applicants must be undergraduate or Post-Baccalaureate students who are United States' citizens, and are pursuing certification and licensure in a Science- or Mathematics-related discipline at an OSGC member university. Underrepresented students including women, minorities and persons with disabilities are encouraged to apply. **Criteria:** Selection is competitive and will be based upon the applicants' academic record, written letters of recommendation and the applicants' personal objective statement and education project proposal.

Funds Avail.: $2,000. **To Apply:** Applicants must submit a complete application package consisting of the following materials: completed education scholarship application form, including personal objective statement and education project proposal; one completed letter of recommendation or education scholarship recommendation form and; transcript(s).

8602 ■ Ohio State University (OSU) - Center for Clinical and Translational Science (CCTS)
260 Prior Hall
376 W 10th Ave.
Columbus, OH 43210
Ph: (614)366-5212
E-mail: ccts-info@osumc.edu
URL: ccts.osu.edu
Social Media: www.facebook.com/OSUCCTS
twitter.com/osu_ccts
www.youtube.com/user/OhioStateCCTS

8603 ■ CCTS services, resources, and pilot awards *(Postdoctorate, Professional development/Grant)*

Purpose: To encourage faculty investigators to address integrated solutions to complex clinical and translational problems. **Focus:** Medical research.

8604 ■ Ohio State University - Kiplinger Program in Public Affairs Journalism
1480 W Lane Ave.
Columbus, OH 43221
Ph: (614)247-0028
E-mail: haddix.12@osu.edu
URL: www.kiplingerprogram.org
Social Media: www.facebook.com/KipProgram
twitter.com/kipprogram

8605 ■ Kiplinger Fellowship *(Professional development/Fellowship)*

Purpose: To help journalists in maximizing the use of new online tools and channels on the online digital revolution. **Focus:** Journalism.

Funds Avail.: Amount not specified. **Duration:** Annual. **Number Awarded:** Varies. **Remarks:** Established in 1973.

Awards are arranged alphabetically below their administering organizations

8606 ■ Ohioana Library Association

274 E 1st Ave., Ste. 300
Columbus, OH 43201
Ph: (614)466-3831
Fax: (614)728-6974
E-mail: ohioana@ohioana.org
URL: www.ohioana.org
Social Media: www.facebook.com/Ohioana
www.instagram.com/ohioanalibrary
twitter.com/Ohioana
www.youtube.com/channel/
   UCQ3TAOhbRpZtNFBsUnlydKg

8607 ■ Walter Rumsey Marvin Grant *(Professional development/Grant)*

Purpose: To recognize an author under 30 years of age who has not had a book published. **Focus:** Literature. **Qualif.:** Applicant must have been born in Ohio or have lived in Ohio for a minimum of five years; must be no older than 30 years of age; must not have had a book published. **Criteria:** Selection are based upon committee criteria.

Funds Avail.: $1,000. **Duration:** Annual. **Number Awarded:** 1. **To Apply:** Application must be submitted online. **Deadline:** January 31. **Contact:** Ohioana Library Association, 274 E. First Ave., Ste. 300, Columbus, OH 43201; David Weaver, Telephone: 614-466-3831; Fax: 614-728-6974; Email: ohioana@ohioana.org.

8608 ■ Oklahoma City University School of Law

800 N Harvey
Oklahoma City, OK 73102
Ph: (405)208-5337
URL: www.okcu.edu
Social Media: www.facebook.com/oculaw
twitter.com/OCULAW

8609 ■ Oklahoma City University Full-Time Merit Scholarships *(Undergraduate/Scholarship)*

Purpose: To provide financial assistance to incoming law students enrolled in the full-time and part-time program who have demonstrated academic excellence at the undergraduate level, and who have a strong performance on the LSAT. **Focus:** Law. **Qualif.:** Applicants must be incoming law students enrolled in the full-time program who have demonstrated academic excellence at the undergraduate level, and a strong performance on the LSAT; must have GPA of 2.0 or above. **Criteria:** Selection will be based on LSAT and GPA average.

Funds Avail.: No specific amount. **Duration:** up to 3 years.

8610 ■ Hatton W. Sumners Scholarships *(Undergraduate/Scholarship)*

Purpose: To provide financial assistance to qualified law students intending to pursue their studies. **Focus:** Law. **Criteria:** Selection will be based on academic proficiency, extra-curricular achievement and demonstrated capacity for public service.

Funds Avail.: No specific amount. **To Apply:** Applicants must complete the application form available online must also submit their undergraduate transcript and three letters of recommendation.

8611 ■ Oklahoma Restaurant Association (ORA)

3800 N Portland Ave.
Oklahoma City, OK 73112
Ph: (405)942-8181
Free: 800-375-8181
URL: www.okrestaurants.com
Social Media: www.facebook.com/okrestaurants
www.instagram.com/okrestaurants/
twitter.com/okrestaurants

8612 ■ Oklahoma Restaurant Association Scholarships *(Other/Scholarship)*

Purpose: To award scholarships to students in pursuit of their undergraduate or continuing education at a post-secondary accredited institution. **Focus:** Culinary arts; Food service careers; Hotel, institutional, and restaurant management.

Funds Avail.: No specific amount. **Duration:** Annual. **To Apply:** Applicants can be submitted online; copies of paycheck stubs from an employer indicating the completion of 250 hours food service related work; two letters of recommendation from a faculty member and industry employer; a copy of high school or college transcript; and (maximum of 500 words, double-spaced) an essay explaining the reasons for applying for the scholarship, plans and career goals. **Deadline:** February 14.

8613 ■ Oklahoma Speech-Language-Hearing Association (OSHA)

3126 S Boulevard St., Ste. 180
Edmond, OK 73013
E-mail: office@oslha.org
URL: www.oslha.org

8614 ■ OSHA Graduate Scholarship *(Doctorate, Master's/Scholarship)*

Purpose: To provide financial assistance to students majoring in speech-language pathology or audiology. **Focus:** Speech and language pathology/Audiology. **Qualif.:** Applicants must be full-time doctoral or masters student in one of the ASHA CAA accredited graduate programs in Oklahoma, majoring in speech-language pathology or audiology. **Criteria:** Selection will be based on the evaluation of submitted documents and specific criteria.

Funds Avail.: $1,000. **Duration:** Annual. **To Apply:** Applicants must submit a completed application form; transcripts; cumulative undergraduate and graduate GPA; description of undergraduate and graduate involvement in pre-professional and volunteer organizations; statement of career objectives and professional interests (not exceeding 500 words); two recommendation letters; brief statement of financial need. Letters of reference should be included in the packet in a sealed envelope with the writer's signature on the outside of the seal. If applicants are incoming first year graduate students, they must submit a copy of acceptance letter into one of the graduate programs in the state. **Deadline:** June 30. **Contact:** Allie Bartlett, 8801 S Olie Ave., Oklahoma City, OK 73139; Phone: 405-601-7192; Email: abartslp@gmail.com.

8615 ■ Olympia Tumwater Foundation (OTF)

110 Deschutes Pky. SW
Tumwater, WA 98501
Ph: (360)943-2550
Fax: (360)943-6755
E-mail: otf@olytumfoundation.org
URL: www.olytumfoundation.org

Awards are arranged alphabetically below their administering organizations

Social Media: www.facebook.com/
 OlympiaTumwaterFoundation
www.instagram.com/olympiatumwaterfoundation

8616 ■ Olympia Tumwater Foundation Traditional Scholarships *(Undergraduate, High School/Scholarship)*

Purpose: To Thurston County graduating high school seniors who plan to attend school within the State of Washington. **Focus:** General studies/Field of study not specified.

Funds Avail.: $5,000-$15,000. **To Apply:** Applicants must submit an application form and following Student Aid Report; School Financial Aid Offers; transcript of records; SAT scores; separate sheet for honors or awards, list of community involvement, essay explaining the reasons for application and describing influential person; letter of recommendation; and applicant's and counselor's signature. **Deadline:** April 22. **Remarks:** Established in 1967. **Contact:** Olympia Tumwater Foundation, PO Box 4098, Tumwater, WA 98501; Phone: 360-943-2550; E-mail: OTF@olytumfoundation.org.

8617 ■ Olympia Tumwater Foundation Transitional (non-traditional) Scholarships *(Undergraduate/Scholarship)*

Purpose: To provide educational assistance for non-traditional students at South Puget Sound Community College, The Evergreen State College and Saint Martin's University. **Focus:** General studies/Field of study not specified. **Qualif.:** Applicants must be a resident of Thurston County; must have completed at least 50% of a degree or certificate program and have an established plan for completion of the program; and must be in good academic standing.

Funds Avail.: No specific amount. **To Apply:** Application forms are available at the financial aid offices of St. Martins University, Sound Puget Community College, and the Evergreen State College. **Remarks:** Established in 1967.

8618 ■ Omicron Delta Kappa Society (ODK)
224 McLaughlin St.
Lexington, VA 24450-2002
Ph: (540)458-5336
Fax: (540)458-5342
Free: 877-635-6437
E-mail: odknhdq@odk.org
URL: www.odk.org
Social Media: www.facebook.com/OmicronDeltaKappa
www.instagram.com/odk_hq
twitter.com/ODK1914

8619 ■ Foundation Scholarships *(Graduate/Scholarship)*

Purpose: To support graduate students with their educational pursuits. **Focus:** General studies/Field of study not specified. **Qualif.:** Applicant must be a voting member of Omicron Delta Kappa as defined in the manual; be a senior at the time of the application or have graduated within the past five years (students who are classified as juniors during the semester/quarter and attain senior standing upon completion of the semester/quarter are not eligible to apply); expected to enroll in an accredited graduate or professional school in the United States or a foreign country within three years of the semester following the award of the

scholarship (students deferring entrance into a graduate school must indicate in the application); and must have earned a cumulative GPA of 3.5 (on a 4.0 scale), or higher, on all academic work attempted for the bachelor's degree. **Criteria:** Selection is based on the application.

Funds Avail.: $1,000 to $2,500. **Duration:** Annual. **Number Awarded:** 25. **To Apply:** Applications can be submitted using the online application. **Deadline:** March 31. **Contact:** Omicron Delta Kappa National Headquarters, c/o Foundation Scholarships Committee, 224 McLaughlin St., Lexington, VA 24450; Associate Executive Director for External Relations, Katy Datz at 540-458-5344, E-mail: scholarships@odk.org.

8620 ■ Omohundro Institute of Early American History and Culture (OIEAHC)
PO Box 8781
Williamsburg, VA 23187-8781
Ph: (757)221-1114
Fax: (757)221-1047
E-mail: oieahc@wm.edu
URL: oieahc.wm.edu

8621 ■ Institute Andrew W. Mellon Postdoctoral Research Fellowships *(Graduate/Fellowship)*

Purpose: To promote study in any area of early American studies. **Focus:** United States studies. **Qualif.:** Applicants must have received their Ph.D. at least 12 months prior to the fellowship; have not previously published a book or have entered into a contract for the publication of a scholarly monograph; proposed fellowship project must not be under contract with another publisher.

Duration: One year. **To Apply:** Applicants must submit one copy of a completed dissertation or book manuscript; completed application form (four copies); curriculum vitae (four copies); samples of work; statement of proposed work; abstract (four copies); and three references sent directly to Beverly Smith, Manager, Institute Administration, Mellon Fellowship. **Deadline:** November 2. **Contact:** ieahc1@wm.edu.

8622 ■ Omohundro Institute-NEH Postdoctoral Fellowships *(Graduate/Fellowship)*

Purpose: To promote study in any area of early American studies. **Focus:** United States studies. **Qualif.:** Applicants must have completed the Ph.D. by the date the fellowship begins; must be a U.S. citizen or have lived in the United States for the three years preceding the fellowship award (required for NEH funding); have not previously published a scholarly book or have entered into a contract for the publication of a scholarly monograph; proposed fellowship project must not be under contract with another publisher. **Criteria:** Selection will be based on candidate's dissertation or other manuscript has significant potential as a distinguished, book-length contribution to scholarship.

Funds Avail.: No specific amount. **Duration:** Annual. **Deadline:** November 1. **Contact:** E-mail: oieahc@wm.edu.

8623 ■ On Q Financial
615 S River Dr., Ste. 170
Tempe, AZ 85281
Free: 866-667-3279
URL: onqfinancial.com
Social Media: www.facebook.com/onqfinancial

Awards are arranged alphabetically below their administering organizations

www.linkedin.com/company/on-q-financial-inc

8624 ■ The Dream is Inclusive Scholarship (Two Year College, Undergraduate, Graduate, Professional development, Vocational/Occupational/Scholarship)

Purpose: To help students pay for higher education. **Focus:** General studies/Field of study not specified. **Qualif.:** Applicants must be of Russian, Spanish, or Chinese descent; high school graduates; legal residents of the United States or the District of Columbia; and currently enrolled or planning to enroll in an accredited post-secondary institution of higher education. **Criteria:** Selection will be based on response to the essay question.

Funds Avail.: $1,500. **Number Awarded:** 3. **To Apply:** Application and essay must be completed online. **Deadline:** July 31. **Contact:** Email: marketingteam@onqfinancial.com; URL: onqfinancial.com/scholarship/.

8625 ■ Oncology Nursing Society Foundation
125 Enterprise Dr.
Pittsburgh, PA 15275-1214
Ph: (412)859-6228
Fax: (412)859-6163
Free: 866-257-4667
E-mail: info@onsfoundation.org
URL: www.onsfoundation.org
Social Media: www.facebook.com/onsfoundation
twitter.com/onsfoundation
youtube.com/user/onsfoundationvideos

8626 ■ Bachelor's in Nursing Degree Scholarship (Undergraduate/Scholarship)

Purpose: To provide funding to individuals interested in and committed to oncology nursing and pursuing a baccalaureate degree in nursing. **Focus:** Nursing, Oncological. **Qualif.:** Applicants must be currently enrolled for their senior year of a bachelor of nursing degree program at an NLN or CCNE accredited School of Nursing in the given academic year.

Funds Avail.: $3,000 to $5,000 each. **Duration:** Annual. **Number Awarded:** Varies. **Deadline:** February 1.

8627 ■ Clinical Project Funding for Advanced Practice Oncology Nurses (Advanced Professional, Professional development/Grant)

Purpose: To provide support for a clinical project for the purpose of facilitating innovative solutions to the challenges of delivering patient-centered, evidenced based and accessible care. **Focus:** Nursing, Oncological. **Qualif.:** Applicants must be graduates Master of Nursing (MN), Master of Science in Nursing (MSN), or Doctor of Nursing Practice (DNP) programs; and must be currently practicing in an Advanced Practice Nurses (APN) role. **Criteria:** Selection will be based on the committee's criteria.

Funds Avail.: Up to $5,000 per year. **Duration:** Two years. **To Apply:** Applicants may contact the Foundation for the application process and other information. **Contact:** ONS Research Department at research@onsfoundation.org.

8628 ■ Oncology Nursing Society Foundation - Doctoral Scholarships (Doctorate/Scholarship)

Purpose: To provide funding to registered nurses interested in and committed to oncology nursing to continue their education by pursuing a doctoral degree. **Focus:** Nursing,

Oncological. **Qualif.:** Applicants must: be currently enrolled in (or applying to) a doctoral nursing degree or related program; have their current licenses to practice as registered nurses; and, have an interest in and commitment to oncology nursing. Applicants entering a doctoral program without master's degree must have completed the first two years of the doctoral program curriculum.

Funds Avail.: $5,000 and $7,500. **Duration:** Annual. **Number Awarded:** Varies. **Deadline:** February 1.

8629 ■ Oncology Nursing Society Foundation - Master's Scholarships (Graduate, Master's/Scholarship)

Purpose: To provide scholarships to registered nurses who are interested in and committed to oncology nursing to continue their education by pursuing a master's degree in nursing. **Focus:** Nursing, Oncological. **Qualif.:** Applicants must: be currently enrolled in (or applying to) a master's nursing degree at an NLN or CCNE accredited School of Nursing; have their current licenses to practice as registered nurses; and, have an interest in and commitment to oncology nursing.

Funds Avail.: $5,000. **Duration:** Annual. **Number Awarded:** Varies. **Deadline:** February 1.

8630 ■ ONS Foundation Congress Scholarships (Professional development/Scholarship)

Purpose: To support registered nurses interested in improving cancer care by developing their personal knowledge as a result of attending the ONS Congress and sharing this new knowledge with others. **Focus:** Nursing, Oncological. **Qualif.:** Applicants must be registered nurses living or working within a 50 mile radius of the conference location.

Funds Avail.: $1,200. **Deadline:** December 1.

8631 ■ Research Career Development Award (Professional development/Grant)

Purpose: To support short-term oncology research training and mentorship. **Focus:** Nursing, Oncological. **Qualif.:** Applicants must be registered nurses with an interest in oncology and with a completed PhD degree in nursing or a related discipline.

Funds Avail.: $20,000 ($18,000 for the fellows; $2,000 for the mentor or mentor's institution). **Deadline:** July 1. **Remarks:** The Research Career Development Award is funded by the ONS Foundation through an unrestricted grant from Genentech BioOncology. **Contact:** Email: info@onsfoundation.org.

8632 ■ Research Grant Funding (RE01) (Advanced Professional/Grant)

Purpose: To support oncology nursing research. **Focus:** Nursing, Oncological. **Qualif.:** Applicants must be principal investigators who are actively involved in some aspect of cancer patient care, education, or research; and must be PhD- or DNSc-prepared. **Criteria:** Selection will be based on the Foundation's criteria. Funding preference will be given to projects that involve nurses in the design and conduct of the research activity and that promote theoretically based oncology practice.

Funds Avail.: $25,000 each. **Duration:** Two years. **To Apply:** Applications should be submitted with prior Letter of Intent approval. **Deadline:** October 1. **Contact:** Email: info@onsfoundation.org.

Awards are arranged alphabetically below their administering organizations

8633 ■ One Source Process Inc.

1133 13th St., NW, Ste. C4
Washington, DC 20005
Ph: (202)459-4760
Fax: (202)449-4115
Free: 800-668-5448
E-mail: info@onesourceprocess.com
URL: onesourceprocess.com

8634 ■ One Source Process Inc. Scholarship
(Undergraduate, Graduate/Scholarship)

Purpose: To help students in the legal field afford a college education. **Focus:** Law. **Qualif.:** Applicants must be U.S. citizens accepted to or currently attending a legal program at a college or university within the United States. **Criteria:** Selection will be made randomly.

Funds Avail.: $1,000. **Number Awarded:** 1. **To Apply:** Applications should be completed online at www.onesourceprocess.com/scholarship. **Deadline:** December 15. **Contact:** Email: kbrown@straightnorth.com.

8635 ■ Ontario Centres of Excellence (OCE)

325 Front St., W Ste. 300
Toronto, ON, Canada M5V 2Y1
Ph: (416)861-1092
Fax: (416)971-7164
Free: 866-759-6014
URL: www.oce-ontario.org

8636 ■ Martin Walmsley Award for Entrepreneurship *(Graduate/Award)*

Purpose: To support a researcher committed to founding in Ontario a new technologically innovative business (TIB) venture. **Focus:** Business. **Qualif.:** Applicant must be a graduate student's business founded on university-based research. **Criteria:** Selection will be based on the committee's criteria.

Funds Avail.: $25,000. **Duration:** Annual. **Number Awarded:** Varies. **To Apply:** The application process is online.

8637 ■ Ontario English Catholic Teachers Association

65 St. Claire Ave. E, Ste. 400
Toronto, ON, Canada M4T 2Y8
Ph: (416)925-2493
Fax: (416)925-7764
Free: 800-268-7230
URL: www.oecta.on.ca
Social Media: www.facebook.com/OECTA
twitter.com/OECTAProv

8638 ■ Cecilia Rowan Memorial Fellowship
(Postgraduate/Fellowship)

Purpose: To support members seeking full-time study in religious education. **Focus:** Education, Religious. **Qualif.:** Applicants must be OECTA members and fully qualified and certificated teacher; Be a statutory or voluntary member in good standing in the Association.

Funds Avail.: 10,000 Canadian Dollars. **Duration:** Annual. **To Apply:** Applicants must include three reference letters, one of which must be from your OECTA Unit President, with your application; must be summit Statement of acceptance for post-graduate study; Statement of Release from the Board; current copy of your Ontario Teaching Certificate; Short resume of studies. **Deadline:** April 1. **Contact:** Awards Committee, c/o OECTA, 65 St. Clair Ave., E., Ste. 400, Toronto, ON, M4T 2Y8; Phone: 416-925-6912; Email: awards@oecta.on.ca.

8639 ■ Doreen Brady Memorial Scholarship
(Postgraduate/Scholarship)

Purpose: To financially assist members with their full-time post-graduate study. **Focus:** General studies/Field of study not specified. **Qualif.:** Applicants must be OECTA members and need to hold a university degree acceptable to the Ontario Ministry of Education for either a Certificate of Qualification from the Ontario College of Teachers or for entrance to a faculty of education.

Funds Avail.: 10,000 Canadian Dollars. **Duration:** Annual. **To Apply:** Applicants must submit a statement of acceptability as a full-time student or equivalent status at the university of choice and submit a resume of the proposed studies. **Deadline:** April 1. **Contact:** Awards Committee, c/o OECTA, 65 St. Clair Ave., E., Ste. 400, Toronto, ON, M4T 2Y8; Phone: 416-925-6912; Email: awards@oecta.on.ca.

8640 ■ Father J. Harold Conway Memorial Scholarship *(Postgraduate/Scholarship)*

Purpose: To financially assist members with their full-time post-graduate study. **Focus:** General studies/Field of study not specified. **Qualif.:** Applicants must be OECTA members and need to hold a university degree acceptable to the Ontario Ministry of Education for either a Certificate of Qualification from the Ontario College of Teachers or for entrance to a faculty of education.

Funds Avail.: 10,000 Canadian Dollars. **Duration:** Annual. **To Apply:** Applicants must submit a statement of acceptability as a full-time student or equivalent status at the university of choice and submit a resume of the proposed studies. **Deadline:** April 1. **Contact:** Awards Committee, c/o OECTA, 65 St. Clair Ave., E., Ste. 400, Toronto, ON, M4T 2Y8; Phone: 416-925-6912; Email: awards@oecta.on.ca.

8641 ■ Joan Rogers Kamps Bursary *(Undergraduate, Postgraduate, Professional development/Scholarship)*

Purpose: To financially assist members with their continuing education. **Focus:** General studies/Field of study not specified. **Qualif.:** Applicants must be a statutory or voluntary member in good standing in the Association. **Criteria:** Selection will be based on committee's criteria; members in pre-degree categories taking undergraduate courses are given priority, but those who want to pursue post-graduate studies or professional development activities are also eligible.

Funds Avail.: 1,000 Canadian Dollars. **Duration:** Annual. **To Apply:** Applicants must submit a current copy of the applicant's Ontario Teaching Certificate of Qualifications and Registration and A copy of the course description, including cost, date of course commencement and name of institution. **Deadline:** May 1. **Contact:** Awards Committee, c/o OECTA, 65 St. Clair Ave., E., Ste. 400, Toronto, ON, M4T 2Y8; Phone: 416-925-6912; Email: awards@oecta.on.ca.

8642 ■ Margaret Lynch Memorial Fellowship
(Postgraduate/Fellowship)

Purpose: To support members seeking full-time study in religious education. **Focus:** Education, Religious. **Qualif.:**

Awards are arranged alphabetically below their administering organizations

Applicants must be OECTA members and fully qualified and certificated teacher; Be a statutory or voluntary member in good standing in the Association. **Funds Avail.:** 10,000 Canadian Dollars. **Duration:** Annual. **To Apply:** Applicants must include three reference letters, one of which must be from your OECTA Unit President, with your application; must be summit Statement of acceptance for post-graduate study; Statement of Release from the Board; current copy of your Ontario Teaching Certificate; Short resume of studies. **Deadline:** April 1. **Contact:** Awards Committee, c/o OECTA, 65 St. Clair Ave., E., Ste. 400, Toronto, ON, M4T 2Y8; Phone: 416-925-6912; Email: awards@oecta.on.ca.

8643 ■ Mary C. Babcock Fellowship (Postgraduate/ Fellowship)

Purpose: To support members seeking full-time study in labour studies. **Focus:** Industrial and labor relations. **Qualif.:** Applicants must be OECTA members and fully qualified and certificated teacher; Be a statutory or voluntary member in good standing in the Association. **Funds Avail.:** 10,000 Canadian Dollars. **Duration:** Annual. **To Apply:** Applicants must include three reference letters, one of which must be from your OECTA Unit President, with your application; must be summit Statement of acceptance for post-graduate study; Statement of Release from the Board; current copy of your Ontario Teaching Certificate; Short resume of studies. **Deadline:** April 1. **Contact:** Awards Committee, c/o OECTA, 65 St. Clair Ave., E., Ste. 400, Toronto, ON, M4T 2Y8; Phone: 416-925-6912; Email: awards@oecta.on.ca.

8644 ■ Rose Cassin Memorial Scholarship (Postgraduate/Scholarship)

Purpose: To financially assist members with their full-time post-graduate study. **Focus:** General studies/Field of study not specified. **Qualif.:** Applicants must be OECTA members and need to hold a university degree acceptable to the Ontario Ministry of Education for either a Certificate of Qualification from the Ontario College of Teachers or for entrance to a faculty of education. **Funds Avail.:** 10,000 Canadian Dollars. **Duration:** Annual. **To Apply:** Applicants must submit a statement of acceptability as a full-time student or equivalent status at the university of choice and submit a resume of the proposed studies. **Deadline:** April 1. **Contact:** Awards Committee, c/o OECTA, 65 St. Clair Ave., E., Ste. 400, Toronto, ON, M4T 2Y8; Phone: 416-925-6912; Email: awards@ oecta.on.ca.

8645 ■ Ontario Medical Association (OMA)

150 Bloor St. W, Ste. 900
Toronto, ON, Canada M5S 3C1
Ph: (416)599-2580
Fax: (416)599-9309
Free: 800-268-7215
E-mail: info@oma.org
URL: www.oma.org
Social Media: www.facebook.com/Ontariosdoctors
www.instagram.com/ontariosdoctors/
www.linkedin.com/company/ontario-medical-association
twitter.com/OntariosDoctors
www.youtube.com/user/OntMedAssociation

8646 ■ Burlington Medical Student Bursary (Undergraduate/Grant)

Purpose: To support a student pursuing a specific medical specialty, or from a certain area of the province. **Focus:** Medicine. **Qualif.:** Applicants must be current residents or high school graduates of Burlington enrolled or planning to enroll in a medical program at an institution of higher education. **Criteria:** Selection will be based on the applicants demonstrated financial need and academic standing. **Funds Avail.:** 2,000 Canadian dollars. **Duration:** Annual. **To Apply:** Application details are available in September of each year online at www.ontariomedicalfoundation.ca/named-bursaries/. **Deadline:** January 31.

8647 ■ Dr. Gilbert Hopson Medical Student Bursary (Undergraduate/Grant)

Purpose: To support a student pursuing a specific medical specialty, or from a certain area of the province. **Focus:** Medicine. **Qualif.:** Applicants must be current residents or high school graduates of Sault Ste. Marie who are enrolled or enrolling in a medical program at an post-secondary institution. **Criteria:** Selection will be based on the applicants' demonstrated financial need and academic standing. **Funds Avail.:** 2,000 Canadian Dollars. **Duration:** Annual. **To Apply:** Application details are available in September of each year online at www.ontariomedicalfoundation.ca/named-bursaries/. **Deadline:** January 31. **Remarks:** Established by Algoma West Academy of Medicine in memory of the late Dr. Gilbert Hopson.

8648 ■ Dr. Arlene MacIntyre Medical Student Bursary (Undergraduate/Grant, Recognition)

Purpose: To support a student pursuing a specific medical specialty, or from a certain area of the province. **Focus:** Medicine. **Qualif.:** Applicants must be in their final year of their study and have a plan to pursue family medicine. **Criteria:** Selection will be based on the applicants' demonstrated financial need and academic standing. **Funds Avail.:** 2,000 Canadian Dollars. **To Apply:** Application details are available in September of each year online at www.ontariomedicalfoundation.ca/named-bursaries/. **Deadline:** January 31. **Remarks:** Established by the estate of the late Doris C. Boes to honor Dr. Arlene MacIntyre for her compassionate care of patients.

8649 ■ OMSBF District Four - Physician Care Bursary (Undergraduate/Grant)

Purpose: To support a student pursuing a specific medical specialty, or from a certain area of the province. **Focus:** Medicine. **Qualif.:** Applicants must be current residents or high school graduates of District 4 (Acton, Alberton, Ancaster, Beamsville, Binbrook, Burlington, Burnaby, Caistor Centre, Caledonia, Campbellville, Canfield, Carlisle, Cayuga, Crystal Beach, Dundas, Dunnville, Fenwick, Fisherville, Flamborough, Fonthill, Fort Erie, Freelton, Fruitland, Greensville, Grimsby, Hagersville, Halton Hills, Hamilton, Hornby, Jarvis, Jerseyville, Jordan, Jordan Station, Kilbride, Lowbanks, Lynden, Millgrove, Milton, Moffat, Mount Hope, Nanticoke, Niagara Falls, Niagara-on-the-Lake, Oakville, Oneida Settlement, Pelham, Port Colborne, Queenston, Ridgeville, Ridgeway, Rockton, Smithville, Snowville, St. Anns, St. Catharine's, St. David's, Stevensville, Stoney Creek, Thorold, Townsend, Troy, Vineland, Vineland Station, Virgil, Wainfleet, Waterdown, Welland, Wellandport, West Flamborough, Winona, York); and have the intention of practicing in a community in District 4. **Criteria:** Selection will be based on the applicants' demonstrated financial need and academic standing. **Funds Avail.:** 2,000 Canadian dollars. **To Apply:** Applicants must provide a brief description of plan in cover

Awards are arranged alphabetically below their administering organizations

letter. Application details are available in September of each year online at www.ontariomedicalfoundation.ca/named-bursaries/. **Deadline:** January 31.

8650 ■ Sun Life Financial Medical Student Bursary
(Undergraduate/Grant)

Purpose: To assist financially challenged medical students. **Focus:** Medicine. **Qualif.:** Applicants must be achieving academic excellence and in good academic standing and enrolled or enrolling in a medical program in a post-secondary institution. **Criteria:** Selection will be based on the applicant's demonstrated financial need and academic standing.

Funds Avail.: 2,000 Canadian Dollars. **To Apply:** Application details are available in September of each year online at www.ontariomedicalfoundation.ca/named-bursaries/. **Deadline:** January 31.

8651 ■ Ontario Ministry of Children and Youth Services
77 Wellesley St. W
Toronto, ON, Canada M7A 1N3
Fax: (416)212-1977
Free: 866-821-7770
E-mail: mcsinfo@mcys.gov.on.ca
URL: www.children.gov.on.ca

8652 ■ Grant Assistance Program for Autism Professionals - College Programs *(Undergraduate/Grant)*

Purpose: To support qualified staff in their college level study. **Focus:** Mental health; Psychology. **Qualif.:** Applicants must be full-time or part-time employees working in MCYS funded Autism Intervention Program or Applied Behaviour Analysis (ABA)-based services and support for at least one year continuously at the time of application and employed as members of the program's team involved directly in the provision of IBI and/or ABA-based interventions; legally entitled to live and work in Canada; and enrolled in or accepted to The Ontario College Graduate Certificate in Autism and Behavioural Science, or any advanced diploma or applied degree in behavioural science or behavioural psychology. **Criteria:** Applicants are selected based on eligibility and compliance with the application process.

Funds Avail.: Up to 5,000 Canadian Dollars. **Duration:** Quarterly; up to two or more years. **To Apply:** Applicants must submit a completed application in addition to that the letter of employment from the regional Autism Intervention Program provider or the ABA-based services and supports provider; documented proof of enrolment in or acceptance to a qualifying academic program; and copy of tuition receipts for courses completed to date. **Deadline:** May 31; August 31; November 30; February 28. **Contact:** Applications must be sent to the Grant Assistance Program Administrator, North Bay Regional Health Centre, 680 Kirkwood Drive, Sudbury, ON P3E 1X3; Phone: 705-675-9193 ext. 8411; Email: info@autismgrantprogram.on.ca.

8653 ■ Grant Assistance Program for Autism Professionals - Doctoral Programs *(Doctorate/Grant)*

Purpose: To support qualified staff in their pursuit of a doctoral degree in clinical or behavioral psychology with a focus on autism or behavior analysis. **Focus:** Mental health; Psychology. **Qualif.:** Applicants must be full-time or part-time employees working in MCYS funded Autism Intervention Program or Applied Behaviour Analysis (ABA)-based services and support for at least one year continuously at the time of application and employed as members of the program's team involved directly in the provision of IBI and/or ABA-based interventions; legally entitled to live and work in Canada; and enrolled in or accepted to any doctoral program in clinical or behavioural psychology with a focus on autism or behaviour analysis. **Criteria:** Applicants are selected based on eligibility and compliance with the application process.

Funds Avail.: 24,000 Canadian Dollars. **Duration:** Quarterly; up to three or more years. **To Apply:** Applicants must submit a completed application in addition to that the letter of employment from the regional Autism Intervention Program provider or the ABA-based services and supports provider; documented proof of enrolment in or acceptance to a qualifying academic program; and copy of tuition receipts for courses completed to date. **Deadline:** May 31; August 31; November 30; February 28. **Contact:** Applications must be sent to the Grant Assistance Program Administrator, North Bay Regional Health Centre, 680 Kirkwood Drive, Sudbury, ON P3E 1X3; Phone: 705-675-9193 ext. 8411; Email: info@autismgrantprogram.on.ca.

8654 ■ Grant Assistance Program for Autism Professionals - Institutional Standards *(Undergraduate, Graduate/Grant)*

Purpose: To support qualified staff in obtaining their degree in clinical or behavioral psychology. **Focus:** Mental health; Psychology. **Qualif.:** Applicants must be full-time or part-time employees working in MCYS funded Autism Intervention Program or Applied Behaviour Analysis (ABA)-based services and support for at least one year continuously at the time of application (or cumulatively in the case of applicants from isolated communities) and employed as members of the program's team involved directly in the provision of IBI and/or ABA-based interventions; legally entitled to live and work in Canada; and enrolled in or accepted to any college diploma or applied degree (toward professional certification) offered by an accredited Ontario college of applied arts and technology or by a college or diploma-granting institution in another jurisdiction operating in conformity with the applicable laws of that jurisdiction; or, any undergraduate, Master's or doctoral degree (toward professional certification) offered by a duly established university or degree-granting institution in Canada or by a university or degree-granting institution in another jurisdiction operating in conformity with the laws of that jurisdiction where available, accredited by a recognized institutional accrediting agency or association. **Criteria:** Applicants are selected based on eligibility and compliance with the application process.

Duration: Quarterly. **To Apply:** Applicants must submit a completed application in addition to that the letter of employment from the regional Autism Intervention Program provider or the ABA-based services and supports provider; documented proof of enrolment in or acceptance to a qualifying academic program; and copy of tuition receipts for courses completed to date. **Deadline:** May 31; August 31; November 30; February 28. **Contact:** Applications must be sent to the Grant Assistance Program Administrator, North Bay Regional Health Centre, 680 Kirkwood Drive, Sudbury, ON P3E 1X3; Phone: 705-675-9193 ext. 8411; Email: info@autismgrantprogram.on.ca.

Awards are arranged alphabetically below their administering organizations

8655 ■ Grant Assistance Program for Autism Professionals - Masters Programs *(Master's/Grant)*

Purpose: To support qualified staff in their graduate level study. **Focus:** Mental health; Psychology. **Qualif.:** Applicants must be full-time or part-time employees working in MCYS funded Autism Intervention Program or Applied Behaviour Analysis (ABA)-based services and support for at least one year continuously at the time of application and employed as members of the program's team involved directly in the provision of IBI and/or ABA-based interventions; legally entitled to live and work in Canada; and enrolled in or accepted to Master of Applied Disability Studies at Brock University or any Master's program specializing in clinical or behavioural psychology or behaviour analysis. **Criteria:** Applicants are selected based on eligibility and compliance with the application process.

Funds Avail.: Up to 12,000 Canadian Dollars. **Duration:** Quarterly; up to three or more years. **To Apply:** Applicants must submit a completed application in addition to that the letter of employment from the regional Autism Intervention Program provider or the ABA-based services and supports provider; documented proof of enrolment in or acceptance to a qualifying academic program; and copy of tuition receipts for courses completed to date. **Deadline:** May 31; August 31; November 30; February 28. **Contact:** Applications must be sent to the Grant Assistance Program Administrator, North Bay Regional Health Centre, 680 Kirkwood Drive, Sudbury, ON P3E 1X3; Phone: 705-675-9193 ext. 8411; Email: info@autismgrantprogram.on.ca.

8656 ■ Grant Assistance Program for Autism Professionals - Professional Certification Programs *(Undergraduate, Professional development/Grant)*

Purpose: To support qualified staff in their pursuit of professional certification. **Focus:** Mental health; Psychology. **Qualif.:** Applicants must be enrolled in any college, undergraduate or graduate course or courses required by a recognized accreditation authority within the field of behavioral analysis in order to qualify for professional certification under the rules of the accreditation authority; be legally entitled to live and work in Canada; be enrolled in or accepted to a qualifying academic program for full or part-time study. **Criteria:** Applicants are selected based on eligibility and compliance with the application process.

Funds Avail.: Up to 1,000 Canadian Dollars after one year or up to 5,000 Canadian Dollars over two or more years. **Duration:** Quarterly; up to two or more years. **To Apply:** Applicants must submit a completed application in addition to that the letter of employment from the regional Autism Intervention Program provider or the ABA-based services and supports provider; documented proof of enrolment in or acceptance to a qualifying academic program; and copy of tuition receipts for courses completed to date. **Deadline:** May 31; August 31; November 30; February 28. **Contact:** Applications must be sent to the Grant Assistance Program Administrator, North Bay Regional Health Centre, 680 Kirkwood Drive, Sudbury, ON P3E 1X3; Phone: 705-675-9193 ext. 8411; Email: info@autismgrantprogram.on.ca.

8657 ■ Grant Assistance Program for Autism Professionals - Retroactive Assistance *(Advanced Professional, Professional development/Grant)*

Purpose: To support qualified staff who are seeking professional development. **Focus:** Mental health; Psychology. **Qualif.:** Applicants must be individuals who qualify for grant assistance but have already completed a qualifying academic program (any of the following: doctoral; profes-

sional certification; master's; undergraduate; college or institutional standards), providing they completed the program within five years prior to application date and they continue in the employment of Autism Intervention Program or ABA-based services and supports for the duration of the funding agreement. **Criteria:** Selection will be based on the applicants' eligibility and compliance with the application process.

Funds Avail.: No specific amount. **Duration:** Quarterly. **To Apply:** Applicants must submit a completed application in addition to a letter of employment from the regional Autism Intervention Program provider or the ABA-based services and supports provider; documented proof of enrolment in or acceptance to a qualifying academic program; and copy of tuition receipts for courses completed to date. **Deadline:** May 31; August 31; November 30; February 28. **Contact:** Applications must be sent to the Grant Assistance Program Administrator, North Bay Regional Health Centre, 680 Kirkwood Drive, Sudbury, ON P3E 1X3; Phone: 705-675-9193 ext. 8411; Email: info@autismgrantprogram.on.ca.

8658 ■ Grant Assistance Program for Autism Professionals - Undergraduate Programs *(Undergraduate/Grant)*

Purpose: To assist qualified staff in their professional development and pursuit of a degree in psychology. **Focus:** Mental health; Psychology. **Qualif.:** Applicants must be full-time or part-time employees working in MCYS funded Autism Intervention Program or Applied Behaviour Analysis (ABA)-based services and support for at least one year continuously at the time of application (or cumulatively in the case of applicants from isolated communities) and employed as members of the program's team involved directly in the provision of IBI and/or ABA-based interventions; legally entitled to live and work in Canada; and enrolled in or accepted to any undergraduate degree in psychology or any undergraduate degree with a major in psychology. **Criteria:** Applicants are selected based on eligibility and compliance with the application process.

Funds Avail.: Up to 12,000 Canadian Dollars. **Duration:** Quarterly; up to three or more years. **To Apply:** Applicants must submit a completed application in addition to that the letter of employment from the regional Autism Intervention Program provider or the ABA-based services and supports provider; documented proof of enrolment in or acceptance to a qualifying academic program; and copy of tuition receipts for courses completed to date. **Deadline:** May 31; August 31; November 30; February 28. **Contact:** Applications must be sent to the Grant Assistance Program Administrator, North Bay Regional Health Centre, 680 Kirkwood Drive, Sudbury, ON P3E 1X3; Phone: 705-675-9193 ext. 8411; Email: info@autismgrantprogram.on.ca.

8659 ■ Ontario Native Education Counselling Association (ONECA)

37 A Reserve Rd.
Naughton, ON, Canada P0M 2M0
Ph: (705)692-2999
Fax: (705)692-9988
E-mail: oneca@oneca.com
URL: www.oneca.com
Social Media: www.facebook.com/Ontario-Native
   -Education-Counselling-Association-375571329178886/
www.instagram.com/oneca_transitional
twitter.com/ONECA_COMMS

Awards are arranged alphabetically below their administering organizations

8660 ■ ONECA Four Directions Scholarship
(Undergraduate/Scholarship)

Purpose: To support graduating aboriginal secondary school/adult students in their continuing education. **Focus:** General studies/Field of study not specified. **Qualif.:** Applicants must be students of aboriginal ancestry graduating from an Ontario Secondary School with O.S.S.D of the current school year; maintain good academic standing throughout the school year; 75% overall average in graduating year; proceeding into a post-secondary institution full time program; be involved in the community and/or school extra-curricular-activities; be recommended by secondary school, First Nation Community or Education Counsellor; and have leadership qualities, dedication and good attendance. **Criteria:** Selection will be based on leadership qualities, dedication and good attendance.

Funds Avail.: 1,000 Canadian Dollars. **Duration:** Annual. **Number Awarded:** 4. **To Apply:** Applicants should complete and submit the application form available online and must include a copy of letter of acceptance into second year of the program; proof of Aboriginal Ancestry; biography and one paragraph describing how a scholarship would assist them; letter of recommendation from school, First Nation or Education Counselor; copy of final marks for 1st year of the program; copies of awards, diplomas or other supporting documents; a recent photo; signed release form which allows the Association to post the applicants' name and picture to the website; signed authorization form agreeing to allow the post-secondary institution to release information regarding the attendance at the time the awards are selected. **Deadline:** June 29; July 31. **Remarks:** Established in 2004. **Contact:** Submissions must be sent to the following address: Ontario Native Education Counselling Association, PO Box 220, 37A Reserve Road, Naughton, Ontario.

8661 ■ Colin Wasacase Scholarship *(Undergraduate/Scholarship)*

Purpose: To support aboriginal post-secondary college students and post-secondary university students who have successfully completed their first year in a full-time program in the field of counseling. **Focus:** Counseling/Guidance. **Qualif.:** Applicants must be full-time post-secondary students of aboriginal ancestry; have successfully completed their first year in a Counseling program at an Ontario Post Secondary Institution; have an good academic standing throughout the first school year; have a 75% overall average in first year; be proceeding into the second year of the same program; and, be involved in the community or school extra-curricular activities. **Criteria:** Selection will be based on leadership qualities, dedication and good attendance.

Funds Avail.: 1,000 Canadian Dollars. **Duration:** Annual. **Number Awarded:** Varies. **To Apply:** Applicants should complete and submit the application form available online and must include a copy of letter of acceptance into second year of the program; proof of Aboriginal Ancestry; biography and one paragraph describing how a scholarship would assist them; letter of recommendation from school, First Nation or Education Counselor; copy of final marks for 1st year of the program; copies of awards, diplomas or other supporting documents; a recent photo; signed release form which allows the Association to post the applicants' name and picture to the website; signed authorization form agreeing to allow the post-secondary institution to release information regarding the attendance at the time the awards are selected; 500-word essay outlining why the applicants

have chosen this career path. **Deadline:** June 30. **Remarks:** Established in 2004.

8662 ■ Open Society Foundations
224 W 57th St.
New York, NY 10019-3212
Ph: (212)548-0600
Fax: (212)548-4600
URL: www.opensocietyfoundations.org
Social Media: www.facebook.com/
  OpenSocietyFoundations
www.instagram.com/opensocietyfoundations
www.linkedin.com/company/open-society-foundations
twitter.com/opensociety
www.youtube.com/c/opensociety

8663 ■ Baltimore Community Fellowships
(Advanced Professional/Fellowship)

Purpose: To seek dynamic activists and social entrepreneurs interested in implementing projects that address problems in underserved communities in Baltimore city. **Focus:** Economics; Social sciences. **Qualif.:** Applicants may come from any field, including, but not limited to law, medicine, drug addiction solutions, education, the arts, race relations, and juvenile and criminal justice; must be from Baltimore city and knowledgeable about social and economic justice issues affecting Baltimore's communities and must be willing to participate fully in meetings scheduled for the Community Fellows. **Criteria:** Selection will be based on the applicant's eligibility and compliance with the application process.

Funds Avail.: $60,000. **To Apply:** Applicants must submit two copies of the application. The application can be found in the Download Files section of the website. **Remarks:** Established in 1998.

8664 ■ Open Society Fellowship *(Other/Fellowship)*

Purpose: To support individuals seeking innovative and unconventional approaches to fundamental open society challenges. **Focus:** General studies/Field of study not specified. **Criteria:** The fellowship does not fund enrollment for degree or nondegree study at academic institutions, including dissertation research.

Funds Avail.: $80,000-$100,000. **To Apply:** Applicants are first required to submit a one- to two page, single-spaced, letter of inquiry that outlines the topic of the project, proposed work product, and relevance to the proposition; A CV should accompany the letter of inquiry. **Remarks:** Established in 2008.

8665 ■ Open Society Presidential Fellowship
(Graduate/Fellowship)

Purpose: To encourage aspiring fellows to pursue work related to human rights, good governance and justice. **Focus:** Business; Law; Public affairs. **Qualif.:** Applicants must be recent J.D., MPA, MPP and MBA graduates from accredited U.S. law, public policy and business schools. **Criteria:** Selection will be based on the applicant's scholarship, leadership and commitment to continued practice in the fields of nonprofit management, human rights, good governance and justice.

Funds Avail.: $65,000. **Duration:** 11/year. **Number Awarded:** 3. **To Apply:** Application must be; resume; official transcript; two letters of recommendation.

Awards are arranged alphabetically below their administering organizations

8666 ■ Soros Justice Advocacy Fellowships - Track I *(Professional development/Fellowship)*

Purpose: To advance professional growth, support career development, and both seed and deepen leadership in the field of criminal justice reform. **Focus:** Criminal justice. **Qualif.:** Applicants must have at least two (2) years of relevant advocacy experience, which may include full-time and part-time employment; paid or unpaid internships; longer term experience as advocates, organizers or researchers; or other pertinent experience (e.g. advocacy while incarcerated). **Criteria:** Applications will be evaluated on the extent to which the applicants possess the vision, drive, and skills required to create and sustain a project that will advance one or more of the Open Society Foundations' U.S. criminal justice reform goals or priorities. In evaluating applications, the program will consider: project need; project approach; project goals, objectives, and activities; and the applicant's eligibility.

Funds Avail.: $87,000 over 18 months. **To Apply:** Applicants must submit their applications via online. On the online system, applicants will have to provide basic contact information and register with the system. Once registered, applicants will be able to proceed to the application itself. All communications from the Open Society Foundations regarding applications will be sent to the email used to register with the online system, so applicants should ensure that email communications from Open Society Foundations do not end up in their "Junk Mail" folder. Complete applications consist of a number of documents that must be uploaded to the online application system: resume, proposal (single-spaced, no more than 3, 000 words), letters of recommendation, and host commitment letter (if applicable). Meanwhile, applicants who are uncertain whether some aspect of their proposed projects fit within the parameters of the Fellowships Program guidelines or whether the projects are otherwise likely to be of interest to the program may submit an email inquiry before proceeding with the full application. The email should provide a brief (no more than 500 words) description of the proposed projects, as well as some background information on the applicants.

8667 ■ Soros Justice Advocacy Fellowships - Track II *(Professional development/Fellowship)*

Purpose: To support seasoned, established, and accomplished leaders and experts in the field of criminal justice. **Focus:** Criminal justice. **Qualif.:** Applicants must have at least ten (10) years of relevant advocacy experience. **Criteria:** Applications will be evaluated on the extent to which the applicants possess the vision, drive, and skills required to create and sustain a project that will advance one or more of the Open Society Foundations' U.S. criminal justice reform goals or priorities. In evaluating applications, the program will consider: project need; project approach; project goals, objectives, and activities; and the applicant's eligibility.

Funds Avail.: $120,000 over 18 months. **To Apply:** Applicants must submit their applications via online. On the online system, applicants will have to provide basic contact information and register with the system. Once registered, applicants will be able to proceed to the application itself. All communications from the Open Society Foundations regarding applications will be sent to the email used to register with the online system, so applicants should ensure that email communications from Open Society Foundations do not end up in their "Junk Mail" folder. Complete applications consist of a number of documents that must be uploaded to the online application system: resume,

proposal (single-spaced, no more than 3, 000 words), letters of recommendation, and host commitment letter (if applicable). Meanwhile, applicants who are uncertain whether some aspect of their proposed projects fit within the parameters of the Fellowships Program guidelines or whether the projects are otherwise likely to be of interest to the program may submit an email inquiry before proceeding with the full application. The email should provide a brief (no more than 500 words) description of the proposed projects, as well as some background information on the applicants. **Deadline:** October 12 letters of intent; September 9 application.

8668 ■ Soros Justice Media Fellowships - Track I *(Professional development/Fellowship)*

Purpose: To support writers, print and broadcast journalists, bloggers, filmmakers, and other individuals with distinctive voices proposing to complete media projects that engage and inform, spur debate and conversation, and catalyze change on important U.S. criminal justice issues. **Focus:** Communications; Criminal justice. **Criteria:** Selection of applicants will be based on the following criteria: project treatment; project viability; project dissemination; project budget and timeline; and the applicant's eligibility.

Funds Avail.: $58,000 over 12 months. **Number Awarded:** Varies. **To Apply:** Applicants must submit their applications via online. On the online system, applicants will have to provide basic contact information and register with the system. Once registered, applicants will be able to proceed to the application itself. All communications from the Open Society Foundations regarding applications will be sent to the email used to register with the online system, so applicants should ensure that email communications from Open Society Foundations do not end up in their "Junk Mail" folder. Complete applications consist of a number of documents that must be uploaded to the online application system: resume, proposal (single-spaced, no more than 3, 000 words), letters of recommendation, and host commitment letter (if applicable). Meanwhile, applicants who are uncertain whether some aspect of their proposed projects fit within the parameters of the Fellowships Program guidelines or whether the projects are otherwise likely to be of interest to the program may submit an email inquiry before proceeding with the full application. The email should provide a brief (no more than 500 words) description of the proposed projects, as well as some background information on the applicants. **Deadline:** November 20.

8669 ■ Soros Justice Media Fellowships - Track II *(Professional development/Fellowship)*

Purpose: To support writers, print and broadcast journalists, bloggers, filmmakers, and other individuals with distinctive voices proposing to complete media projects that engage and inform, spur debate and conversation, and catalyze change on important U.S. criminal justice issues. **Focus:** Communications; Criminal justice. **Qualif.:** Applicants are ideally full-time writers, print or broadcast journalists, filmmakers, bloggers, or other media makers, with well-established records of publication, dissemination or broadcast in local, regional or national markets, or among targeted audiences or constituencies; applicants who are not professional writers, journalists, filmmakers, or other types of media makers must demonstrate that they nonetheless have the experience and capacity to be able to accomplish the project; must have at least two (2) years of relevant full-time experience. **Criteria:** Selection of applicants will be based on the following criteria: project treatment; project viability; project dissemination; project budget

Awards are arranged alphabetically below their administering organizations

and timeline; and the applicant's eligibility.

Funds Avail.: $80,000 over 12 months. **Number Awarded:** 1. **To Apply:** Applicants must submit their applications via online. On the online system, applicants will have to provide basic contact information and register with the system. Once registered, applicants will be able to proceed to the application itself. All communications from the Open Society Foundations regarding applications will be sent to the email used to register with the online system, so applicants should ensure that email communications from Open Society Foundations do not end up in their "Junk Mail" folder. Complete applications consist of a number of documents that must be uploaded to the online application system: resume, proposal (single-spaced, no more than 3,000 words), letters of recommendation, and host commitment letter (if applicable). Meanwhile, applicants who are uncertain whether some aspect of their proposed projects fit within the parameters of the Fellowships Program guidelines or whether the projects are otherwise likely to be of interest to the program may submit an email inquiry before proceeding with the full application. The email should provide a brief (no more than 500 words) description of the proposed projects, as well as some background information on the applicants. **Deadline:** November 20.

8670 ■ Opera Foundation (OF)

c/o Mannheim LLC, 712 5th Ave., 32nd Fl.
New York, NY 10019
Ph: (212)664-8843
E-mail: gala@operafoundation.org
URL: www.operafoundation.org
Social Media: www.facebook.com/The-Opera-Foundation -214806865250691

8671 ■ Opera Foundation Scholarship *(Other/ Scholarship)*

Purpose: To provide the opportunity for young artists to participate in programs offered by one of the three partnering opera houses in Berlin, Turin, and Munich. **Focus:** Opera. **Qualif.:** Scholarship competition is open to American citizens and permanent residents between the ages of 18 and 30 who are beginning their professional careers. Selected candidates will be invited to participate in auditions at a location to be announced by the Foundation. Transportation to and from New York is at the candidate's own expense. **Criteria:** Selection will be based on the committee's criteria.

Funds Avail.: $16,000; and $1,600 (travel expenses). **Duration:** Annual. **Number Awarded:** 3. **To Apply:** Applicants may download or request an application online. Applicants can also request an application directly by contacting the Foundation. Applications must be accompanied by all of the following requirements: a photocopy of birth certificate, Green Card or Passport; two letters of recommendation from a music professional (manager, teacher, coach) dated no later than the deadline; a recent photograph; an application processing fee of $40.00 (non-refundable) paid by certified bank check or money order, payable to The Opera Foundation, Inc.

8672 ■ Opportunity Financial, LLC

130 E Randolph St., Ste. 3400
Chicago, IL 60601
Ph: (312)212-8079
Free: 800-990-9130

E-mail: info@opploans.com
URL: www.opploans.com
Social Media: www.facebook.com/OppLoans
www.instagram.com/opploans
twitter.com/opploans

8673 ■ OppU Achievers Scholarship *(Undergraduate/ Scholarship)*

Purpose: To encourage financial literacy in college students, while giving them a helping hand with the various expenses they incur. **Focus:** General studies/Field of study not specified. **Qualif.:** Applicant must be enrolled full time in high school or at least part time in college, graduate, professional, or trade school; possess a cumulative GPA of at least 3.0/4.0. **Criteria:** Selections are made four times a year.

Funds Avail.: $2,500. **Duration:** Annual. **To Apply:** Complete application and submit essay no more than 500 words that explains "why you're an achiever. How have you created opportunity for yourself". **Deadline:** September 30; December 31; March 31; June 30. **Remarks:** Established in 2016. **Contact:** Email: OppU@opploans.com.

8674 ■ Optical Society of America Foundation (OSAF)

2010 Massachusetts Ave. NW
Washington, DC 20036
Ph: (202)416-1416
Fax: (202)416-1450
E-mail: foundation@osa.org
URL: www.osa.org

8675 ■ Corning Outstanding Student Paper Competition *(Graduate, Undergraduate/Award)*

Purpose: To recognize student innovation, research excellence and presentation abilities in optical communications. **Focus:** Optics. **Qualif.:** Applicants must be an undergraduate or graduate of an educational institution of collegiate grade who is devoting more than half-time to studies within the institution at the time the paper was written. **Criteria:** All properly submitted papers are reviewed and scored according to standard OFC/NFOEC Technical Program Committee review criteria. Finalists are judged on innovation, research excellence and presentation skills.

Funds Avail.: $1,500. **Duration:** Annual. **Number Awarded:** 3. **To Apply:** Applicants must submit their research paper and opt-in to the competition during the submissions process. **Deadline:** October 22. **Remarks:** Established in 2007. **Contact:** OSA Program Management Team; Email: cstech@osa.org.

8676 ■ Harvey M. Pollicove Memorial Scholarship *(Undergraduate, Graduate/Scholarship)*

Purpose: To support student pursuing a degree in the field of precision optics manufacturing. **Focus:** Optics. **Criteria:** Selection is based on the application materials submitted.

Funds Avail.: $4,000. **Duration:** Annual. **To Apply:** Applicants may contact OSA Foundation for the application information. **Remarks:** Established in 2007.

8677 ■ Robert S. Hilbert Memorial Student Travel Grants *(Graduate, Undergraduate/Grant)*

Purpose: To support the students in the areas of optical engineering, lens design and/or illumination design. **Focus:**

Awards are arranged alphabetically below their administering organizations

Engineering, Optical. **Criteria:** Selection is based on the submitted application materials.

Funds Avail.: $1,100. **Duration:** Annual. **Number Awarded:** 3. **To Apply:** Applicants must submit a copy of the paper and abstract; a letter of support from an advisor or professor; statement explaining the value of attending the meeting; and CV/Resume. **Deadline:** May 15. **Remarks:** Established in memory of ORA's former President and Chief Executive Officer Robert S. Hilbert, this program recognizes the research excellence of students in the areas of optical engineering, lens design and illumination design. Established in 2009.

8678 ■ Jean Bennett Memorial Student Travel Grant (Graduate, Undergraduate/Grant)

Purpose: To support students in their educational pursuits. **Focus:** Optics. **Qualif.:** Applicants Must: apply at the time of paper submission; be the presenter of a paper or poster accepted at FiO; be a member of OSA; me an undergraduate or graduate student of an educational institution of collegiate grade who is devoting more than half-time to studies within the institution at the time the paper was written. **Criteria:** Selection is based on the submitted application materials.

Funds Avail.: $1,000. **Duration:** Annual. **Number Awarded:** 1. **To Apply:** Application must submit online. **Deadline:** May 15. **Remarks:** Established in memory of Jean M. Bennett, a highly decorated research physicist who was recognized for her contributions to the studies of optical surfaces and served as OSA's first female president. Established in 2008.

8679 ■ Maiman Student Paper Competition (Graduate, Undergraduate/Award)

Purpose: To recognize student innovation, research excellence and presentation skills in the areas of laser technology and electro-optics. **Focus:** Optics. **Qualif.:** Applicants must be an undergraduate or graduate of an educational institution of collegiate grade who is devoting more than half-time to studies within the institution at the time the paper was written.

Funds Avail.: $3,000. **Duration:** Annual. **Number Awarded:** 3. **To Apply:** Students must submit their research paper during the regular "call for papers" and opt-in to the competition during the submissions process. **Deadline:** December 5. **Remarks:** Endowed by HRL Laboratories, LLC, IEEE Photonics Society and APS Division of Laser Science, to honor Theodore Maiman. Established in 2008.

8680 ■ Emil Wolf Outstanding Student Paper Competition (Graduate, Undergraduate/Award)

Purpose: To recognize innovation, research and excellence in optics students. **Focus:** Optics. **Qualif.:** Applicants must be an undergraduate or graduate of an educational institution of collegiate grade who is devoting more than half-time to studies within the institution at the time the paper was written; the paper must be submitted and accepted during the regular "call for papers" process.

Funds Avail.: $300. **Duration:** Annual. **Number Awarded:** Varies. **To Apply:** Students must submit their research paper and opt-in to the competition during the submissions process. **Deadline:** May 15. **Remarks:** Established to honor Emil Wolf for his many contributions to science and the Optical Society, this competition recognizes the innovation, research and presentation excellence of students

presenting their work during Frontiers in Optics (FiO). Established in 2008.

8681 ■ Oral and Maxillofacial Surgery Foundation (OMS)

9700 W Bryn Mawr Ave.
Rosemont, IL 60018-5701
Ph: (847)233-4304
Free: 866-278-9221
E-mail: info@omsfoundation.org
URL: omsfoundation.org
Social Media: www.linkedin.com/company/oral-and
-maxillofacial-surgery-foundation
twitter.com/oms_foundation

8682 ■ OMSF Clinical Surgery Fellowship (Professional development/Fellowship)

Purpose: To provide to promising oral and maxillofacial surgery faculty members the opportunity to develop specialized surgical skills and to broaden their knowledge, experience and judgment in diverse areas of oral and maxillofacial surgical practice. **Focus:** Dentistry; Surgery. **Criteria:** Selection will be based on committee's criteria.

Funds Avail.: $70,000. **Duration:** Annual. **To Apply:** Applications can be submitted online. **Deadline:** July 15.

8683 ■ Resident Research Summit Scholarship (Professional development, Advanced Professional/Scholarship)

Purpose: To support resident attendance at the Young Investigators Day and the Research Summit. **Focus:** Dentistry; Medical research; Surgery.

Funds Avail.: $1,000 each. **Number Awarded:** Varies.

8684 ■ Order of Omega

300 E Border St.
Arlington, TX 76010
Ph: (817)265-4074
Fax: (817)459-3355
E-mail: hq@orderofomega.org
URL: orderofomega.org

8685 ■ William J. Brennan Graduate Assistant Fellowships (Graduate/Fellowship)

Purpose: To provide financial assistance to students who are pursuing graduate program in higher education. **Focus:** Educational administration.

Funds Avail.: $1,000. **Duration:** Annual. **Number Awarded:** 14. **To Apply:** Applicants must submit a completed application form; two recommendation letters from the previous college or university supervisor and current college or university supervisor; official or unofficial college transcript, photograph. **Remarks:** The Fellowship was established in honor of William J. Brennan. **Contact:** 300 E. Border St. Arlington, TX 76010; Phone: 817-265-4074; Email: hq@orderofomega.org.

8686 ■ Jacque Placette Chapman Master's Fellowships (Graduate, Master's/Fellowship)

Purpose: To provide financial assistance to students who are pursuing graduate program in higher education. **Focus:** Educational administration.

Awards are arranged alphabetically below their administering organizations

Funds Avail.: $1,000. **Duration:** Annual. **To Apply:** Applicants must submit a completed application form; two recommendation letters from the previous college or university supervisor and current college or university supervisor; official or unofficial college transcript, photograph. **Remarks:** The Fellowship was established in honor of Jacque Placette Chapman. **Contact:** Email: fellowship@ orderofomega.org.

8687 ■ Order of Omega Doctoral Fellowships
(Doctorate, Graduate/Fellowship)

Purpose: To provide financial assistance to students who are pursuing graduate program in higher education. **Focus:** Educational administration.

Funds Avail.: $2,000. **Duration:** Annual. **To Apply:** Applicants must submit a completed application form; two recommendation letters from the previous college or university supervisor and current college or university supervisor; official or unofficial college transcript, photograph. **Contact:** Email: scholarship@orderofomega.org.

8688 ■ Order Sons and Daughters of Italy in America (OSDIA)
219 E St. NE
Washington, DC 20002
Ph: (202)547-2900
Fax: (202)546-8168
Free: 800-552-6742
E-mail: nationaloffice@osia.org
URL: www.osia.org
Social Media: www.facebook.com/Sons.of.Italy
www.instagram.com/sons_of_italy
twitter.com/sons_of_italy

8689 ■ Henry Salvatori Scholarship *(Undergraduate/ Scholarship)*

Purpose: To provide financial support to college-bound high school senior demonstrating exceptional leadership, deep understanding and respect for the principles of the nation - liberty, freedom and equality. **Focus:** General studies/Field of study not specified. **Qualif.:** Applicants must be U.S. citizens of Italian descent in their senior year of high school and planning to attend a four-year, accredited institution for the fall term. Previous SIF scholarship recipients are not eligible. **Criteria:** Recipients will be selected based on the submitted application.

Duration: Annual. **Number Awarded:** 1. **To Apply:** Applicants must submit cover sheet; official transcript; test scores; resume; two letters of recommendation from public figures whose careers have demonstrated a commitment to the principles the scholarship embodies; typewritten original essay of 750-1, 000 words concerning the Declaration of Independence, the Constitution and the Bill of Rights - discussion of the relevance of these documents to the principles of liberty, freedom and equality in the United States and the processing fee; and submit a type-written cover letter of 150-250 words outlining the academic and professional goals. **Deadline:** February 29. **Remarks:** Established in 2009.

8690 ■ Italian Language Scholarship
(Undergraduate/Scholarship)

Purpose: To provide financial support for education of US citizens of Italian descent. **Focus:** Foreign languages. **Criteria:** Recipients will be selected based on the submitted application.

Duration: Annual. **Number Awarded:** 1. **To Apply:** Applicants must submit cover sheet; official transcript; test scores; resume outlining extracurricular activities, work, experience, volunteer service and honors, especially as they relate to Italian language, culture and heritage; letters of recommendation; an original, typewritten 500-750-word essay in Italian on why learning Italian is important in today's world and plan of how to use the language degree; and the processing fee. **Deadline:** February 29.

8691 ■ Order Sons of Italy Foundation General Scholarships *(Graduate, Undergraduate/Scholarship)*

Purpose: To support students aiming to a higher education. **Focus:** General studies/Field of study not specified. **Qualif.:** Applicants must be U.S. citizens of Italian descent (at least one Italian or Italian-American grandparent); must be enrolled in undergraduate or graduate program at four-year, accredited academic institutions for the fall term. **Criteria:** Selection will be merit-based.

To Apply: Applicants must submit completed application form; official transcript(s); test scores; resume; letters of recommendation; essay and processing fee. **Deadline:** February 29.

8692 ■ Order of United Commercial Travelers of America (UCT)
1801 Watermark Dr., Ste. 100
Columbus, OH 43215
Ph: (614)487-9680
Fax: (614)487-9675
Free: 800-848-0123
E-mail: customerservice@uct.org
URL: www.uct.org

8693 ■ UCT Scholarship *(Other/Scholarship)*

Purpose: To provide aid to individuals wishing to teach people with intellectual disabilities. **Focus:** Education, Special. **Criteria:** Selection shall be based on the aforementioned qualifications and compliance with the application details.

Funds Avail.: Up to $2,500. **Duration:** Annual. **To Apply:** Applicant should answer all questions and return the completed application, along with other requested information; initial applicants must include a typed resume of work experience in the field of special education with an emphasis on teaching people with intellectual disabilities to UCT's Fraternal Department at the given address. **Deadline:** November 15. **Contact:** Phone: 800-848-0123 Ext. 1100; Email: aneal@uct.org.

8694 ■ L'Oreal USA, Inc.
10 Hudson Yards
New York, NY 10001
Ph: (212)984-4414
Free: 800-345-5012
E-mail: contact@loreal.com
URL: www.lorealusa.com
Social Media: www.facebook.com/lorealusa
www.instagram.com/lorealusa
www.linkedin.com/company/loréal
twitter.com/LOrealUSA

Awards are arranged alphabetically below their administering organizations

www.youtube.com/channel/UCJd9NjTUZZIiH7IYF9c0Uig

8695 ■ L'Oréal-UNESCO For Women in Science International Rising Talents *(Doctorate, Postdoctorate/Fellowship)*

Purpose: To support and encourage promising young women to pursue their scientific careers. **Focus:** Life sciences. **Qualif.:** Applicants must be at their doctoral or postdoctoral level. **Criteria:** Selection will be based on the committee's criteria.

Funds Avail.: 110,055.18 USD. **Duration:** Annual. **Number Awarded:** 15. **Remarks:** Established in 1998.

8696 ■ L'Oréal USA For Women in Science Fellowship *(Postdoctorate/Fellowship)*

Purpose: To reward five U.S.-based women researchers for their outstanding contributions to science, technology, engineering, and math fields. **Focus:** Science.

Funds Avail.: $60,000 each. **Duration:** Annual. **Number Awarded:** 5. **To Apply:** Applicants must complete the online submission and must submit three letters of recommendation, one letter from a mentor or former advisor, one letter from applicant post-doctoral advisor and another one letter from someone of applicant choice. **Remarks:** Established in 2003. **Contact:** L'Oreal USA For Women In Science, C/O AAAS, Attn: Janaya Thompson/Education and Human Resources, 1200 New York Ave., NW, 6th Fl., Washington, DC 20005.

8697 ■ Oregon Association of Broadcasters (OAB)

3422 NW Bryce Canyon Ln
Bend, OR 97701
Ph: (503)443-2299
E-mail: theoab@theoab.org
URL: www.theoab.org

8698 ■ Oregon Association of Broadcasters Scholarships *(Undergraduate/Scholarship)*

Purpose: To promote, enhance, strengthen and defend the broadcast industry. To encourage and promote sound broadcast customs and practices. **Focus:** Broadcasting.

To Apply: Applicants may apply for the scholarship they click the Apply Button next to the scholarship; Then the application will complete the rest of the application and submit. **Deadline:** March 1. **Contact:** OAB address is 3422 NW Bryce Canyon Ln, Bend, OR 97703. The telephone number is (503) 443-2299 and the e-mail address is theoab@theoab.org.

8699 ■ Oregon Association of Independent Accountants (OAIA)

1804 NE 43rd Ave.
Portland, OR 97214
URL: www.oaia.net
Social Media: www.facebook.com/oaia.net

8700 ■ OAIA Scholarships *(Undergraduate, Graduate/Scholarship)*

Purpose: To support the education of accounting students in Oregon. **Focus:** Accounting. **Qualif.:** Applicants must be residents of the State of Oregon; enrolled in, or accepted by, an accredited school for the study of accounting within

the State of Oregon; and, full-time students carrying a minimum of 12 credit hours. **Criteria:** Selection will be based on financial need, scholastics achievement, personal qualifications and professional promise.

Funds Avail.: No specific amount. **Duration:** Annual. **To Apply:** Applicants must submit a completed scholarship application along with high school and college transcripts. **Deadline:** April 1. **Contact:** Oregon Association of Independent Accountants scholarship Foundation; 1804 NE 43rd Ave, Portland, OR, 97213.

8701 ■ Oregon Association of Nurseries (OAN)

29751 SW Town Center Loop W
Wilsonville, OR 97070
Ph: (503)682-5089
Fax: (503)682-5099
Free: 888-283-7219
E-mail: info@oan.org
URL: www.oan.org
Social Media: www.facebook.com/pages/Oregon
  -Association-of-Nurseries/91842024952
twitter.com/diggermag

8702 ■ Bill Egan Memorial Award *(Undergraduate/Scholarship)*

Purpose: To provide opportunities for education, research and business development to members, including landscapers and allied businesses, that supply goods and services to those who grow, handle and retail ornamental horticultural products in Oregon. **Focus:** Horticulture. **Qualif.:** Applicants must be college students majoring in horticulture with an emphasis on the greenhouse/floriculture areas. **Criteria:** Preference will be given to students attending Oregon schools.

Funds Avail.: $500. **Duration:** Annual. **Number Awarded:** Varies. **To Apply:** Applicants must submit one copy of official transcript of records and three current letters of reference supporting the horticulture abilities. **Deadline:** April 15. **Contact:** Stephanie Weihrauch; Phone: 503-682-5089; Email: sweihrauch@oan.org.

8703 ■ Christmas Tree Chapter Scholarship Awards *(Undergraduate/Scholarship)*

Purpose: To provide opportunities for education, research and business development to members, including landscapers and allied businesses, that supply goods and services to those who grow, handle and retail ornamental horticultural products in Oregon. **Focus:** Horticulture. **Qualif.:** Applicants must be students pursuing a degree in the field of horticulture. **Criteria:** Recipients are selected based on academic performance and financial need. Preference will be given to a member, children of members, or an employee of a Christmas Tree Chapter member.

Funds Avail.: $500. **To Apply:** Applicants must submit one copy of an official transcript of records and three current letters of reference supporting the applicant's horticulture abilities. **Contact:** Oregon Nurseries Foundation, 29751 SW Town Center Loop W, Wilsonville, OR 97070; Fax: 503-682-5099; Email: onf@oan.org.

8704 ■ Clackamas Chapter Ed Wood Memorial Award *(Undergraduate/Scholarship)*

Purpose: To provide students preparing for a career in ornamental horticulture and related fields. **Focus:** Horticul-

Awards are arranged alphabetically below their administering organizations

ture. **Qualif.:** Applicants must be currently enrolled in a college horticulture program in Oregon. **Criteria:** Recipients are selected based on the promise and commitment they show toward making significant future contributions to the nursery industry.

Funds Avail.: $1,500. **Duration:** Annual. **Number Awarded:** Varies. **To Apply:** Applicants must submit one copy of official transcript of records and three current letters of reference supporting the horticulture abilities. **Contact:** Stephanie Weihrauch at 503-682-5089 or sweihrauch@oan.org.

8705 ■ Clackamas Chapter Scholarship Awards
(Undergraduate/Scholarship)

Purpose: To provide opportunities for education, research and business development to members, including landscapers and allied businesses, that supply goods and services to those who grow, handle and retail ornamental horticultural products in Oregon. **Focus:** Horticulture.

Funds Avail.: $1,500.

8706 ■ Emerald Empire Chapter Scholarship Awards *(Undergraduate/Scholarship)*

Purpose: To provide opportunities for education, research and business development to members, including landscapers and allied businesses, that supply goods and services to those who grow, handle and retail ornamental horticultural products in Oregon. **Focus:** Horticulture. **Qualif.:** Applicants must be junior or senior college students majoring in horticulture, landscape architecture or landscape construction who have graduated from an Oregon high school. **Criteria:** Preference will be given to a student from the Emerald Empire (Eugene) area.

To Apply: Applicants must submit one copy of official transcript of records and three current letters of reference supporting the horticulture abilities. **Contact:** Oregon Nurseries Foundation, 29751 SW Town Center Loop W, Wilsonville, OR 97070; Fax: 503-682-5099; Email: onf@oan.org.

8707 ■ Joseph H. Klupenger Scholarship Awards
(Undergraduate/Scholarship, Award)

Purpose: To provide opportunities for education, research and business development to members, including landscapers and allied businesses that supply goods and services to those who grow, handle and retail ornamental horticultural products in Oregon. **Focus:** Horticulture. **Qualif.:** Applicants must be students majoring in ornamental horticulture; must intend to work in the ornamental industry. **Criteria:** Recipients are selected based on academic performance and financial need.

Funds Avail.: $550. **Duration:** Annual. **Number Awarded:** 1. **To Apply:** Applicants must submit one copy of official transcript of records and three current letters of reference supporting the horticulture abilities. **Deadline:** April 15. **Contact:** Oregon Nurseries Foundation, 29751 SW Town Center Loop W, Wilsonville, OR 97070; Fax: 503-682-5099; Email: onf@oan.org.

8708 ■ Mt. Hood Chapter Scholarship Awards
(Undergraduate/Scholarship)

Purpose: To provide opportunities for education, research and business development to members, including landscapers and allied businesses, that supply goods and services to those who grow, handle and retail ornamental horticultural products in Oregon. **Focus:** Horticulture. **Qualif.:** Ap-

plicants must be college students majoring in ornamental horticulture. **Criteria:** Preference will be given to applicants from nursery areas east of Portland.

Funds Avail.: $1,000. **Duration:** Annual. **To Apply:** Applicants must submit one copy of official transcript of records and three current letters of reference supporting the horticulture abilities. **Contact:** Oregon Nurseries Foundation, 29751 SW Town Center Loop W, Wilsonville, OR 97070; Fax: 503-682-5099; E-mail: onf@oan.org.

8709 ■ Nurseries Foundation Scholarship Awards
(Undergraduate/Scholarship)

Purpose: To provide opportunities for education, research and business development to members, including landscapers and allied businesses, that supply goods and services to those who grow, handle and retail ornamental horticultural products in Oregon. **Focus:** Horticulture. **Qualif.:** Applicants must be college students majoring in the field of horticulture.

Funds Avail.: $1,000. **Duration:** Annual. **To Apply:** Applicants must submit one copy of official transcript of records and three current letters of reference supporting the horticulture abilities. **Contact:** Oregon Nurseries Foundation, 29751 SW Town Center Loop W, Wilsonville, OR, 97070; Fax: 503-682-5099; Email: onf@oan.org.

8710 ■ Nurseries Memorial Award *(Graduate/Scholarship)*

Purpose: To provide opportunities for education, research and business development to members, including landscapers and allied businesses, that supply goods and services to those who grow, handle and retail ornamental horticultural products in Oregon. **Focus:** Horticulture. **Qualif.:** Applicants must be graduate students pursuing a research project pertaining to ornamental horticulture. **Criteria:** Recipients are selected based on academic performance and financial need.

To Apply: Applicants must submit one copy of official transcript of records and three current letters of reference supporting the horticulture abilities. **Contact:** Oregon Nurseries Foundation, 29751 SW Town Center Loop W, Wilsonville, OR, 97070; Fax: 503-682-5099; Email: onf@oan.org.

8711 ■ Oregon Association of Nurseries Scholarship Program *(Graduate/Scholarship)*

Purpose: To provide opportunities for education, research and business development to members, including landscapers and allied businesses, that supply goods and services to those who grow, handle and retail ornamental horticultural products in Oregon. **Focus:** Horticulture. **Qualif.:** Applicants must be students preparing for a career in ornamental horticulture and related fields. **Criteria:** Recipients are selected based on academic performance and financial need.

Funds Avail.: $1,000. **Duration:** Annual. **Number Awarded:** 1. **To Apply:** Applicants must submit one copy of official transcript of records and three current letters of reference supporting the horticulture abilities. **Deadline:** April 1. **Contact:** Contact Stephanie Weihrauch at 503-582-2001 or scholarships@oan.org.

8712 ■ Retail Chapter Scholarship Awards
(Undergraduate/Scholarship)

Purpose: To provide opportunities for education, research and business development to members, including landscap-

Awards are arranged alphabetically below their administering organizations

ers and allied businesses, that supply goods and services to those who grow, handle and retail ornamental horticultural products in Oregon. **Focus:** Horticulture. **Qualif.:** Applicants must be students majoring in ornamental horticulture and related fields. **Criteria:** Preference will be given to a student who is son or daughter of an OAN member retailer, or one of their employees.

Funds Avail.: $1,000. **Duration:** Annual. **Number Awarded:** Varies. **To Apply:** Applicants must submit one copy of official transcript of records and three current letters of reference supporting the horticulture abilities. **Deadline:** April 15. **Contact:** Oregon Nurseries Foundation, 29751 SW Town Center Loop W, Wilsonville, OR, 97070; Fax: 503-682-5099; Email: onf@oan.org.

8713 ■ Willamette Chapter Scholarship Awards
(Undergraduate/Scholarship)

Purpose: To provide opportunities for education, research and business development to members, including landscapers and allied businesses, that supply goods and services to those who grow, handle and retail ornamental horticultural products in Oregon. **Focus:** Horticulture. **Qualif.:** Applicants must be students majoring in ornamental horticulture and related fields. **Criteria:** Preference will be given to a member, member's child or an employee of a Willamette chapter member.

Funds Avail.: $1,500. **Number Awarded:** Varies. **To Apply:** Applicants must submit one copy of official transcript of records and three current letters of reference supporting the horticulture abilities. **Deadline:** April 15. **Contact:** Oregon Nurseries Foundation, 29751 SW Town Center Loop W, Wilsonville, OR, 97070; Fax: 503-682-5099; Email: onf@oan.org.

8714 ■ Oregon Farm Bureau (OFB)
1320 Capitol St. NE, Ste. 200
Salem, OR 97301
Ph: (503)399-1701
Fax: (503)399-8082
Free: 800-334-6323
E-mail: tiffany@oregonfb.org
URL: www.oregonfb.org
Social Media: www.facebook.com/ofbinfo
www.instagram.com/oregonfarmbureau
twitter.com/OreFarmBureau
www.youtube.com/oregonfarmbureau

8715 ■ Clackamas County Farm Bureau Agricultural Scholarships *(Undergraduate/Scholarship)*

Purpose: To help students pursuing a career in agriculture or related field at a two or four year institution of higher learning. **Focus:** Agriculture, Economic aspects. **Qualif.:** Applicants must be residents of Clackamas County at the time of the application; must be interested in pursuing a career in agriculture or a related field; must have a GPA of at least 2.8; must be Clackamas County high school graduate. **Criteria:** Recipients are selected based on academic performance.

Funds Avail.: $500 to $3,000. **Duration:** Annual. **To Apply:** Applicants must submit two letters of recommendation, from which one must come from an Ag Advisor or teacher and the other from another non-relative; transcript of records from most recent school attended; written statement detailing reasons for interest in an agricultural profession, leadership, community service experience and experi-

ence in agriculture; resume. **Deadline:** March 27. **Contact:** Completed application must be sent to Clackamas County Farm Bureau, Scholarship Committee, PO Box 961, Canby, OR, 97013; Email: ClackamasCountyFB@gmail.com.

8716 ■ Oregon Farm Bureau Memorial Scholarship
(Undergraduate, Graduate, High School/Scholarship)

Purpose: To promote educational improvement, economic opportunity and social achievement for its members and the farming, ranching and natural resources industry as a whole. **Focus:** Agriculture, Economic aspects. **Qualif.:** Applicants must be full-time students pursuing an agriculture-related major; must be an Oregon high school graduate or an Oregon home schoolgraduate with a full year, 24 semester or 36 quarter hours, of completed college coursework; children and grandchildren of voting members of OFB are eligible; students attending institutions outside of Oregon are also eligible. **Criteria:** Recipients are selected based on academic performance and financial need.

Funds Avail.: $1,500. **Duration:** Annual. **Number Awarded:** 2. **To Apply:** Applicants must complete an application form; must submit transcript of records. **Deadline:** March 15. **Contact:** Holly Michaels, Email:scholarship@oregonfb.org.

8717 ■ Yamhill County Farm Bureau Scholarships
(Undergraduate/Scholarship)

Purpose: To assist Yamhill County high school graduates in furthering their education. **Focus:** Agriculture, Economic aspects. **Criteria:** Recipients are selected based on academic performance.

Funds Avail.: $2,000. **Duration:** Annual. **Number Awarded:** 2. **To Apply:** Applicants must submit a completed and signed application form, two letters of recommendation from non-related persons and official transcripts from all colleges attended. **Deadline:** August 1.

8718 ■ Oregon Medical Association (OMA)
11740 SW 68th Pky., Ste. 100
Portland, OR 97223
Ph: (503)619-8000
Fax: (503)619-0609
E-mail: oma@theoma.org
URL: www.theoma.org
Social Media: www.facebook.com/Oregon-Medical
-Association-188934540635
twitter.com/ORmedicine

8719 ■ Linn-Benton County Scholarships
(Undergraduate/Scholarship)

Purpose: To provide educational assistance to students who are seeking a career in medicine or nursing. **Focus:** Medicine; Nursing. **Qualif.:** Applicants must be high school seniors or graduates seeking a career in medicine or nursing. **Criteria:** Recipients are selected based on academic performance.

Funds Avail.: $1,000. **To Apply:** Applicants must complete the application form; must submit their official academic high school transcript in Linn or Benon County; official academic transcript from all subsequent institutions of higher education; letter of recommendation from current academic advisor; one-page essay describing why they are interested in a career in nursing or medicine; and list of all school and community service activities. **Remarks:** Established in 2001.

Awards are arranged alphabetically below their administering organizations

8720 ■ Oregon Society of Certified Public Accountants (OSCPA)
10206 SW Laurel St.
Beaverton, OR 97005-3209
URL: www.orcpa.org

8721 ■ Oregon College/University Scholarships
(Undergraduate/Scholarship)

Purpose: To financially support accounting students. **Focus:** Accounting. **Qualif.:** Applicants must be Oregon high school seniors planning to study accounting or Oregon undergraduates planning to study accounting; must have a minimum required GPA is 3.2 in accounting/business classes and an overall cumulative 3.2 GPA. **Criteria:** Selection is based on academic performance and student's interest in the accounting profession.

Funds Avail.: $1,000 - $3,000 (Post Baccalaureate and Masters Program Students); $500 (Accounting Students). **Duration:** Annual. **To Apply:** Applicants may complete the application online or mail the completed application form; must submit official transcripts and online educator reference must be completed. **Deadline:** January 13.

8722 ■ OSCPA Educational Foundation High School Scholarships (Undergraduate/Scholarship)

Purpose: To financially support accounting students. **Focus:** Accounting. **Criteria:** Selection is based on scholastic ability and a student's interest in the accounting profession.

Funds Avail.: No specific amount. **Duration:** Annual. **To Apply:** Applicants may complete the application online or mail the completed application form; must submit official transcripts and three letters of recommendation (must be completed by the reference listed on the application form).

8723 ■ Carl Orff Canada - Music for Children (COCMC)
3551 Apple Grove
Regina, SK, Canada S4V 2R3
URL: www.orffcanada.ca

8724 ■ Gunild Keetman Scholarship (Other, Undergraduate/Scholarship)

Purpose: To financially assist students or teachers studying in an approved course within a Canadian university. **Focus:** Music. **Qualif.:** Applicants must be members in good standing of Carl Orff Canada who has successfully completed a level 1 Orff course. **Criteria:** Applicants will be judged based on qualifications and submitted documents.

Funds Avail.: No specific amount. **Duration:** Annual. **To Apply:** Applicants must submit a filled-out application form; must obtain a transcript of grades in level I and/or II; and reference letters from two referees (one from a music education professor or music consultant/supervisor and one from a previous Orff instructor). Subject line of the e-mail should be, "Guild Keetman Scholarship Application", followed by the applicant's name. Recipients are required to submit an article to the Ostinato Editor reflecting their course experience(s) and must forward a copy of certificate or transcript of completed course to the National Treasurer. **Deadline:** April 15. **Remarks:** Established in 1976.

8725 ■ Organization of American Historians (OAH)
112 N Bryan Ave.
Bloomington, IN 47408-4141

Ph: (812)855-7311
E-mail: oah@oah.org
URL: www.oah.org

8726 ■ Huggins-Quarles Award (Doctorate, Graduate/Award)

Purpose: To assist qualified individuals with travel expenses related to travel to research collections for the completion of their PhD dissertations. **Focus:** History. **Qualif.:** Applicants must be ALANA (African American, Latino/a, Asian American, Native American) scholar; U.S. residency is not required; must be ABD; applicant's dissertation must focus on U.S. history. **Criteria:** Recipient will be chosen based on the application materials submitted.

Duration: Annual. **Number Awarded:** 1 - 2. **To Apply:** Applicants should submit a five-page dissertation proposal (which should include a definition of the project, and explanation of the project's significance and contribution to the field, and a description of the most important primary sources), along with a one-page itemized budget explaining travel and research plans; cover letter, which should also indicate the candidate's progress on the dissertation, including ABD status; CV. **Deadline:** December 1. **Contact:** Lauren Araiza, Denison University (Committee Chair); Email: araizal@denison.edu.

8727 ■ John Higham Research Fellowship (Postdoctorate/Fellowship)

Purpose: To provide travel grants to graduate students to be used toward costs of attending the OAH/IEHS Annual Meeting. **Focus:** History, American; Immigration. **Qualif.:** Applicants must be graduate students writing doctoral dissertations for a Ph.D. in American history. **Criteria:** Selection will be based on the committee's criteria.

Funds Avail.: $1,000 to $1,500. **Duration:** Annual. **Number Awarded:** 3. **To Apply:** Applicants should submit project proposal of no more than 1, 000 words describing the research project and detailing how the funds will be used; updated curriculum vitae with a list of the names and addresses of references; two signed letters of recommendation on official letterhead submitted independently by referees. **Deadline:** December 1. **Remarks:** The grants are given in memory of John Higham (1920-2003), past president of the OAH and an important figure in immigration, ethnic, and intellectual history. **Contact:** Julian Lim, Arizona State University, Committee Chair jlim42@asu.edu.

8728 ■ Lerner-Scott Prize (Doctorate/Prize)

Purpose: To recognize the best doctoral dissertation in U.S. women's history. **Focus:** History. **Qualif.:** Applicants must be at the doctoral level of study. **Criteria:** Selection will be based on the committee's criteria.

Funds Avail.: No specific amount. **Duration:** Annual. **To Apply:** Applicants must submit an application containing a letter of support from a faculty member at the degree-granting institution, along with an abstract, table of contents and sample chapter from the dissertation; also include email addresses for both the applicants and the adviser, if available; finalist will be asked to submit a complete copy of the dissertation at a later date. **Deadline:** October 1. **Contact:** Email: sjkatz@sfsu.edu.

8729 ■ Louis Pelzer Memorial Award (Graduate/Award)

Purpose: To promote excellence in the scholarship, teaching and presentation of American history. **Focus:** History.

Awards are arranged alphabetically below their administering organizations

Qualif.: Applicants must be in their graduate degree of study. **Criteria:** Selection will be based on the committee's criteria.

Duration: Annual. **To Apply:** Applicants must submit an essay of not more than 10, 000 words (including endnotes). **Deadline:** November 2. **Remarks:** Established in 1949. **Contact:** Benjamin H. Irvin, Executive Editor, OAH/Editor, Journal of American History, Journal of American History, 1215 East Atwater Ave., Bloomington IN 47401.

8730 ■ Organization of American States (OAS)

17th St. & Constitution Ave., NW
Washington, DC 20006-4499
Ph: (202)370-5000
Fax: (202)458-3967
URL: www.oas.org
Social Media: www.facebook.com/OASofficial
www.instagram.com/oea_oficial/?hl=en
twitter.com/oas_official
www.youtube.com/user/OASVideos

8731 ■ OAS Academic Scholarship for Undergraduate Studies *(Undergraduate/Scholarship)*

Purpose: To promote and support human capacity development and the strengthening of bonds among peoples in the hemisphere by maximizing the number of scholarships awarded in reputable educational institutions in its member states with the resources available. **Focus:** General studies/Field of study not specified. **Qualif.:** Applicants must be citizens or permanent residents of an English-speaking Caribbean member state or Suriname; must have completed the first two years of an undergraduate degree, or have an Associate's degree; must have a GPA above the minimum standard required by the university; and be in good physical and mental health to complete the program successfully. **Criteria:** Recipients will be selected based on financial need.

Duration: Annual. **To Apply:** Applicants must include: a copy of the Associate's diploma, if applicable (for those candidates already enrolled in the bachelor's program, copy of the high school diploma); copy of the Associate's degree transcripts, if applicable (for those candidates already enrolled in the bachelor's degree program, latest transcripts from the current program of study); and, three recommendation letters, preferably two different letters from current or former professors using the OAS Recommendation Statement Form, and one from a current or previous employer using the Employer Recommendation Form.

8732 ■ OAS Scholarships for Professional Development - Disaster Communications Management *(Professional development/Scholarship)*

Purpose: To encourage students to complete their short or medium-term, intensive, non-academic courses and training programs offered by its partner offering institutions around the world. **Focus:** Communications technologies; Telecommunications systems. **Qualif.:** Applicants must be citizens or permanent residents of an OAS member state who are policymakers, engineers or managers of all levels with at least three years of experience and working on aspects related to disaster relief; English proficiency is considered for admission, scores must be submitted from either the Test of English as a Foreign Language (TOEFL) or the academic International English Language Testing System (IELTS); exceptions may be made for applicants

who hold a degree from a university located in a country in which English is the official language and also the language of instruction at the university; minimum scores for admission academic IELTS an overall band score of 6.0 with no individual score below 5.0; TOEFL: 550 on paper-based or 80 on Internet-based test. **Criteria:** Scholarship will be awarded based on the following criteria: objective and priorities established in the Strategic Plan for Partnership for Development; training priorities of the member states; merits and overall credentials of the candidates, including their academic and professional background; financial need of the candidates; extensive and equitable geographic distribution for the benefit of all member states and that takes into account the greater needs of the smaller and relatively less developed economies.

Funds Avail.: No specific amount. **Number Awarded:** Varies. **To Apply:** Interested applicants may visit the website for an online application. Applicants must also provide the following documents: copy of diploma for the highest degree obtained; copies of transcripts of grades for all academic degrees completed and to be completed; three recommendation letters. Two different letters must be from current or former professors using the OAS Recommendation Statement Form and one letter from a current or previous employer using the Employer Recommendation Form. If unemployed or never employed, obtain a third recommendation using the Recommendation Statement Form; resume, maximum of four pages, including diplomas from conferences, workshops, seminars, etc.; admission letter. Scan all required documents in one single file in PDF format, shouldn't be larger than 8MB. After the applicants submit their application, they will receive an email with the application they filled out in PDF format. Print the application, add the required documents and submit the package to the National Liaison Agency (ONE) in their country. **Deadline:** November 2.

8733 ■ OAS Scholarships for Professional Development - Radio Spectrum Monitoring Techniques and Procedures *(Professional development/Scholarship)*

Purpose: To support students who are completing their short or medium-term, intensive, non-academic courses and training programs offered by its partner offering institutions around the world. **Focus:** Radio and television; Telecommunications systems. **Qualif.:** Applicants must be citizens or permanent residents of an OAS member state with the exception of the United States since it is the host country; have earned a bachelor's degree in economics, law or engineering; be government policy-makers and regulators, executives and managers of telecommunications companies subject to existing or proposed governmental regulations and government and private sector attorneys who advise them with at least three years of experience; and be proficient in English. **Criteria:** Scholarship will be awarded based on the following criteria: objectives and priorities established in the strategic plan for partnership for development; training priorities of the member states; merits and overall credentials of the candidates, including their academic and professional background; financial need of the candidates; extensive and equitable geographic distribution for the benefit of all member states and that takes into account the greater needs of the smaller and relatively less developed economies.

Funds Avail.: No specific amount. **Number Awarded:** Varies. **To Apply:** Applicants must include a copy of diploma for the highest degree obtained; copies of transcripts of grades for all academic degrees completed and to be

Awards are arranged alphabetically below their administering organizations

completed; three recommendation letters; two different letters must be from current or former professors using the OAS Recommendation Statement Form and one letter from a current or previous employer using the Employer Recommendation Form; if unemployed or never employed, obtain a third recommendation using the Recommendation Statement Form; resume, maximum of four pages, including diplomas from conferences, workshops, seminars, etc.; admission letter; scan all required documents in one single file in PDF format, shouldn't be larger than 8MB; after the applicants submit their application, they will receive an email with the application they filled out in PDF format; print the application, add the required documents and submit the package to the National Liaison Agency (ONE) in their country.

8734 ■ OAS Scholarships for Professional Development - Satellite Communications *(Professional development/Scholarship)*

Purpose: To provide support to students for them to complete their short or medium-term, intensive, non-academic courses and training programs offered by its partner offering institutions around the world. **Focus:** Communications technologies; Telecommunications systems. **Qualif.:** Applicants must be citizens or permanent residents of an OAS member state with the exception of the United States, since it is the host country; and policymakers, engineers and managers of all levels with at least three years of experience and working on aspects related to disaster relief. **Criteria:** Selection will be based on the following criteria: objectives and priorities established in the strategic plan for partnership for development; training priorities of the member states; merits and overall credentials of the candidate, including their academic and professional background; financial need of the candidate; an extensive and equitable geographic distribution for the benefit of all member states and that takes into account the greater needs of the smaller and relatively less developed economies.
Funds Avail.: No specific amount. **Duration:** Annual. **Number Awarded:** Varies. **To Apply:** Applicants must include a copy of diploma for the highest degree obtained; copies of transcripts of grades for all academic degrees completed and to be completed; three recommendation letters; two different letters must be from current or former professors using the OAS Recommendation Statement Form and one letter from a current or previous employer using the Employer Recommendation Form; if unemployed or never employed, obtain a third recommendation using the Recommendation Statement Form; resume, maximum of four pages, including diplomas from conferences, workshops, seminars, etc.; admission letter; scan all required documents in one single file in PDF format, shouldn't be larger than 8MB; after the applicants submit their application, they will receive an email with the application they filled out in PDF format; print the application, add the required documents and submit the package to the National Liaison Agency (ONE) in their country.

8735 ■ OAS Scholarships for Professional Development - The ABC of Telecommunications *(Professional development/Scholarship)*

Purpose: To provide assistance to students to complete their short or medium-term, intensive, non-academic courses and training programs offered by its partner offering institutions around the world. **Focus:** Telecommunications systems.
Funds Avail.: No specific amount. **Number Awarded:** Varies. **To Apply:** Applicants must include the OAS scholar-

ship application form; copy of transcript of the latest degree obtained; updated resume; one letter of recommendation of current or most recent employer; scan all required documents in one single file in PDF format, shouldn't be larger than 8MB; after the applicants submit their application, they will receive an email with the application they filled out in PDF format; print and sign the application add the required documents and submit the package to the National Liaison Agency (ONE) in their country.

8736 ■ Organization of American States AOS-Placed Scholarships *(Graduate, Undergraduate/Scholarship)*

Purpose: To assist the member states with their domestic efforts in pursuit of integral development goals by supporting human resource development in the priority areas; to promote and support human capacity development and the strengthening of bonds among people in the hemisphere by maximizing the number of scholarships awarded in reputable educational institutions in its member states with the resources available. **Focus:** General studies/Field of study not specified. **Qualif.:** Applicants must be enrolled in a university, college, or institution; must be enrolled in a full-time study or research leading to a graduate or undergraduate degree in any AOS member state except the one who is sponsoring the candidate for this scholarship. **Criteria:** Recipients are selected based on the following criteria: (1) objectives and priorities established in the Strategic Plan for Partnership for Integral Development; (2) training priorities of member states; (3) merits and overall credentials of applicants; (4) quality of the written essay; (5) GPA; (6) completeness of the application and required documents; (7) quality of recommendation letter; (8) geographic distribution based on needs of smaller and less developed economies; (9) gender quality and equity; and (10) financial need.
Funds Avail.: No specific amount. **To Apply:** Applicants must include standardized test results (optional); copy of diploma; original transcript of records for the highest degree completed and for the program of studies in which currently enrolled; and not to exceed four pages curriculum vitae.

8737 ■ Organization of American States Graduate Scholarships *(Doctorate, Graduate/Scholarship)*

Purpose: To assist the member states with their domestic efforts in pursuit of integral development goals by supporting human resource development in the priority areas; to promote and support human capacity development and the strengthening of bonds among people in the hemisphere by maximizing the number of scholarships awarded in reputable educational institutions in its member states with the resources available. **Focus:** General studies/Field of study not specified. **Qualif.:** Applicants must be enrolled in a master's or doctorate degree program; Applicants must be citizens or permanent residents of member state; must have a GPA above the minimum standard required by the university; and be in good physical and mental health to complete the program successfully. **Criteria:** Recipients are selected based on financial need.
Funds Avail.: No specific amount. **Duration:** Annual. **To Apply:** Applicants must include: a copy of the Associate's diploma, if applicable (for those candidates already enrolled in the bachelor's program, copy of the high school diploma); copy of the Associate's degree transcripts, if applicable (for those candidates already enrolled in the bachelor's degree program, latest transcripts from the current program of study); and, three recommendation letters, preferably two different letters from current or former professors using the

Awards are arranged alphabetically below their administering organizations

OAS Recommendation Statement Form, and one from a current or previous employer using the Employer Recommendation Form. **Remarks:** Established in 1958.

8738 ■ Organization of American States Self-Placed Scholarships *(Doctorate, Graduate/Scholarship)*

Purpose: To assist the member states with their domestic efforts in pursuit of integral development goals by supporting human resource development in the priority areas; to promote and support human capacity development and the strengthening of bonds among peoples in the hemisphere by maximizing the number of scholarships awarded in reputable educational institutions in its member states with the resources available. **Focus:** General studies/Field of study not specified. **Qualif.:** Applicants must be enrolled in a program of study and be eligible to graduate within 2 academic years from the date of the award, or be accepted into the university for the last two years of the undergraduate degree (admission letter must state that the applicant will complete the program of studies within 2 academic years); must be enrolled in a master's or doctorate degree program. **Criteria:** Recipients are selected based on financial need.

Funds Avail.: No specific amount. **Duration:** Annual. **To Apply:** Applicants must complete the application form; may apply directly to the universities or educational institutions where scholarship is being offered.

8739 ■ Leo S. Rowe Pan American Fund *(Graduate, Undergraduate/Loan)*

Purpose: To help finance higher educational pursuits of Latin American and Caribbean students in the United States. **Focus:** Arts; Latin American studies; Science. **Criteria:** Recipients will be selected based on academic records and financial need.

Funds Avail.: Up to $15,000. **Duration:** Annual. **To Apply:** Applicants must submit an original, duly sealed, stamped, or notarized transcript of grades; diplomas; and foreign student advisor form. **Contact:** URL: www.oas.org/en/rowefund, Email: rowefund@oas.org.

8740 ■ Organization of Black Aerospace Professionals (OBAP)

1 Westbrook Corporate Ctr., Ste. 300
Westchester, IL 60154
Free: 800-538-6227
E-mail: nationaloffice@obap.org
URL: www.obap.org
Social Media: www.facebook.com/OBAP.org
instagram.com/obapexcellence/
twitter.com/OBAPEXCELLENCE

8741 ■ Alaska Airlines Pilot Scholarship *(All/Scholarship)*

Purpose: To promote education in the aviation industry. **Focus:** Aviation. **Qualif.:** Applicant must be an OBAP member pursuing a career in the aviation industry. **Criteria:** Selection is based on achievements; attitude to others; commitment to success; financial need and responsibility.

Funds Avail.: $2,500. **Duration:** Annual. **To Apply:** Applicant must provide evidence of participation in at least one OBAP event; a copy of Private Pilot's license; a resume; two letters of recommendations (one must be from an OBAP member); a copy of medical permit; (two-page) autobiography with recent photo; and an essay on, "What

is/has been your greatest life challenge and how has it enriched you or someone else's life?". **Deadline:** May 10. **Contact:** E-mail: obapscholarships@obap.org.

8742 ■ Edward Horne Scholarship *(Advanced Professional/Scholarship)*

Purpose: To provide individuals retaining a Private Pilot License with the financial support needed to advance careers in aviation through continue education and training. **Focus:** Aviation. **Qualif.:** Applicant must be an OBAP member pursuing a career in the aviation industry.

Funds Avail.: $5,000. **Duration:** Annual. **To Apply:** Applicants must submit their respective documents via email; contents of the email shall include in PDF form application form; essay; two letters of recommendation, and any other required documents as indicated on the scholarship. All documents must be attached to a single email with only the OBAP member number in the subject line. **Remarks:** The scholarship was established to honor Captain Edward L. Horne, Jr., who began his passion for flying in 1969. **Contact:** E-mail: obapscholarships@obap.org.

8743 ■ Organization for Tropical Studies (OTS)

410 Swift Ave.
Durham, NC 27705
Ph: (919)684-5774
Fax: (919)684-5661
E-mail: info@tropicalstudies.org
URL: www.ots.ac.cr
Social Media: www.facebook.com/OTS.OET
linkedin.com/company/organization-for-tropical-studies
twitter.com/ots_oet

8744 ■ David and Deborah Clark Fellowship *(Graduate/Fellowship)*

Purpose: To assist thesis-related field research in tropical biology and similar fields. **Focus:** Biology. **Qualif.:** Applicants must be graduate students enrolled in a degree program at OTS member institutions.

Funds Avail.: Up to $5,200 for 60 days at OTS field stations plus up to $340 toward OTS services to obtain research/export permits. **To Apply:** Applicants must submit the following items: OTS Fellowship Cover Sheet; project abstract, objectives, methods and significance; project schedule and expected outputs; project budget; project justification; literature cited; name, address, telephone, fax and email of four people who can comment on the scientific merit of the proposal; applicant's curriculum vitae; letter of endorsement from the thesis advisor. Materials should be typed in 12-point font and all pages must be numbered. The cover sheet and proposal should be submitted by email. Letter of endorsement from the thesis advisor should be sent directly by the applicant's recommend by email. Proposals may be submitted in English or Spanish. **Deadline:** March 1st and October 1st. **Contact:** Email: guiselle.castro@tropicalstudies.org.

8745 ■ Dole Food Fellowship *(Graduate/Fellowship)*

Purpose: To assist thesis-related field research in tropical biology and similar fields. **Focus:** Biology. **Qualif.:** Applicant must be a graduate students enrolled in degree programs at OTS member institutions and to OTS graduate course alumni. **Criteria:** Selection will be based on the committee criteria.

Funds Avail.: Up to $5,200 for 60 days at OTS field stations plus up to $340 toward OTS services to obtain

Awards are arranged alphabetically below their administering organizations

research/export permits. **Duration:** Semiannual. **To Apply:** Applicants must submit the following items: OTS Fellowship Cover Sheet; project abstract, objectives, methods and significance; project schedule and expected outputs; project budget; project justification; literature cited; name, address, telephone, fax and email of four people who can comment on the scientific merit of the proposal; applicant's curriculum vitae; letter of endorsement from the thesis advisor. Materials should be typed in 12-point font and all pages must be numbered. The cover sheet and proposal should be submitted by email. Letter of endorsement from the thesis advisor should be sent directly by the applicant's recommend by email. Proposals may be submitted in English or Spanish. **Deadline:** October 1; March 1. **Contact:** Email: guiselle.castro@tropicalstudies.org.

8746 ■ Emily P. Foster Fellowship (Graduate/ Fellowship)

Purpose: To assist thesis-related field research in tropical biology and similar fields. **Focus:** Biology. **Qualif.:** Applicants must be graduate students enrolled in a degree program at OTS member institutions.

Funds Avail.: Up to $5,200 for 60 days at OTS field stations plus up to $340 toward OTS services to obtain research/export permits. **To Apply:** Applicants must submit the following items: OTS Fellowship Cover Sheet; project abstract, objectives, methods and significance; project schedule and expected outputs; project budget; project justification; literature cited; name, address, telephone, fax and email of four people who can comment on the scientific merit of the proposal; applicant's curriculum vitae; letter of endorsement from the thesis advisor. Materials should be typed in 12-point font and all pages must be numbered. The cover sheet and proposal should be submitted by email. Letter of endorsement from the thesis advisor should be sent directly by the applicant's recommend by email. Proposals may be submitted in English or Spanish. **Deadline:** October 1; March 1. **Contact:** Email: guiselle.castro@tropicalstudies.org.

8747 ■ F. Christian and Betty Thompson Fellowship (Graduate/Fellowship)

Purpose: To assist thesis-related field research in tropical biology and similar fields. **Focus:** Biology. **Qualif.:** Applicants must be graduate students enrolled in a degree program at OTS member institutions.

Funds Avail.: Up to $5,200 for 60 days at OTS field stations plus up to $340 toward OTS services to obtain research/export permits. **To Apply:** Applicants must submit the following items: OTS Fellowship Cover Sheet; project abstract, objectives, methods and significance; project schedule and expected outputs; project budget; project justification; literature cited; name, address, telephone, fax and email of four people who can comment on the scientific merit of the proposal; applicant's curriculum vitae; letter of endorsement from the thesis advisor. Materials should be typed in 12-point font and all pages must be numbered. The cover sheet and proposal should be submitted by email. Letter of endorsement from the thesis advisor should be sent directly by the applicant's recommend by email. Proposals may be submitted in English or Spanish. **Deadline:** October 1; March 1. **Contact:** Email: guiselle.castro@tropicalstudies.org.

8748 ■ Lillian and Murray Slatkin Fellowship (Graduate/Fellowship)

Purpose: To assist thesis-related field research in tropical biology and similar fields. **Focus:** Biology. **Qualif.:** Ap-

plicants must be graduate students enrolled in a degree program at OTS member institutions. **Criteria:** Selection will be based on the committee's criteria.

Funds Avail.: Up to $5,200 for 60 days at OTS field stations plus up to $340 toward OTS services to obtain research/export permits. **Duration:** Annual. **To Apply:** Applicants must submit the following items: OTS Fellowship Cover Sheet; project abstract, objectives, methods and significance; project schedule and expected outputs; project budget; project justification; literature cited; name, address, telephone, fax and email of four people who can comment on the scientific merit of the proposal; applicant's curriculum vitae; letter of endorsement from the thesis advisor. Materials should be typed in 12-point font and all pages must be numbered. The cover sheet and proposal should be submitted by email. Letter of endorsement from the thesis advisor should be sent directly by the applicant's recommend by email. Proposals may be submitted in English or Spanish. **Deadline:** October 1; March 1. **Contact:** Guiselle Castro, Email: guiselle.castro@tropicalstudies.org.

8749 ■ Andrew W. Mellon Foundation Fellowships (Graduate/Fellowship)

Purpose: To support graduate thesis research on plants and ecosystem-oriented projects. **Focus:** Ecology. **Qualif.:** Applicants must be graduate students with a research focusing on plants and ecosystem. **Criteria:** Selection will be based on the committee's criteria.

Funds Avail.: $4,200 for 50 days at OTS field stations plus $500 in airfare or other permissible expenses. **Duration:** Annual. **To Apply:** Applicants must submit the following items: OTS Fellowship Cover Sheet; project abstract, objectives, methods and significance; project schedule and expected outputs; project budget; project justification; literature cited; name, address, telephone, fax and email of four people who can comment on the scientific merit of the proposal; applicant's curriculum vitae; letter of endorsement from thesis advisor. Materials should be typed in 12-point font and all pages must be numbered. The cover sheet and proposal should be submitted by email. Letter of endorsement from thesis advisor should be sent directly by the applicant's recommender by email. **Deadline:** October 1 and March 1. **Contact:** Organization for Tropical Studies, at the above address.

8750 ■ Peace Frogs Fellowships (Graduate/ Fellowship)

Purpose: To provide funds for graduate students interested in conducting herpetological research, particularly with threatened or endangered species. **Focus:** Herpetology. **Qualif.:** Applicants must be a University of Virginia undergraduate student participating in a U.Va. program or exchange. **Criteria:** Selection will be based on the committee's criteria.

Funds Avail.: $500. **Duration:** Annual. **Number Awarded:** 1. **To Apply:** Applicants must submit the following items: OTS Fellowship Cover Sheet; project abstract, project objectives; project methods; project significance; project schedule and expected outputs; project budget; project justification; literature cited; name, address, telephone, fax and email of four people who can comment on the scientific merit of the proposal; applicant's curriculum vitae; letter of endorsement from thesis advisor. Materials should be typed in 12-point font and all pages must be numbered. The cover sheet and proposal should be submitted by email. Letter of endorsement from thesis advisor should be sent directly by the applicant's recommender by email. Proposals may be

Awards are arranged alphabetically below their administering organizations

submitted in English or Spanish. **Remarks:** Established in 1996.

8751 ■ Rexford Daubenmire Fellowship *(Graduate/ Fellowship)*

Purpose: To assist thesis-related field research in tropical biology and similar fields. **Focus:** Biology. **Qualif.:** Applicants must be graduate students enrolled in a degree program at OTS member institutions.

Funds Avail.: Up to $5,200 for 60 days at OTS field stations plus up to $340 toward OTS services to obtain research/export permits. **To Apply:** Applicants must submit the following items: OTS Fellowship Cover Sheet; project abstract, objectives, methods and significance; project schedule and expected outputs; project budget; project justification; literature cited; name, address, telephone, fax and email of four people who can comment on the scientific merit of the proposal; applicant's curriculum vitae; letter of endorsement from the thesis advisor. Materials should be typed in 12-point font and all pages must be numbered. The cover sheet and proposal should be submitted by email. Letter of endorsement from the thesis advisor should be sent directly by the applicant's recommend by email. Proposals may be submitted in English or Spanish. **Deadline:** October 1; March 1. **Contact:** Email: guiselle.castro@tropicalstudies.org.

8752 ■ Rowe Family Fellowships *(Graduate/ Fellowship)*

Purpose: To enable selected students to conduct their thesis work at an OTS research station in Costa Rica or to receive a post-course award after taking an OTS course. **Focus:** Biology. **Qualif.:** Applicants must be students throughout the United States and Latin America. **Criteria:** Selection will be based on the committee's criteria.

Funds Avail.: $4,200 for 50 days at OTS field stations& $500 in airfare or other permissible expenses. **To Apply:** Applicants must submit the project abstract, objectives, methods and significance; project schedule and expected outputs; project budget; project justification; literature cited; name, address, telephone, fax and email of four people who can comment on the scientific merit of the proposal; a curriculum vitae; letter of endorsement from thesis advisor; should be typed in 12-point font and all pages must be numbered; a cover sheet and proposal should be submitted by email; a letter of endorsement from thesis advisor. **Deadline:** October 1; March 1. **Contact:** Organization for Tropical Studies, at the above address.

8753 ■ Stanley Smith Horticultural Fellowships *(Graduate, Undergraduate/Fellowship)*

Purpose: To provide funds for horticultural work and systematic research on tropical plants of interest to the Wilson Botanical Garden. **Focus:** Horticulture. **Qualif.:** Applicants must be individuals of all levels who are experts in tropical plant groups. **Criteria:** Selection will be based on the committee's criteria.

Funds Avail.: Up to $25,000. **Duration:** Annual. **To Apply:** Applicants must submit the following items: OTS Fellowship Cover Sheet; project abstract, objectives, methods and significance; project schedule and expected outputs; project budget; project justification; literature cited; name, address, telephone, fax and email of four people who can comment on the scientific merit of the proposal; applicant's curriculum vitae; letter of endorsement from thesis advisor. Materials should be typed in 12-point font and all pages must be numbered. The cover sheet and proposal should

be submitted by email. Letter of endorsement from thesis advisor should be sent directly by the applicant's recommender by email. **Deadline:** June 29. **Contact:** Zak Zahawi at zak.zak.zahawi@ots.cr.

8754 ■ William L. Brown Fellowship *(Graduate/ Fellowship)*

Purpose: To assist thesis-related field research in tropical biology and similar fields. **Focus:** Biology. **Qualif.:** Applicants must be graduate students enrolled in a degree program at OTS member institutions.

Funds Avail.: Up to $5,200 for 60 days at OTS field stations plus up to $340 toward OTS services to obtain research/export permits. **To Apply:** Applicants must submit the following items: OTS Fellowship Cover Sheet; project abstract, objectives, methods and significance; project schedule and expected outputs; project budget; project justification; literature cited; name, address, telephone, fax and email of four people who can comment on the scientific merit of the proposal; applicant's curriculum vitae; letter of endorsement from the thesis advisor. Materials should be typed in 12-point font and all pages must be numbered. The cover sheet and proposal should be submitted by email. Letter of endorsement from the thesis advisor should be sent directly by the applicant's recommend by email. Proposals may be submitted in English or Spanish. **Contact:** Email: guiselle.castro@tropicalstudies.org.

8755 ■ Orgone Biophysical Research Laboratory (OBRL)
Greensprings Ctr.
Ashland, OR 97520
Ph: (541)552-0118
Fax: (541)552-0118
URL: www.orgonelab.org

8756 ■ Lou Hochberg Awards - University/College Essay Awards *(Undergraduate/Award, Monetary)*

Purpose: To support the best University/College level student research paper, addressing Wilhelm Reich's findings and discoveries. **Focus:** Biophysics. **Qualif.:** Applicants must be university students and journalists worldwide. **Criteria:** Selection will be based on accuracy, clarity and merit, as determined by our judges.

Funds Avail.: $500. **Duration:** Annual. **To Apply:** Submissions should be made as one good-quality photocopy plus a separate PDF version.

8757 ■ Lou Hochberg Awards - Thesis and Dissertation Awards *(Graduate/Award, Monetary)*

Purpose: To support the outstanding research on Wilhelm Reich's discoveries. **Focus:** Biophysics. **Criteria:** Selection will be based on the submitted essay.

Funds Avail.: $1,000.00. **Duration:** Annual. **To Apply:** Submitted proposals must be in duplicate (good quality photocopy plus PDF if available) and include a letter from the students' home department (or their committee chairperson) indicating the formal acceptance of their proposal. The proposal must be accompanied by a cover letter expressing the amount needed and how it would be spent. **Contact:** The Orgone Biophysical Research Laboratory, PO Box 1148, Ashland, Oregon, 97520, USA; Email: info@orgonelab.org.

8758 ■ Orlando Central Florida Chapter of the Society for Technical Communication
PO Box 540444
Orlando, FL 32804-0444

Awards are arranged alphabetically below their administering organizations

URL: www.stc-orlando.org
Social Media: www.facebook.com/stcorlando
twitter.com/stcorlando

8759 ■ The Melissa Pellegrin Memorial Scholarship Fund *(Undergraduate, Graduate/Scholarship)*

Purpose: To support the education of undergraduate and graduate UCF Technical Communications students. **Focus:** Technical communications; Writing. **Qualif.:** Applicants must be full-time or part-time undergraduate or graduate technical writing students at the University of Central Florida (UCF); must be enrolled in the Technical Communication program at UCF pursuing a career in technical communication. **Criteria:** Selection is based on committee's criteria.

Funds Avail.: $500 - $1,000. **Duration:** Annual. **Number Awarded:** Varies. **To Apply:** Applicants must submit a completed scholarship application form along with a copy of transcripts and a letter to the STC Orlando Chapter Education Committee; send application and supporting materials to the contact provided. **Remarks:** Established to honor and preserve the memory and generous spirit of a valued friend and professional colleague, Melissa Pellegrin. Established in 1997. **Contact:** Wendy Sanchez; Phone: 407-823-2251; E-mail: Wendy.Sanchez@ucf.edu or Lyman Brodie; Phone: 407-823-0743; E-mail: lyman.brodie@ucf.edu.

8760 ■ The Orr Law Firm, LLC
1355 S Colorado Blvd., Ste. C-420
Denver, CO 80222
Ph: (303)818-2448
URL: www.orrlaw.com
Social Media: www.facebook.com/pg/orrlawfirm
twitter.com/theorrlawfirm

8761 ■ A DUI Defense Scholarship *(Graduate/Scholarship)*

Purpose: To provide assistance toward any expense incurred in law school. **Focus:** Law. **Qualif.:** Applicants must be full-time students over the age of 18 enrolled in a current or upcoming accredited law program.**Criteria:** Essays are judged upon content, style, and creativity.

Funds Avail.: $1,000. **Number Awarded:** 1. **To Apply:** Applicants submit an essay answering the prompt, "As a Defense Attorney, would you defend a drunk driver?". **Deadline:** August 15. **Contact:** Email: scholarship@orrlaw.com.

8762 ■ Orthopaedic Trauma Association (OTA)
9400 W Higgins Rd., Ste. 305
Rosemont, IL 60018-4975
Ph: (847)698-1631
Fax: (847)430-5140
E-mail: ota@ota.org
URL: ota.org
Social Media: www.facebook.com/
  OrthopaedicTraumaAssociation
www.instagram.com/otatrauma
twitter.com/OrthoTraumaAssn

8763 ■ OTA Member Full Research Grant *(Other/Grant)*

Purpose: To provide funds that will promote the research endeavors and interests of the OTA members. **Focus:**

Medicine, Orthopedic. **Qualif.:** Applicants must be investigators or co-principal investigators who are OTA or AONA members; must be in good standing and the primary research institution must be located in North America. **Criteria:** Selection will be reviewed by OTA Research Committee based on scientific merit scores and ranking.

Funds Avail.: Clinical Research Grants: $40,000; Basic Research Grants: $50,000; Directed Topic Research Grants: $20,000. **Duration:** Annual. **To Apply:** Applicants Research grants pre-proposal applications are available online; all application materials (Word document only), figures, tables, etc. must be part of the single Word document submitted.

8764 ■ Orthotic and Prosthetic Education and Research Foundation (OPERF)
PO Box 34635
Washington, DC 20043-4635
Ph: (202)380-3663
Fax: (202)380-3447
URL: www.operf.org
Social Media: www.facebook.com/OPERF
www.linkedin.com/company/operf
twitter.com/OPERF_

8765 ■ OPERF/ABC Resident Travel Award *(Professional development/Grant)*

Purpose: To support prosthetics and orthotics residents travel to the American Academy of Orthotists and Prosthetists (AAOP) national meeting so that they may present their NCOPE (National Commission on Orthotic and Prosthetic Education) required Directed Study Report. **Focus:** Orthotics prosthetics technology. **Qualif.:** Applicants must be prosthetics and orthotics residents; must be currently involved in or have completed an NCOPE accredited residency within the last 3 years; project must be relevant to the orthotics and prosthetics profession; Individuals are only eligible to receive this award once. **Criteria:** Selection will be based upon the merit of the residents' project, as determined by the OPERF Research Committee and OPERF Board of Directors.

Funds Avail.: $2,500. **Duration:** Annual. **Number Awarded:** 4. **To Apply:** Applicants must include the application cover page, available at the website; maximum of one page abstract; a one-page brief biosketches for the residents and residency advisor; abstract should describe the residents' NCOPE Directed Study project; typed single-space in 10-12 point font on pages with one inch margins; be formatted according to the conventional format of introduction, methods, results, discussion, conclusion and references; may be included in the one-page abstract, if they are legible. **Deadline:** November 1. **Contact:** OPERF/ABC Resident, Travel Award Program, c/o Manisha Bhaskar, FAAOP, Orthotic and Prosthetic Education and Research Foundation Inc., PO Box 30840, Bethesda, MD, 20824; Phone: 202-380 3663; Email: submissions@operf.org; at (202) 380-3663 or email mbhaskar@operf.org.

8766 ■ OPERF Student Awards *(Professional development/Grant)*

Purpose: To support orthotics and prosthetics educators who currently hold teaching position at CAAHEP-accredited O&P education institutions who are pursuing higher degrees to improve their skills as O&P instructors. **Focus:** Orthotics prosthetics technology. **Qualif.:** Applicants must

Awards are arranged alphabetically below their administering organizations

be employed as faculty members at a CAAHEP-Accredited O&P Program; enrolled in an advanced degree program. **Criteria:** Selection will be based on the review panel's criterla.

Funds Avail.: $10,000. **Duration:** Annual. **Number Awarded:** 10. **To Apply:** Completed application must include the following: current faculty position; degree program; plan of study and progress toward degree; letter of recommendation; applicants' statement describing how the students' academic goals will contribute to excellence as an O&P faculty member and how the OPERF Educator Award will assist the students in pursuing their academic goals; Applicants' CV. **Deadline:** October 1. **Contact:** Orthotic and Prosthetic Education and Research Foundation, Research Committee Chair, PO Box 30840, Bethesda, MD 20824; Manisha Bhaskar; Phone: (202) 380-3663; Fax: (202) 380-3447; Email: mbhaskar@operf.org.

8767 ■ OPERF Fellowships (Graduate, Master's/Fellowship)

Purpose: To support quality graduate education research related to the orthotics and prosthetics profession. **Focus:** Orthotics prosthetics technology. **Qualif.:** Applicants must be students currently enrolled in a Masters and/or PhD educational program within the United States; project must be relevant to the orthotics and prosthetics profession. **Criteria:** Selection will be based on the committee's criteria.

Funds Avail.: $5,000. **Duration:** Annual. **To Apply:** Applicants must submit a letter of intent, maximum of one page in length and must briefly describe the proposed research; proposal should be a maximum of five pages in length, 12 point font, one inch borders and single-space; research proposal must include the following components application cover page, available at the website; abstract, up to 300 words; specific aims; background and significance; previous research; methodology; project timeline, including milestones and deliverables; anticipated results; references; budget and facilities; list of current/pending support related to the proposed research; list of collaborators (including a short biosketch for each); biosketch for the students; letter of faculty support (from the students' advisor). **Deadline:** January 15. **Contact:** Manisha Bhaskar, Phone: 202-380-3663, Email: mbhaskar@operf.org.

8768 ■ OPERF Small Grants (Doctorate/Grant)

Purpose: To support quality investigator-initiated research related to the orthotics and prosthetics profession. **Focus:** Orthotics prosthetics technology. **Criteria:** Selection will be based on the committee's criteria.

Funds Avail.: Up to $25,000. **Duration:** Annual. **To Apply:** Applicants must submit a maximum of one page Letter of Intent and must briefly describe the proposed research; research proposal should be a maximum of 15 pages in length, 12 point font, 1 inch borders, single-spaced; research proposal should include the application cover page, available at the website; abstract, up to 500 words; specific aims; background and significance; previous research; methodology; project timeline, including milestones and deliverables; anticipated results; references; budget and facilities, current/pending support related to proposed research; list of collaborators, including a short biosketch for each; letters of support; biosketch for the principal investigator. **Contact:** Orthotic and Prosthetic Education and Research Foundation, Research Committee Chair, PO Box 30840, Bethesda, MD 20824; Phone: 312-503-5717; Email: smallgrantapplications@operf.org.

8769 ■ OSA Management LLP
43 Bedford St, Ste. 4005
London WC2E 9HA, United Kingdom

8770 ■ Mailcheck Scholarship $1,500 (College, University, Undergraduate/Scholarship)

Purpose: To cover expenses for studying or just self-development. **Focus:** General studies/Field of study not specified. **Qualif.:** Applicant must be a current full-time student or accepted as a full-time student at an accredited college or university.

Funds Avail.: $1,500. **Number Awarded:** 1. **To Apply:** Applicant must write an essay (1,500 to 2,000 words) on the topic and follow all of the instructions. Essays with grammatical, format, and punctuation errors will be disqualified. If application is successful, applicant will receive a confirmation within seven working days. **Deadline:** September 30. **Contact:** Email: scholarship@mailcheck.co; URL: www.mailcheck.co/scholarship.

8771 ■ Osgoode Society for Canadian Legal History
Osgoode Hall
Toronto, ON, Canada M5H 2N6
Ph: (416)947-3321
Fax: (416)947-3447
E-mail: osgoodesociety@lsuc.on.ca
URL: www.osgoodesociety.ca
Social Media: www.facebook.com/osgoodesocietyforcanadianlegalhistory
twitter.com/OsgoodeSociety

8772 ■ R. Roy McMurtry Fellowship in Legal History (Doctorate, Graduate/Fellowship)

Purpose: To provide financial assistance for graduate students in the field of Canadian legal history. **Focus:** Law. **Qualif.:** Applicants must be graduate students or those who recently completed their doctoral degree affiliated by Ontario University and who must conduct research in the field of Canadian legal history. **Criteria:** Recipients will be selected based on financial need.

Funds Avail.: $16,000. **Duration:** Annual. **To Apply:** Applicants must submit a curriculum vitae and statement of the research to be conducted. **Deadline:** May 31. **Remarks:** The fellowship was named in honor of R. Roy McMurtry, Chief Justice of Ontario. Established in 2007. **Contact:** Amanda Campbell, McMurtry Fellowship Selection Committee, Osgoode Society for Canadian Legal History, Osgoode Hall, 130 Queen St., W, Toronto, M5H 2N6; Email: osgoodesociety@lsuc.on.ca.

8773 ■ The OTA Guide
333 Guadalupe, Ste. 2-510
Austin, TX 78701
Ph: (512)305-6900
Fax: (512)305-6970
E-mail: admin@occupational-therapy-assistant.org
URL: occupational-therapy-assistant.org
Social Media: www.facebook.com/pg/OTAGuide
twitter.com/OTAguide

8774 ■ COTA Scholarship for Occupational Therapy Assistants (Undergraduate/Scholarship)

Purpose: To encourage and assist students to achieve their educational goals. **Focus:** Occupational therapy. **Qua-**

Awards are arranged alphabetically below their administering organizations

lif.: Applicants must be enrolled in an occupational therapy assistant program of any age, race, and gender. **Criteria:** Selection will be based on the submitted essay.

Funds Avail.: $500. **Duration:** Annual. **To Apply:** Applicants must submit a 1,000-word essay answering the following questions: "Using your talent and education, what is your plan to improve the world? What career and personal goals have you made for yourself?". **Deadline:** December 1. **Contact:** the.ota.guide@gmail.com.

8775 ■ Our World-Underwater Scholarship Society (OWUSS)
PO Box 6157
Woodridge, IL 60517
Ph: (630)969-6690
E-mail: info@owuscholarship.org
URL: www.owuscholarship.org
Social Media: www.facebook.com/rolexscholarship

8776 ■ Our World Underwater Scholarship Society North American Rolex Scholarships
(Undergraduate, Graduate/Scholarship)

Purpose: To provide hands-on introduction to underwater and other aquatic-related endeavors for a young person considering a career in an underwater-related discipline. **Focus:** Biology, Marine. **Criteria:** Selection will be based on Committee's criteria.

Funds Avail.: $25,000. **Duration:** Annual. **Number Awarded:** 1. **To Apply:** Applicants must submit a completed application form along with the following: a copy of dive scuba diving certification card(s); a copy of dive logs for the last six months; official transcripts or Unofficial Transcript; completed medical form signed by a licensed physician; two letters of recommendation from teachers/professors; two letters of recommendation from persons in the community; statement from certifying agency/school or recent scuba instructor regarding the applicant's diving proficiency; resume including extracurricular activities; personal biography (double spaced, maximum of 2 pages). **Deadline:** January 15. **Remarks:** Established in 1974. **Contact:** Roberta Flanders, Executive Administrator, Email:execadmin@owuscholarship.org.

8777 ■ Out on Bay Street
20 Bloor St. E
Toronto, ON, Canada M4W 3T3
URL: outonbayst.org
Social Media: facebook.com/outonbayst
instagram.com/outonbayst
twitter.com/outonbayst

8778 ■ OOBS Student Leadership Scholarships
(Undergraduate/Scholarship)

Purpose: To support students who make a difference in their LGBTQ and other communities by providing resources to help them achieve their educational goals. **Focus:** General studies/Field of study not specified. **Qualif.:** Applicants must be Canadian legal residents; must be current registered students in an accredited Canadian post-secondary program of study; must exemplify leadership, especially within the LGBTQ communities; and must have demonstrated personal and/or academic success. **Criteria:** Selection will be based on the applicants' eligibility and compliance with the application process.

Funds Avail.: 2,500 Canadian Dollars. **Duration:** Annual. **To Apply:** Applicants must register as Student Members on the Out On Bay Street Student Portal to gain access to the OOBS Student Leadership Scholarship application; must provide supporting documents such as resume and unofficial transcript, and email address; other information regarding the application process can be verified at the program website. **Deadline:** May 29.

8779 ■ Outdoor Power Equipment Aftermarket Association (OPEAA)
1605 King St.
Alexandria, VA 22314
Ph: (703)549-7608
Fax: (703)549-7609
E-mail: info@opeaa.org
URL: www.opeaa.org

8780 ■ Bill Nelson Scholarship Endowment (BNSE)
(Undergraduate, Graduate/Scholarship)

Purpose: To supplement the educational expenses for students in the upcoming academic year for those in a business-related field. **Focus:** General studies/Field of study not specified. **Qualif.:** Applicants can be full time employees of OPEAA members, their children, stepchildren, grandchildren and adopted children; current part-time employees (excluding their children) are also eligible; must be current year high school graduates and college undergraduates; previous applicants and awardees are eligible.

Funds Avail.: No specific amount. **Duration:** Annual. **To Apply:** Completed application (hard copy) with the signature of their company's CEO along with an essay describing aspirations in 250 words or less; two letters of reference; an official copy of ACT/SAT scores and school transcripts and a recent photograph must be submitted. **Deadline:** May 15. **Remarks:** The scholarship was established to honor Bill Nelson, founder of Rotary Corporation and one of the great leaders of the outdoor power equipment aftermarket industry. **Contact:** BNSE Trustees: 1605 King St., Alexandria, VA 22314, Email: infoOPEAA@opeaa.org.

8781 ■ Outdoor Writers Association of America (OWAA)
2814 Brooks St.,
Missoula, MT 59801
Ph: (406)728-7434
E-mail: info@owaa.org
URL: www.owaa.org
Social Media: www.facebook.com/OWAAonline
twitter.com/OWAAonline

8782 ■ Bodie McDowell Scholarship *(Graduate, Undergraduate/Scholarship)*

Purpose: To provide support to talented communicators with outdoor interests. **Focus:** Writing. **Qualif.:** Applicants must be undergraduate or graduate students from any discipline and school; must have a career goal in outdoor communications including print, photography, film, art or broadcasting. **Criteria:** Selection based on the following criteria candidate should have clear, significant goals in outdoor communications; examples of work and letters of recommendation.

Funds Avail.: $1,000 to $5,000. **Duration:** Annual. **Number Awarded:** 3 and more. **To Apply:** Applicants must

Awards are arranged alphabetically below their administering organizations

submit a completed application, letter of recommendation from a faculty advisor, professor or school administrator; grade transcript and example of outdoor communication work; a one- to two-page statement of career goals, and optional letters of recommendation from others familiar with applicant's work. **Deadline:** March 1. **Contact:** Bodie McDowell Scholarship, 615 Oak St., Ste. 201, Missoula, MT, 59801; Email: info@owaa.org.

8783 ■ Overseas Press Club Foundation

c/o Jane Reilly, Executive Director
40 W 45 St.
New York, NY 10036
Ph: (201)493-9087
E-mail: foundation@opcofamerica.org
URL: www.overseaspressclubfoundation.org

8784 ■ Flora Lewis Fellowship *(Graduate, Undergraduate/Scholarship)*

Purpose: To support the education of students who aspire to become foreign correspondents. **Focus:** Journalism. **Qualif.:** Applicants must be graduate or undergraduate students, studying at American colleges and universities, who aspire to become foreign correspondents. **Criteria:** Selection will be made by judges to applications showing strong reporting skills, color, and understanding or passion.

Funds Avail.: $2,000. **Duration:** Annual. **Number Awarded:** 1. **To Apply:** Applicants must submit a cover letter (should be autobiographical in nature addressing such questions as how the applicants developed an interest in this particular part of the world, or how he or she would use the scholarship to further journalistic ambitions); resume; and essay (approximately 500 words concentrating on an area of the world or an international issue that is in keeping with the applicant's interest); applicant's name and school should appear at the top of each page. **Deadline:** December 1. **Contact:** William J. Holstein President; Overseas Press Club Foundation; 40 West 45 Street New York NY 10036; Email: foundation@opcofamerica.org; Jane Reilly, Executive Director; Phone: 201-819-2639.

8785 ■ Emanuel R. Freedman Scholarship *(Graduate, Undergraduate/Scholarship)*

Purpose: To support the education of students who aspire to become foreign correspondents. **Focus:** Journalism.

Funds Avail.: $2,000. **Duration:** Annual. **Number Awarded:** 16. **To Apply:** Applicants must submit a cover letter (should be autobiographical in nature addressing such questions as how the applicants developed an interest in this particular part of the world, or how he or she would use the scholarship to further journalistic ambitions); resume; and essay (approximately 500 words concentrating on an area of the world or an international issue that is in keeping with the applicant's interest); applicant's name and school should appear at the top of each page. **Remarks:** The award was established to honor Emanuel R. Freedman, known as Manny, was the foreign editor of The New York Times for 16 years and then an assistant managing editor.

8786 ■ Harper's Magazine Scholarships *(Graduate, Undergraduate/Scholarship)*

Purpose: To support the education of students who aspire to become foreign correspondents. **Focus:** Journalism. **Criteria:** Selection will be made by judges to applications showing strong reporting skills, color, and understanding or passion.

Funds Avail.: $2,000. **Duration:** Annual. **Number Awarded:** 1. **To Apply:** Applicants must submit a cover letter (should be autobiographical in nature addressing such questions as how the applicants developed an interest in this particular part of the world, or how he or she would use the scholarship to further journalistic ambitions); resume; and essay (approximately 500 words concentrating on an area of the world or an international issue that is in keeping with the applicant's interest); applicant's name and school should appear at the top of each page. **Contact:** Overseas Press Club Foundation, at the above address.

8787 ■ Irene Corbally Kuhn Scholarship *(Graduate, Undergraduate/Scholarship)*

Purpose: To support the education of students who aspire to become foreign correspondents. **Focus:** Journalism. **Qualif.:** Applicants must be graduate or undergraduate students, studying at American colleges and universities, who aspire to become foreign correspondents. **Criteria:** Selection will be made by judges to applications showing strong reporting skills, color, and understanding or passion.

Funds Avail.: $2,000. **Duration:** Annual. **To Apply:** Applicants must submit a cover letter (should be autobiographical in nature addressing such questions as how the applicants developed an interest in this particular part of the world, or how he or she would use the scholarship to further journalistic ambitions); resume; and essay (approximately 500 words concentrating on an area of the world or an international issue that is in keeping with the applicant's interest); applicant's name and school should appear at the top of each page. **Deadline:** December 1. **Contact:** Overseas Press Club Foundation, at the above address.

8788 ■ Reuters Fellowship *(Graduate, Undergraduate/Fellowship)*

Purpose: To support the education of students who aspire to become foreign correspondents. **Focus:** Journalism. **Qualif.:** Applicants must be graduate or undergraduate students, studying at American colleges and universities, who aspire to become foreign correspondents. **Criteria:** Selection will be made by judges to applications showing strong reporting skills, color, and understanding or passion.

Funds Avail.: $2,000. **Duration:** Annual. **To Apply:** Applicants must submit a cover letter (should be autobiographical in nature addressing such questions as how the applicants developed an interest in this particular part of the world, or how he or she would use the scholarship to further journalistic ambitions); resume; and essay (approximately 500 words concentrating on an area of the world or an international issue that is in keeping with the applicant's interest); applicant's name and school should appear at the top of each page. **Deadline:** December 1.

8789 ■ Roy Rowan Scholarship *(Graduate, Undergraduate/Scholarship)*

Purpose: To support the education of students who aspire to become foreign correspondents. **Focus:** Journalism. **Qualif.:** Applicants must be an excellent scholar with a focus on empiricism and an imaginative research agenda assessing natural resource and environmental issues. **Criteria:** Selection will be made by judges to applications showing strong reporting skills, color, and understanding or passion.

Funds Avail.: $2,000. **Duration:** Annual. **Number Awarded:** Varies. **To Apply:** Applicants must submit a cover letter (should be autobiographical in nature address-

Awards are arranged alphabetically below their administering organizations

ing such questions as how the applicants developed an interest in this particular part of the world, or how he or she would use the scholarship to further journalistic ambitions); resume; and essay (approximately 500 words concentrating on an area of the world or an international issue that is in keeping with the applicant's interest); applicant's name and school should appear at the top of each page. **Contact:** Overseas Press Club Foundation, at the above address.

8790 ■ David R. Schweisberg Memorial Scholarship (Graduate, Undergraduate/Scholarship)

Purpose: To support the education of students who aspire to become foreign correspondents. **Focus:** Journalism. **Qualif.:** Applicants must be graduate or undergraduate students, studying at American colleges and universities, who aspire to become foreign correspondents. **Criteria:** Selection will be made by judges to applications showing strong reporting skills, color, and understanding or passion.

Funds Avail.: $2,000. **Duration:** Annual. **To Apply:** Applicants must submit a cover letter (should be autobiographical in nature addressing such questions as how the applicants developed an interest in this particular part of the world, or how he or she would use the scholarship to further journalistic ambitions); resume; and essay (approximately 500 words concentrating on an area of the world or an international issue that is in keeping with the applicant's interest); applicant's name and school should appear at the top of each page. **Contact:** Overseas Press Club Foundation, at the above address.

8791 ■ Standard and Poor's Award for Economic and Business Reporting - S&P Scholarships (Graduate, Undergraduate/Scholarship)

Purpose: To encourage talented young reporters considering careers in financial journalism. **Focus:** Journalism.

Funds Avail.: $2,000. **Duration:** Annual. **To Apply:** Applicants must submit a cover letter (should be autobiographical in nature addressing such questions as how the applicants developed an interest in this particular part of the world, or how he or she would use the scholarship to further journalistic ambitions); resume; and essay (approximately 500 words concentrating on an area of the world or an international issue that is in keeping with the applicant's interest); applicant's name and school should appear at the top of each page. **Remarks:** Endowed by S&P Global.

8792 ■ H.L. Stevenson Fellowship (Graduate, Undergraduate/Fellowship)

Purpose: To support the education of students who aspire to become foreign correspondents. **Focus:** Journalism. **Qualif.:** Applicants must be graduate or undergraduate students, studying at American colleges and universities, who aspire to become foreign correspondents. **Criteria:** Selection will be made by judges to applications showing strong reporting skills, color, and understanding or passion.

Funds Avail.: $2,000. **Duration:** Annual. **Number Awarded:** 1. **To Apply:** Applicants must submit a cover letter (should be autobiographical in nature addressing such questions as how the applicants developed an interest in this particular part of the world, or how he or she would use the scholarship to further journalistic ambitions); resume; and essay (approximately 500 words concentrating on an area of the world or an international issue that is in keeping with the applicant's interest); applicant's name and school should appear at the top of each page. **Contact:** 40 West 45 St., New York NY 10036 USA; Phone:201-493-9087;

Email:foundation@opcofamerica.org.

8793 ■ Stan Swinton Fellowship (Graduate, Undergraduate/Fellowship)

Purpose: To support the education of students who aspire to become foreign correspondents. **Focus:** Journalism.

Funds Avail.: $2,000. **Duration:** Annual. **Contact:** Overseas Press Club Foundation, at the above address.

8794 ■ Theo Wilson Scholarship (Graduate, Undergraduate/Scholarship)

Purpose: To support the education of students who aspire to become foreign correspondents. **Focus:** Journalism. **Qualif.:** Graduate and undergraduate students studying at American colleges and universities who aspire to become foreign correspondents. **Criteria:** Selection will be made by judges to applications showing strong reporting skills, color, and understanding or passion.

Funds Avail.: $2,000. **Duration:** Annual. **Number Awarded:** 1. **To Apply:** Applicants must submit a cover letter (should be autobiographical in nature addressing such questions as how the applicants developed an interest in this particular part of the world, or how he or she would use the scholarship to further journalistic ambitions); resume; and essay (approximately 500 words concentrating on an area of the world or an international issue that is in keeping with the applicant's interest); applicant's name and school should appear at the top of each page. **Deadline:** December 1.

8795 ■ Bill Owen, Cowboy Artist, Memorial Scholarship Fund, Inc. (ACSO)

C/O Dallas Laone Accounting LLC 8610 S Maryland Pkwy Ste. 1005
Las Vegas, NV 89123
E-mail: info@allaboutboca.org
URL: www.allaboutacso.com
Social Media: www.facebook.com/AllAboutBOCA

8796 ■ BOCA Scholarship (Undergraduate/Scholarship)

Purpose: To provide funds for education programs beyond high school for young people of the Arizona ranching community. **Focus:** General studies/Field of study not specified. **Criteria:** Selection will be made by the BOCA Board of Directors.

Duration: Annual. **Number Awarded:** Varies. **To Apply:** Applicant must submit a copy of Official Birth Certificate (first-time applicants only); two letters of recommendation from persons other than family members (first-time applicants only); information about the applicant, including high school, college or trade school achievements and activities, educational plans or goals, Applicant should also provide other scholarships applied for if they have been granted and dollar amount(s) of each, the name, address and phone number of the educational facility plan to attend, and what the tuition, books and lab fees are per semester. **Deadline:** March 15. **Contact:** Bill Owen, Cowboy Artist, Memorial Scholarship Fund, Inc. C/O Valerie Owen-Fillhouer, 9944 W Monte Lindo, St. Peoria, AZ 85383-1933; Email: info@allaboutBOCA.org.

8797 ■ Owner-Operator Independent Drivers Association (OOIDA)

1 NW OOIDA Dr.
Grain Valley, MO 64029-7903

Awards are arranged alphabetically below their administering organizations

Ph: (816)229-5791
Free: 800-444-5791
URL: www.ooida.com
Social Media: twitter.com/OOIDA
www.youtube.com/user/TruckersOOIDA

8798 ■ OOIDA Mary Johnston Scholarship Program
(Undergraduate/Scholarship)

Purpose: To assist the children, grandchildren and legal dependents of OOIDA members in their effort to gain higher education. **Focus:** General studies/Field of study not specified. **Qualif.:** Applicants must be immediate family members of OOIDA; scholarships are available for children, grandchildren and legal dependents of OOIDA members. **Criteria:** Selection will be based on academic merit; applicants are selected in a blind evaluation conducted by the Scholarship Advisory Committee.

Funds Avail.: Four $1,000; One $2,000. **Duration:** Annual. **Number Awarded:** 5. **To Apply:** Applicants must submit an essay (500-word); official certified high school (grades 9-12) transcript; proof of enrollment from institution of higher education. **Deadline:** February 1. **Remarks:** Established in 1998. **Contact:** Andrew King, OOIDA Foundation Inc., PO Box 1000, Ste.1, NW OOIDA Dr., Grain Valley, MO 64029; Phone: 816-229-5791, ext. 1133; E-mail: andrew_king@ooida.com.

8799 ■ Michael Oykhman Criminal Defense Law
840-396 11 Ave., SW
Calgary, AB, Canada T2R 0C5
Ph: (403)266-4440
Fax: (403)234-0337
E-mail: michaeloykhman@so-law.ca
URL: www.oykhmancriminaldefence.com
Social Media: facebook.com/
  OykhmanCriminalDefenceLawCalgary

8800 ■ Michael Oykhman Criminal Law and Evidence Scholarship *(Juris Doctorate, Advanced Professional/Scholarship)*

Purpose: To recognizes a student who has completed their second year of a Juris Doctor program in the Faculty of Law at an accredited. **Focus:** Criminal justice; Law.

Funds Avail.: 1,000 Canadian Dollars. **To Apply:** Application is via online. Applications should contain the subject line "Michael Oykhman Criminal Law and Evidence Scholarship" and should contain the following: the applicant's name, date of birth, address, telephone number and email address; PDF copy of Law School Transcript, with courses fitting the Criminal Law and Evidence criteria highlighted for consideration; and, the applicant's expected date of graduation. **Deadline:** May 31.

8801 ■ Pacific 12 Conference (PAC12)
360 3rd St., 3rd Fl.,
San Francisco, CA 94107
Ph: (415)580-4200
Fax: (415)549-2828
URL: pac-12.com

8802 ■ The Pac-12 Postgraduate Scholarships
(Graduate/Scholarship)

Purpose: To support outstanding student-athletes from member institutions who are also outstanding scholars.

Focus: General studies/Field of study not specified. **Qualif.:** Applicants must have an overall undergraduate minimum cumulative GPA of 3.00 (based on a 4.00 scale) or its equivalent; in the final season of intercollegiate athletics eligibility in all sports or in final year of undergraduate studies; have performed with distinction as a member of the varsity team in the sport in which the student-athlete has been nominated; intend to continue academic work beyond the baccalaureate degree as a full-time graduate student; have behaved, both on and off the field, in a manner that has brought credit to the student-athlete, the institution and intercollegiate athletics. **Criteria:** Selection will be based on participation in campus or community service activities.

Funds Avail.: $9,000. **Duration:** Annual; 3 years. **Number Awarded:** 24. **To Apply:** Applicants must submit data form; student-athlete's statement; and coach endorsement. **Deadline:** June 30.

8803 ■ Pacific Aviation Museum - Pearl Harbor
Historic Ford Island
319 Lexington Blvd.
Honolulu, HI 96818
Ph: (808)441-1000
URL: www.pacificaviationmuseum.org
Social Media: www.facebook.com/PacificAviationMuseum
twitter.com/PacificAviation

8804 ■ Frank Der Yuen Aviation Scholarship
(Undergraduate/Scholarship)

Purpose: To provide financial assistance to Hawaii residents who have been accepted or are enrolled in an aviation-related program at an accredited trade school, college or university. **Focus:** Aviation. **Qualif.:** Applicants must be Hawaii residents who have been accepted, or are enrolled, in an aviation-related program at an accredited trade school, college, or university. **Criteria:** Selection will be made without regard to gender, race, religion, or national origin.

Funds Avail.: $1,000. **Duration:** Annual. **To Apply:** Application and details are available at www.pearlharboraviationmuseum.org/education/scholarships/. **Deadline:** February 14. **Remarks:** To honors the aviation legacy of Frank Der Yuen.

8805 ■ Pacific Institute for the Mathematical Sciences (PIMS)
University of British Columbia
Vancouver, BC, Canada V6T 1Z4
Ph: (604)822-3922
Fax: (604)822-0883
E-mail: reception@pims.math.ca
URL: www.pims.math.ca
Social Media: www.linkedin.com/company/pacific-institute
  -of-mathematical-sciences
twitter.com/pimsmath

8806 ■ PIMS Postdoctoral Fellowship *(Doctorate, Postdoctorate/Fellowship)*

Purpose: To support young researchers in the field of mathematical sciences. **Focus:** Mathematics and mathematical sciences. **Qualif.:** Applicants must have a PhD or equivalent at the time of the nomination. **Criteria:** Selection are based upon committee criteria.

Awards are arranged alphabetically below their administering organizations

Funds Avail.: $25,000. **Duration:** Annual. **To Apply:** Applicants should upload a list of publications, a curriculum vitae and a statement of research interests; special justification statements should be included if the plans to either continue to work with a PhD advisor, or remain at their current institution; should arrange for at least two reference letters to be uploaded to MathJobs; at least one letter should be preferably from an outside referee who is at arms length from the candidate and PhD advisor. **Deadline:** December 14. **Contact:** Executive Assistant, PIMS; Email: reception@pims.math.ca.

8807 ■ David and Lucile Packard Foundation
343 2nd St.
Los Altos, CA 94022-3632
Ph: (650)948-7658
URL: www.packard.org
Social Media: www.facebook.com/PackardFoundation
www.instagram.com/packardfdn
www.linkedin.com/company/packardfoundation
twitter.com/PackardFdn
www.youtube.com/user/ThePackardFoundation

8808 ■ Packard Fellowships for Science and Engineering *(Professional development/Fellowship)*

Purpose: To allow the nation's most promising early career professors to pursue their science and engineering research with few funding restrictions and limited paperwork requirements. **Focus:** Engineering; Science. **Criteria:** Selection will be based Nominations are carefully reviewed by the Fellowship Advisory Panel, comprised of distinguished scientists and engineers.

Funds Avail.: $875,000 ($175,000 per year). **Duration:** Annual; up to five years. **To Apply:** Applications will be through nomination and online; the Foundation invites the presidents of 50 universities to nominate two early-career professors each from their institutions. **Remarks:** Established in 1988. **Contact:** Conservation and Science Program, The David and Lucile Packard Foundation, 343 Second St., Los Altos, CA, 94022; Phone: 650-917-7275; Fax: 650-948-2957; Email: fellows@packard.org.

8809 ■ Paddle Canada (PC)
PO Box 126
Kingston, ON, Canada K7L 4V6
Ph: (613)547-3196
Fax: (613)547-4880
Free: 888-252-6292
E-mail: info@paddlecanada.com
URL: www.paddlecanada.com

8810 ■ Bill Mason Memorial Scholarship Fund *(Undergraduate/Scholarship)*

Purpose: To assist with the education of tomorrow's environmental stewards (those people who help make a difference in the kind of world we live in today and pass on to future generations). **Focus:** Education; Environmental conservation. **Criteria:** Applicants are judged upon the committee's criteria.

Funds Avail.: $1,000. **Duration:** Annual. **Number Awarded:** 1. **To Apply:** Applicants must submit the following: cover letter; confirmation of Eligibility including a copy of birth certificate, Canadian passport or other equivalent document, a confirmation of enrolment letter or related document, current academic year standing and an official, unopened, copy of the most recent transcript; confirmation of Academic Course Content; affirmation of Career Objectives; a brief one-paragraph statement outlining your knowledge of the late Bill Mason; a statement of philosophy regarding your beliefs with reference to the environment, to outdoor education and to how it pertains to the ethics of land and water; a budget outlining both expenses and anticipated revenues during the current academic year; a resume of paddling involvement. **Deadline:** September 30. **Remarks:** Established with a bequest from the Bill Mason, a Canadian recognized both nationally and internationally as an avid canoeist, environmentalist, filmmaker, photographer, artist and public speaker. Established in 1990. **Contact:** Completed scholarship application to: Bill Mason Memorial Scholarship Fund, c/o Paddle Canada | Pagaie Canada, PO Box 126, Station Main, Kingston, Ontario, K7L 4V6, Canada; Toll-free: 888-252-6292; Email: info@paddlecanada.com.

8811 ■ Painting and Decorating Contractors of America (PDCA)
2316 Millpark Dr.
Maryland Heights, MO 63043
URL: www.pdca.org
Social Media: www.facebook.com/PDCANational
www.instagram.com/pdca_national
www.linkedin.com/groups/2390918/profile
twitter.com/PDCANational

8812 ■ A.E. Robert Friedman Scholarship *(Undergraduate, High School/Scholarship)*

Purpose: To provide funds to deserving high school seniors or college aged students who are seeking to further their education through vocational or post-college studies and is based on the students' character and financial need. **Focus:** General studies/Field of study not specified. **Qualif.:** Applicant must be sponsored by a PDCA National Member; must be applying to any state certified University or College. Must be at least a senior in high school at the time of application. Are not required to be a member of PCA, related to a PCA member or an employee of a PCA member, or to have any other connection with PCA. Subject to the above requirements, any individual shall be eligible for a scholarship award. **Criteria:** Applicant will judged based upon character, financial need, and upon full or part-time attendance in an accredited junior college, college, university, vocational, or post-graduate institution.

Funds Avail.: No specific amount. **Duration:** Annual. **Number Awarded:** 3 in 2020. **To Apply:** Applicants must submit a completed application form with two current letters of recommendation, academic transcript, a letter of recommendation by a PDCA national member and an essay (250 words min.) on your career goals. **Remarks:** Established in 1978.

8813 ■ Paleontological Society
9650 Rockville Pike
Bethesda, MD 20814
Ph: (301)634-7231
Fax: (301)634-7099
E-mail: membership@paleosoc.org
URL: paleosoc.org

Awards are arranged alphabetically below their administering organizations

8814 ■ Paleontological Society International Research Program Sepkoski Grants *(Advanced Professional, Graduate/Grant)*

Purpose: To support paleontologists living in Eastern Europe and Republics of the former Soviet Union. **Focus:** Paleontology. **Qualif.:** Applicants must be Paleontologists living in all republics of the former Soviet Union, including the Baltic States, Mongolia, and nations in Eastern Europe (other than East Germany), including Poland, the Czech Republic, Slovakia, Hungary, Romania, Bulgaria, Albania, and the countries of the former Yugoslavia, countries of Central America, Countries of South America, and island nations of the Caribbean (excluding possessions' and territories' of the USA and western European countries). **Criteria:** Grantees will be selected by a committee of the Paleontological Society based on the quality and feasibility of the proposed research.

Funds Avail.: $1,000. **Duration:** Annual. **Number Awarded:** Up to 25. **To Apply:** Applicants must complete the application form providing cover sheet; cover letter; research proposal containing project title, brief description of proposed research; curriculum vitae. **Deadline:** April 1. **Contact:** Dr. Ronald L. Parsley, PalSIRP Sepkoski Grants, Department of Earth & Environmental Sciences, Tulane University, New Orleans, LA 70118, USA; Email: parsley@tulane.edu.

8815 ■ PanHellenic Scholarship Foundation
8501 West Higgins Road Suite 210
Chicago, IL 60631
Ph: (312)357-6432
Fax: (312)872-0090
E-mail: info@panhellenicsf.org
URL: www.panhellenicscholarships.org
Social Media: www.facebook.com/panhellenic
www.instagram.com/panhellenicfoundation/?hl=en
twitter.com/PanHellenicFdn
www.youtube.com/user/ThePanhellenic

8816 ■ The PanHellenic Scholarship *(Undergraduate/Scholarship)*

Purpose: To encourage and support the educational aspirations of gifted high school graduates and university students of Hellenic descent and to provide support for those who have financial need. **Focus:** General studies/Field of study not specified. **Qualif.:** Applicants must be US Citizens or US permanent residents with minimum 3.5 cumulative GPA and Hellenic descent; full-time undergraduate student at an accredited 4-year university in Fall 2018. **Criteria:** Selection is based on academic excellence and financial need.

Funds Avail.: 20 awards of $10,000; 20 awards of $2,500. **Duration:** Annual. **Number Awarded:** 40. **To Apply:** Applicants must submit an essay that addresses the connections between Hellenic contributions to the world and America today; must complete and submit the application form which can be downloaded directly from the website. **Deadline:** April 30. **Contact:** PanHellenic Scholarship Foundation, 8501 West Higgins Road, Ste 210. Chicago, Illinois 60631, USA; Phone: 312 357 6432; Fax: 312 872 0090; Email: info@panhellenicsf.org.

8817 ■ Papercheck, LLC
3905 State St., Ste. 7-516
Santa Barbara, CA 93105-3138
Free: 866-693-3348
E-mail: support@papercheck.com
URL: www.papercheck.com
Social Media: www.facebook.com/papercheck
www.linkedin.com/company/papercheck-llc
twitter.com/papercheck

8818 ■ Charles Shafae Scholarship *(Undergraduate, Four Year College/Scholarship)*

Purpose: To provide funds for the education of qualified individuals through an essay contest. **Focus:** General studies/Field of study not specified. **Criteria:** Selection shall be based on the Papercheck Essay Contest.

Funds Avail.: $1,000. **Duration:** Annual. **Deadline:** January 18. **Contact:** Email: scholarships@papercheck.com.

8819 ■ Paralyzed Veterans of America (PVA)
801 18th St. NW
Washington, DC 20006-3517
Free: 800-424-8200
E-mail: info@pva.org
URL: www.pva.org
Social Media: www.facebook.com/ParalyzedVeterans
www.instagram.com/pva1946
twitter.com/pva1946
www.youtube.com/c/paralyzedveterans1946?reload=9

8820 ■ PVA Research Foundation Fellowships *(Postdoctorate/Fellowship)*

Purpose: To support innovative research and fellowships that improve the lives of those with spinal cord injury and disease. **Focus:** Spinal cord injuries and research. **Qualif.:** Applicants grantee institutions must be located in the United States or Canada; must be postdoctoral students who received their PhD or MD within four years or less; and more than four years of training should apply as principal investigators; must have a designated and identified mentor/sponsor who is a senior-level investigator of the laboratory in which the research is to be conducted. **Criteria:** Selection will be based on scientific/technical merit and relevance to spinal cord dysfunction issues.

To Apply: Applications can be obtained at the website; must submit a proposal and must include the following: one letter of support written by the mentor/sponsor; the letter should identify the mentor and must be submitted as an attachment in the supporting documents section of the online application; the letter should include a statement about the applicant, a brief overview of the sponsor's training and number of fellows and students previously trained, a description of the training environment provided by the laboratory and department, such as seminar program and availability of other investigators for discussion and consultation; two additional letters of support from individuals familiar with the qualifications of the fellows; a biosketch of the mentor/sponsor.

8821 ■ Parapsychological Association (PA)
PO Box 14884
Columbus, OH 43214
Ph: (614)600-2195
URL: www.parapsych.org
Social Media: www.facebook.com/
  ParapsychologicalAssociation

Awards are arranged alphabetically below their administering organizations

www.instagram.com/parapsychologicalassociation
twitter.com/parapsych
www.youtube.com/channel/
  UCs3rgEjohpmCPSWZA2k661Q

8822 ■ Parapsychological Association Research Endowment *(Undergraduate/Recognition, Grant)*

Purpose: To encourage parapsychological research by students and other researchers. **Focus:** Parapsychology. **Qualif.:** Applicants must be involved or interested in doing parapsychological research. **Criteria:** Recipients will be selected based on quality of proposal; prospects for completion as a useful contribution to the field.

Funds Avail.: $2,000-$5,000. **Duration:** Annual. **Number Awarded:** Varies. **To Apply:** Applicants must submit a brief but formal proposal (less than 3000 words), in either plain text or a word document; proposal should have a cover page, title and a brief abstract (50 words or less) of the research, contact information and short statement of personal qualifications; must include letter of support from people involved in supervising or helping the work. **Deadline:** June 30. **Contact:** Dr. David Vernon at grants@ parapsych.org.

8823 ■ Parapsychology Foundation (PF)
PO Box 1562
New York, NY 10021-0043
Ph: (212)628-1550
Fax: (212)628-1559
E-mail: office@parapsychology.org
URL: www.parapsychology.org
Social Media: www.facebook.com/
  parapsychologyfoundation
www.instagram.com/parapsychf
www.pinterest.com/parapsychologyf
twitter.com/parapsychf

8824 ■ Eileen J. Garrett Scholarship *(Undergraduate, Postgraduate/Scholarship)*

Purpose: To assist a student attending an accredited college or university who wishes to pursue the academic study of the science of parapsychology. **Focus:** Parapsychology. **Qualif.:** Applicants must be an accredited college or university who wishes to pursue the academic study of the science of parapsychology; the successful applicant will demonstrate a previous interest in parapsychology.

Funds Avail.: $2,000. **Duration:** Annual. **Number Awarded:** 1. **To Apply:** Applicants must submit an application form together with letters of reference from individuals familiar with the applicant's' work or studies in parapsychology. **Deadline:** July 1. **Contact:** Email: office@ parapsychology.org.

8825 ■ Parent Cooperative Preschools International (PCPI)
PO Box 230327
Portland, OR 97281-0327
E-mail: enquiries@preschools.coop
URL: www.preschools.coop
Social Media: www.facebook.com/parentcooperatives

8826 ■ Katharine Whiteside Taylor Grant *(Professional development/Scholarship)*

Purpose: To help parents and teachers in Canada about cooperative preschools. **Focus:** Education, Early childhood. **Qualif.:** Applicants must be one or more Canadian parent cooperative preschools, or Councils, to help fund a parent education project or other activity that helps members improve in their role as parents.

Funds Avail.: Up to $500. **Duration:** Annual. **Deadline:** December 15. **Remarks:** The grant was established in memory of Dr. Katharine Whiteside Taylor. Established in 1995. **Contact:** E-mail: katharinewhitesidetaylorgrant@ gmail.com.

8827 ■ Park Law Enforcement Association (PLEA)
4397 McCullough St.
Port Charlotte, FL 33948
Ph: (941)286-7410
URL: www.myparkranger.org

8828 ■ Commander Newell S. Rand Jr. Scholarship Program *(Undergraduate/Scholarship)*

Purpose: To provide scholarships to persons pursuing a bachelor's or master's degree in a Park Law Enforcement related course of study. **Focus:** Law enforcement. **Criteria:** Recipients are chosen by the PLEA Board or Committee appointed by the PLEA board.

Funds Avail.: $1,000. **Duration:** Annual. **To Apply:** Applicants must submit the following: three letters of recommendation (one of which must be from a counselor or instructor, principal or college advisor); a one page essay explaining why this scholarship is desired; and, a listing and summary of school and community activities exhibiting leadership and character. **Deadline:** June 1.

8829 ■ Parkersburg Area Community Foundation (PACF)
1620 Park Ave.
Parkersburg, WV 26102-1762
Ph: (304)428-4438
Fax: (304)606-3030
Free: 866-428-4438
E-mail: info@pacfwv.com
URL: www.pacfwv.com
Social Media: www.facebook.com/PACFwv
www.linkedin.com/company/our-community's-foundation
twitter.com/pacfwv
www.youtube.com/channel/
  UCOzCEYkurK30UAM8esTpkgQ

8830 ■ Martin K. Alsup and Frank Schroeder Memorial Music Scholarship *(Undergraduate/Scholarship)*

Purpose: To provide financial assistance to qualified high school seniors from Parkersburg High School. **Focus:** General studies/Field of study not specified; Music; Musicology. **Qualif.:** Applicants must be graduating seniors from Parkersburg High School who have a strong commitment to the field of instrumental music and music-related activities as demonstrated by participation in orchestra or the Big Red Band. **Criteria:** Recipients will be selected based on strong commitment to the field of music and related activities. Preference will be given to students majoring in music or instrumental music; and additional consideration will be given for other music-related activities, such as involvement in performing arts groups.

Funds Avail.: No specific amount. **Duration:** Annual. **To Apply:** Applicants must submit the following: cover sheet

Awards are arranged alphabetically below their administering organizations

(three pages) and application form (four pages); personal essay; high school and/or post-secondary transcripts; a letter of recommendation in a signed and sealed envelope; a copy of the page of their or their parents' most recent tax return that indicates adjusted gross income; and, Student Aid Report showing estimated family contribution from FAFSA. Application form and other supporting documents must be sent to the Foundation's office. **Deadline:** March 1. **Contact:** Rachel Brezler, Regional Scholarships Officer; Phone: 304-428-4438; Email: Rachel.Brezler@pacfwv.com.

8831 ■ The Ambrose-Ramsey Trust *(Undergraduate/ Scholarship)*

Purpose: To provide financial assistance to qualified students from Parkersburg, Parkersburg South, Parkersburg Catholic, or Williamstown High School. **Focus:** Religion. **Qualif.:** Applicants must be graduates from Parkersburg, Parkersburg South, Parkersburg Catholic, or Williamstown High School with the desire to further their education in the study of the Methodist Ministry. **Criteria:** Selection of applicants will be based on the application requirements and scholarship selection criteria.

Funds Avail.: No specific amount. **Duration:** Annual. **To Apply:** Applicants must submit the following: cover sheet (three pages) and application form (four pages); personal essay; high school and/or post-secondary transcripts; a letter of recommendation in a signed and sealed envelope; a copy of the page of their or their parents' most recent tax return that indicates adjusted gross income; and, Student Aid Report showing estimated family contribution from FAFSA. Application form and other supporting documents must be sent to the Foundation's office. **Deadline:** March 1. **Contact:** Rachel Brezler, Regional Scholarships Officer; Phone: 304-428-4438; Email: info@pacfwv.com.

8832 ■ Joe Barbarow Memorial Scholarship *(Undergraduate/Scholarship)*

Purpose: To provide financial support to deserving graduate seniors at Parkersburg High School. **Focus:** General studies/Field of study not specified. **Qualif.:** Applicants must be Parkersburg high school graduating seniors who attended Hamilton Middle School in Wood County. **Criteria:** Selection will be based on academic achievement, school citizenship, moral character, and financial need.

Funds Avail.: No specific amount. **Duration:** Annual. **To Apply:** Applicants must submit the following: cover sheet (three pages) and application form (four pages); personal essay; high school and/or post-secondary transcripts; a letter of recommendation in a signed and sealed envelope; a copy of the page of their or their parents' most recent tax return that indicates adjusted gross income; and, Student Aid Report showing estimated family contribution from FAFSA. Application form and other supporting documents must be sent to the Foundation's office. **Deadline:** March 1. **Contact:** Rachel Brezler, Regional Scholarships Officer; Phone: 304-428-4438; Email: Rachel.Brezler@pacfwv.com.

8833 ■ William (Billbo) Boston/Harold Knopp Scholarship *(Undergraduate/Scholarship)*

Purpose: To provide financial assistance to qualified graduating students from Wood County. **Focus:** Computer and information sciences; Journalism. **Qualif.:** Applicants must be graduating seniors or current undergraduates with a minimum 3.0 GPA who previously graduated from a Wood County high school and are pursuing undergraduate degrees in computer science or journalism (or related fields) at an accredited post-secondary school in West Virginia or

Ohio. **Criteria:** Selection based on financial need, academic achievement, and school/community activities.

Funds Avail.: No specific amount. **Duration:** Annual. **To Apply:** Applicants must submit the following: cover sheet (three pages) and application form (four pages); personal essay; high school and/or post-secondary transcripts; a letter of recommendation in a signed and sealed envelope; a copy of the page of their or their parents' most recent tax return that indicates adjusted gross income; and, Student Aid Report showing estimated family contribution from FAFSA. Application form and other supporting documents must be sent to the Foundation's office. **Deadline:** March 1. **Remarks:** Established in 2012. **Contact:** Rachel Brezler, Regional Scholarships Officer; Phone: 304-428-4438; Email: Rachel.Brezler@pacfwv.com.

8834 ■ Bryce/Lietzke/Martin Scholarship *(Undergraduate/Scholarship)*

Purpose: To provide financial assistance to qualified individuals in Wood County. **Focus:** General studies/Field of study not specified. **Qualif.:** Applicants must: be Wood County residents with interest in golf; have a minimum of 2.5 GPA; and, be accepted or attending a post-secondary educational institution. **Criteria:** Selection of recipients will be based on good moral character, involvement in extracurricular activities and financial need.

Funds Avail.: No specific amount. **Duration:** Annual. **To Apply:** Applicants must submit the following: cover sheet (three pages) and application form (four pages); personal essay; high school and/or post-secondary transcripts; a letter of recommendation in a signed and sealed envelope; a copy of the page of their or their parents' most recent tax return that indicates adjusted gross income; and, Student Aid Report showing estimated family contribution from FAFSA. Application form and other supporting documents must be sent to the Foundation's office. **Deadline:** March 1. **Contact:** Rachel Brezler, Regional Scholarships Officer; Phone: 304-428-4438; Email: Rachel.Brezler@pacfwv.com.

8835 ■ Freda Burge Scholarship *(Undergraduate/ Scholarship)*

Purpose: To encourage graduating students of Williamstown High School to pursue their education. **Focus:** General studies/Field of study not specified. **Qualif.:** Applicants must be Williamstown High School graduating seniors planning to attend West Virginia University-Parkersburg full-time, and have a minimum of 2.5 GPA. **Criteria:** Selection will be based on financial need and application materials.

Funds Avail.: No specific amount. **Duration:** Annual. **To Apply:** Applicants must submit the following: cover sheet (three pages) and application form (four pages); personal essay; high school and/or post-secondary transcripts; a letter of recommendation in a signed and sealed envelope; a copy of the page of their or their parents' most recent tax return that indicates adjusted gross income; and, Student Aid Report showing estimated family contribution from FAFSA. Application form and other supporting documents must be sent to the Foundation's office. **Deadline:** March 1. **Contact:** Rachel Brezler, Regional Scholarships Officer; Phone: 304-428-4438; Email: Rachel.Brezler@pacfwv.com.

8836 ■ Chester H. Bruce Memorial Scholarship *(Undergraduate/Scholarship)*

Purpose: To provide financial support to qualified students of Wirt County High School. **Focus:** Christian education; Education, Vocational-technical. **Qualif.:** Applicants must be graduating seniors of Wirt County High School pursuing

Awards are arranged alphabetically below their administering organizations

vocational or trade studies, Christian ministry or service. They must: be enrolled as full-time students in an undergraduate two or four-year program or a vocational program or graduate school; have a minimum of 2.5 GPA; and, have a strong work ethic. **Criteria:** Selection of recipients will be based on scholarship selection criteria.

Funds Avail.: No specific amount. **Duration:** Annual. **To Apply:** Applicants must submit the following: cover sheet (three pages) and application form (four pages); personal essay; high school and/or post-secondary transcripts; a letter of recommendation in a signed and sealed envelope; a copy of the page of their or their parents' most recent tax return that indicates adjusted gross income; and, Student Aid Report showing estimated family contribution from FAFSA. Application form and other supporting documents must be sent to the Foundation's office. **Deadline:** March 1. **Contact:** Rachel Brezler, Regional Scholarships Officer; Phone: 304-428-4438; Email: info@pacfwv.com.

8837 ■ George H. Clinton Scholarship
(Undergraduate/Scholarship)

Purpose: To provide support for graduating or graduate students from a Wood County high school. **Focus:** Advertising; Broadcasting; Communications; Journalism. **Qualif.:** Applicants must be graduating students or have graduated from a Wood County high school; be attending college full-time and majoring in the media communications field (including, but not limited to, majors in broadcasting, journalism, or advertising); and have a minimum 3.0 GPA. **Criteria:** Selection of applicants will be based on the scholarship selection criteria.

Funds Avail.: No specific amount. **Duration:** Annual. **To Apply:** Applicants must submit the following: cover sheet (three pages) and application form (four pages); personal essay; high school and/or post-secondary transcripts; a letter of recommendation in a signed and sealed envelope; a copy of the page of their or their parents' most recent tax return that indicates adjusted gross income; and, Student Aid Report showing estimated family contribution from FAFSA. Application form and other supporting documents must be sent to the Foundation's office. **Deadline:** March 1. **Contact:** Rachel Brezler, Regional Scholarships Officer; Phone: 304-428-4438; Email: Rachel.Brezler@pacfwv.com.

8838 ■ Dwight O. Connor/Ellen Conner Lepp/Danhart Scholarship *(Undergraduate/Scholarship)*

Purpose: To provide financial assistance to qualified graduating high school students at Parkersburg High School. **Focus:** General studies/Field of study not specified. **Qualif.:** Applicants must be Parkersburg High School graduating seniors. **Criteria:** Selection will be based on financial need.

Funds Avail.: No specific amount. **Duration:** Annual. **To Apply:** Applicants must submit the following: cover sheet (three pages) and application form (four pages); personal essay; high school and/or post-secondary transcripts; a letter of recommendation in a signed and sealed envelope; a copy of the page of their or their parents' most recent tax return that indicates adjusted gross income; and, Student Aid Report showing estimated family contribution from FAFSA. Application form and other supporting documents must be sent to the Foundation's office. **Deadline:** March 1. **Contact:** Rachel Brezler, Regional Scholarships Officer; Phone: 304-428-4438; Email: Rachel.Brezler@pacfwv.com.

8839 ■ David A. Couch Memorial Scholarship
(Undergraduate/Scholarship)

Purpose: To provide financial assistance to qualified individuals intending to pursue studies involving massage

therapy or physical or occupational therapy. **Focus:** Occupational therapy; Physical therapy. **Qualif.:** Applicants must be residents of Wood, Wirt, Jackson, Pleasants, Ritchie, Roane, Mason, Calhoun, Gilmer, or Doddridge in West Virginia or Washington County, Ohio who are actively pursuing a course of study involving massage therapy, or physical/occupational therapy (with preference given to applicants studying massage therapy). **Criteria:** Selection will be based on personal commitment to service for individuals whose lives are affected by ALS or other neuromuscular or disabling disease, as evidenced by related volunteer or community service to individuals whose lives are affected by these diseases or for organizations serving individuals whose lives are affected.

Funds Avail.: No specific amount. **Duration:** Annual. **To Apply:** Applicants must submit the following: cover sheet (three pages) and application form (four pages); personal essay; high school and/or post-secondary transcripts; a letter of recommendation in a signed and sealed envelope; a copy of the page of their or their parents' most recent tax return that indicates adjusted gross income; and, Student Aid Report showing estimated family contribution from FAFSA. Application form and other supporting documents must be sent to the Foundation's office. **Deadline:** March 1. **Contact:** Rachel Brezler, Regional Scholarships Officer; Phone: 304-428-4438; Email: Rachel.Brezler@pacfwv.com.

8840 ■ Jennifer D. Coulter Memorial Scholarship
(Undergraduate/Scholarship)

Purpose: To encourage the graduating seniors of Parkersburg High School to pursue their career in teaching. **Focus:** Teaching. **Qualif.:** Applicants must be graduating seniors from Parkersburg High School interested in pursuing a career in teaching and involved in extracurricular and/or community service activities; and must have a minimum 2.5 GPA and financial need. **Criteria:** Selection will be based on academic achievement or potential to achieve academically with evidence of financial need. Preference will be given to students who have displayed interest in foreign language study during their high school career.

Funds Avail.: No specific amount. **Duration:** Annual. **To Apply:** Applicants must submit the following: cover sheet (three pages) and application form (four pages); personal essay; high school and/or post-secondary transcripts; a letter of recommendation in a signed and sealed envelope; a copy of the page of their or their parents' most recent tax return that indicates adjusted gross income; and, Student Aid Report showing estimated family contribution from FAFSA. Application form and other supporting documents must be sent to the Foundation's office. **Deadline:** March 1. **Contact:** Rachel Brezler, Regional Scholarships Officer; Phone: 304-428-4438; Email: Rachel.Brezler@pacfwv.com.

8841 ■ Cindy Curry Memorial Scholarship
(Undergraduate/Scholarship)

Purpose: To encourage graduating students to pursue higher education. **Focus:** General studies/Field of study not specified. **Qualif.:** Applicants must be graduating high school seniors with outstanding academic achievement and leadership qualities from any Wood County School, including home-schooled students, and who are Wood County residents; be planning to attend an accredited West Virginia college or university full-time; and have a minimum 3.0 GPA and a strong motivation to attend school. **Criteria:** Recipients will be selected based on scholarship selection criteria.

Funds Avail.: No specific amount. **Duration:** Annual. **To Apply:** Applicants must submit the following: cover sheet

Awards are arranged alphabetically below their administering organizations

(three pages) and application form (four pages); personal essay; high school and/or post-secondary transcripts; a letter of recommendation in a signed and sealed envelope; a copy of the page of their or their parents' most recent tax return that indicates adjusted gross income; and, Student Aid Report showing estimated family contribution from FAFSA. Application form and other supporting documents must be sent to the Foundation's office. **Deadline:** March 1. **Contact:** Rachel Brezler, Regional Scholarships Officer; Phone: 304-428-4438; Email: Rachel.Brezler@pacfwv.com.

8842 ■ Kenneth D. and Katherine D. Davis Scholarship (Undergraduate/Scholarship)

Purpose: To encourage graduating seniors of Wirt County High School to pursue their education. **Focus:** Business. **Qualif.:** Applicants must be Wirt County High School graduating seniors. **Criteria:** Recipients will be selected based on financial need, academic achievement, potential, and character. Preference will be given to applicants pursuing a career in business.

Funds Avail.: No specific amount. **Duration:** Annual. **To Apply:** Applicants must submit the following: cover sheet (three pages) and application form (four pages); personal essay; high school and/or post-secondary transcripts; a letter of recommendation in a signed and sealed envelope; a copy of the page of their or their parents' most recent tax return that indicates adjusted gross income; and, Student Aid Report showing estimated family contribution from FAFSA. Application form and other supporting documents must be sent to the Foundation's office. **Deadline:** March 1. **Contact:** Rachel Brezler, Regional Scholarships Officer; Phone: 304-428-4438; Email: Rachel.Brezler@pacfwv.com.

8843 ■ Lawrence E. and Jean L. Davis Scholarship (Undergraduate/Scholarship)

Purpose: To encourage the graduating seniors of Parkersburg High School to pursue their education in either the states of West Virginia or Ohio. **Focus:** General studies/ Field of study not specified. **Qualif.:** Applicants must be graduating seniors from Parkersburg High School who have been admitted to attend an accredited four-year institution of higher education in either the state of West Virginia or Ohio as full-time students; and must have a minimum 2.5 GPA. **Criteria:** Selection of recipients will be based on financial need.

Funds Avail.: No specific amount. **Duration:** Annual. **To Apply:** Applicants must submit the following: cover sheet (three pages) and application form (four pages); personal essay; high school and/or post-secondary transcripts; a letter of recommendation in a signed and sealed envelope; a copy of the page of their or their parents' most recent tax return that indicates adjusted gross income; and, Student Aid Report showing estimated family contribution from FAFSA. Application form and other supporting documents must be sent to the Foundation's office. **Deadline:** March 1. **Contact:** Rachel Brezler, Regional Scholarships Officer; Phone: 304-428-4438; Email: Rachel.Brezler@pacfwv.com.

8844 ■ Doddridge County High School Promise Scholarship in Memory of Hattie Leggett (Undergraduate/Scholarship)

Purpose: To encourage graduating students of Doddridge County High School to pursue higher education. **Focus:** General studies/Field of study not specified. **Qualif.:** Applicants must be graduating high school seniors or graduates of Doddridge County High School who have been admitted to the college of their choice; have a GPA of 3.2

or above, be in the top 20 percent of the class, ACT of 21 or above, or SAT of 1100 or above; have followed a college-bound curriculum; and have financial need. **Criteria:** Recipients will be selected based on the evaluation of the scholarship selection committee.

Funds Avail.: No specific amount. **Duration:** Annual. **To Apply:** Applicants must submit the following: cover sheet (three pages) and application form (four pages); personal essay; high school and/or post-secondary transcripts; a letter of recommendation in a signed and sealed envelope; a copy of the page of their or their parents' most recent tax return that indicates adjusted gross income; and, Student Aid Report showing estimated family contribution from FAFSA. Application form and other supporting documents must be sent to the Foundation's office. **Deadline:** March 1. **Contact:** Rachel Brezler, Regional Scholarships Officer; Phone: 304-428-4438; Email: Rachel.Brezler@pacfwv.com.

8845 ■ David Edward Farson Scholarships (Undergraduate/Scholarship)

Purpose: To encourage graduating seniors at Parkersburg High School to pursue their education. **Focus:** General studies/Field of study not specified. **Qualif.:** Applicants must be Parkersburg High School graduating seniors planning to attend Marshall University. **Criteria:** Selection of applicants will be based on financial need and academic achievements.

Funds Avail.: No specific amount. **Duration:** Annual. **To Apply:** Applicants must submit the following: cover sheet (three pages) and application form (four pages); personal essay; high school and/or post-secondary transcripts; a letter of recommendation in a signed and sealed envelope; a copy of the page of their or their parents' most recent tax return that indicates adjusted gross income; and, Student Aid Report showing estimated family contribution from FAFSA. Application form and other supporting documents must be sent to the Foundation's office. **Deadline:** March 1. **Contact:** Rachel Brezler, Regional Scholarships Officer; Phone: 304-428-4438; Email: Rachel.Brezler@pacfwv.com.

8846 ■ Fostering Hope Scholarship (Undergraduate/ Scholarship)

Purpose: To provide financial assistance to qualified individuals intending to pursue their education. **Focus:** General studies/Field of study not specified. **Qualif.:** Applicants must be students who are actively enrolled or have been enrolled in the foster care system; and, West Virginia residents who are admitted to a course of study at a post-high school educational institution for the upcoming year. **Criteria:** Selection of applicants will be based on academic promise, good character, good citizenship, and financial need. Preference will be given to residents of Wood County, WV.

Funds Avail.: No specific amount. **Duration:** Annual. **To Apply:** Applicants must include cover sheet (three pages) and application form (four pages); personal essay; high school and/or post-secondary transcripts; a letter of recommendation in a signed and sealed envelope; a copy of the page of their or their parents' most recent tax return that indicates adjusted gross income; and, Student Aid Report showing estimated family contribution from FAFSA; application form and other supporting documents must be sent to the Foundation's office. **Deadline:** March 1. **Contact:** Rachel Brezler, Regional Scholarships Officer; Phone: 304-428-4438; Email: Rachel.Brezler@pacfwv.com.

Awards are arranged alphabetically below their administering organizations

8847 ■ William E. "Bill" Gallagher Scholarship
(Undergraduate/Scholarship)

Purpose: To provide financial assistance to qualified graduating seniors at Parkersburg South High School. **Focus:** Arts; Education; Education, Physical; History. **Qualif.:** Applicants must be graduating seniors at Parkersburg South High School who have been admitted to attend Glenville State College in Glenville, WV, or Alderson Broaddus College in Philippi, WV. **Criteria:** Selection of applicants will be based on the knowledge and a love of people as attested to by the guidance counselors and as evidenced by candidates' participation in extracurricular activities and community service; preference will be given to students majoring in education, with further preference given to students intending to major in history, fine arts, physical education, or middle school education. To the extent possible, preference will be given to applicants whose elementary and secondary school careers included terms at Blennerhassett Elementary or Junior High School.

Funds Avail.: No specific amount. **Duration:** Annual. **To Apply:** Applicants must include cover sheet (three pages) and application form (four pages); personal essay; high school and/or post-secondary transcripts; a letter of recommendation in a signed and sealed envelope; a copy of the page of their or their parents' most recent tax return that indicates adjusted gross income; and, Student Aid Report showing estimated family contribution from FAFSA; application form and other supporting documents must be sent to the Foundation's office. **Deadline:** March 1. **Contact:** Rachel Brezler, Regional Scholarships Officer; Phone: 304-428-4438; Email: Rachel.Brezler@pacfwv.com.

8848 ■ Laverne L. Gibson Memorial Scholarship
(Undergraduate/Scholarship)

Purpose: To provide financial assistance to qualified graduating seniors intending to pursue careers in education. **Focus:** Education; Education, Special. **Qualif.:** Applicants must be graduating seniors from Wood County, West Virginia, or Washington County, Ohio, who are majoring in education or special education. **Criteria:** Selection of applicants will be based on academic achievement or potential to achieve, honesty and good moral character, involvement in extracurricular and/or community service activities, and financial need.

Funds Avail.: No specific amount. **Duration:** Annual. **To Apply:** Applicants must submit the following: cover sheet (three pages) and application form (four pages); personal essay; high school and/or post-secondary transcripts; a letter of recommendation in a signed and sealed envelope; a copy of the page of their or their parents' most recent tax return that indicates adjusted gross income; and, Student Aid Report showing estimated family contribution from FAFSA. Application form and other supporting documents must be sent to the Foundation's office. **Deadline:** March 1. **Contact:** Rachel Brezler, Regional Scholarships Officer; Phone: 304-428-4438; Email: Rachel.Brezler@pacfwv.com.

8849 ■ Shane Gilbert Memorial Scholarship
(Undergraduate/Scholarship)

Purpose: To encourage graduating students to pursue their post-secondary education. **Focus:** General studies/Field of study not specified. **Qualif.:** Applicants must be a Wood County Technical/Caperton Canter graduating seniors intending to pursue post-secondary education. **Criteria:** Selection of applicants will be based on achievements, ability, financial need, and citizenship.

Funds Avail.: No specific amount. **Duration:** Annual. **To Apply:** Applicants must submit the following: cover sheet (three pages) and application form (four pages); personal essay; high school and/or post-secondary transcripts; a letter of recommendation in a signed and sealed envelope; a copy of the page of their or their parents' most recent tax return that indicates adjusted gross income; and, Student Aid Report showing estimated family contribution from FAFSA. Application form and other supporting documents must be sent to the Foundation's office. **Deadline:** March 1. **Contact:** Rachel Brezler, Regional Scholarships Officer; Phone: 304-428-4438; Email: Rachel.Brezler@pacfwv.com.

8850 ■ S. William & Martha R. Goff Educational Scholarship *(Undergraduate/Scholarship)*

Purpose: To encourage individuals to pursue their career in medical school. **Focus:** Medicine. **Qualif.:** Applicants must have attended high school in Wood County and must be entering or currently in medical school. **Criteria:** Selection of applicants will be based on merit and need.

Funds Avail.: No specific amount. **Duration:** Annual. **To Apply:** Applicants must submit the following: cover sheet (three pages) and application form (four pages); personal essay; high school and/or post-secondary transcripts; a letter of recommendation in a signed and sealed envelope; a copy of the page of their or their parents' most recent tax return that indicates adjusted gross income; and, Student Aid Report showing estimated family contribution from FAFSA. Application form and other supporting documents must be sent to the Foundation's office. **Deadline:** March 1. **Contact:** Rachel Brezler, Regional Scholarships Officer; Phone: 304-428-4438; Email: Rachel.Brezler@pacfwv.com.

8851 ■ Russ Grant Memorial Scholarship for Tennis
(Undergraduate/Scholarship)

Purpose: To encourage graduating seniors with an interest in tennis to pursue higher level education. **Focus:** General studies/Field of study not specified. **Qualif.:** Applicants must be graduating seniors from Parkersburg High School, Parkersburg South High School, or Parkersburg Catholic High School who have shown evidence of an interest in tennis and have a minimum 2.5 GPA. **Criteria:** Selection of recipients will be based on commitment to tennis, academic achievement, and financial need.

Funds Avail.: No specific amount. **Duration:** Annual. **To Apply:** Applicants must submit the following: cover sheet (three pages) and application form (four pages); personal essay; high school and/or post-secondary transcripts; a letter of recommendation in a signed and sealed envelope; a copy of the page of their or their parents' most recent tax return that indicates adjusted gross income; and, Student Aid Report showing estimated family contribution from FAFSA. Application form and other supporting documents must be sent to the Foundation's office. **Deadline:** March 1. **Contact:** Rachel Brezler, Regional Scholarships Officer; Phone: 304-428-4438; Email: Rachel.Brezler@pacfwv.com.

8852 ■ Clayburn J. Sr. & Garnet R. Hanna Scholarship *(Undergraduate/Scholarship)*

Purpose: To provide financial assistance to the residents or graduates of Wirt County. **Focus:** General studies/Field of study not specified. **Qualif.:** Applicants must be residents of Wirt County or graduates of Wirt County High School planning to attend a post-secondary educational institution full-time. **Criteria:** Selection of applicants will be based on financial need, likelihood of completion of degree and leadership. Preference will be given to students who are not likely to receive other significant scholarship awards.

Funds Avail.: No specific amount. **Duration:** Annual. **To Apply:** Applicants must submit the following: cover sheet

Awards are arranged alphabetically below their administering organizations

(three pages) and application form (four pages); personal essay; high school and/or post-secondary transcripts; a letter of recommendation in a signed and sealed envelope; a copy of the page of their or their parents' most recent tax return that indicates adjusted gross income; and, Student Aid Report showing estimated family contribution from FAFSA. Application form and other supporting documents must be sent to the Foundation's office. **Deadline:** March 1. **Contact:** Rachel Brezler, Regional Scholarships Officer; Phone: 304-428-4438; Email: Rachel.Brezler@pacfwv.com.

8853 ■ H.G. Hardbarger Science - Mathematics Award *(Undergraduate, Vocational/Occupational/Award)*

Purpose: To provide financial assistance to graduating seniors from Ritchie County High School. **Focus:** Mathematics and mathematical sciences; Science. **Qualif.:** Applicants must be graduating seniors from Ritchie County High School who have demonstrated achievement in the fields of Math/Science, and are planning to attend an accredited college, university, or vocational/trade school in West Virginia. **Criteria:** Applicants will be selected based on the scholarship criteria.

Funds Avail.: No specific amount. **Duration:** Annual. **To Apply:** Applicants must submit the following: cover sheet (three pages) and application form (four pages); personal essay; high school and/or post-secondary transcripts; a letter of recommendation in a signed and sealed envelope; a copy of the page of their or their parents' most recent tax return that indicates adjusted gross income; and, Student Aid Report showing estimated family contribution from FAFSA. Application form and other supporting documents must be sent to the Foundation's office. **Deadline:** March 1. **Contact:** Rachel Brezler, Regional Scholarships Officer; Phone: 304-428-4438; Email: Rachel.Brezler@pacfwv.com.

8854 ■ Harrisville Lion's Club Scholarship *(Undergraduate, Vocational/Occupational/Scholarship)*

Purpose: To provide financial support to qualified individuals in Ritchie County intending to pursue their studies. **Focus:** Education, Vocational-technical. **Qualif.:** Applicants must be residents of Ritchie County who are pursuing vocational, technical, or trade related education through an accredited institution or program, and have a minimum 2.0 GPA (if a graduating senior or presently enrolled in school). **Criteria:** Preference will be given to students with financial need.

Funds Avail.: No specific amount. **Duration:** Annual. **To Apply:** Applicants must submit the following: cover sheet (three pages) and application form (four pages); personal essay; high school and/or post-secondary transcripts; a letter of recommendation in a signed and sealed envelope; a copy of the page of their or their parents' most recent tax return that indicates adjusted gross income; and, Student Aid Report showing estimated family contribution from FAFSA. Application form and other supporting documents must be sent to the Foundation's office. **Deadline:** March 1. **Contact:** Rachel Brezler, Regional Scholarships Officer; Phone: 304-428-4438; Email: Rachel.Brezler@pacfwv.com.

8855 ■ Harry C. Hartleben III/Gordon Page Corbitt Scholarship *(Undergraduate/Scholarship)*

Purpose: To provide financial assistance to qualified graduating seniors from Parkersburg High School intending to pursue higher education. **Focus:** General studies/Field of study not specified. **Qualif.:** Applicants must be graduating seniors from Parkersburg High School who plan to pursue higher education, and have a minimum 3.0 GPA. **Criteria:** Recipients of the scholarships will be selected based on academic achievement, motivation, character and involvement in school and community activities; financial need is not a primary consideration.

Funds Avail.: No specific amount. **Duration:** Annual. **To Apply:** Applicants must include cover sheet (three pages) and application form (four pages); personal essay; high school and/or post-secondary transcripts; a letter of recommendation in a signed and sealed envelope; a copy of the page of their or their parents' most recent tax return that indicates adjusted gross income; and, Student Aid Report showing estimated family contribution from FAFSA; application form and other supporting documents must be sent to the Foundation's office. **Deadline:** March 1. **Contact:** Rachel Brezler, Regional Scholarships Officer; Phone: 304-428-4438; Email: Rachel.Brezler@pacfwv.com.

8856 ■ Gail L. Hartshorn Memorial Fund *(Other/Scholarship)*

Purpose: To provide financial assistance to qualified Wood County residents intending to pursue their studies and to support charitable needs. **Focus:** Emergency and disaster services; Paramedics. **Qualif.:** Applicants must be Wood County residents who are pursuing emergency medical technician or paramedic training. **Criteria:** Selection of applicants will be based on financial need and commitment to career in emergency services.

Funds Avail.: No specific amount. **To Apply:** Applicants must submit the following: cover sheet (three pages) and application form (four pages); personal essay; high school and/or post-secondary transcripts; a letter of recommendation in a signed and sealed envelope; a copy of the page of their or their parents' most recent tax return that indicates adjusted gross income; and, Student Aid Report showing estimated family contribution from FAFSA. Application form and other supporting documents must be sent to the Foundation's office. **Contact:** Marian Clowes, Associate Director for Community Leadership: Phone: 304-428-4438: E-mail: marian.clowes@pacfwv.com.

8857 ■ Gregory Linn Haught Citizenship Award *(Undergraduate/Scholarship)*

Purpose: To encourage the graduating students of Ritchie County High School to pursue their education. **Focus:** General studies/Field of study not specified. **Qualif.:** Applicants must be Ritchie County High School graduating seniors. **Criteria:** Selection of applicants will be based on academic achievement, good moral character, service to others, and service in religious activities and endeavours.

Funds Avail.: No specific amount. **Duration:** Annual. **To Apply:** Applicants must submit the following: cover sheet (three pages) and application form (four pages); personal essay; high school and/or post-secondary transcripts; a letter of recommendation in a signed and sealed envelope; a copy of the page of their or their parents' most recent tax return that indicates adjusted gross income; and, Student Aid Report showing estimated family contribution from FAFSA. Application form and other supporting documents must be sent to the Foundation's office. **Deadline:** March 1. **Contact:** Rachel Brezler, Regional Scholarships Officer; Phone: 304-428-4438; Email: Rachel.Brezler@pacfwv.com.

8858 ■ Dorcas Edmonson Haught Scholarship *(Undergraduate/Scholarship)*

Purpose: To provide financial support to qualified students intending to attend Marietta College. **Focus:** General

Awards are arranged alphabetically below their administering organizations

studies/Field of study not specified. **Qualif.:** Applicants must be graduating Parkersburg High School seniors who plan to attend Marietta College. **Criteria:** Selection of applicants will be based on financial need, achievements, and character.

Funds Avail.: No specific amount. **Duration:** Annual. **To Apply:** Applicants must submit the following: cover sheet (three pages) and application form (four pages); personal essay; high school and/or post-secondary transcripts; a letter of recommendation in a signed and sealed envelope; a copy of the page of their or their parents' most recent tax return that indicates adjusted gross income; and, Student Aid Report showing estimated family contribution from FAFSA. Application form and other supporting documents must be sent to the Foundation's office. **Deadline:** March 1. **Contact:** Rachel Brezler, Regional Scholarships Officer; Phone: 304-428-4438; Email: Rachel.Brezler@pacfwv.com.

8859 ■ Ella Beren Hersch Scholarship
(Undergraduate/Scholarship)

Purpose: To encourage graduating students to pursue higher education. **Focus:** General studies/Field of study not specified. **Qualif.:** Applicants must be Parkersburg High School graduating seniors. **Criteria:** Selection will be based on financial need.

Funds Avail.: No specific amount. **Duration:** Annual. **To Apply:** Applicants must submit the following: cover sheet (three pages) and application form (four pages); personal essay; high school and/or post-secondary transcripts; a letter of recommendation in a signed and sealed envelope; a copy of the page of their or their parents' most recent tax return that indicates adjusted gross income; and, Student Aid Report showing estimated family contribution from FAFSA. Application form and other supporting documents must be sent to the Foundation's office. **Deadline:** March 1. **Contact:** Rachel Brezler, Regional Scholarships Officer; Phone: 304-428-4438; Email: Rachel.Brezler@pacfwv.com.

8860 ■ Holly Jackson-Wuller Memorial Scholarship
(Undergraduate/Scholarship)

Purpose: To encourage graduating seniors from Parkersburg South High School to pursue degrees at Marshall University. **Focus:** General studies/Field of study not specified. **Qualif.:** Applicants must be graduating seniors from Parkersburg South High School planning to attend Marshall University, with minimum 2.5 GPA. **Criteria:** Selection of applicants will be based on financial need and participation in school, church, and community activities. Preference may be given to students who have participated in the sports of crew, basketball, or cheerleading.

Funds Avail.: No specific amount. **Duration:** Annual. **To Apply:** Applicants must submit the following: cover sheet (three pages) and application form (four pages); personal essay; high school and/or post-secondary transcripts; a letter of recommendation in a signed and sealed envelope; a copy of the page of their or their parents' most recent tax return that indicates adjusted gross income; and, Student Aid Report showing estimated family contribution from FAFSA. Application form and other supporting documents must be sent to the Foundation's office. **Deadline:** March 1. **Contact:** Rachel Brezler, Regional Scholarships Officer; Phone: 304-428-4438; Email: Rachel.Brezler@pacfwv.com.

8861 ■ K.A.S.A. Memorial Scholarship
(Undergraduate/Scholarship)

Purpose: To provide financial support to graduating high school seniors or graduates of Doddridge County High

School. **Focus:** General studies/Field of study not specified. **Qualif.:** Applicants must be graduating high school seniors or graduates of Doddridge County High School who have a minimum GPA of 2.25. **Criteria:** Preference will be given to students who have been admitted to attend a public college in West Virginia, and to well-rounded, hard working individuals with financial need who are not receiving substantial scholarship aid from other sources.

Funds Avail.: No specific amount. **Duration:** Annual. **To Apply:** Applicants must submit the following: cover sheet (three pages) and application form (four pages); personal essay; high school and/or post-secondary transcripts; a letter of recommendation in a signed and sealed envelope; a copy of the page of their or their parents' most recent tax return that indicates adjusted gross income; and, Student Aid Report showing estimated family contribution from FAFSA. Application form and other supporting documents must be sent to the Foundation's office. **Deadline:** March 1. **Contact:** Rachel Brezler, Regional Scholarships Officer; Phone: 304-428-4438; Email: info@pacfwv.com.

8862 ■ Dr. Charles Kelly Memorial Scholarships
(Undergraduate/Scholarship)

Purpose: To provide financial assistance to qualified graduating seniors of Ravenswood High School. **Focus:** General studies/Field of study not specified. **Qualif.:** Applicants must be Jackson County graduating seniors planning to attend Marshall University. **Criteria:** Selection of applicants will be based on financial need.

Funds Avail.: No specific amount. **Duration:** Annual. **To Apply:** Applicants must include cover sheet (three pages) and application form (four pages); personal essay; high school and/or post-secondary transcripts; a letter of recommendation in a signed and sealed envelope; a copy of the page of their or their parents' most recent tax return that indicates adjusted gross income; and, Student Aid Report showing estimated family contribution from FAFSA; application form and other supporting documents must be sent to the Foundation's office. **Deadline:** March 4.

8863 ■ Langfitt-Ambrose Scholarship
(Undergraduate/Scholarship)

Purpose: To provide financial assistance to deserving students intending to pursue their education. **Focus:** English language and literature; Mathematics and mathematical sciences. **Qualif.:** Applicants must be graduates from Parkersburg, Parkersburg South, Parkersburg Catholic, or Williamstown High School, and have excelled in the combined fields of Mathematics and English desiring to further their education in those fields. Previous recipients may reapply. **Criteria:** Recipients will be selected based on their application materials.

Funds Avail.: No specific amount. **Duration:** Annual. **To Apply:** Applicants must submit the following: cover sheet (three pages) and application form (four pages); personal essay; high school and/or post-secondary transcripts; a letter of recommendation in a signed and sealed envelope; a copy of the page of their or their parents' most recent tax return that indicates adjusted gross income; and, Student Aid Report showing estimated family contribution from FAFSA. Application form and other supporting documents must be sent to the Foundation's office. **Deadline:** March 1. **Contact:** Rachel Brezler, Regional Scholarships Officer; Phone: 304-428-4438; Email: Rachel.Brezler@pacfwv.com.

8864 ■ Megan Nicole Longwell Scholarship
(Undergraduate/Scholarship)

Purpose: To encourage the graduating seniors of Parkersburg South High School to pursue their college degrees.

Awards are arranged alphabetically below their administering organizations

Focus: General studies/Field of study not specified. **Qualif.:** Applicants must be Parkersburg South High School graduating seniors who have been admitted to an accredited institution of higher learning as full-time students and have a minimum 2.5 GPA. **Criteria:** Selection of applicants will be based on financial need and participation in school athletics. Special consideration will be given to applicants whose families have experienced extraordinary special needs that may impact the student's ability to fund their college expenses.

Funds Avail.: No specific amount. **Duration:** Annual. **To Apply:** Applicants must submit the following: cover sheet (three pages) and application form (four pages); personal essay; high school and/or post-secondary transcripts; a letter of recommendation in a signed and sealed envelope; a copy of the page of their or their parents' most recent tax return that indicates adjusted gross income; and, Student Aid Report showing estimated family contribution from FAFSA. Application form and other supporting documents must be sent to the Foundation's office. **Deadline:** March 1. **Contact:** Rachel Brezler, Regional Scholarships Officer; Phone: 304-428-4438; Email: Rachel.Brezler@pacfwv.com.

8865 ■ Dudley Mullins/Cabot Corporation Scholarship *(Undergraduate/Scholarship)*

Purpose: To assist graduating seniors of Williamstown High School in their educational pursuits. **Focus:** General studies/Field of study not specified. **Qualif.:** Applicants must be Williamstown graduating seniors who attended Waverly Elementary School for a minimum of one year and graduated from Waverly Elementary, and have minimum of 2.0 GPA. **Criteria:** Selection of applicants will be based on involvement in school and civic activities, academic achievement, and potential.

Funds Avail.: No specific amount. **Duration:** Annual. **To Apply:** Applicants must submit the following: cover sheet (three pages) and application form (four pages); personal essay; high school and/or post-secondary transcripts; a letter of recommendation in a signed and sealed envelope; a copy of the page of their or their parents' most recent tax return that indicates adjusted gross income; and, Student Aid Report showing estimated family contribution from FAFSA. Application form and other supporting documents must be sent to the Foundation's office. **Deadline:** March 1. **Contact:** Rachel Brezler, Regional Scholarships Officer; Phone: 304-428-4438; Email: Rachel.Brezler@pacfwv.com.

8866 ■ Pennsboro High School Alumni Scholarship *(Undergraduate/Scholarship)*

Purpose: To provide financial assistance to graduating seniors of Ritchie County High School intending to pursue their education. **Focus:** General studies/Field of study not specified. **Qualif.:** Applicants must be Ritchie County High School graduating seniors who demonstrate financial need. **Criteria:** Preference will be given to students who demonstrated academic promise, good character, good citizenship, and financial need.

Funds Avail.: No specific amount. **Duration:** Annual. **To Apply:** Applicants must submit the following: cover sheet (three pages) and application form (four pages); personal essay; high school and/or post-secondary transcripts; a letter of recommendation in a signed and sealed envelope; a copy of the page of their or their parents' most recent tax return that indicates adjusted gross income; and, Student Aid Report showing estimated family contribution from FAFSA. Application form and other supporting documents must be sent to the Foundation's office. **Deadline:** March

1. **Contact:** Rachel Brezler, Regional Scholarships Officer; Phone: 304-428-4438; Email: Rachel.Brezler@pacfwv.com.

8867 ■ William R. Pfalzgraf Memorial Scholarship *(Undergraduate/Scholarship)*

Purpose: To assist graduating students in their educational pursuits. **Focus:** Education, English as a second language; English language and literature; Law; Music; Speech, Debate, and Forensics. **Qualif.:** Applicants must be Parkersburg High School graduating seniors with a minimum 3.0 GPA. **Criteria:** Selection of applicants will be based on merit, motivation toward higher education, character and financial need. Preference will be given to student with interest in or achievement in the areas of law, debating, English, or music.

Funds Avail.: No specific amount. **Duration:** Annual. **To Apply:** Applicants must submit the following: cover sheet (three pages) and application form (four pages); personal essay; high school and/or post-secondary transcripts; a letter of recommendation in a signed and sealed envelope; a copy of the page of their or their parents' most recent tax return that indicates adjusted gross income; and, Student Aid Report showing estimated family contribution from FAFSA. Application form and other supporting documents must be sent to the Foundation's office. **Deadline:** March 1. **Contact:** Rachel Brezler, Regional Scholarships Officer; Phone: 304-428-4438; Email: Rachel.Brezler@pacfwv.com.

8868 ■ Herschel H. Pifer Scholarship *(Undergraduate/Scholarship)*

Purpose: To encourage graduating students to pursue their education. **Focus:** General studies/Field of study not specified. **Qualif.:** Applicants must be Ritchie County High School graduating seniors. **Criteria:** Selection of applicants will be based on financial need, academic achievement and activities. Preference will be given to applicants who have not yet received a scholarship support.

Funds Avail.: No specific amount. **Duration:** Annual. **To Apply:** Applicants must submit the following: cover sheet (three pages) and application form (four pages); personal essay; high school and/or post-secondary transcripts; a letter of recommendation in a signed and sealed envelope; a copy of the page of their or their parents' most recent tax return that indicates adjusted gross income; and, Student Aid Report showing estimated family contribution from FAFSA. Application form and other supporting documents must be sent to the Foundation's office. **Deadline:** March 1. **Contact:** Rachel Brezler, Regional Scholarships Officer; Phone: 304-428-4438; Email: Rachel.Brezler@pacfwv.com.

8869 ■ William R. Reaser Scholarship *(Vocational/Occupational, Undergraduate/Scholarship)*

Purpose: To encourage graduating students to pursue their college education. **Focus:** Education, Vocational-technical. **Qualif.:** Applicants must be Ritchie County High School graduating seniors planning to pursue post-secondary education in a technical or vocational field. **Criteria:** Selection of recipients will be based on academic achievement or potential in the area of vocational/technical studies, honesty and good moral character, community service, and financial need.

Funds Avail.: No specific amount. **Duration:** Annual. **To Apply:** Applicants must submit the following: cover sheet (three pages) and application form (four pages); personal essay; high school and/or post-secondary transcripts; a letter of recommendation in a signed and sealed envelope; a copy of the page of their or their parents' most recent tax

Awards are arranged alphabetically below their administering organizations

return that indicates adjusted gross income; and, Student Aid Report showing estimated family contribution from FAFSA. Application form and other supporting documents must be sent to the Foundation's office. **Deadline:** March 1. **Contact:** Rachel Brezler, Regional Scholarships Officer; Phone: 304-428-4438; Email: Rachel.Brezler@pacfwv.com.

8870 ■ Mary K. Smith Rector Scholarship
(Undergraduate, Vocational/Occupational/Scholarship)

Purpose: To encourage graduating seniors to pursue their education. **Focus:** Education, Vocational-technical; General studies/Field of study not specified. **Qualif.:** Applicants must be graduating seniors from Gilmer County High School who are planning to attend an accredited college or university in West Virginia or pursue a vocational training, and have a minimum 2.5 GPA. Previous recipients are eligible to reapply. **Criteria:** Selection of recipients will be based on academic achievement and financial need.

Funds Avail.: No specific amount. **Duration:** Annual. **To Apply:** Applicants must submit the following: cover sheet (three pages) and application form (four pages); personal essay; high school and/or post-secondary transcripts; a letter of recommendation in a signed and sealed envelope; a copy of the page of their or their parents' most recent tax return that indicates adjusted gross income; and, Student Aid Report showing estimated family contribution from FAFSA. Application form and other supporting documents must be sent to the Foundation's office. **Deadline:** March 1. **Contact:** Rachel Brezler, Regional Scholarships Officer; Phone: 304-428-4438; Email: Rachel.Brezler@pacfwv.com.

8871 ■ Ripley Rotary Scholarship/The Judge Oliver Kessel Scholarship *(Undergraduate, Vocational/Occupational/Scholarship)*

Purpose: To assist Ripley High School graduating seniors in their higher education pursuits. **Focus:** General studies/Field of study not specified. **Qualif.:** Applicants must be Ripley High School graduating seniors or graduates attending accredited college or technical programs. **Criteria:** Selection of recipients will be based on financial need and strong record of community service.

Funds Avail.: $500. **Duration:** Annual.

8872 ■ James H. Roberts Athletic Scholarship
(Undergraduate/Scholarship)

Purpose: To encourage graduating athletic students to continue their education. **Focus:** General studies/Field of study not specified. **Qualif.:** Applicants must be graduating seniors from Wirt County High School who are planning to attend a four-year program of study at a higher education institution in West Virginia; must be student athletes; and have a minimum 2.0 GPA. **Criteria:** Selection of recipients will be based on commitment to athletics, GPA, and test scores.

Funds Avail.: No specific amount. **Duration:** Annual. **To Apply:** Applicants must submit the following: cover sheet (three pages) and application form (four pages); personal essay; high school and/or post-secondary transcripts; a letter of recommendation in a signed and sealed envelope; a copy of the page of their or their parents' most recent tax return that indicates adjusted gross income; and, Student Aid Report showing estimated family contribution from FAFSA. Application form and other supporting documents must be sent to the Foundation's office. **Deadline:** March 1. **Contact:** Rachel Brezler, Regional Scholarships Officer; Phone: 304-428-4438; Email: Rachel.Brezler@pacfwv.com.

8873 ■ Thomas Warren Roberts Memorial Scholarship *(Undergraduate/Scholarship)*

Purpose: To encourage graduating high school students to continue their education. **Focus:** General studies/Field of study not specified. **Qualif.:** Applicants must be Belpre High School graduating seniors. **Criteria:** Selection based on financial need, academic achievement, involvement in school activities, and character.

Funds Avail.: No specific amount. **Duration:** Annual. **To Apply:** Applicants must submit the following: cover sheet (three pages) and application form (four pages); personal essay; high school and/or post-secondary transcripts; a letter of recommendation in a signed and sealed envelope; a copy of the page of their or their parents' most recent tax return that indicates adjusted gross income; and, Student Aid Report showing estimated family contribution from FAFSA. Application form and other supporting documents must be sent to the Foundation's office. **Deadline:** March 1. **Contact:** Rachel Brezler, Regional Scholarships Officer; Phone: 304-428-4438; Email: Rachel.Brezler@pacfwv.com.

8874 ■ Carl M. Rose Memorial Scholarship
(Undergraduate/Scholarship)

Purpose: To encourage graduating high school students to pursue their education. **Focus:** Education, Secondary; Mathematics and mathematical sciences; Science. **Qualif.:** Applicants must be Parkersburg South High School graduating seniors who have a 3.0 GPA and are planning to pursue a major in secondary education. **Criteria:** Selection will be based on financial need, personal statement and academic achievement. Consideration will be given to applicants majoring in math and science secondary education.

Funds Avail.: No specific amount. **Duration:** Annual. **To Apply:** Applicants must submit the following: cover sheet (three pages) and application form (four pages); personal essay; high school and/or post-secondary transcripts; a letter of recommendation in a signed and sealed envelope; a copy of the page of their or their parents' most recent tax return that indicates adjusted gross income; and, Student Aid Report showing estimated family contribution from FAFSA. Application form and other supporting documents must be sent to the Foundation's office. **Deadline:** March 1. **Contact:** Rachel Brezler, Regional Scholarships Officer; Phone: 304-428-4438; Email: Rachel.Brezler@pacfwv.com.

8875 ■ S. Byrl Ross Memorial Scholarship
(Undergraduate/Scholarship)

Purpose: To encourage graduating high school students to pursue their education. **Focus:** Music; Music, Vocal. **Qualif.:** Applicants must be graduating seniors of Wood or Ritchie Counties pursuing a major in music or a music-related field at a post-secondary educational institution. **Criteria:** Selection will be based on financial need, academic achievement, potential, and character.

Funds Avail.: No specific amount. **Duration:** Annual. **To Apply:** Applicants must submit the following: cover sheet (three pages) and application form (four pages); personal essay; high school and/or post-secondary transcripts; a letter of recommendation in a signed and sealed envelope; a copy of the page of their or their parents' most recent tax return that indicates adjusted gross income; and, Student Aid Report showing estimated family contribution from FAFSA. Application form and other supporting documents must be sent to the Foundation's office. **Deadline:** March 1. **Contact:** Rachel Brezler, Regional Scholarships Officer; Phone: 304-428-4438; Email: Rachel.Brezler@pacfwv.com.

Awards are arranged alphabetically below their administering organizations

8876 ■ St. Joseph's Hospital School of Nursing Alumnae Scholarship *(Undergraduate/Scholarship)*

Purpose: To encourage graduating high school students to pursue higher education, especially in the field of nursing. **Focus:** Nursing. **Qualif.:** Applicants must be residents of Wood, Ritchie, Wirt, Calhoun, Jackson, Gilmer, Roane, Pleasants, or Doddridge in WV, or Washington County, OH. Applicants must also be planning to attend an accredited college/nursing school to become registered nurses; have a financial need and a minimum of 2.0 GPA; and, be willing to make a written pledge attesting to their intention to return to the area covered by the service region of the Foundation to practice for at least two years. **Criteria:** Recipients will be selected based on financial need and other scholarship selection criteria.

Funds Avail.: No specific amount. **Duration:** Annual. **To Apply:** Applicants must submit the following: cover sheet (three pages) and application form (four pages); personal essay; high school and/or post-secondary transcripts; a letter of recommendation in a signed and sealed envelope; a copy of the page of their or their parents' most recent tax return that indicates adjusted gross income; and, Student Aid Report showing estimated family contribution from FAFSA. Application form and other supporting documents must be sent to the Foundation's office. **Deadline:** March 1. **Contact:** Rachel Brezler, Regional Scholarships Officer; Phone: 304-428-4438; E-mail: Rachel.Brezler@ pacfwv.com.

8877 ■ Sand Plains & Lewis A. and Gurry F. Batten Education Scholarship *(Undergraduate/Scholarship)*

Purpose: To provide financial assistance to qualified senior high school students at Parkersburg High School. **Focus:** General studies/Field of study not specified. **Qualif.:** Applicants must be Parkersburg High School graduating seniors who have a minimum of 2.5 GPA, and are attending a four-year college or university. **Criteria:** Selection of recipients will be based on merit and financial need.

Funds Avail.: No specific amount. **Duration:** Annual. **To Apply:** Applicants must submit the following: cover sheet (three pages) and application form (four pages); personal essay; high school and/or post-secondary transcripts; a letter of recommendation in a signed and sealed envelope; a copy of the page of their or their parents' most recent tax return that indicates adjusted gross income; and, Student Aid Report showing estimated family contribution from FAFSA. Application form and other supporting documents must be sent to the Foundation's office. **Deadline:** March 1. **Contact:** Rachel Brezler, Regional Scholarships Officer; Phone: 304-428-4438; Email: Rachel.Brezler@pacfwv.com.

8878 ■ Everett Oscar Shimp Memorial Scholarships *(Undergraduate/Scholarship)*

Purpose: To encourage graduating high school students to pursue higher education, especially in the field of mathematics, science and education. **Focus:** Agricultural sciences; Computer and information sciences; Education; History; Life sciences; Mathematics and mathematical sciences; Physical therapy; Science. **Qualif.:** Applicants must: be graduates of Jackson or Roane County high schools who are currently enrolled full-time and have completed college credits equivalent to junior or senior status; have a minimum of 3.0 college GPA; and, be majoring in math, science (biology, zoology, chemistry, geology, forestry), physical therapy, computer science, agriculture, or history or pursuing an education degree majoring in math, science, agriculture, or history. **Criteria:** Selection will be based on

the aforesaid qualifications and compliance with the application process.

Funds Avail.: No specific amount. **Duration:** Annual. **To Apply:** Applicants must submit the following: cover sheet (three pages) and application form (four pages); personal essay; high school and/or post-secondary transcripts; a letter of recommendation in a signed and sealed envelope; a copy of the page of their or their parents' most recent tax return that indicates adjusted gross income; and, Student Aid Report showing estimated family contribution from FAFSA. Application form and other supporting documents must be sent to the Foundation's office. **Deadline:** March 4.

8879 ■ Pat Shimp Memorial Scholarships *(Undergraduate/Scholarship)*

Purpose: To encourage graduating students to pursue their degree in the business, agriculture, nursing or any healthcare related field. **Focus:** Agriculture, Economic aspects; Business; Health care services; Nursing. **Qualif.:** Applicants must be Roane County High School graduating seniors pursuing a degree in a business, agriculture, nursing, or a health-care related field with a minimum of 2.0 GPA. **Criteria:** Preference will be given to students with record of community service.

Funds Avail.: No specific amount. **Duration:** Annual. **To Apply:** Applicants must submit the following: cover sheet (three pages) and application form (four pages); personal essay; high school and/or post-secondary transcripts; a letter of recommendation in a signed and sealed envelope; a copy of the page of their or their parents' most recent tax return that indicates adjusted gross income; and, Student Aid Report showing estimated family contribution from FAFSA. Application form and other supporting documents must be sent to the Foundation's office. **Deadline:** March 4.

8880 ■ Simonton Windows Scholarship *(Undergraduate/Scholarship)*

Purpose: To provide educational assistance to high school graduates or the equivalent who demonstrate academic potential. **Focus:** General studies/Field of study not specified. **Qualif.:** Applicants must be dependent children of employees of Simonton Windows or SimEx currently enrolled in undergraduate studies. Previous recipients of the scholarship may reapply for consideration with new applicants. **Criteria:** Selection of applicants will be based on financial need, academic achievement, leadership abilities, and activities.

Funds Avail.: No specific amount. **Duration:** Annual. **To Apply:** Applicants must submit the following: cover sheet (three pages) and application form (four pages); personal essay; high school and/or post-secondary transcripts; a letter of recommendation in a signed and sealed envelope; a copy of the page of their or their parents' most recent tax return that indicates adjusted gross income; and, Student Aid Report showing estimated family contribution from FAFSA. Application form and other supporting documents must be sent to the Foundation's office. **Deadline:** March 1. **Contact:** Rachel Brezler, Regional Scholarships Officer; Phone: 304-428-4438; Email: Rachel.Brezler@pacfwv.com.

8881 ■ Bill Six Memorial Scholarship *(Undergraduate/Scholarship)*

Purpose: To encourage graduating high school seniors to pursue their education. **Focus:** General studies/Field of study not specified. **Qualif.:** Applicants must be graduating

Awards are arranged alphabetically below their administering organizations

seniors or previous high school graduates who are permanent residents of Vienna, West Virginia, and have at least a 2.0 GPA. **Criteria:** Selection will be based on financial need and potential for successful achievement beyond high school. Preference will be given to the students who appear to be hardworking individuals and are likely to succeed, yet do not necessarily maintain a superior GPA.

Funds Avail.: No specific amount. **Duration:** Annual. **To Apply:** Applicants must submit the following: cover sheet (three pages) and application form (four pages); personal essay; high school and/or post-secondary transcripts; a letter of recommendation in a signed and sealed envelope; a copy of the page of their or their parents' most recent tax return that indicates adjusted gross income; and, Student Aid Report showing estimated family contribution from FAFSA. Application form and other supporting documents must be sent to the Foundation's office. **Deadline:** March 1. **Contact:** Rachel Brezler, Regional Scholarships Officer; Phone: 304-428-4438; Email: Rachel.Brezler@pacfwv.com.

8882 ■ C.R. Thomas Scholarship *(Undergraduate/ Scholarship)*

Purpose: To encourage graduating high school students to pursue their education. **Focus:** General studies/Field of study not specified. **Qualif.:** Applicants must be graduating seniors of Parkersburg High School and willing to help the community and others. **Criteria:** Selection will be based on the aforesaid qualifications and compliance with the application process. In the event of a tie, financial need may be considered.

Funds Avail.: No specific amount. **Duration:** Annual. **To Apply:** Applicants must submit the following: cover sheet (three pages) and application form (four pages); personal essay; high school and/or post-secondary transcripts; a letter of recommendation in a signed and sealed envelope; a copy of the page of their or their parents' most recent tax return that indicates adjusted gross income; and, Student Aid Report showing estimated family contribution from FAFSA. Application form and other supporting documents must be sent to the Foundation's office. **Deadline:** March 1. **Contact:** Rachel Brezler, Regional Scholarships Officer; Phone: 304-428-4438; Email: Rachel.Brezler@pacfwv.com.

8883 ■ Charles A. Townsend Scholarship *(Undergraduate/Scholarship)*

Purpose: To encourage graduating students to pursue their career as education professionals. **Focus:** Education. **Qualif.:** Applicants must be graduates or graduating seniors of Wood County schools planning to attend an accredited post-secondary school, interested in pursuing a career as an education professional. Applicants pursuing a degree at St. John's College in Annapolis, MD, or Santa Fe, NM, will be given first consideration. **Criteria:** Selection of recipients will be based on financial need, achievement, and character.

Funds Avail.: No specific amount. **Duration:** Annual. **To Apply:** Applicants must submit the following: cover sheet (three pages) and application form (four pages); personal essay; high school and/or post-secondary transcripts; a letter of recommendation in a signed and sealed envelope; a copy of the page of their or their parents' most recent tax return that indicates adjusted gross income; and, Student Aid Report showing estimated family contribution from FAFSA. Application form and other supporting documents must be sent to the Foundation's office. **Deadline:** March 1. **Contact:** Rachel Brezler, Regional Scholarships Officer; Phone: 304-428-4438; Email: Rachel.Brezler@pacfwv.com.

8884 ■ Wayne-Meador-Elliott Scholarship *(Undergraduate/Scholarship)*

Purpose: To encourage graduating seniors of Ritchie County High School to pursue their education. **Focus:** Education; Engineering, Petroleum; Geology; Music. **Qualif.:** Applicants must be Ritchie County High School graduating seniors with a minimum 3.0 GPA who are enrolled as full-time students in accredited four-year colleges or universities. **Criteria:** Preference will be given to students planning to major in the field of education administration, music, geology/ petroleum engineering or education. Selection of recipients will be based on ability to overcome obstacles, strong work ethic, interest in community service, leadership ability, and financial need.

Funds Avail.: No specific amount. **Duration:** Annual. **To Apply:** Applicants must submit the following: cover sheet (three pages) and application form (four pages); personal essay; high school and/or post-secondary transcripts; a letter of recommendation in a signed and sealed envelope; a copy of the page of their or their parents' most recent tax return that indicates adjusted gross income; and, Student Aid Report showing estimated family contribution from FAFSA. Application form and other supporting documents must be sent to the Foundation's office. **Deadline:** March 1. **Contact:** Rachel Brezler, Regional Scholarships Officer; Phone: 304-428-4438; Email: Rachel.Brezler@pacfwv.com.

8885 ■ West Virginia Nurses Association District No. 3 Professional Nursing Scholarships *(Undergraduate/Scholarship)*

Purpose: To provide support for qualified individuals intending to pursue their nursing degree. **Focus:** Nursing. **Qualif.:** Applicants must reside in Wood, Wirt, Calhoun, Jackson, or Roane Counties and pursuing an associate nursing degree as full-time students. **Criteria:** Selection of recipients will be based on merit.

Funds Avail.: No specific amount. **Duration:** Annual. **To Apply:** Applicants must submit the following: cover sheet (three pages) and application form (four pages); personal essay; high school and/or post-secondary transcripts; a letter of recommendation in a signed and sealed envelope; a copy of the page of their or their parents' most recent tax return that indicates adjusted gross income; and, Student Aid Report showing estimated family contribution from FAFSA. Application form and other supporting documents must be sent to the Foundation's office. **Deadline:** March 1. **Contact:** Rachel Brezler, Regional Scholarships Officer; Phone: 304-428-4438; E-mail: Rachel.Brezler@ pacfwv.com.

8886 ■ Whitaker-Minard Memorial Scholarship *(Undergraduate/Scholarship)*

Purpose: To encourage graduating seniors to pursue their degrees in any field specializing in services for individuals with disabilities. **Focus:** Disabilities. **Qualif.:** Applicants must be residents of Wood, Pleasants, Ritchie, Wirt, Gilmer, Calhoun, Jackson, Roane, or Tyler Counties, WV, or Washington County, OH. Applicants must also be graduating high school seniors with a minimum 2.5 GPA who are admitted to attend college, or currently enrolled college students, pursuing associate or bachelor level degrees in any field specializing in services for individuals with disabilities. **Criteria:** Preference will be given to applicants who show willingness to volunteer/participate or have previously volunteered/participated in one of Wood County Society's programs within, or the following year after, the scholarship is received.

Awards are arranged alphabetically below their administering organizations

Funds Avail.: No specific amount. **Duration:** Annual. **To Apply:** Applicants must submit the following: cover sheet (three pages) and application form (four pages); personal essay; high school and/or post-secondary transcripts; a letter of recommendation in a signed and sealed envelope; a copy of the page of their or their parents' most recent tax return that indicates adjusted gross income; and, Student Aid Report showing estimated family contribution from FAFSA. Application form and other supporting documents must be sent to the Foundation's office. **Deadline:** March 1. **Contact:** Rachel Brezler, Regional Scholarships Officer; Phone: 304-428-4438; Email: Rachel.Brezler@pacfwv.com.

8887 ■ Glenn Wilson Broadcast Journalism Scholarship *(Undergraduate/Scholarship)*

Purpose: To provide financial support for qualified individuals intending to pursue their education. **Focus:** Broadcasting; Communications; Journalism; Marketing and distribution. **Qualif.:** Applicants must be current or previous Wood or Pleasant County, WV, or Washington County, OH, high school students who are studying broadcast journalism, journalism, communications or marketing, and have a minimum 2.5 GPA. **Criteria:** Preference will be given to students whose main interest is broadcast journalism as demonstrated by candidates' school activities or through study of this field.

Funds Avail.: No specific amount. **Duration:** Annual. **To Apply:** Applicants must include cover sheet (three pages) and application form (four pages); personal essay; high school and/or post-secondary transcripts; a letter of recommendation in a signed and sealed envelope; a copy of the page of their or their parents' most recent tax return that indicates adjusted gross income; and, Student Aid Report showing estimated family contribution from FAFSA; application form and other supporting documents must be sent to the Foundation's office. **Deadline:** March 1. **Contact:** Rachel Brezler, Regional Scholarships Officer; Phone: 304-428-4438; Email: Rachel.Brezler@pacfwv.com.

8888 ■ Wood County Bar Association Memorial Scholarship *(Graduate/Scholarship)*

Purpose: To provide financial assistance to qualified individuals intending to pursue law degrees. **Focus:** Law. **Qualif.:** Applicants must be students attending an accredited law school in the United States and have connections with Wood, Jackson, Ritchie, Wirt, or Pleasant Counties in West Virginia, or Washington County in Ohio. Previous recipients of this scholarship may reapply for consideration with new applicants. **Criteria:** Selection of recipients will be based on scholarship selection criteria.

Funds Avail.: No specific amount. **Duration:** Annual. **To Apply:** Applicants must submit the following: cover sheet (three pages) and application form (four pages); personal essay; high school and/or post-secondary transcripts; a letter of recommendation in a signed and sealed envelope; a copy of the page of their or their parents' most recent tax return that indicates adjusted gross income; and, Student Aid Report showing estimated family contribution from FAFSA. Application form and other supporting documents must be sent to the Foundation's office. **Deadline:** March 1. **Contact:** Rachel Brezler, Regional Scholarships Officer; Phone: 304-428-4438; Email: Rachel.Brezler@pacfwv.com.

8889 ■ Wood County Technical/Caperton Center Scholarship *(Undergraduate/Scholarship)*

Purpose: To assist graduating seniors in their educational pursuits. **Focus:** General studies/Field of study not speci-

fied. **Qualif.:** Applicants must be graduating seniors attending Wood County Technical/Caperton Center who are admitted to a post-secondary educational institution. **Criteria:** Selection of applicants will be based on GPA and financial need.

Funds Avail.: No specific amount. **Duration:** Annual. **To Apply:** Applicants must include cover sheet (three pages) and application form (four pages); personal essay; high school and/or post-secondary transcripts; a letter of recommendation in a signed and sealed envelope; a copy of the page of their or their parents' most recent tax return that indicates adjusted gross income; and, Student Aid Report showing estimated family contribution from FAFSA; application form and other supporting documents must be sent to the Foundation's office. **Deadline:** March 1. **Contact:** Rachel Brezler, Regional Scholarships Officer; Phone: 304-428-4438; Email: Rachel.Brezler@pacfwv.com.

8890 ■ Parkinson Canada
4211 Yonge St., Ste. 316
Toronto, ON, Canada M2P 2A9
Ph: (416)227-9700
Fax: (844)440-8963
Free: 800-565-3000
E-mail: info@parkinson.ca
URL: www.parkinson.ca
Social Media: www.facebook.com/parkinsoncanada
twitter.com/parkinsoncanada
www.youtube.com/channel/UCm_sAjRqhAaiutx2B9dOqng

8891 ■ Parkinson Canada Basic Research Fellowship *(Advanced Professional/Fellowship)*

Purpose: To encourage promising young scientists possessing a doctoral qualification (MD or PhD) in medicine to enter the field of Parkinson's research, and invest in research training that offers promise for future work in the area of Parkinson's disease. **Focus:** Medical research; Parkinson's disease. **Qualif.:** Applications will be accepted from applicants who meet the eligibility criteria established by PSC (as summarized in this Request for Applications) and who propose to continue their training or conduct research with the following organizations (an "Approved Institution"): Canadian post-secondary institutions and their affiliated institutions, including hospitals and research institutes; or other organizations, as determined by the Research Policy Committee of the National Board of PSC in consultation with the Advisory Board, provided that the applicants' research or research-related activities fall within the mandate of PSC; and, candidates for the PSC/FRQS funding opportunity must submit applications to both FRSQ and to PSC. Research supported under this Program must be carried out at a University or affiliated institutions including hospitals and research institutes, within the Province of Quebec. Applicants must hold a doctoral degree (M.D. or Ph.D.) and be graduates of a university recognized by Parkinson Canada. M.D. degree holders may register in a graduate program leading to M.Sc. degree or Ph.D. degree. Post-M.D. applicants must be licensed to practice in Canada or should have a Canadian educational license. **Criteria:** Selection will be based on the aforesaid qualifications and compliance with the application process. The principal consideration for the evaluation of applications (i.e. applicants' respective research proposals) is research excellence potential.

Funds Avail.: 40,000 to 50,000 Canadian Dollars per annum. **Duration:** Annual; Up to 2 years. **To Apply:** Ap-

Awards are arranged alphabetically below their administering organizations

plicants must submit their applications digitally through the Parkinson Canada online website. The applicants must register and complete the provided application form. Applications for Basic Research Fellowship include the following (minimum font size of 12 point, black ink; six lines per inch; 1 inch margin with no condensed type or spacing; references can be printed in smaller font, however they must be legible): Parkinson Canada Face Sheet for signatures (Generated by printing the personal information sheet from the online application system); Project Summary (1 page; to save space, there is not need to include basic information such as the description of Parkinson's disease); Project Narrative, including background rationale (1 page), specific aims and training goals (1/2 page), details of proposed study including methods and procedures (1 page), and statement describing relevance of proposed studies to Parkinson's (1/2 page); listing of all current and pending funding support; curriculum vitae; and Assessment Forms of Candidates for a Fellowship completed by two sponsors. **Deadline:** February 1. **Contact:** Julie Wysocki, Director, National Research Program; Phone: 800-565-3000 or 416-227-3382; Email: Julie.wysocki@parkinson.ca.

8892 ■ Parkinson Canada Clinical Movement Disorder Fellowship *(Advanced Professional, Professional development/Fellowship)*

Purpose: To encourage promising young clinicians to enter into clinical training in the subspecialty of Movement Disorders, which will include Parkinson's disease. **Focus:** Disabilities; Parkinson's disease. **Qualif.:** Applicants must have completed a recognized postgraduate training program in Neurology or Neurosurgery before the start of the proposed post-graduate Movement Disorder program and be eligible to practice in Canada. Trainees must have successfully completed the Royal College of Physicians examinations in Neurology or Neurosurgery, or must show that they are eligible and have been approved by the Royal College to sit the examinations. In specific situations where application has been made to the Royal College and the applicant is waiting for response, Parkinson Canada's Scientific Advisory Board will consider such candidate as an exception. Applicants should also be eligible for licensure in the jurisdiction where the fellowship will be held. Training is to be conducted at an Approved Institution with registration in a post-graduate training position. Parkinson Canada wishes to support training excellence and development of the wide scope of Parkinson's biomedical research in Canada. It will allow fellowship applications from individuals training at the following organizations: Canadian Medical College or Canadian Post-secondary institutions and their affiliated institutions including hospitals and research institutes; other organizations, as determined by the Research Policy Committee of the board of directors of Parkinson Canada in consultation with the Advisory Board, on the condition that their research or research related activity falls within the mandate of the Program. Canadian citizenship is not a requirement; however, in the selection process, preference will be given to candidates who express the intent to practice in Canada. Applicants will be given an opportunity to describe any career interruptions. **Criteria:** The foremost consideration in evaluation of the Fellowship applications is clinical excellence. However, there are also specific criteria that may also be considered: academic competence; clinical competence in Parkinson's disease and related Movement Disorders; quality and relevance of proposed program of study; potential to make a contribution to clinical care of those living with Parkinson's and related Movement Disorders upon completion of train-

ing; and, intention of candidate to remain in Canada upon Completion of Fellowship.

Funds Avail.: 50,000 Canadian Dollars per annum. **Duration:** Annual. **To Apply:** Applicants must submit their applications digitally through the Parkinson Canada online website. The applicants must register and complete the provided application form. Applications for Program include the following: (minimum font size of 12 point, black ink; six lines per inch; 1 inch margin with no condensed type or spacing; references can be printed in smaller font, however they must be legible): Parkinson Canada Face Sheet for signatures (Generated by printing the personal information sheet from the online application system); a statement from the candidates expressing their interests in Parkinson's, career goals and demonstrating evidence of commitment to Parkinson's disease; curriculum vitae; transcript of university record, including all undergraduate medical and postgraduate studies (foreign transcripts must be accompanied by a certified English or French interpretation and a clear explanation of the grading system); description of where the research will be conducted and the resources available there (1/2 to 1 page); and, confidential letters of reference from three professors or supervisors with whom the candidates have taken the majority of their training. **Deadline:** February 1. **Contact:** Julie Wysocki, Director, National Research Program; Phone: 800-565-3000 or 416-227-3382; Email: Julie.wysocki@parkinson.ca.

8893 ■ Parkinson Canada Clinical Research Fellowship *(Professional development/Fellowship)*

Purpose: To encourage promising young scientists possessing a doctoral qualification (MD) in medicine to enter the field of Parkinson's clinical research, and invest in research training that offers promise for future work in the area of Parkinson's disease. **Focus:** Parkinson's disease. **Qualif.:** Applicants must hold a doctoral degree (M.D.) in medicine, with specialty training experience in either clinical neurology or neurosurgery. Applicants must be graduates of and must have completed training at a university recognized by Parkinson Canada. International applicants are encouraged to apply; however, priority will be given to Canadian citizens and/or applicants intending to remain in, or relocate to, Canada to continue their career following completion of the two-year term of the fellowship. Applicants must be licensed to practice in Canada or should have a Canadian educational license. **Criteria:** Selection will be based on the aforesaid qualifications and compliance with the application process.

Funds Avail.: 50,000 Canadian Dollars per year. **Duration:** Annual; Up to 2 years. **To Apply:** Applicants must submit their applications digitally through the Parkinson Canada online website. The applicants must register and complete the provided application form. Applications for Program include the following (minimum font size of 12 points, black ink; six lines per inch; 1 inch margin with no condensed type or spacing; references can be printed in smaller font, however, they must be legible): Parkinson Canada Face Sheet for signatures (Generated by printing the personal information sheet from the online application system); a statement from applicants expressing their interest in the field of Parkinson's, their career goals and evidence of the applicants commitment to Parkinson's disease (the statement should be 1 to 2 pages and include the relevance of proposed training to the applicant's future career); Project Narrative (total of 3 pages), including background rationale (1 page), specific objectives and training goals (1/2 page), details of proposed study, including methods and procedures (1 page), and statement describ-

Awards are arranged alphabetically below their administering organizations

ing relevance of proposed studies in Canada (1/2 page); description of where research will be conducted and the resources available there (1/2 to 1 page); listing of all current and pending funding support; official transcripts of the applicants complete academic record to date, including degrees and specialty certifications (foreign transcripts must be accompanied by a certified English or French interpretation and a clear explanation of the grading system); curriculum vitae; and assessment forms of candidates for the Fellowship completed by a minimum of two, and not more than three, sponsors, accompanied by letters of support from each such sponsor. **Deadline:** February 1. **Contact:** Julie Wysocki, Director, National Research Program; Phone: 800-565-3000 or 416-227-3382; Email: Julie.wysocki@parkinson.ca.

8894 ■ Parkinson Canada Graduate Student Award
(Graduate, Advanced Professional/Award)

Purpose: To encourage continued growth and revitalization in the fields of Parkinson's research in Canada by supporting talented young scientists and providing students with an opportunity to enter into the area of Parkinson's research during the early stages of their training. **Focus:** Parkinson's disease. **Qualif.:** Applicants must be students engaged in full-time research training in a graduate school. At the time of application, all candidates must be enrolled in a graduate study program at the Master's or PhD level. **Criteria:** Selection will be based on the aforesaid qualifications and compliance with the application process. The principal consideration for the evaluate the applications (i.e. applicants' respective research proposals) is research excellence potential.

Funds Avail.: Total of 20,000 Canadian Dollars per year. **Duration:** Annual; Up to 2 years. **To Apply:** Applicants must submit their applications digitally through the Parkinson Canada online website. The applicants must register and complete the provided application form. Applications for Program include the following (minimum font size of 12 point, black ink; six lines per inch; 1 inch margin with no condensed type or spacing; references can be printed in smaller font, however they must be legible): Parkinson Canada Face Sheet for signatures (Generated by printing the personal information sheet from the online application system); Project Summary, stating in 200 words or less, the scientific or clinical question being asked, how they will address it, the expected outcome and the likely impact of Parkinson's disease; Project Narrative (1 page; to save space, there is not need to include basic information such as the description of Parkinson's disease) including the hypothesis to be tested, candidate's role in the project, and the justification of the relevance of the study to the Parkinson's disease; academic transcripts; and three letters of support. **Deadline:** February 1. **Contact:** Julie Wysocki, Director, National Research Program; Phone: 800-565-3000 or 416-227-3382; Email: Julie.wysocki@parkinson.ca.

8895 ■ Parkinson Canada New Investigator Award
(Professional development/Grant)

Purpose: To provide investigators, who have recently completed research training, with an early opportunity to develop and demonstrate ability to initiate and conduct independent health research. **Focus:** Medical research; Parkinson's disease. **Qualif.:** Applicants must hold a M.D. or Ph.D. degree (or equivalent degree) and be graduates of a university recognized by Parkinson Canada. They must be university faculty member with a position ranking of Associate Professor or less, in the first five years of their

career, and must be conducting research for the following institutions and organizations (an "Approved Institution"): Canadian post-secondary institutions and their affiliated institutions including hospitals and research institutes; or, other equivalent organizations, as determined by the Research Policy Committee of the National Board of Parkinson Canada in consultation with the Advisory Board, provided that the applicant's research or research-related activities fall within the mandate of the organization. Furthermore, the applicants must: be researchers who have completed formal training in health-related research; have some form of research appointment with an Approved Institution, typically, an employment relationship with such institution or organization; be responsible for the intellectual direction of the proposed project; and, be willing and able to assume all administrative and financial responsibilities for any funds awarded under the Program. Applicants in junior faculty positions outside of Canada and scientists transferring into the fields of Parkinson's research from another field are both eligible for this award but are subject to the same eligibility criteria established by Parkinson Canada for other eligible candidates and described in this Request for Applications. **Criteria:** Selection will be based on the aforesaid qualifications and compliance with the application process. The principal consideration for the evaluation of applications (i.e. applicants' respective research proposals) is research excellence potential.

Funds Avail.: 45,000 Canadian Dollars per annum. **Duration:** Annual; Up to 2 years. **To Apply:** Applicants must submit their applications digitally through the Parkinson Canada online website. The applicants must register and complete the provided application form. Applications for New Investigator Awards include the following (minimum font size of 12 point, black ink; six lines per inch; 1 inch margin with no condensed type or spacing; references can be printed in smaller font, however they must be legible): Parkinson Canada Face Sheet for signatures (Generated by printing the personal information sheet from the online application system); Project Summary (1 page; to save space, there is no need to include basic information such as the description of Parkinson's disease); Project Narrative (please take note that indicated breakdown of page amounts are suggestions only, including: background of proposed studies (1 page), specific objectives of the proposed studies (1/2 page), details of proposed experiment, including methods and procedures (3 pages), and statement describing the relevance of proposed studies in Canada (1/2 page) for a total of 5 pages); estimated budget (the details for this can be seen at the website); and biographical information/curriculum vitae of both applicants and all other collaborators (4 page Parkinson Canada biosketch format). Applicants must also include accurate and complete information regarding all other sources of funding support (current or pending), including title, funding source, total amount of funds requested or awarded, inclusive funding period, and percentage effort of the applicants. Applications must be submitted with the required signatures by the due date. Prior to submission, applicants should determine what signatures are needed, print the applicant information sheet (face sheet) and obtain all the required signatures for their application. Once obtained, scan the signature page and upload the signed signature page to the PSC online system as part of their submission by the application deadline date. **Deadline:** February 1. **Contact:** Julie Wysocki, Director, National Research Program; Phone: 800-565-3000 or 416-227-3382; Email: Julie.wysocki@parkinson.ca.

Awards are arranged alphabetically below their administering organizations

8896 ■ Parkinson Canada Pilot Project Grant
(Advanced Professional/Grant)

Purpose: To encourage established investigators to enter into the study of Parkinson's disease and perform research in new, specifically targeted, high priority areas. **Focus:** Medical research; Parkinson's disease. **Qualif.:** Applicant must be a Independent researchers. **Criteria:** Selection will be based on the aforesaid qualifications and compliance with the application process. The principal consideration for the evaluation of applications (i.e. applicants' respective research proposals) is research excellence potential.

Funds Avail.: Up to 50,000 Canadian Dollars. **Duration:** Annual. **To Apply:** Applicants must submit their applications digitally through the Parkinson Canada online website. The applicants must register and complete the provided application form. Applications for Program include the following (minimum font size of 12 point, black ink; six lines per inch; 1 inch margin with no condensed type or spacing; references can be printed in smaller font, however they must be legible): Parkinson Canada Face Sheet for signatures (Generated by printing the personal information sheet from the online application system); Project Summary (1 page; to save space, there is no need to include basic information such as the description of Parkinson's disease); Project Narrative (please take note that indicated breakdown of page amounts are suggestions only), including: background of proposed studies (1 page), specific objectives of the proposed studies (1/2 page), details of proposed experiment, including methods and procedures (3 pages), and statement describing the relevance of proposed studies in Canada (1/2 page) for a total of 5 pages; estimated budget (the details for this can be seen at the website); and biographical information/curriculum vitae of both applicants and all other collaborators (4 page Parkinson Canada bio-sketch format). Applicants must also include accurate and complete information regarding all other sources of funding support (current or pending), including title, funding source, total amount of funds requested or awarded, inclusive funding period, and percentage effort of the applicants. Applications must be submitted with the required signatures by the due date. Prior to submission, applicants should determine what signatures are needed, print the applicant information sheet (face sheet) and obtain all the required signatures for their application. Once obtained, scan the signature page and upload the signed signature page to the PSC online system as part of their submission by the application deadline date. **Deadline:** February 1. **Contact:** Julie Wysocki, Director, National Research Program; Phone: 800-565-3000 or 416-227-3382; Email: Julie.wysocki@parkinson.ca.

8897 ■ Parkinson's Foundation (PF)
1359 Broadway, Ste. 1509
New York, NY 10018
Free: 800-473-4636
E-mail: contact@parkinson.org
URL: www.parkinson.org
Social Media: www.facebook.com/parkinsondotorg
www.instagram.com/parkinsondotorg
www.linkedin.com/company/parkinsondotorg
twitter.com/parkinsondotorg
www.youtube.com/ParkinsonDotOrg

8898 ■ Clinician Research Awards *(Postgraduate, Professional development, Other/Fellowship)*
Purpose: To support clinician scientist's research related to Parkinson's disease. **Focus:** Medical research; Parkinson's

disease. **Qualif.:** Applicants must be clinician-scientists who are licensed to care for patients regardless of nationality or location. Physicians must have completed a residency in neurology or be able to justify the relevance of their training pathway is of benefit to people with PD; allied health professionals must hold an advanced research degree, typically a PhD. All applicants must demonstrate a significant research focus on PD. Applicants who are fellows, in a mentored status or within 2 years of starting an independent position must identify an appropriate mentor with research experience to provide oversight of the proposed project. **Criteria:** Preference will be given to the support of junior investigators.

Funds Avail.: $200,000 total over two years. Up to 10% of the award total, i.e., $20,000, may be used to defray indirect costs. Salary support is permitted but for no more than 40% of the recipient's salary and capped at $50,000 per year. **Duration:** Annual. **Number Awarded:** 2 to 3. **To Apply:** Application details are available at www.parkinson.org/research/Grant-Opportunities/clinical-research-awards. **Deadline:** April 10. **Contact:** Email: grants@parkinson.org.

8899 ■ Parkinson's Disease Foundation International Research Grants Program (IRGP)
(Postdoctorate/Grant)

Purpose: To provide financial assistance for projects of the highest scientific caliber from around the world; to promote innovative research with high potential to advance the knowledge of Parkinson's disease. **Focus:** Parkinson's disease. **Qualif.:** Applicants must have completed a PhD or MD and qualified to serve as a principal investigator for the project which is basic, translational and clinical research. **Criteria:** Applicants proposal will be peer-reviewed and competitively evaluated based on the quality of the research proposal and its pertinence to Parkinson's disease; preference will be given to those applicants who are at any early stage of their professional careers.

Duration: Two years. **To Apply:** Applicants must submit the application package which includes the completed PDF application form, which requires the signature of the applicants and the relevant institutional authority; letter of recommendation consisting of the background of proposed study, specific aims, details of proposed experiment including methods, statement describing relevance of proposed studies, budget and justification, curriculum vitae and references. **Contact:** grants@pdf.org.

8900 ■ Postdoctoral Fellowships for Basic Scientists Program *(Postdoctorate/Fellowship)*

Purpose: To support research into Parkinson's disease. **Focus:** Medical research; Parkinson's disease. **Qualif.:** Must be within five years of receiving a Ph.D. at the time the award starts, and must name an individual who will serve as research mentor and supervisor. This program is open to both national and international applicants. If awarded, a Postdoctoral Fellow must commit 90 percent of their effort to the Parkinson's Foundation-funded project. **Criteria:** Selection committee peer-reviews and ranks all proposals based upon scientific merit and impact upon Parkinson's disease.

Funds Avail.: $120,000. **Duration:** 2 years. **To Apply:** Initial letter of intent required, selected participants will be invited to submit full proposals. Application must be submitted online. **Deadline:** February 18. **Contact:** E-mail: grants@parkinson.org; URL: www.parkinson.org/research/information-for-researchers/early-career-fellowships/postdoctoral.

Awards are arranged alphabetically below their administering organizations

8901 ■ Postdoctoral Fellowships for Clinical Neurologists *(Postdoctorate/Fellowship)*

Purpose: To provide financial assistance for young clinicians who have completed their neurology residency and are seeking clinical research experience. **Focus:** Neurology; Parkinson's disease. **Qualif.:** Applicants must possess a M.D. or equivalent and be within three years of having completed a residency in neurology; applicants may not have their own lab and must identify an individual who will serve as their mentor and supervisor of their research; this program is open to both national and international applicants. **Criteria:** Selection committee peer-reviews and ranks all proposals based upon scientific merit and impact upon Parkinson's disease.

Funds Avail.: $140,000. **Duration:** 2 years. **To Apply:** Initial letter of intent required, selected participants will be invited to submit full proposals. Application must be submitted online. **Deadline:** February 18. **Contact:** E-mail: grants@parkinson.org; URL: www.parkinson.org/research/information-for-researchers/early-career-fellowships/postdoctoral.

8902 ■ Summer Student Fellowships *(Undergraduate, Graduate/Fellowship)*

Purpose: To cultivate students' early interest in helping to solve, treat, and end Parkinson's and providing the tools they need to transition into leaders in the field. **Focus:** Parkinson's disease. **Qualif.:** Applicants must be undergraduates and medical students; must identify a mentor with whom they will conduct the proposed project. **Criteria:** Applications are judged based on the relevance of the technique to be learned to advance an applicant's PD research, the overall feasibility of the applicant's project, the background of the applicant, and the appropriateness of the host mentor.

Funds Avail.: $4,000. **Duration:** Up to 10 weeks. **To Apply:** Application available at www.parkinson.org/research/information-for-researchers/early-career-fellowships/summer. **Contact:** Email: grants@parkinson.org.

8903 ■ Partnership for Public Service (PPS)
1100 New York Ave. NW Ste.200 E
Washington, DC 20005
Ph: (202)775-9111
Fax: (202)775-8885
E-mail: othompson@ourpublicservice.org
URL: ourpublicservice.org
Social Media: www.facebook.com/
  partnershipforpublicservice
www.linkedin.com/company/28034
twitter.com/RPublicService

8904 ■ Public Service Fellows Internship Program - Center for Government Leadership *(Undergraduate, Graduate/Internship)*

Purpose: To allow individuals to contribute to the Partnership's mission of revitalizing federal government by transforming the way government works and inspiring a new generation to serve while developing valuable professional skills. **Focus:** General studies/Field of study not specified. **Qualif.:** Applicants must be undergraduate, graduate and recent graduate students; must be willing to relocate to Washington, D.C. for the duration of the term. **Criteria:** Selection will be based on the following requirements: strong communication, customer service, writing

and organizational skills, as well as an ability to adapt and collaborate.

Funds Avail.: $1,000 per month (for full-time fellows with an undergraduate or graduate degree); $800 (for those who are currently undergraduate students). **To Apply:** Applicants may contact the Partnership for Public Service for the available positions and for the application process. **Deadline:** Summer 2017: March 3; Fall 2017: June 30; Spring 2018: November 3. **Contact:** Mollie Allers, Christina Francisco, and Patrick Moniz, Program Coordinators; Phone: (202) 775-9111; Email: fellows@ourpublicservice.org.

8905 ■ Public Service Fellows Internship Program - Education and Outreach *(Undergraduate, Graduate, Professional development/Internship)*

Purpose: To allow individuals to contribute to the Partnership's mission of revitalizing federal government by transforming the way government works and inspiring a new generation to serve while developing valuable professional skills. **Focus:** General studies/Field of study not specified. **Qualif.:** Applicants must be undergraduate, graduate and recent graduate students; must be willing to relocate to Washington, D.C. for the duration of the term. **Criteria:** Selection will be based on the committee's criteria; ideal applicants must possess outstanding written and verbal communication skills, strong attention to detail and excellent time-management abilities.

Funds Avail.: $1,000 per month (for full-time fellows with an undergraduate or graduate degree); $800 (for those who are currently undergraduate students). **To Apply:** Applicants may contact the Partnership for Public Service for the available positions and for the application process. **Deadline:** Summer 2017: March 3; Fall 2017: June 30; Spring 2018: November 3. **Contact:** Mollie Allers, Christina Francisco, and Patrick Moniz, Program Coordinators; Phone: (202) 775-9111; Email: fellows@ourpublicservice.org.

8906 ■ Public Service Fellows Internship Program - Government Transformation and Agency Partnerships *(Undergraduate, Graduate, Professional development/Internship)*

Purpose: To allow individuals to contribute to the Partnership's mission of revitalizing federal government by transforming the way government works and inspiring a new generation to serve while developing valuable professional skills. **Focus:** General studies/Field of study not specified. **Qualif.:** Applicants must be undergraduate, graduate and recent graduate students; must be willing to relocate to Washington, D.C. for the duration of the term. **Criteria:** Selection will be based on the committee's criteria.

Funds Avail.: $1,000 per month (for full-time fellows with an undergraduate or graduate degree); $800 (for those who are currently undergraduate students). **To Apply:** Applicants may contact the Partnership for Public Service for the available positions and for the application process. **Deadline:** Summer 2017: March 3; Fall 2017: June 30; Spring 2018: November 3. **Contact:** Mollie Allers, Christina Francisco, and Patrick Moniz, Program Coordinators; Phone: (202) 775-9111; Email: fellows@ourpublicservice.org.

8907 ■ Public Service Fellows Internship Program - Human Resources *(Professional development, Other/Internship)*

Purpose: To allow individuals to contribute to the Partnership's mission of revitalizing federal government by

---

Awards are arranged alphabetically below their administering organizations

transforming the way government works and inspiring a new generation to serve while developing valuable professional skills. **Focus:** General studies/Field of study not specified. **Qualif.:** Applicants must be undergraduate, graduate or recent graduate students; must be willing to relocate to Washington, D.C. for the duration of the term; must be able to work independently and in a team setting; and must show a demonstrated ability to handle confidential information with discretion and professionalism. **Criteria:** Selection will be based on the committee's criteria.

Funds Avail.: $1,000 per month (for full-time fellows with an undergraduate or graduate degree); $800 (for those who are currently undergraduate students). **To Apply:** Applicants may contact the Partnership for Public Service for the available positions and for the application process. **Deadline:** Summer 2017: March 3; Fall 2017: June 30; Spring 2018: November 3. **Contact:** Mollie Allers, Christina Francisco, and Patrick Moniz, Program Coordinators; Phone: (202) 775-9111; Email: fellows@ourpublicservice.org.

8908 ■ Public Service Internship Program - Communications *(Undergraduate, Graduate, Professional development/Internship)*

Purpose: To allow individuals to contribute to the Partnership's mission of revitalizing federal government by transforming the way government works and inspiring a new generation to serve while developing valuable professional skills. **Focus:** General studies/Field of study not specified. **Qualif.:** Applicants must be undergraduate, graduate and recent graduate students; must be willing to relocate to Washington, D.C. for the duration of the term. **Criteria:** Selection will be based on the committee's criteria; ideal applicants are outgoing, detail-oriented, team players and have excellent writing, organization and public speaking skills.

Funds Avail.: $1,000 per month (for full-time fellows with an undergraduate or graduate degree); $800 (for those who are currently undergraduate students). **To Apply:** Applicants may contact the Partnership for Public Service for the available positions and for the application process. **Deadline:** Fall 2018: July 13; Spring 2019: November 9; Summer 2019: March 8. **Contact:** Victoria Eick; Email: veick@ourpublicservice.org.

8909 ■ Public Service Internship Program - Development *(Undergraduate, Graduate, Professional development/Internship)*

Purpose: To allow individuals to contribute to the Partnership's mission of revitalizing federal government by transforming the way government works and inspiring a new generation to serve while developing valuable professional skills. **Focus:** General studies/Field of study not specified. **Qualif.:** Applicants must be undergraduate, graduate and recent graduate students; must be willing to relocate to Washington, D.C. for the duration of the term. **Criteria:** Selection will be based on the committee's criteria; ideal applicants must also have exceptional written and spoken communication skills which are essential.

Funds Avail.: $1,000 per month (for full-time fellows with an undergraduate or graduate degree); $800 (for those who are currently undergraduate students). **To Apply:** Applicants may contact the Partnership for Public Service for the available positions and for the application process. **Deadline:** Fall 2018: July 13; Spring 2019: November 9; Summer 2019: March 8. **Contact:** Victoria Eick; Email: veick@ourpublicservice.org.

8910 ■ Public Service Internship Program - Government Affairs *(Undergraduate, Graduate, Professional development/Internship)*

Purpose: To allow individuals to contribute to the Partnership's mission of revitalizing federal government by transforming the way government works and inspiring a new generation to serve while developing valuable professional skills. **Focus:** General studies/Field of study not specified. **Qualif.:** Applicants must be undergraduate, graduate and recent graduate students; must be willing to relocate to Washington, D.C. for the duration of the term. **Criteria:** Selection will be based on the committee's criteria.

Funds Avail.: $1,000 per month (for full-time fellows with an undergraduate or graduate degree); $800 (for those who are currently undergraduate students). **To Apply:** Applicants may contact the Partnership for Public Service for the available positions and for the application process. **Deadline:** Fall 2018: July 13; Spring 2019: November 9; Summer 2019: March 8. **Contact:** Victoria Eick; Email: veick@ourpublicservice.org.

8911 ■ Public Service Internship Program - Research and Program Evaluation Focus *(Undergraduate, Graduate, Professional development/ Internship)*

Purpose: To allow individuals to contribute to the Partnership's mission of revitalizing federal government by transforming the way government works and inspiring a new generation to serve while developing valuable professional skills. **Focus:** General studies/Field of study not specified. **Qualif.:** Applicants must be undergraduate, graduate and recent graduate students; must be willing to relocate to Washington, D.C. for the duration of the term. **Criteria:** Selection will be based on the committee's criteria; preference will be given to those with social science research experiences; excel and/or SPSS skills will also be considered.

Funds Avail.: $1,000 per month (for full-time fellows with an undergraduate or graduate degree); $800 (for those who are currently undergraduate students). **To Apply:** Applicants may contact the Partnership for Public Service for the available positions and for the application process. **Deadline:** Fall 2018: July 13; Spring 2019: November 9; Summer 2019: March 8. **Contact:** Victoria Eick; Email: veick@ourpublicservice.org.

8912 ■ Pasteur Foundation
420 Lexington Ave., Ste. 1654
New York, NY 10170
Ph: (212)599-2050
Fax: (212)599-2047
E-mail: director@pasteurfoundation.org
URL: www.pasteurfoundation.org

8913 ■ Pasteur Foundation Postdoctoral Fellowship *(Postdoctorate/Fellowship)*

Purpose: To support postdoctoral researchers who wants to work in Pasteur laboratories in Paris. **Focus:** General studies/Field of study not specified.

Funds Avail.: 3,750 Euros per month. **Duration:** Annual; 3 years. **Number Awarded:** 1. **To Apply:** Applicants must submit the completed Pasteur foundation application form; presentation letter from the host ip lab head; a scanned copy of the candidate's passport or id (pages showing your photograph, identification, and citizenship); to be provided

Awards are arranged alphabetically below their administering organizations

two reference letters recommender. **Deadline:** September 10. **Contact:** Email: bourses@pasteur.fr; Email: director@pasteurfoundation.org.

8914 ■ Patch
560 N Nimitz Highway, Suite 218
Honolulu, HI 96817
Ph: (808)839-1988
Fax: (808)839-1799
E-mail: patch@patch-hi.org
URL: www.patchhawaii.org
Social Media: www.facebook.com/PATCHHI
www.instagram.com/patch_hawaii
www.linkedin.com/company/people-attentive-to-children
twitter.com/PATCH_Hawaii

8915 ■ PATCH Early Childhood Education Scholarships *(Graduate/Scholarship)*
Purpose: To support the quality of care for young people who are entering into the early care and education profession. **Focus:** General studies/Field of study not specified. **Criteria:** Selection will be based on the committee's criteria.
Funds Avail.: $750 per round (3 rounds per year: August, January, May). **Duration:** Annual. **To Apply:** Applicants must submit a proof of payment verifying that funds were debited from your account; a financial aid or award letter; transcript that lists passing grade of eligible coursework. **Deadline:** August 31 (1st Round); January 15 (2nd Round); May 31 (3rd Round). **Contact:** PATCH, Atten: Scholarships, 26 Waianuenue Ave., Hilo, HI, 96720.

8916 ■ Pathways College
320 N Halstead St.
Pasadena, CA 91107
Free: 888-532-7282
E-mail: info@pathwayscollege.org
URL: www.pathwayscollege.org
Social Media: www.facebook.com/pathwayscollege.org
www.instagram.com/pathwayscollege626
www.linkedin.com/company/pathways-college-online

8917 ■ Pathways College Scholarship *(Undergraduate/Scholarship)*
Purpose: To help a student attend Pathways college in the business or liberal arts program. **Focus:** Business; Liberal arts. **Qualif.:** Applicant must have a high school diploma or GED; must want to major in business or liberal studies and be willing to complete 10 hours of community service within a year to the organization of their choice.
Funds Avail.: $5,000 to attend Pathways College. **Duration:** Good for one year, but students in good standing can keep renewing. **To Apply:** Complete the application form at www.pathwayscollege.org/scholarship. **Contact:** Email: egonzalez@pathwayscollege.org.

8918 ■ Patterson, Belknap, Webb and Tyler L.L.P.
1133 Avenue of the Americas
New York, NY 10036
Ph: (212)336-2000
Fax: (212)336-2222
URL: www.pbwt.com
Social Media: www.linkedin.com/company/patterson-belknap-webb-&-tyler-llp

twitter.com/pbwtlaw

8919 ■ Patterson Belknap Webb & Tyler LLP Diversity Fellowships *(Doctorate/Fellowship)*
Purpose: To help students continue their doctoral degree at an ABA accredited law school. **Focus:** Law.
Funds Avail.: $25,000. **Duration:** Annual. **Number Awarded:** Varies.

8920 ■ Pauahi Foundation
567 S King St., Ste. 160
Honolulu, HI 96813
Ph: (808)534-3966
Fax: (808)534-3890
E-mail: info@pauahi.org
URL: www.pauahi.org
Social Media: www.facebook.com/KeAliiPauahiFoundation
twitter.com/kealiipauahi

8921 ■ Dan and Rachel Mahi Educational Scholarship *(Graduate, Undergraduate/Scholarship)*
Purpose: To provide financial support to students pursuing their educational goals. **Focus:** General studies/Field of study not specified. **Qualif.:** Applicants must be students in an undergraduate or graduate degree-seeking program from an accredited post-high educational institution in Hawaii; must demonstrate interest in Hawaiian language, culture, history; must have minimum GPA of 2.0. **Criteria:** Selection will be based on the committee's criteria; financial need.
Funds Avail.: $2,000. **Duration:** Annual. **Number Awarded:** 1. **To Apply:** Applicants must submit two letters of recommendation: one from a teacher or counselor and one from an employer or community organization who can comment on your overall character, achievement and contribution to serve the greater community; Student Aid Report (SAR) from the Free Application for Federal Student Aid (FAFSA).

8922 ■ Daniel Kahikina and Millie Akaka Scholarship *(Graduate, Undergraduate/Scholarship)*
Purpose: To provide financial support to students pursuing their educational goals. **Focus:** General studies/Field of study not specified. **Qualif.:** Applicants must be undergraduate or graduate students that demonstrate a financial need and have a GPA of 3.2 or higher. Recipients are strongly encouraged to provide a minimum of 10 hours of community service to the Council for Native Hawaiian Advancement. **Criteria:** Selection will be based on the committee's criteria.
Funds Avail.: $2,900. **Duration:** Annual. **Number Awarded:** 1. **To Apply:** Applicants must submit completed application form; letters of recommendation; Student Aid Report (SAR) from the Free Application for Federal Student Aid (FAFSA). **Deadline:** January 29.

8923 ■ Denis Wong & Associates Scholarship *(Graduate, Undergraduate/Scholarship)*
Purpose: To support the students degree in liberal arts or science, or a graduate degree in a professional field. **Focus:** Liberal arts; Science. **Qualif.:** Applicants must be outstanding students pursuing an undergraduate degree in liberal arts or science, or a graduate degree in a professional field from an accredited university; must have a

Awards are arranged alphabetically below their administering organizations

minimum GPA of 3.5. **Criteria:** Demonstrate well-rounded and balanced record of achievement in preparation for career objectives.

Funds Avail.: $1,000. **Duration:** Annual. **Number Awarded:** 5. **To Apply:** Applicants must submit completed application form; letters of recommendation, essays or artist portfolios; Student Aid Report (SAR) from the Free Application for Federal Student Aid (FAFSA).

8924 ■ Bruce T. and Jackie Mahi Erickson Scholarship *(Graduate, Undergraduate/Scholarship)*

Purpose: To support students in pursuing studies in S.T.E.A.M (Science, Technology, Engineering, Arts, Math). **Focus:** Arts; Engineering; Mathematics and mathematical sciences; Science; Technology. **Qualif.:** Applicants must pursuing studies in S.T.E.A.M; demonstrate financial need. **Criteria:** Selection will be based on the committee's criteria.

Funds Avail.: $1,400. **Duration:** Annual. **Number Awarded:** 1. **To Apply:** Applicants must submit letters of recommendation, essays or artist portfolios; Student Aid Report; and complete online application.

8925 ■ George Hi'ilani Mills Scholarship *(Graduate/ Scholarship)*

Purpose: To support students in pursuing their educational goals. **Focus:** Health sciences; Medicine. **Qualif.:** Applicants must be graduate students pursuing professional studies in the field of medicine or the allied health-related fields; must also demonstrate financial need. **Criteria:** Selection will be based on the committee's criteria.

Funds Avail.: $1,000. **Duration:** Annual. **Number Awarded:** 7. **To Apply:** Applicants must submit completed application form; one-page essay demonstrating balanced record of achievement, as well as holding the values and tradition of the Hawaiian civic club movement; and Student Aid Report (SAR) from the Free Application for Federal Student Aid (FAFSA).

8926 ■ Goldman Sachs/Matsuo Takabuki Commemorative Scholarship *(Graduate/Scholarship)*

Purpose: To support the students in pursuing their educational goals. **Focus:** Business; Finance. **Qualif.:** Applicants must be students pursuing graduate degrees in business or financial services related fields; must be resident of Hawaii. **Criteria:** Selection given to those demonstrating financial need.

Funds Avail.: $17,500. **Duration:** Annual. **Number Awarded:** Varies. **To Apply:** Applicants must submit completed application form; and Students Aid Report (SAR) from the Free Application for Federal Student Aid (FAFSA).

8927 ■ Isaac and Mary Harbottle Scholarship *(Graduate, Undergraduate/Scholarship)*

Purpose: To support the educational needs and goals of people who wants to enrich the learning in areas of education, community organization, and/or spiritual growth. **Focus:** General studies/Field of study not specified. **Qualif.:** Applicants must be undergraduate or graduate students in the areas of education, community organization, and/or spiritual growth. Students are challenged to create and sustain healthy communities, increase healthy relationships in the community, and keep the native Hawaiian culture and the legacy of Isaac Hakuole and Mary Kaimookalani Kamaolipua Okuu Piikoi Harbottle alive. **Criteria:** Selection will be based on the committee's criteria.

Funds Avail.: $1,300. **Duration:** Annual. **Number Awarded:** 1. **To Apply:** Applicant must submit a College Acceptance Letter; official transcript of grades; and student aid report (SAR). **Deadline:** January 29.

8928 ■ Iwalani Carpenter Sowa Scholarship *(Graduate/Scholarship)*

Purpose: To support anyone pursuing a divinity degree to become a Protestant minister. **Focus:** Religion. **Qualif.:** Applicants must be students pursuing a graduate degree in the Protestant Christian ministry and who have a desire to minister in Hawaii. **Criteria:** Preference will be given to a Kamehameha Schools graduate and those demonstrating financial need.

Funds Avail.: $2,500. **Duration:** Annual. **Number Awarded:** 1. **To Apply:** Applicant must submit a College Acceptance Letter if attending a college or university for the first time, or currently enrolled college student changing schools or degree programs; official transcript of grades; and student aid report (SAR). Applicants must also submit two letter of recommendation from applicant's religion professor, college advisor, church minister or community organization.

8929 ■ Gladys Kamakakokalani 'Ainoa Brandt Scholarships *(Graduate, Undergraduate/Scholarship)*

Purpose: To support the students in pursuing a career in the education field. **Focus:** Education. **Qualif.:** Applicants must be full-time junior, senior or graduate students at an accredited university aspiring to enter the educational profession; must demonstrate financial need; must have a GPA of 2.5 or higher. **Criteria:** Financial need; preference will be given to current or former residents of Kaua'i.

Funds Avail.: $2,500. **Duration:** Annual. **Number Awarded:** 7. **To Apply:** Must submit completed application form; two letters of recommendation; and Student Aid report (SAR) from the Free Application for Federal Student Aid (FAFSA). **Deadline:** January 29.

8930 ■ Kamehameha Schools Class of 1968 "Ka Poli O Kaiona" Scholarships *(Graduate, Undergraduate/Scholarship)*

Purpose: To support students in pursuing their higher education. **Focus:** General studies/Field of study not specified. **Qualif.:** Applicants must be either classified undergraduate or graduate student; must be have minimum GPA of 2.8; and must demonstrate financial need. **Criteria:** Selection will be given to family members (as defined) of KS Class of 1968 graduates.

Funds Avail.: $1,100. **Duration:** Annual. **Number Awarded:** 2. **To Apply:** Applicants must submit two letters of recommendation from school, employer or community organization; submit essay on how this award would support and extend the legacy of Ke Ali'i Bernice Pauahi Bishop; and student Aid Report (SAR) from the Free Application for Federal Student Aid (FAFSA). **Remarks:** Established in 1968.

8931 ■ Kamehameha Schools Class of 1972 Scholarship *(Graduate, Undergraduate/Scholarship)*

Purpose: To assist individuals whose lives have been impacted, and maybe traumatized, by challenging circumstances with educational opportunities. **Focus:** General studies/Field of study not specified. **Qualif.:** Applicants must be either classified undergraduate or graduate students; must be enrolled in a degree-seeking program; must be enrolled in two- or four-year accredited college institution in Hawaii or the continental U.S.; must demon-

Awards are arranged alphabetically below their administering organizations

strate a commitment to contribute to the greater community and interest in Hawaiian language, culture, and history; must be have minimum GPA of 2.8; Must demonstrate financial need. **Criteria:** Selection will be based on the committee's criteria.

Funds Avail.: $1,000. **Duration:** Annual. **Number Awarded:** 2. **To Apply:** Applicants must submit letter of recommendation from social service agency or counselor; and Students Aid Report from Free Application for Federal Student Aid.

8932 ■ Native Hawaiian Chamber of Commerce Scholarship (Graduate, Undergraduate/Scholarship)

Purpose: To provide financial support to students pursuing a degree in business administration. **Focus:** Business administration. **Qualif.:** Applicants must be students in an undergraduate or graduate business administration program from an accredited post-high educational institution in Hawaii; must demonstrate interest in Hawaiian language, culture, history; must have minimum GPA of 3.0. **Criteria:** Financial need.

Funds Avail.: $1,000. **Duration:** Annual. **Number Awarded:** 4. **To Apply:** Apply online.

8933 ■ Native Hawaiian Visual Arts Scholarship (Graduate, Undergraduate/Scholarship)

Purpose: To provide financial support to students majoring in the visual arts. **Focus:** Visual arts. **Qualif.:** Applicants must be undergraduate and graduate students majoring in Art to pursue the area of Visual Arts, including but not limited to, drawing, painting, printmaking, graphic design, fiber arts, sculpture, ceramics, digital art (computer), photography, and film-making/video production; must have a GPA of 3.2 or higher. **Criteria:** Selection will be based on artistic merit as demonstrated by an artistic portfolio and academic achievements.

Funds Avail.: $2,600. **Duration:** Annual. **Number Awarded:** 2. **To Apply:** Applicants must submit letters of recommendation; essays or artist portfolios; Student Aid Report; artistic works created (CDs and DVDs will not be accepted); and complete online application.

8934 ■ William S. Richardson Commemorative Scholarship (Graduate/Scholarship)

Purpose: To provide financial support to students pursuing their educational goals. **Focus:** Law. **Qualif.:** Applicants must be a state resident of Hawaii attending the University of Hawaii-Manoa William S. Richardson School of Law. **Criteria:** Selection will be given to applicants demonstrating financial need.

Funds Avail.: $1,500. to $3,000. **Duration:** Annual. **Number Awarded:** 4. **To Apply:** Applicants must submit completed application form; letters of recommendation, essays; Student Aid Report (SAR) from the Free Application for Federal Student Aid (FAFSA).

8935 ■ PBR Forces Veterans Association (PBR-FVA)
14015 Spanish Point Dr.
Jacksonville, FL 32225
URL: www.pbr-fva.org

8936 ■ BM1 James Elliott Williams Memorial Scholarship Fund (Undergraduate/Scholarship)

Purpose: To provide educational support to students who are in need. **Focus:** Vietnamese studies. **Qualif.:** Applicant

must be a direct descent of an active member of PBR Forces Veterans Association; must be enrolled in a two or four-year accredited college/technical school. **Criteria:** Selection will be awarded to the student who best meets the criteria.

Funds Avail.: Varies. **To Apply:** Applicants must fill out the application form using blue or black ink and must be countersigned by the Sponsor. **Deadline:** August 15. **Remarks:** Established in honor of BM1 James Elliott Williams, who received the Medal of Honor on May 14, 1968 by President Lyndon Baines Johnson for action that took place on October 31, 1966 while he was attached to River Section 531, My Tho, Republic of Vietnam. **Contact:** Application forms must be sent to PBR Forces Veterans Association, Inc, c/o Mr. Rich Fichtelman, 1766 Kirkwood Rd., Corona, CA 92882.

8937 ■ Pediatric Brain Tumor Foundation - Georgia
6065 Roswell Rd. NE, Ste. 505
Atlanta, GA 30328
Ph: (404)252-4107
Fax: (404)252-4108
URL: www.curethekids.org
Social Media: www.facebook.com/curethekids
www.instagram.com/braintumorkids
www.linkedin.com/company/pediatric-brain-tumor
 -foundation
www.pinterest.com/curethekids
twitter.com/braintumorkids
www.youtube.com/channel/
 UCzsxAqMQwVg2uCkYe1Bjx2Q

8938 ■ Larry Dean Davis Scholarship (Undergraduate/Scholarship)

Purpose: To provide financial support to those students who are pursuing their educational degree. **Focus:** General studies/Field of study not specified. **Qualif.:** Applicants must be survivors of pediatric brain or spinal cord tumor who are residents of the state of Georgia; must be entering or currently enrolled in an advanced educational program at a college, university, vocational school, or other setting; and must demonstrate a need for financial assistance. **Criteria:** Selection will be based on the committee's criteria.

Funds Avail.: $2,500. **Duration:** Annual. **Number Awarded:** Up to 2. **To Apply:** Applicants must submit completed application available on the website; two letters of recommendation; and an essay describing the following: 1) brain or spinal cord tumor experience; 2) brief biographical sketch of themselves and future aspirations; and 3) detailed statement of financial need. Applicants may call the foundation for further information or to request an application. **Remarks:** The scholarship was established in memory of Larry Dean Davis, a beloved founding member of the Board of Directors of the Brian Tumor Foundation for Children. Established in 2002. **Contact:** Larry Dean Davis Scholarship Committee, C/o Pediatric Brain Tumor Foundation-GA Chapter, 6065 Roswell Rd. NE, Ste. 505, Atlanta, GA, 30328.

8939 ■ Pediatric Endocrinology Nursing Society (PENS)
4400 College Blvd., Ste. 220
Overland Park, KS 66211

Awards are arranged alphabetically below their administering organizations

Ph: (913)222-8657
Fax: (913)222-8606
Free: 877-936-7367
E-mail: pens@kellencompany.com
URL: www.pens.org
Social Media: www.facebook.com/
pediatricendocrinologynursingsociety

8940 ■ Academic Education Scholarship (Professional development/Scholarship)

Purpose: To provide financial assistance to members who are enrolled in pediatric endocrine nursing programs. **Focus:** Education; Nursing. **Qualif.:** Applicant must be an active PENS member who is pursuing her/his further education in an accredited degree program in nursing; must be currently employed in pediatric endocrine nursing; must have a minimum of 3 years of PENS membership prior to applying. **Criteria:** The board of directors reviews applications which are blinded to ensure anonymity.

Funds Avail.: $1,000. **To Apply:** Applicants must complete the scholarship application form available from the PENS executive office and the PENS web site; must include the following; copy of RN license, curriculum vitae or resume, documentation of registration or receipt from college/university, transcript of grades or acceptance letter. **Deadline:** April 1; September 1.

8941 ■ Pediatric Endocrinology Nursing Society Academic Education Scholarships (Undergraduate/Scholarship)

Purpose: To promote the study and development of pediatric endocrine nursing. **Focus:** Nursing, Pediatric. **Qualif.:** Applicant must be an active pens member who is pursuing her/his further education in an accredited degree program in nursing; applicant must be currently employed in pediatric endocrine nursing; applicant must have a minimum of 3 years of PENS membership prior to applying. **Criteria:** Applicants are judged upon the committee's criteria.

Funds Avail.: $1,000. **Duration:** One year. **To Apply:** Applicants must complete the scholarship application form; copy of RN License; curriculum vitae or resume; documentation of registration or receipt from college/university; transcript of grades or acceptance letter. **Deadline:** April 1; September 1. **Contact:** PENS Executive Office, 4400 College Blvd Ste., 220 Overland Pk., KS, 66211; Fax: 913-222-8606; Email: pens@kellencompany.com.

8942 ■ PENS Conference Reimbursement Scholarship (Undergraduate/Scholarship)

Purpose: To promote the study of endocrine and clinical experience that has affected your pediatric endocrinology nursing practice. **Focus:** Nursing, Pediatric. **Qualif.:** Applicants must be an active PENS member. **Criteria:** Recipients are selected based on the committee's review of the application materials.

Funds Avail.: $1,000. **Duration:** Annual. **Number Awarded:** Up to 12. **To Apply:** Applicants must send a completed application form and a (2-4 page) clinical exemplar or copy of your poster abstract accepted by the PENS Research Committee. Letter from your employer clearly stating the amount of funding received from employer to attend conference. Send documents via email. **Deadline:** June 15. **Contact:** Submit the application materials to the PENS Executive Office at email: PENS@kellencompany.com.

8943 ■ PENS Research Grants (Professional development/Grant)

Purpose: To provide the nursing membership of PENS with the financial support required to advance pediatric endocrine nursing practices through basic and applied research. **Focus:** Nursing, Pediatric.

Funds Avail.: $15,000. **Duration:** Annual. **Contact:** Email: PENS@kellencompany.com.

8944 ■ Pediatric Infectious Diseases Society (PIDS)
4040 Wilson Boulevard, Suite 300
Arlington, VA 22203
Ph: (703)299-6764
Fax: (703)299-0473
E-mail: pids@idsociety.org
URL: www.pids.org
Social Media: www.facebook.com/PIDSociety
twitter.com/PIDSociety

8945 ■ Antimicrobial Stewardship Fellowship Award (Professional development/Fellowship)

Purpose: To support the development of future researchers in pediatric antimicrobial stewardship by providing mentorship to complete a scholarly research project in a timely manner during fellowship or residency. **Focus:** Medicine, Pediatric. **Qualif.:** Applicants must be physicians or pharmacists in training and PIDS members; pediatric residents are also eligible. **Criteria:** Selection will be based on the submitted applications.

Funds Avail.: No specific amount. **Duration:** Annual. **Number Awarded:** Up to 3. **To Apply:** Applicants should include an application including an overview of the aim and research question to be answered; letter of recommendation from a local mentor; copies of applicant's and mentor's curriculum vitae. **Deadline:** June 9. **Contact:** Email: pids@idsociety.org.

8946 ■ Pediatric Orthopedic Society of North America (POSNA)
1 Tower Lane, Ste. 2410
Oakbrook Terrace, IL 60181
Ph: (630)478-0480
Fax: (630)478-0481
E-mail: posna@posna.org
URL: www.posna.org
Social Media: www.facebook.com/POSNA
twitter.com/POSNA_org

8947 ■ Arthur H. Huene Memorial Award (Doctorate/Grant)

Purpose: To recognize and support outstanding researchers for Excellence and Promise in Pediatric Orthopedics, who are active members of POSNA. **Focus:** Medicine, Orthopedic. **Criteria:** Selection will be based on significance, impact, relevance to POSNA mission, originality/innovation, scientific quality of the proposed study, investigator(s) track record, feasibility, and potential for future funding.

Funds Avail.: Up to $30,000. **Duration:** Annual. **Number Awarded:** 1. **To Apply:** Application must be current curriculum vitae with a statement about career goals and one

Awards are arranged alphabetically below their administering organizations

page description of past research accomplishments. **Deadline:** September 13.

8948 ■ St. Giles Young Investigator Award
(Doctorate/Grant)

Purpose: To support a young investigator to initiate a research project which can develop into a research program or allow the young investigator to develop an academic career with a sustained research effort in the area. **Focus:** Medicine, Orthopedic. **Qualif.:** Recipients must be POSNA members for five years or less. **Criteria:** Selection of applicants will be based on significance, impact, relevance to POSNA mission, originality/innovation, scientific quality of the proposed study, investigator(s) track record, feasibility, and potential for future funding.

Funds Avail.: Up to $30,000. **Duration:** Annual. **Deadline:** September 13.

8949 ■ Pedrozzi Scholarship Foundation
1141 Catalina Dr. Ste. 170
Livermore, CA 94550
Ph: (925)456-3700
Fax: (925)456-3701
E-mail: info@pedrozzifoundation.org
URL: pedrozzifoundation.org
Social Media: www.facebook.com/PedrozziFoundation
twitter.com/PEDROZZI
www.youtube.com/channel/
UCLZ3wBwJkOszQFZl6nEYJyg

8950 ■ Mario Pedrozzi Scholarship *(Undergraduate, Graduate/Scholarship)*

Purpose: To support students in their educational pursuit. **Focus:** General studies/Field of study not specified. **Qualif.:** Applicants must have either graduated from a Livermore Valley Joint Unified School District high school (Del Valle or Phoenix, Granada, Livermore or Vineyard) or have been residents of Alameda County upon high school graduation and been accepted at St. Patrick's Seminary and University; students applying for undergraduate or graduate scholarships must have a minimum GPA of 3.0. **Criteria:** Selection are evaluated anonymously based on the combination of: responses to short essay prompts, school and community activities, work experience, reference responses and academic record.

Funds Avail.: Amount varies. **Duration:** Annual; up to four years. **Number Awarded:** Varies. **To Apply:** Applicants are required to apply online; students are to submit official transcript (in an official stamped and sealed envelope); two reference questionnaires. **Deadline:** March 2. **Contact:** Electronic Submission: transcript@Pedrozzi.org; Pedrozzi Scholarship Foundation, 1141 Catalina Dr., Ste. 170, Livermore, CA, 94550.

8951 ■ PEN American
588 Broadway, St. 303
New York, NY 10012
Ph: (212)334-1660
Fax: (212)334-2181
E-mail: info@pen.org
URL: pen.org
Social Media: www.facebook.com/PENamerica
www.instagram.com/penamerica
twitter.com/penamerican

www.youtube.com/c/PENAmerica

8952 ■ PEN/Phyllis Naylor Grant for Children's and Young Adult Novelists *(Other/Grant)*

Purpose: To assist a writer of children's or young adult literature when monetary support is particularly needed. **Focus:** Literature, Children's; Writing. **Qualif.:** Candidate must be a writer of child or young adult fiction in financial need; submitted work must be fiction and a work-in-progress. **Criteria:** Judges will be looking for candidates whose work has not yet attracted a broad readership.

Funds Avail.: $5,000. **Duration:** Annual. **To Apply:** Must submit a manuscript. **Deadline:** August 1. **Remarks:** Established in 2001.

8953 ■ Pennsylvania Association on Probation, Parole and Corrections (PAPPC)
PO Box 5553
Harrisburg, PA 17110-0553
Ph: (724)662-2380
URL: www.pappc.org

8954 ■ Robert E. Kelsey Annual Scholarship
(Undergraduate/Scholarship)

Purpose: To support members and children of members who are pursuing post-secondary education. **Focus:** Humanities; Social sciences. **Qualif.:** Applicants must be current PAPPC members or immediate family members; must be currently enrolled or accepted into a two-year or four-year accredited program of higher education with a concentration of studies in the Humanities and Social Sciences; must be in good academic standing; must demonstrate academic success by holding at least a 2.75 GPA or equivalent at the time of application. **Criteria:** Selection will be based on the committee's criteria.

Funds Avail.: $1,500. **Duration:** Annual. **Number Awarded:** Up to 2. **To Apply:** Applicants must submit three letters of recommendation at the time of application; must submit a personal statement explaining why they chose their field of study and how that field applies to their future aspirations; statements should not exceed 500 words, must be type-written and double-spaced; must submit a copy of their most current transcripts. Must also submit the following information: full name; social security number; address; phone number; email address; high school or college GPA; the name of college or university that the applicant is planning to attend or currently attending, along with major; PAPPC member name and relationship. **Deadline:** March 31. **Contact:** URL: www.pappc.org/robert_e_kelsey_annual_schola.php.

8955 ■ Pennsylvania Dental Hygienists Association (PDHA)
1804 Elmhurst Ave.
Jersey Shore, PA 17740
Ph: (717)766-0334
E-mail: lisandrardh@gmail.com
URL: pdhaonline.org

8956 ■ Bailey/Hollister Scholarship *(Graduate, Professional development/Scholarship)*

Purpose: To help students to pursue a career in the dental hygiene profession. **Focus:** Dental hygiene. **Criteria:** Selection will be based on the committee's criteria.

Awards are arranged alphabetically below their administering organizations

Funds Avail.: No specific amount. **Duration:** Annual. **To Apply:** Applicants must submit the following materials a completed financial need form; a letter of reference from the director of the dental hygiene program, which includes the current GPA which must be 2.5 or higher; a letter of reference from a clinical instructor; a certified copy of the student's academic record; a letter from the applicants stating why they should be awarded the scholarship; a copy of driver's license as a proof of Pennsylvania residency. **Deadline:** July 17. **Contact:** PDHA Central Office, Scholarship Committee, PO Box 606, Mechanicsburg, PA, 17055; Phone: 717-766-0334; Email: pdha@outlook.com.

8957 ■ Pennsylvania Library Association (PALA)
220 Cumberland Pky., Ste. 10
Mechanicsburg, PA 17055
URL: www.palibraries.org
Social Media: www.facebook.com/PALibraries
twitter.com/PALibraryAssoc

8958 ■ Pennsylvania Library Association MLS Scholarships *(Graduate/Scholarship)*

Purpose: To provide opportunities for professional growth, leadership development and continuing education for librarians. **Focus:** Library and archival sciences. **Criteria:** Selection will be based on the committee's criteria.

Funds Avail.: $1,500. **Duration:** Annual. **Number Awarded:** 3. **To Apply:** Application submit online must include your contact info; your current employer info; the names of those who will submit a letter of recommendation; your personal essay of no more than 500 words. **Deadline:** May 15. **Contact:** Email: admin@palibraries.org.

8959 ■ Pennsylvania Music Educators Association (PMEA)
56 S 3rd St.
Hamburg, PA 19526-1828
Ph: (610)562-9757
Fax: (610)562-9760
Free: 888-919-7632
E-mail: abiyoung@pmea.net
URL: www.pmea.net
Social Media: www.facebook.com/pmeamusic
instagram.com/pmeastate/
www.linkedin.com/company/10122472
twitter.com/pmeastate

8960 ■ Irene R. Christman Scholarship *(Undergraduate/Scholarship)*

Purpose: To support students who are planning to pursue music education in college. **Focus:** Music. **Qualif.:** Applicants must be All-State students who will be attending college to major in music education.

Funds Avail.: No specific amount. **Duration:** Annual. **To Apply:** Application details available online at www.pmea.net/resources/scholarships-and-awards/. **Deadline:** May 1. **Remarks:** Established in 1997.

8961 ■ Pennsylvania Society of Land Surveyors (PSLS)
908 N 2nd St.
Harrisburg, PA 17102

Ph: (717)540-6811
Fax: (717)236-2046
E-mail: psls@psls.org
URL: www.psls.org
Social Media: www.facebook.com/PSLSsocial

8962 ■ Pennsylvania Land Surveyors' Foundation Scholarship *(Undergraduate/Scholarship)*

Purpose: To promote, improve and encourage the profession. **Focus:** Cartography/Surveying. **Qualif.:** Applicants must be citizens of the United States and be residents of the Commonwealth of Pennsylvania; be enrolled in or accepted in a two-year Surveying Technology Program or a four-year Bachelor of Science Program in Land Surveying. **Criteria:** Selection will be based on performance factors, applicant's activities, application preparation, guidance counselor/advisor evaluation, applicant's potential as a professional land surveyor, SAT scores and grades.

Funds Avail.: No specific amount. **Duration:** Annual. **To Apply:** Applicants must submit copies of SAT scores and high school or college transcripts with completed transcript release from a guidance office or registrars office. **Deadline:** April 1. **Contact:** Pennsylvania Land Surveyors' Foundation, Board of Trustees, 908 North Second St., Harrisburg, PA, 17102.

8963 ■ Pennsylvania Society of Professional Engineers (PSPE)
908 N 2nd St.
Harrisburg, PA 17102
Ph: (717)441-6051
Fax: (717)236-2046
E-mail: contactpspe@pspe.org
URL: www.pspe.org
Social Media: www.facebook.com/Pennsylvania-Society-of-Professional-Engineers-48421778986
www.linkedin.com/company/pennsylvania-society-of-professional-engineers

8964 ■ Pennsylvania Engineering Foundation (PEF) Grants: Undergraduate *(Undergraduate/Scholarship)*

Purpose: To provide financial assistance for freshmen students to pursue their academic goals in the engineering field of study. **Focus:** Engineering.

Funds Avail.: $1,000. **Duration:** Annual. **Number Awarded:** 2. **To Apply:** Applicants must complete the application form and must include certified copy of transcripts and SAT scores with a copy of the official test report. **Deadline:** April 15. **Contact:** Pennsylvania Engineering Foundation, Scholarships, 908 N. Second St., Harrisburg, PA, 17102; Email: lramsey@wannerassoc.com.

8965 ■ Pennsylvania Space Grant Consortium (PSGC)
118 Engineering Services Bldg
University Park, PA 16802-6813
E-mail: spacegrant@psu.edu
URL: pa.spacegrant.org
Social Media: www.facebook.com/wordspennstate
twitter.com/wordspennstate

8966 ■ PSGC/NASA Space Grant Fellowships at the PSGC Affiliate Institutions *(Graduate/Fellowship)*

Purpose: To recognize outstanding students who pursued graduate degrees in the fields of Science, Technology,

Awards are arranged alphabetically below their administering organizations

Engineering and Mathematics. **Focus:** Aeronautics; Space and planetary sciences. **Qualif.:** Will consider qualified proposals for awards in each of our three program areas: higher education, research infrastructure, pre-college. **Criteria:** Will be awarded based upon merit and funding availability.

Funds Avail.: $6,000, $12,000, and $25,000. **Duration:** Annual. **Number Awarded:** 3. **To Apply:** All proposed budgets must include detailed justification; must include S.M.A.R.T. Goals, align with NASA Education Outcomes and one or more priorities of NASA's Mission Directorates. **Contact:** Email: spacegrant@psu.edu.

8967 ■ Pennsylvania State System of Higher Education Foundation (PASSHE)
2986 N 2nd St.
Harrisburg, PA 17110
Ph: (717)720-4065
Fax: (717)720-7082
URL: www.thepafoundation.org
Social Media: www.facebook.com/statesystem
www.instagram.com/explore/locations/726154646/united
  -states/harrisburg-pennsylvania/pennsylvanias-state
  -system-of-higher-education
www.linkedin.com/company/passhe
twitter.com/statesystem

8968 ■ Minnie Patton Stayman Scholarships
(Undergraduate/Scholarship)

Purpose: To provide educational assistance to all the students who are enrolled at PASSHE universities. **Focus:** General studies/Field of study not specified. **Qualif.:** Applicants must: be residents of Altoona; be full-time undergraduate students who plan to enroll at Indiana University of Pennsylvania or Lock Haven University of Pennsylvania. **Criteria:** Recipients are selected based on financial need.

Funds Avail.: $1,000. **Duration:** Annual. **To Apply:** Applicants must submit all the required application information. **Deadline:** June 30.

8969 ■ Wayne G. Failor Scholarship Fund
(Undergraduate/Scholarship)

Purpose: To provide funding to help cover the cost of the students participating in the summer internship program. **Focus:** Business. **Qualif.:** Applicant must be full-time student at Shippensburg University who is accepted into The Washington Center's 2017 summer internship program. **Criteria:** Selection will be based on the committee's criteria.

Funds Avail.: $1,000. **Duration:** Annual. **Number Awarded:** 1. **Remarks:** The Scholarship was funded by Wayne G. Failor who served as Vice Chancellor for Finance and Administration for the PA State System of Higher Education from 1983 to his retirement in 1997.

8970 ■ PennyGeeks.com
316 California Ave., No. 865
Reno, NV 89509
Ph: (757)447-3950
Free: 855-587-2494
URL: pennygeeks.com
Social Media: www.facebook.com/pennygeekscom
www.linkedin.com/company/pennygeeks-com
twitter.com/pennygeeks

8971 ■ PennyGeeks.com Car Insurance Essay Scholarship *(Undergraduate/Scholarship)*

Purpose: To provide financial support to U.S. students attending an American college or university. **Focus:** General studies/Field of study not specified. **Qualif.:** Applicant must be a U.S. student who is currently enrolled in or has been accepted to a college or university in the United States. **Criteria:** Selection will be based on the submitted essay.

Funds Avail.: $500. **Duration:** Semiannual. **To Apply:** Applicant must submit an essay (700 to 1,200 words) on one of the following topics: 1. How will driverless cars impact the cost of auto insurance?; 2. How can college students save money on auto insurance?; 3. How can recent college graduates save money on car insurance? Applicant should include their city and state of residence. **Contact:** Email: scholarship@pennygeeks.com.

8972 ■ Pension Real Estate Association (PREA)
100 Pearl St., 13th Fl.
Hartford, CT 06103
Ph: (860)692-6341
Fax: (860)692-6351
E-mail: membership@prea.org
URL: www.prea.org
Social Media: twitter.com/preanews

8973 ■ PREA Scholarship *(Undergraduate, Graduate/ Scholarship)*

Purpose: To promote understanding of institutional investment in real estate. **Focus:** Real estate. **Qualif.:** Applicants must be students studying real estate at the undergraduate and graduate levels. **Criteria:** Recipients are selected based on financial need.

Funds Avail.: Total amount of $30,000. **Duration:** Annual.

8974 ■ PEO International (PEO)
3700 Grand Ave.
Des Moines, IA 50312
Ph: (515)255-3153
Fax: (515)255-3820
E-mail: contactus@peodsm.org
URL: www.peointernational.org
Social Media: www.instagram.com/peointernational/

8975 ■ International Peace Scholarship Fund (IPS)
(Graduate, Master's, Doctorate/Scholarship)

Purpose: To provide scholarships for selected women from other countries to study in the United States and Canada. **Focus:** General studies/Field of study not specified. **Qualif.:** Applicant must be qualified for admission to full-time graduate study and working toward a graduate degree in an accredited college or university in the United States or Canada.

Funds Avail.: $12,500. **Duration:** Annual. **Remarks:** Established in 1949.

8976 ■ The P.E.O. Educational Loan Fund (ELF)
(Undergraduate, Master's, Doctorate/Loan)

Purpose: To promote educational opportunities for women who desire higher education and are in need of financial assistance. **Focus:** General studies/Field of study not specified. **Criteria:** Recipients are selected based on financial need.

Awards are arranged alphabetically below their administering organizations

Funds Avail.: $12,000 (associate and bachelor degree programs, technical or professional training, and post-graduate certifications); $15,000 (master's degrees); $20,000 (doctoral degrees). **Duration:** Annual. **To Apply:** Applicants must submit transcript of grades is submitted to the P.E.O. Executive Office as part of the application process and, if requested, before each loan installment is drawn. **Remarks:** Established in 1907.

8977 ■ P.E.O. Scholar Awards (PSA) *(Doctorate/Award, Scholarship)*

Purpose: To provide partial support for study and research for women who will make significant contributions in their varied fields of endeavor. **Focus:** General studies/Field of study not specified. **Qualif.:** Applicant must be a citizen or legal permanent resident of the United States or Canada; must have earned, at minimum, a bachelor's degree; must be within two years of graduating from a doctoral program and have at least one full academic year of work remaining in August of the year you are awarded; must be enrolled in full-time doctoral-level study at an accredited U.S. or Canadian post-secondary institution during the entire academic year of the award. **Criteria:** Selection will be based on the committee's criteria.

Funds Avail.: $15,000. **Duration:** Annual. **Number Awarded:** 3. **To Apply:** Applicants must complete the online request information. **Deadline:** May 1. **Remarks:** Established in 1991.

8978 ■ People for the Ethical Treatment of Animals (PETA)
501 Front St.
Norfolk, VA 23510
Ph: (757)622-7382
Fax: (757)622-0457
URL: www.peta.org
Social Media: www.facebook.com/official.peta
instagram.com/peta
www.linkedin.com/company/peta
pinterest.com/officialpeta
twitter.com/peta
youtube.com/user/officialpeta

8979 ■ PETA Foundation Law Internship *(Graduate/Internship)*

Purpose: To provide assistance to attorneys at the PETA Foundation with a wide range of legal issues that arise in the course of PETA's work to protect animals through public education, cruelty investigations, research, animal rescue, legislation, and protest campaigns. **Focus:** Animal rights; Law. **Criteria:** Selection will be based on the committee's criteria.

Funds Avail.: No specific amount. **To Apply:** Applicants must send a letter of interest, resume, transcript, legal writing sample, and list of three professional references. **Remarks:** The term of employment is temporary, unpaid position. **Contact:** Jared Goodman, Director of Animal Law, at JaredG@petaf.org.

8980 ■ People to People International (PTPI)
2405 Grand Blvd., Ste. 500
Kansas City, MO 64108
Ph: (816)531-4701
Fax: (816)561-7502
E-mail: ptpi@ptpi.org
URL: www.ptpi.org
Social Media: www.facebook.com/PeopletoPeople
www.instagram.com/ptpi_official
twitter.com/ptpi

8981 ■ Joyce C. Hall College Scholarship *(Undergraduate/Scholarship)*

Purpose: To encourage youth participation in international activities. **Focus:** General studies/Field of study not specified. **Qualif.:** Applicants must be current members of People to People International and a full-time student 3.0 GPA or higher. **Criteria:** Recipients will be selected based on the evaluation of all application materials.

Funds Avail.: $2,000 each. **To Apply:** Applicants must submit complete applications, including: an original essay; letters of recommendation from three people not related to the applicant; 1,000-word essay on the following topics. a school transcript.

8982 ■ Peoria County Bar Association (PCBA)
110 SW Jefferson Ave., Ste. 520
Peoria, IL 61602
Ph: (309)674-6049
E-mail: pcba@mtco.com
URL: peoriabar.org

8983 ■ PCBA Diversity Scholarship *(Undergraduate/Scholarship)*

Purpose: To provide financial assistance to law students who show interest in practicing law in the Peoria area and part of a minority group that is historically underrepresented in the legal profession. **Focus:** Law. **Criteria:** Selection will be made by Diversity Committee of the PCBA.

Funds Avail.: $5,000. **Duration:** Annual. **Number Awarded:** Varies. **To Apply:** Completed applications can be submitted electronically, date of submission and further information can be obtained from the website. **Contact:** Chair of the PCBA Diversity Committee, Honorable James E. Shadid; Phone: 309.671.4227 or E-mail: Cathy_Geier@ilcd.uscourts.gov.

8984 ■ Pepperdine University (PU)
24255 Pacific Coast Hwy.
Malibu, CA 90263
Ph: (310)506-4000
URL: www.pepperdine.edu
Social Media: www.facebook.com/pepperdine
www.instagram.com/pepperdine
www.linkedin.com/school/pepperdine-university
twitter.com/pepperdine
www.youtube.com/pepperdine

8985 ■ PLP Scholarships *(Undergraduate/Scholarship, Award, Monetary)*

Purpose: To strengthen churches by financially supporting Christian students at Pepperdine University in their education and spiritual walk. **Focus:** Education; Law; Psychology. **Qualif.:** Applicants must be students admitted at Pepperdine University and members of the Church of Christ.

Funds Avail.: $5,000. **Duration:** Annual. **Number Awarded:** Varies. **To Apply:** Applications can be submitted

Awards are arranged alphabetically below their administering organizations

online; must submit the general Pepperdine admission application; must submit the Free Application for Federal Student Aid; must submit an additional recommendation from a Church of Christ leader. **Remarks:** The scholarships are administered by the Associated Women of Pepperdine.

8986 ■ Pepperdine University Caruso School of Law

24255 Pacific Coast Hwy.
Malibu, CA 90263
Ph: (310)506-4611
E-mail: lawadmis@pepperdine.edu
URL: law.pepperdine.edu
Social Media: www.facebook.com/pepperdinelaw
www.linkedin.com/school/pepperdine-university-school-of
 -law
twitter.com/pepplaw
www.youtube.com/pepperdinelaw

8987 ■ Albert J. and Mae Lee Memorial Scholarship
(Undergraduate/Scholarship)

Purpose: To support students to meet the educational costs of attending the School of Law. **Focus:** Law. **Qualif.:** Applicants must be students with above average scholastic ability who are in need of financial assistance at the School of Law. **Criteria:** Selection will be based on financial need, academic merit, community involvement and personal achievement.

Funds Avail.: No specific amount. **To Apply:** Applicants must submit a completed scholarship application form together with a resume and a letter of qualifications. **Remarks:** The scholarships were established as a gift from the Mae Lee Estate. Established in 2003.

8988 ■ Ann Marie Bredefeld Scholarship
(Undergraduate/Scholarship)

Purpose: To support qualified students to meet the educational costs of attending the School of Law. **Focus:** Law. **Qualif.:** Applicants must be students who share the Christian values of Pepperdine. **Criteria:** Selection will be based on financial need, academic merit, community involvement and personal achievement.

Funds Avail.: No specific amount. **To Apply:** Applicants must submit a completed scholarship application form together with a resume and a letter of qualifications.

8989 ■ Athalie Clarke Endowed Scholarship
(Undergraduate/Scholarship)

Purpose: To support students to meet the educational costs of attending the School of Law. **Focus:** Law. **Qualif.:** Applicants must be Pepperdine University School of Law students. **Criteria:** Selection will be based on financial need, academic merit, community involvement and personal achievement.

Funds Avail.: No specific amount. **To Apply:** Applicants must submit a completed scholarship application form together with a resume and a letter of qualifications. **Remarks:** The scholarship was funded by the late Athalie Irvine Clarke, a community leader in Orange County and Los Angeles and a founding member of the School of Law Board of Visitors.

8990 ■ Barbara A. Shacochis Scholarship
(Undergraduate/Scholarship)

Purpose: To support students to meet the educational costs of attending the School of Law. **Focus:** Law. **Qualif.:**

Applicants must be Pepperdine University School of Law students and member of the Law Review. **Criteria:** Preference will be given to third year Law Review students and/or editors of the Law Review.

Funds Avail.: No specific amount. **To Apply:** Applicants must submit a completed scholarship application form together with a resume and a letter of qualifications. **Remarks:** The scholarship namesake was a 1990 alumna and Pepperdine Law Review editor-in-chief, and School of Law Board of Visitors member.

8991 ■ Beck-Pfann Memorial Scholarship
(Undergraduate/Scholarship)

Purpose: To support qualified students through a tuition credit for them to meet the educational costs of attending the School of Law. **Focus:** Law. **Qualif.:** Applicants must be second-year students at the School of Law. **Criteria:** Selection will based on community service, academic achievement, financial need, and extracurricular activities.

Funds Avail.: No specific amount. **To Apply:** Applicants must submit a completed scholarship application form together with a resume and a letter of qualifications. **Remarks:** Family members and friends have established the scholarship in honor of R. Michael Beck and C. Lori Pfann, who had completed their first year at Pepperdine University School of Law and were engaged to be married at the time of their death in an automobile wreck.

8992 ■ Benjamin G. Shatz Scholarship
(Undergraduate/Scholarship)

Purpose: To support students to meet the educational costs of attending the School of Law. **Focus:** Law. **Qualif.:** Applicants must be second or third-year students and active member of the Jewish Law Student Association. **Criteria:** Selection will be based on merit and financial need.

Funds Avail.: No specific amount. **Duration:** Annual. **To Apply:** Applicants must submit a completed scholarship application form together with a resume and a letter of qualifications.

8993 ■ Brian Dane Cleary Memorial Scholarship
(Undergraduate/Scholarship)

Purpose: To assist a well-rounded, financially-needy student ranked in the bottom 75% of their class. **Focus:** Law. **Qualif.:** Applicants must be Pepperdine University School of Law students. **Criteria:** Selection will be based on financial need, academic merit, community involvement and personal achievement.

Funds Avail.: No specific amount. **To Apply:** Applicants must submit a completed scholarship application form together with a resume and a letter of qualifications. **Remarks:** The scholarship was established by family members and friends of Brian Dane Cleary, a member of the Class of 1991, who died in a car accident 18 days before graduation. Established in 1991.

8994 ■ The Hugh and Hazel Darling Dean's Scholarship *(Undergraduate/Scholarship)*

Purpose: To encourage students to stay at the Caruso School of Law. **Focus:** Law. **Qualif.:** Applicants must be Pepperdine University School of Law students. **Criteria:** Recipients will be selected based on academic excellence as well as school and community involvement.

Funds Avail.: No specific amount. **To Apply:** Applicants must submit a completed scholarship application form together with a resume and a letter of qualifications.

Awards are arranged alphabetically below their administering organizations

8995 ■ Darling Foundation Endowed School of Law Scholarship *(Undergraduate/Scholarship)*

Purpose: To support deserving students in meeting their educational costs of attending the School of Law. **Focus:** Law. **Qualif.:** Applicants must be Pepperdine University School of Law students. **Criteria:** Selection will be based on financial need, academic merit, community involvement and personal achievement.

Funds Avail.: No specific amount. **To Apply:** Applicants must submit a completed scholarship application form together with a resume and a letter of qualifications.

8996 ■ David and Camille Boatwright Endowed Scholarship *(Undergraduate/Scholarship)*

Purpose: To assist students pursuing a Law degree that are in good standing in all areas of the University. **Focus:** Law. **Qualif.:** Applicants must be Pepperdine University School of Law students. **Criteria:** Recipients of the award is determined by the Scholarship Committee.

Funds Avail.: No specific amount. **To Apply:** Applicants must submit a completed scholarship application form together with a resume and a letter of qualifications.

8997 ■ Edward D. Di Loreto-Odell S. McConnell Scholarship *(Undergraduate/Scholarship)*

Purpose: To aid deserving students of high scholastic standing who are in need of financial assistance. **Focus:** Law. **Qualif.:** Applicants must be Pepperdine University School of Law students with high scholastic standing. **Criteria:** Selection will be based on financial need, academic merit, community involvement and personal achievement.

Funds Avail.: No specific amount. **To Apply:** Applicants must submit a completed scholarship application form together with a resume and a letter of qualifications. **Remarks:** The scholarship was established in memory of the late Edward D. Di Loreto, a longtime friend of the University and a major influence in the acquisition of the Orange University College of Law by Pepperdine University, founding member of the School of Law Board of Visitors, and the late Odell S. McConnell, founder of the Odell McConnell Law Center, home of Pepperdine University School of Law. Established in 1969.

8998 ■ Judge McIntyre Faries Scholarship *(Undergraduate/Scholarship)*

Purpose: To support students served on the Superior Court bench for over twenty years. **Focus:** Law. **Qualif.:** Applicants must be Pepperdine University School of Law student. **Criteria:** Selection will be based on the committee's criteria.

Funds Avail.: No specific amount. **Remarks:** The scholarship was established by John Herklotz to honor an exceptional California jurist, the late Judge McIntyre Faries, who served on the Superior Court bench for over twenty years.

8999 ■ Froberg-Suess JD/MBA Scholarship *(Undergraduate/Scholarship)*

Purpose: To support students to meet the educational costs of attending the School of Law. **Focus:** Law. **Qualif.:** Applicants must have successfully completed at least one semester of law school and one semester of business school. **Criteria:** Recipients will be selected based on merit.

Funds Avail.: No specific amount. **Duration:** one academic year. **To Apply:** Applicants must submit a completed scholarship application form together with a resume and a letter of qualifications. **Remarks:** The scholarships were established by alums Jay A. Froberg and Greg Suess.

9000 ■ Gerald Garner Memorial Scholarship *(Undergraduate/Scholarship)*

Purpose: To support students to meet the educational costs of attending the School of Law. **Focus:** Law. **Qualif.:** Applicants must be Pepperdine University School of Law students. **Criteria:** Selection will be based on the committee's criteria.

Funds Avail.: No specific amount. **Remarks:** The scholarship was established in the memory of Gerald Garner who was a member of the George Pepperdine Society Chancellor's Circle and a supporter of many activities of the University.

9001 ■ Terry M. Giles Honor Scholar Program *(Undergraduate/Scholarship)*

Purpose: To support students to meet the educational costs of attending the School of Law. **Focus:** Law. **Qualif.:** Applicants must be third-year students at Pepperdine University School of Law. **Criteria:** Recipients are selected based on scholastic achievement, co-curricular and extracurricular activities, personality and character.

Funds Avail.: No specific amount. **Duration:** Annual. **To Apply:** Applicants must submit a completed scholarship application form together with a resume and a letter of qualifications. **Remarks:** The scholarships are provided each year by Pepperdine University School of Law alumnus and Board of Visitor member Terry M. Giles (class of 1974).

9002 ■ Greg Matthews Memorial Scholarship *(Undergraduate/Scholarship)*

Purpose: To support students to meet the educational costs of attending the School of Law. **Focus:** Law. **Qualif.:** Applicants must be Pepperdine University School of Law students. **Criteria:** Recipients will be selected based on financial need.

Funds Avail.: No specific amount. **To Apply:** Applicants must submit a completed scholarship application form together with a resume and a letter of qualifications. **Remarks:** The scholarship was established in memory of Greg Matthews through private donations made by his family and friends. Greg was a third-year law student at the time of his death. Established in 1982.

9003 ■ Gunnar Nicholson Endowed Scholarship *(Undergraduate/Scholarship)*

Purpose: To provide scholarships to deserving students. **Focus:** Law. **Qualif.:** Applicants must be Pepperdine University School of Law students. **Criteria:** Recipients will be determined by the Scholarship Committee.

Funds Avail.: No specific amount. **To Apply:** Applicants must submit a completed scholarship application form together with a resume and a letter of qualifications. **Remarks:** The endowed scholarship was established through the restricted funds by Gunnar Nicholson Estate.

9004 ■ Guy P. Greenwald Jr. Endowed Scholarship Fund *(Undergraduate/Scholarship)*

Purpose: To provide scholarships for worthy and needy law students. **Focus:** Law. **Qualif.:** Applicants must be Pepperdine University School of Law students. **Criteria:** Selection will be based on financial need, academic merit, community involvement and personal achievement.

Awards are arranged alphabetically below their administering organizations

Funds Avail.: No specific amount. **To Apply:** Applicants must submit a completed scholarship application form together with a resume and a letter of qualifications. **Remarks:** The scholarship was established by the late Guy P. Greenwald, attorney and Pepperdine friend.

9005 ■ Howard A. White Endowed Scholarship
(Undergraduate/Scholarship)

Purpose: To support students to meet the educational costs of attending the School of Law. **Focus:** Law.

Funds Avail.: No specific amount. **Remarks:** This scholarship program has been established in honor of Howard A. White, President Emeritus of Pepperdine University.

9006 ■ J. McDonald and Judy Williams School of Law Scholarship *(Undergraduate/Scholarship)*

Purpose: To support students to meet the educational costs of attending the School of Law. **Focus:** Law. **Qualif.:** Applicants must be admitted at Pepperdine University Caruso School of Law; and must be members of the Church of Christ. **Criteria:** Selection will be based on merit and financial need.

Funds Avail.: No specific amount. **To Apply:** Applicants must submit a completed scholarship application form together with a resume, letter of qualifications, and a letter confirming active membership in a local Church of Christ congregation.

9007 ■ Jamie Phillips Endowed Scholarship Fund
(Undergraduate/Scholarship)

Purpose: To support students to meet the educational costs of attending the School of Law. **Focus:** Law. **Qualif.:** Applicants must be Pepperdine University School of Law students. **Criteria:** Recipients will be determined by the Scholarship Committee.

Funds Avail.: No specific amount. **To Apply:** Applicants must submit a completed scholarship application form together with a resume and a letter of qualifications. **Remarks:** The scholarship was established in memory of Jamie Phillips, wife of School of Law Dean Emeritus Ronald F. Phillips.

9008 ■ John Purfield Endowed Scholarship
(Undergraduate/Scholarship)

Purpose: To assist qualified students who have demonstrated academic excellence. **Focus:** Law. **Qualif.:** Applicants must be Pepperdine University School of Law students. **Criteria:** Selection will be based on academic excellence.

Funds Avail.: No specific amount. **To Apply:** Applicants must submit a completed scholarship application form together with a resume and a letter of qualifications.

9009 ■ JSR Foundation Endowed School of Law Scholarship *(Undergraduate/Scholarship)*

Purpose: To assist deserving students with financial need. **Focus:** Law. **Qualif.:** Applicants must be Pepperdine University School of Law students. **Criteria:** Selection will be based on financial need.

Funds Avail.: No specific amount. **To Apply:** Applicants must submit a completed scholarship application form together with a resume and a letter of qualifications. **Remarks:** The endowed scholarships are generously funded by the John Stuart Richard Foundation.

9010 ■ Julia Kwan Endowed Scholarship *(Graduate/Scholarship)*

Purpose: To assist students with financial need who are pursuing a graduate degree at the School of Law. **Focus:**
Law. **Qualif.:** Applicants must be Pepperdine University School of Law students pursuing a graduate degree. **Criteria:** Recipients will be selected based on financial need.

Funds Avail.: No specific amount. **Duration:** Annual. **To Apply:** Applicants must submit a completed scholarship application form together with a resume and a letter of qualifications. **Remarks:** The scholarship was established with a generous gift by Julia Kwan.

9011 ■ Kae and Kay Brockermeyer Endowed Scholarship Fund *(Undergraduate/Scholarship)*

Purpose: To promote deserving law students who have an interest in a trial advocacy and are residents of the state of Texas. **Focus:** Law. **Qualif.:** Applicants must be law students interested in trial advocacy; they must also be residents of the state of Texas. **Criteria:** Selection will be based on financial need, academic merit, community involvement and personal achievement.

Funds Avail.: No specific amount. **To Apply:** Applicants must submit a completed scholarship application form together with a resume and a letter of qualifications. **Deadline:** January 14. **Remarks:** The scholarship was established by Kae and Kay Brockermeyer of Wilson, Wyoming.

9012 ■ Kerrigan Scholarship Foundation
(Undergraduate/Scholarship)

Purpose: To assist single-parent mothers at the School of Law. **Focus:** Law. **Qualif.:** Applicants must be single-parent mothers enrolled at the Caruso School of Law. **Criteria:** Selection will based on financial need, academic merit, community involvement and personal achievement.

Funds Avail.: No specific amount. **To Apply:** Applicants must submit a completed scholarship application form together with a resume and a letter of qualifications. **Remarks:** The scholarships were established by Sharon Kerrigan, a 1992 School of Law alumna, and the Kerrigan Family Charitable Foundation. Established in 1992.

9013 ■ Krist-Reavley Minority Scholarship
(Undergraduate/Scholarship)

Purpose: To support students to meet the educational costs of attending the School of Law. **Focus:** Law. **Qualif.:** Applicants must be ethnically diverse students at Pepperdine University School of Law and longtime members of the Caruso School of Law Board of Visitors. **Criteria:** Selection will be based on financial need, academic merit, community involvement and personal achievement.

Funds Avail.: No specific amount. **Duration:** one academic year. **To Apply:** Applicants must submit a completed scholarship application form together with a resume and a letter of qualifications. **Remarks:** The scholarships have been established by noted trial attorney Ronald D. Krist and his wife, Carole.

9014 ■ Margaret Martin Brock Scholarship in Law
(Undergraduate, Juris Doctorate/Scholarship)

Purpose: To support students to meet the educational costs of attending the School of Law. **Focus:** Law. **Qualif.:** Applicants must be designated as Margaret Martin Brock Scholars. **Criteria:** Selection will be based on financial need, academic merit, community involvement and personal achievement.

Funds Avail.: No specific amount. **Duration:** Annual. **To Apply:** Applicants must submit a completed scholarship application form together with a resume and a letter of qualifications. **Remarks:** The scholarship fund was estab-

Awards are arranged alphabetically below their administering organizations

lished by the late Mrs. Margaret Martin Brock, nationally recognized civic leader and longtime friend of the University and a founding member of the Law School Board of Visitors.

9015 ■ Mark and Michelle Hiepler Endowed Scholarship Fund (Undergraduate/Scholarship)

Purpose: To support students to meet the educational costs of attending the School of Law. **Focus:** Law. **Qualif.:** Applicants must be the writers of the Best Respondent's Brief and Best Petitioner's Brief in the yearly Vincent S. Dalsimer Moot Court Competition. **Criteria:** Scholarships will be awarded based on financial need, academic study, community involvement, and health care law interest or health care background.

Funds Avail.: No specific amount. **Duration:** Annual. **To Apply:** Applicants must submit a completed scholarship application form together with a resume and a letter of qualifications. **Remarks:** The scholarships were established by Mark (class of 1988) and Michelle (class of 1989) Hiepler in memory of Nelene Hiepler Fox.

9016 ■ Martha Delman and Milton Arthur Krug Endowed Law Scholarship (Undergraduate/Scholarship)

Purpose: To promote and provide funds for qualified law students. **Focus:** Law. **Qualif.:** Applicants must be Pepperdine University School of Law students. **Criteria:** Recipients of the award will be determined by the Scholarship Committee.

Funds Avail.: No specific amount. **To Apply:** Applicants must submit a completed scholarship application form together with a resume and a letter of qualifications. **Remarks:** The funds for the scholarship are provided by the late Martha Delman Krug, a loyal friend of Pepperdine University and a respected leader in the Law Affiliates of Los Angeles. Her late husband, Milton Arthur Krug, was a distinguished attorney.

9017 ■ John Merrick Law Scholarship (Undergraduate/Scholarship)

Purpose: To support students to meet the educational costs of attending the Caruso School of Law. **Focus:** Law. **Qualif.:** Applicants must be to the community and to Pepperdine University and its School of Law. **Criteria:** Preference for this scholarship is given to those with an interest in public service.

Funds Avail.: No specific amount. **To Apply:** Applicants must submit a completed scholarship application form together with a resume and a letter of qualifications. **Remarks:** Friends of long-time Malibu judge John Merrick have established the fund to honor his extraordinary service to the community and to Pepperdine University and its School of Law.

9018 ■ Charles I. Nelson Endowed Scholarship Fund (Undergraduate/Scholarship)

Purpose: To support students to meet the educational costs of attending the School of Law. **Focus:** Law. **Qualif.:** Applicants must be Pepperdine University School of Law students. **Criteria:** Recipients will be determined by the Scholarship Committee.

Funds Avail.: No specific amount. **To Apply:** Applicants must submit a completed scholarship application form together with a resume and a letter of qualifications. **Remarks:** The endowed scholarship fund honoring Professor

Charles I. Nelson, was established by Kae Brockemeyer, a former law school classmate, and his wife, Kay, and by Pepperdine alumni, faculty and friends.

9019 ■ Pepperdine University Diversity Scholarships (Doctorate, Graduate/Scholarship)

Purpose: To support students to meet the educational costs of attending the School of Law. **Focus:** Law. **Qualif.:** Applicants must be admitted as full-time students of the Juris Doctor program at Pepperdine University School of Law in the fall or spring semesters only. Applicants must have the ability to bring significant diversity to the student body. **Criteria:** Selection award is given based on merit.

Funds Avail.: No specific amount. **To Apply:** Applicants must submit a completed Diversity Scholarship application to the Admissions Office. **Contact:** Pepperdine University School of Law, at the above address.

9020 ■ Pepperdine University School of Law Armenian Student Scholarship (Undergraduate/Scholarship)

Purpose: To assist and promote law students of Armenian heritage. **Focus:** Law. **Qualif.:** Applicants must be law students of Armenian heritage, and admitted at Pepperdine University School of Law. **Criteria:** Selection will be based on financial need, academic merit, community involvement and personal achievement.

Funds Avail.: No specific amount. **To Apply:** Applicants must submit a completed application form together with a resume and a letter of qualifications. **Remarks:** The scholarship was established by Khajak Kassabian, a 1997 School of Law alum. Established in 1997.

9021 ■ Pepperdine University School of Law Dean's Merit Scholarship (Doctorate, Undergraduate/Scholarship)

Purpose: To assist students in the Juris Doctor program at Pepperdine University School of Law. **Focus:** Law. **Qualif.:** Applicants must be admitted to the full-time Juries Doctor program at Pepperdine University School of Law with an undergraduate GPA of 3.3 or higher and an LSAT score in the 82nd percentile. **Criteria:** Selection will be based on merit.

Funds Avail.: No specific amount. **Duration:** Annual; one year. **To Apply:** Applicants admitted full-time will be automatically considered.

9022 ■ Pepperdine University School of Law Faculty Scholars Award (Doctorate, Graduate/Award)

Purpose: To support applicants who demonstrate academic excellence and personal achievement, without regard to financial need. **Focus:** Law. **Qualif.:** Applicants must have a minimum undergraduate GPA of 3.65 and an LSAT score in the 87th percentile. **Criteria:** Recipients will be selected based on academic excellence and personal achievement, without regard to financial need.

Funds Avail.: No specific amount. **Duration:** Annual. **To Apply:** Applicants must submit a complete JD application and Faculty Scholars Award application; and a letter to the Office of Admissions. **Deadline:** January 11. **Contact:** E-mail: lawadmis@pepperdine.edu.

9023 ■ Pepperdine University School of Law JD/MBA Endowed Scholarship (Undergraduate/Scholarship)

Purpose: To support students to meet the educational costs of attending the School of Law. **Focus:** Business;

Awards are arranged alphabetically below their administering organizations

Law. **Qualif.:** Applicants must be students enrolled in the joint JD and MBA program at the School of Law and Graziadio School of Business and Management. They must be in good standing in all areas of the University. **Criteria:** Selection will be based on merit.

Funds Avail.: No specific amount. **Duration:** Annual. **To Apply:** Applicants must submit a completed scholarship application form together with a resume and a letter of qualifications.

9024 ■ Pepperdine University School of Law Special Law School Scholarship (Undergraduate/Scholarship)

Purpose: To support students to meet the educational costs of attending the School of Law. **Focus:** Law. **Qualif.:** Applicants must be Pepperdine University School of Law students with a special financial need. **Criteria:** Selection will be based on financial need.

Funds Avail.: No specific amount. **To Apply:** Applicants must submit a completed scholarship application form together with a resume and a letter of qualifications.

9025 ■ R. Wayne Estes Endowed Scholarship Fund (Undergraduate/Scholarship)

Purpose: To promote the professional careers of students and to develop an enviable reputation in the field of arbitration. **Focus:** Law. **Qualif.:** Applicants must be Pepperdine University School of Law students. **Criteria:** Selection will be based on financial need, academic merit, community involvement and personal achievement.

Funds Avail.: No specific amount. **To Apply:** Applicants must submit a completed scholarship application form together with a resume and a letter of qualifications. **Remarks:** The endowed scholarship was established by former students of Professor Emeritus R. Wayne Estes, along with colleagues and friends.

9026 ■ Shirley J. Brooke Endowed Scholarship (Undergraduate/Scholarship)

Purpose: To support the education of qualified female Law students who demonstrate above average academic achievement. **Focus:** Law. **Qualif.:** Applicants must be female law students who demonstrate above average academic achievement. **Criteria:** Selection will be based on financial need, academic merit, community involvement and personal achievement.

Funds Avail.: No specific amount. **Duration:** Annual. **To Apply:** Applicants must submit a completed scholarship application form together with a resume and a letter of qualifications.

9027 ■ Stuart Silverman Scholarship (Undergraduate/Scholarship)

Purpose: To support students to meet the educational costs of attending the School of Law. **Focus:** Law. **Qualif.:** Applicants must be Pepperdine University School of Law students pursuing a Juries Doctorate degree at the School of Law, and have overcome a major tragedy or hardship. **Criteria:** Selection will be based on need.

Funds Avail.: No specific amount. **To Apply:** Applicants must submit a completed scholarship application form together with a resume and a letter of qualifications. **Remarks:** The scholarship was established in memory of alumnus Stuart Silverman. Established in 1974.

9028 ■ Thomas and Glenna Trimble Endowed Scholarship (Graduate/Scholarship)

Purpose: To support students to meet the educational costs of attending the School of Law. **Focus:** Law. **Qualif.:**

Applicants must be admitted at Pepperdine University; and must be members of the Church of Christ. **Criteria:** Selection will be based on financial need, merit, character, and church membership.

Funds Avail.: No specific amount. **To Apply:** Applicants must submit a completed scholarship application form together with a resume, letter of qualifications, and a letter confirming active membership in a local Church of Christ congregation.

9029 ■ The Honorable Raymond Thompson Endowed Scholarship (Undergraduate/Scholarship)

Purpose: To support students to meet the educational costs of attending the School of Law. **Focus:** Law. **Qualif.:** Applicants must be Pepperdine University School of Law students. **Criteria:** Selection will be based on public service, extracurricular activities, financial need and merit.

Funds Avail.: No specific amount. **To Apply:** Applicants must submit a completed scholarship application form together with a resume and a letter of qualifications. **Remarks:** The scholarship was established in memory of the late Raymond H. Thompson, Superior Court Judge and Professor Emeritus at the School of Law, through private donations made by his family and friends.

9030 ■ Warren and Rosalie Gummow Endowed Scholarship (Undergraduate/Scholarship)

Purpose: To support students to meet the educational costs of attending the School of Law. **Focus:** Law. **Qualif.:** Applicants must be Pepperdine University School of Law students. **Criteria:** Selection will be based on financial need, academic merit, community involvement and personal achievement.

Funds Avail.: No specific amount. **To Apply:** Applicants must submit a completed scholarship application form together with a resume and a letter of qualifications. **Remarks:** The endowed scholarship was funded by Rosalie and the late Warren Gummow, strong supporters of Pepperdine University School of Law and parents of Todd A. Gummow, a 1986 School of Law graduate. Established in 1986.

9031 ■ The Brian J. White Endowed Law Scholarship (Undergraduate/Scholarship)

Purpose: To support students to meet the educational costs of attending the School of Law. **Focus:** Law. **Qualif.:** Applicants must be practicing Christians committed to pursuing a career in criminal defense; must actively worship with a local congregation and be committed to Christ. **Criteria:** Selection will be based on a review of all application materials.

Funds Avail.: No specific amount. **To Apply:** Applicants must submit a completed scholarship application form together with a resume, letter of qualifications, and a letter of confirmation from a minister or priest.

9032 ■ Woodrow Judkins Endowed Scholarship (Undergraduate/Scholarship)

Purpose: To support students to meet the educational costs of attending the School of Law. **Focus:** Law. **Qualif.:** Applicants must be Pepperdine University School of Law students with good academic standing. **Criteria:** Recipients of the award will be determined by the Scholarship Committee.

Funds Avail.: No specific amount. **Duration:** Annual. **To Apply:** Applicants must submit a completed scholarship

Awards are arranged alphabetically below their administering organizations

application form together with a resume and a letter of qualifications.

9033 ■ PepsiCo Foundation, Inc.
700 Anderson Hill Rd.
Purchase, NY 10577
Ph: (914)253-3153
Fax: (914)253-3553
URL: www.pepsico.com/Purpose/Corporate-Contributions
.aspx

9034 ■ PepsiCo Foundation Scholarships
(Undergraduate/Scholarship)

Purpose: To provide financial support to those students who are pursuing hospitality-related degree programs. **Focus:** Hotel, institutional, and restaurant management. **Qualif.:** Applicants must be an incoming freshman for the upcoming fall semester, which is defined as a student who has never been enrolled in a college or university; an undergraduate hospitality management major at a U.S. college or university; enrolled in at least 12 credit hours for the upcoming fall and spring semesters; a minimum overall GPA of 2.0; must be U.S. citizens or permanent U.S. residents. **Criteria:** Recipients are selected based on academic performance, hospitality work experience, financial need, extracurricular/professional attributes and honors, as well as personal attributes as defined in their career goal statement.

Funds Avail.: Baccalaureate Majors: $4,000; Associate Majors: $2,000. **To Apply:** Preference will be given to high school graduates of the Hospitality & Tourism Management Program (HTMP) or Lodging Management Program (LMP); applicants must complete sections 1-8 of the AHLEF Scholarship Application.

9035 ■ Perfect Plants Nursery
PO Box 442
Lloyd, FL 32337
Ph: (850)997-3008
URL: www.myperfectplants.com
Social Media: www.facebook.com/PerfectPlants
www.instagram.com/myperfectplants
www.linkedin.com/company/myperfectplants
www.pinterest.com/perfectplantsnu
twitter.com/myperfectplants

9036 ■ Perfect Plants Scholarship *(Community College/Scholarship)*

Purpose: To assist students pursuing a degree in the horticultural industry. **Focus:** Horticulture. **Qualif.:** Applicant must be an incoming freshman, sophomore, junior, or senior enrolled full- or part-time in a course of study at a community college or university program leading to a career in the horticultural industry; must have a minimum 3.0 GPA. **Criteria:** Selection will be Minimum 500 words; 1,000 Maximum

Funds Avail.: $1,000. **Duration:** Annual. **Number Awarded:** 1. **To Apply:** Applicant must submit completed application, transcripts, essay, and two letters of recommendation. Application materials may be submitted by mail to the address above or via email to contact@myperfectplants.com. **Deadline:** August 20. **Contact:** Email: Scholars@myperfectplants.com, Address: P.O. Box 442 Lloyd, FL 32337.

9037 ■ Perkins Coie L.L.P.
1201 3rd Ave., Ste. 4900
Seattle, WA 98101-3099
Ph: (206)359-8000
Fax: (206)359-9000
URL: www.perkinscoie.com

9038 ■ Perkins Coie 1L Diversity Fellowship
(Undergraduate/Fellowship)

Purpose: To support students from a diversity of backgrounds in their pursuit of legal education, as well as for their preparation in legal careers. **Focus:** Law. **Qualif.:** Applicant must has paved a steady road to change by opening the door for diverse students to experience practice at a large law firm. **Criteria:** Selection will be based on the basis of their academic record, interests and meaningful contributions to diversity programs at their law schools.

Funds Avail.: $15,000. **Duration:** Annual. **Number Awarded:** Varies. **To Apply:** Interested applicants may contact the Firm for the application process and other information.

9039 ■ Perkins Coie 1L Patent Litigation and Patent Fellowships *(Undergraduate/Fellowship)*

Purpose: To allow those law students to further their knowledge and interest in patent litigation and/or patent prosecution. **Focus:** Law. **Qualif.:** Applicants must be students with particular technical backgrounds and an interest in patent litigation and/or patent prosecution.

Funds Avail.: $15,000. **To Apply:** Interested applicants may contact the Firm for the application process and other information.

9040 ■ Perkins Coie 1L Political Law Diversity Fellowships *(Undergraduate/Fellowship)*

Purpose: To assist students with their political law careers. **Focus:** Law; Political science. **Qualif.:** Applicants must be law students who are interested in political law. **Criteria:** Applicants must have a demonstrated interest in politics and a desire to specialize in political law after law school graduation.

Funds Avail.: $15,000. **To Apply:** Applicants must contact the Firm for the application process and other information.

9041 ■ Personal Money Service
1001 Bayhill Dr., Ste. 200
San Bruno, CA 94066
Free: 888-373-0748
URL: personalmoneyservice.com
Social Media: linkedin.com/company/personal-money
-service
www.pinterest.com/personalms
twitter.com/money_service

9042 ■ $1,000 Scholarship for Veterans
(Undergraduate/Scholarship)

Purpose: To support veterans who aim for superior educational heights. **Focus:** General studies/Field of study not specified. **Qualif.:** Applicant must be a high school senior or high school graduate; be an active duty member of the U.S. military or a veteran; be a legal resident or citizen of the U.S.; and not have previously earned a bachelors degree. **Criteria:** Selection is based on the most impressive post.

Awards are arranged alphabetically below their administering organizations

Funds Avail.: $1,000. **Number Awarded:** 1. **To Apply:** Applicant must write a post explaining why they should be awarded this scholarship and make this post public on their Facebook or YouTube account. Applicant must also link to Personal Money Service's Facebook or YouTube page and link the post. Application should be submitted via email. **Contact:** Email: admin@personalmoneyservice.com; URL: personalmoneyservice.com/veterans-scholarship/.

9043 ■ Pet Insurance U

633 7th Ave.
San Diego, CA 92101
Ph: (858)230-1220
E-mail: help@petinsuranceu.com
URL: www.petinsuranceu.com

9044 ■ Animal Compassion Undergraduate Scholarships *(Undergraduate/Scholarship)*

Purpose: To support students pursuing veterinary medicine or animal-related careers. **Focus:** Veterinary science and medicine. **Qualif.:** Applicants must be undergraduate students, year 1 through year 4, currently attending an accredited college or university in the United States; must have a minimum 3.0 GPA. **Criteria:** Selection will be based on the applicants' demonstrated interest or experience in animal advocacy, animal care, veterinary volunteering or related endeavors.

Duration: Annual. **To Apply:** Applicants must visit the scholarship page and submit all applications via email. **Contact:** Email: scholarships@usattorneys.com.

9045 ■ Petro Law Firm

2260 Rocky Ridge Rd., Ste. C
Birmingham, AL 35203
Ph: (205)327-8311
E-mail: mark@petrolawfirm.com
URL: www.petrolawfirm.com
Social Media: www.facebook.com/petrolawfirm
www.linkedin.com/company/petro-law-firm
twitter.com/petrolawfirmpc

9046 ■ Petro Law Firm Scholarship Contest *(Graduate, College/Scholarship)*

Purpose: To provide financial aid to a college students; encourage students to explore the role personal injury lawyers play in minimizing hazards, helping those injured, and encouraging people everywhere to think about consumer safety; and inspire students to pursue a career in any legal field. **Focus:** Law. **Qualif.:** Applicant must be a high school senior or college freshman and a U.S. citizen or permanent resident attending college, or planning to attend college, in the United States in the field of law. **Criteria:** Selection is based on the best video or written essay submitted.

Funds Avail.: $1,000. **Number Awarded:** 1. **To Apply:** Applicant must record a video (one to two minutes long, in plain English) explaining how lawyers make the world a safer place. Video must be published to applicant's YouTube channel with the title "Petro Law Firm Scholarship Contest" and include this link in the description: www.petrolawfirm.com/scholarship-for-college-students/. Instead of a video essay, applicant may submit a 1,000 to 1,500 word essay on the same subject and place on the webpage. **Deadline:** August 15. **Contact:** Mark Petro;

Email: mark@petrolawfirm.com.

9047 ■ Petroleum History Society (PHS)

1638 Broadview Rd. NW
Calgary, AB, Canada T2N 3H1
E-mail: info@petroleumhistory.ca
URL: www.petroleumhistory.ca

9048 ■ Petroleum History Society Graduate Scholarships *(Graduate/Scholarship)*

Purpose: To support a graduate student working in a field of study related to historical aspects of the Canadian petroleum industry. **Focus:** History. **Criteria:** Selection is based on the application.

Funds Avail.: 1,700. **Duration:** Annual. **Number Awarded:** 1. **To Apply:** Applicant must submit an online application form. **Remarks:** Established in 1991. **Contact:** E-mail: gsaward@ucalgary.ca.

9049 ■ Petroleum Packaging Council (PPC)

c/o ATD Management Inc.
1519 via Tulipan
San Clemente, CA 92673-3715
Ph: (949)369-7102
Fax: (949)366-1057
E-mail: ppc@atdmanagement.com
URL: www.ppcouncil.org
Social Media: twitter.com/PetroPackaging

9050 ■ Member Student Scholarships *(Undergraduate/Scholarship)*

Purpose: To provide technical leadership and education for the petroleum packaging industry. **Focus:** Packaging. **Qualif.:** Applicants must be a child of a PPC member in good standing. **Criteria:** Scholarships are given based on the academic performance of the student.

Funds Avail.: $3,500. **Duration:** Annual. **Number Awarded:** 2. **To Apply:** Applicants must be a member to access the links; applications are available online. **Deadline:** May 1.

9051 ■ Pew Charitable Trusts

1 Commerce Sq.
2005 Market St., Ste. 2800
Philadelphia, PA 19103-7077
Ph: (215)575-9050
E-mail: info@pewtrusts.org
URL: www.pewtrusts.org
Social Media: www.facebook.com/pewcharitabletrusts
www.instagram.com/pewenvironment
www.linkedin.com/company/20974
www.linkedin.com/company/the-pew-charitable-trusts
twitter.com/pewtrusts
www.youtube.com/user/Pew

9052 ■ Pew Latin American Fellows Program in the Biomedical Sciences *(Other/Fellowship)*

Purpose: To support young scientists from Latin America to receive postdoctoral training in the United States. **Focus:** Biomedical research. **Qualif.:** Applicants must be scientists from Latin America. **Criteria:** Selection will be evaluated by

Awards are arranged alphabetically below their administering organizations

the Scholarship Selection Committee.

Deadline: September 26. **Contact:** Email: fellowsapp@pewtrusts.org.

9053 ■ PFLAG Columbia/Howard County

Owen Brown Interfaith Center
7246 Cradlerock Way
Columbia, MD 21045
Ph: (443)953-8631
E-mail: info@pflaghoco.org
URL: www.pflaghoco.org
Social Media: www.facebook.com/PflagHowardCounty
www.instagram.com/pflag/
twitter.com/pflag
twitter.com/pflaghoco
www.youtube.com/user/pflagnational

9054 ■ PFLAG Howard County Scholarship
(Undergraduate/Scholarship)

Purpose: To support outstanding lesbian, gay, bisexual, transgender and allied students; to encourage the pursuit of post-secondary education for self-identified LGBT and allies; to foster a positive image of the LGBT society. **Focus:** General studies/Field of study not specified. **Criteria:** Selection will be based on the committee's criteria.

Funds Avail.: $2,000. **Duration:** Annual. **Number Awarded:** 1. **To Apply:** Applicants must include general application form; PFLAG scholarship questionnaire; two sealed letters of recommendation; academic transcripts (unofficial copies). **Deadline:** May 11. **Contact:** Email: info@pflaghoco.org.

9055 ■ Pharmaceutical Research and Manufacturers of America Foundation

950 F St. NW, Ste. 300
Washington, DC 20004
Ph: (202)572-7756
E-mail: foundation@phrma.org
URL: www.phrmafoundation.org
Social Media: www.facebook.com/PhRMAFoundation
www.linkedin.com/company/phrma-foundation
twitter.com/PhRMAfoundation

9056 ■ Informatics Post Doctoral Fellowships
(Doctorate/Fellowship)

Purpose: To support the post doctoral career development of individuals preparing to engage in research that will bridge the gap between experimental and computational approaches in genomic and biomedical studies. **Focus:** General studies/Field of study not specified. **Qualif.:** Applicants must either hold a Ph.D. degree in a field of study logically or functionally related to the proposed post doctoral activities or expect to receive the Ph.D. before activating the award; must also have a firm commitment from an accredited U.S. university and be a U.S. citizen or permanent resident.

Funds Avail.: $40,000. **Duration:** Annual. **To Apply:** Applicants must submit the application by an accredited U.S. college or university. **Deadline:** September 1.

9057 ■ Informatics Pre Doctoral Fellowships
(Doctorate/Fellowship)

Purpose: To promote the use of informatics in an integrative approach to the understanding of biological and

disease processes. **Focus:** General studies/Field of study not specified. **Qualif.:** Applicants must be full-time, in-residence Ph.D. candidates in the fields of informatics who are enrolled in M.D., Ph.D. program; must be U.S. citizens or permanent residents. **Criteria:** Selection based on high demand for this fellowship, the PhRMA Foundation will accept only two applications per academic institution.

Funds Avail.: $20,000 in stipend support per year for one or two years. **Duration:** Annual; 1 - 2 years. **To Apply:** Applicants must submit the application by an accredited U.S. college or university. **Deadline:** September 1.

9058 ■ Informatics Sabbatical Fellowships *(Doctorate, Postdoctorate, Master's/Fellowship)*

Purpose: To enable faculty with active research programs to work outside of their home institutions for periods of six months to one year to learn new skills or develop new collaborations that will enhance their research and research training capabilities in informatics. **Focus:** General studies/Field of study not specified. **Qualif.:** Applicants must 1) hold a PhD, Pharm.D, MD or Sc.D degree in a field of study logically or functionally related to the proposed post doctoral activities, 2) hold a faculty appointment that presents eligibility for sabbatical leave from their institution, 3) have institutional approval of a sabbatical plan that includes partial salary matching the PhRMA Foundation stipend, and 4) have an endorsement from a mentor who agrees to sponsor the applicant's visiting scientist activity; must be U.S. citizens or permanent residents. **Criteria:** Selection will be based on the committee criteria.

Funds Avail.: $40,000. **Duration:** Annual; minimum of six months and a maximum of one year. **Number Awarded:** 1. **To Apply:** Applicants should include general registration information; curriculum vitae or biosketch; extended letter; thesis project description; a titled abstract of approximately 200 words concerning proposed research plan; official transcripts; thesis advisor information and letter of reference; reference letter from an individual other than the thesis advisor, who is knowledgeable about the candidate's scientific skills, must comment on the candidate's potential for a career in research. **Deadline:** September 1.

9059 ■ Pharmaceutics Post Doctoral Fellowships
(Doctorate/Fellowship)

Purpose: To assist individuals doing post-doctoral research. **Focus:** Pharmacy. **Qualif.:** Applicants must hold a Ph.D. degree in pharmaceutics or a related discipline from an accredited U.S. university or expect to receive such a degree before activating the award; should indicate strong determination to continue research careers in pharmaceutics following completion of the fellowship; must be U.S. citizens or permanent residents. **Criteria:** Selection will be based on the committee's criteria.

Funds Avail.: $40,000. **Duration:** Annual. **To Apply:** Applicants should include general registration information; curriculum vitae or biosketch; extended letter; thesis project description; a titled abstract of approximately 200 words concerning proposed research plan; official transcripts; thesis advisor information and letter of reference; reference letter from an individual other than the thesis advisor, who is knowledgeable about the candidate's scientific skills, must comment on the candidate's potential for a career in research. **Deadline:** September 1. **Contact:** PhRMA Foundation, 950 F St., NW, Ste. 300, Washington, DC, 20004.

Awards are arranged alphabetically below their administering organizations

9060 ■ Pharmaceutics Research Starter Grants
(Doctorate/Grant)

Purpose: To offer financial support to individuals beginning their independent research careers at the faculty level. **Focus:** Pharmacy. **Criteria:** Selection will be judged on the scientific merit of the proposed research, and on the degree of financial need.

Funds Avail.: $100,000. **Duration:** Annual. **To Apply:** Applicants should include general registration information; curriculum vitae or biosketch; extended letter; thesis project description; a titled abstract of approximately 200 words concerning proposed research plan; official transcripts; thesis advisor information and letter of reference; reference letter from an individual other than the thesis advisor, who is knowledgeable about the candidate's scientific skills, must comment on the candidate's potential for a career in research.

9061 ■ Pharmaceutics Sabbatical Fellowships
(Master's, Doctorate/Fellowship)

Purpose: To provides support for individuals engaged in a multidisciplinary research training program that will extend their credentials in pharmaceutics. **Focus:** Pharmacy.

Funds Avail.: $40,000. **Duration:** Annual. **Number Awarded:** 1. **To Apply:** Applicants should include general registration information; curriculum vitae or biosketch; extended letter; thesis project description; a titled abstract of approximately 200 words concerning proposed research plan; thesis advisor information and letter of reference; reference letter from an individual other than the thesis advisor, who is knowledgeable about the candidate's scientific skills, must comment on the candidate's potential for a career in research. **Deadline:** September 1.

9062 ■ Pharmacology/Toxicology Pre Doctoral Fellowships *(Doctorate/Fellowship)*

Purpose: To assist in the candidate's pre doctoral training. **Focus:** Pharmacology; Toxicology. **Qualif.:** Applicants must hold a PhD, Pharm.D, MD or Sc.D degree in a field of study logically or functionally related to the proposed post doctoral activities; must hold a faculty appointment that presents eligibility for sabbatical leave from their institution; must have salary matching the PhRMA Foundation stipend; must have an endorsement from a mentor who agrees to sponsor the applicant's visiting scientist activity. All applicants must be U.S. citizens or permanent residents. **Criteria:** Selection will be based on a university.

Funds Avail.: $20,000. **Duration:** Annual; up 2 years. **Number Awarded:** 1. **To Apply:** Applicants should include general registration information; curriculum vitae or biosketch; extended letter; thesis project description; a titled abstract of approximately 200 words concerning proposed research plan; official transcripts; thesis advisor information and letter of reference; reference letter from an individual other than the thesis advisor, who is knowledgeable about the candidate's scientific skills, must comment on the candidate's potential for a career in research. **Deadline:** September 1.

9063 ■ PhRMA Foundation Health Outcomes Pre Doctoral Fellowships *(Doctorate/Fellowship)*

Purpose: To assist full-time, in-residence PhD candidates in the fields of health outcomes. **Focus:** Health sciences; Public health. **Qualif.:** Applicants must be Ph.D. candidates in the fields of health outcomes must be a full-time, in-residence who will have completed most of their pre-thesis requirements (at least two years of study); candidate; must be U.S. citizens or permanent residents.

Funds Avail.: $25,000 in stipend support per year for one or two years. **Duration:** Annual; 2 years. **To Apply:** Applicants should include general registration information; curriculum vitae or biosketch; extended letter; thesis project description; a titled abstract of approximately 200 words concerning proposed research plan; official transcripts; thesis advisor information and letter of reference; reference letter from an individual other than the thesis advisor, who is knowledgeable about the candidate's scientific skills, must comment on the candidate's potential for a career in research. **Deadline:** February 3.

9064 ■ PhRMA Foundation Health Outcomes Research Starter Grants *(Doctorate/Grant)*

Purpose: To offer financial support to individuals beginning their independent research careers at the faculty level. **Focus:** Health sciences; Public health. **Qualif.:** Applicants must be submitted by an accredited U.S. University; will have a firm commitment from the university; must be sponsored by the department or unit in which the proposed research is to be undertaken; will not have other substantial sources of research funding; must be U.S. citizens or permanent residents. **Criteria:** Applicants will be judged on the scientific merit of the proposed research and degree of financial need.

Funds Avail.: $100,000. **Duration:** Annual. **Number Awarded:** 1. **To Apply:** Applicants should include general registration information; curriculum vitae or biosketch; extended letter; thesis project description; a titled abstract of approximately 200 words concerning proposed research plan; official transcripts; thesis advisor information and letter of reference; reference letter from an individual other than the thesis advisor, who is knowledgeable about the candidate's scientific skills, must comment on the candidate's potential for a career in research. **Deadline:** February 3.

9065 ■ PhRMA Foundation Health Outcomes Sabbatical Fellowships *(Postdoctorate, Master's/Fellowship)*

Purpose: To enable faculty with active research programs to work outside of their home institution. **Focus:** Health sciences; Public health. **Qualif.:** Applicants must hold a Ph.D., MD, PharmD, or ScD degree in a field of study logically or functionally related to the proposed post doctoral activities; hold a faculty appointment that impacts eligibility for a sabbatical leave from their home institution; have institutional approval of a sabbatical plan that includes partial salary that matches the PhRMA stipend; hold an endorsement from a mentor who agrees to sponsor the applicant's visiting scientist activity; and be a U.S. citizen or permanent resident.

Funds Avail.: A stipend of $40,000, payable quarterly for a minimum of six months and a maximum of one year. **Duration:** Annual. **To Apply:** Applicants should include general registration information; curriculum vitae or biosketch; extended letter; thesis project description; a titled abstract of approximately 200 words concerning proposed research plan; official transcripts; thesis advisor information and letter of reference; reference letter from an individual other than the thesis advisor, who is knowledgeable about the candidate's scientific skills, must comment on the candidate's potential for a career in research. **Deadline:** February 1.

Awards are arranged alphabetically below their administering organizations

9066 ■ PhRMA Foundation Informatics Research Starter Grants (Doctorate/Grant)

Purpose: To provide financial support to individuals beginning their independent research careers at the faculty level. **Focus:** General studies/Field of study not specified. **Qualif.:** Applicants must be holding an academic rank of Assistant Professor (or Research Assistant Professor) within a tenure-track (or Research track) appointment; must be sponsored by the department or unit in which the proposed research is to be undertaken; must be U.S. citizens or permanent residents. **Criteria:** Judged on the scientific merit of the proposed research, and on the degree of financial need.

Funds Avail.: $100,000. **Duration:** Annual; one year. **To Apply:** Applicants should include general registration information; curriculum vitae or biosketch; extended letter; thesis project description; a titled abstract of approximately 200 words concerning proposed research plan; official transcripts; thesis advisor information and letter of reference; reference letter from an individual other than the thesis advisor, who is knowledgeable about the candidate's scientific skills, must comment on the candidate's potential for a career in research. **Deadline:** September 1.

9067 ■ PhRMA Foundation Pharmaceutics Pre Doctoral Fellowships (Postdoctorate/Fellowship)

Purpose: To support advanced students who will have completed the bulk of their pre-thesis requirements and are starting their thesis research by the time the award is activated. **Focus:** Pharmacy. **Qualif.:** Applicants must hold a Pharm.D. or a B.S. or M.S. from an accredited school in pharmacy or a related area, such as chemistry, biology or engineering; should expect to complete the requirements for the Ph.D. in two years or less from the time the fellowship begins; must be U.S. citizens or permanent residents.

Funds Avail.: $20,000. **Duration:** Annual; up 2 years. **To Apply:** Applicants should include general registration information; curriculum vitae or biosketch; extended letter; thesis project description; a titled abstract of approximately 200 words concerning proposed research plan; official transcripts; thesis advisor information and letter of reference; reference letter from an individual other than the thesis advisor, who is knowledgeable about the candidate's scientific skills, must comment on the candidate's potential for a career in research. **Deadline:** September 1.

9068 ■ PhRMA Foundation Pharmacology/ Toxicology Post Doctoral Fellowships (Postdoctorate/Fellowship)

Purpose: To support post-doctoral career development activities of individuals prepared to engage in research that integrates information on molecular or cellular mechanisms of action with information on the effect of an agent in the intact organism. **Focus:** Pharmacology; Toxicology. **Qualif.:** Applicants must either hold a Ph.D. degree or appropriate terminal research doctorate in a field of study logically or functionally related to the proposed post doctoral activities, or expect to receive the Ph.D. before activating the award; must also have a firm commitment from a mentor at an accredited U.S. university and be a U.S. citizen or permanent resident.

Funds Avail.: $40,000 in stipend support per year for one or two years. **Duration:** Annual; 2 years. **Number Awarded:** 1. **To Apply:** Applicants should include general registration information; curriculum vitae or biosketch; extended letter; thesis project description; a titled abstract of approximately 200 words concerning proposed research

plan; official transcripts; thesis advisor information and letter of reference; reference letter from an individual other than the thesis advisor, who is knowledgeable about the candidate's scientific skills, must comment on the candidate's potential for a career in research. **Deadline:** September 1.

9069 ■ PhRMA Foundation Pharmacology/ Toxicology Research Starter Grants (Doctorate/ Grant)

Purpose: To provide financial To provide research careers to support and reward innovation in disciplines essential to the development. **Focus:** Pharmacology; Toxicology. **Qualif.:** Applicants may All applicants have a firm commitment from an accredited U.S. school or university. **Criteria:** Applicants will be judged on the scientific merit of the proposed research and degree of financial need.

Funds Avail.: $100,000. **Duration:** Annual. **To Apply:** Applicants should include general registration information; curriculum vitae or biosketch; extended letter; thesis project description; a titled abstract of approximately 200 words concerning proposed research plan; official transcripts; thesis advisor information and letter of reference; reference letter from an individual other than the thesis advisor, who is knowledgeable about the candidate's scientific skills, must comment on the candidate's potential for a career in research. **Deadline:** September 1.

9070 ■ PhRMA Foundation Pharmacology/ Toxicology Sabbatical Fellowships (Postdoctorate, Master's/Fellowship)

Purpose: To enable faculty with active research programs to work outside of their home institutions for periods of 6 months to one year to learn new skills or develop new collaborations that will enhance their research training capabilities in pharmacology/toxicology. **Focus:** Pharmacology; Toxicology.

Funds Avail.: $40,000 for a minimum of six months to a maximum of 12 months. **Duration:** Annual. **To Apply:** Applicants should include general registration information; curriculum vitae or biosketch; extended letter; thesis project description; a titled abstract of approximately 200 words concerning proposed research plan; official transcripts; thesis advisor information and letter of reference; reference letter from an individual other than the thesis advisor, who is knowledgeable about the candidate's scientific skills, must comment on the candidate's potential for a career in research. **Deadline:** September 1.

9071 ■ PhRMA Foundation Post Doctoral Health Outcomes Fellowships (Postdoctorate/Fellowship)

Purpose: To provide stipend support for individuals engaged in a research training program that will create or extend their credentials in health outcomes. **Focus:** Health sciences; Public health. **Qualif.:** Applicants must be PharmD, MD, and Ph.D. graduates; must have a firm commitment from an accredited U.S. university; must be U.S. citizens or permanent residents.

Funds Avail.: $55,000. **Duration:** Annual. **Number Awarded:** 2. **To Apply:** Applicants should include general registration information; curriculum vitae or biosketch; extended letter; thesis project description; a titled abstract of approximately 200 words concerning proposed research plan; official transcripts; thesis advisor information and letter of reference; reference letter from an individual other than the thesis advisor, who is knowledgeable about the

Awards are arranged alphabetically below their administering organizations

candidate's scientific skills, must comment on the candidate's potential for a career in research. **Deadline:** February 3.

9072 ■ Phi Alpha Theta

University of South Florida
4202 E Fowler Ave., SOC107
Tampa, FL 33620-8100
Fax: (813)974-8215
Free: 800-394-8195
E-mail: info@phialphatheta.org
URL: www.phialphatheta.org
Social Media: www.instagram.com/phialphatheta
www.linkedin.com/company/phi-alpha-theta
twitter.com/PAT_History
www.youtube.com/channel/
  UCUQzwQkvF3V70NdPK4izqkA

9073 ■ A.F. Zimmerman Scholarship *(Graduate, Master's/Scholarship)*

Purpose: To support Phi Alpha Theta graduate students and their educational goals. **Focus:** History. **Qualif.:** Applicant must be a Phi Alpha Theta member entering graduate school for the first time and enrolled in a Master's program in History. **Criteria:** Selection is based on the application.

Funds Avail.: $1,250. **Duration:** Annual. **To Apply:** Applicants must submit six copies of the completed application form together with six copies of official transcripts (one official copy from each undergraduate and graduate institution where work was credited toward a degree); six copies of curriculum vitae or resume; GRE scores; letter of recommendation from each of the three individuals listed in the application (original only); letter from the Department Chair confirming the student is not enrolled in an online program. **Deadline:** March 1. **Contact:** Graduate Scholarship Committee, Phi Alpha Theta History Honor Society, University of South Florida, 4202 E Fowler Ave., SOC107, Tampa, Florida 33620-8100; Phone: 800-394-8195; Fax: 813-974-8215; Email: info@phialphatheta.org.

9074 ■ Graydon A. Tunstall Undergraduate Student Scholarship *(Undergraduate/Scholarship)*

Purpose: To support student members and their educational goals. **Focus:** History. **Qualif.:** Applicants must be exceptional student members entering the fall semester of their senior year and majoring in Modern European History 1815 to present. **Criteria:** Selection is based on the application.

Funds Avail.: $1,000. **Duration:** Annual. **To Apply:** Applicants must submit three copies of the completed application form together with official transcripts (one official copy from each undergraduate institution where work was credited toward a degree); three copies of curriculum vitae or resume; letter of recommendation from each of the three individuals listed in the application form (original only); and a letter from the Department Chair confirming the applicants is not enrolled in an online program. **Deadline:** March 1. **Contact:** Undergraduate Scholarship Committee, Phi Alpha Theta History Honor Society, University of South Florida, 4202 E Fowler Ave., SOC107, Tampa, Florida 33620-8100; Phone: 800-394-8195; Fax: 813-974-8215; Email: info@ phialphatheta.org.

9075 ■ Thomas S. Morgan Memorial Scholarship *(Graduate, Master's/Scholarship)*

Purpose: To support Phi Alpha Theta graduate students and their educational goals. **Focus:** History. **Qualif.:** Ap-

plicant must be a Phi Alpha Theta member entering graduate school for the first time and enrolled in a Master's program in History. **Criteria:** Selection is based on the application.

Funds Avail.: $1,000. **Duration:** Annual. **To Apply:** Applicants must submit six copies of the completed application form together with six copies of official transcripts (one official copy from each undergraduate and graduate institution where work was credited toward a degree); six copies of curriculum vitae or resume; GRE scores; letter of recommendation from each of the three individuals listed in the application (original only); letter from the Department Chair confirming the student is not enrolled in an online program. **Deadline:** March 1. **Contact:** Graduate Scholarship Committee, Phi Alpha Theta History Honor Society, University of South Florida, 4202 E Fowler Ave., SOC107, Tampa, Florida 33620-8100; Phone: 800-394-8195; Fax: 813-974-8215; Email: info@phialphatheta.org.

9076 ■ Phi Alpha Theta Doctoral Scholarship *(Doctorate/Scholarship)*

Purpose: To financially support graduate student members who are pursuing a PhD in History. **Focus:** History. **Qualif.:** Applicant must be a graduate student member pursuing a PhD in History and have passed the general examination. **Criteria:** Selection is based on the application.

Funds Avail.: $1,000. **Duration:** Annual. **To Apply:** Applicants must submit six copies of the completed application and supporting materials including: official transcripts; curriculum vitae or resume; writing sample; letter of recommendation; dissertation prospectus of no more than 3 double-spaced pages; letter from the History Department Chair confirming the applicants is not enrolled in an online degree program. **Deadline:** March 1. **Contact:** Doctoral Scholarship Committee, Phi Alpha Theta History Honor Society, University of South Florida, 4202 E Fowler Ave., SOC107, Tampa, FL 33620-8100.

9077 ■ Phi Alpha Theta Faculty Advisor Research Grant *(Other/Grant)*

Purpose: To support the advancement of a faculty advisor's career. **Focus:** History. **Qualif.:** Applicant must be a faculty advisor who has served as a chapter advisor for five or more years and is currently advising. **Criteria:** Selection is based on years of service to Phi Alpha Theta; compliance with honor society procedures and guidelines (i.e. submitting initiates) and the merit of the proposal.

Funds Avail.: $1,000. **Duration:** Annual. **To Apply:** Applicants must submit four copies of the completed application form and all supporting materials; four copies of a current curriculum vitae including a selected list of the applicant's publications; and the original and three copies of a letter of support from Department Chair or Dean. **Deadline:** July 1. **Contact:** Phi Alpha Theta National Headquarters, Phi Alpha Theta History Honor Society, University of South Florida, 4202 E Fowler Ave., SOC107, Tampa, Florida 33620-8100; Phone: 800-394-8195; Fax: 813-974-8215; Email: info@phialphatheta.org.

9078 ■ The John Pine Memorial Award *(Doctorate, Graduate, Undergraduate/Scholarship)*

Purpose: To financially support graduate student members who are pursuing a PhD in History. **Focus:** History. **Qualif.:** Applicant must be a graduate student member pursuing a PhD in History and have passed the general examination. **Criteria:** Selection is based on the application.

Funds Avail.: $1,000. **Duration:** Annual. **To Apply:** Applicants must submit six copies of completed application

Awards are arranged alphabetically below their administering organizations

and supporting materials including: official transcripts; curriculum vitae or resume; writing sample; letter of recommendation; dissertation prospectus of no more than 3 double-spaced pages; letter from the History Department Chair confirming the applicants is not enrolled in an online degree program. **Contact:** Doctoral Scholarship Committee, Phi Alpha Theta History Honor Society, University of South Florida, 4202 E Fowler Ave., SOC107, Tampa, Florida 33620-8100; Phone: 800-394-8195; Fax: 813-974-8215; Email: info@phialphatheta.org.

9079 ■ William E. Parrish Scholarship *(Graduate, Master's/Scholarship)*

Purpose: To support Phi Alpha Theta graduate students and their educational goals. **Focus:** History. **Qualif.:** Applicant must be a Phi Alpha Theta member entering graduate school for the first time and enrolled in a Master's program in History. **Criteria:** Selection is based on the application.

Funds Avail.: $1,000. **Duration:** Annual. **To Apply:** Applicants must submit six copies of the completed application form together with six copies of official transcripts (one official copy from each undergraduate and graduate institution where work was credited toward a degree); six copies of curriculum vitae or resume; GRE scores; letter of recommendation from each of the three individuals listed in the application (original only); letter from the Department Chair confirming the student is not enrolled in an online program. **Deadline:** March 1. **Contact:** Graduate Scholarship Committee, Phi Alpha Theta History Honor Society, University of South Florida, 4202 E Fowler Ave., SOC107, Tampa, Florida 33620-8100; Phone: 800-394-8195; Fax: 813-974-8215; Email: info@phialphatheta.org.

9080 ■ The Phi Beta Kappa Society
1606 New Hampshire Ave. NW
Washington, DC 20009
Ph: (202)265-3808
Fax: (202)986-1601
URL: www.pbk.org
Social Media: www.facebook.com/phibetakappa
www.instagram.com/phibetakappasociety
twitter.com/PhiBetaKappa
www.youtube.com/user/phibetakappa

9081 ■ Walter J. Jensen Fellowships *(Other/ Fellowship)*

Purpose: To help educators and researchers improve education in standard French language, literature and culture and in the study of standard French in the United States. **Focus:** French studies. **Qualif.:** Applicants must be U.S. citizens under the age of 40 who can demonstrate their career does or will involve active use of the French language; they must have earned a bachelor's degree from an accredited four-year institution with a 3.0 minimum GPA in French language and literature as a major; they must demonstrate superior competence in French, according to the standards established by the American Association of Teachers of French. **Criteria:** Application must be given to members of Phi Beta Kappa and educators at the secondary school level or higher.

Funds Avail.: $15,900. **Duration:** Annual. **To Apply:** Applicants must complete an online application form; must submit an official transcript; GPA in French and Literature; list of scholarships, fellowships and prizes received; refer-

ence letter; and attach a statement including; description and impact of the study, place where the project would be conducted and expectations when report of studies would be published in France. **Remarks:** The fellowship established by Professor Walter J. Jensen for the study of French Language, Literature, and Culture. Established in 2001. **Contact:** Jen Horneman; Phone: 202-745-3287; Email: jhorneman@pbk.org.

9082 ■ Mary Isabel Sibley Fellowship *(Doctorate/ Fellowship)*

Purpose: To increase interest in the study of Greek language, history, literature or archaeology, or the study of French language or literature. **Focus:** French studies; Greek studies; Linguistics. **Qualif.:** Applicants must be unmarried women 25 to 35 years of age who have demonstrated their ability to carry on with an original research; must hold a doctoral degree or have fulfilled all the requirements for a doctorate except for the dissertation; and must plan to work full-time on research during the fellowship year; award is not restricted to Phi Beta Kappa members or U.S citizens. **Criteria:** Selection of applicants will be based on the criteria of the Fellowship Committee.

Funds Avail.: $20,000. **Duration:** Annual. **To Apply:** Applicant must submit the completed application form; official transcript; list of scholarships, fellowships and prizes received; and three letters of reference. Must attach a statement including; description/state of the project, place where project would be carried out, and expectations with regards to study; applicant must also include four copies of each letter of recommendation in a single envelope signed and sealed by the reference. **Remarks:** The fellowship established by Isabelle Stone in honor of her mother, Mary Isabel Sibley, this fellowship was designed to reward women pursuing graduate work in one of two fields of study, French or Greek, with the experience of researching and living abroad. Established in 1934. **Contact:** Jen Horneman; Phone: 202-745-3287; Email: jhorneman@pbk.org.

9083 ■ Phi Chi Theta
PO Box 113394
Carrollton, TX 75011-3394
Ph: (972)245-7202
URL: www.phichitheta.org
Social Media: www.facebook.com/phichitheta
www.linkedin.com/company/phi-chi-theta-business
  -fraternity
twitter.com/PhiChiTheta

9084 ■ Anna E. Hall Memorial Scholarships
(Undergraduate, Graduate, Doctorate/Scholarship)

Purpose: To support students who have made a substantial contribution and impact to the organization or local community intending to pursue a degree in the fields of business and/or economics. **Focus:** Business; Economics. **Qualif.:** Applicants must be national members of Phi Chi Theta in good standing who are students who have completed at least one semester or two quarters of college in United States, and will be enrolled or attending classes during the forthcoming academic year at an approved college or university in United States (in pursuit of a degree in the fields of Business and/or Economics). **Criteria:** Applicants will be selected based on achievements and contributions to the Phi Chi Theta; scholastic achievement; courses enrolled during the Spring Semester; school and community involvement.

Awards are arranged alphabetically below their administering organizations

Funds Avail.: No specific amount. **To Apply:** Applicants must submit a completed application form; one copy of an official transcript (mailed directly from Registrar's Office to the Scholarship Committee); two letters of recommendation from a Phi Chi Theta Fraternity officer; an essay explaining of how they see themselves in the next 3-5 years; resume; and professional or business photo. **Deadline:** June 1. **Remarks:** The scholarship was established to honor the memory of Anna E. Hall, Founder (Colorado Alpha Chapter - University of Denver). Established in 1989. **Contact:** Email: PCTEdScholarship@aol.com.

9085 ■ Helen D. Snow Memorial Scholarship
(Undergraduate, Graduate, Doctorate/Scholarship)

Purpose: To support students who have made a substantial contribution and impact to the organization or local community pursuing a degree in the fields of business and/or economics. **Focus:** Business; Economics. **Qualif.:** Applicants must be national members of Phi Chi Theta in good standing; must be students who have completed at least one semester or two quarters of college in United States; and must be enrolled or attending classes during the forthcoming academic year at an approved college or university in United States in pursuit of a degree in the fields of business and/or economics. **Criteria:** Candidates will be selected based on achievements and contributions to the Phi Chi Theta; scholastic achievement as demonstrated in transcript; courses enrolled during the Spring Semester; school and community achievement and activities.

Funds Avail.: No specific amount. **Duration:** Annual. **To Apply:** Applicants must submit a completed application form; one copy of an official transcript (mailed directly from Registrar's Office to the Scholarship Committee); two letters of recommendation from a Phi Chi Theta Fraternity officer; an essay explaining of how they see themselves in the next 3-5 years; resume; and professional or business photo. **Deadline:** June 1. **Remarks:** The scholarship was established to honor the late memory of Helen Snow, Honorary Member (Delta Chapter -Northwestern University. Established in 2003. **Contact:** Email: PCTEdScholarship@aol.com.

9086 ■ Phi Delta Phi International Legal Honor Society
PO Box 11570
Fort Lauderdale, FL 33339
Ph: (202)223-6801
Fax: (202)223-6808
E-mail: info@phideltaphi.org
URL: www.phideltaphi.org
Social Media: www.facebook.com/groups/2220670257
twitter.com/phideltaphi

9087 ■ Balfour Scholarship *(Graduate/Scholarship)*

Purpose: To support students who have made an outstanding service to the Inn, to Phi Delta Phi and academic achievements. **Focus:** General studies/Field of study not specified; Law. **Qualif.:** Applicant must have completed one full year of legal study; prior winners of Balfour Scholarships are precluded from entering subsequent competitions. **Criteria:** Selection will be based on academic merits.

Funds Avail.: $2,500. **Duration:** Annual. **Number Awarded:** 3. **To Apply:** Applicants submit a copy of application Form BSA-I for each candidate to International

Headquarters. **Deadline:** September 1;November 1.

9088 ■ Phi Eta Sigma National Honor Society, Inc.
Western Kentucky University
Bowling Green, KY 42101-1062
Ph: (270)745-2333
URL: www.phietasigma.org
Social Media: www.linkedin.com/company/phietasigmahq

9089 ■ Phi Eta Sigma Graduate Scholarships
(Graduate, Other/Scholarship)

Purpose: To support members who are pursuing higher education. **Focus:** General studies/Field of study not specified. **Qualif.:** Applicants must be a member of Phi Eta Sigma. **Criteria:** Selection will be based on a high scholastic record with a minimum 3.5 cumulative GPA.

Funds Avail.: $7,000 each. **Duration:** Annual. **Number Awarded:** 6. **To Apply:** Application form for undergraduate scholarships may be obtained from the chapter adviser; members applying for graduate scholarships may contact the chapter adviser. **Deadline:** May 01.

9090 ■ Phi Eta Sigma Undergraduate Scholarship Awards *(Undergraduate/Scholarship)*

Purpose: To support members who are pursuing higher education. **Focus:** General studies/Field of study not specified. **Qualif.:** Candidates applying for scholarships on either the graduate or undergraduate level.

Funds Avail.: $1,000 each. **Duration:** Annual. **Number Awarded:** one or more awards. **To Apply:** Applicant must be submitted to the national office. **Deadline:** May 1.

9091 ■ Phi Eta Sigma Undergraduate Scholarships
(Undergraduate/Scholarship)

Purpose: To support members who are pursuing higher education. **Focus:** General studies/Field of study not specified. **Qualif.:** Applicant must be a full-time undergraduate student member of Phi Eta Sigma. **Criteria:** Selection will be based on a high scholastic record with a minimum 3.5 cumulative GPA.

Funds Avail.: $6,000 each. **Duration:** Annual. **Number Awarded:** Varies. **To Apply:** Application form for undergraduate scholarships may be obtained from the chapter adviser; members applying for graduate scholarships may contact the chapter adviser. **Deadline:** May 1.

9092 ■ Thomas Arkle Clark Scholar-Leader of the Year *(Graduate, Undergraduate/Scholarship)*

Purpose: To help and support students with their educational goals. **Focus:** General studies/Field of study not specified. **Qualif.:** Applicants must be a member of Phi Eta Sigma. **Criteria:** Selection will be based on high scholastic records with a minimum 3.5 cumulative GPA.

Funds Avail.: $10,000. **Duration:** Annual. **To Apply:** Application form for undergraduate scholarships may be obtained from the chapter adviser; members applying for graduate scholarships may contact the chapter adviser. **Deadline:** May 1.

9093 ■ Phi Gamma Delta
1201 Red Mile Rd.
Lexington, KY 40544-4599
Ph: (859)255-1848

Awards are arranged alphabetically below their administering organizations

Fax: (859)253-0779
E-mail: phigam@phigam.org
URL: www.phigam.org
Social Media: www.facebook.com/PhiGammaDelta
www.instagram.com/phigamhq/
www.linkedin.com/company/phi-gamma-delta
twitter.com/PhiGamHQ
www.youtube.com/user/PhiGamHeadquarters

9094 ■ Peale Scholarship Grant *(Professional development/Scholarship)*

Purpose: To support Phi Gamma Delta brothers who have chosen careers in the ministry. **Focus:** Religion. **Qualif.:** Applicants must be member of a Phi Gamma Delta chapter or colony choosing a career in ministry. **Criteria:** Selection will be based on the committee's criteria.

Funds Avail.: No specific amount. **To Apply:** Interested applicants may contact Virginia Miller to request an application and other information. **Contact:** Ben Robinson; Email: brobinson@phigam.org.

9095 ■ Phi Delta Gamma Academic Achievement Awards *(Undergraduate/Scholarship)*

Purpose: To support undergraduate members who need a healthy academic environment for their scholastic aspirations. **Focus:** General studies/Field of study not specified. **Qualif.:** Applicants must be initiated member of a Phi Gamma Delta chapter or colony; must have 3.2 on a 4.0 GPA scale during their pledging semester; must complete a minimum 12 credit hours for the semester. Chapter must have properly pledged and initiated the applicants; must have turned in all pledge and initiation forms and fees to the International Fraternity. Chapter President must verify memberhip by signing the application. **Criteria:** Selection will be based on the committee's criteria.

Funds Avail.: $250. **To Apply:** Application form can be obtained at the website. Applicants must insure that their application and all attachments are received at the Foundation offices on or before the deadline.

9096 ■ Phi Kappa Phi

7576 Goodwood Blvd.
Baton Rouge, LA 70806
Ph: (225)388-4917
Fax: (225)388-4900
Free: 800-804-9880
E-mail: info@phikappaphi.org
URL: www.phikappaphi.org
Social Media: www.facebook.com/phikappaphi
www.instagram.com/phikappaphi
www.linkedin.com/company/phikappaphi
www.pinterest.com/phikappaphi
twitter.com/phikappaphi
www.youtube.com/user/thephikappaphi

9097 ■ Phi Kappa Phi DissertationFellowships *(Doctorate/Fellowship)*

Purpose: To support students in the dissertation stage of doctoral study. **Focus:** General studies/Field of study not specified. **Qualif.:** Applicants must be a members or those who have accepted membership; and attend a US regionally accredited, doctoral granting institution of higher education. **Criteria:** Selection will be based on the committee's criteria.

Funds Avail.: $10,000. **Duration:** Annual. **Number Awarded:** 10. **To Apply:** Applications can be submitted online and further details can be obtained from the website. **Deadline:** November 30.

9098 ■ Phi Kappa Phi Fellowship *(Graduate, Undergraduate/Fellowship)*

Purpose: To provide financial support for members entering the first year of graduate or professional study. **Focus:** General studies/Field of study not specified. **Qualif.:** Applicants must be active members of Phi Kappa Phi and have applied to enroll as a full-time student in a post-baccalaureate program of study for the current academic year, at an accredited American Institution of higher learning. **Criteria:** Candidates will be evaluated based on academic achievement, including transcripts, honors and awards, relevant research experience, standardized test scores, and samples of creative work, service and leadership experience, on and off campus letters of recommendation, personal statement and career goals, and acceptance at an approved graduate or professional program.

Duration: Annual. **To Apply:** Applicants must complete application online, print, and submit it with the other required materials to respective chapters. **Deadline:** April 15.

9099 ■ Phi Kappa Sigma (PKS)

2 Timber Dr.
Chester Springs, PA 19425
Ph: (610)469-3282
Fax: (610)469-3286
URL: www.pks.org
Social Media: www.facebook.com/phikap
www.instagram.com/phikappasigmahq/
www.linkedin.com/groupinvitation?groupid
 =2392&sharedkey=23a3b4284044
twitter.com/phikappasigma

9100 ■ Need-Based Scholarships *(Undergraduate/ Scholarship)*

Purpose: To provide financial support to students who are in need. **Focus:** General studies/Field of study not specified. **Qualif.:** Applicants must be officially registered members of Phi Kappa Sigma Fraternity; with initiation fee having been remitted by the chapter to the Fraternity Headquarters; and must be at undergraduate level entering a bachelor's degree; must be full time and graduate students working towards first bachelor degree are not eligible. **Criteria:** Selection is based on financial need and scholastic achievement.

Funds Avail.: No specific amount. **Duration:** One academic year. **Number Awarded:** Varies. **To Apply:** Applicants must submit/upload completed application form along with the required materials: a resume, financial Information of the applicant (most recent tax return of the applicant or parents), completed and signed Chapter Advisor check-off form, and letter of intent (optional). Official transcript of grades must be forwarded directly by the college registrar. **Deadline:** April 15.

9101 ■ Participation-Based Scholarships *(Undergraduate/Scholarship)*

Purpose: To provide financial support to students who are in need. **Focus:** General studies/Field of study not specified. **Qualif.:** Applicants must be officially registered members of Phi Kappa Sigma Fraternity, with initiation fee

Awards are arranged alphabetically below their administering organizations

having been remitted by the chapter to the Fraternity Headquarters, and must be an undergraduate entering a bachelor's degree program. **Criteria:** Selection will be based on the applicant's chapter, campus, and community involvement and scholastic achievement.

Funds Avail.: No specific amount. **Duration:** One academic year. **Number Awarded:** Varies. **To Apply:** Applicants must submit/upload a completed application form along with the required materials: resume, basic financial information (electronic copy of most recent tax return of the applicant and their parents), completed and signed Chapter Advisor check-off form, letter of intent (optional), Official transcript of grades must be forwarded directly by the college registrar. **Deadline:** April 15.

9102 ■ Phi Kappa Sigma Foundation Scholarship
(Undergraduate/Scholarship)

Purpose: To support students with financial needs who want to continue their education. **Focus:** General studies/ Field of study not specified. **Qualif.:** Applicants must be full-time students and active members of Phi Kappa Sigma Fraternity; previous award winners are eligible if qualified, as long as their undergraduate status remains, including five-year degree programs. **Criteria:** Selection will be based on the applicants' financial need, scholastic achievement, chapter, campus and community involvement.

Funds Avail.: Up to $5,000. **Duration:** Annual. **To Apply:** Applicants must visit the website to complete the online application process. **Deadline:** April 15.

9103 ■ Phi Sigma Pi National Honor Fraternity
2119 Ambassador Cir.
Lancaster, PA 17603
Ph: (717)299-4710
E-mail: pspoffice@phisigmapi.org
URL: www.phisigmapi.org
Social Media: www.facebook.com/phisigmapifraternity
www.instagram.com/phisigmapi
www.linkedin.com/company/phi-sigma-pi-national-honor
  -fraternity
twitter.com/phisigmapi
www.youtube.com/user/PhiSigmaPi

9104 ■ Richard Cecil Todd and Clauda Pennock Todd Tripod Scholarship *(Graduate, Undergraduate/ Scholarship)*

Purpose: To promote the future academic opportunity of Phi Sigma Pi Members by providing educational support. **Focus:** General studies/Field of study not specified. **Qualif.:** Applicant must be an undergraduate student pursuing a Bachelor's Degree; or graduating senior entering a graduate school (must provide a proof of enrollment to a graduate program); an active Phi Sigma Pi member; and have a GPA of 3.00 on a 4.0 scale. **Criteria:** Selection is based on application.

Funds Avail.: No specific amount. **Duration:** Annual. **To Apply:** Applicants must submit a completed application form; letters of recommendation; official transcript; and notification from the Financial Aid Office (if applicable). **Deadline:** August 1. **Remarks:** Established in 1991. **Contact:** Email: pspoffice@phisigmapi.org.

9105 ■ Rolla F. Wood Graduate Scholarships
(Graduate, Undergraduate/Scholarship)

Purpose: To support the education of the Alumnus who has excelled in undergraduate studies. **Focus:** General studies/Field of study not specified. **Qualif.:** Applicants must be Phi Sigma Pi alumni who have graduated in good standing and are pursuing a postgraduate degree or certification (proof of enrollment in a graduate/professional school program must be submitted); must be members of the National Alumni Association; and have a GPA of 3.0. **Criteria:** Selection will be based on the submitted application.

Funds Avail.: No specific amount. **Deadline:** April 15. **Remarks:** Established in 2004.

9106 ■ Phi Upsilon Omicron, Inc. (PHI U)
PO Box 50970
Bowling Green, KY 42102-4270
Ph: (270)904-1340
E-mail: national@phiu.org
URL: www.phiu.org
Social Media: www.facebook.com/phiunational
www.instagram.com/PhiUNational
www.linkedin.com/company/phi-upsilon-omicron
twitter.com/PhiUNational
youtube.com/embed/upSymqpJnaw

9107 ■ Geraldine Clewell Fellowships - Doctoral Student *(Graduate/Fellowship)*

Purpose: To promote the study of family and consumer sciences. **Focus:** Consumer affairs; Family planning. **Qualif.:** Applicant must be a Phi U member; have doctoral students in family and consumer sciences or a related area. **Criteria:** Selection will be based on the applicants' scholastic record; honors and recognitions; participation in honor society, professional, community, and other organizations; scholarly work; statement of professional goals; and recommendations. Preference will be given to students who desire to teach at the college/university level.

Funds Avail.: $500 and up. **Duration:** Annual. **To Apply:** Applicants must visit the website for procedures and required materials. **Deadline:** February 1.

9108 ■ Geraldine Clewell Fellowships - Masteral
(Graduate/Fellowship)

Purpose: To promote the study of family and consumer sciences. **Focus:** Consumer affairs; Family planning. **Qualif.:** Applicant must be a Phi U member; pursuing a master's degree in family and consumer sciences or related area; atleast one recommendation must be from the student's major advisor. **Criteria:** Selection will be based on the applicants' scholastic record; honors and recognitions; participation in honor society, professional, community, and other organizations; scholarly work; statement of professional goals; and recommendations. Preference will be given to students majoring in family and consumer sciences education and who desires to teach at the elementary/secondary level.

Funds Avail.: $500 and up. **Duration:** Annual. **To Apply:** Applicants must visit the website for procedures and required materials. **Deadline:** February 1.

9109 ■ Closs/Parnitzke/Clarke Scholarship
(Undergraduate/Scholarship)

Purpose: To promote education in advance family and consumer sciences and related areas. **Focus:** Consumer affairs; Family planning. **Qualif.:** Applicants must be Phi U members; enrolled full-time in a baccalaureate degree

Awards are arranged alphabetically below their administering organizations

program in family and consumer sciences or a related area. **Criteria:** Selection will be based on the applicants' scholastic record; participation in Phi U and other collegiate activities; a statement of professional aims and goals; professional services; and recommendations.

Funds Avail.: $500 and up. **Duration:** Annual. **To Apply:** Applicants must visit the website for procedures and required materials. **Deadline:** February 1.

9110 ■ Margaret Drew Alpha Scholarship *(Graduate/Scholarship)*

Purpose: To promote the study of family and consumer sciences. **Focus:** Consumer affairs; Family planning; Nutrition. **Qualif.:** Applicant must be a Phi U member; graduate student in the field of family and consumer sciences. **Criteria:** Selection will be based on the applicants' scholastic record; honors and recognitions; participation in honor society, professional, community, and other organizations; scholarly work; statement of professional goals; and recommendations. Preference will be given to a dietetics or food and nutrition major.

Funds Avail.: No specific amount. **Duration:** Annual. **To Apply:** Applicants must submit an application; transcripts; recommendations. **Deadline:** February 1.

9111 ■ Genevieve Forthun Scholarships *(Undergraduate/Scholarship)*

Purpose: To promote education in advance family and consumer sciences and related areas. **Focus:** Consumer affairs; Family planning. **Qualif.:** Applicant must be a Phi U member; enrolled full-time in a baccalaureate degree program in family and consumer sciences or a related area. **Criteria:** Selection will be based on the committee's criteria.

Funds Avail.: No specific amount. **Duration:** Annual. **To Apply:** Applicants must visit the website for procedures and required materials. **Deadline:** February 1. **Remarks:** Applicants may apply for more than one fellowship.

9112 ■ Mary Weiking Franken Scholarships *(Undergraduate/Scholarship)*

Purpose: To promote education in advance family and consumer sciences and related areas. **Focus:** Consumer affairs; Family planning. **Qualif.:** Applicant must be a Phi U member; enrolled full-time in a baccalaureate degree program in family and consumer sciences or a related area. **Criteria:** Preference is given to students majoring in child/family or family and consumer sciences education.

Funds Avail.: No specific amount. **To Apply:** Applicants must visit the website for procedures and required materials. **Deadline:** February 1. **Remarks:** Applicants may apply for more than one fellowship.

9113 ■ Geraldine Clewell Scholarship *(Undergraduate/Scholarship)*

Purpose: To promote education in advance family and consumer sciences and related areas. **Focus:** Consumer affairs; Family planning. **Qualif.:** Applicant must be Phi U member; must be enrolled full-time in a baccalaureate degree program in family and consumer sciences or a related area. **Criteria:** Selection will be based on the applicant's scholastic record; participation in Phi U and other collegiate activities; a statement of professional aims and goals; professional services; and recommendations.

Funds Avail.: $500 and up. **Duration:** Annual. **To Apply:** Applicants must visit the website for procedures and required materials. **Deadline:** February 1.

9114 ■ Jackman Scholarships *(Undergraduate/Scholarship)*

Purpose: To provide educational support to Phi U members pursuing baccalaureate degrees. **Focus:** Consumer affairs; Family planning. **Qualif.:** Applicant must be a Phi U member; enrolled full-time in a baccalaureate degree program in family and consumer sciences or a related area, and have shown exemplary commitment to Phi Upsilon Omicron. **Criteria:** Selection will be based on the applicants' scholastic record; participation in Phi U and other collegiate activities; a statement of professional aims and goals; professional services; and recommendations.

Funds Avail.: $500 and up. **Duration:** Annual. **To Apply:** Applicants must visit the website for procedures and required materials. **Deadline:** February 1.

9115 ■ Jean Dearth Dickerscheid Fellowship *(Graduate/Fellowship)*

Purpose: To promote education in advance family and consumer sciences and related areas. **Focus:** Consumer affairs; Family planning. **Qualif.:** Applicant must be a Phi U member; pursuing a Ph.D. in family and consumer sciences or related area and has earned at least one other degree in family and consumer sciences and interested in a career in academia. **Criteria:** Selection will be based on the applicants' scholastic record; honors and recognitions; participation in honor society, professional, community, and other organizations; scholarly work; statement of professional goals; and recommendations. Preference will be given to students majoring in family and consumer sciences education and who desires to teach at the elementary/secondary level.

Funds Avail.: $500 and up. **Duration:** Annual. **To Apply:** Applicants must visit the website for procedures and required materials. **Deadline:** February 1.

9116 ■ Treva C. Kintner Scholarships *(Undergraduate/Scholarship)*

Purpose: To promote education in advance family and consumer sciences and related areas. **Focus:** Consumer affairs; Family planning. **Qualif.:** Applicant must be a Phi U member; a non-traditional student; completed at least half of the academic work toward a baccalaureate degree in family and consumer sciences or a related area. **Criteria:** Selection will be based on the committee's criteria.

Funds Avail.: No specific amount. **To Apply:** Applicants must visit the website for procedures and required materials. **Deadline:** February 1. **Remarks:** Applicants may apply for more than one fellowship.

9117 ■ Martha Combs Jenkins Scholarship *(Undergraduate/Scholarship)*

Purpose: To promote education in advance family and consumer sciences and related areas. **Focus:** Consumer affairs; Family planning. **Qualif.:** Applicant must be a Phi U member; pursuing a baccalaureate degree in family and consumer sciences or one of its related areas and have shown exemplary commitment to Phi Upsilon Omicron. **Criteria:** Selection will be based on the applicants' scholastic record; participation in Phi U and other collegiate activities; a statement of professional aims and goals; professional services and recommendations.

Funds Avail.: $500 and up. **Duration:** Annual. **To Apply:** Applicants must visit the website for procedures and required materials. **Deadline:** February 1.

Awards are arranged alphabetically below their administering organizations

9118 ■ Nell Bryant Robinson Scholarship
(Undergraduate/Scholarship)

Purpose: To provide educational support to Phi U members pursuing baccalaureate degrees. **Focus:** Consumer affairs; Family planning; Nutrition. **Qualif.:** Applicant must be a Phi U member; must be pursuing a baccalaureate degree in family and consumer sciences or in one of its related areas. **Criteria:** Selection will be based on the applicants' scholastic record; participation in Phi U and other collegiate activities; statement of professional aims and goals; professional services; and recommendations; Preference is given to students majoring in dietetics or food and nutrition.

Funds Avail.: $500 and up. **Duration:** Annual. **To Apply:** Applicants must visit the website for procedures and required materials. **Deadline:** February 1.

9119 ■ Phi Upsilon Omicron Candle Fellowships
(Graduate, Postgraduate/Fellowship)

Purpose: To provide educational support to students planning to study a master's degree program. **Focus:** Consumer affairs; Family planning. **Qualif.:** Applicant must be Phi U member; enrolled full-time in a baccalaureate degree program in family and consumer sciences or a related area. **Criteria:** Selection will be based on the applicants' scholastic record; participation in Phi U and other collegiate activities; a statement of professional aims and goals; professional services; and recommendations.

Funds Avail.: No specific amount. **Duration:** Annual. **To Apply:** Applications can be submitted and further details can be obtained from the website. **Deadline:** February 1.

9120 ■ Phi Upsilon Omicron Challenge Scholarships
(Undergraduate/Scholarship)

Purpose: To provide educational support to members enrolled in baccalaureate degree programs. **Focus:** Consumer affairs; Family planning. **Qualif.:** Applicants must be Phi U members; enrolled full-time in a baccalaureate degree program in family and consumer sciences or a related area. **Criteria:** Selection will be based on the applicants' scholastic record; participation in Phi U and other collegiate activities; a statement of professional aims and goals; professional services; and recommendations.

Funds Avail.: $500 and up. **Duration:** Annual. **To Apply:** Applicants must visit the website for procedures and required materials. **Deadline:** February 1.

9121 ■ Phi Upsilon Omicron Diamond Anniversary Fellowships
(Graduate/Fellowship)

Purpose: To promote education in advance family and consumer sciences and related areas. **Focus:** Consumer affairs; Family planning. **Qualif.:** Applicant must be a Phi U member; accepted into or currently enrolled in a graduate program; studying at the master's or doctoral level in the family and consumer sciences or a related area. **Criteria:** Selection will be based upon applicant's scholastic record; honors and recognition; participation in honor society, professional, community, and other organizations; scholarly work; statement of professional goals; and recommendations; must be a Phi U member.

Funds Avail.: $500 and up. **Duration:** Annual. **To Apply:** Applications can be submitted and further details can be obtained from the website. **Deadline:** February 1.

9122 ■ Phi Upsilon Omicron Founders Fellowship
(Graduate/Fellowship)

Purpose: To promote education in advance family and consumer sciences and related areas. **Focus:** Consumer

affairs; Family planning. **Qualif.:** Applicant must be a Phi U member; have completed at least half the credit-hour requirements toward the doctorate in some area of family and consumer sciences and have had several years of successful employment in the profession. **Criteria:** Selection will be based on the applicants' scholastic record; participation in Phi U and other collegiate activities; statement of professional aims and goals; professional services; and recommendations; must be Phi U member.

Funds Avail.: $500 and up. **Duration:** Annual. **To Apply:** Applicants must visit the website for procedures and required materials. **Deadline:** February 1.

9123 ■ Phi Upsilon Omicron Golden Anniversary Scholarships
(Undergraduate/Scholarship)

Purpose: To promote education in advance family and consumer sciences and related areas. **Focus:** Consumer affairs; Family planning. **Qualif.:** Applicant must be a Phi U member; enrolled full-time in a baccalaureate degree program in family and consumer sciences or a related area. **Criteria:** Selection will be based on the applicants' scholastic record; participation in Phi U and other collegiate activities; statement of professional aims and goals; professional services; and recommendations.

Funds Avail.: $500 and up. **Duration:** Annual. **To Apply:** Applicants must visit the website for procedures and required materials. **Deadline:** February 1.

9124 ■ Phi Upsilon Omicron Past Presidents Scholarships
(Undergraduate/Scholarship)

Purpose: To promote education in advance family and consumer sciences and related areas. **Focus:** Consumer affairs; Family planning. **Qualif.:** Applicant must be a Phi U member; enrolled full-time in a Master degree program in family and consumer sciences or a related area. **Criteria:** Selection will be based on the committee's criteria.

Funds Avail.: No specific amount. **Duration:** Annual. **To Apply:** Applicants must visit the website for procedures and required materials. **Deadline:** February 1.

9125 ■ Phi Upsilon Omicron Presidents Research Fellowship
(Graduate, Master's, Doctorate, Postdoctorate/Fellowship)

Purpose: To promote education in advance family and consumer sciences and related areas. **Focus:** Consumer affairs; Family planning. **Qualif.:** Applicants must be a Phi U member; on a graduate research at the master's, doctoral or post-doctoral level in the family and consumer sciences or a related area. **Criteria:** Selection will be based on the applicants' scholastic record; honors and recognitions; participation in honor society, professional, community, and other organizations; scholarly work; statement of professional goals; and recommendations. Preference will be given to students majoring in family and consumer sciences education and who desires to teach at the elementary/secondary level.

Funds Avail.: $500 and up. **Duration:** Annual. **To Apply:** Application must include research prospectus exhibiting organization and need for the research. **Deadline:** February 1.

9126 ■ Lucile Rust Scholarships
(Undergraduate/Scholarship)

Purpose: To promote education in advance family and consumer sciences and related areas. **Focus:** Consumer affairs; Family planning. **Qualif.:** Applicant must be a Phi U

Awards are arranged alphabetically below their administering organizations

member; enrolled full-time in a baccalaureate degree program in family and consumer sciences or a related area. **Criteria:** Selection will be based on the applicants' scholastic record; participation in Phi U and other collegiate activities; statement of professional aims and goals; professional services; and recommendations.

Funds Avail.: No specific amount. **To Apply:** Applicants must visit the website for procedures and required materials. **Deadline:** February 1. **Remarks:** Applicants may apply for more than one fellowship.

9127 ■ S. Penny Chappell Scholarship
(Undergraduate/Scholarship)

Purpose: To promote the study of advance family and consumer sciences and related areas. **Focus:** Fashion design; Textile science. **Qualif.:** Applicant must be a Phi U member; pursuing a baccalaureate degree in fashion design and construction, textile design, and development and/or textile preservation. **Criteria:** Selection will be based on the applicants' scholastic record; participation in Phi U and other collegiate activities; a statement of professional aims and goals; professional services; and recommendations.

Funds Avail.: $500 and up. **Duration:** Annual. **To Apply:** Applicants must visit the website for procedures and required materials. **Deadline:** February 1.

9128 ■ Margaret Jerome Sampson Scholarships
(Undergraduate/Scholarship)

Purpose: To provide educational support to Phi U members pursuing baccalaureate degrees. **Focus:** Consumer affairs; Family planning; Nutrition. **Qualif.:** Applicant must be a Phi U member; must be enrolled full-time in a baccalaureate degree program in family and consumer sciences or a related area. **Criteria:** Selection will be based on the applicants' scholastic record; participation in Phi U; professional aims and goals. Preference is given to students majoring in dietetics or food and nutrition, at least one recommendation required from the student's Phi U chapter advisor.

Funds Avail.: $5,000. **Duration:** Annual. **Number Awarded:** 8. **To Apply:** Applicants must visit the website for procedures and required materials. Must provide a financial statement and complete the justification statement. **Deadline:** February 1.

9129 ■ Lillian P. Schoephoerster Scholarships
(Undergraduate/Scholarship)

Purpose: To promote education in advance family and consumer sciences and related areas. **Focus:** Consumer affairs; Family planning. **Qualif.:** Applicant must be a Phi U member; a non-traditional student enrolled full-time in a baccalaureate degree program in family and consumer sciences or a related area. **Criteria:** Selection will be based on the committee's criteria.

Funds Avail.: $2,000. **To Apply:** Applicants must visit the website for procedures and required materials. **Deadline:** February 1. **Remarks:** Applicants may apply for more than one fellowship.

9130 ■ Sutherland/Purdy Scholarship
(Undergraduate/Scholarship)

Purpose: To promote the study of advance family and consumer sciences and related areas. **Focus:** Fashion design; Textile science. **Qualif.:** Applicants must be Phi U member; enrolled full-time in a baccalaureate degree

program in clothing and textiles; must have held a leadership position in her/his Phi U chapter and have earned at least a 3.0 out of 4.0 overall point average. **Criteria:** Selection will be based on the applicants' scholastic record; participation in Phi U and other collegiate activities; a statement of professional aims and goals; professional services; and recommendations.

Funds Avail.: $500 and up. **Duration:** Annual. **To Apply:** Applicants must visit the website for procedures and required materials. **Deadline:** February 1.

9131 ■ Tommie J. Hamner Scholarship
(Undergraduate/Scholarship)

Purpose: To provide educational support to Phi U members pursuing baccalaureate degrees. **Focus:** Consumer affairs; Family planning. **Qualif.:** Applicant must be a Phi U member; enrolled full-time in a baccalaureate degree program in family and consumer sciences or a related area and have shown exemplary commitment to Phi Upsilon Omicron. **Criteria:** Selection will be based on the applicants' scholastic record; participation in Phi U and other collegiate activities; a statement of professional aims and goals; professional services; and recommendations.

Funds Avail.: $500 and up. **To Apply:** Applicants must visit the website for procedures and required materials. **Deadline:** February 1.

9132 ■ Philadelphia Bar Association
1101 Market St., 11th Fl.
Philadelphia, PA 19107
Fax: (215)238-1159
E-mail: Iris@philabar.org
URL: www.philadelphiabar.org
Social Media: www.facebook.com/philadelphiabar
www.linkedin.com/groups/1882313/profile
twitter.com/PhilaBar

9133 ■ The Philadelphia Public Interest Fellowship Program *(Undergraduate/Fellowship)*

Purpose: To provide an extraordinary opportunity for new attorneys at participating firms to defer private practice for a year while they perform valuable public service at one of Philadelphia's legal services agencies. **Focus:** Law. **Qualif.:** Applicants must be third year law students who have received and accepted an offer from a participating private law firm employer.

Funds Avail.: No specific amount. **To Apply:** Applicants and private employer are encouraged to consider a written agreement that outlines procedures such as payroll, conflicts checking and participation in the firm's own training and other activities during the year of the fellowship; a letter of intent from the agency to the fellow will suffice, with copies to the employer and Bar Foundation. **Remarks:** Established in 1992. **Contact:** Gene Sirni, Executive Director, Philadelphia Bar Foundation; Phone: 215-238-6334; Email: gsirni@philabar.org.

9134 ■ Philippine Nurses Association of America (PNAA)
7725 Gateway Blvd., No. 4448
Irvine, CA 92618
E-mail: infomypnaa@gmail.com
URL: mypnaa.org
Social Media: www.instagram.com/mypnaa

Awards are arranged alphabetically below their administering organizations

twitter.com/mypnaa

9135 ■ PNAA Nursing Scholarship Award *(Master's, Doctorate/Scholarship)*

Purpose: To encourage and provide support to members to obtain a Master's Degree in Nursing, Post Master's Program or Doctoral Program. **Focus:** Nursing. **Criteria:** Selection will be based on the Chair of the PNAA Scholarship Committee's criteria.

Funds Avail.: $2,000. **Duration:** Annual. **To Apply:** Applicants must be endorsed/recommended by the Chapter President; must submit a progress report at the end of each academic year (must have served PNAA as an Officer, Board, Committee Member, etc. at the Chapter and/or at the National level); submit brief essay (150 words) describing professional career goals; and include: letter of Acceptance to an accredited program; academic transcript of records; three letters of recommendations (one from employer, one from a faculty or supervisor and one from the Chapter President); resume/curriculum vitae; and passport picture. **Deadline:** May 13. **Contact:** Nini C. Jurado, Chair, PNAA Scholarship Committee, 48 Milburn Dr., Hillsborough, NJ, 08844-2266; E-mail: nicju@icloud.com; Phone: 908-431-9268.

9136 ■ Phoenix Pride Community Foundation
PO Box 16847
Phoenix, AZ 85011-6847
Ph: (602)277-7433
Fax: (602)687-9225
E-mail: info@phoenixpride.org
URL: phoenixpride.org
Social Media: www.facebook.com/PhoenixPrideAZ
www.instagram.com/phoenixprideaz
twitter.com/PhoenixPrideAZ

9137 ■ Phoenix Pride Scholarship *(Undergraduate/Scholarship)*

Purpose: To provide scholarships for students who identify as Lesbian, Gay, Bisexual, Transgender, or Queer, as an LGBTQ ally, or are the dependents of a self-identified LGBTQ parent, and help them achieve their educational goals. **Focus:** General studies/Field of study not specified. **Qualif.:** Applicant must be college students in the local community who are LGBTQ member or ally.

Funds Avail.: $47,000. **Number Awarded:** Multiple. **Remarks:** Established in 2008.

9138 ■ Photographic Historical Society of Canada (PHSC)
4335 Bloor St. W
Toronto, ON, Canada M9C 2A5
E-mail: info@phsc.ca
URL: phsc.ca
Social Media: www.facebook.com/
  PHSCPhotographicHistoricalSocietyofCanada

9139 ■ PHSC Publication Grant *(Professional development/Grant)*

Purpose: To aid the publication, in book or monograph form, of original research into Canada's photographic history. **Focus:** Publishing. **Qualif.:** Applicant must be a PHSC member at time of application and at time of publication.

Criteria: Recommendations for acceptance to be made by a PHSC panel, for approval by the PHSC executive.

Funds Avail.: Up to 1,000 Canadian Dollars. **Duration:** Annual. **Number Awarded:** 1. **To Apply:** Submit a written proposal (maximum one page) outlining topic, format, print run, cost and timing, together with a copy of the material if available and a sample of any previously published work.

9140 ■ PHSC Research Grant *(Professional development/Grant)*

Purpose: To recognize a current member of the PHSC for original research into Canada's photographic history. **Focus:** Publishing. **Qualif.:** Must be a PHSC member.

Funds Avail.: 500 Canadian Dollars. **Duration:** Annual. **To Apply:** Applicants must submit a proposal (maximum four pages) outlining intended avenue of research. Proposals should indicate the topic, rationale for its choice and what it contributes to photographic history, intended research sources/techniques, previous completed research, expected schedule to complete research, and proposed final form for the research.

9141 ■ PHS Commissioned Officers Foundation
8201 Corporate Dr., Ste. 1170
Landover, MD 20785
Ph: (301)731-9080
URL: www.phscof.org
Social Media: www.linkedin.com/company/phs
  -commissioned-officers-fdn-for-the-advancement-of-public
  -health
twitter.com/phscof

9142 ■ COF Dependent Scholarship Program *(Undergraduate, Graduate/Scholarship)*

Purpose: To provide financial support to dependent children or dependent spouses of active duty, retired, or deceased officers of the USPHS Commissioned Corps. **Focus:** General studies/Field of study not specified. **Criteria:** Applicants are evaluated based on criteria designed by the scholarship selection committee.

Funds Avail.: No specific amount. **Duration:** Annual. **To Apply:** Applicants must submit the online application; two letters of recommendation; current academic documentation; extracurricular school and community activities; honors and awards; include a one page essay addressing what they intend to accomplish with their degree and how their area of focus may relate to any of the PHS professional categories. **Contact:** URL: www.phscof.org/dependent-scholarship.html; Email: scholarship@coausphs.org.

9143 ■ Phycological Society of America (PSA)
PO Box 90001
Blacksburg, VA 24062-9001
Ph: (540)231-6170
URL: www.psaalgae.org
Social Media: twitter.com/PSAAlgae

9144 ■ Hannah T. Croasdale Fellowships *(Graduate/Fellowship)*

Purpose: To encourage graduate students to broaden their phycological training by attending phycology courses at biological field stations. **Focus:** Botany. **Qualif.:** Applicants must be members of PSA; must be currently enrolled in a

Awards are arranged alphabetically below their administering organizations

graduate program or formally admitted at the time of the submission of the application. **Criteria:** Selection will be based on the overall merit and need of the applicant; will be evaluated by the members of the PSA Grants and Fellowships committee, and will be notified of the committee's decision.

Funds Avail.: Up to $1,500. **Duration:** Annual. **Number Awarded:** 5. **To Apply:** Applicants must submit the completed application; a letter of recommendation from the applicant's major professor; copy of transcripts (unofficial copies are acceptable). **Deadline:** March 1. **Remarks:** Established in 1987. **Contact:** Sophie McCoy, mccoy@ bio.fsu.edu.

9145 ■ Physical and Health Education Canada (PHE Canada)
2451 Riverside Dr.
Ottawa, ON, Canada K1H 7X7
Ph: (613)523-1348
Fax: (613)523-1206
E-mail: info@phecanada.ca
URL: www.phecanada.ca
Social Media: www.facebook.com/PHECanada
twitter.com/PHECanada
www.youtube.com/user/phecanada

9146 ■ Dr. Andy Anderson Young Professional Awards *(Professional development/Award)*

Purpose: To recognize individuals who epitomize exemplary work on behalf of the physical and health education profession. **Focus:** Education, Physical; Health education. **Qualif.:** Applicants must be 35 years of age or younger who are member of PHE Canada or a Liaison group. **Criteria:** Candidates will be evaluated based on their contribution to the profession.

Funds Avail.: No specific amount. **Duration:** One year. **To Apply:** Applicants must complete the online application form.

9147 ■ North American Society Fellowship Award (NAS Fellowship) *(Professional development/ Fellowship)*

Purpose: To recognize outstanding professionals related to health education, physical education, recreation, sport and dance in North America. **Focus:** Education, Physical; Health education. **Qualif.:** Applicants should be individuals who are currently members of Shape America or PHE Canada, are leaders of the profession, and have provided extensive contributions to the profession over the course of their careers. **Criteria:** Applicants will be evaluated based on completeness and eligibility of the submitted nomination package.

Funds Avail.: No specific amount. **Duration:** Annual. **Number Awarded:** Varies. **To Apply:** Applicants must submit completed nomination form; three letters of reference that outline how the nominee meets at least two of the six professional endeavors listed under the eligibility section; biographical sketch of the nominee that is 250- 300 words in length; the biographical sketch should highlight the professional contributions made by the nominee that is relevant to the criteria of the award; supporting documentation (not exceeding five pages), that showcases the nominee's contribution to the field. **Remarks:** Established in 1999.

9148 ■ PHE Canada National Award for Teaching Excellence in Physical Education *(Professional development/Recognition)*

Purpose: To recognize and support elementary, middle and secondary teachers who have the ability to motivate students to participate in physical activity. **Focus:** Education, Physical. **Qualif.:** Applicants must be a member/ supporter of their respective provincial organization and/or PHE Canada; teaching responsibility for physical education in one or more grades from kindergarten to grade 12; must be fully certified by their respective province to teach and follows provincial curriculum using sound pedagogical principles; must be a minimum of 7 years teaching experience in physical education; must have a permanent teaching contract, at the time of nomination and selection; must be a candidate must not be a previous PETE Award recipient or have previously received the National Award for Teaching Excellence in Physical Education. **Criteria:** Award will be given to applicants who demonstrate the following qualifications: a) conduct a quality physical education program as reflected in PHE Canada's definition; b) serve as role models epitomizing personal health and fitness, enjoyment of activity, sportspersonship and sensitivity to the needs of students; and c) able to participate in professional development related to teaching of physical education; d) has made a substantial contribution to the field by positively impacting the teaching of physical education curriculum in the school, region, and province; e) participates in professional development opportunities related to the teaching of physical education and also shares their expertise with colleagues locally, regionally, provincially or nationally.

Funds Avail.: No specific amount. **Duration:** Periodic. **Number Awarded:** 3. **To Apply:** Applicants must include nomination forms should be submitted online; with accompanying documentation submitted electronically, by fax or by mail; incomplete or late applications will not be considered.

9149 ■ PHE Canada Student Awards *(Undergraduate/ Award)*

Purpose: To recognize undergraduate student leadership in the field of physical education or a related discipline. **Focus:** Education, Physical; Health education. **Qualif.:** Applicants must be in the second, third or fourth year of undergraduate studies in physical education, health education, or a related discipline; must be in the first or second year of an undergraduate teacher education program. **Criteria:** Recipients will be selected based on submitted materials.

Funds Avail.: Amount not specified. **Duration:** Annual. **Number Awarded:** Varies.

9150 ■ R. Tait Mckenzie Award *(Professional development/Award)*

Purpose: To advance the knowledge and understanding of physical and health education, recreation and dance. **Focus:** Education, Physical; Health education. **Qualif.:** Applicants must be nominated by an individual who is a member of PHE Canada; must be a teacher, coach, supervisor, or administrator with 20 years experience and has performed as a recognized leader locally, regionally, nationally and internationally; nominees need not be members of PHE Canada. **Criteria:** Recipients will be chosen based on completeness and eligibility of the submitted nomination package.

Funds Avail.: Amount not specified. **Duration:** Annual. **Number Awarded:** Varies. **To Apply:** Applicants must

Awards are arranged alphabetically below their administering organizations

include information forms, 250-300 word biographical sketch, three letters of reference and supporting documents that show contribution to the field.

9151 ■ Physicians Group Management (PGM)

1050 Wall St. W
Lyndhurst, NJ 07071
Free: 877-531-5835
URL: www.pgmbilling.com
Social Media: www.facebook.com/pgmbilling
linkedin.com/company/physicians-group-management
twitter.com/pgmbilling
youtube.com/user/pgmbilling

9152 ■ PGM Graduate Scholarship *(Graduate/ Scholarship)*

Purpose: To assist medical school students. **Focus:** Medicine. **Qualif.:** Applicants must be entering or already established in an accredited medical school in the United States. **Criteria:** Essay submission reflecting leadership, academics, and achievements.

Funds Avail.: $500. **Number Awarded:** 3. **To Apply:** Submit completed essay question, official transcript, and copy of resume at www.pgmbilling.com/about-us/pgm-scholarship-program/. **Deadline:** June 30. **Contact:** ATTN: Scholarship Committee; Email: scholarship@pgmbilling.com.

9153 ■ PGM Undergraduate Scholarship *(Undergraduate/Scholarship)*

Purpose: To assist undergraduate students pursuing a career in computer science and demonstrating an interest in the health care industry. **Focus:** Computer and information sciences. **Qualif.:** Applicants must be pursuing a career related to computer science; entering into college in the fall. **Criteria:** Essay submission reflecting leadership, academics, and achievements.

Funds Avail.: $500. **Duration:** Annual. **Number Awarded:** 3. **To Apply:** Submit completed essay question, official transcript, and copy of resume at www.pgmbilling.com/about-us/pgm-scholarship-program/. **Deadline:** June 30. **Contact:** ATTN: Scholarship Committee; Email: scholarship@pgmbilling.com.

9154 ■ Physicians' Services Incorporated Foundation

4773 Yonge St., Ste. 5G
North York, ON, Canada M2N 6L9
Ph: (416)226-6323
Fax: (416)226-6080
E-mail: psif@psifoundation.org
URL: www.psifoundation.org

9155 ■ Educational Fellowship For Practicing Physicians *(Advanced Professional, Professional development/Fellowship)*

Purpose: To encourage practicing physicians to undertake training to acquire a clinical skill or knowledge currently lacking in the community or to undertake training in research methodology. **Focus:** Medical research. **Qualif.:** Applicants must be Ontario physicians in established practice and residing outside of the teaching center communities; general practitioners and specialists are also

eligible but they must have the approval and support of the local medical society or the physicians within their community. **Criteria:** Selection will be based on the Foundation's criteria. Preference is given to a training program involving active participation by the applicants rather than mere observation.

Funds Avail.: No specific amount. **To Apply:** Applications will be considered for support of physicians who have undertaken training courses that commenced up to three months prior to the time the application is considered at a meeting of the Foundation's Grants Committee. **Remarks:** Established in 1970. **Contact:** Phone: 416-226-6323; Email: psif@psifoundation.org.

9156 ■ PSI Graham Farquharson Knowledge Translation Fellowship *(Advanced Professional, Professional development/Fellowship)*

Purpose: To provide salary support to new Ontario investigators who have demonstrated the ability to successfully complete high impact knowledge translation research. **Focus:** Medical research. **Qualif.:** Applicants must be either within five years of their first academic appointment and have demonstrated potential for high impact research work or who have dedicated at least 50% of a full-time schedule to the Fellowship or practicing physicians having direct patient care responsibilities and an academic appointment. **Criteria:** Selection will be based on the following: candidates' past research productivity; research plan; leveraging PSI fund; and institutional support and in-kind support.

Funds Avail.: A maximum of $150,000 per year for two years or a maximum of $100,000 per year for for three years. **Duration:** Annual. **To Apply:** Applicants must submit a letter of support from this supervisor; applications are submitted through the appropriate academic health science center; Candidate's past performance. **Contact:** Phone: 416-226-6323; Email: psif@psifoundation.org.

9157 ■ PSI Healthcare Research by Community Physicians Grants *(Advanced Professional, Professional development/Grant)*

Purpose: To assist physicians practicing in a community setting to undertake a review of their practice patterns which would enhance the effectiveness of practice and patient care in their own clinic, hospital or region. **Focus:** Medical research. **Qualif.:** Applicants must be Ontario physicians.

Funds Avail.: Up to 20,000 Canadian Dollars (500 will be for travel costs). **Duration:** Annual. **To Apply:** Applicants must submit a letter from the appropriate person at the hospital or institution should accompany applications for support of the healthcare research by a community physician; authorized officer of the hospital or institution should also sign the application. **Remarks:** Established in 1970.

9158 ■ Resident Research Grant *(Postgraduate, Professional development/Grant)*

Purpose: To support professionals in their research. **Focus:** Health education; Medical research. **Qualif.:** Applicants must be resident researchers in one of the following three areas: clinical research, medical education research and health systems research); must have a salary as Residents (such is being provided by the Ontario Ministry of Health and Long-Term Care); must be registered in a recognized program leading to certification by the Royal College of Physicians and Surgeons or the College of Fam-

Awards are arranged alphabetically below their administering organizations

ily Physicians; and must be registered as postgraduate students at the university where residency training is being taken. **Criteria:** Selection will be on a competitive basis due to grants allocated.

Funds Avail.: Up to a maximum of $20,000 Canadian Dollars. **Duration:** up to 2 years. **To Apply:** Applicants must new online application system is now in use for Resident Research Grant applications. may verify the website for further instructions regarding the application.

9159 ■ Pi Gamma Mu (PGM)
1001 Millington St., Ste. B
Winfield, KS 67156
Ph: (620)221-3128
URL: www.pigammamu.org
Social Media: www.facebook.com/
   PiGammaMuHonorSociety
www.linkedin.com/in/pi-gamma-mu-international-honor
   -society-45733695
www.linkedin.com/public-profile/in/pi-gamma-mu
   -international-honor-society-45733695
twitter.com/PiGammaMu1

9160 ■ Pi Gamma Mu Scholarships *(Graduate/ Scholarship)*
Purpose: To provide financial support to qualified individuals to pursue graduate education. **Focus:** Anthropology; Criminal justice; Economics; Geography; History; International affairs and relations; Law; Political science; Psychology; Public administration; Social work; Sociology. **Criteria:** Application will be evaluated based upon the degree to which the social sciences are an integral component of the overall course of study.

Funds Avail.: $1,000 - $2,000. **Duration:** Annual. **Number Awarded:** Upto 10. **To Apply:** Applicants must include personal statement; resume; three letters of recommendation from individuals qualified to assess the academic merit; recommendation letters should specifically address the student's merit related to Pi Gamma Mu scholarship application, intellectual qualities, and chance for success in graduate school rather than a generic letters recommending acceptance into a graduate program or other general recommendations; official transcripts from all institutions of higher learning attended; transcripts should be official and include the school's stamp or seal. **Deadline:** February 15. **Contact:** Pi Gamma Mu, 1001 Millington St., Ste B, Winfield, KS 67156.

9161 ■ Pi Kappa Phi Fraternity
2015 Ayrsley Town Blvd., Ste. 200
Charlotte, NC 28273
Ph: (704)504-0888
Fax: (980)318-5295
E-mail: pikapphq@pikapp.org
URL: pikapp.org
Social Media: www.instagram.com/pikappaphi
twitter.com/pikappaphi

9162 ■ Pi Kapp Scholars Award *(Undergraduate/ Scholarship)*
Purpose: To support undergraduate student leaders for their commitment to academic excellence. **Focus:** General studies/Field of study not specified. **Qualif.:** Applicants

must be juniors or seniors; must have a cumulative GPA of 3.3 or better; must have demonstrated leadership within the chapter or within chapter community; be an initiated member of Pi Kappa Phi Fraternity. **Criteria:** Selection will be based on Pi Kappa Phi Foundation.

Funds Avail.: $1,000. **Duration:** Annual. **Number Awarded:** Up to 7. **To Apply:** Applicants Complete the entire application. **Deadline:** March 5. **Contact:** Vicky Halsey, Executive Assistant; Email: vhalsey@pikapp.org.

9163 ■ Pi Lambda Theta (PLT)
1820 N Fort Myer Dr., Ste. 320
Arlington, VA 22209
Free: 800-766-1156
E-mail: pilambdatheta@pdkintl.org
URL: www.pilambda.org
Social Media: www.facebook.com/pilambda
www.linkedin.com/company/pi-lambda-theta
twitter.com/pilambdatheta¿lang=en

9164 ■ Graduate Student Scholar Award *(Graduate/ Scholarship)*
Purpose: To recognize an outstanding graduate student who is an education major. **Focus:** Education. **Qualif.:** Applicant must have a cumulative GPA of at least 3.5 on a 4.0 scale.

Funds Avail.: $1,000. **Duration:** Biennial. **Remarks:** Established in 1993.

9165 ■ Pi Sigma Epsilon (PSE)
4811 S 76th St.,Ste. 310
Greenfield, WI 53220
Ph: (414)328-1952
Fax: (414)235-3425
E-mail: pse@pse.org
URL: www.pse.org
Social Media: www.facebook.com/PiSigmaEpsilon
www.instagram.com/pisigmaepsilon
www.linkedin.com/company/pi-sigma-epsilon
twitter.com/pse

9166 ■ Anchor Plastics Scholarships *(Graduate, Undergraduate/Scholarship)*
Purpose: To provide financial support to sales and marketing students to advance their education. **Focus:** Marketing and distribution. **Criteria:** Selection is based on Pi Sigma Epsilon activities; career objectives/ educational goals; educational financing; overall and major GPA; and non-PSE activities/work experience.

Funds Avail.: $1,000. **Number Awarded:** 3. **Contact:** Email: scholarships@pse.org.

9167 ■ Debbie Khalil Memorial Scholarship *(Graduate, Undergraduate/Scholarship)*
Purpose: To provide financial support to sales and marketing students to advance their education. **Focus:** Marketing and distribution. **Criteria:** Selection is based on Pi Sigma Epsilon activities; career objectives/ educational goals; educational financing; overall and major GPA; and non-PSE activities/work experience.

Funds Avail.: $1,000. **Number Awarded:** 1. **Contact:** Email: scholarships@pse.org.

Awards are arranged alphabetically below their administering organizations

9168 ■ Enterprise Schlorship *(Graduate, Undergraduate/Scholarship)*

Purpose: To advance education of Pi Sigma Epsilon student member in sales and marketing. **Focus:** Marketing and distribution.
Funds Avail.: $1,500.

9169 ■ Federated Insurance Scholarship *(Graduate, Undergraduate/Scholarship)*

Purpose: To advance education of Pi Sigma Epsilon student member in sales and marketing. **Focus:** Marketing and distribution.
Funds Avail.: $1,000.

9170 ■ William H. Harris Memorial Scholarships *(Graduate, Undergraduate/Scholarship)*

Purpose: To provide financial support to sales and marketing students to advance their education. **Focus:** Marketing and distribution. **Criteria:** Selection is based on Pi Sigma Epsilon activities; career objectives/ educational goals; educational financing; overall and major GPA; and non-PSE activities/work experience.
Funds Avail.: $1,500. **Number Awarded:** 1. **Contact:** Email: scholarships@pse.org.

9171 ■ Northwestern Mutual Scholarship *(Graduate, Undergraduate/Scholarship)*

Purpose: To advance education of Pi Sigma Epsilon student member in sales and marketing. **Focus:** Marketing and distribution. **Criteria:** Selection is based on Pi Sigma Epsilon activities; career objectives/ educational goals; educational financing; overall and major GPA; and non-PSE activities/work experience.
Funds Avail.: $1,500. **Number Awarded:** 1. **Contact:** Email: scholarships@pse.org.

9172 ■ Phi Sigma Epsilon Past National President Scholarships *(Graduate, Undergraduate/Scholarship)*

Purpose: To provide financial support to sales and marketing students to advance their education. **Focus:** Marketing and distribution. **Qualif.:** Applicants must be enrolled in an undergraduate program and working toward an undergraduate degree with at least one semester, two quarters or summer session left before graduation; or enrolled or planning to enroll in a Graduate Program and working toward a post graduate degree (such as an MBA) with at least one semester, two quarters or summer session left before graduation; be students studying abroad; or graduating seniors with outstanding loans to their university. **Criteria:** Selection is based on Pi Sigma Epsilon activities; career objectives/ educational goals; educational financing; overall and major GPA; and non-PSE activities/work experience.
Funds Avail.: No specific amount. **To Apply:** Applicants must submit a completed application form together with a one page description of qualifications (Pi Sigma Epsilon activities; Mu Kappa Tau activities; Career objectives; Educational goals; Campus/Community activities; Special achievements/awards; Employment history; Percent of education financed by self, parents, scholarships, other); and two letters of recommendation. Applicants must also submit/bring a college transcript and resume. **Contact:** Send materials electronically to scholarships@pse.org.

9173 ■ Vector Marketing Scholarship *(Graduate, Undergraduate/Scholarship)*

Purpose: To advance education of Pi Sigma Epsilon student member in sales and marketing. **Focus:** Marketing and distribution.

Funds Avail.: $1,500.

9174 ■ Whan Memorial Scholarships *(Graduate, Undergraduate/Scholarship)*

Purpose: To provide financial support to sales and marketing students to advance their education. **Focus:** Marketing and distribution. **Criteria:** Selection is based on Pi Sigma Epsilon activities; career objectives/ educational goals; educational financing; overall and major GPA; and non-PSE activities/work experience.
Funds Avail.: $1,500. **Number Awarded:** 1. **Remarks:** Established in 1989. **Contact:** Email: scholarships@pse.org.

9175 ■ Pinnacol Foundation
7501 E Lowry Blvd.
Denver, CO 80230
Ph: (303)361-4005
Fax: (303)361-5000
Free: 800-873-7242
URL: pinnacol.com
Social Media: www.facebook.com/Pinnacol
www.instagram.com/pinnacol
www.linkedin.com/company/pinnacol-assurance
twitter.com/pinnacol

9176 ■ Pinnacol Foundation Scholarship *(Undergraduate, Community College, Vocational/ Occupational/Scholarship)*

Purpose: To ensure that children of seriously injured Colorado workers have the opportunity to pursue their dreams by continuing their education. **Focus:** General studies/Field of study not specified. **Qualif.:** Applicant must be the natural child, adopted child, stepchild, or full dependent of a worker who was injured or killed in a compensable work-related accident during the course and scope of employment with a Colorado-based employer and was entitled to receive benefits under the Colorado Workers' Compensation Act. Applicant must be between the ages of 16 and 25 at the time of the application deadline, have and maintain a minimum cumulative GPA of 2.0 or higher, and have a high school diploma or GED, or be a high school senior. **Criteria:** Selection is based on five categories: severity of the parent's workplace injury, academic performance, financial need, civic involvement, and motivation (as assessed through their essay and other application requirements).
Funds Avail.: $4,700. **To Apply:** Applications must be submitted through the sponsor's online application system. **Deadline:** February 15. **Contact:** Chris Sautter, Director; Email: pinnacol.foundation@pinnacol.com.

9177 ■ PinProsPlus
573 N Main St.
Kaysville, UT 84037
Ph: (801)544-1005
Free: 866-345-7467
E-mail: sales@pinprosplus.com
URL: www.pinprosplus.com
Social Media: www.facebook.com/pinprosplus
www.linkedin.com/company/pinpros
twitter.com/pinprosplus

9178 ■ The PinProsPlus Scholarship *(College, University, Graduate/Scholarship)*

Purpose: To help further the education of motivated and committed students. **Focus:** General studies/Field of study

Awards are arranged alphabetically below their administering organizations

not specified. **Qualif.:** Applicant must be accepted into or already a student of an accredited university, college, trade, or technical school in the United States. **Criteria:** Selection is based on the stories submitted.

Funds Avail.: $500. **Duration:** Semiannual. **Number Awarded:** 2. **To Apply:** Applicant needs to fill out the form online and submit an essay (800 to 1,000) words telling their story. **Deadline:** December 1. **Contact:** www.pinprosplus.com/about/scholarship/.

9179 ■ Pinto Ranch

1717 Post Oak Blvd.
Houston, TX 77056
Ph: (713)333-7900
Fax: (813)579-1390
Free: 800-393-8001
E-mail: houston@pintoranch.com
URL: www.pintoranch.com
Social Media: www.facebook.com/pintoranch
instagram.com/pintoranch/
www.pinterest.com/pintoranch/
twitter.com/pintoranch

9180 ■ The Pinto Ranch Western Achievement Scholarship *(Graduate/Scholarship)*

Purpose: To foster American heritage through Western culture and recognize hardworking high school seniors who have an appreciation for Western history and traditions. **Focus:** General studies/Field of study not specified. **Qualif.:** Applicant must be a graduating high school senior and a U.S. citizen or permanent legal resident; must have a minimum 3.5 GPA; must be an active member of FFA or similar agricultural or environmental organization; must plan to enroll in an accredited college/university in fall of the scholarship year; must have a minimum 24 hours of community service.

Funds Avail.: $2,000. **Duration:** Annual. **Number Awarded:** 1. **To Apply:** Applicants must submit Official High School transcript; copy of the college acceptance letter; Applicant must submit a 500-word essay on one of three topics: 1. What does it mean to live in America? What would you change? How can you help make that change?; 2. Describe how you are a leader in both your school and in your community.; 3. A long-standing Western tradition is to apprentice under a tradesman or craftsman to carry on that job or tradition. Who would you apprentice under and why? Further application details are available online at www.pintoranch.com/scholarships. **Deadline:** March 31. **Contact:** Email: scholarship@pintoranch.com.

9181 ■ Pipe Line Contractors Association of Canada (PLCAC)

1075 N Service Rd. W, Ste. 201
Oakville, ON, Canada L6M 2G2
Ph: (905)847-9383
Fax: (905)847-7824
E-mail: plcac@pipeline.ca
URL: www.pipeline.ca
Social Media: facebook.com/pages/Pipe-Line-Contractors
 -Association-of-Canada/521400631226999
www.linkedin.com/company/pipe-line-contractors
 -association-of-canada
twitter.com/PLCAC_Canada

www.youtube.com/channel/UCvzvbVVTNEq9Ty6olh9RNvA

9182 ■ PLCAC Student Award Program *(Postgraduate/Award)*

Purpose: To assist students with their educational expenses. **Focus:** Construction. **Criteria:** Selection will be based on the committee's criteria.

Funds Avail.: No specific amount. **Duration:** Annual. **Number Awarded:** Varies. **To Apply:** The application process is online. **Deadline:** October 11. **Remarks:** Established in 1974.

9183 ■ PKD Foundation

1001 E. 101st Terrace, Ste.220
Kansas City, MO 64131
Ph: (816)931-2600
Fax: (816)931-2600
Free: 800-753-2873
E-mail: pkdcure@pkdcure.org
URL: www.pkdcure.org
Social Media: www.facebook.com/pkdfoundation
twitter.com/pkdfoundation
www.youtube.com/user/PKDFoundation

9184 ■ PKD Foundation Fellowships *(Doctorate, Graduate/Fellowship)*

Purpose: To foster further research in all hereditary cystic disorders and to address the structure and function of polycystic kidney disease related genes in health and disease. **Focus:** Medicine. **Criteria:** Applications are reviewed based on the scientific merit of the project and its relevance to PKD research.

Funds Avail.: $60,000 each. **Duration:** Annual; two years. **Number Awarded:** Varies. **To Apply:** Applicants must submit the information via online; the sections of the applications and submitting instructions can be founded in the website. **Deadline:** January 18. **Contact:** Email: research@pkdcure.org.

9185 ■ A Place for Mom, INC.

701 5th Ave., Ste. 3200
Seattle, WA 98104
Free: 866-518-0936
URL: www.aplaceformom.com

9186 ■ Senior Wisdom Scholarship *(Undergraduate, Graduate/Scholarship, Award)*

Purpose: To support the training and education of future senior care leaders. **Focus:** Nursing. **Qualif.:** Applicants must be enrolled in an undergraduate or graduate degree program at an accredited U.S. or Canadian college (excluding Quebec); must be citizens or permanent residents of the U.S. or Canada (excluding Quebec); must maintain a satisfactory academic performance. **Criteria:** Selection will be based on the committee's criteria.

Funds Avail.: $2,000. **Duration:** Annual. **To Apply:** Applicants must submit a 500 words essay on the most important lesson they have learned from a senior citizen. More details on the essay topic and the agreement form can be found on the web site; must complete the online student information form; must submit a signed copy of the scholarship award agreement; submissions should have the student's name as the title/file name and all emails

Awards are arranged alphabetically below their administering organizations

should include the student's name in the subject line. **Deadline:** May 1. **Contact:** Email: scholarship@ aplaceformom.com.

9187 ■ Plan New Hampshire

273 Corporate Dr.,Suite 100
Portsmouth, NH 03801
Ph: (603)452-7523
URL: plannh.org
Social Media: www.facebook.com/pages/Plan-New
-Hampshire-The-Foundation-for-Shaping-the-Built
-Environment/103620672760
www.linkedin.com/company/plan-new-hampshire
twitter.com/#!/PlanNH

9188 ■ Plan NH's Scholarship and Fellowship Program *(Community College, Four Year College, Undergraduate, Graduate, Vocational/Occupational/ Scholarship)*

Purpose: To encourage and support students interested in some aspect of the built environment and its impact on the social, economic, and/or environmental capital of a community. **Focus:** Architecture; Construction; Environmental design; Historic preservation; Interior design; Landscape architecture and design. **Qualif.:** Applicant must be a resident of NH; must be in College (must be at least in first year when applying) or Grad School in an accredited program studying in the built environment (architecture, landscape architecture, studio art, engineering, interior design, construction, environmental, land or community planning, historic preservation, etc.), and must have a superior GPA. **Criteria:** Applications will be reviewed by a committee of diverse professionals, and those selected for interviews will be notified. Where applicable, the applicant may be asked to bring a portfolio of her/his work.

Duration: Annual. **Number Awarded:** 8-10. **To Apply:** Applicant should send a PDF of the online application, personal reference assessments, and other written requirements to r_leblanc@plannh.org. **Deadline:** April 17.

9189 ■ Plastic Surgery Foundation (PSF)

444 E Algonquin Rd.
Arlington Heights, IL 60005-4664
Ph: (847)228-9900
Free: 800-766-4955
E-mail: giving@plasticsurgery.org
URL: www.thepsf.org
Social Media: www.facebook.com/
ThePlasticSurgeryFoundation
twitter.com/ASPS_News
twitter.com/ASPSMembers

9190 ■ PSF Research Fellowship Grants *(Master's, Doctorate/Grant, Fellowship)*

Purpose: To encourage research and academic career development in plastic surgery. **Focus:** Medical research; Surgery. **Criteria:** Evaluation of the application will place emphasis on the research training experience, research project, applicant potential, and mentor qualifications and commitment to mentoring.

Funds Avail.: Up to $50,000. **Duration:** Annual. **To Apply:** Applications must be submitted online. **Deadline:** December 1.

9191 ■ PlasticPlace

300 Boulevard of the Americas, Ste. 1
Lakewood, NJ 08701
Free: 877-343-2247
E-mail: info@plasticplace.com
URL: www.plasticplace.com
Social Media: www.facebook.com/PlasticPlace
twitter.com/Plasticplace

9192 ■ PlasticPlace Young Entrepreneurs Scholarship Award *(Undergraduate/Scholarship)*

Purpose: To help students who have the aptitude to become America's future entrepreneurs primarily those who belong to any underrepresented minority demographic. **Focus:** Business; Economics. **Qualif.:** Applicants must be incoming students for the next academic year, who are U.S. citizens, and have an average SAT score of 1070, GPA of 3.5 or above. **Criteria:** Preference will be given to applicants who are female, or belong to any minority group, including; African American, Asian American, Native American, and Hispanic; the winning essay will be chooses on the basis of quality of research, originality, and presentation.

Funds Avail.: $1,500. **Duration:** Annual. **To Apply:** Applicants must fill out an application form, produce a thoughtful, well-written essay on the topic listed to enter into the contest and submit the name and contact information of their chosen college/university for verification of registration and payment of the scholarship directly to the school. **Deadline:** November 1. **Contact:** Email: scholarships@ plasticplace.com.

9193 ■ Platinum Educational Group

2644 Sun Valley
Jenison, MI 49428
Ph: (616)818-7877
E-mail: marketing@platinumed.com
URL: platinumed.com
Social Media: www.facebook.com/
PlatinumEducationalGroup
www.linkedin.com/company/platinum-educational-group-llc/
products
twitter.com/PlatinumEdGroup
www.youtube.com/user/platinumeducational

9194 ■ Platinum Educational Groups Annual Scholarships Program *(All/Scholarship)*

Purpose: To provide students entering the EMS, Nursing, and Allied Health fields assistance in funding their education **Focus:** Paramedics. **Qualif.:** Applicants must be students entering the EMS, Nursing, and Allied Health fields.

Funds Avail.: $1,000. **Duration:** Annual. **Number Awarded:** 3. **To Apply:** Applicant must submit full details and to apply for the Platinum Educational Group Scholarships Program contact Director of Marketing. **Contact:** Director of Marketing, Jeremy M. Johnson; Email: marketing@ platinumed.com.

9195 ■ Playwrights' Center

2301 E Franklin Ave.
Minneapolis, MN 55406
Ph: (612)332-7481

Awards are arranged alphabetically below their administering organizations

Fax: (612)332-6037
E-mail: info@pwcenter.org
URL: pwcenter.org
Social Media: www.facebook.com/pwcenter
instagram.com/pwcenter
twitter.com/pwcenter

9196 ■ Jerome Fellowships *(Other/Fellowship)*

Purpose: To provide funds and services to emerging American playwrights and to aid them in the development of their craft. **Focus:** Theater arts. **Qualif.:** Applicants must be citizens or permanent residents of the United States who may have had more than two different works fully produced by professional theaters at the time of application, defined as productions for which the author or primary artists (actors, directors). Recipients must commit to spending the 12-month fellowship period in Minnesota and actively participating in the Center's programs.

Funds Avail.: $18,000 stipend and $2,500 in development support. **Duration:** Annual. **To Apply:** Applicant must submit the following: completed application form, playwriting resume, one page artistic statement and goals, full-length play script, and two letters of recommendation. **Remarks:** Awarded in partnership with the Jerome Foundation. Established in 1976. **Contact:** Julia Brown, Artistic Programs Manager; Email: juliab@pwcenter.org; URL: pwcenter.org/programs/jerome-fellowships.

9197 ■ Many Voices Fellowships *(Other/Fellowship)*

Purpose: To support early career playwrights of color and Indigenous playwrights who demonstrate artistic potential. **Focus:** Theater arts. **Qualif.:** Applicants must be playwrights of color or indigenous playwrights who reside in and have the legal right to work in the U.S; may not have had more than one playfully produced by professional theaters at the time of the application. Recipients must commit to spending the 12-month fellowship period in Minnesota and actively participating in the Center's programs.

Funds Avail.: $18,000 stipend and $2,500 in development funds. **Duration:** Annual. **Number Awarded:** 2. **To Apply:** Applicants must submit the following: completed application form, playwrighting resume, one page artistic statement and goals, full-length play script, and two letters of recommendations. **Contact:** Julia Brown, Artistic Programs Manager; Email: juliab@pwcenter.org; URL: pwcenter.org/programs/many-voices-fellowships.

9198 ■ McKnight Fellowships *(Other/Fellowship)*

Purpose: To recognize and support playwrights whose work demonstrates exceptional artistic merit and potential. **Focus:** Theater arts. **Qualif.:** Applicants must be citizens or permanent residents of the United States; must be a resident of Minnesota and must maintain residency in Minnesota during the fellowship year; must have a minimum of one work fully produced by a professional theater at the time of the application. **Criteria:** Selection will be based on artistic excellence, professional achievement, and proposed residency plans.

Funds Avail.: $25,000 stipend; $1,400 travel support; $2,500 to support a play development workshop and other professional expenses. **To Apply:** Applicants must submit the following: completed application form, playwriting resume, artistic statement, full-length play script, and two references. **Remarks:** Sponsored by the McKnight Foundation Arts Funding Plan. **Contact:** Julia Brown, Artistic Programs Manager; Email: juliab@pwcenter.org; URL:

pwcenter.org/programs/mcknight-fellowships-in-playwriting.

9199 ■ McKnight Theater Artist Fellowships *(Other/Fellowship)*

Purpose: To support outstanding work by professional artists whose skill and talent contribute to theatrical productions. **Focus:** Theater arts. **Qualif.:** Applicants must be professional artists who have been continuous residents of Minnesota; fellowship is open to actors, directors, dramaturgs, stage managers, and theatrical designers (including puppetry). It is also open to those choreographers and composers whose main body of work is in theater. Only individual artists are eligible. **Criteria:** Selection will be based on a commitment to theater arts, evidence of professional achievements, and a sustained level of excellence in the work.

Funds Avail.: $25,000 each. **To Apply:** Applicants must declare their intent to apply and inform the playwrights' center where and when the performances will take place. In final application, must submit six collated sets of the following items; cover sheet; one-page artist statement; resume (2 pages maximum); statements of working process; work sample information sheet (2 pages maximum); work samples; submit samples in no more than two of the following formats; video, 3-4 minutes of video in DVD format; photographs, up to 10 images in JPEG or TIFF format on a CD; audio, 3-4 minutes in audio CD format or MP3 format. **Deadline:** April 16. **Contact:** Julia Brown, Artistic Programs Manager; Email: juliab@pwcenter.org; URL: pwcenter.org/programs/mcknight-theater-artist-fellowships.

9200 ■ PWC Core Apprentice Program *(Other/Internship)*

Purpose: To foster deeper connections between professional playwrights and emerging playwrights, and to encourage further development in the student writer's work and career. **Focus:** Performing arts; Theater arts. **Qualif.:** Applicants must be playwrights who are current or recently graduated (within one year) students of New Plays on Campus(NPOC) member colleges or universities and are nominated by their schools.

Number Awarded: 3. **To Apply:** Applicants must submit the following: a recommendation letter written by a faculty member detailing why this student would benefit from a workshop at this time, the student's strengths, and areas in which the student has room for growth in their craft; a 25-page script sample of the student's proposed play, with a brief play synopsis and a casting description; one-page development project proposal written by the student stating how they would benefit from a workshop of this play at the Playwrights' Center and a 9-month mentorship; and a professional resume. **Deadline:** February 20. **Contact:** All application materials can be emailed to Hannah Joyce-Hoven at hannahj@pwcenter.org; URL: pwcenter.org/programs/core-apprentice.

9201 ■ D.F. Plett Historical Research Foundation, Inc.

515 Portage Ave.
Winnipeg, MB, Canada R3B 2E9
Ph: (204)786-9352
E-mail: info@plettfoundation.org
URL: www.plettfoundation.org

Awards are arranged alphabetically below their administering organizations

9202 ■ D.F. Plett Graduate Fellowship *(Graduate/ Fellowship)*

Purpose: To encourage graduate students who are pursuing studies and research in the history of the forerunners and descendants of the 1870s Mennonite migrants to Manitoba. **Focus:** History. **Qualif.:** Applicants must be admitted or applying to complete a master of arts degree in history in the Joint Master's Program of the University of Winnipeg and the University of Manitoba or a PhD in history at the University of Manitoba. **Criteria:** Selection is based on the submitted application and materials.

Funds Avail.: Postdoctoral Fellowship - $40,000; Ph.D. Fellowship - $20,000; Master's Fellowship - $15,000. **Number Awarded:** 2. **To Apply:** Applicants must submit a completed application form along with a photocopy of official transcripts, a summary of the proposed research (not more than 250 words); and sealed letters from two referees. **Deadline:** January 1.

9203 ■ Plumbing-Heating-Cooling Contractors Association (PHCC)

180 S Washington St., Ste. 100
Falls Church, VA 22046
Ph: (703)237-8100
Fax: (703)237-7442
Free: 800-533-7694
URL: www.phccweb.org
Social Media: www.facebook.com/PHCCNational
www.linkedin.com/company/plumbing-heating-cooling
  -contractors--national-association
www.linkedin.com/company/phccnational
twitter.com/phccnatl
www.youtube.com/user/NationalPHCC

9204 ■ Delta Faucet Scholarships *(Undergraduate/ Scholarship)*

Purpose: To help students prepare for careers in the plumbing-heating-cooling profession. **Focus:** Business. **Criteria:** Selection will be made up of selection committee.

Funds Avail.: $2,500. **Number Awarded:** 6. **To Apply:** Applicant must complete the online application. **Deadline:** May 1. **Contact:** PHCC Educational Foundation at scholarships@naphcc.org.

9205 ■ Plumbing-Heating-Cooling Contractors Association Educational Foundation Massachusetts Auxiliary Scholarships *(Undergraduate/Scholarship)*

Purpose: To help students prepare for careers in the plumbing-heating-cooling profession. **Focus:** Business. **Qualif.:** Applicants must be high school seniors who are citizens of the United States and residents of the Commonwealth of Massachusetts, planning to enroll in a full-time undergraduate degree program at an accredited four-year college or university. **Criteria:** Recipients are selected based on academic performance and financial need.

Funds Avail.: $2,500. **Number Awarded:** 1. **To Apply:** Applicants must complete the application form and submit an official transcript of high school grades; letter of recommendation from high school principal or counselor; SAT and ACT scores and cumulative GPA; and a letter of recommendation from an active member of the Plumbing-Heating-Cooling Contractors Association National Auxiliary. **Deadline:** May 1. **Contact:** PHCC Educational Foundation at scholarships@naphcc.org.

9206 ■ Plumbing-Heating-Cooling Contractors Association Educational Foundation Need-Based Scholarships *(Undergraduate/Scholarship)*

Purpose: To help students prepare for careers in the plumbing-heating-cooling profession. **Focus:** Business.

Funds Avail.: $2,500. **To Apply:** Applicants must complete the application form and submit an official transcript of high school grades; letter of recommendation from high school principal or counselor; SAT and ACT scores and cumulative GPA; and a letter of recommendation from an active member of the Plumbing-Heating-Cooling Contractors Association National Association. **Contact:** PHCC Educational Foundation; Email: E: foundation@naphcc.org.

9207 ■ PHCC of Texas Auxiliary and PHCC Educational Foundation funds *(Undergraduate/ Scholarship)*

Purpose: To help students prepare for careers in the plumbing-heating-cooling profession. **Focus:** Business. **Qualif.:** Applicants must be citizens of the United States or Canada and must be enrolled full-time in an undergraduate degree program at an accredited four-year college or university with a major directly to plumbing-heating-cooling profession. **Criteria:** Recipients are selected based on academic performance and financial need.

Funds Avail.: $2,500. **Number Awarded:** 1. **To Apply:** Applicants must complete the application form and submit an official transcript of the high school grades; letter of recommendation from high school principal or counselor; SAT and ACT scores as well as cumulative GPA; and a letter of recommendation from an active member of the Plumbing-Heating-Cooling Contractors Association National Association. **Deadline:** May 1. **Contact:** PHCC Educational Foundation at scholarships@naphcc.org.

9208 ■ A.O. Smith Scholarships *(Undergraduate/ Scholarship)*

Purpose: To help students prepare for careers in the plumbing-heating-cooling profession. **Focus:** Business. **Qualif.:** Applicants must be citizens of the United States or Canada and must be enrolled full-time in an undergraduate degree program at an accredited four-year college or university with a major directly to plumbing-heating-cooling profession. **Criteria:** Recipients are selected based on academic performance.

Funds Avail.: $2,500. **Number Awarded:** Up to 4. **To Apply:** Applicants must complete the application form and must submit an official transcript of the high school grades; letter of recommendation from high school principal or counselor, college/university dean, academic advisor or apprentice program instructor; SAT and ACT scores as well as cumulative GPA; and a letter of recommendation from an active member of the plumbing-heating-cooling contractors. **Deadline:** May 1. **Contact:** PHCC Educational Foundation at scholarships@naphcc.org.

9209 ■ Bradford White Corporation Scholarships *(Undergraduate/Scholarship)*

Purpose: To help students prepare for careers in the plumbing-heating-cooling profession. **Focus:** Business. **Criteria:** Recipients are selected based on academic performance.

Funds Avail.: $2,500. **Number Awarded:** Up to 3. **To Apply:** Applicants must complete the application form and submit an official transcript of the high school grades; letter of recommendation from high school principal or counselor,

Awards are arranged alphabetically below their administering organizations

college/university dean, academic advisor or apprentice program instructor; SAT and ACT scores and cumulative GPA; and a letter of recommendation from an active member of the plumbing-heating-cooling contractors. **Deadline:** May 1. **Contact:** PHCC Educational Foundation at scholarships@naphcc.org.

9210 ■ Plus Foundation
5353 Wayzata Blvd., Ste. 600
Minneapolis, MN 55416
Ph: (952)746-2590
Fax: (952)746-2599
E-mail: info@plusweb.org
URL: www.plusfoundation.org

9211 ■ Leo Gilmartin Scholarship *(Undergraduate/Scholarship)*

Purpose: To assist deserving PLUS member students with their college education. **Focus:** General studies/Field of study not specified. **Qualif.:** Applicants must be high school seniors who are children of current PLUS member or children of employees of current PLUS corporate sponsors. **Criteria:** Applicants are evaluated based on scholastic merit and extracurricular activity.

Funds Avail.: Up to $12,000. **Duration:** Annual. **Number Awarded:** Up to 4. **To Apply:** Applicants must submit college entrance exam scores; GPA and class rank; essay and letters of recommendation; list of extracurricular and community service activities.

9212 ■ PLUS Foundation Financial Aid Scholarship *(Undergraduate/Scholarship)*

Purpose: To provide educational assistance to students who wants to advance their education. **Focus:** General studies/Field of study not specified. **Qualif.:** Applicants must be high school seniors who are children of current PLUS member or children of employees of current PLUS corporate sponsors. **Criteria:** Recipients are selected based on family financial need and proof of average to above average high school performance.

Funds Avail.: Up to $12,000. **Duration:** Annual. **Number Awarded:** Up to 4. **To Apply:** Applicants must submit the household adjusted gross income; total number in household and number of dependent children attending college; estimated cost of tuition; GPA, class rank, college entrance exams scores. **Deadline:** January 31.

9213 ■ PM Business Advisors
333 Westchester Ave., East Building, Ste. E-1101
White Plains, NY 10604
Ph: (914)218-1300
E-mail: info@pmbusinessadvisors.com
URL: www.pmbusinessadvisors.com

9214 ■ Striving for Greatness Accounting & Finance Scholarship *(Undergraduate/Scholarship)*

Purpose: To support well-rounded individuals who display both academic excellence in accounting and/or finance as well as an involvement in their community. **Focus:** Accounting; Finance. **Qualif.:** Applicants must follow a course of study in accounting or finance; plan to sit for the CPA exam within three years; be enrolled full-time in a college or university; have a cumulative GPA of at least 3.0; demonstrate leadership ability and involvement in community

service organizations; be a U.S. citizen or permanent U.S resident.

Funds Avail.: $2,500. **Duration:** Annual. **Deadline:** December 31. **Contact:** PM Business Advisors, LLC, 333 Westchester Ave., E bldg. Ste. E-1500, White Plains, NY, 10604; Phone: 914-218-1300; Email: nsgueglia@pmbusinessadvisors.com.

9215 ■ Poetry
61 West Superior Street
Chicago, IL 60654
Ph: (312)787-7070
E-mail: mail@poetryfoundation.org
URL: www.poetrymagazine.org
Social Media: www.facebook.com/poetryfoundation
www.instagram.com/poetryfoundation
twitter.com/poetryfound

9216 ■ Ruth Lilly and Dorothy Sargent Rosenberg Poetry Fellowships *(Professional development/Fellowship, Prize)*

Purpose: To recognize and encourage young, emerging American poets. **Focus:** Poetry. **Qualif.:** Applicants must reside in the U.S. or be U.S. citizens; must be at least 21 years of age and no older than 31 years of age as of April 30, 2017.

Funds Avail.: $25,800. **Duration:** Annual. **Number Awarded:** Varies. **To Apply:** Applicants must be submit an introduction to work approximately 250-word (not to exceed one page);Ten pages of poems must be include multiple poems on one page, but the total pages of poems must not exceed ten. **Deadline:** April 30. **Remarks:** Established in 1989.

9217 ■ Point Foundation (PF)
6320 Wilshire Blvd., Ste. 890
Los Angeles, CA 90036
Ph: (323)933-1234
Free: 866-337-6468
E-mail: info@pointfoundation.org
URL: www.pointfoundation.org
Social Media: www.facebook.com/pointfoundation
instagram.com/pointfoundation
linkedin.com/company/point-foundation
twitter.com/PointFoundation
youtube.com/user/UTubePointFoundation

9218 ■ George Benes, MD & Michael Mallee, EdD Point Scholarships *(Undergraduate, Graduate, Doctorate/Scholarship)*

Purpose: To assist students in achieving their higher education degree to make a significant impact on the society no matter what gender preferences they have. **Focus:** General studies/Field of study not specified. **Qualif.:** Applicants must attain the following qualifications: must be enrolled or intending to enroll at an accredited college or university based in the United States, including Hawaii and Alaska - applicants enrolled or intending to enroll in a college or university in a United States territory are not eligible; must be enrolled full-time for the full academic year and in a degree-granting undergraduate or graduate or doctoral program; must be at least senior in high school and; must be "out" as a person who identifies as a member

Awards are arranged alphabetically below their administering organizations

of the LGBTQ community. Community college applicants must be transferring to a four-year college or university.

Duration: Annual. **To Apply:** Application form and details are available online at: pointfoundation.org/point-apply/community-college/. **Contact:** David Garza at davidg@pointfoundation.org; Phone: 212-512-5339; Adam Crowley at adam@pointfoundation.org; Phone: 323-933-1234.

9219 ■ Calamus Foundation Point Scholarship
(Undergraduate, Graduate, Doctorate/Scholarship)

Purpose: To help LGBTQ+ students pay for higher education and impact the lives of the next generation of leaders. **Focus:** General studies/Field of study not specified. **Qualif.:** Applicants must attain the following qualifications: must be enrolled or intending to enroll at an accredited college or university based in the United States, including Hawaii and Alaska - applicants enrolled or intending to enroll in a college or university in a United States territory are not eligible; must be enrolled full-time for the full academic year and in a degree-granting undergraduate or graduate or doctoral program; must be at least senior in high school and; must be "out" as a person who identifies as a member of the LGBTQ community. Community college applicants must be transferring to a four-year college or university.

Duration: Annual. **To Apply:** Application form and details are available online at: pointfoundation.org/point-apply/community-college/.

9220 ■ Walter M. Decker Point Scholarship *(Graduate, Undergraduate/Scholarship)*

Purpose: To support LGBT students to achieve their full academic and leadership potential. **Focus:** General studies/Field of study not specified. **Qualif.:** Applicant must be part of the LGBT community, or have a history of leadership in the LGBT community and plan to be a LGBT leader in the future. **Criteria:** Award is given based on the application.

To Apply: Applicants must complete the online scholarship application before the deadline. If chosen as semi-finalists, students are requested to submit supplemental materials, in one envelope: two to three letters of recommendation; official transcripts; test score verification; and resume. **Remarks:** Established by the Point Foundation in honor of Walter M. Decker, an accomplished radiologist, who was a fine example of an individual who lived simply, but wanted others to benefit from his success. **Contact:** David Garza at davidg@pointfoundation.org; Phone: 212-512-5339; Adam Crowley at adam@pointfoundation.org; Phone: 323-933-1234.

9221 ■ Steven Esposito Memorial Scholarship
(Undergraduate, Graduate, Doctorate/Scholarship)

Purpose: To assist students in achieving their higher education degree to make a significant impact on the society no matter what gender preferences they have. **Focus:** General studies/Field of study not specified. **Qualif.:** Applicants must attain the following qualifications: must be enrolled or intending to enroll at an accredited college or university based in the United States, including Hawaii and Alaska - applicants enrolled or intending to enroll in a college or university in a United States territory are not eligible; must be enrolled full-time for the full academic year and in a degree-granting undergraduate or graduate or doctoral program; must be at least senior in high school and; must be "out" as a person who identifies as a member of the LGBTQ community. Community college applicants must be transferring to a four-year college or university.

To Apply: Application form and details are available online at: pointfoundation.org/point-apply/community-college/. **Contact:** David Garza at davidg@pointfoundation.org; Phone: 212-512-5339; Adam Crowley at adam@pointfoundation.org; Phone: 323-933-1234.

9222 ■ HBO Point Scholarship *(Graduate, Undergraduate, Doctorate/Scholarship)*

Purpose: To help a creative and dynamic individual who intends to pursue a career in the media. **Focus:** Media arts. **Qualif.:** Applicants must attain the following qualifications: must be enrolled or intending to enroll at an accredited college or university based in the United States, including Hawaii and Alaska - applicants enrolled or intending to enroll in a college or university in a United States territory are not eligible; must be enrolled full-time for the full academic year and in a degree-granting undergraduate or graduate or doctoral program; must be at least senior in high school and; must be "out" as a person who identifies as a member of the LGBTQ community. Community college applicants must be transferring to a four-year college or university.

To Apply: Applicants must complete the online scholarship application on or before the deadline. If chosen as semi-finalists, students are requested to submit supplemental materials, in one envelope: two to three letters of recommendation; official transcripts; test score verification; and resume. **Contact:** David Garza at davidg@pointfoundation.org; Phone: 212-512-5339; Adam Crowley at adam@pointfoundation.org; Phone: 323-933-1234.

9223 ■ Kevin Hummer Point Scholarship *(Graduate, Undergraduate, Doctorate/Scholarship)*

Purpose: To support LGBT students to achieve their full academic and leadership potential. **Focus:** General studies/Field of study not specified. **Qualif.:** Applicants must attain the following qualifications: must be enrolled or intending to enroll at an accredited college or university based in the United States, including Hawaii and Alaska - applicants enrolled or intending to enroll in a college or university in a United States territory are not eligible; must be enrolled full-time for the full academic year and in a degree-granting undergraduate or graduate or doctoral program; must be at least senior in high school and; must be "out" as a person who identifies as a member of the LGBTQ community. Community college applicants must be transferring to a four-year college or university.

Funds Avail.: No specific amount. **To Apply:** Applicants must complete the online scholarship application on or before the deadline. If chosen as semi-finalists, students are requested to submit supplemental materials, in one envelope: two to three letters of recommendation; official transcripts; test score verification; and resume. Application form and details are available online at: pointfoundation.org/point-apply/community-college/. **Remarks:** Named in honor of Kevin Hummer, who desired to create something to leave behind — something that could have helped someone like him growing up. **Contact:** David Garza at davidg@pointfoundation.org; Phone: 212-512-5339; Adam Crowley at adam@pointfoundation.org; Phone: 323-933-1234.

9224 ■ Janssen Infectious Disease Point Scholarships *(Undergraduate, Graduate, Doctorate/Scholarship)*

Purpose: To assist students in achieving their higher education degrees to make a significant impact on the society no matter what gender preferences they have.

Awards are arranged alphabetically below their administering organizations

Focus: General studies/Field of study not specified. **Qualif.:** Applicants must attain the following qualifications: must be enrolled or intending to enroll at an accredited college or university based in the United States, including Hawaii and Alaska; must be enrolled full-time for the full academic year and in a degree-granting undergraduate or graduate/doctoral program; must be at least senior in high school and; must be "out" as a person who identifies as a member of the LGBTQ community. Community college applicants must be transferring to a four-year college or university. **Criteria:** Selection will be based on the committees' criteria. **Duration:** Annual. **To Apply:** Application form and details are available online at: pointfoundation.org/point-apply/community-college/. **Contact:** David Garza at davidg@pointfoundation.org; Phone: 212-512-5339; Adam Crowley at adam@pointfoundation.org; Phone: 323-933-1234.

9225 ■ Larry King/Jeffrey Fashion Cares Point Scholarship *(Undergraduate, Graduate, Doctorate/Scholarship)*

Purpose: To assist students in achieving a higher education degrees to make a significant impact on the society no matter what gender preferences they have. **Focus:** Sexuality. **Qualif.:** Applicants must attain the following qualifications: must be enrolled or intending to enroll at an accredited college or university based in the United States, including Hawaii and Alaska - applicants enrolled or intending to enroll in a college or university in a United States territory are not eligible; must be enrolled full-time for the full academic year and in a degree-granting undergraduate or graduate/doctoral program; must be at least a senior in high school and; must be "out" as a person who identifies as a member of the LGBTQ community. Community college applicants must be transferring to a four-year college or university. **Criteria:** Selection will be based on the committees' criteria.

To Apply: Application form and details are available online at: pointfoundation.org/point-apply/community-college/. **Contact:** David Garza at davidg@pointfoundation.org; Phone: 212-512-5339; Adam Crowley at adam@pointfoundation.org; Phone: 323-933-1234.

9226 ■ William J. Levy Point Scholarship *(Undergraduate, Graduate, Doctorate/Scholarship)*

Purpose: To assist students in achieving a higher education degree to make a significant impact on the society no matter what gender preferences they have. **Focus:** General studies/Field of study not specified. **Qualif.:** Applicants must attain the following qualifications: must be enrolled or intending to enroll at an accredited college or university based in the United States, including Hawaii and Alaska - applicants enrolled or intending to enroll in a college or university in a United States territory are not eligible; must be enrolled full-time for the full academic year and in a degree-granting undergraduate or graduate/doctoral program; must be at least senior in high school and; must be "out" as a person who identifies as a member of the LGBTQ community. Community college applicants must be transferring to a four-year college or university.

To Apply: Application form and details are available online at: pointfoundation.org/point-apply/community-college/. **Contact:** David Garza at davidg@pointfoundation.org; Phone: 212-512-5339; Adam Crowley at adam@pointfoundation.org; Phone: 323-933-1234.

9227 ■ Minton-Spidell-Jackowski Point Scholarship *(Undergraduate, Graduate, Doctorate/Scholarship)*

Purpose: To assist students in achieving a higher education degree to make a significant impact on the society no matter what gender preferences they have. **Focus:** General studies/Field of study not specified. **Qualif.:** Applicants must attain the following qualifications: must be enrolled or intending to enroll at an accredited college or university based in the United States, including Hawaii and Alaska - applicants enrolled or intending to enroll in a college or university in a United States territory are not eligible; must be enrolled full-time for the full academic year and in a degree-granting undergraduate or graduate or doctoral program; must be at least senior in high school and; must be "out" as a person who identifies as a member of the LGBTQ community. Community college applicants must be transferring to a four-year college or university.

Funds Avail.: No specific amount. **To Apply:** Application form and details are available online at: pointfoundation.org/point-apply/community-college/. **Contact:** David Garza at davidg@pointfoundation.org; Phone: 212-512-5339; Adam Crowley at adam@pointfoundation.org; Phone: 323-933-1234.

9228 ■ NBCUniversal Point Scholarship *(Undergraduate, Graduate, Doctorate/Scholarship)*

Purpose: To assist students in achieving a higher education degree to make a significant impact on the society no matter what gender preferences they have. **Focus:** General studies/Field of study not specified. **Qualif.:** Applicants must attain the following qualifications: must be enrolled or intending to enroll at an accredited college or university based in the United States, including Hawaii and Alaska - applicants enrolled or intending to enroll in a college or university in a United States territory are not eligible; must be enrolled full-time for the full academic year and in a degree-granting undergraduate or graduate or doctoral program; must be at least senior in high school and; must be "out" as a person who identifies as a member of the LGBTQ community. Community college applicants must be transferring to a four-year college or university.

To Apply: Application form and details are available online at: pointfoundation.org/point-apply/community-college/. **Contact:** David Garza at davidg@pointfoundation.org; Phone: 212-512-5339; Adam Crowley at adam@pointfoundation.org; Phone: 323-933-1234.

9229 ■ Point Community College Scholarship Program *(Undergraduate, Community College/Scholarship)*

Purpose: To assist students in achieving a higher education degrees to make a significant impact on the society no matter what gender preferences they have. **Focus:** General studies/Field of study not specified. **Qualif.:** Applicants must be enrolled or intending to enroll at an accredited community college based in the United States, including Hawaii and Alaska; must have one to two years of community college left and be intending to transfer to a bachelor's degree program at a four-year college or university; must be "out" as a person who identifies as a member of the LGBTQ community. **Criteria:** Applicants are evaluated on many criteria, including: financial need or independence; personal history; academic achievement; community involvement and work experience.

Funds Avail.: $2,000 to $4,800 per year. **To Apply:** Application and details are available at: pointfoundation.org/point-apply/community-college/. **Deadline:** May 4. **Contact:** Email: applications@pointfoundation.org.

9230 ■ Rim-Freeman Point Scholarship *(Undergraduate/Scholarship)*

Purpose: To assist students in achieving a higher education degrees to make a significant impact on the society no

Awards are arranged alphabetically below their administering organizations

matter what gender preferences they have. **Focus:** General studies/Field of study not specified. **Qualif.:** Applicants must attain the following qualifications: must be enrolled or intending to enroll at an accredited college or university based in the United States, including Hawaii and Alaska - applicants enrolled or intending to enroll in a college or university in a United States territory are not eligible; must be enrolled full-time for the full academic year and in a degree-granting undergraduate program; must be at least senior in high school and; must be "out" as a person who identifies as a member of the LGBTQ community. Community college applicants must be transferring to a four-year college or university. **Criteria:** Selection will be based on the committees' criteria.

To Apply: Application form and details are available online at: pointfoundation.org/point-apply/community-college/. **Contact:** David Garza at davidg@pointfoundation.org; Phone: 212-512-5339; Adam Crowley at adam@pointfoundation.org; Phone: 323-933-1234.

9231 ■ Rand Skolnick Point Scholarship
(Undergraduate, Graduate, Doctorate/Scholarship)

Purpose: To assist students in achieving a higher education degree to make a significant impact on the society no matter what gender preferences they have. **Focus:** General studies/Field of study not specified. **Qualif.:** Applicants must attain the following qualifications: must be enrolled or intending to enroll at an accredited college or university based in the United States, including Hawaii and Alaska - applicants enrolled or intending to enroll in a college or university in a United States territory are not eligible; must be enrolled full-time for the full academic year and in a degree-granting undergraduate or graduate or doctoral program; must be at least senior in high school and; must be "out" as a person who identifies as a member of the LGBTQ community. Community college applicants must be transferring to a four-year college or university.

Funds Avail.: No specific amount. **Duration:** Annual. **To Apply:** Application form and details are available online at: pointfoundation.org/point-apply/community-college/. **Remarks:** Established to honor Rand Skolnick's commitment to education and to support young people as they explore careers in philanthropy and service to the LGBT community. **Contact:** David Garza at davidg@pointfoundation.org; Phone: 212-512-5339; Adam Crowley at adam@pointfoundation.org; Phone: 323-933-1234.

9232 ■ Took Trust Point Scholarship *(Undergraduate, Graduate/Scholarship)*

Purpose: To assist students in achieving a higher education degree to make a significant impact on the society no matter what gender preferences they have. **Focus:** General studies/Field of study not specified. **Qualif.:** Applicants must attain the following qualifications: must be enrolled or intending to enroll at an accredited college or university based in the United States, including Hawaii and Alaska - applicants enrolled or intending to enroll in a college or university in a United States territory are not eligible; must be enrolled full-time for the full academic year and in a degree-granting undergraduate or graduate/doctoral program; must be at least senior in high school and; must be "out" as a person who identifies as a member of the LGBTQ community. Community college applicants must be transferring to a four-year college or university. **Criteria:** Selection will be based on the committee's criteria.

To Apply: Application form and details are available online at: pointfoundation.org/point-apply/community-college/.

Contact: David Garza at davidg@pointfoundation.org; Phone: 212-512-5339; Adam Crowley at adam@pointfoundation.org; Phone: 323-933-1234.

9233 ■ Toyota Point Scholarship *(Undergraduate, Graduate, Doctorate/Scholarship)*

Purpose: To assist students in achieving a higher education degree to make a significant impact on the society no matter what gender preferences they have. **Focus:** General studies/Field of study not specified. **Qualif.:** Applicants must attain the following qualifications: must be enrolled or intending to enroll at an accredited college or university based in the United States, including Hawaii and Alaska - applicants enrolled or intending to enroll in a college or university in a United States territory are not eligible; must be enrolled full-time for the full academic year and in a degree-granting undergraduate or graduate/doctoral program; must be at least senior in high school and; must be "out" as a person who identifies as a member of the LGBTQ community. Community college applicants must be transferring to a four-year college or university. **Criteria:** Selection will be based on the committee's criteria.

To Apply: Application form and details are available online at: pointfoundation.org/point-apply/community-college/. **Contact:** David Garza at davidg@pointfoundation.org; Phone: 212-512-5339; Adam Crowley at adam@pointfoundation.org; Phone: 323-933-1234.

9234 ■ Wells Fargo Point Scholarship *(Undergraduate, Graduate/Scholarship)*

Purpose: To assist students in achieving a higher education degree to make a significant impact on the society no matter what gender preferences they have. **Focus:** General studies/Field of study not specified. **Qualif.:** Applicants must attain the following qualifications: must be undergraduate students enrolled or intending to enroll at an accredited college or university based in the United States, including Hawaii and Alaska - applicants enrolled or intending to enroll in a college or university in a United States territory are not eligible; must be enrolled full-time for the full academic year and in a degree-granting undergraduate program; must be at least senior in high school and; must be "out" as a person who identifies as a member of the LGBTQ community. Community college applicants must be transferring to a four-year college or university.

To Apply: Application form and details are available online at: pointfoundation.org/point-apply/community-college/. **Contact:** David Garza at davidg@pointfoundation.org; Phone: 212-512-5339; Adam Crowley at adam@pointfoundation.org; Phone: 323-933-1234.

9235 ■ Pointe Pest Control
334 Dekalb St.
Bridgeport, PA 19405
Ph: (610)277-7575
URL: pointe-pest.com
Social Media: www.facebook.com/PointePest
twitter.com/pointepc

9236 ■ ROFL Scholarship *(Undergraduate, College, University/Scholarship)*

Purpose: To help students pay for further education. **Focus:** General studies/Field of study not specified. **Qualif.:** Any high school senior or college freshman from the state of Pennsylvania, New Jersey or Delaware. **Criteria:** Selec-

Awards are arranged alphabetically below their administering organizations

tion will be based on making the sponsor laugh the hardest.

Funds Avail.: $500. **Duration:** Annual. **Number Awarded:** 1. **To Apply:** Complete the application including an original funny joke, story or quick video.

9237 ■ PolicyPak

506 Wildflower Ln.
Media, PA 19063
Free: 800-883-8002
E-mail: sales@policypak.com
URL: www.policypak.com
Social Media: www.facebook.com/policypak
www.linkedin.com/company/policypak-inc.
twitter.com/policypak
www.youtube.com/user/policypak

9238 ■ PolicyPak Scholarship *(Undergraduate, Graduate/Scholarship)*

Purpose: To provide college scholarships to entrepreneurial students with big dreams. **Focus:** General studies/Field of study not specified. **Qualif.:** Applicant must be currently enrolled in an accredited graduate or undergraduate educational institution or recently graduated with the three months of the scholarship award distribution. **Criteria:** Selection will be made by a panel of PolicyPak judges who will review application essays and award the applicant with the greatest entrepreneurial idea related to security.

Funds Avail.: $1,500. **Duration:** Biennial. **To Apply:** Applicant must present an entrepreneurial idea focused on security and explain how the entrepreneur aspires to make the world more secure. Application form needs to be completed online. **Deadline:** March 30. **Contact:** Email: scholarships@policypak.com.

9239 ■ Polish-American Engineers Association

1 Watergate Dr.
South Barrington, IL 60010
URL: www.polishengineers.org

9240 ■ Ralph Modjeski Scholarship *(Graduate, Undergraduate/Scholarship)*

Purpose: To provide financial assistance to qualified engineering students. **Focus:** Engineering. **Qualif.:** Applicants must be engineering students at junior year, academic year college or university or can also be graduates of engineering who demonstrate excellent academic achievements and proven commitment to engineering.

Funds Avail.: No specific amount. **Duration:** Annual. **To Apply:** Applicants must complete the application form, available online; must submit an official transcript, a 200-word letter describing the student's short and long term goals with any other information deemed pertinent; and must have three references with addresses and telephone numbers. **Deadline:** May 30. **Contact:** Polish-American Engineers Association, c/o Michael Niedzinski; 1 Watergate Drive South Barrington Illinois 60010, USA; Email: administration@polishengineers.org.

9241 ■ Polish Falcons of America (PFA)

1016 Greentree Rd.,Ste 201
Pittsburgh, PA 15220
Ph: (412)922-2244

Fax: (412)922-5029
Free: 800-535-2071
E-mail: info@polishfalcons.org
URL: www.polishfalcons.org
Social Media: www.facebook.com/pfanational
www.linkedin.com/company/polish-falcons-of-america
www.pinterest.com/pfanational
twitter.com/pfanational
www.youtube.com/pfanational

9242 ■ Falcon Achievement Scholarships *(Undergraduate/Scholarship)*

Purpose: To provide financial support for deserving Falcon members aspiring to attend institutions of higher learning. **Focus:** Polish studies. **Qualif.:** Candidates must be graduating high school seniors or presently enrolled undergraduates intending to pursue further education as full time students in an accredited two or four year college, university or trade school; must have a minimum cumulative GPA of 2.0 out of 4.0. **Criteria:** Selection will be based on the academic achievements and leadership qualities.

Funds Avail.: $1,500. **To Apply:** Applicants must complete and sign the application form available online; must provide a community service information, essay, and photo; must submit an official transcript, counselor recommendation, and net information form and letter. **Deadline:** February 15.

9243 ■ General Falcon Scholarships *(Undergraduate/Scholarship)*

Purpose: To provide financial support for deserving Falcon members who are aspiring to attend institutions of higher learning. **Focus:** General studies/Field of study not specified. **Qualif.:** Candidates must be graduating high school seniors or presently enrolled undergraduates intending to pursue further education as full time students in an accredited two- or four-year college, university or trade school; must have a minimum cumulative GPA of 3.0 out of 4.0; must have taken an active participation in the Polish Falcon programs. **Criteria:** Selection will be based on the criteria of the selection committee.

Funds Avail.: $750. **To Apply:** Applicants must complete and sign the application form available online; must provide a community service information, essay and photo; must submit an official transcript, counselor recommendation and net information form and letter. **Deadline:** February 15. **Contact:** Patricia Del Busse, National First Vice President at vptrish@polishfalcons.org.

9244 ■ Richard C. Gorecki Scholarships *(Graduate/Scholarship)*

Purpose: To provide financial assistance for deserving individuals intending to pursue their education. **Focus:** General studies/Field of study not specified. **Qualif.:** Applicant must be a PFA member for at least six years; must have a minimum GPA of 3.0 out of 4.0; must be enrolled full-time in a four-year college or university, or full-time postgraduate studies. **Criteria:** Selection of applicant will be based on the academic achievements and leadership qualities. Decisions of the selection board are subject to the approval of the National Board of Directors.

Duration: Annual. **Number Awarded:** 3. **To Apply:** Applicant must complete the scholarship application; must have a two part essay (minimum 500 words for each part); must provide at least three letters of recommendation. **Deadline:** April 15. **Remarks:** Established in 1998. **Con-**

Awards are arranged alphabetically below their administering organizations

tact: PFA National Headquarters,Gorecki Scholarship Committee, ATTN: Druhna Del Busse, Toll-free 1-800-535-2071, E-mail: vptrish@polishfalcons.org.

9245 ■ Pontifical Institute of Mediaeval Studies (PIMS)

59 Queen's Park Cres. E
Toronto, ON, Canada M5S 2C4
Ph: (416)926-7142
Fax: (416)926-7292
E-mail: pontifex@chass.utoronto.ca
URL: www.pims.ca
Social Media: twitter.com/PIMS_Mediaeval

9246 ■ Post-Doctoral Mellon Fellowships
(Postdoctorate/Fellowship)

Purpose: To support the professional development of young medievalists of exceptional promise who have completed their doctoral work, ordinarily within the previous five years, and have defended their thesis successfully. **Focus:** Medieval studies.

Funds Avail.: Approximately Can $40,000. Canadian Dollars. **Duration:** Annual. **Number Awarded:** 4. **To Apply:** Applicant must submit letters of references; letters can be sent directly by the referees by email (preferred); applicants should submit a proposal indicating the nature of the research they would undertake and letters of support from two scholars who are familiar with their work, together with a curriculum vitae and the official transcripts of their graduate studies; completed applications and supporting documents can be sent by email in PDF; official confirmation of the PhD should be sent directly to PIMS by the awarding university, in hard copy stating that the PhD has been examined and that its award has been approved by the appropriate authority. **Contact:** Pontifical Institute of Mediaeval Studies, 59 Queen's Park Crescent East, Toronto, Ontario, Canada, M5S 2C4; Phone: 416-926-7142; Barbara North, Institute Secretary; Email: barbara.north@utoronto.ca.

9247 ■ Portable Sanitation Association International (PSAI)

2626 E 82nd St., Ste. 175
Bloomington, MN 55425
Ph: (952)854-8300
Fax: (952)854-7560
E-mail: info@psai.org
URL: psai.org
Social Media: www.instagram.com/psai_org
www.linkedin.com/company/psai
twitter.com/psaiorg
www.youtube.com/channel/UCa-_cl8-46VYWiB2J2WEG3g

9248 ■ PSAI Scholarship Fund *(Undergraduate/ Scholarship)*

Purpose: To assist individuals in the portable sanitation industry who have made a commitment to advancing themselves through higher education. **Focus:** Technology. **Qualif.:** Applicants must be employees of a PSAI Member company or children or spouses of full-time employees who have been with the member company for at least two years; be high school senior or college undergraduate students enrolled full-time at a four-year or two-year college,

vocational or technical school; have GPA of 3.0 or above; obtain a minimum SAT score of 1000, ACT score of 21, or country equivalent.

Funds Avail.: $5,000. **Duration:** Annual. **Number Awarded:** Up to 5. **Remarks:** Established in 2004. **Contact:** Lee Sola, PSAI Scholarship Committee Chair; 3263 Oakland St., Aurora, CO, 80010; Email: lsola@sbprestrooms.com.

9249 ■ Portuguese American Leadership Council of the United States (PALCUS)

9255 Center St., Ste. 404
Manassas, VA 20110
Ph: (202)466-4664
E-mail: palcus@palcus.org
URL: www.palcus.org
Social Media: www.facebook.com/groups/palcus
twitter.com/palcus
www.youtube.com/user/PALCUS91

9250 ■ PALCUS National Scholarship Program
(Undergraduate/Scholarship)

Purpose: To supporting Portuguese-American students in the pursuit of their higher education goals. **Focus:** General studies/Field of study not specified. **Qualif.:** Applicants must be young Portuguese-American at $25 per year; U.S. citizenship or a permanent legal U.S. resident (proof of I551 card with no restrictions required); Portuguese ancestry of an aggregate of least 25%, i.e. total Portuguese ancestry of the applicant; student attending a baccalaureate or graduate degree program at an accredited college or university in the United States (high school seniors or entering freshmen are not eligible); cumulative Grade point average (GPA) of a minimum of 3.0.**Criteria:** Scholarship will be evaluated based on the academic record; extracurricular activities; community service; essay.

Funds Avail.: $1,000. **Number Awarded:** 5. **To Apply:** Applicants must submit complete application. **Deadline:** July 31. **Contact:** Gracielle Camilo, Executive Assistant, PALCUS, 9255 Center St., Ste 404, Manassas, VA, 20110; Phone: 202-466-4664; Fax: 202-466-4661; Email: palcus@palcus.org.

9251 ■ Portuguese-American Police Association of Massachusetts, Lodge II

PO Box 51523
New Bedford, MA 02745
URL: papamass.com

9252 ■ Portuguese American Police Association Scholarships *(Undergraduate/Scholarship)*

Purpose: To assist individuals for a career in law enforcement. **Focus:** Health care services; Law enforcement; Social work. **Qualif.:** Applicants must be of Portuguese descent; must be residents of Massachusetts; must be enrolled full-time in an accredited college or university or graduating seniors applying to full-time status in an accredited or another college or university; must be majoring in either health care, social services, law enforcement or another related field; must maintain a GPA of 2.0 or higher. **Criteria:** Selection will be selected based on their academic standing.

Funds Avail.: $500. **Duration:** Annual; one year. **Number Awarded:** 6. **To Apply:** Application forms are available

Awards are arranged alphabetically below their administering organizations

online; must submit an essay of not more than three paragraphs stating the reasons and their career goals; must have a high school transcript that includes the class rank; must have the current college/university transcript; must have a letter of reference from a guidance counselor or advisor and personal reference, preferably from someone with whom they have worked.

9253 ■ Post-Polio Health International (PHI)
50 Crestwood Executive Ctr.,Ste. 440
Saint Louis, MO 63126
Ph: (314)534-0475
Fax: (314)534-5070
E-mail: info@post-polio.org
URL: www.post-polio.org
Social Media: www.facebook.com/polioplace
twitter.com/PolioPlace

9254 ■ PHI Research Fund Grant *(Other/Grant)*

Purpose: To support the work of researchers investigating the late effects of poliomyelitis and/or neuromuscular respiratory disease. **Focus:** Business. **Criteria:** Selection is based on which projects have the potential to improve the lives of polio survivors or users of home mechanical ventilation; it may be quantitative or qualitative and must follow accepted research Methodology.

Funds Avail.: Up to $50,000. **Duration:** Annual. **Number Awarded:** 2. **To Apply:** Applicants must submit Project summary; detailed proposal; proposed budget. **Remarks:** Established in 1995. **Contact:** Joan L. Headley, Executive Director; Phone: 314-534-0475; E-mail: director@post-polio.org.

9255 ■ Poteet Strawberry Festival Association (PSFA)
9199 N State Hwy. 16
Poteet, TX 78065
Ph: (830)742-8144
Fax: (888)742-3608
URL: www.strawberryfestival.com

9256 ■ Poteet Strawberry Festival Association Scholarships *(Graduate, Undergraduate/Scholarship)*

Purpose: To increase the number of minority students who want to attain higher education. **Focus:** General studies/Field of study not specified. **Qualif.:** Applicants must be students who are still in college. **Criteria:** Applications will be reviewed by the selection committee.

Funds Avail.: No specific amount. **Duration:** Annual. **To Apply:** For further information about the scholarship, applicants are advised to contact the Foundation.

9257 ■ Potential Magazine
61 Marekt Pl. E
Montgomery, AL 36117
Ph: (334)578-7810
URL: potentialmagazine.com
Social Media: www.facebook.com/PotentialMagazine
www.instagram.com/potential_mag
www.pinterest.com/potentialmag
twitter.com/Potential_Mag
www.youtube.com/user/PotentialMagazine1

9258 ■ Don't Wait to Reach Your Potential *(High School/Scholarship)*

Purpose: To help college-bound teens residing in Alabama. **Focus:** General studies/Field of study not specified. **Qualif.:** Applicant must be an college bound high school student in grades 9-12 in the state of Alabama; must be a current C2C eNews subscriber at the time of the drawing. **Criteria:** Selection is via a random drawing.

Funds Avail.: $500. **Number Awarded:** 1. **To Apply:** Application is available online at potentialmagazine.com/college-scholarships/Alabama-scholarship-signup. **Deadline:** January 6. **Contact:** Email: editor@potentialmagazine.com.

9259 ■ Pound Coffee
2028 E Ben White Blvd., No. 240
Austin, TX 78741
Ph: (512)539-0410
URL: poundcoffee.com

9260 ■ $600 Scholarship Opportunity by Pound Coffee *(All/Scholarship)*

Purpose: To assist existing and future students in finding their dream careers. **Focus:** General studies/Field of study not specified. **Qualif.:** Applicant must be at least 18 years old and a current or future student enrolled in an academic course for the upcoming school year. **Criteria:** Selection is based on the submitted essay which will be judged by a panel of Pound Coffee members.

Funds Avail.: $600. **Number Awarded:** 1. **To Apply:** Applicant must submit a 1,500 to 2,000 word essay written on one subject from the three essay subjects offered: 1. How Coffee Exports Help Third-World Countries Thrive; 2. Use Of Coffee And Its Correlation To Academic Success;3. Are Coffee Drinkers More Productive In The Workplace Than Non-Coffee Drinkers? Why Or Why Not? Essays must be in a Word document. All received materials will be considered property of Pound Coffee and deemed eligible for later marketing use. **Deadline:** December 31. **Contact:** Sam Rosario; Email: allthecoffee@gmail.com; URL: poundcoffee.com/scholarship-opportunity/.

9261 ■ Practising Law Institute (PLI)
1177 Avenue of the Americas, 2nd Fl.
New York, NY 10036
Ph: (212)626-2680
E-mail: info@pli.edu
URL: www.pli.edu
Social Media: www.linkedin.com/company/practising-law-institute
twitter.com/PractLawInst
www.youtube.com/user/pliiscle

9262 ■ Practising Law Institute Scholarships *(Advanced Professional, Professional development/Scholarship)*

Purpose: To provide financial assistance to qualified students who want to pursue their career. **Focus:** Law. **Criteria:** Selection will be based on the committee's criteria.

Funds Avail.: No specific amount. **To Apply:** Applicants must complete the application forms available online; must have a legible copy of a student ID for the current term, and complete the Statement of Need on the respective let-

Awards are arranged alphabetically below their administering organizations

ter head. **Contact:** Scholarship Committee, Practising Law Institute, 1177 Avenue of the Americas, New York, NY, 10036; Phone: 212-824-5700; Fax: 212-824-5925; Email: scholarship@pli.edu or patentexam@pli.edu.

9263 ■ Presbyterian Association of Musicians (PAM)

100 Witherspoon St.
Louisville, KY 40202-1396
Ph: (502)569-5288
Fax: (502)569-8465
Free: 888-728-7228
E-mail: pam@pcusa.org
URL: www.presbymusic.org
Social Media: www.facebook.com/PresbyMusic
www.instagram.com/presbymusic/
twitter.com/Presbymusic

9264 ■ PAM General Conference Scholarships
(Other/Scholarship)

Purpose: To support members to attend any PAM sponsored conference. **Focus:** General studies/Field of study not specified. **Qualif.:** Applicants must be PAM members.

Funds Avail.: Varies.

9265 ■ PAM Scholarship for Montreat *(All/Scholarship)*

Purpose: To provide financial assistance for students for summer worship and music conferences. **Focus:** Music. **Qualif.:** Applicant must be a participant in the conference. **Criteria:** The recipient will be selected based on financial need.

Funds Avail.: $500-$5,000. **Duration:** Annual. **To Apply:** •Applicants who are adults must write and submit a short essay of qualifications and why they would like to attend a PAM conference and a letter of recommendation from pastor or music director; for children and youth applicants, their music director must write an evaluation statement including their musical experience and involvement in the church, how the applicants would benefit from the conference and perception of the applicants' financial need.

9266 ■ Presbyterian Church

100 Witherspoon St.
Louisville, KY 40202
Free: 800-728-7228
E-mail: info@pcusa.org
URL: www.pcusa.org
Social Media: www.facebook.com/pcusa
twitter.com/Presbyterian
www.youtube.com/user/presbyterianchurch

9267 ■ Samuel Robinson Award *(Undergraduate/Award)*

Purpose: To stimulate interest in the Westminster shorter Catechism. **Focus:** Religion. **Qualif.:** Applicants must be Presbyterian Church members who are: full-time students at a Presbyterian-related college or university; a junior or senior of the current college and university.

Funds Avail.: $2,000-$7,500. **Duration:** Annual. **Number Awarded:** 2. **To Apply:** Applicants must submit an essay of at least 2,000 words on a related assigned topic. **Dead-**

line: June 1, September 1, and December 1.

9268 ■ Prescott Center for the Arts (PCA)

208 N Marina St.
Prescott, AZ 86301
Ph: (928)445-3286
Fax: (928)778-7888
E-mail: tickets@pca-az.net
URL: www.pca-az.net
Social Media: www.facebook.com/PrescottCenterForTheArts/?fref=ts
www.instagram.com/officialpcatheater
www.youtube.com/channel/UCm-V7MVVmtXqVyrsUj__9Eg/playlists?view_as=subscriber

9269 ■ Prescott Fine Arts Association Scholarship Program *(Undergraduate/Scholarship)*

Purpose: To recognize and support the talented young people of Yavapai County. **Focus:** Arts. **Qualif.:** Applicants must be high school students. **Criteria:** Recipients are selected based on financial need.

Funds Avail.: $10,000. **To Apply:** Applicants must complete the application form.

9270 ■ President's Commission on White House Fellowships

Room 6400 1900 E Street, N.W.
Washington, DC 20415
Ph: (202)395-4522
E-mail: whfapplication@opm.gov
URL: www.whitehouse.gov
Social Media: www.facebook.com/WhiteHouse
www.instagram.com/whitehouse
twitter.com/whitehouse

9271 ■ White House Fellows *(Other/Fellowship)*

Purpose: To provide gifted and highly motivated young Americans with some firsthand experience in the process of governing the Nation and a sense of personal involvement in the leadership of society; to enhance the leadership and other learning experiences in the work assignment. **Focus:** General studies/Field of study not specified.

Funds Avail.: No specific amount. **Duration:** Annual. **To Apply:** Applications forms are available online and must be sent together with the other supporting documents. **Deadline:** January 8. **Remarks:** Established in 1964.

9272 ■ Pretty Photoshop Actions

1029 Lake St.
Oak Park, IL 60301
URL: www.photoshopactions.com
Social Media: www.facebook.com/prettyphotoshopactions
instagram.com/pretty_photoshop_actions
twitter.com/PrettyPSActions

9273 ■ Pretty Photoshop Actions Bi-Annual Scholarship *(Undergraduate, Graduate/Scholarship)*

Purpose: To provide college and university students an opportunity to earn money to further their education. **Focus:** General studies/Field of study not specified. **Qualif.:** Applicants must be either a high school senior, transitioning

Awards are arranged alphabetically below their administering organizations

from high school to a college or university, or enrolled in a college or university in Canada or the U.S. Employees and their immediate family members of PhotoshopActions.com are not eligible. **Criteria:** Quality of essay-style Adobe Photoshop tutorial, with screenshots and photos.

Funds Avail.: $500. **Duration:** Semiannual. **To Apply:** Tutorial should be between 800 and 1,000 words, with screenshots and photos to illustrate your points on one of the following topics: how Photoshop has changed photography, how to re-touch skin in Photoshop for photographers, favorite tips for enhancing color in Photoshop, or three must-know Photoshop overlays ideas for adding "wow" to portraits. Include the name of your college, the mailing address of its financial aid office, and a headshot of yourself in .JPG or .PNG format that is at least 300 pixels wide. **Deadline:** April 15; October 15. **Contact:** E-mail: scholarship@photoshopactions.com.

9274 ■ Prevent Blindness

225 W Wacker Dr., Ste. 400
Chicago, IL 60606
Free: 800-331-2020
E-mail: info@preventblindness.org
URL: preventblindness.org
Social Media: www.facebook.com/preventblindness
www.instagram.com/prevent_blindness
twitter.com/PBA_savingsight

9275 ■ Joanne Angle Investigator Award *(Professional development/Award, Grant)*

Purpose: To support research investigating public health related to eye health and safety. **Focus:** Visual impairment. **Qualif.:** Investigators must be citizens or permanent residents of either the United States or Canada; level of experience and related field work will be taken into consideration by the reviewers.

Funds Avail.: Up to $25,000. **Duration:** Annual. **To Apply:** Application Form must be completed online in one session; application Form must include 2-3 sentences describing in non-technical terms your project's relevance to the core mission of Prevent Blindness; 4 pieces of supporting documentation must be transmitted as PDF attachments. **Deadline:** March 6. **Contact:** Email: npatelsinha@ preventblindness.org.

9276 ■ Prevent Cancer Foundation (PCF)

1600 Duke St., Ste. 500
Alexandria, VA 22314
Ph: (703)836-4412
Free: 800-227-2732
E-mail: pcf@preventcancer.org
URL: preventcancer.org
Social Media: www.facebook.com/preventcancer
www.instagram.com/preventcancer
www.linkedin.com/company/prevent-cancer-foundation
www.pinterest.com/preventcancerf
twitter.com/preventcancer
www.youtube.com/user/preventcancerfound

9277 ■ Prevent Cancer Foundation Fellowships *(Postdoctorate/Fellowship)*

Purpose: To provide funding for innovative projects expected to lead to future funding from other peer-reviewed sources. **Focus:** Oncology.

Funds Avail.: $50,000. **Duration:** Annual; up to two years. **Number Awarded:** Varies. **To Apply:** Applicants must complete application form; letters of support. **Remarks:** Established in 1985. **Contact:** Email: Ximena.Marquez@ preventcancer.org.

9278 ■ Price Benowitz LLP

409 7th St. NW, Ste. 100
Washington, DC 20004
Ph: (202)558-4397
Fax: (202)664-1331
E-mail: info@pricebenowitz.com
URL: pricebenowitz.com
Social Media: www.facebook.com/PriceBenowitz
www.linkedin.com/company/price-benowitz-llp
twitter.com/PriceBenowitz
youtube.com/user/PriceBenowitz

9279 ■ Kush Arora Federal Criminal Justice Reform Scholarships *(Undergraduate, Graduate/Scholarship)*

Purpose: To support students pursuing law degrees. **Focus:** Law. **Qualif.:** Applicants must be undergraduate, graduate, and law school students, as well as incoming college freshmen; must be in good academic standing and possess a minimum cumulative GPA of 3.0 or higher. **Criteria:** Selection will be based on the applicants' qualifications and their submitted application documents.

Funds Avail.: $500. **To Apply:** Applicant must submit a current resume, an academic transcript, and a 1,000-word essay providing a well-reasoned argument about whether a specific policy in the criminal justice system (applicant's choice) is unjust and requires reform, or is just and should stay the same. Essay will be judged on the best-reasoned response, not on the position of the applicant. **Deadline:** December 15. **Contact:** Email: scholarships@maryland-criminallawyer.com.

9280 ■ Kerri Castellini Women's Leadership Scholarship *(Undergraduate, Graduate, Community College/Scholarship)*

Purpose: To support educated women who have the power to act as strong leaders both in their respective fields and in the community at large. **Focus:** General studies/Field of study not specified. **Qualif.:** Applicants must be female students enrolled in a community college, private or public undergraduate college or university, graduate program, business school, or law school in the United States, and first-year college students are also eligible to apply if they possess a valid GED or high school diploma; must exhibit strong leadership skills, as demonstrated by past and present educational, professional, and volunteer experiences; must be in good academic standing with a minimum cumulative 3.0 GPA. **Criteria:** Selection will be based on the aforementioned qualifications and compliance with the application details.

Funds Avail.: $1,000. **To Apply:** Applicants must submit the following requirements: a 500-word essay addressing the following prompt: "Describe an ideal woman leader in the 21st century. How do you believe that you exemplify the role in your daily life and career aspirations?"; an official academic transcript demonstrating a GPA of 3.0 or greater (if not available due to lack of grades, an unofficial transcript may be submitted, as well as an official transcript from the applicant's most recent educational institution); and a recommendation letter written by someone who can

Awards are arranged alphabetically below their administering organizations

attest to the applicant's leadership goals, achievements, and capabilities. Applications should be submitted via email on or before the given deadline. **Deadline:** December 31. **Contact:** Email: info@trustandestateslawyers.com.

9281 ■ Steve Duckett Local Conservation Scholarship *(Undergraduate, Postgraduate, Community College, Graduate/Scholarship)*

Purpose: To support the education of an individual who demonstrates exceptional commitment to natural conservation and environmental stewardship. **Focus:** General studies/Field of study not specified. **Qualif.:** Applicants must be entering an accredited community college, college, university, or post-graduate program; must be in good academic standing with their current educational institution, with a GPA of 3.0 or greater; and must also be able to demonstrate a commitment to environmental conservation using past and present volunteer, professional, and educational experiences. **Criteria:** Selection will be based on the aforesaid qualifications and compliance with the application process.

Funds Avail.: $1,000. **To Apply:** Applicants must submit a complete application that consist of the following: an updated resume that highlights the individuals' conservation and natural stewardship accomplishments, listing volunteer, professional, and academic experience; a 500-word personal statement explaining the candidates' dedication to local conservation and detailing the efforts, past and current, they have made to contribute to conservation and natural preservation efforts; an official transcript from the applicants' respective current schools or educational institutions that shows the candidates' GPA to be 3.0 or greater (note that if applicants do not have an official transcript available from their current institution, please submit an unofficial transcript, as well as their most recent official transcript from the last school attended). The materials should be submitted all together via email. **Deadline:** October 31. **Contact:** Email: info@virginiacriminallaws.com.

9282 ■ Healthy Communities Scholarship *(Undergraduate, Graduate, Community College/ Scholarship)*

Purpose: To support students in a post-secondary education who seek to encourage sustainable and local health-initiatives in their respective communities. **Focus:** General studies/Field of study not specified. **Qualif.:** Applicants must be students currently enrolled in an accredited community college, undergraduate, or graduate program in the United States, including incoming first-year college students who are high school graduates or possess a GED; must possess a proven record of interest in healthy communities through past and present volunteer, professional, or educational experiences; and must be in good academic standing, maintaining a cumulative average grade of a B (3.0 GPA). **Criteria:** Selection will be based on the aforesaid qualifications and compliance with the application process.

Funds Avail.: $1,000. **To Apply:** Applicant must submit the following: contact information, updated resume, and status as a student in the U.S; a 500-word statement identifying the applicant and their past and future dedication to healthy communities and sustainable initiatives (the personal statement should make clear how the candidate would use their continued education to champion accessible health- and local-activities programs); a current transcript. Application materials should be submitted via email. **Deadline:** December 31. **Contact:** Email: info@virginialawfirm.net.

9283 ■ Seth Okin Good Deeds Scholarships *(Undergraduate, Graduate, Community College/ Scholarship)*

Purpose: To enable those in pursuit of educational goals with the ultimate purpose of creating a meaningful life of service to others. **Focus:** Business; General studies/Field of study not specified; Law. **Qualif.:** Applicants must be students pursuing a post-secondary education (community college, undergraduate or graduate degree programs, law school, or business school); must be both interested and engaged in serving their community; and must have a GPA of 3.0 or greater (indicating good academic standing). **Criteria:** Selection will be based on the aforesaid qualifications and compliance with the application process.

Funds Avail.: $500. **To Apply:** Applicants must submit a resume that reflects their interest in service and activism by presenting relevant professional, academic, and volunteer experience. They must submit a 500-word essay that responds to the following question: "With so many people and organizations in today's world in need of volunteers and financial assistance, how should people decide where to direct their time and donations?" And they must also submit the most recent available academic transcript. If no official transcript is available from the applicants' current institution, an up-to-date unofficial transcript shall be submitted in addition to the most recent official transcript available. **Deadline:** November 30. **Contact:** Email: scholarships@criminallawyermaryland.net.

9284 ■ Karin Riley Porter Good Works Scholarships *(Undergraduate, Graduate/Scholarship)*

Purpose: To support students in their pursuit of law degrees. **Focus:** Law. **Qualif.:** Applicants must be undergraduate, graduate, or law school students, or incoming college freshmen at an accredited U.S. educational institution; must be in good academic standing with a minimum cumulative GPA of 3.0; must show a dedicated interest in community service and projects pertaining to criminal justice. **Criteria:** Selection will be based on the aforementioned qualifications and compliance with the application details.

Funds Avail.: $500. **To Apply:** Applicants must complete the Scholarship Application cover sheet. They must also submit the following requirements: a 500-word letter of intent that identifies them and describes their leadership and dedication in giving back to their respective communities through community service projects, including projects involving criminal justice issues; a current, unofficial academic transcript from their respective schools; a recommendation letter from a teacher, principal, school administrator, work supervisor, or member of clergy who has known the applicants at least one year and can speak to why the applicants deserve the scholarship. Applicants must submit the complete application by no later than the deadline. Materials should be submitted all together by U.S. mail or fax. **Deadline:** October 31. **Contact:** Email: scholarships@virginia-criminallawyer.com.

9285 ■ Price Benowitz Social Justice Scholarships *(Undergraduate, Graduate, Community College/ Scholarship)*

Purpose: To encourage young future leaders to pursue social justice causes through higher education and fight for a better future for all people. **Focus:** General studies/Field of study not specified. **Qualif.:** Applicants must be students currently enrolled in an accredited community college, undergraduate, or graduate program in the United States,

Awards are arranged alphabetically below their administering organizations

including incoming first-year college students who are high school graduates or possess a GED; must possess an interest in social justice, as demonstrated by past and present volunteer, professional, and educational experiences; must be in good academic standing, with a minimum cumulative 3.0 GPA.

Funds Avail.: $2,000. **To Apply:** Applicant must submit an updated resume, current transcript, and a 750-word essay in response to the essay prompt: What are some significant challenges people with disabilities encounter on a regular basis? What are some practicable public policies that could address these challenges? Applicant should feel free to speak about the challenges they have experienced or witnessed in a loved-one's life. **Deadline:** February 28. **Contact:** Email: scholarships@pricebenowitz.com.

9286 ■ White Collar Defense Diversity Scholarships (Undergraduate, Graduate/Scholarship)

Purpose: To support African American and Hispanic students with single mothers who are committed to pursuing quality education and who have demonstrated their ability in overcoming adversity and challenges related to their backgrounds. **Focus:** General studies/Field of study not specified. **Qualif.:** Applicants must be African American or Hispanic undergraduate or law school students, as well as incoming college freshmen; must be in good academic standing with a minimum cumulative GPA of 3.0 or higher. **Criteria:** Selection will be based on the applicants' qualifications, submitted application requirements, and demonstrated financial need.

Funds Avail.: $500. **Number Awarded:** 1. **To Apply:** Applicant must submit a 1,000-word essay describing the applicant's personal situation as a minorities with single mothers, the impact that it has had on their lives, and how they have overcome those challenges. They should also address their college, law school and/or career plans and how the scholarship will help them achieve those plans. Other requirements are: a current. unofficial academic transcript from the applicants' school; a recommendation letter from a teacher, principal, school administrator, work supervisor or a member of clergy who has known the applicant at least three years or more and can speak to why the applicants deserve the scholarship; and the completed Scholarship Application cover sheet found at the website. **Deadline:** September 30. **Contact:** Email: scholarships@whitecollarattorney.net.

9287 ■ Pride Foundation
2014 E Madison St., Ste. 300
Seattle, WA 98122
Ph: (206)323-3318
Free: 800-735-7287
URL: www.pridefoundation.org
Social Media: www.facebook.com/PrideFoundation
www.instagram.com/PrideFdn
twitter.com/PrideFdn

9288 ■ Paul Arnold Memorial Scholarships (Other/ Scholarship)

Purpose: To support students studying interior, fashion, or graphic design. **Focus:** Fashion design; Graphic art and design; Interior design. **Qualif.:** Applicants must be young men and women studying interior, fashion, graphic design; must be a resident of Alaska, Idaho, Montana, Oregon or Washington but may study elsewhere.

Funds Avail.: No specific amount. **Duration:** Annual. **Number Awarded:** 1. **To Apply:** Applicants must include official

or unofficial copy of transcript; resume - concise overview of your personal, educational, and professional experience; letter of recommendation; complete application. **Remarks:** Established in 1996. **Contact:** Phone: 206-323-3318; Toll Free: 800-735-7287; Email: scholarships@pridefoundation.org.

9289 ■ Asian and Pacific Islander Queer Sisters Scholarship (APIQS) (Undergraduate/Scholarship)

Purpose: To provide scholarship to students who have been stigmatized, isolated or closeted because of sexual identity issues. **Focus:** General studies/Field of study not specified. **Qualif.:** Applicants must be Asian/Pacific Islander lesbians, bisexual females, and transgender (both MTF and FTM spectrum) students; must be resident of Alaska, Idaho, Montana, Oregon, and Washington (currently live within that state and have done so for at least three months prior to the application deadline or have lived within that state for at least one year at any time within the five years prior to the application deadline); must be pursuing post secondary education and attending or planning to attend an accredited institution or program.

Funds Avail.: No specific amount. **To Apply:** Completed applications along with an academic transcript, resume, letter of recommendation (optional) from an individual who can speak to your qualifications, such as a teacher, instructor, mentor, supervisor, or religious leader must be submitted online. **Deadline:** January 12. **Contact:** Educational Programs Officer; Phone: 206-323-3318; Toll Free: 800-735-7287; Email: scholarships@pridefoundation.org.

9290 ■ Associates in Behavioral Health Scholarships (Graduate/Scholarship)

Purpose: To support LGBTQ students pursuing graduate education in psychology, psychiatry, social work, or psychiatric nursing. **Focus:** Nursing, Psychiatric; Psychiatry; Psychology; Social work. **Qualif.:** Applicants must be LGBT students pursuing graduate education in psychology, psychiatry, social work, or psychiatric nursing; residents of Alaska, Idaho, Montana, Oregon or Washington. **Criteria:** Preference given to individuals with demonstrated financial needs and to those entering or already enrolled in an accredited graduate program.

Funds Avail.: No specific amount. **Duration:** Annual. **To Apply:** Applicants may download an application form from the Foundation's website and submit complete application including essays, as completely as possible; include Letter(s) of Recommendation and Transcript. **Deadline:** January 11. **Remarks:** Established in 2007. **Contact:** scholarships@pridefoundation.org.

9291 ■ Barbara Bailey Scholarship (Undergraduate/ Scholarship)

Purpose: To encourage students of different backgrounds, educational interests and to promote leadership and diversity in the LGBTQ community. **Focus:** General studies/Field of study not specified. **Qualif.:** Applicant must be lesbians who are residents of Washington. **Criteria:** Selection will be based on the committee criteria.

Funds Avail.: No specific amount. **To Apply:** Applicants must include official or unofficial copy of transcript; resume - concise overview of personal, educational, and professional experience; letter of recommendation; complete application. **Deadline:** January 12.

9292 ■ Bellevue PFLAG Scholarships (Graduate, High School/Scholarship)

Purpose: To support East King County High School seniors who have demonstrated their ability to promote leadership

Awards are arranged alphabetically below their administering organizations

in the LGBTQ community through their actions as volunteers and advocates. **Focus:** General studies/Field of study not specified. **Qualif.:** Applicants must be graduating high school seniors currently attending a greater East King County high school.

Funds Avail.: No specific amount. **To Apply:** Applicants may download an application form from the Foundation's website and submit complete application including essays, as completely as possible; include Letter(s) of Recommendation and Transcript. **Remarks:** Established in 1999.

9293 ■ Bill Bendiner and Doug Morgenson Scholarship *(Undergraduate/Scholarship)*

Purpose: To support students pursuing a career in human services, health sciences, or visual arts. **Focus:** Health sciences; Human relations; Visual arts. **Qualif.:** Applicants must be students pursuing a career in human services, health sciences, or visual arts.

Funds Avail.: No specific amount. **Number Awarded:** 1. **To Apply:** Applicants may download an application form from the Foundation's website and submit complete application including essays, as completely as possible; include Letter(s) of Recommendation and Transcript. **Deadline:** January 12. **Remarks:** Established in 2001.

9294 ■ Cole Family Scholarships *(All/Scholarship)*

Purpose: To encourage students of different backgrounds, educational interests and to promote leadership and diversity in the LGBTQ community. **Focus:** General studies/Field of study not specified. **Qualif.:** Applicants must be Washington residents under age 25 raised by one or more LGBTQ parent.

Funds Avail.: No specific amount. **To Apply:** Applicants may download an application form from the Foundation's website and submit complete application including essays, as completely as possible; include Letter(s) of Recommendation and Transcript. **Contact:** Phone: 206-323-3318; Toll Free: 800-735-7287; Email: scholarships@pridefoundation.org.

9295 ■ Brian M. Day Scholarships *(Undergraduate, Graduate/Scholarship)*

Purpose: To support Puget Sound area gay men of color in their continuing education. **Focus:** General studies/Field of study not specified. **Qualif.:** Applicants must be: puget sound area gay men of color who have significant financial need and demonstrate activism in the gay/lesbian community and their communities of color; and, residents of Alaska, Idaho, Montana, Oregon or Washington but may study elsewhere.

Funds Avail.: No specific amount. **To Apply:** Applicants may download an application form from the Foundation's website and submit complete application including essays, as completely as possible; include Letter(s) of Recommendation and Transcript. **Deadline:** March 13. **Remarks:** Established in 1993. **Contact:** Phone: 206-323-3318; Toll Free: 800-735-7287; Email: scholarships@pridefoundation.org.

9296 ■ Deloris Carter Hampton Scholarship *(Undergraduate/Scholarship)*

Purpose: To support the education of those women of color who are advocates of LGBTQ community. **Focus:** Dance; Education. **Qualif.:** Applicants must be women of color who have demonstrated history of activism and/or leadership in the LGBTQ community pursuing a degree in educa-

tion, women's health, or dance. **Criteria:** Selection will be based on the committee criteria.

Funds Avail.: No specific amount. **To Apply:** Completed applications along with an academic transcript, resume, letter of recommendation (optional) from an individual who can speak to your qualifications, such as a teacher, instructor, mentor, supervisor, or religious leader must be submitted online. **Remarks:** Established in 2001. **Contact:** URL: pridefoundation.org/find-funding/scholarships/scholarship-opportunities/.

9297 ■ Dennis Coleman Scholarship *(Undergraduate/Scholarship)*

Purpose: To provide a scholarship to the students who have been stigmatized, isolated or closeted because of sexual identity issues. **Focus:** Music. **Qualif.:** LGBTQ students studying choral conducting or music with preference given to those committed to creating social change through music. **Criteria:** Preference will be given to those who are committed to creating social change through music.

Funds Avail.: No specific amount. **To Apply:** Applicants may download an application form from the Foundation's website and submit complete application including essays, as completely as possible; include Letter(s) of Recommendation and Transcript. **Deadline:** January 25. **Contact:** Phone: 206-323-3318; Toll Free: 800-735-7287; Email: scholarships@pridefoundation.org.

9298 ■ Dennis Coleman Scholarships *(Undergraduate/Scholarship)*

Purpose: To support LGBTQ students that are studying choral conducting or music. **Focus:** Music. **Qualif.:** Applicants must be LGBTQ students studying choral conducting or music. **Criteria:** Preference will be given to those committed to creating social change through music.

Funds Avail.: No specific amount. **To Apply:** Applicants must include official or unofficial copy of transcript; resume - concise overview of personal, educational, and professional experience; letter of recommendation; complete application. **Deadline:** January 12. **Contact:** Phone: 206-323-3318; Toll Free: 800-735-7287; Email: scholarships@pridefoundation.org.

9299 ■ Derivative Duo Scholarships *(Undergraduate/Scholarship)*

Purpose: To provide a scholarship to the students who have been stigmatized, isolated or closeted because of sexual identity issues. **Focus:** Human relations; Mental health. **Qualif.:** Applicants must be residents of Washington studying mental health or human services.

Funds Avail.: No specific amount. **To Apply:** Applicants may download an application form from the Foundation's website and submit complete application including essays, as completely as possible; include Letter(s) of Recommendation and Transcript. **Remarks:** The scholarship was founded by Sue Nivert & Barb Glenn for LGBTQ and straight ally Washington residents pursuing careers in nursing, mental health, or social services. Established in 2002. **Contact:** Phone: 206-323-3318; Toll Free: 800-735-7287; Email: scholarships@pridefoundation.org.

9300 ■ Donald O. Coffman Scholarship *(Graduate, Undergraduate/Scholarship)*

Purpose: To encourage students of different backgrounds, educational interests and to promote leadership and

Awards are arranged alphabetically below their administering organizations

diversity in the LGBTQ community. **Focus:** General studies/ Field of study not specified. **Qualif.:** Applicants must be current and future LGBT and straight-ally leaders and role models that are residents of Alaska, Idaho, Montana, Oregon or Washington but may study elsewhere. **Criteria:** Selection will be based on the committee's criteria.

Funds Avail.: No specific amount. **Contact:** Phone: 206-323-3318; Toll Free: 800-735-7287; Email: scholarships@ pridefoundation.org.

9301 ■ Fargo Supplier Diversity Scholarship (Undergraduate/Scholarship)

Purpose: To provide scholarship to the students who have been stigmatized, isolated or closeted because of sexual identity issues. **Focus:** General studies/Field of study not specified. **Qualif.:** Applicants must be current or future LGBT and straight-ally leaders and role models and residents of Alaska, Idaho, Montana, Oregon or Washington but may study elsewhere. **Criteria:** Preference will be given to students who are self-identified LGBTQ, members of LGBTQ families or straight-allies who have been strongly supportive of the LGBTQ community.

To Apply: Qualified students are asked to submit an application to determine eligibility for scholarships. Applicants may download an application form from the Foundation's website.

9302 ■ Inland Northwest Business Alliance Scholarships (INBA) (Undergraduate/Scholarship)

Purpose: To encourage students of different backgrounds, educational interests and to promote leadership and diversity in the LGBTQ community. **Focus:** General studies/ Field of study not specified. **Qualif.:** Applicants must be undergraduate students who are also residents of Eastern Washington and Northern Idaho.

Funds Avail.: No specific amount. **To Apply:** Applicants may download an application form from the Foundation's website and submit complete application including essays, as completely as possible; include Letter(s) of Recommendation and Transcript. **Deadline:** January 12. **Contact:** Phone: 206-323-3318; Toll Free: 800-735-7287; Email: scholarships@pridefoundation.org.

9303 ■ Obrzut Ling Scholarships (Graduate/ Scholarship)

Purpose: To provide scholarship to the students who have been stigmatized, isolated or closeted because of sexual identity issues. **Focus:** General studies/Field of study not specified. **Qualif.:** Applicant must be a student enrolled or entering a vocational or technical program at an accredited learning institution. Preference is given to students who are self-identified lesbian, gay, bisexual or transgender (LGBT). **Criteria:** Selection will be based on the committee's criteria.

To Apply: Qualified students are asked to submit an application to determine eligibility for scholarships. Applicants may download an application form from the Foundation's website.

9304 ■ McFarffels Scholarships (Undergraduate/ Scholarship)

Purpose: To provide scholarship to the students who have been stigmatized, isolated or closeted because of sexual identity issues. **Focus:** General studies/Field of study not specified. **Qualif.:** Applicants must be: lesbians with financial need entering a field that promotes social change and/or social justice; and, residents of Alaska, Idaho,

Montana, Oregon or Washington but may study elsewhere. **Criteria:** Preference will be given to students who are self-identified LGBTQ, members of LGBTQ families or straight-allies who have been strongly supportive of the LGBTQ community.

Funds Avail.: No specific amount. **Duration:** Annual. **To Apply:** Applicants must submit an application to determine eligibility for scholarships. Applicants may download an application form from the Foundation's website.

9305 ■ Jack D. Motteler Scholarship (Undergraduate/ Scholarship)

Purpose: To help so many incredibly talented but financially strained students succeed academically. **Focus:** Visual arts. **Qualif.:** Applicants must be undergraduate students in the visual arts; and residents of Alaska, Idaho, Montana, Oregon or Washington but may study elsewhere. **Criteria:** Selection will be based on the committee's criteria.

Funds Avail.: No specific amount. **To Apply:** Applicants must include official or unofficial copy of transcript; resume - concise overview of personal, educational, and professional experience; letter of recommendation; complete application. **Deadline:** January 25. **Remarks:** Established in 2000. **Contact:** Phone: 206-323-3318; Toll Free: 800-735-7287; Email: scholarships@pridefoundation.org.

9306 ■ Pride Foundation Political Leadership Scholarships (Undergraduate/Scholarship)

Purpose: To encourage students of different backgrounds, educational interests and to promote leadership and diversity in the LGBTQ community. **Focus:** Law; Political science; Public administration. **Qualif.:** Applicants must be students studying law, political science, public policy, or public administration with the goal of improving rights for LGBTQ people. **Criteria:** Preference is given to LGBTQ students of color and low-income or first-generation college students.

Funds Avail.: No specific amount. **To Apply:** Applicants must include official or unofficial copy of transcript; resume - concise overview of personal, educational, and professional experience; letter of recommendation; complete application. **Contact:** Phone: 206-323-3318; Toll Free: 800-735-7287; Email: scholarships@pridefoundation.org.

9307 ■ Pride Foundation Regional Scholarships (Undergraduate/Scholarship)

Purpose: To encourage students of different backgrounds, educational interests and to promote leadership and diversity in the LGBTQ community. **Focus:** General studies/ Field of study not specified. **Qualif.:** Applicants must be residents of areas outside of King County where Pride Foundation is working to enhance the leadership of the LGBTQ and ally community: Alaska, Idaho, Montana, Oregon, Eastern Washington, and Northwest/Southwest Washington.

Funds Avail.: No specific amount. **To Apply:** Applicants may download an application form from the Foundation's website and submit complete application including essays, as completely as possible; include Letter(s) of Recommendation and Transcript. **Deadline:** March 13. **Contact:** Phone: 206-323-3318; Toll Free: 800-735-7287; Email: scholarships@pridefoundation.org.

9308 ■ Pride Foundation Social Work Scholarships (Undergraduate/Scholarship)

Purpose: To encourage students of different backgrounds, educational interests and to promote leadership and

Awards are arranged alphabetically below their administering organizations

diversity in the LGBTQ community. **Focus:** Social work.

Contact: Phone: 206-323-3318; Toll Free: 800-735-7287; Email: scholarships@pridefoundation.org.

9309 ■ Pride of the Rose Scholarship
(Undergraduate/Scholarship)

Purpose: To provide financial assistance to those students who are in need. **Focus:** General studies/Field of study not specified. **Qualif.:** Applicants must be post-secondary education to members of the gay, lesbian, bisexual and transgender communities and their children residing in the Quad-county area of Portland, OR and Clark County, WA.

Funds Avail.: No specific amount. **To Apply:** Applicants must provide a resume, Transcript, Letter of recommendation. **Contact:** For more information, Educational Programs Officer; Phone: 206-323-3318; Tollfree: 800-735-7287; Email: scholarships@pridefoundation.org.

9310 ■ Don Renschler Scholarships *(Graduate/Scholarship)*

Purpose: To encourage students of different backgrounds, educational interests and to promote leadership and diversity in the LGBTQ community. **Focus:** Mental health. **Qualif.:** Applicants must be residents of Washington who are graduate students in the study of mental health.

Funds Avail.: No specific amount. **To Apply:** Applicants may download an application form from the Foundation's website and submit complete application including essays, as completely as possible; include Letter(s) of Recommendation and Transcript. **Contact:** Phone: 206-323-3318; Toll Free: 800-735-7287; Email: scholarships@pridefoundation.org.

9311 ■ Robert Browning Scholarships
(Undergraduate/Scholarship)

Purpose: To support students studying health sciences or health services. **Focus:** Health sciences.

Funds Avail.: No specific amount. **Remarks:** Established in 1993.

9312 ■ Rosenberg-Ibarra Scholarships *(Graduate/Scholarship)*

Purpose: To encourage students of different backgrounds, educational interests and to promote leadership and diversity in the LGBTQ community. **Focus:** General studies/Field of study not specified. **Qualif.:** Applicants must be LGBTQ students who either graduated from a high school in Idaho or will be attending a college or university within the state of Idaho. They must also be residents of Alaska, Idaho, Montana, Oregon or Washington.

Funds Avail.: No specific amount. **To Apply:** Applicants may download an application form from the Foundation's website and submit complete application including essays, as completely as possible; include Letter(s) of Recommendation and Transcript. **Contact:** Phone: 206-323-3318; Toll Free: 800-735-7287; Email: scholarships@pridefoundation.org.

9313 ■ Kathy Spadoni Memorial Scholarships
(Graduate/Scholarship)

Purpose: To encourage students of different backgrounds, educational interests and to promote leadership and diversity in the LGBTQ community. **Focus:** General studies/Field of study not specified.

Funds Avail.: No specific amount. **To Apply:** Applicants must include official or unofficial copy of transcript; resume

- concise overview of personal, educational, and professional experience; letter of recommendation; complete application. **Contact:** Phone: 206-323-3318; Toll Free: 800-735-7287; Email: scholarships@pridefoundation.org.

9314 ■ Phil Sullivan Scholarships *(Undergraduate/Scholarship)*

Purpose: To provide scholarship to the students who have been stigmatized, isolated or closeted because of sexual identity issues. **Focus:** General studies/Field of study not specified.

Funds Avail.: No specific amount. **To Apply:** Qualified students are asked to submit an application to determine eligibility for scholarships. Applicants may download an application form from the Foundation's website.

9315 ■ Ric Ulrich and Chuck Pischke Scholarships
(Undergraduate/Scholarship)

Purpose: To support LGBTQ and allied students studying visual arts and design. **Focus:** Visual arts. **Qualif.:** Candidates must intend to study in visual arts and design.

Funds Avail.: No specific amount. **To Apply:** Applicants may download an application form from the Foundation's website and submit complete application including essays, as completely as possible; include Letter(s) of Recommendation and Transcript. **Deadline:** October 11. **Remarks:** Established in 1998. **Contact:** Phone: 206-323-3318; Toll Free: 800-735-7287; Email: scholarships@pridefoundation.org.

9316 ■ Patricia Van Kirk Scholarship
(Undergraduate/Scholarship)

Purpose: To support lesbians studying theater or visual arts with a commitment to social justice. **Focus:** Theater arts; Visual arts. **Qualif.:** Applicants must be: lesbians studying theater or visual arts; and, resident of Alaska, Idaho, Montana, Oregon or Washington but may study elsewhere. **Criteria:** Selection will be based on the committee criteria.

Funds Avail.: No specific amount. **Duration:** Annual. **To Apply:** Applicants may download an application form from the Foundation's website and submit complete application including essays, as completely as possible; include Letter(s) of Recommendation and Transcript. **Deadline:** January 12. **Remarks:** Established in 2007.

9317 ■ Whidbey Island Giving Circle Scholarships
(Undergraduate/Scholarship)

Purpose: To encourage students of different backgrounds, educational interests and to promote leadership and diversity in the LGBTQ community. **Focus:** General studies/Field of study not specified. **Qualif.:** Applicants must be current and future LGBTQ and ally leaders and role models. **Criteria:** Preference will be given to residents of Whidbey Island.

Funds Avail.: No specific amount. **To Apply:** Applicants may download an application form from the Foundation's website and submit complete application including essays, as completely as possible; include Letter(s) of Recommendation and Transcript. **Remarks:** Established in 2007. **Contact:** Co-chairs Marsha Morgan, Claire Moore, Harry Anderson, and Terry Bible; Phone: 206-323-3318; Email: whidbeygivingcircle@whidbey.com.

9318 ■ Wozumi Family Scholarships *(Undergraduate/Scholarship)*

Purpose: To encourage students of different backgrounds, educational interests and to promote leadership and

Awards are arranged alphabetically below their administering organizations

diversity in the LGBTQ community. **Focus:** General studies/ Field of study not specified. **Qualif.:** Applicants must be students who are goal-oriented, HIV-positive, and/or focusing on the treatment and/or eradication of HIV.

Funds Avail.: No specific amount. **Number Awarded:** 1. **To Apply:** Applicants may download an application form from the Foundation's website and submit complete application including essays, as completely as possible; include Letter(s) of Recommendation and Transcript. **Contact:** Phone: 206-323-3318; Toll Free: 800-735-7287; Email: scholarships@pridefoundation.org.

9319 ■ You Go Girl! Scholarships *(Undergraduate/ Scholarship)*

Purpose: To provide scholarship to the students who have been stigmatized, isolated or closeted because of sexual identity issues. **Focus:** General studies/Field of study not specified.

To Apply: Qualified students are asked to submit an application to determine eligibility for scholarships. Applicants may download an application form from the Foundation's website.

9320 ■ Urashi Zen Scholarships *(Undergraduate/ Scholarship)*

Purpose: To provide scholarship to the students who have been stigmatized, isolated or closeted because of sexual identity issues. **Focus:** Business administration; Computer and information sciences; Political science. **Qualif.:** Applicants must be students studying business administration, computer science, or political science; and residents of Alaska, Idaho, Montana, Oregon or Washington but may study elsewhere. **Criteria:** Preference will be given to students who are self-identified LGBTQ, members of LGBTQ families or straight-allies who have been strongly supportive of the LGBTQ community.

Funds Avail.: No specific amount. **To Apply:** Qualified students are asked to submit an application to determine eligibility for scholarships. Applicants may download an application form from the Foundation's website.

9321 ■ Pride Law Fund (PLF)
PO Box 2602
San Francisco, CA 94126-2602
E-mail: info@pridelawfund.org
URL: www.pridelawfund.org
Social Media: www.facebook.com/pridelawfund
twitter.com/PrideLawFund

9322 ■ Tom Steel Post-Graduate Fellowships
(Postgraduate, Professional development/Fellowship)

Purpose: To support unmet legal needs in the LGBT community are addressed and prioritized on an ongoing basis, and that the next generation of legal advocates for the LGBT community develops the critical skills necessary to secure civil rights into the future. **Focus:** Law. **Qualif.:** Applicants must be law students who are about to graduate in the Spring semester or lawyers within three years of their graduation from law school; must complete full-time work within 12 months. **Criteria:** Need for the project, anticipated impact of the project, organization and structure of the proposal, stability and supportiveness of the sponsoring organization or attorney, past community or public service, demonstrate a connection and involvement with the LGBTQ community.

Funds Avail.: $30,000. **Duration:** Annual. **Number Awarded:** 1. **To Apply:** Applicants must submit a cover page; one-page overview of project; full description of the project; applicant's qualifications; estimated budget; resume; law transcript; description of the sponsoring organization and/or Supervising Attorney; list of any other people involved in the project and a description of their respective roles and relevant experiences; letter of support from the sponsoring organization; two additional letters of support; timetable; a signed "usage agreement and certification". **Deadline:** January 31. **Contact:** Pride Law Fund Steel Fellowship, P.O. Box 2602, San Francisco CA 94126-2602; Email: steel@pridelawfund.org; URL: www.pridelawfund.org/fellowships/tom-steel.

9323 ■ Primate Conservation, Inc.
1411 Shannock Rd.
Charlestown, RI 02813-3726
Ph: (401)364-7140
Fax: (401)364-6785
E-mail: nrowe@primate.org
URL: www.primate.org

9324 ■ Primate Conservation Grants *(Graduate, Professional development/Grant)*

Purpose: To fund field research that supports conservation programs for wild populations of primates. **Focus:** Zoology. **Qualif.:** Applicants must be graduate students, qualified conservationists and primatologists to study rare and endangered primates and their conservation in their natural habitat.**Criteria:** Applicants are evaluated on competitive basis; applications are screened by outside reviewers and the Board of Directors of PCI. All appropriate projects will be considered, but the regions of current interest are Asia and West Africa.

Funds Avail.: $2,500-$5,000. **To Apply:** Applicants must fill out the cover sheet and institutional agreement forms and submit three copies of the complete proposal via regular airmail. Email one digital copy of the proposal with applicants name and species in the file name in an MS doc file or RTF. Proposals must be typed, double-spaced, in English, and limited to 20 pages total. Proposal should consist of the following: introduction; background information; project description; methods; post-project follow-up; timetable; budget; bibliography; CV of principal personnel, maximum of two pages; copies of permissions from appropriate governmental agencies, or statement that permits and permissions are not needed; completed and signed institution agreement form; names and addresses of three people qualified to review the applicants proposal.

9325 ■ Prince Henry Society - New Bedford Chapter
508 Coming-Soon The Prince Henry Society
New Bedford, MA 02742
URL: princehenrysociety.com

9326 ■ Prince Henry Society Scholarships
(Undergraduate/Scholarship)

Purpose: To provide opportunities for deserving students who want to pursue a higher education. **Focus:** General studies/Field of study not specified. **Qualif.:** Applicants must be a members of the PHS.

Funds Avail.: No specific amount. **Duration:** Annual. **Contact:** Prince Henry Society, New Bedford Chapter, PO Box

Awards are arranged alphabetically below their administering organizations

6726, New Bedford, MA 02742.

9327 ■ Pringle Chivers Sparks Teskey
300-10150 100 St., NW
Edmonton, AB, Canada T5J 0P6
Ph: (780)424-8866
URL: www.pringlelaw.ca

9328 ■ Alexander D. Pringle Memorial Scholarship
(Advanced Professional/Scholarship)

Purpose: To enhance the educational opportunities of young scholars who wish to study or are studying law at a Canadian university in pursuit of an LLB. or J.D. degree. **Focus:** Law. **Qualif.:** Applicants must be law students who are currently admitted to or attending an undergraduate degree program in law at a Canadian university. **Criteria:** Selection will be based on the students who demonstrate financial need and who have made recognized community contributions.

Funds Avail.: 1,000 Canadian Dollars. **Number Awarded:** 1. **To Apply:** Applicants must write a 500-word essay on their respective community contributions and their current financial situation. Their essay should be in a Word document, Pages or PDF attachment. Furthermore, they are also required to include the following information in application: full name, address, and contact details including phone number and email address, as well as the copy of their current law school transcripts. **Deadline:** December 1. **Contact:** Email: scholarship@pringlelaw.ca.

9329 ■ Print and Graphics Scholarship Foundation (PGSF)
301 Brush Creek Rd.
Warrendale, PA 15086-7529
Ph: (412)259-1740
Free: 800-910-4283
E-mail: pgsf@printing.org
URL: pgsf.org
Social Media: www.facebook.com/printscholarships
www.instagram.com/pgsfscholar/

9330 ■ Print and Graphics Scholarship Foundation Awards *(Graduate, Undergraduate/Award)*

Purpose: To provide financial assistance to students pursuing graphic communications careers, in order to strengthen the print and graphics industry. **Focus:** Communications; Graphic art and design. **Qualif.:** Applicants must have a 3.0 GPA or better; full-time status; student who is enrolled in a printing or graphic program at a technical school, college or university within the United States; student must be pursuing a career in printing technology, printing management, or graphic communication. **Criteria:** Recipients are selected based on academic records; recommendations offered from instructors, advisors, and employers; biographical records, which indicate academic honors; extracurricular interests.

Funds Avail.: $1,000-$5,000. **Duration:** up to 4 years. **To Apply:** Applicants must complete an application form; must have two letters of recommendation; must have official transcripts or a copy of official transcripts; for High school students - if SAT's or ACT scores are not recorded on official transcripts email or send separately to the foundation address. **Deadline:** May 1. **Contact:** PGSF, 301 Brush Creek Rd., Warrendale, PA, 15086.; Phone: 866-556-

PGSF; Email: contact@pgsf.org.

9331 ■ Printing Industries of America's Center for Technology and Research
301 Brush Creek Rd.
Warrendale, PA 15086
Ph: (412)741-6860
Fax: (412)741-2311
Free: 800-910-4283
E-mail: info@printing.org
Social Media: www.facebook.com/printingunited
www.instagram.com/printingind
www.linkedin.com/company/printingunited
twitter.com/PrintingInd

9332 ■ PGSF Scholarship *(Undergraduate/Scholarship)*

Purpose: To encourage and support talented men and women who are interested in graphic communication careers. **Focus:** Graphic art and design. **Criteria:** Selection shall be based on high school/college academic records, rank in class, recommendations and biographical information, which includes extracurricular interests and academic honors.

Funds Avail.: range of $1,000 to 5,000 per academic year. **Duration:** Annual. **Number Awarded:** Varies. **To Apply:** Applicants may visit the program website for further information regarding the application details/instructions. **Deadline:** MAY 1. **Contact:** Canadian Printing Industry Association, 151 Rue Slater St., Ste. 1110, Ottawa, ON, K1P 5H3; E-mail: pgsf@printing.org; Phone: 412-259-1740.

9333 ■ Prism Foundation
PO Box 22155
Oakland, CA 94623
Ph: (415)857-4272
E-mail: info@theprismfoundation.org
URL: theprismfoundation.org
Social Media: www.facebook.com/prismqtapi
www.instagram.com/prismqtapi
twitter.com/prismqtapi
www.youtube.com/channel/UCPsdZZuAtAT9p0fXnjZ4Lsw

9334 ■ GAPA Foundation Scholarship *(Undergraduate, Graduate, High School, Vocational/Occupational/Scholarship)*

Purpose: To provide financial assistance to lesbian, gay, bisexual and transgender Asian and Pacific Islanders in educational pursuits. **Focus:** Homosexuality. **Qualif.:** Applicant must be attending in a post-secondary institution in the United States in the fall of current year; should have a strong history of activism within the API and/or LGBTQ communities; open to students who attend community college, university, and trade/vocational school.

Funds Avail.: $1,000-$5,000. **To Apply:** Applicants must submit a completed Horizons Foundation's scholarship application form together with a transcript, a letter of recommendation. **Deadline:** June 30. **Contact:** E-mail: scholarship@theprismfoundation.org.

9335 ■ Professional Beauty Association (PBA)
7755 E Gray Rd.
Scottsdale, AZ 85260

Awards are arranged alphabetically below their administering organizations

E-mail: info@probeauty.org
URL: probeauty.org
Social Media: www.facebook.com/
  professionalbeautyassociation
www.instagram.com/probeautyassoc
www.linkedin.com/company/professional-beauty
  -association
twitter.com/probeautyassoc
www.youtube.com/user/professionalbeauty

9336 ■ Sally Beauty Scholarships for High School Graduates *(High School/Scholarship)*

Purpose: To support high school graduates, desiring to enter the cosmetology profession. **Focus:** Cosmetology. **Qualif.:** Applicants must be high school graduates under the age of 26 who want to enter the cosmetology profession. **Criteria:** Recipients are selected based on academic performance and interest in a cosmetology program.

Funds Avail.: $1,000. **Duration:** Annual. **Number Awarded:** 10. **To Apply:** Applicants must submit a completed application form along with two letters of recommendation; personal essay; and high school transcript. **Deadline:** January 15.

9337 ■ Professional Construction Estimators Association of America, Inc. (PCEA)

PO Box 680336
Charlotte, NC 28216
Free: 877-521-7232
E-mail: pcea@pcea.org
URL: www.pcea.org
Social Media: www.facebook.com/pceanational
www.linkedin.com/in/pcea
twitter.com/wildapricot

9338 ■ Ted G. Wilson Memorial Scholarships *(Undergraduate/Scholarship)*

Purpose: To provide financial assistance for individuals intending to further their education in the construction industry. **Focus:** Construction; Engineering. **Qualif.:** Applicants must be high school seniors and above; must resident of, or plan to attend a school or university in the states where PCEA has an established Chapter will qualify; must reside North Carolina, South Carolina, Georgia and Florida. **Criteria:** Applicants are selected based on their academic ability, need, and desire to enter the construction industry.

Funds Avail.: $1,500. **Duration:** One Year. **Number Awarded:** Varies. **To Apply:** Applicants must submit a completed application form; one evaluation form completed by the high school Guidance Counselor or College Faculty Advisor, whichever is applicable at time of application; one evaluation form completed by an adult not related to the applicant; official transcript of high school/college grades and latest S.A.T. scores if available; finalists may be interviewed by the Scholarship Committee. **Deadline:** March 31. **Remarks:** Established in memory of Ted Wilson (1932-1987), the first National Executive Director of the PCEA. Established in 1988. **Contact:** National PCEA Scholarship Committee, PO Box 9146, Charlotte, NC, 28299; Phone: 704- 421-4601.

9339 ■ Professional Employees Association (PEA)

505-1207 Douglas St.
Victoria, BC, Canada V8W 2E7

Ph: (250)385-8791
Fax: (250)385-6629
Free: 800-779-7736
URL: www.pea.org
Social Media: www.facebook.com/peainbc
www.instagram.com/peainbc/
twitter.com/pea_online
www.youtube.com/user/PEAblogger

9340 ■ PEA Bursaries *(Undergraduate/Scholarship)*

Purpose: To provide support to members and/or relative of the Association. **Focus:** General studies/Field of study not specified. **Qualif.:** Applicants must: be current member of PEA; be registered, or in the process of being registered, in a part-time post-secondary educational program for an upcoming educational session; and, demonstrate financial need.

Funds Avail.: $500 each. **Duration:** Annual. **Number Awarded:** Up to 10. **To Apply:** Applicants must submit a complete application form available at the website; must include (a) a typed letter setting out the applicants' education and career goals, (b) a statutory declaration that the applicants meet the criteria set out in the qualifications. **Contact:** PEA Bursary Committee, c/o Professional Employees Association 505 - 1207 Douglas Street, Victoria, BC, V8W 2E7 or email to bursaries@pea.org.

9341 ■ PEA Scholarships *(Undergraduate/Scholarship)*

Purpose: To provide support to members and/or relative of the Association. **Focus:** General studies/Field of study not specified. **Qualif.:** Applicants must be current member or relatives of PEA staff; must also be registered, or in the process of being registered, in a full-time post-secondary educational program for an upcoming educational session. **Criteria:** Award is given based on the worthiness of the essay considering content, analysis and literary style, as selected by the scholarships committee.

Duration: Annual. **To Apply:** Applicants must submit a 1,500-word essay discussing the impact of provincial government funding cuts on unionized public sector workers and the public they serve. **Deadline:** March 15. **Contact:** Email: scholarships@pea.org.

9342 ■ Professional Insurance Agents of Arkansas (PIAA)

10809 Executive Center Dr., Pla. 4
Little Rock, AR 72211
Ph: (501)225-1645
URL: www.piaar.com
Social Media: www.facebook.com/pia.arkansas.94
twitter.com/arkansaspia

9343 ■ Randy Henry Memorial Scholarship *(Undergraduate/Scholarship)*

Purpose: To support a high school senior or current college undergraduate. **Focus:** Insurance and insurance-related fields. **Criteria:** Selection will be based on extracurricular activities, community service or job experience.

Funds Avail.: $1,000 ($500 per semester). **Duration:** Annual. **To Apply:** Applicants must submit current photo; stay in school throughout the semester with at least 12 credit hours. **Remarks:** The award was established in honor of Randy Henry.

Awards are arranged alphabetically below their administering organizations

9344 ■ Professional Manufacturing Confectioners Association (PMCA)

2980 Linden St., Ste. E3
Bethlehem, PA 18017
Ph: (610)625-4655
E-mail: info@pmca.com
URL: pmca.com
Social Media: www.instagram.com/pmca1907

9345 ■ Allen Allured Fellowship (Graduate/Fellowship)

Purpose: To recognize and support outstanding graduate students enrolled or planning to enroll in the Department of Food Science at the Pennsylvania State University, as well as to promote and enhance the knowledge and image of the confectionery industry. Focus: Food science and technology. Qualif.: Applicants must be individuals that have earned an undergraduate degree, have some confectionery experience and are interested in furthering their education. Criteria: Selection shall be based on the aforementioned qualifications and compliance with the application details. Preference is given to the candidates who have some experience in confectionery manufacture.

Funds Avail.: No specific amount. Duration: Annual. To Apply: Applicant must submit an online application form along with the following: a nonrefundable application fee is required; Graduate Record Examination (GRE) scores (an original report of scores form is required), the institution code is 2660, Penn State Univ., University Park, PA & the department code is 0107; language of instruction at Penn State is English, all international applicants must take and submit scores for the TOEFL (Test of English as a Foreign Language) or the IELTS (International English Language Testing System); transcripts (or equivalent documents for institutions outside the U.S., e.g., degree/study certificates, diplomas, etc.) from all post-secondary institutions attended, in the language of instruction (and copies of an official English translation if English is not the language of instruction; a completed background and interest form (in PDF) indicating your interest in research of specific Food Science faculty members; personal statement (2-3 pages maximum), must include the following information: reasons for choosing food science as a career and your plans for the future; particular research interests and career goals; hobbies or other special interests; if applicable, previous graduate work or research experience; if applicable, internship and/or co-op experience; if applicable, previous experience in food industry or elsewhere; External financial means (scholarships etc.) to support graduate work; three letters of recommendation. Deadline: December 15. Remarks: Established in 1989. Contact: Dr. Swamy Anantheswaran, Professor, Department of Food Science, Penn State University, 202 Food Science Bl. University Park, Pennsylvania 16802; Phone: 814-865-3004; Fax: 814-863-6132; E-mail: rca3@psu.edu.

9346 ■ Professional Woman's Magazine

18 Technology Dr., Ste. 170
Irvine, CA 92618
Fax: (800)453-8201
Free: 888-562-9662
URL: professionalwomanmag.com
Social Media: www.facebook.com/professionalwomansmagazine
www.instagram.com/profwomansmag
www.linkedin.com/company/professionalwomanmag
twitter.com/profwomansmag

9347 ■ Professional Woman's Magazine Scholarship Opportunity (Undergraduate/Scholarship)

Purpose: To promote the advancement of multicultural, diverse women in all aspects of business and employment to ensure equal opportunity. Focus: General studies/Field of study not specified. Qualif.: Applicant must be a Undergraduate and graduate students can search for scholarships that fit their interests. Criteria: Selection is based on essay submitted.

Funds Avail.: $500. Number Awarded: 1. To Apply: Applicant must submit a application in form; essay.

9348 ■ Project Management Association of Canada (PMAC)

1234 Kingston Rd., Ste. 125
Toronto, ON, Canada M1N 1P3
Fax: (416)986-5777
URL: www.pmac-ampc.ca

9349 ■ Fellowship in the PMAC-AGPC (Professional development/Fellowship)

Purpose: To recognize and support individuals who have made significant contribution to the development of the art and science project, program or portfolio management, either as practitioners, teachers, or researchers. Focus: General studies/Field of study not specified. Qualif.: Applicants must be regular members of the association for at least five years; interested individuals who have been members with less than five years will be considered depending on the contribution made to the field or the association.

Funds Avail.: No specific amount. Duration: Annual. To Apply: Applicants must submit a completed application form, curriculum vitae, personal statement, portfolio of evidence, documentary and letter of support.

9350 ■ Property and Environment Research Center (PERC)

2048 Analysis Dr., Ste. A
Bozeman, MT 59718
Ph: (406)587-9591
URL: www.perc.org
Social Media: www.facebook.com/PERCgroup
www.linkedin.com/company/perc
twitter.com/PERCtweets

9351 ■ Property and Environment Research Center Graduate Fellowships (Graduate/Fellowship)

Purpose: To provide opportunities for those who are interested in researching issues related to natural resources and the environment. Focus: Environmental law; Natural resources. Qualif.: Applicants must be graduates or law students interested in natural resources and environmental issues and show potential for research and writing in these areas. Criteria: Selection is given to those who are working on a research paper, thesis or dissertation on a natural resource or environmental topic.

Funds Avail.: $2,250 per month. Duration: 3/year. Number Awarded: Varies. Deadline: December 31.

9352 ■ Property and Environment Research Center Lone Mountain Fellowships (Other/Fellowship)

Purpose: To advance understanding of the role of markets and property rights in protecting and enhancing environmental resources. **Focus:** Natural resources. **Qualif.:** Applicants must be a scholar, journalist, policy-maker or environmentalist interested in undertaking a project that advances understanding of the role of markets and property rights in protecting and enhancing environmental resources. **Criteria:** Selection is based on the submitted applications.

Funds Avail.: No specific amount.

9353 ■ Property and Environment Research Center Media Fellowships *(Other/Fellowship)*

Purpose: To help journalists examine how property rights and markets can improve the environment. **Focus:** Natural resources. **Qualif.:** Applicant must be a reporter, editorial writer, broadcaster, producer or other working in the field of journalism, primarily covering the environment; a journalist who is skeptical but open-minded; or a journalist who is familiar with property rights and markets and their affect on the environment. **Criteria:** Preference may be given to journalists who specialize in environmental reporting.

To Apply: Applicants must complete the application online; in addition, applicants must provide and upload a statement (one page or less) explaining why they want to be fellows; resume; clippings or other indications of writing or broadcasting experience (may be sent as attachments or URLs or mailed separately); and two references.

9354 ■ Julian Simon Fellowships *(Postgraduate/ Fellowship)*

Purpose: To develop policy-oriented research on natural resource and environmental conservation. **Focus:** Natural resources.

Funds Avail.: No specific amount. **To Apply:** Applicants must complete the application online; in addition, applicants must provide and upload a vita; a short (2-3 page) research proposal summarizing the work to undertake while at PERC; and individuals who are at a relatively early stage of their career (untenured faculty) should have a senior scholar in their field write a letter of recommendation on their behalf.

9355 ■ ProQuest L.L.C.
789 E. Eisenhower Pkwy.
Ann Arbor, MI 48108
Ph: (800)521-0600
E-mail: info@proquest.com
URL: www.proquest.com
Social Media: www.facebook.com/proquest
www.linkedin.com/company/proquest
www.pinterest.com/proquest/
twitter.com/proquest
www.youtube.com/user/proquestvideo

9356 ■ Roger K. Summit Scholarship *(Graduate/ Scholarship)*

Purpose: To assist students studying library science and related disciplines. **Focus:** Library and archival sciences. **Qualif.:** Applicants must be students who are currently enrolled in an accredited library or information science program. **Criteria:** Selection of recipient shall be based on academic achievement; demonstrated interest in electronic information services, based on course work, research, and experience; and, faculty recommendations.

Funds Avail.: $5,000. **Duration:** Annual. **To Apply:** Applicants may visit the scholarship section of the bestowing

organization's website for further information regarding the application details. **Deadline:** March 30. **Remarks:** Established in 1993.

9357 ■ ProSocial
1625 Stanford St.
Santa Monica, CA 90404
Ph: (310)826-0123
URL: www.purposechallenge.org
Social Media: facebook.com/ThePurposeChallenge
instagram.com/thepurposechallenge

9358 ■ The Purpose Challenge *(Undergraduate/ Scholarship)*

Purpose: To help high school seniors reflect on and refine their sense of purpose. **Qualif.:** Applicant must be a high school senior currently planning to attend college in the fall semester; must be residing in the 50 United States or the District of Columbia; must be at least 16 years old at date of entry.

Funds Avail.: $25,000 (one); $5,000 (five). **Number Awarded:** 6. **To Apply:** Applicant must write an essay that identifies a long-term goal and succinctly articulates why this goal is personally meaningful and will positively contribute to the world at large. Application and details are available online at www.purposechallenge.org/contest. **Contact:** Email: opportunities@purposechallenge.org.

9359 ■ Prospanica
2711 LBJ Fwy., Ste. 800
Dallas, TX 75234
Free: 877-467-4622
E-mail: info@prospanica.org
URL: www.prospanica.org
Social Media: www.facebook.com/ProspanicaNational
www.instagram.com/prospanicanational
www.linkedin.com/company/nshmba
twitter.com/Prospanica
www.youtube.com/channel/UCbG7LZJxFtw0IAwBCFzcd-g

9360 ■ Prospanica Scholarship *(Graduate, Undergraduate/Scholarship)*

Purpose: To assist qualified Hispanics to pursue MBAs. **Focus:** Business. **Qualif.:** Applicants must be a United States Citizen or Legal Permanent Resident; be of Hispanic heritage; have a minimum GPA of 3.0 on a 4.0 scale (or equivalent) from either a bachelor's degree or master's degree OR have a minimum GPA of 2.75 on a 4.0 scale (or equivalent) from a bachelor's degree in combination with two years of full-time work experience; a current NSHMBA member (Applicants who are not currently a NSHMBA member may apply); and be enrolled in a graduate business program in a college/university in the United States or Puerto Rico, accredited by the AACSB (AACSB International) at the time of award. **Criteria:** Selection is based on academic achievement, work experience, financial need, personal statement of goals and aspirations, community service, letters of recommendation, and NSHMBA ambassadorship.

Funds Avail.: No specific amount. **Duration:** Annual. **To Apply:** Applicants must include personal Statement (maximum 300 words/3, 000 characters); prospanica essay; college academic information, including complete

Awards are arranged alphabetically below their administering organizations

transcripts of grades from all colleges attended; list of work, Prospanica participation, and community service experience; financial information from the family's most recently submitted tax return; two recommendation forms from professors, advisors, or employers.

9361 ■ Prostate Cancer Canada (PCC)

55 St Clair Ave W Ste 500
Toronto, ON, Canada M5C 1M1
URL: www.prostatecancer.ca

9362 ■ Movember Clinical Trials *(Advanced Professional/Grant)*

Purpose: To support outstanding innovative clinical trials that will lead to significant advancements in the understanding of prostate cancer. **Focus:** Medical research; Oncology. **Qualif.:** Applicants must be professionals who want to conduct research on prostate cancer in Canada and have the following: a single Principal Investigator who is an independent investigator; co-applicants (Co-Principal Investigators and Co-Investigators) who are independent investigators, formally affiliated with eligible institutions; written support from the coordinating center that will participate in carrying out the study. Candidates' respective "eligible institutions", as mentioned, are those that fall under the following categories: Canadian post-secondary institutions and their affiliated institutions including hospitals and research institutes; Canadian non-governmental, not-for-profit organizations (including charitable or community organizations) with an explicit research or knowledge translation mandate; and Canadian non-federal government departments or agencies, including regional health authorities, where specific programs of those departments or agencies do not fund the activity that forms the subject matter of the grant. **Criteria:** Applicants will be evaluated based on their express of intent (EOI). EOIs will be evaluated based on the following evaluation criteria: overall objective and extent of innovation of the program of research; significance of the trial results and likelihood of its impact on policy or practice in Canada; and ability of the research team to conduct the trial including the identification of a coordinating center.

Funds Avail.: 3,500,000 Canadian Dollars. **Duration:** Up to 5 years. **To Apply:** The program has a two phase application process. Phase 1 requires the completion of an Expression of Interest (EOI). Phase 2 requires the completion of a full application upon invitation. All applications must conform to the specific requirements. For the General EOI Submission, please include the following: title of the proposal; new application or re-application (for re-applications, provide a response to previous critiques (maximum 400 words) and upload previous reviews, one document); lay summary (maximum 250 words; please provide a brief summary in non-scientific language of the proposal); applicant table (using the spreadsheet provided, applicant table, available in the resources section of the online application, list all applicants with their affiliations and expertise keywords; the list need not be final at the expression of interest stage; attach the completed spreadsheet); objectives (maximum 400 words; list the objectives of the proposal); project information (the research program proposal must include an overall description of the research program (maximum of 1,500 words not including references) and must clearly outline the following elements: background; a brief description of the importance of the research hypotheses or questions to be addressed and expected findings; list of the research disciplines and/or

aspects that make up the research program; the capacity of the research team to carry out the program of research proposed; a plan, including proposed organizational structures for engaging and linking with those who will ultimately use the research findings; the nature and extent of the host institutions' financial and other forms of long-term commitment to the team's research, and to ensuring a favorable environment for carrying out the research activities; the roles of partners in the planning and execution of the research program and the dissemination and utilization of the research results; summary of trials; other items that can be attached such as reference bibliography, tables and figures (maximum of 5 pages), and written support from the coordinating center that will participate in carrying out the study; curriculum vitae (2-page free-form); letter of support from the coordinating center; recommended reviewers (minimum of 3 required); and reviewers to exclude (optional). **Deadline:** January 23. **Contact:** Jenna Fong Ph.D., Manager, Research, Prostate Cancer Canada; Phone: 416-441-2131, ext. 243; E-mail: jenna.fong@prostatecancer.ca.

9363 ■ Movember Discovery Grants *(Advanced Professional, Professional development/Grant)*

Purpose: To support researchers to generate preliminary data in prostate cancer research that would provide the basis for a more substantial research grant from another agency. **Focus:** Medical research; Oncology. **Qualif.:** Awards are open to new investigators and established investigators. The former must have held academic or research appointment(s) for no more than five years at the commencement of the award, while the latter must have held academic or research appointment(s) for a period of five years or more at the commencement of the award. Furthermore, they must be: independent investigators; applied health researchers and/or hold an M.D. degree (or equivalent) and/or Ph.D. degree (or equivalent); and, licensed to practice medicine in Canada (if holding an M.D. degree). Candidates' respective "eligible institutions", as mentioned, are those that fall under the following categories: Canadian post-secondary institutions and their affiliated institutions including hospitals and research institutes; Canadian non-governmental, not-for-profit organizations (including charitable or community organizations) with an explicit research or knowledge translation mandate; and Canadian non-federal government departments or agencies, including regional health authorities, where specific programs of those departments or agencies do not fund the activity that forms the subject matter of the grant. **Criteria:** Applicants will be evaluated based on their excellence as judged against the following evaluation criteria: track record of investigator team; feasibility of the proposed work; innovation: innovative research (a novel, inventive and transformative approach or design that might be high risk, high gain); and potential impact on prostate cancer.

Funds Avail.: 200,000 Canadian Dollars. **Duration:** Annual. **To Apply:** Application is via online. The online application is two-stage process, each with a specific deadline. Key components for the grant application are registration (no attachments) and full application. For registration: select new or established investigators; project title; area of research; keywords; review panel election; principal investigator (PI) profile; update profile to include: date of first faculty/research appointment; co-principal investigator (maximum 1) and co-investigator names; dean of faculty/head of division information; financial officer information recommended reviewers with whom they are not in conflict (3 minimum required); reviewers to exclude (optional). For full application: upload curriculum vitae for PI, co-PI and co-investigators; collaborator information;

Awards are arranged alphabetically below their administering organizations

upload letters of collaboration as appropriate; new application or re-application; response to previous reviews (re-application only); lay summary; scientific abstract; research proposal; references; tables/figures; innovation (describe how the proposal is innovative: innovative research is a novel, inventive and transformative approach or design that might be high risk, high gain); certificates required; current and pending funding; abstracts for current and pending funding; reprints/preprints/abstracts (optional); proposed budget; signature page. **Deadline:** February 15 (registration); April 3 (full application). **Contact:** Jenna Fong Ph.D., Manager, Research, Prostate Cancer Canada; Phone: 416-441-2131, ext. 243; Email: jenna.fong@prostatecancer.ca; Joanne Reynolds Manager, Research Operations Prostate Cancer Canada; Phone: 416-441-2131, Ext. 226; Email: joanne.reynolds@prostatecancer.ca.

9364 ■ Movember Rising Star in Prostate Cancer Research Awards (Advanced Professional, Professional development/Grant)

Purpose: To provide salary and research support for outstanding researchers initiating a career as independent investigators in prostate cancer research. **Focus:** Medical research; Oncology. **Qualif.:** Applicants must, at the commencement of the award that is September 1: be independent investigators; be applied health researchers and/or hold an M.D. degree (or equivalent) and/or Ph.D. degree (or equivalent); have an academic or research appointment at an eligible institution; and, have held an academic or research appointment as an independent investigator for no longer than 5 years at September 1, the start date of the award. Candidates' respective "eligible institutions", as mentioned, are those that fall under the following categories: Canadian post-secondary institutions and their affiliated institutions including hospitals and research institutes; Canadian non-governmental, not-for-profit organizations (including charitable or community organizations) with an explicit research or knowledge translation mandate; and Canadian non-federal government departments or agencies, including regional health authorities, where specific programs of those departments or agencies do not fund the activity that forms the subject matter of the grant. **Criteria:** Applications for the award will be evaluated based on their excellence as judged against the following evaluation criteria. For the applicants: potential to develop as researchers; quality of the applicants' academic achievements, extracurricular activities, characteristics and abilities; commitment to meeting the program objectives to become an independent researcher; quality of the letters of reference from three referees. For the supervisor(s)/mentor(s): appropriateness of the supervisor/mentor's research qualifications; quality and extent of the supervisor/mentor's proposed role in providing guidance and advice to the applicants; previous experience in fostering the development of trainees; history of research productivity and peer-reviewed support; strength of the supervisor/mentors statement. For the research project: scientific and technical merit of the research question, feasibility, design and methodology; significance of the proposed research on our understanding prostate cancer. And for the environment and institutional commitment to the applicants: adequacy of research facilities and training opportunities; quality and relevance of the environment for the scientific and professional development of the applicants.

Funds Avail.: 150,000 Canadian Dollars per annum (75,000 for salary support; 75,000 for research expenses). **To Apply:** Application is via online. The online application is two-stage process, each with a specific deadline. Key

components for the grant application are registration (no attachments) and full application. For registration: applicant details, date of first faculty appointment, and host institution; mentor(s); project title, area of research, keywords; and recommended reviewers and reviewers to exclude. For full application: training, experience, career plans (maximum 2,000 words); up to 3 mentor(s) (with mentor statement); for those re-applying on the program, provide a response to previous critiques (maximum 400 words); must attach copies of previous reviews in pdf format; lay summary (maximum 250 words); scientific abstract (maximum 250 words); research proposal (maximum 2,000 words not including reference bibliography, tables and figures); current and pending funding; budget; letters of reference (3 required); and signature page. **Deadline:** September 30 (registration; October 30 (full application). **Contact:** Jenna Fong Ph.D., Manager, Research, Prostate Cancer Canada; Phone: 416-441-2131, ext. 243; E-mail: jenna.fong@ prostatecancer.ca.

9365 ■ Movember Team Grants (Advanced Professional, Professional development/Grant)

Purpose: To support Canadian research programs in prostate cancer that generate new knowledge that improves our understanding of prostate cancer and accelerates progress to a practice or policy change. **Focus:** Medical research; Oncology. **Qualif.:** Applicants will be made up of at least three independent investigators, one of which will be identified as the Program Director. All identified independent investigators must contribute substantially to the primary research goal of the program. **Criteria:** Applicants will be evaluated based on their express of intent (EOI). EOIs will be evaluated based on the following evaluation criteria: overall objective and extent of innovation of the program of research; and significance of the research on our understanding of prostate cancer.

Funds Avail.: 10,000,000 Canadian Dollars. **To Apply:** The program has a two phase application process. Phase 1 requires the completion of an Expression of Interest (EOI). Phase 2 requires the completion of a full application upon invitation. All applications must conform to the specific requirements. For the General EOI Submission, please include the following: title of the proposal; new application or re-application (for re-applications, provide a response to previous critiques (maximum 400 words) and upload previous reviews, one document); lay summary (maximum 250 words; please provide a brief summary in non-scientific language of the proposal); applicants table (using the spreadsheet provided, list all applicants with their affiliations and expertise keywords); objectives (maximum 400 words; list the objectives of the proposal); project information (the research program proposal must include an overall description of the research program (maximum of 1,500 words not including references) and must clearly outline the following elements: background; a brief description of the importance of the research hypotheses or questions to be addressed and expected findings; list of the research disciplines and/or aspects that make up the research program; the nature of the team and extent of collaboration between investigators, with an explanation of the anticipated value added to the research program through the synergy of the research team; the capacity of the research team to carry out the program of research proposed; the research training and mentoring environment that will provide a superior experience for undergraduate, graduate and/or post-doctoral trainees, including those with a health professional background; a plan, including proposed organizational structures for engaging and linking with those who will ultimately use the research findings; ap-

Awards are arranged alphabetically below their administering organizations

plicants should be considering their KT plans from the inception of their project the nature and extent of the host institutions' financial and other forms of long-term commitment to the team's research, and to ensuring a favorable environment for carrying out the research activities; if the team involves partners, the proposed roles of partners in the planning and execution of the research program and the dissemination and utilization of the research results; summaries of each of the highly-integrated projects (minimum 3 projects) summaries of shared infrastructure support core (if applicable) and must clearly outline how the core will enhance the productivity, cost-effectiveness, and/or research outcomes of the proposed research program and provide the opportunity for downstream leveraging; and other items that can be attached such as reference bibliography (provide a short bibliography for any references cited in the expression of interest; attach one document), tables and figures (maximum 5 pages; attach one document); and lastly, curriculum vitae (attach one document that includes brief 2-page free-form curriculum vitaes for the program director and each principal investigator; this include training and education, degrees, positions and honors, a list of relevant publications (past 5 years) and information on grants and awards held (source, type, title, amount/year, duration)., The program has a two phase application process. Phase 1 requires the completion of an Expression of Interest (EOI). Phase 2 requires the completion of a full application upon invitation. All applications must conform to the specific requirements. For the General EOI Submission, please include the following: title of the proposal; new application or re-application (for re-applications, provide a response to previous critiques (maximum 400 words) and upload previous reviews, one document); lay summary (maximum 250 words; please provide a brief summary in non-scientific language of the proposal); applicant table (using the spreadsheet provided, applicant table, available in the resources section of the online application, list all applicants with their affiliations and expertise keywords; the list need not be final at the expression of interest stage; attach the completed spreadsheet.); objectives (maximum 400 words; list the objectives of the proposal); project information (the research program proposal must include an overall description of the research program (maximum of 1,500 words not including references) and must clearly outline the following elements: background; a brief description of the importance of the research hypotheses or questions to be addressed and expected findings; list of the research disciplines and/or aspects that make up the research program; the nature of the team and extent of collaboration between investigators, with an explanation of the anticipated value added to the research program through the synergy of the research team; the capacity of the research team to carry out the program of research proposed; the research training and mentoring environment that will provide a superior experience for undergraduate, graduate and/or post-doctoral trainees, including those with a health professional background; a plan, including proposed organizational structures for engaging and linking with those who will ultimately use the research findings; applicants should be considering their KT plans from the inception of their project the nature and extent of the host institutions' financial and other forms of long-term commitment to the team's research, and to ensuring a favorable environment for carrying out the research activities; if the team involves partners, the proposed roles of partners in the planning and execution of the research program and the dissemination and utilization of the research results; summaries of each of the highly-integrated projects (minimum 3 projects)

summaries of shared infrastructure support core (if applicable) and must clearly outline how the core will enhance the productivity, cost-effectiveness, and/or research outcomes of the proposed research program and provide the opportunity for downstream leveraging; and other items that can be attached such as reference bibliography (provide a short bibliography for any references cited in the expression of interest; attach one document), tables and figures (maximum 5 pages; attach one document); and lastly, curriculum vitae (attach one document that includes brief 2-page free-form curriculum vitaes for the program director and each principal investigator; this include training and education, degrees, positions and honors, a list of relevant publications (past 5 years) and information on grants and awards held (source, type, title, amount/year, duration). **Deadline:** March 16. **Contact:** Jenna Fong Ph.D., Manager, Research, Prostate Cancer Canada; Phone: 416-441-2131, ext. 243; E-mail: jenna.fong@ prostatecancer.ca.

9366 ■ Prostate Cancer Canada Clinical Research Fellowships (Advanced Professional/Fellowship)
Purpose: To support high-potential trainees to develop their skills in an outstanding research environment under the guidance of an experienced supervisor/mentor. **Focus:** Medical research; Oncology. **Qualif.:** Applicants must, at the time the award commences: be studying at an eligible institution; hold a regulated professional degree; and, be at least one year from the completion of their research fellowship. Candidates' respective "eligible institutions", as mentioned, are those that fall under the following categories: Canadian post-secondary institutions and their affiliated institutions including hospitals and research institutes; Canadian non-governmental, not-for-profit organizations (including charitable or community organizations) with an explicit research or knowledge translation mandate; and Canadian non-federal government departments or agencies, including regional health authorities, where specific programs of those departments or agencies do not fund the activity that forms the subject matter of the grant. **Criteria:** Applications will be evaluated based on excellence as judged against the following evaluation criteria. For the applicants: potential to develop as researchers; quality of the applicants' academic achievements, extracurricular activities, characteristics and abilities; commitment to meeting the program objectives to become an independent researcher; quality of the letters of reference from three referees. For the supervisor(s)/mentor(s): appropriateness of the supervisor/mentor's research qualifications; quality and extent of the supervisor/mentor's proposed role in providing guidance and advice to the applicants; previous experience in fostering the development of trainees; history of research productivity and peer-reviewed support; strength of the supervisor/mentors statement. For the research project: scientific and technical merit of the research question, feasibility, design and methodology; significance of the proposed research on our understanding prostate cancer. And for the environment and institutional commitment to the applicants: adequacy of research facilities and training opportunities; quality and relevance of the environment for the scientific and professional development of the applicants.
Funds Avail.: 75,000 canadian Dollars. **Duration:** Annual. **To Apply:** Application is via online. The online application is two-stage process, each with a specific deadline. Key components for the grant application are registration (no attachments) and full application. For registration: application details; supervisor/mentor details; dean of the faculty/head of division and finance officer details; project title, area of

Awards are arranged alphabetically below their administering organizations

research, keywords. For full application: for applicants' training and experience (maximum of 1,000 words); curriculum vitae (approximately 3 pages); for supervisor(s)/mentor(s) letter of reference; curriculum vitae (approximately 3 pages); research project application (non-scientific summary: maximum 250 words, scientific summary: maximum 250 words, research proposal: maximum 1,000 words not including references, tables and figures); letters of references (total of 3); and signature pages (applicants, supervisor/mentor(s), dean of faculty/head of division and financial officer). **Contact:** Jenna Fong Ph.D., Manager, Research, Prostate Cancer Canada; Phone: 416-441-2131, ext. 243; E-mail: jenna.fong@prostatecancer.ca.

9367 ■ Prostate Cancer Canada Graduate Studentships (Graduate, Doctorate/Grant)

Purpose: To support doctoral students to advance their research training and studies. **Focus:** Medical research; Oncology.

Funds Avail.: 35,000 Canadian Dollars per annum, plus 5,000 knowledge exchange stipend. **To Apply:** Application is via online. The online application has a two-stage process, registration (no attachments) and full application, each with a specific deadline. For registration, applicants must prepare the following: application details; supervisor/mentor details; dean of the faculty/head of division and finance officer details; project title, area of research, keywords. For full application: applicants' training and experience (maximum of 1,000 words); curriculum vitae (approximately 3 pages); supervisors'/mentors' letter of reference; curriculum vitae (approximately 3 pages); research project application (maximum 250 words for non-scientific summary; maximum 250 words for scientific summary. Research proposals must be maximum of 1,000 words not including references, tables and figures); letters of references (total of 3); and signature pages (applicants, supervisor/mentor(s), dean of faculty/head of division and financial officer). **Deadline:** February 10 (registration); March 9 (full application). **Contact:** Jenna Fong Ph.D., Manager, Research, Prostate Cancer Canada; Phone: 416-441-2131, ext. 243; E-mail: jenna.fong@prostatecancer.ca.

9368 ■ Prostate Cancer Canada Postdoctoral Research Fellowships (Postdoctorate, Advanced Professional/Fellowship)

Purpose: To support high-potential trainees to develop their skills in an outstanding research environment. **Focus:** Medical research; Oncology. **Qualif.:** Applicants must be studying at an eligible institution and hold a Ph.D. degree. Candidates' respective "eligible institutions", as mentioned, are those that fall under the following categories: Canadian post-secondary institutions and their affiliated institutions including hospitals and research institutes; Canadian non-governmental, not-for-profit organizations (including charitable or community organizations) with an explicit research or knowledge translation mandate; and Canadian non-federal government departments or agencies, including regional health authorities, where specific programs of those departments or agencies do not fund the activity that forms the subject matter of the grant. **Criteria:** Applications will be evaluated based on excellence as judged against the following evaluation criteria. For the applicants: potential to develop as researchers; quality of the applicants' academic achievements, extracurricular activities, characteristics and abilities; commitment to meeting the program objectives to become an independent researcher; quality of the letters of reference from three referees. For the supervisor(s)/mentor(s): appropriateness of the supervisor/

mentor's research qualifications; quality and extent of the supervisor/mentor's proposed role in providing guidance and advice to the applicants; previous experience in fostering the development of trainees; history of research productivity and peer-reviewed support; strength of the supervisor/mentors statement. For the research project: scientific and technical merit of the research question, feasibility, design and methodology; significance of the proposed research on our understanding prostate cancer. And for the environment and institutional commitment to the applicants: adequacy of research facilities and training opportunities; quality and relevance of the environment for the scientific and professional development of the applicants.

Funds Avail.: 50,000 Canadian Dollars per annum, plus 5,000 knowledge exchange stipend. **Duration:** Annual. **To Apply:** Application is available online. The online application has a two-stage process, registration (no attachments) and full application, each with a specific deadline. For registration, applicants must prepare the following: application details; supervisor/mentor details; dean of the faculty/head of division and finance officer details; project title, area of research, keywords. For full application: applicants' training and experience (maximum of 1,000 words); curriculum vitae (approximately 3 pages); supervisors'/mentors' letter of reference; research project application (maximum 250 words for non-scientific summary; maximum 250 words for scientific summary. Research proposals must be maximum of 1,000 words not including references, tables and figures); letters of references (total of 3); and signature pages (applicants, supervisor/mentor(s), dean of faculty/head of division and financial officer). **Contact:** Jenna Fong Ph.D., Manager, Research, Prostate Cancer Canada; Phone: 416-441-2131, ext. 243; E-mail: jenna.fong@prostatecancer.ca.

9369 ■ Prostate Cancer Foundation

1250 Fourth St.
Santa Monica, CA 90401
Ph: (310)570-4700
Fax: (310)570-4701
Free: 800-757-2873
E-mail: info@pcf.org
URL: www.pcf.org
Social Media: www.facebook.com/PCF.org
www.instagram.com/pcfnews/
www.linkedin.com/company/prostate-cancer-foundation/
twitter.com/PCFnews

9370 ■ PCF Challenge Awards (Professional development/Award)

Purpose: To support cross-disciplinary teams of investigators in strategic areas. **Focus:** Oncology.

Funds Avail.: $300,000 to $1,500,000 per year. **Duration:** Annual. **Number Awarded:** Varies. **To Apply:** Applicant must be submitted scientific abstract concisely describing the background, rationale, specific aims, experimental approach andanticipated outcomes and impact of the project is required (fill-in form field); Statement of Originality (1-page limit); research proposal; NIH Bio sketch; budget page(s); supplemental information (Optional). **Remarks:** Established in 2008. **Contact:** Howard R. Soule, Ph. D. Executive Vice President, Chief Science Officer, Prostate Cancer Foundation; Email: applications@pcf.org.

Awards are arranged alphabetically below their administering organizations

9371 ■ PCF Young Investigator Award *(Professional development, Postdoctorate/Award)*

Purpose: To support future research leaders who will keep the field of prostate cancer research vibrant with new ideas. **Focus:** Oncology. **Qualif.:** Applicants must be young (generally 35 and younger) investigators who have achieved junior faculty positions and are committing their lives to the field of prostate cancer.

Funds Avail.: No specific amount. **Duration:** Annual. **Number Awarded:** Varies. **To Apply:** Applicants must submit three-year research proposal no greater than five (5) pages; letter of support from the applicant's mentor(s); letter of support from the applicant's departmental chairperson or cancer center director; 1-2 page mentorship plan from the mentor; applicant's NIH bio sketch is required (5 pages maximum); must be combined into a single PDF document for upload. **Remarks:** Established in 2008. **Contact:** Howard R. Soule, Ph. D. Executive Vice President, Chief Science Officer, Prostate Cancer Foundation; Email: applications@pcf.org.

9372 ■ Proven Data Recovery
590 Madison Ave., Ste. 2155
New York, NY 10022
Ph: (212)729-8690
Free: 877-364-5161
URL: www.provendatarecovery.com
Social Media: facebook.com/ProvenDataRecovery
linkedin.com/company/proven-data-recovery
twitter.com/ProvenDR
youtube.com/user/ProvenDataRecoveryUS

9373 ■ Proven Data Recovery Technology Scholarships *(All/Scholarship)*

Purpose: To inspire those that are committed to the growth and movement of technology and to take on the journey that will continue to be an integrated part of humanity's social structure and assist in the protection and security of a global community. **Focus:** Technology. **Qualif.:** Those who have an interest in the growth of technology, and the protection and security of the global community are eligible. **Criteria:** Selection will be based on creativity, the ability to engage readers, and presentation of interesting subject matter in the submitted essay.

Funds Avail.: $1,000. **Number Awarded:** 1. **To Apply:** Application form and process are available at www.provendatarecovery.com/about/scholarship-opportunities/. **Deadline:** January 30.

9374 ■ Psi Chi, The International Honor Society in Psychology
651 E 4th St. Ste. 600
Chattanooga, TN 37403
Ph: (423)756-2044
Fax: (423)265-1529
URL: www.psichi.org
Social Media: www.facebook.com/PsiChiCentralOffice
instagram.com/psichihonor
www.linkedin.com/company/
  psichitheinternationalhonorsocietyinpsychology
twitter.com/PsiChiHonor

9375 ■ APA Society Convention Research Awards *(Undergraduate, Graduate/Award)*

Purpose: To recognize the best research papers and poster abstracts submitted by graduate and undergraduate Psi Chi students at APA. **Focus:** Psychology. **Qualif.:** Applicants must be graduate or undergraduate students who have done research they believe is competitive and can attend the APA annual convention; Applicant must be the first author of the proposal; Applicant must be a student Psi Chi member. **Criteria:** Selection will be based on the quality of the following: rationale/background; methodology; analysis and results; conclusion.

Funds Avail.: $400 for undergraduate students; $500 for graduate students. **Duration:** Annual. **Number Awarded:** 4. **To Apply:** Applicants must present their research at the APA Convention. **Deadline:** April 15.

9376 ■ APS Convention Society Research Awards *(Undergraduate, Graduate/Award)*

Purpose: To recognize the best research papers and posters submitted by graduate and undergraduate Psi Chi students at the APS Annual Convention. **Focus:** Psychology. **Qualif.:** Applicants must be graduate or undergraduate students who have done research they believe is competitive and can attend the APA annual convention; Applicant must be the first author of the proposal; Applicant must be a student Psi Chi member; Applicant must be a have an APS member as a sponsor. **Criteria:** Proposals will be evaluated on the following: 50-word abstract; rationale/hypothesis; participants; methods section; results and; conclusion/discussion.

Funds Avail.: $400 for undergraduate students; $500 for graduate students. **Duration:** Annual. **Number Awarded:** 4. **To Apply:** Applicants must present their research at the APS Convention. **Deadline:** February 1.

9377 ■ Psychology Association of Saskatchewan
PO Box 4528
Regina, SK, Canada S4P 3W7
E-mail: info@psychsask.ca
URL: psychsask.ca

9378 ■ Psychology Association of Saskatchewan Student Scholarships - Academic Achievement *(Master's, Doctorate/Scholarship)*

Purpose: To support students to further develop psychological research, education and training in the Province of Saskatchewan. **Focus:** Psychology. **Qualif.:** Applicants must be full-time students (Honors, Masters, or Doctoral) who do not currently hold any major scholarships or departmental awards over $10, 000; preference will be given to student representatives of Psychology Association of Saskatchewan (PAS). **Criteria:** Selection will be judged based on their academic standing, or thesis/dissertation work.

Funds Avail.: $500. **Duration:** Annual. **To Apply:** Applicants must submit all required documents most recent transcript from an accredited Saskatchewan University; one letter of recommendation from a supervisor; and a written statement, no more than 500 words describing educational and work goals. **Deadline:** April 30. **Contact:** PAS Award Chairperson, Christina Scott M.Ed. R., Psych (Provisional); Email: crs753@mail.usask.ca.

9379 ■ Psychology Association of Saskatchewan Student Scholarships - Research Based *(Master's, Doctorate/Scholarship)*

Purpose: To support students to further develop psychological research, education and training in the Province of

Awards are arranged alphabetically below their administering organizations

Saskatchewan. **Focus:** Psychology. **Qualif.:** Applicants must be full-time students (Honors, Masters, or Doctoral) who do not currently hold any major scholarships or departmental awards over $10, 000; preference will be given to student representatives of Psychology Association of Saskatchewan (PAS). **Criteria:** Selection will be judged based on their academic standing, or thesis/dissertation work.

Funds Avail.: $500. **Duration:** Annual. **To Apply:** Applicants must submit all required documents most recent transcript from an accredited Saskatchewan University; one letter of recommendation from a supervisor; and a written statement, no more than 500 words describing educational and work goals. **Deadline:** April 30. **Contact:** PAS Award Chairperson, Christina Scott M.Ed. R., Psych (Provisional); Email: crs753@mail.usask.ca.

9380 ■ PTAC Crew

7450 Chapman Hwy., No. 303
Knoxville, TN 37920
Free: 888-458-7822
URL: ptaccrew.com

9381 ■ PTAC Crew Scholarship for HVAC Students
(Vocational/Occupational/Scholarship)

Purpose: To help an HVAC student attend college. **Focus:** Heating, air conditioning, and refrigeration. **Qualif.:** Applicant must be a registered student at a vocational or technical college in the United States and enrolled in an HVAC or HVAC-related program. **Criteria:** Selection will be based on the quality and creativity of the scholarship essay.

Funds Avail.: $1,500. **Number Awarded:** 1. **To Apply:** Submit application and 500-1,000 word essay. **Deadline:** August 1. **Contact:** Marshall Stephens; E-mail: marshall@ptaccrew.com; scholarship@ptaccrew.com; URL: ptaccrew.com/scholarship.

9382 ■ Public Accountants Association of Kansas (PAAK)

PO Box 2732
Salina, KS 67402-2732
Ph: (785)827-7225
Fax: (785)827-0283
URL: www.paak.org
Social Media: www.facebook.com/PAAK-Public
 -Accountants-Association-of-Kansas-Inc-174588207102
twitter.com/PAAKansas

9383 ■ Floyd E. Lietz Scholarship Fund
(Undergraduate/Scholarship)

Purpose: To support accounting students in Kansas and assist with their financial education needs at Kansas Universities. **Focus:** Accounting. **Qualif.:** Applicants must be junior or senior students with an accounting major.
Funds Avail.: No specific amount. **Duration:** Annual.

9384 ■ Public Agency Risk Management Association

c/o Carrie Willson, Chair
707 3rd St.
West Sacramento, CA 95605
Ph: (916)376-5271

URL: parma.com
Social Media: www.facebook.com/
 PublicAgencyRiskManagementAssociation
instagram.com/parma2762
www.linkedin.com/groups/144680
twitter.com/PARMA2762

9385 ■ Ben C. Francis Risk Management Education Fund *(Undergraduate/Scholarship)*

Purpose: To promote, develop, and facilitate education and leadership in public agency risk management. **Focus:** Management. **Qualif.:** Applicants should be an employee of a member public agency pursuing an associate in Risk Management, Risk Management for Public Entities, and Associate in Risk Pool Management. **Criteria:** Committee appointed by the president of PARMA will select the candidates based on their goals in risk management and other related information.

Funds Avail.: $500. **Number Awarded:** Up to 4. **To Apply:** Applicants must fill out the application form; attach a written sponsorship statement by a PARMA member agency; must submit a paper detailing goals in the field of risk management; a description of the participation in PARMA including the local Chapter level; and attach any other related experience or information that will support the scholarship request.

9386 ■ Public Education Foundation

4350 S Maryland Pky.
Las Vegas, NV 89119
Ph: (702)799-1042
Fax: (702)799-5247
E-mail: info@thepef.org
URL: thepef.org
Social Media: www.facebook.com/pg/pefoz
www.facebook.com/ThePublicEducationFoundation
www.linkedin.com/company/the-public-education
 -foundation
twitter.com/ThePEFtoday
www.youtube.com/user/ThePublicEdFoundatio

9387 ■ Adelson Scholarship *(Undergraduate/Scholarship)*

Purpose: To assist the education of the dependents of Venetian Resort Hotel Casino Employees. **Focus:** General studies/Field of study not specified. **Qualif.:** Applicants must be CCSD seniors who are dependents of a Venetian/Palazzo Resort Hotel Casino Team Member, Sands Expo Team Member or Las Vegas Sands Corp. Team Member and who plan to attend an accredited college or university; must have a minimum 3.5 cumulative GPA, and demonstrate financial need. **Criteria:** Selection will be given based on the application materials.

Funds Avail.: $3,000 each. **Duration:** Annual; up to 3 years. **Number Awarded:** 3. **To Apply:** Applicants must submit completed application form along with essay, copy of a pay stub from the Venetian Resort Hotel Casino for the qualifying parent/guardian; copy of your parent's most recent tax return; current transcript; resume; letter of recommendation from someone who can speak to your determination and ability to succeed; letter of recommendation (a second letter; any source other than a peer or relative); "Financial Need Letter" explaining why you need assistance with your college/school expenses. **Deadline:** February 18.

Awards are arranged alphabetically below their administering organizations

9388 ■ Agustin Cano Memorial Scholarship
(Undergraduate/Scholarship)

Purpose: To provide financial assistance for tuition, fees and other appropriate educational expenses to the Valley High School in Clark County, Nevada seniors who plan to attend a college/university as a full-time student beginning in the fall. **Focus:** General studies/Field of study not specified.

Funds Avail.: $500. **Duration:** Annual. **Number Awarded:** 1. **Remarks:** The scholarship was established in the remembrance of Agustin Cano.

9389 ■ Alliance of Black Culinarians Scholarships
(Undergraduate/Scholarship)

Purpose: To promote education in culinary arts. **Focus:** Culinary arts. **Qualif.:** Applicants must be CCSD seniors; have a minimum 2.5 GPA; and, demonstrate financial needs. **Criteria:** Preference is given to minority students and those interested in a career in culinary arts.

Funds Avail.: No specific amount. **To Apply:** Interested applicants may contact the Foundation for more information. **Contact:** For further inquiry, please contact Scholarship Office at 702-221-7422; E-mail: csdonnelly@ccpef.org.

9390 ■ American Nuclear Society Nevada Section Scholarship *(Undergraduate/Scholarship)*

Purpose: To provide financial assistance for tuition, fees and other appropriate educational expenses for CCSD Nevada seniors who plan to major in a Nuclear Engineering or a Nuclear Science related field at UNLV. **Focus:** Engineering, Nuclear; Nuclear science. **Qualif.:** Applicants must be CCSD seniors planning to major in nuclear engineering or a nuclear science related field at UNLV with a minimum 3.8 cumulative GPA. **Criteria:** Selection will be based on the application materials.

Funds Avail.: $1,000. **Duration:** Annual. **Number Awarded:** 1. **To Apply:** Applicants must submit a completed application form with an essay; two letters of recommendation; transcript; and resume of awards; a letter of recommendation from a teacher, counselor, administrator, coach or advisor. **Deadline:** January 31. **Contact:** Phone: 702-221-7422; Email: csdonnelly@ccpef.org.

9391 ■ Susan Ayers Memorial Scholarships
(Undergraduate/Scholarship)

Purpose: To provide a financial assistance to independent women, mothers and Teachers. **Focus:** General studies/Field of study not specified. **Qualif.:** Applicants must be an independent women or mothers or a teacher. **Criteria:** Selection will be based on the compliance with submission of the necessary application materials.

Funds Avail.: No specific amount. **To Apply:** Interested applicants may contact the Foundation for more information. **Remarks:** The scholarship was established in the remembrance of Susan Ayers.

9392 ■ Cheyenne High School Desert Shields Scholarship *(Undergraduate/Scholarship)*

Purpose: To provide financial assistance for tuition, fees and other appropriate educational expenses to the Cheyenne High School Clark County, Nevada seniors who plan to attend a college or university as a full-time student. **Focus:** General studies/Field of study not specified. **Qualif.:** Applicants must be Cheyenne High School seniors planning to attend college or university as a full time student and have a minimum 3.1 unweighted GPA. **Criteria:** Selec-

tion will be given based on the application materials.

Funds Avail.: $1,000 each. **Duration:** Annual. **Number Awarded:** 2. **To Apply:** Applicant must submit a completed application form together with two letters of recommendation, a resume, essay; a letter of recommendation from a teacher; and applicant's most current transcript. **Contact:** Phone: 702-221-7422; Email: csdonnelly@ccpef.org.

9393 ■ Cimarron-Memorial Spartan Staff Scholarships *(Undergraduate/Scholarship)*

Purpose: To provide financial assistance for tuition, fees and other appropriate educational expenses for Cimarron-Memorial High School Clark County, Nevada seniors who are interested in pursuing a degree at an accredited college or university. **Focus:** General studies/Field of study not specified. **Qualif.:** Applicants must be Cimarron-Memorial High School seniors who are interested in pursuing a degree at an accredited college or university; must have a minimum 3.0 unweighted cumulative GPA. **Criteria:** Selection is given based on the compliance with submission of the necessary application materials.

Funds Avail.: $500 each. **Duration:** Annual. **Number Awarded:** 10. **To Apply:** Applicants must submit a completed application form along with an essay, two letters of recommendation, transcript, and resume of awards. **Deadline:** January 31. **Remarks:** The scholarship was established in the remembrance of Cimarron. **Contact:** Phone: 702-221-7422; Email: csdonnelly@ccpef.org.

9394 ■ Clark High School Academy of Finance Scholarship *(Undergraduate/Scholarship)*

Purpose: To support students who want to pursue education in business, economics or finance. **Focus:** Business; Economics; Finance. **Qualif.:** Applicants must be Clark High School Academy of Finance (AOF) seniors who are interested in pursuing a degree in business, economics or finance at any accredited college/university and who have a minimum 3.0 GPA. **Criteria:** Selection will be given based on the application materials.

Funds Avail.: $1,000. **Duration:** Annual. **Number Awarded:** 1. **To Apply:** Applicants must submit a completed application form together with the following: an essay (200 words) explaining career goals and aspirations; a letter of recommendation from a teacher, counselor, administrator, coach or advisor; letter of recommendation from a community or faith based organization which speaks to your volunteerism with their organization; transcript, resume. **Contact:** Phone: 702-221-7422; Email: csdonnelly@ccpef.org.

9395 ■ Coronado High School Counselors' Scholarship *(Undergraduate/Scholarship)*

Purpose: To provide financial assistance for tuition, fees and other appropriate educational expenses to the Coronado High School Clark County, Nevada seniors who have overcome adversities and plan to attend an accredited post-secondary institution. **Focus:** General studies/Field of study not specified. **Qualif.:** Applicants must be Coronado High School Clark County seniors who plan to attend an accredited post-secondary institution. **Criteria:** Selection will be based on the application materials.

Funds Avail.: $1,000. **Duration:** Annual. **Number Awarded:** 2. **To Apply:** Applicants must provide resume; current transcript (unofficial); 400-500 word essay, "Why I feel I deserve this scholarship."; brief essay about overcoming a serious challenge or circumstance in life. **Deadline:** January 31.

Awards are arranged alphabetically below their administering organizations

9396 ■ Corporal Joseph Martinez U.S. Army/ Durango High School AFJROTC Scholarship *(Undergraduate/Scholarship)*

Purpose: To provide financial assistance for tuition, fees and other appropriate educational expenses for Durango High School AFJROTC Program Clark County, Nevada seniors who plan to attend an accredited post-secondary institution either during or immediately following enlistment in any branch of the U.S. military. **Focus:** General studies/ Field of study not specified. **Qualif.:** Applicants must be Durango High School AFJROTC program seniors planning to attend any accredited post-secondary institution either during or immediately following enlistment in any branch of the U.S. military. **Criteria:** Selection will be based on compliance with the submission of necessary application materials; preference will be given to those who have excelled in the areas of leadership, community service and extracurricular activities.

Funds Avail.: $1,000. **Duration:** Annual. **Number Awarded:** 1. **To Apply:** Applicants must submit completed application form along with the letter from military recruiter, one letter of recommendation, transcript, and resume; a letter of recommendation from a teacher, counselor, administrator, coach or advisor. **Deadline:** February 20. **Contact:** Phone: 702-221-7422; Email: csdonnelly@ccpef.org.

9397 ■ Edwin F. Wiegand Science & Technology Scholarship *(Undergraduate/Scholarship)*

Purpose: To provide educational opportunities for individuals intending to pursue higher studies. **Focus:** Computer and information sciences; Information science and technology.

Funds Avail.: $1,250.

9398 ■ Elizabeth Shafer Memorial Scholarship *(Undergraduate/Scholarship)*

Purpose: To provide financial assistance for tuition, fees and other appropriate educational expenses. **Focus:** Culinary arts.

Funds Avail.: $1,000. **Remarks:** The scholarship was established in the remembrance of Elizabeth Shafer.

9399 ■ Evelyn Abrams Memorial Scholarship *(Undergraduate/Scholarship)*

Purpose: To provide financial assistance for tuition, fees and other appropriate educational expenses to the CCSD Nevada female seniors who are pursuing a degree in teacher education or business. **Focus:** Business; Education. **Qualif.:** Applicants must be CCSD female seniors interested in pursuing a degree in education or business at an accredited college/university; have a minimum 3.0 unweighted cumulative GPA; and, demonstrate financial need. **Criteria:** Selection will be based on the aforesaid qualifications and compliance with the application process.

Funds Avail.: $1,000. **Duration:** Annual. **Number Awarded:** 1. **To Apply:** Applicant must submit a completed application form, essay, letter of recommendation f from a community or faith based organization which speaks to your volunteerism with their organization; "Financial Need Letter" explaining why you need assistance with your college/school expenses; resume; most current transcript. **Deadline:** March 1. **Remarks:** The scholarship was established in the remembrance of Evelyn Abrams. **Contact:** Phone: 702-221-7422; Email: csdonnelly@ccpef.org.

9400 ■ Brendan Flores Alumni Leadership Circle Scholarship - Clark High School *(Undergraduate/ Scholarship)*

Purpose: To support students who want to pursue education in business, economics or finance. **Focus:** Business; Economics; Finance. **Qualif.:** Applicants must be Clark High School Academy of Finance (AOF) seniors who are interested in pursuing a degree in business, economics or finance at an accredited college/university with a minimum 3.0 GPA. **Criteria:** Selection will be given based on the application materials.

Funds Avail.: $500. **Duration:** Annual. **Number Awarded:** 1. **To Apply:** Applicants must submit a completed application form together with an essay, transcript, resume; a letter of recommendation from a teacher, counselor, administrator, coach or advisor; provide a copy of your letter of admission to a college or university. **Deadline:** February 18. **Contact:** Phone: 702-221-7422; Email: csdonnelly@ccpef.org.

9401 ■ Fraser Family Scholarships *(Undergraduate/ Scholarship)*

Purpose: To provide educational opportunities for individuals intending to pursue higher studies. **Focus:** General studies/Field of study not specified.

Funds Avail.: No specific amount. **Contact:** For further inquiry, please contact Scholarship Office at 702-221-7422; E-mail: csdonnelly@ccpef.org.

9402 ■ Glazing Industry Scholarship *(Advanced Professional/Scholarship)*

Purpose: To provide financial assistance for tuition, fees and other appropriate educational expenses for the High school seniors and post-secondary students in Nevada who are children or grandchildren of individuals actively participating in the glazing industry. **Focus:** General studies/Field of study not specified. **Qualif.:** Applicants must be members engaged in the auto glass, commercial glass, residential glass and all other related glazing industries. **Criteria:** Selection will be based on the aforesaid qualifications and compliance with the application process.

Funds Avail.: $1,000 each. **Duration:** Annual. **Number Awarded:** 3.

9403 ■ Gordy Fink Memorial Scholarship *(Undergraduate/Scholarship)*

Purpose: To provide financial assistance for tuition, fees and other appropriate educational expenses for residents of Clark County, Nevada who are graduating seniors from Valley High School that will be enrolling full-time at the University of Nevada-Las Vegas. **Focus:** General studies/ Field of study not specified. **Qualif.:** Applicants must be Valley High School seniors planning to attend the University of Nevada, Las Vegas as full-time students; must describe their leadership roles and any community service involvement. **Criteria:** Selection will be given to students with financial need.

Funds Avail.: $1,000. **Duration:** Annual. **Number Awarded:** 2. **To Apply:** Applicants should submit a completed application form together with the following: two letters of recommendation from a teacher, school counselor, club advisor, coach or employer; an essay (of 200 words) explaining careers and aspirations; and resume, as well as a letter of admission from UNLV. **Deadline:** March 11. **Remarks:** The scholarship was established in the remembrance of Gordy Fink. **Contact:** Phone: 702-221-7422;

Awards are arranged alphabetically below their administering organizations

Email: csdonnelly@ccpef.org.

9404 ■ Gretchen Hauff Memorial Scholarship
(Undergraduate/Scholarship)

Purpose: To provide financial assistance for tuition, fees and other appropriate educational expenses for college-bound female seniors living in Clark County, Nevada who are pursuing a degree in physical education (PE teacher) at an accredited college or university. **Focus:** Education, Physical. **Qualif.:** Applicants must be CCSD female seniors who are interested in pursuing a degree in physical education at an accredited college/university; must also have a minimum 2.5 unweighted cumulative GPA, and demonstrated financial need. **Criteria:** Selection will be based on the aforesaid qualifications and compliance with the application process.

Funds Avail.: $1,000. **Duration:** Annual. **Number Awarded:** 1. **To Apply:** Applicants should submit a completed application form together with the following: letters of recommendation from a teacher, school counselor, club advisor, coach or employer; an essay (of 400 to 500 words) describing the hope to accomplish with a degree in physical education; a Financial Need Letter; and resume; current transcript. **Deadline:** March 4. **Remarks:** The scholarship was established in the remembrance of Gretchen Hauff. **Contact:** Phone: 702-221-7422; Email: csdonnelly@ccpef.org.

9405 ■ JMA Architecture Studios Scholarship
(Undergraduate/Scholarship)

Purpose: To provide financial assistance for tuition, fees and other appropriate educational expenses for seniors interested in pursuing a career in architecture and plan to enroll as a full-time student at a university with an accredited School of Architecture. **Focus:** Architecture. **Qualif.:** Applicants must be CCSD seniors interested in pursuing a career in architecture and planning to attend a university with an accredited School of Architecture;. They must also demonstrate financial need and have a minimum 3.0 unweighted cumulative GPA. **Criteria:** Preference will be given to students who have participated in the Clark County School District's drafting program.

Funds Avail.: $5,000. **Duration:** Annual. **Number Awarded:** 3. **To Apply:** Applicants should submit a completed application form together with the following: two letters of recommendation from a teacher, school counselor, club advisor, coach or employer; a copy of letter of admission to a college or university; and upload a work sample or portfolio; resume; current transcript; "Financial Need Letter" explaining why you need assistance with your college/school expenses. **Deadline:** January 31. **Contact:** Phone: 702-221-7422; Email: csdonnelly@ccpef.org.

9406 ■ John Caoile Memorial Scholarship *(Other/Scholarship)*

Purpose: To provide financial assistance for tuition, fees and other appropriate educational expenses to the Durango High School Clark County, Nevada, AFJROTC Program seniors who plan to attend an accredited post-secondary institution and have excelled in the areas of leadership, community service and extra-curricular activities. **Focus:** General studies/Field of study not specified. **Qualif.:** Applicants must be Durango High School AFJROTC program seniors planning to attend at any accredited post-secondary institution and have excelled in the areas of leadership, community service and extra-curricular activities, and have a minimum of 3.0 GPA. **Criteria:** Selec-

tion will be based on the submitted application materials. **Funds Avail.:** $1,000. **Duration:** Annual. **Number Awarded:** 1. **To Apply:** Applicants must submit a completed application form together with a letter of recommendation, transcript and a resume. **Deadline:** January 31. **Remarks:** The scholarship was established in the remembrance of John Caoile. **Contact:** Phone: 702-221-7422; Email: csdonnelly@ccpef.org.

9407 ■ Josef Princ Memorial Scholarship
(Undergraduate/Scholarship)

Purpose: To provide financial assistance for tuition, fees and other appropriate educational expenses for CCSD Nevada male seniors who are of European descent. **Focus:** Engineering; Mathematics and mathematical sciences. **Qualif.:** Applicants must be CCSD male seniors of European descent; maintaining a minimum 3.5 cumulative GPA; planning to attend any accredited post-secondary college/university majoring in engineering, mathematics or science. **Criteria:** Must demonstrate financial need.

Funds Avail.: $2,000 each. **Duration:** Annual. **Number Awarded:** 4. **To Apply:** Must submit completed application form, an essay, amount of your personal savings and that of your family, a copy of your parent's most recent tax return; two letters of recommendation who can speak to your determination and ability to succeed, transcript; a financial need letter; and resume. **Deadline:** January 31. **Remarks:** The scholarship was established in the remembrance of Josef Princ. **Contact:** Phone: 702-221-7422; Email: csdonnelly@ccpef.org.

9408 ■ Judith Warner Memorial Scholarship
(Undergraduate/Scholarship)

Purpose: To provide educational opportunities for individuals intending to pursue higher studies. **Focus:** General studies/Field of study not specified.

Funds Avail.: $600. **Remarks:** The scholarship was established in the remembrance of Judith Warner.

9409 ■ Las Vegas Chinatown Scholarship
(Undergraduate/Scholarship)

Purpose: To provide financial assistance for tuition, fees and other appropriate educational expenses for CCSD Nevada seniors of Asian descent who plan to attend an accredited college or university in Nevada. **Focus:** Business. **Qualif.:** Applicants must be CCSD seniors of Asian descent planning to attend any accredited college/university in Nevada and have a minimum 3.5 cumulative GPA. **Criteria:** Selection will be given to students planning to major in Business.

Funds Avail.: $1,000 each. **Duration:** Annual. **Number Awarded:** 2. **To Apply:** Applicants must submit a completed application form with an essay; two letters of recommendation; transcript; and resume of awards; a letter of recommendation from a teacher, counselor, administrator, coach or advisor. **Deadline:** January 31. **Contact:** Phone: 702-221-7422; Email: csdonnelly@ccpef.org.

9410 ■ Mesquite Club Evening Chapter Inc. Scholarship *(Undergraduate/Scholarship)*

Purpose: To provide financial assistance for tuition, fees and other appropriate educational expenses to the CCSD Nevada female high school seniors who plan to attend an accredited post-secondary institution in Nevada as a full-time student beginning in the fall. **Focus:** General studies/Field of study not specified. **Qualif.:** Applicants must be

Awards are arranged alphabetically below their administering organizations

CCSD female seniors planning to attend an accredited post-secondary institution in Nevada as full-time students; must have a minimum 3.0 GPA and have demonstrated financial need. **Criteria:** Selection will be given based on the application materials.

Funds Avail.: $1,500 each. **Duration:** Annual. **Number Awarded:** 3. **To Apply:** Applicants should submit a completed application form together with the following: one letter of recommendation from a teacher, school counselor, club advisor, coach or employer; an essay explaining careers, aspirations, leadership roles and any community service involvement; and resume; current transcript; "Financial Need Letter" explaining why you need assistance with your college expenses. **Deadline:** January 31. **Contact:** Phone: 702-221-7422; Email: csdonnelly@ccpef.org.

9411 ■ Michael J. Hoggard Memorial Scholarship
(Undergraduate/Scholarship)

Purpose: To provide financial assistance for tuition, fees and other appropriate educational expenses for Green Valley High School Clark County, Nevada seniors who have been on the school's soccer team for at least two years, including their senior year and plan to attend an accredited post-secondary college or university. **Focus:** General studies/Field of study not specified. **Qualif.:** Applicants must be Green Valley High School seniors who have been on the school's soccer team for at least two years (including senior year), planning to attend any accredited post-secondary college/university, and have a minimum 3.0 cumulative GPA. **Criteria:** Selection will be based on the aforesaid qualifications; and financial need will be considered.

Funds Avail.: $1,000. **Duration:** Annual. **Number Awarded:** 1. **To Apply:** Applicants should submit a completed application form together with the following: two letters of recommendation from a teacher, school counselor, club advisor, coach or employer; an essay (of 500 words, should be double spaced) describing the reason or reasons why they are applying for the award and address both of the following questions: (a) How would the award benefit or impact the applicants' ability to obtain an education? (b) How has soccer impacted the applicants' life?; a Financial Need Letter; and resume; current transcript. **Remarks:** The scholarship was established in the remembrance of Michael J. Hoggard. **Contact:** Phone: 702-221-7422; Email: csdonnelly@ccpef.org.

9412 ■ Mickey Donnelly Memorial Scholarship
(Undergraduate/Scholarship)

Purpose: To provide financial assistance for tuition, fees and other appropriate educational expenses to the CCSD Nevada seniors who attended Walter Johnson Junior High School for a minimum of one year and plan to attend an accredited post-secondary institution in Nevada. **Focus:** General studies/Field of study not specified. **Qualif.:** Applicants must be CCSD seniors. **Criteria:** Selection will be given based on the application materials.

Funds Avail.: $1,000. **Duration:** Annual. **Number Awarded:** 1. **To Apply:** Applicants must submit a completed application form together with an essay; two letters of recommendation; transcript; and resume of awards; a letter of recommendation from a teacher, counselor, administrator, coach or advisor. **Remarks:** The scholarship was established in the remembrance of Mickey Donnelly. **Contact:** Phone: 702-221-7422; Email: csdonnelly@ccpef.org.

9413 ■ Nate Mack/Cindi Turner Scholarship
(Undergraduate/Scholarship)

Purpose: To provide financial assistance for tuition, fees and other appropriate educational expenses for CCSD Nevada seniors who attended Nate Mack Elementary School for three (3) or more years. **Focus:** General studies/Field of study not specified. **Qualif.:** Applicants must be CCSD seniors who attended Nate Mack Elementary School for at least three years, planning to attend any accredited college/university, have a minimum 3.0 cumulative GPA, and demonstrate financial need. **Criteria:** Selection will be based on the aforesaid qualifications.

Funds Avail.: $1,000. **Duration:** Annual. **Number Awarded:** 1. **Remarks:** The scholarship was established in the remembrance of Nate Mack and Cindi Turner.

9414 ■ National Security Technologies Engineering and Science Scholarships *(Undergraduate/Scholarship)*

Purpose: To support CCSD seniors who are pursuing technical degrees that are vital to the future of the Nevada National Security Site. **Focus:** Engineering; Science. **Qualif.:** Applicants must be CCSD seniors planning to major in engineering or science at a four-year institution with a minimum 3.5 cumulative GPA. **Criteria:** Selection will be based on the compliance with the submission of necessary application materials.

Funds Avail.: No specific amount. **Duration:** Annual. **To Apply:** Applicants may contact the Foundation for more information. **Remarks:** The scholarship is sponsored by National Security Technologies, LLC. **Contact:** For further inquiry, please contact Scholarship Office at 702-221-7422; E-mail: csdonnelly@ccpef.org.

9415 ■ North Las Vegas Firefighters William J. Harnedy Memorial Scholarship *(Undergraduate/Scholarship)*

Purpose: To provide financial assistance for tuition, fees and other appropriate educational expenses for CCSD Nevada seniors who attend a high school in the City of North Las Vegas. **Focus:** General studies/Field of study not specified.

Funds Avail.: $1,000. **Remarks:** The scholarship was established in the remembrance of William J. Harnedy who is a North Las Vegas Firefighters.

9416 ■ Palo Verde High School Barbara Edwards Memorial Scholarship *(Undergraduate/Scholarship)*

Purpose: To provide financial assistance for tuition, fees and other appropriate educational expenses for Palo Verde High School seniors living in Clark County, NV who will have completed seven semesters of the same foreign language by January of their senior year and have demonstrated academic excellence. **Focus:** Foreign languages.

Funds Avail.: $1,000. **Remarks:** The scholarship was established in the remembrance of Barbara Edwards.

9417 ■ Palo Verde High School Faculty Follies Scholarship *(Undergraduate/Scholarship)*

Purpose: To provide educational opportunities for individuals intending to pursue higher studies. **Focus:** General studies/Field of study not specified. **Qualif.:** Applicants must be Palo Verde High School seniors who have completed six semesters of theater classes; must be planning to attend any accredited college/university; and must

Awards are arranged alphabetically below their administering organizations

have a minimum 2.5 cumulative GPA. **Criteria:** Selection will be based on the compliance with submission of the necessary application materials.

Funds Avail.: $500. **Duration:** Annual. **Number Awarded:** 2. **To Apply:** Applicants must submit a completed application form with an essay; resume of awards; and most current transcript. **Deadline:** February 18. **Contact:** Phone: 702-221-7422; Email: csdonnelly@ccpef.org.

9418 ■ Panther Cafe Scholarships (Undergraduate/ Scholarship)

Purpose: To provide financial assistance by profits from the cafe are utilized to help the students make the transition from school to careers through field trips, securing health cards, and scholarships for post-secondary education. **Focus:** General studies/Field of study not specified. **Qualif.:** Applicants must be Palo Verde High School seniors who have participated in a class that is directly associated with the operation of the Panther Cafe and planning to attend any accredited post-secondary college or institution. **Criteria:** Selection will be based on the compliance with the submission of the necessary application materials.

Funds Avail.: $1,000. **Duration:** Annual; up to 3 years. **Number Awarded:** 2. **To Apply:** Applicants must submit a completed application form with an essay; two letters of recommendation; transcript; and resume of awards; a letter of recommendation from a teacher, counselor, administrator, coach or advisor. **Deadline:** March 15. **Remarks:** Established in 1998. **Contact:** For further inquiry, please contact Scholarship Office at 702-221-7422; E-mail: csdonnelly@ccpef.org.

9419 ■ Pardee Community Building Scholarship (Undergraduate/Scholarship)

Purpose: To recognized as a premier supporter of education as well as a pioneer in master planning for quality of life. **Focus:** Architecture; Business; Construction; Engineering, Civil.

Funds Avail.: $1,500 each. **Duration:** up to 3 years.

9420 ■ Rich Abjian Leadership Scholarship (Undergraduate/Scholarship)

Purpose: To provide educational opportunities for individuals intending to pursue higher studies. **Focus:** General studies/Field of study not specified. **Qualif.:** Applicants must be CCSD seniors who have participated in athletics for the past four years with a minimum 3.2 unweighted cumulative GPA. **Criteria:** Selection is given based on the compliance with submission of the necessary application materials.

Funds Avail.: $2,500 each. **Duration:** Annual. **Number Awarded:** 5. **To Apply:** Applicants must submit a completed application form along with an essay describing each of the athletic sports areas you participated in, letters received in each of those sports. Also list all sports honors you may have received and leadership roles that you have held on the sports field, how being an athlete has impacted your life. The length of your typed essay should be 400-500 words and your ability to be a leader; two letters of recommendation, transcript, and resume. **Deadline:** March 1. **Remarks:** The scholarship is sponsored by Southern Nevada Sports Hall of Fame. **Contact:** Phone: 702-221-7422; Email: csdonnelly@ccpef.org.

9421 ■ Rose Marie Princ Memorial Scholarship (Undergraduate/Scholarship)

Purpose: To provide educational opportunities for individuals intending to pursue higher studies. **Focus:** Education,

Elementary; Education, Secondary. **Criteria:** Selection will be based on demonstrated financial need.

Funds Avail.: $2,000 each. **Duration:** Annual. **Number Awarded:** Up to 4. **To Apply:** Applicants must submit completed application form along with essay, two letters of recommendation, transcript; a financial need letter; resume; amount of your personal savings and that of your family; copy of your parent's most recent tax return; explain your exact involvement in community service and the name of any supervisor(s) and hours of participation as well as years. Ex. 4 years or Freshman through senior years; note all AP Classes as well as Honor Classes that you have taken in High School, including second semester. **Deadline:** January 31. **Remarks:** The scholarship was established in the remembrance of Rose Marie Princ. **Contact:** Phone: 702-221-7422; Email: csdonnelly@ccpef.org.

9422 ■ Sheila Tarr-Smith Memorial Scholarship (Undergraduate/Scholarship)

Purpose: To provide educational opportunities for individuals intending to pursue higher studies. **Focus:** Public service.

Funds Avail.: $2,500.

9423 ■ Smith's Personal Best Scholarships (Undergraduate/Scholarship)

Purpose: To provide financial assistance for tuition, fees and other appropriate educational expenses for high school seniors who show promise in non-traditional ways. **Focus:** General studies/Field of study not specified. **Qualif.:** Applicants must be high school seniors who show promise in non-traditional ways; need non-traditional incentives for graduation. **Criteria:** Selection will be based on the aforesaid qualifications.

Funds Avail.: $2,000 each.

9424 ■ Susan Brager Occupational Education Scholarship (Undergraduate/Scholarship)

Purpose: To provide financial assistance for tuition, fees and other appropriate educational expenses to the CCSD seniors living in Clark County, Nevada who have completed a minimum of two years of an established occupational education program. **Focus:** Education.

Funds Avail.: $1,000. **Duration:** Annual. **Number Awarded:** 1.

9425 ■ Tall Awareness Scholarships (Graduate/ Scholarship)

Purpose: To assist a tall student in his/her academic endeavors. **Focus:** General studies/Field of study not specified. **Qualif.:** Applicants must be graduate in high school seniors of Clark County School District.

Funds Avail.: $1,000.

9426 ■ Tarkanian Teacher Education Academy at Clark High School Scholarship (Undergraduate/ Scholarship)

Purpose: To provide educational opportunities for individuals intending to pursue higher studies. **Focus:** Education. **Funds Avail.:** Varies.

9427 ■ Travis Dunning Memorial Scholarship (Undergraduate/Scholarship)

Purpose: To provide financial assistance tuition, fees, and other appropriate educational expenses to the Green Val-

Awards are arranged alphabetically below their administering organizations

ley, Coronado, and Foothill High School seniors living in Clark County, Nevada who plan to attend an accredited four-year college or university. **Focus:** General studies/ Field of study not specified. **Qualif.:** Applicants must be high school seniors from Green Valley, Coronado, Foothill, Silverado or Liberty planning to attend an accredited four-year college/university, and who have a 3.0 weighted or unweighted GPA. **Criteria:** Selection will be based on demonstrated financial need.

Funds Avail.: $1,500. **Duration:** Annual; up to 3 years. **Number Awarded:** 1. **To Apply:** Applicants must submit completed application form along with essay, two letters of recommendation, transcript; a financial need letter; and resume. **Deadline:** January 31. **Remarks:** The scholarship was established in the remembrance of Travis Dunning. **Contact:** Phone: 702-221-7422; Email: csdonnelly@ ccpef.org.

9428 ■ Tsutako Curo Scholarship (Undergraduate/ Scholarship)

Purpose: To support single mothers desiring to advance their education. **Focus:** General studies/Field of study not specified.

Funds Avail.: $2,000. **Duration:** Annual. **Number Awarded:** 1.

9429 ■ Veronica Gantt Memorial Scholarship (Undergraduate/Scholarship)

Purpose: To provide financial assistance for tuition, fees and other appropriate educational expenses for the Del Sol High School seniors living in Clark County, Nevada who are active in sports and their community and plan to attend an accredited college or university. **Focus:** Education, Physical; Sports studies.

Funds Avail.: $500 each. **Duration:** Annual. **Number Awarded:** 2. **Remarks:** The scholarship was established in the remembrance of Veronica Gantt. **Contact:** 4350 S. Maryland Pkwy, Las Vegas, NV 89119; Phone: 702-799-1042; Email: info@ccpef.org.

9430 ■ Public Library Association (PLA)
225 N Michigan Ave., Ste. 1300
Chicago, IL 60601
Ph: (312)280-5047
Free: 800-545-2433
E-mail: pla@ala.org
URL: www.ala.org/pla
Social Media: www.facebook.com/pla.org
instagram.com/ala_pla
twitter.com/ALA_PLA

9431 ■ Baker and Taylor Entertainment Audio Music/Video Product Award (Other/Award)

Purpose: To promote the development of a circulating audio music/video product collection in public libraries and increase the exposure of the format within the community. **Focus:** Library and archival sciences. **Qualif.:** Any public library is eligible.

Funds Avail.: $2,500. **Duration:** Annual. **Remarks:** Established in 1997. **Contact:** Phone: 800-545-2433, ext. 5PLA (5752); Email: pla@ala.org.

9432 ■ DEMCO New Leaders Travel Grants (Professional development/Grant)

Purpose: To enhance the professional development and improve the expertise of public librarians new to the field by making possible their attendance at major professional development activities. **Focus:** Library and archival sciences. **Qualif.:** Applicants must be members of the public library association; must be practicing librarians for five years or less; must not be officers or members of the PLA board of directors; and must not be members or supervisors of the new leaders travel grant jury; cannot have attended a major PLA continuing education program in the last five years due to limited or non-existent funding for professional travel; supervisor or supervising authority cannot be a current member of the new leaders travel grant jury. **Criteria:** Selection is based on quality and appropriateness of the submitted proposals; Preference will be given to applicants who can document the fiscal need for travel fund based on their institution's budget and those whose continuing education falls within the framework of PLA priority concerns.

Funds Avail.: Up to $1,500. **Duration:** Annual. **Number Awarded:** Varies. **To Apply:** Applicants are advised to visit the website for the PLA's awards online application. **Contact:** E-mail: pla@ala.org; Phone: 800-545-2433.

9433 ■ Public Relations Society of America Maryland Chapter (PRSAMD)
c/o Mariner Management and Marketing
PO Box 1640
Columbia, MD 21044-0640
Ph: (443)283-8060
Fax: (301)238-4579
Free: 866-868-7772
E-mail: info@prsamd.org
URL: www.prsamd.org
Social Media: www.facebook.com/PRSAMaryland
twitter.com/PRSA_MD
www.youtube.com/channel/UCc2I1DoykPk6CUSBild7dXQ

9434 ■ Kathleen Kelly Undergraduate Scholarship (Undergraduate/Scholarship)

Purpose: To support students who demonstrates excellent academic credentials and hold promise for successful careers in public relations. **Focus:** Public administration. **Qualif.:** Applicants must be college-level students, sophomore or junior status; must be enrolled in a Maryland college or university; or residents of Maryland attending college outside of the state; concentrated study in an area of communications with the intention to pursue a career in public relations; must have a minimum 3.0 GPA overall and grades of B or better in all public relations English and/or writing courses; commitment to public relations as demonstrated by campus public relations activities, membership in PRSSA and/or other career-related student organizations, public relations work experience (paid, volunteer or internship); active involvement in campus and/or community organizations. **Criteria:** Awarded at the discretion of PRSA Maryland's Executive Board to a student who demonstrates excellent academic credentials and the potential for a successful public relations career.

Funds Avail.: No specific amount. **Duration:** Annual. **To Apply:** Applicants must submit a completed application including an essay, along with a resume covering all areas outlined in award criteria; official transcripts from all colleges and universities attended and currently enrolled required; two recommendation letter. **Remarks:** The award is established in honor of Kathleen S. Kelly, Ph.D., in honor of her contributions to the Maryland Chapter of PRSA and

Awards are arranged alphabetically below their administering organizations

public relations education. **Contact:** URL: prsamd.org/scholarship/.

9435 ■ Public Relations Student Society of America (PRSSA)
120 Wall St., 21st Fl.
New York, NY 10005
Ph: (212)460-1474
Fax: (212)995-0757
E-mail: prssa@prsa.org
URL: prssa.prsa.org
Social Media: www.facebook.com/prssanational
twitter.com/prssanational

9436 ■ Stephen D. Pisinski Memorial Scholarship
(Undergraduate/Scholarship)

Purpose: To provide educational assistance for qualified students intending to pursue a career in the field of public relations. **Focus:** Communications; Journalism; Public administration; Public relations. **Qualif.:** Applicants must be journalism, communications, or public relations majors; be in junior or senior year of college; have at least a 3.3 overall GPA on a 4.0 system and be members of the Public Relations Student Society of America. **Criteria:** Selection will be based on the aforesaid qualifications and compliance with the application process.

Funds Avail.: $1,500. **Duration:** Annual. **To Apply:** Applicants must submit the following: completed application form; a resume including academic honors, special projects, activities and work experience; an official transcript of all college studies, including grades of the preceding semester; an essay of 1,000 words or less stating career goals; two strong writing samples; and two letters of academic and/or professional recommendations. Application and details available online at prssa.prsa.org/scholarships-and-awards/individual-scholarships/. **Remarks:** The scholarship was developed by Allison & Partners in memory of Steve Pisinski, APR, Fellow PRSA, and founder of The Montgomery Group. Established in 2002.

9437 ■ Betsy Plank/PRSSA Scholarships
(Undergraduate/Scholarship)

Purpose: To provide educational support for deserving students intending to pursue a career in public relations. **Focus:** Public relations. **Qualif.:** Applicants must be PRSSA members who are in junior or senior year of college, preparing for a career in public relations. **Criteria:** Applicants will be judged on the following criteria: academic achievement in public relations and overall studies; demonstrated leadership; practical experience (e.g. internships, other work/service, student firm work); and, commitment to public relations, particularly as expressed in the candidates' statement.

Funds Avail.: $5,000 (First honor); $1,500 (Second honor); $1,000 (Third honor). **Duration:** Annual. **Number Awarded:** 3. **To Apply:** Applicant must a letter of recommendation from their faculty or professional adviser; a signed statement of 300 words or fewer that outlines applicant's commitment to public relations and its ethical practice; and optional additional letters of recommendation from previous employers or professors. Application and details available online at prssa.prsa.org/scholarships-and-awards/individual-scholarships/. **Remarks:** Honors Betsy Plank, APR, Fellow PRSA, the PRSA President in 1973, the first

woman to lead the Society, and chair of the U.S. Section of International Public Relations Association (1980–1981).

9438 ■ PRSA Diversity Multicultural Scholarships
(Undergraduate/Scholarship)

Purpose: To assist and recognize young men and women for outstanding academic achievement and commitment to the practice of public relations. **Focus:** Communications; Public relations. **Qualif.:** Applicants must be full-time undergraduate students at an accredited four-year college/university; membership in the Public Relations Student Society of America (PRSSA) is preferred, but is not a requirement; a major or minor in public relations is also preferred; student who attends a school that does not offer a public relations degree or program must be enrolled in a communications degree program; must maintain a 3.0 GPA on a 4.0 scale in all courses; must have African-American/Black, Hispanic/Latino, Asian, Native American, Alaskan Native or Pacific Islander ancestry. **Criteria:** Selection is based on the submitted application materials.

Funds Avail.: $1,500 each. **Duration:** Annual. **Number Awarded:** 2. **To Apply:** Applicants must submit a completed application form together with an official transcript; a brief letter of recommendation from a PRSA member or an individual associated with public relations or higher education; a typed, double-spaced essay (maximum of three pages); and statement of Financial Status. Application and details available online at prssa.prsa.org/scholarships-and-awards/individual-scholarships/. **Remarks:** Established in 1989.

9439 ■ Gary Yoshimura Scholarship *(Undergraduate/Scholarship)*

Purpose: To provide support to qualified PRSSA members who demonstrate a financial need for the pursuit of higher education in the public relations field. **Focus:** Public administration; Public relations. **Qualif.:** Applicants must be PRSSA member pursuing a higher education in the public relations field; have a minimum 3.0 GPA; and demonstrate financial need. **Criteria:** Selection will be based on the aforesaid qualifications and compliance with the application process.

Funds Avail.: $2,400. **Duration:** Annual. **Number Awarded:** 1. **To Apply:** Application forms are available at the website; must also submit the following: official transcript, letter of recommendation from the internship supervisor/employer or faculty advisor; must prepare a 1,000-word essay describing the challenges they have faced, either personally or professionally, and how they overcame it; must complete the statement of intent and financial need section. Application and details available online at prssa.prsa.org/scholarships-and-awards/individual-scholarships/.

9440 ■ Public Schools of Hawaii Foundation (PSHF)
PO Box 4148
Honolulu, HI 96812
E-mail: pshf88@gmail.com
URL: pshf.org
Social Media: www.facebook.com/pshf808
twitter.com
www.youtube.com/user/pshf808

9441 ■ PSHF Good Idea Grant *(Other/Grant)*
Purpose: To provide assistance to teachers in helping all children to reach high levels of achievements. **Focus:**

Awards are arranged alphabetically below their administering organizations

General studies/Field of study not specified. **Qualif.:** Applicants must be classroom teachers in a Hawaii public school during the current school year; a team of teachers from the same school may apply, but one teacher on the team; must be designed to enhance innovation in the classroom and challenge teachers to think creatively and boldly. **Criteria:** Selection will be based on the committee's criteria.

Funds Avail.: Maximum of $3,000. **Duration:** Annual. **Number Awarded:** 1. **To Apply:** Applicants may download application form online. **Deadline:** July 10.

9442 ■ Public Service Alliance of Canada (PSAC)
233 Gilmour St.
Ottawa, ON, Canada K2P 0P1
Ph: (613)560-4200
Free: 888-604-7722
E-mail: info@psac-afpc.com
URL: psacunion.ca
Social Media: www.facebook.com/psac.national
www.instagram.com/psacafpc
twitter.com/psacnat
twitter.com/psac_afpc
www.youtube.com/channel/UCoFoscofcn-mysgl_bU95nQ

9443 ■ J.R. (Joe) Power National Scholarship
(Postgraduate/Scholarship, Monetary)

Purpose: To provide financial assistance to children and dependents of PSAC members. **Focus:** General studies/Field of study not specified. **Qualif.:** Applicants must be PSAC member or their children who are returning to university, college or a recognized institute of higher learning; must have a good standing in PSAC. **Criteria:** Selection based on the merit of the 800-word essay, YouTube video, infographic, song or other creative submission according to the topic determined for the given year

Funds Avail.: 2,000 Canadian Dollars. **Duration:** Annual. **Number Awarded:** 1. **To Apply:** Applicants must submit an 800-word essay on the topic chosen by the PSAC scholarship committee OR A YouTube video, infographic or audio recording song (submitted on-line in mp3 format or via YouTube, or by mail on a CD); application form are available from the website and must be completed and mailed to Public Service Alliance of Canada. **Deadline:** June 26. **Contact:** Completed applications should be mailed to: Public Service Alliance of Canada, Attn: Scholarship Committee, 233 Gilmour St., 9th Fl., Ottawa, Ontario, K2P 0P1; For questions: Phone: 613-560-4347; Email: scholarships@psac-afpc.com.

9444 ■ PSAC-AGR National Scholarship
(Postgraduate/Scholarship, Monetary)

Purpose: To provide financial assistance to children and dependents of PSAC members. **Focus:** General studies/Field of study not specified. **Qualif.:** Applicants must be PSAC members or their children who are returning to university, college or a recognized institute of higher learning; must have a good standing in PSAC. **Criteria:** Selection based on the merit of the 800-word essay, YouTube video, infographic, song or other creative submission according to the topic determined for the given year

Funds Avail.: 3,000 Canadian Dollars; 4,000 Canadian Dollars. **Duration:** Annual. **Number Awarded:** 2. **To Apply:** Applicants must submit an 800-word essay on the

topic chosen by the PSAC scholarship committee OR A YouTube video, infographic or audio recording song (submitted on-line in mp3 format or via YouTube, or by mail on a CD); application form are available from the website and must be completed and mailed to Public Service Alliance of Canada. **Deadline:** June 26. **Contact:** Completed applications should be mailed to: Public Service Alliance of Canada, Attn: Scholarship Committee, 233 Gilmour St., 9th Fl., Ottawa, Ontario, K2P 0P1; For questions: Phone: 613-560-4347; Email: scholarships@psac-afpc.com.

9445 ■ PSAC - Coughlin National Scholarships
(Postgraduate/Scholarship, Monetary)

Purpose: To provide financial assistance to children and dependents of PSAC members. **Focus:** General studies/Field of study not specified. **Qualif.:** Applicants must be PSAC member or their children who are returning to university, college or a recognized institute of higher learning; must have a good standing in PSAC. **Criteria:** Selection based on the merit of the 800-word essay, YouTube video, infographic, song or other creative submission according to the topic determined for the given year

Funds Avail.: 3,000 Canadian Dollars; 4,000 Canadian Dollars. **Duration:** Annual. **Number Awarded:** 2. **To Apply:** Applicants must submit an 800-word essay on the topic chosen by the PSAC scholarship committee OR A YouTube video, infographic or audio recording song (submitted on-line in mp3 format or via YouTube, or by mail on a CD); application form are available from the website and must be completed and mailed to Public Service Alliance of Canada. **Deadline:** June 26. **Contact:** Completed applications should be mailed to: Public Service Alliance of Canada, Attn: Scholarship Committee, 233 Gilmour St., 9th Fl., Ottawa, Ontario, K2P 0P1; For questions: Phone: 613-560-4347; Email: scholarships@psac-afpc.com.

9446 ■ PSAC National Member Scholarship
(Postgraduate/Scholarship, Monetary)

Purpose: To assist and support dependent children of PSAC members who are planning to attend university, college or recognized institute of higher learning on a full-time basis. **Focus:** Education; Public service. **Qualif.:** Applicants must be PSAC member or their children who are returning to university, college or a recognized institute of higher learning; must have a good standing in PSAC. **Criteria:** Selection are awarded based on the impact of the 800-word essay, scholastic achievement, and community and union involvement as reviewed by the PSAC scholarship committee.

Funds Avail.: 2,000 Canadian Dollars. **Duration:** Annual. **Number Awarded:** 5. **To Apply:** Applicants must submit an 800-word essay on the topic chosen by the PSAC scholarship committee OR A YouTube video, infographic or audio recording song (submitted on-line in mp3 format or via YouTube, or by mail on a CD); application form are available from the website and must be completed and mailed to Public Service Alliance of Canada. **Deadline:** June 26. **Contact:** Completed applications should be mailed to: Public Service Alliance of Canada, Attn: Scholarship Committee, 233 Gilmour St., 9th fl., Ottawa, Ontario, K2P 0P1; For questions: Phone: 613-560-4347; Email: scholarships@psac-afpc.com.

9447 ■ PSAC Regional Scholarships *(Postgraduate/Scholarship, Monetary)*

Purpose: To provide financial assistance to children and dependents of PSAC members. **Focus:** General studies/

Awards are arranged alphabetically below their administering organizations

Field of study not specified. **Qualif.:** Applicants must be PSAC member or their children who are returning to university, college or a recognized institute of higher learning; must have a good standing in PSAC. **Criteria:** Selection based on the merit of the 800-word essay, YouTube video, infographic, song or other creative submission according to the topic determined for the given year; one for each of the seven regions (Atlantic, Quebec, National Capital Region, Ontario, Prairies, British Columbia, and the North)

Funds Avail.: 1,000 Canadian Dollars each. **Duration:** Annual. **Number Awarded:** 7. **To Apply:** Applicants must submit an 800-word essay on the topic chosen by the PSAC scholarship committee OR A YouTube video, infographic or audio recording song (submitted on-line in mp3 format or via YouTube, or by mail on a CD); application form are available from the website and must be completed and mailed to Public Service Alliance of Canada. **Deadline:** June 26. **Contact:** Completed applications should be mailed to: Public Service Alliance of Canada, Attn: Scholarship Committee, 233 Gilmour St., 9th Fl., Ottawa, Ontario, K2P 0P1; For questions: Phone: 613-560-4347; Email: scholarships@psac-afpc.com.

9448 ■ Pulmonary Hypertension Association
8401 Colesville Road, Suite 200
Silver Spring, MD 20910
Ph: (301)565-3004
Fax: (301)565-3994
Free: 800-748-7274
URL: www.phassociation.org
Social Media: www.facebook.com/
  PulmonaryHypertensionAssociation
www.instagram.com/phassociation
twitter.com/PHAssociation
www.youtube.com/user/PHAssociation

9449 ■ PHA Research Fellowships *(Professional development/Fellowship)*

Purpose: To support faculty-level researchers who are in the field of pulmonary arterial hypertension. **Focus:** Medical research; Medicine, Pulmonary.

Funds Avail.: Up to $50,000. **Duration:** Annual. **Number Awarded:** Varies. **Remarks:** Established in 2006.

9450 ■ Purdue University School of Mechanical Engineering - Ray W. Herrick Laboratories
177 S Russell St.
West Lafayette, IN 47907-2099
URL: engineering.purdue.edu
Social Media: www.facebook.com/PurdueEngineering
www.youtube.com/user/PurdueEngineering

9451 ■ Purdue University Ray W. Herrick Laboratories Research Fellowship *(Graduate/Fellowship)*

Purpose: To assist individuals in their research related to energy, the environment, quality of life and sustainability. **Focus:** Energy-related areas; Engineering. **Qualif.:** Applicants must be outstanding students who have earned their bachelor's or masters' degree in engineering or related sciences. **Criteria:** Selection will be based on the committee's criteria.

Funds Avail.: No specific amount. **To Apply:** Interested applicants may contact the Herrick Laboratories for the application process and other information.

9452 ■ Quality Bath
1144 E County Line Rd.
Lakewood, NJ 08701
Free: 800-554-3210
E-mail: info@qualitybath.com
URL: www.qualitybath.com
Social Media: www.facebook.com/QualityBath
instagram.com/qualitybath
www.pinterest.com/qualitybath
twitter.com/TheQualityBath

9453 ■ Quality Bath.com Scholarship *(Community College, College, University, Undergraduate, Graduate/Scholarship)*

Purpose: To celebrate the beauty in our world and a belief in an even more beautiful future. **Focus:** Arts; Design. **Qualif.:** Applicant must be enrolled in a college or university in the United States, or a high school students planning to enroll, pursuing a degree in the arts or design fields; must be a U.S. citizen or permanent resident alien; must have a minimum 3.0 GPA.

Funds Avail.: $1,500. **Number Awarded:** 1.

9454 ■ Quality Company Formations
71-75 Shelton St.
London WC2H 9JQ, United Kingdom
Ph: 20 3 9080044
URL: www.qualitycompanyformations.co.uk
Social Media: www.facebook.com/pages/Quality
  -Formations/604953572949509
twitter.com/Q_Formations

9455 ■ Quality Company Formations Scholarship *(College, University, Undergraduate/Scholarship)*

Purpose: To help students pay for college or university. **Focus:** General studies/Field of study not specified. **Qualif.:** Applicant must a both current and incoming undergraduate or postgraduate students, currently enrolled at an accredited learning institution in the UK or US.

Funds Avail.: $1,250. **Number Awarded:** Up to 3. **To Apply:** Applicant must submit an essay (1,000 words) outlining their business proposal, the steps the applicant has taken to realize this ambition, and details of how applicant would use the scholarship to further develop their idea; must also send the completed student application form and proof or enrollment or acceptance letter from their university or college. **Deadline:** June 26. **Contact:** Email: scholarships@qualityformations.co.uk.

9456 ■ Quarter Century Wireless Association Inc. (QCWA)
c/o Roberta Cohen, Office Manager
WA2FRW, 1972 Martina St.
Apopka, FL 32703-1558
Ph: (403)226-5840
URL: www.qcwa.org
Social Media: www.linkedin.com/groups/150709/profile
twitter.com/QCWA

Awards are arranged alphabetically below their administering organizations

9457 ■ Quarter Century Wireless Association Scholarship Program *(Undergraduate/Scholarship)*

Purpose: To provide financial support for students intending to pursue higher education. **Focus:** Radio and television. **Qualif.:** Applicants must be radio amateurs enrolled or planning to enroll in a full-time course which leads to a degree at an accredited college/university. **Criteria:** Applications will be reviewed by the Foundation for Amateur Radio.

Funds Avail.: $500 each. **Duration:** Annual. **Number Awarded:** 532. **To Apply:** Applications are requested from the Foundation for Amateur Radio Scholarship Committee; applicants must be recommended by a QCWA member. **Deadline:** April 15. **Remarks:** Established in 1977. **Contact:** Glen Reid, K5FX - Scholarship Chairman, 1305Carlotta Ln Austin, TX 78733; Phone: 512-263-5700; E-Mail: k5fx@qcwa.org.

9458 ■ Queens County Women's Bar Association (QCWBA)

PO Box 585
Kew Gardens, NY 11424
Ph: (718)595-0585
E-mail: info@qcwba.org
URL: www.qcwba.org
Social Media: www.facebook.com/QCWBA

9459 ■ Faith E. O'Neal Scholarship *(Graduate/Scholarship)*

Purpose: To financially assist students who have demonstrated a dedication to public interest. **Focus:** Law. **Criteria:** Scholarship committee shall make its determination based on the following: Community service, Financial need, Academics, Written personal statements.

Funds Avail.: $2,000. **Duration:** Annual. **Number Awarded:** 2. **To Apply:** Application must include college or law school transcript(s) and written personal statement. **Remarks:** Established in 2005. **Contact:** Queens County Women's Bar Foundation, P.O. Box 585, Borough Hall Station, Kew Gardens, New York 11424.

9460 ■ Queen's University - Stephen J.R. Smith School of Business

Goodes Hall
Kingston, ON, Canada K7L 3N6
URL: smith.queensu.ca

9461 ■ Robert Sutherland/Harry Jerome Entrance Award *(Undergraduate/Scholarship)*

Purpose: To support students pursuing an undergraduate degree at Queen's University. **Focus:** General studies/Field of study not specified. **Qualif.:** Applicant must be a black student entering the first year of any direct-entry undergraduate degree program at Queen's University. **Criteria:** Selection is base on demonstrated financial need, academic achievement and contribution to the community or other volunteer activities, reviewed by a committee of the Student Awards Office at Queen's Univ.

Funds Avail.: $5,000 Canadian Dollars. **Duration:** 3 Year. **To Apply:** Applicants must complete the online application form and attach the following: Letter of Recommendation from teacher, guidance counsellor, principal or vice-principal who knows applicant well and can write about academic

accomplishments and other outstanding attributes written on official letterhead; letter of Recommendation from a member of applicant community, high-school transcript (attachments in PDF format); hardcopy original of high school transcript must be sent to NSF Office within 14 days of application online deadline. **Deadline:** March 1. **Remarks:** The scholarship honors Robert Sutherland (BA, 1852), the first student of African heritage to graduate from Queen's University, Ontario, Canada. Established in 2008.

9462 ■ Quill and Scroll International Honorary Society (QSS)

University of Iowa
100 Adler Journalism Bldg.
Iowa City, IA 52242
Ph: (319)335-3457
E-mail: quill-scroll@uiowa.edu
URL: quillandscroll.org
Social Media: www.facebook.com/QuillandScrollSociety
twitter.com/QuillandScroll
www.youtube.com/user/quillscroll?feature=watch

9463 ■ Lester G. Benz Memorial Scholarship for College Journalism Study *(Other/Scholarship)*

Purpose: To identify and reward experienced journalism teachers and publication advisers who seek the opportunity to upgrade journalism skills, teaching methodologies and advising techniques. **Focus:** Journalism. **Qualif.:** Applicants must be high-school journalism teachers and newspaper and yearbook advisers who have had at least six semester hours of journalism courses; must have minimum of four years of teaching experience and advising school publications; must be currently teaching a journalistic writing class; and must have definite commitment to return to the high school classroom and publication. **Criteria:** Selection will be based on scholarship committee.

Funds Avail.: $500 for actual tuition, room, board and transportation costs. **To Apply:** Applicants must submit the completed application form; two letters of recommendation that will attest to their journalism teaching skills, publication advising, quality of the journalistic writing courses the applicants teach and the quality of the publications the applicants advises; the letters of recommendation should come from any of the following sources superintendent; principal; vice principal; department chairperson; regional or state scholastic press association director; scholastic journalism workshop director; a faculty member of the school of Journalism or Dept. of journalism from whom the applicants has taken a journalism course recently (2-4 years). **Deadline:** April 15. **Contact:** Lester G. Benz Memorial Scholarship Quill And Scroll Foundation, School of Journalism and Mass Communication, The University of Iowa, 100 Adler Journalism Building, Room E346, Iowa City, Iowa 52242.

9464 ■ Edward J. Nell Memorial Scholarships in Journalism *(Undergraduate/Scholarship)*

Purpose: To provide financial assistance to well-qualified individuals who wish to attend any college or university that offers a major in journalism. **Focus:** Journalism. **Qualif.:** Applicants must be national winners of the Yearbook Excellence Contest or the international writing, photography and multimedia contest and blogging competition; the scholarships are awarded for the freshman year only and are paid in two installments (fall semester and spring semester). **Criteria:** Selection will be major in journalism or a related area of communications.

Awards are arranged alphabetically below their administering organizations

To Apply: Applicants must submit completed application form; two letters of recommendation, one from their principal or counselor; one from a media adviser/teacher (see guidelines on Request for Letter of Recommendation form); a small, color photo with name on the back; a statement of not more than 500 words (see Personal Statement Guidelines sheet); three examples of their journalistic work. **Deadline:** May 15.

9465 ■ Radio-Television Digital News Association (RTDNA)

529 14th St. NW, Ste. 1240
Washington, DC 20045
Ph: (941)896-4246
URL: rtdna.org
Social Media: www.facebook.com/RTDNA.RTDNF
www.instagram.com/rtdna.rtdnf
www.linkedin.com/company/rtdna
twitter.com/RTDNA
www.youtube.com/user/rtndaf

9466 ■ Ken Kashiwahara Scholarships
(Undergraduate/Scholarship)

Purpose: To provide financial assistance to students who have demonstrated their interest in the field of radio and television news. **Focus:** Radio and television. **Qualif.:** Applicant must be an officially enrolled college sophomore and have at least one full academic year; must be fully enrolled college sophomore or higher to receive a scholarship; must be enrolled in any major involved in electronic journalism. **Criteria:** Selection is based on the submitted application materials and financial need.

Funds Avail.: No specific amount. **To Apply:** Applicant must submit a completed application form available on the website accompanied by the following materials: (1) copy of resume, (2) one to three examples of their journalistic skills on audio CD or DVD, with scripts, (3) one page statement, with specific career preferences (radio, TC, online, reporting, producing, or newsroom management), and (4) letter of reference from dean or faculty. **Remarks:** Established in 1998.

9467 ■ Abe Schechter Graduate Scholarships
(Graduate/Scholarship)

Purpose: To provide financial assistance to students who have demonstrated their interest in the field of radio and television news. **Focus:** Radio and television. **Qualif.:** Applicants must be enrolled in a graduate program and must be in good standing in the field of radio and television news. **Criteria:** Selection is based on the application materials submitted.

Funds Avail.: No amount specific. **Duration:** Annual. **To Apply:** Applicants must submit a completed application form available online along with a copy of an updated resume, one-page statement stating their merits and career objectives, and letter of reference from dean or faculty.

9468 ■ Radio Television Digital News Association (RTDNA)

529 14th St. NW, Ste. 1240
Washington, DC 20045
Ph: (202)221-4282
URL: www.rtnda.org
Social Media: www.facebook.com/RTDNA.RTDNF
www.instagram.com/rtdna.rtdnf
www.linkedin.com/company/rtdna
twitter.com/RTDNA
www.youtube.com/user/rtndaf

9469 ■ N.S. Beinstock Fellowships *(Other/Fellowship)*

Purpose: To recognize a promising minority journalist in radio or television news. **Focus:** Journalism. **Qualif.:** Applicant must be long-time member of RTDNA; promising minority journalist in radio or television news. **Criteria:** Selection will be based on the committee's criteria.

Funds Avail.: $2,500. **Number Awarded:** 1. **To Apply:** Complete the online application form; provide three to five samples of work, cover letter, resume, letter of recommendation from a professor, advisor, or supervisor. **Deadline:** May. **Remarks:** The award was established by Richard Leibner and Carole Cooper, the original owners of N.S. Bienstock. Established in 1999. **Contact:** Kate McGarrlty, Email: katem@rtdna.org.

9470 ■ Ed Bradley Scholarships *(Undergraduate/Scholarship)*

Purpose: To provide educational support to aspiring and early-career electronic journalists. **Focus:** Journalism. **Qualif.:** Applicants must be enrolled in radio and television news; must be a full-time college student with at least one full year of college remaining whose career objective is to enter into the electronic journalism field.

Funds Avail.: $10,000. **Duration:** Annual. **Number Awarded:** 1. **To Apply:** Complete the online application form; provide three to five samples of work, cover letter, resume, letter of recommendation from a professor, advisor, or supervisor. **Remarks:** The scholarship was named in the honor of Ed Bradley. Established in 1994. **Contact:** Kate McGarrity, Email: katem@rtdna.org.

9471 ■ Michele Clark Fellowships *(Undergraduate/Fellowship)*

Purpose: To provide educational support to a minority professional in television or radio news. **Focus:** Journalism. **Qualif.:** Applicants must be a young, promising minority professional in television or radio news.

Funds Avail.: $1,000. **Duration:** Annual. **Number Awarded:** 1. **To Apply:** Complete the online application form; provide three to five samples of work, cover letter, resume, letter of recommendation from a professor, advisor, or supervisor. **Deadline:** January 31. **Remarks:** The Fellowship was named in the honor of Michele Clark. **Contact:** Kate McGarrity, Email: katem@rtdna.org.

9472 ■ George Foreman Tribute to Lyndon B. Johnson *(Undergraduate/Scholarship)*

Purpose: To support a journalism student attending the University of Texas at Austin. **Focus:** Journalism. **Qualif.:** Applicant must be attending the University of Texas at Austin; students who will be sophomores, juniors or seniors at the time the scholarship is awarded, pursuing careers in radio, television, or digital journalism; must be officially enrolled, full-time sophomores or above in good standing when scholarships are awarded. **Criteria:** Selection will be based on judges decisions.

Funds Avail.: $6,000. **Duration:** Annual. **Number Awarded:** 1. **To Apply:** Applicants must include contact information; experience; URL links to 3-5 work samples;

Awards are arranged alphabetically below their administering organizations

cover letter; resume; letter of recommendation. **Remarks:** This award is a recognition for George Foreman is a boxing champion, Lyndon Johnson and by RTDNF founder Barney Oldfield. Established in 1998. **Contact:** Kate McGarrity, Email: katem@rtdna.org.

9473 ■ Mike Reynolds Scholarship *(Undergraduate/ Scholarship)*

Purpose: To provide educational support to a journalism student with a good writing ability, excellent grades, a dedication to the news business, strong interest in pursuing a career in electronic journalism. **Focus:** Journalism. **Qualif.:** Applicants who will be sophomores, juniors or seniors at the time the scholarship is awarded and are pursuing careers in radio, television, or digital journalism are eligible must be apply for only one RTDNF scholarship, and past RTDNF scholarship winners are not eligible.

Funds Avail.: $1,000. **Duration:** Annual. **Number Awarded:** 1. **To Apply:** Applicants must include contact information; experience; URL links to 3-5 work samples, either broadcast or online news pieces which should also be uploaded to a host site (like YouTube, Vimeo, SoundCloud, etc.); cover letter discussing the current and past journalism experience, how the applicants intend to use the funds, the applicants' choice to pursue a career in journalism; resume; letter of recommendation from a professor, advisor or supervisor. **Remarks:** The scholarship was established in memory of Mike Reynolds. **Contact:** Kate McGarrity, Email: katem@rtdna.org.

9474 ■ Jacque I. Minnotte Health Reporting Fellowship *(Other/Fellowship)*

Purpose: To recognizes excellence in health or medical television and radio reporting. **Focus:** Journalism. **Qualif.:** Applicant must be a professional broadcast or digital journalists with fewer than 10 years of experience; journalists may apply for only one RTDNF fellowship; past RTDNF fellows are not eligible. **Criteria:** Selection will be based on the committee criteria.

Funds Avail.: $2,000. **Duration:** Annual. **Number Awarded:** 1. **To Apply:** Applicants must complete and submit the following online: an application form; a cover letter discussing journalism experiences, use of fellowship funds, discussing choosing career in electronic journalism; three to five links to the best and most relevant work samples discussing the roles in each of the pieces; a letter of reference from news manager or higher. **Remarks:** The award was created to honor former news director and Medstar executive Jacque Minnotte. **Contact:** Kate McGarrity, Email: katem@rtdna.org.

9475 ■ Lou and Carole Prato Sports Reporting Scholarship *(Undergraduate/Scholarship)*

Purpose: To provide educational support to aspiring journalism students covering sports. pursuing careers in radio, television, or digital journalism. **Focus:** Journalism. **Criteria:** Selection will be based on the committee's criteria.

Funds Avail.: $1,000. **Duration:** Annual. **Number Awarded:** 1. **To Apply:** Applicants must include contact information; experience; URL links to 3-5 work samples, either broadcast or online news pieces which should also be uploaded to a host site (like YouTube, Vimeo, SoundCloud, etc.); cover letter discussing the current and past journalism experience, how the applicants intend to use the funds, the applicants' choice to pursue a career in journalism; resume; letter of recommendation from a professor, advisor or supervisor. **Remarks:** This award is a recogni-

tion for Lou's service to RTDNA. Established in 2001. **Contact:** Kate McGarrity, Email: katem@rtdna.org.

9476 ■ Presidents Scholarship *(Undergraduate/ Scholarship)*

Purpose: To provide educational support to aspiring and early-career electronic journalists. **Focus:** Journalism. **Qualif.:** Applicants must be currently enrolled as college sophomores, juniors and seniors in good standing with career goal in radio, television or digital journalism.

Funds Avail.: $2,500. **Duration:** Annual. **Number Awarded:** 2. **To Apply:** Applicants must include contact information; experience; URL links to 3-5 work samples, either broadcast or online news pieces which should also be uploaded to a host site (like YouTube, Vimeo, SoundCloud, etc.); cover letter discussing the current and past journalism experience, how the applicants intend to use the funds, the applicants' choice to pursue a career in journalism; resume; letter of recommendation from a professor, advisor or supervisor. **Remarks:** To honor RTDNA Presidents Theodore Koop, Bruce Dennis, James McCulla, John Salisbury, Bruce Palmer, Dick Cheverton, Jim Byron, Ben Chatfield and John Hogan. **Contact:** Kate McGarrity, Email: katem@rtdna.org.

9477 ■ Carole Simpson Scholarship *(Undergraduate/ Scholarship)*

Purpose: To provide educational support to minority students pursuing careers as electronic journalists. **Focus:** Journalism. **Qualif.:** Applicants must be full-time sophomore, junior or senior students, in good standing, pursuing careers in radio, television or digital journalism; must be apply for only one RTDNF scholarship, and past RTDNF scholarship winners are not eligible.

Funds Avail.: $2,000. **Duration:** Annual. **Number Awarded:** 1. **To Apply:** Applicants must include contact information; experience; URL links to 3-5 work samples, either broadcast or online news pieces which should also be uploaded to a host site (like YouTube, Vimeo, SoundCloud, etc.); cover letter discussing the current and past journalism experience, how the applicants intend to use the funds, the applicants' choice to pursue a career in journalism; resume; letter of recommendation from a professor, advisor or supervisor. **Remarks:** The scholarship was named in the honor of Carole Simpson. Established in 1992. **Contact:** Kate McGarrity, Email: katem@rtdna.org.

9478 ■ Pete Wilson Journalism Scholarship *(Graduate, Undergraduate/Scholarship)*

Purpose: To provide educational support to aspiring and early-career electronic journalists. **Focus:** Journalism. **Qualif.:** Applicant must be pursuing a career in radio and television news; must be full-time undergraduate or graduate students, in good standing, from or studying in the San Francisco Bay area.

Funds Avail.: $2,000. **Duration:** Annual. **Number Awarded:** 1. **To Apply:** Applicants must include contact information; experience; URL links to 3-5 work samples, either broadcast or online news pieces which should also be uploaded to a host site (like YouTube, Vimeo, SoundCloud, etc.); cover letter discussing the current and past journalism experience, how the applicants intend to use the funds, the applicants' choice to pursue a career in journalism; resume; letter of recommendation from a professor, advisor or supervisor. **Remarks:** The scholarship was named in the honor of Pete Wilson. Established in 2007. **Contact:** Kate McGarrity, Email: katem@rtdna.org.

Awards are arranged alphabetically below their administering organizations

9479 ■ Radio-Television News Directors Foundation Canada (RTDNF)

2800-14th Ave., Ste. 210
Markham, ON, Canada L3R 0E4
Ph: (416)491-2886
Fax: (416)491-1670
E-mail: sherry@rtdnfcanada.com
URL: rtdnfcanada.com
Social Media: www.facebook.com/RTDNFCanada
www.linkedin.com/company/rtdnf-canada
twitter.com/RTDNFCanada

9480 ■ RTDNF Scholarships *(Undergraduate/ Scholarship)*

Purpose: To offer financial assistance to broadcast journalism students in Canada. **Focus:** Radio and television. **Qualif.:** Applicant must be a Canadian citizen; must be a second year, third year, or graduating student enrolled in a broadcast journalism course at either a college or university, college or university programs with a broadcast journalism option, or actively involved in news at a radio or TV station on or off campus.

Funds Avail.: 2,000 Canadian dollars. **To Apply:** Applicants must submit a completed entry form online a radio or TV documentary, feature, newscast, sportscast, or spot news or sports report; the total presentation time must not exceed 10 minutes. Application can be completed and submitted online at submissions.rtdnfcanada.com/login. **Deadline:** April 30. **Remarks:** Established in 1978.

9481 ■ Radiological Society of North America (RSNA)

820 Jorie Blvd.
Oak Brook, IL 60523-2251
Ph: (630)571-2670
Fax: (630)571-7837
Free: 800-381-6660
E-mail: membership@rsna.org
URL: www.rsna.org
Social Media: www.facebook.com/RSNAfans
www.instagram.com/rsnagram
www.linkedin.com/company/rsna
twitter.com/rsna
www.youtube.com/user/RSNAtube

9482 ■ R&E Foundation Education Scholar Grant *(Graduate, Other/Scholarship)*

Purpose: To develop teachers and educational leaders in radiology who can effectively share their knowledge with the radiology community. **Focus:** Education; Medicine, Nuclear; Radiology. **Qualif.:** Applicants must hold a faculty position in a department of radiology, radiation oncology, or nuclear medicine within an educational institution; must hold an MD degree or equivalent; must have completed advanced training and be certified by the American Board of Radiology (ABR) or its equivalent or be on track for certification; must not be agents of any for-profit, commercial company in the radiologic sciences; and may not have concurrent RSNA grants; if the applicant's membership category is Member-in-Training or any other non-dues paying category, the scientific advisor or one of the co-investigators must be a dues-paying member. **Criteria:** Selection is based on the application materials.

Funds Avail.: Up to $75,000. **Duration:** Annual. **To Apply:** Applications must be completed online using the online grant application system. **Contact:** Scott Walter, Assistant Director, Grant Administration; E-mail: swalter@rsna.org; Phone: 630-571-7816.

9483 ■ Research Resident/Fellow Grant *(Professional development/Grant)*

Purpose: To provide young investigators the opportunity to gain further insight into scientific investigation and to gain competence in research techniques and methods in anticipation of establishing a career in academic radiologic science. **Focus:** Radiology. **Qualif.:** Applicants from outside North America must already be accepted into a one or two-year fellowship position at a North American education institution, one-year research project must be completed while the recipient is at the North American institution, must be certified, or on track for certification, by the radiology board in their home country; must be in the last year of, or have completed, the prescribed residency training; must not have ever held a faculty position in the radiologic sciences at or above the level of assistant professor; must not have been principal investigator on external/extramural grant/contract amounts totaling more than $60, 000 in a single year; must not be agents of any for-profit, commercial company in the radiologic sciences. **Criteria:** Selection will be based on the committee's criteria.

Funds Avail.: $30,000 - Research resident project; $50,000 - Research fellow project. **Duration:** Annual. **To Apply:** Applications can be submitted online. **Deadline:** January 15. **Contact:** Scott A. Walter, MS, Assistant Director - Grant Administration, Radiological Society of North America, R&E Foundation, 820 Jorie Blvd., Oak Brook, IL, 60523; Phone: 630-571-7816; E-mail: swalter@rsna.org.

9484 ■ RSNA/AUR/APDR/SCARD Radiology Education Research Development Grant *(Professional development/Grant)*

Purpose: To encourage innovation and improvement in health sciences education by providing research opportunities to individuals throughout the world who are in pursuit of advancing the science of radiology education. **Focus:** Radiology. **Qualif.:** Applicants must be individuals, at any level of career development, who have a primary appointment in a radiology department; must be members of one or more of the sponsoring organizations; did not have concurrent RSNA grants. **Criteria:** Selection will be based on the committee's criteria.

Funds Avail.: $10,000. **Duration:** Annual. **To Apply:** Applications can be submitted online. **Deadline:** January 10.

9485 ■ RSNA Education Scholar Grant *(Professional development/Grant)*

Purpose: To provide funding opportunities for individuals with an active interest in radiologic education. **Focus:** Radiology. **Qualif.:** Applicant must be a RSNA member at the time of the application; co-principal investigator(s) must not be agents of any for-profit, commercial company in the radiologic sciences; do not have concurrent RSNA grants. **Criteria:** Selection will be based on the committee's criteria.

Funds Avail.: $75,000. **Duration:** Annual. **To Apply:** Applications can be submitted online.

9486 ■ Research Scholar Grant *(Professional development/Grant)*

Purpose: To support junior faculty members who have completed the conventional resident/fellowship training program(s) but have not yet been recognized as indepen-

Awards are arranged alphabetically below their administering organizations

dent investigators. **Focus:** Radiology. **Qualif.:** Applicant must be any junior radiology faculty member may apply for the Research Scholar Grant, as long as you are an RSNA member and meet the following criteria: must hold a full-time faculty position in a department of radiology, radiation oncology or nuclear medicine within a North American educational institution; must have been hired within the last 5 years with an academic rank of instructor, assistant professor or an equivalent title; must have completed advanced training and be certified by either the American Board of Radiology (ABR), The Royal College of Physicians and Surgeons of Canada or are on track for certification; cannot have been a principal investigator on a grant or contract totaling more than $60,000 in a single year; this includes single and combined grants and contracts from government, private and commercial sources; you and your principal investigators cannot be employed by any for-profit, commercial company in the radiologic sciences; cannot submit more than one grant application to the RSNA R&E Foundation a year and cannot have a concurrent RSNA grant; must have funding from other grant sources must be approved by Foundation staff if it wasn't described in the original research plan; cannot have previously accepted any of the following grants: ARRS Scholar Award, AUR GE-Radiology Research Academic Fellowship (GERRAF), RSNA Research Scholar Grant. **Criteria:** Selection will be based on the committee's criteria.

Funds Avail.: $75,000. **Duration:** Annual. **Number Awarded:** Varies. **To Apply:** Applicants can submitted online; must use their RSNA membership username and password to login. Applicants' project must: be in any area of research related to the radiologic sciences; describe the unique nature of the research effort independent of existing research efforts. Greater emphasis will be place on the likelihood of this research to attract future funding given the nature and extent of the preliminary data collected within the cycle of the grant; focused on advancing imaging science, developing or evaluating medical imaging technology or making innovative use of imaging science to answer important biologic or clinical questions. **Deadline:** January 16. **Contact:** Email: grants@rsna.org.

9487 ■ RSNA Research Seed Grant *(Professional development/Grant)*

Purpose: To enable all levels of investigators throughout the world in defining objectives and testing hypotheses in preparation of major grant applications to the corporation, foundations and governmental agencies. **Focus:** Radiology. **Qualif.:** Applicant must be an RSNA member at the time of application; must hold a full-time faculty position in a department of radiology, radiation oncology, or nuclear medicine within an educational institution; if the applicant is not a full-time faculty member at the time of application but will become a full-time faculty members when the award commences, a letter from the department chair attesting to this appointment must be included; must have completed advanced training and be certified by the American Board of Radiology, or equivalent, or on track for certification; institutions outside North America must have completed advanced training and be certified by the radiology board in their country. **Criteria:** Selection will be based on the committee's criteria.

Funds Avail.: $40,000. **Duration:** Annual. **To Apply:** Applicants must use their RSNA membership username and password to login on the website. Applicant's project must: be in any area of research related to the radiologic sciences; describe the unique nature of the research effort independent of existing research efforts. Greater emphasis

will be place on the likelihood of this research to attract future funding given the nature and extent of the preliminary data collected within the cycle of the grant; focused on advancing imaging science, developing or evaluating medical imaging technology or making innovative use of imaging science to answer important biologic or clinical questions. **Deadline:** January 15. **Contact:** Keshia Osley, Assistant Director, Grant Administration Radiological Society of North America, R&E Foundation, 820 Jorie Blvd., Oak Brook, IL, 60523; Phone: 630-571-7816; E-mail: kosley@rsna.org.

9488 ■ Railway Tie Association (RTA)
115 Commerce Dr., Ste. C
Fayetteville, GA 30214-7335
Ph: (770)460-5553
Fax: (770)460-5573
E-mail: ties@rta.org
URL: www.rta.org
Social Media: www.facebook.com/American.Counseling
.Association
www.facebook.com/RTAHQ
www.linkedin.com/company/railway-tie-association/

9489 ■ John Mabry Forestry Scholarships
(Undergraduate/Scholarship)

Purpose: To provide financial support for students attending technical schools, colleges and universities. **Focus:** General studies/Field of study not specified. **Qualif.:** Applicants must be college Juniors and Seniors of four-year institutions (not graduating before the end of the school year) and also open to second-year students in a two-year institution (not graduating before the end of the school year) who will be enrolled in accredited Forestry programs. **Criteria:** Recipients are selected based on leadership qualities, career objectives, scholastic achievement, and financial need.

Funds Avail.: $2,000 each. **Duration:** One year. **Number Awarded:** 2. **To Apply:** Completed application must be submitted along with personal narrative; black and white photo; one transcript copy; Employer, University Department Head, or Major Forestry Professor reference. **Deadline:** June 30. **Contact:** The Railway Tie Association, 115 Commerce Dr., Ste C, Fayetteville, GA 30214; Phone: 770-460-5553; Fax: 770 460-5573; Email: ties@rta.org.

9490 ■ Rain Bird Corp.
970 W Sierra Madre Ave.
Azusa, CA 91702
Ph: (626)812-3400
Free: 800-724-6247
URL: www.rainbird.com
Social Media: www.facebook.com/RainBirdCorp
www.linkedin.com/company/rain-bird
www.linkedin.com/company/rainbirdcorporation
twitter.com/RainBirdCorp
www.youtube.com/user/rainbirdcorp

9491 ■ Rain Bird Intelligent Use of Water Scholarship *(Undergraduate/Scholarship)*

Purpose: To support an outstanding landscape architecture, horticulture or irrigation science student. **Focus:** Horticulture; Landscape architecture and design. **Qualif.:** Ap-

Awards are arranged alphabetically below their administering organizations

plicants must be students in the final two years of undergraduate study (third, fourth, or fifth-year students) who have demonstrated commitment to these professions through participation in extracurricular activities and exemplary scholastic achievements. **Criteria:** Selection will be based on the aforementioned applicant's qualifications and compliance with the application details.

Funds Avail.: $2,500. **Duration:** Annual. **To Apply:** Applicants must submit an entry form; a photo; bio for the LAF Website (150 word max), resume; financial aid form; 2 letters of recommendation; essay (2 page max). **Deadline:** February 1. **Contact:** E-mail: scholarships@lafoundation.org; Phone: 202-331-7070 x14.

9492 ■ Rainbow Business Professionals Association (RBPA)
PO Box 11148
Portland, ME 04104
Ph: (207)775-0077
URL: www.rbpa.org

9493 ■ RBPA Scholarship *(Undergraduate, Graduate, Doctorate/Scholarship)*

Purpose: To promote positive role models for gay, lesbian, bisexual, and transgendered individuals in the academic environment and community at large. **Focus:** Sexuality. **Qualif.:** Applicants must be gay, lesbian, bisexual, or transgendered students with residency within the New England area (Maine, Vermont, New Hampshire, Massachusetts, Rhode Island, and Connecticut); must be entering an accredited institution of higher learning no later than the following fall semester from the award year. **Criteria:** Scholarship recipients are selected by the Scholarship Committee.

Duration: Annual. **Number Awarded:** 3. **To Apply:** Applicants must fully complete either the online application or the downloadable application and ensure that all required documentation (references, certificates, etc.) are attached and sent it to the Scholarship Committee. **Remarks:** The Scholarship was established in memory of Carolyn Jalbert partner, Donna Tennant, one of the founding members of RBPA. Established in 1997. **Contact:** RBPA Scholarship Fund, Inc., PO Box 11148, Portland, ME, 04104; Phone: 207-775-0077.

9494 ■ Rainforest Alliance
233 Broadway, 28th Fl.
New York, NY 10279
Ph: (212)677-1900
Fax: (212)677-2187
E-mail: info@ra.org
URL: www.rainforest-alliance.org

9495 ■ The Kleinhans Fellowship *(Professional development/Fellowship)*

Purpose: To provide funds for research that is oriented toward solving real-world problems as defined by CFEs. **Focus:** Conservation of natural resources.

Duration: Triennial. **Number Awarded:** 1. **Deadline:** August 31.

9496 ■ R&D Systems Inc.
614 McKinley Pl. NE
Minneapolis, MN 55413

Free: 800-343-7475
URL: www.rndsystems.com
Social Media: www.facebook.com/RnDSystems
twitter.com/RnDSystems
www.youtube.com/user/RnDSystems

9497 ■ R&D Systems Scholarship *(All/Scholarship)*

Purpose: To support students who are pursuing a degree in a science related field. **Focus:** Science. **Qualif.:** Applicant must be pursuing a science related degree. **Criteria:** Selection is based on the responses provided by the applicant.

Funds Avail.: $1,500. **Duration:** Annual. **Number Awarded:** 1, twice a year. **To Apply:** Application should be completed online. **Deadline:** July 29. **Contact:** Email: scholarship@novusbio.com.

9498 ■ Charles B. Rangel International Affairs Program
2218 6th St. NW
Washington, DC 20059
Ph: (202)806-4367
Fax: (202)806-5424
Free: 877-633-0002
E-mail: rangelprogram@howard.edu
URL: www.rangelprogram.org/?contentid=0
Social Media: www.facebook.com/pages/Charles-B-Rangel-International-Affairs-Program/153923151284576
www.facebook.com/RangelProgram
twitter.com/RangelProgram

9499 ■ Rangel Graduate Fellowship *(Graduate/Fellowship)*

Purpose: To attract and prepare outstanding young people for careers in the Foreign Service in which they can help formulate, represent and implement U.S. foreign policy. **Focus:** International affairs and relations.

Funds Avail.: Up to $37,500. **Duration:** Annual; two years. **Number Awarded:** 30. **To Apply:** Applicants must complete the application online; applicants must submit, in one package, proof of U.S. citizenship with a notarized copy of: birth certificate, certificate of U.S. citizenship, U.S. passport; Student Aid Report (SAR) generated from the Free Application for Federal Student Aid (FAFSA) form; and GRE or GMAT Scores (copy of report sent to student). In addition, the institution or individual must submit the official transcript from all colleges and universities that the applicants has attended (in a sealed/signed envelope either by applicants or by institution); official Financial Aid Statement from applicant's senior year; and two letters of recommendation: (can be sent directly from the recommender or from the applicants in a sealed and signed envelope) one from a faculty member, and one from a community leader or other individual who can comment on the applicant's non-academic accomplishments and potential. **Contact:** Email: rangelprogram@howard.edu.

9500 ■ Jeannette Rankin Women's Scholarship Fund (JRF)
1 Huntington Road, Suite 701
Athens, GA 30606
Ph: (706)208-1211
E-mail: info@rankinfoundation.org

Awards are arranged alphabetically below their administering organizations

URL: www.rankinfoundation.org
Social Media: www.facebook.com/jeannetterankinfund
www.instagram.com/rankinfund
www.linkedin.com/company/jeannette-rankin-women's
  -scholarship-fund
twitter.com/rankinfund
www.youtube.com/channel/UChpB
  -L1oYWX1wHFtkCB9IVQ

9501 ■ Jeannette Rankin Scholarships *(Undergraduate, Vocational/Occupational/Scholarship)*

Purpose: To financially support low-income female students pursuing post-secondary education. **Focus:** General studies/Field of study not specified. **Qualif.:** Applicant must be enrolled in, or accepted to an accredited school; have low-income according to the U.S. Department of Labor's Lower Living Standard. **Criteria:** Awards are given based on goals; plans in reaching those goals; challenges the applicants may have faced; and financial situation.

Funds Avail.: Varies. **Duration:** Annual. **Number Awarded:** Varies. **To Apply:** Applicants must submit a proof of enrollment or acceptance.

9502 ■ Raptor Research Foundation (RRF)
Boise, ID
URL: www.raptorresearchfoundation.org
Social Media: www.facebook.com/pg/
raptorresearchfoundation
twitter.com/research_raptor

9503 ■ Leslie Brown Memorial Grant *(Advanced Professional/Grant)*

Purpose: To promote the research and/or the dissemination of information on African birds of prey. **Focus:** Wildlife conservation, management, and science.

Funds Avail.: Up to $1,400. **Duration:** Annual. **Number Awarded:** 1. **To Apply:** Applicants must include resume; specific study objectives; an account of how funds will be spent; an indication of how the proposed work would relate to other work; other sources of funding. **Deadline:** June 30. **Remarks:** The award was established in the memory of late Leslie H. Brown (1917-1980). Established in 1986.

9504 ■ Stephen R. Tully Memorial Grant *(Advanced Professional/Grant)*

Purpose: To support research and conservation of raptors, particularly to students and amateurs with limited access to alternative funding. **Focus:** Wildlife conservation, management, and science.

Funds Avail.: $500. **Duration:** Annual. **Number Awarded:** 1. **To Apply:** Applicants must submit cover letter; proposal; background; objectives of study. **Deadline:** June 30. **Remarks:** The grant honor the memory of Steve Tully, a falconer with an enthusiastic interest in raptor biology. Established in 1983.

9505 ■ Ratingle
8345 NW 66 St., No. C7592
Miami, FL 33166
URL: ratingle.com
Social Media: www.facebook.com/Ratingle
twitter.com/RatingleCom

9506 ■ Ratingle Scholarship Program *(College, University, Community College, Undergraduate, Graduate/Scholarship)*

Purpose: To help students pay for higher education. **Focus:** General studies/Field of study not specified. **Qualif.:** Applicant must be currently enrolled, or enrolled to begin, in higher education in the upcoming semester; must be permanent residents of the United States; must allow sponsor all rights to the submitted content.

Funds Avail.: $1,000. **Number Awarded:** 1. **To Apply:** Applicant must submit a video review of the coolest gadget they have used recently. Application and video details are available online at www.ratingle.com/scholarship.

9507 ■ Raytheon Co.
870 Winter St.
Waltham, MA 02451-1449
Ph: (781)522-3000
E-mail: sales@raytheoncyber.com
URL: www.raytheon.com
Social Media: www.facebook.com/raytheon
www.instagram.com/raytheoncompany
www.linkedin.com/company/raytheon
twitter.com/raytheon
www.youtube.com/raytheoncompany

9508 ■ Raytheon Scholars *(Undergraduate/ Scholarship)*

Purpose: To assist employee's children who plan to continue their education in college. **Focus:** General studies/ Field of study not specified. **Qualif.:** Applicants must be dependent children of active Raytheon Company employees who have a minimum of one year of full-time employment with the company as of the application deadline date; children of part-time employees working 20 hours or more per week are also eligible; dependent children are defined as natural and legally adopted children or stepchildren living in the employee's household or primarily supported by the employee; college or postsecondary students who have completed at least one full quarter or semester and who plan to enroll in full-time undergraduate study at an accredited two- or four-year college, university or vocational-technical school for the academic year; under the age of 24 as of the application deadline date; applicants may receive only one Raytheon scholarship in any academic year; applicant has received another scholarship from Raytheon in the same academic year, they will not be eligible for Raytheon Scholars, and vice versa. **Criteria:** Recipients are selected on the basis of academic record, demonstrated leadership, participation in school and community activities, honors, work experience, statement of goals and aspirations, and unusual personal or family circumstances.

Funds Avail.: $2,000. **Duration:** Annual. **To Apply:** Applicants must submit the application and current complete official transcript of grades to Scholarship America. **Deadline:** March 31. **Contact:** Email: raytheon@scholarshipamerica.org.

9509 ■ Real Estate Elevated
9550 S Eastern Ave., Ste. 253
Las Vegas, NV 89123
Free: 800-388-7046
URL: reelevatedevents.com
Social Media: facebook.com/reelevatedevents

Awards are arranged alphabetically below their administering organizations

instagram.com/reelevatedevents
pinterest.com/reelevatedevents

9510 ■ Real Estate Elevated Scholarship *(Community College, Undergraduate, Graduate/Scholarship)*

Purpose: To provide additional financial support for students wanting to pursue an entrepreneurial career. **Focus:** General studies/Field of study not specified. **Qualif.:** Applicant must be a U.S. citizen enrolled full-time in an institution of higher learning. **Criteria:** Preference will be given to applicants with a passion for business and entrepreneurial goals.

Funds Avail.: $1,500. **Duration:** Annual. **Number Awarded:** 1. **To Apply:** Applicants must submit a three-minute video explaining or showing the value of education and how gaining a higher education can help establish success in the world of business and entrepreneurship. Video should be uploaded to YouTube and the link, along with answers to the prompted questions, should be submitted via email to toscholarship@REElevatedEvents.com, with "Entry for Real Estate Elevated Scholarship" in the subject line. **Deadline:** April 1.

9511 ■ RealtyHop
335 Madison Ave.
New York, NY 10017
URL: www.realtyhop.com
Social Media: www.facebook.com/realtyhop
www.instagram.com/realtyhop
www.pinterest.com/realtyhop
twitter.com/realtyhop

9512 ■ RealtyHop Scholarship *(Undergraduate, Two Year College/Scholarship)*

Purpose: To assist eligible undergraduate students and high school seniors working towards bachelors or associates degrees and who demonstrate ambition, diligence, leadership, and entrepreneurial spirit. **Focus:** General studies/Field of study not specified. **Qualif.:** Applicant must be a current student in an eligible undergraduate program or a graduating high school senior planning to enroll and be working towards a bachelors or associates degree. **Criteria:** Submitted essays are judged based on how they answer the scholarship prompts and how well they follow the essay instructions.

Funds Avail.: $1,000. **Duration:** Semiannual. **To Apply:** Applicant must submit an essay (under 500 words) on the following topic via email: How have your family, friends, and life at home influenced you decision on your future career? **Deadline:** April 30; August 31.

9513 ■ The Recovery Village
633 Umatilla Blvd.
Umatilla, FL 32784
Ph: (352)771-2700
URL: www.therecoveryvillage.com
Social Media: www.facebook.com/therecoveryvillage
twitter.com/recoveryvillage
www.youtube.com/user/recoveryvillage

9514 ■ The Recovery Village Health Care Scholarship *(Undergraduate/Scholarship)*

Purpose: To help students pursuing medical-related courses of study. **Focus:** Health education; Medicine; Substance abuse.

Funds Avail.: $1,000. **Contact:** www.therecoveryvillage.com/scholarships/.

9515 ■ Red Olive
9980 S 300 W, Ste. 803
Sandy, UT 84070
Ph: (801)658-0330
URL: www.redolive.com
Social Media: www.facebook.com/redolive
www.instagram.com/redolive
www.linkedin.com/company/red-olive-design-inc.
www.youtube.com/redolive

9516 ■ Red Olive Women in STEM Scholarship *(Undergraduate, Graduate/Scholarship)*

Purpose: To encourage female students to study in STEM fields. **Focus:** Engineering; Mathematics and mathematical sciences; Science; Technology. **Qualif.:** Applicant must be a female student currently enrolled or planning to enroll in a fully accredited university in a STEM field, and must be female. **Criteria:** Selection is based online application.

Funds Avail.: $1,000. **Number Awarded:** 1. **To Apply:** Applicant must write an 800-word essay on the following question: How does she plan to make the future better with technology? Applicant must submit essay and required information online through the scholarship URL. **Deadline:** August 1.

9517 ■ Redlands Community Scholarship Foundation (RCSF)
PO Box 1683
Redlands, CA 92373
Ph: (909)307-9892
E-mail: president@redlandsscholarships.org
URL: www.redlandsscholarships.org

9518 ■ The Patty Ahearn-Victoria Elementary School Scholarship *(Undergraduate/Scholarship)*

Purpose: To encourage educational pursuits among Redlands Unified School District graduates by providing educational assistance. **Focus:** General studies/Field of study not specified. **Qualif.:** Applicants must be a graduating senior; must have a 2.5 GPA or higher; must have attended Victoria Elementary School for at least three years and must have continued to follow the Victoria Peace Builder's Pledge.

Funds Avail.: $500. **To Apply:** Applicants must submit a completed application form together with the scantron sheet; cover sheet; student activity and community activity sheets; personal essay and a copy of unofficial transcript (signed by the counselor); cover sheet with student and parent signature. **Deadline:** February 6. **Contact:** Suzanne Trad, President; Email: suztrad@aol.com.

9519 ■ William A. Allen Memorial Metal Shop/Auto Body Scholarships *(Undergraduate/Scholarship)*

Purpose: To support the continuing education of an outstanding metal shop or auto body student. **Focus:** General studies/Field of study not specified. **Qualif.:** Applicant must be an outstanding metal shop or auto body student who displays dedication, skill and desire to become a true craftsman. **Criteria:** Selection shall be based on the applicant's demonstration of: creativity, show problem solving

Awards are arranged alphabetically below their administering organizations

abilities, and exhibit good social skills.

Funds Avail.: $400. **To Apply:** Applicant may visit the scholarship section of the bestowing organization's website for further information regarding the application details.

9520 ■ Annette and Ernest Keith Memorial Scholarship *(Undergraduate/Scholarship)*

Purpose: To support the continuing education of an exceptional student who wishes to study in California. **Focus:** General studies/Field of study not specified. **Qualif.:** Applicant must be a graduating student who is in the top ten percent (10%) of the class and will be attending a four-year California college or university on a full-time basis.

Funds Avail.: $500. **To Apply:** Applicants must submit a completed application form together with the cover sheet; Personal Information; Education; Future Plans; School Activities; Non-School Activities; Community Service; essay and an explanation of any suspension during your "High School" years. **Deadline:** February 2. **Contact:** Redlands Community Scholarship Foundation, PO Box 1683, Redlands, California, 92373; Phone: 909-307-9892; Fax: 909-792-7035.

9521 ■ Connie "Chelo" Armendariz Memorial Scholarships *(Undergraduate/Scholarship)*

Purpose: To provide financial assistance to those graduating seniors who are planning to continue their education at a vocational school, junior college, or university. **Focus:** General studies/Field of study not specified. **Qualif.:** Applicants must be graduating seniors planning to continue their education at a vocational school, junior college, or University. **Criteria:** Preference shall be given to students who attended the former Saint Mary's Catholic Church in Redlands.

Funds Avail.: $500. **To Apply:** Applicants must submit a completed application form together with the cover sheet; Personal Information; Education; Future Plans; School Activities; Non-School Activities; Community Service; essay and an explanation of any suspension during your "High School" years. **Deadline:** February 2. **Contact:** Pam Bibo, Administrative Assistant; Email: admin@redlandsscholarships.org.

9522 ■ Arthur H. Daniels Memorial Scholarship *(Undergraduate/Scholarship)*

Purpose: To encourage educational pursuits among Redlands Unified School District graduates by providing educational assistance. **Focus:** General studies/Field of study not specified. **Qualif.:** Applicants must be a graduating senior demonstrating good citizenship, academic accomplishment, contribution to school and community; student should be college-bound who plans to attend on a full-time basis.

Funds Avail.: $500. **To Apply:** Applicants must submit a completed application form together with the scantron sheet; cover sheet; student activity and community activity sheets; personal essay and a copy of unofficial transcript (signed by the counselor); cover sheet with student and parent signature. **Deadline:** February 6. **Contact:** Suzanne Trad, President; Email: suztrad@aol.com.

9523 ■ Arthur and Juna Fisher Memorial Track Scholarship *(Undergraduate/Scholarship)*

Purpose: To support educational pursuits among Redlands Unified School District graduates by providing educational assistance. **Focus:** General studies/Field of study not specified. **Qualif.:** Applicants must be a graduating senior who has been active in track activities for at least two years and has maintained a 3.0 or better GPA.

Funds Avail.: $500. **To Apply:** Applicants must submit a completed application form together with the scantron sheet; cover sheet; student activity and community activity sheets; personal essay and a copy of unofficial transcript (signed by the counselor); cover sheet with student and parent signature. **Deadline:** February 6. **Contact:** Suzanne Trad, President; Email: suztrad@aol.com.

9524 ■ Baha'i Faith Scholarship for Racial Harmony *(Undergraduate/Scholarship)*

Purpose: To support the education of graduating high school students for their promotion of racial and intercultural harmony on campus. **Focus:** General studies/Field of study not specified. **Qualif.:** Applicants must be graduating seniors from Orangewood High School who have promoted racial and intercultural harmony on campus.

Funds Avail.: $400 each. **To Apply:** Applicants must submit a completed application form together with the cover sheet; Personal Information; Education; Future Plans; School Activities; Non-School Activities; Community Service; essay and an explanation of any suspension during your "High School" years. **Deadline:** February 2. **Contact:** Pam Bibo, Administrative Assistant; Email: admin@redlandsscholarships.org.

9525 ■ Barbara Bonnema Memorial Scholarship *(Undergraduate/Scholarship)*

Purpose: To encourage educational pursuits among Redlands Unified School District graduates by providing educational assistance. **Focus:** General studies/Field of study not specified. **Qualif.:** Applicant must be a college-bound graduating senior who will be attending school on a full-time basis. **Criteria:** Awards are given based academic excellence and financial need.

Funds Avail.: Minimum of $500. **Number Awarded:** Varies. **To Apply:** Applicants must submit a completed application form together with the scantron sheet; cover sheet; student activity and community activity sheets; personal essay and a copy of unofficial transcript (signed by the counselor); cover sheet with student and parent signature. **Deadline:** February 6. **Contact:** Suzanne Trad, President; Email: suztrad@aol.com.

9526 ■ Timothy Baylink Good Fellowship Awards *(Undergraduate/Fellowship)*

Purpose: To encourage educational pursuits among Redlands Unified School District graduates by providing educational assistance. **Focus:** General studies/Field of study not specified. **Qualif.:** Applicant must be a graduating senior who possesses some of the attributes of Dr. Timothy Baylink, which include athleticism, sense of adventure, friendliness, free spirit, interest in computers and commitment to learning. **Criteria:** Award is given based on merit.

Funds Avail.: $1,000. **To Apply:** Applicants must submit a completed application form together with the scantron sheet; cover sheet; student activity and community activity sheets; personal essay; and a copy of unofficial transcript (signed by the counselor). **Deadline:** February 3.

9527 ■ Beaver Medical Clinic Foundation - Dr. Glenn Adams Memorial Award *(Undergraduate/Scholarship)*

Purpose: To encourage educational pursuits among Redlands Unified School District graduates by providing

Awards are arranged alphabetically below their administering organizations

educational assistance. **Focus:** General studies/Field of study not specified. **Qualif.:** Applicants must be a graduating senior seeking a career in the field of medicine and must be outstanding academically; leadership skills and in sports participation.

Funds Avail.: $750. **To Apply:** Applicants must submit a completed application form together with the scantron sheet; cover sheet; student activity and community activity sheets; personal essay and a copy of unofficial transcript (signed by the counselor); cover sheet with student and parent signature. **Deadline:** February 6. **Contact:** Suzanne Trad, President; Email: suztrad@aol.com.

9528 ■ Beaver Medical Clinic Foundation - H.E.A.R.T. Academy Award (Undergraduate/Scholarship)

Purpose: To provide financial assistance to a graduating student attending Redlands High School seeking a career in medical field. **Focus:** General studies/Field of study not specified. **Qualif.:** Applicant must be a graduating senior seeking a career in the field of medicine; student must have participated in the HEART Academy program for three years.

Funds Avail.: $750. **To Apply:** Applicants must submit a completed application form together with the scantron sheet; cover sheet; student activity and community activity sheets; personal essay and a copy of unofficial transcript (signed by the counselor); cover sheet with student and parent signature. **Deadline:** February 6. **Contact:** Suzanne Trad, President; Email: suztrad@aol.com.

9529 ■ Beaver Medical Clinic Foundation - Premedical Award (Undergraduate/Scholarship)

Purpose: To encourage educational pursuits among Redlands Unified School District graduates by providing educational assistance. **Focus:** General studies/Field of study not specified. **Qualif.:** Applicants must be a graduating senior seeking a career in the field of medicine; student must be outstanding both academically and in leadership skills.

Funds Avail.: $2,500. **To Apply:** Applicants must submit a completed application form together with the scantron sheet; cover sheet; student activity and community activity sheets; personal essay and a copy of unofficial transcript (signed by the counselor); cover sheet with student and parent signature. **Deadline:** February 6. **Contact:** Suzanne Trad, President; Email: suztrad@aol.com.

9530 ■ Garvin L. Beck Scholarships (Undergraduate/Scholarship)

Purpose: To encourage educational pursuits among Redlands Unified School District graduates by providing educational assistance. **Focus:** General studies/Field of study not specified. **Qualif.:** Applicant must be enrolled at a four-year college, junior college or trade school. **Criteria:** Award is given based on merit.

Funds Avail.: $500 and $1,000. **To Apply:** Applicants must submit a completed application form together with the scantron sheet; cover sheet; student activity and community activity sheets; personal essay; and a copy of unofficial transcript (signed by the counselor). **Deadline:** February 3.

9531 ■ Benchwarmers Club of Redlands Scholarship- Jess Mercado Memorial (Undergraduate/Scholarship)

Purpose: To encourage educational pursuits among Redlands Unified School District graduates by providing

educational assistance. **Focus:** General studies/Field of study not specified. **Qualif.:** Applicant must be a three-year member of the Redlands High School sports program; who has been a starter for at least one year, exhibits good citizenship, with dedication; student must have maintained at least a 2.0 GPA.

Funds Avail.: $1,000. **To Apply:** Applicants must submit a completed application form together with the scantron sheet; cover sheet; student activity and community activity sheets; personal essay and a copy of unofficial transcript (signed by the counselor); cover sheet with student and parent signature. **Deadline:** February 6. **Contact:** Suzanne Trad, President; Email: suztrad@aol.com.

9532 ■ Boy Scouts of America Troop 3 Art Till/ Nathan E. Smith Memorial Scholarship (Undergraduate, Vocational/Occupational/Scholarship)

Purpose: To encourage educational pursuits among Redlands Unified School District graduates by providing educational assistance. **Focus:** General studies/Field of study not specified. **Qualif.:** Applicant must be a graduating senior with at least a 2.0 GPA; must be planning to attend an accredited college, university, or vocational program and must have continuous involvement in scouting and community service. **Criteria:** Preference is given to individuals who have attained the rank of Eagle Scout.

Funds Avail.: $500. **Number Awarded:** 2. **To Apply:** Applicants must submit a completed application form together with the scantron sheet; cover sheet; student activity and community activity sheets; personal essay and a copy of unofficial transcript (signed by the counselor); cover sheet with student and parent signature. **Deadline:** February 6. **Contact:** Suzanne Trad, President; Email: suztrad@aol.com.

9533 ■ Brian Jimenez Memorial Scholarship (Undergraduate/Scholarship)

Purpose: To assist male baseball or soccer athletes planning to take criminal law or criminal justice studies. **Focus:** Criminal justice. **Qualif.:** Applicants must be a senior male from Redlands High School who has participated in baseball or soccer, has a GPA of 2.5 or higher, and is intending to attend an institution of higher learning on a full-time basis. **Criteria:** Preference is given to a student who plans to major in criminal justice or criminal law. applicants should also demonstrate a love of family, be a strong but quiet role model, be respected by peers, and be goal-oriented in his tasks.

Funds Avail.: $500. **To Apply:** Applicants must submit a completed application form together with the cover sheet; Personal Information; Education; Future Plans; School Activities; Non-School Activities; Community Service; essay and an explanation of any suspension during your "High School" years. **Deadline:** February 2. **Contact:** Redlands Community Scholarship Foundation, PO Box 1683, Redlands, California, 92373; Phone: 909-307-9892; Fax: 909-792-7035.

9534 ■ Cindy Andrews Educational Scholarship (Undergraduate/Scholarship)

Purpose: To support educational pursuits among Redlands Unified School District graduates by providing educational assistance. **Focus:** Educational administration; Teaching. **Qualif.:** Applicants must be graduating seniors from Redlands High School who have been CSF members for at least 4 semesters and plan to be teachers and eventually administrators in the public school system.

Awards are arranged alphabetically below their administering organizations

Funds Avail.: $500. To Apply: Applicants must submit a completed application form together with the cover sheet; Personal Information; Education; Future Plans; School Activities; Non-School Activities; Community Service; essay and an explanation of any suspension during your "High School" years. Deadline: February 2. Contact: Redlands Community Scholarship Foundation, PO Box 1683, Redlands, California, 92373; Phone: 909-307-9892; Fax: 909-792-7035.

9535 ■ Community Bank - Lee Guggisberg Foundation Memorial Scholarships (Undergraduate/Scholarship)

Purpose: To provide scholarship to those students who are planning to further their education in the field of business management or accounting. Focus: Accounting; Business. Qualif.: Applicants must be students from Redlands East Valley High School and Redlands High School; complete the graduation requirements of the Redlands Unified School District; be enrolled as full-time students at an accredited college/university prior to Community Bank releasing the scholarship money; and, plan to further education in the field of business management or accounting. Criteria: Selection will be based on merit.

Funds Avail.: $300 each. Duration: Annual. Number Awarded: 3. To Apply: Applicants must submit a completed application form together with the scantron sheet; cover sheet; student activity and community activity sheets; personal essay; and a copy of unofficial transcript (signed by the counselor). Deadline: February 3. Contact: Pam Bibo, Administrative Assistant, at admin@redlandsscholarships.org.

9536 ■ Contemporary Club Scholarship (Undergraduate/Scholarship)

Purpose: To encourage educational pursuits among Redlands Unified School District graduates by providing educational assistance. Focus: Music. Qualif.: Applicants must be a graduating senior who will continue to further their education.

Funds Avail.: $1,000. To Apply: Applicants must submit a completed application form together with the scantron sheet; cover sheet; student activity and community activity sheets; personal essay and a copy of unofficial transcript (signed by the counselor); cover sheet with student and parent signature. Deadline: February 6. Contact: Suzanne Trad, President; Email: suztrad@aol.com.

9537 ■ Cope Middle School PTSA Scholarship (Undergraduate/Scholarship)

Purpose: To encourage educational pursuits among Redlands Unified School District graduates by providing educational assistance. Focus: General studies/Field of study not specified. Qualif.: Applicant must be a graduating senior who attended Cope Middle School for two years; citizenship and a desire to continue education after high school are also a requirement. Criteria: Priority will be given to a student whose parents were PTA volunteers.

Funds Avail.: $400. To Apply: Applicants must submit a completed application form together with the scantron sheet; cover sheet; student activity and community activity sheets; personal essay and a copy of unofficial transcript (signed by the counselor); cover sheet with student and parent signature. Deadline: February 6. Contact: Suzanne Trad, President; Email: suztrad@aol.com.

9538 ■ Crafton Elementary School PTA Scholarship (Undergraduate/Scholarship)

Purpose: To encourage educational pursuits among Redlands Unified School District graduates by providing educational assistance. Focus: General studies/Field of study not specified. Qualif.: Applicants must be a graduating senior who has a financial need and have demonstrated outstanding community service through their high school years; student must have attended Crafton Elementary School.

Funds Avail.: $500. To Apply: Applicants must submit a completed application form together with the scantron sheet; cover sheet; student activity and community activity sheets; personal essay and a copy of unofficial transcript (signed by the counselor); cover sheet with student and parent signature. Deadline: February 6. Contact: Suzanne Trad, President; Email: suztrad@aol.com.

9539 ■ Crafton Hills College Foundation Scholarship (Undergraduate/Scholarship)

Purpose: To provide a scholarship to those students who are in need to achieve their educational goal. Focus: General studies/Field of study not specified. Qualif.: Applicants must be currently enrolled in 6 or more units at CHC, completed a total of 12 or more CHC college units, must be enrolled in 6 or more units at CHC or a four year college for the 2020-2021 academic year when you claim your scholarship.

Funds Avail.: $500. Duration: Annual. To Apply: Applicants must submit a online scholarship application form together with Once you get to the AcademicWorks website, click on "Sign in" and "Sign in with your Institution". Use your WebAdvisor username and password to login. Application will determine if you are eligible for Crafton Scholarships or Valley Scholarships. Make sure you answer all questions as accurately as you can. click on "Finish and Submit" to finish and submit your application. need to make changes after submitting your application, you can click on "Update Your Application". Deadline: February 28. Contact: Crafton Hills College, 11711 Sand Canyon Road, Yucaipa, CA 92399, 909-794-2161.

9540 ■ David Beltran Memorial Scholarship (Undergraduate/Scholarship)

Purpose: To encourage educational pursuits among Redlands Unified School District graduates by providing educational assistance. Focus: Theater arts. Qualif.: Applicants must be a college-bound graduating senior planning to major in drama, theater arts or thespian studies.

Funds Avail.: $500. To Apply: Applicants must submit a completed application form together with the scantron sheet; cover sheet; student activity and community activity sheets; personal essay and a copy of unofficial transcript (signed by the counselor); cover sheet with student and parent signature. Deadline: February 6. Contact: Suzanne Trad, President; Email: suztrad@aol.com.

9541 ■ Dorothy Mitchell Memorial Scholarship (Undergraduate/Scholarship)

Purpose: To support educational pursuits among Redlands Unified School District graduates by providing educational assistance. Focus: General studies/Field of study not specified. Qualif.: Applicants must be a graduating senior from Redlands High School who plans to enter the teaching profession.

Funds Avail.: $500. To Apply: Applicants must submit a completed application form together with the cover sheet;

Awards are arranged alphabetically below their administering organizations

Personal Information; Education; Future Plans; School Activities; Non-School Activities; Community Service; essay and an explanation of any suspension during your "High School" years. **Deadline:** February 2. **Contact:** Redlands Community Scholarship Foundation, PO Box 1683, Redlands, California, 92373; Phone: 909-307-9892; Fax: 909-792-7035.

9542 ■ Eric L. Jacobson Memorial Scholarship
(Undergraduate/Scholarship)

Purpose: To support educational pursuits among Redlands Unified School District graduates by providing educational assistance. **Focus:** General studies/Field of study not specified. **Qualif.:** Applicant must be a graduating student from Redlands High School who has maintained a 3.0 or higher GPA, has participated on the speech or debate team for at least two years (one of which must be the senior year), and plans to attend a four-year college or university on a full-time basis.

Funds Avail.: $1,500. **To Apply:** Applicants must submit a completed application form together with the scantron sheet; cover sheet; student activity and community activity sheets; personal essay and a copy of unofficial transcript (signed by the counselor); cover sheet with student and parent signature. **Deadline:** February 6. **Contact:** Suzanne Trad, President; Email: suztrad@aol.com.

9543 ■ James Mackenzie Fallows Scholarships Honoring Gertrude Baccus *(Undergraduate/Scholarship)*

Purpose: To support students who produce the best piece of expository writing. **Focus:** General studies/Field of study not specified. **Qualif.:** Applicants must be students from Redlands High School who are about to write an essay, article, speech, or some other work of non-fiction designed to explore an idea or explain a situation with the clarity and logic that Mrs. Baccus insisted on from her students. **Criteria:** Scholarships will be given to students who will produce the best piece of expository writing.

Funds Avail.: $1,000. **Duration:** Annual. **To Apply:** Applicants must submit a completed application form together with the scantron sheet; cover sheet; student activity and community activity sheets; personal essay; and a copy of unofficial transcript (signed by the counselor). **Deadline:** February 6. **Contact:** Pam Bibo, Administrative Assistant, at admin@redlandsscholarships.org.

9544 ■ James Mackenzie Fallows Scholarships Honoring William Cunningham *(Undergraduate/Scholarship)*

Purpose: To provide scholarship to those students who are in need to achieve their educational goal. **Focus:** Public service. **Qualif.:** Applicants must be students from Redlands High School who show great promise for public service in their career. Public service could include teaching, medical care, religious or volunteer work, or other expressions of the use of private talent for the public good. **Criteria:** Selection will be based on the qualifications and compliance with the application process.

Funds Avail.: $1,000. **Duration:** Annual. **To Apply:** Applicants must submit a completed application form together with the scantron sheet; cover sheet; student activity and community activity sheets; personal essay; and a copy of unofficial transcript (signed by the counselor). **Deadline:** February 6. **Contact:** Pam Bibo, Administrative Assistant, at admin@redlandsscholarships.org.

9545 ■ Frank G. Araujo Memorial Scholarship
(Undergraduate/Scholarship)

Purpose: To assist Mexican-American graduate seniors in their pursuit of higher education. **Focus:** General studies/Field of study not specified. **Qualif.:** Applicants must be students of Mexican-American descent; recipient must have a 3.0 or higher GPA, demonstrate good citizenship and participate in school or community activities.

Funds Avail.: $500. **To Apply:** Applicants must submit a completed application form together with the cover sheet; Personal Information; Education; Future Plans; School Activities; Non-School Activities; Community Service; essay and an explanation of any suspension during your "High School" years. **Deadline:** February 2. **Contact:** Redlands Community Scholarship Foundation, PO Box 1683, Redlands, California, 92373; Phone: 909-307-9892; Fax: 909-792-7035.

9546 ■ Franklin Elementary School PTA Scholarship
(Undergraduate/Scholarship)

Purpose: To support educational pursuits among Redlands Unified School District graduates by providing educational assistance. **Focus:** General studies/Field of study not specified. **Qualif.:** Applicants must be students who attended Franklin Elementary School and have extensive volunteer service in both school and community. **Criteria:** Selection is based on academic standing and financial need.

Funds Avail.: $600. **To Apply:** Applicants must submit a completed application form together with the scantron sheet; cover sheet; student activity and community activity sheets; personal essay and a copy of unofficial transcript (signed by the counselor); cover sheet with student and parent signature. **Deadline:** February 6. **Contact:** Suzanne Trad, President; Email: suztrad@aol.com.

9547 ■ Friends and Family of Christopher J. Kohlmeier Scholarship *(Undergraduate/Scholarship)*

Purpose: To support students who are interested in a career in law enforcement or firefighting. **Focus:** Fires and fire prevention; Law enforcement. **Qualif.:** Applicants must be graduating students from Citrus Valley High School who plan to attend a two-year or four-year college or university and who have strong test scores, but whose C average in high school could easily have been higher. **Criteria:** Preference will be given to students who are interested in a career in law enforcement or firefighting.

Funds Avail.: $750. **To Apply:** Applicants must submit a completed application form together with the cover sheet; Personal Information; Education; Future Plans; School Activities; Non-School Activities; Community Service; essay and an explanation of any suspension during your "High School" years. **Deadline:** February 2. **Contact:** Redlands Community Scholarship Foundation, PO Box 1683, Redlands, California, 92373; Phone: 909-307-9892; Fax: 909-792-7035.

9548 ■ Gail Garner Memorial R.I.S.E. Scholarship
(Undergraduate/Scholarship)

Purpose: To support educational pursuits among Redlands Unified School District graduates by providing educational assistance. **Focus:** General studies/Field of study not specified. **Qualif.:** Applicant must be a student graduating from the Redlands Independent Study Education (R.I.S.E.) program.

Funds Avail.: $500. **To Apply:** Applicants must submit a completed application form together with the scantron

Awards are arranged alphabetically below their administering organizations

sheet; cover sheet; student activity and community activity sheets; personal essay and a copy of unofficial transcript (signed by the counselor); cover sheet with student and parent signature. **Deadline:** February 6. **Contact:** Suzanne Trad, President; Email: suztrad@aol.com.

9549 ■ Guzkowski Family Scholarships
(Undergraduate/Scholarship)

Purpose: To support the continuing education of students who want to pursue further learning in the area of government and public policy. **Focus:** Political science; Public administration. **Qualif.:** Applicant must be a graduating student by the Guzkowski Family to recognize critical thinking in the area of government and public policy. **Criteria:** Selection shall be based on the aforementioned applicants' qualifications and compliance with the application details.

Funds Avail.: $600. **Duration:** Annual. **To Apply:** Applicant must submit a 500-word essay that demonstrates an appreciation for and understanding of objective analysis and some of the problems and challenges confronting contemporary society, as well as the role that can be played by government through rational public policy in addressing these issues. Applicant should include the information required by the scholarship using the specific essay listed on the Directory Page. (RCSF web pages 28 through 34).

9550 ■ Harry Munoz Memorial Scholarship
(Undergraduate/Scholarship)

Purpose: To provide a scholarship to those students who are in need to achieve their educational goal. **Focus:** General studies/Field of study not specified. **Qualif.:** Applicants must be graduate students from Redlands East Valley High School and/or Redlands High School who have demonstrated academic achievement, outstanding citizenship and a desire to continue their education.

Funds Avail.: $1,000. **To Apply:** Applicants must submit a completed application form together with the cover sheet; Personal Information; Education; Future Plans; School Activities; Non-School Activities; Community Service; essay and an explanation of any suspension during your "High School" years. **Deadline:** February 2. **Remarks:** The scholarship award was established in the memory of Harry Munoz, a Redlands High School graduate of the Class. **Contact:** Pam Bibo, Administrative Assistant; Email: admin@redlandsscholarships.org.

9551 ■ Jack M. Nagasaka Memorial Scholarship
(Undergraduate/Scholarship)

Purpose: To support and encourage those graduating high school students who are outstanding in the field of math or science. **Focus:** General studies/Field of study not specified. **Qualif.:** Applicants must be a graduating senior who is outstanding in the field of math or science. **Criteria:** Selection will be based on grades and achievement test scores in chemistry, physics and or math.

Funds Avail.: $300. **To Apply:** Applicants must submit a completed application form together with the cover sheet; Personal Information; Education; Future Plans; School Activities; Non-School Activities; Community Service; essay and an explanation of any suspension during your "High School" years. **Deadline:** February 2. **Contact:** Redlands Community Scholarship Foundation, PO Box 1683, Redlands, California, 92373; Phone: 909-307-9892; Fax: 909-792-7035.

9552 ■ Kimberly Elementary School PTA Scholarship *(Undergraduate/Scholarship)*

Purpose: To support educational pursuits among Redlands Unified School District graduates by providing educational assistance. **Focus:** General studies/Field of study not specified. **Qualif.:** Applicants must be graduating seniors who attended Kimberly Elementary School for a minimum of three years; average or above-average achievers, demonstrate good citizenship and preferably have not received other scholarships.

Funds Avail.: $500. **To Apply:** Applicants must submit a completed application form together with the cover sheet; Personal Information; Education; Future Plans; School Activities; Non-School Activities; Community Service; essay and an explanation of any suspension during your "High School" years. **Deadline:** February 2. **Contact:** Redlands Community Scholarship Foundation, PO Box 1683, Redlands, California, 92373; Phone: 909-307-9892; Fax: 909-792-7035.

9553 ■ Kingsbury Elementary School PTA Scholarship *(Undergraduate/Scholarship)*

Purpose: To support educational pursuits among Redlands Unified School District graduates by providing educational assistance. **Focus:** General studies/Field of study not specified. **Qualif.:** Applicants must be students who attended Kingsbury Elementary School for at least three years, have a minimum of a C average, and have demonstrated good citizenship and leadership. **Criteria:** Selection shall be based on the financial need; involvement in extracurricular and community activities.

Funds Avail.: $300. **To Apply:** Applicants must submit a completed application form together with the cover sheet; Personal Information; Education; Future Plans; School Activities; Non-School Activities; Community Service; essay and an explanation of any suspension during your "High School" years. **Deadline:** February 2. **Contact:** Redlands Community Scholarship Foundation, PO Box 1683, Redlands, California, 92373; Phone: 909-307-9892; Fax: 909-792-7035.

9554 ■ Kiwanis Club of Redlands Foundation Academic Excellence Scholarship *(Undergraduate/Scholarship)*

Purpose: To encourage educational pursuits among Redlands Unified School District graduates by providing educational assistance. **Focus:** General studies/Field of study not specified. **Qualif.:** Applicants must be a graduating senior an with outstanding GPA upon graduation from high school, with good citizenship, extracurricular activity involvement and demonstrated leadership abilities. **Criteria:** Recipients will be selected through an interview process conducted by the kiwanis club foundation scholarship committee.

Funds Avail.: $6,000. **Duration:** Up to 4 years. **To Apply:** Applicants must submit a completed application form together with the cover sheet; Personal Information; Education; Future Plans; School Activities; Non-School Activities; Community Service; essay and an explanation of any suspension during your "High School" years. **Deadline:** February 2. **Contact:** Redlands Community Scholarship Foundation, PO Box 1683, Redlands, California, 92373; Phone: 909-307-9892; Fax: 909-792-7035.

9555 ■ Kiwanis Club of Redlands Foundation - Martin and Dorothy Munz Scholarship
(Undergraduate/Scholarship)

Purpose: To provide financial support to students who are in need of help in pursuing higher education. **Focus:** General studies/Field of study not specified. **Qualif.:** Applicants

Awards are arranged alphabetically below their administering organizations

must be graduating seniors who meet the following criteria: has a 3.0 GPA in all subjects, has an interest in or aptitude for education or a business career; has been involved in community service such as scouting and church; highly motivated to obtain a four-year college degree, and demonstrates a financial need.

Funds Avail.: $1,500. **To Apply:** Applicants must submit a completed application form together with the cover sheet; Personal Information; Education; Future Plans; School Activities; Non-School Activities; Community Service; essay and an explanation of any suspension during your "High School" years. **Deadline:** February 2. **Contact:** Redlands Community Scholarship Foundation, PO Box 1683, Redlands, California, 92373; Phone: 909-307-9892; Fax: 909-792-7035.

9556 ■ Doreen Legg Memorial Scholarships
(Undergraduate/Scholarship)

Purpose: To support educational pursuits among Redlands Unified School District graduates by providing educational assistance. **Focus:** Business; Teaching. **Qualif.:** Applicants must be graduating seniors who will enroll full-time at a four-year college or university pursuing a business or teaching career; must have a minimum 3.0 GPA and attended a RUSD High School for three consecutive years.

Funds Avail.: $500. **To Apply:** Applicants must submit a completed application form together with the cover sheet; Personal Information; Education; Future Plans; School Activities; Non-School Activities; Community Service; essay and an explanation of any suspension during your "High School" years. **Deadline:** February 2. **Contact:** Redlands Community Scholarship Foundation, PO Box 1683, Redlands, California, 92373; Phone: 909-307-9892; Fax: 909-792-7035.

9557 ■ Jack A. and Louise S. Levine Memorial Scholarships *(Undergraduate/Scholarship)*

Purpose: To support educational pursuits among Redlands Unified School District graduates by providing educational assistance. **Focus:** General studies/Field of study not specified. **Qualif.:** Applicants must be graduating seniors from Citrus Valley High School, Redlands eAcademy, Redlands East Valley High School, and/or Redlands High School who plan to continue their education, have 3.0 or higher GPA, demonstrate good citizenship, and have participated in school and/or community activities. **Criteria:** Selection shall be based on the aforementioned applicants' qualifications and compliance with the application details.

Funds Avail.: $500. **Duration:** Annual. **To Apply:** Applicants may visit the scholarship section of the bestowing organization's website for further information regarding the application details.

9558 ■ Lugonia Alumni/Harrison Lightfoot Scholarship *(Undergraduate/Scholarship)*

Purpose: To support educational pursuits among Redlands Unified School District graduates by providing educational assistance. **Focus:** General studies/Field of study not specified. **Qualif.:** Applicants must be graduating seniors from Lugonia Elementary School; must have extensive community service and/or be involved in school activities, demonstrate good citizenship and have a GPA of 2.5 or higher; scholarship may be used at any college, university, or vocational school.

Funds Avail.: $1,500. **Number Awarded:** Varies. **To Apply:** Applicants must submit a completed application form

together with the cover sheet; Personal Information; Education; Future Plans; School Activities; Non-School Activities; Community Service; essay and an explanation of any suspension during your "High School" years. **Deadline:** February 2. **Contact:** Redlands Community Scholarship Foundation, PO Box 1683, Redlands, California, 92373; Phone: 909-307-9892; Fax: 909-792-7035.

9559 ■ Mariposa Elementary School PTA Scholarship *(Undergraduate/Scholarship)*

Purpose: To support educational pursuits among Redlands Unified School District graduates by providing educational assistance. **Focus:** General studies/Field of study not specified. **Qualif.:** Applicants must be graduating seniors who attended Mariposa Elementary School for at least three years; recipient must be pursuing an education at a two or four-year university and show academic excellence with a minimum 3.0 GPA as well as community service. **Criteria:** Preference will be given to those who meet the criteria and demonstrate financial need.

Funds Avail.: $500. **To Apply:** Applicants must submit a completed application form together with the cover sheet; Personal Information; Education; Future Plans; School Activities; Non-School Activities; Community Service; essay and an explanation of any suspension during your "High School" years. **Deadline:** February 2. **Contact:** Redlands Community Scholarship Foundation, PO Box 1683, Redlands, California, 92373; Phone: 909-307-9892; Fax: 909-792-7035.

9560 ■ Marshall Phelps Athletic Memorial Scholarship *(Undergraduate/Scholarship)*

Purpose: To encourage educational pursuits among Redlands Unified School District graduates by providing educational assistance. **Focus:** General studies/Field of study not specified. **Qualif.:** Applicants must be graduating male or female from Redlands High School with proven athletic ability and interest in a career involving some phase of athletics, such as sports medicine, coaching, or physical therapy; community service and leadership qualities are desirable but not essential; student must plan to enroll in a two-year or four-year college program and have a minimum 2.0 GPA. **Criteria:** Selection will be based upon high school counselor's recommendations.

Funds Avail.: $1,000. **To Apply:** Applicants must submit a completed application form together with the cover sheet; Personal Information; Education; Future Plans; School Activities; Non-School Activities; Community Service; essay and an explanation of any suspension during your "High School" years. **Deadline:** February 2. **Contact:** Redlands Community Scholarship Foundation, PO Box 1683, Redlands, California, 92373; Phone: 909-307-9892; Fax: 909-792-7035.

9561 ■ McKinley Elementary School PTA Scholarship *(Undergraduate/Scholarship)*

Purpose: To support educational pursuits among Redlands Unified School District graduates by providing educational assistance. **Focus:** General studies/Field of study not specified. **Qualif.:** Applicant must be a graduating senior who attended McKinley Elementary School for at least three years and plans to attend a college, university, or vocational school.

Funds Avail.: $300. **To Apply:** Applicants must submit a completed application form together with the cover sheet; Personal Information; Education; Future Plans; School Activities; Non-School Activities; Community Service; essay

Awards are arranged alphabetically below their administering organizations

and an explanation of any suspension during your "High School" years. **Deadline:** February 2. **Contact:** Redlands Community Scholarship Foundation, PO Box 1683, Redlands, California, 92373; Phone: 909-307-9892; Fax: 909-792-7035.

9562 ■ Michael A. Russo Memorial Scholarship
(Undergraduate/Scholarship)

Purpose: To support students who are planning to pursue a career in a medical or medically-allied profession or career. **Focus:** Medicine. **Qualif.:** Applicants must be graduating seniors who plan to pursue a career in a medical or medically-allied profession or career.

Funds Avail.: $1,000. **Number Awarded:** 2. **To Apply:** Applicants must submit a completed application form together with the cover sheet; Personal Information; Education; Future Plans; School Activities; Non-School Activities; Community Service; essay and an explanation of any suspension during your "High School" years. **Deadline:** February 2. **Contact:** Pam Bibo, Administrative Assistant; Email: admin@redlandsscholarships.org.

9563 ■ Mike Niemeyer Memorial Football Scholarship *(Undergraduate/Scholarship)*

Purpose: To support educational pursuits among Redlands Unified School District graduates by providing educational assistance. **Focus:** Athletics; General studies/Field of study not specified. **Qualif.:** Applicants must be graduating seniors from Redlands High School who are members of the Redlands High School Terrier football team; recipient must demonstrate academic achievement and good citizenship. **Criteria:** Preference will be given to those who are able to demonstrate high academic achievement and good citizenship, as well as those offensive or defensive linemen.

Funds Avail.: $500. **To Apply:** Applicants must submit a completed application form together with the cover sheet; Personal Information; Education; Future Plans; School Activities; Non-School Activities; Community Service; essay and an explanation of any suspension during your "High School" years. **Deadline:** February 2. **Contact:** Redlands Community Scholarship Foundation, PO Box 1683, Redlands, California, 92373; Phone: 909-307-9892; Fax: 909-792-7035.

9564 ■ Moore Middle School PTA Scholarship
(Undergraduate/Scholarship)

Purpose: To support educational pursuits among Redlands Unified School District graduates by providing educational assistance. **Focus:** General studies/Field of study not specified. **Qualif.:** Applicants must be a graduating senior who attended Moore Middle School for three years and plans to attend college or a trade school.

Funds Avail.: $500. **To Apply:** Applicants must submit a completed application form together with the cover sheet; Personal Information; Education; Future Plans; School Activities; Non-School Activities; Community Service; essay and an explanation of any suspension during your "High School" years. **Deadline:** February 2. **Contact:** Redlands Community Scholarship Foundation, PO Box 1683, Redlands, California, 92373; Phone: 909-307-9892; Fax: 909-792-7035.

9565 ■ Robert L. Morlan Redlands Area Interfaith Council Scholarships *(Undergraduate/Scholarship)*

Purpose: To support educational pursuits among Redlands Unified School District graduates by providing educational assistance. **Focus:** General studies/Field of study not specified. **Qualif.:** Applicants must be graduating senior; created from the long history of promoting love and respect among all of the people of faith in our community.

Funds Avail.: $400. **To Apply:** Applicants must submit a completed application form together with the cover sheet; Personal Information; Education; Future Plans; School Activities; Non-School Activities; Community Service; essay and an explanation of any suspension during your "High School" years. **Deadline:** February 2. **Contact:** Redlands Community Scholarship Foundation, PO Box 1683, Redlands, California, 92373; Phone: 909-307-9892; Fax: 909-792-7035.

9566 ■ Robyn Nance Memorial Scholarships
(Undergraduate/Scholarship)

Purpose: To support educational pursuits among Redlands Unified School District graduates by providing educational assistance. **Focus:** General studies/Field of study not specified. **Qualif.:** Applicants must be graduating seniors from Redlands High School who are active in dramatic arts, have utilized their talents to the utmost, display love and enthusiasm for the theater, and participate whenever and wherever needed. **Criteria:** Selection shall be based on the aforementioned applicants' qualifications and compliance with the application details.

Funds Avail.: $500. **To Apply:** Applicants may visit the scholarship section of the bestowing organization's website for further information regarding the application details. **Contact:** Redlands Community Scholarship Foundation, at the above address.

9567 ■ Northside Booster Club - Felix R. Sepulveda Memorial Scholarship *(Undergraduate/Scholarship)*

Purpose: To support students who have maintain a good academic average. **Focus:** Sports studies. **Qualif.:** Applicants must be graduating male or female who have maintained at least a 2.5 GPA and participated in at least one sport.

Funds Avail.: $500 each. **To Apply:** Applicants must submit a completed application form together with the cover sheet; Personal Information; Education; Future Plans; School Activities; Non-School Activities; Community Service; essay and an explanation of any suspension during your "High School" years. **Deadline:** February 2. **Contact:** Pam Bibo, Administrative Assistant; Email: admin@redlandsscholarships.org.

9568 ■ Optimist Club of Redlands Scholarship- Ralph Maloof *(Undergraduate/Scholarship)*

Purpose: To support educational pursuits among Redlands Unified School District graduates by providing educational assistance. **Focus:** General studies/Field of study not specified. **Qualif.:** Applicants must be a male graduating senior from Redlands High School who has a minimum 3.0 GPA, has a positive attitude, and involved in service to the community.

Funds Avail.: $2,000. **To Apply:** Applicants must submit a completed application form together with the cover sheet; Personal Information; Education; Future Plans; School Activities; Non-School Activities; Community Service; essay and an explanation of any suspension during your "High School" years. **Deadline:** February 2. **Contact:** Redlands Community Scholarship Foundation, PO Box 1683, Redlands, California, 92373; Phone: 909-307-9892; Fax: 909-792-7035.

Awards are arranged alphabetically below their administering organizations

9569 ■ Optimist Club of Redlands Scholarship- Virgina Elliott (*Undergraduate/Scholarship*)

Purpose: To encourage educational pursuits among Redlands Unified School District graduates by providing educational assistance. **Focus:** General studies/Field of study not specified. **Qualif.:** Applicant must be a female graduating senior from Redlands High School who has a minimum 3.0 GPA, has a positive attitude, and involved in service to the community.

Funds Avail.: $2,000. **To Apply:** Applicants must submit a completed application form together with the cover sheet; Personal Information; Education; Future Plans; School Activities; Non-School Activities; Community Service; essay and an explanation of any suspension during your "High School" years. **Deadline:** February 2. **Contact:** Redlands Community Scholarship Foundation, PO Box 1683, Redlands, California, 92373; Phone: 909-307-9892; Fax: 909-792-7035.

9570 ■ Pat Dermargosian Memorial Scholarship (*Undergraduate/Scholarship*)

Purpose: To support educational pursuits among Redlands Unified School District graduates by providing educational assistance. **Focus:** General studies/Field of study not specified. **Qualif.:** Applicant must be a graduating senior whose parent has been actively involved in the PTA.

Funds Avail.: $300. **To Apply:** Applicant must submit a completed application form together with the scantron sheet; cover sheet; student activity and community activity sheets and a copy of unofficial transcript (signed by the counselor). In addition, applicant must also submit a one page essay stating the effect of parent's participation in school PTA. **Deadline:** February 6. **Contact:** Suzanne Trad, President; Email: suztrad@aol.com.

9571 ■ PCH Architects LLP - Steven J. Lehnhof Memorial Architectural Scholarship (*Undergraduate/Scholarship*)

Purpose: To support those who want to study architecture or architectural engineering at an accredited college or university. **Focus:** Architecture; Engineering, Architectural. **Qualif.:** Applicants must be graduating seniors who will be majoring in architecture or architectural engineering at an accredited college or university.

Funds Avail.: $1,000. **To Apply:** Applicants must submit a completed application form together with the cover sheet; Personal Information; Education; Future Plans; School Activities; Non-School Activities; Community Service; essay and an explanation of any suspension during your "High School" years. **Deadline:** February 2. **Remarks:** The scholarship award was established in the memory of Steven J. Lehnhof, an architecture and drafting teacher at Redlands High School for many years. **Contact:** Redlands Community Scholarship Foundation, PO Box 1683, Redlands, California, 92373; Phone: 909-307-9892; Fax: 909-792-7035.

9572 ■ Professional Women of Redlands, PoWeR to Continue Learning Scholarships (*Undergraduate/Scholarship*)

Purpose: To encourage educational pursuits among Redlands Unified School District graduates by providing educational assistance. **Focus:** General studies/Field of study not specified. **Qualif.:** Applicants must be a graduating young woman from any of the Redlands Unified Schools, except Redlands eAcademy; must have a minimum 2.5 GPA; must have participated in at least one school activity; must have demonstrated some type of community service and must be planning to attend a two-year or four-year college or a vocational program. **Criteria:** Preference will be given to a student who will be the first in their family to obtain a college degree or professional certification program.

Funds Avail.: $1,000. **To Apply:** Applicants must submit a completed application form together with the cover sheet; Personal Information; Education; Future Plans; School Activities; Non-School Activities; Community Service; essay and an explanation of any suspension during your "High School" years. **Deadline:** February 2. **Contact:** Redlands Community Scholarship Foundation, PO Box 1683, Redlands, California, 92373; Phone: 909-307-9892; Fax: 909-792-7035.

9573 ■ Quincy Brown Memorial Scholarship (*Undergraduate/Scholarship*)

Purpose: To encourage educational pursuits among Redlands Unified School District graduates by providing educational assistance. **Focus:** Business; Teaching. **Qualif.:** Applicant must be a graduating senior enrolled as a full-time student in a four-year college or university; must be pursuing a business or teaching career; must have a 3.0 or higher GPA and must have attended Redlands High School for at least three consecutive years.

Funds Avail.: $500 or greater scholarship. **To Apply:** Applicants must submit a completed application form together with the scantron sheet; cover sheet; student activity and community activity sheets; personal essay and a copy of unofficial transcript (signed by the counselor); cover sheet with student and parent signature. **Deadline:** February 6. **Contact:** Suzanne Trad, President; Email: suztrad@aol.com.

9574 ■ R. Garn Haycock Memorial Scholarship (*Undergraduate/Scholarship*)

Purpose: To support educational pursuits among Redlands Unified School District graduates by providing educational assistance. **Focus:** General studies/Field of study not specified. **Qualif.:** Applicant must be a deserving senior who displays good citizenship, character and academic potential; has a need for financial assistance, and will attend an institution of higher learning on a full-time basis.

Funds Avail.: $1,000. **To Apply:** Applicants must submit a completed application form together with the scantron sheet; cover sheet; student activity and community activity sheets; personal essay and a copy of unofficial transcript (signed by the counselor); cover sheet with student and parent signature. **Deadline:** February 6. **Contact:** Suzanne Trad, President; Email: suztrad@aol.com.

9575 ■ Rachel Graham Memorial Scholarship (*Undergraduate/Scholarship*)

Purpose: To support educational pursuits among Redlands Unified School District graduates by providing educational assistance. **Focus:** General studies/Field of study not specified. **Qualif.:** Applicants must be graduating seniors from Citrus Valley High School, Redlands eAcademy, Redlands East Valley High School, and Redlands High School who will attend a four-year college or university on a full-time basis; must also have maintained at least a 3.0 GPA; shown good citizenship and participated in school and community activities.

Funds Avail.: $500. **Number Awarded:** Varies. **To Apply:** Applicants must submit a completed application form

Awards are arranged alphabetically below their administering organizations

together with the scantron sheet; cover sheet; student activity and community activity sheets; personal essay and a copy of unofficial transcript (signed by the counselor); cover sheet with student and parent signature. **Deadline:** February 6. **Contact:** Suzanne Trad, President; Email: suztrad@aol.com.

9576 ■ Raymond and Donald Beeler Memorial Scholarship *(Undergraduate/Scholarship)*

Purpose: To encourage educational pursuits among Redlands Unified School District graduates by providing educational assistance. **Focus:** General studies/Field of study not specified. **Qualif.:** Applicants must be a student with at least a 3.0 GPA intending to attend a community or four-year college on a full-time basis. **Criteria:** Selection is based on merit.

Funds Avail.: $500. **To Apply:** Applicants must submit a completed application form together with the scantron sheet; cover sheet; student activity and community activity sheets; personal essay and a copy of unofficial transcript (signed by the counselor); cover sheet with student and parent signature. **Deadline:** February 6. **Contact:** Suzanne Trad, President; Email: suztrad@aol.com.

9577 ■ Redlands Baseball/Softball for Youth Scholarship *(Undergraduate/Scholarship)*

Purpose: To support the continuing education of those who have participated in the Redlands Baseball/Softball for Youth program for a given period of time. **Focus:** General studies/Field of study not specified. **Qualif.:** Applicants must be graduating seniors who have participated in the Redlands Baseball/Softball for Youth program including scorekeepers or umpires for a minimum of three years; student must have exemplified good sportsmanship and academic achievement.

Funds Avail.: $350. **To Apply:** Applicants must submit a completed application form together with the scantron sheet; cover sheet; student activity and community activity sheets; personal essay and a copy of unofficial transcript (signed by the counselor); cover sheet with student and parent signature; essay (200 words) essay entitled How Redlands Baseball/Softball for Youth Has Impacted My Life. **Deadline:** February 6. **Contact:** Suzanne Trad, President; Email: suztrad@aol.com.

9578 ■ Redlands Community Scholarship Foundation Awards *(Undergraduate/Scholarship)*

Purpose: To assist graduate seniors in their pursuit of higher education. **Focus:** General studies/Field of study not specified. **Qualif.:** Applicants must be graduating senior to assist in their pursuit of higher education.

Funds Avail.: $500. **To Apply:** Applicants must submit a completed application form together with the cover sheet; Personal Information; Education; Future Plans; School Activities; Non-School Activities; Community Service; essay and an explanation of any suspension during your "High School" years. **Deadline:** February 2. **Contact:** Redlands Community Scholarship Foundation, PO Box 1683, Redlands, California, 92373; Phone: 909-307-9892; Fax: 909-792-7035.

9579 ■ Redlands Council PTA - Dorathy Jolley Memorial Scholarship *(Undergraduate/Scholarship)*

Purpose: To support educational pursuits among Redlands Unified School District graduates by providing educational assistance. **Focus:** General studies/Field of study not

specified. **Qualif.:** Applicants must be a graduating senior who has a minimum 3.0 GPA and are active in a non-school service group such as church, scouts, or a community service club.

Funds Avail.: $400. **To Apply:** Applicants must submit a completed application form together with the cover sheet; Personal Information; Education; Future Plans; School Activities; Non-School Activities; Community Service; essay and an explanation of any suspension during your "High School" years. **Deadline:** February 2. **Contact:** Redlands Community Scholarship Foundation, PO Box 1683, Redlands, California, 92373; Phone: 909-307-9892; Fax: 909-792-7035.

9580 ■ Redlands Evening Lions Club - Barbara Westen Memorial Scholarship *(Undergraduate/Scholarship)*

Purpose: To help a deserving graduate pursue training beyond high school. **Focus:** General studies/Field of study not specified. **Qualif.:** Applicant must be awarded to help a deserving graduate pursue training beyond high school. **Criteria:** Preference is given to a student with a hearing or sight disability. Financial need is also considered.

Funds Avail.: $350. **To Apply:** Applicants must submit a completed application form together with the cover sheet; Personal Information; Education; Future Plans; School Activities; Non-School Activities; Community Service; essay and an explanation of any suspension during your "High School" years. **Deadline:** February 2. **Contact:** Redlands Community Scholarship Foundation, PO Box 1683, Redlands, California, 92373; Phone: 909-307-9892; Fax: 909-792-7035.

9581 ■ Redlands Footlighters, Inc. - Merle and Peggy Williams Scholarship *(Undergraduate/Scholarship)*

Purpose: To provide a scholarship to those students who have made major contributions in the theater. **Focus:** Theater arts. **Qualif.:** Applicants must be graduating seniors from Redlands High School who have made major contributions in theater, either as actors or as theater technicians, and intend to continue involvement in theater activities in the future.

Funds Avail.: $500. **To Apply:** Applicants must submit a completed application form together with the cover sheet; Personal Information; Education; Future Plans; School Activities; Non-School Activities; Community Service; essay and an explanation of any suspension during your "High School" years. **Deadline:** February 2. **Contact:** Pam Bibo, Administrative Assistant; Email: admin@redlandsscholarships.org.

9582 ■ Redlands High School Academic Decathlon Scholarship *(Undergraduate/Scholarship)*

Purpose: To assist outstanding seniors who have participated in Academic Decathlon, in their pursuit of higher education. **Focus:** General studies/Field of study not specified. **Qualif.:** Applicants must be outstanding seniors from Redlands High School who participated in the Academic Decathlon program for a minimum of three years, have played on the varsity team at least one year and whose performances have contributed to a successful program.

Funds Avail.: $300. **Number Awarded:** 4. **To Apply:** Applicants must submit a completed application form together with the cover sheet; Personal Information; Education; Future Plans; School Activities; Non-School Activities; Com-

Awards are arranged alphabetically below their administering organizations

munity Service; essay and an explanation of any suspension during your "High School" years. **Deadline:** February 2. **Contact:** Redlands Community Scholarship Foundation, PO Box 1683, Redlands, California, 92373; Phone: 909-307-9892; Fax: 909-792-7035.

9583 ■ Redlands High School Aquatics Booster Club Scholarship (Undergraduate/Scholarship)

Purpose: To encourage educational pursuits among Redlands Unified School District graduates by providing educational assistance. **Focus:** General studies/Field of study not specified. **Qualif.:** Applicants must be graduating seniors from who have participated for at least three consecutive years in the water polo and/or swimming program. Must have maintained a minimum 3.0 GPA and are planning on continuing in an aquatics program in college.

Funds Avail.: $500. **Number Awarded:** Varies. **To Apply:** Applicants must submit a completed application form together with the cover sheet; Personal Information; Education; Future Plans; School Activities; Non-School Activities; Community Service; essay and an explanation of any suspension during your "High School" years. **Deadline:** February 2. **Remarks:** No electronic submissions of application will be accepted. Submit two printed copies of the application and use a No. 2 pencil on the scantron sheet.

9584 ■ Redlands High School Boy's Varsity Volleyball Scholarships (Undergraduate/Scholarship)

Purpose: To provide financial support to students who are in need of help in pursuing higher education. **Focus:** Athletics; General studies/Field of study not specified. **Qualif.:** Applicants must be graduating male seniors from Redlands High School who are members of the Varsity Volleyball team. **Criteria:** Selection shall be based on the aforementioned applicants' qualifications and compliance with the application details.

Funds Avail.: $300. **Duration:** Annual. **To Apply:** Applicants must submit a completed application form together with the scantron sheet; cover sheet; student activity and community activity sheets; personal essay; and a copy of unofficial transcript (signed by the counselor). **Deadline:** February 3.

9585 ■ Redlands High School Girls' Volleyball Boosters Scholarship Awards (Undergraduate/ Scholarship)

Purpose: To encourage educational pursuits among Redlands Unified School District graduates by providing educational assistance. **Focus:** General studies/Field of study not specified. **Qualif.:** Applicant must be a graduating senior volleyball player with good academic standing and citizenship; must be a dedicated team player; and must have positive leadership skills and a positive attitude. **Criteria:** Award is given based on the application.

Funds Avail.: No specific amount. **To Apply:** Applicants must submit a completed application form together with the scantron sheet; cover sheet; student activity and community activity sheets; personal essay; and a copy of unofficial transcript (signed by the counselor). **Deadline:** February 3.

9586 ■ Redlands High School Mock Trial Scholarship (Undergraduate/Scholarship)

Purpose: To provide financial support to students who are in need of help in pursuing higher education. **Focus:** General studies/Field of study not specified. **Qualif.:** Applicants

must be graduating seniors who are members of the RHS Mock Trial team; minimum of 1 year, and whose performances have contributed to a successful program.

Funds Avail.: One $800 and four $300. **To Apply:** Applicants must submit a completed application form together with the cover sheet; Personal Information; Education; Future Plans; School Activities; Non-School Activities; Community Service; essay and an explanation of any suspension during your "High School" years. **Deadline:** February 2. **Contact:** Redlands Community Scholarship Foundation, PO Box 1683, Redlands, California, 92373; Phone: 909-307-9892; Fax: 909-792-7035.

9587 ■ Redlands High School-PTSA Scholarship (Undergraduate/Scholarship)

Purpose: To provide financial support to students who are in need of help in pursuing higher education. **Focus:** General studies/Field of study not specified. **Qualif.:** Applicants must be graduating seniors from Redlands High School pursuing careers in a vocational field and who have a 2.0 or higher GPA. Also eligible are graduating seniors with a 3.0 or higher GPA who plan to pursue careers in a four-year college. Recipients must demonstrate good citizenship, a high work capacity, and service to school and or community; PTSA membership is a strong consideration.

Funds Avail.: $500. **To Apply:** Applicants must submit a completed application form together with the cover sheet; Personal Information; Education; Future Plans; School Activities; Non-School Activities; Community Service; essay and an explanation of any suspension during your "High School" years. **Deadline:** February 2. **Contact:** Redlands Community Scholarship Foundation, PO Box 1683, Redlands, California, 92373; Phone: 909-307-9892; Fax: 909-792-7035.

9588 ■ Redlands High School Softball Booster Scholarship (Undergraduate/Scholarship)

Purpose: To encourage educational pursuits among Redlands Unified School District graduates by providing educational assistance. **Focus:** General studies/Field of study not specified. **Qualif.:** Applicants must be graduating seniors who have earned a varsity letter in senior year and who have a minimum 3.25 weighted GPA.

Funds Avail.: $300. **Number Awarded:** 2. **To Apply:** Applicants must submit a completed application form together with the scantron sheet; cover sheet; student activity and community activity sheets; personal essay and a copy of unofficial transcript (signed by the counselor); cover sheet with student and parent signature. **Deadline:** February 6. **Contact:** Suzanne Trad, President; Email: suztrad@aol.com.

9589 ■ Redlands High School Spiritleaders Scholarship (Undergraduate/Scholarship)

Purpose: To encourage educational pursuits among Redlands Unified School District graduates by providing educational assistance. **Focus:** General studies/Field of study not specified. **Qualif.:** Applicant must be a graduating senior who has been in Spiritleaders for a minimum of two years; one recipient will be the student with the highest cumulative GPA. **Criteria:** Selection will be based on the committee's criteria.

Funds Avail.: $300. **Number Awarded:** 3. **To Apply:** Applicants must submit a completed application form together with the scantron sheet; cover sheet; student activity and community activity sheets; personal essay and a copy of

Awards are arranged alphabetically below their administering organizations

unofficial transcript (signed by the counselor); cover sheet with student and parent signature. **Deadline:** February 6. **Contact:** Suzanne Trad, President; Email: suztrad@aol.com.

9590 ■ Redlands High School Terrier Band Boosters Club Scholarship *(Undergraduate/Scholarship)*

Purpose: To encourage educational pursuits among Redlands Unified School District graduates by providing educational assistance. **Focus:** Music. **Qualif.:** Applicant must be a graduating senior who participated in the Redlands High School instrumental music program and plans to continue with instrumental music in some capacity (not necessarily majoring in music).

Funds Avail.: $250. **To Apply:** Applicants must submit a completed application form together with the scantron sheet; cover sheet; student activity and community activity sheets; personal essay and a copy of unofficial transcript (signed by the counselor); cover sheet with student and parent signature. **Deadline:** February 6. **Contact:** Suzanne Trad, President; Email: suztrad@aol.com.

9591 ■ Redlands High School Vocal Music Boosters Scholarship *(Undergraduate/Scholarship)*

Purpose: To encourage educational pursuits among Redlands Unified School District graduates by providing educational assistance. **Focus:** Music. **Qualif.:** Applicant must be a graduating senior who has participated in the Redlands High School choral program and plans to continue with music in some capacity.

Funds Avail.: $500 and $250. **To Apply:** Applicants must submit a completed application form together with the scantron sheet; cover sheet; student activity and community activity sheets; personal essay and a copy of unofficial transcript (signed by the counselor); cover sheet with student and parent signature. **Deadline:** February 6. **Contact:** Suzanne Trad, President; Email: suztrad@aol.com.

9592 ■ Redlands Morning Kiwanis Club Foundation Scholarships *(Graduate/Scholarship)*

Purpose: To supports the Hope of America program awarding recognition and scholarships to outstanding elementary and middle school students. **Focus:** General studies/Field of study not specified. **Qualif.:** Applicants must be graduating seniors from Redlands Unified School District high schools to assist those graduates in obtaining post secondary technical or college educations; must be planning to attend an accredited college, university, or vocational program. **Criteria:** Preference is given to those who were members of Kiwanis Club of Redlands Foundation.

Funds Avail.: $500. **To Apply:** Applicants may visit the scholarship section of the bestowing organization's website for further information regarding the application details. **Contact:** Redlands Community Scholarship Foundation; Post Office Box 1683; Redlands, CA 92373; Telephone: (909) 307-9892; Website: www.redlandsscholarship.org; Email: admin@redlandsscholarship.org.

9593 ■ Redlands Rotary Club Foundation Discretionary Scholarship *(Undergraduate/ Scholarship)*

Purpose: To assist outstanding students who are pursuing a higher education at a two-year or four-year college. **Focus:** General studies/Field of study not specified. **Qualif.:** Applicants must be graduating seniors from either Citrus Valley High School, Orangewood High School, Red-

lands East Valley High School and/or Redlands High School pursuing higher education at a two- or four-year college.

Funds Avail.: $500. **To Apply:** Applicants must submit a completed application form together with the cover sheet; Personal Information; Education; Future Plans; School Activities; Non-School Activities; Community Service; essay and an explanation of any suspension during your "High School" years. **Deadline:** February 2. **Contact:** Pam Bibo, Administrative Assistant; Email: admin@redlandsscholarships.org.

9594 ■ Redlands Rotary Club Scholarship - Donald C. Anderson *(Undergraduate/Scholarship)*

Purpose: To provide financial support to students who are in need of help in pursuing higher education. **Focus:** General studies/Field of study not specified. **Qualif.:** Applicants must be graduating seniors who have shown the highest academic achievement, outstanding citizenship and service to school and community. **Criteria:** Applicants will be selected through an interview process conducted by the Redlands Rotary Club scholarship committee.

Funds Avail.: $2,500. **To Apply:** Applicants must submit a completed application form together with the cover sheet; Personal Information; Education; Future Plans; School Activities; Non-School Activities; Community Service; essay and an explanation of any suspension during your "High School" years. **Deadline:** February 2. **Contact:** Redlands Community Scholarship Foundation, PO Box 1683, Redlands, California, 92373; Phone: 909-307-9892; Fax: 909-792-7035.

9595 ■ Redlands Rotary Club Scholarship - Ernest L. Cronemeyer *(Undergraduate/Scholarship)*

Purpose: To assist graduating high school students in their continuing education. **Focus:** General studies/Field of study not specified. **Qualif.:** Applicants must be graduating seniors who have shown the highest in academic achievements, outstanding citizenship and service to school and community. **Criteria:** Recipients will be selected through an interview process conducted by the Redlands Rotary Club scholarship committee.

Funds Avail.: $4,000. **To Apply:** Applicants must submit a completed application form together with the cover sheet; Personal Information; Education; Future Plans; School Activities; Non-School Activities; Community Service; essay and an explanation of any suspension during your "High School" years. **Deadline:** February 2. **Contact:** Pam Bibo, Administrative Assistant; Email: admin@redlandsscholarships.org.

9596 ■ Redlands Teachers Association Scholarship *(Undergraduate/Scholarship)*

Purpose: To provide a scholarship to graduating seniors who are committed to the profession of teaching. **Focus:** Teaching. **Qualif.:** Applicants must be graduating seniors who are committed to the profession of teaching; recipients must be in good standing scholastically and have good citizenship; qualified children with R.T.A. affiliations will be considered first.

Funds Avail.: $500. **Number Awarded:** Varies. **To Apply:** Applicants must submit a completed application form together with the cover sheet; Personal Information; Education; Future Plans; School Activities; Non-School Activities; Community Service; essay and an explanation of any suspension during your "High School" years. **Deadline:** February 2. **Contact:** Pam Bibo, Administrative Assistant;

Awards are arranged alphabetically below their administering organizations

Email: admin@redlandsscholarships.org.

9597 ■ Rick Munoz Memorial Scholarship
(Undergraduate/Scholarship)

Purpose: To support Redlands Unified School District graduates with their educational pursuit. **Focus:** General studies/Field of study not specified. **Qualif.:** Applicants must have lettered in at least one sport in their senior year; demonstrated high academic achievement, outstanding citizenship and a desire to continue their education. **Criteria:** Selection will be based on academic achievement, outstanding citizenship, and a desire to continue education.

Funds Avail.: $500. **To Apply:** Applicants must submit a completed application form together with the cover sheet; Personal Information; Education; Future Plans; School Activities; Non-School Activities; Community Service; essay and an explanation of any suspension during your "High School" years. **Deadline:** February 2. **Remarks:** The scholarship award was established in the memory of Rick Munoz. **Contact:** Redlands Community Scholarship Foundation, PO Box 1683, Redlands, California, 92373; Phone: 909-307-9892; Fax: 909-792-7035.

9598 ■ Robert G. Campbell Scholarship
(Undergraduate/Scholarship)

Purpose: To provide a scholarship to an outstanding student who is highly motivated, and plans to attend either a junior college or a vocational school. **Focus:** General studies/Field of study not specified. **Qualif.:** Applicant must be an above-average student who is highly motivated and planning a career.

Funds Avail.: $7,000. **Duration:** Up to 4 years. **To Apply:** Applicants must submit a completed application form together with the cover sheet; Personal Information; Education; Future Plans; School Activities; Non-School Activities; Community Service; essay and an explanation of any suspension during your "High School" years. **Deadline:** February 2. **Contact:** Pam Bibo, Administrative Assistant; Email: admin@redlandsscholarships.org.

9599 ■ Robinson G. Allen Athletic Memorial Scholarship *(Undergraduate/Scholarship)*

Purpose: To support educational pursuits among Redlands Unified School District graduates by providing educational assistance. **Focus:** General studies/Field of study not specified. **Qualif.:** Applicant must be a senior whose athletic prowess has been limited, for the most part to junior varsity teams; recipient must attend an institution of higher learning on a full-time basis. **Criteria:** Award is given based on sportsmanship, citizenship, scholarship and financial need.

Funds Avail.: $500. **To Apply:** Applicants must submit a completed application form together with the scantron sheet; cover sheet; student activity and community activity sheets; personal essay and a copy of unofficial transcript (signed by the counselor); cover sheet with student and parent signature. **Deadline:** February 6. **Contact:** Suzanne Trad, President; Email: suztrad@aol.com.

9600 ■ Charles and Ruth Ronin Memorial Scholarships *(Undergraduate/Scholarship)*

Purpose: To provide scholarship to those students who are in need to achieve their educational goal. **Focus:** Education; History; Political science. **Qualif.:** Applicants must be graduating seniors from Redlands High School with a 3.5 or higher GPA who are going to attend a four-year college/university on a full-time basis in pursuit of a bachelor's degree in political science, history, or education. **Criteria:** Primary considerations for the selection of recipients are the qualifications stated above, and financial need.

Funds Avail.: $1,000. **Duration:** Annual. **Number Awarded:** Varies. **To Apply:** Applicants must submit a completed application form together with the scantron sheet; cover sheet; student activity and community activity sheets; personal essay; and a copy of unofficial transcript (signed by the counselor). **Deadline:** February 6. **Contact:** Pam Bibo, Administrative Assistant, at admin@redlandsscholarships.org.

9601 ■ Ruth Adams Memorial Scholarship
(Undergraduate/Scholarship)

Purpose: To encourage educational pursuits among Redlands Unified School District graduates by providing educational assistance. **Focus:** General studies/Field of study not specified.

Funds Avail.: $500. **Remarks:** The award was established to Ruth Adams, a science teacher at RHS from 1951 to 1957. **Contact:** Benton Community Foundation, 660 NW Harrison Blvd; Corvallis, OR 97330; (541) 753-1603.

9602 ■ Schools first Federal Credit Union Scholarship *(Undergraduate/Scholarship)*

Purpose: To encourage educational pursuits among Redlands Unified School District graduates by providing educational assistance. **Focus:** General studies/Field of study not specified. **Qualif.:** Applicants must be high school seniors. **Criteria:** Selection is based on scholarship, participation in school and community activities.

Funds Avail.: $600. **To Apply:** Applicants must submit a completed application form together with the scantron sheet; cover sheet; student activity and community activity sheets; personal essay and a copy of unofficial transcript (signed by the counselor); cover sheet with student and parent signature. **Deadline:** February 6. **Contact:** Suzanne Trad, President; Email: suztrad@aol.com.

9603 ■ Smiley Elementary School PTA Scholarship - Beverly Roberts Memorial *(Undergraduate/Scholarship)*

Purpose: To provide a scholarship to those students who are in need to achieve their educational goal. **Focus:** General studies/Field of study not specified. **Qualif.:** Applicants must be graduating seniors from Redlands High School who attended Smiley Elementary School and are well-rounded students. **Criteria:** Primary considerations for the selection of recipients are the qualifications stated above, and financial need.

Funds Avail.: $500. **Number Awarded:** 2. **To Apply:** Applicants must submit a completed application form together with the cover sheet; Personal Information; Education; Future Plans; School Activities; Non-School Activities; Community Service; essay and an explanation of any suspension during your "High School" years. **Deadline:** February 2. **Contact:** Pam Bibo, Administrative Assistant; Email: admin@redlandsscholarships.org.

9604 ■ Soroptimist International of Redlands Scholarship *(Undergraduate/Scholarship)*

Purpose: To provide a scholarship to those students who are in need to achieve their educational goal. **Focus:** General studies/Field of study not specified. **Qualif.:** Applicants must be outstanding graduating female seniors

Awards are arranged alphabetically below their administering organizations

from Citrus Valley High School, Orangewood High School, Redlands East Valley High School and/or Redlands High School who have participated in the community service and will be attending an accredited four-year college or university, community college, or trade school in a full- or part-time basis.

Funds Avail.: $500. **To Apply:** Applicants must submit a completed application form together with the cover sheet; Personal Information; Education; Future Plans; School Activities; Non-School Activities; Community Service; essay and an explanation of any suspension during your "High School" years. **Deadline:** February 2. **Contact:** Pam Bibo, Administrative Assistant; Email: admin@redlandsscholarships.org.

9605 ■ William T. Hartzell Memorial Scholarship
(Undergraduate/Scholarship)

Purpose: To encourage educational pursuits among Redlands Unified School District graduates by providing educational assistance. **Focus:** General studies/Field of study not specified. **Qualif.:** Applicants must be a graduating senior who has maintained at least a 3.5 GPA; must attend a four year college or university on a full time basis and has attended Redlands area schools for three years or more.

Funds Avail.: $500. **To Apply:** Applicants must submit a completed application form together with the scantron sheet; cover sheet; student activity and community activity sheets; personal essay and a copy of unofficial transcript (signed by the counselor); cover sheet with student and parent signature. **Deadline:** February 6. **Remarks:** This scholarship is in memory of William T. Hartzell, a lifetime resident of Redlands who was very active in community affairs. **Contact:** Suzanne Trad, President; Email: suztrad@aol.com.

9606 ■ Reedsy Ltd.
Seedcamp 4-5 Bonhill St.
Shoreditch
London, United Kingdom
Ph: 44 20 3108 9367
URL: blog.reedsy.com
Social Media: facebook.com/wearereedsy
linkedin.com/company/reedsy
twitter.com/reedsyhq

9607 ■ The Reedsy National Creative Writing Scholarship *(Undergraduate/Scholarship)*

Purpose: To reward students who write the best first chapter of a novel. **Focus:** Creative writing. **Qualif.:** Applicant must be a U.S. citizen or permanent resident accepted to or currently enrolled in an accredited college, university, or undergraduate program in the United States, Canada, or Australia. **Criteria:** Selection will be based on the best submission.

Funds Avail.: $1,000. **Duration:** Semiannual. **Number Awarded:** 1 award twice a year. **To Apply:** Applicant must submit the first chapter (1,500 to 7,500 words) of an original novel they have written but not yet published. The application must be submitted via the online form and include the following: name, email, address, and contact number; a short bio, name or college or university attending or planning to attend; sample chapter. **Contact:** Email: scholarship@reedsy.com, Address: Reedsy Ltd. Seedcamp 4-5 Bonhill St, Shoreditch, London EC2A 4BX, Phone: +44 20 3108 9367.

9608 ■ The Clifford H. "Ted" Rees, Jr. Scholarship Foundation
2311 Wilson Blvd., Ste. 400
Arlington, VA 22201
Ph: (703)293-4854
E-mail: sperez@ahrinet.org
URL: reesscholarship.org
Social Media: www.facebook.com/ReesScholarship
twitter.com/reesscholarship
www.youtube.com/channel/UCc9xu5qFQ5zl2LeeQjgyE4g

9609 ■ Donald L. Frendberg Program *(Undergraduate, Vocational/Occupational/Scholarship)*

Purpose: To help HVAC students afford an education. **Focus:** Heating, air conditioning, and refrigeration. **Qualif.:** Must be enrolled in an HVACR training program at an institutionally accredited school in Florida.

Funds Avail.: Up to $2,000. **To Apply:** Submit application, background questions, 500-word essay, two recommendation letters, official transcripts from high school, college, or university. **Deadline:** June 1; October 1. **Contact:** Sue Perez, Program Coordinator; Phone: 703-293-4854; Email: sperez@ahrinet.org; URL: reesscholarship.org/site/292/Apply.

9610 ■ Rees Scholarship Foundation - HVACR and Water Heating Technician Program *(Community College, Undergraduate, Vocational/Occupational/Scholarship)*

Purpose: To assist with the education, recruitment, and competency of future HVACR and water heating technicians. **Focus:** Heating, air conditioning, and refrigeration. **Qualif.:** Applicant must be a U.S. citizen or permanent resident enrolled in an HVACR training program at an institutionally accredited school. **Criteria:** Selection will be based on the following criteria: personal statements, academic performance, interest in HVACR field, career goals and overcoming personal obstacles, and demonstration of financial need.

Funds Avail.: Up to $2,000. **Number Awarded:** 70. **To Apply:** Applicant must submit completed form, background questions, 500-word essay and two recommendation letters, along with official transcripts (sealed or sent directly from school). Application can be submitted at reesscholarship.org/site/292/Apply, or mailed to the address above. **Deadline:** June 1; October 1. **Contact:** Sue Perez, Program Coordinator; Phone: 703-293-4854; E-mail: sperez@ahrinet.org.

9611 ■ Rees Scholarship Foundation - Veterans Program *(Vocational/Occupational, Undergraduate/Scholarship)*

Purpose: To help a veterans attain education in the HVAC field. **Focus:** Heating, air conditioning, and refrigeration. **Qualif.:** Applicant must be a veteran enrolled in an HVACR training program at an institutionally accredited school. **Criteria:** Personal statements, academic performance, interest in the HVAC field, career goals, overcoming personal obstacles, and demonstration of financial need will be taken into consideration in committee selection of recipients.

Funds Avail.: Up to $2,000. **To Apply:** Applicant must submit completed application, background questions, 500-word essay, two recommendation letters, copy of DD214, and official transcripts from high school, college, or

Awards are arranged alphabetically below their administering organizations

university. **Deadline:** June 1; October 1. **Contact:** Sue Perez, Program Coordinator; Phone: 703-293-4854; Email: sperez@ahrinet.org; URL: reesscholarship.org/site/292/Apply.

9612 ■ Reflex Sympathetic Dystrophy Syndrome Association (RSDSA)

99 Cherry St.
Milford, CT 06460
Ph: (203)877-3790
Free: 877-662-7737
E-mail: info@rsds.org
URL: www.rsds.org
Social Media: www.facebook.com/RSDSA
www.instagram.com/rsdsa_official
www.pinterest.com/RSDSA_Official
twitter.com/RSDSA
www.youtube.com/user/RSDSAofAmerica/

9613 ■ RSDSA Research Grants *(Other/Grant)*

Purpose: To seek relevant research that will improve understanding and treatment of RSD/CRPS-1. **Focus:** Medicine; Muscular dystrophy. **Qualif.:** Applicants must be basic science or clinical research project will advance our understanding of Complex Regional Pain Syndrome. **Criteria:** Recipients are selected based on a committee's review of the proposal.

Funds Avail.: No specific amount. **Duration:** Annual. **To Apply:** Applications should contain cover page with name and all affiliations, principal supporting institution and department, administrative support, Include a letter of support from the research administration/department chairman of the research organization, contact information, principal investigator and project coordinator and proposal outline in the form of summary, background, significance, rationale, preliminary data, specific aim(s), methods, design and recruitment strategy, statistical approach including power analysis, scientific summary, detailed budget. **Remarks:** Established in 1992. **Contact:** Jim Broatch; RSDSA, 99 Cherry Street, Milford, CT 06460.

9614 ■ REFORMA: National Association to Promote Library & Information Services to Latinos and the Spanish Speaking

PO Box 832
Anaheim, CA 92815-0832
E-mail: info@reforma.org
URL: www.reforma.org
Social Media: www.facebook.com/REFORMAnational/
instagram.com/reformanational
www.youtube.com/user/REFORMAnational

9615 ■ REFORMA Scholarship *(Undergraduate, Graduate/Scholarship)*

Purpose: To provide financial assistance and to encourage Spanish-speaking individuals to pursue a career in the library or information science. **Focus:** Library and archival sciences.

Funds Avail.: $1,500 maximum. **Duration:** Annual. **To Apply:** Applicants must submit a current resume; two letters of reference from professors, employers, librarians or other professionals; an official transcript, either graduate or undergraduate. **Deadline:** March 15. **Remarks:** Established

in 1971. **Contact:** Delores Carlito, E-mail: dcarlito@uab.edu.

9616 ■ REFORMA Scholarship Program
(Undergraduate/Scholarship)

Purpose: To encourage Spanish-speaking individuals to pursue or advance a career in library and information science. **Focus:** Library and archival sciences. **Qualif.:** Applicants must be students who qualify for graduate study in Library andInformation Science; should be pursuing a degree in children andyoung adult librarianship. **Criteria:** Selection shall be based on the aforementioned applicant's qualifications and compliance with the application details; Preference is given to applicants who plan on serving Hispanic/Latinos and the Spanish-speaking community.

Funds Avail.: Up to $1,500. **Duration:** One academic year. **Number Awarded:** Varies. **To Apply:** Applicants must submit a completed application form together with official copies of college transcripts, resume and two letters of reference from professors, employers, librarians or other professionals. **Deadline:** March 15.

9617 ■ Regions Financial Corporation

1900 Fifth Ave. N
Birmingham, AL 35203-2610
Free: 800-734-4667
URL: www.regions.com
Social Media: www.facebook.com/RegionsBank
www.linkedin.com/company/regions-financial-corporation
www.pinterest.com/regionsbank
twitter.com/askregions

9618 ■ Regions Riding Forward Scholarship Essay Contest *(Undergraduate, High School/Scholarship)*

Purpose: To support the education of those who are inspired by the African-American individuals and to celebrate Black History Month. **Focus:** General studies/Field of study not specified. **Qualif.:** Applicants must either be high school seniors or college students who live in states with Regions branches (Alabama, Arkansas, Florida, Georgia, Illinois, Indiana, Iowa, Kentucky, Louisiana, Mississippi, Missouri, North Carolina, South Carolina, Tennessee or Texas) and will attend an accredited college in the United States; must be at least 13 years old and have a minimum 2.0 GPA. **Criteria:** Selection will be based on the decisions from independent panel of judges.

Funds Avail.: $5,000 each for 15 high school seniors; $3,500 each for 15 college students. **Duration:** Annual. **Number Awarded:** 30. **To Apply:** Application form must be completed online at www.regions.com/promo/black-history-scholarship. Applicant must also submit an essay (500 words or less) on the following subject: Is there a particular African-American who inspires you? Address how an African-American has been an inspiration in your life. Discuss the contributions of the African-American individual who has served to inspire and motivate you. **Deadline:** February 28.

9619 ■ Registered Psychiatric Nurses Association of Saskatchewan (RPNAS)

2055 Lorne St.
Regina, SK, Canada S4P 2M4
Ph: (306)586-4617
Fax: (306)586-6000

Awards are arranged alphabetically below their administering organizations

URL: www.rpnas.com

9620 ■ RPNAS Baccalaureate Level Program Scholarship *(Undergraduate/Scholarship)*

Purpose: To provide financial assistance to qualified individuals who want to pursue their Baccalaureate degree in psychiatric nursing. **Focus:** Nursing, Psychiatric. **Qualif.:** Applicants must hold active practicing membership with the registered Psychiatric Nurses Association of Saskatchewan with at least five successive years of psychiatric nursing practice as a Registered Psychiatric Nurse immediately preceding the current membership year; must have made a significant contribution to the profession and/or the Association beyond job responsibilities. **Criteria:** Recipient will be selected by the RPNAS Selection Committee.

Funds Avail.: $1,000. **Duration:** Annual. **Number Awarded:** 1. **To Apply:** Applicants must provide a proof of formal enrollment in a recognized, post-diploma program leading to a Baccalaureate related to psychiatric nursing; must provide a full course outline of the program; must complete the attached questionnaire. **Deadline:** May 1.

9621 ■ RPNAS Doctorate Level Program Scholarship *(Doctorate/Scholarship)*

Purpose: To provide financial assistance to qualified individuals who want to pursue their doctorate degree in psychiatric nursing. **Focus:** Nursing, Psychiatric. **Qualif.:** Applicants must hold active practicing membership with the registered Psychiatric Nurses Association of Saskatchewan, with at least five successive years of psychiatric nursing practice as a Registered Psychiatric Nurse immediately preceding the current membership year; must have made a significant contribution to the profession and/or the Association beyond job responsibilities. **Criteria:** Recipient will be selected by the RPNAS Selection Committee.

Funds Avail.: $2,000. **Duration:** Annual. **Number Awarded:** 1. **To Apply:** Applicants must provide a proof of formal enrollment in a recognized, doctorate level program leading to a doctorate degree; must provide an overview of how the doctorate will enhance the profession of psychiatric nursing (1, 000-1, 500 words, 4-6 pages); must provide a copy of dissertation to RPNAS. **Deadline:** May 1. **Contact:** Registered Psychiatric Nurses Association of Saskatchewan, 2055 Lorne St., Regina, SK, S4P 2M4; Phone: 586-4617; Fax: 586-6000.

9622 ■ RPNAS Master's Level Program Scholarship *(Master's/Scholarship)*

Purpose: To provide financial assistance to qualified individuals who want to pursue their Master's degree in psychiatric nursing. **Focus:** Nursing, Psychiatric. **Qualif.:** Applicants must hold active practicing membership with the registered Psychiatric Nurses Association of Saskatchewan with at least five successive years of psychiatric nursing practice as a Registered Psychiatric Nurse immediately preceding the current membership year; must have made a significant contribution to the profession and/or the Association beyond job responsibilities. **Criteria:** Recipient will be selected by the RPNAS Selection Committee.

Funds Avail.: $1,000 each. **Duration:** Annual. **Number Awarded:** 2. **To Apply:** Applicants must provide proof of formal enrollment in a recognized, master level program leading to a Master's degree; must complete attached questionnaire; must have made a significant contribution to the profession and/or the Association beyond the responsibilities of their job; must provide a copy of research proposal. **Deadline:** May 1. **Contact:** Registered Psychiat-

ric Nurses Association of Saskatchewan, 2055 Lorne St., Regina, SK, S4P 2M4; Phone: 586-4617; Fax: 586-6000.

9623 ■ Registry of Interpreters for the Deaf, Inc. (RID)
333 Commerce St.
Alexandria, VA 22314
Ph: (703)838-0030
Fax: (703)838-0454
E-mail: ridinfo@rid.org
URL: rid.org
Social Media: www.facebook.com/RIDInc

9624 ■ Daniel H. Pokorny Memorial Scholarship Award *(Undergraduate/Scholarship)*

Purpose: To provide financial assistance to members applying for certification. **Focus:** Hearing and deafness. **Qualif.:** Applicant must be a member in good standing at either the associate or student level for the 12 months prior toapplying; must be a current member at either the associate or student level on July 1 of the award year; must have successfully passed all portions of the written test prior to applying for performance test funding.

Funds Avail.: No specific amount. **Duration:** Annual. **Deadline:** June 1. **Contact:** Scholarship and Awards Committee, Registry of Interpreters for the Deaf, Inc., 333 Commerce St., Alexandria, VA, 22314; Email: Info@rid.org.

9625 ■ Elizabeth Benson Scholarship Award *(Undergraduate/Scholarship)*

Purpose: To provide financial assistance to members enrolled to ITP or IPP. **Focus:** Hearing and deafness. **Qualif.:** Applicants must have dual memberships; enrolled full-time or nine hours in an interpreter or transliterator program; must have completed at least one semester of ITP or IPP; have 3.0 GPA in ITP or IPP.

Funds Avail.: $500. **Duration:** Annual. **To Apply:** Applicants must submit a letter of interest or video specifying financial need; an application form (can be downloaded from the website); transcripts; three letters of recommendation (must be from an ITP or IPP chair, instructor and personal reference); copies of current RID and affiliate chapter membership card. **Deadline:** June 1. **Contact:** Scholarship and Awards Committee, Registry of Interpreters for the Deaf, Inc., 333 Commerce St., Alexandria, VA, 22314; Email: Info@rid.org.

9626 ■ Rehabmart.com
1353 Athens Hwy.
Elberton, GA 30635
Free: 800-827-8283
E-mail: assistance@rehabmart.com
URL: www.rehabmart.com
Social Media: www.facebook.com/Rehabmart
www.instagram.com/rehabmartcom
www.pinterest.com/rehabmart
twitter.com/rehabmart
www.youtube.com/user/rehabmart

9627 ■ Rehabmart.com $25,000 Scholarship Fund *(Undergraduate/Scholarship)*

Purpose: To promote awareness to the cause of making higher education accessible for students living with dis-

Awards are arranged alphabetically below their administering organizations

abilities. **Focus:** Health sciences. **Qualif.:** Applicants must be any students with disability, anyone enrolling as health sciences students, or any special education students who are currently attending a secondary school, or have been accepted to attend a secondary school, technical college, junior college, 4-year college or university; should be matriculating students and non-matriculating students. **Criteria:** Selection will be based on the submitted biography and essay.

Funds Avail.: $250 - $2,500. **Duration:** Annual. **Number Awarded:** Varies. **To Apply:** Applicants are advised to visit the website to fill out the requested information on the online application. **Deadline:** May 31.

9628 ■ J.H. Stewart Reid Memorial Fellowship Trust

c/o Canadian Association of University Teachers
Ottawa, ON, Canada K2B 8K2
E-mail: stewartreid@caut.ca
URL: stewartreid.caut.ca

9629 ■ J.H. Stewart Reid Memorial Fellowship Trust *(Doctorate/Fellowship)*

Purpose: To support students registered in a doctoral program at a Canadian University. **Focus:** General studies/ Field of study not specified. **Criteria:** Selection will be based on committee's criteria.

Funds Avail.: $5,000. **Duration:** Annual. **Number Awarded:** 1. **To Apply:** Applicants must complete the online application form and must contact the trustees through postal service, electronic mail and telephone conference call. **Deadline:** April 30. **Remarks:** Established in 1999.

9630 ■ Reiff & Bily

1500 John F. Kennedy Blvd. 501
Philadelphia, PA 19102
Ph: (215)709-6940
Fax: (215)246-9012
URL: www.reiffandbily.com

9631 ■ Reiff & Bily Legal Scholarship *(Graduate, Undergraduate/Scholarship)*

Purpose: To encourage more students to pursue the study of law. **Focus:** Law. **Qualif.:** Applicant must be current full-time student pursuing a degree in law, or pre-law; must be a citizen of the United States; must have a minimum 3.0 GPA.

Funds Avail.: $1,000. **Duration:** Annual. **Number Awarded:** 1. **To Apply:** Applicant should submit a completed application, a 650-word essay, and an official transcript. Application form available online at www.reiffandbily.com/legal-scholarship/. **Deadline:** July 1. **Contact:** Email: scholarships@reifflawfirm.com.

9632 ■ Religion Newswriters Association (RNA)

30 Neff Annex
Columbia, MO 65211-2600
Ph: (740)263-7875
URL: www.rna.org
Social Media: www.facebook.com/ReligionNewswriters
twitter.com/religionreport

9633 ■ Lilly Scholarships in Religion for Journalists *(Other/Scholarship)*

Purpose: To help journalists achieve excellence in writing and reporting in faith, values, ethics and spirituality in the news media. **Focus:** Journalism. **Qualif.:** Applicants must be journalists interested in taking college courses in religion or spirituality may apply for a scholarship program; must be full-time print and broadcast journalists in the U.S. and Canada. **Criteria:** Recipients are selected based on demonstrated interest in the field of journalism.

Funds Avail.: Up to $5,000. **To Apply:** Applications can be submitted online. **Deadline:** February 10. **Contact:** Amy Schiska at 573-355-5201, ext. 3 or email at schiska@rna.org.

9634 ■ Rentec Direct

231 SW I St.
Grants Pass, OR 97526
Ph: (541)216-6000
Fax: (888)882-1062
Free: 800-881-5139
E-mail: info@rentecdirect.com
URL: www.rentecdirect.com
Social Media: www.facebook.com/rentecdirect
twitter.com/rentec
www.youtube.com/rentecdirect

9635 ■ Tech Mastery Scholarships *(Undergraduate, Graduate/Scholarship)*

Purpose: To further support the goals and dreams of future technology influencers. **Focus:** Computer and information sciences. **Qualif.:** Applicant must be enrolled, or intend to be enrolled, full-time in a computer science degree program, or a related field, at an accredited U.S. college or university; must be in a good-standing and should have a GPA of 3.0 or higher; high school seniors planning to attend an accredited university for computer science of the following term are encouraged to apply. **Criteria:** Selection of submitted essay will be judged on the level of creativity, humor, and content.

Funds Avail.: $500. **Duration:** Annual. **Number Awarded:** Up to 4. **To Apply:** Applicants must submit an essay not to exceed 1,000 words explaining, in their view, how technology evolved to make an everlasting impact for internet based organizations in the last five years; must also submit a brief cover letter explaining why they are pursuing the degree they have chosen and how it will benefit them in their future,contact information, copy of academic transcript, and university enrollment status for current students or university acceptance letter for high school seniors or new graduate students. **Deadline:** April 15. **Contact:** Email: scholarship@rentecdirect.com; URL: www.rentecdirect.com/scholarship/.

9636 ■ RentHop

335 Madison Ave.
New York, NY 10017
URL: www.renthop.com

9637 ■ RentHop Scholarship *(Undergraduate, Two Year College/Scholarship)*

Purpose: To support eligible undergraduate students who demonstrate ambition, diligence, leadership, and entrepreneurial spirit. **Focus:** General studies/Field of study not specified. **Qualif.:** Applicant must be a current student in an eligible undergraduate program, or a graduating high school senior planning to enroll in college, who is working towards a bachelors or associates degree. **Criteria:** Es-

Awards are arranged alphabetically below their administering organizations

says are judged based on how the prompts were answered and how well essay instructions were followed.

Funds Avail.: $1,000. **Duration:** Semiannual. **To Apply:** Applicant must submit an essay on the following topic via email: Technology is changing every aspect of our daily lives, from searching for real estate to phones in our pocket that are more powerful than anyone could have imagined in previous generations. In the next five years, what do you feel will be the most profound changes that impact college graduates, their careers, and their personal lives? To what extent are these cultural and societal shifts aligned with your personal ambitions, your school degree program, and the RentHop values? **Deadline:** April 30; August 31. **Contact:** Email:college-scholarship@renthop.com.

9638 ■ Research Corporation for Science Advancement (RCSA)

4703 E Camp Lowell Dr., Ste. 201
Tucson, AZ 85712
Ph: (520)571-1111
Fax: (520)571-1119
E-mail: awards@rescorp.org
URL: www.rescorp.org
Social Media: www.facebook.com/Rescorp.org
www.linkedin.com/company/research-corporation-for
  -science-advancement
twitter.com/RCSA1

9639 ■ Cottrell Scholar Award (CSA) (Graduate, Advanced Professional, Professional development/ Award)

Purpose: To provide funding for early career faculty at US research universities and primarily undergraduate institutions. **Focus:** Science. **Qualif.:** Applicants must be tenure-track faculty members at U.S. institutions whose primary appointment is in a Bachelor's and Ph.D.-granting department of astronomy, biochemistry, biophysics, chemistry, or physics, but not in a school of medicine or engineering. **Criteria:** Selection will be based on strong and innovative research program and achieve excellence in education and their academic citizenship skills.

Funds Avail.: $100,000. **Duration:** Annual; for three years. **To Apply:** Applicants must be completed and submitted online. **Deadline:** April 15; July 1. **Remarks:** Established in 1994. **Contact:** Silvia Ronco, Senior Program Director; Email: sronco@rescorp.org; Email Richard Wiener at rwiener@rescorp.org.

9640 ■ Research and Development Corporation, Newfoundland and Labrador

68 Portugal Cove Rd.
Saint John, NL, Canada A1B 2L9
Ph: (709)758-0913
Fax: (709)758-0927
URL: www.rdc.org

9641 ■ Ocean Industry Student Research Awards (Undergraduate, Graduate, Postdoctorate/Award)

Purpose: To attract, retain and develop highly qualified people and the next generation of R&D leaders for Newfoundland and Labrador's ocean industries. **Focus:** Engineering; Science; Technology.

9642 ■ Research, Education, Advancement & Philanthropy, Inc. (REAP)

PO Box 656
Zoar, OH 44697
URL: reap2sow.org

9643 ■ The 86211 Scholarship (Undergraduate/ Scholarship)

Purpose: To help full-time entering college students with educational expenses. **Focus:** General studies/Field of study not specified. **Qualif.:** Applicant must be a U.S. citizen, 17 years of age or older, who will be entering full-time studies at an accredited postsecondary institution that offers bachelor degrees. **Criteria:** Selection based on the criteria set forth in the requirements section and documents reviewed by a panel.

Funds Avail.: $2,500. **To Apply:** Application must contain completed form and a copy each of the applicant's government-issued photo identification and of the results from admission test/s (SAT and/or ACT). **Remarks:** Limited to the first eight applicants from each high school preselected by REAP each year, for a total of 30 applicants. **Contact:** reap2sow.org/86211-scholarship.html.

9644 ■ Resources for the Future (RFF)

1616 P St. NW, Ste. 600
Washington, DC 20036
Ph: (202)328-5000
E-mail: info@rff.org
URL: www.rff.org

9645 ■ Joseph L. Fisher Doctoral Dissertation Fellowships (Graduate/Fellowship)

Purpose: To support graduate students in the final year of their dissertation research. **Focus:** Energy-related areas; Environmental conservation. **Qualif.:** Applicants must be graduate students in the final year of their dissertation research; must also have completed the preliminary examinations for their doctorate prior to the application deadline.

Funds Avail.: $18,000. **Duration:** Annual. **To Apply:** Applicants must submit a completed application form, cover letter, curriculum vitae, transcript of records, one-page abstract of the dissertation, 2,500 words technical summary of the dissertation, letter from the department chair or other university officials certifying the student's doctoral candidacy and two letters of recommendation from faculty members on the student's dissertation committee. **Deadline:** February 21. **Remarks:** Established in 1998. **Contact:** Email at: fisher-award@rff.org.

9646 ■ Responsify

495 Flatbush Ave.
Brooklyn, NY 11225
Social Media: linkedin.com/company/responsify
twitter.com/responsifynyc

9647 ■ The Responsify Empowering Others Scholarship (Undergraduate/Scholarship)

Purpose: To help students pay for college. **Focus:** General studies/Field of study not specified. **Qualif.:** Applicant must be enrolled or enrolling at a U.S. college or university in an undergraduate program. Undocumented, domestic, interna-

Awards are arranged alphabetically below their administering organizations

tional, and online students are welcome to apply. **Criteria:** Essays will be judged by a team at Responsive; they will consider personality and commitment, as well as grammar and structure.

Funds Avail.: $1,000. **Duration:** Annual. **Number Awarded:** 1. **To Apply:** Applications must be submitted online through the scholarship page. **Deadline:** October 5. **Contact:** www.responsify.com/scholarship/.

9648 ■ Restaurant Association of Maryland Education Foundation (RAMEF)

6301 Hillside Ct.
Columbia, MD 21046
Ph: (410)290-6800
Fax: (410)290-6882
Free: 800-874-1313
E-mail: mthompson@marylandrestaurants.com
URL: www.marylandrestaurants.com/foundation.html
Social Media: www.facebook.com/marylandrestaurants
www.linkedin.com/company/restaurant-association-of
  -maryland/
twitter.com/RestaurantsinMD

9649 ■ Letitia B. Carter Scholarships *(Undergraduate, Advanced Professional/Scholarship)*

Purpose: To support students who are interested in pursuing hospitality-related coursework. **Focus:** Culinary arts; Food science and technology; Food service careers; Hotel, institutional, and restaurant management. **Qualif.:** Applicants must be Maryland residents; must be high school, college, corporate instructor/teacher or hospitality industry professionals; must be pursuing hospitality-related coursework; must have applied to an RAMEF-recognized professional development program in hospitality or enrolled in a RAMEF-recognized food service/hospitality program. **Criteria:** Recipients will be selected on a competitive basis.

Funds Avail.: $500 to $2,000. **Duration:** Annual. **To Apply:** Applicants must complete the provided application form which can be downloaded from the program website. Such must be submitted together with the other prescribed requirements. Other procedures must also be followed and complied with. **Deadline:** March 24. **Remarks:** The scholarship was named in the honor of George J. Mitchell.

9650 ■ Marcia S. Harris Legacy Fund Scholarships *(Undergraduate, Advanced Professional/Scholarship)*

Purpose: To support students in the restaurant and food service industry. **Focus:** Culinary arts; Food science and technology; Food service careers; Hotel, institutional, and restaurant management. **Qualif.:** Applicants must be Maryland residents; must be high school or college students, or high school or postsecondary instructors who teach culinary arts or hospitality management courses; must be enrolled in a postsecondary or professional development course; must be pursuing hospitality-related coursework in culinary arts, hospitality management or bartending academy programs. **Criteria:** Selection will be on a competitive basis. Preference will be given to those who possess the qualities of passion and dedication and have a strong desire to improve the foodservice industry through the personal pursuit of professionalism.

Funds Avail.: $500 to $2,000. **Duration:** Annual. **To Apply:** Applicants must complete the provided application form which can be downloaded from the program website.

Such must be submitted together with the other prescribed requirements. Other procedures must also be followed and complied with. **Deadline:** March 24. **Remarks:** The scholarship was named in the honor of Marcia S. Harris.

9651 ■ NRAEF Scholarship *(Undergraduate/Scholarship)*

Purpose: To provide financial assistance to students and educators pursuing restaurant-related studies and training. **Focus:** Culinary arts; Food science and technology; Food service careers; Hotel, institutional, and restaurant management. **Qualif.:** Applicants must be graduating high school seniors; college undergraduates or GED credential holders; acceptance to, or enrollment in, an accredited restaurant or foodservice-related, post-secondary program, either full-time or substantial part-time (minimum 9 credit hours); must be Massachusetts resident; must have a minimum cumulative GPA of 2.65 on a 4.0 scale, or GED test results of 470 or more. **Criteria:** Applicants will be selected on a competitive basis by judges.

Funds Avail.: $2, 500 to $10, 000. **Duration:** Annual. **To Apply:** Applicants must submit an official current school transcript with cumulative Grade Point Average (GPA) or GED transcript with test scores; must have Guidance translate GPA to a 4.0 scale, circle GPA, and sign the transcript; signed letter of recommendation; college acceptance letter. **Deadline:** March 25. **Contact:** Stacey Sawyer, Director of Education, Massachusetts Restaurant Association Educational Foundation, 333 Turnpike Rd., Ste. 102, Southborough, MA 01772-1775; Phone: 508-573-192; E-mail: ssawyer@themassrest.org.

9652 ■ Retail Print Music Dealers Association (RPMDA)

14070 Proton Rd., Ste. 100
Dallas, TX 75244
Ph: (972)233-9107
Fax: (972)490-4219
E-mail: office@printmusic.org
URL: printmusic.org

9653 ■ RPMDA/Ed Adams Memorial Scholarships *(Other/Scholarship)*

Purpose: To encourage individuals working for print music retailers to further their education and professional development by attending the annual RPMDA convention. **Focus:** Music. **Qualif.:** Applicants must be currently working for an RPMDA member or associate member establishment; have worked for a minimum of 400 hours in the print music industry; and, exhibit a strong desire to continue to work in the print music industry; they must be under the age of 40; applicant may not have received this award previously. **Criteria:** Selection will be evaluated by the Scholarship Selection Committee.

Funds Avail.: No specific amount. **Duration:** Annual. **To Apply:** Applicants must submit a completed RPMDA or Ed Adams scholarship award application; completed employment verification from the sponsoring RPMDA member company. **Deadline:** March 8. **Remarks:** The award was established in honor of Ed Adams, an idependent sales representative, and his dedicated service to the print music industry.

9654 ■ Retired League Postmasters (RLP)

1 Beltway Ctr.
Alexandria, VA 22303

Awards are arranged alphabetically below their administering organizations

URL: www.postmasters.org/membership/become

9655 ■ Retired League Postmasters Scholarship Program (Undergraduate/Scholarship)

Purpose: To provide financial assistance for the education of children or grandchildren of active Postmasters or retired postmasters, who are members of the National League of Postmasters. **Focus:** General studies/Field of study not specified. **Qualif.:** Applicants must be children or grandchildren of active Postmasters or Retired Postmasters who are members of The National League of Postmasters. They must: be high school graduates accepted as first year students for fall admission to an accredited college, university or trade school; and, have a 3.0 Grade Point Average (GPA) overall including a 3.0 average for the last full year of high school. **Criteria:** Applicants will be evaluated based on academic performance by a certain committee for the program.

Funds Avail.: No specific amount. **To Apply:** Applicants should include a biographical letter (not more than 400 words) discussing their plans for the college years and their life goals; latest transcript from high school. **Deadline:** June 30. **Contact:** Hazel Boettcher, Scholarship Committee Chair, at hazldb@aol.com.

9656 ■ The W. Reymont Foundation
14 Hester St.
Hamilton, ON, Canada L9A 2N2
Ph: (905)574-9212
Fax: (905)574-9212
E-mail: president@reymontfoundation.com
URL: www.reymontfoundation.com

9657 ■ Blaski Alex Memorial Scholarship (Undergraduate/Scholarship)

Purpose: To provide financial support for Polish individuals in Canada who want to pursue their studies. **Focus:** General studies/Field of study not specified. **Qualif.:** Applicants must be students of Polish descent; must be either citizens or landed Immigrants; must be registered in at least the second year of a recognized program at a post secondary institution. **Criteria:** Selection will be based on scholastic achievements.

Funds Avail.: No specific amount. **Duration:** Annual. **To Apply:** Applicants may apply to the scholarship committee or download an application form from the website. **Deadline:** October 13. **Contact:** Witold Jaroszewski, Chairman, The W. Reymont Foundation, Scholarship Committee, 4949 Eramosa, 6th Ln., Rockwood, ON, N0B 2K0; Phone: 519-856-4874; Email: scholarship@reymontfoundation.com.

9658 ■ Borek Maria and Czeslaw Scholarship (Undergraduate/Scholarship)

Purpose: To provide financial support for Polish individuals in Canada who want to pursue their studies. **Focus:** General studies/Field of study not specified. **Qualif.:** Applicants must be students of Polish descent; must be either Canadian citizens or landed immigrants; must be registered in at least the second year of a recognized program at a post secondary institution; must be students from Durham/Oshawa area. **Criteria:** Selection will be based on scholastic achievements.

Funds Avail.: No specific amount. **Duration:** Annual. **To Apply:** Applicants may apply to the scholarship committee or download an application form from the website. **Deadline:** October 13. **Contact:** Witold Jaroszewski, Chairman, The W. Reymont Foundation, Scholarship Committee, 4949 Eramosa, 6th Ln., Rockwood, ON, N0B 2K0; Phone: 519-856-4874; Email: scholarship@reymontfoundation.com.

9659 ■ Dobranowski Julian Memorial Scholarship (Undergraduate/Scholarship)

Purpose: To provide financial support for Polish individuals in Canada who want to pursue their studies. **Focus:** General studies/Field of study not specified. **Qualif.:** Applicants must be students of Polish descent; must be either Canadian citizens or landed immigrants; must be registered in at least the second year of a recognized program at a post secondary institution. **Criteria:** Selection will be based on scholastic achievements.

Funds Avail.: No specific amount. **Duration:** Annual. **To Apply:** Applicants may apply to the scholarship committee or download an application form from the website. **Deadline:** October 13. **Contact:** Witold Jaroszewski, Chairman, The W. Reymont Foundation, Scholarship Committee, 4949 Eramosa, 6th Ln., Rockwood, ON, N0B 2K0; Phone: 519-856-4874; Email: scholarship@reymontfoundation.com.

9660 ■ Dr Piotrowski Adolph Memorial Art Scholarship (Undergraduate/Scholarship)

Purpose: To provide financial support for Polish individuals in Canada who want to pursue their studies. **Focus:** Visual arts. **Qualif.:** Applicants must be students of Polish descent; must be either Canadian citizens or landed immigrants; must be registered in at least the second year of a recognized program at a post secondary institution; must be paint and sculpture students. **Criteria:** Selection will be based on scholastic achievements.

Funds Avail.: No specific amount. **Duration:** Annual. **To Apply:** Applicants may apply to the scholarship committee or download an application form from the website. **Deadline:** October 13. **Contact:** Witold Jaroszewski, Chairman, The W. Reymont Foundation, Scholarship Committee, 4949 Eramosa, 6th Ln., Rockwood, ON, N0B 2K0; Phone: 519-856-4874; Email: scholarship@reymontfoundation.com.

9661 ■ Drzymala Janusz & Roma Scholarship (Undergraduate/Scholarship)

Purpose: To provide financial support for Polish individuals in Canada who want to pursue their studies. **Focus:** Engineering, Architectural; Science. **Qualif.:** Applicants must be students of Polish descent; must be either Canadian citizens or landed immigrants; must be registered in at least the second year of a recognized program at a post secondary institution; must be science and engineering students. **Criteria:** Selection will be based on scholastic achievements.

Funds Avail.: No specific amount. **Duration:** Annual. **To Apply:** Applicants may apply to the scholarship committee or download an application form from the website. **Deadline:** October 13. **Contact:** Witold Jaroszewski, Chairman, The W. Reymont Foundation, Scholarship Committee, 4949 Eramosa, 6th Ln., Rockwood, ON, N0B 2K0; Phone: 519-856-4874; Email: scholarship@reymontfoundation.com.

9662 ■ Dulemba Aleksander & Stefania Scholarship (Undergraduate/Scholarship)

Purpose: To provide financial support for Polish individuals in Canada who want to pursue their studies. **Focus:** Education, Medical. **Qualif.:** Applicants must be students of Polish descent; must be either Canadian citizens or landed im-

Awards are arranged alphabetically below their administering organizations

migrants; must be registered in at least the second year of a recognized program at a post secondary institution; must be medical students and students in financial needs. **Criteria:** Selection will be based on scholastic achievements.

Funds Avail.: No specific amount. **Duration:** Annual. **To Apply:** Applicants may apply to the scholarship committee or download an application form from the website. **Deadline:** October 13. **Contact:** Witold Jaroszewski, Chairman, The W. Reymont Foundation, Scholarship Committee, 4949 Eramosa, 6th Ln., Rockwood, ON, N0B 2K0; Phone: 519-856-4874; Email: scholarship@reymontfoundation.com.

9663 ■ Flis Walter & Anna Memorial Scholarship
(Undergraduate/Scholarship)

Purpose: To provide financial support for Polish individuals in Canada who want to pursue their studies. **Focus:** General studies/Field of study not specified. **Qualif.:** Applicants must be students of Polish descent; must be either Canadian citizens or landed immigrants; must be registered in at least the second year of a recognized program at a post secondary institution. **Criteria:** Selection will be based on scholastic achievements.

Funds Avail.: No specific amount. **Duration:** Annual. **To Apply:** Applicants may apply to the scholarship committee or download an application form from the website. **Deadline:** October 13. **Contact:** Witold Jaroszewski, Chairman, The W. Reymont Foundation, Scholarship Committee, 4949 Eramosa, 6th Ln., Rockwood, ON, N0B 2K0; Phone: 519-856-4874; Email: scholarship@reymontfoundation.com.

9664 ■ Gadzala Franciszek Memorial Scholarship
(Undergraduate/Scholarship)

Purpose: To provide financial support for Polish individuals in Canada who want to pursue their studies. **Focus:** History. **Qualif.:** Applicants must be from the University of Toronto; must be Polish history faculty students; must be born in Canada; must be registered in at least the second year of a recognized program at a post secondary institution. **Criteria:** Selection will be based on scholastic achievements.

Funds Avail.: No specific amount. **Duration:** Annual. **To Apply:** Applicants may apply to the scholarship committee or download an application form from the website. **Deadline:** October 13. **Contact:** Witold Jaroszewski, Chairman, The W. Reymont Foundation, Scholarship Committee, 4949 Eramosa, 6th Ln., Rockwood, ON, N0B 2K0; Phone: 519-856-4874; Email: scholarship@reymontfoundation.com.

9665 ■ Glogowski Franciszek Memorial Scholarship
(Undergraduate/Scholarship)

Purpose: To provide financial support for Polish individuals in Canada who want to pursue their studies. **Focus:** General studies/Field of study not specified. **Qualif.:** Applicants must be students of Polish descent; must be either Canadian citizens or landed immigrants; must be registered in at least the second year of a recognized program at a post secondary institution. **Criteria:** Selection will be based on scholastic achievements.

Funds Avail.: No specific amount. **Duration:** Annual. **To Apply:** Applicants may apply to the scholarship committee or download an application form from the website. **Deadline:** October 13. **Contact:** Witold Jaroszewski, Chairman, The W. Reymont Foundation, Scholarship Committee, 4949 Eramosa, 6th Ln., Rockwood, ON, N0B 2K0; Phone: 519-856-4874; Email: scholarship@reymontfoundation.com.

9666 ■ Juchniewicz Kazimiera Memorial Scholarship
(Undergraduate/Scholarship)

Purpose: To provide financial support for Polish individuals in Canada who want to pursue their studies. **Focus:** General studies/Field of study not specified. **Qualif.:** Applicants must be students of Polish descent; must be either Canadian citizens or landed immigrants; must be registered in at least the second year of a recognized program at a post secondary institution. **Criteria:** Selection will be based on scholastic achievements.

Funds Avail.: No specific amount. **Duration:** Annual. **To Apply:** Applicants may apply to the scholarship committee or download an application form from the website. **Deadline:** October 13. **Contact:** Witold Jaroszewski, Chairman, The W. Reymont Foundation, Scholarship Committee, 4949 Eramosa, 6th Ln., Rockwood, ON, N0B 2K0; Phone: 519-856-4874; Email: scholarship@reymontfoundation.com.

9667 ■ Kacperski Stefan & Weronika Memorial Scholarship
(Undergraduate/Scholarship)

Purpose: To provide financial support for Polish individuals in Canada who want to pursue their studies. **Focus:** General studies/Field of study not specified. **Qualif.:** Applicants must be students of Polish descent; must be either Canadian citizens or landed immigrants; must be registered in at least the second year of a recognized program at a post secondary institution. **Criteria:** Selection will be based on scholastic achievements.

Funds Avail.: No specific amount. **Duration:** Annual. **To Apply:** Applicants may apply to the scholarship committee or download an application form from the website. **Deadline:** October 13. **Contact:** Witold Jaroszewski, Chairman, The W. Reymont Foundation, Scholarship Committee, 4949 Eramosa, 6th Ln., Rockwood, ON, N0B 2K0; Phone: 519-856-4874; Email: scholarship@reymontfoundation.com.

9668 ■ Klimt Stefan & Janina Scholarship
(Undergraduate/Scholarship)

Purpose: To provide financial support for Polish individuals in Canada who want to pursue their studies. **Focus:** General studies/Field of study not specified. **Qualif.:** Applicants must be from Cambridge and other local areas; must be either Canadian citizens or landed immigrants; must be registered in at least the second year of a recognized program at a post secondary institution. **Criteria:** Selection will be based on scholastic achievements.

Funds Avail.: No specific amount. **Duration:** Annual. **To Apply:** Applicants may apply to the scholarship committee or download an application form from the website. **Deadline:** October 13. **Contact:** Witold Jaroszewski, Chairman, The W. Reymont Foundation, Scholarship Committee, 4949 Eramosa, 6th Ln., Rockwood, ON, N0B 2K0; Phone: 519-856-4874; Email: scholarship@reymontfoundation.com.

9669 ■ George Kokociski Memorial Scholarships
(Undergraduate/Scholarship)

Purpose: To provide financial support for Polish individuals in Canada who want to pursue their studies. **Focus:** General studies/Field of study not specified. **Qualif.:** Applicants must be students of Polish descent; must be either Canadian citizens or landed immigrants; must be registered in at least the second year of a recognized program at a post secondary institution. **Criteria:** Selection will be based on scholastic achievements.

Funds Avail.: No specific amount. **Duration:** Annual. **To Apply:** Applicants may apply to the scholarship committee

Awards are arranged alphabetically below their administering organizations

or download an application form from the website. **Deadline:** October 13. **Contact:** Witold Jaroszewski, Chairman, The W. Reymont Foundation, Scholarship Committee, 4949 Eramosa, 6th Ln., Rockwood, ON, N0B 2K0; Phone: 519-856-4874; Email: scholarship@reymontfoundation.com.

9670 ■ Kuropas Jan Memorial Scholarship
(Undergraduate/Scholarship)

Purpose: To provide financial support for Polish individuals in Canada who want to pursue their studies. **Focus:** General studies/Field of study not specified. **Qualif.:** Applicants must be open to students of Polish descent; must be either Canadian citizens or landed immigrants; must be registered in at least the second year of a recognized program at a post secondary institution. **Criteria:** Selection will be based on scholastic achievements.

Funds Avail.: No specific amount. **Duration:** Annual. **To Apply:** Applicants may apply to the scholarship committee or download an application form from the website. **Deadline:** October 13. **Contact:** Witold Jaroszewski, Chairman, The W. Reymont Foundation, Scholarship Committee, 4949 Eramosa, 6th Ln., Rockwood, ON, N0B 2K0; Phone: 519-856-4874; Email: scholarship@reymontfoundation.com.

9671 ■ Maziarz Tadeusz Scholarship (Undergraduate/Scholarship)

Purpose: To provide financial support for Polish individuals in Canada who want to pursue their studies. **Focus:** General studies/Field of study not specified. **Qualif.:** Applicants must be students of Polish descent; must be either Canadian citizens or landed immigrants; must be registered in at least the second year of a recognized program at a post secondary institution. **Criteria:** Selection will be based on scholastic achievements.

Funds Avail.: No specific amount. **Duration:** Annual. **To Apply:** Applicants may apply to the scholarship committee or download an application form from the website. **Deadline:** October 13. **Contact:** Witold Jaroszewski, Chairman, The W. Reymont Foundation, Scholarship Committee, 4949 Eramosa, 6th Ln., Rockwood, ON, N0B 2K0; Phone: 519-856-4874; Email: scholarship@reymontfoundation.com.

9672 ■ Michno Bronislaw Memorial Scholarship
(Undergraduate/Scholarship)

Purpose: To provide financial support for Polish individuals in Canada who want to pursue their studies. **Focus:** General studies/Field of study not specified. **Qualif.:** Applicants must be students of Polish descent; must be either Canadian citizens or landed immigrants; must be registered in at least the second year of a recognized program at a post secondary institution. **Criteria:** Selection will be based on scholastic achievements.

Funds Avail.: No specific amount. **Duration:** Annual. **To Apply:** Applicants may apply to the scholarship committee or download an application form from the website. **Deadline:** October 13. **Contact:** Witold Jaroszewski, Chairman, The W. Reymont Foundation, Scholarship Committee, 4949 Eramosa, 6th Ln., Rockwood, ON, N0B 2K0; Phone: 519-856-4874; Email: scholarship@reymontfoundation.com.

9673 ■ Nawrot Marek Memorial Scholarship
(Undergraduate/Scholarship)

Purpose: To provide financial support for Polish individuals in Canada who want to pursue their studies. **Focus:** Cartography/Surveying. **Qualif.:** Applicants must be York University students of geography or environment; must be

either Canadian citizens or landed immigrants; must be registered in at least the second year of a recognized program at a post secondary institution. **Criteria:** Selection will be based on scholastic achievements.

Funds Avail.: No specific amount. **Duration:** Annual. **To Apply:** Applicants may apply to the scholarship committee or download an application form from the website. **Deadline:** October 13. **Contact:** Witold Jaroszewski, Chairman, The W. Reymont Foundation, Scholarship Committee, 4949 Eramosa, 6th Ln., Rockwood, ON, N0B 2K0; Phone: 519-856-4874; Email: scholarship@reymontfoundation.com.

9674 ■ Pidperyhora Eleonora Scholarship
(Undergraduate/Scholarship)

Purpose: To provide financial support for Polish individuals in Canada who want to pursue their studies. **Focus:** General studies/Field of study not specified. **Qualif.:** Applicants must be students of Polish descent; must be either citizens or landed Immigrants; must be registered in at least the second year of a recognized program at a post secondary institution. **Criteria:** Selection will be based on scholastic achievements.

Funds Avail.: No specific amount. **Duration:** Annual. **To Apply:** Applicants may apply to the scholarship committee or download an application form from the website. **Deadline:** October 13. **Contact:** Witold Jaroszewski, Chairman, The W. Reymont Foundation, Scholarship Committee, 4949 Eramosa, 6th Ln., Rockwood, ON, N0B 2K0; Phone: 519-856-4874; Email: scholarship@reymontfoundation.com.

9675 ■ W. Reymont Scholarships (Undergraduate/Scholarship)

Purpose: To provide financial support for Polish individuals in Canada who want to pursue their studies. **Focus:** General studies/Field of study not specified. **Qualif.:** Applicants must be students of Polish descent; must be either Canadian citizens or landed immigrants; must be registered in at least the second year of a recognized program at a post secondary institution. **Criteria:** Selection will be based on scholastic achievements.

Funds Avail.: No specific amount. **Duration:** Annual. **To Apply:** Applicants may apply to the scholarship committee or download an application form from the website. **Deadline:** October 13. **Contact:** Witold Jaroszewski, Chairman, The W. Reymont Foundation, Scholarship Committee, 4949 Eramosa, 6th Ln., Rockwood, ON, N0B 2K0; Phone: 519-856-4874; Email: scholarship@reymontfoundation.com.

9676 ■ Rodziny Krawczyk-Krane Family Scholarship
(Undergraduate/Scholarship)

Purpose: To provide financial support for Polish individuals in Canada who want to pursue their studies. **Focus:** General studies/Field of study not specified. **Qualif.:** Applicants must be students of Polish descent; must be either Canadian citizens or landed immigrants; must be registered in at least the second year of a recognized program at a post secondary institution. **Criteria:** Selection will be based on scholastic achievements.

Funds Avail.: No specific amount. **Duration:** Annual. **To Apply:** Applicants may apply to the scholarship committee or download an application form from the website. **Deadline:** October 13. **Contact:** Witold Jaroszewski, Chairman, The W. Reymont Foundation, Scholarship Committee, 4949 Eramosa, 6th Ln., Rockwood, ON, N0B 2K0; Phone: 519-856-4874; Email: scholarship@reymontfoundation.com.

Awards are arranged alphabetically below their administering organizations

9677 ■ Chester & Maria Sadowski Memorial Scholarships (Undergraduate/Scholarship)

Purpose: To provide financial support for Polish individuals in Canada who want to pursue their studies. **Focus:** Science. **Qualif.:** Applicants must be students of Polish descent; must be either citizens or landed Immigrants; must be registered in at least the second year of a recognized program at a post secondary institution. **Criteria:** Selection will be based on scholastic achievements.

Funds Avail.: No specific amount. **Duration:** Annual. **To Apply:** Applicants may apply to the scholarship committee or download an application form from the website. **Deadline:** October 13. **Contact:** Witold Jaroszewski, Chairman, The W. Reymont Foundation, Scholarship Committee, 4949 Eramosa, 6th Ln., Rockwood, ON, N0B 2K0; Phone: 519-856-4874; Email: scholarship@reymontfoundation.com.

9678 ■ Boleslaw & Irena Sobczak Scholarships (Undergraduate/Scholarship)

Purpose: To provide financial support for Polish individuals in Canada who want to pursue their studies. **Focus:** General studies/Field of study not specified. **Qualif.:** Applicants must be students of Polish descent; must be either citizens or landed Immigrants; must be registered in at least the second year of a recognized program at a post secondary institution. **Criteria:** Selection will be based on scholastic achievements.

Funds Avail.: No specific amount. **Duration:** Annual. **To Apply:** Applicants may apply to the scholarship committee or download an application form from the website. **Deadline:** October 13. **Contact:** Witold Jaroszewski, Chairman, The W. Reymont Foundation, Scholarship Committee, 4949 Eramosa, 6th Ln., Rockwood, ON, N0B 2K0; Phone: 519-856-4874; Email: scholarship@reymontfoundation.com.

9679 ■ Lasek Stanisław and Aniela Scholarship (Undergraduate/Scholarship)

Purpose: To provide financial support for Polish individuals in Canada who want to pursue their studies. **Focus:** General studies/Field of study not specified. **Qualif.:** Applicants must be students of Polish descent; must be either Canadian citizens or landed immigrants; must be registered in at least the second year of a recognized program at a post secondary institution. **Criteria:** Selection will be based on scholastic achievements.

Funds Avail.: No specific amount. **Duration:** Annual. **To Apply:** Applicants may apply to the scholarship committee or download an application form from the website. **Deadline:** October 13. **Contact:** Witold Jaroszewski, Chairman, The W. Reymont Foundation, Scholarship Committee, 4949 Eramosa, 6th Ln., Rockwood, ON, N0B 2K0; Phone: 519-856-4874; Email: scholarship@reymontfoundation.com.

9680 ■ Reynoldsburg-Pickerington Rotary Club
PO Box 1155
Reynoldsburg, OH 43068-6155
E-mail: info@rprotaryclub.com
URL: www.rprotaryclub.com
Social Media: www.facebook.com/rprotary
www.instagram.com/rprotary

9681 ■ Reynoldsburg-Pickerington Rotary Club High School Scholarship (Undergraduate/Scholarship)

Purpose: To support graduating seniors at high schools in Reynoldsburg and Pickerington. **Focus:** General studies/

Field of study not specified. **Qualif.:** Applicants must be graduating seniors in the Reynoldsburg or Pickerington high schools and enrolled in the Eastland/Fairfield Career Center.

Funds Avail.: $1,000. **Number Awarded:** 2. **Deadline:** March 31. **Remarks:** Established in 1986.

9682 ■ The Rho Chi Society
c/o UNC Eshelman School of Pharmacy
University of North Carolina
3210 Kerr Hall, CB 7569
Chapel Hill, NC 27599-7569
Ph: (734)615-4898
E-mail: rhochisociety@umich.edu
URL: www.rhochi.org
Social Media: twitter.com/RhoChiSociety

9683 ■ Rho Chi, AFPE First Year Graduate Fellowships (Graduate/Fellowship)

Purpose: To defray the cost in conducting student's research. **Focus:** Pharmacy. **Criteria:** Selection will be based on academic achievement; research achievement; personal achievement.

Funds Avail.: $7,500. **Duration:** Annual. **Number Awarded:** 1. **To Apply:** Applicants must submit three letters of recommendation. **Deadline:** May 1. **Contact:** The Rho Chi Society, National Office, Attn: Fellowship Committee, USC School of Pharmacy, University of Southern California, 1985 Zonal Ave., PSC 700D, Los Angeles, CA, 90089-9121; Email: rhochi@usc.edu.

9684 ■ Rho Chi Society Clinical Research Scholarships (Postdoctorate/Scholarship)

Purpose: To help post-doctoral members pursue their education. **Focus:** Pharmacy. **Qualif.:** Applicants must be clinical research fellows who have completed professional studies in an ACPE accredited school or college of pharmacy; must be members of the Rho Chi Honor Society; must be U.S. citizens or permanent residents. **Criteria:** Selection will be based on academic achievement.

Funds Avail.: $7,500. **Duration:** Annual. **Number Awarded:** 1. **To Apply:** Applicants must submit three letters of recommendation. **Deadline:** December 15; February 1. **Contact:** The Rho Chi Society, C/O University of Michigan, College of Pharmacy Attn: Clinical Research Scholarship Committee, 428 Church Street Ann Arbor, MI, 48109-1065; Office: (734) 615-4898 ~ Email: RhoChiSociety@umich.edu.

9685 ■ Rhode Island Bar Association (RIBA)
41 Sharpe Dr.
Cranston, RI 02920
Ph: (401)421-5740
Fax: (401)421-2703
E-mail: info@ribar.com
URL: www.ribar.com
Social Media: www.facebook.com/RIBarAssociation
twitter.com/ribarassoc

9686 ■ Thomas F. Black Jr. Memorial Scholarship (Undergraduate/Scholarship)

Purpose: To help full-time students who are Rhode Island residents who will be entering their first year of law school.

Awards are arranged alphabetically below their administering organizations

Focus: Law. **Qualif.:** Applicants must be Rhode Island residents; must be full-time students in programs leading to the award of the LLB or JD degree offered by law schools located in the United States and accredited by the American Bar Association.

Funds Avail.: $20,000. **Duration:** Annual. **Number Awarded:** 2. **To Apply:** Applicants must submit the completed application form together with their personal statement; two letter of recommendation. **Deadline:** March 27. **Remarks:** Established in 1989. **Contact:** Rhode Island Bar Association Foundation; Phone: 401-421-5740; Fax 401-421-2703 Email: info@ribar.com.

9687 ■ Rhode Island Foundation (RIF)

1 Union Sta.
Providence, RI 02903
Ph: (401)274-4564
E-mail: info@rifoundation.org
URL: www.rifoundation.org
Social Media: www.facebook.com/rhodeislandfoundation
twitter.com/rifoundation
www.youtube.com/TheRIFoundation

9688 ■ Antonio Cirino Memorial Scholarship
(Graduate/Scholarship)

Purpose: To provide financial assistance for qualified individuals pursuing graduate education toward a master's or doctorate in order to pursue a teaching career in the arts. **Focus:** Arts. **Criteria:** Preference will be given to rhode island residents.

Funds Avail.: $2,000 to $12,000. **Duration:** Annual; up to 2 years. **To Apply:** Applicants must submit resume; one proof of Rhode Island residency (new applicants only) e.g., driver's license, voter registration card, lease samples of your work. **Remarks:** The scholarship was established in honor of antonio cirino. **Contact:** Kelly Riley, Donor Services Administrator; Phone: 401-427-4028; Email: kriley@rifoundation.org.

9689 ■ Bach Organ Scholarship (Undergraduate/ Scholarship)

Purpose: To provide financial assistance to promising music students to pursue their career. **Focus:** Education, Music. **Qualif.:** Applicants must be residents of the state of Rhode Island. Students must be currently enrolled in a college music program, majoring in organ music and they must show financial need. **Criteria:** Selection will be based on financial need.

Funds Avail.: $800 - $1,000. **Duration:** Annual. **Number Awarded:** Varies. **To Apply:** Interested applicants may contact the Foundation for more information. **Deadline:** April 21. **Remarks:** Established in 1985.

9690 ■ Bruce and Marjorie Sundlun Scholarship
(Undergraduate/Scholarship)

Purpose: To assist single parents in the pursuit of education beyond high school. **Focus:** General studies/Field of study not specified. **Qualif.:** Applicants must be Rhode island residents who are low-income single parents (men or women). **Criteria:** Preference will be given to parents currently or previously receiving state aid or those who have been previously incarcerated.

Funds Avail.: $500 to $2,000. **Duration:** Annual. **To Apply:** Applications can be submitted online. **Contact:** Kelly

Riley, Donor Services Administrator; Phone: 401-427-4028; Email: kriley@rifoundation.org.

9691 ■ Constant Memorial Scholarship
(Undergraduate/Scholarship)

Purpose: To provide support to deserving visual art or music major students intending to pursue their education. **Focus:** Education, Music; Visual arts. **Qualif.:** Applicants must be aquidneck island residents who are music or art students enrolled as freshman, sophomores, juniors, or seniors in a four-year accredited institution of higher learning. **Criteria:** Selection of applicants will be based on the scholarship selection criteria.

Funds Avail.: $2,000 to $5,000. **Duration:** Annual. **To Apply:** Applicants must complete the application form, available online; must have a copy of their financial aid award letter; must submit a recent official college transcript; three proofs of Rhode island residency; one essay; copy of their final student aid report; one letter of recommendation; and a sample of work done within the last 12 months. application forms and other supporting documents must be sent to Rhode island foundation. **Contact:** Kelly Riley, Donor Services Administrator; Phone: 401-427-4028; Email: kriley@rifoundation.org.

9692 ■ Edward Leon Duhamel Freemasons Scholarship (Undergraduate/Scholarship)

Purpose: To provide financial assistance to descendants of members of the Franklin Lodge of Freemasons in Wesley, RI. **Focus:** General studies/Field of study not specified. **Criteria:** Applicants will be selected based on the scholarship selection criteria. Preference will be given to prior year's recipients.

Funds Avail.: $500 - $1,000. **Duration:** Annual. **To Apply:** Interested applicant may contact Edward Lowe for the application process and other information. **Remarks:** Established in 1991. **Contact:** Edward Lowe, Franklin Lodge, Ste. 20, 20 Elm St, Westerly, RI, 02891; Email: ed01lowe@aol.com.

9693 ■ GFWC Women's Club of South County scholarship program (Undergraduate/Scholarship)

Purpose: To provide support for females living in Washington County who need financial assistance in order to pursue education or job training. **Focus:** General studies/Field of study not specified. **Criteria:** Selection will be based on the committee criteria.

Funds Avail.: No specific amount. **Duration:** Annual. **To Apply:** Application must submit online. **Remarks:** Established in 1997. **Contact:** Email:jcohoon@rifoundation.org.

9694 ■ Lily and Catello Sorrentino Memorial Scholarship (Undergraduate/Scholarship)

Purpose: To encourage older students to return to undergraduate school for further education. **Focus:** General studies/Field of study not specified. **Qualif.:** Applicants must be Rhode island residents who are 25 years of age or older pursuing an undergraduate degree in degree-conferring non-parochial institution in Rhode island; must also demonstrate financial need. **Criteria:** Selection will be based on the aforesaid qualifications. preference will be given to first-time applicants and to students attending rhode island college, community college of rhode island, or university of rhode island.

Funds Avail.: No specific amount. **Duration:** Annual. **Contact:** Kelly Riley, Donor Services Administrator; Phone:

Awards are arranged alphabetically below their administering organizations

401-427-4028; Email: kriley@rifoundation.org.

9695 ■ Marilynne Graboys Wool Scholarship
(Graduate/Scholarship)

Purpose: To provide tuition support to women with financial need planning to attend graduate school to attain a law degree at an accredited institution. **Focus:** Law. **Qualif.:** Applicants must be females planning to attend or registered in an accredited law school; Rhode island residents; accepted into an accredited law school; and able to demonstrate financial need. **Criteria:** Selection of will be based on the aforesaid qualifications.

Funds Avail.: $2,000. **Duration:** Annual. **To Apply:** Applications can be submitted online. **Contact:** Kelly Riley, Donor Services Administrator; Phone: 401-427-4028; Email: kriley@rifoundation.org.

9696 ■ Rhode Island Association of Former Legislators Scholarship *(Graduate/Scholarship)*

Purpose: To provide financial assistance to promising students with a distinguished record of public services. **Focus:** General studies/Field of study not specified. **Qualif.:** Applicants must be graduating high school seniors, residents of Rhode Islands and outstanding community service. **Criteria:** Selection of applicants will be based on scholarship selection criteria.

Funds Avail.: $1,500 range. **Duration:** Annual. **To Apply:** Interested applicants may contact the Foundation for more information. **Deadline:** April 27. **Remarks:** Established in 1996. **Contact:** Kelly Riley, Donor Services Administrator; Phone: 401-427-4028; Email: kriley@rifoundation.org.

9697 ■ Rhode Island Commission on Women/Freda H. Goldman Education Award *(Undergraduate/Award)*

Purpose: To provide support to individuals intending to pursue their education or job training, and assist with transportation, child-care, tutoring, educational materials, and/or other support services. **Focus:** General studies/Field of study not specified. **Qualif.:** Applicants must be Rhode island women pursuing education or job training beyond high school. **Criteria:** Preference will be given to highly motivated, self-supporting, low-income women completing first undergraduate degree or certificate program.

Funds Avail.: $500 to $2,000. **Duration:** Annual.

9698 ■ Rhode Island Space Grant Consortium
Lincoln Field Rm. 313, Box 1846
Brown University
Providence, RI 02912
E-mail: nancy_ciminelli@brown.edu
URL: www.brown.edu/initiatives/ri-space-grant
Social Media: instagram.com/brownu
twitter.com/BrownUniversity
www.youtube.com/brownuniversity

9699 ■ NASA RISGC Graduate Fellowships
(Master's, Postdoctorate, Graduate/Fellowship)

Purpose: To support graduate students who are interested in carrying out NASA-related research projects. **Focus:** Space and planetary sciences. **Criteria:** Selection will be based on the committee's criteria.

Funds Avail.: No specific amount. **To Apply:** Applicants must submit the following requirements online application;

personal information; mentors' name and email addresses; title or short description of the project; one page of.

9700 ■ Rhode Island Student Loan Authority
935 Jefferson Blvd., Ste. 3000
Warwick, RI 02886
Ph: (401)468-1700
Fax: (401)468-2196
Free: 800-758-7562
E-mail: info@risla.com
URL: www.risla.com

9701 ■ RISLA Student Loans *(Undergraduate, Graduate/Loan)*

Purpose: To cover the educational expenses of students attending eligible Rhode Island schools. **Focus:** General studies/Field of study not specified. **Qualif.:** Applicants must be Rhode Island residents attending eligible in-state schools or out-of-state schools and students from outside of Rhode Island who are attending eligible Rhode Island schools; must be either undergraduate or graduate students; must be full-time, half-time, less than half-time, matriculating or non-matriculating students. **Criteria:** Selection will be based on credit check approval and other eligibility requirements.

Funds Avail.: Varies. **Duration:** Annual. **To Apply:** Applicants must visit the website for the online application process and to choose the loan term.

9702 ■ Bryon Riesch Paralysis Foundation (BRPF)
PO Box 1388
Waukesha, WI 53187-1388
Ph: (262)547-2083
E-mail: info@brpf.org
URL: www.brpf.org
Social Media: www.facebook.com/American.Counseling.Association
twitter.com/BRPFcure

9703 ■ Bryon Riesch Paralysis Foundation Research Grants *(Professional development/Grant)*

Purpose: To promote new and exciting research in the field of paralysis. **Focus:** Spinal cord injuries and research. **Criteria:** Selection will be based on the submitted applications.

Funds Avail.: No specific amount. **Duration:** Annual. **To Apply:** Applicants must submit an application in the following order title of research; principal investigator; title (title and degrees of PI and co-investigator if applicable); principal investigator present appointment; signature of principal investigator; fiscal officer; contract officer; check payable to; personnel; equipment; animal and supplies itemize purchases over $1000; nontechnical abstract; key words; relationship to BROF priorities; narrative describing the specific objective of the project and hypothesis, the prior research/theory behind the project; the methods and experimental design; and equipment/facilities to be used; must be maximum of five pages, single-space and 12 pt. Font; must also include references. **Deadline:** December 20. **Contact:** Bryon Riesch Paralysis Foundation, PO Box 1388, Waukesha, WI, 53187-1388; Phone: 262-547-2083; E-mail: info@brpf.org.

Awards are arranged alphabetically below their administering organizations

9704 ■ The Right Staff, LLC

7550 France Ave. S
Edina, MN 55435
Ph: (952)546-1100
Fax: (952)544-6967
URL: www.therightstaff.com
Social Media: www.facebook.com/therightstaff
www.linkedin.com/company/78521
twitter.com/THERIGHTSTAFF1
www.youtube.com/user/therightstaff

9705 ■ Amy Affolter Memorial Scholarship Program
(College, Vocational/Occupational/Scholarship)

Purpose: To provide financial assistance to external employees of THE RIGHT STAFF. **Focus:** General studies/Field of study not specified. **Qualif.:** Applicants must be students working on assignment through the Right Staff firm. **Criteria:** The organization's scholarship committee will make the selection.

Funds Avail.: $500. **Duration:** Annual. **Number Awarded:** 2. **Remarks:** The scholarship was named in memory of Amy Affolter, Vice President and Managing Partner of THE RIGHT STAFF. **Contact:** Email: hr@therightstaff.com.

9706 ■ Rising Farmworker Dream Fund (RFDF)

171 Main St., Ste. 230
Los Altos, CA 94022
E-mail: exchange@risingfarmworkers.org
URL: rfdf.org
Social Media: www.facebook.com/groups/rfdfexchange/about
www.linkedin.com/in/rfdf-exchange
twitter.com/rfdf_exchange

9707 ■ RFDF-MBA Fellowship *(Graduate/Fellowship)*

Purpose: To encourage the sons and daughters of farmworkers to purse MBA degrees and in turn, develop more leaders who will channel resources to the U.S. farmworking community. **Focus:** Business. **Qualif.:** Applicants must be a sons and daughters of U.S. Based Farmworkers applying to a graduate business school program within 3 years.

Funds Avail.: $250-$10,000. **Duration:** Annual; 3 years. **To Apply:** Applicants must complete the application online.

9708 ■ RFDF MBA Preparation Fellowships
(Graduate/Fellowship)

Purpose: To encourage the sons and daughters of farmworkers to purse MBA degrees and in turn, develop more leaders who will channel resources to the U.S. farmworking community. **Focus:** Business. **Qualif.:** Applicants must be a sons and daughters of U.S. Based Farm workers.

Funds Avail.: $250-$10,000. **Duration:** Annual; 3 years. **To Apply:** Applicants must complete the application online.

9709 ■ Riverside Sheriffs Association (RSA)

21810 Cactus Ave.
Riverside, CA 92518
Ph: (951)653-5152
Fax: (951)653-1943
Free: 800-655-4772
URL: www.rcdsa.org
Social Media: www.facebook.com/RiversideSheriffsAssoc

www.instagram.com/rsa1943
twitter.com/rsa1943

9710 ■ Riverside Sheriffs Association Member Scholarship Program *(Graduate, Undergraduate/Scholarship)*

Purpose: To assist members of the Riverside Sheriffs' Association (RSA) who have plans to continue their education in college or university. **Focus:** General studies/Field of study not specified. **Qualif.:** Applicants must be members of RSA; have earned at least an associate or equivalent degree; and must be accepted or plan to enroll in an undergraduate or graduate course of study on a full-time or part-time basis. **Criteria:** Awards will be given to applicants who meet the required qualifications.

Funds Avail.: $5,000. **Duration:** Annual. **Number Awarded:** 4. **To Apply:** Applicants must complete the application form and mail it along with a current transcript of grades. **Deadline:** March 31. **Contact:** Riverside Sheriffs' Association Member Scholarship Program, Scholarship America, 1 Scholarship Way, Saint Peter, MN, 56082; Phone: 507-931-1682.

9711 ■ RJT Criminal Defense Lawyers

2820 Camino Del Rio S, Ste. 110
San Diego, CA 92108
Ph: (619)577-0868
E-mail: info@sandiegocriminallawyerrt.com
URL: www.sandiegocriminallawyerrt.com
Social Media: www.facebook.com/RJT-Criminal-Defense-945251592197944
www.instagram.com/rjtdefense/
linkedin.com/company/rjt-criminal-defense/about

9712 ■ Autism Scholarship *(Two Year College, Four Year College, Vocational/Occupational/Scholarship)*

Purpose: To help students with autism attend college. **Focus:** General studies/Field of study not specified. **Qualif.:** Applicants must be an U.S. citizen who has been diagnosed with autism spectrum disorder (ASD) who would like to pursue their education at a trade school, college, junior college, university.

Funds Avail.: $1,000. **To Apply:** Applicants must complete online application; upload a short statement (150 words or less) setting forth educational goals. Optional: upload an essay (750 words or less) discussing the impact autism has had on applicant's education. **Deadline:** February 14. **Contact:** Email: mike@sandiegocriminallawyerrt.com.

9713 ■ Disabled Veteran Scholarship *(College, Vocational/Occupational/Scholarship)*

Purpose: To offset some of the tuition cost associated with attendance at a trade school or college. **Focus:** General studies/Field of study not specified. **Qualif.:** Applicants must a disabled veteran of any branch of the U.S. Armed Forces with a disability of at least 30%.

Funds Avail.: $1,000. **To Apply:** Applicants must complete online application; upload a short statement setting forth your educational goals. Optional: upload an essay consisting of 1,000 words or less discussing how your military service has affected applicant's life. **Deadline:** February 13.

9714 ■ Law School Scholarship *(Graduate/Scholarship)*

Purpose: To ease the road toward completion of a student's legal education. **Focus:** Law. **Qualif.:** Applicants

---

Awards are arranged alphabetically below their administering organizations

must be a U.S. citizens currently attending ABA-accredited law school or who will be attending law school in the near future.

Funds Avail.: $1,000. **To Apply:** Applicants must complete online application; upload a brief statement (175 words or less) describing how they intend to utilize their law degree. Optional: upload a statement (1,000 words or less) of how they think their law degree will enable them to make a positive impact on society. **Deadline:** February 22.

9715 ■ RKT Publishing LLC
PO Box 1033
East Dennis, MA 02641
URL: girlswhostem.com

9716 ■ Girls in Stem (GIS) Scholarship
(Undergraduate/Scholarship)

Purpose: To help students pursuing careers in STEM fields. **Focus:** Engineering; Mathematics and mathematical sciences; Science; Technology. **Qualif.:** Applicant must be currently enrolled in good standing in any STEM related area of study at an accredited undergraduate program in the United States; have a demonstrated history of working in (through advocacy, community involvement, or research efforts) any STEM field or any involvement in programs that advocates access to STEM education and professions for girls and women; have a demonstrated financial need; and have a current overall GPA of 3.0 or higher. **Criteria:** Selection will be made by the GIS Scholarship Award committee members, who will score each submission and essay on a scale of 1 to 20 based on merit and need factors.

Funds Avail.: $500. **Duration:** Annual. **Number Awarded:** 1. **To Apply:** Applicant must submit first and last name, email address, phone number, current college or university, current GPA, expected graduation date, and current course of study, along with a one to two page essay covering the following: 1. Why you've chose to pursue a career in stem; 2. What your specific extracurricular experience is working with STEM related projects; and 3. How you intend to use this award (include any pictures that demonstrate extracurricular efforts). All information should be submitted via email. **Deadline:** December 31.

9717 ■ Roanoke Bar Association (RBA)
PO Box 18183
Roanoke, VA 24014
Ph: (540)342-4905
E-mail: rba@roanokebar.com
URL: www.roanokebar.com

9718 ■ Jane S. Glenn Memorial Endowed Scholarship *(Undergraduate/Scholarship)*

Purpose: To provide financial assistance to those deserving law students. **Focus:** Law. **Criteria:** Selection shall be based on demonstrated diligence in and commitment to studies, academic excellence and an interest in the pursuit of law.

Funds Avail.: No specific amount. **Duration:** Annual. **Number Awarded:** 1. **To Apply:** Applicants must include an original application, typewritten or completed in black ink, which must be postmarked no later than the deadline, and must be accompanied by the two letters of recommendation dated during the current school year, one of which must be from a teacher or instructor; a statement of 250

words or less on why the applicants has chosen to pursue an education in the law; and an official copy of the applicant's latest grade transcript (3.0 GPA minimum required). **Deadline:** March 31. **Remarks:** The Scholarship was established in memory of Jane S. Glenn. Established in 2007. **Contact:** Roanoke Law Foundation, PO Box 18183, Roanoke, VA 24014; Email: rba@roanokebar.com.

9719 ■ James N. Kincanon Scholarship
(Undergraduate/Scholarship)

Purpose: To provide financial assistance to those students who want to pursue a legal education. **Focus:** Law. **Criteria:** Selection shall be based on demonstrated diligence in and commitment to studies, academic excellence and an interest in the pursuit of law.

Funds Avail.: No specific amount. **Duration:** Annual. **Number Awarded:** 1. **To Apply:** Applicants must include an original application, typewritten or completed in black ink, which must be postmarked no later than the deadline, and must be accompanied by the two letters of recommendation dated during the current school year, one of which must be from a teacher or instructor; a statement of 250 words or less on why the applicants has chosen to pursue an education in the law; and an official copy of the applicant's latest grade transcript (3.0 GPA minimum required). **Deadline:** March 31. **Remarks:** The Scholarship was established in honor of James N. Kincanon, Esq., by the Roanoke Law Foundation (formerly known as the Roanoke Bar Association Foundation). Established in 1997. **Contact:** Roanoke Law Foundation, PO Box 18183, Roanoke, VA 24014; Email: rba@roanokebar.com.

9720 ■ Robert and Patricia Switzer Foundation
94 Main St.
Belfast, ME 04915
Ph: (207)338-5654
Fax: (207)338-5655
E-mail: info@switzernetwork.org
URL: www.switzernetwork.org
Social Media: www.facebook.com/SwitzerFoundation
twitter.com/switzernetwork

9721 ■ Switzer Environmental Fellowship *(Graduate/Fellowship)*

Purpose: To support highly talented graduate students in New England and California whose studies are directed toward improving environmental quality and who are able to demonstrate potential leadership in their field. **Focus:** Environmental conservation; Environmental law; Environmental science; Environmental technology. **Qualif.:** Applicants must be U.S. citizens; must be enrolled full-time in an accredited graduate institution in California or New England; must have strong academic qualifications; must have academic and career goals focused on environmental improvement. **Criteria:** Selection will be based on leadership experience and potential; applied focus; career goals and commitment.

Funds Avail.: $15,000. **Duration:** Annual. **To Apply:** Applicants must submit a completed application form; original essay (maximum of three pages); two professional recommendation letters; resume; most recent academic transcripts; brief outline of general course of study; evidence of financial need. **Remarks:** Established in 1986.

9722 ■ Jackie Robinson Foundation (JRF)
1 Hudson Sq., 2nd Fl.
75 Varick St.
New York, NY 10013-1917

Awards are arranged alphabetically below their administering organizations

Ph: (212)290-8600
Fax: (212)290-8081
URL: www.jackierobinson.org
Social Media: www.facebook.com/jrf42
instagram.com/jrfoundation
www.linkedin.com/jackie-robinson-foundation
pinterest.com/jackierobinsonf
twitter.com/JRFoundation

9723 ■ Jackie Robinson Scholarship Award
(Undergraduate/Scholarship)

Purpose: To financially support minority students in attaining higher educational pursuits. **Focus:** General studies/Field of study not specified. **Qualif.:** Applicant must be a minority high school student showing leadership potential and demonstrating financial need to attend an accredited 4-year college or university; be a graduating high school senior;be a United States citizen; have a minimum SAT score of 1,000 combined on the math and critical reading sections or a composite ACT score of 21. **Criteria:** Awards are given based on leadership potential, dedication to community service, financial need.

Funds Avail.: Up to $30,000. **Duration:** Up to 4 years. **Number Awarded:** 1. **To Apply:** Applicants must submit online application, which includes four essay questions; a letter of recommendation; professional, hi-resolution digital photo; SAT or ACT scores. **Deadline:** February 1. **Contact:** Infosnap, Inc., Email: customerservice@infosnap.com.

9724 ■ Rocky Mountain American Association of Collegiate Registrars and Admission Officers (RMACRAO)
c/o Stacy Sharp, President
University of Northern Colorado
Greeley, CO 80639
URL: www.rmacrao.org

9725 ■ RMACRAO Professional Development Scholarship *(Professional development/Scholarship)*

Purpose: To assist the RMACRAO membership and RMACRAO member institutions in its commitment to professional development for registrar and admissions officers. **Focus:** General studies/Field of study not specified. **Qualif.:** Applicants must be Individuals who are awarded this scholarship will be expected to either write an article for the RMACRAO Newsletter about their professional development opportunity or make a presentation.

Funds Avail.: $750. **Duration:** Annual. **Number Awarded:** 2. **To Apply:** Applicants must provide a photocopy of expense report to the RMACRAO Treasurer. **Deadline:** October 1.

9726 ■ Rocky Mountain Coal Mining Institute (RMCMI)
3900 S. Wadsworth Blvd, Suite 365
Lakewood, CO 80235
Ph: (303)948-3300
Fax: (303)954-9004
URL: www.rmcmi.org
Social Media: www.facebook.com/Rocky-Mountain-Coal-Mining-Institute-RMCMI-196321237078383

9727 ■ Rocky Mountain Coal Mining Institute Engineering/Geology Scholarships *(Four Year College/Scholarship)*

Purpose: To provide financial aid for junior and senior year students who are looking for a career in the coal industry.

Focus: Engineering; Engineering, Geological. **Qualif.:** Applicants must be full-time college sophomores or juniors at the time of selection; must be both U.S. citizens and legal residents of one of the Rocky Mountain Coal Mining Institute member states Arizona, Colorado, Montana, New Mexico, North Dakota, Texas, Utah, or Wyoming; must be pursuing a degree in a mining-related field or in the engineering disciplines; and must be interested in coal as a career path. **Criteria:** Recipients are selected based on Scholarship committee's review of the application materials.

Funds Avail.: $2,750 per year. **Duration:** Annual; two years. **To Apply:** Applicants must include the following: an autobiography (150 words or less), any academic and athletic honors, extra-curricular activities, and why you feel you deserve this scholarship; three references; work experience and answers to the following questions (limiting each to 100 words or less): why are you pursuing your present degree?; hat do you envision doing after graduation?. **Deadline:** February 1. **Contact:** The Rocky Mountain Coal Mining Institute; 3900 S. Wadsworth Blvd., Ste 365, Lakewood, CO 80235; Phone: 303/948-3300; Fax: 303/954-9004; mail@rmcmi.org.

9728 ■ Rocky Mountain Coal Mining Institute Technical Scholarships *(Two Year College/Scholarship)*

Purpose: To provide financial aid for students enrolled in technical programs who would like to pursue their education in the coal industry. **Focus:** Energy-related areas. **Qualif.:** Applicants must be first-year students at a two-year Technical/Trade School in a good standing at the time of selection; must be U.S. citizens and legal residents of one of the Rocky Mountain Coal Mining Institute member states - Arizona, Colorado, Montana, New Mexico, North Dakota, Texas, Utah, or Wyoming; must be studying an applicable trade and interested in coal as a career path. **Criteria:** Recipients are selected based on the scholarship committee's review of the application materials.

Funds Avail.: $1,000. **Duration:** Annual; one year. **To Apply:** Applicants must include the following: Three references. Include name, address, business and home phone number, company or business name, and years acquainted; three references; work experience and answers to the following questions (limiting each to 100 words or less): If you could pick any job, what would it be and why?; why are you pursuing your present degree?; what are your plans after graduation?; personal statement (i.e. why you are applying for this scholarship, special skills or training, etc.). **Deadline:** February 1. **Remarks:** Established in 2007. **Contact:** The Rocky Mountain Coal Mining Institute; 3900 S. Wadsworth Blvd., Ste 365, Lakewood, CO 80235; Phone: 303/948-3300; Fax: 303/954-9004; mail@rmcmi.org.

9729 ■ Rocky Mountain Conservancy
PO Box 3100
Estes Park, CO 80517-3100
Ph: (970)586-0108
URL: www.rmconservancy.org
Social Media: www.facebook.com/RockyMountainConservancy
www.instagram.com/rmconservancy

9730 ■ RMNP Research Fellowship *(Graduate/Fellowship)*

Purpose: To encourage highly qualified graduate students to apply their talents to conducting research in the national

Awards are arranged alphabetically below their administering organizations

parks. **Focus:** General studies/Field of study not specified. **Criteria:** Selection will be based on committee's criteria.

Funds Avail.: $8,000; plus up to $3,000 for expenses related to research. **Duration:** Annual; from 3 to 4 months. **Number Awarded:** 1. **To Apply:** Applicants must submit a preliminary research proposal and the chosen fellow will be expected to convey research findings to the general public as well as to professional audiences. **Deadline:** February 1. **Contact:** Rachel Balduzzi, Field Institute Director; Phone: 970-586-3262 ext. 301; Email: rachel.balduzzi@ rmconservancy.org.

9731 ■ Rocky Mountain Mineral Law Foundation (RMMLF)

9191 Sheridan Blvd. Suite 203
Westminster, CO 80031
Ph: (303)321-8100
Fax: (303)321-7657
Free: 844-838-0790
E-mail: info@rmmlf.org
URL: www.rmmlf.org
Social Media: www.facebook.com/
   rockymountainminerallawfoundation
twitter.com/rmmlf

9732 ■ Joe Rudd Scholarships *(Graduate/ Scholarship)*

Purpose: To encourage the study of natural resources law by well-qualified law students who have the potential to make significant contributions to scholarship in natural resources law. **Focus:** Law. **Criteria:** Selection will be based on the following criteria:potential to make a significant contribution to the field of natural resources law;academic ability;leadership ability;year in law school;financial need.

Funds Avail.: Amount varies. **Duration:** Annual. **Number Awarded:** Varies. **To Apply:** Applicants must download the application form (in Word or PDF format); please email the complete application form and supporting documents. **Deadline:** February 28. **Remarks:** The scholarship was established in honor of Joe Rudd, a prominent natural resources attorney in Alaska. Established in 1979. **Contact:** Email: scholarships@rmmlf.org; Phone: 303-321-8100.

9733 ■ Ronald McDonald House Charities (RMHC)

110 North Carpenter St.
Chicago, IL 60607
Ph: (630)623-7048
E-mail: info@rmhc.org
URL: www.rmhc.org
Social Media: www.facebook.com/rmhcglobal
instagram.com/rmhc
pinterest.com/rmhc
twitter.com/rmhc
youtube.com/user/RMHCGlobal

9734 ■ RMHC African American Future Achievers Scholarship *(Undergraduate/Scholarship)*

Purpose: To support students to afford the education of their dreams. **Focus:** General studies/Field of study not specified. **Qualif.:** Applicants must be current high school senior; must be less than 21 years of age; must be eligible to attend a two- or four-year college or university vocational/

technical school; must be legal residents of the United States; must be living in a participating local RMHS Chapter's geographic area. **Criteria:** Selection will be based on financial need, community involvement, essay content, academic achievements and records.

Funds Avail.: Minimum of $1,000. **To Apply:** Applicants must complete the online application form providing supporting documents, recommendation letter, official & unofficial transcripts. **Deadline:** January 18. **Contact:** Phone: 866-664-0236; Email: RMHC@applyISTS.com.

9735 ■ RMHC Asia Scholarship *(Undergraduate/ Scholarship)*

Purpose: To support students to afford the education of their dreams. **Focus:** General studies/Field of study not specified. **Qualif.:** Applicants must be current high school senior; must be less than 21 years of age; must be eligible to attend a two- or four-year college or university vocational/ technical school; must be legal residents of the United States; must be living in a participating local RMHS Chapter's geographic area. **Criteria:** Selection will be based on financial need, community involvement, essay content, academic achievements and records.

Funds Avail.: Minimum of $1,000. **To Apply:** Applicants must complete the online application form providing supporting documents, recommendation letter, official & unofficial transcripts. **Deadline:** January 18. **Contact:** Phone: 866-664-0236; Email: RMHC@applyISTS.com.

9736 ■ RMHC HACER Scholarship *(Undergraduate/ Scholarship)*

Purpose: To support students to afford the education of their dreams. **Focus:** General studies/Field of study not specified. **Qualif.:** Applicants must be current high school senior; must be less than 21 years of age; must be eligible to attend a two- or four-year college or university vocational/ technical school; must be legal residents of the United States; must be living in a participating local RMHS Chapter's geographic area. **Criteria:** Selection will be based on financial need, community involvement, essay content, academic achievements and records.

Funds Avail.: Minimum of $1,000. **To Apply:** Applicants must complete the online application form providing supporting documents, recommendation letter, official & unofficial transcripts. **Deadline:** January 18. **Contact:** Phone: 866-664-0236; Email: RMHC@applyISTS.com.

9737 ■ Ronald McDonald House Charities Scholarship *(Undergraduate/Scholarship)*

Purpose: To help high school seniors to pursue their educational goals. **Focus:** General studies/Field of study not specified. **Qualif.:** Applicants must be current high school senior; must be less than 21 years of age; must be eligible to attend a two- or four-year college or university vocational/technical school; must be legal residents of the United States; must be living in a participating local RMHS Chapter's geographic area. **Criteria:** Selection will be based on financial need, community involvement, essay content, academic achievements and records.

Funds Avail.: Minimum of $1,000. **To Apply:** Applicants must complete the online application form providing supporting documents, recommendation letter, official & unofficial transcripts. **Deadline:** January 18. **Contact:** Phone: 866-664-0236; Email: RMHC@applyISTS.com.

9738 ■ Roofing Industry Alliance for Progress

10255 W Higgins Rd., Ste. 600
Rosemont, IL 60018

Awards are arranged alphabetically below their administering organizations

URL: www.roofingindustryalliance.net
Social Media: www.facebook.com/RoofingAlliance
www.linkedin.com/company/roofingalliance
www.instagram.com/roofingalliance
twitter.com/alliancenrca

9739 ■ Melvin Kruger Endowed Scholarship Program *(Graduate, Undergraduate/Scholarship)*

Purpose: To help employees and their families who plan to pursue post-secondary education in college and vocational programs. **Focus:** General studies/Field of study not specified.

Remarks: The scholarship was established in memory of Melvin Kruger. **Contact:** Bennett Judson, Executive Director; Toll: 800-323-9545 ext. 7513; Email: bjudson@ roofingalliance.net.

9740 ■ The Roothbert Fund, Inc.

475 Riverside Dr., Rm. 1622
New York, NY 10115
Ph: (212)870-3116
E-mail: mail@roothbertfund.org
URL: www.roothbertfund.org
Social Media: www.pinterest.com/pin/
526287906441668479

9741 ■ Roothbert Fund Scholarships *(Undergraduate, Graduate/Scholarship)*

Purpose: To provide financial assistance to both men and women who wants to further their education. **Focus:** General studies/Field of study not specified. **Criteria:** Preference will be given to those who can satisfy high scholastic requirements and are considering careers in education.

Funds Avail.: Averaging $2,000-$3,000. **Duration:** Annual. **Number Awarded:** 20. **To Apply:** Completed online application form along with all letters of recommendation and transcripts must be submitted.

9742 ■ Rosenfeld Injury Lawyers LLC

225 W Wacker Dr., No. 1760
Chicago, IL 60606
Ph: (847)835-8895
Fax: (847)572-1331
Free: 888-424-5757
URL: www.rosenfeldinjurylawyers.com
Social Media: www.facebook.com/Rosenfeld.Injury
.Lawyers
www.linkedin.com/company/rosenfeld-injury-lawyers
www.youtube.com/user/rosenfeldinjurylaw

9743 ■ Single Mother Scholarship *(Undergraduate, Graduate, College, University/Scholarship)*

Purpose: To expand opportunities for single mothers who want to go back to school. **Focus:** General studies/Field of study not specified; Law. **Qualif.:** Applicant must be enrolled in an accredited high school, college, or university in the U.S. and enrolled or planning to enroll in an undergraduate or law degree program; must maintain a minimum 3.0 GPA; and must be a single mother. **Criteria:** One scholarship will go to an undergraduate student and one to a law student.

Funds Avail.: $1,000 each. **Number Awarded:** 2. **To Apply:** Submit copy of transcripts, write a 500+ word essay

on the advantages of going back to school while caring for children as a mother. Email submission to Jonathan@ rosenfeldinjurylawyers.com, must include "Scholarship" in the subject field. **Deadline:** December 5. **Contact:** URL: www.rosenfeldinjurylawyers.com/scholarship.html.

9744 ■ The Rotary Foundation

1560 Sherman Ave.
Evanston, IL 60201
URL: www.ilsos.gov

9745 ■ Rotary Foundation Global Grant Scholarships Supplement *(Graduate/Scholarship, Grant)*

Purpose: To support graduate students who are planning a career in a fields that support the Rotary's efforts to promote peace, fight disease, provide clean water, save mother and children, support education, and grow local economies. **Focus:** General studies/Field of study not specified. **Criteria:** Selection will be based on the Rotary's criteria.

Funds Avail.: No specific amount. **To Apply:** Applicants may contact their respective local Rotary clubs for further information.

9746 ■ Rove Pest Control

1043 Grand Ave.
Saint Paul, MN 55105
Ph: (651)433-6355
URL: www.rovepestcontrol.com
Social Media: www.facebook.com/roveminnesota
twitter.com/RovePestControl

9747 ■ Rove Pest Control Scholarships *(Undergraduate/Scholarship)*

Purpose: To support students seeking higher education. **Focus:** Entomology. **Qualif.:** Applicants must be high school seniors or high school graduates nationwide in United States of America.; must be accepted to a college and enrolled in courses full-time; must have a minimum GPA of 3.0. **Criteria:** Selection will be judged primarily on academic achievement, but financial need may also be considered; special consideration will be given to anyone pursuing a degree in entomology or a related field.

Funds Avail.: $500. **To Apply:** Applications can be submitted online; Applicants must submit a completed application and a transcript with counselor or school representative signature. **Deadline:** January 31.

9748 ■ Travis Roy Foundation

60 State St., 8th Fl.
Boston, MA 02109
Ph: (617)619-8257
Fax: (617)227-0781
E-mail: contact@travisfoundation.org
URL: www.travisfoundation.org
Social Media: www.facebook.com/travisroyfoundation
www.linkedin.com/company/travis-roy-foundation
twitter.com/TRFoundation

9749 ■ Travis Roy Foundation Individual Grants *(All/Grant)*

Purpose: To provide assistance to spinal cord injury survivors. **Focus:** Spinal cord injuries and research. **Qua-**

Awards are arranged alphabetically below their administering organizations

lif.: Applicants must be spinal cord injury survivors with paraplegia and quadriplegia; must demonstrate financial need and may be required to provide documentation; must be US residents.

Funds Avail.: No specific amount. **To Apply:** Applicants must complete all questions of the applications in order to be considered for a Travis Roy Foundation Individual Grant, including contact information and estimates from at least two suppliers and/or contractors for the equipment or renovations requested in the application. **Contact:** Travis Roy Foundation, 101 Huntington Ave., Ste 520, Boston, MA 02199.

9750 ■ Royal Canadian Regiment Association (RCR)
PO Box 9999
Petawawa, ON, Canada K8H 2X3
URL: thercr.ca

9751 ■ Royal Canadian Regiment Association Bursaries *(Undergraduate/Scholarship)*

Purpose: To support the education of the relatives of serving, former serving or deceased members of The Royal Canadian Regiment. **Focus:** General studies/Field of study not specified. **Criteria:** Selection will be based on scholastic achievement, community service activities, military/cadet service (if any) and family financial position.

Duration: Annual. **To Apply:** Completed application along with a secondary school principal's recommendation (A letter from the applicant's homeroom teacher in lieu of the principal's recommendation would be acceptable); letter of acceptance for first-year enrolment from an institute of higher learning; a letter of recommendation from unit CO or ERE mentor (for serving members, spouse or a cadet); transcript of your final grades from a secondary school must be submitted.**Contact:** Bursary Committee, The RCR Association, RHQ, The Royal Canadian Regiment, PO Box 9999 Station Main, Petawawa, ON K8H 2X3.

9752 ■ Lucille and Edward R. Roybal Foundation
5253 East Beverly Boulevard
Los Angeles, CA 90022
E-mail: info@roybalfoundation.org
URL: www.roybalfoundation.org
Social Media: www.facebook.com/theroybalfoundation/?hc
_ref=SEARCH

9753 ■ Lucille and Edward R. Roybal Foundation Public Health Scholarships *(Graduate, Undergraduate/Scholarship)*

Purpose: To support graduate and undergraduate Hispanic students pursuing degrees in public health related programs. **Focus:** Nursing; Optometry; Pharmacy; Public health. **Qualif.:** Applicants must be Hispanic students in their junior or senior year or in a graduate program of an accredited college or university in Pharmacy, Optometry, Nursing, or Public Health; must have a minimum GPA of 2.5. **Criteria:** Recipients will be selected based on their commitment to serve the interests of low-income Latino communities in the United States, and on financial need.

Funds Avail.: $1,500. **Number Awarded:** 2. **To Apply:** Applicants must submit a completed application form available online; must provide two letters of recommendation, one from an academic source and another from a com-

munity leadership source, resume, and school transcript with current GPA. **Contact:** Lucille and Edward R. Roybal Foundation, at the above address or Email: mgroybalfoundation@att.net.

9754 ■ RSL Funding LLC
1980 Post Oak Blvd., Ste. 1975
Houston, TX 77056
Free: 800-543-6513
URL: www.rslfunding.com
Social Media: www.facebook.com/rslfundingcompany
www.instagram.com/rsl_funding
twitter.com/rslfundingcom

9755 ■ $5000 Imagine Scholarship *(College, University/Scholarship)*

Purpose: To help students pay for higher education. **Focus:** General studies/Field of study not specified. **Qualif.:** Applicant must be a U.S. citizen or permanent resident enrolled, or in the enrollment process, at an accredited college, university, or trade school in the United States. **Criteria:** Selection is based on the essay using the following criteria: demonstration of effective financial management, spelling and grammar, creativity, thoroughness, and organization.

Funds Avail.: Up to $5,000. **Number Awarded:** 1. **To Apply:** Applicant must write an essay detailing a sound financial and investment plan they would utilize if they were awarded a structured settlement. Essay and bio must be up uploaded to the scholarship website at www.rslfunding.com/scholarship/. **Deadline:** December 31.

9756 ■ Damon Runyon Cancer Research Foundation (DRCRF)
1 Exchange Plz.
55 Broadway, Ste. 302
New York, NY 10006-3720
Ph: (212)455-0520
Free: 877-722-6237
E-mail: info@damonrunyon.org
URL: www.damonrunyon.org
Social Media: www.facebook.com/damonrunyon
instagram.com/damon_runyon
linkedin.com/company/damonrunyon
twitter.com/damonrunyon
youtube.com/user/DamonRunyonFnd/videos

9757 ■ Damon Runyon Cancer Research Foundation Fellowships *(Graduate, Postdoctorate/Fellowship)*

Purpose: To support the training of the brightest postdoctoral scientists as they embark upon their research careers. **Focus:** Medical research. **Qualif.:** Applicants must have completed one or more degrees or its equivalent: MD, PhD, MD/PhD, DDS, DVM (applicants must include a copy of their diploma to confirm date of conferral); application must be under the guidance of a Sponsor - a scientist (tenured, tenure-track or equivalent position); applicants who have already accepted a postdoctoral research fellowship award are not eligible. **Criteria:** Selection is based on the quality of the research proposal; qualifications, experience and productivity of both the candidate and the Sponsor; and the quality of the research training environment in which the proposed research is to be conducted.

Awards are arranged alphabetically below their administering organizations

Funds Avail.: $50,000-$60,000. **Duration:** Annual. **Number Awarded:** Varies. **To Apply:** Applicants must submit an application cover sheet with all required original signatures; the Sponsor's biographical sketch in NIH format and a list of current funding; sponsor's letter including: a)description of training plan for the candidate, b) track record of mentorship with list of graduate and postdoctoral fellows trained, c) percentage of proposal written by the candidate (numerical percentage); applicant's curriculum vitae, including a bibliography of all published works; a letter from the applicant describing previous research and teaching experience (the letter must state that the applicant is committed to a career in cancer research); and the research proposal, which shall not exceed five pages of single-spaced 12-point type with at least 0.5 inch margins. **Deadline:** March 15.

9758 ■ Damon Runyon Physician-Scientist Training Awards (Postdoctorate, Professional development/ Award)

Purpose: To provide funds to developing physician-scientists to pursue research intensively. **Focus:** General studies/Field of study not specified. **Criteria:** Selection is based on the following: quality of a format research proposal written by the applicants; commitment of the institution to the development and training of future physician-scientists, including providing the necessary protected time for research; importance of the proposed research to the understanding of cancer and/or prevention, diagnosis or treatment of cancer; and capacity of the mentor to provide a robust training experience that will accelerate the development of the applicant's scientific skills and prepare them to independently conduct high quality, innovative cancer-related research.

Funds Avail.: $460,000. **Number Awarded:** 3. **To Apply:** Applicant must propose a research project together with the help of a mentor and submit a letter of commitment from their Institution/Department. A letter endorsed by both the Dean or Center Director, and the Head/Chair of the Department, should confirm the applicant's and mentor's academic appointments, state the institution's commitment to support the applicant's research efforts, the nature of the support that will be provided, and guarantee a minimum of 80% protected time for the applicant's research to fulfill the terms of the award. **Deadline:** December 3. **Contact:** Phone: 212-455-0520; E-mail: awards@damonrunyon.org.

9759 ■ Damon Runyon-Rachleff Innovation Awards (Postdoctorate/Award)

Purpose: To provide funding for extraordinary early career researchers who have an innovative new idea but lack sufficient preliminary data to obtain traditional funding. **Focus:** Medical research. **Qualif.:** Applicants, including non-U.S. citizens, must be conducting independent research at a U.S. research institution. must have a background in multiple disciplines; must belong to either tenure-track Assistant Professors within the first four years of obtaining the position, Clinical Instructors and Senior Clinical Fellows (with an MD) pursuing a period of independent research before taking a faculty position, or Postdoctoral Fellows and highly motivated recent PhD and MD graduates pursuing a period of independent research before taking a faculty position; must commit 80% of their time to conducting research; and must demonstrate access to the resources and infrastructures necessary to conduct the research. **Criteria:** Recipients are chosen based on the applicant's capacity to conduct bold, exceptionally creative research; the novelty and potential for breakthrough innovation of the

proposed research; the likelihood of impact to cancer understanding if research is successful; and the applicant's lack of resources to pursue the proposed research.

Funds Avail.: $150,000 per year. **Duration:** Annual. **To Apply:** Applicants must submit the pre-proposal materials including the following: (1) a completed cover sheet; (2) one-page description of the proposed research; (3) one paragraph description of the resources and core facilities; (4) NIH biosketch; (5) three reference letters from a Tenure-track Assistant professor and clinical instructors and/or Senior Clinical Fellows. Semi finalist applicants will be asked to submit a full proposal including the following: (a) an expanded description of the research proposal (maximum of three pages); (b) full curriculum vitae; (c) a proposed budget for the term of the award; (d) a written statement guaranteeing adequate safety precautions and approved by the appropriate Institutional Review Board; and two letters of reference. **Deadline:** July 1. **Contact:** E-mail: awards@damonrunyon.org.

9760 ■ Damon Runyon-Sohn Pediatric Cancer Fellowship Award (Master's, Doctorate/Fellowship)

Purpose: To provide funds to basic scientists and clinicians who conduct research with the potential to significantly impact the prevention, diagnosis or treatment of one or more pediatric cancers. **Focus:** Medical research. **Qualif.:** Applicants must have completed one or more of the following degrees or its equivalent: MD, PhD, MD/PhD, DDS, DVM, DO. **Criteria:** Applicants are evaluated based on the following criteria: potential impact of the research on pediatric cancer; the quality of the research proposal (importance of the problem, originality of approach, and appropriateness of techniques and clarity of presentation); the qualifications, experience and productivity of both the candidate and the sponsor; the quality of the research training environment in which the proposed research is to be conducted and its potential for broadening and strengthening the applicant's ability to conduct innovative and substantive research.

Funds Avail.: $50,000-$60,000. **To Apply:** Applicants must propose a research that conducted at a university, hospital or research institution. **Deadline:** March 15. **Contact:** Phone: 212-455-0520; E-mail: awards@damonrunyon.org.

9761 ■ Damon Runyon Clinical Investigator Awards (Postgraduate/Award)

Purpose: To increase the number of physicians capable of moving seamlessly between the laboratory and the patient's bedside in search of breakthrough treatments. **Focus:** Medical research. **Qualif.:** Applicants must be U.S. citizens or permanent legal residents; must be nominated by their institution; must have received an MD or MD/PhD degree(s) from an accredited institution and are board-eligible; must be committed to spending 80% of their time conducting research; must apply in conjunction with a mentor who is established in the field of clinical translational cancer research. **Criteria:** Recipients are chosen based on excellence of the applicant and the mentor; innovation, creativity, quality and originality of research proposal; commitment of the mentor and institution to the development and training of the applicant as an independent clinical research investigator; evidence of the applicant's commitment to clinical translational and/or cancer prevention research and their ability to apply these advances; importance of the proposed research; and adherence of the proposal to the definition of clinical research.

Funds Avail.: No specific amount. **Duration:** Three years. **To Apply:** Applicants submit a curriculum vitae; cover

Awards are arranged alphabetically below their administering organizations

sheet; at-a-Glance form; nomination letter from institution/department; applicant's letter and accomplishments; mentor's biographical sketch and letter of support; mentor's proposal training; research proposal; human subjects, radiation safety and environmental health issues statement; summary of research form; and two letters of recommendation; all application materials should be sent in a CD/DVD. **Deadline:** July 1. **Contact:** E-mail: awards@damonrunyon.org.

9762 ■ Russell & Lazarus

1401 Dove St., No. 310
Newport Beach, CA 92660
Ph: (949)344-2349
Free: 888-539-3154
URL: www.russellandlazarus.com
Social Media: www.facebook.com/RussellLazarusAPC
www.linkedin.com/company/russell-&-lazarus
twitter.com/russelllazarus
www.youtube.com/channel/
   UCwAInOwqULAJIGRVhgoKbjQ

9763 ■ Russell & Lazarus Safety Scholarship Contest *(Undergraduate, College, University/Scholarship)*

Purpose: To provide financial aid to college students, inspire students to pursue a career in any legal field, and encourage students to explore the role personal injury lawyers play in minimizing hazards, helping those injured, and encouraging people to think about consumer safety. **Focus:** Law. **Qualif.:** Applicant must be a high school student enrolled or enrolling in college or a college freshman; must be in the United States. **Criteria:** Selection is based on the video essay or written essay.

Funds Avail.: $1,000. **Number Awarded:** 1. **To Apply:** Applicant must create a one- to two-minute video explaining how lawyers make the world a safer place and publish the video to their YouTube channel; the video should be titled "Russell & Lazarus Safety Scholarship" and should include this link in the description: www.russellandlazarus.com/our-firm/safety-scholarship-for-law-students/. Applicant should also share the video on their Facebook page and the sponsor's Facebook page. Instead of a video essay, applicant may submit a 1,000 to 1,500 word essay on the same subject and submit to rlscholarship@gmail.com. **Deadline:** August 15.

9764 ■ Russian Brotherhood Organization of the U.S.A. (RBOUSA)

301 Oxford Valley Rd., Ste. 1602B
Yardley, PA 19067-7721
Ph: (215)563-2537
Fax: (215)563-8106
E-mail: info@rbo.org
URL: www.rbo.org

9765 ■ Mihaly Russin Scholarship Awards *(Graduate/Scholarship)*

Purpose: To provide aid to students seeking higher education in helping the future generation to prosper. **Focus:** General studies/Field of study not specified. **Qualif.:** Applicants must have life insurance policy of $10, 000 or more with the RBO; remained active within the society; must be a Christian; if the membership of the Applicants is termi-

nated, then in that event the RBO reserves the right to cancel the scholarship award. **Criteria:** Selection is based on the application.

Funds Avail.: $1,000 per year not to exceed 3 years. **To Apply:** Applicants must submit a completed application form together with two letters of recommendation, a picture, a copy of transcripts and acceptance letter.

9766 ■ Saints Cyril and Methodius Scholarships *(Undergraduate/Scholarship)*

Purpose: To support the education of a student member. **Focus:** General studies/Field of study not specified. **Qualif.:** Applicant must be a high school graduate or prep school; hold a Russian Brotherhood Organization life insurance certificate of not less than $10000; and a member of the society in good standing. **Criteria:** Recipients are selected by an independent scholarship committee.

Funds Avail.: $10,000. **Duration:** Annually. **To Apply:** Applicants must submit a completed application form, photograph and copy of college acceptance letter to SS. Cyril and Methodius Scholarships. **Deadline:** September 30.

9767 ■ The Ryan Law Group

2101 Rosecrans Ave., Ste. 5290
El Segundo, CA 90245
Ph: (310)321-4800
Fax: (310)496-1435
URL: theryanlawgroup.com
Social Media: www.facebook.com/TheRyanLawGroup
twitter.com/RyanLawGroup

9768 ■ The Ryan Law Group Scholarship *(Undergraduate/Scholarship)*

Purpose: To help a student afford an undergraduate education. **Focus:** General studies/Field of study not specified. **Qualif.:** Applicant must be an incoming freshman or sophomore in an undergraduate program at a college or university in the United States; must be a U.S. citizen. **Criteria:** Senior attorneys at the law firm will select recipient based on submitted essays.

Funds Avail.: $1,000. **Number Awarded:** 1. **To Apply:** Application is available online at theryanlawgroup.com/scholarship/. **Deadline:** July 31.

9769 ■ Safe Schools Coalition (SSC)

PO Box 2388
Seattle, WA 98111
Ph: (206)957-1621
Fax: (206)325-2689
Free: 877-723-3723
E-mail: info@equalrightswashington.org
URL: safeschoolscoalition.org

9770 ■ The Davis-Putter Scholarship Fund *(Undergraduate, Graduate/Scholarship)*

Purpose: To provide scholarships for individuals who are able to do academic work at the university level and who are part of the progressive movement on the campus and in the community. **Focus:** General studies/Field of study not specified. **Qualif.:** Must be enrolled at an institution of higher learning; demonstrate involvement in the fight for social and economic justice. **Criteria:** Selection will be based on academic merit and financial need.

Awards are arranged alphabetically below their administering organizations

Funds Avail.: $15,000. **Duration:** Annual. **To Apply:** Must submit the personal statement no more than 1000 words; letters of recommendation; upload a copy of the Student Aid Report (SAR). **Deadline:** April 1. **Contact:** Davis-Putter Scholarship Fund, PO Box 7307, New York, NY, 10116-7307; Email: davisputter@davisputter.org.

9771 ■ Pride Foundation Scholarships
(Undergraduate/Scholarship)

Purpose: To provide financial assistance for gay, lesbian, bisexual and transgender students pursuing higher education. **Focus:** General studies/Field of study not specified. **Qualif.:** Applicants must be gay, lesbian, bisexual, transgender, queer and straight-ally students as well as students raised by LGBT families; must be residents of Alaska, Idaho, Montana, Oregon and Washington. **Criteria:** Preference will be given to those who meet the scholarship criteria: Seattle-area gay men of color; Latin youth involved in athletics; students of health sciences; interior, fashion or graphic arts; design; or performing arts and former TRIO students from a NASP member program.

Funds Avail.: Up to $10,000. **Number Awarded:** Varies. **To Apply:** Applicants must check the available website for the required materials. **Contact:** URL: pridefoundation.org/find-funding/scholarships.

9772 ■ University of Puget Sound LGBT Leadership Scholarship *(Undergraduate/Scholarship)*

Purpose: To support students who have demonstrated leadership and involvement in the lesbian, gay, bisexual, and transgender (LGBT) community at the University of Puget Sound. **Focus:** General studies/Field of study not specified. **Qualif.:** Applicants must be currently enrolled University of Puget Sound students in good academic standing; demonstrate leadership in the promotion of a positive identity for LGBT students throughout the University and local community. **Criteria:** Recipients will be chosen by a staff and faculty committee appointed by the Dean of Students.

Duration: Annual. **To Apply:** Applicants must check the available website for the required materials. **Remarks:** Established in 2000. **Contact:** Student Financial Services, Mail: 1500 N Warner St., Ste. 1039, Tacoma, WA 98416-1039; Phone: 253-879-3214; URL: www.pugetsound.edu/student-life/center-for-student-support/office-of-intercultural-engagement/programs/lgbt-resources/lgbt-leadership-scholarship/.

9773 ■ Russell Sage Foundation (RSF)
112 E 64th St.
New York, NY 10065
Ph: (212)750-6000
E-mail: pubs@rsage.org
URL: www.russellsage.org
Social Media: www.facebook.com/russellsagefoundation
twitter.com/russellsagefdn
www.youtube.com/user/RussellSageFdn

9774 ■ Russell Sage Foundation's Visiting Scholars Program *(Postdoctorate, Doctorate/Fellowship)*

Purpose: To promote writing and research in the social sciences. **Focus:** Behavioral sciences; Social sciences. **Criteria:** Selection is based on both an individual's demonstrated record of research accomplishment and the merit of the applicant's proposed project. Several criteria

are given special consideration in the selection process.
Funds Avail.: Up to $110,000. **Duration:** Annual; up to 10 months. **Number Awarded:** Up to 19. **Deadline:** June 30.

9775 ■ Saint Andrew's Society of the State of New York
150 E 55th St., 3rd Fl.
New York, NY 10022
Ph: (212)223-4248
E-mail: office@standrewsny.org
URL: www.standrewsny.org
Social Media: www.facebook.com/standrewsny
www.linkedin.com/company/saint-andrews-new-york
twitter.com/NyScots

9776 ■ Saint Andrews Scholarships *(Undergraduate/Scholarship)*

Purpose: To provide significant funding for two Scottish graduate students to study in the United States and two American students of Scottish heritage to study in Scotland. **Focus:** General studies/Field of study not specified. **Qualif.:** Applicants must be senior undergraduate students who will obtain a bachelor's degree from an accredited college or university and who can demonstrate the significance of studying in Scotland; must be a resident of uk. **Criteria:** Recipients are selected based on academic achievement, extracurricular activities, financial need, statement of personal objectives, Scottish descent and proof of citizenship.

Funds Avail.: $30,000 - $35,000. **Duration:** Annual. **To Apply:** Applicants must submit application and letters of reference from appropriate professors. **Deadline:** December 15.

9777 ■ St. Croix Valley Foundation
516 2nd St., Ste. 214
Hudson, WI 54016
Ph: (715)386-9490
E-mail: info@SCVFoundation.org
URL: www.scvfoundation.org

9778 ■ Sterbenz-Ryan Scholarship *(Undergraduate, Vocational/Occupational/Scholarship)*

Purpose: To assist traditional and non-traditional students in Wisconsin or Minnesota who otherwise may not have the opportunity to pursue post-secondary education due to changing life circumstances and financial constraints. **Focus:** General studies/Field of study not specified. **Qualif.:** Applicant must be a graduating senior or non-traditional student to attend any public post-secondary school (technical, community, university) in Minnesota or Wisconsin (must reside in one of the following counties: Burnett, Pierce, Polk, St. Croix in Wisconsin, or Chisago, Washington in Minnesota, or be a student seeking to attend Century College, Metropolitan State University, or WITC. Recipients may reapply annually.

Funds Avail.: $1,500 each. **Duration:** Annual. **Number Awarded:** Approximately 100. **To Apply:** Application details are available at: scvfoundation.org/scholarships. **Deadline:** March 31. **Remarks:** Established by local businessmen Richard Sterbenz and Martin Ryan who wanted to "give kids like them a shot at life they never had.". Established in 2016.

Awards are arranged alphabetically below their administering organizations

9779 ■ St. James Armenian Apostolic Church

465 Mt. Auburn St.
Watertown, MA 02472
Ph: (617)953-8860
E-mail: info@sthagop.com
URL: stjameswatertown.org
Social Media: www.facebook.com/stjameswatertown
twitter.com/stjamesarmenian

9780 ■ St. James Armenian Apostolic Church Scholarships *(Undergraduate, Vocational/ Occupational/Scholarship)*

Purpose: To provide financial assistance to students of Armenian descent associated with St. James Armenian Apostolic Church. **Focus:** General studies/Field of study not specified. **Qualif.:** Applicants must be enrolled in, or high school graduates who have been accepted to, a college or post-high school technical and vocational program; at least one parent of the student must be a dues-paid member of St. James for a period of more than one year, and, if an applicant is 18 years of age or over, the student applying for a scholarship must also be a dues-paid member of St. James; must be attending school or a training/vocational program full-time during the normal academic year. **Criteria:** Scholarships will be awarded based on the academic achievement, financial need, service to school, community and church and seriousness of purpose.

To Apply: Interested applicants may contact the sponsor for the application process and other required materials.

9781 ■ St. Louis Paralegal Association

714 Locust Street
Saint Louis, MO 63169-0218
Social Media: instagram.com/stlparalegals
twitter.com/stlparalegals

9782 ■ CLA/CP Scholarship *(Other/Scholarship)*

Purpose: To support legal assistants with their CP exam fees. **Focus:** Paralegal studies. **Qualif.:** Application must be a Association membership. **Criteria:** Selection will be based upon references, recommendations and participation in the community.

Funds Avail.: $750. **Duration:** Annual. **Number Awarded:** 1. **To Apply:** Application must letter of recommendation from a supervisor at your employer; typewritten paper indicating career Objectives. **Deadline:** April 1.

9783 ■ St. Louis Paralegal Student Scholarships *(Undergraduate/Scholarship)*

Purpose: To assist students with the cost of required books for legal assistants program classes. **Focus:** Paralegal studies. **Qualif.:** Applicants must be enrolled in a study leading to a position as a legal assistant; must be members of the St. Louis Association of Legal Assistants (SLALA); and must maintain at least a "B" average in all legal assistant program classes. **Criteria:** Recipients will be selected based on scholastic achievement; participation in campus, paralegal and community activities; and review of the writing sample. Applicants who have demonstrated a financial need will be given consideration.

Funds Avail.: $500. **Duration:** Biennial. **To Apply:** Applicants must submit the following: a letter of recommendation from a director, faculty member, Legal Assistant

Program, or employer; an official transcript of records; and personal statement (maximum of three pages, double-spaced) indicating the applicant's career objectives. **Deadline:** April 1.

9784 ■ Saint Paul University Canada (SPU)

223 Main St.
Ottawa, ON, Canada K1S 1C4
Ph: (613)236-1393
Fax: (613)782-3005
Free: 800-637-6859
E-mail: info@ustpaul.ca
URL: www.ustpaul.ca
Social Media: www.facebook.com/
  UniversiteSaintPaulUniversity
instagram.com/ustpaul_ca
www.linkedin.com/school/saint-paul-university-cp
twitter.com/ustpaul_ca
www.youtube.com/user/uspottawa

9785 ■ Saint Paul University Financial Aid Bursaries *(Undergraduate, Graduate/Scholarship)*

Purpose: To provide educational assistance for all students in Saint Paul University. **Focus:** General studies/Field of study not specified. **Qualif.:** Applicants must be full-time students enrolled in an undergraduate or graduate program at Saint Paul University; available to Canadian citizens, permanent residents, and international students alike. **Criteria:** Applicants will be evaluated by a committee according to financial necessity or very special conditions.

Funds Avail.: No specific amount. **Duration:** Annual. **Number Awarded:** Varies. **To Apply:** Applications can be submitted online. **Contact:** Email: financialaid@ustpaul.ca.

9786 ■ St. Petersburg Personal Injury Attorneys McQuaid & Douglas

5858 Central Ave., Ste. A
Saint Petersburg, FL 33707
Ph: (721)381-2300
E-mail: smcqu@brdwlaw.com
URL: www.727injury.com
Social Media: www.facebook.com/727injury
www.linkedin.com/company/st-petersburg-personal-injury
  -attorneys-mcquaid-douglas
www.pinterest.com/727injury
twitter.com/727injury
www.youtube.com/channel/UC1RDpVj8WknIgoFU0FjnIkA

9787 ■ St. Petersburg Personal Injury Attorneys McQuaid & Douglas $2,000 Scholarship Contest *(College, Undergraduate, Vocational/Occupational, Professional development/Scholarship)*

Purpose: To help students pay for higher education. **Focus:** General studies/Field of study not specified. **Qualif.:** Applicant must be currently enrolled or accepted into an accredited college or university in the United States. **Criteria:** Submissions will be posted on the website and voted on.

Funds Avail.: $1,250 First Place; $500 Second Place; $250 Third Place. **Duration:** Biennial. **Number Awarded:** 3. **To Apply:** Applicant must write a 1,000-word essay on the topic of: The Importance of Hiring a Car Accident Attorney

Awards are arranged alphabetically below their administering organizations

After an Auto Accident. Essay must be posted online to the applicant's blog, a university blog site, or a blog platform such as medium.com, blogger.com, or the like. The essay must cite at least three authoritative sources on car accident injury law, and must include a link to www.727injury.com. Application must also be completed on sponsors website. **Deadline:** January 31. **Contact:** Email: scholarship@727injury.com; URL: hwww.727injury.com/st-petersburg-p ersonal-injury-attorneys-mcquaid-douglas-2000-scholarship-contest/.

9788 ■ Salon Supply Store
350 Hiatt Dr.
Palm Beach Gardens, FL 33418
URL: www.salonsupplystore.com

9789 ■ Salon Supply Store Cosmetology Scholarships *(Undergraduate/Scholarship)*

Purpose: To award and inspire cosmetology students. **Focus:** Cosmetology. **Qualif.:** Applicants must be legal residents of the United States; must be at least 18 years old at the time of application; must be currently enrolled or have been accepted to enroll in an accredited postsecondary institution of higher learning. **Criteria:** Selection will be based on the following criteria: GPA; originality and creativity of the submitted essay; emotional impact; relevance of topic.

Funds Avail.: $1,000. **Duration:** Biennial. **Number Awarded:** 1. **To Apply:** Applicants must submit a complete scholarship online application at Salon Supply Store's website. **Deadline:** October 1. **Contact:** scholarship@salonsupplystore.com.

9790 ■ Salvadoran American Leadership and Education Fund (SALEF)
421 S Bixel St. Ste. A
Los Angeles, CA 90017
Ph: (213)480-1052
URL: www.salef.org
Social Media: www.facebook.com/salefonline
www.instagram.com/_salef

9791 ■ SALEF Health Career Scholarships *(Undergraduate, Graduate/Scholarship)*

Purpose: To support students pursuing health related fields. **Focus:** Health care services; Health education. **Qualif.:** Applicants must: be pursuing health related degrees and careers; be of Central American or other Latino ethnicity; demonstrate proven financial need; demonstrate a history of community involvement; possess a minimum 2.5 GPA; and, be either of the following: graduating high school seniors; current undergraduate, graduate, MPH, MD or Dentistry School students; community college students; or enrolled/studying at vocational/trade schools; they must also reside in the following areas: Los Angeles Area (specifically from those who are from Pico Union, South Los Angeles, Central LA, and surrounding schools). **Criteria:** Selection shall be based on the aforementioned applicants' qualifications and compliance with the application details.

Funds Avail.: Amount varies. **Duration:** Annual. **Number Awarded:** Varies. **To Apply:** Applicants must submit a completed application form along with two letters of recommendation (on official letterhead when applicable); a personal statement (maximum of 800 words); resume; official transcripts (have school seal and/or authorized signature); copy of applicants' or applicants' parents' Federal Tax Return or Proof of Family Income (include a written statement with explanation, if not applicable); and a colored photograph (wallet size, 3 1/2 x 5) and the attached Release Authorization Form. **Deadline:** May 31. **Contact:** Lea Gonzalez, Civic Engagement & Scholarship Programs Coordinator; Email: lmgonzalez@salef.org.

9792 ■ The SAMFund
89 South St., Ste.701
Boston, MA 02111
Ph: (617)938-3484
Fax: (866)496-8070
E-mail: info@thesamfund.org
URL: thesamfund.org
Social Media: www.facebook.com/thesamfund
www.instagram.com/thesamfund
twitter.com/TheSAMFund
www.youtube.com/user/SAMFundTV

9793 ■ Samfund grants *(Other/Grant)*

Purpose: To provide financial assistance to young adults as they move forward with their lives after cancer. **Focus:** General studies/Field of study not specified. **Criteria:** Selection is based on the submitted application materials.

Funds Avail.: $1,500. **Number Awarded:** Varies. **To Apply:** Applicant must include basic personal and contact information; current financial picture including monthly income, monthly expenses, assets applicant may own, and liabilities/debts; completion of a medical history verification form, signed by a licensed medical professional with whom applicant has a relationship (e.g., oncologist, primary care physician, nurse practitioner). **Remarks:** Established in 2005. **Contact:** Phone: 617-938-3484; Email: grants@thesamfund.org.

9794 ■ San Angelo Area Foundation (SAAF)
221 S Irving St.
San Angelo, TX 76903-6421
Ph: (325)947-7071
Fax: (325)947-7322
E-mail: infosaaf@saafound.org
URL: www.saafound.org
Social Media: www.facebook.com/sanangelofoundation

9795 ■ San Angelo Area Foundation Scholarship *(All/Scholarship)*

Purpose: To support the education of students from the San Angelo area. **Focus:** General studies/Field of study not specified. **Qualif.:** Applicants must be from San Angelo area. **Criteria:** Selection is based on submitted application materials.

Funds Avail.: Varies. **Duration:** Annual. **Number Awarded:** Varies. **To Apply:** Applicants must submit ACT & SAT test scores; documentation of college credit hours from the Institution awarding the credits; current transcript; two letters of recommendation - 1 personal & 1 academic. **Deadline:** March 1. **Contact:** Phone: 325-947-7071; Email: scholarship@saafound.org.

9796 ■ San Antonio Paralegal Association (SAPA)
PO Box 90037
San Antonio, TX 78209

Awards are arranged alphabetically below their administering organizations

Fax: (210)734-9965
URL: www.saparalegal.org
Social Media: www.facebook.com/San-Antonio-Paralegal
-Association-169111429781139

9797 ■ Professional Certification Exam Scholarship
*(Undergraduate, Professional development/
Scholarship)*

Purpose: To promote excellence, education, ethical conduct, and the enhancement of the paralegal profession. **Focus:** Paralegal studies. **Qualif.:** Applicants must be current voting, associate, or student members of SAPA. An applicant may apply for the scholarship in more than one category. **Criteria:** Selection will be based on the committee's criteria.

Funds Avail.: Half of the exam fee. **Duration:** Annual. **To Apply:** Applicant must provide a written essay on a topic listed in Section VII of the application (two-pages, doubled-spaced). **Deadline:** June 8. **Contact:** SAPA's Education Director; Email: educationdirector@saparalegal.org.

9798 ■ The San Diego Foundation (TSDF)
2508 Historic Decatur Rd., Ste. 200
San Diego, CA 92106
Ph: (619)235-2300
Fax: (619)239-1710
E-mail: info@sdfoundation.org
URL: www.sdfoundation.org
Social Media: www.facebook.com/TSDF1
www.instagram.com/sandiegofoundation
www.linkedin.com/company/the-san-diego-foundation
twitter.com/sd_fdn
www.youtube.com/user/tsdf01

9799 ■ Athena San Diego Pinnacle Scholarship
(Undergraduate/Scholarship)

Purpose: To support outstanding female high school students in San Diego County who are entering STEM fields. **Focus:** Engineering; Mathematics and mathematical sciences; Science. **Qualif.:** Applicants must be female high school seniors in San Diego County planning to enter a four-year university to study in the sciences, math, or engineering fields. **Criteria:** Selection is based on academic excellence, leadership in school organizations, and community involvement.

Funds Avail.: $2,500. **Duration:** 2 Year. **To Apply:** Application and details available at www.sdfoundation.org/students/other-tsdf-scholarships/. **Deadline:** May 31. **Contact:** Email: staff@athenasd.org.

9800 ■ Ballard Family Foundation Scholarships
(Undergraduate/Scholarship)

Purpose: To support the education of students from California. **Focus:** General studies/Field of study not specified. **Criteria:** Special consideration will be given to African-American students.

Funds Avail.: No specific amount. **To Apply:** Applicants must submit a completed Common Scholarship Application together with personal statement; two letters of recommendation on official letterhead (written within the last six months); official transcript in an official and sealed envelope; and a letter of recommendation from the applicant's social worker indicating the applicant is or has been in foster care. **Deadline:** February 1.

9801 ■ Barta-Lehman Musical Scholarship
(Undergraduate/Scholarship)

Purpose: To support the education of students from California. **Focus:** Music. **Qualif.:** Applicants must be graduating high school seniors, or current undergraduate or graduate college students who are serious and talented musicians planning to pursue a career in music or play professionally (string instruments preferred) and plan to enroll full-time at an accredited four-year university or music academy in the United States; must have a minimum of 3.0 GPA on a 4.0 scale; must be San Diego County residents.

Funds Avail.: No specific amount. **Duration:** Annual. **Number Awarded:** Varies. **To Apply:** Applicants should include letter of recommendation (on official letterhead) from music teacher indicating his or her level of talent and seriousness about pursuing music as a career; a CD or DVD of applicant's music; materials will not be returned. **Deadline:** February 5.

9802 ■ James R. and Geraldine F. Bertelsen Scholarship *(Undergraduate/Scholarship)*

Purpose: To support the education of students from California. **Focus:** General studies/Field of study not specified. **Qualif.:** Applicants must be practicing Roman Catholics who are: graduating high school seniors who have applied to, been accepted by, and will attend a four-year Roman Catholic college or university in the U.S.; or students currently enrolled at a Catholic college or university in the United States; they must also be residents of Carlsbad, CA for a minimum of one full year enrolling in or currently enrolled in a course of instruction that will enable to obtain an undergraduate degree within four years. **Criteria:** Selection is given based on achievement with need being a secondary consideration.

Funds Avail.: No specific amount. **Deadline:** February 5. **Remarks:** The scholarship was established by Bertelsens to assist Catholic college-bound students. **Contact:** San Diego Foundation; Email: scholarships@sdfoundation.org.

9803 ■ Breslauer Family Scholarships
(Undergraduate/Scholarship)

Purpose: To support the education of students from California. **Focus:** General studies/Field of study not specified. **Qualif.:** Applicants must: be San Diego county residents; be graduating seniors from San Diego High School (in downtown San Diego only) who plan to attend an accredited four-year university in the United States; have a minimum unweighted GPA of 3.5 on a 4.0 scale; show a strong commitment to their community as demonstrated by their involvement in extra-curricular activities and/or work/volunteer experience; and, have a demonstrated financial need, as evidenced by an adjusted gross family income of equal to or less than $40,000. **Criteria:** Selection shall be based on the aforementioned qualifications and compliance with the application details.

Funds Avail.: No specific amount. **Duration:** Annual. **To Apply:** Applicants may visit the website to verify the application process and other pieces of information. Required additional materials: 1) Unofficial copy of your current transcript. 2) At least one letter of reference from a teacher at your high school or school employee. **Deadline:** February 4.

9804 ■ Louise A. Broderick San Diego County Scholarship *(Undergraduate/Scholarship)*

Purpose: To support the education of students from California. **Focus:** General studies/Field of study not speci-

Awards are arranged alphabetically below their administering organizations

fied. **Qualif.:** Applicants must be single parents with dependent children who are re-entering college or are already in college; must have a minimum of 2.0 GPA on a 4.0 scale; plan to attend a two-year community college, four-year university, or trade and vocational school; united states citizens and permanent residents. **Criteria:** Selection will be based on financial need.

Funds Avail.: No specific amount. **Duration:** Annual. **Number Awarded:** 12. **To Apply:** Applicants should include required additional materials: first page of prior year federal tax form showing filing status and dependent child(ren). **Deadline:** February 5.

9805 ■ California Association of Family and Consumer Sciences - San Diego Chapter Scholarship (Undergraduate, Graduate/Scholarship)

Purpose: To support the education of students from California. **Focus:** Fashion design; Food science and technology; Food service careers; Home Economics; Housing; Management; Nutrition; Textile science. **Qualif.:** Applicants must be reside in California, though priority will be given to applicants who have resided in San Diego County for at least one year, Be graduating high school seniors, current college students, or graduate students majoring in Culinary Arts; Dietetics; Nutrition; Hospitality and Tourism; Human, Child and Family Development; Apparel Services; Fashion Design; Textile Design; Interior Design; Consumer Economics or Family and Consumer Science Education, Plan to attend or currently attend an accredited four-year university, community college, or licensed career/ technical school in the United States (undergraduate recipients must be enrolled full-time (12 units per semester or 9 per quarter); graduate students may be enrolled full-time or part-time with awards allocated appropriately based upon enrollment units), Have a cumulative unweighted GPA of 2.5 or higher on a 4.0 scale.

Funds Avail.: No specific amount. **To Apply:** Applicants must submit a letter of recommendation on official letterhead from an instructor or other professional indicating your interest in pursuing a career in one of above listed fields. **Deadline:** February 5.

9806 ■ The Club at Morningside Scholarship (Undergraduate, Graduate/Scholarship)

Purpose: To support the education of students from California. **Focus:** General studies/Field of study not specified. **Criteria:** Selection will be based on academic achievement, involvement in extra-curricular activities and community service, work experience, and financial need.

Funds Avail.: No specific amount. **Duration:** Annual. **To Apply:** Applicant should include letter on official letterhead from the human resources department verifying they or their parent is employed at the club at Morningside, including position held, length of employment and a description of job responsibilities. **Deadline:** February 1.

9807 ■ Madison and Edith Cooper Scholarships (Undergraduate/Scholarship)

Purpose: To support the education of students from California. **Focus:** General studies/Field of study not specified. **Qualif.:** Applicants must be young adults in San Diego County (up to age 24); have been in the foster care system; planning to attend an accredited two-year college, four-year university, or licensed trade/vocational school in the U.S.; have a minimum of 2.50 GPA on a 4.0 scale; demonstrated financial need; and involved in serving the community through extra-curricular activities, community

service, or work experience. **Criteria:** Awards are given based on the application materials.

To Apply: Applicants may visit the website to verify the application process and other pieces of information. Additional material(s) required: letter on official letterhead from a social worker verifying applicants are currently or have been in foster care. **Contact:** San Diego Foundation, at the above address.

9808 ■ Crawford Scholarship (Undergraduate/Scholarship)

Purpose: To support the education of students from California. **Focus:** General studies/Field of study not specified. **Qualif.:** Applicants must be: graduating seniors of Crawford Educational Complex who plan to attend an accredited community college or four-year university in the United States; previous Crawford Scholarship recipients who had to forfeit their scholarship who are attending an accredited community college or four-year university in the United States; have a minimum 2.50 GPA on a 4.0 scale (high school GPAs are unweighted); those who are engaged in their community through their involvement in extracurricular, church, volunteer activities or work experience. They must have a demonstrated financial need.

Funds Avail.: No specific amount. **Number Awarded:** 17. **Deadline:** February 5.

9809 ■ Davis Family Scholarship (Undergraduate/Scholarship)

Purpose: To support the education of students from California. **Focus:** General studies/Field of study not specified.

9810 ■ Hans and Margaret Doe Charitable Trust Scholarship (Community College, Vocational/Occupational, College, University, Undergraduate, Graduate/Scholarship)

Purpose: To help children of employees at the Vista Irrigation District to attend college. **Focus:** General studies/Field of study not specified. **Qualif.:** Applicants must be biological, adopted, or stepchildren of the employees at the Vista Irrigation District who plan to attend an accredited career/ technical school, community college, four-year university, or graduate school (including medical and law) in the United States. May be renewable for up to eight consecutive years. **Criteria:** Selection is based on academic achievement, financial need, extracurricular activities, work experience, demonstrated leadership, good citizenship, and potential for future development.

To Apply: Application and details available at www.sdfoundation.org/students/other-tsdf-scholarships/. **Deadline:** February 5. **Remarks:** Established to honor Hans and Margaret Doe, tireless water crusaders for all Californians. **Contact:** Email: scholarships@sdfoundation.org.

9811 ■ Doris Hendren Memorial Scholarship (Undergraduate/Scholarship)

Purpose: To support the education of students from California. **Focus:** Liberal arts. **Criteria:** Applicants must be demonstrated financial need.

Duration: Annual. **To Apply:** Applicants must submit a unofficial copy of current transcript. **Deadline:** February 5.

9812 ■ Dorothy M. Bolyard Memorial Scholarship (Undergraduate/Scholarship)

Purpose: To support the education of students from California. **Focus:** General studies/Field of study not speci-

Awards are arranged alphabetically below their administering organizations

fied. **Qualif.:** Applicants must be San Diego residents (age 25 years and older) pursuing a degree at an accredited two-year college or four-year university in San Diego County; have a minimum 3.0 GPA on a 4.0 scale; and demonstrated financial need. **Criteria:** Selection is given to applicants who have a record of involvement in their community as demonstrated by their extra-curricular activities, community or church service, or work experience.

Deadline: February 5.

9813 ■ Escondido High School (EHS) Class of '56 Scholarship (Community College, Vocational/Occupational/Scholarship)

Purpose: To assist current graduating Escondido High School seniors who plan to attend a community college or trade school. **Focus:** General studies/Field of study not specified. **Qualif.:** Applicants must be graduating seniors from Escondido High School (EHS) who have attended EHS for all four years; be U.S. citizens or legal residents; planning to attend an accredited two-year community college or trade school in the United States in the fall semester; have a cumulative unweighted 2.0 to 3.0 GPA; have a demonstrated commitment to community service; have a demonstrated financial need. **Criteria:** Preference given to applicants who enroll/participate in First Year Experience (FYE) and Summer Bridge program for entering Community College students.

Duration: Annual. **To Apply:** Applicants should contact the counselor at Escondido High School for application details.

9814 ■ Frank H. Ault Scholarship (Undergraduate/Scholarship)

Purpose: To support the education of students from California. **Focus:** Accounting. **Qualif.:** Applicants must be graduating high school students or junior college students planning to major in accounting or finance at an accredited four-year university; current college student (sophomore, junior, or senior year) have declared a major in finance or accounting; students must have a minimum of 3.0 GPA on a 4.0 scale; and have participated in extra-curricular or community service activities. **Criteria:** Selection will be given to students who are active members of or have taken leadership in their school's accounting society.

Funds Avail.: No specific amount. **Duration:** Annual. **Number Awarded:** 6. **To Apply:** Applicants must submit a unofficial copy of current transcript. **Deadline:** February 5.

9815 ■ Arthur H. Goodman Memorial Scholarship (Undergraduate, University/Scholarship)

Purpose: To provide financial assistance to dynamic, community-minded women and minority students transitioning from a community college in California or Arizona to four-year universities. **Focus:** General studies/Field of study not specified. **Qualif.:** Applicants must be women or minorities who are committed and engaged in their communities and our graduating from a community college in California or Arizona to a four-year university.

To Apply: Application form and details available at www.sdfoundation.org/students/other-tsdf-scholarships/. **Deadline:** June 19. **Contact:** Robert Villarreal; Phone: 619.243.8652; Email: RVillarreal@cdcloans.com.

9816 ■ Leslie Jane Hahn Memorial Scholarships (Undergraduate/Scholarship)

Purpose: To support the education of students from California. **Focus:** General studies/Field of study not speci-

fied. **Qualif.:** Applicants must be graduating high school senior females from a public school who plan to enroll full-time at an accredited four-year college/university in the U.S.; have at least a 3.75 GPA on a 4.0 scale; demonstrated financial need; and have a history of active involvement in athletics, other extracurricular activities, community service or work experience. **Criteria:** Preference will be given to applicants who most closely reflect Jane's qualities and background.

Funds Avail.: No specific amount. **To Apply:** Applicants may visit the website to verify the application process and other pieces of information. **Deadline:** February 1.

9817 ■ Hans H. and Margaret B. Doe Scholarship (Graduate, Undergraduate/Scholarship)

Purpose: To support the education of students from California. **Focus:** Law; Medicine. **Qualif.:** Applicants must be biological, adopted or stepchildren of the employees at the Vista Irrigation District; may attend a career or technical school, community college, four-year university or graduate school, including medicine and law; recipient maintains a positive academic GPA of 2.0 on a 4.0 scale. **Criteria:** Selection will be made on the basis of academic achievement; financial need; extra-curricular activities/work experience; demonstrated leadership; good citizenship and potential for future development.

Funds Avail.: No specific amount. **Duration:** Annual. **Deadline:** June 1. **Contact:** San Diego Foundation; Email: scholarships@sdfoundation.org.

9818 ■ Viginia & Susan Hawk Scholarship (Other/Scholarship)

Purpose: To support aspiring opera and concert singers. **Focus:** Music, Vocal; Opera. **Qualif.:** Applicants must be aspiring opera and concert singers; must be between the ages of 20 to 35; be a resident of San Diego or Imperial County **Criteria:** Vocal audition judged on the following criteria: vocal potential, Musicianship and language skills, technique, artistry.

To Apply: Email the completed application, audition Information for judges, proof of birth date, teacher's letter of recommendation, winner's pledge, and digital photo for publicity. **Remarks:** Mrs. Virginia Fletcher Hawk, wife of Captain C.V. Hawk, USN, established this award in memory of their daughter, Susan. Established in 1979. **Contact:** Shirley Towers; Email: shirleytowers@me.com; URL: www.sdfoundation.org/students/other-tsdf-scholarships/.

9819 ■ Helm Family Scholarship (Undergraduate/Scholarship)

Purpose: To support the education of students from California. **Focus:** Biology; Chemistry; Computer and information sciences; Engineering; Physics; Technology. **Qualif.:** Applicants must be entering junior or senior students at San Diego State University or the University of California, San Diego; have declared a major in mathematics or a scientific field such as, but not limited to, biology, computer science, chemistry, technology, engineering, physics; have a minimum of 3.0 GPA on a 4.0 scale; have demonstrated financial need. **Criteria:** Selection will be given to students who are employed or have participated in extra-curricular activities or community service.

Funds Avail.: No specific amount. **Number Awarded:** 1. **Deadline:** February 5.

9820 ■ Herman H. Derksen Scholarship (Undergraduate/Scholarship)

Purpose: To support the education of students from California. **Focus:** General studies/Field of study not speci-

Awards are arranged alphabetically below their administering organizations

fied. **Criteria:** Preference is given to applicants who have a record of involvement in their community as demonstrated by their extra-curricular activities, community or church service, or work experience.

Funds Avail.: No specific amount. **Duration:** Annual.

9821 ■ Cathy Hopper Memorial Scholarship
(Undergraduate/Scholarship)

Purpose: To help future teachers in California afford a college education. **Focus:** Education; Teaching. **Qualif.:** Applicants must have graduated from a public high school in San Diego County and resided in San Diego County for at least one year; must be current college/university students currently pursuing teaching credentials and/or student teaching at a university in California with the goal of a career as a K-12 public school teacher in California; must have a cumulative minimum 3.0 GPA, shown a commitment to their community through meaningful community service, and have a demonstrated financial need.

Duration: Annual. **To Apply:** Application and details available at www.sdfoundation.org/students/other-tsdf-scholarships/. **Deadline:** May 22. **Remarks:** Established in memorial of Cathy Hopper, a long-time educator and resident of San Diego County. **Contact:** Email: scholarships@sdfoundation.org.

9822 ■ Albert W. and Mildred Hubbard Scholarships
(Undergraduate/Scholarship)

Purpose: To support the education of students from California. **Focus:** General studies/Field of study not specified. **Criteria:** Selection shall be based on the aforementioned qualifications and compliance with the application details.

Funds Avail.: No specific amount. **Duration:** Annual. **To Apply:** Applicants may visit the website to verify the application process and other pieces of information. Applicants must also submit the following required materials: unofficial copy of current transcript, and unofficial copy of the SAT or ACT scores. **Deadline:** February 1.

9823 ■ Jean Wright-Elson Scholarship *(Doctorate, Graduate, Undergraduate/Scholarship)*

Purpose: To support the education of students from California. **Focus:** Nursing. **Criteria:** Selection shall be based on demonstrated financial need.

Funds Avail.: No specific amount. **Duration:** Annual. **To Apply:** Applicants must submit a unofficial copy of current transcript. **Deadline:** February 5.

9824 ■ Judith Keller Marx Krumholz Scholarship
(Graduate/Scholarship)

Purpose: To support the education of students from California. **Focus:** General studies/Field of study not specified.

Funds Avail.: No specific amount. **Number Awarded:** Varies. **Deadline:** February 5.

9825 ■ Kawano Family Scholarships *(Undergraduate/ Scholarship)*

Purpose: To support the education of students with arthritis from California. **Focus:** General studies/Field of study not specified. **Qualif.:** Applicants must be students from San Diego County who have arthritis or have an immediate family member affected by arthritis, which impact the applicants on a daily basis. They must have a minimum of 3.0

GPA on a 4.0 scale; demonstrated financial need; and planning to attend, or attending an accredited four-year university in the U.S. **Criteria:** Selection shall be based on the aforementioned qualifications and compliance with the application details.

Funds Avail.: No specific amount. **To Apply:** Applicants may visit the website to verify the application process and other pieces of information.

9826 ■ Kiwanis Club of Escondido Scholarship
(Undergraduate/Scholarship)

Purpose: To support the education of students from California. **Focus:** General studies/Field of study not specified. **Qualif.:** Applicants must be graduating high school seniors in the Escondido High School District planning to enroll full-time at anaccredited four-year university in the United States; minimum unweighted GPA of 3.0 on a 4.0 scale; an active member of a Key Club (sponsored by an Escondido Kiwanis Club); have a demonstrated financial need. **Criteria:** Preference is given to applicants who have a record of involvement in their community as demonstrated by their extra-curricular activities, community or church service, or work experience.

Funds Avail.: No specific amount. **Number Awarded:** 1. **To Apply:** Applicants must submit an application form; required additional materials: letter of recommendation from their respective Key Club advisors indicating their degree of involvement. **Deadline:** February 5. **Contact:** San Diego Foundation; Email: scholarships@sdfoundation.org.

9827 ■ Patrick Ledden Honorary Scholarships
(Undergraduate/Scholarship)

Purpose: To support the education of students from California. **Focus:** General studies/Field of study not specified. **Qualif.:** Applicants must be graduating seniors at the Preuss School, UCSD; have a minimum 3.50 GPA on a 4.0 scale; and planning to attend a public or private four-year university in United States. **Criteria:** Special consideration is given to students who have participated in extra-curricular activities and community service or have work experience.

Funds Avail.: No specific amount. **Duration:** Annual. **To Apply:** Applicants may visit the website to verify the application process and other pieces of information. Required additional materials: essay (typed, double-spaced, maximum one page) answering "What have you learned from your experience at The Preuss School, UCSD that you feel will best benefit you in college?". **Deadline:** February 1.

9828 ■ Lehman Family Scholarship *(Undergraduate/ Scholarship)*

Purpose: To support the education of students from California. **Focus:** General studies/Field of study not specified. **Qualif.:** Applicants must be graduating seniors from Lincoln, Morse, or San Diego (downtown San Diego) high schools; have a minimum of 3.00 GPA on a 4.0 scale; planning to attend an accredited four-year university in the U.S; have financial need; and have demonstrated commitment to the community through involvement in extra-curricular activities, work or volunteer experience, or church activities. **Criteria:** Preference will be given to foreign born children of immigrant parents.

Funds Avail.: No specific amount. **Number Awarded:** 2. **Deadline:** February 5.

9829 ■ Lemon Grove Education Foundation Scholarship *(Undergraduate, Graduate/Scholarship)*

Purpose: To support the education of students from California. **Focus:** General studies/Field of study not speci-

Awards are arranged alphabetically below their administering organizations

fied. **Qualif.:** Applicants must be graduating high school seniors or adults (ages 18 or over) residing within the boundaries of the Lemon Grove School District; have a minimum of 2.0 GPA on a 4.0 scale; and, planning to attend a four-year public university, two-year community college, licensed career or technical school or regional occupational program in San Diego County; united States citizens or permanent residents.

Funds Avail.: No specific amount. **Duration:** Annual. **Deadline:** February 5.

9830 ■ Rebecca Christine Lenci Thespian Memorial Scholarship *(Undergraduate/Scholarship)*

Purpose: To support a student who exhibits the qualities necessary to be a positive, creative force in and around the world of theatre. **Focus:** General studies/Field of study not specified. **Qualif.:** Applicants must be seniors from Natick High School in Natick, Massachusetts; have a connection with the theatre program at Natick High School and a passion for theatre; have demonstrated financial need; have a cumulative 2.5 or higher GPA. **Criteria:** Selection based primarily on the essay submitted, financial need is also a factor. Preference given to applicants who participated in two theatre-related classes and/or participated in the after-school theatre program.

Duration: Annual. **To Apply:** Essay required, application and guidelines available via email. **Deadline:** February 5. **Remarks:** Established by the Lenci family in memory of their daughter and sister, Rebecca, who passed away. **Contact:** Email: scholarships@sdfoundation.org; URL: www.sdfoundation.org/students/other-tsdf-scholarships/.

9831 ■ Luis Arreola Memorial Scholarship *(Undergraduate/Scholarship)*

Purpose: To support the education of students from California. **Focus:** General studies/Field of study not specified. **Qualif.:** Applicants must be graduating seniors from Sweetwater Union High School District who plan to attend an accredited four-year university, community college or licensed career or technical school in the United States; must also have a minimum GPA of 3.0 on an 4.0 scale, have demonstrated both commitment to serving their community and financial need. **Criteria:** Selection will be based on financial need and preference will be given to students who are ambitious, have shown success and potential in the courses related to their chosen career and have persevered in spite of their obstacles.

Funds Avail.: No specific amount. **Duration:** Annual. **Deadline:** February 5.

9832 ■ Malini E. Sathyadev Memorial Scholarship *(Undergraduate/Scholarship)*

Purpose: To support the education of students from California. **Focus:** General studies/Field of study not specified. **Qualif.:** Applicants must be graduating high school seniors from Horizon High School and Cathedral Catholic High School who plan to enroll full-time at an accredited four-year university in the United States; have a minimum of 3.50 GPA on a 4.0 scale; attending an accredited four-year university in the U.S. **Criteria:** Selection will be based on involvement in community service and extracurricular activities such as sports and music.

Funds Avail.: No specific amount. **Duration:** Annual. **To Apply:** Applicants should include required additional materials: essay (maximum 500 words) on the role that Jesus Christ plays in their life. **Deadline:** February 1.

9833 ■ Marvin Arnold and Irene Jaquetta Heye Scholarship *(Undergraduate/Scholarship)*

Purpose: To provide financial assistance to graduating high school seniors planning to attend, or current students who are attending California Polytechnic State University-San Luis Obispo. **Focus:** Engineering. **Qualif.:** Applicants must be graduating high school seniors planning to attend California Polytechnic State University or current students attending California Polytechnic State University; must be majoring in engineering (aerospace, civil and environmental, electrical, general, industrial and manufacturing, materials or mechanical engineering); have a minimum 3.33 grade point average on a 4.0 scale. **Criteria:** Selection will be based on financial need; involved in extra-curricular activities, community service, or work experience; preference will be given to students with a high financial need, former military personnel and dependents of active military personnel.

Funds Avail.: No specific amount. **Duration:** Annual; up to four years. **To Apply:** Applicants must submit their letters of recommendation, transcripts of record and personal statement together with their completed application form. **Deadline:** June 1. **Contact:** San Diego Foundation, Marvin Arnold and Irene Jaquetta Heye Scholarship, 2508 Historic Decatur Rd., Ste. 200, San Diego, CA, 92106; Phone: 619-814-1343; Email: scholarships@sdfoundation.org.

9834 ■ Mission Bay Hospital Auxiliary Scholarship *(Undergraduate/Scholarship)*

Purpose: To support the education of students from California. **Focus:** Medicine. **Qualif.:** Applicants must be graduating college seniors pursuing a career in medicine; residents of San Diego County planning to attend an accredited medical school in the U.S.; have a minimum 3.50 GPA on a 4.0 scale; and demonstrate financial need; United States citizens or permanent residents. **Criteria:** Special consideration is given to applicants who are involved in their community and exhibit a need for financial aid.

Funds Avail.: No specific amount. **Duration:** Annual. **Number Awarded:** 1. **Deadline:** February 5.

9835 ■ MKC/Preuss Scholarship *(Undergraduate, Community College, University/Scholarship)*

Purpose: To support the education of students from California. **Focus:** General studies/Field of study not specified. **Qualif.:** Applicants must be current graduating seniors and students who have already graduated from the Preuss School, UCSD; planning to attend an accredited two-year college or four-year university in the U.S.; have a minimum 3.30 GPA on a 4.0 scale. **Criteria:** Selection will be based on commitment to serving the community through involvement in community service, church or extra-curricular activities.

Funds Avail.: No specific amount. **Duration:** Annual. **Number Awarded:** 1. **To Apply:** Applicants should include unofficial copy of your current transcript; letter of recommendation on official letterhead from someone who knows you from an academic perspective. **Deadline:** February 5.

9836 ■ Music Teachers' Association of California Goodlin Scholarship *(High School/Scholarship)*

Purpose: To seek out and support talented youth musicians in San Diego county. **Focus:** Music. **Qualif.:** Applicants must be music students in San Diego County under the age of 18.

Funds Avail.: $2,000 each. **Number Awarded:** 2. **To Apply:** Application details available via email. **Deadline:** April

Awards are arranged alphabetically below their administering organizations

25. **Contact:** Leah Rogers; Email: learogers@icloud.com; URL: www.sdfoundation.org/students/other-tsdf-scholarships/.

9837 ■ Napoleon A. Jones, III Memorial Scholarship
(Undergraduate/Scholarship)

Purpose: To support the education of students from California. **Focus:** General studies/Field of study not specified. **Qualif.:** Applicant must be a graduating high school senior residing within the zip codes of 92113, 92114 and 92115; or a graduating senior attending one of the following public high schools: Crawford, Hoover, Lincoln, Morse, San Diego High (located in downtown San Diego), and School for the Creative and Performing Arts; must have a minimum 3.0 GPA on a 4.0 scale; planning to attend an accredited four-year university in the U.S. **Criteria:** Selection will be based on commitment to serving the community through involvement in community service, church or extra-curricular activities.

Funds Avail.: No specific amount. **Duration:** Annual. **Number Awarded:** 1. **To Apply:** The application process is online. **Deadline:** February 5.

9838 ■ Pacific Beacon Scholarship *(Community College, University, Undergraduate, Vocational/Occupational/Scholarship)*

Purpose: To benefit the educational pursuits of active duty military residents in San Diego. **Focus:** General studies/Field of study not specified. **Qualif.:** Applicants must be active-duty enlisted unaccompanied United States navy personnel; must be planning to attend or currently attending a four-year university, community college, or career/technical school in the United States in the fall.

Funds Avail.: Up to $1,500 per award. **Duration:** Annual. **To Apply:** Application details available via email. **Deadline:** May 20. **Contact:** Email: scholarships@sdfoundation.org; URL: www.sdfoundation.org/students/other-tsdf-scholarships/.

9839 ■ Pearman Family Scholarship *(Undergraduate/Scholarship)*

Purpose: To support the education of students from California. **Focus:** General studies/Field of study not specified. **Qualif.:** Applicants must be graduating African-American high school seniors from San Diego County; must have a minimum of 3.4 GPA on a 4.0 scale; planning to attend an accredited four-year university in the U.S.; and be United States citizens and permanent residents. **Criteria:** Preference may be given to applicants whose parents have not graduated from college.

Funds Avail.: No specific amount. **Duration:** Annual. **Deadline:** February 5.

9840 ■ Pollard-Bailey Scholarship *(Undergraduate/Scholarship)*

Purpose: To support the education of students from California. **Focus:** General studies/Field of study not specified. **Qualif.:** Applicants must be graduating high school seniors who will attend an accredited two-year community college in San Diego County; must have a minimum 2.50 GPA on a 4.0 scale; must be San Diego County residents; United States citizens or permanent residents. **Criteria:** Selection will be based on financial need; involvement in extra-curricular activities, church or volunteer activities or work experience.

Funds Avail.: No specific amount. **Duration:** Annual. **Number Awarded:** 5. **Deadline:** February 5.

9841 ■ Qualcomm San Diego Science, Technology, Engineering and Mathematics Scholarship
(Undergraduate/Scholarship)

Purpose: To support the education of students from California. **Focus:** General studies/Field of study not specified. **Qualif.:** Applicants must be graduating high school seniors; or students currently attending a local community college and transferring to either the University of California, San Diego, San Diego State University or California State University, San Marcos; must have a minimum of 3.50 GPA on a 4.0 scale. **Criteria:** Selection will be based on financial need; consideration will be given to students who have participated in extracurricular activities, community service or work experience.

Funds Avail.: No specific amount. **Duration:** Annual. **Deadline:** February 1.

9842 ■ Rancho Bernardo/Smith Scholarship
(Undergraduate/Scholarship)

Purpose: To support the education of students from California. **Focus:** General studies/Field of study not specified. **Qualif.:** Applicant must be graduating high school senior from Rancho Bernardo, who will attend an accredited, public four-year university in the state of California; have a minimum of 3.50 GPA on a 4.0 scale. **Criteria:** Selection will be based on financial need; demonstrated commitment to the Rancho Bernardo community through their involvement in extracurricular activities, community service, sports or work experience; special consideration will be given to applicants who have lost one or both parents while in high school.

Funds Avail.: No specific amount. **Duration:** Annual. **Deadline:** February 5.

9843 ■ Randy Williams Scholarship *(Undergraduate/Scholarship)*

Purpose: To support the education of students from California. **Focus:** General studies/Field of study not specified.

Funds Avail.: No specific amount. **Duration:** Annual. **To Apply:** Applicants must submit the following: completed application; letter of recommendation on official letterhead from swimming coach; essay (maximum of 250 words) describing the benefits they have enjoyed from being involved in competitive swimming and emphasizing how they will utilize the skills they learned in swimming to reach their goals. **Deadline:** February 5.

9844 ■ Ray And Mary Bell Scholarship
(Undergraduate/Scholarship)

Purpose: To support the education of students from California. **Focus:** General studies/Field of study not specified. **Qualif.:** Applicants must be graduating high school seniors from Fallbrook High School who will attend an accredited two-year college or four-year university in the U.S; have a minimum 3.0 GPA on a 4.0 scale. **Criteria:** Selection will be based on commitment to serving the community through involvement in community service, church or extra-curricular activities.

Funds Avail.: No specific amount. **Duration:** Annual. **To Apply:** Applicants should include required additional materials: essay (maximum 250 words) answering What have applicant learned from your experience at The Preuss School, UCSD that applicant feel will best benefitApplicant in college. **Deadline:** February 5.

Awards are arranged alphabetically below their administering organizations

9845 ■ Reuben H. Fleet Memorial Scholarship
(Undergraduate/Scholarship)

Purpose: To support the education of students from California. **Focus:** Engineering; Mathematics and mathematical sciences; Science. **Qualif.:** Applicants must be college students pursuing an undergraduate degree in science, engineering or math; have completed 54 semester units or 72 quarter units; have maintained a minimum of 3.5 GPA on a 4.0 scale; be enrolled at a four-year university in San Diego County; or be San Diego County residents attending a four-year university in the U.S. **Criteria:** Selection will be based on commitment in community service.

Funds Avail.: No specific amount. **Duration:** Annual. **To Apply:** Applicants should include unofficial copy of current transcript. **Deadline:** February 5.

9846 ■ The Rotary Club of Rancho Bernardo Sunrise Community Service Scholarships
(Undergraduate/Scholarship)

Purpose: To support the education of students from California. **Focus:** General studies/Field of study not specified. **Qualif.:** Applicants must be one of the following: graduating high school seniors living in or attending high school in Rancho Bernardo or Poway who plan to attend an accredited four-year university; current community college students whose high school home residence would have qualified them as graduating high school seniors who will transfer to a four-year college/university; current four-year university students whose high school hime residence would have qualified them as graduating high school seniors; or current Interact or Rotoract members residing in the communities of Scripps Ranch, Rancho Penasquitos or Rancho Bernardo, CA and/or who attend Abraxas High School, Del Norte High School, Mount Carmel High School, Poway High School, Scripps Ranch High School, or Westview High School. Furthermore, they must meet all of the following criteria: have a GPA of 3.25 on a 4.0 scale (high school GPAs are unweighted); be actively involved (more than 500 hours total during high school) in serving their community through their involvement in in extra-curricular activities, community service, or work experience in areas benefiting the greater San Diego community; and have demonstrated financial need. **Criteria:** Selection will be based on the submitted application materials.

Funds Avail.: No specific amount. **To Apply:** Applicants may visit the website to verify the application process and other pieces of information.

9847 ■ Ruth E. Jenkins Scholarship *(Undergraduate/Scholarship)*

Purpose: To support the education of African-American students from California. **Focus:** General studies/Field of study not specified. **Criteria:** Selection will be based on financial need; involvement in extra-curricular activities, church or volunteer activities or work experience.

Funds Avail.: No specific amount. **Duration:** Annual. **Deadline:** February 5.

9848 ■ The San Diego Foundation Community Scholarship I *(Undergraduate/Scholarship)*

Purpose: To support the education of students from California. **Focus:** General studies/Field of study not specified. **Criteria:** Selection will be based on financial need; involvement in extracurricular, work, religious or volunteer activities.

Funds Avail.: No specific amount. **Duration:** Annual.

9849 ■ The San Diego Foundation Community Scholarship II *(Undergraduate/Scholarship)*

Purpose: To support the education of students from California. **Focus:** General studies/Field of study not specified. **Qualif.:** Applicants must be graduating high school seniors who plan to enroll full-time at an accredited community college in San Diego County; have a minimum of 2.50 GPA on a 4.0 scale; United States citizens or permanent residents. **Criteria:** Selection will be based on financial need; and by their involvement in extracurricular, work, religious or volunteer activities.

Funds Avail.: No specific amount. **Duration:** Annual. **Deadline:** February 5.

9850 ■ San Pasqual Academy Scholarship
(Undergraduate/Scholarship)

Purpose: To support the education of students from California. **Focus:** General studies/Field of study not specified.

Funds Avail.: No specific amount. **Duration:** Annual. **To Apply:** Applicants must submit the completed application; required additional material is letter of recommendation on official letterhead from staff or faculty at San Pasqual Academy. **Deadline:** February 1.

9851 ■ Harvey L. Simmons Memorial Scholarships
(Undergraduate/Scholarship)

Purpose: To support the education of students from California. **Focus:** General studies/Field of study not specified. **Qualif.:** Applicants must be graduating high school seniors who will attend an accredited two-year college or four-year university in the U.S.; have a minimum of 3.0 GPA on a 4.0 scale; have demonstrated financial need; and committed in serving the community through involvement in community service, church or extra-curricular activities. **Criteria:** Preference will be given to applicants who have participated in high school sports for at least three years, two at the varsity level, and are intending to play at the college level.

Funds Avail.: No specific amount. **To Apply:** Applicants may visit the website to verify the application process and other pieces of information. Required additional materials: letter on official letterhead from their coach detailing the sport(s) played, level, years of participation and achievements. **Deadline:** February 1.

9852 ■ David C. Sommerville Memorial Scholarship
(Undergraduate, Graduate/Scholarship)

Purpose: To provide financial assistance to college bound children and grandchildren of Local Union 230 members. **Focus:** General studies/Field of study not specified. **Qualif.:** Applicants must be high school students graduating in the current year and planning on attending college or students currently enrolled in college full-time; must have achieved at least a 2.5 GPA in high school, or be maintaining at least a 2.5 GPA in college; must be the child, stepchild, or grandchild of a member of Local 230.

Funds Avail.: $1,000. **To Apply:** Application and details available at www.ualocal230.org/scholarships/. **Remarks:** Established by Plumbers & Pipefitters, Local Union 230. **Contact:** Phone: 858-554-0586.

9853 ■ Steve Petix Journalism Scholarship
(Undergraduate/Scholarship)

Purpose: To support the education of students from California. **Focus:** Journalism. **Qualif.:** Applicants must be

Awards are arranged alphabetically below their administering organizations

graduating seniors attending schools in the Grossmont Union High School District who are interested in pursuing a career in journalism or related writing career; have a minimum of 2.50 GPA on a 4.0 scale; and planning to attend an accredited two-year college or four-year university in the U.S. **Criteria:** Preference will be given to students who have been involved in their school newspaper or serve as yearbook staff.

Funds Avail.: No specific amount. **Duration:** Annual. **Deadline:** January 8.

9854 ■ Mark and Karla Stuart Family Scholarship
(Undergraduate/Scholarship)

Purpose: To support the education of students from California. **Focus:** General studies/Field of study not specified.

Funds Avail.: No specific amount. **Deadline:** February 1.

9855 ■ Stuart L. Noderer Memorial Scholarship
(Undergraduate/Scholarship)

Purpose: To support the education of students from California. **Focus:** Architecture; Engineering; Science. **Qualif.:** Applicants must be graduating seniors from Mission Bay High School; planning to attend an accredited four-year university in the U.S.; have a minimum of 3.50 GPA on a 4.0 scale; and will major in science, engineering or architecture.

Funds Avail.: No specific amount. **Duration:** Annual. **Deadline:** February 5.

9856 ■ Katrina Thompson Scholarship *(Community College, College, University, Undergraduate, Vocational/Occupational/Scholarship)*

Purpose: To encourage students from Garfield-Palouse High School to attend college. **Focus:** General studies/Field of study not specified. **Qualif.:** Applicants must be U.S. citizens or permanent residents; be graduating seniors from Garfield-Palouse High School in Palouse, Washington; planning to enroll full-time in an accredited public community college, four-year college, or career/technical school in the United States in the fall; have a cumulative unweighted 2.5 or higher GPA; be actively involved in serving their community as demonstrated by their involvement in extracurricular activities, community service, or work experience.

To Apply: Application and details available at www.sdfoundation.org/students/other-tsdf-scholarships/. **Deadline:** February 5. **Contact:** Email: scholarships@sdfoundation.org.

9857 ■ UCSD Black Alumni Scholarship for Arts and Humanities *(Undergraduate/Scholarship)*

Purpose: To support the education of African-American students from California. **Focus:** Arts; Humanities. **Qualif.:** Applicants must be African-American students currently attending the University of California, San Diego (UCSD); or prospective African-American students enrolling at UCSD; must be majoring in the arts or humanities; United States citizens and permanent residents. **Criteria:** Selection will be based on the student's involvement in the community; and financial need.

Funds Avail.: No specific amount. **Deadline:** February 1.

9858 ■ UCSD Black Alumni Scholarships for Engineering, Mathematics and Science
(Undergraduate/Scholarship)

Purpose: To support the education of African-American students from California. **Focus:** Engineering; Mathematics

and mathematical sciences; Science. **Qualif.:** Applicants must be African-American students currently enrolled full-time at the University of California, San Diego (UCSD); or prospective African-American students who are current California residents and will be enrolling at UCSD; must be majoring in engineering, mathematics or science; must have a 3.0 GPA on a 4.0 scale while current UCSD students must have maintained at least a 2.7 GPA on a 4.0 scale; United States citizens and permanent residents. **Criteria:** Selection will be based on the student's involvement in the community; and financial need.

Funds Avail.: No specifc amount. **Deadline:** February 1.

9859 ■ U.S. Bank Scholarships *(Undergraduate/ Scholarship)*

Purpose: To support the education of students from California. **Focus:** General studies/Field of study not specified. **Qualif.:** Applicants must be adults (ages 25 or older) with income levels less than or equal to 50% of the prevailing San Diego County Metropolitan Statistical Area HUD median income level (currently $37,950); have earned a high school diploma or GED; have demonstrated financial need; working either full-time or part-time; either re-entering college after a break or are starting college for the first time in fall of the current year. **Criteria:** Selection will be based on aforesaid qualifications.

Funds Avail.: No specific amount. **Duration:** Annual. **To Apply:** Applicants may visit the website to verify the application process and other pieces of information. **Deadline:** February 4.

9860 ■ University Club Lamp of Learning Scholarship *(Undergraduate, University/Scholarship)*

Purpose: To provide financial assistance to San Diego students attending four-year universities. **Focus:** General studies/Field of study not specified. **Qualif.:** Applicants must be high school juniors who plan to enroll full-time at accredited four-year university in the United States upon graduation from high school; have resided in San Diego County for at least one year; have been enrolled in AVID (Achievement via Individual Determination) a minimum of two years in high school (including junior year) and preferably at least one year in middle school; have been enrolled in honors/accelerated courses in addition to a minimum of two AP or IB courses and AP exams; have a cumulative unweighted 3.2 or higher GPA; have demonstrated financial need; have a history of community service, employment, and/or responsibilities within the family; and have demonstrated maturity or leadership abilities in extracurricular activities and school or community activities.

Duration: Annual. **To Apply:** Application and details available via email. **Deadline:** February 5. **Remarks:** Sponsored by Lamp of Learning, a fundraising organization providing scholarships to San Diego students. **Contact:** Email: scholarships@sdfoundation.org; URL: www.sdfoundation.org/students/other-tsdf-scholarships/.

9861 ■ Diana Venable Scholarship *(Undergraduate, Community College/Scholarship)*

Purpose: To enable low to moderate-income students who have a record of academic achievement and personal growth, along with leadership potential for both professional careers and civic contributions, to attend a college program. **Focus:** General studies/Field of study not specified. **Qualif.:** Applicants must be U.S. citizens and high school juniors who are or were previously involved in a Rotary Club partnership at Hoover High School, Monarch

Awards are arranged alphabetically below their administering organizations

School, or San Diego High School, or other high schools within the city of San Diego; have a minimum unweighted 2.5 GPA; be enrolling in a full-time accredited community college or four-year college in the fall after their senior year; be actively involved in their community as demonstrated by involvement in extracurricular activities, community service, work experience, or other responsibilities; be highly motivated to succeed; have exemplary citizenship and attendance records; and have demonstrated financial need. **Criteria:** Preference will be given to Rotary-involved students from Hoover High School, Monarch School, and San Diego High School.

Funds Avail.: $20,000. **Duration:** 4 to 5 years. **To Apply:** Application is available at www.sdfoundation.org/students/other-tsdf-scholarships/. **Deadline:** February 5. **Remarks:** Dedicated to carrying on a small portion of the legacy of Ms. Venable, a successful San Diego entrepreneur who spent much of her adult life devoted to helping financially disadvantaged children and young adults achieve a sense of respect, responsibility, and academic achievement in order to overcome the repeated cycle of poverty. **Contact:** Email: scholarships@sdfoundation.org.

9862 ■ Vincent Trotter Health Care Scholarship
(Undergraduate/Scholarship)

Purpose: To support the education of students from California. **Focus:** Health care services. **Qualif.:** Applicants must be current college students or adult re-entry students pursuing a career in the health care field (nurse practitioner, nurse, paramedic, health care aide or hospice aide) who plan to attend an accredited four-year university, community college or licensed career or technical school in the United States; and have a minimum GPA of 3.0 or better on a 4.0 scale. **Criteria:** Selection will be based on activities like extra-curricular clubs, community service or internships.

Funds Avail.: No specific amount. **Duration:** Annual. **Deadline:** February 5.

9863 ■ Marjorie Rose Warren Scholarship
(Undergraduate/Scholarship)

Purpose: To support students at San Diego State University who are working towards their teaching credentials to become public school teachers. **Focus:** Education; Teaching. **Qualif.:** Applicants must be United States citizens, permanent residents, or undocumented students; be current San Diego State University students currently pursuing their teaching credentials and/or student teaching at a public school with the goal of careers as K-12 public school teachers; have resided in San Diego county for at least one year; be actively student teaching; have a cumulative 3.0 or higher GPA; have demonstrated financial need.

To Apply: Application details available via email. **Deadline:** May 22. **Remarks:** Established in honor of dedicated public school teacher Marjorie Rose Warren by her daughter and son-in-law Betsey and Vincent Biondo. **Contact:** Email: scholarships@sdfoundation.org; URL: www.sdfoundation.org/students/other-tsdf-scholarships/.

9864 ■ Weissbuch Family Scholarship
(Undergraduate/Scholarship)

Purpose: To support the education of students from California. **Focus:** General studies/Field of study not specified. **Qualif.:** Applicants must be students enrolled at the University of California, San Diego (UCSD) in their freshman, sophomore or junior year; have a minimum of 2.50 GPA on a 4.0 scale; must also be residents of San Diego county for a minimum of four years. **Criteria:** Selection will be based on financial needs.

Funds Avail.: No specific amount. **Duration:** Annual. **To Apply:** Applicants should include letter from current employer on official letterhead verifying employment, including position held and length of employment. **Deadline:** February 5.

9865 ■ Robert L. Wiegel Scholarship for Coastal Studies *(Graduate/Scholarship)*

Purpose: To honor a graduate student whose work best exemplifies passion for coastal science and engineering. **Focus:** Oceanography. **Qualif.:** Applicant must be a graduate student pursuing, or having recently received, a graduate degree at a California university or college; student's study must deal with a coast problem occurring in a marine environment (such as beaches, the nearshore zone, ports/harbors, coastal rivers and bluffs, lagoons, and wetlands) preferably in California, and the work must identify the importance of the research and the inter-related nature of the scientific/engineering findings with the social, economic, and environmental issues so common to coastal issues. **Criteria:** Preference will be given to students who undertake field work with the intent of discovering the true nature of the problem while experiencing a wide range of ocean conditions.

Funds Avail.: $1,000 to $4,000. **Duration:** Annual. **To Apply:** Provide a description of the study that includes final results; annotated bibliography showing knowledge of pertinent prior research; statement of support from an academic advisor or educational mentor; a personal statement regarding the research effort; completed application. **Remarks:** Sponsored by the California Shore and Beach Preservation Society to honor Prof. Robert L. Wiegel and his coastal and oceanographic research. **Contact:** Wiegel Scholarship for Coastal Studies, c/o CSBPA, 882A Patriot Dr., Moorpark, CA 93021; Email: pgadd@coastalfrontiers.com; URL: www.sdfoundation.org/students/other-tsdf-scholarships/.

9866 ■ The Leon And Margaret Williams Scholarship *(Undergraduate/Scholarship)*

Purpose: To support the education of students from California. **Focus:** Health care services. **Criteria:** Selection is based on financial need.

Funds Avail.: No specific amount. **To Apply:** Applicants must be submit an Essay (maximum 500 words) on "Improving the Health of our Underserved Community". **Deadline:** February 5.

9867 ■ San Diego Pan-Pacific Law Enforcement Association (PANPAC)
PO Box 122924
San Diego, CA 92112
E-mail: sdpanpacfamily@gmail.com
URL: www.sdpanpac.org

9868 ■ Pan Pacific Law Enforcement Scholarships
(Undergraduate/Scholarship)

Purpose: To provide financial assistance to San Diego students interested in law enforcement careers. **Focus:** Law enforcement. **Criteria:** Applicants are selected based on committee's review of the application materials.

Funds Avail.: No specific amount. **To Apply:** Applicants must submit a completed application form available online; must provide an autobiography (one-page maximum, 12-Font, 1 inch margins), high school transcript, two recom-

Awards are arranged alphabetically below their administering organizations

mendation letters (community, school, government agency) and a 250-word essay describing, "How can Law Enforcement better serve the Asian and Pacific Island Community".

9869 ■ San Francisco Foundation (SFF)

One Embarcadero Ctr., Ste. 1400
San Francisco, CA 94111
Ph: (415)733-8500
Fax: (415)477-2783
E-mail: info@sff.org
URL: sff.org
Social Media: www.facebook.com/
  TheSanFranciscoFoundation
www.instagram.com/sanfranciscofoundation
www.linkedin.com/company/the-san-francisco-foundation
twitter.com/tsff
www.youtube.com/user/tsffvideo

9870 ■ Edwin Anthony and Adelaide Boudreaux Cadogan Scholarships *(Graduate/Fellowship)*

Purpose: To provide financial assistance to Bay area Fine Arts students in their academic studies. **Focus:** Art. **Criteria:** Selection will be judged by a panel of art professionals.

Funds Avail.: $6,500. **Duration:** Annual. **To Apply:** Applicants must submit a completed online application form; work samples; description of work submitted; numbered list or work samples as detailed in the online application. **Deadline:** June 30. **Remarks:** Established in 1986. **Contact:** San Francisco Foundation, at the above address.

9871 ■ The Jack K. & Gertrude Murphy Award *(Graduate/Award)*

Purpose: To provide financial assistance to Bay area Fine Arts students in their academic studies. **Focus:** Art. **Criteria:** Selection will be judged by a panel of art professionals. The jurors' decisions will be based solely on merit and are final.

Funds Avail.: $40,000. **Duration:** Annual. **To Apply:** Applicants must submit a completed online application form; work samples; description of work submitted; a numbered list or work samples as detailed in the online application. **Deadline:** June 30. **Remarks:** Established in 1986. **Contact:** Phone: 415-733-8500; Email: artsinfo@sff.org.

9872 ■ San Francisco State University Disability Programs and Resource Center

Student Service Bldg., Rm. 110
San Francisco, CA 94132
Ph: (415)338-2472
Fax: (415)338-1041
E-mail: dprc@sfsu.edu
URL: www.sfsu.edu/~dprc
Social Media: twitter.com/SFSU

9873 ■ P. Johnson and C. Kolb Memorial Scholarships *(Undergraduate, Graduate, Master's, Doctorate/ Scholarship)*

Purpose: To provide financial support for students with disabilities to achieve their academic goals. **Focus:** Disabilities. **Qualif.:** Applicants must be students with disabilities who will be entering or are currently enrolled in graduate school with a minimum of 4 units; can be

undergraduate, graduating senior, graduate, masters/ credential or in PhD level of study (undergraduate and graduate applicants must have a minimum of 3.0 for their GPA). **Criteria:** Selection will be based on the committee's criteria.

Funds Avail.: $500. **To Apply:** Applicants must contact the Center for the application process and other information. **Deadline:** May 15.

9874 ■ Dale M. Schoettler Scholarship for Visually Impaired Students *(Undergraduate, Graduate/ Scholarship)*

Purpose: To assist visually impaired students with their educational expenses. **Focus:** Arts; Business; Humanities; Science. **Qualif.:** Applicants must currently have a minimum cumulative GPA of 2.8 on a 4.0 scale and must maintain a minimum GPA of 2.8 on a 4.0 scale during the academic year in which the award is received; must be currently enrolled in 6.1 units or more as a CSU undergraduate or graduate student in any major field and must remain enrolled in 6.1 units during the academic year in which the award is received; must have a visual disability and provide verification from a medical health professional, which includes the best corrected visual acuity notations.

Funds Avail.: $10,000. **Duration:** Annual. **Number Awarded:** 39. **To Apply:** Applicants must submit the following application requirements; completed scholarship applicants information form (typed); calculation of unmet financial need and calculation of grade point average to be verified by the Financial Aid before submission to DPRC; medical health professional's verification of visual disability, which includes the best corrected visual acuity notations using the "Confirmation of Visual Disability"; brief personal statement of the students describing the applicants' background, personal achievements, challenges encountered, educational pursuits and goals and aspirations for the future; and complete application checklist with initials from the Financial Aid office before submission to the DPRC; be sure to print out and complete both the scholarship information form and the application checklist; and do not leave any line blank on the applicants information form; if there is no information to provide, "N/A" should be used; each item submitted with the application packet (i.e., "Personal Statement") should be clearly labeled; all application requirements must be submitted to the DPRC, no fax submissions will be accepted. **Remarks:** Established in 1991.

9875 ■ Amato Sanita Attorney at Law

1518 Walnut St., Ste. 808
Philadelphia, PA 19102
Ph: (215)515-9088
URL: www.pennsylvaniacriminallawyer.com

9876 ■ The Amato Sanita Brighter Future Scholarship *(Undergraduate, Graduate, Advanced Professional/Scholarship)*

Purpose: To assist a student who exemplifies the pursuit of a better world through education. **Focus:** General studies/Field of study not specified. **Qualif.:** Applicants must be those seeking to enroll in undergraduate, graduate, or law school programs in the United States; and must be in good academic standing, with a minimum cumulative GPA of 3.0 or greater based on the most recent transcript available from the current institution or one attended immediately prior. **Criteria:** Selection will be based on the

Awards are arranged alphabetically below their administering organizations

aforesaid qualifications and compliance with the application process.

Funds Avail.: $500. **To Apply:** Interested applicants must send the following via U.S. mail or fax: a completed application; a 500-word letter of intent that identifies a problem and explains how the applicants intend to use their education as a way to begin solving that problem and creating a brighter future; and academic transcript. **Deadline:** March 31.

9877 ■ Santa Clara County La Raza Lawyers Association
552 NORTH SECOND STREET
San Jose, CA 95112
Ph: (555)555-5555
URL: lrla.clubexpress.com
Social Media: www.facebook.com/SCCLRLA

9878 ■ Law Student Scholarship *(Graduate/Scholarship)*
Purpose: To support the education of law students. **Focus:** Law.
Funds Avail.: $5,000. **Duration:** Annual.

9879 ■ Saratoga County Bar Association (SCBA)
PO Box 994
Saratoga Springs, NY 12866
Ph: (518)280-1974
Fax: (518)280-1974
E-mail: pclute@saratogacountybar.org
URL: www.saratogacountybar.org
Social Media: www.facebook.com/saratogacountybar

9880 ■ Saratoga County Bar Association Law Student Scholarship *(Undergraduate/Scholarship)*
Purpose: To support residents of Saratoga County who are studying to enter the legal profession. **Focus:** Law. **Qualif.:** Applicants must be residents of Saratoga County who are in their second or third year of law school. **Criteria:** Recipients are selected based on class rank, demonstrated leadership, community involvement and financial need.
Funds Avail.: $1,000 each. **Duration:** Annual. **Number Awarded:** 2. **To Apply:** Applicants must submit a completed application form; and must attach graduate and professional school financial aid report, if available. **Deadline:** March 15. **Contact:** Saratoga County Bar Association, PO Box 994, Saratoga Springs, NY, 12866; E-mail: pclute@saratogacountybar.org.

9881 ■ Saskatchewan Association of Recreation Professionals
PO Box 583
Moose Jaw, SK, Canada S6H 4P2
E-mail: office@sarponline.ca
URL: www.sarponline.ca
Social Media: www.facebook.com/saskrecprof
www.instagram.com/saskrecprof
twitter.com/saskrecprof

9882 ■ SARP Professional Development Grant *(Professional development/Grant)*
Purpose: To provide opportunities for members to access financial assistance to host conferences, workshops and, seminars in their community. **Focus:** General studies/Field of study not specified. **Qualif.:** Applicants must be either professional, affiliate, associate or student members in good standing that have host groups or organizations.
Funds Avail.: Maximum of $500. **Duration:** Biennial. **To Apply:** Applicants must obtain a PD grant application form, complete and sign it then send it in to the provincial office. **Contact:** Saskatchewan Association of Recreation Professionals, PO Box 583, Moose Jaw, SK, S6H 4P2; Email: office@sarponline.ca.

9883 ■ Saskatchewan Government Insurance (SGI)
2260 11th Ave.
Regina, SK, Canada S4P 0J9
Free: 844-855-2744
E-mail: sgiinquiries@sgi.sk.ca
URL: www.sgi.sk.ca
Social Media: www.facebook.com/SGIcommunity
www.linkedin.com/company/sgi_5
twitter.com/SGItweets

9884 ■ Auto Body Technician Certificate Scholarship *(Graduate/Scholarship)*
Purpose: To help Saskatchewan students accomplish their education goals. **Focus:** Automotive technology. **Qualif.:** Applicants must be students enrolled in the Auto Body Technician Certificate program at SIAST Wascana Campus and SIAST Kelsey Campus for the diversity scholarship, self-declared as a diversity student with Saskatchewan Polytechnic Wascana Campus. **Criteria:** Selection will be based on academic achievement (75% weighting) and financial need (25% weighting).
Funds Avail.: $2,500. **Duration:** Annual. **Number Awarded:** 2. **To Apply:** Applicants apply directly to SIAST; students may download the application from the SIAST website or pick up applications at the Wascana and Kelsey Campuses.

9885 ■ Stan Hamilton Scholarship *(Graduate/Scholarship)*
Purpose: To help Saskatchewan aboriginal students for them to accomplish their education goals. **Focus:** General studies/Field of study not specified. **Qualif.:** Applicants must be aboriginal (First Nations - Treaty or non-status, Metis or Inuit); must be full-time students at FNUC; must be enrolled in the last 12 credit hour classes in Administration Qualifying, Faculty of Administration, or in at least the second year of a computer science degree; maintain an overall average of at least 65%; and, show their contribution to the community, extracurricular activities or commitments made in balancing work, education and home responsibilities.
Funds Avail.: $2,500. **Duration:** Annual. **Number Awarded:** 1. **To Apply:** Applicants must complete and submit the application form; applications can be obtained from the FNUC website or from the FNUC Student Success Services. **Deadline:** October 31. **Remarks:** The award was established in honor of Stan Hamilton, SGI Vice President of Human Resources (1982 to 1983).

9886 ■ Risk Management and Insurance Scholarship *(Graduate/Scholarship)*
Purpose: To help Saskatchewan students accomplish their education goals. **Focus:** Insurance and insurance-related

Awards are arranged alphabetically below their administering organizations

fields; Risk management. **Qualif.:** Applicant must be a resident of Saskatchewan, Ontario, Alberta or Manitoba; must be registered in the 2nd, 3rd, or 4th year of studies in Risk Management and Insurance (RMIN); must have a GPA of 3.20.

Funds Avail.: $3,000. **Duration:** Annual. **Number Awarded:** 1. **To Apply:** No application is required for this scholarship; eligible students will automatically be considered by their faculty.

9887 ■ Saskatchewan Government Insurance Actuarial Science Scholarship (Graduate/Scholarship)

Purpose: To help Saskatchewan students accomplish their education goals in the field of actuarial science. **Focus:** Actuarial science. **Qualif.:** Applicants must be students enrolled in the third, fourth or fifth year of studies in the Faculty of Science, actuarial science program; have successfully completed 60 or more credit hours towards a Bachelor of Science Degree, major in Actuarial Science; have completed or enrolled in ASC 116, 216 and 317 and have a GPA of 80% or higher in the completed course stated; and, be registered in a minimum of 12 credit hours in the semester the scholarship is paid.

Funds Avail.: $2,000. **Duration:** Annual. **Number Awarded:** 1. **To Apply:** Applicants are considered through the recommendation of the University of Regina Department of Mathematics and Statistics.

9888 ■ Saskatchewan Government Insurance Anniversary Scholarships (Undergraduate/Scholarship)

Purpose: To help Saskatchewan students accomplish their education goals. **Focus:** General studies/Field of study not specified. **Qualif.:** Applicants must be children or legal dependents of an employee of SGI or its wholly-owned subsidiaries; be enrolled full-time in a certificate, diploma or degree program at an accredited post-secondary campus; provide proof of enrollment in the fall semester of the current academic year. **Criteria:** Selection will be based on the eligibility criteria.

Funds Avail.: $2,500. **Duration:** Annual. **Number Awarded:** 4. **To Apply:** Applicants must complete and submit the application form together with proof of enrollment of the current academic year and a transcript demonstrating a minimum average of 70% in the last academic year of study. **Deadline:** September 30. **Contact:** Email: scholarships@sgi.sk.ca.

9889 ■ Saskatchewan Government Insurance Corporate Scholarships (Undergraduate/Scholarship)

Purpose: To help Saskatchewan students accomplish their education goals. **Focus:** General studies/Field of study not specified. **Qualif.:** Applicants must: be residents of Saskatchewan, Alberta or Manitoba; not be legal dependents of an employee of SGI or its wholly owned subsidiaries (legal dependents of SGI employees are eligible for the SGI Anniversary Scholarships only); be enrolled full-time in a certificate, diploma or degree program (related to the business needs of SGI) at an accredited post-secondary campus in Saskatchewan, Alberta or Manitoba; business needs of SGI are defined broadly to include all aspects and departments in the corporation; must demonstrate a contribution to the community, extracurricular activities or commitments made in balancing work, education and home responsibilities. **Criteria:** Selection will be based on the eligibility criteria.

Funds Avail.: $2,500. **Duration:** Annual. **Number Awarded:** 7. **To Apply:** Applicants must complete and

submit the application form together with proof of enrollment of the current academic year and a transcript demonstrating a minimum average of 70% in the last academic year of study. **Deadline:** September 30. **Contact:** Email: scholarships@sgi.sk.ca.

9890 ■ SGI Business Insurance Diploma Scholarships (Undergraduate/Scholarship)

Purpose: To help Saskatchewan students accomplish their education goals. **Focus:** Business. **Qualif.:** Applicants must be enrolled full-time in the Business Insurance Diploma Program - Year 2 at the SIAST Palliser campus; must have earned a minimum 70% average in their 1st year (Business Certificate Program); must self-declare as a diversity student with SIAST (for the diversity scholarship); for the diversity scholarship, self-declared as a diversity student with Saskatchewan Polytechnic. **Criteria:** Selection will be based on the following criteria: academic achievement, as reflected in their overall GPA of all classes required to complete their Business Certificate (75% Weighting); financial need (25% Weighting).

Funds Avail.: $2,500. **Duration:** Annual. **Number Awarded:** 4. **To Apply:** Download the application from the Saskatchewan Polytechnic website or pick up an application at the Moose Jaw Palliser Campus.

9891 ■ SGI Graduate Research Grant (Graduate/Grant)

Purpose: To support development of ideas which may be applied to the solution of problems in traffic safety in Saskatchewan. **Focus:** Engineering; Social sciences. **Qualif.:** Applicant must be a University of Regina graduate student who meets the following criteria: has a proposed research which involves engineering or human factors issues related to traffic safety; has a minimum cumulative grade point average (CGPA) of 80%; and, be registered full-time (minimum 6 credit hours) in the semester the award is presented. Continuing students must be in good standing and have demonstrated satisfactory achievement in coursework as well as appropriate progress toward the completion of the research requirement. **Criteria:** Selection will be based on the Graduate Studies and Research Scholarship Committee will review applications, select a recipient.

Funds Avail.: $5,000. **Duration:** Annual. **To Apply:** Applications for the award are available on the University of Regina website; applicants should include a research proposal along with an outline of their relevant experience related to their project; applications must also be supported by a confidential letter of reference from the student's supervising faculty member. **Deadline:** September 30.

9892 ■ Saskatchewan Hockey Association
Ste. 2 - 575 Park St.
Regina, SK, Canada S4N 5B2
Ph: (306)789-5101
Fax: (306)789-6112
E-mail: kellym@sha.sk.ca
URL: www.sha.sk.ca
Social Media: www.facebook.com/SaskHockey
twitter.com/sask_hockey

9893 ■ Saskatchewan Hockey Association Scholarships (Undergraduate/Scholarship)

Purpose: To provide financial assistance to the SHA registered member to further their education. **Focus:** Sports

Awards are arranged alphabetically below their administering organizations

studies. **Qualif.:** Applicant must have been registered for three years; be a registrant in good standing in the SHA; be a graduating Grade 12 student during that year for Junior A, B and C players or Senior players 20 years of age or under as of December 31 of the current year; be going to attend a Saskatchewan based University, affiliate College or SIAST; and, attend an institution within four years to take advantage of the grant. **Criteria:** Selection will be based on the committee's criteria.

Funds Avail.: 1,000 Canadian Dollars. **Duration:** Annual. **Number Awarded:** Minimum of 11. **To Apply:** Application form can be obtained from the SHA office; and will be required to fill out and return an application on or before the deadline; must submit two letters of reference. **Deadline:** August 31.

9894 ■ Saskatchewan Music Festival Association (SMFA)
4623 Albert St.
Regina, SK, Canada S4S 7K3
URL: www.smfa.ca

9895 ■ Mary Anderson Memorial Intermediate Woodwind Scholarship *(Other/Scholarship)*

Purpose: To recognize the best performance in the Intermediate Woodwind in the Provincial Finals Competitions. **Focus:** Music.

9896 ■ L.I. Bryson Memorial Senior Speech Arts Scholarship *(Other/Scholarship)*

Purpose: To recognize the most promising competitor in the Senior Speech Arts Classes 10050, 10080, 10110, 10120, and 10170 in the Provincial Finals Competitions. **Focus:** Speech and language pathology/Audiology.

Funds Avail.: 400 Canadian Dollars. **Duration:** Annual. **Remarks:** The scholarship was established in memory of Iris Bryson, by her family whose passion for music and literature greatly enriched the lives of those around her.

9897 ■ Covey Intermediate Female Voice Scholarship *(Graduate/Scholarship)*

Purpose: To recognize the most promising competitor in the Girls' Voice Classes 1042 and 1043 in the Provincial Finals Competitions. **Focus:** Music, Vocal.

Funds Avail.: 300 Canadian Dollars. **Duration:** Annual. **Remarks:** Endowed by Edna Covey and Doris Covey Lazecki in memory of their mother, Jessie Covey, who was an avid supporter of young female singers.

9898 ■ Daryl Cooper Intermediate Piano Beethoven Scholarship *(Other/Scholarship)*

Purpose: To recognize the best performance in the Intermediate Beethoven Class 2061 in the Provincial Finals Competitions. **Focus:** Music.

Funds Avail.: 300 Canadian Dollars. **Duration:** Annual.

9899 ■ Frances England & Hugheen Ferguson Memorial Intermediate Piano Haydn & Mozart Scholarship *(Other/Scholarship)*

Purpose: To recognize the best performance in the Intermediate Haydn and Mozart Class 2064 in the Provincial Finals Competitions. **Focus:** Music.

Funds Avail.: 300 Canadian Dollars. **Duration:** Annual.

9900 ■ Goodfellow Memorial Canadian Vocal Music Scholarship *(Other/Scholarship)*

Purpose: To recognize the competitor presenting the best performance in the Senior Canadian Vocal Music Class 1220 in the Provincial Finals Competitions. **Focus:** Music, Vocal.

Funds Avail.: 400 Canadian Dollars. **Duration:** Annual.

9901 ■ Goodfellow Memorial Grade A Female Voice Scholarship *(Undergraduate/Scholarship)*

Purpose: To recognize the most accomplished singer in the Grade A Female Voice Classes 1000, 1001, and 1002 in the Provincial Finals Competition. **Focus:** Music, Vocal. **Qualif.:** Applicants should be Grade A Female Voice Classes 1000, 1001, and 1002.

Funds Avail.: 400 Canadian Dollars. **Duration:** Annual. **Remarks:** Endowed by the late S. J. Goodfellow of Regina, who established the Trust Fund in honor of his wife, Nancy Goodfellow. During her lifetime, Mrs. Goodfellow had many and varied community interests to which she gave of herself unstintingly.

9902 ■ Goodfellow Memorial Oratorio Scholarship *(Other/Scholarship)*

Purpose: To recognize the winner of the Senior Oratorio Classes 1100, 1101, and 1106 in the Provincial Finals Competitions. **Focus:** Music.

Duration: Annual.

9903 ■ Goodfellow Memorial Senior Grade A Male Voice Scholarship *(Other/Scholarship)*

Purpose: To recognize the most accomplished singer in the Grade A Male Voice Classes 1010, 1011, 1012, and 1013 in the Provincial Finals Competitions. **Focus:** Music, Vocal.

Funds Avail.: 400 Canadian Dollars. **Duration:** Annual. **Remarks:** The scholarship was established in honor of Madame Alicia Birkett, A.R.C.M., L.R.A.M., was an inspirational and successful teacher of her many students from the southern area of this province.

9904 ■ Goodfellow Memorial Senior Operatic Scholarship *(Graduate/Scholarship)*

Purpose: To recognize the most accomplished singer in the Senior Operatic Classes 1120 and 1125 in the Provincial Final Competitions. **Focus:** Music, Vocal.

Funds Avail.: 400 Canadian Dollars. **Remarks:** The scholarship was established in memory of Hazel Farnsworth of Regina and she was being a choir member of St. Paul's Cathedral for many years.

9905 ■ Jackson Memorial Intermediate Piano Recital Scholarship *(Graduate/Scholarship)*

Purpose: To recognize the best performance in the Intermediate Recital Class 2142 in the Provincial Finals Competitions. **Focus:** Music.

Funds Avail.: 300 Canadian Dollars.

9906 ■ Johanna Mitchell Memorial Intermediate Viola/ Cello/ Double Bass Scholarship *(Graduate, Undergraduate/Scholarship)*

Purpose: To recognize the best performance in the Intermediate Cello/Viola/Double Bass Classes in the Provincial Finals Competitions. **Focus:** Music.

Awards are arranged alphabetically below their administering organizations

Funds Avail.: 300 Canadian Dollars. **Duration:** Annual. **Remarks:** The scholarship was established by Camille and Charles Mitchell of Saskatoon, in memory of Johanna Mitchell.

9907 ■ Kipling and District Music Festival Intermediate Chopin Scholarship *(Other/Scholarship)*

Purpose: To recognize the winner of the Intermediate Chopin Class 2091 in the Provincial Finals Competitions. **Focus:** Music, Piano.

Funds Avail.: 300 Canadian Dollars. **Duration:** Annual.

9908 ■ Kiwanis of Wascana Senior Cello/Viola/ Double Bass Scholarship *(Graduate/Scholarship)*

Purpose: To recognize the best performance in the Senior Cello/Viola/Double Bass Classes 3200, 3220, 3240, 3270, 3290, 3320, 3340, 3400, 3420, 3440, 3461, 3480, 3500, 3510, 3530, 3600, 3620, 3630, 3650, and 3660 in the Provincial Finals Competitions. **Focus:** Music.

Funds Avail.: 300 Canadian Dollars.

9909 ■ Heather Laxdal Memorial Grade B Female Voice Scholarship *(Undergraduate/Scholarship)*

Purpose: To recognize the most promising competitor in the Grade B Female Voice Classes 1020, 1021, and 1022 in the Provincial Finals Competitions. **Focus:** Music, Vocal.

9910 ■ Mary Anderson Memorial (Sacred) Choral Scholarship *(Undergraduate/Scholarship)*

Purpose: To recognize the most outstanding Senior Woodwind competitor in Classes 5000, 5010, 5020, 5030, 5040, 5050, 5060, 5070, 5080, 5100, 5110, 5120, 5130, 5140, 5150, 5160, 5170, 5180, 5200, 5300, 5310, and 5400 in the Provincial Finals Competitions. **Focus:** Music.

Funds Avail.: 500 Canadian Dollars.

9911 ■ Mrs. Clare K. Mendel Memorial Senior Violin Recital Scholarship *(Graduate/Scholarship)*

Purpose: To recognize the finest performance in the Senior Violin Classes 3000, 3080, 3120, 3180, 3240, and 3290 in the Provincial Finals Competitions. **Focus:** Music, Violin.

Funds Avail.: 400 Canadian Dollars. **Duration:** Annual. **Remarks:** The scholarship was established in memory of Mrs. Clare K. Mendel.

9912 ■ Music for Young Children Saskatchewan Teachers' Association Senior Chopin Scholarship *(Other/Scholarship)*

Purpose: To recognize the winner of the Senior Chopin Class 2085 in the Provincial Finals Competitions. **Focus:** Music.

Funds Avail.: 400 Canadian Dollars. **Duration:** Annual.

9913 ■ Music for Young Children Saskatchewan Teachers' Association Senior Piano Chopin Scholarship *(Other/Scholarship)*

Purpose: To recognize the winner of the Senior French Music Class 2100 in the Provincial Finals Competitions. **Focus:** Music.

Funds Avail.: 400 Canadian Dollars. **Duration:** Annual.

9914 ■ Regan Grant Memorial Intermediate Musical Theatre Ballad Scholarship *(Other/Scholarship)*

Purpose: To recognize the finest performance in the Senior Musical Theatre Classes 9001, 9011, 9021, 9031, 9041,

and 9051 in the Provincial Final Competitions. **Focus:** Music, Vocal.

Funds Avail.: 300 Canadian Dollars. **Duration:** Annual. **Remarks:** The scholarship was established in memory of Regan Grant and he was following graduation from MUCC, Regan earned a double Major in Voice and Drama in 1984 from the University of Regina.

9915 ■ Saskatchewan Choral Federation Open Choral Scholarship *(Graduate/Award, Scholarship)*

Purpose: To recognize the most outstanding performance by a Senior Choir in Classes 140, 141, 142, 143, 144, 145, 170, 171, 172, 173, 174, and 175 in the Provincial Finals Competitions. **Focus:** Music, Vocal.

Funds Avail.: 300 Canadian Dollars. **Duration:** Annual.

9916 ■ Saskatchewan Registered Music Teachers' Association Senior Romantic Music Scholarship *(Other/Scholarship)*

Purpose: To recognize the best performance in the Senior Romantic Music Piano Class 2085 in the Provincial Finals Competitions. **Focus:** Music.

Funds Avail.: 400 Canadian Dollars. **Duration:** Annual.

9917 ■ Blanche Squires Memorial Senior Brass Scholarship *(Undergraduate/Scholarship)*

Purpose: To recognize the finest performance in the Senior Brass Classes 6000, 6010, 6020, 6030, 6040, 6100, 6110, 6120, 6130, 6140, 6200, 6300, and 6400 in the Provincial Finals Competitions. **Focus:** Music.

Funds Avail.: $400. **Duration:** Annual.

9918 ■ Thomas and Don Hatton Memorial Senior Grade B Male Voice Scholarship *(Graduate/Scholarship)*

Purpose: To recognize the most promising competitor in the Grade B Male Voice Classes 1030, 1031, 1032, and 1033 in the Provincial Finals Competitions. **Focus:** Music, Vocal.

Funds Avail.: 400 Canadian Dollars. **Duration:** Annual. **Remarks:** The scholarship was established in memory of Thomas and Don Hatton.

9919 ■ Gordon C. Wallis Memorial Senior Piano Beethoven Scholarship *(Other/Scholarship)*

Purpose: To recognize the Senior Beethoven Class 2060 in the Provincial Finals Competitions. **Focus:** Music.

Funds Avail.: $400. **Duration:** Annual. **Remarks:** The scholarship was established in honor of the late Gordon C. Wallis of Regina.

9920 ■ Saskatchewan Pulse Growers (SPG)
207-116 Research Dr.
Saskatoon, SK, Canada S7N 3R3
Ph: (306)668-5556
Fax: (306)668-5557
E-mail: pulse@saskpulse.com
URL: saskpulse.com
Social Media: www.facebook.com/saskpulse
twitter.com/saskpulse

9921 ■ Dr. Alfred E. Slinkard Scholarship *(Graduate/Scholarship)*

Purpose: To promote academic excellence within the area of pulse crop research in Saskatchewan. **Focus:** Agricul-

Awards are arranged alphabetically below their administering organizations

tural sciences. **Qualif.:** Applicants must be full-time students entering or continuing studies pursuing a Masters of Science degree or Doctor of Philosophy degree who are conducting pulse crop research at the University of Saskatchewan. **Criteria:** Selection will be based on academic achievement, as determined by the Award Committee.

Funds Avail.: $20,000. **Duration:** Annual. **Number Awarded:** 1.

9922 ■ Don Jaques Memorial Fellowship (Graduate/ Fellowship)

Purpose: To recognize and support outstanding academic achievement and research interests in pulse crops. **Focus:** Agricultural sciences. **Qualif.:** Applicants must be either Canadian citizens or landed immigrants who are full-time, post-graduate students in an M.Sc. or Ph.D. degree program at the University of Saskatchewan, and are conducting thesis research on some aspect of pulse crop development. **Criteria:** Selection will be made on the basis of a proven record of outstanding academic achievement and research interest in pulse crops development; preference will be given to Saskatchewan residents.

Funds Avail.: $20,000. **Duration:** Annual. **Number Awarded:** 1.

9923 ■ Saskatchewan Pulse Growers Undergraduate Scholarships (Undergraduate/Scholarship)

Purpose: To promote the interest in pursuing a career related to agriculture and pulse industry. **Focus:** Agricultural sciences; Engineering; Natural sciences; Nutrition. **Qualif.:** Applicants must be students and they, or their parents, must be registered as Saskatchewan pulse growers; must not be immediate family members of current SPG staff or directors; have a minimum average of 70% on five high school average; and, be accepted as full-time students in a Saskatchewan-based post-secondary program that is associated with the pulse industry or agriculture (e.g. agriculture, natural sciences, nutrition, and engineering). **Criteria:** Selection will be based on the premises that students must have an interest in pursuing a career related to agriculture and the pulse industry; have a history of demonstrated leadership; and, have made contributions to school and community life.

Funds Avail.: No specific amount. **Duration:** Annual. **To Apply:** Applicants must submit the following application requirements: unofficial transcript at the time of application followed by Official Transcript upon receipt; proof of acceptance (conditional or otherwise) to a post-secondary program, followed by proof of registration; one headshot photo; written permission to use photo and name in promotional materials (if candidate is successful); applicants must also submit a maximum of 500 words essay on: career plans and how applicants plan to contribute to the pulse industry; situations where the applicant has demonstrated leadership; contributions the applicants have made to school and community life. **Contact:** Saskatchewan Pulse Growers, 207-116 Research Dr., Saskatoon, SK, S7N 3R3, Phone: 306- 668-0116, Email: pulse@ saskpulse.com.

9924 ■ Saskatchewan School Boards Association

400 - 2222 13th Ave.
Regina, SK, Canada S4P 3M7
Ph: (306)569-0750

Fax: (306)352-9633
E-mail: admin@saskschoolboards.ca
URL: www.saskschoolboards.ca
Social Media: www.facebook.com/saskschoolboards
twitter.com/saskschoolboard

9925 ■ Saskatchewan School Boards Association Education Scholarships (Graduate/Scholarship)

Purpose: To support students who remain in Saskatchewan for acquiring post-secondary education. **Focus:** Science technologies. **Qualif.:** Applicants must be graduating Saskatchewan high school students. **Criteria:** Selection will be based on demonstrated good character, community leadership, financial need and a 500-word essay.

Funds Avail.: $2,500. **Duration:** Annual. **Number Awarded:** 2. **Deadline:** August 31.

9926 ■ Saskatchewan School Boards Association Graduate Student Award (Graduate/Award)

Purpose: To recognize leadership in education and to advance informed decision making in education. **Focus:** General studies/Field of study not specified. **Qualif.:** Applicants should be individuals who have recently completed a doctoral dissertation, master's thesis or project in education. Such study must contribute to advancing K-12 education in Saskatchewan.

Funds Avail.: $2,000. **Duration:** Annual. **Number Awarded:** Up to 4. **Deadline:** September 1.

9927 ■ Saskatchewan Trucking Association (STA)

103 Hodsman Rd.
Regina, SK, Canada S4N 5W5
Ph: (306)569-9696
Free: 800-563-7623
E-mail: info@sasktrucking.com
URL: www.sasktrucking.com
Social Media: www.facebook.com/sasktrucking
www.instagram.com/sasktrucking
www.linkedin.com/company/saskatchewan-trucking
 -association
twitter.com/sasktrucking
www.youtube.com/channel/UC68_B4OUbiU1BqiB5-z0fdw

9928 ■ Saskatchewan Trucking Association Scholarships (Undergraduate/Scholarship)

Purpose: To support those that are wishing to further their education into post-secondary. **Focus:** General studies/ Field of study not specified. **Qualif.:** Applicant must be a dependent of an employee or an employee of a STA member company; must be a high school graduate; must confirmation of application to a post-secondary institution. **Criteria:** Special consideration is given to those that are specializing in an area within the truck transport industry.

Funds Avail.: $3,000; $1,000. **Duration:** Annual. **Number Awarded:** 3. **To Apply:** Applicants must submit a transcript of record and the application form and must send it to scholarship selection committee. **Deadline:** June. **Contact:** Susan Ewart, Executive Director; 103 Hodsman Rd., Regina, Saskatchewan, S4N 5W5; Phone: 306-569-9696; Toll Free: 800-563-7623; Email: sewart@sasktrucking.com.

9929 ■ Scandinavian Society of Cincinnati (SSOC)

1279 Sweetwater Dr.
Cincinnati, OH 45215

Awards are arranged alphabetically below their administering organizations

URL: www.scandinaviansoc.org
Social Media: facebook.com/scandinaviansoc
twitter.com/ScandinavianSOC

9930 ■ SSOC Scholarship *(Undergraduate/ Scholarship)*

Purpose: To foster the development of ideas, knowledge, culture and understanding between the people of the United States of America and Scandinavian countries. **Focus:** General studies/Field of study not specified. **Qualif.:** Applicants must be persons or students from the Greater Cincinnati area, students from Scandinavia studying in the Greater Cincinnati, or persons or groups putting on Scandinavian cultural events in this area.

Funds Avail.: $1,000. **To Apply:** Applicants must complete the application form and must prepare a 10-page, double-spaced reviewed paper. **Contact:** For questions, Shirley Ekvall, 549 Tohatchi Dr., Cincinnati, Oh, 4521; Email: scholarships@scandinaviansoc.org.

9931 ■ Leopold Schepp Foundation
950 Third Ave., 31st Fl.
New York, NY 10022
Ph: (212)692-0191
URL: www.scheppfoundation.org

9932 ■ Leopold Schepp Foundation Scholarship *(Undergraduate, Graduate/Scholarship)*

Purpose: To provide educational support for students pursuing higher education. **Focus:** General studies/Field of study not specified. **Criteria:** Selection shall be based on the following: character; ability; and financial need.

Funds Avail.: $9,000. **Duration:** Annual. **Number Awarded:** Varies. **To Apply:** Applicants must submit copies of their and their parents' most recently filed income tax returns; detailed estimate of academic expenses and resources is required. **Deadline:** July 20.

9933 ■ Schmeelk Canada Foundation
1 Place Ville Marie, 39th Fl.
Montreal, QC, Canada H3B 4M7
URL: www.schmeelk.ca/foundation
Social Media: facebook.com/SchmeelkCanada

9934 ■ Richard J. Schmeelk Fellowship *(Graduate/ Fellowship)*

Purpose: To promote intercultural awareness and interprovincial studies. **Focus:** Foreign languages. **Qualif.:** Applicant must be a Canadian citizen or landed immigrant; must have completed a bachelor's degree and pursuing studies in Canada's other official language at one of the Richard J. Schmeelk Fellowship partner universities.

Funds Avail.: No specific amount. **To Apply:** Applicants must submit a completed application form and attach the required supporting documents. Submit complete application package to the participating university of the applicant's choice.

9935 ■ Schmidt Kramer Injury Lawyers
209 State St.
Harrisburg, PA 17101
Ph: (717)888-8888
Fax: (717)232-6467

Free: 888-476-0807
URL: www.schmidtkramer.com
Social Media: www.facebook.com/SchmidtKramer
www.linkedin.com/company/schmidt-kramer-p.c.
twitter.com/DialThe8s
www.youtube.com/user/schmidtkramerlaw

9936 ■ Schmidt Kramer Annual Scholarship For Academic Excellence *(Undergraduate/Scholarship)*

Purpose: To support outstanding Pennsylvania college students. **Focus:** General studies/Field of study not specified. **Qualif.:** Applicants must be Pennsylvania college students with a minimum 3.0 GPA. **Criteria:** Selection will be based on the foresaid qualifications and compliance with the application process.

Funds Avail.: $1,500. **Duration:** Annual. **Number Awarded:** 1. **To Apply:** Applicants must submit the completed online application form along with the required documents. They must also include a written, original essay of at least 500 words regarding the topic of how the youth of today can help to positively shape the legal system in the future. **Deadline:** December 1.

9937 ■ Scholarship America
7900 International Dr., Ste. 500
Minneapolis, MN 55425
Ph: (952)830-7300
Free: 800-537-4180
E-mail: development@scholarshipamerica.org
URL: scholarshipamerica.org
Social Media: www.facebook.com/ScholarshipAmerica
www.instagram.com/scholamerica
www.linkedin.com/company/scholarship-america
twitter.com/scholamerica
youtube.com/user/ScholarshipAmerica

9938 ■ AbbVie Immunology Scholarship *(Community College, Undergraduate, Graduate, Vocational/ Occupational, Doctorate/Scholarship)*

Purpose: To provide financial support for exceptional students living with chronic inflammatory diseases. **Focus:** General studies/Field of study not specified. **Qualif.:** Applicant must be legal residents of the U.S. and diagnosed by a healthcare professional with one of the following conditions: ankylosing spondylitis (AS), Crohn's disease (CD), hidradenitis suppurativa (HS), juvenile idiopathic arthritis (JIA), psoriasis (Ps), psoriatic arthritis (PsA), rheumatoid arthritis (RA), ulcerative colitis (UC), or uveitis (UV); must plan to enroll in undergraduate (associate or bachelor) or graduate (master's, MD, JD, doctorate) study at an accredited two- or four-year college, university, or vocational school in the United States. **Criteria:** Selection will be based on academic excellence, community involvement, and ability to serve as a positive role model in the immunology community.

Funds Avail.: Up to $15,000 (dependent on degree pursued). **Duration:** Annual. **To Apply:** Application and details are available online at: abbvieimmunologyscholarship.com. **Deadline:** December 4. **Contact:** Email: AbbVieimmunology@scholarshipamerica.org.

9939 ■ James Beard Foundation Scholarship Program *(College, Community College, Undergraduate, Professional development/Scholarship)*

Purpose: To assist aspiring and established culinary professionals who plan to further their education. **Focus:**

Awards are arranged alphabetically below their administering organizations

Culinary arts. **Qualif.:** Applicant must be a high school student or graduate planning to start or continue a course of study at a licensed culinary school or food-focused program.

Funds Avail.: Up to $20,000. **Number Awarded:** Over 100. **To Apply:** Application available at www.scholarsapply.org/jamesbeard/. **Deadline:** May 15. **Contact:** URL: www.jamesbeard.org/scholarships.

9940 ■ Bristol-Myers Squibb Scholarship for Cancer Survivors (Community College, Four Year College, Vocational/Occupational, Undergraduate/Scholarship)

Purpose: To assist cancer survivors who plan to continue their education in college or vocational school programs. **Focus:** General studies/Field of study not specified. **Qualif.:** Applicants must be cancer survivors, age 25 and under, who are high school seniors or graduates, or current postsecondary undergraduates; must be enrolled or planning to enroll in full-time undergraduate study at an accredited two- or four-year college, university, or vocational-technical school for the entire upcoming academic year. Scholarships are not renewable, but applicants may reapply each year as long as they meet eligibility requirements.

Funds Avail.: $10,000 each. **Duration:** Annual. **Number Awarded:** Up to 25. **To Apply:** Application can be completed online at: scholarshipamerica.org/students/browse-scholarships/. **Deadline:** April 23. **Remarks:** Funds for this scholarship were provided by a donation from Bristol-Myers Squibb. **Contact:** Email: scholarsapply.org/cancer-survivors.

9941 ■ Dunkin' Donuts Philadelphia Regional Scholarship Program (Undergraduate/Scholarship)

Purpose: To help Philadelphia area students attain undergraduate degrees. **Focus:** General studies/Field of study not specified. **Qualif.:** Applicant must be high school seniors who plan to enroll full-time undergraduate course of study at an accredited two- or four-year college, university, or vocational-technical school for the entire academic year; must also reside in Kent or New Castle counties, DE; Atlantic, Burlington, Camden, Cape May, Cumberland, Gloucester, Mercer or Salem counties, NJ; Berks, Bucks, Chester, Delaware, Lehigh, Montgomery, Northampton or Philadelphia counties, PA. **Criteria:** Selection is based on applicant's demonstration of a well-rounded character: positive academic record, demonstrated leadership, commitment to school and community activities, and experience in a work environment.

Funds Avail.: $2,000 each. **Duration:** Annual. **Number Awarded:** Up to 25. **To Apply:** Application is available online at: learnmore.scholarsapply.org/dunkinphilly. **Deadline:** April 15. **Contact:** Email: dunkindonutsphil@scholarshipamerica.org.

9942 ■ Future of School Scholarship Program (Undergraduate/Award)

Purpose: To provide graduates of blended and online programs with access to financial support that will allow them to achieve their educational goals beyond high school. **Focus:** General studies/Field of study not specified. **Qualif.:** Applicant must be a high school senior who has completed a minimum of five blended or online courses during the last two years of high school and is planning to enroll full-time in undergraduate study at an accredited two- or four-year college, university, or vocational-technical school; must have demonstrated academic achievement or improvement as a direct result of their enrollment in the blended/online learning curriculum.

Funds Avail.: Up to $10,000. **Duration:** Annual. **Number Awarded:** 30. **To Apply:** Application is available online at scholarsapply.org/fbol-scholarship. **Deadline:** March 19. **Contact:** Email: fbol-scholarship@scholarshipamerica.org.

9943 ■ NANOG Scholarship Program (Undergraduate, Graduate/Scholarship)

Purpose: To support the next generation of network operators by assisting current undergraduate and graduate level students pursuing a degree in computer engineering, computer science, electrical engineering, network engineering, or telecommunications. **Focus:** Computer and information sciences; Engineering, Computer; Engineering, Electrical; Telecommunications systems. **Qualif.:** Applicants must plan to enroll part-time (at least six credits) or full-time in undergraduate or graduate study at an accredited two- or four-year college or university for the entire academic year; must be pursuing degrees in Computer Engineering, Computer Science, Electrical Engineering, Network Engineering, or Telecommunications (Telecommunication for graduate students only); must have a minimum 3.0 GPA.

Funds Avail.: $10,000. **Duration:** Annual. **To Apply:** Application and details are available online at: learnmore.scholarsapply.org/nanog/. **Deadline:** April 16.

9944 ■ Wells Fargo Scholarship Program for People with Disabilities (Undergraduate/Scholarship)

Purpose: To help people with disabilities obtain the education or training necessary to succeed in the career path of their choice. **Focus:** General studies/Field of study not specified. **Qualif.:** Applicants must have an identified disability (defined as someone who has, or considers themselves to have, a long-term or recurring issue that impacts one or more major life activity); must be high school seniors or graduates planning to enroll, or who are already enrolled, in full- or half-time undergraduate study at an accredited two- or four-year college or university in the United States for the upcoming school year.

Funds Avail.: $2,500 for full-time students; $1,250 for half-time students. **Duration:** Annual. **To Apply:** Submit application at: learnmore.scholarsapply.org/pwdscholarship/. **Deadline:** December 4. **Remarks:** Provided in partnership with Wells Fargo. **Contact:** Email: pwdscholarship@scholarshipamerica.org.

9945 ■ Wells Fargo Veterans Scholarship Program (Undergraduate, Graduate, Two Year College, Four Year College/Scholarship)

Purpose: To help fill financial aid gaps for veterans and the spouses of disabled veterans, after military benefits and other grants and scholarships have been utilized. **Focus:** General studies/Field of study not specified. **Qualif.:** Applicants must be honorably-discharged (no longer drilling) veterans or spouses of disabled veterans who have served in the United States military, including the Reserves and National Guard, and have received a Certificate of Eligibility from the Department of Veterans Affairs or another document of service; must be high school or GED graduates who plan to enroll or students who are already enrolled in full-time undergraduate (first Associates or Bachelor's) or graduate (first Master's degree) study at an accredited two-year or four-year college, university, or vocational-technical school; must have a minimum cumulative grade point average of 2.0 on a 4.0 scale, or its equivalent. **Criteria:** Selection will be based on academic performance, demonstrated leadership and participation in school and community activi-

Awards are arranged alphabetically below their administering organizations

ties, work experience, and two essays. Financial need will be considered.

Funds Avail.: Up to $5,000 per year, renewable. **Duration:** Annual. **To Apply:** Application and details are available online at: learnmore.scholarsapply.org/wellsfargoveterans/. **Deadline:** February 28. **Remarks:** Provided in partnership with Wells Fargo. **Contact:** E-mail: wellsfargoveterans@scholarshipamerica.org.

9946 ■ Scholarship Foundation of the Pacific
c/o Beverley Kniffen, Executive Director
6 - 3415 Chancellor Place
West Kelowna, BC, Canada V4T 2S9
Ph: (604)916-7881
E-mail: sfotpbeverley@gmail.com
URL: www.sfotp.com

9947 ■ SFP Scholarships *(Undergraduate/Scholarship)*

Purpose: To support undergraduate students in the area of marine science. **Focus:** General studies/Field of study not specified. **Qualif.:** Applicants must maintain at least a 3.5 GPA; must be in communities of the Queen Charlotte Islands, must be in conjunction with one of our University partners: Hawaii Pacific University, University of Hawaii and Simon Fraser University. **Criteria:** The Foundation will select the scholarship recipient.

Funds Avail.: No specific amount. **Duration:** Annual. **To Apply:** Applicants must submit the required documentation includes transcripts, letters of recommendation from school officials and community representatives and a letter from the applicant describing their educational and career goals.

9948 ■ The Scholarship Foundation of St. Louis
6825 Clayton Ave., Ste. 100
Saint Louis, MO 63139
Ph: (314)725-7990
Fax: (314)725-5231
E-mail: info@sfstl.org
URL: www.sfstl.org
Social Media: www.facebook.com/ScholarshipFoundationSTL
twitter.com/SfofStL

9949 ■ Ava's Grace Scholarship Program *(Graduate, Undergraduate/Scholarship)*

Purpose: To provide financial assistance to members who want to pursue their educational goals. **Focus:** General studies/Field of study not specified.

Funds Avail.: $5,000. **Duration:** Annual. **Deadline:** May 15. **Remarks:** Established in 2010. **Contact:** The Scholarship Foundation of St. Louis, 6825 Clayton Ave, Ste. 100, St. Louis, MO, 63139; Phone: 314-725-7990; Email: info@sfstl.org.

9950 ■ Scholarship Foundation of Santa Barbara (SFSB)
2253 Las Positas Rd.
Santa Barbara, CA 93105
Ph: (805)687-6065
URL: www.sbscholarship.org
Social Media: www.facebook.com/sbscholarship

www.instagram.com/sbscholarship
twitter.com/sbscholarship
www.youtube.com/user/sbscholarship

9951 ■ Scholarship Foundation of Santa Barbara General Scholarship Program *(Undergraduate, Graduate/Scholarship)*

Purpose: To assist applicants studying in standard academic programs on a traditional academic calendar. **Focus:** General studies/Field of study not specified.

Duration: Annual. **To Apply:** Applicants must provide a following information: personal essay; personal profile; Citizenship and additionally following materials are required: two letters of recommendation; High school transcript; College transcript (if applicable); Student Aid Report (SAR) and College enrollment history. **Deadline:** January 15. **Contact:** Phone: 805-687-6065; Email: info@sbscholarship.org.

9952 ■ Art Competition Scholarship Program *(Undergraduate/Scholarship)*

Purpose: To provide financial assistance to students who are planning to major in Art or an art-related major at college. **Focus:** Arts. **Criteria:** Selection will be based on the committee criteria.

Funds Avail.: No specific amount. **Duration:** Annual. **To Apply:** Applicants must upload their high school transcripts to their online application. **Deadline:** November 15. **Contact:** Phone: 805-687-6065; Email: info@sbscholarship.org.

9953 ■ South Coast High School Senior Honors Scholarship Program *(Graduate/Scholarship)*

Purpose: To provide assistance to those students who are pursuing their chosen education. **Focus:** General studies/Field of study not specified. **Criteria:** Selection are evaluated based on academic achievement.

Funds Avail.: No specific amount. **Duration:** Annual. **To Apply:** Applicants must submit completed application form; personal statement/essay; academic transcript; academic recommendation letter; copy of SAT/ACT scores; and employer/supervisor recommendation letter in order to qualify for an interview; only qualified applicants will be considered for a personal interview. **Deadline:** November 15. **Contact:** Phone: 805-687-6065; Email: info@sbscholarship.org.

9954 ■ The Scholarship Foundation of Wakefield
Americal Civic Ctr.
467 Main St.
Wakefield, MA 01880
Ph: (781)245-4890
E-mail: tsfofwakefield@earthlink.net
URL: www.tsfofwakefield.org
Social Media: www.facebook.com/tsfofwakefield
twitter.com/tsfofwakefield

9955 ■ The Scholarship Foundation of Wakefield Scholarships *(All/Scholarship)*

Purpose: To support the education of Wakefield students. **Focus:** General studies/Field of study not specified. **Qualif.:** Applicants must be residents of Wakefield who will attend school in a full-time basis and must demonstrate financial need. **Criteria:** Selection is based on financial need and merit.

Funds Avail.: Amount varies. **Duration:** Annual. **Number Awarded:** Varies. **To Apply:** Applicants must complete a

Awards are arranged alphabetically below their administering organizations

TSF of wakefield student application, as well as submit a copy of curent year confirmation page from the free application for federal student aid (FAFSA) or page one of current year student aid report (SAR) from the FAFSA.

9956 ■ Scholarships for a Cause

2329 Humboldt St.
Denver, CO 80205
Ph: (303)335-9968
URL: www.scholarshipsforacause.com

9957 ■ Ugly Sweater Scholarship *(High School, College, University, Graduate, Undergraduate/Scholarship)*

Purpose: To show off the best "ugly" sweaters and support the Salvation Army's Brighten the Holidays program. **Focus:** General studies/Field of study not specified. **Qualif.:** Applicant must be a junior or senior in high school, in postsecondary school (university, college, or community college), or in graduate school in the United States; must be legal U.S. residents. **Criteria:** Selection is based on whichever entry gets the most votes.

Funds Avail.: $250 (voting award); $100 (judged award). **Number Awarded:** 2. **To Apply:** Applicant must complete the entry form, upload a picture of self wearing their ugliest holiday sweater, and submit a short story (250 words or less) on how they acquired their ugly sweater. Entry form is available online at my.360photocontest.com/uglysweaterscholarship/. **Deadline:** December 31. **Contact:** Email: scholarshipsforacause@gmail.com.

9958 ■ School Nutrition Association (SNA)

2900 S Quincy St., Ste. 700
Arlington, VA 22206
Ph: (703)824-3000
Fax: (703)824-3015
E-mail: servicecenter@schoolnutrition.org
URL: schoolnutrition.org
Social Media: www.facebook.com/
  SchoolNutritionAssociation
www.instagram.com/schoolnutritionassoc
www.linkedin.com/company/school-nutrition-association
twitter.com/SchoolLunch
www.youtube.com/user/SchoolNutrition

9959 ■ GED Jump Start Scholarships *(Professional development/Scholarship)*

Purpose: To support members who are planning on getting their GEDs within one year. **Focus:** Food service careers. **Qualif.:** Applicants must be SNA members who want a General Education Development (GED) diploma.

Funds Avail.: $200. **To Apply:** Applications are accepted throughout the year. **Contact:** Toll-free: 800-877-8822.

9960 ■ Nancy Curry Scholarship *(Vocational/Occupational, Undergraduate, Graduate, Postgraduate/Scholarship, Award)*

Purpose: To provide members the opportunity to explore higher education options with the help of financial assistance. **Focus:** Food service careers. **Qualif.:** Applicants must be an active SNA member, who has been a SNA member for at least one year (since at least January 1, 2017); currently employed in school foodservice as an operator or state agency (Industry and student members

are not eligible.; enrolled or will be enrolled in a degree or certificate program at a vocational/technical, undergraduate, graduate or post-graduate level in the United States in a program of study which falls into one or more of the USDA Professional Standards subject areas; children of SNA members are not eligible.

Funds Avail.: $500. **Duration:** Annual. **Number Awarded:** 1 in 2018. **To Apply:** Applicant Should submit application in worksheet format into online form. **Deadline:** April 2. **Contact:** Toll-free: 800-877-8822.

9961 ■ Schwan's Food Service Scholarship *(Vocational/Occupational, Professional development/Scholarship, Award)*

Purpose: To provide members the opportunity to explore higher education options with the help of financial assistance. **Focus:** Food service careers. **Qualif.:** Applicants must be an active SNA member, who has been a SNA member for at least one year; currently employed in school foodservice as an operator or state agency (Industry and student members are not eligible.; enrolled or will be enrolled in a degree or certificate program at a vocational/technical, undergraduate, graduate or post-graduate level in the United States in a program of study which falls into one or more of the USDA Professional Standards subject areas; children of SNA members are not eligible.

Funds Avail.: Up to $2,500 each. **Duration:** One academic year. **Number Awarded:** 1 in 2018. **To Apply:** Applicant Should submit application in worksheet format into online form. **Deadline:** April 2. **Contact:** Toll-free: 800-877-8822.

9962 ■ SNF Professional Growth Scholarship *(Graduate, Undergraduate, Vocational/Occupational, Postgraduate/Scholarship, Award)*

Purpose: To provide members the opportunity to explore higher education options with the help of financial assistance. **Focus:** Food service careers. **Qualif.:** Applicants must be an active SNA member, who has been a SNA member for at least one year (since at least January 1, 2017); currently employed in school foodservice as an operator or state agency (Industry and student members are not eligible.; enrolled or will be enrolled in a degree or certificate program at a vocational/technical, undergraduate, graduate or post-graduate level in the United States in a program of study which falls into one or more of the USDA Professional Standards subject areas; children of SNA members are not eligible.

Funds Avail.: Up to $2,500 each. **Duration:** Annual. **Number Awarded:** 1 in 2018. **To Apply:** Applicant Should submit application in worksheet format into online form. **Deadline:** April 2. **Contact:** Toll-free: 800-877-8822.

9963 ■ Winston Build Your Future Scholarship *(Graduate, Undergraduate, Vocational/Occupational/Scholarship)*

Purpose: To provide members the opportunity to explore higher education options through financial assistance. **Focus:** Food service careers. **Qualif.:** Applicant must be employed as a School Food Service Professional; must be a dependent of an employee, employed as a School Food Service Professional; must be a registered at, or have plans to attend an accredited college, university or vocational/technical institution. **Criteria:** Selection will be based on the submitted application.

Funds Avail.: Up to $2,500 each. **To Apply:** Applicant must submit a completed Winston Scholarship application

Awards are arranged alphabetically below their administering organizations

form along with the required materials and information.

9964 ■ School Nutrition Association of Kansas (SNA-KS)

c/o Tara Grindol-Cox, President
5720 SW 13th St.
Topeka, KS 66604
URL: snaks.wordpress.com/home

9965 ■ School Nutrition Association of Kansas Education Scholarship *(Undergraduate/Scholarship)*

Purpose: To support school food service personnel who have an interest in furthering their career and refining their skills in school food service. **Focus:** General studies/Field of study not specified. **Qualif.:** Applicants must be school food service personnel who have an interest in furthering their career and refining their skills in school food service; must be current members of SNA-KS. **Criteria:** Applications are accepted for classes or courses taken in the current year only. The number of scholarships awarded will be determined by the funds available annually by the SNA-KS Board.

Funds Avail.: No specific amount. **Duration:** Annual. **Number Awarded:** Varies. **To Apply:** Applicants must submit a copy of the current membership card; personal information; course information; education history; essay. **Deadline:** May 31.

9966 ■ Evalee C. Schwarz Charitable Trust for Education

c/o Private Foundation Services, Inc.
4265 San Felipe, Ste. 1100
Houston, TX 77027-2913
E-mail: pfs@privatefoundationservices.com
URL: www.evaleeschwarztrust.org

9967 ■ Evalee C. Schwarz Educational Loans *(Undergraduate, Graduate/Loan)*

Purpose: To provide interest-free loans to undergraduate and graduate students who demonstrate exceptional academic performance and significant financial need. **Focus:** General studies/Field of study not specified. **Qualif.:** Applicants must be U.S. citizens; qualify for financial need in the form of government grants (Please complete the Free Application for Federal Student Aid); be enrolled in a school in the state in which the students reside; demonstrate outstanding combination of class rank and standardized test scores (scores must be in the top 15% of nationwide scores); and, not be seeking a law degree. **Criteria:** Selection shall be based on academic performance and financial need.

Funds Avail.: Varies. **Duration:** Annual. **Number Awarded:** Varies. **To Apply:** Applicants must submit a completed typed or printed application form along with a copy of official picture I.D.; official transcripts; copy of Student Aid Report (SAR); three letters of recommendation; a personal essay; copy of admissions test score (SAT, ACT, GRE, GMAT, MCAT, etc.); copy of brochure or other document stating current school costs (tuition, room, board, fees). **Deadline:** April 10. **Contact:** Evalee C. Schwarz Charitable Trust for Education, c/o Private Foundation Services, Inc., 4265 San Felipe, Ste. 1100, Houston, TX, 77027-2913.

9968 ■ Science Foundation Arizona (SFAZ)

1475 N Scottsdale Rd., Ste. 200
Scottsdale, AZ 85257
Ph: (480)884-1786
URL: www.sfaz.org
Social Media: www.facebook.com/
  ScienceFoundationArizona
twitter.com/sciencefoundaz

9969 ■ Graduate Research Fellows (GRF) *(Graduate/ Fellowship)*

Purpose: To strengthen existing research programs at universities in Arizona. **Focus:** Engineering, Aerospace/ Aeronautical/Astronautical. **Qualif.:** Applicant must be a VP of Research at a 501(C)(3) educational institution that grants PhD or higher-level degrees or a Master's degree in aeronautical sciences. Applicant must be selected by the educational institution where undergraduate or some postgraduate studies have been completed. **Criteria:** Submitted proposals are reviewed by a panel of expert outside reviewers.

Funds Avail.: No specific amount. **Duration:** Annual. **To Apply:** Applicants must complete the application online.

9970 ■ Science History Institute

315 Chestnut St.
Philadelphia, PA 19106
Ph: (215)925-2222
URL: www.sciencehistory.org
Social Media: www.facebook.com/SciHistoryOrg
twitter.com/scihistoryorg

9971 ■ CHF Travel Grants *(Professional development/ Grant)*

Purpose: To provide financial support for researchers who wish to use the collections at the Beckman Center for the History of Chemistry for short-term research. **Focus:** Chemistry; History. **Qualif.:** Applicants must reside more than 75 miles from Philadelphia to be eligible.

Funds Avail.: $750 per week for travel; $45,000 stipend for postdoctoral; $3,000 per month for short-term fellowships. **Duration:** Annual. **Number Awarded:** 1.

9972 ■ Science History Institute Travel Grants *(All/ Grant)*

Purpose: To recognize a individuals with a research proposal that also details how the applicant will make use of the Science History Institute's collections. **Focus:** Chemistry. **Criteria:** Recipients are selected based on committee's review of the research.

To Apply: Applicants should submit a research proposal that also details how the applicant will make use of the Science History Institute's collections (one page); a curriculum vitae (up to three pages); one reference letter; referees should submit letters directly to the Science History Institute.

9973 ■ Science, Mathematics and Research for Transformation (SMART)

c/o American Society for Engineering Education
1818 N St. NW, Ste. 600
Washington, DC 20036
Ph: (202)331-3544
E-mail: smart@asee.org
URL: smart.asee.org

Awards are arranged alphabetically below their administering organizations

9974 ■ Science, Mathematics And Research for Transformation Scholarship for Service Program (SMART) *(Undergraduate, Graduate/Scholarship)*

Purpose: To increase the number of civilian scientists and engineers working at Department of Defense laboratories. **Focus:** Engineering; Mathematics and mathematical sciences; Science; Technology. **Qualif.:** Applicants must be U.S., Australia, Canada, New Zealand, or United Kingdom citizens; 18 years old and above; able to participate in summer internships at Department of Defense (DoD) facility; willing to accept post-graduate employment with the DoD; students in good standing with a minimum cumulative GPA of 3.0 on a 4.0 scale; and, pursuing undergraduate or graduate degree in one of the science, technology, engineering and mathematics (STEM) disciplines; in addition, undergraduate applicants must be enrolled in a regionally accredited U.S. college/university and have their respective high school diplomas/GED's while graduate applicants can be either currently enrolled in a regionally accredited U.S. college or university or awaiting notification of admission to such. **Criteria:** Selection shall be based on the aforementioned applicant's qualifications and compliance with the application details.

Funds Avail.: $25,000-$38,000 stipend; $1,200 for Health Insurance; $1,000 for Miscellaneous Supplies. **Duration:** Annual. **To Apply:** All applicants are required to submit applications online; applicants will need to register for a new account before they will be able to start the application; the applicant will input their name and email address and choose a password. **Deadline:** December 3. **Contact:** Phone: 202-331-3544; Fax: 202-265-8504; Email: smartparticipant@asee.org.

9975 ■ ScienceSoft USA Corp.
5900 S Lake Forest Dr., Ste. 300
McKinney, TX 75070
Ph: (214)306-6837
E-mail: contact@scnsoft.com
URL: www.scnsoft.com
Social Media: www.facebook.com/sciencesoft.solutions
www.linkedin.com/company/sciencesoft
twitter.com/ScienceSoft

9976 ■ ScienceSoft Scholarship *(Graduate, Undergraduate/Scholarship)*

Purpose: To help students pay for an education and to raise awareness of artificial intelligence (AI) technologies and popularize their real-life applications. **Focus:** General studies/Field of study not specified. **Qualif.:** Applicant must be a full-time student at a U.S. college or university who has already finished there first year of studies, or a graduate student. **Criteria:** Based on quality of essay.

Funds Avail.: $2,000 First Place; $1,000 Second Place; $500 Third Place. **Number Awarded:** 3. **To Apply:** Applicant must write a 1,000 - 2,000 word essay with the requirements specified on the sponsor's website and submit it along with proof of enrollment. **Deadline:** December 31. **Contact:** Email: submissions@scnsoft.com; URL: www.scnsoft.com/about/scholarship.

9977 ■ Scleroderma Foundation (SF)
300 Rosewood Dr., Ste. 105
Danvers, MA 01923
Ph: (978)463-5843

Fax: (978)463-5809
Free: 800-722-4673
E-mail: sfinfo@scleroderma.org
URL: www.scleroderma.org
Social Media: www.facebook.com/SclerodermaUS
twitter.com/scleroderma
www.youtube.com/user/SclerodermaUS

9978 ■ New Investigator Grant *(Postdoctorate/Grant)*

Purpose: To support promising new Scleroderma investigators in research that is likely to lead to individual research project grants. **Focus:** Medical research.

Funds Avail.: $50,000 per year. **Duration:** Three years.

9979 ■ Scleroderma Foundation Established Investigator Grants *(Doctorate/Grant)*

Purpose: To provide assistance for established investigators in areas of research related to SSc who are pursuing highly innovative and meritorious pilot projects; to facilitate highly innovative and meritorious pilot projects in areas of research related to scleroderma. **Focus:** Medicine, Osteopathic. **Qualif.:** Applicants must have a doctoral degree in Medicine, Osteopathy, Veterinary Medicine or one of the sciences and must have completed a postdoctoral fellowship; have been a principal investigator on grants from the Scleroderma Foundation or other national, private or government agencies in the past. **Criteria:** Recipients are selected based on a committee's review of the proposal.

Funds Avail.: $150,000. **Duration:** Annual. **To Apply:** Applicants must submit one original copy in PDF format via CD and five hard copies of completed application along with five sets of appendices. **Deadline:** September 15.

9980 ■ Scleroderma Foundation New Investigator Grants *(Doctorate/Grant)*

Purpose: To provide financial assistance to promising new investigators in areas of research related to SSc. **Focus:** Medicine, Osteopathic. **Qualif.:** Applicants must have a doctoral degree in Medicine, Osteopathy, Veterinary Medicine or one of the sciences and must have completed a postdoctoral fellowship. **Criteria:** Recipients are selected based on a committee's review of the proposal.

Funds Avail.: $150,000. **Duration:** Annual. **To Apply:** Applicants must submit one original copy in PDF format via CD and five hard copies of completed application and five sets of appendices. **Deadline:** September 15.

9981 ■ Scleroderma Research Foundation (SRF)
220 Montgomery St., Ste. 484
San Francisco, CA 94104
Ph: (415)834-9444
E-mail: info@srfcure.org
URL: www.srfcure.org
Social Media: www.facebook.com/SRFcure
www.instagram.com/srfcure
www.linkedin.com/company/scleroderma-research
 -foundation
twitter.com/srfcure
www.youtube.com/channel/UCsTzCavzIctmsu6i7Hm-gLg

9982 ■ SRF Post-doctoral Fellowships *(Postdoctorate/Fellowship)*

Purpose: To raise interest in exploring new approaches and hypotheses on the pathogenesis of scleroderma

Awards are arranged alphabetically below their administering organizations

among young scientists by providing funding support. **Focus:** Biomedical research. **Qualif.:** Applicants must be U.S. citizens or permanent residents and must be Ph.D. or M.D. degree holders; must also identify a sponsoring private or public non-profit institution and an individual who will serve as a sponsor and will directly supervise and document everything that is involved in the training and research experience of the candidate. **Criteria:** Award is given based on merit.

Funds Avail.: $35,000-$55,000. **Duration:** Two years. **Number Awarded:** 2. **To Apply:** Applicants must submit completed and signed application along with letter from sponsoring principle investigator; relevant supplemental material appended to application; research proposal; and three letters of recommendation. **Deadline:** December 15 for new grants; December 31 for continuing grants. **Contact:** Phone: 415-834-9444; Fax: 415-834-9177; Email: info@sclerodermaresearch.org.

9983 ■ Scottish Rite Foundation of Colorado
1370 Grant Street
Denver, CO 80203-2347
Ph: (303)861-2410
Fax: (303)861-2411
Free: 866-289-6797
E-mail: ritecare@scottishritefoundation.org
URL: www.scottishritefoundation.org

9984 ■ Dwight A. Hamilton Scottish Rite Foundation of Colorado Graduate Scholarship in Speech-Language Pathology *(Graduate/Scholarship)*

Purpose: To provide scholarship to graduate students in speech-language pathology. **Focus:** Speech and language pathology/Audiology. **Criteria:** Applicants who are interested in serving children in rural or underserved areas of Colorado are given preference.

Funds Avail.: $5,000. **Duration:** Annual. **Number Awarded:** 6. **To Apply:** Applicants must submit official transcript or academic progress report (first year graduate study); proof of Colorado residency as defined by the university's criteria; one-page, double-spaced statement on career goals and aspirations including a description of student's interest in serving children with language disorders and intention to remain in Colorado; one letter of recommendation from university faculty; one letter of recommendation from clinical supervisor; one-page professional resume; application checklist showing application completeness. **Deadline:** June 15. **Remarks:** The scholarship was named in honor of former Sovereign Grand Inspector General and President of the Foundation, Dwight A. Hamilton. Established in 2005. **Contact:** E-mail: ritecare@scottishritefoundation.org.

9985 ■ Scouts Canada (SC)
1345 Baseline Rd.
Ottawa, ON, Canada K2C 0A7
Free: 888-855-3336
E-mail: helpcenter@scouts.ca
URL: www.scouts.ca
Social Media: www.facebook.com/scoutscanada
www.linkedin.com/company/scouts-canada
twitter.com/scoutscanada
www.youtube.com/c/scoutscanadaOfficial

9986 ■ Reginald K. Groome Memorial Scholarships *(Undergraduate/Scholarship)*

Purpose: To enhance the mission of Scouts Canada through recognition of scholastic and other achievement by youth members of Scouts Canada; to encourage continuous self-development on the part of active youth members of Scouts Canada through institutions of post secondary education. **Focus:** General studies/Field of study not specified. **Qualif.:** Applicants must be a post secondary school (Venturer Scouts, Rover Scouts, SIT's, young leaders). **Criteria:** Candidates will be selected based on leadership contribution; scholastic achievement; attitude and aptitude.

Duration: Annually. **To Apply:** Application form is available at the website. Applicants must submit an official transcript of records; must attach a typed statement (200 words) discussing the value of scouting in their life; authorized report card; one passport/school-sized photo; and two letters of recommendation from Scouting and outside organization.

9987 ■ Herbert Scoville Jr. Peace Fellowship
820 1st St. NE, Ste. LL-180
Washington, DC 20002
Ph: (202)446-1565
E-mail: info@scoville.org
URL: www.scoville.org
Social Media: www.facebook.com/ScovilleFellowship
www.instagram.com/scovillefellowship
www.linkedin.com/company/herbert-scoville-jr-peace
-fellowship
twitter.com/ScovillePF
www.youtube.com/channel/UCvbihyZqtwINdjjdtg-X_sQ

9988 ■ Herbert Scoville Jr. Peace Fellowship *(Graduate/Fellowship)*

Purpose: To provide an opportunity for college graduates to gain practical knowledge and experience by contributing to the efforts of nonprofit, public-interest organizations working on peace and security issues. **Focus:** Peace studies. **Qualif.:** Applicants must required to have completed a baccalaureate degree by the time the fellowship commences. Preference is given to United States citizens; Non-U.S. citizens living outside the United States are not eligible to apply. **Criteria:** Selection shall be based on academic accomplishments and interest in issues of peace and security.

Funds Avail.: No specific amount. **Duration:** Semiannual. **Number Awarded:** Varies. **To Apply:** Application materials must include a cover sheet (applicant's name, semester for which they are applying, contact details); a signed letter indicating the applicants' desire to apply, addresses and telephone numbers of two references (letter should indicate how the applicants first learned of the Scoville Peace Fellowship); a full CV (educational and professional data, and extracurricular activities); a personal essay discussing the applicants' qualifications, interests, Fellowship objectives and career goals (should also list 5-6 organizations they would like to work with); a policy or opinion essay of no more than 1, 000 words relevant to the field of peace and security taking a position on a contemporary, contentious issue (must be titled); official transcript(s) detailing the candidates' entire college academic record including undergraduate, graduate and foreign study; and two signed letters of reference; electronic applications must be submitted as one compiled Adobe PDF file or Microsoft Word, subject must be scoville Application-name of the applicant;

Awards are arranged alphabetically below their administering organizations

paper applications must be submitted in a single envelope (each page must be numbered, do not staple pages together). **Deadline:** October 2. **Remarks:** Established in 1987. **Contact:** 820 1st St., NE, Ste. LL-180, Washington, DC 20002.

9989 ■ Screen Actors Guild - American Federation of Television and Radio Artists (SAG-AFTRA)
5757 Wilshire Blvd., 7th Fl.
Los Angeles, CA 90036
Ph: (323)954-1600
Free: 855-724-2387
E-mail: info@sagaftra.org
URL: www.sagaftra.org
Social Media: www.facebook.com/SAGAFTRA
twitter.com/SAGAFTRA

9990 ■ John L. Dales Standard Scholarship
(Undergraduate/Scholarship)

Purpose: To support members and their dependents for study at accredited institutions of higher education. **Focus:** Performing arts. **Qualif.:** Applicants must be a SAG-AFTRA member or dependent of a member; must be enrolled in an accredited institution of higher learning; Applicants under 22 applying for scholarship must have been a member in a good standing for five years and have a lifetime earnings of $30, 000 within SAG-AFTRA jurisdiction; a member parent or guardian whose dependent is applying for the scholarship must have 10 years of vested pension credits or a lifetime $150, 000 within the SAG-AFTRA jurisdiction. **Criteria:** Selection for scholarship awards of the John L. Dales Scholarship Fund will be selected in accordance of the criteria.

Funds Avail.: No specific amount. **Duration:** Annual. **To Apply:** Applicants shall submit a transcript of all high school, college and university course and evaluations, SAT scores, and any other relevant information; applicants shall submit the Confidential Financial Aid Form for applicants and a copy of their most recent Federal Income Tax Returns for applicants and parent; if either applicants or parents are incorporated, the Corporate Tax Return must be submitted. All submitted tax returns must be complete; applicants shall submit an essay of 350 to 750 words on one of the topics provided with the application and two personal letters of recommendation. **Deadline:** March 15. **Remarks:** Established in 1973.

9991 ■ SE Ranking
228 Hamilton Ave.
Palo Alto, CA 94301
Ph: (415)704-4387
URL: seranking.com
Social Media: www.facebook.com/serankingcom
www.linkedin.com/company/se-ranking
www.pinterest.com/seranking
twitter.com/SERanking
www.youtube.com/channel/
  UCtUeek7hmkByxGbiOZNgB3w

9992 ■ The SE Rankings Scholarship Program
(Undergraduate, Graduate, Professional development/ Scholarship)

Purpose: To encourage students to learn more about marketing and entrepreneurship. **Focus:** General studies/

Field of study not specified. **Qualif.:** Applicant must be enrolled or accepted into an accredited university in the United States or Europe. **Criteria:** Selection will be done by an internal committee who will pick the best essay.

Funds Avail.: $1,000. **To Apply:** Applicant must important to stay abreast everything that marketing is using to reach your ultimate goals. Application and essay details are available online at seranking.com/scholarship.html. **Contact:** Email: scholarship@seranking.com.

9993 ■ Seasons in Malibu
31739 Pacific Coast Hwy.
Malibu, CA 90265
Free: 866-780-8539
URL: seasonsmalibu.com
Social Media: www.facebook.com/SeasonsInMalibu
www.instagram.com/seasonsmalibu
twitter.com/SeasonsMalibu

9994 ■ Seasons in Malibu Annual Scholarship
(Undergraduate, Graduate/Scholarship)

Purpose: To highlight the importance of mental health and provide financial aide to students in need. **Focus:** Mental health; Rehabilitation, Physical/Psychological. **Qualif.:** Applicant must be enrolled in an institute of higher education in the fields of mental health or addiction. **Criteria:** Selection is based on applicant's essay.

Funds Avail.: $1,500. **Duration:** Annual. **Number Awarded:** 1. **To Apply:** Applicant must submit an 800-word essay on the importance of mental health and fill out an application form at seasonsofmalibu.com/general-education-and-mental-health-education-scholarship.

9995 ■ Seldovia Native Association (SNA)
PO Drawer L
Seldovia, AK 99663
Ph: (907)234-7625
Fax: (907)234-7637
Free: 800-478-7898
E-mail: info@snai.com
URL: www.snai.com
Social Media: www.facebook.com/
  seldovianativeassociationinc/

9996 ■ Seldovia Native Association Achievement Scholarships *(Undergraduate, Graduate/Scholarship)*

Purpose: To assist Alaska Natives in their pursuit of education. **Focus:** General studies/Field of study not specified. **Qualif.:** Applicants must be Alaska Natives who are shareholders and their lineal descendants (children, grandchildren, natural or adopted and spouses); must be enrolled at an accredited college or university and must maintain 3.0 GPA. Undergraduate applicants must have enrolled 12 or more credit hours per semester and nine or more credit hours per semester for graduate students. **Criteria:** Recipients will be evaluated based on the following categories; scholastic achievement; previous work performance, education and community involvement; financial need; recommendations and demonstrated potential to succeed in a chosen career; seriousness of purpose; major field of study; and practicality of education, professional goals and completeness of the application.

Funds Avail.: $2,500. **Duration:** Annual. **To Apply:** Applicants must submit a completed, signed and dated ap-

Awards are arranged alphabetically below their administering organizations

plication form, an official copy of transcript, two letters of recommendation, proof of acceptance and photo. **Deadline:** July 1.

9997 ■ Seldovia Native Association General Scholarships *(Undergraduate, Graduate/Scholarship)*

Purpose: To assist Alaska Natives in their pursuit of education. **Focus:** General studies/Field of study not specified. **Qualif.:** Applicants must be Alaska Natives who are shareholders and their lineal descendants (children, grandchildren, natural or adopted and spouses); must be enrolled at an accredited college or university and must maintain 2.0 GPA. Undergraduate applicants must have enrolled 12 or more credit hours per semester and nine or more credit hours per semester for graduate students. **Criteria:** Recipients will be evaluated based on the following categories; scholastic achievement; previous work performance, education and community involvement; financial need; recommendations and demonstrated potential to succeed in a chosen career; seriousness of purpose; major field of study; and practicality of education, professional goals and completeness of the application.

Funds Avail.: $500. **Duration:** Annual. **To Apply:** Applicants must submit a completed, signed and dated application form, an official copy of transcript, two letters of recommendation, proof of acceptance and photo. **Deadline:** July 1. **Contact:** Deliver or mail, postmarked no later than the deadline to: The SNA Foundation; PO Drawer L Seldovia Alaska, 99663; TEL (907) 234-7625 1-800-478-7898; Fax: 234-7637.

9998 ■ Semiconductor Research Corporation (SRC) - Global Research Collaboration (GRC)
4819 Emperor Blvd., Ste. 300
Durham, NC 27703
URL: www.src.org

9999 ■ Graduate Fellowship Program - Robert M. Burger Fellowships *(Doctorate, Graduate/Fellowship)*

Purpose: To encourage academically gifted students to pursue doctoral degrees relevant to microelectrics. **Focus:** Engineering; Science; Technology. **Qualif.:** Applicant must be a U.S. citizen; has completed a Master's degree; pursuing, or planning to pursue a doctoral program.

Funds Avail.: No specific amount. **Duration:** Annual. **Number Awarded:** Varies. **To Apply:** Applicants must submit resume; faculty advisor reference; two additional References (from scientists, engineers, or faculty members who have recent or current knowledge of the applicant's academic accomplishments and professional or research experience); official transcripts of all accredited baccalaureate and graduate work completed, including the first semester or quarter of the current academic year. **Remarks:** The Fellowship was named in recognition of Dr. Burger's ten years of service to SRC as Vice President and Chief Scientist. Established in 1992. **Contact:** Semiconductor Research Corporation Education Alliance, Fellowship/Scholarship Program, 4819 Emperor Blvd., Ste. 300, Durham, NC, 27703; Phone: 919-941-9400; Email: apply@src.org.

10000 ■ Graduate Fellowship Program - Mahboob Khan/Advanced Micro Devices Fellowships *(Doctorate, Graduate/Fellowship)*

Purpose: To encourage academically gifted students to pursue doctoral degrees relevant to microelectrics. **Focus:** Engineering; Science; Technology. **Qualif.:** Applicant must be a U.S. citizen; has completed a Master's degree; pursuing, or planning to pursue a doctoral program.

Funds Avail.: No specific amount. **Duration:** Annual. **To Apply:** Applicants must submit resume; faculty advisor reference; two additional References (from scientists, engineers, or faculty members who have recent or current knowledge of the applicant's academic accomplishments and professional or research experience); official transcripts of all accredited baccalaureate and graduate work completed, including the first semester or quarter of the current academic year. **Remarks:** The Fellowship was named in memory of Dr. Khan. **Contact:** Semiconductor Research Corporation Education Alliance, Fellowship/Scholarship Program, 4819 Emperor Blvd., Ste. 300, Durham, NC, 27703; Phone: 919-941-9400; Email: apply@src.org.

10001 ■ SRC Master's Scholarships Program *(Graduate, Master's/Scholarship)*

Purpose: To attract qualified students who are also in underrepresented minority categories to graduate study in areas of interest to the semiconductor industry. **Focus:** Engineering; Science; Technology. **Criteria:** Selection is based on minority or female status and outstanding academic achievement.

Funds Avail.: No specific amount. **Duration:** Annual. **To Apply:** Applicants must submit a completed Personal Information Form (may be submitted electronically from the applicant's university e-mail address or in hard copy) along with official transcripts of all accredited baccalaureate and graduate work completed; three Reference Report Forms completed by scientists, engineers or faculty members; and official report of test results from the Graduate Record Examination (SRC institution code 2800). **Contact:** Semiconductor Research Corporation Education Alliance, Fellowship/Scholarship Program, 4819 Emperor Blvd., Ste. 300, Durham, NC, 27703; Phone: 919-941-9400; Email: apply@src.org.

10002 ■ Graduate Fellowship Program - Peter Verhofstadt Fellowships *(Graduate/Fellowship)*

Purpose: To encourage academically gifted students to pursue doctoral degrees relevant to microelectrics. **Focus:** Biophysics; Chemistry; Mathematics and mathematical sciences; Physical sciences; Physics. **Qualif.:** Applicant must study in the physical sciences, specifically chemistry, physics, mathematics, or biophysics. This Fellowship is to stimulate non-traditional thinking and encourage exploratory, high-risk research leading to novel, high-payoff solutions for challenges faced by the semiconductor industry at and beyond the time horizons of the International Technology Roadmap for Semiconductors.

Funds Avail.: No specific amount. **Duration:** Annual. **To Apply:** Applicants must submit resume; faculty advisor reference; two additional References (from scientists, engineers, or faculty members who have recent or current knowledge of the applicant's academic accomplishments and professional or research experience); official transcripts of all accredited baccalaureate and graduate work completed, including the first semester or quarter of the current academic year. **Remarks:** The Fellowship was named in memory of Peter Verhofstadt, SRC Chief Scientist and Co-Executive Director of MARCO. Established in 2002. **Contact:** Semiconductor Research Corporation Education Alliance, Fellowship/Scholarship Program, 4819 Emperor Blvd., Ste. 300, Durham, NC, 27703; Phone: 919-941-9400; Email: apply@src.org.

Awards are arranged alphabetically below their administering organizations

10003 ■ Semiconductor Research Corporation (SRC) - Nanoelectronics Research Initiative (NRI)
4819 Emperor Blvd., Ste. 300
Durham, NC 27703
Ph: (919)941-9400
Fax: (919)941-9450
E-mail: students@src.org
URL: src.org

10004 ■ SRC NRI Hans J. Coufal Fellowships
(Graduate/Fellowship)

Purpose: To increase the number of graduate students being educated to enter the semiconductor and nanoelectronics fields. **Focus:** Electronics; Physics. **Qualif.:** Applicant must be in nanoelectronics-related disciplines.

Funds Avail.: No specific amount. **Duration:** Annual. **To Apply:** Applicants must submit resume; faculty advisor reference; two additional References (from scientists, engineers, or faculty members who have recent or current knowledge of the applicant's academic accomplishments and professional or research experience); official transcripts of all accredited baccalaureate and graduate work completed, including the first semester or quarter of the current academic year. **Remarks:** The Fellowship was named in memory of Hans J. Coufal, the founding director of the Nanoelectronics Research Initiative. Established in 2006. **Contact:** Semiconductor Research Corporation Education Alliance, Fellowship/Scholarship Program, 4819 Emperor Blvd., Ste. 300, Durham, NC, 27703; Phone: 919-941-9400; Email: apply@src.org.

10005 ■ Seneca Family of Companies
90201 Hwy. 99
Eugene, OR 97402
Ph: (541)689-1011
E-mail: seneca@senecasawmill.com
URL: senecasawmill.com
Social Media: www.facebook.com/
  SenecaSawmillCompany

10006 ■ The Seneca Scholarship *(High School, College/Scholarship)*

Purpose: To educate students on the sustainability of Oregon's viable timber. **Focus:** General studies/Field of study not specified. **Qualif.:** Applicant must be a resident of Oregon and a senior in high school heading to higher education.

Funds Avail.: $10,000; $7,000; $5,000. **Number Awarded:** 3. **To Apply:** Applicant must submit a five- to seven-page research essay. Application is available online through OSAC at app.oregonstudentaid.gov. **Deadline:** March 1. **Contact:** Ashley Jones; Email: ss@senecasawmill.com; URL: www.senecascholarship.org.

10007 ■ SeniorAdvice
2525 S Lamar, Ste. 8
Austin, TX 78704
Fax: (800)244-2575
E-mail: customersupport@senioradvice.com
URL: www.senioradvice.com
Social Media: www.facebook.com/senioradvice
www.instagram.com/senior_advice
www.linkedin.com/company/senioradvice-com
www.pinterest.com/senioradvice
twitter.com/senior_advice

10008 ■ SeniorAdvice Caregiver Scholarships
(Undergraduate/Scholarship)

Purpose: To assist those who give back to the elderly community. **Focus:** General studies/Field of study not specified. **Qualif.:** Applicants must be students attending a two or four-year university or college in the fall of current year; must have been involved in caregiving for a family member. **Criteria:** Selection will be based on the following criteria, that include, but are not limited to: quality of submission content; impact the scholarship will make on the life of the students; and whether the applicants have addressed the application questions and satisfied the application guidelines.

Funds Avail.: $1,000. **To Apply:** Applicants must e-mail their completed questions and two required attachments (copy of transcript and video file or essay). **Deadline:** July 15.

10009 ■ SeniorAdvice Volunteer Scholarships
(Undergraduate/Scholarship)

Purpose: To assist those who give back to the elderly community. **Focus:** General studies/Field of study not specified. **Qualif.:** Applicants must be students attending a two or four-year university or college in the fall of current year; must have been involved in caregiving for a family member. **Criteria:** Selection will be based on the following criteria, that include, but are not limited to: quality of submission content; impact the scholarship will make on the life of the students; and whether the applicants have addressed the application questions and satisfied the application guidelines.

Funds Avail.: $1,000. **To Apply:** Applicants must e-mail their completed questions and two required attachments (copy of transcript and video file or essay). **Deadline:** July 15.

10010 ■ Sentinels of Freedom (SOF)
PO Box 1316
San Ramon, CA 94583
Ph: (925)380-6342
Fax: (925)867-1078
E-mail: info@sentinelsoffreedom.org
URL: www.sentinelsoffreedom.org
Social Media: www.facebook.com/sentinelsoffreedom
www.instagram.com/sentinelsoffreedom
www.linkedin.com/company/sentinels-of-freedom
  -scholarship-foundation/

10011 ■ Sentinels of Freedom Scholarship
(Advanced Professional/Scholarship)

Purpose: To provide life-changing opportunities for men and women of the U.S. Armed Forces who have suffered severe injuries and need the support of grateful communities to realize their dreams. **Focus:** General studies/Field of study not specified.

Funds Avail.: No specific amount. **Duration:** Semiannual. **To Apply:** Applications can be submitted online; must submit authorization for disclosure; request for Information Packet- Personal & Military information, including housing, education, and injury information; personal statement outlining education, career, and personal goals; financial

Awards are arranged alphabetically below their administering organizations

worksheet; photograph and video release and 2 photos; and DD 214 (Only Member 4 Form will be accepted); letter of recommendation; college transcripts, if applicable; and VA rating statement; and background or credit report. **Deadline:** June 1 (Fall school enrollment); November 1 (Spring school enrollment).

10012 ■ SEO Architect

Raiya Rd., near ramdevpir chowk
Vision 2020 Complex
Rajkot 360007, Gujarat, India
Ph: 91 84 6064 0779
URL: top10bestbudget.com
Social Media: facebook.com/Top-10-Best-Budget
  -122834515150557
pinterest.com/top10bestbudget
twitter.com/top10bestbudget

10013 ■ Top10bestbudget Annual Scholarship Award *(Undergraduate, Postgraduate/Scholarship)*

Purpose: To help talented students pursue an education. **Focus:** General studies/Field of study not specified. **Qualif.:** Applicant must be an undergraduate or graduate student pursuing a degree at a college, university, or trade school.

Funds Avail.: $1,000. **Duration:** Annual. **Number Awarded:** 1. **To Apply:** Applicant must submit an essay, 600 to 1,000 words, on the subject of "How to use Facebook as a marketing tool". Essay should be in a doc or pdf file and emailed to scholarship@ top10bestbudget.com. **Deadline:** December 31. **Contact:** Email: scholarship@top10bestbudget.com.

10014 ■ SEO Optimizers

1509 Westmont Dr.
Los Angeles, CA 90001
Ph: (310)940-9463
E-mail: info@seooptimizers.com
URL: seooptimizers.com
Social Media: www.facebook.com/seooptimizers
www.linkedin.com/company/seo-optimizers
twitter.com/seooptimizers

10015 ■ SEO Optimizers Scholarships *(All/Scholarship)*

Purpose: To provide students the opportunity of gaining real-working experience in a chosen field. **Focus:** General studies/Field of study not specified. **Qualif.:** Applicants must be American citizens, permanent residents, or hold a valid student visa; must be currently enrolled as high school or college/university students within the United States; must have a cumulative GPA of at least 3.0 (or the equivalent); and must have designed an innovative project that makes a difference in the lives of others (could be a website, series of blogs, an app, fundraising event, etc.). **Criteria:** Selection will be based on grounds of user experience, innovation, and its own originality; and reviewed by the panel of two judges.

Funds Avail.: $500. **Duration:** Annual. **To Apply:** Applicants must submit an essay describing the goal of the particular project and provide supporting documentation; the essay, idea, or creation must be the original work. **Deadline:** 20th of each month.

10016 ■ Serbian Bar Association of America (SBAA)

1 N LaSalle, Ste. 300
Chicago, IL 60602
E-mail: sbaa@serbbar.org
URL: www.serbbar.org
Social Media: www.facebook.com/serbbar
twitter.com/SerbBar

10017 ■ Serbian Bar Association of America Scholarships *(Graduate/Scholarship)*

Purpose: To assist Serbian-American law students across the country. **Focus:** Law. **Qualif.:** Applicants must be of Serbian birth or ancestry and/or their spouses who are enrolled in an accredited law school in the US. **Criteria:** Selection is based on merit.

Funds Avail.: No specific amount. **Duration:** Annual. **To Apply:** Applicant should complete the free online membership application and submit a resume, official transcript, and answers to the below essay; submit a brief personal statement (750 words or less); this is an opportunity for the applicant to introduce themselves and explain why obtaining a law degree is important to them. **Deadline:** October 5. **Contact:** E-mail: sbaa@serbbar.org.

10018 ■ Sertoma Inc.

1912 E Meyer Blvd.
Kansas City, MO 64132
Ph: (816)333-8300
Fax: (816)333-4320
E-mail: infosertoma@sertomahq.org
URL: www.sertoma.org
Social Media: www.facebook.com/SertomaInc
www.linkedin.com/company/sertoma-inc-/
twitter.com/sertomahq
www.youtube.com/embed/BfOAHPMpcr8

10019 ■ Sertoma Communicative Disorders Scholarship *(Undergraduate/Scholarship)*

Purpose: To fund graduate students pursuing advanced degrees in audiology or speech-language pathology from institutions in the U.S. **Focus:** Hearing and deafness; Speech and language pathology/Audiology. **Qualif.:** Applicants must be US citizens accepted into a graduate level program in speech language pathology and/or audiology at a college or university in the United Sates, accredited by ASHA's Council on Academic Accreditation; must have a minimum cumulative 3.5 on a 4.0 scale for all undergraduate, graduate and doctoral level course work. **Criteria:** Selection will be based on the committee's criteria.

Funds Avail.: $1,000. **Duration:** Annual. **To Apply:** Application form and details are available online at: sertoma.org/what-we-do/scholarships/.

10020 ■ Sertoma Hard of Hearing and Deaf Scholarship *(Undergraduate/Scholarship)*

Purpose: To support hard of hearing and deaf students pursuing post-secondary education. **Focus:** General studies/Field of study not specified. **Qualif.:** Applicants must have a minimum 40dB bilateral hearing loss as evidenced on audiogram by an SRT of 40dB or greater in both ears; must be citizens of the United States; must be either entering college on a full time basis or currently at-

Awards are arranged alphabetically below their administering organizations

tending college in a full time basis at a college or university in the United States; must be pursuing a Bachelor's degree in any discipline; must have a minimum unweighted GPA of 3.2 on a 4.0 scale. **Criteria:** Selection will be based on the committee's criteria.

Funds Avail.: $1,000. **Duration:** Annual. **To Apply:** Application form and details are available online at: sertoma.org/what-we-do/scholarships/. **Deadline:** May 1. **Remarks:** Established in 1994.

10021 ■ ServiceMaster By Glenns

1505 10th Ave.
Vero Beach, FL 32960
E-mail: info@waterdamagespecialists.com
URL: waterdamagespecialists.com
Social Media: www.facebook.com/ServiceMasterByGlenns
www.instagram.com/servicemasterbyglenns

10022 ■ ServiceMaster By Glenns Preparation Scholarship *(University, Undergraduate, Vocational/Occupational/Scholarship)*

Purpose: To help Florida students pay for college or trade school and to demonstrate knowledge in how to prepare for a disaster. **Focus:** General studies/Field of study not specified. **Qualif.:** Applicant must be a high school or college student with plans to attend, or already accepted to, a Florida trade school or university; and be a Florida resident and be able to provide two proofs of Florida residency. Scholarship will be awarded after six weeks of enrollment in a Florida university or trade school. **Criteria:** Selection will be based on content, originality, creativity, and the sponsor's branding.

Funds Avail.: $500. **Number Awarded:** 2. **To Apply:** Create a video or design an infographic using visual aids and proper citation on how a business or individual can properly prepare for a disaster; fill out application. **Deadline:** May 31. **Contact:** Email: Marygrella@gmail.com; URL: waterdamagespecialists.com/scholarship.

10023 ■ ServiceScape Inc.

27 Congress St., Ste. 510
Salem, MA 01970
E-mail: info@servicescape.com
URL: www.servicescape.com
Social Media: www.facebook.com/servicescape
twitter.com/servicescapeinc
www.youtube.com/c/ServiceScape

10024 ■ ServiceScape Scholarship *(College, University/Scholarship)*

Purpose: To help a student pay for books, supplies, or other educational expenses. **Focus:** General studies/Field of study not specified. **Qualif.:** Applicant must be at least 18 years old and attending an accredited college, university, or trade school in the upcoming school year.

Funds Avail.: $1,000. **Number Awarded:** 1. **To Apply:** Applicant must write a 300-word essay on the following question: How does writing impact today's world? Applicant can fill out form and submit essay online at www.servicescape.com/scholarship. **Deadline:** November 30. **Contact:** David Costello; Email: info@servicescape.com.

10025 ■ Seton Hall University (SHU)

400 S Orange Ave.
South Orange, NJ 07079

Ph: (973)761-9000
URL: www.shu.edu
Social Media: www.facebook.com/setonhall
www.instagram.com/setonhall
www.linkedin.com/edu/seton-hall-university-18877
www.linkedin.com/school/seton-hall-university
twitter.com/setonhall
www.youtube.com/user/setonhall

10026 ■ Frances M. Schwartz Fellowship *(Other/Fellowship)*

Purpose: To support the study of numismatic and museum methodology at the American Numismatic Society. **Focus:** Numismatics. **Qualif.:** Applicant must have the B.A. or the equivalent.

Funds Avail.: $5,000. **Duration:** Annual. **Remarks:** Established in 1985.

10027 ■ Seton Hall University College of Arts and Sciences - Center for Public Service

Jubilee Hall
400 S Orange Ave.
South Orange, NJ 07079
Ph: (973)761-9501
E-mail: servicedesk@shu.edu
URL: www.shu.edu/academics/artsci/public-service
Social Media: www.facebook.com/setonhallartscience
www.instagram.com/shuathletics
twitter.com/setonhall
www.youtube.com/user/setonhall

10028 ■ Goya Scholarships *(Graduate/Scholarship)*

Purpose: To support outstanding students in the Master of Public Administration (MPA) program seeking careers in the public and nonprofit sectors. **Focus:** Public administration. **Qualif.:** Applicants must be a graduates. **Criteria:** Selection will be based on the committees' criteria with demonstrated financial need.

Funds Avail.: No specific amount. **To Apply:** Applicants must submit completed requirements: Application for Graduate Programs; Partial Scholarship Application and; FAFSA. **Contact:** Monica Mckie or Ryan Ouellette at 973-761-9510.

10029 ■ Thomas J. Stanton, Jr. Scholarships *(Graduate/Scholarship)*

Purpose: To support outstanding students in the Master of Public Administration (MPA) program seeking careers in the public and nonprofit sectors. **Focus:** Public administration. **Qualif.:** All applicants must have a bachelor's degree from an accredited college or university; degree applicants must have a minimum of a 3.0 grade point average; certificate applicants must have a minimum of a 2.75 grade point average. **Criteria:** Selection will be based on the committee's criteria.

Funds Avail.: No specific amount. **To Apply:** Applicants must complete the application for graduate programs and attach the completing the partial scholarship application; personal statement; resume. **Deadline:** December 30.

10030 ■ Seton Hall University School of Law

1 Newark Ctr.
Newark, NJ 07102

Awards are arranged alphabetically below their administering organizations

Ph: (973)761-9000
E-mail: admitme@shu.edu
URL: law.shu.edu
Social Media: www.facebook.com/SetonHallLaw
www.linkedin.com/school/seton-hall-law-school

10031 ■ Seton Hall Law Merit Scholarships
(Graduate/Scholarship)

Purpose: To reward the hard work and academic success of students. **Focus:** Law. **Qualif.:** Applicants must be incoming law students of the university.

Funds Avail.: $10,000 - $38,000 per year. **Duration:** Annual. **To Apply:** All applications for school admission are considered as application for the program since no separate application is required. **Contact:** Phone 973-642-8502; Email: law_financial@shu.edu.

10032 ■ SGM Law Group PLLC
800 Corporate Dr., Ste. 206
Fort Lauderdale, FL 33334
Ph: (954)604-6406
Fax: (888)279-9618
E-mail: info@immi-usa.com
URL: www.immi-usa.com
Social Media: www.facebook.com/SGMImmigrationLaw
twitter.com/ShilpaMalikEsq

10033 ■ SGM Law Group $1,000 Bi-Annual Scholarship (Undergraduate, Graduate/Scholarship)

Purpose: To provide financial assistance to help cover educational expenses. **Focus:** Law. **Qualif.:** Applicants must be currently enrolled in an accredited university, college, or law school within the U.S.; have a cumulative GPA of 3.0 or higher; must be a full-time student.

Funds Avail.: $1,000. **Duration:** Biennial. **To Apply:** Submit essay (500-1,000 words) on any of the following topics: 1) What hardship did you conquer to achieve your goal of pursuing law studies? 2) Explain your motivation for becoming a lawyer and what about the law inspires you. 3) Discuss the impact of employment immigration on U.S. economy, including the effects of related immigration reforms. 4) What field of law are you interested in and how will you help others with your earned law degree? Submit along with your contact information and current unofficial transcript in your submission that serves as proof of enrollment and displays your GPA. **Deadline:** December 15.

10034 ■ Sharp Criminal Lawyers
3600 Lime St., Ste. 111
Riverside, CA 92501
Ph: (951)777-1111
E-mail: info@sharpcriminallawyers.com
URL: www.sharpcriminallawyers.com
Social Media: www.facebook.com/sharpcriminallawyers
www.linkedin.com/in/stephen-sweigart-75306a29
twitter.com/NotGuiltyCA
www.youtube.com/channel/UCtdiEJR73O5d4IRLIyQ7rxA

10035 ■ Sharp Criminal Lawyers Autism Scholarship (College, Undergraduate, Vocational/Occupational/Scholarship)

Purpose: To provide encouragement to those with autism who wish to continue their education. **Focus:** General

studies/Field of study not specified. **Qualif.:** Applicant must be a U.S. citizen diagnosed with ASD (DSM-V) seeking a higher education.

Funds Avail.: $1,000. **Duration:** Annual. **Number Awarded:** 1. **To Apply:** Complete online application, provide a statement of 125 words or less outlining education goals and / or optional 750 word statement telling the selection committee how ASD has effected your education. May be asked to provide evidence of diagnosis, acceptance at an educational institution. **Deadline:** February 17. **Contact:** Stephen Swiegart, Esq.; Email: scholarshipcontests@gmail.com.

10036 ■ Shastri L'Institut Indo-Canadien
1418 Education Twr.
2500 University Dr. NW
Calgary, AB, Canada T2N 1N4
Ph: (403)220-7467
Fax: (403)289-0100
E-mail: sici@ucalgary.ca
URL: www.shastriinstitute.org
Social Media: www.facebook.com/OfficialSICI
twitter.com/OfficialSICI
www.youtube.com/channel/UCPH_Z2EGJWIBb
  -XWjyOh9Og

10037 ■ Shastri Scholar Travel Subsidy Grants (SSTSG) (Graduate, Professional development/Grant)

Purpose: To assist faculty members and graduate students with travel subsidies. **Focus:** Canadian studies; Indian studies (Asia). **Qualif.:** Applicants must be citizens or permanent residents of India and Canada; must have been invited to participate by an academic institution and be affiliated with, or traveling to a Shastri Institute member institutions. **Criteria:** Selection will be based on Institution or Event; contribution to own development and potential institutional linkages; professional background; contribution to promoting or building academic linkages between India-Canada.

Funds Avail.: 1,000 Canadian Dollars. **Duration:** Annual. **Number Awarded:** 10. **To Apply:** Applicants must submit the completed electronic application form to Shastri Institute's Canada office along with the following documents: curriculum vitae that is not more than three pages; letter of invitation from the host institution/organization; and proof of residency either copy of passport. **Contact:** Mahmuda Aldeen, Program and Member Relations Officer, Shastri Indo-Canadian Institute, 1418 Education Twr., 2500 University Dr NW, Calgary, AB, T2N 1N4.

10038 ■ Sheet Metal and Air Conditioning Contractors' National Association (SMACNA)
4201 Lafayette Center Dr.
Chantilly, VA 20151-1209
Ph: (703)803-2980
Fax: (703)803-3732
E-mail: order@smacna.org
URL: www.smacna.org
Social Media: www.facebook.com/SMACNA
www.instagram.com/smacna4201/
www.linkedin.com/company/122248
www.linkedin.com/company/smacna
twitter.com/smacna

Awards are arranged alphabetically below their administering organizations

www.youtube.com/user/SMACNAnational/feed

10039 ■ Sheet Metal And Air Conditioning Contractors' National Association College of Fellows Scholarship Program (Undergraduate/Scholarship)

Purpose: To provide financial assistance for the discovery, interpretation and dissemination of new knowledge that promotes leadership development and personal growth. **Focus:** Metallurgy. **Criteria:** Recipients are selected based on the following demonstrated academic excellence; academic goals; involvement in extracurricular activities; community involvement; leadership ability; and good character.

Funds Avail.: No specific amount. **Duration:** Annual. **To Apply:** Applicants must complete the application form; must submit an essay; high school transcripts; three letters of recommendation; college aptitude scores; indication of an acceptance at an accredited four-year college or university; and recent photograph. **Contact:** SMACNA College of Fellows Scholarship Program, PO Box 221230, Chantilly, VA, 20153-1230.

10040 ■ Shell Oil Co.
PO Box 2463
Houston, TX 77252-2463
Ph: (281)544-2600
Free: 888-467-4355
URL: www.shell.us
Social Media: www.facebook.com/Shell
www.linkedin.com/company/shell
twitter.com/shell

10041 ■ Shell Incentive Fund Scholarship
(Undergraduate/Scholarship)

Purpose: To support underrepresented students pursuing an undergraduate degree in a specific technical field of study at certain universities. **Focus:** Engineering; Geosciences. **Qualif.:** Applicant must be enrolled as a freshman, sophomore, or junior for the current academic year; must be enrolled full-time students in the year of the scholarship award. If the candidate is not a full-time student (i.e., not taking a full course load or will be taking on a co-op opportunity), the candidate will not be considered for a scholarship; must be enrolled in one of the specified institutions (See list) for the year of the scholarship award. Transfers between Shell-approved institutions are permitted during the year of the scholarship award; must have a minimum 3.20 cumulative GPA (will not be rounded) on a 4.0 scale, which must be maintained throughout any participation in the scholarship program; must major in one of the following disciplines: geology, geophysics or physics, chemical, civil, electrical, environmental, mechanical, petroleum, geological, or geophysical engineering; must be a member of at least one of the following under-represented minorities: Black (Not of Hispanic Origin), Hispanic/Latino, American Indian or Alaskan Native.

Funds Avail.: $2,500. **Duration:** Annual; four-year renewable. **Number Awarded:** Up to 20. **To Apply:** Applicants must complete an online application; must include a copy of high school transcript and standardized test score and to provide the names & email addresses for two individuals to provide recommendations on the applicant's behalf. **Deadline:** December 15. **Contact:** ISTS; Phone: 855-670-ISTS or E-mail: contactus@applyists.com.

10042 ■ Shell Oil Company Technical Scholarship
(Undergraduate/Scholarship)

Purpose: To help students pursuing an undergraduate degree in a specific technical field of study at certain colleges. **Focus:** Engineering; Geosciences. **Qualif.:** Applicant must be enrolled as a freshman, sophomore, or junior for the current academic year; must be enrolled full-time students in the year of the scholarship award. If the candidate is not a full-time student (i.e., not taking a full course load or will be taking on a co-op opportunity), the candidate will not be considered for a scholarship; must be enrolled in one of the specified institutions (See list) for the year of the scholarship award. Transfers between Shell-approved institutions are permitted during the year of the scholarship award; must have a minimum 3.20 cumulative GPA (will not be rounded) on a 4.0 scale, which must be maintained throughout any participation in the scholarship program; must major in one of the following disciplines: geology, geophysics or physics; chemical, civil, electrical, environmental, mechanical, petroleum, geological, or geophysical engineering.

Funds Avail.: $2,500. **Duration:** Annual; four-year renewable. **Number Awarded:** Up to 20. **To Apply:** Applicants must complete an online application; must include a copy of high school transcript and standardized test score and to provide the names & email addresses for two individuals to provide recommendations on the applicant's behalf. **Deadline:** December 15. **Contact:** ISTS; Phone: 855-670-ISTS or E-mail: contactus@applyists.com.

10043 ■ Shell Process Technology Scholarships
(Undergraduate/Scholarship)

Purpose: To aid students who seek an education to obtain employment in the industries that use and control mechanical, physical or chemical processes to produce a final product. **Focus:** Engineering; Geosciences. **Qualif.:** Applicants must be US citizens or authorized to work on a full-time basis in the United States; enrolled full or part-time in a Process Technology (or Instrumentation Technology) two-year degree program or be high school seniors planning to enroll in the Process Technology (or Instrumentation Technology) two-year degree program; and enrolled in at least one Process Technology or Instrumentation Technology course per semester unless pursuing a four-year degree. **Criteria:** Recipients are selected based on financial need.

Funds Avail.: Amount varies. **Duration:** Annual; two-year. **To Apply:** Applicants must submit a completed application form.

10044 ■ Sheriff's Law Enforcement Association of McLennan County
PO Box 23475
Waco, TX 76702

10045 ■ SLEAMC Scholarships (Graduate, Undergraduate/Scholarship)

Purpose: To provide financial assistance to those students with good scholastic records. **Focus:** General studies/Field of study not specified. **Qualif.:** Applicants must be U.S. citizens; must be high school seniors, graduates, or GED recipients at time of application; must be enrolled in a college or university in an academic course of study; must be 25 years of age or less at time of application; must have a cumulative GPA of at least 2.5; must be enrolled as full-time students during semester for which the application is

Awards are arranged alphabetically below their administering organizations

submitted; must not have been convicted of a crime. **Criteria:** Preference will be given to those students residing in McLennan County, Texas and will be based on academic achievement.

Funds Avail.: $500. **To Apply:** Applicants must complete the application form available online. Must submit the following application requirements: official high school transcript or GED certification; current official college transcript; work history (summer and/or part time, volunteer; indicate number of hours worked). **Contact:** Sheriff's Law Enforcement Association of McLennan County, at the above address.

10046 ■ Joseph Shinoda Memorial Scholarship Foundation, Inc.
c/o Patricia Broering, Executive Assistant
962 Pecho St.
Morro Bay, CA 93442
Ph: (805)704-2408
URL: www.shinodascholarship.org

10047 ■ Joseph Shinoda Memorial Scholarship
(Undergraduate/Scholarship)

Purpose: To encourage creative young talent to pursue careers in floriculture. **Focus:** Floriculture. **Qualif.:** Applicant must be an undergraduate student enrolled in an accredited four-year college/university in the U.S. (or in a California community college) majoring in a degree program related to the field of floriculture. **Criteria:** Selection is based on the application materials submitted.

Funds Avail.: $1,000 - $5,000. **Duration:** Annual. **Number Awarded:** Varies. **To Apply:** Applicants must submit a completed application form together with a letter of recommendation from the faculty evaluating the applicants as a student; another letter of recommendation from an employer or community service organization evaluating the applicants as a worker or volunteer; and transcript of grades.

10048 ■ Shoreline Community College Foundation
16101 Greenwood Ave. N
Shoreline, WA 98133-5696
Ph: (206)546-4101
Fax: (206)546-4630
URL: www.shoreline.edu
Social Media: www.facebook.com/
ShorelineCommunityCollege
www.instagram.com/shorelinecollege
twitter.com/shorelinecc
www.youtube.com/user/ShorelineCCvideos

10049 ■ Beta Sigma Phi Visual Arts Scholarship
(Undergraduate/Scholarship)

Purpose: To increase access and success of Shoreline Community College students; to attract, encourage and assist talented students enrolled in Fine Arts programs at SCC. **Focus:** Art. **Qualif.:** Applicants must be Washington state residents; must be part-time or full-time students; must have applied or be currently enrolled in the visual arts courses at SCC. **Criteria:** Recipients will be selected based on academic performance and financial needs.

Funds Avail.: $250. **Duration:** Annual. **Number Awarded:** 2. **To Apply:** Applicants must complete and submit the ap-

plication form online providing essays; unofficial transcripts; budget worksheet and references. **Deadline:** March 22. **Contact:** Contact: Foundation Scholarship Office Bldg 5000 (FOSS), Room 5218 Shoreline Community College 16101 Greenwood Avenue N Shoreline, WA 98133-5696; 206-533-6783; Email: scholarships@shoreline.edu.

10050 ■ Boeing Company Scholarship
(Undergraduate/Scholarship)

Purpose: To support a student pursuing a degree in math, manufacturing or engineering. **Focus:** Engineering; Information science and technology; Manufacturing. **Qualif.:** Applicant must be a student pursuing a degree in math, manufacturing or engineering at SCC. **Criteria:** Recipients will be selected based on academic performance and financial needs.

Duration: Annual. **To Apply:** Applicants must complete and submit the application form online providing essays; unofficial transcripts; budget worksheet and references. **Contact:** Alysen Laakso, Bldg., 1000, Rm. 1005; Phone: 206-533-6783; Email: scholarships@shoreline.edu.

10051 ■ Carli Edwards Memorial Scholarship
(Undergraduate/Scholarship)

Purpose: To provide Shoreline Community College students who are survivors of domestic abuse with financial assistance toward the purchase of textbooks. **Focus:** Criminal justice. **Criteria:** Recipients are selected based on academic standing and financial needs; preference will be given to singlemothers with minor children living at home.

Funds Avail.: $200. **Duration:** Quarterly. **To Apply:** Applicants must complete and submit the application form including letter of recommendation; statement/documentation of income and need for financial assistance; current class schedule; unofficial SCC transcript.

10052 ■ Friends of Mary Automotive Scholarship
(Undergraduate/Scholarship)

Purpose: To provide financial assistance to women who are taking automotive program. **Focus:** Automotive technology. **Qualif.:** Applicants must be returning female students at Shoreline Community College. **Criteria:** Recipients will be selected based on academic performance and financial needs.

Funds Avail.: $500. **Duration:** Annual. **Number Awarded:** 1. **To Apply:** Applicants must complete and submit the application form online providing essays; unofficial transcripts; budget worksheet and references. **Deadline:** April 11. **Remarks:** The Scholarship was established in honor of Mary Nelson. **Contact:** Julianne Scott, International Admissions, Phone: 206-546-6995, Email: international@shoreline.edu; Alysen Laakso, Scholarship Manager, Foundation, Phone: 206- 533-6783, Email: scholarships@shoreline.edu.

10053 ■ High School Academic Scholarship
(Undergraduate/Scholarship)

Purpose: To provide financial assistance to students who are in need. **Focus:** General studies/Field of study not specified. **Qualif.:** Applicants must be graduating Washington State high school seniors in the Shoreline area who are enrolling at SCC; must have demonstrated strong academic improvement. **Criteria:** Recipients will be selected based on academic performance; leadership qualities and involvement in school and community activities.

Funds Avail.: $1,500. **Duration:** Annual. **Number Awarded:** 3. **To Apply:** Applicants must complete and

Awards are arranged alphabetically below their administering organizations

submit the application form online providing essays; unofficial transcripts; budget worksheet and references. **Contact:** Alysen Laakso, Bldg., 1000, Rm. 1005; Phone: 206-533-6783; Email: scholarships@shoreline.edu.

10054 ■ Ina Knutsen Scholarship *(Undergraduate/ Scholarship)*

Purpose: To provide financial support to students who are in need. **Focus:** General studies/Field of study not specified. **Qualif.:** Applicant must be a U.S. citizen or legal U.S. resident or permanent U.S. resident with an I-551 Card or a student in F-1 non-immigrant status (if applicable); must have completed at least 24 college level credits at Shoreline CC; must have a minimum Shoreline GPA of 3.0 for college level classes only; must have completed at least 2 quarters at Shoreline Community College. **Criteria:** Recipients will be selected based on academic performance and financial needs.

Funds Avail.: $3,000. **Duration:** Annual. **Number Awarded:** 5. **To Apply:** Applicants must complete and submit the application form online providing essays; unofficial transcripts; budget worksheet and references. **Deadline:** April 16. **Contact:** FOSS Bldg (5000) - Rm 5218; Phone: 206-533-6783; Email:scholarships@shoreline.edu.

10055 ■ Joseph Wood Rogers Memorial Scholarship in Mathematics *(Undergraduate/Scholarship)*

Purpose: To provide financial support to students who are in need. **Focus:** Mathematics and mathematical sciences. **Qualif.:** Applicants must be Washington state residents (as defined by the college). Must have completed at least 30 credits at Shoreline Community College; must have completed at least two mathematic courses at or above the calculus level at SCC; must have at least a 3.5 grade point average in mathematic courses taken at SCC; must Intend to pursue a degree in "pure" mathematics at an accredited college or university; must show promise of continued growth in mathematics. **Criteria:** Recipients will be selected based on academic performance and financial needs.

Funds Avail.: $1,000. **Duration:** Annual. **Number Awarded:** 2. **To Apply:** Applicants must complete and submit four collated packets (typed) including current class schedule; SCC unofficial transcript; one (two page maximum) typed personal essay describing interest in mathematics and your professional goals; three references. **Deadline:** April 11. **Remarks:** The scholarship was established in memory of Joseph Wood Rogers. **Contact:** Alysen Laakso, Bldg., 1000, Rm. 1005; Phone: 206-533-6783; Email: scholarships@shoreline.edu.

10056 ■ Ken LaFountaine First Nations Scholarship *(Undergraduate/Scholarship)*

Purpose: To provide First Nation students (indigenous to the Americas and associated territories) with financial assistance in times of need. **Focus:** Dental hygiene. **Qualif.:** Applicants must be full-time or part-time students at the Shoreline Community College(students indigenous to the Americas and associated territories). **Criteria:** Recipients are selected based on academic standing and financial needs.

Funds Avail.: $500. **Duration:** Annual. **To Apply:** Applicants must complete and submit the application form online providing essays; unofficial transcripts; budget worksheet and references. **Deadline:** April 11. **Contact:** Alysen Laakso, Bldg., 1000, Rm. 1005; Phone: 206-533-6783; Email: scholarships@shoreline.edu.

10057 ■ Ron LaFreniere Business Administration Scholarship *(Undergraduate/Scholarship)*

Purpose: To provide students they need like tuition fees, books, and/or any class related fees. **Focus:** Business administration. **Qualif.:** Applicants must be Washington state residents (as defined by the college); must have completed a minimum of two quarters at SCC and taken at least 12 credits in Business Administration, have a strong emphasis of study in Business Administration, have a minimum SCC cumulative grade point average of 3.0, and must have applied for Financial Aid. **Criteria:** Recipients will be selected based on academic performance and financial needs.

Funds Avail.: $1,000. **Duration:** Annual. **Number Awarded:** 1. **To Apply:** Applicants must complete and submit the application form. **Contact:** Phone: 206-533-6783; E-mail: lyaw@shoreline.edu.

10058 ■ Margaret Mallett Nursing Scholarship *(Undergraduate/Scholarship)*

Purpose: To provide financial support to students who are in need. **Focus:** Nursing.

Funds Avail.: $1,000. **Duration:** Annual. **Number Awarded:** 9. **To Apply:** Applicants must complete and submit the application form online providing essays; unofficial transcripts; budget worksheet and references. **Remarks:** The fund was established in memory of Margaret by her son.

10059 ■ Margaret Svec Scholarship *(Undergraduate/ Scholarship)*

Purpose: To provide financial support to students who are in need. **Focus:** Mathematics and mathematical sciences.

Funds Avail.: $1,000. **Duration:** Annual. **Number Awarded:** 2. **To Apply:** Applicants must complete and submit the application form online providing essays; unofficial transcripts; budget worksheet and references. **Deadline:** April 16. **Remarks:** The scholarship was established by Margaret E. Svec, before her death.

10060 ■ Eric Niemitalo Scholarship in Earth and Environmental Science *(Undergraduate/Scholarship)*

Purpose: To provide financial support to students who are pursuing a degree in sciences. **Focus:** Environmental science; Geography; Geology.

Duration: Annual. **To Apply:** Applicants must complete and submit the application form online providing essays; unofficial transcripts; budget worksheet and references. **Deadline:** April 16. **Remarks:** The Scholarship was established in honor of Eric Niemitalo.

10061 ■ Professor Emeritus Dr. Bill Johnson Memorial Scholarship *(Undergraduate/Scholarship)*

Purpose: This scholarshipis intended for students who are within three quarters of graduation from SCC and have shown a strong emphasis of study in mathematics or science. **Focus:** Mathematics and mathematical sciences. **Qualif.:** Applicant must be a student pursuing a degree in mathematics or science at SCC. **Criteria:** Recipient will be selected based on academic performance and financial needs.

Duration: Annual. **To Apply:** Applicants must complete and submit the application form online providing essays; unofficial transcripts; budget worksheet and references. **Deadline:** April 11. **Contact:** URL: www.shoreline.edu/

Awards are arranged alphabetically below their administering organizations

Sponsors and Their Scholarships

scholarships; Phone: 206-533-6783; Email: scholarships@shoreline.edu.

10062 ■ SCC Full-Time Continuing Student Scholarship *(Undergraduate/Scholarship)*

Purpose: To provide financial assistance to students who are in need. **Focus:** General studies/Field of study not specified. **Qualif.:** Applicants must be full-time students at Shoreline Community College. **Criteria:** Recipients will be selected based on academic performance and financial needs.

Duration: Annual. **To Apply:** Applicants must complete and submit the application form online providing essays; unofficial transcripts; budget worksheet and references. **Deadline:** September 2. **Contact:** Alysen Laakso, Bldg., 1000, Rm. 1005; Phone: 206-533-6783; Email: scholarships@shoreline.edu.

10063 ■ SCC Part-Time Continuing Student Scholarship *(Undergraduate/Scholarship)*

Purpose: To provide financial assistance to students who are in need. **Focus:** General studies/Field of study not specified. **Qualif.:** Applicants must be part time students at Shoreline Community College. **Criteria:** Recipients will be selected who demonstrate good academic performance.

Duration: Annual. **To Apply:** Applicants must complete and submit the application form online providing essays; unofficial transcripts; budget worksheet and references. **Deadline:** March 22. **Contact:** Alysen Laakso, Bldg., 1000, Rm. 1005; Phone: 206-533-6783; Email: scholarships@shoreline.edu.

10064 ■ Shoreline and Lake Forest Park scholarship *(Undergraduate/Scholarship)*

Purpose: To provide financial assistance to students who are in need. **Focus:** General studies/Field of study not specified. **Qualif.:** Applicants must be graduating high school seniors in the Shoreline/Lake Forest Park area who are enrolling at SCC; must have demonstrated strong academic performance; must live in the city of Shoreline or Lake Forest Park. **Criteria:** Recipients will be selected based on academic performance and financial needs.

Duration: Annual. **Number Awarded:** 1. **To Apply:** Applicants must complete and submit the application form online providing essays; unofficial transcripts; budget worksheet and references. **Deadline:** April 23.

10065 ■ Elizabeth R. Thomas Alumni Nursing Scholarship *(Undergraduate/Scholarship)*

Purpose: To provide financial assistance to students who are in need. **Focus:** General studies/Field of study not specified.

Funds Avail.: $500. **Duration:** Annual. **Number Awarded:** 2. **To Apply:** Applicants must complete and submit the application form online providing essays; unofficial transcripts; budget worksheet and references.

10066 ■ SHPE Foundation
1765 Duke St.
Alexandria, VA 22314
Ph: (703)647-2122
Fax: (323)622-1046
URL: www.shpefoundation.org

10067 ■ AHETEMS/ExxonMobil Scholarships *(Undergraduate/Scholarship)*

Purpose: To enhance and achieve the potential of students pursuing degrees in engineering. **Focus:** Engineering, Civil; Engineering, Electrical; Engineering, Mechanical; Engineering, Petroleum. **Qualif.:** Applicant must be a U.S. citizen; enrolled full-time (12 hrs undergraduate) during the academic year at an accredited university in the U.S. or Puerto Rico; have a minimum GPA of 3.0 on a 4.0 scale; majoring in civil, chemical, electrical, mechanical, or petroleum engineering. **Criteria:** Selection is based on demonstrated significant motivation and aptitude for a career in science, technology, engineering or mathematics.

Funds Avail.: No specific amount. **Duration:** Annual. **To Apply:** Applicant must complete the application form online. In addition, applicants must submit via mail the Scholarship Certification Form along with the personal statement, official transcript, letter of recommendation, and a resume to AHETEMS. **Deadline:** April 1. **Contact:** SHPE Foundation, at the above address.

10068 ■ AHETEMS General Scholarships *(Undergraduate, Graduate/Scholarship)*

Purpose: To enhance and achieve the potential of Latino students pursuing degrees in engineering, math and science. **Focus:** Engineering; Mathematics and mathematical sciences; Science; Technology. **Qualif.:** Applicant must be of Hispanic-descent; accepted into or attending an accredited 2-year or 4-year college/university in the U.S. or Puerto Rico; enrolled full-time (12 hrs undergraduate, 9 hrs graduate) during the academic year; or a high school graduating senior graduating from an accredited U.S. high school with a diploma; have a minimum GPA of 3.00 on a 4.0 (high school senior and undergraduate), or 3.25 on a 4.0 scale (graduate student); majoring in science, technology, engineering, mathematics or a related field; and pursuing first bachelors, masters or doctoral degree (students pursuing a second bachelors, etc. are not eligible). **Criteria:** Selection is based on demonstrated significant motivation and aptitude for a career in science, technology, engineering or mathematics.

Funds Avail.: No specific amount. **Duration:** Annual. **To Apply:** Applicant must complete the application form online. In addition, applicants must submit via mail the Scholarship Certification Form along with the personal statement, official transcript, letter of recommendation, and a resume to AHETEMS. **Deadline:** May 1. **Contact:** SHPE Foundation, at the above address.

10069 ■ AHETEMS Professional Scholarships *(Graduate/Scholarship)*

Purpose: To enhance and achieve the potential of Latino students pursuing degrees in engineering, math and science. **Focus:** Engineering; Mathematics and mathematical sciences; Science; Technology. **Qualif.:** Applicant must be employed full-time in the U.S. or Puerto Rico in a technical career field; enrolled in a science, technology, engineering, or mathematics graduate degree program at an accredited university in the U.S. or Puerto Rico at least half-time (6 hrs/credits) throughout the academic year; have a minimum 3.25 on a 4.0 GPA; be a SHPE member in good standing both at the time of application and throughout the academic year (non-member may become member at the time of application); pursuing a first masters or doctoral degree. **Criteria:** Selection is based on demonstrated significant motivation and aptitude for a career in science, technology, engineering or mathematics.

Funds Avail.: No specific amount. **Duration:** Annual. **To Apply:** Applicant must complete the application form online. In addition, applicants must submit via mail the Scholarship Certification Form along with the personal statement, of-

Awards are arranged alphabetically below their administering organizations

Scholarships, Fellowships and Loans, 38th Ed.

ficial transcript, letter of recommendation, and a resume to AHETEMS. **Deadline:** May 1. **Contact:** SHPE Foundation, at the above address.

10070 ■ Shred Nations

777 S Wassworth Blvd. 3-250
Lakewood, CO 80123
Free: 800-747-3365
E-mail: info@shrednations.com
URL: www.shrednations.com
Social Media: www.facebook.com/shred.nations
www.linkedin.com/company/shred-nations
www.in.pinterest.com/shrednations
twitter.com/shred_nations

10071 ■ Shred Nations Scholarship *(Undergraduate, Graduate/Scholarship)*

Purpose: To promote education in the shredding and secure destruction industries. **Focus:** Environmental conservation; Environmental technology. **Criteria:** Selection priority will be given to family and friends of members of the Shred Nations partner network. Applicant's character will also be evaluated and academic merit will be considered.

Funds Avail.: $5,000. **Duration:** Annual. **Number Awarded:** 1. **To Apply:** Applicant must submit an essay of 500 to 1,000 words about how they will use their studies to improve business and environmental responsibility, and make contributions to the community. Essay should also include the applicant's interest in the secure destruction industry and demonstrate what value the they can provide to a potential employer.

10072 ■ Sickle Cell Disease Association of America (SCDAA)

3700 Koppers St., Ste. 570
Baltimore, MD 21227
Free: 800-421-8453
URL: www.sicklecelldisease.org
Social Media: www.facebook.com/sicklecellcampaign
www.instagram.com/scdaa/
twitter.com/SCDAAorg

10073 ■ Kermit B. Nash Academic Scholarships *(Graduate/Scholarship)*

Purpose: To promote educational pursuits of individuals with sickle cell disease. **Focus:** General studies/Field of study not specified. **Qualif.:** Applicants must have minimum of 3.0 GPA unless special hardship demonstrated; must be severity of academic challenges and obstacles posed by sickle cell disease. **Criteria:** Selection will be based on general academic achievement; promise leadership and community service.

Funds Avail.: Total of $20,000 (2,500 per semester). **Duration:** 4 years. **Number Awarded:** 1. **Deadline:** May 20.

10074 ■ SCDAA Post-Doctoral Research Fellowships *(Postdoctorate/Fellowship)*

Purpose: To provide financial support for young investigators conducting research in sickle cell disease. **Focus:** specific diseases. **Qualif.:** Applicants must have completed a doctoral degree (MD, PhD or equivalent); must have completed clinical training; must not have more than a total

of five years of post-doctoral research experience by the award date; and must be affiliated with a non-profit institution of higher learning or non-profit research facility in the United States.

Duration: Two years. **To Apply:** Applicants must submit three copies of application and research mentor's supporting documents including a letter of commitment and the biographical sketch of the mentor. The research proposal must address the broad subject of sickle cell disease in basic laboratory, clinical or psychosocial research areas.

10075 ■ Sidley Austin LLP

1 S Dearborn
Chicago, IL 60603
Ph: (312)853-7000
Fax: (312)853-7036
E-mail: area@sidley.com
URL: www.sidley.com
Social Media: www.facebook.com/sidleyaustinllpofficial
www.linkedin.com/company/sidley-austin
twitter.com/sidleylaw

10076 ■ Sidley Diversity and Inclusion Scholarships *(Undergraduate/Scholarship)*

Purpose: To promote creating opportunities for lawyers of all backgrounds, regardless of gender, race, ethnicity, national origin, disability status, sexual orientation or beliefs. **Focus:** Law. **Qualif.:** Applicants must: have demonstrated ability to contribute meaningfully to the diversity of the law school, the firm, and the legal profession; be second year law students; have demonstrated academic achievement and leadership qualities. Preference is given to students at schools where Sidley conducts on-campus interviews or participates in resume collections. **Criteria:** Selection will be based on the committee's criteria.

To Apply: Applicants should submit an application, including resume, official law school transcript, legal writing sample and personal statement; an optional letter of recommendation from a professor, employer or personal acquaintance who can meaningfully comment on academic and intellectual strengths, demonstrated commitment to diversity, and/or ability to contribute to Sidley's diversity efforts.

10077 ■ Sidley Prelaw Scholars Program *(Undergraduate/Scholarship)*

Purpose: To increase diversity in law schools by subsidizing the cost of applying to law school for talented, financially needy minority students. **Focus:** Law. **Qualif.:** Applicant must be a second semester junior or senior graduating from college in good standing; a native-born or naturalized U.S. citizen; and has demonstrated financial need. **Criteria:** Selection is based on merit and need.

Duration: Annual. **To Apply:** Applicants must submit a completed scholarship application form along with a copy of most recent FAFSA SAR; a copy of current transcript; resume or curriculum vitae (maximum of two pages); and completed recommendation form from one academic reference. **Contact:** Email: sidleyscholars@sidley.com.

10078 ■ Siemens Canada Ltd.

1577 N Service Rd. E
Oakville, ON, Canada L6H 0H6
URL: new.siemens.com

10079 ■ Siemens Canada Academic Awards *(Undergraduate/Scholarship)*

Purpose: To help students across Canada reach their education and career objectives. **Focus:** Engineering,

Awards are arranged alphabetically below their administering organizations

Electrical; Engineering, Mechanical. **Qualif.:** Applicants must be university or college students who have completed at least their second year of study in an electrical, mechanical engineering/technology program with a minimum 80% average. **Criteria:** Selection will be based on the applicants' eligibility and other criteria of the committee.

Funds Avail.: 3,500 Canadian Dollars each. **Duration:** Annual. **To Apply:** Applicants may visit the website for them to create an account to apply for the scholarship, as well as for the other application materials required. **Deadline:** May 31. **Remarks:** The scholarship is co-sponsored by the Siemens Canada.

10080 ■ The Sigma Chi Foundation
1714 Hinman Ave.
Evanston, IL 60201
Ph: (847)869-3655
Fax: (847)869-4906
E-mail: foundation@sigmachi.org
URL: sigmachi.org
Social Media: www.facebook.com/sigmachi
www.instagram.com/sigmachi
twitter.com/sigmachi
www.youtube.com/user/SigmaChiFraternity

10081 ■ Denton Scholarship (Graduate/Scholarship)

Purpose: To assist students pursuing a career in the field of international affairs. **Focus:** Business; Economics; International affairs and relations; Political science. **Criteria:** Selection will be based on academic performance and demonstrated leadership.

Funds Avail.: $1,000. **To Apply:** Applicants must present the following requirements: a copy of most recent transcript; two letters of recommendation, one must be from a dean, professor or professional colleague and the other letter should be from a Sigma Chi alumnus that the applicants known for at least a year. **Remarks:** Established in 1929.

10082 ■ Herschede Engineering Scholarship (Graduate/Scholarship)

Purpose: To assist students pursuing a career in the area of engineering. **Focus:** Engineering. **Qualif.:** Applicants must be members in good standing of Sigma Chi Fraternity; must be pursuing graduate degree in the field of engineering; must have a cumulative GPA of 3.0 on a 4.0 scale. **Criteria:** Selection will be based on academic performance and demonstrated leadership.

Funds Avail.: $1,000. **Duration:** Annual. **To Apply:** Applicants must present the following requirements: a copy of most recent transcript; two letters of recommendation, one must be from a dean, professor or professional colleague and the other letter should be from a Sigma Chi alumnus that the applicants known for at least a year. **Remarks:** Established in 1940.

10083 ■ Madson Graduate Scholarship (Graduate/Scholarship)

Purpose: To assist students pursuing a career in any academic field. **Focus:** General studies/Field of study not specified. **Qualif.:** Applicants must be members in good standing of Sigma Chi Fraternity; must be pursuing their first year of graduate level study in any academic field; must have a cumulative GPA of 3.0 on a 4.0 scale. **Criteria:** Selection will be based on academic performance and demonstrated leadership.

Funds Avail.: $1,000. **Duration:** Annual. **To Apply:** Applicants must present the following requirements: a copy of most recent transcript; two letters of recommendation, one must be from a dean, professor or professional colleague and the other letter should be from a Sigma Chi alumnus that the applicants known for at least a year. **Remarks:** Established in 1925.

10084 ■ Military Service Scholarship (Graduate, Undergraduate/Scholarship)

Purpose: To provide scholarships to undergraduate and graduate Sigma Chi Brothers who are currently serving or have served in army, navy, air force, marines, coast guard, or national guard. **Focus:** General studies/Field of study not specified. **Qualif.:** Applicants must be undergraduate or graduate Sigma Chi Brothers who are currently serving or have served on active duty in their country's military; must have a cumulative undergraduate GPA of 3.0 on a 4.0 scale for graduate students and GPA of 2.5 on a 4.0 scale for undergraduate students. **Criteria:** Selection will be based on academic performance and demonstrated leadership.

Funds Avail.: $1,000. **Duration:** Annual. **To Apply:** Applicants must present the following requirements: a copy of most recent transcript; two letters of recommendation, one letter of recommendation must be from a dean, professor or professional colleague and the other letter should be from a Sigma Chi alumnus you have known for at least a year; letters of Recommendation from family members and friends are not acceptable.

10085 ■ Sigma Delta Chi Foundation (SDX)
3909 N Meridian St.
Indianapolis, IN 46208
Ph: (317)927-8000
Fax: (317)920-4789
URL: www.spj.org
Social Media: www.facebook.com/SocietyofProfessional
 Journalists
www.instagram.com/spj_pics
www.linkedin.com/company/society-of-professional
 -journalists
twitter.com/spj_tweets

10086 ■ Eugene C. Pulliam Fellowships for Editorial Writing (Other/Fellowship)

Purpose: To provide financial assistance to outstanding editorial writers to help broaden their journalistic horizons and knowledge of the world. **Focus:** Editors and editing. **Qualif.:** Applicants must be part-time or full-time editorial writers at a news publication located in the United States; with at least three years experience as an editorial writer; demonstrate outstanding writing and analytical abilities and ability and intent to publish work within 18 months of selection. **Criteria:** Selection will be reviewed and evaluated by a panel of judges.

Funds Avail.: $75,000. **Duration:** Annual. **To Apply:** Applicants must submit a cover letter (containing complete contact information) stating the purpose and nature of the proposed study, a timeline for accomplishing the work and a plan for how the stipend will be used; editor's endorsement; a (one-page) professional biography and summary of professional experience; and five samples of editorials. **Deadline:** June 22. **Remarks:** The Fellowship was established to honor Eugene C. Pulliam. Established in 1978. **Contact:** SPJ Headquarters; Phone: 317-927-8000; Email: awards@spj.org.

Awards are arranged alphabetically below their administering organizations

10087 ■ Sigma Iota Epsilon (SIE)

c/o Dr. G. James Francis, President
Colorado State University
213 Rockwell Hall
Fort Collins, CO 80521
Ph: (970)491-6265
Fax: (970)491-3522
URL: www.sienational.com

10088 ■ Sigma Iota Epsilon Undergraduate National Scholar Awards *(Undergraduate/Scholarship)*

Purpose: To support students with their studies. **Focus:** Management. **Criteria:** Selection will be based on a level of activity in SIE and other university organizations; leadership interest and offices held - community service involvement; academic excellence.

Funds Avail.: $1,000 each for top five students; $250-$500 for additional scholars. **Duration:** Annual. **Number Awarded:** Varies.

10089 ■ Sigma Kappa Foundation

695 Pro Med Ln., Ste. 300
Carmel, IN 46032-5323
Ph: (317)872-3275
URL: www.sigmakappa.org
Social Media: www.facebook.com/sigmakappa
www.instagram.com/sigmakappasorority
www.linkedin.com/company/the-sigma-kappa-foundation
www.pinterest.com/sigmakappa
twitter.com/SigmaKappa
www.youtube.com/sigmakappasorority

10090 ■ Alice Hersey Wick Award *(Undergraduate/Scholarship)*

Purpose: To support initiated undergraduate members who are in good standing. **Focus:** General studies/Field of study not specified. **Qualif.:** Applicants must be members of Gamma Lambda Chapter who are in good standing; must have minimum cumulative GPA of 3.0 on 4.0 scale and had sustained or improved in the area of scholarship, and exhibited outstanding leadership and service to the chapter, Panhellenic and university. **Criteria:** Preference will be given to rising seniors and then juniors who live in chapter housing.

Funds Avail.: No specific amount. **Contact:** Email at foundationscholarships@sigmakappa.org.

10091 ■ Alpha Kappa Trust Scholarship-Beta Omega *(Undergraduate/Scholarship)*

Purpose: To support initiated undergraduate sophomore, junior or senior members of Sigma Kappa with good standing. **Focus:** General studies/Field of study not specified. **Qualif.:** Applicants must be initiated member of Beta Sigma Chapter of Sigma Kappa; must have minimum GPA of 3.00 on 4.00; must be residents in the chapter house; must have demonstrated leadership in their chapter and on campus and are in need of financial assistance.**Criteria:** Applicants will be judge based on their active participation in a variety of the foundation and academic activities.

Funds Avail.: No specific amount. **To Apply:** Applicants must submit the transcript through online, financial aid details, personal essay and two recommendation letters. **Contact:** Teresa Glassman; Phone: 317-381-5548; E-mail: foundationscholarships@sigmakappa.org.

10092 ■ Alzheimer's/Gerontology Scholarship *(Graduate/Scholarship)*

Purpose: To support initiated members of Sigma Kappa who are in good standing. **Focus:** Gerontology. **Qualif.:** Applicants must be junior, senior or graduate Sigma Kappa members majoring in Gerontology or related field with at least one year of study remaining; must have minimum GPA of 3.00. **Criteria:** Selection of candidates will be based on GPA and other basic demographic criteria.

Funds Avail.: No specific amount. **Contact:** Teresa Glassman; Phone: 317-381-5548; E-mail: foundationscholarships@sigmakappa.org.

10093 ■ Andrea Will Memorial Scholarship *(Undergraduate/Scholarship)*

Purpose: To support initiated undergraduate members of Sigma Kappa with good standing. **Focus:** General studies/Field of study not specified. **Qualif.:** Applicants must be initiated member of the Gamma Mu Chapter of Sigma Kappa; must have minimum GPA of 3.0 on a 4.00 scale; must have demonstrated leadership qualities and involvement in co-curricular activities. **Criteria:** Applicants will be judge based on their active participation in a variety of the foundation and academic activities.

Funds Avail.: No specific amount. **Contact:** Teresa Glassman; Phone: 317-381-5548; E-mail: foundationscholarships@sigmakappa.org.

10094 ■ Francis Warren Baker Memorial Scholarships *(Undergraduate/Scholarship)*

Purpose: To support initiated undergraduate members who are in good standing. **Focus:** Communications; Journalism. **Qualif.:** Applicants must be initiated member of Sigma Kappa with a minimum GPA of 2.5; must be majoring in journalism or communications (print media); must have demonstrated leadership within the chapter, campus, and community. **Criteria:** Preference will be given to sophomores and juniors with at least one year's study remaining.

Funds Avail.: No specific amount. **To Apply:** Applicants must submit the transcript through online, financial aid details, personal essay and two recommendation letters. **Contact:** Email at foundationscholarships@sigmakappa.org.

10095 ■ Barber-Owen-Thomas Scholarship *(Undergraduate/Scholarship)*

Purpose: To support initiated undergraduate junior or senior members of Sigma Kappa with good standing. **Focus:** General studies/Field of study not specified. **Qualif.:** Applicants must be initiated member of Beta Sigma Chapter of Sigma Kappa; must have minimum GPA of 3.00 on a 4.00 scale; must be residents in the chapter house and are in need of financial assistance. **Criteria:** Applicants will be judge based on their active participation in a variety of the foundation and academic activities.

Funds Avail.: No specific amount. **Contact:** Teresa Glassman; Phone: 317-381-5548; E-mail: foundationscholarships@sigmakappa.org.

10096 ■ Beta Sigma Scholarship *(Undergraduate/Scholarship)*

Purpose: To support initiated undergraduate members who are in good standing. **Focus:** General studies/Field of study not specified. **Qualif.:** Applicants must be an active member

Awards are arranged alphabetically below their administering organizations

of Beta Sigma Chapter (Purdue University); must be a sophomore, junior, or senior class status (mid-year graduating seniors are eligible); must have a minimum cumulative GPA of 2.5; must be in need of financial assistance; must be Residing in the chapter house; must demonstrate leadership in their chapter and on campus. **Criteria:** Applicants will be selected based on their active participation in a variety of the foundation and academic activities.

Funds Avail.: No specific amount. **Contact:** Email at foundationscholarships@sigmakappa.org.

10097 ■ Christine Kerr Cawthorne Scholarship
(Undergraduate/Scholarship)

Purpose: To support initiated undergraduate members who are in good standing. **Focus:** General studies/Field of study not specified. **Qualif.:** Applicants must be matriculated rising sophomore at the time the application is completed, and therefore a matriculated junior in the academic year for which the scholarship is issued; must have minimum cumulative GPA of 3.0. **Criteria:** Applicants will be judged on leadership and service provided to the chapter and campus community.

Funds Avail.: No specific amount. **Contact:** Email at foundationscholarships@sigmakappa.org.

10098 ■ Maridell Braham Condon Scholarships
(Undergraduate/Scholarship)

Purpose: To provide support to initiated undergraduate members of Sigma Kappa with good standing. **Focus:** Education. **Qualif.:** Applicants must be initiated members of Sigma Kappa; must have minimum GPA of 3.0; must be majoring in education; must be in need of financial assistance and have demonstrated involvement in their chapter and on campus. **Criteria:** Applicants will be judged based on the demonstrated financial need and active participation in a variety of Sigma Kappa and academic activities. Preference will be given to juniors and seniors with at least one year study remaining.

Funds Avail.: No specific amount. **To Apply:** Applicants must submit the transcript through online, financial aid details, personal essay and two recommendation letters. **Contact:** Email at foundationscholarships@sigmakappa.org.

10099 ■ Delta Chi Alumnae Memorial Scholarship
(Undergraduate/Scholarship)

Purpose: To support initiated undergraduate members who are in good standing. **Focus:** General studies/Field of study not specified. **Qualif.:** Applicants must be initiated member of Delta Chi Chapter (University of Central Oklahoma); must be junior or senior class status; must have a minimum cumulative GPA of 3.25; must be currently enrolled in 12 hours or more. **Criteria:** Consideration will be given for leadership and service provided to the chapter and to the campus community.

Funds Avail.: No specific amount. **Contact:** Email at foundationscholarships@sigmakappa.org.

10100 ■ Beta Nu/Caryl Cordis D'hondt Scholarship
(Undergraduate/Scholarship)

Purpose: To support initiated undergraduate members of Sigma Kappa with good standing. **Focus:** General studies/Field of study not specified. **Qualif.:** Applicants must be initiated member of the Beta Nu Chapter of Sigma Kappa; must be involved in chapter and campus activities and are in need of financial assistance. **Criteria:** Applicants will be

judge based on their active participation in a variety of the foundation and academic activities.

Funds Avail.: No specific amount. **Contact:** Teresa Glassman; Phone: 317-381-5548; E-mail: foundationscholarships@sigmakappa.org.

10101 ■ Theta/Caryl Cordis D'hondt Scholarship
(Undergraduate/Scholarship)

Purpose: To support initiated undergraduate junior or senior members who are in good standing. **Focus:** General studies/Field of study not specified. **Qualif.:** Applicants must be initiated member of Theta Chapter of Sigma Kappa; must have minimum GPA of 3.25 on a 4.00 scale; must have demonstrated involvement in the chapter. **Criteria:** Financial need will be considered.

Funds Avail.: No specific amount. **Contact:** Teresa Glassman; Phone: 317-381-5548; E-mail: foundationscholarships@sigmakappa.org.

10102 ■ Dr. Nancy Smith Midgette Scholarship
(Undergraduate/Scholarship)

Purpose: To support initiated undergraduate members who are in good standing. **Focus:** General studies/Field of study not specified. **Qualif.:** Applicants must be active member of Kappa Zeta Chapter (Elon University); must demonstrate outstanding leadership and service to the chapter, Panhellenic, and the University; must have a minimum cumulative GPA of 3.4.

Funds Avail.: No specific amount. **Contact:** Email at foundationscholarships@sigmakappa.org.

10103 ■ Elin J. Stene/Xi Scholarship *(Undergraduate/Scholarship)*

Purpose: To support initiated undergraduate members who are in good standing. **Focus:** General studies/Field of study not specified. **Qualif.:** Applicants must be active member of Xi Chapter (University of Kansas); must be juniors or seniors class status (mid-year graduating seniors are eligible); must have a minimum cumulative GPA of 3.0; must be in need of financial assistance.

Funds Avail.: No specific amount. **Contact:** Email at foundationscholarships@sigmakappa.org.

10104 ■ Elise Reed Jenkins Memorial Scholarship
(Undergraduate/Scholarship)

Purpose: To support initiated undergraduate members who are in good standing. **Focus:** General studies/Field of study not specified. **Qualif.:** Applicants must be members of the Alpha Delta, Gamma Lambda and Gamma Psi Chapters of Sigma Kappa who are in good standing; must have a minimum cumulative GPA of 3.0 on 4.0 scale; must be loyal members of Sigma Kappa for at least two years.

Funds Avail.: No specific amount. **Contact:** Email at foundationscholarships@sigmakappa.org.

10105 ■ Epsilon Epsilon Scholarship
(Undergraduate/Scholarship)

Purpose: To support initiated undergraduate members who are in good standing. **Focus:** General studies/Field of study not specified. **Qualif.:** Applicants must be an active member in good standing of Epsilon Chapter (University of Georgia); must be a junior or senior class status; must have a minimum cumulative GPA of 3.00. **Criteria:** Candidate will be selected based on financial need and leadership qualities as an officer or former officer of the chapter.

Awards are arranged alphabetically below their administering organizations

Funds Avail.: No specific amount. **Contact:** Email at foundationscholarships@sigmakappa.org.

10106 ■ Epsilon Tau Scholarship *(Undergraduate/ Scholarship)*

Purpose: To support initiated undergraduate members who are in good standing. **Focus:** General studies/Field of study not specified. **Qualif.:** Applicants must be active member in good standing (scholastic, financial, membership) of Epsilon Tau Chapter (California State University at Fullerton); must demonstrate financial need and involvement in Sigma Kappa, campus, and the community. **Criteria:** Candidates will be selected based on their financial need and involvement to the foundation.

Funds Avail.: No specific amount. **Contact:** Email at foundationscholarships@sigmakappa.org.

10107 ■ Evelyn S. Nish Scholarship *(Undergraduate/ Scholarship)*

Purpose: To support initiated undergraduate members who are in good standing. **Focus:** General studies/Field of study not specified. **Qualif.:** Applicants must be active member in good standing of the Theta Chapter (University of Illinois); must be junior or senior students enrolled during the academic year that the scholarship is granted; must have a minimum cumulative GPA of 2.50. **Criteria:** Consideration will be given for leadership and service provided to the chapter and to the campus community.

Funds Avail.: No specific amount. **Contact:** Email at foundationscholarships@sigmakappa.org.

10108 ■ Gamma Iota Scholarship *(Undergraduate/ Scholarship)*

Purpose: To support initiated undergraduate members who are in good standing. **Focus:** General studies/Field of study not specified. **Qualif.:** Applicants must be active members of Zeta Nu, Gamma Tau, or Zeta Kappa; must have a minimum cumulative GPA of 3.0; must have held or currently hold a Sorority position; must demonstrate involvement in campus and community activities; must be in need of financial assistance. **Criteria:** Candidates will be selected based on their financial need and involvement to the foundation.

Funds Avail.: No specific amount. **Contact:** Email at foundationscholarships@sigmakappa.org.

10109 ■ Gamma Iota Scholarships - Gamma Tau *(Undergraduate/Scholarship)*

Purpose: To support initiated undergraduate members who are in good standing. **Focus:** General studies/Field of study not specified. **Qualif.:** Applicants must be active members attending Kappa Eta (Texas Christian University), Zeta Nu (University of Texas at San Antonio), Gamma Tau (Midwestern State), or Zeta Kappa (Angelo State); must have a minimum cumulative GPA of 3.0; must held or currently hold a Sorority position; must demonstrate involvement in campus and community activities; must be in need of financial assistance. **Criteria:** Candidates will be selected based on their financial need and involvement to the foundation.

Funds Avail.: No specific amount. **To Apply:** Applicants must submit the transcript through online, financial aid details, personal essay and two recommendation letters. **Contact:** Email at foundationscholarships@ sigmakappa.org.

10110 ■ Gamma Iota Scholarships - Zeta Kappa *(Undergraduate/Scholarship)*

Purpose: To support initiated undergraduate members who are in good standing. **Focus:** General studies/Field of study not specified. **Qualif.:** Applicants must be active member attending Kappa Eta (Texas Christian University), Zeta Nu (University of Texas at San Antonio), Gamma Tau (Midwestern State), or Zeta Kappa (Angelo State); must have minimum cumulative GPA of 3.0; must have held or currently hold a Sorority position; must demonstrate involvement in campus and community activities; must be in need of financial assistance. **Criteria:** Candidates will be selected based on their financial need and involvement to the foundation.

Funds Avail.: No specific amount. **To Apply:** Applicants must submit the transcript through online, financial aid details, personal essay and two recommendation letters. **Contact:** Email at foundationscholarships@ sigmakappa.org.

10111 ■ Gamma Iota Scholarships - Zeta Nu *(Undergraduate/Scholarship)*

Purpose: To support initiated undergraduate members who are in good standing. **Focus:** General studies/Field of study not specified. **Qualif.:** Applicants must be active member attending Kappa Eta (Texas Christian University), Zeta Nu (University of Texas at San Antonio), Gamma Tau (Midwestern State), or Zeta Kappa (Angelo State); must have minimum cumulative GPA of 3.0; must have held or currently hold a Sorority position; must have demonstrate involvement in campus and community activities; must be in need of financial assistance. **Criteria:** Candidates will be selected based on their financial need and involvement to the foundation.

Funds Avail.: No specific amount. **To Apply:** Applicants must submit the transcript through online, financial aid details, personal essay and two recommendation letters. **Contact:** Email at foundationscholarships@ sigmakappa.org.

10112 ■ Gamma Lambda Scholarship *(Undergraduate/Scholarship)*

Purpose: To support initiated undergraduate members who are in good standing. **Focus:** General studies/Field of study not specified. **Qualif.:** Applicants must be members of Gamma Lambda Chapter who are in good standing; must have minimum cumulative GPA of 3.0 on 4.0 scale and had sustained or improved in the area of scholarship, and exhibited outstanding leadership and service to the chapter, Panhellenic and university. **Criteria:** Preference will be given to rising seniors and then juniors who live in chapter housing.

Funds Avail.: No specific amount. **Contact:** Email at foundationscholarships@sigmakappa.org.

10113 ■ Irma E. Voigt Memorial Scholarship *(Undergraduate/Scholarship)*

Purpose: To support initiated undergraduate members who are in good standing. **Focus:** General studies/Field of study not specified. **Qualif.:** Applicants must be initiated member of Beta Upsilon Chapter (Ohio University); must be a junior class status, currently enrolled in 12 or more hours; must have a minimum cumulative GPA of 3.0; must be actively involved in a chapter, on campus, and in the community. **Criteria:** Candidates will be selected based on their academic achievements and involvement to the foundation.

Awards are arranged alphabetically below their administering organizations

Funds Avail.: No specific amount. **Contact:** Email at foundationscholarships@sigmakappa.org.

10114 ■ Lorraine E. Swain Scholarship
(Undergraduate/Scholarship)

Purpose: To support initiated undergraduate members who are in good standing. **Focus:** General studies/Field of study not specified. **Qualif.:** Applicants must be active member of Sigma Kappa. **Criteria:** Consideration will be given for leadership and service provided to the chapter and to the campus community.

Funds Avail.: No specific amount. **Contact:** Email at foundationscholarships@sigmakappa.org.

10115 ■ Lucile Cheever Graubart/Lambda Scholarship *(Undergraduate/Scholarship)*

Purpose: To support initiated undergraduate members who are in good standing. **Focus:** General studies/Field of study not specified. **Qualif.:** Applicants must be member of Lambda Chapter of Sigma Kappa. **Criteria:** Candidates will be selected based on their financial need.

Funds Avail.: No specific amount. **Contact:** Teresa Glassman; Phone: 317-381-5548; E-mail: foundationscholarships@sigmakappa.org.

10116 ■ Margaret J. Andrew Memorial Scholarship
(Undergraduate, Graduate/Scholarship)

Purpose: To support initiated undergraduate junior, senior or graduate members of Sigma Kappa with good standing. **Focus:** Food science and technology. **Qualif.:** Applicants must be initiated member of Sigma Kappa; must have minimum GPA of 3.00 on a 4.00 scale; must be majoring in food science, food technology or a related field. **Criteria:** Selection will be based on GPA and other basic demographic criteria.

Funds Avail.: No specific amount. **Contact:** Teresa Glassman; Phone: 317-381-5548; E-mail: foundationscholarships@sigmakappa.org.

10117 ■ Marian Johnson Frutiger Sisterhood Scholarship *(Undergraduate/Scholarship)*

Purpose: To support initiated undergraduate members of Sigma Kappa with good standing. **Focus:** General studies/Field of study not specified. **Qualif.:** Applicants must be initiated member of Sigma Kappa; must have minimum GPA of 3.0 on a 4.00 scale; must exemplify the ideals and standards of Sigma Kappa; must exhibit outstanding sisterhood and have demonstrated leadership within the fraternal community. **Criteria:** Candidates will be judged based on leadership, academic excellence and financial standing.

Funds Avail.: No specific amount. **Contact:** Teresa Glassman; Phone: 317-381-5548; E-mail: foundationscholarships@sigmakappa.org.

10118 ■ Mary Turnbull Schacht Memorial Scholarship *(Undergraduate/Scholarship)*

Purpose: To support initiated undergraduate members who are in good standing. **Focus:** General studies/Field of study not specified. **Qualif.:** Applicants must be active member of Lambda Chapter (University of California, Berkeley); must demonstrate outstanding leadership and service provided to the chapter, Panhellenic and university; must have a minimum cumulative GPA of 3.0. **Criteria:** Candidates will be selected based on their involvement to the foundation.

Funds Avail.: No specific amount. **Contact:** Teresa Glassman; Phone: 317-381-5548; E-mail:

foundationscholarships@sigmakappa.org.

10119 ■ Joan Reagin McNeill Scholarships - Alpha Theta *(Undergraduate/Scholarship)*

Purpose: To support initiated undergraduate sophomore, junior or senior members who are in good standing. **Focus:** General studies/Field of study not specified. **Qualif.:** Applicants must be active member of Alpha Theta Chapter (University of Louisville) or Theta Phi Chapter (University of Tennessee, Chattanooga) with at least one year remaining for completion of an undergraduate degree; must have a minimum cumulative GPA of 3.25. **Criteria:** Financial need will be considered.

Funds Avail.: No specific amount. **Contact:** Email at foundationscholarships@sigmakappa.org.

10120 ■ Joan Reagin McNeill Scholarships - Theta Phi *(Undergraduate/Scholarship)*

Purpose: To support initiated undergraduate sophomore, junior or senior members who are in good standing. **Focus:** General studies/Field of study not specified. **Qualif.:** Applicants must be active sophomore, junior, or senior members of Alpha Theta Chapter (University of Louisville) or Theta Phi Chapter (University of Tennessee, Chattanooga) with at least one year remaining for completion of an undergraduate degree; must have a minimum cumulative GPA of 3.25. **Criteria:** Financial need will be considered.

Funds Avail.: No specific amount. **Contact:** Email at foundationscholarships@sigmakappa.org.

10121 ■ Sigma Kappa Foundation Alumnae Continuing Education Scholarship *(Graduate, Undergraduate/Scholarship)*

Purpose: To support initiated alumnae members of Sigma Kappa with good standing. **Focus:** General studies/Field of study not specified. **Qualif.:** Applicants must be alumnae possessing undergraduate degree from a four year institution; must have cumulative GPS of 3.0. **Criteria:** Selection will be based on applicant's academic standing.

Funds Avail.: No specific amount. **Contact:** Teresa Glassman; Phone: 317-381-5548; E-mail: foundationscholarships@sigmakappa.org.

10122 ■ Sigma Kappa Foundation Alzheimer's/Gerontology Scholarship *(Graduate/Scholarship)*

Purpose: To encourage and support the scholastic development of the collegiate and alumnae sisters of the foundation. **Focus:** Alzheimer's disease; Gerontology. **Qualif.:** Applicants must be gerontology majors in good standing with the sorority, have at least one year of study left, and maintain a 3.0 GPA. **Criteria:** Selection of candidate will be based on the scholarship criteria.

Funds Avail.: No specific amount. **Remarks:** The scholarship was established in honor of Ben C. Francis.

10123 ■ Sigma Kappa Foundation Founders' Scholarships *(Undergraduate/Scholarship)*

Purpose: To support initiated undergraduate members who are in good standing. **Focus:** General studies/Field of study not specified. **Qualif.:** Applicants should be active, initiated, continuing members in good standing; must have a minimum cumulative GPA of 3.0; must demonstrate a leadership role on campus (student government, chapter officer, Panhellenic officer). **Criteria:** Preference will be

Awards are arranged alphabetically below their administering organizations

given to sophomores and juniors with at least one year study remaining.

Funds Avail.: No specific amount. **Contact:** Email at foundationscholarships@sigmakappa.org.

10124 ■ Sigma Kappa Foundation Michigan Scholarship *(Undergraduate/Scholarship)*

Purpose: To support initiated undergraduate and graduate members who are in good standing. **Focus:** General studies/Field of study not specified. **Qualif.:** Applicants must be initiated member of Sigma Kappa; must have minimum GPA of 2.5 on a 4.00 scale; must be attending college or university in Michigan; must have at least one year remaining for the completion of an undergraduate degree or current enrollment in a graduate level program; must have not previously awarded the scholarship.**Criteria:** Candidate will be selected based on their academic achievements and involvement to the foundation.

Funds Avail.: No specific amount. **Contact:** Teresa Glassman; Phone: 317-381-5548; E-mail: foundationscholarships@sigmakappa.org.

10125 ■ Walta Wilkinson Carmichael Scholarship *(Graduate/Scholarship)*

Purpose: To support initiated alumnae members of Sigma Kappa with good standing. **Focus:** General studies/Field of study not specified. **Qualif.:** Applicants must be initiated alumnae member of Sigma Kappa; must have minimum GPA of 3.0 on a 4.00 scale; must be enrolled in a graduate program; must demonstrate participation in collegiate chapter activities. **Criteria:** Candidate will be selected based on academic standing.

Funds Avail.: No specific amount. **Contact:** Teresa Glassman; Phone: 317-381-5548; E-mail: foundationscholarships@sigmakappa.org.

10126 ■ Wilma Sackett Dressel Scholarship *(Undergraduate/Scholarship)*

Purpose: To provide financial support to initiated undergraduate members of Alpha Tau Chapter. **Focus:** General studies/Field of study not specified. **Qualif.:** Applicants must be initiated member of Alpha Tau Chapter of Sigma Kappa; must be in need of financial assistance. **Criteria:** Selection of applicant will be based on their financial need.

Funds Avail.: No specific amount. **Contact:** Teresa Glassman; Phone: 317-381-5548; E-mail: foundationscholarships@sigmakappa.org.

10127 ■ Sigma Xi, The Scientific Research Honor Society

3200 E NC Hwy. 54, Ste. 300
Research Triangle Park, NC 27709
Ph: (919)549-4691
Fax: (919)549-0090
Free: 800-243-6534
URL: www.sigmaxi.org
Social Media: instagram.com/sigma_xi_society
linkedin.com/company/sigma-xi-the-scientific-research
-honor-society
twitter.com/SigmaXiSociety
youtube.com/user/sigmaxisociety

10128 ■ Grants-in-Aid of Research (GIAR) *(Graduate, Undergraduate/Grant)*

Purpose: To give graduate and undergraduate students the opportunity to have close working relationships with the faculty, promoting scientific excellence and achievement through hands-on learning. Students use the funding to pay for travel expenses to and from a research site, or for the purchase of non-standard laboratory equipment necessary to complete a specific research project. **Focus:** Astronomy and astronomical sciences; Engineering; Science. **Qualif.:** Applicants must be undergraduate and graduate students with valuable educational.

Funds Avail.: up to $5,000 in astronomy, $2,500 in eye or vision research, and up to $1,000 in all other fields. **Duration:** Annual. **To Apply:** All applications must be submitted online using the web site's application portal. **Deadline:** March 15; October 1. **Contact:** E-mail: giar@sigmaxi.org.

10129 ■ Silicon Valley Community Foundation (SVCF)

2440 W El Camino Real, Ste. 300
Mountain View, CA 94040-1498
Ph: (650)450-5400
Fax: (650)450-5401
E-mail: info@siliconvalleycf.org
URL: www.siliconvalleycf.org
Social Media: www.facebook.com/siliconvalleycf
instagram.com/siliconvalleycf
www.linkedin.com/company/silicon-valley-community
-foundation
twitter.com/siliconvalleycf
youtube.com/TheSVCF

10130 ■ Hazel Reed Baumeister Scholarship Program *(Undergraduate/Scholarship)*

Purpose: To support high school graduates of high academic achievement who would be unable to pursue higher education without financial assistance. **Focus:** General studies/Field of study not specified. **Qualif.:** Applicants must be United States citizen; current graduating seniors or graduates of a public or private high school in San Mateo County or Santa Clara County; must have demonstrated financial hardship; minimum cumulative grade point average of 3.5 on a 4.0 scale. **Criteria:** Selection will be demonstrated community involvement over a period of several years.

Funds Avail.: Up to $5,000. **Number Awarded:** Up to 15. **To Apply:** Applications can be submitted online on sponsor's website; must submit personal statement (PDF or Word doc); financial need documentation (PDF); two letters of recommendation (PDF); official transcripts of grades (Submit both PDFs and hard copies). **Deadline:** February 14. **Remarks:** The scholarship was established through the Trust of Mrs. Hazel Reed Baumeister, a longtime resident of Burlingame. Mrs. Baumeister attended business school and worked from 1933 to 1939 as confidential executive secretary to United States Senator Pat McCarran of Nevada. Established in 2001. **Contact:** Email: scholarships@siliconvalleycf.org.

10131 ■ Crain Scholarship Program *(Undergraduate/Scholarship)*

Purpose: To enable high school graduates to pursue courses of study they would otherwise be unable to follow due to limited financial means. **Focus:** General studies/Field of study not specified. **Qualif.:** Applicants must be current graduating seniors or graduates of a public or private high school in San Mateo County or Santa Clara Counties; must be U.S. citizens; must have demonstrated

Awards are arranged alphabetically below their administering organizations

financial hardship; must have a minimum cumulative grade point average of 3.5 on a 4.0 scale. **Criteria:** Selection will be evaluated based on demonstrated academic promise, documented perseverance in activities outside the classroom, quality of the personal statement and personal characteristics such as honesty, good judgment and commitment to serving the community.

Funds Avail.: Up to $5,000. **Duration:** Annual. **Number Awarded:** Up to 10. **To Apply:** Applicants must submit statement with their full name and date at the top of every page; personal statement must be 500-850 words, double-spaced (approximately 2-3 pages); two letters of recommendation must be signed and dated; must obtain a recommendation from both teacher or academic advisor on school letterhead; volunteer or work supervisor, community leader or personal acquaintance; (volunteer or work supervisor letters must be on the organization's letterhead; official transcripts of official high school transcript and official college transcripts grades (submit both PDFs and hard copies). **Remarks:** Established in 1987. **Contact:** Email: scholarships@siliconvalleycf.org.

10132 ■ Curry Awards for Girls and Young Women (Undergraduate/Scholarship)

Purpose: To help young women who are self-motivated, need financial support and attempt to achieve despite tremendous obstacles. **Focus:** General studies/Field of study not specified. **Qualif.:** Applicants must be young woman aged 18 to 26; maximum cumulative grade point average of 3.3 on a 4.0 scale; current resident of San Mateo County, preference given to residents of East Palo Alto, East Menlo Park, Redwood City and San Mateo; current graduating high school senior, graduate or G.E.D. certificate holder: preference given to students who attend(ed) East Palo Alto Academy, East Side College Prep, Menlo Atherton, Sequoia, Carlmont and San Mateo high schools; planning to enroll or currently enrolled in a two- or four-year college or university as a full-time student; must be United States citizen or eligible non-citizen. **Criteria:** Selection committee also considers circumstances related to possible ethnic or racial discrimination, physical disability or the choice of a nontraditional area of study; preference given to residents of East Palo Alto, East Menlo Park, Redwood City and San Mateo; preference given to students who attend(ed) East Palo Alto Academy, East Side College Prep, Menlo Atherton, Sequoia, Carlmont and San Mateo high schools.

Funds Avail.: $1,000. **Number Awarded:** Up to 10. **To Apply:** Applications can be submitted online; must submit personal statement (PDF or Word doc); financial need documentation (PDF); two letters of recommendation (PDF); official transcripts of grades (Submit both PDFs and hard copies). **Contact:** Email: scholarships@siliconvalleycf.org.

10133 ■ Bobette Bibo Gugliotta Memorial Scholarships for Creative Writing (Undergraduate/Scholarship)

Purpose: To help students majoring in the creative writing field and who have demonstrated creative writing ability. **Focus:** General studies/Field of study not specified. **Qualif.:** Applicant must have demonstrated passion for creative writing; must be graduating high school senior or graduate of a public or private high school in San Mateo county or Santa Clara counties; must be planning to enroll or currently enrolled in a four-year college or university as a full-time student; must be U.S. citizen or eligible non-citizen (eligible non-citizens include United States legal residents

and A.B. 540 students). **Criteria:** Preference will be given to those students who meet the criteria.

Funds Avail.: Up to $1,000. **Number Awarded:** Up to 2. **To Apply:** Applications can be submitted online; must submit personal statement (PDF or Word doc); financial need documentation (PDF); two letters of recommendation (PDF); official transcripts of grades (Submit both PDFs and hard copies); two creative writing samples (PDF or Word). **Remarks:** Established in 1995. **Contact:** Email: scholarships@siliconvalleycf.org.

10134 ■ Ralph Hale and Martha L. Ruppert Educational Scholarship (Undergraduate/Grant)

Purpose: To support "late bloomers" - those students who show academic promise and improvement during the last years of high school or in the first few years of college, but are unlikely to receive other scholarships because of their low GPAs. **Focus:** General studies/Field of study not specified. **Qualif.:** Applicants must be is a "late bloomer" who demonstrates academic promise and continuous grade point average improvement during high school or college; must demonstrate community involvement; maximum cumulative grade point average of 3.3 on a 4.0 scale; demonstrated financial hardship; must be graduating high school senior or graduate of a public or private high school in San Mateo County, San Francisco County, or Santa Clara County; planning to enroll or enrolled in two- or four-year college, university or vocational school as a full-time student; and United States citizen or eligible non-citizen. **Criteria:** Selection will be based on demonstrated financial need.

Funds Avail.: Up to $10,000. **Number Awarded:** Up to 30. **To Apply:** Applications can be submitted online at sponsor's website; must submit personal statement (PDF or Word doc); financial need documentation (PDF); two letters of recommendation (PDF); official transcripts of grades (Submit both PDFs and hard copies). **Deadline:** February 14. **Remarks:** The grant program was established through a trust and bequest agreement by Ralph Hale Ruppert and Lenore Martha Ruppert in memory of their mothers, Nellie Hale Ruppert and Amanda Miller Edwards. **Contact:** Email: scholarships@siliconvalleycf.org.

10135 ■ Dr. James L. Hutchinson and Evelyn Ribbs Hutchinson Medical School Scholarship (Undergraduate/Scholarship)

Purpose: To support students who demonstrate excellence in both character and academic achievement by helping them attend medical school. **Focus:** Medicine. **Qualif.:** Applicants must be United States citizens; must be college seniors and accepted to medical school, or currently enrolled full-time in an accredited medical school program; must demonstrate personal motivation for excellence in both character and academic achievement; personal integrity, as exemplified by leadership, community involvement, and concern for others. **Criteria:** Preference will be given to those students who meet the criteria.

Funds Avail.: Up to $2,000. **Duration:** Annual. **Number Awarded:** 1. **To Apply:** Applicants must submit statement with their full name and date at the top of every page; personal statement must be 500-850 words, double-spaced (approximately 2-3 pages); two letters of recommendation must be signed and dated; must obtain a recommendation from both teacher or academic advisor on school letterhead; volunteer or work supervisor, community leader or personal acquaintance; (volunteer or work supervisor letters must be on the organization's letterhead; official

Awards are arranged alphabetically below their administering organizations

transcripts of official high school transcript and official college transcripts grades (submit both PDFs and hard copies). **Deadline:** May 4. **Remarks:** The scholarship was established to honor of Dr. and Mrs. Hutchinson by numerous friends, colleagues, patients and community leaders who honored them at a gala dinner in 1994 and, at the same time, contributed generously toward the establishment of this medical school scholarship. **Contact:** Email: scholarships@siliconvalleycf.org.

10136 ■ Latinos in Technology Scholarship
(Undergraduate/Scholarship)

Purpose: To support students who have a declared major in a science, technology, engineering and math (STEM)-related field. **Focus:** Engineering; Mathematics and mathematical sciences; Science; Technology. **Qualif.:** Applicants must be of Latino or Hispanic origin; have a declared major in and been accepted into a STEM program; be current college students entering their junior or senior year and planning to enroll on a full-time or part-time basis for the next academic school year; graduates of a high school in the Greater Silicon Valley (includes Santa Clara County, San Mateo County, San Francisco County; Fremont, Newark, and Union City in Alameda County and Scotts Valley in Santa Cruz County); minimum cumulative college GPA of 2.5; demonstrated financial need; and U.S. citizens or eligible non-citizens. **Criteria:** Preference is given to San Mateo and Santa Clara County high school graduates.

Funds Avail.: $30,000 (paid over three years, provided renewal eligibility requirements are met). **Number Awarded:** Up to 100. **To Apply:** Applications can be submitted online at sponsor's website; must submit personal statement (PDF or Word doc); financial need documentation (PDF); two letters of recommendation (PDF); official transcripts of grades (Submit both PDFs and hard copies). **Contact:** Email: scholarships@siliconvalleycf.org.

10137 ■ Fauneil J. Rinn Scholarships
(Undergraduate/Scholarship)

Purpose: To help woman student in political science or the master's in public administration program. **Focus:** Political science; Public administration. **Qualif.:** Applicants must be women who are current students in good standing in the Political Science or Master of Public Administration programs at San Jose State University; a minimum 3.0 grade point average is required. **Criteria:** Selection will be based on their achievements and abilities as reflected in a brief application form, a resume and a 500-word essay on a subject relevant to the political or governmental role of women.

Funds Avail.: Up to $5,000. **Duration:** Annual. **Number Awarded:** 1. **To Apply:** Applicants must check the sponsor's website for the required materials. **Contact:** Kenneth Peter; E-mail: kenneth.peter@sjsu.edu.

10138 ■ Leo and Trinidad Sanchez Scholarships
(Undergraduate/Scholarship)

Purpose: To help Hispanic American students enrolled or planning to enroll in a program leading to a degree in architecture. **Focus:** Architecture. **Qualif.:** Applicants must be Hispanic/American (with at least one parent of Hispanic or Hispanic/American heritage); must be residents of Santa Clara or Santa Cruz County; must be seniors in high school or students at West Valley College enrolled in a program leading to a degree in architecture, or students in any

architectural school. **Criteria:** Preference will be given to those who meet the criteria.

Funds Avail.: Up to $4,500. **Duration:** Annual. **Number Awarded:** 1. **To Apply:** Application details are available on the sponsor's website. **Contact:** Amy Ress; Email: director@aiasiliconvalley.org; URL: www.siliconvalleycf.org/scholarships/sanchez.

10139 ■ Simon Youth Foundation (SYF)
225 W Washington St.
Indianapolis, IN 46204
Fax: (317)263-2371
Free: 800-509-3676
E-mail: syf@simon.com
URL: www.syf.org
Social Media: www.facebook.com/simonyouthfoundation
www.instagram.com/simonyouthfoundation
www.linkedin.com/company/simonyouthfoundation
www.pinterest.com/simonyouth
twitter.com/simon_youth
www.youtube.com/user/simonyouthfoundation

10140 ■ Simon Youth Community Scholarship Program *(Undergraduate/Scholarship)*

Purpose: To provide scholarships to the promising students in communities that host Simon properties. **Focus:** General studies/Field of study not specified. **Qualif.:** Applicant must be a high school senior attending school and living in a Simon community; must be a legal U.S. resident; must be enroll full-time in an accredited two- or four-year college, university or vocational/technical school in the current year. **Criteria:** Selection based on academic promise, financial need, written response, work experience and community/extracurricular involvement.

Funds Avail.: $1,500. **Duration:** Annual. **Number Awarded:** 1.

10141 ■ The Simons Foundation
PO Box 2163
Vancouver, BC, Canada V6B 3V3
Ph: (778)782-7779
Fax: (778)782-7781
E-mail: info@thesimonsfoundation.ca
URL: www.thesimonsfoundation.ca

10142 ■ Graduate Research Awards for Disarmament, Arms Control and Non-Proliferation *(Master's, Doctorate/Award)*

Purpose: To enhance Canadian graduate level scholarship on disarmament, arms control and non-proliferation issues. **Focus:** Law. **Qualif.:** Applicants must be citizens and Canadian permanent residents/landed immigrants currently enrolled in a graduate programme; graduate students studying outside Canada are eligible; must be in a masters or doctoral program. **Criteria:** Selection will be reviewed by an Expert Review Panel.

Funds Avail.: $5,000 Canadian Dollars. **Duration:** Annual. **Number Awarded:** 4. **To Apply:** Applicants must include a resume, including proof of citizenship status; complete, official transcript of grades (electronic copies of official transcripts are acceptable); an academic paper (1,500 words, MLA format) responding to one of the specific Non-Proliferation, Arms Control and Disarmament issues. **Dead-**

Awards are arranged alphabetically below their administering organizations

line: February 1. **Remarks:** Established in 2003. **Contact:** Elaine Hynes; Phone: 778-782-7779; Email: ehynes@thesimonsfoundation.ca.

10143 ■ Sindhi Association of North America (SANA)
1805 N Greenleese Dr.
Frederick, MD 21701
E-mail: sananotification@gmail.com
URL: sanaonline.org
Social Media: www.facebook.com/sanasindh2017
www.instagram.com/sindhiassociation
twitter.com/sana_sindh2017?lang=en
www.youtube.com/channel/
  UC7FMKTaFFb7xSR3sWcszmqw

10144 ■ Dr. Feroz Ahmed Memorial Educational Post-Graduate Scholarships *(Doctorate, Postgraduate/Scholarship)*

Purpose: To financially support the education of meritorious Sindhi students who are pursuing higher degrees in research topics at a university in Pakistan. **Focus:** History; Humanities; Nursing; Pharmaceutical sciences; Social sciences; Sociology. **Criteria:** Selection will be based on academic excellence and financial need.

Duration: Annual. **To Apply:** Applicants must submit a completed application form; attendance record of the current semester; proof of admission in the university; attested mark sheets for Class X, Class XII and university examinations mentioned in this form; two recommendation letters; original family income certificate; autobiographical essay stating why do applicants deserve the award.

10145 ■ SINFONIA Educational Foundation (SEF)
10600 Old State Rd.
Evansville, IN 47711
E-mail: scholarship@sinfonia.org
URL: www.sinfonia.org
Social Media: www.facebook.com/phimualphasinfonia
www.linkedin.com/company/phi-mu-alpha-sinfonia
  -fraternity-of-america
youtube.com/user/sinfonianhq

10146 ■ Delta Iota Alumni Scholarship
(Undergraduate/Scholarship)

Purpose: To keep with the strong tradition of fraternal interaction and support for the national fraternity exemplified by delta iota brothers and to aid all undergraduate members of the fraternity. **Focus:** General studies/Field of study not specified.

Funds Avail.: $500. **Duration:** Annual. **To Apply:** Applicants must submit a typed or computer-generated application with 1-2 page essay on the topic: How has your membership in Phi Mu Alpha developed in you the tools to instill in others an awareness of music's important role in the enrichment of the human spirit?; minimum of three letters and a maximum of five letters of support, one from a Sinfonian and one from a non-Sinfonian, that address evidence of the applicants' integrity, ethics, initiative and overall devotion to the Object of Phi Mu Alpha Sinfonia Fraternity; composite style coat and tie photo for promotional purposes only; name and address of hometown newspaper for promotional purposes. **Deadline:** April 26.

10147 ■ James H. Patrenos Memorial Scholarship
(Undergraduate/Scholarship)

Purpose: To provide educational assistance for American college students. **Focus:** General studies/Field of study not specified. **Qualif.:** Applicants must be in good standing; must maintain good standing status during the academic year of scholarship; full-time undergraduate or graduate degree enrollment as defined by the policies of the institution. **Criteria:** Applicants are evaluated based on merit.

Funds Avail.: $2,500. **Duration:** Annual. **To Apply:** Applicants must submit typed or computer-generated application with 1-2 page essay on the topic: How has your membership in Phi Mu Alpha developed in you the tools to instill in others an awareness of music's important role in the enrichment of the human spirit?; minimum of three letters and a maximum of five letters of support, one from a Sinfonian and one from a non-Sinfonian, that address evidence of the applicant's integrity, ethics, initiative and overall devotion to the Object of Phi Mu Alpha Sinfonia Fraternity; composite style coat and tie photo for promotional purposes only; name and address of hometown newspaper for promotional purposes. **Deadline:** April 15.

10148 ■ W. Eldridge and Emily Lowe Scholarship
(Undergraduate, Graduate/Scholarship)

Purpose: To provide educational assistance for American college students. **Focus:** General studies/Field of study not specified.

Funds Avail.: $1,000. **To Apply:** Applicants must submit a typed or computer-generated application with 1-2 page essay on the topic: How has your membership in Phi Mu Alpha developed in you the tools to instill in others an awareness of music's important role in the enrichment of the human spirit?; minimum of three letters and maximum of five letters of support, one from a Sinfonian and one from a non-Sinfonian, that address evidence of the applicants' integrity, ethics, initiative and overall devotion to the Object of Phi Mu Alpha Sinfonia Fraternity; composite style coat and tie photo for promotional purposes only; name and address of hometown newspaper for promotional purposes. **Deadline:** April 26.

10149 ■ Sino-American Pharmaceutical Professionals Association (SAPA)
PO Box 282
Nanuet, NY 10954
E-mail: information@sapaweb.org
URL: www.sapaweb.org
Social Media: www.linkedin.com/company/sapa-hq

10150 ■ Sino-American Pharmaceutical Professionals Association Scholarships *(Undergraduate/Scholarship)*

Purpose: To recognize and support excellence on the part of outstanding high school students and to encourage the finest high school graduates to develop careers in life science. **Focus:** Life sciences. **Qualif.:** Applicant must be a full-time high school graduate who plans full-time undergraduate study at an accredited four-year college in the upcoming academic year; must have GPA above 3.3, a minimum SAT 2000; must be a United States citizen, or a legal resident alien. **Criteria:** Selection will be evaluated based on their merit and outstanding potential to pursue careers in life sciences; SAPA Scholars are selected by the Board of SAPA Scholarship and Excellence in Education for Life Science Foundation.

Awards are arranged alphabetically below their administering organizations

Funds Avail.: $1,000. **Duration:** One year. **To Apply:** Applicants must submit an essay of approximately 600 words; two letters of recommendation from teachers who can discuss the nominee's potential for a career in life sciences including a teacher in the applicant's field of study and another who can attest the nominee's potential; must have a list of awards received; must have a list of Advanced Placement of Honors courses with grades and awards received. **Deadline:** May 30. **Remarks:** Established in 1999. **Contact:** SAPA Scholarship Office, P.O. Box 3228, 212 Carnegie Center Princeton, NJ 08543; Email: sapa_scholarship@yahoo.com.

10151 ■ Sixt Rent a car
2901 SE 6th Ave.
Fort Lauderdale, FL 33316
Free: 888-749-8227
E-mail: customerservice-usa@sixt.com
URL: www.sixt.com
Social Media: www.facebook.com/sixt.rentacar.usa
www.instagram.com/sixtusa
www.pinterest.com/sixtrentacarusa
twitter.com/sixtusa

10152 ■ Sixt Rent a Car Scholarships
(Undergraduate/Scholarship)

Purpose: To assist high school students who plan to continue their education in college. **Focus:** General studies/ Field of study not specified. **Qualif.:** Applicants must be graduating high school seniors in the United States and planning to enroll full-time in an accredited institution, college or university; must have a minimum 3.7 GPA on a 4.0 scale. **Criteria:** Selection will be based on the financial need and extracurricular activities.

Funds Avail.: $5,000 each. **Number Awarded:** 5. **To Apply:** Applicants must submit a completed application appraisal form and a copy of high school transcript. **Deadline:** November 30. **Remarks:** Established in 2014.

10153 ■ Sjogren's Syndrome Foundation (SSF)
6707 Democracy Blvd., Ste. 325
Bethesda, MD 20817
Ph: (301)530-4420
Fax: (301)530-4415
Free: 800-475-6473
E-mail: tms@sjogrens.org
URL: www.sjogrens.org
Social Media: www.facebook.com/SjogrensFoundation
instagram.com/sjogrensfoundation
www.linkedin.com/company/sjogrens-syndrome-foundation
www.pinterest.com/sjogrensorg
twitter.com/SjogrensOrg

10154 ■ SSF Research Grants *(Other/Grant)*

Purpose: To encourage therapeutic development in Sjogren's syndrome by funding potential researches on further treatment and understanding of the disease. **Focus:** Medical research. **Qualif.:** Applicants must be basic scientists and clinical investigators and holding an advanced degree (MD, DDS, DMD, or PhD); or junior or senior investigators conducting research at an institution in the United States. **Criteria:** Applicants are selected based on the application package.

Funds Avail.: $15,000-$50,000 a year for two years. **Deadline:** February 1. **Contact:** https://www.sjogrens.org/news/ 2019/apply-for-an-ssf-research-grant.

10155 ■ SSF Student Fellowships *(Doctorate, Undergraduate/Fellowship)*

Purpose: To provide financial support for students working on a semester or summer research project in Sjogren's Syndrome. **Focus:** Medical research. **Qualif.:** Applicants must be medical or dental students and must be conducting research at an institution in the United States. **Criteria:** Applicants are selected based on the application package.

Funds Avail.: No specific amount. **Duration:** Annual. **Number Awarded:** 1. **To Apply:** Applicants must submit a complete application package which includes: an Application Face page; abstract for the research proposal; publications; budget; letters of recommendation; statement of guarantee of adequate facilities and budget for the research proposal; and a principal investigators signed statement of responsibility. Applicants must send the documents electronically with a subject line: (Applicant Name) Research Grant Application, or send on a CD.

10156 ■ Skadden Fellowship Foundation
c/o Kathleen Rubenstein,Executive Director
One Manhattan West 46th Floor
New York, NY 10001-8602
URL: www.skaddenfellowships.org

10157 ■ Skadden Fellowship *(Graduate/Fellowship)*

Purpose: To provide funding for graduating law students who wish to devote their professional lives to providing legal services to the poor (including the working poor), the elderly, the homeless and the disabled, as well as those deprived of their civil or human rights. **Focus:** Law. **Qualif.:** Applicants must be law school graduates or outgoing judicial law clerks; grants are made to organizations only, not to individuals. **Criteria:** Selection will be based on a variety of factors, including the qualifications (competency, academic performance, character and demonstrated commitment to the public interest).

Duration: Annual; up to two years. **Number Awarded:** Varies. **To Apply:** Applicants must submit a completed application form with the official law school transcripts; two letters of recommendation (from former employer, and law school professor); a commitment letter from a potential sponsoring organization; and three essays. **Deadline:** September 14. **Remarks:** Established in 1988. **Contact:** Email: skadden.foundation@skadden.com.

10158 ■ Skidmore, Owings and Merrill Foundation (SOM)
224 S Michigan Ave., Ste. 1000
Chicago, IL 60604
Ph: (312)427-4202
Fax: (312)360-4545
URL: www.somfoundation.som.com
Social Media: www.facebook.com/
  SkidmoreOwingsMerrillFoundation
www.instagram.com/somfoundation
twitter.com/SOM_Foundation

10159 ■ SOM Foundation Architecture, Design and Urban Design Prize *(Graduate/Prize)*

Purpose: To identify and nurture emerging talent by sponsoring prestigious research awards and traveling study

Awards are arranged alphabetically below their administering organizations

grants to students of architecture, design and urban design. **Focus:** Architecture; Design.

10160 ■ SOM Foundation Structural Engineering Travel Fellowships *(Doctorate, Graduate, Master's, Undergraduate/Fellowship)*

Purpose: To foster an appreciation of the aesthetic potential in the structural design of buildings and bridges by enabling a gifted graduate to experience works of architecture and engineering first hand. **Focus:** Engineering, Architectural; Engineering, Civil. **Qualif.:** Applicants must be graduating with a bachelor's degree, master's degree, or Ph.D. in Civil or Architectural Engineering with a specialization in Structural Engineering from a U.S. school. **Funds Avail.:** $20,000. **Duration:** Annual.

10161 ■ SOM Foundation Travel Fellowships in Architecture, Design and Urban Design *(Graduate, Undergraduate/Fellowship)*

Purpose: To support students with the highest design aspirations and enable them, through research and travel, to broaden their horizons and achieve excellence in their professional or academic careers. **Focus:** Architecture; Design. **Funds Avail.:** $20,000.

10162 ■ Skooblie
PO Box 1165
Wheeling, IL 60090-4756
Free: 866-705-3581
URL: www.skooblie.com

10163 ■ Skooblie Scholarships *(Undergraduate/ Scholarship)*

Purpose: To provide assistance to students who are pursuing higher education. **Focus:** Education. **Qualif.:** Applicants must be students who successfully complete six credit hours at a college that they were matched with through the college match process. **Criteria:** Selection will be based on the committee's criteria.

Funds Avail.: Varies. **Duration:** One-time. **Number Awarded:** Varies. **To Apply:** Applicants must accomplish the following steps: complete a profile, match and save a Skooblie Scholarship; enroll and notify Skooblie by sending an email along with class schedule of credits intended; complete the six hours credit hours within one year of enrolling and send via scanning and emailing or mailing a final report card showing credits earned to Skooblie within 60 days of completion.

10164 ■ Skubiak & Rivas
1516 E Robinson
Orlando, FL 32801
Ph: (407)894-4449
URL: trafficlawfirm.com
Social Media: www.facebook.com/trafficlawfirm

10165 ■ Skubiak & Rivas - Justice in Action Scholarship *(College, University, Vocational/ Occupational, Undergraduate/Scholarship)*

Purpose: To help a young person succeed. **Focus:** General studies/Field of study not specified. **Qualif.:** Applicant must be a high school senior accepted to a college, university, or

trade school, or a student currently attending a college, university, or trade school. **Criteria:** Selection is based on the submitted image or video and accompanying essay.

Funds Avail.: $1,000. **Number Awarded:** 1. **To Apply:** Applicant must submit a video or image capturing the idea of "Justice in Action" and submit a 300-word essay explaining their entry. Applications available at trafficlawfirm.com/scholarship/. **Deadline:** December 1.

10166 ■ Skylights for Less
20 Lewis St.
Oneonta, NY 13820
Ph: (607)353-8088
Free: 800-284-5194
URL: www.skylightsforless.com
Social Media: www.facebook.com/SkylightsForLess
twitter.com/skylights4less

10167 ■ The Skylight Effect Scholarship Contest *(Undergraduate, Graduate/Scholarship)*

Purpose: To reward prospective students, with a preference on those studying in art, architecture, graphic and interior design, and photography. **Focus:** General studies/Field of study not specified. **Qualif.:** Applicant must be enrolled or planning to enroll in an undergraduate or graduate program at any accredited college or university with the United States for the upcoming school year; have a minimum 2.5 GPA on a 4.0 scale; and be a U.S. citizen or have a student visa.

Funds Avail.: $1,000. **Number Awarded:** 1. **To Apply:** Applicant must capture the before and after effects of a skylight installation in a building using photos, photo edited mock-ups, digitized sketches, drawings, or paintings. Applicant must submit the following via email: a description of applicant's completed work (150 to 400 words); a brief biography or statement of goals in college (150 to 400 words); applicant's legal name, mailing address, telephone number, and email address; and name of college university and proposed year of graduation. Applicant must also follow the sponsor on Facebook or Instagram. **Deadline:** October 1. **Contact:** Email: scholarship@skylightsforless.com; URL: https://www.petersons.com/scholarship/the-skylight-effect-scholarship-contest-111_222523.aspx.

10168 ■ Sleeping Angels Co.
528 Arizona Ave., Ste. 300
Santa Monica, CA 90401
Ph: (310)451-5692
Fax: (310)451-8548
E-mail: info@sleepingangelsco.com
URL: www.sleepingangelsco.com
Social Media: www.facebook.com/sleepingangelsco
instagram.com/sleepingangelsco
www.linkedin.com/company/sleeping-angeles-co.
twitter.com/sleepingangels

10169 ■ Sleeping Angels Co. Scholarships *(College, University/Scholarship)*

Purpose: To help students get a foothold in college and some extra money. **Focus:** General studies/Field of study not specified. **Qualif.:** Applicants must be currently enrolled as high school or college/university students within the

Awards are arranged alphabetically below their administering organizations

United States; must have a cumulative GPA of at least 3.0; must be U.S. citizens. **Criteria:** Selection will be on the based on the essay submitted.

Funds Avail.: $500.

10170 ■ Alfred P. Sloan Foundation

630 5th Ave., Ste. 2200
New York, NY 10111
Ph: (212)649-1649
Fax: (212)757-5117
URL: www.sloan.org
Social Media: www.facebook.com/sloanfoundation

10171 ■ Sloan Research Fellowships *(Doctorate/ Fellowship)*

Purpose: To stimulate fundamental research by early-career scientists and scholars of outstanding promise. **Focus:** Biology, Molecular; Chemistry; Computer and information sciences; Economics; Mathematics and mathematical sciences; Neuroscience; Physics. **Qualif.:** Applicants must hold a PhD (or equivalent) in chemistry, physics, mathematics, computer science, economics, neuroscience or computational and evolutionary molecular biology, or in a related interdisciplinary field; must be a member of the regular faculty (tenure track) of a college/university in the United States or Canada; be no more than six years from completion of the most recent PhD or equivalent and must be nominated by department heads or other senior researchers for the fellowship. **Criteria:** Selection will be based on their independent research accomplishments, creativity, and potential to become leaders in the scientific community through their contributions to their field.

Funds Avail.: $65,000. **Duration:** Two years. **Number Awarded:** 126. **To Apply:** Applicants must submit materials for nomination must include a completed nomination form; a letter from a department head or other senior researcher officially nominating the candidate and describing his or her qualifications, initiative, and research; a brief (one-page) statement by the candidate describing his or her significant scientific work and immediate research plans; curriculum vitae (including a list of the candidates scientific publications); two representative articles by the candidate; three letters from other researchers (preferably not all from the same institution) written in support of the candidate's nomination. **Deadline:** September 15. **Remarks:** Established in 1955.

10172 ■ SmartMeasurement (SMC)

10437 Innovation Dr., Ste. 315
Wauwatosa, WI 53226
Ph: (414)299-3896
Fax: (414)433-1606
Free: 866-404-5415
E-mail: sales@smartmeasurement.com
URL: www.smartmeasurement.com
Social Media: www.facebook.com/SmartMeasurementLLC
www.linkedin.com/company/smartmeasurement-llc
twitter.com/SMC_Measurement

10173 ■ SmartMeasurement's Dream for a Better Future: Student Scholarship *(High School, Vocational/Occupational, College, University, Undergraduate/Scholarship)*

Purpose: To support students attending higher education. **Focus:** General studies/Field of study not specified. **Qua-**

lif.: Applicant needs to be a high school, trade school, or college or university student attending school in the united states; need an average gpa of at least 3.0 for applying. **Criteria:** Selection is based on submitted video.

Funds Avail.: $1,000. **Number Awarded:** 1. **To Apply:** Applicant needs to submit an 8-10 minute video on why they should receive the scholarship; the following points should be covered in the video: How do you plan to address the different needs of flow technologies to satisfy a wide range of customers from all kinds of industries? Do you have a working model of flow meters, industrial flow measurement instruments, and other related utilities? Do you have a proposal for the improvement of our technical infrastructure (SmartMatrix)? video must be in a standard format (AVI, WMP, MP3, and MOV). Video should be submitted via email to scholarship@ smartmeasurement.com. **Deadline:** March 31. **Contact:** Email: scholarship@smartmeasurement.com.

10174 ■ Smartways Marketing

24 Drinkwater Cres.
Sunshine West, VIC 3020, Australia
Ph: 61 3 9005 8320
URL: www.smartwaysmarketing.com
Social Media: www.facebook.com/smartwaysmarketing
in.linkedin.com/in/smartwaysmarketing1
twitter.com/SmartWays_M

10175 ■ Smartways Marketing Scholarship *(Undergraduate, Postdoctorate/Scholarship)*

Purpose: To provide financial assistance to undergraduate or postgraduate student in need. **Focus:** General studies/ Field of study not specified. **Qualif.:** Undergraduate and postgraduate students with financial need. **Criteria:** Applicants should have Interest in internet marketing is preferred. Essays must demonstrate quality writing and powerful logics.

Funds Avail.: $500. **To Apply:** Select topic and submit essay from website. **Deadline:** October 20. **Contact:** Email: scholarship@smartwaysmarketing.com.

10176 ■ SmileMarketing

PO Box 37
Palmer Lake, CO 80133
E-mail: nhlbiinfo@nhlbi.nih.gov
URL: www.smilemarketing.com
Social Media: www.facebook.com/smile.marketing.dental
 .websites
www.linkedin.com/company/smile-marketing-dental
 -websites
twitter.com/smilemarketing

10177 ■ Smile Marketing Dental Scholarship *(Doctorate/Scholarship)*

Purpose: To help students ease some financial burdens in attending dental school. **Focus:** Dentistry. **Qualif.:** Applicants must be currently enrolled in an accredited dental school. **Criteria:** Selection will review all submissions carefully and select the winning essay for each submission.

Funds Avail.: $500. **Duration:** Biennial. **Number Awarded:** 1. **To Apply:** Applicants must send a completed email of 500-word essay response to the question. **Deadline:** March 15.

Awards are arranged alphabetically below their administering organizations

10178 ■ The Smith Cos.
PO Box 560219
Orlando, FL 32856
URL: www.smithcompanies.com

10179 ■ Ryan and Jamie Smith Essay Contest
(Graduate, Postgraduate/Scholarship)

Purpose: To support individuals for their financial needs. **Focus:** General studies/Field of study not specified. **Qualif.:** Applicants must be continuing education, graduate or post-graduate students who are enrolled in an accredited institution; must be 18 years of age or older. U.S. citizens and international students are eligible. **Criteria:** Selection will be based on the submitted application.

Funds Avail.: $5,000. **To Apply:** Applicants must submit an essay of less than 1000 words answering the question "What do you feel is an appropriate balance between being successful financially and the need to serve others by giving back?" Applicants must check the website www.smithcompanies.com for the complete application process.

10180 ■ Michael Smith Foundation for Health Research
200 - 1285 W Broadway
Vancouver, BC, Canada V6H 3X8
URL: www.msfhr.org

10181 ■ MSFHR Research Trainee Award *(Postdoctorate, Professional development/Grant)*

Purpose: To support highly qualified applicants at the post-PhD and post-health professional degree stages to prepare for careers as independent health researchers. **Focus:** Medical research. **Qualif.:** Applicants must be individuals in the postdoctoral (PhD) and post-health professional degree (MD, DDS, DVM or DPharm) stages.

Funds Avail.: No specific amount. **Duration:** Annual. **Number Awarded:** Varies. **To Apply:** Interested applicants may contact the Program Manager for the application process and other information; Submit Reference and Supervisor Approval. **Deadline:** January 31. **Remarks:** Established in 2001.

10182 ■ MSFHR Scholar Awards *(Advanced Professional, Professional development/Grant)*

Purpose: To support new investigators to launch independent research careers and build strong research programs that could benefit the British Columbia area. **Focus:** Medical research. **Qualif.:** Applicants must have a PhD or equivalent and commit to a minimum of 75 percent of their time conductingResearch.

Funds Avail.: No specific amount. **Duration:** Annual; Up to five years. **To Apply:** Applicants must submit letter of intent; program of research and appendices; Canadian Common CV – MSFHR full version; list of publications, patents & intellectual property rights uploaded as an attachment to CCV; department head/chair form; dean of faculty Form; three letters of reference. **Remarks:** Established in 2001.

10183 ■ Robert H. Smith International Center for Jefferson Studies (ICJS)
PO Box 316
Charlottesville, VA 22902
Ph: (434)984-9800

URL: www.monticello.org
Social Media: www.facebook.com/TJMonticello
www.instagram.com/tjmonticello
www.pinterest.com/VisitMonticello
twitter.com/TJMonticello
www.youtube.com/user/MonticelloVisit

10184 ■ ICJS Short-Term Fellowships *(Doctorate, Postdoctorate, Advanced Professional/Fellowship)*

Purpose: To support research on Jefferson-related projects. **Focus:** History, American. **Qualif.:** Applicants may be academics from any country, subject to selection by committee. **Criteria:** Priority is given to Jefferson-related projects using the Digital Archeological Archive of Comparative Slavery or Getting Word.

Funds Avail.: $2,000-$3,000. **Duration:** Monthly. **Number Awarded:** Varies. **To Apply:** Applicants must submit a succinct description of the research project (500 words), a one-paragraph summary of the project, and a resume; two letters of reference should be emailed directly to the Center. **Deadline:** November 1; April 1. **Contact:** Fellowship Committee, Robert H. Smith International Center for Jefferson Studies, Monticello, Phone: 434-984-7500; Email: icjsfellowships@monticello.org.

10185 ■ Smith Scholarship Foundation (SSF)
400 Caldwell Trace
Birmingham, AL 35242
URL: www.smithscholarships.com

10186 ■ J. Craig and Page T. Smith Scholarship *(Undergraduate/Scholarship)*

Purpose: To support the education of Alabama high school seniors. **Focus:** General studies/Field of study not specified. **Qualif.:** Applicants must be graduating Alabama high school seniors entering an Alabama 4-year college; must have a minimum grade of C+. **Criteria:** Selection is based on a number of factors related to financial need and academic readiness.

Funds Avail.: $15,000. **Duration:** Annual. **Number Awarded:** Varies. **To Apply:** Applicants must complete the application form online; ACT or SAT, OR college entry test and a copy of those scores must be attached; proof of acceptance; three letters of recommendation. **Deadline:** December 1. **Remarks:** The scholarship was established by Mignon C. Smith in honor of J. Craig and Page T. Smith, president and CEO of Avondale Mills in Sylacauga. **Contact:** Email: appsupport@smithscholarships.com.

10187 ■ Smithsonian Center for Learning and Digital Access (SCLDA)
600 Maryland Ave., Ste. 1005
Washington, DC 20024
Ph: (202)633-5335
Fax: (202)633-5344
E-mail: learning@si.edu
URL: www.smithsonianeducation.org
Social Media: www.facebook.com/smithsonianeducation
twitter.com/Smithsonianlab

10188 ■ Smithsonian Fellowships in Museum Practice *(Professional development, Graduate/Fellowship)*

Purpose: To help learners of all ages discover the Learning Lab's digital images, recordings, texts, and lesson plans

Awards are arranged alphabetically below their administering organizations

regardless of a user's physical proximity to these assets. **Focus:** Museum science. **Qualif.:** Applicants must be mid- and senior-level museum personnel, researchers and training providers. Applicants must be employed by a not-for-profit cultural or educational institution that deals directly with the public or is an independent scholar.

Funds Avail.: A monthly stipend of $3,500. **Duration:** Annual; for a period of six months. **To Apply:** Applicants must include abstract of the proposed research not more than one page and; include the project title curriculum vitae or resume including previous and current fellowships, grants, and/or awards, and a description of your research interests; bibliography an annotated literature review relevant to the proposed research; the full statement of your research that should not exceed 1,500 words (maximum six pages, 12 point type, double-spaced); names and email addresses of two people familiar with your work., Applicants must include abstract of the proposed research not more than one page and include the project title; curriculum vitae or resume including previous and current fellowships, grants, and/or awards, and a description of your research interests; bibliography, an annotated literature review relevant to the proposed research; and full statement of your research that should not exceed 1,500 words (maximum six pages, 12 point type, double-spaced); names and email addresses of two people familiar with your work.

10189 ■ Smithsonian Institution - National Air and Space Museum

National Air & Space Museum, Rm. 3100
Independence Ave. SW & 6th St.
Washington, DC 20560-0314
URL: airandspace.si.edu
Social Media: www.facebook.com/airandspace
www.instagram.com/airandspacemuseum/
twitter.com/airandspace
www.youtube.com/user/airandspace

10190 ■ A. Verville Fellowship (*Professional development/Fellowship*)

Purpose: To support candidates to pursue programs of research and writing professional in tone and substance, but addresses to an audience with broad interests. **Focus:** Aerospace sciences; Aviation. **Qualif.:** Applicants should be interested candidates who can provide a critical analytical approach to major trends, developments and accomplishments in some aspect of aviation and/or space history.

Funds Avail.: $55,000. **Duration:** Annual; from nine to twelve months. **To Apply:** Applicants must apply through the Smithsonian Online Academic Appointment system; as part of the application, applicants will be required to include the following supplemental files: a maximum of 250 words summary description of the proposed research; a maximum of 1,500 words of a research proposal; this statement should set forth the research plan, indicating the importance of the work both in relation to the larger discipline and to their own intellectual goals; a research budget for equipment, supplies, travel costs and other support required to conduct the research itself; a bibliography of literature relevant to the applicants' proposed research, especially that cited in the research proposal; an estimated schedule for each phase of the proposed research; a curriculum vitae or resume, not longer than three pages, including pertinent publications, fellowships or accomplishments relevant to their proposal. **Contact:** Email: NASM-Fellowships@si.edu; Phone: 202-633-2648.

10191 ■ Charles A. Lindbergh Fellowships (*Graduate/Fellowship*)

Purpose: To promote research into, and writing about, the history of aviation and space flight. **Focus:** Aerospace sciences; Aviation. **Qualif.:** Applicants must be senior scholars with distinguished records of publication who are at work on or anticipate being at work on, books in aerospace history.

Funds Avail.: Maximum of $100,000. **Duration:** Annual; 12 months. **To Apply:** Applicants must apply through the Smithsonian Online Academic Appointment system; as part of the application, applicants will be required to include the following supplemental files: a maximum of 250 words summary description of the proposed research; a maximum of 1, 500 words of a research proposal; this statement should set forth the research plan, indicating the importance of the work both in relation to the larger discipline and to their own intellectual goals; a research budget for equipment, supplies, travel costs and other support required to conduct the research itself; a bibliography of literature relevant to the applicants' proposed research, especially that cited in the research proposal; an estimated schedule for each phase of the proposed research; a curriculum vitae or resume, not longer than three pages, including pertinent publications, fellowships or accomplishments relevant to their proposal. **Deadline:** December 1.

10192 ■ Guggenheim Fellowships (*Doctorate/Fellowship*)

Purpose: To support candidates in pursuing programs of research and writing that support publication of works. **Focus:** Aerospace sciences; Aviation. **Qualif.:** Applicants should have completed preliminary coursework and examinations and be engaged in dissertation research; have received their Ph.D. within the past seven years.

Funds Avail.: $30,000 for predoctoral candidates and $45,000 for postdoctoral candidates. **Duration:** Annual; from three to twelve months. **To Apply:** Applicants must apply through the Smithsonian Online Academic Appointment system; as part of the application, applicants will be required to include the following supplemental files: a maximum of 250 words summary description of the proposed research; a maximum of 1,500 words of a research proposal; this statement should set forth the research plan, indicating the importance of the work both in relation to the larger discipline and to their own intellectual goals; a research budget for equipment, supplies, travel costs and other support required to conduct the research itself; a bibliography of literature relevant to the applicants' proposed research, especially that cited in the research proposal; an estimated schedule for each phase of the proposed research; a curriculum vitae or resume, not longer than three pages, including pertinent publications, fellowships or accomplishments relevant to their proposal. **Deadline:** December 1. **Contact:** Email: NASM-Fellowships@si.edu; Phone: 202-633-2648.

10193 ■ Smithsonian Institution - National Museum of American History

12th St. & Constitution Ave. NW
Washington, DC 20560-0601
Ph: (202)633-3270
Fax: (202)312-1990
E-mail: archivescenter@si.edu
URL: americanhistory.si.edu
Social Media: www.facebook.com/americanhistory

Awards are arranged alphabetically below their administering organizations

www.instagram.com/amhistorymuseum
www.pinterest.com/amhistorymuseum
twitter.com/amhistorymuseum
www.youtube.com/SmithsonianAmHistory

10194 ■ Lemelson Center Fellowships *(Doctorate, Postdoctorate, Professional development/Fellowship)*

Purpose: To support projects that present creative approaches to the study of invention and innovation in American society. **Focus:** General studies/Field of study not specified. **Qualif.:** Applicants must be pre-doctoral graduate students, post-doctoral scholars and other professional who have completed advanced training; fellows are expected to reside in the Washington, DC area, to participate in the Center's activities, and to make presentations on their work to colleagues at the museum. **Criteria:** Selection will be based on the committee's criteria.

Funds Avail.: $630/week (pre-doctoral); $925/week (post-doctoral/professional). **Duration:** Annual. **Number Awarded:** Varies. **To Apply:** Applicants must include a complete application consisting of an abstract, bibliography, curriculum vitae, project/research proposal, and three references from people familiar with their work. **Deadline:** November 1.

10195 ■ Lemelson Center Travel to Collections Awards *(Graduate, Professional development/Award)*

Purpose: To support research on the history of invention and innovation based on the holding of the Museum's Archives Center and curatorial divisions. **Focus:** General studies/Field of study not specified. **Qualif.:** Applicants must be scholars, graduate students and independent researchers not residing or attending school within commuting distance of the National Museum of American History. **Criteria:** Selection will be based on the committee's criteria.

Funds Avail.: No specific amount. **To Apply:** Applicants must include application form and current curriculum vitae or resume; bibliography of relevant secondary sources; statement of purpose summarizing their project and detailing why the Archives Center's collections are essential to their research; list of specific collections or resources to be consulted; must consult with the Travel Award Coordinator prior to submitting a proposal. **Remarks:** Established in 1999. **Contact:** Alison L. Oswald; Phone: 202-633-3726, Fax: 202-633-4593; Email: oswalda@si.edu.

10196 ■ Smithsonian Institution - National Museum of the American Indian
4th St. and Independence Ave., SW
Washington, DC 20560
Ph: (202)633-1000
E-mail: nmai-groupreservations@si.edu
URL: nmai.si.edu

10197 ■ Andrew W. Mellon Fellowships For Conservation Training Programs *(Graduate/Fellowship)*

Purpose: To cultivate practical skills as well as foster a solid understanding of the contexts of material culture, the philosophies of conservation at the NMAI, and the ethics of the conservation profession. **Focus:** Archeology; Culture; Ethnography. **Qualif.:** Applicants must be currently enrolled in a conservation training program or recent graduate; should have a proven record of research, writing ability and

proficient English language skills.
Duration: Annual. **To Apply:** Applicants must visit the website for the Smithsonian online application system. Applicants must also prepare the following materials: a no more than two pages cover letter explaining candidate's interests and intent; curriculum vitae including basic biographical information, current and permanent addresses, phone numbers and email address; at least two examples of pertinent publications, lectures or other written materials; unofficial transcripts of both undergraduate and graduate courses of academic study with an explanation of the evaluation system if it is not equivalent to that of the united states; three letters of recommendation: two are from conservation professionals familiar with the candidate's work and one letter of personal reference. **Deadline:** March 15.

10198 ■ Smithsonian Institution - National Museum of Natural History (NMNH)
SI Bld., Room 153, MRC 010
Washington, DC 20013-7012
Ph: (202)633-0821
URL: www.mnh.si.edu
Social Media: www.facebook.com/SmithsonianNMNH
instagram.com/smithsoniannmnh
twitter.com/NMNH

10199 ■ Peter Buck Fellowships Program - Graduate *(Graduate/Fellowship)*

Purpose: To provide opportunities to pursue independent research projects in association with members of the Smithsonian professional research staff. **Focus:** General studies/Field of study not specified. **Criteria:** Selection will be based on the committee's criteria.

Funds Avail.: No specific amount. **Duration:** Annual; up to 1 to 2 years. **Number Awarded:** Varies. **To Apply:** Applicants must contact the Smithsonian Institution - National Museum of Natural History for the application process and requirements.

10200 ■ Peter Buck Fellowships Program - Postdoctoral *(Postdoctorate/Fellowship)*

Purpose: To provide opportunities to pursue independent research projects in association with members of the Smithsonian professional research staff. **Focus:** General studies/Field of study not specified. **Qualif.:** Applicants must be scientists who have received their Ph.D. or equivalent degree in the last five years; fellowships are open to citizens of any country. **Criteria:** Selection will be based on the committee's criteria.

Funds Avail.: No specific amount. **Duration:** Annual; up to 2 to 3 years. **To Apply:** Applicants must contact the Smithsonian Institution - National Museum of Natural History for the application process and requirements.

10201 ■ Link Foundation/Smithsonian Graduate Fellowships in Marine Science *(Graduate/Fellowship)*

Purpose: To support and conduct of scholarly research in the marine sciences, including collection, documentation and preservation of south Florida's marine biodiversity and ecosystems, as well as education, training and public service. **Focus:** Biology, Marine. **Qualif.:** Applicants must be students enrolled in a graduate program of study at a degree-granting institution, and have completed at least

Awards are arranged alphabetically below their administering organizations

one semester before the appointment period, are eligible for 12-week graduate student fellowships. **Criteria:** Selection will be based on the committee's criteria.

Funds Avail.: $6,500. **Duration:** Annual; up to 12 weeks. **To Apply:** Applicants must visit the website for the online application process. **Deadline:** February 15. **Remarks:** Established in 1998.

10202 ■ NMHM Global Volcanism Program for Visiting Scientist/Postdoctoral Fellowships (Postdoctorate, Advanced Professional/Fellowship)

Purpose: To understand global patterns in volcanism in space and time. **Focus:** Geosciences. **Criteria:** Selection will be based on the committee's criteria.

Funds Avail.: No specific amount. **Duration:** Annual.

10203 ■ NMNH American Indian Program Fellowships (Graduate/Fellowship)

Purpose: To encourage participation of Native Americans in Smithsonian activities, and support collection research, exhibitions and public programming as they relate to Native peoples. **Focus:** Culture; History. **Qualif.:** Applicants must be students of Native American history and culture. **Criteria:** Selection will be based on the committee's criteria.

Funds Avail.: No specific amount. **Duration:** Annual. **To Apply:** Applicants may apply through the online application process (SOLAA) and review other application requirements. **Remarks:** Established in 1986. **Contact:** JoAllyn Archambault at 202-633-1936; E-mail: archambj@si.edu.

10204 ■ Smithsonian Institution - Office of Fellowships and Internships

470 L'Enfant Pl., SW, Ste. 7102
Washington, DC 20013-7012
Ph: (202)633-7070
E-mail: siofi@si.edu
URL: www.smithsonianofi.com
Social Media: www.facebook.com/SmithsonianOFI
www.pinterest.com/smithsonianofi
twitter.com/SmithsonianOFI
www.youtube.com/channel/UC
__qpDDrKJtVSZOt4KRnEsQ

10205 ■ Smithsonian Institution Graduate Student Fellowships (Graduate/Fellowship)

Purpose: To provide students and scholars with opportunities to pursue independent research projects in association with members of the Smithsonian professional research staff. **Focus:** Animal science and behavior; Anthropology; Archeology; Art history; Astronomy and astronomical sciences; Biological and clinical sciences; Earth sciences; Folklore; History; United States studies. **Qualif.:** Applicants must be formally enrolled in a graduate program of study at a degree-granting institution; must still be enrolled and must have completed at least one full-time semester or its equivalent, or have completed the graduate program within the past four months; must be interested in conducting independent research or study related to Smithsonian collections, facilities, and/or research interests of the Institution and its staff. **Criteria:** Selection will be made by scholars in appropriate fields based on the following: the proposal's merit, the applicant's ability to carry out the proposed research and study, the likelihood that the research could be completed in the requested time, and the extent to which the Smithsonian, through its research

staff members and resources, could contribute to the proposed research.

Funds Avail.: $7,500 stipend. **Duration:** Annual; 10 weeks. **Number Awarded:** Varies. **To Apply:** Application details are available online at www.smithsonianofi.com/fellowship-opportunities/smithsonian-institution-fellowship-program/. **Deadline:** November 1.

10206 ■ Smithsonian Institution Postdoctoral Researcher Fellowships (Postdoctorate/Fellowship)

Purpose: To provide students and scholars with opportunities to pursue independent research projects in association with members of the Smithsonian professional research staff. **Focus:** Animal science and behavior; Anthropology; Archeology; Art history; Astronomy and astronomical sciences; Biological and clinical sciences; Earth sciences; Folklore; History; United States studies. **Qualif.:** Applicants must have completed by their doctorate degree by the time the fellowship begins; must be interested in conducting independent research or study related to Smithsonian collections, facilities, and/or research interests of the Institution and its staff. **Criteria:** Selection will be made by scholars in appropriate fields based on the following: the proposal's merit, the applicant's ability to carry out the proposed research and study, the likelihood that the research could be completed in the requested time, and the extent to which the Smithsonian, through its research staff members and resources, could contribute to the proposed research.

Funds Avail.: $50,400 annual stipend, along with a research allowance up to $4,000. **Duration:** 3 to 24 months. **Number Awarded:** Varies. **To Apply:** Application details are available online at www.smithsonianofi.com/fellowship-opportunities/smithsonian-institution-fellowship-program/. **Deadline:** November 1.

10207 ■ Smithsonian Institution Predoctoral Student Fellowships (Doctorate, Postgraduate/Fellowship)

Purpose: To provide students and scholars with opportunities to pursue independent research projects in association with members of the Smithsonian professional research staff. **Focus:** Animal science and behavior; Anthropology; Archeology; Art history; Astronomy and astronomical sciences; Biological and clinical sciences; Earth sciences; Folklore; History; United States studies. **Qualif.:** Applicant must be enrolled at a university as a candidate for the Ph.D. or equivalent; the university must approve the undertaking of dissertation research at the Smithsonian Institution and certify that requirements for the doctorate, other than the dissertation, have been met at the time of appointment; must be interested in conducting independent research or study related to Smithsonian collections, facilities, and/or research interests of the Institution and its staff. **Criteria:** Selection will be made by scholars in appropriate fields based on the following: the proposal's merit, the applicant's ability to carry out the proposed research and study, the likelihood that the research could be completed in the requested time, and the extent to which the Smithsonian, through its research staff members and resources, could contribute to the proposed research.

Funds Avail.: $36,000 annual stipend, along with a research allowance up to $4,000. **Duration:** Annual; 3 to 12 months. **Number Awarded:** Varies. **To Apply:** Application details are available online at www.smithsonianofi.com/fellowship-opportunities/smithsonian-institution-fellowship-program/. **Deadline:** November 1.

Awards are arranged alphabetically below their administering organizations

10208 ■ Smithsonian Institution Senior Researcher Fellowships *(Professional development/Fellowship)*

Purpose: To provide students and scholars with opportunities to pursue independent research projects in association with members of the Smithsonian professional research staff. **Focus:** Animal science and behavior; Anthropology; Archeology; Art history; Astronomy and astronomical sciences; Biological and clinical sciences; Earth sciences; Folklore; History; United States studies. **Qualif.:** Applicants must have held a Ph.D. or equivalent for at least 7 years; must be interested in conducting independent research or study related to Smithsonian collections, facilities, and/or research interests of the Institution and its staff. **Criteria:** Selection will be made by scholars in appropriate fields based on the following: the proposal's merit, the applicant's ability to carry out the proposed research and study, the likelihood that the research could be completed in the requested time, and the extent to which the Smithsonian, through its research staff members and resources, could contribute to the proposed research.

Funds Avail.: $50,400 annual stipend, along with a research allowance up to $4,000. **Duration:** Annual; 3 to 24 months. **Number Awarded:** Varies. **To Apply:** Application details are available online at www.smithsonianofi.com/fellowship-opportunities/smithsonian-institution-fellowship-program/. **Deadline:** November 1.

10209 ■ Smithsonian Minority Awards Program - Visiting Student *(Graduate/Fellowship)*

Purpose: To provide graduate students the opportunity to learn more about the Smithsonian and their academic fields through direct experience in research or museum-related internship projects under the supervision of research and professional staff members at the Institution's many museums, research institutes, and offices. **Focus:** Animal science and behavior; Anthropology; Arts; Culture; Earth sciences; Social sciences. **Qualif.:** Applicants must be currently engaged in graduate study, and have an overall GPA of 3.0 or its equivalent; must be U.S. citizens or U.S. permanent residents; must be actively engaged in a field of study that relates to current Smithsonian research. **Criteria:** Selection will be based on the following: the merit of the proposal; the ability of the applicant to carry out the proposed research and study; and the extent to which the Smithsonian, through its staff members and resources, can contribute to the proposed research.

Funds Avail.: $600 per week stipend. **Duration:** Semiannual; 10 weeks. **Number Awarded:** Varies. **To Apply:** Applicants must complete the online application process; maximum 6 pages double spaced; Unofficial transcripts are acceptable; reference letters are considered confidential unless confidentiality has been waived by the reference; Curriculum Vitae or Resume. **Deadline:** February 1; October 1. **Contact:** Pamela Hudson Veenbaas, Phone: 202-633-7070.

10210 ■ Smithsonian Native American Awards Program - Community Scholars *(Graduate, Doctorate, Postdoctorate, Professional development/Fellowship)*

Purpose: To provide Native American students and scholars with opportunities to pursue independent research projects in association with members of the Smithsonian professional research staff. **Focus:** Native American studies. **Qualif.:** Applicants must be Native Americans who are formally or informally related to a Native American community, to undertake projects on a Native American subject

and utilize the Native American resources of the Institution. **Criteria:** Selection will be based on the following: the merit of the proposal; the ability of the applicant to carry out the proposed research and study; and, the extent to which the Smithsonian, through its staff members and resources, can contribute to the proposed research.

Funds Avail.: $175 per day up to 21 days. **Duration:** Semiannual. **Number Awarded:** Varies. **To Apply:** Application details are available online at www.smithsonianofi.com/fellowship-opportunities/native-american-community-scholars-awards/. **Deadline:** February 1; October 1. **Contact:** Pamela Hudson Veenbaas, Phone: 202-633-7070.

10211 ■ Smithsonian Native American Awards Program - Visiting Student *(Graduate/Fellowship)*

Purpose: To support students, who are formally or informally affiliated with a Native American community or tribe, to visit the Institution to conduct independent research using its Native American-related resources in with the advice and guidance of Smithsonian research staff. **Focus:** Native American studies. **Qualif.:** Applicants must be currently enrolled advanced Native American graduate students who are formally or informally related to a Native American community; must be interested in pursuing an independent research project related to Native American resources; good academic standing with an overall G.P.A. of 3.0 or equivalent; graduate study at the time of the appointment. **Criteria:** Selection will be based on the following: the merit of the proposal; the ability of the applicant to carry out the proposed research and study; and, the extent to which the Smithsonian, through its staff members and resources, can contribute to the proposed research.

Funds Avail.: $175 per day or $600 per week (up to 21 days). **Duration:** Semiannual. **Number Awarded:** Varies. **To Apply:** Application details are available online at www.smithsonianofi.com/fellowship-opportunities/native-american-visiting-student-awards/. **Deadline:** February 1; October 1. **Contact:** Pamela Hudson Veenbaas, Phone: 202-633-7070.

10212 ■ Smithsonian Postgraduate/Postdoctoral Fellowships in Conservation of Museum Collections *(Postgraduate, Postdoctorate/Fellowship)*

Purpose: To create opportunity for recent graduates of masters programs in art and archaeological conservation and conservation scientists to conduct research and gain further training in the conservation of museum collection objects. **Focus:** Art conservation; Museum science; Preservation. **Qualif.:** Applicants must be recent graduates of masters programs in art conservation or the equivalent or conservation scientists, including those at the postdoctoral level, who wish to conduct research and gain further training in Smithsonian conservation laboratories for a period of one year. **Criteria:** Selection will be based on the merit of the submitted research proposals; applicants' ability to carry out the proposed research and study; the likelihood that the research could be completed in the requested time; and, the extent to which the Smithsonian, through its research staff members and resources, could contribute to the proposed research.

Funds Avail.: $36,000 annually, along with a research allowance up to $4,000 (postgraduate conservation/predoctoral fellowship; $50,400 annually, along with a research allowance of up to $4,000 (postdoctoral fellowship). **Duration:** Annual; 3 to 12 months. **Number Awarded:** Varies. **To Apply:** Applicants must visit the

Awards are arranged alphabetically below their administering organizations

website for the online application process and other application requirements. Applicants are strongly encouraged to contact staff members to help identify potential advisors, determine the feasibility of the proposed research being conducted at the Smithsonian Institution, and the availability of relevant resources such as staff, collections, archives and library materials during the proposed tenure dates. **Deadline:** November 1.

10213 ■ Smithsonian Institution - Smithsonian American Art Museum (SAAM)

750 9th St. NW, Ste. 3100
Washington, DC 20001
Ph: (202)633-7970
Fax: (202)633-8493
E-mail: americanartinfo@si.edu
URL: americanart.si.edu
Social Media: www.facebook.com/americanart
twitter.com/americanart

10214 ■ Douglass Foundation Fellowship in American Art *(Doctorate/Fellowship)*

Purpose: To support individuals who planned to conduct pre-doctoral research in American art. **Focus:** Art; Museum science. **Qualif.:** Applicants must be pre-doctoral students that have completed coursework and preliminary examinations for their doctoral degree and must be engaged in dissertation research. **Criteria:** Selection will be evaluated based on the quality of the proposed research project, academic standing, scholarly qualifications, and experience. The project's compatibility with Smithsonian collections, facilities, staff and programs will also be considered; a committee of curators and historians will review the applications.

Duration: Annual. **To Apply:** Applicants should apply to the Smithsonian Institution Fellowship Program, found under the Office of Fellowships in the online application system (SOLAA), and not under the museum's name; must propose a primary advisor/supervisor from SAAM to be eligible for a fellowship at this museum. **Deadline:** November 1. **Contact:** Amelia Goerlitz, Chair of Academic Programs; Phone 202-633-8353; Email: AmericanArtFellowships@si.edu.

10215 ■ Patricia and Phillip Frost Fellowships *(Doctorate, Postdoctorate/Fellowship)*

Purpose: To support individual who planned to conduct research in American art and visual culture. **Focus:** Art; Museum science. **Qualif.:** Applicants must be pre- and postdoctoral scholars who wish to work with Smithsonian American Art Museum advisors. **Criteria:** Selection will be evaluated based on the quality of the proposed research project, academic standing, scholarly qualifications and experience. The project's compatibility with Smithsonian collections, facilities, staff and programs will be also considered; a committee of curators and historians will review the applications.

Duration: Annual. **To Apply:** Applicants should apply to the Smithsonian Institution Fellowship Program, found under the Office of Fellowships in the online application system (SOLAA), and not under the museum's name; must propose a primary advisor/supervisor from SAAM to be eligible for a fellowship at this museum. **Deadline:** November 1. **Contact:** Amelia Goerlitz, Chair of Academic Programs; Phone 202-633-8353; Email:

AmericanArtFellowships@si.edu.

10216 ■ The George Gurney Fellowship Endowment Fund *(Doctorate, Postdoctorate/Fellowship)*

Purpose: To support a one-to three-month research appointment in American art and to honor the distinguished career of SAAM's former curator of sculpture. **Focus:** Art; Museum science. **Qualif.:** Applicants must be pre- and postdoctoral scholars who wish to work with Smithsonian American Art Museum advisors. **Criteria:** Selection will be evaluated based on the quality of the proposed research project, academic standing, scholarly qualifications and experience; the project's compatibility with Smithsonian collections, facilities, staff and programs will be also considered; a committee of curators and historians will review the applications.

To Apply: Applicants should apply to the Smithsonian Institution Fellowship Program, found under the Office of Fellowships in the online application system (SOLAA), and not under the museum's name; must propose a primary advisor/supervisor from SAAM to be eligible for a fellowship at this museum. **Deadline:** November 1. **Contact:** Amelia Goerlitz, Chair of Academic Programs; Phone 202-633-8353; Email: AmericanArtFellowships@si.edu.

10217 ■ James Renwick Fellowship in American Craft *(Doctorate, Postdoctorate/Fellowship)*

Purpose: To support research that is related to American studio crafts or decorative arts from the nineteenth century to the present. **Focus:** Art; Museum science. **Qualif.:** Applicants must be pre- and postdoctoral scholars who wish to work with Renwick Gallery and Smithsonian American Art Museum advisors; seniors' scholars who do not hold a Ph.D. will be accepted provided applicants demonstrate an equivalent record of professional accomplishment at the time of application. **Criteria:** Selection will be evaluated based on the quality of the proposed research project, academic standing, scholarly qualifications and experience; the project's compatibility with Smithsonian collections, facilities, staff and programs will be also considered; a committee of curators and historians will review the applications.

To Apply: Applicants should apply to the Smithsonian Institution Fellowship Program, found under the Office of Fellowships in the online application system (SOLAA), and not under the museum's name; must propose a primary advisor/supervisor from SAAM to be eligible for a fellowship at this museum. **Contact:** Emily D. Shapiro, 202-633-8335, shapiroed@si.edu, Amelia Goerlitz, 202-633-8353, goerlitza@si.edu, americanartfellowships@si.edu.

10218 ■ Sara Roby Fellowship in Twentieth-Century American Realism *(Doctorate, Postdoctorate/Fellowship)*

Purpose: To support scholar whose topic is in the area of twentieth-century American realism. **Focus:** Art; Museum science. **Qualif.:** Applicants must be pre- and postdoctoral scholars researching twentieth-century American realism who wishes to work with Smithsonian American Art Museum advisors. **Criteria:** Selection will be evaluated based on the quality of the proposed research project, academic standing, scholarly qualifications and experience; the project's compatibility with Smithsonian collections, facilities, staff and programs will be also considered; a committee of curators and historians will review the applications.

Funds Avail.: $32,700 to $48,000. **To Apply:** Applicants should apply to the Smithsonian Institution Fellowship

Awards are arranged alphabetically below their administering organizations

Program, found under the Office of Fellowships in the online application system (SOLAA), and not under the museum's name; must propose a primary advisor/supervisor from SAAM to be eligible for a fellowship at this museum. **Contact:** Emily D. Shapiro, 202-633-8335, shapiroed@si.edu, Amelia Goerlitz, 202-633-8353, goerlitza@si.edu, americanartfellowships@si.edu.

10219 ■ Joshua C. Taylor Fellowships *(Doctorate, Postdoctorate/Fellowship)*

Purpose: To support independent research and study related to Smithsonian facilities, experts or collection for the increase and diffusion of knowledge. **Focus:** Art; Museum science. **Qualif.:** Applicants must be pre- and postdoctoral scholars who wish to work with Smithsonian American Art Museum advisors. **Criteria:** Selection will be evaluated based on the quality of the proposed research project, academic standing, scholarly qualifications and experience; the project's compatibility with Smithsonian collections, facilities, staff and programs will be also considered; a committee of curators and historians will review the applications.

To Apply: Applicants should apply to the Smithsonian Institution Fellowship Program, found under the Office of Fellowships in the online application system (SOLAA), and not under the museum's name; must propose a primary advisor/supervisor from SAAM to be eligible for a fellowship at this museum. **Deadline:** November 1. **Contact:** Amelia Goerlitz, Chair of Academic Programs; Phone: Email: GoerlitzA@si.edu.

10220 ■ The Terra Foundation Fellowships in American Art *(Undergraduate, Doctorate, Postdoctorate/Fellowship)*

Purpose: To support individuals that foster cross-cultural dialogue about the history of art of the United States up to 1980. **Focus:** Art; Museum science. **Qualif.:** Applicants must be pre- and postdoctoral scholars and also in senior levels from abroad or U.S. who are investigating international contexts for American art. **Criteria:** Selection will be evaluated based on the quality of the proposed research project, academic standing, scholarly qualifications and experience; the project's compatibility with Smithsonian collections, facilities, staff and programs will be also considered; a committee of curators and historians will review the applications.

Funds Avail.: $36,000 to $50,400. **Duration:** Annual. **To Apply:** Applicants should apply to the Smithsonian Institution Fellowship Program, found under the Office of Fellowships in the online application system (SOLAA), and not under the museum's name; must propose a primary advisor/supervisor from SAAM to be eligible for a fellowship at this museum. **Deadline:** November 1. **Remarks:** Established in 1980. **Contact:** Amelia Goerlitz, Chair of Academic Programs; Phone: Email: GoerlitzA@si.edu.

10221 ■ The William H. Truettner Fellowship Endowment Fund *(Undergraduate, Doctorate, Postdoctorate/Fellowship)*

Purpose: To support one to three months of research, in recognition of Mr. Truettner's career of nearly fifty years as a curator of painting and sculpture at SAAM. **Focus:** Art; Museum science. **Qualif.:** Applicants must be pre- and postdoctoral scholars and also in senior levels from abroad or U.S.; must propose a Smithsonian American Art Museum primary advisor/supervisor. **Criteria:** Selection will be evaluated based on the quality of the proposed research project,

academic standing, scholarly qualifications and experience; the project's compatibility with Smithsonian collections, facilities, staff and programs will be also considered; a committee of curators and historians will review the applications.

To Apply: Applicants should apply to the Smithsonian Institution Fellowship Program, found under the Office of Fellowships in the online application system (SOLAA), and not under the museum's name; must propose a primary advisor/supervisor from SAAM to be eligible for a fellowship at this museum. **Deadline:** November 1. **Contact:** Amelia Goerlitz, Chair of Academic Programs; Phone: Email: GoerlitzA@si.edu.

10222 ■ Wyeth Foundation Predoctoral Fellowship *(Postdoctorate/Fellowship)*

Purpose: To support the advancement and completion of a doctoral dissertation that concerns the study, appreciation and recognition of excellence in all aspects of American art. **Focus:** Art; Museum science. **Qualif.:** Applicants must be Ph.D. candidates who wish to work with Smithsonian American Art Museum advisors. **Criteria:** Selection will be evaluated based on the quality of the proposed research project, academic standing, scholarly qualifications and experience; the project's compatibility with Smithsonian collections, facilities, staff and programs will be also considered; a committee of curators and historians will review the applications.

To Apply: Applicants should apply to the Smithsonian Institution Fellowship Program, found under the Office of Fellowships in the online application system (SOLAA), and not under the museum's name; must propose a primary advisor/supervisor from SAAM to be eligible for a fellowship at this museum. **Deadline:** November 1. **Contact:** Amelia Goerlitz, Chair of Academic Programs; Phone: Email: GoerlitzA@si.edu.

10223 ■ Smithsonian Tropical Research Institute (STRI)
PO Box 37012, MRC 705
Washington, DC 20013-7012
Ph: (202)633-4014
Fax: (202)786-2557
URL: www.stri.si.edu
Social Media: www.facebook.com/SmithsonianPanama
www.instagram.com/smithsonianpanama/
twitter.com/stri_panama
www.youtube.com/user/TheSmithsonianPanama

10224 ■ A. Stanley Rand Fellowship Program *(Undergraduate, Doctorate, Postdoctorate/Fellowship)*
Purpose: To foster and promote the careers of young biologists, especially those from Latin America, and his belief in the importance of tropical research. **Focus:** Animal science and behavior; Biology; Ecology; Environmental science; History.

To Apply: Applicants must submit one printed copy, plus one electronic copy of all requested materials; electronic copy should be submitted on a CD or by e-mail, as a single file in Word or preferably PDF. **Deadline:** March 15; May 15; August 15; November 15. **Contact:** STRI/Office of Academic Programs, MRC 0580-12, Unit 9100 Box 0948, DPO AA 34002-9998.

10225 ■ ForestGEO Research Grants *(Graduate, Postdoctorate, Professional development/Grant)*
Purpose: To provide opportunities for senior researchers, postdoctoral fellows and graduate students to use existing

CTFS plots to conduct research with scientists affiliated with them. **Focus:** Environmental science; Natural sciences. **Qualif.:** Applicants must be senior researchers, postdoctoral fellows, or graduate students; all nationalities are welcome to apply. **Criteria:** Preference will be given to scientists in the countries with CTFS (Center for Tropical Forest Science) site and to all graduate students and postdoctoral researchers; awards are made on the basis of the proposal's merit, the applicant's ability to carry out the proposed research, the likelihood that the research can be carried out in the proposed time frame, and the extent to which CTFS plots contribute to the proposed research.

Duration: From 3 months to 2 years. **To Apply:** Applicants must include one single PDF document with information; a research proposal (1000-word limit, research proposals that exceed 1000 words will be disqualified prior to review); list of project collaborators; a Curriculum Vitae (limit 2 pages), including the applicant's contact information, educational background, current and previous fellowships and grants, and research interests; a detailed budget. **Deadline:** May 29. **Contact:** Email: forestgeo@si.edu; URL: forestgeo.si.edu/opportunities/grants-program.

10226 ■ STRI Short-Term Fellowships *(Undergraduate, Graduate, Postdoctorate/Fellowship)*

Purpose: To support students and introduce them to tropical research. **Focus:** Animal science and behavior; Anthropology; Biology; Ecology; Neuroscience; Paleontology; Physiology; Soil science. **Qualif.:** Applicants must be undergraduate, graduate, or postdoctoral students. **Criteria:** Selection are evaluated on the scientific merits of the proposed research relative to its costs; the applicant's ability to conduct the proposed research in the time available; and the relevance of the proposed research to STRI research programs and interests. Availability of space at the particular facility will also be considered.

Funds Avail.: $1,000/month, a total amount of $3,000 for stipend; up to $2,000 research budget; and a round-trip coach airfare. **Duration:** Annual; up to three months. **To Apply:** Applicants must include a two-page application form available online with the requested information, including the names of main advisors and consultants; a non-technical abstract of not more than 250 words; a research proposal with a narrative of not more than 1, 500 words, plus a bibliography that is not included in the word count; narrative should include a description of the research to be undertaken at STRI, including a general introduction to the research topic, the methodology to be used, and expected results; a detailed 3-month timetable for the proposed research; research budget and justification; curriculum vitae; copies of academic transcripts; must arrange to have two letters of recommendation sent directly to STRI's Office of Academic Programs; before submitting a formal application, all applicants should consult with STRI scientific staff, who will serve as potential advisors, to confirm that they are willing to supervise and support the proposed project. **Deadline:** February 15; April 15; July 15; October 15. **Contact:** Email: fellows@si.edu.

10227 ■ Earl S. Tupper Three-year Postdoctoral Fellowship *(Postdoctorate/Fellowship)*

Purpose: To provide complete freedom to pursue intellectual curiosity among biology students and professionals. **Focus:** Animal science and behavior; Anthropology; Biology; Ecology; Neuroscience; Paleontology; Physiology; Soil science. **Qualif.:** Applicants must be individuals who already have their postdoctoral degrees.

Funds Avail.: $50,400 yearly stipend and up to $16,000 research budget. **Duration:** Annual. **To Apply:** Applications

must be completed online at: solaa.si.edu/solaa/#/public. **Deadline:** August 15.

10228 ■ Smithsonian Tropical Research Institute (STRI) - Center for Tropical Forest Science - ForestGEO (CTFS-ForestGEO)
West Loading Dock MRC-166
10th and Constitution Ave., NW
Washington, DC 20560
Ph: (202)633-1836
Fax: (202)786-2563
E-mail: forestgeo@si.edu
URL: www.ctfs.si.edu,www.forestgeo.si.edu
Social Media: www.facebook.com/ForestGEO
twitter.com/forestgeo

10229 ■ CTFS-ForestGEO Research Grants Program *(Graduate, Postdoctorate, Advanced Professional/Grant)*

Purpose: To provide opportunities for researchers, post doctorate fellows, and graduate students to use existing CTFS-ForestGEO plots to conduct research with scientists affiliated with them. **Focus:** Natural sciences; Social sciences. **Qualif.:** Application is open to all researchers, from graduate students to senior scientists; in some cases, advanced undergraduates will also be considered; all nationalities are welcome to apply; everyone working directly in CTFS-ForestGEO plots, analyzing plot data, or generating complementary data that strengthen CTFS-ForestGEO programs are eligible. **Criteria:** Preference will be given to scientists in the countries with CTFS-ForestGEO sites and to all graduate students and postdoctoral researchers.

Funds Avail.: $ 15,000. **Duration:** Up to 2 years. **To Apply:** Applicants must submit application form including the CTFS-ForestGEO cover letter; research proposal of 1,000 words; list of collaborators; two-page curriculum vitae; contact references; and detailed budget and time. All of these need to be submitted to Delaney Rakosnik. **Deadline:** April 13. **Contact:** Email: ForestGEO@si.edu.

10230 ■ SMSA Scholarship (SMSA)
PO Box 391
Springfield, VA 22150
E-mail: smsa@seabee.org
URL: www.seabee.org
Social Media: www.facebook.com/
SeabeeMemorialScholarshipAssociation
www.instagram.com/seabeememorial
www.linkedin.com/company/seabee-memorial-scholarship
 -association
twitter.com/SeabeeMemorial
www.youtube.com/channel/UCrBHWDjzvv1FkZbgAijA_aw

10231 ■ Seabee Memorial Scholarship Association Scholarships *(Undergraduate/Scholarship)*

Purpose: To support officers who have served or are serving in a Naval Construction Force Unit. **Focus:** General studies/Field of study not specified. **Criteria:** Recipients will be selected based on financial need, scholastic record, leadership, good citizenship and character.

Funds Avail.: No specific amount. **Duration:** Annual. **To Apply:** Applicants must attach a copy of an official docu-

Awards are arranged alphabetically below their administering organizations

ment that verifies the rate/rank, service number and a Seabee/CEC unit in which the sponsor served; two pages of military sponsor's information; Student Aid Report (SAR); complete list of extracurricular activities and awards; list of work experiences; and high school or college transcript. **Deadline:** January 1. **Contact:** Seabee Memorial Scholarship Association, PO Box 391, Springfield, VA, 22150.

10232 ■ SMUD
6301 South St.
Sacramento, CA 95817
Ph: (916)732-6119
URL: www.smud.org
Social Media: www.facebook.com/mysmud
www.instagram.com/mysmud
www.linkedin.com/company/smud
twitter.com/SMUDUpdates
www.youtube.com/channel/UCG
-JNJVBZJ5d5BOXZqOFT1g

10233 ■ SMUD Powering Futures Scholarship
(Undergraduate, Two Year College, University/ Scholarship)

Purpose: To help fund college for students. **Focus:** General studies/Field of study not specified. **Qualif.:** Applicant must be a high school senior or graduate, have earned a GED certificate, or currently be a postsecondary undergraduate student; have a minimum 3.0 GPA on a 4.0 scale; are enrolled or plan to enroll in a two- or four-year college or university in the U.S. for the fall semester; and be a SMUD customer living in SMUD's service area, or have a SMUD customer as a legal guardian. **Criteria:** Awards will be based on merit and financial need with preference for students with majors relevant to SMUD.

Funds Avail.: Up to $5,000. **Number Awarded:** 21. **To Apply:** Application should be completed online. **Deadline:** February 24. **Contact:** Email: SMUDRecruiter@smud.org; URL: www.smud.org/en/Giving-Back-to-Community/College-Scholarships.

10234 ■ Snowmobile Association of Massachusetts (SAM)
PO Box 386
Conway, MA 01341
Ph: (413)369-8092
Fax: (413)369-0203
URL: www.sledmass.com
Social Media: www.facebook.com/sledmass
twitter.com/sledmass

10235 ■ Snowmobile Association of Massachusetts Awards / Scholarships *(Undergraduate/Scholarship)*

Purpose: To develop and maintain an expanding interconnected snowmobile trail system, allowing snowmobile enthusiasts to travel from Worcester County. **Focus:** Transportation. **Qualif.:** Applicants must be parents or students who are members of Snowmobile Association of Massachusetts and local clubs.

Funds Avail.: A total of $5,000. **Duration:** Annual. **To Apply:** Applicants must submit a completed application form; an official high school or college transcript; recommendations in writing by at least two teachers; recommendations in writing by one or two friends, employers or clergy; proof

of acceptance at the listed college, university or vocational school; a written essay about snowmobiling in the state (500 words or less); overview of extracurricular activity or snow mobile associated volunteerism (within the last year of application); all required documents must be provided in five copies.

10236 ■ Sobeys Inc.
115 King St.
Stellarton, NS, Canada B0K 1S0
URL: www.sobeys.com

10237 ■ D&R Sobey Scholarships *(Undergraduate/ Scholarship)*

Purpose: To help young people attain the education needed to succeed today. **Focus:** General studies/Field of study not specified. **Qualif.:** Applicants must be students from Atlantic Canada pursuing first year of the undergraduate Commerce program at the Smith School of Business at Queen's University. **Criteria:** Selection will be based on the academic excellence; involvement in school or community activities; proven leadership.

Funds Avail.: 80,000 Canadian Dollars. **Duration:** Annual. **Number Awarded:** 6. **To Apply:** Applicants may contact the company for the application process and other requirements. **Deadline:** December 1.

10238 ■ The Frank H. Sobey Awards for Excellence in Business Studies *(Undergraduate/Award)*

Purpose: To provide financial support to students who are in need of help in pursuing higher education. **Focus:** Business. **Qualif.:** Applicants must be full-time undergraduate students of Business Studies in universities in the Atlantic Provinces. **Criteria:** Selection will be based on the committee's criteria.

Funds Avail.: 25,000 Canadian Dollars. **Duration:** Annual. **Number Awarded:** 8. **To Apply:** Applicants must complete the application form along must include: three letters of personal reference, sent directly by your referees to the Dean of the faculty in which you are enrolled for full-time studies in 2018-2019; recent head and shoulders photograph of yourself suitable for possible publication. **Deadline:** November 14. **Remarks:** Established in 1989.

10239 ■ Sobeys & Empire Work Experience & Scholarship Program - Future Leaders Awards *(Other/Scholarship)*

Purpose: To help young people attain the education needed to succeed today. **Focus:** General studies/Field of study not specified. **Qualif.:** Applicants must be employees of Sobeys across Canada. **Criteria:** Selection will be based on the committee's criteria.

Funds Avail.: $120,000. **Duration:** Annual. **To Apply:** Applicants may contact the company for the application process and other requirements.

10240 ■ Social Science Research Council (SSRC)
300 Cadman Plz. W, 15th Fl.
Brooklyn, NY 11201
Ph: (212)377-2700
URL: www.ssrc.org
Social Media: www.facebook.com/SSRC.org
twitter.com/SSRC_org
www.youtube.com/user/SSRCorg

Awards are arranged alphabetically below their administering organizations

10241 ■ Abe Fellowship (Professional development/Fellowship)

Purpose: To foster the development of a new generation of researchers who are interested in policy-relevant topics of long-range importance and who are willing to become key members of a bilateral and global research network built around international multidisciplinary research on topics of pressing global concern. **Focus:** Social sciences. **Qualif.:** Open to citizens of the United States and Japan, nationals of other countries affiliated with research communities in Japan or the United States, must hold a PhD or the terminal degree in their field, or have attained an equivalent level of professional experience at the time of application.

Funds Avail.: No specific amount. **Duration:** Annual; every 3 to 12 months. **To Apply:** Applications can be submitted online at: https://soap.ssrc.org. **Deadline:** September 1. **Contact:** Email: abe@ssrc.org; URL: www.ssrc.org/fellowships/view/abe-fellowship/.

10242 ■ Abe Fellowships for Journalists (Professional development/Fellowship)

Purpose: To encourage in-depth coverage of topics of pressing concern to the United States and Japan through individual short-term policy-related projects. **Focus:** Journalism. **Qualif.:** Applicants must be citizens of the United States and Japan with at least five years of professional journalistic experience with newspapers, news magazines, wire services and online news organizations; freelancers are also eligible; nationals of other countries must be permanent residents of the United States or Japan, or have a long-term affiliation with the American or Japanese journalistic communities; US-based with no previous journalistic employment in Japan or Japan-based with no previous journalistic employment in the United States will be given priority; proposals must be non-partisan. **Criteria:** Selection will be based on the committee's criteria.

Funds Avail.: $23,500. **Duration:** Annual. **To Apply:** Applications can be submitted online. **Deadline:** September 15. **Contact:** For U.S: Abe Fellowship Program, Social Science Research Council, One Pierrepont Plz., 15th Fl. Brooklyn, NY, 11201, USA; Phone: 212-377-2700; Fax: 212 377-2727; Email: abe@ssrc.org; For Japan: Abe Fellowship Program, SSRC Tokyo Office, c/o Japan Foundation Center for Global Partnership, Shinjuku Gyoenmae Bldg., 6F 4-16-3 Yotsuya, Shinjuku-ku, Tokyo, 160-0004; Phone: 3-5369-6085; Fax: 3-5369-6142; Email: abetokyo@ssrc.org.

10243 ■ Dissertation Proposal Development Fellowship (Doctorate/Fellowship)

Purpose: To help early-stage doctoral students in the humanities and social sciences formulate innovative dissertation research proposals through workshops, explanatory summer research, and writing guided by peer review and faculty mentorship. **Focus:** Humanities; Social sciences. **Qualif.:** Applicants must be students in the humanities and social sciences undertaking doctoral dissertation research; must be currently matriculated in PhD programs at accredited universities in the United States; must be U.S. citizens or non-citizens; must have completed at least two full years of graduate study (MA and/or PhD) by the end of June of the current year; must commit to attend the spring and fall workshops. **Criteria:** Selection applications will be evaluated based on the following criteria: (1) potential significance of proposed dissertation topic; (2) applicant's readiness for proposal development; (3) interest in

and potential benefit from other disciplines in the humanities and social sciences; (4) connection between summer research plans and proposal development.

Funds Avail.: Up to $5,000. **Duration:** Annual. **To Apply:** Applications can be submitted online. **Remarks:** Established in 2006. **Contact:** Social Science Research Council;300 Cadman Plaza West, 15th Floor Brooklyn, NY 11201, USA; Phone: 212-377-2700 ext. 3672; Email: korea@ssrc.org.

10244 ■ Eurasia Program Fellowships - Dissertation Development Awards (Doctorate/Fellowship)

Purpose: To provide financial and academic support to graduate students in the early stages of dissertation development and PhD candidates near completion of their doctoral programs in the social sciences and related humanities. **Focus:** Humanities; Social sciences.

Funds Avail.: Stipends up to $20,000. **Duration:** One year. **Number Awarded:** 10.

10245 ■ Eurasia Program Fellowships - Pre-Dissertation Awards (Doctorate/Fellowship)

Purpose: To provide financial and academic support to graduate students in the early stages of dissertation development and PhD candidates near completion of their doctoral programs in the social sciences and related humanities. **Focus:** Humanities; Social sciences. **Qualif.:** Applicants must be graduate students in the first three years of study in a PhD program; awards require evidence of ethics training and recipients will be required to obtain University IRB approval for their project, if necessary. **Criteria:** Selection of applications are reviewed by an interdisciplinary panel of experts that reward proposals with clear arguments, carefully considered theory and methodology and a writing style accessible to readers both inside and outside the applicants' discipline. Proposals should be intriguing for both a specialist and generalist audience; all proposals are expected to meet high levels of academic merit and to address the current needs of the field of Eurasian studies.

Funds Avail.: No specific amount. **Duration:** Annual. **Number Awarded:** 6. **To Apply:** Applicants may visit the website for the online application process and must complete all the required documents; research proposals and bibliographies should be: collated as one continuous PDF document not exceeding 12 pages in total; times New Roman, 12-point font type with at least one inch margins on all sides; double-spaced for the proposals and single-spaced for the bibliography; name and page numbers should appear on each page. **Contact:** Denise Mishiwiec, eurasia@ssrc.org.

10246 ■ International Dissertation Research Fellowship (IDRF) (Graduate, Doctorate/Fellowship)

Purpose: To provide assistance in fostering innovative research and mobilizing necessary knowledge on important public issues to new generations of social scientists. **Focus:** Humanities; Social sciences. **Qualif.:** Applicants must be graduates of humanities and social sciences enrolled in PhD programs in the United States. **Criteria:** Preference will be given to applicants who write their prose clearly and intelligibly; proposal that shows major concepts, theories, and methods; and applicants who will provide evidence of having attained an appropriate level of training to do the proposed research.

Funds Avail.: Amount varies. **Duration:** Annual; 9-12 months. **To Apply:** Applicants must fill out the online ap-

Awards are arranged alphabetically below their administering organizations

plication through the SSRC Online Application Portal; must complete the research relevance section must upload their research proposal and bibliography; and must send reminders to referees and language evaluators. **Deadline:** November 4. **Remarks:** Established in 1997.

10247 ■ Japan Society for the Promotion of Science Fellowship (JSPS) *(Doctorate/Fellowship)*

Purpose: To encourage and to advance recent Ph.D. recipients and ABDs' own research and at the same time closely collaborate with young Japanese researchers and contribute to Japanese research communities. **Focus:** Humanities; Social sciences. **Qualif.:** Applicants for the long-term and short-term fellowships must possess US citizenship or permanent residency status and must provide a copy of a permanent resident card; citizens of other countries may be eligible if they have completed a master's or PhD course at a US university, and upon completing the course, have at least three continuous years conducted high-level research in the US. **Criteria:** Fellows will be selected by the JSPS based on nominations made by the SSRC Japan Advisory Board.

Funds Avail.: No specific amount. **Duration:** Annual. **To Apply:** Applicants must submit the following an application form, a project description; two letters of recommendation; a letter of invitation from a host institution in Japan; must also submit a copy of PhD diploma from a university outside Japan dated no more than six years or, for a short-term fellowship, a letter from their institution stating that the applicants is a PhD candidate within two years of receiving a PhD. **Deadline:** December 1. **Contact:** Email: japan@ssrc.org.

10248 ■ Korean Studies Dissertation Workshop *(Graduate/Fellowship)*

Purpose: To create a sustained network of advanced graduate students and faculty by providing the opportunity to give and receive critical feedback on dissertations in progress. **Focus:** Humanities; Social sciences. **Qualif.:** Applicants must be a full-time advanced graduate student enrolled at a U.S. or Canadian institution; must have an approved dissertation prospectus at the time of application, but cannot have completed writing for final submission. **Criteria:** Special consideration will be given to students from universities that are not major Korea Studies institutions; selection of applicant will be based on the narrative project descriptions as part of the application.

Funds Avail.: No specific amount. **Duration:** Annual. **To Apply:** Applicants must complete and sign a short application form; must have a narrative description of the dissertation topic; letter of recommendation from the student's primary adviser. **Contact:** Social Science Research Council;300 Cadman Plaza West, 15th Floor Brooklyn, NY 11201, USA; Phone: 212-377-2700 ext. 3672; Email: korea@ssrc.org.

10249 ■ Next Generation Social Sciences in Africa: Doctoral Dissertation Completion Fellowship *(Doctorate/Fellowship)*

Purpose: To support the advancement of social science faculty toward completion of doctoral degrees and to promote next-generation social science research in Ghana, Nigeria, South Africa, Tanzania, and Uganda. **Focus:** Social sciences. **Criteria:** Selection will be based on the committee's criteria.

Funds Avail.: $15,000. **Duration:** Annual. **Number Awarded:** 1. **To Apply:** Applications must be submitted us-

ing the online application portal; strong proposals will offer clear and concise descriptions of the project and its significance; proposals should display thorough knowledge of the relevant social science literature that will engage and the methodologies relevant to the project; in addition, must demonstrate that all proposed activities are feasible and can be completed in a timely manner; fellows must be willing to attend two workshops sponsored by the SSRC each year that are intended to help early-career faculty produce scholarly publications. **Deadline:** January 10. **Contact:** Email: nextgenafrica@ssrc.org.

10250 ■ Next Generation Social Sciences in Africa: Doctoral Dissertation Proposal Fellowship *(Doctorate/Fellowship)*

Purpose: To support short-term research costs to develop a doctoral dissertation proposal. **Focus:** Social sciences. **Qualif.:** Applicants must be citizens of and reside in a sub-Saharan African country while holding a current faculty position at an accredited college or university in Ghana, Nigeria, South Africa, Tanzania or Uganda; must have a master's degree and be working toward completion of a doctoral degree; must be admitted to a graduate program but have yet to undertake dissertation research. **Criteria:** Selection will be based on the committee's criteria.

Funds Avail.: $3,000. **Duration:** Annual. **To Apply:** Applications must be submitted using the online application portal; strong proposals will offer clear and concise descriptions of the project and its significance; proposals should display thorough knowledge of the relevant social science literature that will engage and the methodologies relevant to the project; in addition, must demonstrate that all proposed activities are feasible and can be completed in a timely manner; fellows must be willing to attend two workshops sponsored by the SSRC each year that are intended to help early-career faculty produce scholarly publications. **Deadline:** November 17. **Contact:** Email: nextgenafrica@ssrc.org.

10251 ■ Next Generation Social Sciences in Africa: Doctoral Dissertation Research Fellowship *(Doctorate/Fellowship)*

Purpose: To support the advancement of social science faculty toward completion of doctoral degrees and to promote next-generation social science research in Ghana, Nigeria, South Africa, Tanzania, and Uganda. **Focus:** Social sciences. **Criteria:** Selection will be based on the committee's criteria.

Funds Avail.: $15,000. **Duration:** Annual; 6-12 months. **To Apply:** Applicants must be submitted online. **Deadline:** January 10. **Contact:** Email: nextgenafrica@ssrc.org.

10252 ■ Sociedad Interamericana de Prensa (SIP)
3511 NW 91st Ave.
Doral, FL 33172
Ph: (305)634-2465
Fax: (305)860-4264
E-mail: info@sipiapa.org
URL: www.sipiapa.com
Social Media: www.facebook.com/institutodeprensa
twitter.com/sip_oficial
www.youtube.com/channel/UCn2bPI
  -MyxGlx8FpWuGbugw?view_as=subscriber

10253 ■ Inter American Press Association Scholarships *(Undergraduate/Scholarship)*

Purpose: To defend and promote the right of the peoples of the Americas to be fully and freely informed through an

Awards are arranged alphabetically below their administering organizations

independent press. **Focus:** Journalism. **Criteria:** Recipients are selected based on academic achievement and financial need.

Funds Avail.: $20,000. **Duration:** Annual. **To Apply:** Applicants must complete the application form and submit along with an autobiography around 200 words; transcripts of the university studies; three letters of recommendation; curriculum vitae; and proof of certification. **Deadline:** January 31. **Remarks:** Established in 1942.

10254 ■ Societe des designers graphiques du Canada (GDC)

Arts Ct.
2 Daly Ave.
Ottawa, ON, Canada K1N 6E2
URL: www.gdc.net

10255 ■ Society of Graphic Designers of Canada Adobe Scholarships *(Undergraduate/Scholarship)*

Purpose: To support students in taking their design education to a level that will prepare them for professional practice. **Focus:** Graphic art and design. **Qualif.:** Applicants must be full-time students enrolled in a two, three, or four-year design degree or diploma program; must be members of Graphic Designers of Canada (GDC), SDGQ, or RGD Ontario. **Criteria:** Recipients will be selected based on qualifications and submitted materials.

Funds Avail.: $2,000. **Duration:** Annual. **To Apply:** Applicants must provide a transcript of grades, letter of reference from an instructor, one sample of work to be accompanied by a detailed rationale, photo and electronic files of their work; must also draft a personal letter (250 words) describing their design history, previous design education, reason(s) for applying, career aspirations and goals. **Contact:** GDC National Scholarship Program, c/o Hudson Design Group, at the above address.

10256 ■ Society of Graphic Designers of Canada Applied Arts Scholarships *(Undergraduate/Scholarship)*

Purpose: To support students in taking their design education that will prepare them for professional practice. **Focus:** Graphic art and design. **Qualif.:** Applicants must be full-time students enrolled in a two, three, or four-year design degree or diploma program; must be members of Graphic Designers of Canada (GDC), SDGQ, or RGD Ontario. **Criteria:** Recipients will be selected based on qualifications and submitted materials.

Funds Avail.: $1,000. **Duration:** Annual. **To Apply:** Applicants must provide a transcript of grades, letter of reference from an instructor, one sample of work to be accompanied by a detailed rationale, photo and electronic files of their work; must also draft a personal letter (250 words) describing their design history, previous design education, reason(s) for applying, career aspirations and goals. **Contact:** GDC National Scholarship Program, c/o Hudson Design Group, at the above address.

10257 ■ Society of Graphic Designers of Canada Veer Scholarships *(Undergraduate/Scholarship)*

Purpose: To support students in taking their design education to a level that will prepare them for professional practice. **Focus:** Graphic art and design. **Qualif.:** Applicants must be full-time students enrolled in a two, three, or four-year design degree or diploma program; must be

members of Graphic Designers of Canada (GDC), SDGQ, or RGD Ontario. **Criteria:** Recipients will be selected based on qualifications and submitted materials.

Funds Avail.: $2,500. **Duration:** Annual. **To Apply:** Applicants must provide a transcript of grades, letter of reference from an instructor, one sample of work to be accompanied by a detailed rationale, photo and electronic files of their work; must also draft a personal letter (250 words) describing their design history, previous design education, reason(s) for applying, career aspirations and goals. **Deadline:** April 20. **Contact:** GDC National Scholarship Program, c/o Hudson Design Group, at the above address.

10258 ■ Société Canadienne des études Classiques

Lawson Hall, Rm. 3205
Western University
London, ON, Canada N6A 5B8
Ph: (519)661-3045
Fax: (519)850-2388
E-mail: classics@uwo.ca
URL: cac-scec.ca

10259 ■ Desmond Conacher Scholarship *(Graduate/Scholarship)*

Purpose: To assist and encourage young scholars entering graduate study in classics. **Focus:** Classical studies. **Qualif.:** Applicants must be Canadian citizens or permanent residents; must be entering the first year of graduate studies in classics or similar program in a Canadian university. **Criteria:** Selection will be given to applicants who have demonstrated academic achievement, professional promise, and an appropriate undergraduate preparation.

Funds Avail.: $2,500. **Duration:** Annual. **Number Awarded:** 1. **To Apply:** Applicants must submit a completed application form; personal statement (maximum of 1,000 words) describing the previous academic career, employment experience, academic and career objectives; list of academic awards and honors received at the post-secondary level; transcript of records; two letters of recommendation from university teachers. **Remarks:** The scholarship was offered in memory of Desmond Conacher, formerly Professor of Classics at Trinity College, Toronto, Fellow of the Royal Society of Canada, and Honorary President of the CAC, which have been endowed through donations from his family, friends, colleagues, and universities with which Desmond Conacher was associated. **Contact:** For electronic submissions and questions: Professor Allison Glazebrook, Chair of the CAC Awards Committee; Email: aglazebrook@brocku.ca.

10260 ■ Société Canadienne pour l'Étude de l'Éducation (SCEE)

260 Dalhousie St., Ste. 204
Ottawa, ON, Canada K1N 7E4
Ph: (613)241-0018
Fax: (613)241-0019
E-mail: csse-scee@csse.ca
URL: www.csse-scee.ca
Social Media: www.facebook.com/csse.scee
twitter.com/CSSESCEE

10261 ■ CCGSE Mentorship Award *(Graduate/Award)*

Purpose: To recognize a faculty member who has provided outstanding support and encouragement for graduate

Awards are arranged alphabetically below their administering organizations

students. **Focus:** General studies/Field of study not specified. **Qualif.:** Applicants must be a faculty member mentoring graduate students which include, but is not limited to encouraging contributions to the knowledge base of graduate students; providing opportunities for student's professional growth as teachers and researchers; and modeling active membership in professional societies and encouraging students to do the same. **Criteria:** Award will be given to applicants who can provide evidence of recognition from graduate students.

Funds Avail.: No specific amount. **Duration:** Annual. **To Apply:** Applicants must submit a cover letter; a blind letter of nomination describing why the nominee deserves to be recognized for mentoring graduate students; and three letters of support from other mentees and colleagues. **Deadline:** April 15. **Contact:** CCGSE Mentorship Award Committee Chair: Frances Kalu at fukalu@ucalgary.ca.

10262 ■ CSSE New Scholar Fellowship (CSSE)
(Professional development/Fellowship)

Purpose: To provide support for travel to the CSSE Annual Conference, registration, and accommodation. **Focus:** Education. **Qualif.:** Applicant must be a full-time, tenure-track assistant professor in Education in an academic unit in Canada. **Criteria:** Selection will be made based on submitted application and project.

Funds Avail.: No specific amount. **Duration:** Annual. **To Apply:** Applicants must submit a copy of their full paper for adjudication by the CSSE New Scholar Advisory Board.

10263 ■ Société Canadienne de Recherches Cliniques (SCRC)
114 Cheyenne Way
Ottawa, ON, Canada K2J 0E9
Fax: (613)491-0073
Free: 877-968-9449
E-mail: info@csci-scrc.ca
URL: www.csci-scrc.ca

10264 ■ CSCI Distinguished Scientist Lectures and Awards *(Advanced Professional/Award)*

Purpose: To recognize the medical scientists who has made significant contributions to new knowledge and is generally recognized in her/his field as expert, innovative, and in the forefront of research endeavour. **Focus:** Medical research. **Qualif.:** Applicants must be MD or PhD medical students who made significant contributions to new knowledge and are generally recognized in their respective fields as experts, innovative, and in the forefront of research endeavor. **Criteria:** Recipients will be selected based on submitted materials.

Funds Avail.: 2,000 Canadian Dollars. **Duration:** Annual. **Number Awarded:** 1. **To Apply:** Applicants should include letters of support from two supporters and curriculum vitae. **Deadline:** June 3. **Remarks:** Established in 1987. **Contact:** CSCI National Office; 114 Cheyenne Way, Ottawa, ON, K2J 0E9; Phone: 877-968-9449; Fax: 613-491-0073.

10265 ■ Henry Friesen Awards and Lecture
(Doctorate/Award)

Purpose: To support scientists for their contribution to biomedical research and to cover travel and hotel expenses. **Focus:** Biomedical research. **Criteria:** Selection will be selected based on submitted materials.

Funds Avail.: $3,000. **Duration:** Annual. **Number Awarded:** 1. **To Apply:** Applicants should include letters

from two sponsors, curriculum vitae, and two of the nominees' best publications; the article should be 2,000-3,000 words. **Deadline:** June 3. **Contact:** Email: admin@csci-scrc.ca.

10266 ■ Society of Allied Weight Engineers (SAWE)
5734 E Lucia Walk
Long Beach, CA 90803
Ph: (562)596-2873
Fax: (562)596-2874
URL: www.sawe.org
Social Media: www.linkedin.com/groups/8566430/profile
twitter.com/saweorg

10267 ■ Frank Fong Scholarships *(Undergraduate/Scholarship)*

Purpose: To provide financial assistance for the education of the dependents of SAWE members. **Focus:** Computer and information sciences; Engineering; Mathematics and mathematical sciences; Physics. **Qualif.:** Applicants must be children or grandchildren (age 25 or below) of SAWE members (living or deceased) that are students enrolled in a technical course of study (e.g. engineering, physics, mathematics, computer sciences, etc.). **Criteria:** Selection are given based on academic merit; work experience; extracurricular activities; and goal for the application.

Funds Avail.: $1,000 each. **Duration:** Annual. **Number Awarded:** Up to 4. **To Apply:** Applicants must complete and submit the application form available at the website together with their transcript of grades. **Deadline:** May 1. **Contact:** Questions regarding the scholarship program should be addressed to: Society of Allied Weight Engineers Scholarship Program, Scholarship Management Services, One Scholarship Way, St. Peter, MN 56082 U.S.A.; Telephone: 507-931-1682; Toll-free Phone: 800-537-4180.

10268 ■ Society of Allied Weight Engineers Scholarships *(Undergraduate/Scholarship)*

Purpose: To provide financial assistance for the education of the dependents of SAWE members. **Focus:** General studies/Field of study not specified. **Qualif.:** Applicants must be children or grandchildren of SAWE members; must be aged 25 or below; and must be full-time undergraduate students. **Criteria:** Selection are given based on academic merit; work experience; extracurricular activities; and goal for the application.

Funds Avail.: $1,000. **Duration:** Annual. **Number Awarded:** Up to 4. **To Apply:** Application forms are available at the website; applicants must submit completed application form and send together with a complete transcript of grades. **Deadline:** May 1. **Contact:** Scholarship Management Services, One Scholarship Way, St. Peter, MN 56082; Telephone: 507-931-1682, Toll-free: 800-537-4180.

10269 ■ Society for American Archaeology (SAA)
1111 14th St. NW, Ste. 800
Washington, DC 20005-5622
Ph: (202)789-8200
E-mail: headquarters@saa.org
URL: www.saa.org
Social Media: www.facebook.com/SAAorgfb
www.instagram.com/societyforamericanarchaeology
www.linkedin.com/company/society-for-american
-archaeology

Awards are arranged alphabetically below their administering organizations

twitter.com/saaorg
www.youtube.com/channel/UCJ54dtuh9q8zAjCBaHna6eQ

10270 ■ Arthur C. Parker Scholarship (Undergraduate, Graduate/Scholarship)

Purpose: To support archaeological training for Native American students. **Focus:** Archeology. **Qualif.:** Applicants must be current high school seniors, college undergraduates and graduate students, or personnel of a Tribal or other Native cultural preservation programs. **Criteria:** Selection is based on the application or nomination.

Funds Avail.: Up to $5,000. **Duration:** Annual. **Number Awarded:** 1. **Remarks:** The SAA Native American Scholarships are offered in the following: the SAA Arthur C. Parker Scholarship or NSF Scholarship for Archaeological Training; SAA Native American Undergraduate Archaeology Scholarship; SAA Native American Graduate Archaeology Scholarship. Established in 1998.

10271 ■ Society for Applied Anthropology (SFAA)
3000 United Founders Blvd., Ste. 102G
Oklahoma City, OK 73112
Ph: (405)843-5113
Fax: (405)843-8553
E-mail: info@sfaa.net
URL: www.appliedanthro.org
Social Media: www.facebook.com/
  societyforappliedanthropology
twitter.com/SfAAnthro

10272 ■ Margaret Mead Award (Doctorate/Award)

Purpose: To support young scholars for a book, film, monograph or service which interprets anthropological data and principles in ways that make them meaningful to a broadly concerned public. **Focus:** Anthropology. **Qualif.:** Applicants must have received their PhD degree after January 1 (ten years or less). **Criteria:** Selection will be judged based on intellectual quality, clarity and understandability, extent or depth of the impact and breadth of the impact.

Funds Avail.: No specific amount. **Duration:** Annual. **To Apply:** Applicants must include a curriculum vitae, two letters of recommendation and must submit five copies of the book or film. **Deadline:** February 15. **Remarks:** Established in 1979. **Contact:** Margaret Mead Selection Committee, Society for Applied Anthropology, 3000 United Founders Blvd., Ste. 102G, Oklahoma City, OK, 73112; Phone: 405-843-5113; Fax: 405-843-8553; E-mail info@sfaa.net.

10273 ■ Society of Architectural Historians (SAH)
1365 N Astor St.
Chicago, IL 60610
Ph: (312)573-1365
E-mail: info@sah.org
URL: www.sah.org

10274 ■ Edilia and François Auguste de Montêquin Fellowships (Doctorate/Fellowship)

Purpose: To provide support for travel related to research on Spanish, Portuguese, or Ibero-American architecture. **Focus:** Engineering, Architectural. **Qualif.:** Applicants must be member of the Society of Architectural Historians; must be full-time junior graduate students engaged in a doctoral dissertation research, or senior graduate students with a completed PhD or equivalent with a research focusing on Spanish, Portuguese, or Ibero-American architecture. **Criteria:** Selection will be based on the submitted applications.

Funds Avail.: $2,000 for junior scholars and $6,000 for senior scholars. **Duration:** Annual. **To Apply:** Applicants must need two recommendations to apply for this fellowship, a description of research project on Iberian or Ibero-American architecture to be funded (500 words maximum), a current curriculum vitae (5 pages max), and a statement of purpose. **Deadline:** September 30.

10275 ■ Keepers Preservation Education Fund Fellowship (Graduate/Fellowship)

Purpose: To provide support to students in Historic Preservation to attend the annual meeting. **Focus:** Historic preservation. **Qualif.:** Applicant must be a graduate student in Historic Preservation at the SAH annual international conference; must be US residents. **Criteria:** Preference will be given to a graduate student whose paper has been accepted for delivery at the conference.

Funds Avail.: Up to $1,000. **Duration:** Annual. **To Apply:** Applications can be submitted online. **Remarks:** Established in 1989. **Contact:** Email: fellowships@sah.org.

10276 ■ SAH Study Tour Fellowships (Graduate/Fellowship)

Purpose: To provide travel opportunities that focus on the history of architecture and landscapes. **Focus:** Architecture. **Qualif.:** Applicant must be a member of the Society of Architectural Historians and a Ph.D. student. **Criteria:** Recipients are selected by a committee by the SAH President.

To Apply: Applicants are advised to visit the website for the online Study Tour Fellowship application; students must submit maximum of five pages curriculum vitae and a 300-word statement explaining how this fellowship will advance their studies or interests.

10277 ■ Samuel H. Kress Foundation Fellowships (Doctorate/Fellowship)

Purpose: To provide assistance for the professional development of graduate students in architectural history. **Focus:** Architecture. **Qualif.:** Application must be graduate students, international speakers, and independent scholars presenting at the SAH Annual International Conference; All recipients are required to submit a minimum of 25 annotated images. **Criteria:** Selection will be based on the committee's criteria.

Funds Avail.: Up to $1,000. **To Apply:** Applications can be submitted online. **Contact:** Email: fellowships@sah.org.

10278 ■ Sally Kress Tompkins Fellowship (Graduate/Fellowship)

Purpose: To support and assist the students to work as a summer intern on a 12-week Historic American Buildings Survey project. **Focus:** Architecture. **Qualif.:** Applicant should be pursuing graduate studies in architectural history or other related fields; applicants do not have to be a member of SAH. **Criteria:** Selection will be based on the committee's criteria.

Funds Avail.: $10,000-$12,000. **Duration:** Annual. **To Apply:** Applicants must submit final project/written history, recipients are required to upload a minimum of 50 images documenting their summer HABS project to the SAHARA image database prior to completion of the fellowship. **Deadline:** December 31. **Contact:** Lisa Davidson; Phone: 202-354-2179.

Awards are arranged alphabetically below their administering organizations

10279 ■ Beverly Willis Architecture Foundation Travel Fellowship *(Doctorate/Fellowship)*

Purpose: To support travel expenses of a speaker whose paper has been accepted for delivery at the SAH annual conference. **Focus:** Architecture. **Qualif.:** Applicants must be enrolled in a PhD program conducting a dissertation research about the contribution of women to the production of architecture in the United States in the mid-twentieth century (should be submitted in English). **Criteria:** Recipient is selected based on the submitted materials.

Duration: Annual. **To Apply:** Applicants are advised to visit the website for the online Fellowship Application. Applicants must also submit a Word document which contains a summary or abstract; a budget detailing the use of the funds (one to two pages); a curriculum vitae; and letters of recommendation.

10280 ■ Society for the Arts in Healthcare (SAH)
2647 Connecticut Ave. NW, Ste. 200
Washington, DC 20008
Ph: (202)299-9770
Fax: (202)299-9887
URL: www.thesah.org

10281 ■ Society for the Arts in Healthcare Student Scholarships *(Doctorate, Graduate, Undergraduate/ Scholarship)*

Purpose: To support the education of students enrolled in the field of Arts in Healthcare curriculum. **Focus:** Health care services. **Qualif.:** Applicants must be undergraduate, graduate or doctoral student members of the Society for the Arts in Healthcare who are in good standing; must show a documentation of at least part-time enrollment; and must demonstrate specific contributions to the field through development of student activities, community outreach and/or similar actions that support the integration of the arts in the healthcare experience. **Criteria:** Applications will be judged based on creativity, uniqueness and ability to implement thoughts and ideas regarding the future of the field.

Funds Avail.: $1,000. **Duration:** Annual. **To Apply:** Applicants must submit an application form, references and proof of enrollment. Materials must be submitted in Word or PDF file and should be written in English. **Deadline:** November 15.

10282 ■ Society of Biological Psychiatry (SOBP)
5034A Thoroughbred Ln.
Brentwood, TN 37027
Ph: (615)432-0096
E-mail: sobp@sobp.org
URL: www.sobp.org
Social Media: www.facebook.com/SOBP.ORG
www.linkedin.com/company/society-of-biological-psychiatry
twitter.com/SOBP
www.youtube.com/channel/
    UCdTv6HfK7Zo2RlATnOdDBmA

10283 ■ SOBP Travel Fellowship Award-Early Career Investigator-International *(Postdoctorate/ Fellowship)*

Purpose: To provide travel support to outstanding individuals who wish to participate in professional meetings. **Focus:**

Psychiatry. **Criteria:** Selection will be based on the committee's criteria.

Funds Avail.: $2,000. **Duration:** Annual. **Deadline:** September 25. **Contact:** Society of Biological Psychiatry, Phone: 615-432-0096, Email: sobp@sobp.org.

10284 ■ Society of Broadcast Engineers (SBE)
9102 N Meridian St., Ste. 150
Indianapolis, IN 46260
Ph: (317)846-9000
Fax: (317)846-9120
URL: www.sbe.org
Social Media: www.facebook.com/SBEorg
www.linkedin.com/in/sbe-national-office-11701349
twitter.com/sbeorg
www.youtube.com/user/sbenational

10285 ■ Harold E. Ennes Scholarship *(Graduate/ Scholarship)*

Purpose: To provide an educational fund to deserving candidates who aspire to a career in the technical aspects of broadcasting. **Focus:** Broadcasting; Engineering. **Qualif.:** Applicants must be SBE member; have work experience in broadcasting engineering and interested in continuing their education in order to advance their careers. **Criteria:** Selection will be given to those who are SBE members and employed in broadcasting engineering.

Funds Avail.: $1,000-$1,500. **Duration:** Annual. **Number Awarded:** 3. **To Apply:** Application forms are available at the website; complete only the A and C sections of the application form and send together with a brief autobiography; a summary of technical changes; and a copy of recent college transcripts (if applicable); recipients will be expected to submit a technical paper of 400-500 words on a broadcast-engineering topic. **Deadline:** July 1. **Remarks:** Established in memory of Harold E. Ennes.

10286 ■ Robert D. Greenberg Scholarship *(Graduate, Other/Scholarship)*

Purpose: To provide an educational fund to deserving candidates who aspire to a career in the technical aspects of broadcasting. **Focus:** Broadcasting; Engineering. **Qualif.:** Applicants must be SBE member; have work experience in broadcasting engineering and interested in continuing their education in order to advance their careers. **Criteria:** Selection will be given to those who are SBE members and employed in broadcasting engineering.

Funds Avail.: $1,000-$1,500. **Duration:** Annual. **Number Awarded:** Up to 3. **To Apply:** Application forms are available at the website; complete only the A and C sections of the application form and send together with a brief autobiography; a summary of technical changes; and a copy of recent college transcripts (if applicable); recipients will be expected to submit a technical paper of 400-500 words on a broadcast-engineering topic. **Deadline:** July 1. **Contact:** Society of Broadcast Engineers, 9102 N Meridian St., Ste. 150, Indianapolis, IN, 46260; Phone: 317-846-9000; Email: dhennessey@sbe.org.

10287 ■ SBE/Ennes Youth Scholarships *(Graduate/ Scholarship)*

Purpose: To provide educational fund to deserving candidates who aspire to a career in the technical aspects of broadcasting. **Focus:** Broadcasting; Technical com-

Awards are arranged alphabetically below their administering organizations

munications. **Qualif.:** Applicants must be in their senior year of high school, anticipating graduation by the spring of the current year; intend to enroll at a technical school, college or university in the fall of the current year; and, have a serious interest in pursuing studies leading to a career in broadcast engineering or closely related technical field.

Funds Avail.: $1,500. **Duration:** Annual. **Number Awarded:** Up to 3. **To Apply:** Application forms are available at the website; complete only the A and C sections of the application form and send together with a brief autobiography; a summary of technical changes; and a copy of recent college transcripts (if applicable). **Deadline:** July 1. **Contact:** Society of Broadcast Engineers, 9102 North Meridian St, Ste 150, Indianapolis, IN, 46260; Phone: 317-846-9000; Email: dhennessey@sbe.org.

10288 ■ Society of Building Science Educators (SBSE)

c/o Reichard, Georg President 410 Bishop-Favrao Hall
1345 Perry St
Blacksburg, VA 24060
URL: www.sbse.org
Social Media: facebook.com/sbse
instagram.com/sbse
pinterest.com/sbse
youtube.com/sbse

10289 ■ Jeffrey Cook Student Travel Scholarships to PLEA *(Postgraduate/Scholarship)*

Purpose: To support students presenting papers at the PLEA Conference. **Focus:** Science. **Qualif.:** Applicant must be a student at the time of abstract submission to PLEA, must have a paper/poster accepted for publication at the PLEA conference, and must present the paper/poster at the conference. **Criteria:** Selection will be based upon review of the application materials, including the abstract submitted to PLEA; second stage will include consideration of the full draft paper submitted to PLEA.

Funds Avail.: $1,000. **Duration:** Annual. **To Apply:** Applicants must submit a copy of the proposal (abstract) acceptance notification from PLEA and a copy of the draft completed paper/poster; an electronically submitted form that provides the information requested and addresses. **Deadline:** May 31; June 15. **Remarks:** The scholarship was established in honor of late Jeffrey Cook. **Contact:** Scholarship Coordinator, Jonathan Bean; E-mail: j.bean@arizona.edu.

10290 ■ Jeffrey Cook Memorial Faculty Retreat Scholarship *(Professional development/Scholarship)*

Purpose: To help defray the cost of attending the SBSE Retreat. **Focus:** Science. **Qualif.:** Applicant must be from a SBSE members (currently, there is no membership fee for those from developing countries); recipient is encouraged to seek additional support from home institution (department, college and/or university). **Criteria:** Selection will be based on the applicant's teaching, research, professional service, and networking activities and on the potential for benefits to the applicant's institution and country.

Funds Avail.: $1,500. **Duration:** Annual. **To Apply:** Applications will consist of an electronically submitted Word or pdf document that provides the information noted below; applications must be submitted by e-mail; attach with this application are contact information, impact statement, building science teaching background, PLEA experiences,

special circumstances. **Remarks:** The scholarship was established in honor of late Jeffrey Cook. **Contact:** Scholarship Coordinator, Jonathan Bean; E-mail: j.bean@arizona.edu.

10291 ■ SBSE Ases Student Travel Scholarship *(Graduate/Scholarship)*

Purpose: To provide assistance to students who are presenting papers at (or otherwise actively participating in) Solar, the annual conference of the American Solar Energy Society (ASES). **Focus:** Science.

Funds Avail.: $700. **Duration:** Annual. **To Apply:** Applications will consist of an electronically submitted. **Deadline:** June 1. **Contact:** Scholarship Coordinator, Jonathan Bean; E-mail: j.bean@arizona.edu.

10292 ■ SBSE Student Retreat Scholarship *(Master's, Doctorate/Scholarship)*

Purpose: To support for students who are interested in teaching environmental control systems (or a closely related area of building science). **Focus:** Science. **Criteria:** Selection process will favor those who have never attended an SBSE retreat, geographic diversity among applicants, and balanced representation from institutions.

Funds Avail.: $700. **Duration:** Annual. **Number Awarded:** Up to 6. **To Apply:** Applications will consist of an electronically submitted form that provides the information requested and addresses. **Contact:** Scholarship Coordinator, Jonathan Bean; E-mail: j.bean@arizona.edu.

10293 ■ Society of Canadian Ornithologists (SCO)

PO Box 128
Rocky Harbour, NL, Canada A0K 4N0
URL: www.sco-soc.ca
Social Media: www.facebook.com/sco.soc
twitter.com/sco_soc

10294 ■ Fred Cooke Student Award *(Undergraduate/Grant)*

Purpose: To support ornithological conference travel or research activities by a student at a Canadian university. **Focus:** Ornithology. **Qualif.:** Applicant must be any student who is enrolled in a Canadian university; must be SCO-SOC members to be eligible. **Criteria:** Selection will be based on the committee's criteria.

Funds Avail.: 1,000 Canadian Dollars. **Duration:** Annual. **Number Awarded:** 1. **Deadline:** March 2. **Remarks:** Established to honor the contributions of Professor Fred Cooke to Canadian ornithology by supporting ornithological conference travel or research activities by a student at a Canadian university. **Contact:** Applications should be emailed to: Dr. Nicola Koper Chair, SCO-SOC Student Awards Committee Natural Resources Institute, University of Manitoba Winnipeg, MN R3T 2M6 E-mail: Nicola Koper (nicola.koper@umanitoba.ca).

10295 ■ James L. Baillie Student Research Award *(Undergraduate/Grant)*

Purpose: To support students in their research of Canadian birds in their natural environment, projects which contribute to preservation of birds, and projects which disseminate knowledge of birds. **Focus:** Ornithology. **Qualif.:** Applicants must be SCO-SOC members to be eligible (Note: Member-

Awards are arranged alphabetically below their administering organizations

ship is based on the calendar year so will expire on December 31st of the year in which you register, while registration after October 1st will be valid through December 31st of the following year. Multi-year memberships will be treated similarly, expiring on December 31st of the last year for which you register.). **Criteria:** Selection will be based on the committee's criteria.

Funds Avail.: 2,000 Canadian Dollars. **Duration:** Annual. **Number Awarded:** 1. **To Apply:** A single application can be made to apply for all 3 types of student research awards. Download the application form (including instructions) for the 2020 awards. **Deadline:** March 2. **Remarks:** Established in memory of James L. Baillie and shall be for research that is consistent with the objectives of the James L. Baillie Memorial Fund. **Contact:** Dr. Nicola Koper Chair, SCO-SOC Student Awards Committee Natural Resources Institute, University of Manitoba Winnipeg, MN R3T 2M6 E-mail: Nicola Koper (nicola.koper@umanitoba.ca).

10296 ■ Taverner Awards *(Undergraduate/Grant)*

Purpose: To support people with limited or no access to major funding, regardless of professional status, who are undertaking ornithological work in Canada. **Focus:** Ornithology. **Qualif.:** Applicant must be any student who is enrolled in a Canadian university; must be SCO-SOC members to be eligible. **Criteria:** Selection will be based on the committee's criteria.

Funds Avail.: 2,000 Canadian Dollars each. **Duration:** Annual. **Number Awarded:** 2. **Remarks:** Established to honor Percy A. Taverner and to further his accomplishments in increasing the knowledge of Canadian birds through research, conservation, and public education. **Contact:** Applications should be emailed to: Colleen Barber, Chair, SCO-SOC Student Awards Committee, Department of Biology, St. Mary's University, Halifax, NS B3H 3C3; Phone: 902-496-8126; Email: colleen.barber@smu.ca.

10297 ■ Society of Cardiovascular Anesthesiologists (SCA)

8735 W Higgins Rd., Ste. 300
Chicago, IL 60631
Ph: (847)375-6313
Free: 855-658-2828
E-mail: info@scahq.org
URL: www.scahq.org
Social Media: www.facebook.com/
SocietyofCardiovascularAnesthesiologists
www.instagram.com/sca.hq
twitter.com/scahq

10298 ■ SCA/IARS Starter Grant *(Graduate/Grant)*

Purpose: To support research in cardiac, vascular, and thoracic anesthesiology. **Focus:** Anesthesiology.

Funds Avail.: $25,000. **Duration:** Annual; For Two Years. **Number Awarded:** varies. **To Apply:** Curriculum Vitae of the PI & scientific mentor; Letter from the department Chair; Letters of support from all co-investigators; Research Plan; 2 Pages of Budget; 1 page of Budget Justification; 1 page of study Approval; 1 page of Related studies; 1 page of other Grants. **Contact:** Phone: 855-658-2828; E-mail: info@scahq.org.

10299 ■ Society of Children's Book Writers and Illustrators (SCBWI)

4727 Wilshire Blvd., Ste. 301
Los Angeles, CA 90010

Ph: (323)782-1010
Fax: (323)782-1892
E-mail: scbwi@scbwi.org
URL: www.scbwi.org
Social Media: www.facebook.com/SCBWI
instagram.com/scbwi
pinterest.com/scbwi
twitter.com/scbwi

10300 ■ Don Freeman Illustrator Grants *(Advanced Professional/Grant)*

Purpose: To enable picture book illustrators to further their understanding, training and work in the picture book genre. **Focus:** Literature, Children's. **Qualif.:** Applicants must be published or pre-published illustrators who are currently members of SCBWI (regardless of membership level) that are working on a picture book or their portfolio. **Criteria:** Selection will be based on the committee's criteria.

Funds Avail.: $1,000. **Duration:** Annual. **Number Awarded:** 2. **To Apply:** Applicants who are published illustrators must submit a rough picture book dummy that includes the entire text of the story and two finished illustrations; pre-published illustrator applicants must submit ten finished illustrations that would make a suitable portfolio presentation expressly intended for children's picture books; at least eight illustrations must be in color; send one of these requirements as a single PDF entitled with the applicants' name (first name_last name.pdf). **Deadline:** March 31. **Contact:** Sarah Baker, sarahbaker@scbwi.org.

10301 ■ Martha Weston Grant *(Advanced Professional/Grant)*

Purpose: To encourage authors and illustrators to nurture their creativity in a different genre of children's books. **Focus:** Literature, Children's. **Qualif.:** Applicants must be current SCBWI member and a PAL published author or illustrator trying another genre of children's books. **Criteria:** Selection will be based on the committee's criteria.

Funds Avail.: $1,500. **Duration:** Annual. **Number Awarded:** 1. **To Apply:** Applicants must send a 500 to 1000 word letter explaining about the applicants' publishing history, how they switched to another genres, concrete information about what they want to work on and why, and expectations of what they can get from the conference; only e-mail submissions (with no attachments) will be accepted. **Deadline:** May 1. **Contact:** Lissa Rovetch, Martha Weston Grant Coordinator, mwestgrant@gmail.com.

10302 ■ Multicultural Work-in-Progress Grant *(Advanced Professional/Grant)*

Purpose: To assist children's books writers and illustrators in the publication of a specific project currently not under contract. **Focus:** Literature, Children's. **Qualif.:** Applicants must be a current SCBWI member when their work is submitted and when the award is announced in September. **Criteria:** Selection will be based on the committee's criteria.

Funds Avail.: No specific amount. **Duration:** Annual. **Number Awarded:** 1. **To Apply:** Applicants must submit the application electronically in the form of one PDF. Application must include: a first page that contains the name, manuscript title, grant category, a doubled-spaced synopsis maximum of 250 words and; the first 10 pages of the completed manuscript; application can be no longer than 11 pages total and must title the PDF with the applicants' name (first_last.pdf). **Deadline:** March 31. **Contact:** grants@scbwi.org.

Awards are arranged alphabetically below their administering organizations

10303 ■ SCBWI Work-in-Progress Awards (WIP)
(Advanced Professional/Award)

Purpose: To assist children's books writers and illustrators in the publication of a specific project currently not under contract. **Focus:** Literature, Children's. **Qualif.:** Applicants must be a current SCBWI member when your work is submitted and when the award is announced in September. **Criteria:** Selection will be based on the committee's criteria.

Funds Avail.: No specific amount. **Duration:** Annual. **Number Awarded:** 1. **To Apply:** Applicant must submit the application electronically in the form of one PDF file. Application must include a first page that contains the applicant's name, manuscript title, grant category, a doubled-spaced synopsis, maximum of 250 words; and the first 10 pages of the completed manuscript. Application can be no longer than 11 pages total and must title the PDF with the applicants name (first_last.pdf). **Deadline:** March 31. **Remarks:** Established in 1998. **Contact:** E-mail: wipgrant@scbwi.org.

10304 ■ Student Illustrator Scholarship *(Undergraduate, Graduate/Scholarship)*

Purpose: To provide conference tuition for outstanding students studying illustration. **Focus:** Literature, Children's. **Qualif.:** Applicants must be currently enrolled as full time graduate or undergraduate students at an accredited educational institution; cannot have published a picture book or have received this scholarship before; interested applicants may apply even if they have applied to the SIS in the past, as long as they are still full time students and have not won. **Criteria:** Selection will be chosen by a rotating jury composed of three industry professionals.

Funds Avail.: No specific amount. **Duration:** Annual. **Number Awarded:** 4. **To Apply:** Applicants must include a description in 250 words or less of why the applicants wish to attend the SCBWI Conference (description must be in the body of the email, not in a separate attachment); three samples of the applicants' children's books-style illustrations in separate attachments (not in one pdf) - the title of each file must have the format of "first name_last name_1" (please do not include titles of the pieces besides this naming convention); a letter of recommendation from an illustration faculty member - the letter should be emailed directly from the faculty member, it must be in the body of the email, not in a separate attachment with the subject label "SIS recommendation (Student Name)" and; applicants' address, full name as it is listed in their school's records, phone number and a photo of the applicants' current student I.D; the subject line of the email must be structured as follows: SIS (applicant's name). **Deadline:** Summer Conference May 21; Winter Conference November 1. **Contact:** E-mail: sarahbaker@scbwi.org.

10305 ■ Student Writer Scholarship *(Graduate, Doctorate, Undergraduate/Scholarship)*

Purpose: To support outstanding students in the Summer and Winter Conferences for full-time university students in an English or Creative Writing program. **Focus:** Literature, Children's. **Qualif.:** Applicants must be full-time students enrolled in an accredited educational institution, at least eighteen years old and must be unpublished writers and don't have any contract prior to receiving the award. **Criteria:** Selection will be one winner chosen from a graduate or doctoral program and one winner will be chosen from an undergraduate program.

Funds Avail.: No specific amount. **Duration:** Annual. **Number Awarded:** 2. **To Apply:** Applicants must submit the fol-

lowing requirements short cover letter stating the reasons why applicants want to attend at the conference and a synopsis of their work; five-page sample of a manuscript; copy of the applicants' student ID and; letter of recommendation sent directly from a professor at the applicants' university; must be electronically submitted as one PDF and letters of recommendation can be sent separately as a Word document; and Label the subject of the e-mail "First Name_Last Name Application". **Deadline:** Summer Conference May 21; Winter Conference October 2. **Contact:** Email: sarahdiamond@scbwi.org.

10306 ■ Tribute Fund Community Grant *(Professional development/Grant)*

Purpose: To commemorate members of the children's book community, their lives, and their work by funding all-expense scholarships to the SCBWI International Summer and Winter Conferences for the general membership. **Focus:** Literature, Children's. **Qualif.:** Regional advisors nominate members from their region who are on the verge of a breakthrough, have given a significant contribution to their region, and could not afford to attend the conference otherwise. **Criteria:** Selection will be based on application process.

Funds Avail.: No specific amount. **To Apply:** Applicants may contact the Association for nomination process and other information. **Contact:** Submissions must be sent to the following address: SCBWI Amber Brown Grant, 4727 Wilshire Blvd., Ste. 301, Los Angeles, CA, 90010; Phone: 323-782-1010.

10307 ■ Jane Yolen Mid-List Author Grant *(Professional development/Grant)*

Purpose: To honor and recognize the contribution of mid-list authors. **Focus:** Literature, Children's. **Qualif.:** Must be a current SCBWI member who has published at least two PAL books, but has not sold anything for at least five years.

Funds Avail.: $3,000. **Duration:** Annual. **Number Awarded:** 2. **To Apply:** Applicants must fill out the online application form available in website including career statement. **Deadline:** November 1. **Contact:** Email: sarahdiamond@scbwi.org.

10308 ■ Society for Cinema and Media Studies (SCMS)
Wallace Old Science Hall, Rm. 300
640 Parrington Oval
Norman, OK 73019
Ph: (405)325-8075
E-mail: scms-office@ou.edu
URL: www.cmstudies.org

10309 ■ Anne Friedberg Innovative Scholarship Award *(Other/Scholarship)*

Purpose: To recognize innovative works that expand the discipline of film and media studies, emphasizing its relationship to other visual fields, including architect, art history and digital media. **Focus:** Filmmaking; Media arts. **Qualif.:** Applicants must be authors of books or media projects; first books are eligible, but no book may compete for more than one SCMS award.

Funds Avail.: $1,000. **Duration:** Annual. **To Apply:** Applicants must complete the nomination form and send four copies of eligible books or include instructions for accessing online media projects to the SCMS office. **Contact:**

Awards are arranged alphabetically below their administering organizations

Society for Cinema and Media Studies, Anne Friedberg Award, 640 Parrington Oval Old Science Hall, Rm. 300 Norman, Oklahoma, 73019.

10310 ■ Society for Classical Studies (SCS)

New York University
20 Cooper Sq., 2nd Fl.
New York, NY 10003
Fax: (212)995-3931
E-mail: info@classicalstudies.org
URL: classicalstudies.org
Social Media: twitter.com/scsclassics

10311 ■ Minority Scholarship in Classics and Classical Archaeology *(Undergraduate/Fellowship)*

Purpose: To provide financial assistance for undergraduate students who wish to pursue their preparation for graduate work in classical archeology. **Focus:** Archeology; Classical studies. **Qualif.:** Applicant must have (but not limited to) participated in classical summer programs or field schools in Italy, Greece or Egypt or language training at institutions in the U.S., Canada or Europe. **Criteria:** Candidates will be judged based on academic qualifications, quality of proposal and financial need.

Funds Avail.: $4,500. **Duration:** Annual. **Number Awarded:** 2. **To Apply:** Applicants must complete the application form together with a letter of application describing the applicant's career goals and plans with a list of other programs applied to; must have an undergraduate transcript; must provide two letters of recommendation by a faculty member or other professionals who have worked with the applicant during the past two years (at least one must be an APA or AIA member); one-page summary of the projected or actual budget. **Remarks:** Established in 1994. **Contact:** Helen Cullyer; E-mail: helen.cullyer@nyu.edu.

10312 ■ Thesaurus Linguae Latinae Fellowship (TTL) *(Doctorate/Fellowship)*

Purpose: To support American scholars who wish to broaden their knowledge in the work of Thesaurus Linguae Latinae Institute in Munich. **Focus:** Latin American studies; Philology. **Criteria:** Fellowships will be awarded to applicants who possess a thorough familiarity and special interest in the Latin languages, as well as advanced competence in Greek.

Funds Avail.: $50,400. **Duration:** Annual. **To Apply:** Applicants must submit a curriculum vitae and a statement of what benefits the applicants expects to derive from the fellowship for his or her research and teaching. Applicants must also provide three references. **Deadline:** November 6. **Contact:** Yelena Baraz; E-mail: ybaraz@princeton.edu; Phone: 212-992-7840.

10313 ■ Society for Conservation Biology (SCB)

1133 15th St. NW, Ste. 300
Washington, DC 20005
Ph: (202)234-4133
Fax: (703)995-4633
Free: 855-523-6070
E-mail: info@conbio.org
URL: www.conbio.org
Social Media: www.facebook.com/Society4ConBio
www.linkedin.com/company/society-for-conservation
-biology

twitter.com/Society4ConBio

10314 ■ David H. Smith Conservation Research Fellowship *(Postdoctorate/Fellowship)*

Purpose: To create opportunities for leading conservation scientists to strengthen their skills through two years of applied post-doctoral research, supplemented by training programs, peer networking, and field learning experiences. **Focus:** Biology.

Funds Avail.: $32,000 research fund; $57,000 annual salary; $8,000 travel budget. **Duration:** Annual; Two years. **To Apply:** Applications must be submitted electronically and must be in PDF or MS Word format; please include the applicants' last name in some part of the file name; research approaches may include comparative studies, synthetic analyses across sites, experimentation or observational studies, applied modelling or any combination; proposed research may include intensive work at one site, work at multiple sites, or comparative evaluations of studies by other scientists across many sites; in all cases, the central questions of the inquiry must be clearly articulated; proposed study sites must be noted; an explanation of how the results will inform conservation practice is required; the research plan, excluding literature cited, must not under any circumstances exceed 8 pages; font size must be at least 11 point, 2.5 cm margins; at least 1.5 line spacing; the cover letter, literature cited, personal statement, and curriculum vitae are not included in the 8-page limit for the research plan; the research plan should include the following; abstract, background section, statement of objectives, approaches and methods, anticipated results, research schedule and relevance to conservation science and practice; the complete application must include the following; cover letter; title page; research plan; applicants' curriculum vitae; personal statement; three letters of recommendation addressing the merits of the candidate and the candidate's proposal; sponsor support letter; sponsor's abbreviated curriculum vitae; support letter from practitioner mentor; indirect cost waiver; the personal statement should address the following questions, in at least 200 words; give an example(s) of an accomplishment you believe demonstrates your leadership skills or entrepreneurial abilities; how is your research cutting edge or innovative?; what will be the greatest impact of your research? who or what will be most greatly affected. **Deadline:** October 2. **Contact:** Email: smithinfo@smithfellows.org.

10315 ■ Society of Critical Care Medicine (SCCM)

500 Midway Dr.
Mount Prospect, IL 60056
Ph: (847)827-6869
Fax: (847)439-7226
E-mail: info@sccm.org
URL: www.sccm.org
Social Media: www.facebook.com/SCCM1
www.linkedin.com/company/society-of-critical-care
-medicine
twitter.com/SCCM
www.youtube.com/user/SCCM500

10316 ■ Norma J. Shoemaker Award for Critical Care Nursing Excellence *(Professional development/ Award)*

Purpose: To encourage research in critical care nursing and to provide funding for the continuation of research

Awards are arranged alphabetically below their administering organizations

endeavors. **Focus:** Medicine. **Criteria:** Selection will be on a competitive basis.

Funds Avail.: $1,000.00. **Duration:** Annual. **To Apply:** Applicants must provide one nomination letter and two letters of support are required. Individuals must be nominated by an active SCCM member; nomination letter must detail the nominee's contribution to critical care nursing excellence. This letter should validate the nominee's clinical, educational and/or leadership contributions relevant to critical care. The nominee's involvement in local, chapter or national SCCM committees or activities must be addressed; letters of support must be from SCCM Nursing Section members who are in good standing. Letters of support are preferred, but not required, upon submission of the nomination letter; must provide a resume or curriculum vitae. **Deadline:** September 1. **Remarks:** The award honors Norma J. Shoemaker, RN, MN, FCCM, the Society's first Executive Director. Established in 1992. **Contact:** For more information: Carol Prendergast.

10317 ■ Society of Dance History Scholars (SDHS)
3416 Primm Ln.
Birmingham, AL 35216
Ph: (414)908-4959
Fax: (414)768-8001
URL: sdhs.org
Social Media: www.facebook.com/Society-of-Dance
-History-Scholars-314188591925030
twitter.com/SDanceHS

10318 ■ Graduate Student Travel Grants *(Graduate, Other/Grant)*

Purpose: To help graduate students to defray costs of attending the annual conference. **Focus:** Dance. **Qualif.:** Applicants must be student members of SDHS; must be enrolled in a graduate degree program; and must be engaged in dance research. **Criteria:** Selection will be based on the committee's review of application materials.

Funds Avail.: No specific amount. **Duration:** Annual. **To Apply:** Applicants must submit application form online. **Deadline:** March 1. **Contact:** Ashanti Pretlow, Accounts Manager; info@sdhs.org.

10319 ■ Society for Economic Botany
PO Box 299
Saint Louis, MO 63166-0299
E-mail: seb@botany.org
URL: www.econbot.org
Social Media: www.facebook.com/SocietyEconomicBotany
twitter.com/SEBotany

10320 ■ Richard Evans Schultes Research Award *(Graduate/Award)*

Purpose: To provide funding support for research related to economic botany. **Focus:** Botany. **Qualif.:** Applicants must be graduate students who have received their degree within a year and must be members of the society. **Criteria:** Applicants will be judged by an ad-hoc committee of Society members.

Funds Avail.: $2,500. **Duration:** Annual. **Number Awarded:** Varies. **To Apply:** Applicants major advisor must confirm current MS, PhD or Post-doctoral status of the ap-

plicants through email message and must also provide a recommendation letter; must prepare in MS Word a 2-page description of the proposed research; a 1-page tabular budget; and a 1-page resume. Files must be named using first initial_lastname and must be sent electronically; selected recipients must submit a 1-2-page, double-spaced narrative of their project within nine months of receiving the award. **Deadline:** March 30. **Remarks:** Founded in honor of Dr. Richard Evans Schultes, the society's economic botanist. Established in 2001. **Contact:** Email: schultesaward@econbot.org.

10321 ■ Society of Emergency Medicine Physician Assistants (SEMPA)
4950 W Royal Ln.
Irving, TX 75063
Free: 877-297-7594
E-mail: sempa@sempa.org
URL: www.sempa.org
Social Media: www.facebook.com/sempa.org
twitter.com/sempa360

10322 ■ Paul S. Robinson Award *(Postgraduate/Award)*

Purpose: To financially support students who are pursuing a career in emergency medicine. **Focus:** Medicine. **Qualif.:** Applicants must be Physician Assistant students who plan to pursue a career in emergency medicine; must be current SEMPA members; a student in good standing of an ARC-PA accredited PA training program or a student in a post-graduate emergency medicine training program; should be in the final year of training; should be nominated by a program director or could be self-nomination. **Criteria:** Selection will be selected based on the initial review of completed application by the SEMPA award committee Chair; will be based on the submitted applications.

Funds Avail.: $3,000. **Duration:** Annual. **To Apply:** Applications can be submitted by online; must submit letter of endorsement from your program's director that includes declaration that you are in good standing with the training program; some indication of the applicant's academic performance should be included such as overall GPA while in the PA Program, class ranking, academic awards and clinical rotation evaluations; a current curriculum vitae; written narrative statement that is no more than two pages, single-spaced, 12-point font that addresses your dedication to emergency medicine, leadership and humanism; a letter of recommendation from a peer, colleague, co-worker, clinical preceptor or other faculty addressing the tenets of professionalism, leadership, and humanistic qualities and more than one letter is acceptable; a summary of any leadership positions held within your program, community, and/or service to other medical organizations; include any pertinent information on extent and duration of service or leadership position held; a brief description of any community service in which you've been involved in; this can include activities prior to and during your training program. **Deadline:** January 15. **Contact:** Paul Robinson Award, 4950 W. Royal Ln., Irving, TX, 75063-2524; Email: sempa@sempa.org.

10323 ■ Society of Environmental Toxicology and Chemistry (SETAC)
229 S Baylen St., 2nd Fl.
Pensacola, FL 32502

Awards are arranged alphabetically below their administering organizations

Ph: (850)469-1500
Fax: (888)296-4136
E-mail: setac@setac.org
URL: www.setac.org
Social Media: www.facebook.com/setacworld
www.linkedin.com/company/setacworld
twitter.com/SETAC_world
www.youtube.com/user/setacworld

10324 ■ SETAC/EA Jeff Black Fellowship Award
(Postgraduate/Fellowship)

Purpose: To recognize and support an outstanding Master's level student from anywhere in the world. **Focus:** Chemistry. **Qualif.:** Applicants must be current SETAC members (worldwide) and Master's students in any field of study encompassed by SETAC, or entering Master's students. **Criteria:** Selection will be evaluating all proposals by using a standardized score sheet.

Funds Avail.: $2,000. **Duration:** Annual. **To Apply:** Applications must include a cover page containing title of award, name and mailing address of applicant; a statement of interest in their field of study (including research interests, if formulated) 3 page maximum; transcripts of all completed undergraduate course work; three letters of recommendation; letter from applicant's Master's program advisor (could be one of the three above); curriculum vitae (resume); one Master's degree research proposal; one high resolution photo. **Deadline:** June 12. **Remarks:** The award was established in recognition of Jeff Black's life in science and his contributions to SETAC. Established in 1998. **Contact:** Laura Swanson; Email: laura.swanson@setac.org.

10325 ■ Society for Ethnomusicology (SEM)
Indiana University
800 E 3rd St.
Bloomington, IN 47405
Ph: (812)855-6672
E-mail: sem@indiana.edu
URL: www.ethnomusicology.org
Social Media: twitter.com/SEM_Office

10326 ■ Ida Halpern Fellowship and Award
(Doctorate/Fellowship)

Purpose: To help support research on Native American Music of the United States and Canada and to recognize the publication of said research. **Focus:** Musicology. **Qualif.:** Applicants must be recent Ph.Ds. or Ph.D. candidates who have completed all program requirements except dissertation research. **Criteria:** Preference will be given to a person planning to do research based on Dr. Halpern's collection of Northwest Coast music.

Funds Avail.: $1,000 - post-publication; $4,000 - research fellowship. **Duration:** Biennial. **To Apply:** Applicant application consists of: Research proposal, typed, not to exceed four single-spaced pages; proposed budget; current vita; names, addresses, and phone numbers of two references; letter from Graduate Program advisor verifying completion of all program requirements except dissertation research if applicant is a Ph.D. candidate; letter indicating Native American community support, if new research is proposed. **Deadline:** April 1.

10327 ■ Society of Exploration Geophysicists (SEG)
8801 S Yale, Ste. 500
Tulsa, OK 74137

Ph: (918)497-5581
E-mail: advertising@seg.org
URL: www.seg.org
Social Media: www.facebook.com/SEGeophysicists
www.instagram.com/segeophysicists/
www.linkedin.com/company/seg
twitter.com/SEG_org
www.youtube.com/user/segeophysicists

10328 ■ Society of Exploration Geophysicists Scholarships *(Graduate, Undergraduate/Scholarship, Monetary, Award)*

Purpose: To encourage the study of geophysics and related geosciences provide financial support to students who are studying geophysics'. **Focus:** Geosciences. **Qualif.:** Applicant must be a student pursuing a college curriculum directed toward a career in applied geophysics, or a closely related field such as geosciences, physics, geology, or earth and environmental sciences; must be attending high school and planning to enter college next fall or be an undergraduate or graduate college student whose grades are above average. **Criteria:** Selection will be based on merit.

Funds Avail.: $500-$10,000. **Number Awarded:** Varies. **To Apply:** Applicants must submit a completed scholarship application form; must include current transcripts; include email addresses for two faculty members who have agreed to serve as references. **Deadline:** March 1. **Contact:** Nominations should be sent to: SEG Honors and Awards Committee, c/o SEG Business Office, 8801 S Yale Ave., Ste. 500, Tulsa, OK 74137-2740; Fax: 918-497-5558; E-mail: honorsandawards@seg.org.

10329 ■ Society of Family Planning (SFP)
PO Box 18342
Denver, CO 80218
Free: 866-584-6758
E-mail: info@societyfp.org
URL: www.societyfp.org
Social Media: www.facebook.com/societyfp
twitter.com/SocietyFP

10330 ■ SFP Junior Investigator's Career Development Awards *(Other/Grant)*

Purpose: To support the achievement of health objectives. **Focus:** Family planning. **Qualif.:** Applicants must be SFP full or junior fellows who hold full-time assistant professor faculty positions, function at that rank in an academic setting, or function at an equivalent level in a nonacademic setting; must be within five years from the granting of their last graduate degree. **Criteria:** Selection will be based on academic and intellectual background; motivation; commitment to pursue clinical and translational research; assessment of candidate's potential; dedication to the clinical or translational research; the degree of support from the department.

Funds Avail.: Amount varies. **Duration:** Two years. **To Apply:** Applicants must provide contact details for the applicant, institution, and parties responsible for accounts payable and grants management should the project be funded; provide a summary description of the proposedResearch; do not include proprietary information:if the proposal is funded, the abstract may beused by SFPRF for

Awards are arranged alphabetically below their administering organizations

informational purposes todescribe its program activities. **Deadline:** March 8.

10331 ■ SFP Mid-Career/Mentor Award *(Other/Grant)*

Purpose: To support junior researchers conducting clinical/social science research in family planning and provides additional funding for pilot studies. **Focus:** Biological and clinical sciences; Family planning; Social sciences.

Funds Avail.: $40,000.

10332 ■ SFP Student Research Grants *(Graduate/Grant)*

Purpose: To aid the development of graduate-level students who want to pursue research-oriented careers in the field of family planning. **Focus:** Family planning. **Qualif.:** Applicants must be actively pursuing their medical degree; enrolled in a residency or graduate program at the time of application and award.

Funds Avail.: $150,000. **Duration:** Annual. **To Apply:** Applicants must submit a completed application form; a narrative with a maximum of four pages (font must be at least 11 points, all margins at least one inch and 1.5 spacing - applications that do not adhere to these requirements will be disqualified); letter from project supervisor; IRB documentation.

10333 ■ Society For Industrial and Organizational Psychology (SIOP)

440 E Poe Rd., Ste. 101
Bowling Green, OH 43402
Ph: (419)353-0032
Fax: (419)352-2645
E-mail: siop@siop.org
URL: www.siop.org
Social Media: www.linkedin.com/company/society-for
  -industrial-and-organizational-psychology-siop-/
twitter.com/SIOPtweets

10334 ■ Lee Hakel Graduate Student Scholarship *(Graduate/Scholarship)*

Purpose: To support the research of graduate students pursuing doctoral study in industrial-organizational psychology. **Focus:** Psychology. **Qualif.:** Applicants must be student affiliates of SIOP; must have an approved plan for their dissertation; each program may endorse no more than one student per year; if more than one student from a program wishes to apply for a scholarship, the program must perform an initial screening; those who have already defended their dissertations or are past recipients or recipients of other SIOP sponsored scholarships are not eligible. **Criteria:** Selection proposals will be evaluated with respect to the following criteria: clearly expressed understanding of the field of inquiry; ability of the research design to provide meaningful answers to questions posed by the researcher; potential of the proposed study to make significant theoretical and application contributions to the field of Industrial-Organizational Psychology.

Funds Avail.: $3,500. **Duration:** Annual. **Number Awarded:** 1. **To Apply:** Applicants must submit a 12-page maximum summary of the dissertation research, including an explanation of research design and other important aspects of the project; must provide a two-page maximum curriculum vitae including scientific publications and presentations; must have a letter from the advisor indicating that the dissertation plan has been approved; must

have a letter of endorsement from the chair or director of the program in which the applicant is enrolled. **Deadline:** June 30.

10335 ■ Leslie W. Joyce and Paul W. Thayer Graduate Fellowship in I-O Psychology *(Graduate/Fellowship)*

Purpose: To provide financial support to doctoral students in industrial-organizational (I-O) psychology who are specializing in training and development and/or selection and placement. **Focus:** Psychology.

Funds Avail.: $10,000. **Duration:** Annual. **Number Awarded:** 1. **To Apply:** Applicants must submit an electronic copy of undergraduate and graduate transcripts; statement of graduate program goals and career aspirations; summary of the nominee's master's thesis or summary of the other completed research not to exceed 10 pages; resume that includes work assignments, paid or unpaid, related to I-O psychology; letter of recommendation from the graduate faculty and endorsement letter from the university.

10336 ■ Mary L. Tenopyr Graduate Student Scholarship *(Graduate/Scholarship)*

Purpose: To support the research of graduate students pursuing doctoral study in industrial-organizational psychology. **Focus:** Psychology. **Qualif.:** Applicant must be a full time and in good standing in a doctoral program in Industrial-Organizational Psychology or a closely related field (e.g., organizational behavior) at a regionally accredited university or college; must be a Student Affiliate of SIOP; dissertation plan has been approved by the student's advisor; is not limited to U.S students. **Criteria:** Selection proposals will be evaluated with respect to the following criteria: clearly expressed understanding of the field of inquiry; ability of the research design to provide meaningful answers to questions posed by the researcher; potential of the proposed study to make significant theoretical and application contributions to the field of Industrial-Organizational Psychology.

Funds Avail.: $3,000. **Duration:** Annual. **Number Awarded:** 1. **To Apply:** Applicants must submit a 12-page maximum summary of the dissertation research, including an explanation of research design and other important aspects of the project; a two-page maximum curriculum vitae including scientific publications and presentations; a letter from the advisor indicating that the dissertation plan has been approved; a letter of endorsement from the chair or director of the program in which the applicant is enrolled. **Deadline:** June.

10337 ■ Society of General Internal Medicine (SGIM)

1500 King St., Ste. 303
Alexandria, VA 22314
Ph: (202)887-5150
Free: 800-822-3060
URL: www.sgim.org
Social Media: www.facebook.com/SocietyGIM
www.linkedin.com/society-of-general-internal-medicine
  -sgim-
twitter.com/SocietyGIM

10338 ■ Lawrence S. Linn Research Grant *(Undergraduate, Graduate, Advanced Professional/Grant)*

Purpose: To provide financial support to young researchers and practitioners working to improve the quality of HIV/

Awards are arranged alphabetically below their administering organizations

AIDS care. **Focus:** Medicine. **Qualif.:** Applicants may include SGIM members (associates or full), students, degree candidates, fellows, or faculty members early in their research careers. **Criteria:** Selection will be based on originality, significance, methodological rigor, Likelihood of being completed.

Funds Avail.: $5,000. **Duration:** Annual. **Deadline:** January 8. **Remarks:** Established in 1999.

10339 ■ Scholarship in Medical Education Award
(Advanced Professional, Professional development/ Scholarship)

Purpose: To improve medical education on a national level. **Focus:** Medicine. **Qualif.:** Applicant must be a member or an associate member of SCIM who is in the early or middle phases of their career. **Criteria:** Selection will be judged based on the originality, quality, and generalizability of their work.

Duration: Annual. **To Apply:** Application must be attached with one or two page letter of recommendation from the nominee's supervisor or mentor, that should include a description of the nominee's role in one of the above three types of scholarship; Curriculum Vitae. **Deadline:** January 8. **Remarks:** Established in 1998.

10340 ■ Society of Georgia Archivists (SGA)
PO Box 688
Decatur, GA 30031
E-mail: president@soga.org
URL: soga.wildapricot.org
Social Media: www.facebook.com/
 SocietyOfGeorgiaArchivists
www.instagram.com/society_of_ga_archivists
twitter.com/GA_Archivists

10341 ■ Brenda S. Bank Educational Workshop Scholarship *(Undergraduate/Scholarship)*

Purpose: To provide funding to attend the SGA-sponsored Spring/Summer Workshop as scheduled by the Education Committee. **Focus:** General studies/Field of study not specified. **Criteria:** Preference will be given to applicants who do not have access to institutional support for attending the SGA Spring/Summer Workshop.

Funds Avail.: No specific amount. **Duration:** Annual. **Number Awarded:** 2. **To Apply:** Applicants must submit their details in online scholarship application form. **Deadline:** March 20. **Remarks:** Established in 2008. **Contact:** Muriel Jackson, SGA Scholarship Committee, Washington Memorial Library, 1180 Washington Ave., Macon, Georgia 31201; E-mail: scholarships@soga.org.

10342 ■ Anthony R. Dees Educational Workshop Scholarship *(Graduate/Scholarship)*

Purpose: To provide funding to attend the SGA-sponsored Pre-Conference Workshop. **Focus:** General studies/Field of study not specified. **Criteria:** Recipients are selected based on the academic performance and financial need; Preferences will be given to applicants who do not have access to institutional support for attending the Georgia Archives Institute.

Funds Avail.: No specific amount. **Duration:** Annual. **To Apply:** Applicants must submit their details in online scholarship application form; strongly encouraged to submit their applications well in advance of the deadline to avoid

problems. **Deadline:** September 7. **Remarks:** The scholarship was named by SGA members at the 2007 SGA Annual Meeting in honor of long-time member Tony Dees. Established in 2008. **Contact:** Muriel Jackson, SGA Scholarship Committee, Washington Memorial Library, 1180 Washington Ave., Macon, Georgia 31201; E-mail: scholarships@soga.org.

10343 ■ Larry Gulley Scholarship *(Undergraduate/ Scholarship)*

Purpose: To enhance archival education, membership, and participation in the profession. **Focus:** General studies/ Field of study not specified. **Criteria:** Recipients are selected based on the academic performance and financial need; Preferences will be given to applicants who do not have access to institutional support for attending the Georgia Archives Institute.

Funds Avail.: Varies. **Duration:** Annual. **To Apply:** Applicants must submit their details in online scholarship application form; strongly encouraged to submit their applications well in advance of the deadline to avoid problems. **Deadline:** August 31. **Remarks:** The scholarship is named for Larry Gulley, a loyal member of the Society of Georgia Archivists who gave stellar service to the organization in many capacities. **Contact:** Muriel Jackson, SGA Scholarship Committee, Washington Memorial Library, 1180 Washington Ave., Macon, Georgia 31201; E-mail: scholarships@soga.org.

10344 ■ Carroll Hart Scholarship *(Graduate/ Scholarship)*

Purpose: To enhance archival education and membership. **Focus:** General studies/Field of study not specified. **Qualif.:** Applicants who are eligible are those engaged in compensated or volunteer archival work at any level in an institution in the state of Georgia, SGA members employed outside the state of Georgia, graduate students preparing for a career in archives at a college or university in Georgia or SGA students studying outside of Georgia. **Criteria:** Recipients are selected based on the academic performance and financial need; Preferences will be given to applicants who do not have access to institutional support for attending the Georgia Archives Institute.

Funds Avail.: $500. **Duration:** Annual. **To Apply:** Applicants must submit their details in online scholarship application form. Applicants are strongly encouraged to submit their applications well in advance of the deadline to avoid problems. **Deadline:** March 15. **Contact:** E-mail: scholarships@soga.org.

10345 ■ Society of Health and Physical Educators (SHAPE)
1900 Association Dr.
Reston, VA 20191
Ph: (703)476-3400
Fax: (703)476-9527
Free: 800-213-7193
E-mail: education@shapeamerica.org
URL: www.shapeamerica.org

10346 ■ Ruth Abernathy Presidential Scholarship
(Professional development, Graduate/Scholarship)

Purpose: To recognize and support individuals for their significant contributions in the field of sport and physical activity. **Focus:** General studies/Field of study not speci-

Awards are arranged alphabetically below their administering organizations

fied. **Qualif.:** Applicant must be a current member of SHAPE America; must be graduate students; must be majoring in the field of health, physical education, recreation or dance; must be enrolled in a matriculated full-time masters or doctoral program; must have a minimum grade point average of 3.5 overall on a 4.0 grade point scale. **Criteria:** Selection will be based on scholastic proficiency, evidence of leadership, school, community, professional activity/service, character attributes.

Funds Avail.: $1,750. **Duration:** Annual. **Number Awarded:** 2. **To Apply:** Applications can be submitted online; should submit a letter from your school's dean or registrar indicating full-time status; documentation must be provided in a Microsoft Word or PDF format; three letters of recommendation signed and titled; scanned copy of official transcripts from all colleges or universities attended; biographical sketch. **Deadline:** October 15. **Remarks:** Established in 1995. **Contact:** CEO Office, SHAPE America, 1900 Association Dr., Reston, VA, 20191; Email Patti Hartle at phartle@shapeamerica.org.

10347 ■ Ruth Abernathy Presidential Undergraduate Scholarship (Undergraduate/Scholarship, Fellowship, Award, Monetary)

Purpose: To honor and support deserving students in their educational pursuit. **Focus:** Education, Physical; Health education. **Qualif.:** Applicant must be a current member of SHAPE America(may join at the time of application) and be majoring in the field of health, physical education, recreation or dance; must have college junior or senior class standing at a baccalaureate granting College or university (completed a minimum of 60 semester/90 quarter units of college Courses); must have a minimum grade point average of 3.5 overall on a 4.0 grade point scale; must be a first time Ruth Abernathy Presidential Scholarship recipient. **Criteria:** Selection will be based on scholastic proficiency, evidence of leadership, school, community, professional activity services and character attributes.

Funds Avail.: $1,250 each. **Duration:** Annual. **Number Awarded:** Varies. **To Apply:** Applications must be submitted along with a letter from your school's dean or registrar indicating full-time status; three letters of recommendation signed and titled which address all aspects of the selection criteria (two pages each); scanned copy of official transcripts from all colleges or universities attended in pursuit of current degree; biographical sketch to be used for publication and for the official convention award presentation. **Deadline:** October 15. **Remarks:** Established in 1995. **Contact:** Patti Hartle; Email: phartle@shapeamerica.org.

10348 ■ Barbara A. Cooley Master's Scholarship (Master's/Scholarship, Award, Monetary)

Purpose: To provide support to a master's level student who is currently enrolled in a health education program. **Focus:** Health education. **Qualif.:** Applicant must be master's level student who is currently enrolled in a health education program at an accredited college/university in the United States or a U.S. territory; must have a minimum current overall grade point average of 3.0 on a 4.0 scale.

Funds Avail.: $1,000. **Duration:** Annual. **Number Awarded:** 1. **To Apply:** Applicant must submit curriculum vitae; attach a narrative three-part essay that includes your philosophy of health education, your professional goals, and your assessment of current and future issues in health education; two letters of recommendation; current official transcript. **Deadline:** October 15.

10349 ■ Bill Kane Undergraduate Scholarship (Undergraduate/Scholarship, Award, Monetary)

Purpose: To provide support to an undergraduate health education major. **Focus:** Health education. **Qualif.:** Applicant must be student officially recognized as an undergraduate health education major at an accredited college/university in the United States or a U.S. Territory; must currently be enrolled at a university/college full time (12 hrs.) for both the fall and spring semesters of the academic year during which the recipient is applying; must have sophomore, junior, or senior status at the time of application; must have a minimum, current overall GPA of 3.25 on a 4.0 scale; must be active in health education profession related activities, organizations, at the university/college, and/or the community. **Criteria:** Selection will be based on evidence of leadership potential; be academically talented; be active in health education profession-related activities or organizations at the college or university and/or community level.

Funds Avail.: $1,000. **Duration:** Annual. **Number Awarded:** 1 in 2018. **To Apply:** Applicant must submit a double-spaced, typed personal essay including health education, career interests, life goals, what applicant hopes to accomplish as a health educator in training and in the future, and the attributes and aspirations the applicant brings to the field of health education (essay must be approximately 400-450 words in length). Must also submit three letters of recommendation from professors; a current, official transcript of all college study completed including the fall semester; and current resume. **Deadline:** October 15.

10350 ■ Society of Hispanic Professional Engineers (SHPE)

13181 Crossroads Pky. N, Ste. 450
City of Industry, CA 91746
Ph: (323)725-3970
Fax: (323)725-0316
E-mail: shpenational@shpe.org
URL: www.shpe.org
Social Media: www.facebook.com/shpenational
www.instagram.com/shpenational/
www.linkedin.com/company/society-of-hispanic
  -professional-engineers/
twitter.com/SHPE
www.youtube.com/user/SHPENational

10351 ■ SHPE Dissertation Scholarship (Doctorate/Scholarship)

Purpose: To financially assist doctoral candidates who demonstrate both significant motivation and aptitude for a career in science, technology, engineering or mathematics. **Focus:** Engineering; Mathematics and mathematical sciences; Science; Technology. **Qualif.:** Applicants must be STEM doctoral degree program in the U.S. or Puerto Rico; must have minimum 2.75 GPA; must be full time student; must be a member of SHPE. **Criteria:** Applicants will be selected based on merit and financial need.

Funds Avail.: $5,000. **Duration:** Annual; Fall and Spring terms. **Number Awarded:** 1. **To Apply:** Applicants must submit a photo/video release form, a student profile including a professional head-shot photo, updated resume, transcripts, and any other official documentation. **Deadline:** May 31. **Contact:** E-mail: scholarships@shpe.org.

Awards are arranged alphabetically below their administering organizations

10352 ■ SHPE Professional Scholarship (Master's, Doctorate/Scholarship)

Purpose: To help defray the cost of SHPE professionals who demonstrate significant motivation in pursuing their graduate education. **Focus:** Engineering; Mathematics and mathematical sciences; Science; Technology. **Qualif.:** Applicants must be employed full-time in the U.S. or Puerto Rico in a technical career field; must be enrolled in a STEM masters or doctoral degree program; must have minimum 2.75 GPA; must be a half-time student; must be a member of SHPE. **Criteria:** Recipients will be selected based on merit.

Funds Avail.: $2,000. **Duration:** Fall and Spring terms. **To Apply:** Applicants must submit a photo/video release form, a student profile including a professional head-shot photo, updated resume, transcripts, and any other official documentation. **Deadline:** May 31.

10353 ■ Society for Historians of American Foreign Relations (SHAFR)
1301 E Main St.
Murfreesboro, TN 37132
Ph: (617)458-6156
Fax: (615)898-5881
URL: www.shafr.org
Social Media: www.facebook.com/shafr

10354 ■ Samuel Flagg Bemis Dissertation Research Grants (Graduate/Grant)

Purpose: To help defray the costs of domestic or international travel necessary to conduct research on significant scholarly projects. **Focus:** International affairs and relations. **Qualif.:** Applicants must be actively working on dissertations dealing with some aspect of U.S. foreign relations history; membership in SHAFR is required. **Criteria:** Selection will be based on the committee's criteria.

Funds Avail.: Up to $2,000. **Duration:** Annual. **Number Awarded:** Varies. **To Apply:** Applicants must complete application which can be downloaded at the website; must submit a cover sheet (available at website) with project narrative; budget and justification; one-page CV; and a letter of recommendation; all application materials (including the cover sheet but excluding letters of recommendation), should be in a single document (doc, pdf, rtf) and submit it via e-mail with a subject line which contains the last name of the applicant only; letters of recommendation should be sent separately. **Deadline:** October 15. **Contact:** E-mail: fellowships@shafr.org.

10355 ■ Robert A. and Barbara Divine Graduate Student Travel Fund (Graduate/Grant)

Purpose: To assist graduate students who present papers at the conference. **Focus:** International affairs and relations. **Qualif.:** Applicants must be graduate students who will present papers at the annual meetings of SHAFR. **Criteria:** Selection will be based on the committee's criteria.

Funds Avail.: Amount varies. **Duration:** Annual. **Remarks:** The award was established to honor Professor and Mrs. Robert A. Divine. Established in 2006. **Contact:** E-mail: program-chair@shafr.org.

10356 ■ The Michael J. Hogan Foreign Language Fellowship (Graduate/Fellowship)

Purpose: To support graduate students defray the costs of studying foreign languages needed for research. **Focus:**

Foreign languages. **Qualif.:** Applicants must be graduate students conducting research on some aspect of U.S. foreign relations history, and be members of SHAFR. **Criteria:** Recipients will be selected based on submitted application.

Funds Avail.: Up to $4,000. **Number Awarded:** 1. **To Apply:** Applicants must complete application can be downloaded at the website; must submit a cover sheet (available at website) with project narrative; budget and justification; one-page CV; and a letter of recommendation; all application materials (including the cover sheet but excluding letters of recommendation), should be in a single document (doc, pdf, rtf) and submit it via e-mail with a subject line which contains the last name of the applicant only; letters of recommendation should be sent separately. **Deadline:** October 15. **Remarks:** The fellowship was established to honor Michael J. Hogan, long-time editor of Diplomatic History. **Contact:** E-mail: hogan-fellowships@shafr.org.

10357 ■ Lawrence Gelfand - Armin Rappaport - Walter LaFeber Dissertation Fellowship (Graduate/Fellowship)

Purpose: To help defray the costs of travel in conducting a research on a significant dissertation project. **Focus:** International affairs and relations. **Qualif.:** Applicants must be actively working on dissertations dealing with some aspect of U.S. foreign relations history; membership in SHAFR is required. **Criteria:** Selection will be based on the committee's criteria.

Funds Avail.: Up to $4,000. **Duration:** Annual. **Number Awarded:** 1. **To Apply:** Applicants must complete application can be downloaded at the website; must submit a cover sheet (available at website) with project narrative; budget and justification; one-page CV; and a letter of recommendation; all application materials (including the cover sheet but excluding letters of recommendation), should be in a single document (doc, pdf, rtf) and submit it via e-mail with a subject line which contains the last name of the applicant only; letters of recommendation should be sent separately. **Deadline:** October 15. **Remarks:** The fellowship was established to honor Lawrence Gelfand, founding member and former SHAFR president; Armin Rappaport, founding editor of Diplomatic History; and Walter LaFeber, former president of SHAFR. **Contact:** E-mail: fellowships@shafr.org.

10358 ■ Myrna F. Bernath Fellowship (Doctorate, Graduate/Fellowship)

Purpose: To defray the costs of scholarly research by women. **Focus:** International affairs and relations. **Qualif.:** Applicants must be women from U.S. universities or women abroad pursuing a research in the United States; membership in SHAFR is required. **Criteria:** Selection will be given to graduate students who will be completing their Ph.D. within five years.

Funds Avail.: Up to $2,500. **Duration:** Biennial; in odd-numbered years. **Number Awarded:** 1. **To Apply:** Applicants must complete application can be downloaded at the website; must submit a cover sheet (available at website) with project narrative; budget and justification; one-page CV; and a letter of recommendation; all application materials (including the cover sheet but excluding letters of recommendation), should be in a single document (doc, pdf, rtf) and submit it via e-mail with a subject line which contains the last name of the applicant only; letters of recommendation should be sent separately. **Deadline:** October 15 of even years. **Remarks:** The fellowship was

Awards are arranged alphabetically below their administering organizations

established by the Bernath family to promote scholarship in U.S. foreign relations history by women. Established in 1992. **Contact:** E-mail: myrnabernath-committee@shafr.org.

10359 ■ SHAFR Dissertation Completion Fellowship
(Doctorate/Fellowship)

Purpose: To support the writing and completion of doctoral dissertation. **Focus:** Humanities; International affairs and relations; Social sciences. **Qualif.:** Applicants must be candidates for the Ph.D. in humanities or social science doctoral program (most likely history); must have been admitted to candidacy; and must be at the writing stage, with all substantial research completed by the time of the award; also, they must be working on a topic in the field of U.S. foreign relations history or international history, broadly defined; and must be current members of SHAFR. **Criteria:** Selection will be based on the committee's criteria.

Funds Avail.: $25,000 each. **Duration:** Annual. **Number Awarded:** 1. **To Apply:** Applicants must submit an application letter stating the project's significance, applicant's status and other received support; a statement of research (3 pages, 750 words); a curriculum vitae; and a recommendation letter from the doctoral advisor. **Deadline:** April 24. **Contact:** E-mail: dissertation-fellowships@shafr.org.

10360 ■ Stuart L. Bernath Dissertation Research Grant *(Graduate/Grant)*

Purpose: To help graduate students defray expenses encountered in the writing of their dissertations. **Focus:** International affairs and relations. **Qualif.:** Applicants must be actively working on dissertations dealing with some aspect of U.S. foreign relations history; membership in SHAFR is required. **Criteria:** Selection will be based on the committee's criteria.

Funds Avail.: Up to $4,000. **Duration:** Annual. **Number Awarded:** 1. **To Apply:** Applicants must complete application can be downloaded at the website; must submit a cover sheet (available at website) with project narrative; budget and justification; one-page CV; and a letter of recommendation; all application materials (including the cover sheet but excluding letters of recommendation), should be in a single document (doc, pdf, rtf) and submit it via e-mail with a subject line which contains the last name of the applicant only; letters of recommendation should be sent separately. **Deadline:** October 15. **Remarks:** Established in 1995. **Contact:** E-mail: fellowships@shafr.org.

10361 ■ W. Stull Holt Dissertation Fellowship
(Graduate/Fellowship)

Purpose: To defray the costs of travel in conducting a research on a significant dissertation project. **Focus:** International affairs and relations. **Qualif.:** Applicants must be working on a dissertation dealing with some aspect of U.S. foreign relations history and must have completed all requirements for the doctoral degree except the dissertation; must be member of SHAFR. **Criteria:** Selection will be based on the committee's criteria.

Funds Avail.: Up to $4,000. **Duration:** Annual. **Number Awarded:** 1. **To Apply:** Applicants must submit a cover sheet (available at website) with project narrative; budget and justification; one-page CV; and a letter of recommendation; all application materials (including the cover sheet but excluding letters of recommendation), should be in a single document (doc, pdf, rtf) and submit it via e-mail with a subject line which contains the last name of the applicant only; letters of recommendation should be sent separately.

Deadline: October 15. **Contact:** E-mail: fellowships@shafr.org.

10362 ■ Society for the History of Technology (SHOT)
Dept. of History
310 Thach Hall, Auburn University
Auburn, AL 36849-5207
Ph: (334)844-6770
Fax: (334)844-6673
URL: www.historyoftechnology.org
Social Media: www.facebook.com/historyoftechnology
www.linkedin.com/company/society-for-the-history-of-technology/about
twitter.com/sochisttech?lang=en

10363 ■ Brooke Hindle Postdoctoral Fellowships
(Postdoctorate, Doctorate/Fellowship)

Purpose: To support of a scholar researching or writing the history of technology or a related field. **Focus:** History. **Qualif.:** Applicants must hold a doctorate in the history of technology or a related field. **Criteria:** Selection of awardees is based on the committee's criteria.

Funds Avail.: $10,000. **Duration:** Annual. **Number Awarded:** 1. **To Apply:** Applicants must a proposal of no more than 3000 words, which should outline the focus of the project, relevant literature, sources to be used, plan of work, and originality of the expected contribution. If the proposal involves revising the dissertation, the applicant should specify the new work to be done. A dissertation summary (no more than 1000 words). A writing sample. A current CV. Two letters of recommendation. If the applicant has not yet completed the Ph.D., one letter should be from the chair of the dissertation committee, and this letter should confirm that the dissertation will be completed by the start of the next calendar year. **Deadline:** April 15. **Remarks:** The Fellowship was established in honor of Brooke Hindle.

10364 ■ Melvin Kranzberg Dissertation Fellowships
(Doctorate/Fellowship)

Purpose: To support a doctoral student engaged in the preparation of a dissertation on the history of technology, broadly defined. **Focus:** History. **Qualif.:** Applicants must be working on projects in the history of technology and have completed all requirements for their doctorate except for the dissertation by September 1 of the year in which the award is made; doctoral candidates from outside the United States are especially encouraged to submit application materials. **Criteria:** Committee is charged with selecting the most promising proposal from among those submitted.

Funds Avail.: $4,000. **Duration:** Annual. **Number Awarded:** 1. **To Apply:** Applicants must submit: a curriculum vitae; a 3-5 page (750-1250 words) summary of abstract of the proposed dissertation, in which applicants should describe how their research contributes to the history of technology; a 1-2 page (250-500 words) description of how the applicants intend to use the funds; and a letter of recommendation from the student's respective dissertation director. **Deadline:** April 15. **Remarks:** The award was established in memory of the co-founder of the Society and honors Melvin Kranzberg's many contributions to developing the history of technology as a field of scholarly endeavor and SHOT as a professional organization. Established in 1997.

Awards are arranged alphabetically below their administering organizations

10365 ■ SHOT-NASA Fellowship *(Doctorate/ Fellowship)*

Purpose: To support fellow's advanced research related to all aspects of space history. **Focus:** Indian studies (Asia). **Qualif.:** Applicant must possess a doctorate in history of technology or in a closely related field, or be enrolled as a student in a doctoral degree program and have completed all requirements for the Ph.D., except the dissertation in history of technology or a related field; is limited to U.S. Citizens. **Criteria:** Preference will be given to scholars at early stages in their careers.

Funds Avail.: $21,250. **Duration:** Annual. **Number Awarded:** 1. **To Apply:** Applicant must submit a completed application including a specific and detailed research proposal that will be the basis of the fellow's research during the term. Applicant's CV, A proposal describing your qualifications for a fellowship, detailing briefly the research project you propose to undertake, relating your anticipated experiences as a fellow to your goals, indicating clearly why NASA is the appropriate place to conduct the proposed research. At least two and not more than four letters of recommendation that address the historical competence of the applicant, his/her ability to apply historical concepts and methods to aerospace science, technology, management or policy, and his/her ability to communicate both orally and in writing. **Deadline:** April 20. **Contact:** Jan Korsten; E-mail: shot.secretariaat@tue.nl.

10366 ■ Society for Human Resource Management (SHRM)
1800 Duke St.
Alexandria, VA 22314
Ph: (703)548-3440
Free: 800-283-7476
E-mail: shrm@shrm.org
URL: www.shrm.org
Social Media: www.facebook.com/
  societyforhumanresourcemanagement
instagram.com/shrmofficial/
www.linkedin.com/company/11282?trk=NUS_CMPY_TWIT
twitter.com/SHRM
www.youtube.com/shrmofficial

10367 ■ Susan R. Meisinger Fellowship for Graduate Study in HR *(Graduate, Master's, Advanced Professional/Fellowship)*

Purpose: To support master's degree students who are either members of SHRM or certified HR professionals. **Focus:** Personnel administration/human resources; Resource management. **Qualif.:** Applicants must be members of SHRM; must be master's degree students or certified HR professionals. **Criteria:** Selection will be based on the committee's criteria.

Funds Avail.: Up to $20,000. **Duration:** Annual; up to 2 years. **Number Awarded:** 1. **To Apply:** Applications can be submitted online; must submit application form; current resume or curriculum vitae; undergraduate college transcript and graduate transcript; copy of acceptance letter; two or three letters of reference. **Deadline:** August 15.

10368 ■ Michael R. Losey Excellence In HR Research Award *(Graduate, Undergraduate/Award, Recognition)*

Purpose: To encourage interest and education in the field of human resources. **Focus:** Personnel administration/ human resources. **Qualif.:** Nominee must possess a broad and deep track record of contributions to the HR discipline through research; evidence of the development of research appropriate to the focus of the research; depth of scholarship, criticality and originality. **Criteria:** Scholarship recipients will be selected based primarily on merit and will be evaluated according to the criteria set by the reviewing committee.

Funds Avail.: $50,000. **Duration:** Annual. **Number Awarded:** 1. **To Apply:** Applicants must submit complete application form including current detailed CV or resume and a letter of no more than two pages; summary of the nominee's significant past and continuing contributions related to the HR field; description detailing why the individual is beingNominated; complete list of all publications and significant speaking Engagements. **Deadline:** July 15. **Contact:** Elissa Soares; Email: elissa.soares@ shrm.org.

10369 ■ SHRM Certification Scholarships - Individual *(Professional development/Scholarship)*

Purpose: To provide education scholarships to individuals pursuing study in Human Resource Management. **Focus:** Personnel administration/human resources. **Qualif.:** Applicants must be current member of SHRM that are preparing to sit for the SHRM-CP or SHRM-SCP certification exam. **Criteria:** Selection will based on work experience/ progression (HR involvement and future career plans); volunteer activity; and financial need.

Funds Avail.: $750 each. **Duration:** Annual. **Number Awarded:** Varies. **To Apply:** Applicants may visit the website to verify the application process and other pieces of information online; must provide resume; one letter of reference. **Deadline:** September 1.

10370 ■ Society for Imaging Science and Technology
7003 Kilworth Ln.
Springfield, VA 22151
Ph: (703)642-9090
Fax: (703)642-9094
E-mail: info@imaging.org
URL: www.imaging.org
Social Media: www.linkedin.com/company/society-for
  -imaging-science-and-technology-is&t-
twitter.com/ImagingOrg

10371 ■ Raymond Davis Scholarships *(Undergraduate, Graduate/Scholarship)*

Purpose: To support students who pursue full time study, in a field related to imaging, leading to an academic degree. **Focus:** Engineering, Optical; Photography. **Criteria:** Selection is based on the application materials submitted.

Funds Avail.: $1,000. **Duration:** Annual. **Number Awarded:** Varies. **To Apply:** Applicants must submit a completed scholarship application form together with the letters of nomination from at least two faculty members; an official transcript of college record; and a letter stating the applicant's goals and interests.**Remarks:** Established in 1977. **Contact:** info@imaging.org.

10372 ■ The Society for Integrative and Comparative Biology (SICB)
950 Herndon Pkwy., Ste. 450
Herndon, VA 20170

Awards are arranged alphabetically below their administering organizations

Ph: (703)790-1745
Fax: (703)790-2672
Free: 800-955-1236
E-mail: questions@sicb.org
URL: www.sicb.org
Social Media: www.facebook.com/groups/SICBmembers/

10373 ■ Libbie H. Hyman Memorial Scholarship
(Graduate, Undergraduate/Scholarship)

Purpose: To provide assistance to students to take courses or to pursue research on invertebrates at a marine, freshwater, or terrestrial field station. **Focus:** Zoology. **Qualif.:** Applicants must be a first or second year graduate students or advanced undergraduates currently enrolled in degree programs. **Criteria:** Selection is based on submitted proposals.

Funds Avail.: $700 - $1,900 each. **Duration:** Annual. **To Apply:** Applicants must submit completed applications consisting of a proposal, two letters of reference from faculty members, and copies of undergraduate and graduate transcripts. Applications and letters of recommendation must be submitted electronically following the instructions and using the forms provided at sicb.burkclients.com/grants/hyman/. **Deadline:** Febuary 4. **Remarks:** The award was established in memory of Libbie H. Hyman, one of America's foremost invertebrate zoologists.

10374 ■ SICB Fellowship of Graduate Student Travel (FGST) *(Graduate/Fellowship)*

Purpose: To provide funds for travel and other expenses for students to work at distant research laboratories, museums, or field sites. **Focus:** Biology. **Qualif.:** Applicants must be a graduate student currently enrolled in a degree program and an active member of SICB. **Criteria:** Selection is based on submitted proposals.

Funds Avail.: $2,000. **Duration:** Annual. **Number Awarded:** 3-4. **To Apply:** Applicants must submit a research proposal; must be filed electronically using the forms provided at the website; all fields in the electronic form must be completed unless noted otherwise. **Deadline:** October 25. **Remarks:** Established in 2002. **Contact:** Chair of the Student Support Committee; Email; chair.ssc@sicb.org.

10375 ■ SICB Grants-in-Aid of Research Program (GIAR) *(Graduate/Grant)*

Purpose: To support graduate students who conduct research in the fields of integrated and comparative biology. **Focus:** Biology. **Qualif.:** Applicants must be graduate students currently enrolled in degree programs who are active members of SICB.

Duration: Annual. **Number Awarded:** 25 to 35. **To Apply:** Application and details are available online at sicb.burkclients.com/grants/giarinfo.php. **Deadline:** October 17. **Remarks:** Established in 1996. **Contact:** Chair of the Student Support Committee; Email: Chair.SSC@sicb.org.

10376 ■ Society for Judgment and Decision Making (SJDM)
College of Business
Florida State University
Tallahassee, FL 32306-1110
Ph: (850)644-8231
Fax: (850)644-8234
URL: www.sjdm.org

Social Media: twitter.com/SJDM_Tweets

10377 ■ Hillel Einhorn New Investigator Award
(Doctorate/Award)

Purpose: To encourage outstanding work by new researchers. **Focus:** General studies/Field of study not specified. **Qualif.:** Applicants must have not yet completed their PhD, or if completed, it should be within the last five years. Articles based on a dissertation are encouraged; must be an SJDM member at the time of submission. **Criteria:** Selection will be based on the committee's criteria.

Duration: Annual. **To Apply:** Applicants must submit four copies of a journal-style manuscript on any topic related to judgment and decision making accompanied by: the case of co-authored papers, if the authors are all new investigators they can be considered jointly; otherwise, the new investigator(s) must be the primary author(s) and should be the primary source of ideas. **Deadline:** June 22. **Remarks:** Established in 1998. **Contact:** Susann Fiedler (fiedler@coll.mpg.de).

10378 ■ Jane Beattie Memorial Scholarship
(Graduate/Scholarship)

Purpose: To provide funds to subsidize travel to North America or Europe for purposes of scholarly activity by foreign scholars in the area of judgment and decision research. **Focus:** General studies/Field of study not specified. **Qualif.:** Applicants should be scholars living and working outside the destination who will use the award to help pay for travel for scholarly activities associated with research in judgment and decision making; most awards will be granted to early-career faculty or advanced graduate students at colleges and universities, but others will also be considered. **Criteria:** Selection will be granted on the basis of the committee's estimate of the prospective value of the proposed activity, its relevance to the field of judgment and decision research; the scholarly credentials of the applicant; and the extent to which the award would contribute to the applicant's success (including considerations of financial and academic need).

Funds Avail.: $750. **Duration:** Annual. **Number Awarded:** 1. **To Apply:** Applicants should submit the application form, along with a one page (single-spaced) description of the planned scholarly activity and a copy of their curriculum vitae; the activity may consist of attendance at a relevant conference or a visit to a North American or European institution; the description of activities should indicate the nature of the planned scholarly activity, with whom the applicant plans to work (if applicable), what the applicant hopes to accomplish with the visit, and why travel to North America is important to its accomplishment; submit applications via E-mail via attachments in Word, rtf or pdf format to the contact provided, with the subject "Beattie Application". **Contact:** Luxi Shen; Email: luxi.shen@cuhk.edu.hk.

10379 ■ Society for Linguistic Anthropology (SLA)
c/o Prof. Brigittine M. French, Editor
306 Goodnow Hall ,1118 Park St.
Grinnell College
306 Goodnow Hall
1118 Park St.
Grinnell, IA 50112
E-mail: soclinganth@gmail.com
URL: linguisticanthropology.org
Social Media: www.facebook.com/SocLingAnth

Awards are arranged alphabetically below their administering organizations

twitter.com/soclinganth

10380 ■ Society for Linguistic Anthropology Annual Student Essay Prize (Graduate, Undergraduate/Monetary)

Purpose: To support students with their Linguistic Anthropology studies. **Focus:** Anthropology. **Qualif.:** Applicants must be either undergraduate or graduate students in a degree-granting program when the paper was written; must be the sole author of the paper; and must submit the paper no more than two years after it was written. **Criteria:** Submitted essay will be evaluated on the basis of clarity, significance to the field and substantive contribution.

Funds Avail.: $500 and runner up will receive $250. **Duration:** Annual. **Number Awarded:** Varies. **To Apply:** Applicants must submit a paper of original work based on original research conducted by the author; the paper should be suitable for submission to the Journal of Linguistic Anthropology and must not exceed 25 double-spaced pages, not including bibliography; the paper must be submitted electronically in either pdf or doc format to Jillian Cavanaugh at jcavanaugh@brooklyn.cuny.edu; the cover sheet should include the title of the paper, the author's name, the author's email address, the author's college or university affiliation, the prize category (undergraduate or graduate) for which the paper is being submitted, and the name of the faculty member who served as the student's advisor with respect to the writing of the paper.

10381 ■ Society of Louisiana Certified Public Accountants (LCPA)

2400 Veterans Memorial Blvd., Ste. 500
Kenner, LA 70062
Ph: (504)464-1040
Free: 800-288-5272
URL: www.lcpa.org
Social Media: www.facebook.com/lcpa.org
www.instagram.com/louisianacpas
www.linkedin.com/company/society-of-louisiana-cpas
twitter.com/louisianacpas

10382 ■ Society of Louisiana Certified Public Accountants Scholarships (Undergraduate, Master's, Doctorate/Scholarship)

Purpose: To further develop the accounting education and the accounting profession. **Focus:** Accounting.

Funds Avail.: $500 - $2,000 for undergraduate; $1,000 for masters or doctoral. **Duration:** Annual. **Number Awarded:** Varies. **To Apply:** Applicants must complete the application form online and must submit all required materials, including essay, unofficial and official transcripts, and letters of recommendation.

10383 ■ Society of Manufacturing Engineers Education Foundation (SME)

1000 Town Ctr., Ste. 1910
Southfield, MI 48075
Ph: (313)425-3300
E-mail: foundation@sme.org
URL: www.smeef.org
Social Media: www.facebook.com/SME.Education.Foundation
www.linkedin.com/company/sme-education-foundation

twitter.com/mfgeducation
www.youtube.com/user/pmcsmeef

10384 ■ Walt Bartram Memorial Education Scholarship (Undergraduate/Scholarship)

Purpose: To provide assistance to students who are pursuing manufacturing engineering. **Focus:** Manufacturing. **Qualif.:** Applicant must be a graduating high school senior or undergraduate student pursuing studies in manufacturing engineering or closely related fields; must be a current SME member (except for high school students); must have a GPA of 2.5 on a 4.0 scale; must reside in New Mexico, Arizona, or Southern California. **Criteria:** Preference is given to the applicants who best meet the requirements.

Funds Avail.: No specific amount. **Duration:** Annual. **To Apply:** Applicants must include reference letter, most recent transcript(s), a resume, and supporting materials. **Deadline:** February 1.

10385 ■ Arthur and Gladys Cervenka Scholarship (Undergraduate/Scholarship)

Purpose: To provide assistance to students who are pursuing manufacturing engineering. **Focus:** Manufacturing; Technology. **Qualif.:** Applicant must be an undergraduate student enrolled full-time in a degree program in manufacturing engineering or technology; have completed a minimum of 30 college credit hours; have a GPA of 3.0 on a 4.0 scale. **Criteria:** Preference is given, but not limited to, students in the state of Florida.

Funds Avail.: No specific amount. **Duration:** Annual. **To Apply:** Applicants must include reference letter, most recent transcript(s), a resume, and supporting materials. **Deadline:** February 1.

10386 ■ Chapter 1 - Detroit Associate Scholarship (Graduate, Undergraduate, Vocational/Occupational, Two Year College, Four Year College/Award)

Purpose: To provide assistance to students seeking degrees in manufacturing engineering, manufacturing engineering technology, or a closely related degree or certificate program. **Focus:** Engineering; Manufacturing. **Qualif.:** Applicants must be graduating high school seniors, first time college applicants (such as displaced workers, non-traditional students, veterans), undergraduate students, or graduate students pursuing full-time or part-time studies at an accredited post-secondary two- or four-year college or trade school in Michigan; must be enrolled in manufacturing engineering, manufacturing engineering technology, or a closely related degree or certificate program; must have an overall minimum grade point average of 3.0 on a 4.0 scale; must be citizens of the United States or Canada; must demonstrate good character and leadership.

Duration: Annual. **To Apply:** Applicants must include reference letter, most recent transcript(s), a resume, and supporting materials. **Deadline:** February 1.

10387 ■ Chapter 1 – Detroit Undergraduate Scholarship (Undergraduate, Vocational/Occupational, Two Year College, Four Year College/Scholarship)

Purpose: To provide assistance to students who are pursuing manufacturing engineering. **Focus:** Manufacturing. **Qualif.:** Applicants must be graduating high school seniors, first time college applicants (such as displaced workers, veterans, non-traditional students), or undergraduate students enrolled full-time or part-time in a manufacturing, manufacturing engineering technology, or any related

Awards are arranged alphabetically below their administering organizations

degree or certificate program; must have a minimum GPA of 3.0 on a 4.0 scale and demonstrate good character and leadership; must be citizen of United States or Canada; must be entering an accredited post-high school program at a two- or four-year college or trade school in Michigan. **Funds Avail.:** No specific amount. **Duration:** Annual. **To Apply:** Applicants must include reference letter, most recent transcript(s), a resume, and supporting materials. **Deadline:** February 1.

10388 ■ Chapter 17 - St. Louis Scholarship
(Undergraduate/Scholarship)

Purpose: To provide assistance to students who are pursuing manufacturing engineering, industrial technology, or other manufacturing related programs. **Focus:** Engineering, Industrial; Manufacturing. **Qualif.:** Applicants must be enrolled full-time or part-time undergraduates in a manufacturing engineering, industrial technology or other manufacturing related degree program with a GPA of 2.5. **Criteria:** Recipient selection is based on: first preference, residing within the boundaries of St. Lewis Chapter 17; second preference, residing within the state of Missouri.

Funds Avail.: No specific amount. **Duration:** Annual. **To Apply:** Applicants must include reference letter, most recent transcript(s), a resume, and supporting materials. **Deadline:** February 1.

10389 ■ Chapter 23 - Quad Cities Scholarship
(Undergraduate/Scholarship)

Purpose: To provide assistance to students who are pursuing manufacturing engineering, industrial engineering, manufacturing technology, or integrated manufacturing systems. **Focus:** Engineering, Industrial; Manufacturing. **Qualif.:** Applicant must be seeking a Bachelor's degree in manufacturing engineering, industrial engineering, manufacturing technology, or integrated manufacturing systems; must possess an overall minimum 2.5 GPA. **Criteria:** Preference will be given in the following order: an applicant who is an active SME Student Chapter member, is an SME Member or is a child, grandchild, or step child of a registered SME member or student member; an applicant who are residents of Iowa or Illinois and attending an Iowa or Illinois college or university; students who are residents of the state of Iowa or Illinois; applicants who attend a college or university located in Iowa or Illinois.

Funds Avail.: No specific amount. **Duration:** Annual. **To Apply:** Applicants must include reference letter, most recent transcript(s), a resume, and supporting materials. **Deadline:** February 1.

10390 ■ Chapter 31 - Peoria Scholarship
(Undergraduate/Scholarship)

Purpose: To provide assistance to students who are pursuing manufacturing engineering, industrial engineering, manufacturing technology, or a manufacturing related degree program. **Focus:** Engineering, Industrial; Manufacturing. **Qualif.:** Applicants must be pursuing a bachelor's degree in manufacturing engineering, industrial engineering, manufacturing technology, or a manufacturing related degree program at Bradley University (Peoria, Illinois) or Illinois University (Normal, Illinois); have a GPA of 3.0 on a 4.0 scale. **Criteria:** Preference will be given in the following order: applicants who are North Central Peoria-Chapter 31 members, their spouse, and/or children or grandchildren; applicants who are Illinois Central College transfer students; SME Student Chapter members.

Funds Avail.: No specific amount. **Duration:** Annual. **To Apply:** Applicants must include reference letter, most

recent transcript(s), a resume, and supporting materials. **Deadline:** February 1.

10391 ■ Chapter 4 - Lawrence A. Wacker Memorial Scholarship *(Undergraduate/Scholarship)*

Purpose: To provide assistance to students pursuing degrees in manufacturing, mechanical, or industrial engineering at a college or university in the state of Wisconsin. **Focus:** Engineering, Industrial; Engineering, Mechanical; Manufacturing. **Qualif.:** Applicants must be graduating seniors or current undergraduate students; be enrolled in or accepted to a Bachelor's degree program in manufacturing, mechanical, or industrial engineering at a college or university in the state of Wisconsin; have a GPA of 3.0 on a 4.0 scale; must plan on attending a four year program at an accredited, public or private college or university within the state of Wisconsin. **Criteria:** Selection will be based on preferences in the following order: applicants who are Chapter 4 members, their spouse, and/or their children or grandchildren; applicants who reside within the following Wisconsin counties: Milwaukee, Ozaukee, Washington and Waukesha; applicants who reside within the State of Wisconsin.

Funds Avail.: No specific amount. **Duration:** Annual. **To Apply:** Applicants must include reference letter; most recent transcript(s); resume; and supporting materials. **Deadline:** February 1.

10392 ■ Chapter 52 - Wichita Scholarship *(Graduate, Undergraduate, Vocational/Occupational, Community College/Scholarship)*

Purpose: To provide assistance to students pursuing degrees in manufacturing, mechanical, or industrial engineering, engineering technology, or industrial technology at an accredited public or private college or university in Kansas. **Focus:** Engineering, Industrial; Engineering, Mechanical; Manufacturing. **Qualif.:** Applicants must be pursuing an Associate's, Bachelor's, or Graduate degree in manufacturing, mechanical, or industrial engineering, engineering technology, or industrial technology at an accredited public or private college or university in Kansas; must possess a minimum GPA of 2.5 on a 4.0 point scale. **Criteria:** Preference will be given in the following order: applicants who are a child, grandchild, or relative of a current SME Wichita Chapter No. 52 member; applicants who reside within the state of Kansas; applicants who are planning to attend a college or university located in the state of Kansas.

Funds Avail.: No specific amount. **Duration:** Annual. **To Apply:** Applicants must include reference letter; most recent transcript(s); resume; and supporting materials. **Deadline:** February 1.

10393 ■ Chapter 56 - Ft. Wayne Scholarship *(Graduate, Undergraduate, Vocational/Occupational, Community College/Scholarship)*

Purpose: To provide assistance to students seeking degrees in manufacturing, mechanical, or industrial engineering, engineering technology, or industrial technology at an accredited public or private college or university located in the state of Indiana. **Focus:** Engineering, Industrial; Engineering, Mechanical; Manufacturing. **Qualif.:** Applicants must be pursuing an Associate's, Bachelor's, or Graduate degree in manufacturing, mechanical, or industrial engineering, engineering technology, or industrial technology at an accredited public or private college or university located in the state of Indiana; must possess an

---

Awards are arranged alphabetically below their administering organizations

overall minimum GPA of 2.5. **Criteria:** Preference will be given in the following order: applicants who are a child or grandchild of a current SME Fort Wayne Chapter No. 56 member; SME student members of student chapters that SME Fort Wayne Chapter No. 56 sponsor; applicants who reside within the state of Indiana; applicants who are planning to attend a college or university located in the state of Indiana.

Funds Avail.: No specific amount. **Duration:** Annual. **To Apply:** Applicants must include reference letter; most recent transcript(s); resume; and supporting materials. **Deadline:** February 1.

10394 ■ Chapter 6 - Fairfield County Scholarship
(Undergraduate/Scholarship)

Purpose: To provide assistance to students who are pursuing manufacturing engineering. **Focus:** Manufacturing; Technology. **Qualif.:** Applicants must be undergraduate students enrolled full-time in a degree program in manufacturing, technology, or a closely related field in the United States or Canada; have a GPA of 3.0 on a 4.0 scale. **Criteria:** Preference is given, but not limited to, applicants residing in the eastern part of the United States.

Funds Avail.: No specific amount. **Duration:** Annual. **To Apply:** Applicants must include reference letter, most recent transcript(s), a resume, and supporting materials. **Deadline:** February 1.

10395 ■ Chapter 63 - Morrow Scholarship
(Undergraduate/Scholarship)

Purpose: To support students seeking degrees in manufacturing engineering or closely related fields. **Focus:** Manufacturing. **Qualif.:** Applicants must be students pursuing a degree in manufacturing or any related field; must have a GPA of 2.5 on a 4.0 scale. **Criteria:** Preference will be given in the following order: applicant who is a child/grandchild/step child of a current Chapter 63 member or membership in SME student chapters in Oregon and southwest Washington; students planning to attend Oregon or southwest Washington schools; applicants who reside within the states of Oregon and Washington.

Funds Avail.: No specific amount. **Duration:** Annual. **To Apply:** Applicants must include reference letter; most recent transcript(s); resume; and supporting materials. **Deadline:** February 1.

10396 ■ Chapter 63 - Smith Memorial Scholarship
(Undergraduate/Scholarship)

Purpose: To support students seeking degrees in manufacturing engineering or closely related fields. **Focus:** Manufacturing. **Qualif.:** Applicant must be a student pursuing a career in manufacturing or any related field at an accredited college or university; must have a GPA of 2.5 on a 4.0 scale. Non-SME member students applying for this scholarship must be a first blood relative and/or a legal dependent family member of a current participating SME Chapter 63 member. **Criteria:** Preference will be given in the following order: current active membership in an SME student chapter in the states of Oregon and southwest Washington; students planning to attend Oregon or southwest Washington schools; applicants who reside within the states of Oregon and Washington.

Funds Avail.: No specific amount. **Duration:** Annual. **To Apply:** Applicants must include reference letter; most recent transcript(s); resume; and supporting materials. **Deadline:** February 1.

10397 ■ Chapter 67 - Phoenix Scholarship
(Undergraduate/Scholarship)

Purpose: To provide assistance to students seeking degrees in manufacturing engineering, industrial engineering, manufacturing technology programs, or closely related fields. **Focus:** Engineering, Industrial; Manufacturing. **Qualif.:** Applicant must be a high school senior planning to enroll, or an undergraduate student currently enrolled, in a manufacturing engineering technology, manufacturing technology, industrial technology, or related program at an accredited college or university in Arizona; must have a GPA of 3.0 on a 4.0 scale; must maintain an overall GPA of 2.5, and a 3.0 GPA in their manufacturing courses to continue their eligibility in subsequent years. **Criteria:** Preference is given to applicants who best meet the requirements.

Funds Avail.: No specific amount. **Duration:** Annual. **To Apply:** Applicants must include reference letter; most recent transcript(s); resume; and supporting materials. **Deadline:** February 1.

10398 ■ Chapter 79/198/311 Scholarship *(Graduate, Undergraduate, Vocational/Occupational, Community College/Scholarship)*

Purpose: To provide assistance to students seeking degrees in technology, engineering, mathematics, or manufacturing. **Focus:** Engineering; Manufacturing; Mathematics and mathematical sciences. **Qualif.:** Applicants must be enrolled full-time seeking an associate's degree, bachelor's degree or graduate degree technology, engineering, mathematics, or manufacturing at an accredited public or private college or university in the United States or Canada; must have a minimum 2.5 GPA on a 4.0 scale. **Criteria:** Preference may be given for the following: child, grandchild, related dependent of a member Chapter 079 or former member of Chapter(s) 198 or 311; SME student members of student chapter University of Michigan-Dearborn S326 sponsored by Chapter 079; applicants who reside within the state of Michigan or are studying in the state of Michigan.

Funds Avail.: No specific amount. **Duration:** Annual. **To Apply:** Applicants must include reference letter; most recent transcript(s); resume; and supporting materials. **Deadline:** February 1.

10399 ■ Chapter 93 - Albuquerque Scholarship
(Undergraduate/Scholarship)

Purpose: To provide assistance to students pursuing degrees in manufacturing engineering or related field at a New Mexico college or university. **Focus:** Manufacturing. **Qualif.:** Applicant must be pursuing a Bachelor's degree in manufacturing engineering or related field at a New Mexico college or university; must have a GPA of 2.5 on a 4.0 scale. **Criteria:** Preference will be given in the following order: applicant who is a child/grandchild/step child of a current Chapter 93 member; a SME student member attending a New Mexico university; applicant who resides within the state of New Mexico; applicant who is planning to attend an engineering college or university located in the state of New Mexico.

Funds Avail.: No specific amount. **Duration:** Annual. **To Apply:** Applicants must include reference letter; most recent transcript(s); resume; and supporting materials. **Deadline:** February 1.

Awards are arranged alphabetically below their administering organizations

10400 ■ Chapter 116 - Roscoe Douglas Scholarship
(Undergraduate/Scholarship)

Purpose: To provide assistance to students who are pursuing manufacturing engineering or manufacturing engineering technology degrees. **Focus:** Manufacturing. **Qualif.:** Applicants must be full-time undergraduate students at the Western Michigan University and have completed at least 30 college credit hours; be pursuing a career in manufacturing engineering or manufacturing engineering technology; have a GPA of 3.0 on a 4.0 scale. **Criteria:** Preference is given to applicants who best meet the requirements.

Funds Avail.: No specific amount. **Duration:** Annual. **To Apply:** Applicants must include reference letter; most recent transcript(s); resume and supporting materials. **Deadline:** February 1.

10401 ■ Connie and Robert T. Gunter Scholarship
(Undergraduate/Scholarship)

Purpose: To support students seeking degrees in manufacturing engineering or technology in Georgia. **Focus:** Manufacturing. **Qualif.:** Applicants must be a full-time undergraduate students enrolled in a degree program in manufacturing engineering or technology at one of the following approved institutions: Georgia Institute of Technology - Atlanta; Georgia Southern College - Statesboro; Southern College of Technology - Marietta; must have completed a minimum of 30 college credit hours; must possess an overall minimum GPA of 3.5 on a 4.0 scale.

Duration: Annual. **To Apply:** Applicants must include reference letter, most recent transcript(s), a resume, and supporting materials. **Deadline:** February 1.

10402 ■ Clinton J. Helton Manufacturing Scholarship *(Undergraduate/Scholarship)*

Purpose: To provide students with the assistance they need in furthering their education in manufacturing engineering or technology, or other closely related engineering disciplines. **Focus:** Manufacturing. **Qualif.:** Applicants must be enrolled as full-time undergraduate students in a degree seeking program in manufacturing engineering, technology, or related field; must have completed a minimum of 30 college credit hours; must have a GPA of 3.0 on a 4.0 scale. Recipients may submit applications in succeeding years. **Criteria:** Preference will be given, but not limited to, students attending one of the following approved Colorado institutions: Colorado State University, or University of Colorado - all campuses.

Funds Avail.: No specific amount. **Duration:** Annual. **To Apply:** Applicants must include reference letter; most recent transcript(s); resume; and supporting materials. **Deadline:** February 1.

10403 ■ Lucile B. Kaufman Women's Scholarship
(Undergraduate/Scholarship)

Purpose: To support female students pursuing degrees in manufacturing engineering, technology, or a closely related field in the United States or Canada. **Focus:** Manufacturing; Technology. **Qualif.:** Applicants must be enrolled full-time undergraduate students in a degree program in manufacturing engineering, technology, or related field in the United States or Canada; must be female; must have a GPA of 3.0 on a 4.0 scale and have completed at least 30 college credits.

Funds Avail.: No specific amount. **Duration:** Annual. **To Apply:** Applicants must include reference letter; most recent transcript(s); resume; and supporting materials. **Deadline:** February 1.

10404 ■ E. Wayne Kay Co-op Scholarship
(Undergraduate/Scholarship)

Purpose: To support students pursuing studies in a manufacturing engineering or technology degree program in the United States or Canada. **Focus:** Manufacturing. **Qualif.:** Applicant must be a full time undergraduate student enrolled in a manufacturing engineering or technology degree program in the United States or Canada and working through a Co-Op program in a manufacturing related environment; must have completed a minimum of 30 college credit hours; should possess an overall minimum GPA of 3.0 on 4.0 scale. **Criteria:** Preference is given to applicants who best meet the requirements.

Duration: Annual. **To Apply:** Applicants must provide two letters of recommendation one from their Co-Op employer and one letter of support from a faculty member at their college or university; one copy of high school or college transcript of records; must present a letter of recommendation from an employer, and a letter of support from a current faculty. **Deadline:** February 1.

10405 ■ E. Wayne Kay Community College Scholarship *(Undergraduate, Community College/Scholarship)*

Purpose: To support students pursuing degrees in manufacturing or closely related fields at community colleges and trade schools. **Focus:** Manufacturing. **Qualif.:** Applicant must be a graduating high school senior or a full-time undergraduate student enrolled in a degree program in manufacturing or related field at a two-year community college or trade school in the U.S. or Canada; freshman or sophomore with less than 60 college credit hours completed and pursuing a career in manufacturing engineering or technology; must have a GPA of 3.0 on a 4.0 scale. **Criteria:** Preference is given to applicants who best meet the requirements.

Funds Avail.: No specific amount. **Duration:** Annual. **To Apply:** Applicants must include reference letter; most recent transcript(s); resume; and supporting materials. **Deadline:** February 1.

10406 ■ E. Wayne Kay Graduate Scholarships
(Graduate, Doctorate/Scholarship)

Purpose: To support graduate and doctoral students pursuing advanced degrees in manufacturing or industrial engineering. **Focus:** Engineering, Industrial; Manufacturing. **Qualif.:** Applicants must be accepted in a graduate or doctoral program for manufacturing engineering or industrial engineering. Applicants must also have an overall minimum of a 3.0 GPA on a 4.0 scale; scholastic ability, exemplary character and leadership capability, along with demonstrated potential for future leadership in the profession.

Duration: Annual. **To Apply:** Application form and details are available on the Sponsor's website. **Deadline:** February 1.

10407 ■ E. Wayne Kay High School Scholarship
(Undergraduate/Scholarship)

Purpose: To provide students the assistance they need in attending an accredited college or university in manufacturing engineering or technology programs. **Focus:** Manufacturing. **Qualif.:** Applicants must be graduating high school seniors enrolling in a manufacturing engineering or technology program at an accredited college or university as a full-time freshman in the current summer or fall semester with an overall GPA of 3.0 on a 4.0 scale for high school senior year. **Criteria:** Preference is given to applicants who best meet the requirements.

Awards are arranged alphabetically below their administering organizations

Funds Avail.: No specific amount. **Duration:** Annual. **To Apply:** Applicants must include reference letter; most recent transcript(s); resume; and supporting materials. **Deadline:** February 1.

10408 ■ Giuliano Mazzetti Scholarship
(Undergraduate/Scholarship)

Purpose: To provide students the assistance they need in studying manufacturing engineering or technology in the United States or Canada. **Focus:** Manufacturing; Technology. **Qualif.:** Applicant must be full-time undergraduate student enrolled in a degree program in manufacturing engineering, technology, or a closely related field in the United States or Canada; must have completed a minimum of 30 college credit hours possess an overall minimum GPA of 3.0 on a 4.0 scale. **Criteria:** Preference is given to applicants who best meet the requirements.

Funds Avail.: No specific amount. **Duration:** Annual. **To Apply:** Applicants must include reference letter; most recent transcript(s); resume; and supporting materials. **Deadline:** February 1.

10409 ■ Clarence & Josephine Myers Undergraduate Scholarships *(Graduate, Undergraduate, Vocational/Occupational, Community College/ Scholarship)*

Purpose: To support students pursuing degrees in manufacturing, mechanical, or industrial engineering in the state of Indiana. **Focus:** Engineering, Industrial; Engineering, Mechanical; Manufacturing. **Qualif.:** Applicant must be pursuing an Associate, Bachelor, or Graduate degree in manufacturing, mechanical, or industrial engineering in the state of Indiana; must have a GPA of 3.0 on a 4.0 scale. **Criteria:** Preference will be given for the following: applicant who attended Aresenal Technological High School in Indianapolis; SME student members of SME Chapter 37 sponsored chapters; applicant who is a child or grandchild of a current SME Chapter 37 member.

Funds Avail.: No specific amount. **Duration:** Annual. **To Apply:** Applicants must include reference letter; most recent transcript(s); resume; and supporting materials. **Deadline:** February 1.

10410 ■ North Central Region 9 Scholarship
(Undergraduate/Scholarship)

Purpose: To support students pursuing degrees in manufacturing, mechanical, or industrial engineering, or industrial technology. **Focus:** Engineering, Industrial; Engineering, Mechanical; Manufacturing. **Qualif.:** Applicants must be pursuing Bachelor's or Associate's degrees in manufacturing, mechanical, or industrial engineering, or industrial technology at a two- or four-year college/university within the North Central Region (Iowa, Minnesota, Nebraska, North Dakota, South Dakota, Wisconsin and the upper peninsula of Michigan); must have a GPA of 3.0 on a 4.0 scale. **Criteria:** Preference will be given to applicants who are North Central Region 9 members, their spouse, and/or children or grandchildren.

Funds Avail.: No specific amount. **Duration:** Annual. **To Apply:** Applicants must include reference letter; most recent transcript(s); resume; and supporting materials. **Deadline:** February 1.

10411 ■ Edward S. Roth Scholarship *(Graduate, Undergraduate/Scholarship)*

Purpose: To provide assistance to students who are pursuing manufacturing engineering. **Focus:** Manufacturing.

Qualif.: Applicants must be U.S. citizens; must have a GPA of 3.0 on a 4.0 scale; must be graduating high school seniors or current full-time graduate or undergraduate students pursuing Bachelor's or Master's degrees in manufacturing engineering from one of the following ABET-accredited school: California Polytechnic State University, CA; California State Polytechnic University, CA; University of Miami, FL; Bradley University, IL; Central State University, OH; Miami University, OH; Boston University, MA; Worcester Polytechnic Institute, MA; University of Massachusetts, MA; St. Cloud State University, MN; The University of Texas - Pan American, TX; Brigham Young University, UT; Utah State University, UT. **Criteria:** Preference is given to applicants with demonstrated financial need, minority students, and students participating in a Co-Op program.

Funds Avail.: No specific amount. **Duration:** Annual. **To Apply:** Applicants must include reference letter, most recent transcript(s), a resume, and supporting materials. **Deadline:** February 1.

10412 ■ Schneider/Bingle PLTW Scholarship
(Undergraduate/Scholarship)

Purpose: To support students seeking degrees in manufacturing engineering, industrial engineering, or closely related degree programs. **Focus:** Engineering, Industrial; Manufacturing. **Qualif.:** Applicant must be a full-time student seeking a Bachelor's degree in manufacturing engineering, industrial engineering, or a closely related degree program at a four-year college or university in the United States or Canada; must be a citizen of the United States or Canada; must have a minimum 3.0 GPA on a 4.0 scale; must have completed three or more Project Lead The Way (PLTW) courses.

Funds Avail.: No specific amount. **Duration:** Annual. **To Apply:** Applicants must include reference letter; most recent transcript(s); resume; and supporting materials. **Deadline:** February 1.

10413 ■ Prof. George Schneider Scholarship
(Undergraduate/Scholarship)

Purpose: To support students pursuing degrees in manufacturing, technology, or closely related fields. **Focus:** Manufacturing; Technology. **Qualif.:** Applicants must be enrolled at least 6 credit hours per semester; pursuing a Bachelor's degree in manufacturing engineering, manufacturing engineering technology, or related field at Lawrence Technological University (MI) or Kent State University (OH); have a GPA of 2.5 on a 4.0 scale; have completed at least 60 and less than 90 college credit hours. **Criteria:** Preference is given to applicants who best meet the requirements.

Funds Avail.: No specific amount. **Duration:** Annual. **To Apply:** Applicants must include reference letter; most recent transcript(s); resume; and supporting materials; must provide two letters of recommendation. one must come from the Dean of the College of Engineering. The second letter must come from the Chair of the school in which the student is enrolled. **Deadline:** February 1.

10414 ■ SME Directors Scholarships
(Undergraduate/Scholarship)

Purpose: To support SME members pursuing undergraduate degrees in manufacturing or closely related fields of study in the United States or Canada. **Focus:** Manufacturing. **Qualif.:** Applicants must be full-time undergraduate students enrolled in a manufacturing degree or closely related field of study in the United States or Canada; have completed a minimum of 30 college credit hours and be

Awards are arranged alphabetically below their administering organizations

seeking a career in manufacturing; an overall minimum GPA of 3.5 on a 4.0 scale; be a current member of an SME Professional or Student Chapter. **Criteria:** Preference will be given to students who demonstrate leadership skills in a community, academic, or professional environment.

Funds Avail.: $5,000. **Duration:** Annual. **Number Awarded:** 3. **Deadline:** February 1.

10415 ■ SME Education Foundation Family Scholarships (Undergraduate/Scholarship)

Purpose: To support the children or grandchildren of SME members who are pursuing degrees in manufacturing engineering, manufacturing engineering technology, or closely related engineering fields of study. **Focus:** Engineering; Manufacturing. **Qualif.:** Applicants must pursue a degree in manufacturing engineering, manufacturing engineering technology, or a related manufacturing field of study; must be a resident and attending in an accredited institution in the United States or Canada; must have at least one parent or grandparent that has been a SME member for two years in good standing; must be graduating high school senior or undergraduate with up to 30 credit hours completed; enrolled or enrolling full-time at a college or university; have a GPA of 3.0 on a 4.0 scale; have a minimum 1000 SAT score and/or 21 ACT score; must reside within the United States or Canada; demonstrate academic excellence and an interest in manufacturing engineering or related technology. **Criteria:** Recipient selection is based on academic excellence; communication and interpersonal skills; interest in manufacturing engineering or related field.

Funds Avail.: $40,000 payable over four years (1); $20,000 payable over four years (3). **Duration:** Annual. **Number Awarded:** 4. **To Apply:** Application form and details are available on the Sponsor's website. Recipients must submit intent to renew form and copies of the previous year's transcripts to the foundation prior to the start of the next academic year. **Deadline:** February 1.

10416 ■ SME Future Leaders of Manufacturing Scholarship (Graduate, Undergraduate/Scholarship)

Purpose: To support students pursuing degrees in manufacturing engineering, engineering technology, industrial technology, technical or related engineering fields at colleges or universities in the United States or Canada. **Focus:** Engineering; Engineering, Industrial; Manufacturing. **Qualif.:** Applicants must have a current SME student membership; must be undergraduate or graduate students enrolled in a manufacturing engineering, engineering technology, industrial technology, technical, or related engineering major at an accredited college or university in the United States or Canada; must be enrolled on a full-time (12 credit) basis during the academic year. **Criteria:** Preference is given to candidates who best meet the requirements.

Funds Avail.: No specific amount. **Duration:** Annual. **To Apply:** Applicants must include reference letter; most recent transcript(s); resume; and supporting materials. A letter of recommendation is required from applicant's SME Student Chapter Advisor. **Deadline:** February 1.

10417 ■ Myrtle & Earl Walker Scholarships (Undergraduate/Scholarship)

Purpose: To provide students the assistance they need in studying manufacturing engineering or technology. **Focus:** Manufacturing; Technology. **Qualif.:** Applicant must be an undergraduate student enrolled full-time in a degree program in manufacturing engineering or technology in the U.S. or Canada; must have completed at least 15 college

credit hours or one semester; must have a GPA of 3.0 on a 4.0 scale. **Criteria:** Preference is given to applicants who best meet the requirements.

Funds Avail.: No specific amount. **Duration:** Annual. **To Apply:** Applicants must include reference letter; most recent transcript(s); resume; and supporting materials. **Deadline:** February 1.

10418 ■ William E. Weisel Scholarship (Undergraduate/Scholarship)

Purpose: To support students pursuing engineering or technology programs in the United States or Canada. **Focus:** Engineering; Technology. **Qualif.:** Applicants must be U.S. or Canada citizens pursuing undergraduate degrees in engineering or technology programs in the U.S. or Canada; must be full-time students who have completed at least 30 college credit hours; must have a GPA of 3.0 on a 4.0 scale. **Criteria:** Preference will be given to a student seeking a career in robotics or automated systems used in manufacturing; Consideration will be given to students who intend to apply their knowledge in the sub-specialty of medical robotics.

Funds Avail.: No specific amount. **Duration:** Annual. **To Apply:** Applicants must include reference letter; most recent transcript(s); resume; and supporting materials. **Deadline:** February 1.

10419 ■ Albert E. Wischmeyer Scholarship (Undergraduate/Scholarship)

Purpose: To provide assistance to students who are pursuing manufacturing engineering. **Focus:** Engineering, Mechanical; Manufacturing. **Qualif.:** Applicants must be graduating high school seniors or undergraduates pursuing a degree in manufacturing engineering, manufacturing engineering technology, or mechanical technology; attending an accredited institution in New York State; must be residents of Western New York; must have a GPA of 2.5 on a 4.0 scale. **Criteria:** Recipients will be selected based on the application materials submitted.

Funds Avail.: No specific amount. **Duration:** Annual. **To Apply:** Applicants must include reference letter, most recent transcript(s), a resume, and supporting materials. **Deadline:** February 1.

10420 ■ The Society of Marine Port Engineers of New York (SMPE)
111 Broad St.
Eatontown, NJ 07724
Ph: (732)389-2009
Fax: (732)389-2264
E-mail: info@smpe.org
URL: www.smpe.org

10421 ■ The SMPE NY Scholarship Loan Program (Undergraduate/Scholarship, Loan)

Purpose: To assist members of SMPE and their families in pursuing higher studies. **Focus:** General studies/Field of study not specified. **Qualif.:** Applicants must be SMPE NY members in good standing for a minimum of three (3) consecutive years. **Criteria:** Recipients are selected based on merit.

Funds Avail.: No specific amount. **Duration:** Annual. **To Apply:** Applicants must submit the online application form.

Awards are arranged alphabetically below their administering organizations

10422 ■ Society for Maternal-Fetal Medicine (SMFM)

409 12th St. SW
Washington, DC 20024
URL: www.smfm.org

10423 ■ SMFM/AAOGF Scholarship Awards
(Graduate/Scholarship)

Purpose: To support a single scholarship in maternal-fetal medicine. **Focus:** Medicine, Gynecological and obstetrical. **Qualif.:** Applicants must be members or associate members of SMFM and must be eligible for the certificationprocess of ABOG at the time of the award; those who are in their second year of an ABOG-approved fellowship can apply for funding through this mechanism to start in the 3rd year of fellowship, as long as that year is devoted to research for at least 75% of the year. **Criteria:** Preference may be given to candidates training in areas currently underrepresented in academic obstetrics and gynecology (e.g., urogynecology, family planning).

Funds Avail.: $120,000. **Duration:** One year. **To Apply:** Applicants must include a curriculum vita (complete, not merely-NIH biosketch style), bibliography, prior training, past research experience, evidence of completion of residency training in obstetrics and gynecology; research project should be described in detail using an NIH grant format but should not exceed 6 pages, using number 11 Arial font, including all figures and tables but not bibliography; list of other research grants, training grants, or scholarships previously or currently held by the applicant. **Remarks:** With the enthusiastic support of the Board of Directors of the SMFM and the Council of the American Association of Obstetrical Society and the Endowment Fund Committee of the American Association of Obstetricians and Gynecologists Foundation (AAOGF), the SMFM and AAOGF has entered into a partnership to support a single scholarship in maternal-fetal medicine. **Contact:** SMFM at the above address.

10424 ■ Society for Military History (SMH)

George C. Marshall Library
Virginia Military Institute
Lexington, VA 24450-1600
Ph: (540)464-7468
Fax: (540)464-7330
URL: www.smh-hq.org
Social Media: twitter.com/smh_historians

10425 ■ ABC-Clio Research Grants *(Graduate/Grant)*

Purpose: To support the work of advanced graduate students and those scholars who do not hold a doctoral degree but are employed full-time as historians. **Focus:** History, Military. **Qualif.:** Applicants must be members of the Society for military history; must be employed full-time as professional historians without a doctoral degree. **Criteria:** Selection will be based on originality and quality of the proposed research, the cost-effectiveness of the proposal, and the likelihood that the research will contribute to the development of the field of military history.

Funds Avail.: $500. **Duration:** Annual. **Number Awarded:** 2. **To Apply:** Applicants must submit brief cover letter outlining the specific research needs to be addressed by this funding, CV, and a budget; a letter of reference from the doctoral advisor or another individual familiar with the scholarship should be sent separately. **Deadline:** January

15. **Contact:** Adam Seipp (aseipp@tamu.edu).

10426 ■ Society for Mining, Metallurgy, and Exploration (SME)

12999 E Adam Aircraft Cir.
Englewood, CO 80112
Ph: (303)948-4200
Fax: (303)973-3845
Free: 800-763-3132
E-mail: cs@smenet.org
URL: www.smenet.org
Social Media: www.facebook.com/SocietyForMining
twitter.com/smecommunity

10427 ■ Gerald V. Henderson Memorial Scholarship
(Undergraduate, Graduate/Scholarship)

Purpose: To award scholarships to promising college students who are pursuing degrees in geology, mining engineering or mineral economics with special interests in an industrial minerals and aggregates-oriented program. **Focus:** Metallurgy; Mining. **Qualif.:** Applicants must be graduate or undergraduate student members of SME; must have completed at least two years of undergraduate studies with a minimum cumulative GPA of 3.0; must attend a school that is ABET-accredited and/or has an SME Student Chapter; and must demonstrate a desire for and probability of success in a career in industrial minerals and/or aggregates industries. **Criteria:** Selection of scholarship recipients is at the discretion of SME's Industrial Minerals & Aggregates Division Scholarship Committee.

Funds Avail.: No specific amount. **Duration:** Annual. **Number Awarded:** 1 or more. **To Apply:** Applicant should submit demographic and contact information; short statement (one page) describing applicant's interest in/passion for a career in mining and the environment; two references, one from university faculty and one from an appropriate industry professional; a résumé detailing past education and work experience; copy of most recent transcripts (unofficial transcripts are OK); and anticipated expenses/income for the current academic year. **Deadline:** October 15. **Contact:** Scholarship Coordinator; Phone: 303-948-4200; Email: scholarships@smenet.org.

10428 ■ Mineral & Metallurgical Processing Division Scholarships and Richard Klimpel Memorial Scholarships (MPD) *(Undergraduate, Graduate/Scholarship)*

Purpose: To support outstanding students interested in pursuing careers in the area of mineral and metallurgical processing. **Focus:** Metallurgy; Mineralogy. **Qualif.:** Applicants must be graduate or undergraduate student members of SME; must have completed at least two years of undergraduate studies with a minimum cumulative GPA of 3.0; must attend a school that is ABET-accredited and/or has an SME Student Chapter; and must demonstrate a desire for and probability of success in a career in mineral/metallurgical processing. **Criteria:** Selection of scholarship recipients is at the discretion of SME's Mineral & Metallurgical Processing Division Scholarship Committee.

Funds Avail.: $5,000. **Duration:** Annual. **Number Awarded:** 18. **To Apply:** Applicant should submit demographic and contact information; short statement (one page) describing applicant's interest in/passion for a career in mining and the environment; two references, one from university faculty and one from an appropriate industry

Awards are arranged alphabetically below their administering organizations

professional; résumé detailing past education and work experience; copy of most recent transcript (unofficial transcripts are OK); anticipated expenses/income for the current academic year. **Deadline:** October 15. **Contact:** Phone: 303-948-4200; Email: scholarships@smenet.org.

10429 ■ SME Coal & Energy Division Scholarship
(Undergraduate/Scholarship)

Purpose: To support promising college students who have chosen as a career path the field of mining engineering with an emphasis on coal. **Focus:** Engineering, Mining and Mineral; Metallurgy; Mineralogy; Mining. **Qualif.:** Applicants must have completed at least two years of undergraduate studies with a minimum cumulative GPA of 2.50; must be a SME student member in good standing; attend a school that is ABET accredited; attend a school that has an SME student chapter; must demonstrate a desire for and a probability of success in a career in coal mining. **Criteria:** Selection of scholarship recipients is at the discretion of SME's Coal & Energy Division Scholarship Committee.

Funds Avail.: No specific amount. **Duration:** Annual. **Number Awarded:** 1. **To Apply:** Applicants should submit demographic and contact information; short statement (one page) describing interest in/passion for a career in mining and the environment; two references, one from university faculty and one from an appropriate industry professional; resume detailing past education and work experience; copy of most recent transcript (unofficial transcripts are OK); and anticipated expenses/income for the current academic year. **Deadline:** October 15. **Contact:** Scholarship Coordinator, Phone: 303-948-4200; E-mail: scholarships@smenet.org.

10430 ■ SME Environmental Division Scholarship
(Undergraduate, Graduate/Scholarship)

Purpose: To support promising college students who have chosen as a career path the field of mining and the environment. **Focus:** Engineering, Mining and Mineral; Metallurgy; Mineralogy; Mining. **Qualif.:** Applicants must have completed at least two years of undergraduate studies with a minimum cumulative GPA of 3.0; be an SME student member in good standing; attend a school that is ABET accredited, has an SME Student Chapter, or offers a B.S., B.A., or M.S., or Ph.D. in Geological Sciences; demonstrate a desire for and a probability of success in a career in mining and the environment. **Criteria:** Selection of scholarship recipients is at the discretion of SME's Environmental Division Scholarship Committee.

Funds Avail.: $2,000. **Duration:** Annual. **Number Awarded:** Varies. **To Apply:** Applicants should submit demographic and contact information; short statement (one page) describing applicant's interest in/passion for a career in mining and the environment; two references, one from university faculty and one from an appropriate industry professional; resume detailing past education and work experience; copy of most recent transcript (unofficial transcripts are OK); and anticipated expenses/income for the current academic year. **Deadline:** October 15. **Contact:** Scholarship Coordinator, Phone: 303-948-4200; E-mail: scholarships@smenet.org.

10431 ■ Henry DeWitt Smith Graduate Scholarship
(Graduate/Scholarship)

Purpose: To assist worthy students in the pursuit of their graduate education in the mining, metallurgical, materials or petroleum departments of leading universities and colleges in the United States and Canada. **Focus:** Metallurgy; Mining. **Qualif.:** Applicants must be student member of

SME; must have completed an undergraduate degree in mining engineering with a minimum cumulative GPA of 2.75; must attend a school that is ABET-accredited and/or has an SME student chapter; and must demonstrate a desire for, and a probability of success in, a career in the mining industry. **Criteria:** Selection of scholarship recipients is at the discretion of SME's Mining & Exploration Division Scholarship Committee.

Funds Avail.: No specific amount. **Duration:** Annual. **To Apply:** Applicants should submit demographic and contact information; short statement (one page) describing applicant's interest in/passion for a career in mining and the environment; two references, one from university faculty and one from an appropriate industry professional; must résumé detailing past education and work experience; copy of most recent transcript (unofficial transcripts are OK); must anticipated expenses/income for the current academic year. **Deadline:** October 15. **Remarks:** Named in the honor of Henry DeWitt Smith's contributions to the mining industry. Established in 1967. **Contact:** Phone: 303-948-4200; Email: scholarships@smenet.org.

10432 ■ Society of Naval Architects and Marine Engineers (SNAME)
99 Canal Center Plz., Ste. 310
Alexandria, VA 22314
Ph: (703)997-6701
Fax: (703)997-6702
E-mail: sname@sname.org
URL: www.sname.org
Social Media: www.facebook.com/SNAMEOfficial
www.linkedin.com/company/sname
pinterest.com/sname3503
twitter.com/SNAME_HQ

10433 ■ Robert N. Herbert Undergraduate Scholarships *(Undergraduate/Scholarship)*

Purpose: To encourage study in naval architecture, marine engineering, ocean engineering or marine industry-related fields. **Focus:** Architecture, Naval; Engineering, Marine; Engineering, Ocean.

Funds Avail.: $6,000. **Duration:** Annual. **To Apply:** Applicants must complete the application form and provide evidence of sound academic achievement; should submit the following: a 500-600 word application essay; three letters of professional recommendations in which the two must be NA/ME/OE faculty who have had the student in class and at least two of whom are SNAME members; must give evidence of their passion for naval architecture, marine engineering, ocean engineering and/or other marine field, as well as of their professionalism, commitment and prior. **Deadline:** June 1 - application; June 15 - supporting documents. **Remarks:** The scholarship was established to honor Robert N. Herbert, an innovative employer who realized the importance of providing employees with a stake in the company. His keen sense for innovation, and his honest, straightforward manner helped build long term relationships with his clients. Established in 2008. **Contact:** Sofia Iliogrammenou; E-mail: scholarships@sname.org.

10434 ■ Mandell and Lester Rosenblatt Undergraduate Scholarship *(Undergraduate/Scholarship)*

Purpose: To encourage study in naval architecture, marine engineering, ocean engineering or marine industry-related

Awards are arranged alphabetically below their administering organizations

fields. **Focus:** Architecture, Naval; Engineering, Marine; Engineering, Ocean. **Criteria:** Recipients will be selected based on the scholarship committee's recommendations and the executive committee's approval.

Funds Avail.: $6,000. **Duration:** Annual. **To Apply:** Applicants must complete the application form and provide evidence of sound academic achievement; should submit the following: a 500-600 word application essay; three letters of professional recommendations in which the two must be NA/ME/OE faculty who have had the student in class and at least two of whom are SNAME members; must give evidence of their passion for naval architecture, marine engineering, ocean engineering and/or other marine field, as well as of their professionalism, commitment and prior. **Deadline:** February 1 - application; February 15 - supporting documents. **Remarks:** The scholarship was established to honor the combined legacy of Mandell and Lester Rosenblatt, the founders of M. Rosenblatt & Son, Inc. Established in 2007. **Contact:** Sofia Iliogrammenou; E-mail: scholarships@sname.org.

10435 ■ John V. Wehausen Graduate Scholarships for Advanced Study in Ship Hydrodynamics and Wave Theory *(Graduate/Scholarship)*

Purpose: To support students of naval architecture and marine engineering with their educational expenses. **Focus:** Engineering, Marine. **Qualif.:** Applicants must be graduate students and members of SNAME or another recognized marine society. **Criteria:** Selection will be based on committee's criteria.

Funds Avail.: Up to $20,000. **Duration:** Annual. **To Apply:** Application can be submitted online; must include three letters of reference; supporting documents. **Deadline:** February 15. **Remarks:** The award was named in the honor of John Vroman Wehausen, professor of engineering science, emeritus, at the University of California, Berkeley, and a world leader in the field of marine hydrodynamics. **Contact:** Sofia Iliogrammenou; Email: scholarships@sname.org.

10436 ■ Society of Nuclear Medicine and Molecular Imaging (SNMMI)
1850 Samuel Morse Dr.
Reston, VA 20190
Ph: (703)708-9000
Fax: (703)708-9015
E-mail: education@snmmi.org
URL: www.snmmi.org
Social Media: www.facebook.com/mysnmmi
www.instagram.com/snm_mi
twitter.com/SNM_MI
www.youtube.com/user/SNMChannel1

10437 ■ Mitzi & William Blahd, MD, Pilot Research Grant *(Professional development/Grant)*

Purpose: To help basic or clinical scientists in the early stages of their career conduct research that may lead to further funding. **Focus:** Medicine, Nuclear. **Qualif.:** Applicants must be basic or clinical scientists with an advanced degree, such as MD, PhD or equivalent; hold a full-time position in an educational institution when the award starts; be no more than five years post nuclear medicine/molecular imaging training; not have served as the principal investigator of a peer-reviewed grant for more than $50, 000 in a single calendar year; and be members of SNMMI at the time of award. **Criteria:** Preference will be

given to individuals who have demonstrated great potential for a research career in the field of nuclear medicine/ molecular imaging and whose research focuses on translational in vivo studies that include radionuclide imaging or therapy.

Funds Avail.: $25,000. **Duration:** Annual. **To Apply:** Applicants must be completed in its entirety and submitted along with principal investigator's current curriculum vitae, A research abstract, and a detailed research proposal not to exceed 10 pages, excluding references.; one letter of recommendation from the program director or research supervisor; one letter of recommendation from a professional colleague. **Deadline:** December.

10438 ■ Paul Cole Student Technologist Scholarship *(Undergraduate/Scholarship)*

Purpose: To provide financial assistance to students aiming educational career in nuclear medicine technology. **Focus:** Medicine, Nuclear.

Funds Avail.: $1,000. **Duration:** Annual. **Number Awarded:** 10. **To Apply:** Applicants must submit completed application including statement and program director's signature; official transcripts of all formal education; and complete evaluation from the program director whose signature verifies the applicant's acceptance into or enrollment in the nuclear medicine technology program; applicants should a statement not to exceed 1000 words. **Deadline:** February 17. **Remarks:** The scholarship was named in memory of Paul Cole, CNMT, who served as President of the SNMMI Technologist Section (SNMMI-TS) in 1986 and who was known as a champion of education for technologists. **Contact:** K. Malaika Walton, Associate Director of Governance; Phone: 703-652-6782; Email: Grants&Awards@snmmi.org.

10439 ■ SNMMI Robert E. Henkin, MD, Government Relations Fellowship *(Professional development/ Fellowship)*

Purpose: To provide young professionals in nuclear medicine and molecular imaging direct personal exposure to government relations activities of the SNMMI as well as the state and federal legislative and regulatory process. **Focus:** Medicine, Nuclear. **Qualif.:** Applicants must be young professionals who are resident or fellow physicians, scientists or technologists who have completed their training within the last 10 years. **Criteria:** Selection will be based on a record of professional achievement in one's career; evidence of leadership skills and the potential for further growth; demonstrated commitment to public service evidenced by prior government relations positions; sincere desire to achieve the goals and objectives of the Fellowship in the form of an essay on why the applicants thinks they should be selected; skills to succeed at the highest levels in nuclear medicine and molecular imaging, and the ability to work effectively as part of a team; exceptional writing ability, a positive attitude, and strong leadership skills.

Funds Avail.: $1,000. **Duration:** Annual. **To Apply:** Applicants will be asked to provide curriculum vitae and a written statement of their interest in health policy and regulatory affairs. Two letters of recommendation in support of the application may be submitted, but will not be required. **Deadline:** March 1. **Remarks:** Established in 2013.

10440 ■ PDEF Professional Development Scholarship *(Professional development/Scholarship)*

Purpose: To support students who are employed as technologists and actively pursuing an advanced degree

Awards are arranged alphabetically below their administering organizations

related to their nuclear medicine career. **Focus:** Medicine, Nuclear. **Criteria:** Selection will be based on the committee's criteria.

Funds Avail.: $5,000. **Duration:** Annual.

10441 ■ SNMMI-TS Advanced Practitioner Program Scholarship *(Professional development/Scholarship)*

Purpose: To support students who are pursuing an advanced practitioner program to advance their career in nuclear medicine. **Focus:** Medicine, Nuclear.

Funds Avail.: No specific amount. **Duration:** Annual. **To Apply:** Applicants must complete and submit completed application, which includes personal and financial information; current resume or curriculum vitae; official transcripts of all formal education issued directly from the institution's registrar office; a statement, not to exceed two pages. The brief statement should detail their activity level in the SNMMI Technologist Section and should address their professional achievements and their career and educational goals, and how the advanced practitioner program in the field of nuclear medicine will help them to achieve their goals; a scanned copy of original program acceptance notification.

10442 ■ SNMMI-TS Bachelor's Degree Completion Scholarships *(Undergraduate/Scholarship)*

Purpose: To support students pursuing a Bachelor's degree completion program related to their nuclear medicine career. **Focus:** General studies/Field of study not specified. **Qualif.:** Applicants must demonstrate financial need; hold a certificate or associate's degree in nuclear medicine technology; currently enrolled in a bachelor's level program to advance their career in nuclear medicine; have a minimum cumulative GPA of 2.5 or better (on 4.0 scale) or B average in the program's core curriculum, and member of the SNMTS. **Criteria:** Candidates will be judged based on the criteria designed by the Scholarship Committee.

Funds Avail.: No specific amount. **Duration:** Annual. **To Apply:** Applicants must submit a completed application, which includes applicant's statement and recommenders' signature; official transcripts of all formal education (high school transcripts are not necessary if transcripts of college level work are submitted); a letter of recommendation from an educational or professional reference; an official transcript or letter from the institution's registrar's office verifying the applicant's enrollment or acceptance in the Bachelor's degree program. **Deadline:** January 27.

10443 ■ SNNMI Predoctoral Molecular Imaging Scholar Program *(Doctorate/Scholarship)*

Purpose: To be used for salary support of the principal investigator, as well as direct costs of supplies and equipment. **Focus:** Medicine, Nuclear.

Duration: Annual.

10444 ■ Marc Tetalman, MD, Memorial Award *(Professional development, Doctorate/Recognition)*

Purpose: To honor the research accomplishments of a young investigator who is pursuing a career in nuclear medicine. **Focus:** Medicine, Nuclear. **Criteria:** Selection will be based on the committee's criteria.

Funds Avail.: $1,000. **Duration:** Biennial. **To Apply:** Applicants may be nominated by a member of the SNMMI or they may apply themselves.

10445 ■ Wagner-Torizuka Fellowship *(Professional development/Fellowship)*

Purpose: To provide experience and training in nuclear medicine/molecular imaging modalities in the areas of

cardiology, neurology, and oncology. **Focus:** Medicine, Cardiology; Neurology; Oncology. **Qualif.:** Applicants must be permanent residents of Japan and must have received their Japanese MD license no more than 15 years from the time of application. **Criteria:** Selection will be based on the committee's criteria.

Funds Avail.: $48,000 over 2 years. **Duration:** Annual. **Number Awarded:** Varies. **To Apply:** All applications must be completed online; In addition, two letters of support are required, one from the applicants' supervisor or mentor in Japan and the other from an independent, qualified source from the applicants' US/Canadian institution. **Deadline:** January 30. **Remarks:** Established in 2008. **Contact:** K. Malaika Walton, Associate Director of Governance, at Grants&Awards@snmmi.org. Phone: 703-652-6782.

10446 ■ Susan C. Weiss Clinical Advancement Scholarship *(Other/Scholarship)*

Purpose: To support technologists who are pursuing clinical advancement through didactic educational programs. **Focus:** Biological and clinical sciences. **Qualif.:** Applicants must demonstrate financial need; be currently enrolled in didactic educational programs (ex. CT, DEXA, physics, statistics); complete the said class or program; and members of the SNMTS;active member of the SNMMI-TS. **Criteria:** Candidates will be judged based on the criteria designed by the Scholarship Committee.

Funds Avail.: $500. **Duration:** Annual. **To Apply:** Applicants must provide a current resume or curriculum vitae; demonstrate financial need; provide a professional reference letter as either a signed original on institution letterhead or a scanned copy of the signed original. **Deadline:** March 2. **Remarks:** The scholarship was established in honor of Susan C. Weiss, SNMMI-TS Past-President and former Executive Director of the Education and Research Foundation for SNMMI. **Contact:** K. Malaika Walton, Associate Director of Governance; Phone: 703-652-6782; Email: Grants&Awards@snmmi.org.

10447 ■ Society for Obstetric Anesthesia and Perinatology (SOAP)
6737 W Washington St., Ste. 4210
Milwaukee, WI 53214
Ph: (414)389-8611
Fax: (414)276-7704
E-mail: soap@soap.org
URL: www.soap.org
Social Media: www.facebook.com/SOAPHQ
twitter.com/SOAPHQ

10448 ■ SOAP/Kybele International Outreach Grant *(Advanced Professional, Professional development/Grant)*

Purpose: To provide funding needed to get involved with international outreach projects in order to identify and train future leaders in international outreach from SOAP members; to encourage research in collaboration with host countries with the goal of enhancing the practice of obstetric anasthesia in those countries. **Focus:** Anesthesiology. **Criteria:** Selection will be based on the committee's criteria.

Funds Avail.: $5,000. **Duration:** Annual. **Number Awarded:** 6. **To Apply:** All documents should be in 12-point font, with at least 0.75-inch margins and must include a letter from the chair of the department confirming the department commitment to granting the time needed to

Awards are arranged alphabetically below their administering organizations

fulfill the requirements of the grant; if the applicants are fellows, a letter from the fellowship director is needed highlighting the fellow's suitability for the program; curriculum vitae of the applicants; one page highlighting previous experience and motivation for seeking the grant; 1-3 pages for a proposed research project; letter of support from at least one SOAP member with international outreach experience. The letter must address the applicant's suitability for the program and budget. The proposed research project should include the following section: title; specific aims; significance; methods; anticipated impact; potential collaborators; country of proposed work. Application materials to be submit by either email or mail. **Deadline:** April. **Contact:** SOAP/ Kybele International Outreach Grant, Society for Obstetric Anesthesia and Perinatology, 6737 W. Washington St., Ste., 4210, Milwaukee, WI, 5321; Phone: 414-389-8611; Email: soap@soap.org.

10449 ■ Society of Otorhinolaryngology and Head-Neck Nurses (SOHN)

207 Downing St.
New Smyrna Beach, FL 32168
Ph: (386)428-1695
Fax: (386)423-7566
E-mail: info@sohnnurse.com
URL: sohnnurse.com
Social Media: www.facebook.com/sohnnurse
www.linkedin.com/groups/4245782/profile
twitter.com/sohnnurse
youtube.com/user/sohnnurse

10450 ■ SOHN Allied Health to BSN Degree Scholarship *(Undergraduate/Scholarship)*

Purpose: To provide opportunities for professional interaction, education and growth. **Focus:** Medicine; Nursing. **Qualif.:** Applicants must be current members of SOHN. **Criteria:** Selection will be based on the committee's criteria.

Funds Avail.: No specific amount. **Duration:** Annual. **To Apply:** Applicants must complete and submit the application form and must include the following: a copy of current enrollment in a graduate in nursing program (min.6 hours/semester); recent transcripts (must be min. 3.0 GPA on a 4.0 scale); tuition cost per hour; a statement/documentation of need for financial assistance and current assistance received; letters of recommendation from; SOHN member, an instructor or manager (not the same person as SOHN member), any person applicant may wish to select (letters should contain statements identifying the commitment, learning ability, and quality of performance of the applicant); narrative (750-1000 words) describing applicant's past or current SOHN involvement, future SOHN goals and desire for advancing degree in nursing. **Deadline:** July 1.

10451 ■ SOHN Graduate Degree Scholarship *(Undergraduate/Scholarship)*

Purpose: To provide opportunities to deserving students who exemplify interests in the professional growth of the ORL. **Focus:** Nursing. **Qualif.:** Applicants must be current members of SOHN and may not be members of SOHN board of directors. **Criteria:** Selection will be based on the committee's criteria.

Funds Avail.: $1,000 - $1,500. **Duration:** Annual. **To Apply:** Applicants must include the following together with the application; copy of current enrollment in a graduate in nursing program (minimum of 6 hours/semester); copy of

resent transcripts (must be minimum 3.0 GPA on 4.0 scale); tuition cost per hour including a statement/documentation of need for financial assistance and current assistance received; letters of recommendation from SOHN members, instructors or managers or from any person that the applicants wish to select and; narrative composed of 750-1000 words describing the applicant's past or current SOHN involvement, future SOHN goals and desire for advancing the applicant's degree in nursing. **Deadline:** July 1.

10452 ■ SOHN RN to BSN Degree Scholarship *(Undergraduate/Scholarship)*

Purpose: To provide opportunities to deserving students who exemplify interests in the professional growth of the ORL. **Focus:** Nursing. **Qualif.:** Applicants must be current members of SOHN and may not be members of SOHN board of directors. **Criteria:** Selection will be based on the committee's criteria.

Funds Avail.: No specific amount. **Duration:** Annual. **To Apply:** Applicants must include the following together with the application; copy of current enrollment in a graduate in nursing program (minimum of 6 hours/semester); copy of resent transcripts (must be minimum 3.0 GPA on 4.0 scale); tuition cost per hour including a statement/documentation of need for financial assistance and current assistance received; letters of recommendation from SOHN members, instructors or managers or from any person that the applicants wish to select and; narrative composed of 750-1000 words describing the applicant's past or current SOHN involvement, future SOHN goals and desire for advancing the applicant's degree in nursing. **Deadline:** July 1.

10453 ■ Society of Outdoor Recreation Professionals (SORP)

PO Box 221
Marienville, PA 16239
Ph: (814)927-8212
Fax: (814)927-6659
E-mail: brenda@recpro.org
URL: www.recpro.org
Social Media: www.facebook.com/SORP2
www.linkedin.com/groups/1400127
www.youtube.com/channel/UCTDbU22qy1rPo-ZUDdr8Kvw

10454 ■ SORP Student Conference Scholarship *(Graduate, Undergraduate/Scholarship)*

Purpose: To support undergraduate or graduate students enrolled full-time in an outdoor recreation research, planning, management, policy or closely related degree program. **Focus:** General studies/Field of study not specified. **Qualif.:** Applicants must be undergraduate or graduate students enrolled full-time in an SORP accredited recreation management, planning or closely related degree program.

Funds Avail.: $500 for lodging and travel-related expenses; $275 (250+25) is for full-conference registration and a one-year membership to SORP. **Duration:** Annual. **Number Awarded:** Varies. **To Apply:** Applicants must complete the application form and submit the current resume and transcript; 500-word narrative statement of academic and career goals, and how attending the SORP Conference will be helpful towards achieving these goals; and letter of recommendation from Major Professor/Academic Advisor. **Deadline:** January 16. **Contact:** For application questions: Michael Bradley; Email: michael.bradley@eku.edu; For as-

Awards are arranged alphabetically below their administering organizations

sistance with the online form: Brenda Adams-Weyant; Email: Brenda@RecPro.org.

10455 ■ Society for Pediatric Dermatology (SPD)

8365 Keystone Crossing, Ste. 107
Indianapolis, IN 46240
Ph: (317)202-0224
Fax: (317)205-9481
E-mail: info@pedsderm.net
URL: pedsderm.net
Social Media: www.facebook.com/SocietyforPedsDerm
www.linkedin.com/company/5136777
twitter.com/SocietyPedsDerm

10456 ■ Pilot Project Grant *(Professional development/Award, Grant)*

Purpose: To support the initiation of studies important to Pediatric Dermatology. **Focus:** Child care.

Funds Avail.: Up to $7,500. **Duration:** Annual. **Deadline:** May 1; December 1. **Contact:** Jennifer Hand, MD, SPD Awards & Grants Committee Chair at hand.jennifer@mayo.edu; Joyce Teng, MD, PhD, PeDRA Grants Committee Chair at jteng3@stanford.edu.

10457 ■ William Weston Research Award *(Postgraduate/Grant)*

Purpose: To support young investigators seeking to establish a research program and to members of the Society. **Focus:** Dermatology; Medical research; Medicine, Pediatric.

Funds Avail.: Up to $15,000. **Duration:** Annual. **Deadline:** May 1 first cycle; December 7 second cycle.

10458 ■ Society of Pediatric Nurses (SPN)

330 N Wabash Ave., Ste. 2000
Chicago, IL 60611-7621
Ph: (312)321-5154
Fax: (312)673-6754
E-mail: info@pedsnurses.org
URL: www.pedsnurses.org
Social Media: www.facebook.com/PedsNurses
www.linkedin.com/company/society-of-pediatric-nurses
twitter.com/PedsNurses

10459 ■ Society of Pediatric Nurses Academic Educational Scholarship *(Undergraduate, Graduate/Scholarship)*

Purpose: To help SPN members meet academic goals. **Focus:** Nursing. **Qualif.:** Applicants must be SPN members and may include research studies or EBP projects ranging from pilot work to large, multisite studies.

Duration: Annual. **Deadline:** November 30.

10460 ■ Society for Pediatric Pathology (SPP)

111 West Jackson Blvd.Suite 1412
Chicago, IL 60604
Ph: (212)297-2196
E-mail: spp@kellencompany.com
URL: www.spponline.org

10461 ■ A. James McAdams Short-Term Study Stipend *(Professional development/Grant)*

Purpose: To facilitate training and expertise of pediatric pathologists in a specialized area of pediatric pathology.

Focus: Medicine, Pediatric. **Criteria:** Selection will be based on the committee's criteria.

Funds Avail.: Up to $5,000. **Duration:** Annual. **Number Awarded:** 1. **To Apply:** Application Cover Sheet download: MS Word | PDF. **Deadline:** May 1. **Contact:** Applications and inquiries should be directed to Dr. Gino Somers, Email: gino.somers@sickkids.ca.

10462 ■ SPP Young Investigator Research Grant *(Postdoctorate, Master's/Grant)*

Purpose: To foster research within the Society by providing funds to young investigators in the field of pediatric pathology and to fund a pilot project which will lead to long-term research support from the other granting agencies. **Focus:** Medicine, Pediatric; Pathology. **Qualif.:** Applicants must be hold the degree of MD, PhD, DDS, DVM, or DO. **Criteria:** Selection will be based on financial need.

Funds Avail.: $15,000. **Duration:** Annual. **Number Awarded:** 1. **To Apply:** Application Cover Sheet download: MS Word | PDF, Itemized budget, Personal Statement. **Deadline:** February 21.

10463 ■ Gordon F. Vawter Pathologist-in-Training Award *(Graduate, Postgraduate/Grant)*

Purpose: The purpose of this award is to recognize meritorious work of medical students, residents, and fellows. **Focus:** Pathology. **Qualif.:** Applicant must be the first author of a platform or poster presentation at an interim or annual SPP meeting.

Funds Avail.: $500. **Duration:** Annual. **Number Awarded:** 1. **Remarks:** Established in 1991.

10464 ■ Society for Pediatric Radiology (SPR)

1891 Preston White Dr.
Reston, VA 20191
Ph: (703)648-0680
E-mail: spr@acr.org
URL: www.pedrad.org
Social Media: www.facebook.com/SocPedRad
twitter.com/SocPedRad

10465 ■ Heidi Patriquin Award for International Education *(Advanced Professional, Professional development/Fellowship)*

Purpose: To subsidize the expenses of a pediatric radiologist per year who practices outside of North America. **Focus:** Medicine, Pediatric; Radiology. **Qualif.:** Applicants should be pediatric radiologists who reside and practice outside of North America. **Criteria:** Selection priority will be given to applicants who have never attended an SPR meeting.

Funds Avail.: $3,000. **Duration:** Annual. **Number Awarded:** 1. **To Apply:** Applicants should submit a copy of his or her CV and a personal statement as to why attending the SPR meeting would be personally beneficial. **Deadline:** October 15. **Remarks:** Established in 2003. **Contact:** Jennifer K. Boylan, MA, Managing Director, The SPR Research & Education Foundation, 1891 Preston White Dr., Reston, VA, 20191; Email: jboylan@acr.org.

10466 ■ Society for Pediatric Radiology Research Fellows *(Graduate, Other/Fellowship)*

Purpose: To provide young investigators an opportunity to gain further insight into scientific investigation and to

Awards are arranged alphabetically below their administering organizations

develop competence in research techniques and methods. **Focus:** Radiology.

Duration: One year. **Deadline:** March 15.

10467 ■ Society for Pediatric Radiology Seed Grants *(Graduate, Other/Grant)*

Purpose: To foster research and education in pediatric radiology. **Focus:** Radiology. **Qualif.:** One of the member of the investigator team must be a member of the Society for the Pediatric Radiology (SPR); holds a full-time faculty position in an educational institution; and in a department of diagnostic radiology, radiation oncology or nuclear medicine and have completed all advanced training. **Criteria:** Selection is based on scientific merit and appropriateness.

Funds Avail.: $10,000 or less. **Duration:** One year. **To Apply:** Applicants must submit one printed copy (with signatures) and one electronic version of the completed application.**Deadline:** March 15. **Contact:** Jennifer Boylan, Email: jboylan@acr.org.

10468 ■ The Society for Pediatric Urology (SPU)
500 Cummings Center Suite 4400
Beverly, MA 01915
Ph: (978)927-8330
Fax: (978)524-0498
URL: www.spuonline.org

10469 ■ John W. Duckett Jr., AFUD Pediatric Research Scholarships *(Undergraduate/Scholarship)*

Purpose: To promote pediatric urology, appropriate practice, education as well as exchanges between practitioners involved in the treatment of genito urinary disorders of children. **Focus:** Medicine, Pediatric. **Qualif.:** Applicant must be taking up pediatric medicine. **Criteria:** Application will be evaluated by the Scholarship Committee.

Funds Avail.: $10,000. **To Apply:** Applicant must fill out the application form and submit to the American Foundation of Urologic Disease. **Contact:** 1000 Corporate Blvd., Ste. 410, Linthicum, MD 21090, Phone: 410-689-3990, Fax: 410-689-3998, Toll free: 800-828-7866.

10470 ■ SPU Research Grant *(Undergraduate/Grant)*

Purpose: To promote pediatric urological research and to develop innovation and impact-creating research proposals that are competitive for sustainable outside funding. **Focus:** Medicine, Pediatric. **Qualif.:** Applicant must be a pediatric urological clinicians in practice or clinicians and researchers serving within divisions or departments of pediatric urology; must be member if the SPU or have member sponsorship. **Criteria:** Selection is based on the SPU research grant committee.

Funds Avail.: Up to $30,000. **Duration:** Annual; one year. **Number Awarded:** 1. **To Apply:** Applicants must submit 2-page Letter of Intent (LOI) summarizing the proposal; letter of commitment from the Chairman of the department; curriculum vitae and complete application form. **Deadline:** January 16.

10471 ■ Society of Petroleum Engineers - Evangeline Section (SPE)
PO Box 52356
Lafayette, LA 70505-2356
URL: connect.spe.org/evangeline/home

10472 ■ Children of Evangeline Section Scholarships *(Graduate, Undergraduate/Scholarship)*

Purpose: To provide support to eligible children of Evangeline Section members pursuing a master's degree program. **Focus:** General studies/Field of study not specified. **Criteria:** Selection is based on the submitted application and materials.

Funds Avail.: $1,000 each (paid in two installments). **Duration:** Annual. **To Apply:** Applicants must submit a completed application form along with a certified college (last semester available) or high school transcript (ACT/SAT score reports are also required for entering freshmen). **Deadline:** July 1. **Contact:** Scholarship Committee Chairman, Children of the Evangeline Section Membership Scholarship, SPE Evangeline Section, PO Box 52356, Lafayette, LA, 70505-2356.

10473 ■ Petroleum Engineering Scholarships *(Undergraduate/Scholarship)*

Purpose: To support the education of students majoring in petroleum engineering at Louisiana State University (LSU) or the University of Louisiana at Lafayette (ULL). **Focus:** Engineering, Petroleum. **Qualif.:** Applicants must be petroleum engineering students at LSU or ULL. **Criteria:** Selection is based on academic excellence and application materials.

Funds Avail.: No specific amount. **Duration:** Annual.

10474 ■ Society for Photographic Education (SPE)
2530 Superior Ave. E, Ste. 407
Cleveland, OH 44114
Ph: (216)622-2733
Fax: (216)622-2712
URL: www.spenational.org
Social Media: www.facebook.com/
  SocietyforPhotographicEducation
instagram.com/spenational/
twitter.com/spenational

10475 ■ SPE Student Awards for Innovations in Imaging *(Undergraduate, Graduate/Scholarship)*

Purpose: To offset the cost of attending SPE's national conference. **Focus:** Photography. **Qualif.:** Applicants must be current, matriculated undergraduate or graduate students enrolled at a post-secondary institution majoring/concentrating in photography and not graduating before the end of the academic year; must be student members of SPE or become members before submitting their scholarship application. **Criteria:** Selection will be based on the committee's criteria and on merits of submitted portfolios.

Funds Avail.: $500 travel stipend. **Duration:** Annual. **To Apply:** Applicants must submit brief resume, including name, address, phone number,email address and current institutional affiliation, andeducational and professional experience; cohesive body of work with no more than five images;images around 1280 x 1280 px @ 72 ppi are ideal for goodimage quality and fast upload. **Deadline:** October 15.

10476 ■ Society of Physics Students (SPS)
1 Physics Ellipse
College Park, MD 20740
Ph: (301)209-3007

Awards are arranged alphabetically below their administering organizations

Fax: (301)209-3082
E-mail: sps@aip.org
URL: www.spsnational.org
Social Media: www.facebook.com/SPSNational
www.instagram.com/spsnational
www.youtube.com/user/SPSnational

10477 ■ Peggy Dixon Two-Year Scholarships
(Undergraduate/Scholarship)

Purpose: To support students from a two-year college transitioning into a physics bachelor's degree program. **Focus:** Physics. **Qualif.:** Applicants must be undergraduate member of the SPS national organization; have completed at least one semester or quarter of the introductory physics sequence; and be transitioning from a two-year college into a physics bachelor's degree program. **Criteria:** Selection is based on high scholarship performance both in physics and overall studies; exhibition of the potential and intention for continued scholastic development in physics; active participation in SPS programs.

Funds Avail.: $2,000. **Duration:** Annual. **Number Awarded:** 1. **To Apply:** Applicants must submit completed application form; certified and official transcript (submitted directly by the applicant's college/university); letters from at least two full-time members of the faculty; certification from the Department Chair; Written statement of the applicant's participation in SPS activities; Written statement from the applicant's SPS Advisor; Written statement of the applicant's career objectives, including experiences and ambitions with regard to teaching physics. **Deadline:** March 15. **Remarks:** The scholarship is named in memory of Dr. Peggy A. Dixon, SPS and Sigma Pi Sigma Historian from 1992-2003. **Contact:** SPS Scholarship Program 1 Physics Ellipse College Park, MD 20740; E-mail: SPS-Programs@aip.org.

10478 ■ Leadership Scholarships *(Undergraduate/Scholarship)*

Purpose: To encourage the study of physics and the pursuit of high scholarship. **Focus:** Physics. **Qualif.:** Applicants must be undergraduate members of the SPS national organization; must be a junior according to institution's definition, and plan to be enrolled as an undergraduate for at least one more semester. **Criteria:** Selection will be based on SPS scholarship committee, high scholarship performance both in physics and overall studies; the exhibition of the potential and intention for continued scholastic development in physics, and active participation in SPS programs.

Funds Avail.: $2,000-$5,000. **Duration:** Annual. **Number Awarded:** Varies. **To Apply:** Applications can be submitted online; must include an official, current transcript must be sent directly to the SPS scholarship program by the college or university; two letters of recommendation from faculty members familiar with the applicant and his or her qualifications; written statement of the career objectives; written statement of the participation in SPS activities. **Deadline:** March 15. **Contact:** E-mail: SPS-Programs@aip.org.

10479 ■ Herbert Levy Memorial Scholarship
(Undergraduate/Scholarship)

Purpose: To support worthy, needy physics students to attain a quality physics education. **Focus:** Physics. **Qualif.:** Applicants must be undergraduate member of the SPS national organization; must demonstrate financial need through a written statement; Students who expect to complete their bachelor's degree in physics in the spring or summer following the March 22 deadline are not eligible.

Funds Avail.: $2,000. **Duration:** Annual. **Number Awarded:** 1. **To Apply:** Applicants must submit completed application form; general information form; Transcript: An official, current transcript must be sent directly to the SPS Scholarship Program by the applicant's college or university; Two letters of recommendation from faculty members familiar with the applicant and his or her qualifications; Written statement of financial need from the applicant; Written statement of career objectives; Certification from the Department Chair that the applicant is in good standing with the department and making satisfactory progress toward the degree. **Deadline:** March 15. **Remarks:** The scholarship was named in honor of Dr. Herbert Levy. **Contact:** SPS Scholarship Program, 1 Physics Ellipse College Pk., MD, 20740; E-mail: SPS-Programs@aip.org.

10480 ■ SPS Future Teacher Scholarships
(Undergraduate/Scholarship)

Purpose: To support an SPS member who is participating in a teacher education program and who plans to pursue a career in physics education. **Focus:** Physics. **Qualif.:** Applicants must be undergraduate member of the SPS national organization; participating in a teacher education program.

Funds Avail.: $2,000. **Duration:** Annual. **Number Awarded:** 1. **To Apply:** Applicants must submit completed application form; certified and official transcript (submitted directly by the applicant's college/university); letters from at least two full-time members of the faculty; certification from the Department Chair; Written statement of the applicant's participation in SPS activities; Written statement from the applicant's SPS Advisor; Written statement of the applicant's career objectives, including experiences and ambitions with regard to teaching physics. **Deadline:** March 15. **Contact:** SPS Scholarship Program 1 Physics Ellipse College Park, MD 20740; E-mail: SPS-Programs@aip.org.

10481 ■ SPS Leadership Scholarships
(Undergraduate/Scholarship)

Purpose: To encourage the students to pursue their career in study of physics. **Focus:** Physics. **Qualif.:** Applicants must be undergraduate members of the SPS national organization; must be a junior according to institution's definition, and plan to be enrolled as an undergraduate for at least one more semester.

Funds Avail.: $2,000 - $5,000. **Duration:** Annual. **Number Awarded:** Varies. **To Apply:** Applicants must submit completed application form; certified and official transcript (submitted directly by the applicant's college/university); letters from at least two full-time members of the faculty; certification from the Department Chair; Written statement of the applicant's participation in SPS activities; Written statement from the applicant's SPS Advisor; Written statement of the applicant's career objectives, including experiences and ambitions with regard to teaching physics. **Deadline:** March 15. **Contact:** E-mail: SPS-Programs@aip.org.

10482 ■ Society of Plastics Engineers (SPE)
100 Reserve Rd., Ste. B310
Danbury, CT 06810
Ph: (203)740-5400
Fax: (203)740-5405
E-mail: customerrelations@4spe.org
URL: www.4spe.org

Awards are arranged alphabetically below their administering organizations

Social Media: www.facebook.com/4SPEplastics
instagram.com/4spe_plastics
www.linkedin.com/company/4spe
twitter.com/4spe_plastics

10483 ■ Robert E. Cramer Product Design & Development Scholarship *(Undergraduate/ Scholarship)*

Purpose: To support those who are studying in the field(s) of plastics engineering. **Focus:** Engineering, Chemical; Engineering, Industrial; Engineering, Materials; Science. **Qualif.:** Applicants must be undergraduate in institutions, colleges, or universities in a science, technology, or engineering discipline that is associated with the Plastics Industry **Criteria:** Recipients will be selected based on financial need and academic standing.

Funds Avail.: $1,000. **Duration:** Annual. **To Apply:** Applicants must include completed application form; two from a teacher or school official and one from an employer or non-relative; a high school and/or college transcript for the past two years; a list of current and past school activities, community activities, and honors; a listing of employment history; a one-to-two-page typewritten statement telling why they are applying for the scholarship, qualifications, educational and career goals in the plastic industry. **Deadline:** April 1. **Contact:** The SPE Foundation, 6 Berkshire Blvd., Ste. 306, Bethel, CT 06801; Phone: 203-740-5457; E-mail: foundation@4spe.org.

10484 ■ Robert G. Dailey SPE Detroit Section Scholarship *(Undergraduate/Scholarship)*

Purpose: To support those who are studying in the field(s) of plastics engineering. **Focus:** Engineering, Biomedical; Engineering, Industrial; Engineering, Materials; Science. **Qualif.:** Applicants must be undergraduate students in institutions, colleges, or universities in a science, technology, or engineering discipline that is associated with the Plastics Industry. **Criteria:** Recipients will be selected based on financial need and academic standing.

Funds Avail.: $3,000. **Duration:** Annual. **To Apply:** Applicants must include completed application form (attached); two recommendation letters (one from a teacher or school official and one from an employer or non-relative, all of whom know the applicants well); copy of college transcript for the past school year; a resume noting items like school and community activities, awards and honors, previous employment information, and any other plastics specific items of interest; and, one to two page statement telling why they are applying for the scholarship, why consider themselves as good candidates, and their educational and career goals in the plastics industry. **Deadline:** April 1. **Contact:** The SPE Foundation, 6 Berkshire Blvd., Ste. 306, Bethel, CT 06801; Phone: 203-740-5457; E-mail: foundation@4spe.org.

10485 ■ Lew Erwin Extrusion Division Scholarship *(Master's, Postgraduate, Doctorate/Scholarship)*

Purpose: To promote scientific and engineering knowledge relating to plastics, and support research in polymer extrusion. **Focus:** Engineering, Chemical; Engineering, Industrial; Engineering, Materials; Science. **Qualif.:** Applicants must be Ph.D. candidates, or Seniors/Masters research in polymer extrusion. **Criteria:** Recipients will be selected based on financial need and academic standing.

Funds Avail.: $5,000. **Duration:** Annual. **To Apply:** Applicants must include completed application form; one

recommendation letter which must be from the Faculty Advisor associated with the Senior, MS, or Ph.D. project; a high school and/or college transcript for the past two years; a list of current and past school activities, community activities, and honors; a listing of employment history. **Deadline:** April 1. **Contact:** The SPE Foundation, 6 Berkshire Blvd., Ste. 306, Bethel, CT 06801; Phone: 203-740-5457; E-mail: foundation@4spe.org.

10486 ■ Fleming/Blaszcak Scholarships *(Undergraduate, Graduate/Scholarship)*

Purpose: To promote scientific and engineering knowledge relating to plastics, as well as to encourage Mexican-American students in the plastics field. **Focus:** Engineering, Chemical; Engineering, Industrial; Engineering, Materials; Science. **Qualif.:** Applicants must be full-time undergraduate or graduate students of Mexican or Mexican-American descent who have expressed an interest in plastics and are majoring in or taking courses beneficial to a career in the plastics industry. **Criteria:** Recipients will be selected based on financial need and academic standing.

Duration: Annual. **To Apply:** Applicants must include completed application form; two from a teacher or school official and one from an employer or non-relative; a high school and/or college transcript for the past two years; a list of current and past school activities, community activities, and honors; a listing of employment history; a one-to-two-page typewritten statement telling why they are applying for the scholarship, qualifications, educational and career goals in the plastic industry. **Deadline:** April 1. **Contact:** The SPE Foundation, 6 Berkshire Blvd., Ste. 306, Bethel, CT 06801; Phone: 203-740-5457; E-mail: foundation@4spe.org.

10487 ■ Composites Division/Harold Giles Scholarship *(Undergraduate, Graduate/Scholarship)*

Purpose: To support those who are studying in the field(s) of plastics engineering. **Focus:** Engineering, Chemical; Engineering, Industrial; Engineering, Materials; Science. **Qualif.:** Applicants must be undergraduate or graduate students in institutions, colleges, or universities; must have demonstrated or expressed interest in the plastic industry and be in good academic standing who have experience in the thermoforming industry, such as courses taken, research conducted, or jobs held. **Criteria:** Recipients will be selected based on financial need and academic standing.

Funds Avail.: $3,500 each. **Duration:** Annual. **Number Awarded:** 2. **To Apply:** Applicants must include completed application form; two from a teacher or school official and one from an employer or non-relative; a high school and/or college transcript for the past two years; a list of current and past school activities, community activities, and honors; a listing of employment history; a one-to-two-page typewritten statement telling why they are applying for the scholarship, qualifications, educational and career goals in the plastic industry. **Deadline:** April 1. **Contact:** The SPE Foundation, 6 Berkshire Blvd., Ste. 306, Bethel, CT 06801; Phone: 203-740-5457; E-mail: foundation@4spe.org.

10488 ■ Gulf Coast Hurricane Scholarship *(Undergraduate/Scholarship)*

Purpose: To promote scientific and engineering knowledge relating to plastics, and encourage students in plastics engineering. **Focus:** Engineering, Chemical; Engineering, Industrial; Engineering, Materials; Science. **Qualif.:** Applicants must be residents of, and attending college in,

Awards are arranged alphabetically below their administering organizations

Florida, Alabama, Mississippi, Louisiana, or Texas; must be undergraduate students who have expressed an interest in plastics and are majoring in or taking courses beneficial to a career in the plastics industry. **Criteria:** Recipients will be selected based on financial need and academic standing.

Duration: Annual. **To Apply:** Applicants must include completed application form; two from a teacher or school official and one from an employer or non-relative; a high school and/or college transcript for the past two years; a list of current and past school activities, community activities, and honors; a listing of employment history; a one-to-two-page typewritten statement telling why they are applying for the scholarship, qualifications, educational and career goals in the plastic industry. **Deadline:** April 1. **Contact:** The SPE Foundation, 6 Berkshire Blvd., Ste. 306, Bethel, CT 06801; Phone: 203-740-5457; E-mail: foundation@4spe.org.

10489 ■ Injection Molding Division Scholarship
(Undergraduate, Graduate/Scholarship)

Purpose: To support those who are studying in the field(s) of plastics engineering. **Focus:** Engineering, Chemical; Engineering, Industrial; Engineering, Materials; Science. **Qualif.:** Applicants must be undergraduate or graduate students in institutions, colleges, or universities; must have demonstrated or expressed interest in the plastic industry and be in good academic standing who have experience in the injection molding industry, such as courses taken, research conducted, or jobs held. **Criteria:** Recipients will be selected based on financial need and academic standing.

Funds Avail.: $3,000. **Duration:** Annual. **To Apply:** Applicants must include completed application form; two from a teacher or school official and one from an employer or non-relative; a high school and/or college transcript for the past two years; a list of current and past school activities, community activities, and honors; a listing of employment history; a one-to-two-page typewritten statement telling why they are applying for the scholarship, qualifications, educational and career goals in the plastic industry. **Deadline:** April 1. **Contact:** The SPE Foundation, 6 Berkshire Blvd., Ste. 306, Bethel, CT 06801; Phone: 203-740-5457; E-mail: foundation@4spe.org.

10490 ■ Thermoset Division/James I. Mackenzie and James H. Cunningham Scholarships
(Undergraduate, Graduate/Scholarship)

Purpose: To support those who are studying in the field(s) of plastics engineering. **Focus:** Engineering, Chemical; Engineering, Industrial; Engineering, Materials; Science. **Qualif.:** Applicants must be undergraduate or graduate students in institutions, colleges, or universities; must have demonstrated or expressed interest in the plastic industry and be in good academic standing who have experience in the thermoset industry, such as courses taken, research conducted, or jobs held. **Criteria:** Recipients will be selected based on financial need and academic standing.

Funds Avail.: $2,500 each. **Duration:** Annual. **Number Awarded:** 2. **To Apply:** Applicants must imclude completed application form (attached); two recommendation letters (one from a teacher or school official and one from an employer or non-relative, all of whom know the applicants well); copy of college transcript for the past school year; a resume noting items like school and community activities, awards and honors, previous employment information, and any other plastics specific items of interest; and, one to two page statement telling why they are applying for the

scholarship, why consider themselves as good candidates, and their educational and career goals in the plastics industry; moreover they must also document their experience in the thermoforming industry (courses taken, research conducted or jobs held). **Deadline:** April 1. **Contact:** SPE Foundation at foundation@4spe.org.

10491 ■ Salvatore J. Monte Thermoplastic Materials & Foams Division Scholarship *(Undergraduate/Scholarship)*

Purpose: To support those who are studying in the field(s) of plastics engineering. **Focus:** Engineering; Science. **Qualif.:** Applicants must be graduate or undergraduate; must document their experience in the thermoplastic materials & foams industry (courses taken, research conducted, or jobs held). **Criteria:** Recipients will be selected based on financial need and academic standing.

Funds Avail.: $2,500. **Duration:** Annual. **To Apply:** Applicants must include completed application form; two from a teacher or school official and one from an employer or non-relative; a high school and/or college transcript for the past two years; a list of current and past school activities, community activities, and honors; a listing of employment history; a one-to-two-page typewritten statement telling why they are applying for the scholarship, qualifications, educational and career goals in the plastic industry. **Deadline:** April 1. **Contact:** The SPE Foundation, 6 Berkshire Blvd., Ste. 306, Bethel, CT 06801; Phone: 203-740-5457; E-mail: foundation@4spe.org.

10492 ■ Ted and Ruth Neward Scholarships
(Undergraduate, Graduate/Scholarship)

Purpose: To support those who are studying in the field(s) of plastics engineering. **Focus:** Engineering, Chemical; Engineering, Industrial; Engineering, Materials; Science. **Qualif.:** Applicants must be U.S. citizens who are undergraduate or graduate students in institutions, colleges, or universities in a science, technology, or engineering discipline that is associated with the Plastics Industry. **Criteria:** Recipients will be selected based on financial need and academic standing; preference will be given to female students for the Ruth Neward Scholarship.

Funds Avail.: $3,000 each. **Duration:** Annual. **Number Awarded:** 4 (1 is restricted to a female student). **To Apply:** Applicants must include completed application form; two from a teacher or school official and one from an employer or non-relative; a high school and/or college transcript for the past two years; a list of current and past school activities, community activities, and honors; a listing of employment history; a one-to-two-page typewritten statement telling why they are applying for the scholarship, qualifications, educational and career goals in the plastic industry. **Deadline:** April 1. **Contact:** SPE Foundation at foundation@4spe.org.

10493 ■ Polymer Modifiers and Additives Division (PMAD) Scholarship (PMAD) *(Undergraduate, Graduate/Scholarship)*

Purpose: To support those who are studying in the field(s) of plastics engineering. **Focus:** Engineering; Science. **Qualif.:** Applicants must be undergraduate or graduate students in institutions, colleges, or universities; must have demonstrated or expressed interest in the plastic industry and be in good academic standing who have experience in the PMAD industry, such as courses taken, research conducted, or jobs held. **Criteria:** Recipients will be selected based on financial need and academic standing.

Awards are arranged alphabetically below their administering organizations

Funds Avail.: $2,000 each. **Duration:** Annual. **To Apply:** Applicants must include completed application form; two from a teacher or school official and one from an employer or non-relative; a high school and/or college transcript for the past two years; a list of current and past school activities, community activities, and honors; a listing of employment history; a one-to-two-page typewritten statement telling why they are applying for the scholarship, qualifications, educational and career goals in the plastic industry. **Deadline:** April 1. **Contact:** The SPE Foundation, 6 Berkshire Blvd., Ste. 306, Bethel, CT 06801; Phone: 203-740-5457; E-mail: foundation@4spe.org.

10494 ■ Carrie Fox Solin Blow Molding Division Memorial Scholarships *(Undergraduate/Scholarship)*

Purpose: To support those who are studying in the field(s) of plastics engineering. **Focus:** Engineering, Chemical; Engineering, Industrial; Engineering, Materials; Science. **Qualif.:** Applicants must be undergraduate students in a science, technology, or engineering discipline that is associated with the Plastics Industry (Plastics Engineering, Plastic Technology, Mechanical Engineering, Chemical Engineering, Industrial Engineering, or Materials Science) enrolled at any four-year program; must be SPE members; must have an accepted offer to work as a Co-op or Intern at a blow molding company or a company that services the blow molding industry with a duration of at least 2 months. **Criteria:** Recipients will be selected based on financial need and academic standing.

Duration: Annual. **To Apply:** Applicants must include completed application form (attached); two recommendation letters (one from a teacher or school official and one from an employer or non-relative, all of whom know the applicants well); copy of college transcript for the past school year; a resume noting items like school and community activities, awards and honors, previous employment information, and any other plastics specific items of interest; and, one to two page statement telling why they are applying for the scholarship, why consider themselves as good candidates, and their educational and career goals in the plastics industry; moreover, they must also submit an essay explaining importance of blow molding to the technical parts and packaging industries and why a career in the plastics industry is desired. **Deadline:** April 1. **Contact:** The SPE Foundation, 6 Berkshire Blvd., Ste. 306, Bethel, CT 06801; Phone: 203-740-5457; E-mail: foundation@4spe.org.

10495 ■ SPE Foundation General Scholarships *(Undergraduate, Graduate/Scholarship)*

Purpose: To support students who have demonstrated or expressed an interest in the plastics industry. **Focus:** Engineering, Chemical; Engineering, Industrial; Science. **Qualif.:** Applicants must be undergraduate and graduate students who have demonstrated or expressed an interest in the plastics industry; must be majoring in or taking courses that would be beneficial to a career in the plastics industry; include, but is not limited to, plastics engineering, polymer science, chemistry, physics, chemical engineering, mechanical engineering, and industrial engineering; must be in good standing with their colleges. **Criteria:** Recipients will be selected based on financial need and academic standing.

Funds Avail.: No specific amount. **Duration:** Annual. **To Apply:** Applicants must include a completed application form; three letters of recommendation, two from a teacher or school official and one from an employer or non-relative; a high school and/or college transcript for the past two

years; a list of current and past school activities, community activities, and honors; a listing of employment history; a one-to-two-page typewritten statement telling why they are applying for the scholarship, qualifications, educational and career goals in the plastic industry. **Deadline:** April 1. **Contact:** SPE Foundation at foundation@4spe.org.

10496 ■ SPE Vinyl Plastics Division Educational Grants *(Undergraduate/Grant)*

Purpose: To support those who are studying in the field(s) of plastics engineering. **Focus:** Engineering, Chemical; Engineering, Industrial; Engineering, Materials; Science. **Qualif.:** Applicants must be sons or daughters of the SPE Vinyl Division members in good standing for a minimum of two years; must be students who will be enrolled in college in the autumn of the award year. **Criteria:** Selection will be based on the Division's criteria.

Funds Avail.: $2,500 each. **Duration:** Annual. **Number Awarded:** Varies. **To Apply:** High school seniors must provide a school transcript for the last two years and college students must provide a transcript of their college courses. **Deadline:** April 29. **Contact:** David Owen; E-mail: david.owen.9@outlook.com.

10497 ■ Thermoforming Division Scholarship *(Undergraduate, Graduate/Scholarship)*

Purpose: To support those who are studying in the field(s) of plastics engineering. **Focus:** Engineering, Chemical; Engineering, Industrial; Engineering, Materials; Science. **Qualif.:** Applicants must be undergraduate or graduate students including those enrolled in AS or technical degree programs; must have experience in the thermoforming industry, such as courses taken, research conducted, or jobs held. **Criteria:** Recipients will be selected based on financial need and academic standing.

Funds Avail.: $2,500. **Duration:** Annual. **To Apply:** Applicants must include completed application form (attached); two recommendation letters (one from a teacher or school official and one from an employer or non-relative, all of whom know the applicants well); copy of college transcript for the past school year; a resume noting items like school and community activities, awards and honors, previous employment information, and any other plastics specific items of interest; and, one to two page statement telling why they are applying for the scholarship, why consider themselves as good candidates, and their educational and career goals in the plastics industry; moreover they must also document their experience in the thermoforming industry (courses taken, research conducted or jobs held). **Deadline:** April 1. **Contact:** The SPE Foundation, 6 Berkshire Blvd., Ste. 306, Bethel, CT 06801; Phone: 203-740-5457; E-mail: foundation@4spe.org.

10498 ■ Thermoplastic Elastomers Special Interest Group Scholarship *(Undergraduate, Graduate/Scholarship)*

Purpose: To support those who are studying in the field(s) of plastics engineering. **Focus:** Engineering, Chemical; Engineering, Industrial; Engineering, Materials; Science. **Qualif.:** Applicants must be rising graduate or junior/senior undergraduate students majoring in Plastics Engineering, Plastics Technology, Polymer Science, Polymer Engineering, Chemistry, Material Science, or Chemical Engineering; must be currently studying at a U.S. or Canadian college or university. **Criteria:** Recipients will be selected based on financial need and academic standing.

Funds Avail.: $1,000. **Duration:** Annual. **To Apply:** Applicants must include completed application form (at-

Awards are arranged alphabetically below their administering organizations

tached); two recommendation letters (one from a teacher or school official and one from an employer or non-relative, all of whom know the applicants well); copy of college transcript for the past school year; a resume noting items like school and community activities, awards and honors, previous employment information, and any other plastics specific items of interest; and, one to two page statement telling why they are applying for the scholarship, why consider themselves as good candidates, and their educational and career goals in the plastics industry; moreover, they must also document their experience in the thermoplastic elastomers industry (courses taken, research conducted or jobs held). **Deadline:** April 1. **Contact:** The SPE Foundation, 6 Berkshire Blvd., Ste. 306, Bethel, CT 06801; Phone: 203-740-5457; E-mail: foundation@4spe.org.

10499 ■ Society for the Preservation of Old Mills (SPOOM)
152 E Swamp Rd.
Doylestown, PA 18901
Ph: (847)255-0210
Fax: (312)573-1141
Free: 866-457-2582
URL: www.spoom.org

10500 ■ SPOOM Research Grants *(Graduate/Grant)*
Purpose: To provide financial assistance to researches on mills or milling-related subjects. **Focus:** Preservation. **Qualif.:** Applicants must be individuals seeking support for their research on mills or milling-related subject; must be active members of SPOOM; must be full-time students and in good standing. **Criteria:** Awards are granted based on the significance of the contribution that the proposed project will make to the preservation or understanding of mills or milling; conception, definition, organization and description of the requested project; likelihood that the applicants will complete the entire project; and support of a mill-related group with the eligibility criteria.

Funds Avail.: No specific amount. **Duration:** Annual. **Number Awarded:** Varies. **To Apply:** Applicants must prepare a one-page outline of the project; official graduate transcript; resume detailing applicable work experiences; and must complete application form available in the SPOOM office or website. **Deadline:** August 1. **Contact:** Sandy Jones Birkland, 122 Calistoga Road #134, Santa Rosa, CA 95409; Email: omnedit@sonic.net.

10501 ■ Society of Professional Journalists (SPJ)
Eugene Pulliam National Journalism Ctr.
3909 N Meridian St., Ste. 200
Indianapolis, IN 46208
Ph: (317)927-8000
URL: www.spj.org
Social Media: www.facebook.com/SocietyofProfessionalJournalists
www.instagram.com/spj_pics
www.linkedin.com/company/society-of-professional-journalists
twitter.com/spj_tweets

10502 ■ Eugene C. Pulliam Fellowship for Editorial Writing *(Other/Fellowship)*
Purpose: To enable a mid-career editorial writer or columnist to have time away from daily responsibilities for study and research. **Focus:** Writing. **Qualif.:** Applicant must hold a position as a part-time or full-time editorial writer or columnist at a news publication located in the United States; must have at least three years experience as an editorial writer or columnist; demonstrate outstanding writing and analytical abilities; all entries must be in English. **Criteria:** Selection is evaluated by a panel of judges, will review materials submitted by all the applicants and select the fellow.

Funds Avail.: $75,000. **Duration:** Annual. **Deadline:** June 22. **Remarks:** Established in 1977. **Contact:** E-mail:awards@spj.org.

10503 ■ Pulliam/Kilgore Freedom of Information Internships *(Undergraduate/Internship)*
Purpose: To encourage the free practice of journalism and stimulate high standards of ethical behavior. **Focus:** Journalism. **Qualif.:** Applicants must be journalism students who are entering or just completing their senior year, graduate journalism students or law students with a journalism background.

Funds Avail.: $400 per week. **Duration:** Annual; ten weeks. **Deadline:** December 7.

10504 ■ Society for Psychological Anthropology (SPA)
641 Huntington Ave.
Boston, MA
Ph: (617)432-2612
URL: www.aaanet.org/sections/SPA

10505 ■ Condon Prize for Best Student Essay in Psychological Anthropology *(Graduate, Undergraduate/Prize, Recognition)*
Purpose: To promote the study of adolescence, family and change among the Canadian Inuit. **Focus:** Anthropology. **Qualif.:** Applicants must be graduate or undergraduate students. **Criteria:** Selection will be based on the submitted essays.

Funds Avail.: $500. **Duration:** Annual. **Number Awarded:** 1. **To Apply:** Applicants Papers submitted for consideration should follow these guidelines: No evidence of the author's identity may be provided in any way through the text or by reference in the paper; the author's name and address, student affiliation, and the title of the paper must be provided on a separate cover sheet accompanying the manuscript, which should be identified by the title; all authors of papers submitted for this prize must either be in Doctoral, Master's or undergraduate degree programs at the time of submission. An entry should be accompanied by a photocopy of each author's student identification card or a photocopy of each author's most recent diploma. Only one entry is allowed per author; Papers must not exceed 35 double-spaced pages and must follow the style of Ethos; an electronic version of the paper must be submitted too. **Deadline:** July 10. **Contact:** Dr. Cameron Hay, SPA's Secretary; Email: hayrolmc@miamioh.edu.

10506 ■ SPA/Lemelson Fellowship Program *(Graduate/Award)*
Purpose: To provide graduate students working in the field of psychological anthropology with funding to pursue exploratory research on their dissertation research. **Focus:** Anthropology; Psychology. **Qualif.:** Applicants must student members of SPA enrolled in a graduate program at the

Awards are arranged alphabetically below their administering organizations

time and during the period of fellowship; must work in the field of psychological anthropology. **Criteria:** Selection will be based on the committee's criteria.

Funds Avail.: $3,000 - $6,000. **Duration:** Annual. **Number Awarded:** 6. **Deadline:** February 3. **Contact:** Harold Odden; Email: oddenh@ipfw.edu.

10507 ■ Society for the Psychological Study of Social Issues (SPSSI)
700 7th St. SE
Washington, DC 20003
Ph: (202)675-6956
Fax: (202)675-6902
Free: 877-310-7778
URL: www.spssi.org
Social Media: www.facebook.com/spssi?fref=ts
www.linkedin.com/company/society-for-the-psychological
-study-of-social-issues
twitter.com/spssi

10508 ■ Applied Social Issues Internship Program
(Undergraduate, Graduate, Doctorate/Internship)

Purpose: To encourage intervention projects, non-partisan advocacy projects, applied research, and writing and implementing public policy. Proposals are invited for applying social science principles to social issues, in cooperation with a community, city, or state government organization, public interest group, or other not-for-profit entity. **Focus:** Psychology; Social sciences. **Qualif.:** Applicants must be college seniors, graduate students or first-year postdoctoral students in psychology, applied social science and related disciplines; must be a SPSSI member.

Funds Avail.: $300-$2,500. **Duration:** Annual. **Number Awarded:** Varies. **To Apply:** Application should include: 3-6 page proposal including the proposed budget and a cover sheet with your name, address, phone number, e-mail address and title; short resume; letter from a faculty sponsor/supervisor; letter from an organizational sponsor. **Deadline:** March 15.

10509 ■ The Gordon Allport Intergroup Relations Prize *(Professional development/Monetary, Prize)*

Purpose: To recognize the best paper or article of the year on intergroup relations. **Focus:** Psychology; Social sciences. **Qualif.:** Applicants must submit works published during the calendar year preceding the year of submission; submissions are limited to articles, chapters, or other works published in their primary form (e.g., appearing in print for print journals or books or online for online-only journals or other volumes). **Criteria:** Selection will be based on originality of the contribution, whether theoretical or empirical, will be given special weight; the research area of intergroup relations includes such dimensions as age, gender, and socioeconomic status, as well as ethnicity.

Funds Avail.: $1,000. **Duration:** Annual. **Number Awarded:** Varies. **To Apply:** Applications can be submitted online. **Deadline:** June 15. **Remarks:** The prize was established to honor the memory of the late Dr. Gordon W. Allport, a founder and past president of SPSSI. Established in 1968.

10510 ■ The Clara Mayo Grants *(Graduate/Grant)*

Purpose: In support of masters' theses and pre-dissertation research on sexism, racism, or prejudice. **Focus:** Psychol-

ogy; Social sciences. **Criteria:** Preference given to students enrolled in a terminal master's program. Studies of the application of theory or the design of interventions or treatments to address these problems are welcome.

Funds Avail.: $1,000. **Duration:** Annual. **Number Awarded:** 6. **To Apply:** Applicants must submit complete Clara Mayo grants proposal form; faculty advisor's recommendation; institutional letter of agreement to match the funds requested, if available; can be submitted online. **Deadline:** May 15 Spring; October 10 Fall. **Remarks:** Established in 1998.

10511 ■ SPSSI Grants-In-Aid Program *(Graduate, Postdoctorate/Grant)*

Purpose: To support scientific research in social problem areas related to the basic interests and goals of SPSSI. **Focus:** Psychology. **Qualif.:** Applicants must be SPSSI member. **Criteria:** Preference will be given to students at the dissertation stage of their graduate careers.

Funds Avail.: Up to $2,000 for post-doctoral work; up to $1,000 for pre-doctoral work. **Duration:** Semiannual; twice a year. **To Apply:** Applicants must submit the following a cover letter with name, address, phone number, e-mail address and title for the proposal; an abstract of 100 words or less summarizing the proposed research; project purposes, theoretical rationale, and research methodology and analytical procedures to be employed; relevance of research to SPSSI goals and grants-in-aid criteria; status of human subjects review process (which must be satisfactorily completed before grant funds can be forwarded); resume of investigator (a faculty sponsor's recommendation must be provided if the investigator of a graduate student; support is seldom awarded to students who have not yet reached the dissertation stage); specific amount requested including a budget; for co-authored submissions, please indicate only one name and institution to whom a check should be jointly issued if selected for funding. **Deadline:** May 15 Spring; October 15 Fall. **Contact:** Email to awards@spssi.org.

10512 ■ Society for Public Health Education (SO-PHE)
10 G St. NE, Ste. 605
Washington, DC 20002-4242
Ph: (202)408-9804
Fax: (202)408-9815
E-mail: info@sophe.org
URL: www.sophe.org
Social Media: www.facebook.com/
SocietyforPublicHealthEducation
www.linkedin.com/company/791701
twitter.com/SOPHEtweets
www.youtube.com/user/sophestats

10513 ■ SOPHE/ATSDR Student Fellowships in Environmental Health or Emergency Preparedness *(Graduate/Fellowship)*

Purpose: To recognize, assist and train students working on projects that address environmental health or emergency preparedness from the perspective of health education or the behavioral sciences. **Focus:** Behavioral sciences; Health education. **Qualif.:** Applicants must be enrolled as a full-time student (9 credit hours or more) in a Master's or Doctoral degree program in environmental health, health education, health promotion, behavioral sciences or a

Awards are arranged alphabetically below their administering organizations

related field. Proposed projects should be either research or practice-based and focus on environmental health education/health promotion or environmental justice from the perspective of health education or the behavioral sciences. Proposed projects may be new or on-going, and the Applicants must have the primary role in conducting the project. Projects may be related to surveillance, risk factor identification, or intervention development, evaluation, or dissemination. Projects related to the development or use of theory in environmental health also are acceptable. **Criteria:** Proposals will be reviewed by a SOPHE/ATSDR Environmental Health Promotion Fellowship Selection Committee for their scientific and/or theoretical basis, originality and potential contribution to health education's role in environmental health promotion.

Funds Avail.: $1,500. **Duration:** Annual. **To Apply:** Applicants must submit a completed application form; a current resume or curriculum vitae; and a project proposal describing the rationale, intended purpose, process/ methodology, and potential contribution or impact of the project in 800 words or less. In addition, applications should include one letter of recommendation (from an internship coordinator, preceptor, faculty member or other professional); and one letter of support from a designated faculty member who plans to work with the applicants on the proposed project and can verify that the student is following a course of study. Letters should be sealed in envelopes with authors' signatures across the seal. **Deadline:** September 20. **Contact:** Application form and supporting documents must be submitted to Nicolette Warren at nwarren@ sophe.org.

10514 ■ SOPHE/CDC Student Fellowship in Unintentional Injury Prevention *(Doctorate, Master's/ Fellowship)*

Purpose: To assist and train graduate students working on unintentional injury prevention projects from the perspective of health education or behavioral sciences. **Focus:** Behavioral sciences; Health education. **Qualif.:** Applicants must be a full time student (9 credit hours or more) in a masters or doctoral degree program in health education, health promotion, behavioral sciences or a related field. **Criteria:** Proposals will be reviewed by the SOPHE/CDC Fellowship Selection Committee for their scientific and/or theoretical basis, originality, and potential contribution to health education's role in injury prevention and control.

Funds Avail.: $2,000. **Duration:** Annual. **To Apply:** Applicants must submit current resume or curriculum vitae; project proposal describing the rationale, intended purpose, process/methodology, and potential contribution or impact of the project in 800 words or less titled with applicant name; one letter of recommendation (from an internship coordinator, preceptor, faculty member or other professional); one letter of support from a designated faculty member who plans to work with the applicant on the proposed project and can verify the student is following a course of study in one of the above mentioned disciplines titled with applicant name. **Deadline:** May 15.

10515 ■ SOPHE/CDC Student Fellowships in Child, Adolescent and School Health *(Doctorate, Graduate, Master's/Fellowship)*

Purpose: To recognize, assist and train students working on projects that address aspects of child, adolescent, and school health from the perspective of health education, health promotion or the behavioral sciences. **Focus:** Behavioral sciences; Health education. **Qualif.:** Applicant must

be enrolled as a full-time student in a Master's or Doctoral degree program in health education, health promotion, behavioral sciences, or a related field. **Criteria:** Proposals will be reviewed by a SOPHE/CDC Child and Adolescent School Health Committee for their scientific and/or theoretical basis, originality, and potential contribution to health education's role in promoting Child, Adolescent and School Health.

Funds Avail.: $1,500. **Duration:** Annual. **To Apply:** Applicants must submit a completed application including resume/CV and project proposal; one letter of recommendation; and one letter of support. **Deadline:** September 20. **Contact:** Bryan Damis at bdamis@sophe.org, 202-408-9804.

10516 ■ Vivian Drenckhahn Student Scholarship *(Undergraduate, Graduate/Scholarship)*

Purpose: To provide support to both undergraduate and graduate level full-time students in their pursuit of educational and professional development in health education. **Focus:** Education; Public health. **Qualif.:** Applicants must be full-time undergraduate or graduate students who are national SOPHE members and who have excelled academically, demonstrated a commitment to addressing the public's health through a career in health education, and who have demonstrated financial need; must have completed at least one-third of coursework required for major; must currently be pursuing a health education degree.

Funds Avail.: $2,500. **Duration:** Annual. **Number Awarded:** 3. **To Apply:** Application can be submitted in online; must submit evidence of current enrollment in an appropriate full-time academic program; copy of the degree requirements for the program of study; current, official transcript including course titles; evidence of National SOPHE membership for at least 3 month; faculty mentor letter of recommendation (including required elements); student applicant statement (including required elements); must complete the SOPHE Vivian Drenckhahn Student Scholarship Demonstrated financial need form. **Deadline:** September 30. **Remarks:** Established in 2000. **Contact:** E-mail: mailto:bjohnson@sophe.org.

10517 ■ Society of Punjabi Engineers and Technologists of British Columbia (SPEATBC)
Ste. 101, 13049 76th Ave.
Surrey, BC, Canada V3W 2V7
Free: 888-907-7328
E-mail: speatbc@gmail.com
URL: speatbc.org
Social Media: www.facebook.com/SPEATBC
www.linkedin.com/company/speatbc

10518 ■ SPEATBC Entrance Scholarship *(Graduate, High School/Scholarship)*

Purpose: To provide financial assistance to qualified students pursuing a degree in Technical Engineering or any related fields of study. **Focus:** Engineering; Technology.

Funds Avail.: $1,000. **Duration:** Annual. **Number Awarded:** 5. **Deadline:** January 5. **Contact:** For queries:President, Jatinderpal Sandhu at speatbc@gmail.com; For application: application.speatbc@gmail.com.

10519 ■ Society for Range Management (SRM)
6901 S Pierce St., Ste. 230
Littleton, CO 80128

Awards are arranged alphabetically below their administering organizations

Ph: (303)986-3309
Fax: (303)986-3892
E-mail: info@rangelands.org
URL: rangelands.org
Social Media: www.facebook.com/
societyforrangemanagement
www.linkedin.com/groups/3841425/profile
twitter.com/rangelands

10520 ■ Masonic-Range Science Scholarship
(Undergraduate/Scholarship)

Purpose: To provide financial assistance to students that will help to aim their educational goal. **Focus:** Science. **Criteria:** Selection will be based upon how the applicant answers section D in the application form.

Funds Avail.: Varies. **Duration:** Annual; maximum of 8 semesters. **Number Awarded:** 1. **To Apply:** Applicants must submit a completed application form; copy of high school transcripts; official/certified copy of your SAT or ACT scores; two (2) letters of reference from teachers, county agents, employers, etc. **Deadline:** March 1.

10521 ■ Society of Satellite Professionals International (SSPI)
The New York Information Technology Ctr.
250 Park Ave., 7th Fl.
New York, NY 10177
Ph: (212)809-5199
Fax: (212)825-0075
E-mail: rbell@sspi.org
URL: www.sspi.org
Social Media: www.facebook.com/SSPIglobal
twitter.com/sspi
www.youtube.com/user/SSPIVideo

10522 ■ The SSPI Mid-Atlantic Chapter Scholarship
(Graduate, Undergraduate/Scholarship)

Purpose: To bring in and foster opportunities for the next generation of satellite professionals. **Focus:** Telecommunications systems. **Qualif.:** Candidates must be professionals showcasing the hard work, creativity, and vision of the next generation of satellite and aerospace; must be SSPI member. **Criteria:** Selection is based on different criteria by a panel of satellite industry professionals.

Funds Avail.: No specific amount. **Duration:** Annual. **Deadline:** April 13.

10523 ■ Society for a Science of Clinical Psychology (SSCP)
CO
URL: www.sscpweb.org
Social Media: twitter.com/_SSCP

10524 ■ SSCP Dissertation Grant Award *(Graduate/Grant)*

Purpose: To recognize and support students who have already received approval for their dissertation project. **Focus:** Psychology. **Qualif.:** Applicant must be a member of SSCP; should have current enrollment in an APA or CPA approved doctoral program in Clinical Psychology.

Funds Avail.: $500. **Duration:** Annual. **Number Awarded:** Up to 5. **To Apply:** Application should include Cover letter;

Research Plan; Abstract; CV; A letter from dissertation advisor; should submit via electronically. **Deadline:** November 15. **Contact:** Submit application electronically to Dr. Carolyn Becker, Email: cbecker@trinity.edu.

10525 ■ Society for the Scientific Study of Religion (SSSR)
Calvin College, Dept. of Sociology
Grand Rapids, MI 49546
Ph: (616)526-6026
URL: sssreligion.org
Social Media: www.facebook.com/pg/SSSReligion
twitter.com/sssreligion

10526 ■ Jack Shand Research Grants. *(Advanced Professional/Grant)*

Purpose: To support research in the social scientific study of religion. **Focus:** Religion. **Qualif.:** Applicants must have finished the Ph.D. degree and must be members of SSSR. In the case of co-authored requests, one author must be a member. **Criteria:** Intellectual merit is the criterion by which proposals will be evaluated.

Funds Avail.: $40,000. **Duration:** Annual. **Number Awarded:** Varies. **To Apply:** Applicants should email a proposal, in PDF, to Nancy Nason-Clark, chair of the Shand Research Award committee, no later than the set deadline. The proposal should be no longer than 4 single-spaced pages of 12-point type, including a budget. The limit of 4 pages does not include references. **Deadline:** May 1.

10527 ■ Society for the Scientific Study of Sexuality (SSSS)
1874 Catasauqua Rd., No. 208
Allentown, PA 18109
Ph: (610)443-3100
Free: 866-457-2582
E-mail: thesociety@sexscience.org
URL: www.sexscience.org
Social Media: twitter.com/Sex_Science

10528 ■ Society for the Scientific Study of Sexuality Student Research Grant *(Undergraduate/Grant)*

Purpose: To support students who are doing human sexuality research. **Focus:** Sexuality. **Qualif.:** Applicants must be students enrolled in a degree-granting program and members of SSSS who are doing human sexuality research. **Criteria:** Selection will be based on submitted requirements.

Funds Avail.: $1,000 each. **Duration:** Annual. **Number Awarded:** 2. **To Apply:** Applicants must obtain IRB approval for the project; must prepare a 150-word abstract of the proposed research; prepare a short biographical sketch suitable for the use of the society's newsletter; must prepare a ten-page, double-spaced abstract of the proposed research and bibliography in MS Word; must prepare a proposed budget for the project. **Contact:** SSSS Office: 881 3rd St., Ste. B5, Whitehall, PA 18052; Phone: 610-443-3100; Fax: 610-443-3105. thesociety@sexscience.org.

10529 ■ Society for the Study of Reproduction (SSR)
11130 Sunrise Valley Dr, Ste 350
Reston, VA 20191

Awards are arranged alphabetically below their administering organizations

Ph: (703)885-3502
Fax: (703)435-4390
E-mail: ssr@ssr.org
URL: www.ssr.org
Social Media: www.facebook.com/SSRepro
linkedin.com/company/ssrepro
twitter.com/SSRepro

10530 ■ Asia-Pacific Biomedical Research Foundation Merit Awards *(Postdoctorate/Award, Recognition, Prize)*

Purpose: To recognize the two best abstracts presented at the SSR Annual Meeting. **Focus:** Medical research; Science. **Qualif.:** Applicant must be a native Korean who is in a mentored research training program in Korea; must be a predoctoral trainee, a postdoctoral trainee who has completed a doctoral degree within four years prior to the submission deadline, or a physician-scientist who is currently in a mentored research training program. **Criteria:** Selection will be based on the SSR Awards committee rating the abstracts according to how well each meets the following criteria: scientific merit; interpretation and impact of the results and; clarity of the abstract.

Funds Avail.: $1,000. **Duration:** Annual. **Number Awarded:** 2. **To Apply:** Applicants must submit an abstract through online for presentation at the annual meeting and be able to attend and present their works on the same event and it must be based on work performed primarily by the applicants (presenter) for the award; while submitting the abstract online, must have checked "Yes" in the "SSR Trainee Merit Award" section and then checked the box for Asia-Pacific Biomedical Research Foundation Merit Award. **Deadline:** March 9.

10531 ■ Burroughs Wellcome Travel Fellowships *(Undergraduate, Graduate/Fellowship)*

Purpose: To defray the travel costs of the outstanding students associated with attending and presenting at the SSR Annual Meeting. **Focus:** Biological and clinical sciences. **Qualif.:** Applicants must be members of underrepresented minorities, be residents of U.S. or Canada, and enrolled as students in or teaching at an accredited, degree-granting institution in the U.S. or Canada. **Criteria:** Selection will be done by the SSR Diversity Committee in accordance with the following criteria: will evaluate all complete applications received: applicants will be ranked on the basis of their responses to the questions posed in the application, their coursework and letters (for trainees), biographical sketch (for junior faculty), and demonstrated commitment to the field of reproductive biology; eligible for attending or teaching at minority-serving institutions or non-research intensive institutions will be given preference in an effort to increased awareness and extend the outreach of the Society for the Study of Reproduction; preference will be given to applicants who have not previously received a Burroughs Wellcome Travel Fellowship.

Funds Avail.: $1,200. **Duration:** Annual. **To Apply:** Applicants must include completed application, recommendation letter from their mentor, and an unofficial transcript (with completed course and grades) demonstrating a training emphasis in the biological sciences and reproductive biology; junior faculty applicants must provide a completed application and a biographical sketch maximum of two pages. **Deadline:** May 15.

10532 ■ FASEB MARC Travel Awards *(Undergraduate, Graduate, Postdoctorate/Award)*

Purpose: To defray certain expenses associated with attending scientific meetings. **Focus:** Biological and clinical sciences. **Qualif.:** Applicants must be underrepresented students and postdoctoral fellows. **Criteria:** Selection will be based on the committees' criteria.

To Apply: Applicants may contact the Association for application process and other information.

10533 ■ Lalor Foundation Merit Awards *(Postdoctorate/Award, Recognition, Prize)*

Purpose: To recognize the best-researched and most well presented abstracts. **Focus:** Medical research; Science. **Qualif.:** Applicant must be an SSR Trainee whose membership dues are paid, with their mentor's signature on file in the SSR business office by the abstract submission deadline; must be a predoctoral trainee, a postdoctoral trainee who has completed a doctoral degree within four years prior to the submission deadline, or a physician-scientist who is currently in a mentored research training program. **Criteria:** The SSR Awards committee rates the abstracts according to how well each meets the following criteria: scientific merit; interpretation and impact of the results and; clarity of the abstract.

Duration: Annual. **Number Awarded:** 20. **To Apply:** Applicants must submit an abstract through online for presentation at the annual meeting, abstract must be based on work performed primarily by the applicants for the award; while submitting the abstract online, applicants must have checked "Yes" in the "SSR Trainee Merit Award" section and then checked the box for Lalor Foundation Trainee Merit Award. **Deadline:** March 9.

10534 ■ USDA-NIFA-AFRI Merit Awards *(Postdoctorate/Award, Recognition, Prize)*

Purpose: To recognize research that most benefits or enhances scientific understanding of reproduction in agriculturally important species. **Focus:** Agricultural sciences; Medical research. **Qualif.:** Applicant must be an SSR Trainee whose membership dues are paid, with their mentor's signature on file in the SSR business office by the abstract submission deadline; must be a predoctoral trainee, a postdoctoral trainee who has completed a doctoral degree within four years prior to the submission deadline, or a physician-scientist who is currently in a mentored research training program. **Criteria:** The SSR Awards committee rates the abstracts according to how well each meets the following criteria: relevance of research to the goal of enhancing understanding of reproduction in agriculturally important species; scientific merit; interpretation and impact of the results and; clarity of the abstract.

Funds Avail.: $500. **Duration:** Annual. **Number Awarded:** 10. **To Apply:** Applicants must submit an abstract online for presentation at the annual meeting, abstract must be based on work performed primarily by the applicants and must relate to the goal of benefiting or enhancing the understanding of reproduction in agriculturally important species; while submitting the abstract online, applicants must have checked "Yes" in the "SSR Trainee Merit Award" section and then checked the box for USDA-NIFA-AFRI Trainee Merit Award. **Deadline:** March 9.

10535 ■ Society for the Study of Social Problems (SSSP)
University of Tennessee
901 McClung Twr.
Knoxville, TN 37996-0490

Awards are arranged alphabetically below their administering organizations

Ph: (865)689-1531
Fax: (865)689-1534
E-mail: sssp@utk.edu
URL: www.sssp1.org
Social Media: www.facebook.com/SSSP1org
twitter.com/sssp1org

10536 ■ Lee Student Support Fund *(Undergraduate, Graduate/Award, Monetary, Recognition)*

Purpose: To recognize the individual for their commitment to diversity. **Focus:** Sociology. **Qualif.:** Applicants must be current SSSP members; must be undergraduate and graduate students.

Funds Avail.: $500. **Duration:** Annual. **Deadline:** March 15. **Remarks:** The fund is established in recognition of Al Lee's commitment to social justice and his history of critical contributions to the Society for the Study of Social Problems. **Contact:** For submission: Dr. Meghan G. Mc-Dowell, Chair, Lee Student Support Fund; Email: mcdowellmg@wssu.edu; For questions: Administrative Office, Email: sssp@utk.edu.

10537 ■ SSSP Racial/Ethnic Minority Graduate Fellowship *(Graduate/Fellowship, Award, Monetary)*

Purpose: To identify and support developing minority scholars who exemplify and give fresh voice to the SSSP history and commitment to scholar activism. **Focus:** Social sciences. **Criteria:** Applicants are evaluated based on financial need.

Funds Avail.: $15,000 fellowship and $500 for attendance. **Duration:** Annual. **Number Awarded:** 2. **To Apply:** Applicant must include an official transcript from Doctoral Program; resume or curriculum vitae; three letters of recommendation addressing the student's work and progress in program, including one from the student's dissertation advisor; personal statement of commitment to a career of scholar activism; fifteen or more double spaced pages of applicant's dissertation proposal. **Deadline:** February 1. **Remarks:** Established in 1993. **Contact:** Dr. Ana Muniz, Chair; Racial/Ethnic Minority Graduate Fellowship Committee; Email: anamuniz@uci.edu.

10538 ■ Society for Technical Communication Lone Star Community (STC LSC)

3601 Palmer Court
Arlington, TX 76014
E-mail: president@stcdfw.org
URL: stcdfw.org
Social Media: www.facebook.com/stclonestar
twitter.com/STCLoneStar

10539 ■ STC-Lone Star Chapter Traditional Education Scholarships *(Graduate, Undergraduate/ Scholarship)*

Purpose: To support students pursuing a traditional bachelor's or continued education degree/certificate in a technical communications field. **Focus:** Technical communications. **Criteria:** Selection is based on the completeness and accuracy of the application; demonstration of excellent writing skills; presentation-usage of whitespace, color and graphical elements and financial need.

Funds Avail.: No specific amount. **Duration:** Annual. **To Apply:** Applicant must submit an application that would demonstrate excellent organization, writing and design

skills. Applications (maximum of 1500 words and three graphics) must explain how the student meets the eligibility requirements (degree/certificate plan and plans to accomplish with the degree/certificate); special honors/ achievements; other degrees held; and professional experiences in the technical communications field (if any); applicant's name, address, student ID number, phone number, email address; name of college and department; expected graduation date; expected hours for the upcoming semester; estimation of tuition, fees and book expenses for the following semester; estimation of funds to offset the above costs; information on where to send funds to the school on the student's behalf; Office/Department name, address, phone number In addition applicants must include two school faculty member letters of recommendation (or one faculty member and one employer letter of recommendation) on official letterhead; an unofficial current transcript; degree/certificate plan (from school's website or catalog); and tuition estimate for the current year (from school's website or catalog). Applications are only accepted in electronic format (PDF or HTML) by email to the Lone Star Chapter of STC. **Contact:** Society for Technical Communication Lone Star Community, at the above address, or Email: scholarships@stc-dfw.org.

10540 ■ Society for Technical Communication Puget Sound Chapter (STC-PSC)

4001 E Stevens Way NE
Seattle, WA 98105
URL: www.stc-psc.org
Social Media: www.facebook.com/stcpsc
twitter.com/STCPugetSound

10541 ■ STC-PSC Scholarships *(Undergraduate, Graduate/Scholarship)*

Purpose: To support students who wish to further their education in technical communication. **Focus:** Technical communications. **Criteria:** Selection will be based on the submitted application materials by Committee.

Funds Avail.: $1,000. **Duration:** Annual. **Number Awarded:** 2. **To Apply:** Applicants must submit a completed scholarship application form; one-page description of career goals in the field of technical communication; recommendation letter; One to two samples from coursework or profession / workplace. **Deadline:** May 31. **Remarks:** Established in 1986. **Contact:** Email: pr@stc-psc.org.

10542 ■ Society of Thoracic Surgeons (STS)

633 N St. Clair St., Ste. 2100
Chicago, IL 60611
Ph: (312)202-5800
Fax: (312)202-5801
E-mail: membership@sts.org
URL: www.sts.org
Social Media: www.facebook.com/
  societyofthoracicsurgeons
www.instagram.com/thesocietyofthoracicsurgeons/
www.linkedin.com/company/society-of-thoracic-surgeons
twitter.com/sts_ctsurgery
www.youtube.com/user/ThoracicSurgeons/videos

10543 ■ AATS/STS Cardiothoracic Ethics Forum Scholarships *(Professional development/Scholarship)*

Purpose: To support CT surgeons who are interested in biomedical ethics and show promise of providing leader-

Awards are arranged alphabetically below their administering organizations

ship for the continuing development and flourishing of ethics education for CT surgery. **Focus:** Health sciences; Surgery.

Deadline: October 30. **Remarks:** Established in 2000.

10544 ■ Society of Toxicology (SOT)
11190 Sunrise Valley Dr., Suite 300
Reston, VA 20191
Ph: (703)438-3115
Fax: (703)438-3113
Free: 800-826-6762
E-mail: sothq@toxicology.org
URL: www.toxicology.org
Social Media: www.facebook.com/societyoftoxicology
www.linkedin.com/company/society-of-toxicology-sot-
twitter.com/SOToxicology

10545 ■ Colgate-Palmolive PostDoctoral Fellowship Award in In Vitro Toxicology *(Postdoctorate/ Fellowship)*
Purpose: To advance the development of alternatives to animal testing in toxicological research. **Focus:** Toxicology. **Qualif.:** Applicants must be postdoctoral trainees in their first year of study beyond the Ph.D., MD, or DVM degree who are at academic institutions, federal/national laboratories, or research institutes worldwide; postdoctoral advisor must be a member or pending member of the Society. **Criteria:** Applicants are judged upon the following criteria: proposed research should involve in vitro or animal alternative methods; potential of the proposed work to contribute to the advancement of the field of alternatives.

Funds Avail.: Up to $44,000. **Duration:** Annual. **Number Awarded:** 1. **Deadline:** October 9.

10546 ■ Society for Underwater Technology Houston
5090 Richmond Ave.
Houston, TX 77056
URL: www.suthouston.com
Social Media: www.facebook.com/societyforunderwater
  technology.us
www.linkedin.com/company/society-for-underwater
  -technology
twitter.com/SUT_US

10547 ■ SUT Houston Graduate Scholarships *(Graduate/Scholarship)*
Purpose: To support students who wish to pursue their studies with a relevant component area of marine science, underwater technology or offshore engineering. **Focus:** Engineering, Marine. **Criteria:** Selection of applicants will be based on the following criteria: career goals; recommendation letters; extracurricular activities; and optional information.

Funds Avail.: $3,000. **Duration:** Annual. **To Apply:** Applicants must submit complete application form available online with career essays (500- 1000 word typewritten essay), official transcript and three letters of recommendation. **Deadline:** June 1.

10548 ■ SUT Houston Undergraduate Scholarships *(Undergraduate/Scholarship)*
Purpose: To support students who with to pursue their studies with a relevant component area of marine science,

underwater technology or offshore engineering. **Focus:** Engineering, Marine. **Qualif.:** Applicant must be at least a rising sophomore (someone completing the first half of their sophomore academic year of full-time college work), and must continue as a full-time student while receiving this scholarship; must be enrolled in an accredited college or university; and does not have to be an SUT student member in good standing to apply, but must become one before receiving a scholarship; scholarship plan shall be such as to provide entry into some field of science or engineering encompassed by the technical activities of the SUT; provided they maintain at least the equivalent of a 3.3 on a 4.0 scale, have excellent references, and submit well designed career goals in line with objectives stated above; may be students of any nationality, unrestricted by the US State Department, and in full-time study at any accredited college or university within the United States. **Criteria:** Selection of applicants will be based on the following criteria: career goals; recommendation letters; extracurricular activities; and optional information.

Funds Avail.: $3,000. **Duration:** Annual. **To Apply:** Applicants must submit complete application form available online with career essays (500- 1000 word typewritten essay), official transcript and three letters of recommendation. **Deadline:** September 15.

10549 ■ Society of University Surgeons (SUS)
11300 W Olympic Blvd., Ste. 600
Los Angeles, CA 90064
Ph: (310)986-6442
Fax: (310)437-0585
E-mail: info@susweb.org
URL: www.susweb.org
Social Media: www.facebook.com/susweb
twitter.com/univsurg

10550 ■ SUS Foundation Junior Faculty Research Scholar Award *(Other/Scholarship)*
Purpose: To promote research and training for young surgeons who wish to pursue academic careers in medicine. **Focus:** Surgery. **Qualif.:** Applicants must be tenure-track faculty members in a Department of Surgery; and within three years of their first facility appointment. Individuals with research suite such as national extramural grants are eligible. **Criteria:** Grant is awarded based on the eligibility of the applicants. Officers and members of the SUS Committee are excluded from mentioning Fallow.

Funds Avail.: $30,000. **Duration:** One year. **To Apply:** Applicants must also fill out an authorization form online. **Deadline:** May 8. **Remarks:** Established in 1997. **Contact:** Catherine Sutherland; Phone: 310-986-6442 ext. 107; Email: catherine@susweb.org.

10551 ■ Wyeth-SUS Clinical Scholar Awards *(Postgraduate, Professional development/Award)*
Purpose: To support the research of surgeons whose works involve the basic science that underlies a surgical disease. **Focus:** Surgery.

Funds Avail.: No specific amount. **Duration:** Annual. **To Apply:** Must submit application online using the submission system. Applicant must download and print a hardcopy of the Award Authorizations Form which will verify various institutional requirements and approvals. A completed Award Authorization form must be submitted via mail to the Society offices prior to the application deadline.

Awards are arranged alphabetically below their administering organizations

Contact: SUS at the above address.

10552 ■ Society of Vacuum Coaters Foundation (SVCF)

8100 M-4 Wyoming Blvd. NE, No. 243
Albuquerque, NM 87113
Ph: (505)897-7743
Fax: (866)577-2407
E-mail: info@svcfoundation.org
URL: www.svcfoundation.org

10553 ■ Society of Vacuum Coaters Foundation Scholarship *(Undergraduate, Graduate/Scholarship)*

Purpose: To further the education of people entering or already participating in a course of study related to vacuum coating technology at an accredited institution. **Focus:** Vacuum science and technology. **Qualif.:** Applicants must be students attending an accredited technical, vocational, two-year, undergraduate or graduate school. Students and practitioners already working in the vacuum coating technology field may apply. **Criteria:** Applicants will be evaluated based on academic achievement, personal qualities, financial need and applicant's field of study to vacuum coating technology. Preference will be given to practitioners, undergraduate and graduate students whose major is Engineering, Physics, Material Science and other fields related to vacuum coating.

Duration: Annual. **Number Awarded:** Varies. **To Apply:** Applicants must complete and sign the application form; must submit one current official certified transcript and two recommendation forms (at least one from a professor). **Deadline:** December 1. **Contact:** SVC Foundation, Inc., PO Box 10202, Albuquerque, NM 87184, Email: svcfoundation@svc.org.

10554 ■ Society for Vascular Surgery (SVS)

9400 W. Higgins Rd., Suite 315
Rosemont, IL 60018-4975
Ph: (312)334-2300
Fax: (312)334-2320
Free: 800-258-7188
E-mail: vascular@vascularsociety.org
URL: vascular.org
Social Media: www.facebook.com/VascularHealth/
www.instagram.com/societyforvascularsurgery/
www.linkedin.com/company/1235746

10555 ■ International Scholars Program for Young Vascular Surgeons *(Graduate/Scholarship)*

Purpose: To defray the travel costs and living expenses to visit various universities and clinics in the U.S. and attend the Vascular annual meeting. **Focus:** Medicine; Medicine, Cardiovascular; Medicine, Cerebrovascular. **Criteria:** Applications are reviewed by the International Relations Committee.

Funds Avail.: $5,000. **Duration:** Annual. **Number Awarded:** 4. **To Apply:** Applicants must submit their applications from their intended permanent location; personal statement; 3 letters of recommendation; list of publications; three completed publication reprints; curriculum Vitae of no more than 10 pages; headshot/photograph. **Deadline:** June 3.

10556 ■ SVS Vascular Surgery Trainee Advocacy Travel Scholarship *(Advanced Professional, Professional development/Scholarship, Grant)*

Purpose: To enhance the health policy and advocacy development of the trainee's career. **Focus:** Medicine; Medicine, Cardiovascular; Medicine, Cerebrovascular. **Qualif.:** Applicants must be SVS candidate members currently enrolled in a vascular surgery training program, and have earnest interests in health policy and advocacy issues relating to vascular surgery. **Criteria:** Selection will be based on the committee's criteria.

Funds Avail.: $1,500. **Duration:** Annual. **Number Awarded:** 1. **To Apply:** Applicants must submit the necessary application materials which include curriculum vitae and 300-word essay describing interest in health policy/advocacy and why the applicants wish to receive the scholarship; application materials should be submitted to the SVS Resident and Student Outreach Committee. **Contact:** Phone: 800-258-7188; Email: studentresident@vascularsociety.org.

10557 ■ Women's Leadership Training Grant *(Advanced Professional, Professional development/Grant)*

Purpose: To enhance the health policy and advocacy development of the vascular surgery trainee's career. **Focus:** Medicine; Medicine, Cardiovascular; Medicine, Cerebrovascular. **Qualif.:** Applicants must be female U.S. citizens engaging in vascular surgery profession. **Criteria:** Selection will be based on the committee's criteria.

Funds Avail.: $5,000. **Duration:** Annual. **Number Awarded:** 3. **To Apply:** Applicants must submit completely answered application form; two-page letter of intent that indicates how applicants would use the award to advance personal leadership training and specific career goals; curriculum vitae; three complete publications (reprints or manuscripts); and two letters of recommendation (from the chair of the department in which an academic appointment is held and the other from a colleague). **Contact:** Email: membership@vascularsociety.org; Phone: 800-258-7188.

10558 ■ Society of Vertebrate Paleontology (SVP)

9650 Rockville Pke.
Bethesda, MD 20814
Ph: (301)634-7024
Fax: (301)634-7455
E-mail: svp@vertpaleo.org
URL: vertpaleo.org
Social Media: www.facebook.com/vertpaleo
twitter.com/SVP_vertpaleo

10559 ■ Estes Memorial *(Graduate/Grant)*

Purpose: To support graduate student research in non-mammalian vertebrate paleontology, with emphasis on systematics, morphology, biogeography, and paleoecology. **Focus:** Paleontology. **Qualif.:** Applicants must be graduate students at the time of application; must be SVP members.

Funds Avail.: $1,800. **Duration:** Annual. **Number Awarded:** 1. **To Apply:** Applicants must complete the application form providing detailed budget information including travel and living expenses, permit and material costs and additional expenses; Project Description (3 pages, single-spaced maximum); Letter of Support from project advisor or major professor including full contact information; photo. **Remarks:** Named in the honor of late Dr.

Awards are arranged alphabetically below their administering organizations

Richard Estes (1932-1990), an internationally-recognized paleo herpetologist who wrote over 100 scholarly papers and four edited or authored books. **Contact:** Johannes Muller, Museum fur Naturkunde, Leibniz-Institute for Research on Evolution & Biodiversity at Humboldt, University Berlin, GERMANY; Email: johannes.mueller@mfn-berlin.de.

10560 ■ Patterson Memorial (Graduate, Undergraduate/Grant, Monetary)

Purpose: To support student field work in vertebrate paleontology. **Qualif.:** Applicants and their sponsors must be current SVP members; must be undergraduate and graduate students.

Funds Avail.: $2,500. **Duration:** Annual. **Number Awarded:** Varies. **To Apply:** Applications can be submitted online; must include written statement of how the award would contribute to the success of the work (3000 character limit, includes all characters (letters, numbers, special hidden characters, spaces); budget; title and description of the project (3000 character limit, includes all characters (letters, numbers, special hidden characters, spaces); photo. **Remarks:** Named in the honor of late Bryan Patterson (1909 - 1979), a charter member of the SVP, its third secretary-treasurer (1946-48), and its seventh president (1948-49). **Contact:** Dr. Sarah Werning, Des Moines University, 3200 Grand Ave., Des Moines, IA, 50312-4198; Email: sarah.werning@dmu.edu.

10561 ■ Society of Wetland Scientists (SWS)
22 N Carroll St., Ste. 300
Madison, WI 53703-2798
Ph: (608)310-7855
Fax: (608)251-5941
E-mail: membership@sws.org
URL: www.sws.org
Social Media: www.facebook.com/societywetlandscientists
www.instagram.com/societywetlandscientists
twitter.com/SWS_org
www.youtube.com/channel/
　UCLtuVCqUbRGJ91kwlv6WfAQ

10562 ■ SWS Student Scholarships (Undergraduate/Scholarship)

Purpose: To support student wetland research. **Focus:** Science. **Qualif.:** Applicant must be conducting undergraduate or graduate level research in wetland science at an accredited college or university; must have not previously been awarded an SWS Research Grant.

Duration: Annual. **To Apply:** Applicants must submit a full proposal (3000-word limit), a CV, cited literature, a budget, and the contact information for two referees who will write letters of recommendation. **Deadline:** March 2.

10563 ■ Society of Women Engineers (SWE)
130 E Randolph St., Ste. 3500
Chicago, IL 60601
Ph: (312)596-5223
E-mail: hq@swe.org
URL: societyofwomenengineers.swe.org
Social Media: www.facebook.com/SWEorg
instagram.com/swetalk
www.linkedin.com/company/society-of-women

-engineers?trk=biz-companies-cym
twitter.com/SWETalk
www.youtube.com/user/societywomenengineer

10564 ■ SWE Scholarships (Undergraduate, Graduate/Scholarship)

Purpose: To help women achieve full potential in careers as engineers and leaders, expand the image of the engineering profession as a positive force improving the quality of life, and demonstrate the value of diversity. **Focus:** Engineering. **Qualif.:** Applicants must be incoming freshmen women who are accepted for enrollment in a baccalaureate ABET/CSAB accredited engineering or computer science degree program; Masters and PhD candidates must be enrolled or accepted at a school with ABET-accredited programs in engineering, computing, or technology. **Criteria:** Recipients will be selected based on academic standing.

Funds Avail.: $1,000 - $15,000. **Duration:** Annual. **Number Awarded:** Varies. **To Apply:** Applicants must fill out the online application form and provide the following materials: a current school stamp and signature official transcript from high school or where the applicants have taken courses; a copy of letter of acceptance from ABET accredited college or university indicating acceptance into an engineering or computer science curriculum for the coming academic year; and two letters of recommendation of which one must be from a high school teacher and the other must be from a person who has known the for two or more years and who is not a relative or member of the family. **Deadline:** February 15 (Sophomores through Graduate students); May 1(Freshmen). **Contact:** E-mail: scholarships@swe.org; URL: swe.org/scholarships/.

10565 ■ Sociologists for Women in Society (SWS)
PO Box 150
South Glastonbury, CT 06073
Ph: (860)989-5651
URL: www.socwomen.org
Social Media: www.facebook.com/SocWomen
twitter.com/socwomen

10566 ■ Beth B. Hess Memorial Scholarship (Doctorate, Graduate/Fellowship, Award)

Purpose: To support graduate students who are pursuing doctoral degrees in sociology. **Focus:** Sociology. **Criteria:** Selection of applicants will be based on the criteria given by the scholarship committee.

Funds Avail.: $15,000. **Duration:** Annual. **Number Awarded:** 2. **To Apply:** Applicants must submit a letter of application that describes the student's decision to study sociology, career goals, research, activism and service; must provide a letter confirming enrollment in or admission to a sociology PhD program; must enclose a recommendation letter from a sociologist, full curriculum vitae, including schools, degrees awarded, years of study and full or part-time status in each; must provide a one-page letter describing a community college faculty member who particularly contributed in a significant way to the decision to study sociology or pursue higher education; must provide a cover sheet with the following: (1) name and full contact information, including phone and email address; (2) current academic or organizational affiliation, with years; (3) if not currently enrolled, future PhD program and proposed entry

Awards are arranged alphabetically below their administering organizations

date; (4) community college attended, with years and credits taken, or transcripts; (5) name and contact information for graduate faculty reference; (6) if included, name of honored faculty member. **Deadline:** April 1. **Contact:** Sarah Bruch: sarah-bruch@uiowa.edu.

10567 ■ The Cheryl Allyn Miller Award *(Doctorate, Graduate/Award)*

Purpose: To recognize a sociology graduate student or a recent doctorate who have made outstanding contribution to the field of women and work. **Focus:** Sociology. **Qualif.:** Applicants must be graduate students and recent Ph.D.'s working in the area of women and paid work: employment and self-employment, informal market work, illegal work. They must belong to SWS, and may join at the same time they apply for the award. **Criteria:** Selection will be based on research or activism in the field of women and work.

Funds Avail.: $500. **Duration:** Annual. **Number Awarded:** 1. **To Apply:** Applicants must submit a 2-3 page curriculum vitae; a cover page with the author's name, affiliation and contact information; an abstract and paper of article length (no more than 30 double-spaced pages) in a style suitable for submission to a scholarly journal (should include applicant's name, address, telephone number, email address and, for applicants with PhD, the date the PhD was completed). **Deadline:** October 1.

10568 ■ SWS Barbara Rosenblum Scholarship *(Doctorate/Fellowship, Scholarship)*

Purpose: To encourage doctoral research on women's experience of breast cancer and other reproductive cancers. **Focus:** Oncology. **Criteria:** Selection of applicants will be based on the criteria of the scholarship committee.

Funds Avail.: $2,500. **Duration:** Annual. **Number Awarded:** 1. **To Apply:** Applicants must have use electronic copy of the application form available online; must provide an electronic copy of the CV and a copy of the dissertation proposal or prospectus. **Deadline:** April 1. **Contact:** Subcommittee Chair: Eleanor Miller; Email: Eleanor.Miller@uvm.edu.

10569 ■ Sodowsky Law Firm

12500 Fair Lakes Cir., Ste. 100
Fairfax, VA 22033
Ph: (703)457-1629
Fax: (703)968-9123
URL: sodowskylaw.com
Social Media: www.facebook.com/taxproblemsolver/?rf
=232032086813188
www.youtube.com/user/Fairfaxtaxman

10570 ■ Sodowsky Law Firm Scholarship *(College, University, Undergraduate/Scholarship)*

Purpose: To provide financial aid to deserving law students, encourage students to explore the law and legal careers, and improve understanding of the importance of attorneys in U.S. society. **Focus:** Business; Law. **Qualif.:** Applicant must be a high school student (enrolled or enrolling in college) or a college freshman in the United States. **Criteria:** Selection is based on the video essay.

Funds Avail.: $1,000. **Number Awarded:** 1. **To Apply:** Applicant must create a video (no longer than 3 minutes) discussing one of the following: the importance of consulting a business attorney before starting one's own business, or how tax attorneys improve modern society. Applicant must appear at least once in the video, voice over must be in the voice of the applicant, video should be titled "Sodowsky Law Firm Scholarship, " and include this link in the description: www.sodowskylaw.com/safety-scholarship-for-law-students/. Applicant must share the video on the sponsor's Facebook page and on their own YouTube channel or publicly-shared Facebook page. **Deadline:** August 15. **Contact:** Contact: Elden Sodowsky; Email: info@sodowskylaw.com.

10571 ■ Softer H2O

Polo Rd. W
Wellington, FL 33414
Ph: (561)793-3682
URL: softerh2o.com

10572 ■ Softer H2O Scholarship Program *(Undergraduate, Graduate/Scholarship)*

Purpose: To support students pursuing higher education in the U.S. **Focus:** General studies/Field of study not specified. **Qualif.:** Applicants must be a high school seniors or college/university students. **Criteria:** Essays are judged on overall quality, structure, depth of response, creativity, and originality.

Funds Avail.: $500. **Duration:** Annual. **Number Awarded:** 1. **To Apply:** Applicant must compose a 500-800-word essay on the effect hard water is having on People's Lives; the body of the email should contain full name, contact information, name of college, major, and documentation showing enrollment at the attending institution. **Deadline:** June 15. **Contact:** Email: scholarship@softerh2o.com.

10573 ■ SOKOL U.S.A.

301 Pine St.
Boonton, NJ 07005-0677
Ph: (973)676-0281
E-mail: sokolusahqs@aol.com
URL: www.sokolusa.org

10574 ■ Milan Getting Scholarship *(Undergraduate/Scholarship)*

Purpose: To support Sokol USA student members in furthering their education. **Focus:** General studies/Field of study not specified. **Qualif.:** Applicants must be a Sokol USA member; furthering education in a two or four-year college or university; applicant must maintain membership and minimum grade point average of 2.5 to renew the scholarship. **Criteria:** Selection is based on the application.

Funds Avail.: First year: $1,000; renewal of $500 for three more years. **Duration:** Four years. **To Apply:** Applicant must submit the completed applications along with the high school or college transcript containing GPA, class rank and SAT/ACT scores; Three letters of reference one from each category below: sokol officer or member (non-related) knowledgeable of your involvement in the organization; school personnel such as a principal, teacher or guidance counselor; personal friend, coach, social or recreational group leader (non-related). **Contact:** Milan Getting Scholarship Committee, SOKOL USA, 301 Pine St., PO Box 0677, Boonton, NJ, 07005-0677.

10575 ■ Solano Law Firm

1900 Centrury Pl. NE
Atlanta, GA 30345

Awards are arranged alphabetically below their administering organizations

Ph: (404)800-9213
Fax: (404)662-2526
URL: www.solanofirm.com

10576 ■ The Solano Law Firm Scholarship Contest
(College, University, Undergraduate/Scholarship)

Purpose: To provide financial aid to college students, encourage students to understand their personal motivation for a career in the legal field, inspire students to purse a career in law, and explore the obstacles that immigrant communities face. **Focus:** Business; Law. **Qualif.:** Applicant should be a high school student (enrolled or enrolling in college) or a college freshman in the United States. **Criteria:** Selection is based on the video essay or written essay.

Funds Avail.: $1,000. **Number Awarded:** 1. **To Apply:** Applicant must record a one- to two-minute video explaining either why they want to be a lawyer or what obstacles immigrants face. Applicant should publish the video to their YouTube channel or publicly shared Facebook page (along with the sponsor's Facebook page) with the following link in the description: solanofirm.com/scholarship-college-students. Instead of a video, applicant may submit a 500 to 1,000 word essay on the same subject and submit it to scholarship@solanofirm.com. **Deadline:** July 31.

10577 ■ Soldotna Chamber of Commerce (SCC)
44790 Sterling Hwy.
Soldotna, AK 99669-7940
Ph: (907)262-9814
Fax: (907)262-3566
E-mail: info@animalsandsociety.org
URL: visitsoldotna.com
Social Media: www.facebook.com/SoldotnaAlaska
www.instagram.com/visitsoldotna
www.pinterest.com/visitsoldotna
twitter.com/visitsoldotna

10578 ■ Soldotna Chamber of Commerce/Vera Howarth Memorial Scholarship *(Undergraduate/Scholarship)*

Purpose: To honor to give back to our community through our youth development programs. **Focus:** General studies/Field of study not specified. **Criteria:** Selection will be based on the committee's criteria.

Funds Avail.: $19,000 each. **Number Awarded:** 2. **To Apply:** Applicants must submit a completed application form, including attached essay; one-page letter of recommendation from two individuals attesting to student's positive attitude; letter must be type written and signed by its author; official transcript through senior year. **Deadline:** March 20. **Contact:** Sara Hondel; Phone: 907-262-1337, ext. 15; E-mail: sara@soldotnachmber.com.

10579 ■ Solid Waste Association of North America (SWANA)
1100 Wayne Ave., Ste. 650
Silver Spring, MD 20910
Fax: (301)589-7068
Free: 800-467-9262
URL: swana.org
Social Media: www.facebook.com/
 SolidWasteAssocationOfNorthAmerica

instagram.com/swanahq
www.linkedin.com/groups/45037/profile
twitter.com/swana

10580 ■ Grant H. Flint International Scholarship Program - Category I *(Undergraduate/Scholarship)*

Purpose: To promote education and professional development of dependents of SWANA members. **Focus:** General studies/Field of study not specified. **Qualif.:** Applicants must be graduating high school seniors or graduate equivalent certified candidates who have been accepted for enrollment in a junior college, a four-year college, or a university (any program); must be the children or grandchildren of a SWANA Member (sponsor) in good standing.

Funds Avail.: $20,000 total fund. **Duration:** Annual. **To Apply:** Applicants may visit SWANA website for scholarship forms and instructions. **Deadline:** May 1. **Contact:** Email: techdivisions@swana.org.

10581 ■ Grant H. Flint International Scholarship Program - Category II *(Undergraduate/Scholarship)*

Purpose: To promote education and professional development of dependents of SWANA members. **Focus:** Engineering; Environmental science. **Qualif.:** Applicants must be currently enrolled full-time college or university students who are entering their junior or senior undergraduate year and pursuing a degree in environmental science, engineering, or other suitable major related to the field of solid waste management; must be the children or grandchildren of a SWANA Member (sponsor) in good standing.

Funds Avail.: $20,000 total fund. **Duration:** Annual. **To Apply:** Application forms and instructions are available at SWANA website. **Deadline:** May 1. **Contact:** Email: techdivisions@swana.org.

10582 ■ The Robert P. Stearns/SCS Engineers Scholarship Award *(Graduate/Scholarship)*

Purpose: To promote education and professional development in areas of solid waste management by providing financial aid. **Focus:** Engineering; Environmental science. **Qualif.:** Applicants must be full-time students who are entering or are in graduate school pursuing a degree in environmental science, engineering or other suitable major related to the field of solid waste management; must be sons, daughters, grandsons or granddaughters of a SWANA member (sponsor) in good standing.

Funds Avail.: $5,000. **Duration:** Annual. **Number Awarded:** 1. **To Apply:** Application forms and instructions are available at SWANA website. **Deadline:** May 1. **Contact:** Email: techdivisions@swana.org.

10583 ■ Solvable.com
530 Technology Dr,No.100
Irvine, CA 92618
Free: 855-276-2130
URL: www.solvable.com
Social Media: www.facebook.com/solvable
 -1527214687350549
www.linkedin.com/company/trysolvable
twitter.com/trysolvable

10584 ■ Solvable.com Debt-Free Scholarship *(Two Year College, College, University, Undergraduate/Scholarship)*

Purpose: To provide financial aid to college students who are passionate about personal financial wellness. **Focus:**

Awards are arranged alphabetically below their administering organizations

General studies/Field of study not specified. **Qualif.:** Applicant must be enrolled in a two- or four-year college or university, part-time or full-time, or will be enrolled in the fall in a program; have a minimum 3.0 GPA; and be a U.S. citizen or legal resident. **Criteria:** Selection is based on the submitted essay.

Funds Avail.: $1,000. **Number Awarded:** 1. **To Apply:** Application and essay (500 to 1,000 words) must be submitted online. **Deadline:** November 15. **Contact:** Email: scholarship@solvable.com; Phone: 855-732-7164; URL: www.solvable.com/scholarship/.

10585 ■ Sonoma County Mycological Association (SOMA)
PO Box 7147
Santa Rosa, CA 95407
URL: www.somamushrooms.org
Social Media: www.facebook.com/SOMA-Sonoma-County -Mycological-Association-172451922783550

10586 ■ Herbert M. Saylor Memorial Scholarship *(Graduate/Scholarship)*

Purpose: To recognize student achievement and stimulate further interest and study in the world of fungi; encourage graduate level students to pursue a course of study in Mycolo. **Focus:** Agricultural sciences; Biology. **Qualif.:** Applicants must be graduate students. **Criteria:** Selection will be based on the committee's criteria.

Funds Avail.: $2,500. **Duration:** Annual. **To Apply:** Applicant must complete and submit the application form; a brief letter on what they are studying, their major, and whom they are working under. This should also include a list of college courses taken about fungi; a statement confirming applicant's willingness to present a talk/slideshow at a monthly meeting of SOMA in Santa Rosa, CA; a brief letter or recommendation from someone connected to applicant's academic pursuits. Bring in application materials to a monthly SOMA meeting or mail to the SOMA Scholarship Committee. **Deadline:** May 31. **Contact:** Email: scholarships@somamushrooms.org.

10587 ■ Sons of Confederate Veterans (SCV)
PO Box 59
Columbia, TN 38402
Fax: (931)381-6712
Free: 800-380-1896
URL: www.scv.org
Social Media: www.facebook.com/SCVOfficialPage

10588 ■ Stand Watie Scholarship *(Undergraduate/ Scholarship)*

Purpose: To encourage educational pursuits by providing educational assistance. **Focus:** General studies/Field of study not specified. **Qualif.:** Applicant must be a member in good standing in one of these organizations: Sons of Confederate Veterans, Children of the Confederacy, or United Daughters of the Confederacy; must be a student at an accredited college or university; must be an undergraduate classified as a sophomore, junior, or senior; must be enrolled at accredited college, university or post secondary vocational/technical schools within the United States. **Criteria:** Selection committee is based on information provided in the application letter and associated documents.

Funds Avail.: $1,000. **Duration:** Annual. **To Apply:** Application package includes a personal letter of application;

proof of membership in one of the organizations named; a complete personal data; three letters of recommendation; and copies of transcripts, diplomas and/or certificates. **Deadline:** June 15. **Remarks:** The scholarship was founded by Dr. James M.Edwrards to memorialize Stand Watie for his cheroke heritage and remarkable courage and record of fighting for the confedarate states of America in Indian territory and for being the last confederate general to surrender in the field. **Contact:** Send materials to Chair Vernon R. Padgett, Ph. D., Stand Watie Scholarship Fund, 5412 Citrus Grove Pl, Whittier, California, 90601-2311, Email: vp09@earthlink.net.

10589 ■ Sons of Norway Foundation (SOFN)
1455 W Lake St.
Minneapolis, MN 55408
URL: mblsportal.sos.state.mn.us
Social Media: www.facebook.com/sonsofnorway
www.instagram.com/sonsofnorway
www.linkedin.com/company/sons-of-norway

10590 ■ Nancy Lorraine Jensen Memorial Scholarship Fund *(Undergraduate/Scholarship)*

Purpose: To encourage young women to enter the field of science and engineering. **Focus:** Engineering; Science.

Funds Avail.: No specific amount. **Duration:** Annual. **To Apply:** Applicants must submit an application form only via online; must send SAT or ACT scores; a 500-word essay giving proof of their accomplishments and describing how they intend to pursue their career; a sealed, official copy of their latest grade transcript; and three sealed letters of recommendation; a short autobiography, 150 words or less; essay of 500 words or less addressing one of the core values listed in the application form; financial need. **Deadline:** January 15. **Remarks:** Nancy Lorraine Jensen Memorial Scholarship Fund was established by Dr. and Mrs. Arthur S. Jensen in memory of their remarkable daughter. By age 35, when she died suddenly, Nancy had already distinguished herself as an outstanding chemical engineer whose work resulted in important advanceswithin the field of weather satellite photography. It is the wish of Dr. and Mrs. Jensen to encourage young women to enter the field of science and engineering by offering scholarships in Nancy's memory.

10591 ■ Oslo International Summer School Scholarship *(Undergraduate/Scholarship)*

Purpose: To support students who attend Oslo International Summer School. **Focus:** Engineering; Science. **Qualif.:** Applicants must be admitted to Oslo International Summer · School; Applicants between the ages of 17-26; must be current members of the Sons of Norway, or children or grandchildren of current members; must have a certificate of completion from high school or expect to graduate from high school during the current academic school year; seeking tuition assistance for the summer of 2019; membership must be in effect at least one calendar year prior to application. **Criteria:** Recipients are selected based on the submitted applications and financial need; Scoring is dependent on the use of complete sentences, proper grammar,and inclusion of information outlined in the essay requirements.

Funds Avail.: $1,500. **Duration:** Annual. **Number Awarded:** 2. **To Apply:** Applicants must submit an applica-

Awards are arranged alphabetically below their administering organizations

tion form only via online;a short autobiography, 150 words or less; essay of 500 words or less addressing one of the core values listed in the application form; financial need; Upload the latest completed term's transcripts; two letters of recommendation. **Deadline:** January 15. **Contact:** Email: scholarships@sofn.com.

10592 ■ Sons of Scotland Benevolent Association (SSBA)

505 Consumers Rd., Ste. 801
Toronto, ON, Canada M2J 4V8
Ph: (416)482-1250
Fax: (416)482-9576
Free: 800-387-3382
E-mail: info@sonsofscotland.com
URL: www.sonsofscotland.com
Social Media: www.facebook.com/Sons1876
www.linkedin.com/company/sons-of-scotland-benevolent
  -assn
twitter.com/sonsscotlandca

10593 ■ Sons of Scotland Past Grand Chiefs Scholarship *(Undergraduate/Scholarship)*

Purpose: To support individuals entering their second year of full-time education at a recognized Canadian post-secondary institution. **Focus:** Education. **Qualif.:** Applicant must be Sons of Scotland members in good standing, or their children or grandchildren; applicants must have successfully completed one year/semester of full-time study at a recognized Canadian post-secondary institution; selection will be made mainly on the basis of academic achievement. **Criteria:** Applicants are judged upon the committee's criteria.

Funds Avail.: $1,000 each. **Duration:** Annual. **Number Awarded:** 2 (1 male; 1 female). **To Apply:** Applicants must fill out and submit the questionnaire, transcripts of first-year of post secondary education and secondary school, and three references. **Deadline:** June 30.

10594 ■ Sons of Union Veterans of the Civil War (SUVCW)

National Civil War Museum
1 Lincoln Circle at Reservoir Park, Ste. 240
Harrisburg, PA 17103-2411
Ph: (717)232-7000
Fax: (717)412-7492
URL: www.suvcw.org

10595 ■ SUVCW Scholarships *(Undergraduate/Scholarship)*

Purpose: To promote for tuition and books to high school seniors and college students. **Focus:** General studies/Field of study not specified. **Qualif.:** Male applicants must be current members or Associate of Sons of Union Veterans of the Civil War; female applicants must be the daughters or granddaughters of a current member or Associate of Sons of Union Veterans of the Civil War and must be current members of at least one of the following organizations: Woman's Relief Corps, Ladies of the Grand Army of the Republic, Daughters of Union Veterans of the Civil War 1861-1865, or Auxiliary to the Sons of Union Veterans of the Civil War; must rank in the upper one-fourth of high school graduating class, preferably in the upper one-tenth;

must have a record of performance in activities both in school and in the community; must have a sound interest and positive attitude toward college work. **Criteria:** Recipients are chosen based on merit.

Funds Avail.: $2,500. **Duration:** One year. **Number Awarded:** 2. **To Apply:** Applicants may download forms at the website; must provide three letters of recommendation; these recommendations must be from school counselor, a teacher, and a responsible person in applicants community; photocopies of current membership cards; and transcripts. **Deadline:** March 31. **Contact:** John R. Ertell, SUVCW Scholarship Committee Chair Phone: (610) 948-1278 • Email: jertell@verizon.net.

10596 ■ Paul and Daisy Soros Fellowships for New Americans (PDSFA)

11 West 42nd Street, 3rd fl.
New York, NY 10036
Ph: (212)405-8234
E-mail: pdsoros@pdsoros.org
URL: www.pdsoros.org
Social Media: www.facebook.com/pdsoros
www.instagram.com/pdsoros
twitter.com/pdsoros

10597 ■ Paul & Daisy Soros Fellowships *(Graduate/Fellowship)*

Purpose: To honor the contributions of continuing generations of immigrants and refugees to the United States. **Focus:** General studies/Field of study not specified.

Funds Avail.: $45,000. **Duration:** Annual; up to two years. **To Apply:** Applicants are required to complete the online application form. applicants must submit two essays on specified topics; a 1-2 page resume; three recommendation letters; an institutional status form from the institution attended indicating when and whether the present degree program will be completed; a copy of transcripts; a documentary evidence that the applicant meets the definition of New American. **Deadline:** November 1. **Remarks:** Established in 1997. **Contact:** Email: pdsoros@pdsoros.org.

10598 ■ South Asian Bar Association of Northern California (SABA-NC)

PO Box 26755
San Francisco, CA 94126
Ph: (571)572-2262
E-mail: president@southasianbar.org
URL: www.southasianbar.org
Social Media: www.facebook.com/sabanorcal
www.linkedin.com/company/south-asian-bar-association
  ---northern-california
twitter.com/sabanorcal

10599 ■ SABA NC - Public Interest Post-Bar Fellowships *(Professional development/Fellowship)*

Purpose: To provide financial assistance to recent law school graduates who are working in public interest. **Focus:** Law. **Qualif.:** Applicants must be recent law school graduates who have just completed the bar and who will be working at a public interest or government agency. **Criteria:** Selection may be based on commitment to public service, financial need, academic achievement, and other personal circumstances.

Awards are arranged alphabetically below their administering organizations

Duration: Annual. **To Apply:** Application is available online at www.southasianbar.org/fellowships.

10600 ■ SABA NC - Public Interest Summer Fellowships *(Undergraduate/Fellowship)*

Purpose: To provide stipend for law students to spend a summer working with public interest law organizations in the San Francisco Bay area. **Focus:** Law. **Qualif.:** Applicants must be law students with an interest in interning with a public interest organization or government agency in the San Francisco Bay area; must have demonstrated commitment to serve the South Asian community. **Criteria:** Selection will be based on the submitted application with particular weight given to the applicants' essay. Other factors that may consider include commitment to public service, financial need, academic achievement and other personal circumstances. Preference will be given to applicants who are enrolled in a Northern California law school and employed at a Northern California organizations doing work that directly impacts the South Asian community.

Funds Avail.: No specific amount. **To Apply:** Applicants must submit the completed application form; essay responses; resume with two references; completed employer form; completed financial information form; unofficial law school transcript. Applicants may also submit the following optional materials: letters of recommendation and any additional evidence of financial need. **Contact:** Email: foundation.sabanc@gmail.com; URL: http://www.southasianbar.org/fellowships.

10601 ■ South Asian Bar Association of San Diego

c/o Tarina Mand
501 W Broadway, Ste. 600
San Diego, CA 92101
URL: www.sabasandiego.org

10602 ■ California Bar Foundation 3L Diversity Scholarship *(Undergraduate/Scholarship)*

Purpose: To help offset high cost of law school education. **Focus:** Law. **Qualif.:** Candidate must be diverse 3L who intends to take the California bar exam, has a commitment to social justice/public interest, and can demonstrate their California-oriented career goals. **Criteria:** Selection will be based on the committee's criteria.

Funds Avail.: No specific amount. **Duration:** Annual. **Deadline:** February 15. **Contact:** Email: scholarships@calbarfoundation.org.

10603 ■ South Asian Journalists Association (SAJA)

541 WEST 113TH STREET APT. 3A
New York, NY 10025
URL: www.saja.org
Social Media: www.facebook.com/South.Asian.Journalists.Association
twitter.com/sajahq

10604 ■ SAJA Student Scholarship *(Undergraduate, Graduate/Scholarship)*

Purpose: To help graduate, undergraduate and high school students pursue their education and future careers in journalism. **Focus:** Journalism. **Qualif.:** Applicants must be Undergraduates and graduate students continuing their

year. Students from across the United States, Canada, and South Asia can apply for the scholarships. **Criteria:** Recipients will be selected based on submitted application.

Funds Avail.: $2,000 each. **Duration:** Annual. **Number Awarded:** 10. **To Apply:** Applicants must submit a resume and 350-word essay on why you should be awarded the fund. Non-South Asians should demonstrate their interest in covering South Asia or diaspora. **Deadline:** April 20. **Contact:** Ali I. Rizvi at SAJAprograms@gmail.com.

10605 ■ South Carolina Association for Financial Professionals (SCAFP)

PO Box 5272
Columbia, SC 29250-5272
E-mail: admin@scafponline.org
URL: scafp.wildapricot.org

10606 ■ South Carolina Association for Financial Professionals Certified Treasury Professional Scholarships *(Other/Scholarship)*

Purpose: To establish an additional scholarship award for students to obtain Treasury Professional certification. **Focus:** Finance. **Qualif.:** Applicants must be employed in South Carolina; must be prepared to lead the treasury and finance profession in pursuit of excellence. **Criteria:** Recipients are selected based on their performance and demonstrated interest in the field of treasury and finance.

Funds Avail.: No specific amount. **Duration:** Annual. **Number Awarded:** 2. **To Apply:** Applicants must complete the application form; must submit a one page summary of specific treasury qualifications; must provide resume of work history; must provide a three-to-five page, double-spaced discussion document based on the latest developments in the Treasury Management field and why they should be awarded the scholarship. **Deadline:** March 31. **Contact:** Will Taylor, President, SCAFP; Phone: 843-937-4573; E-mail: will.taylor@wellsfargo.com.

10607 ■ South Carolina Association for Financial Professionals College Education Scholarships *(Undergraduate/Scholarship)*

Purpose: To provide a forum for the exchange of ideas and discussion of legislative, regulatory, and banking issues and developments and the opportunity to network with other Treasury Management professionals; to award an academic scholarship to an outstanding undergraduate student pursuing a degree in business in the areas including, but not limited to, accounting, economics, finance, business administration and management. **Focus:** Finance. **Qualif.:** Applicants must be South Carolina residents; must be U.S. citizens or legal permanent residents; must earn a cumulative 3.0 GPA on a 4.0 scale and a GPA in their major area of 3.5 on a 4.0 scale; must be enrolled as degree-seeking students at eligible South Carolina public or independent (private) institutions; must not be current recipients of a full-tuition scholarship. **Criteria:** Recipients are selected based on their academic performance.

Funds Avail.: No specific amount. **To Apply:** Applicants must complete the application form; must submit a one page summary of academic achievement including the applicant's GPA (overall and major area) and a list of all relevant courses in the Treasury Management field; must submit a letter of recommendation from their major field faculty member; must provide a three-to-five page, double-spaced discussion of the Treasury Management field.

Awards are arranged alphabetically below their administering organizations

10608 ■ South Carolina Law Enforcement Officers Association (SCLEOA)

PO Box 210709
Columbia, SC 29221-0709
Ph: (803)781-5913
Fax: (803)781-9208
URL: www.scleoa.org
Social Media: www.facebook.com/scleoa
twitter.com/scleoa

10609 ■ SCLEOA Scholarships *(Undergraduate, Professional development/Scholarship)*

Purpose: To provide financial assistance graduating high school seniors. **Focus:** General studies/Field of study not specified. **Criteria:** Applicants will be selected by the Scholarship Committee of the SCLEOA based on the application requirements submitted by the student.

Funds Avail.: $7,000. **Duration:** Annual. **Number Awarded:** 3. **To Apply:** Applicants must complete the application form and must submit an essay with a minimum of 1000 words, double-spaced, on the following topics given in the website; must provide a bibliography of cited sources; must attach a copy of high school transcript to the application. **Deadline:** February 21. **Contact:** SCLEOA, PO Box 210709, Columbia, South Carolina 29221-0709; Location: 4921 Broad River Rd., Columbia, South Carolina, 29212; Phone: 803-781-5913; Fax; 800-922-0038.

10610 ■ South Carolina Public Health Association (SCPHA)

PO Box 11061
Columbia, SC 29211
Ph: (803)736-9461
Fax: (803)788-0128
E-mail: scpha@scpha.com
URL: www.scpha.com
Social Media: www.facebook.com/SCPHAinfo

10611 ■ Malcolm U. Dantzler Scholarships *(Graduate/Scholarship)*

Purpose: To protect and promote personal, community and environmental health; to exercise leadership in health policy development and action; to foster scientific and professional development among its members. **Focus:** Public health. **Criteria:** Applications and nominations are to be mailed to the chair of the SCPHA Scholarship Committee.

Funds Avail.: $500. **Duration:** Annual. **Number Awarded:** 1. **Deadline:** March 29.

10612 ■ South Carolina Public Health Association Scholarships *(Professional development/Scholarship, Monetary)*

Purpose: To financially support students with their studies. **Focus:** Public health. **Qualif.:** Candidates in the field of Public Health, continued awareness of the role of public health depends upon the enthusiasm and commitment of existing and future public health professionals. **Criteria:** Selection will be based on scientific and professional development of the membership.

Funds Avail.: $500. **Number Awarded:** 2. **To Apply:** Applications are also available on the SCPHA website. **Deadline:** March 27.

10613 ■ South Carolina Restaurant and Lodging Association (SCRLA)

1122 Lady St., Ste. 1210
Columbia, SC 29201
Ph: (803)765-9000
Fax: (803)252-7136
E-mail: info@scrla.org
URL: www.scrla.org
Social Media: www.facebook.com/
  SCRestaurantAndLodgingAssociation
www.linkedin.com/company/south-carolina-restaurant-and
  -lodging-association
twitter.com/SCRLA

10614 ■ South Carolina Tourism and Hospitality Educational Foundation Scholarships *(Undergraduate/Scholarship)*

Purpose: To provide educational assistance for students who demonstrate an interest in and commitment to the hospitality (restaurant, lodging tourism) industry. **Focus:** Travel and tourism. **Qualif.:** Applicants must be students seeking post-secondary education and careers in the restaurant/hospitality industry.

Funds Avail.: No specific amount. **To Apply:** Applicants must submit a completed application form; three letters of reference; three completed Character Reference Forms; current official transcript; and a double-spaced essay (minimum of 500 words and maximum of 1, 000 words); scholarship application can be downloaded and filled-out at the website. **Deadline:** May 1.

10615 ■ South Carolina Undergraduate Scholarships *(Undergraduate/Scholarship)*

Purpose: To assist students who demonstrate an interest in and commitment to the hospitality (restaurant, foodservice, lodging, tourism) industry. **Focus:** Culinary arts. **Qualif.:** Applicants must be enrolled in a post-secondary restaurant/hospitality program and must be attending an accredited college or university in South Carolina. **Criteria:** Recipients are selected based on financial need and academic performance.

Funds Avail.: Unspecified. **To Apply:** Applicants must submit a completed application form; three letters of reference; three completed character reference forms; current official transcript; and (minimum of 500 words and maximum of 1, 000 words, double-spaced) essay. Scholarship application can be downloaded and filled out at the website. **Deadline:** June 11.

10616 ■ South Carolina Scholastic Press Association (SCSPA)

School of Journalism and Mass Communications
University of South Carolina
Columbia, SC 29208
Ph: (803)777-6284
Fax: (803)777-4103
URL: www.sc.edu
Social Media: www.facebook.com/uofsc
twitter.com/uofsc

10617 ■ McClatchy Minority Scholarship and Fellowship *(Undergraduate/Scholarship)*

Purpose: To provide financial assistance to those students who are in need. **Focus:** Journalism. **Qualif.:** Applicants

Awards are arranged alphabetically below their administering organizations

must be minority continuing students, and graduate students pursuing print/new media journalism careers in the school of journalism and mass communications. **Criteria:** Selection will be based on need and merit as determined by the school of journalism.

Funds Avail.: No specific amount. **To Apply:** Applicants may contact the Association for the scholarship application process.

10618 ■ SCSPA Scholarship (Graduate/Scholarship)

Purpose: To provide financial assistance to students who plans to attend the USC School of Journalism and Mass Communications. **Focus:** Journalism. **Criteria:** Selection will be based on scholastic journalism involvement as well as academic achievements while in high school.

Funds Avail.: $1,000. **Duration:** One year. **Number Awarded:** 1. **To Apply:** Completed application along with high school transcript, 2 letters of recommendation must be submitted. **Deadline:** February 7.

10619 ■ SCSPA Yearbook Scholarship (Undergraduate/Scholarship)

Purpose: To provide financial assistance to deserving students. **Focus:** Journalism. **Criteria:** Preference will be given to those students who meet the criteria.

Funds Avail.: $500. **Duration:** One year. **Number Awarded:** 1. **To Apply:** Applicants must submit a completed application form; a copy of high school transcript; two letters of recommendation. **Deadline:** February 3, 2017. **Contact:** SCSPA, Attn: Leslie Dennis, 800 Sumter St., SJMC/USC, Columbia, SC 29208.

10620 ■ South Central Power Co.
PO Box 250
Lancaster, OH 43130
Ph: (740)653-4422
Fax: (740)681-4488
Free: 800-282-5064
E-mail: bainter@southcentralpower.com
URL: www.southcentralpower.com
Social Media: www.facebook.com/SouthCentralPower
www.instagram.com/south_central_power_company
www.linkedin.com/company/south-central-power-company
www.pinterest.com/southcentralpow
twitter.com/SouthCentralPow
www.youtube.com/channel/UCs2IkdT6xMRckMsr6l-0iIg

10621 ■ Technical, vocational or associate's degree programs (Undergraduate/Scholarship)

Purpose: To support high school seniors who are pursuing their education at a college, vocational or technical school. **Focus:** General studies/Field of study not specified. **Criteria:** Selection will be based on the board's criteria.

Funds Avail.: $1,000 each. **Number Awarded:** Varies. **To Apply:** Application completely filled out the application and obtained your transcript and scholastic record & teacher evaluation. **Deadline:** February 1. **Contact:** South Central Power Company, PO Box 250, Lancaster, OH, 43130; Phone:800-282-5064 ext 6252; Email: Bainter@southcentralpower.com; Liz Bainter Community Development Ambassador; Fax: 740-681-4488.

10622 ■ South Dakota Nurses Association (SDNA)
PO Box 1015
Pierre, SD 57501-1015

Ph: (605)945-4265
Fax: (888)600-1232
URL: www.sdnursesassociation.org
Social Media: www.facebook.com/SDNurses

10623 ■ Marianne M. Stenvig Scholarship (Master's, Doctorate/Scholarship)

Purpose: To support male registered nurses in pursuit of their educational goals. **Focus:** Nursing. **Criteria:** Selection will be based on the committee's criteria.

Funds Avail.: $1,000. **Duration:** Annual. **Number Awarded:** 1. **To Apply:** Applicants must provide the following materials: evidence of current student status, either copy of admission letter if admitted but not yet enrolled, or current transcript if enrolled; two letters of recommendation describing the personal qualities and activities that exemplify leadership, compassion, and involvement in professional organizations(s), professional activities and community service. At least one letter of recommendation should be from a faculty member and one letter may be from a professional colleague; current resume; personal statement addressing career goals, personal qualities that affect their nursing practice, and how their career goals and personal qualities reflect South Dakota Nurses Foundation purposes of education, research, and service. Please limit personal statement to 500 words or less. **Deadline:** October 1. **Contact:** South Dakota Nurses Foundation; Phone: 605-271-7708.

10624 ■ South Dakota Retailers Association (SDRA)
320 E Capitol Ave.
Pierre, SD 57501
E-mail: info@sdra.org
URL: www.sdra.org

10625 ■ Jerry Wheeler Scholarships (Undergraduate/Scholarship)

Purpose: To assist students who wish to pursue studies in a retail field. **Focus:** Business.

Number Awarded: Varies. **To Apply:** Applications can be submitted online. **Deadline:** August 20.

10626 ■ South Jersey Golf Association (SJGA)
PO Box 884
North Cape May, NJ 08204
URL: www.sjgolf.org
Social Media: www.facebook.com/South-Jersey-Golf-Association-558773420820355
twitter.com/SouthJerseyGolf

10627 ■ South Jersey Golf Association Scholarships (Undergraduate/Scholarship)

Purpose: To provide support for deserving high school seniors intending to pursue their education. **Focus:** General studies/Field of study not specified. **Qualif.:** Applicants must be graduating high school seniors who have been members in good standing of their golf team and who plan to enroll as full-time undergraduate students at an accredited college or university within the United States. **Criteria:** Selection will be based College Board SAT (or ACT) scores, Academic Record, Financial need, Qualities of Character and Leadership, Golf Club's financial support of the Program.

Awards are arranged alphabetically below their administering organizations

Funds Avail.: $1,500 to $500. **Duration:** Annual. **To Apply:** Applicants must have a copy of their college/university letter of acceptance or waitlist deferral; must provide a copy of their transcript which must include mid-year grades through the fall semester of senior year; must provide a copy of their SATI or ACT Score Reports; must have a typed essay, three letters of recommendation, completed resume and a senior yearbook photograph. **Contact:** Ms. Gail Reilly, SJGA President, 103 East Hollywood Ave., Wildwood Crest, NJ 08260; Phone: 732-539-3334; Email: gareilly@aol.com.

10628 ■ South Kentucky Rural Electric Cooperative Corp. (SKRECC)

200 Electric Avenue
Somerset, KY 42501
Ph: (606)678-4121
Fax: (606)679-8279
Free: 800-264-5112
E-mail: skrecc@skrecc.com
URL: www.skrecc.com
Social Media: www.facebook.com/South-Kentucky-RECC
-111609522182933
www.instagram.com/sokyrecc
twitter.com/skrecc
www.youtube.com/channel/
UCVJsY17XPgqL5HKd6r7BMsw

10629 ■ Sam J. Hord Memorial Scholarship
(Undergraduate/Scholarship)

Purpose: To provide financial assistance to those who are pursuing higher education. **Focus:** General studies/Field of study not specified. **Qualif.:** Applicants must be members of South Kentucky rural electric cooperative, or whose parents are members, or dependent students whose parents are members.

Duration: Annual. **To Apply:** Applicants should submit a copy of grade transcript; copy of most recent family federal tax return; and, ACT, SAT or COMPASS results. **Deadline:** March 1. **Contact:** Alan Coffey; Phone: 606-678-4121; Toll Free: 800-264-5112.

10630 ■ South Kentucky RECC High School Senior Scholarship Program *(Undergraduate/Scholarship)*

Purpose: To provide financial assistance to those who are pursuing higher education. **Focus:** General studies/Field of study not specified. **Qualif.:** Applicants must be full-time high school seniors whose principal residences are active accounts of South Kentucky RECC. **Criteria:** Applicants are evaluated based on criteria of the Scholarship Committee without regard to race, religion, sex, age or physical capability.

Funds Avail.: $1,000. **Duration:** Annual. **To Apply:** Applicants must submit a completed application form along with an essay (between 350 and 500 words) about. **Contact:** Alan Coffey; Phone: 606-678-4121; Toll Free: 800-264-5112.

10631 ■ Women In Rural Electrification Scholarships (W.I.R.E.) *(Undergraduate/Scholarship)*

Purpose: To provide financial assistance to those who are pursuing higher education. **Focus:** General studies/Field of study not specified. **Qualif.:** Applicants must be students whose immediate family is served by a Kentucky rural electric cooperative, such as South Kentucky RECC; must be full-time juniors or seniors with at least 60 hours of credits at a Kentucky college or university by the start of the fall term. **Criteria:** Applicants will be evaluated based on criteria designed by the committee of the Kentucky W.I.R.E. and chosen applicants will be notified.

Funds Avail.: $1,000 each. **Duration:** Annual. **Number Awarded:** 3. **Contact:** Alan Coffey; Phone: 606-678-4121; Toll Free: 800-264-5112.

10632 ■ Southeastern Library Association (SELA)

PO Box 950
Rex, GA 30273
E-mail: selaadminservices@selaonline.org
URL: selaonline.org
Social Media: www.facebook.com/SELAnews
twitter.com/SELA_Libraries

10633 ■ The Ginny Frankenthaler Memorial Scholarships *(Undergraduate/Scholarship)*

Purpose: To recruit beginning professional librarians who have potential for leadership and have made a commitment to service in the libraries of the Southeastern United States; to provide financial assistance towards the completion of their graduate degree in library science from an institution accredited by the American Library Association. **Focus:** Science.

Funds Avail.: $1,000. **Duration:** Biennial. **To Apply:** Applicants must submit an official application form; letter of acceptance from a library school accredited by the American Library Association; three letters of reference and an official transcript of all academic works sent directly to the chair of the committee. **Deadline:** June 1. **Remarks:** The scholarship was established in memory of Ginny Frankenthaler by her husband, Bud Frankenthaler. **Contact:** Laura Slavin, The University of Alabama in Huntsville, M. Louis Salmon Library, 301 Sparkman Dr., Huntsville, AL, 35899.

10634 ■ Southeastern Theatre Conference Inc. (SETC)

1175 Revolution Mill Dr., Studio 14
Greensboro, NC 27405
Ph: (336)272-3645
E-mail: info@setc.org
URL: www.setc.org
Social Media: www.facebook.com/setc.org
instagram.com/setc
www.linkedin.com/company/southeastern-theatre
-conference
twitter.com/SETCTweet

10635 ■ Leighton M. Ballew Directing Scholarship
(Undergraduate/Scholarship)

Purpose: To recognize and support a graduate student studying directing at an accredited university. **Focus:** Theater arts. **Qualif.:** Applicants must be planning to attend an accredited program of graduate studies in Theatre Directing during the 2020-2021 academic year; must have graduated from, be currently attending, or have plans to attend an accredited academic institution in one of the following 10 states: Alabama, Florida, Georgia, Kentucky, Mississippi, North Carolina, South Carolina, Tennessee, Virginia

Awards are arranged alphabetically below their administering organizations

or West Virginia.**Criteria:** Selections will be based on the replies and recommendations as candidates for the award.

Funds Avail.: $3,000. **Duration:** Annual. **Number Awarded:** 1. **To Apply:** Applicants should include a personal letter outlining plans and objectives for graduate work or internship; a complete resume, including work in stage management or play direction; names, addresses, and telephone numbers of three references who have had agreed, at the request of the award committee, to write letters recommending the applicant; complete undergraduate and graduate transcripts; letter of acceptance by an accredited graduate program in directing. **Deadline:** April 1. **Contact:** Questions about submitting application materials should be sent to info@setc.org.

10636 ■ Marian A. Smith Costume Scholarship Award *(Graduate/Scholarship)*

Purpose: To provide services and educational programs for those individuals and organizations engaged in theatre in the southeast. **Focus:** Theater arts. **Qualif.:** Applicants must be planning to attend an accredited program of graduate studies in Costume Design and/or Costume Technology as a full-time student during the 2020-2021 academic year. **Criteria:** Selection will be based on their replies and recommendations as the candidates for the award.

Funds Avail.: $1,500. **Duration:** One year. **Number Awarded:** 1. **To Apply:** Applicants should include a completed application form; a personal letter outlining plans and objectives; a complete resume; ten slides or photographs of completed work or renderings; names, addresses and phone numbers of three to five references; complete college transcripts. **Deadline:** April 1. **Contact:** Carey Hanson, University of Mississippi, Department of Theatre, Isom Hall, Room 110 A, University, MS 38677; 662-915-6990; costumes@olemiss.edu.

10637 ■ Polly Holliday Scholarship Award *(Undergraduate/Scholarship, Monetary)*

Purpose: To support a qualified high school senior planning to attend an accredited college or university in the SETC region to major in theatre. **Focus:** Theater arts. **Qualif.:** Applicant must be current high school senior in the SETC region; must be planning to attend an accredited program of theatre studies in the SETC region during the 2018-2019 academic year.

Funds Avail.: $500. **Duration:** Annual. **To Apply:** Applicants should include a completed application form; a personal letter outlining plans and objectives; a complete resume; three letters of reference, one from high school principal.

10638 ■ Robert Porterfield Graduate Scholarship *(Graduate/Scholarship)*

Purpose: To provide services and educational programs for those individuals and organizations engaged in theatre in the southeast. **Focus:** Theater arts. **Qualif.:** Applicants must accredited program of graduate studies in Theatre Directing during academic year; must graduated from Alabama, Florida, Georgia, Kentucky, Mississippi, North Carolina, South Carolina, Tennessee, Virginia or West Virginia only these states.**Criteria:** Applicants may be selected as finalists on the basis of their materials.

Funds Avail.: $2,000. **Duration:** Annual. **Number Awarded:** 1. **To Apply:** Applicants should submit completed application; personal letter outlining plans and objectives; a complete resume; three reference letters speaking specifi-

cally to the potential as a graduate student; complete, official transcripts from all colleges/universities attended; and submit all materials in a single, multi-page PDF document. **Deadline:** April 1.

10639 ■ Robert Porterfield Scholarship *(Graduate/ Scholarship)*

Purpose: To recognize a student entering or attending a graduate school or conservatory to study theater in the southeast region of the United States. **Focus:** Theater arts. **Qualif.:** Applicants must accredited program of graduate studies in Theatre Directing during academic year; must graduated from Alabama, Florida, Georgia, Kentucky, Mississippi, North Carolina, South Carolina, Tennessee, Virginia or West Virginia only these states. **Criteria:** Applicants may be selected as finalists on the basis of their materials.

Funds Avail.: $2,000. **Duration:** Annual. **Number Awarded:** 1. **To Apply:** Applicants should submit completed application; personal letter outlining plans and objectives; a complete resume; three reference letters speaking specifically to the potential as a graduate student; complete, official transcripts from all colleges/universities attended; and submit all materials in a single, multi-page PDF document. **Deadline:** April 1. **Remarks:** Established in honor of Robert Porterfield who was the founder and longtime director of the Barter Theatre in Abingdon, VA. **Contact:** Questions about submitting application materials should be sent to info@setc.org. Other questions about this scholarship should be sent to the Porterfield Scholarship Chair.

10640 ■ Southeastern Theatre Conference Secondary School Scholarship *(Undergraduate/Scholarship)*

Purpose: To support a High School student on entering a College or University in the SETC region to major in theatre. **Focus:** Theater arts. **Qualif.:** Applicants must be legal residents of a state in the SETC region, and must have at least one year of experience as a full-time teacher and director of theatre in a regionally accredited secondary school in the SETC region; must enroll in a regionally accredited graduate program within one year of being selected for the scholarship.**Criteria:** Selection is based on the aptitude in theatrical practices and the potential for academic success in college.

Funds Avail.: $1,500. **Duration:** Annual. **Number Awarded:** 1. **To Apply:** Applicants must include an official transcript, along with verification of class rank and available SAT or ACT scores from the high-school guidance counselor or principal; three completed recommendation forms, with one being from the nominee's high-school principal; the student's completed nominee resume form.

10641 ■ William E. Wilson Scholarship *(Graduate/ Scholarship)*

Purpose: To support a secondary school teacher pursuing a graduate degree in theatre, or speech and theatre at a regionally accredited graduate program. **Focus:** Theater arts. **Qualif.:** Applicants must be legal residents of a state in the SETC region, and must have at least one year of experience as a full-time teacher and director of theatre in a regionally accredited secondary school in the SETC region; must enroll in a regionally accredited graduate program within one year of being selected for the scholarship. **Criteria:** Selection will be based on their replies and recommendations as the candidates for the award.

Funds Avail.: $5,000. **Duration:** Annual. **To Apply:** Applicants should submit a personal letter outlining plans and

Awards are arranged alphabetically below their administering organizations

objectives; A complete two letters of recommendation. **Deadline:** April 1. **Contact:** Questions about submitting application materials should be sent to info@setc.org. Other questions about this scholarship should be sent to the Wilson Scholarship Chair, Dean Slusser at dslusser@camden.k12.ga.us.

10642 ■ Southern Appalachian Botanical Society (SABS)

c/o Christopher P. Randle
Department of Biological Sciences, Sam Houston State University
1900 Avenue I, LDB 300
Huntsville, TX 77340
URL: sabs.us

10643 ■ Earl Core Student Research Award *(Professional development/Grant)*

Purpose: To provide financial assistance in support of student research projects in plant taxonomy, systematics, and ecology. **Focus:** Botany. **Qualif.:** Applicant and research advisor must be members of the Southern Appalachian Botanical Society (SABS); research advisor will attest to the applicant's student status and validity of the research proposal. **Criteria:** Selection will be based on the committee's criteria.

Funds Avail.: $1,200. **Duration:** Annual. **Number Awarded:** 1. **To Apply:** Applications can be submitted online. **Deadline:** February 21. **Remarks:** The Award was established by the Society in 1996 in honor of Earl L. Core, who was a major force in the founding of the Southern Appalachian Botanical Club. Established in 1996. **Contact:** Application form and the proposal must be sent to Joe Pollard as an e-mail attachment pdf format to joe.pollard@furman.edu.

10644 ■ Southern Arizona Environmental Management Society, Inc (SAEMS)

PO Box 41433
Tucson, AZ 85717
E-mail: saemstucson@gmail.com
URL: www.saems.org
Social Media: www.facebook.com/saems.org/
www.instagram.com/saems_ehs/

10645 ■ SAEMS Environmental Scholarships *(Undergraduate, Graduate/Scholarship)*

Purpose: To encourage students pursuing a career in an environmental field who are planning to work on solutions to environmental problems. **Focus:** Environmental science. **Qualif.:** Applicants must be undergraduate or graduate students attending the University of Arizona, pursuing studies in the environmental field; must have a minimum 2.5 GPA and satisfactory degree progress. **Criteria:** Selection will be based on the committee's criteria.

Funds Avail.: $500 to $2,500. **Duration:** Annual. **To Apply:** Application form and details available online at saems.org/scholarships/. **Deadline:** May 1. **Contact:** B.J. Cordova, SAEMS Education Chair; Phone: 520-481-3223; Email: bcordova26@gmail.com.

10646 ■ Southern California Chinese Lawyers Association (SCCLA)

PO Box 711114
Los Angeles, CA 90086-1959

E-mail: info@sccla.org
URL: www.sccla.org
Social Media: www.facebook.com/SCCLA

10647 ■ SCCLA Fellowships *(Graduate/Fellowship)*

Purpose: To provide an opportunity for local Asian/Pacific American law students to work with an organization serving the Asian and Pacific Islander (API) community. **Focus:** Law. **Qualif.:** Applicants Program is open to Asian/Pacific American law students at all levels. **Criteria:** Selection is based on need, academic accomplishments, and/or potential contribution to the Chinese-American community.

Funds Avail.: $2,000. **Duration:** Annual. **To Apply:** Applicants may visit the website to obtain an application form and other details. **Contact:** Email: info@sccla.org.

10648 ■ SCCLA Scholarships *(Graduate/Scholarship)*

Purpose: To support the education of local Asian/Pacific American law students. **Focus:** Law. **Qualif.:** Applicants must be Chinese-American community law students at all levels. **Criteria:** Selection is based on need, academic accomplishments, and/or potential contribution to the Chinese American and/or Asian Pacific American community.

Funds Avail.: $1,000. **Duration:** Annual. **To Apply:** Applicants may visit the website and must submit all applications electronically, to obtain an application form and other details. **Deadline:** April 6. **Contact:** contact scholarships@sccla.org.

10649 ■ Southern California Lambda Medical Association (SCLMA)

8265 W Sunset Blvd., Ste. 204
West Hollywood, CA 90046
Ph: (323)465-2322
E-mail: lambdamedical@gmail.com
URL: sclma.net
Social Media: www.facebook.com/groups/SCLMA
twitter.com/sclmaorg

10650 ■ Southern California Lambda Medical Student Scholarships *(Undergraduate, Graduate/Scholarship)*

Purpose: To support gay, lesbian, and bisexual physicians-in-training. **Focus:** Medicine. **Qualif.:** Applicants must be students who are currently in or have been accepted into a Southern California MD or DO program. **Criteria:** Selection is based on the application materials submitted.

Funds Avail.: $500. **Duration:** Annual. **Number Awarded:** 5. **To Apply:** Applicants is required to apply online. **Contact:** Email to support@sclma.org.

10651 ■ The Southern California Research Center for ALPD & Cirrhosis

1333 San Pablo St., MMR-402
Los Angeles, CA 90089-9141
E-mail: htsukamo@usc.edu
URL: keck.usc.edu

10652 ■ Lee Summer Student Fellowship *(Undergraduate, Master's/Fellowship)*

Purpose: To provide hands-on research training for undergraduate and Master students with interest in the sciences and exposure to laboratory medicine. **Focus:** Medi-

Awards are arranged alphabetically below their administering organizations

cal research. **Qualif.:** Applicants must be active under-graduate, Master's or medical students or lab volunteers while in transition to graduate or medical school; must be available to work full-time for 8 to 10 weeks (no exceptions) during the summer under the supervision of a center member.

Funds Avail.: Varies. **Duration:** Annual. **To Apply:** Project must be related to the pathogenesis of alcoholic liver or pancreatic diseases, cirrhosis or related biology. Interested candidates must submit the following: curriculum vitae; title of project; proposed project start and end dates; summary of project; mentor's contact information; mentor's mentorship confirmation. **Deadline:** May 29. **Remarks:** The program was implemented with funds donated by Dr. Sheng-Pu Lee. Established in 2001. **Contact:** Southern California Research Center for ALPD and Cirrhosis, Keck School of Medicine of USC, 1333 San Pablo St., MMR 4th fl., Los Angeles, CA, 90089-9141; Phone: 323-442-3109; Fax: 323-442-3126; gencie turner; Email: gencie.turner@med.usc.edu.

10653 ■ Southern Conference (SOCON)

c/o Jason Yaman, Associate Commissioner
702 North Pine St.
Spartanburg, SC 29303
Ph: (864)591-5100
URL: www.soconsports.com
Social Media: www.facebook.com/SouthernConference
www.instagram.com/southernconference
twitter.com/SoConSports

10654 ■ Dave Hart Graduate Scholarship *(Graduate/Scholarship)*

Purpose: To support a deserving male student-athlete who is interested in continuing his education in graduate school. **Focus:** General studies/Field of study not specified. **Criteria:** A committee comprised of three conference faculty athletic representatives and one athletic director is responsible for selecting the winner of the award.

Funds Avail.: $2,000. **Duration:** Annual. **Remarks:** Established in 1991.

10655 ■ Dorothy Hicks Graduate Scholarship *(Graduate/Scholarship)*

Purpose: To support a female student-athlete who is interested in pursuing a graduate degree. **Focus:** General studies/Field of study not specified.

Funds Avail.: $2,000. **Duration:** Annual. **Remarks:** Established in 1991.

10656 ■ David Knight Graduate Scholarship *(Graduate/Scholarship)*

Purpose: To support a student-athlete who is interested in pursuing a graduate degree. **Focus:** General studies/Field of study not specified.

Funds Avail.: $2,000. **Duration:** Annual.

10657 ■ Southern Nursing Research Society (SNRS)

10200 W 44th Ave., Ste. 304
Wheat Ridge, CO 80033
Ph: (303)327-7548
Free: 877-314-7677

E-mail: info@snrs.org
URL: www.snrs.org
Social Media: www.facebook.com/SNRSociety
www.linkedin.com/in/southern-nursing-research-society
  -snrs-080353121
twitter.com/SNRSociety

10658 ■ CANS/SNRS Dissertation Research Grant *(Doctorate/Grant)*

Purpose: To support doctoral students in the Southern region enrolled in research-focused programs as they initiate a program of nursing research to advance nursing science and practice. **Focus:** Nursing. **Qualif.:** Applicants must be current SNRS members (students or regulars) when the application is received; currently enrolled in doctoral study at a School or College of Nursing in the southern region; and current members (full or student members) of The Council for the Advancement of Nursing Science (CANS). They must also show evidence that the proposed study has met the requirements for the dissertation (proposal has been successfully defended) and that it can be supported at the institution/facility proposed. **Criteria:** Recipients will be selected through a peer review process using the significance to nursing; scientific merit; innovation; appropriateness of methodology given the research question; qualifications of the investigators (research teams) to conduct study; adequacy of human subjects/animal protection; and appropriate environment, budget, and time frame.

Funds Avail.: $5,000. **To Apply:** Applicants may visit the website for the online application and submission process. **Deadline:** March 1. **Contact:** Email the completed form to info@snrs.org.

10659 ■ SNRS Dissertation Research Grants *(Doctorate/Grant)*

Purpose: To support doctoral students in the Southern region enrolled in research-focused programs as they initiate a program of nursing research to advance nursing science and practice. **Focus:** Nursing.

Funds Avail.: $5,000. **Duration:** Annual. **To Apply:** Applicants must submit a proposal and all required materials as one electronic document through the Society's website and are required to pay the application fee. **Deadline:** March 1. **Contact:** Submit required materials with the subject line, SNRS Dissertation Funding Application at info@snrs.org.

10660 ■ SNRS Research Grants *(Professional development/Grant)*

Purpose: To support and promote new investigators in initiating or building a program of research, which advances nursing science and practice. **Focus:** Nursing.

Funds Avail.: $7,500. **Duration:** Annual. **Number Awarded:** 1. **To Apply:** Applicants must submit a proposal and all required materials as one electronic document through the Society's website and are required to pay the application fee. **Deadline:** October 1. **Contact:** Email the completed form to info@snrs.org.

10661 ■ SNRS/STTI Research Grants *(Professional development/Grant)*

Purpose: To encourage qualified nurses to contribute to the advancement of nursing through research. **Focus:** Nursing. **Criteria:** Selection will be based on the committee's criteria.

Awards are arranged alphabetically below their administering organizations

Funds Avail.: Up to $5,000. **Duration:** Annual. **Number Awarded:** 1. **To Apply:** Applicant must submit completed research application packet and a signed research agreement via our on-line submission system; final report; completed abstract. **Deadline:** April 1. **Remarks:** The grant is jointly administered and bestowed by the Southern Nursing Research Society, and Sigma Theta Tau International. **Contact:** Research Services, Sigma Theta Tau International; Phone: 888-634-7575 (US/Canada) or 317-634-8171 (International); Fax: 317-634-8188; Email: research@stti.iupui.edu.

10662 ■ Southern Regional Education Board (SREB)

592 10th St. NW
Atlanta, GA 30318-5776
URL: www.sreb.org
Social Media: www.linkedin.com/company/southern
-regional-education-board
twitter.com/srebeducation

10663 ■ SREB-State Doctoral Scholars Program - Dissertation Award *(Doctorate/Scholarship, Award)*

Purpose: To provide financial assistance and career counseling for students to become faculty members. **Focus:** General studies/Field of study not specified.

Funds Avail.: A stipend of $20,000. **Duration:** Annual; One Year. **To Apply:** Applicants must submit a completed doctoral awards application form along with the following; letter of interest; three letters of recommendation; transcript(s); verification of U.S. citizenship or permanent U.S. resident status; verification from the university of in-state residency status if applying in GA, MS, SC, TN or VA; and verification from the university of passing score on preliminary/comprehensive exams. **Deadline:** April 30. **Contact:** Email: monique.waddell@sreb.org.

10664 ■ SREB-State Doctoral Scholars Program - Doctoral Award *(Doctorate, Graduate/Scholarship)*

Purpose: To increase the number of minority students who earn their respective doctoral degrees and wanting to become college/university professors. **Focus:** Engineering; Mathematics and mathematical sciences; Science; Technology.

Funds Avail.: $20,000 stipend. **Duration:** Annual; up to 3-5 years. **To Apply:** Applicants must submit a completed doctoral awards application form along with the following; letter of interest; three letters of recommendation; transcript(s); verification of U.S. citizenship or permanent U.S. resident status; verification from the university of in-state residency status if applying in GA, MS, SC, TN or VA; and verification from the university of passing score on preliminary/comprehensive exams. **Contact:** ANSLEY ABRAHAM Director, SREB-State Doctoral Scholars Program 592 Tenth Street, NW Atlanta, GA 30318-5776. Phone: 404-875-9211, ext. 269 Direct: 404-879-5569 Fax: 404-872-1477, (404) 879-5573 ansley.abraham@sreb.org.

10665 ■ Southern Scholarship Foundation (SSF)

322 Stadium Dr.
Tallahassee, FL 32304
Ph: (850)222-3833
Fax: (850)222-6750
E-mail: admissions@southernscholarship.org
URL: www.southernscholarship.org

Social Media: www.facebook.com/SouthernScholarship
www.instagram.com/ssfpics
twitter.com/ssftweets
www.youtube.com/user/SouthernScholarship

10666 ■ Southern Scholarship Foundation Scholarships *(Undergraduate, Graduate, Postgraduate/Scholarship)*

Purpose: To support students attending the four major universities in Florida. **Focus:** General studies/Field of study not specified. **Qualif.:** Applicants must be students attending one of our seven university partners: FGCU, UF, SC, TCC, FAMU, FSU, FCT; must have minimum 3.0 unweighted state GPA or 675 GED score; EFC below 7,500. **Criteria:** Selection will be based on the financial resources, excellent character.

Duration: Annual. **To Apply:** Applicants must submit a completed application form along with letters of recommendation. **Deadline:** November 1. **Contact:** Email: admissions@southernscholarship.org.

10667 ■ Southern Section Air and Waste Management Association (SS-A&WMA)

c/o Maya Rao, Chairperson
Trinity Consultants,1000 Highland Colony Pky, Ste.5203
Ridgeland, MS 39157
E-mail: mrao@trinityconsultants.com
URL: www.ss-awma.org

10668 ■ Southern Section A&WMA Scholarships *(Graduate/Scholarship)*

Purpose: To assist students pursuing careers in the areas of air and water pollution control and hazardous waste management, such as transportation control measures, acidic deposition, indoor air quality, new or improved control technology, and physical or chemical characterization of pollutants. **Focus:** Air pollution; Environmental law; Waste management. **Qualif.:** Applicants must be pursuing a graduate-level course of study and research leading to a career related to air or water quality, waste management, pollution prevention, environmental policy/compliance/law, or sustainability; must also be attending a full-time graduate school program at a university within the area of the A&WMA Southern Section (Alabama, Georgia, Mississippi & Tennessee) for the academic year. **Criteria:** Awards will be given based on academic records and career goals without consideration of sex, race, national origin, age, or physical disability.

Funds Avail.: $1,500. **Duration:** Annual. **Number Awarded:** 2. **To Apply:** Applicants are encouraged to be student members of the A&WMA or environmental professionals returning to school for graduate study. **Deadline:** June 21. **Contact:** Dr. John Koehler, A&WMA-GWS Education Committee Chair, E-mail: jkoehler@yorkeengr.com.

10669 ■ Southwest Florida Community Foundation

2031 Jackson Street Suite 100
Fort Myers, FL 33901
Ph: (239)274-5900
Fax: (239)274-5930
URL: www.floridacommunity.com
Social Media: www.facebook.com/SWFLcommunity

Awards are arranged alphabetically below their administering organizations

www.instagram.com/swflcommunity
www.linkedin.com/company/southwest-florida-community
-foundation
twitter.com/SWFLcommunity
www.youtube.com/user/SWFLCF

10670 ■ American Association of University Women(AAUW) Sue Gottcent Memorial Scholarship Fund (Undergraduate, Graduate/Scholarship)

Purpose: To support lee county women in their education. **Focus:** General studies/Field of study not specified. **Qualif.:** Applicants must be female residents of lee county who demonstrate financial need; enrolled or will be enrolled in state of florida college/university system. **Criteria:** Preference will be given to females over 25 years of age.

Funds Avail.: $2,000. **Duration:** Annual; up to 4 years. **To Apply:** Applicants must submit application via online; the federal student financial aid application (fafsa) opens for all individuals who are pursuing postsecondary education. the student aid report (sar) that shows each student's estimated family contribution (efc) score is required for all scholarships and the most up-to-date transcript, official or unofficial, will be required for all scholarships fall 2019 grades should be included in the transcript that you upload into your scholarship application with SAT and/or ACT test scores; at least one reference letter is required. applicants should obtain a reference letter from a person who is outside of the applicant's family and can attest to the applicant's character while knowing the applicant well enough to pass judgement with credibility. **Deadline:** February 24. **Contact:** Phone: (239) 274-5900; Email: scholarships@floridacommunity.com.

10671 ■ Anne M. Fassett Scholarship Fund (Undergraduate, Graduate/Scholarship)

Purpose: To support physical disability students to continue their higher educations. **Focus:** General studies/Field of study not specified. **Qualif.:** Applicants must have graduated from a public or private high school in charlotte, collier, glades, hendry or lee county and currently enrolled or planning to attend a Florida state college, community college or technical school; physical disability and use a wheelchair and demonstrate financial need. **Criteria:** Selection will be based on the committee's criteria.

Funds Avail.: $4,000. **Duration:** Annual. **To Apply:** Applicants should submit a FAFSA Form; Applicants must submit application via online. **Deadline:** February 24. **Contact:** Phone: (239) 274-5900; Email: scholarships@floridacommunity.com.

10672 ■ Anne Sturrock Nursing Scholarship Fund (Undergraduate, Graduate/Scholarship)

Purpose: To support nursing students who are members or children of members of st. andrew catholic church in cape coral. **Focus:** Nursing. **Qualif.:** Applicants must be members or children of members of St. Andrew catholic church; must be pursuing a career in nursing; and demonstrate financial need. **Criteria:** Selection will be based on the committee's criteria.

Funds Avail.: $7,800. **Duration:** Annual. **Number Awarded:** 1. **To Apply:** Applicants should submit a FAFSA Form; Applicants must submit application via online. **Deadline:** February 24. **Contact:** Phone: (239) 274-5900; Email: scholarships@floridacommunity.com.

10673 ■ Carl E. Brooks Scholarship Fund (Undergraduate/Scholarship)

Purpose: To fund tuition for college-bound students of one or more immigrant parents. **Focus:** General studies/Field of study not specified. **Qualif.:** Applicants must have graduated from public or private high school in charlotte, collier, glades, hendry or lee county and able to demonstrate financial need; provide proof of parent's immigrant status (copy of immigration card or birth certificate) & be a child of an immigrant parent. **Criteria:** Selection will be based on the committee's criteria.

Funds Avail.: $2,900 each. **Duration:** Annual. **Number Awarded:** 1. **To Apply:** Applicants should submit a FAFSA Form; Applicants must submit application via online. **Deadline:** February 24. **Contact:** Phone: (239) 274-5900; Email: scholarships@floridacommunity.com.

10674 ■ Chet And Janett Perry Rotary Club Of Fort Myers Scholarship Fund (Undergraduate/Scholarship)

Purpose: To provide funding support for students pursuing a career in accounting. **Focus:** Accounting. **Qualif.:** Applicants must be graduating from a public or private high school in charlotte, hendry, glades or lee county; pursue a degree in accounting; and, enter college within a year following high school graduation. **Criteria:** Selection will be based on the committee's criteria.

Duration: Annual. **Number Awarded:** 1. **To Apply:** Applicants must submit application via online; the federal student financial aid application (fafsa) opens for all individuals who are pursuing postsecondary education. the student aid report (sar) that shows each student's estimated family contribution (efc) score is required for all scholarships and the most up-to-date transcript, official or unofficial, will be required for all scholarships fall 2019 grades should be included in the transcript that you upload into your scholarship application with SAT and/or ACT test scores; at least one reference letter is required. applicants should obtain a reference letter from a person who is outside of the applicant's family and can attest to the applicant's character while knowing the applicant well enough to pass judgement with credibility. **Deadline:** February 10. **Contact:** Phone: (239) 274-5900; Email: scholarships@floridacommunity.com.

10675 ■ Chip Johnson Memorial Scholarship Fund (Undergraduate/Scholarship)

Purpose: To fund scholarships for students who have completed 60 hours of college and plan to attend one of named colleges. **Focus:** General studies/Field of study not specified. **Qualif.:** Applicants must have complete 60 semester hours of college and plan to continue study toward a 4-year degree at Barry university, fgcu, nova, Edison state college or Hodges university, or a regionally accredited college in the 5-county area and have a gpa of 3.5 or above and an outstanding record of academic achievement; live in the 5-county area served by the community foundation (charlotte, collier, glades, hendry and lee); demonstrate leadership, community service and service to school. **Criteria:** Selection will be based on the committee's criteria.

Funds Avail.: $4,000. **Duration:** Annual. **Number Awarded:** Varies. **To Apply:** Applicants should submit a FAFSA Form; Applicants must submit application via online. **Deadline:** February 10. **Remarks:** The scholarship was established in honor of chip johnson. **Contact:** Phone: (239) 274-5900; Email: scholarships@floridacommunity.com.

10676 ■ City Of Sanibel Employee Dependent Scholarship Fund (Undergraduate/Scholarship)

Purpose: To provide financial assistance for qualified dependents of sanibel city employees to attend a college

Awards are arranged alphabetically below their administering organizations

or university. **Focus:** General studies/Field of study not specified. **Qualif.:** Applicants must be dependent of a Sanibel city employee; attending a college or university; need financial assistance. **Criteria:** Selection will be based on the committee's criteria.

Funds Avail.: $750. **Duration:** Annual. **Number Awarded:** Up to 4. **To Apply:** Applicants should submit a FAFSA Form; Applicants must submit application via online.**Deadline:** February 24. **Contact:** Phone: (239) 274-5900; Email: scholarships@floridacommunity.com.

10677 ■ COUSE-Gram Scholarship Fund
(Undergraduate/Scholarship)

Purpose: To provide educational assistance to moore haven high school students pursuing post-secondary education. **Focus:** General studies/Field of study not specified. **Qualif.:** Applicants must be Moore haven high school seniors pursuing post-secondary education. **Criteria:** Selection will be based on the committee's criteria.

Funds Avail.: $900. **Duration:** Annual. **Number Awarded:** 1. **To Apply:** Applicants should submit a FAFSA Form; Applicants must submit application via online.**Deadline:** February 10. **Contact:** Phone: (239) 274-5900; Email: scholarships@floridacommunity.com.

10678 ■ D&A Florida Scholarships *(Undergraduate/ Scholarship)*

Purpose: To fund a student who will attend: fgcu, university of florida/ gainesville, florida state university/tallahassee, flagler college, stetson university/deland, university of miami, university of tampa, or embry riddle aeronautical university/daytona beach. **Focus:** Architecture; Business; Chemistry; Computer and information sciences; Engineering; International affairs and relations; Journalism; Law; Literature; Medicine; Physics; Political science. **Qualif.:** Applicants must have graduated from a public or private high school in charlotte, glades, hendry or lee county; must pursue a degree in architecture, business, engineering, international affairs and relations, journalism, computer and information sciences, law, literature, medicine, physics, chemistry, or political science; must document financial need; must possess a 3.5 GPA or higher; must be 23 years of age or younger and a first-time college student. **Criteria:** Selection will be based on the committee's criteria.

Funds Avail.: No specific amount. **Duration:** Annual. **To Apply:** Applicants must submit application via online; the federal student financial aid application (fafsa) opens for all individuals who are pursuing postsecondary education. the student aid report (sar) that shows each student's estimated family contribution (efc) score is required for all scholarships and the most up-to-date transcript, official or unofficial, will be required for all scholarships fall 2019 grades should be included in the transcript that you upload into your scholarship application with SAT and/or ACT test scores; at least one reference letter is required. applicants should obtain a reference letter from a person who is outside of the applicant's family and can attest to the applicant's character while knowing the applicant well enough to pass judgement with credibility. **Deadline:** February 24. **Contact:** Phone: (239) 274-5900; Email: scholarships@floridacommunity.com.

10679 ■ David G. Robinson Arts Scholarship Fund
(Undergraduate/Scholarship)

Purpose: To fund tuition for high school seniors who plan to study the arts in an accredited school. **Focus:** Art. **Qualif.:** Applicants must be graduate from a high school in lee county and plan to study the arts with industrious student with good moral character; document financial need; show leadership and community service. **Criteria:** Selection will be based on the committee's criteria.

Funds Avail.: $2,300. **Duration:** Annual. **Number Awarded:** 1. **To Apply:** Applicants must submit application via online; the federal student financial aid application (fafsa) opens for all individuals who are pursuing postsecondary education. the student aid report (sar) that shows each student's estimated family contribution (efc) score is required for all scholarships and the most up-to-date transcript, official or unofficial, will be required for all scholarships fall 2019 grades should be included in the transcript that you upload into your scholarship application with SAT and/or ACT test scores; at least one reference letter is required. applicants should obtain a reference letter from a person who is outside of the applicant's family and can attest to the applicant's character while knowing the applicant well enough to pass judgement with credibility. **Deadline:** February 24. **Contact:** Phone: (239) 274-5900; Email: scholarships@floridacommunity.com.

10680 ■ Doc Keen Memorial Scholarship Fund
(Undergraduate/Scholarship)

Purpose: To assist students who were active members of 4-h or a FFA organization for two consecutive years. **Focus:** General studies/Field of study not specified. **Qualif.:** Applicants must be graduate from Clewiston or LaBelle high school; must pursue post-secondary education; must have been active member of 4-H or FFA for 2 consecutive years. **Criteria:** Selection will be based on the committee's criteria.

Funds Avail.: $750. **Duration:** Annual. **Number Awarded:** 2. **To Apply:** Applicants must submit application via online; the federal student financial aid application (fafsa) opens for all individuals who are pursuing postsecondary education. the student aid report (sar) that shows each student's estimated family contribution (efc) score is required for all scholarships and the most up-to-date transcript, official or unofficial, will be required for all scholarships fall 2019 grades should be included in the transcript that you upload into your scholarship application with SAT and/or ACT test scores; at least one reference letter is required. applicants should obtain a reference letter from a person who is outside of the applicant's family and can attest to the applicant's character while knowing the applicant well enough to pass judgement with credibility. **Deadline:** February 10. **Contact:** Phone: (239) 274-5900; Email: scholarships@floridacommunity.com.

10681 ■ Doris W. Frey Memorial Scholarship Fund
(Graduate/Scholarship)

Purpose: To support students studying christian ministry/youth ministry, christian counseling, nursing, or medicine. **Focus:** Christian education; Medicine; Nursing; Religion. **Qualif.:** Applicants must be graduates from a public or private high school in charlotte, collier, hendry, glades or lee counties; pursue a degree in any of the following fields (Christian ministry/youth ministry, Christian counseling, nursing, or medicine); maintain satisfactory grades; be committed to a life of Christian service; demonstrate a commitment through action in ministering to others; and, have recognized ability and academic performance with standard measures of grades and appropriate test scores.**Criteria:** Selection will be based on the committee's criteria.

Funds Avail.: $2,800 each. **Duration:** Annual. **Number Awarded:** Varies. **To Apply:** Applicants should submit a FAFSA Form; Applicants must submit application via online.

Awards are arranged alphabetically below their administering organizations

Deadline: February 10. **Remarks:** The scholarship was established in honor of Doris W. Frey. **Contact:** Phone: (239) 274-5900; Email: scholarships@floridacommunity.com.

10682 ■ Drs. Ira and Udaya Dash Nursing Scholarship Fund *(Undergraduate, Graduate/Scholarship)*

Purpose: To assist students studying nursing at florida southwestern or florida gulf coast university. **Focus:** Nursing. **Qualif.:** Applicants must reside in charlotte, collier, glades, hendry or lee county; plan to attend (or be attending) Edison college or Florida gulf coast university; be enrolled in a nursing program; and, demonstrate financial need. **Criteria:** Selection will be based on the committee's criteria.

Funds Avail.: $900. **Duration:** Annual. **To Apply:** Applicants should submit a FAFSA Form; Applicants must submit application via online. **Deadline:** February 24. **Contact:** Phone: (239) 274-5900; Email: scholarships@floridacommunity.com.

10683 ■ Dunbar Heritage Scholarship Fund *(Undergraduate/Scholarship)*

Purpose: To support research in human-animal studies as well as to promote interdisciplinary exchange among the fellows. **Focus:** General studies/Field of study not specified. **Qualif.:** Applicants must be graduating member of Dunbar high school; be of african-american descent; have financial need; have a GPA of 2.5 or higher; and, enter college within the year following high school graduation. **Criteria:** Selection will be based on the committee's criteria.

Funds Avail.: $1,900 each. **Duration:** Annual. **Number Awarded:** 2. **Deadline:** March 4. **Contact:** Phone: (239) 274-5900; Email: scholarships@floridacommunity.com.

10684 ■ Faye Lynn Roberts Education Scholarship Fund *(Undergraduate, Graduate/Scholarship)*

Purpose: To fund scholarships for female students pursuing a career in technical studies, court reporting, computer training or nursing. **Focus:** Computer and information sciences; Education, Vocational-technical; Nursing. **Qualif.:** Applicants must be women of 21 years of age or older who are residents of lee county, and able to demonstrate financial need; Must be a single mother. **Criteria:** Selection will be based on the committee's criteria.

Funds Avail.: $750. **Duration:** Annual. **Number Awarded:** 1. **To Apply:** Applicants should submit a FAFSA Form; Applicants must submit application via online.**Deadline:** February 24. **Contact:** Phone: (239) 274-5900; Email: scholarships@floridacommunity.com.

10685 ■ Francis Harris Gresham Scholarship Fund *(Undergraduate/Scholarship)*

Purpose: To provide tuition for college-bound seniors from lee county high schools. **Focus:** General studies/Field of study not specified. **Qualif.:** Applicants must have graduated from a public or private high school in lee county. **Criteria:** Selection will be based on the committee's criteria.

Funds Avail.: $1,450. **Duration:** Annual. **To Apply:** Applicants must submit application via online; the federal student financial aid application (fafsa) opens for all individuals who are pursuing postsecondary education. the student aid report (sar) that shows each student's estimated family contribution (efc) score is required for all scholarships; the most up-to-date transcript, official or unofficial, will be required for all scholarships fall 2019 grades should

be included in the transcript that you upload into your scholarship application; SAT and/or ACT test scores will be required; at least one reference letter is required. applicants should obtain a reference letter from a person who is outside of the applicant's family and can attest to the applicant's character while knowing the applicant well enough to pass judgement with credibility. **Deadline:** February 24. **Contact:** Phone: (239) 274-5900; Email: scholarships@floridacommunity.com.

10686 ■ George E. Judd Scholarship Fund *(Undergraduate/Scholarship)*

Purpose: To provide tuition for graduating seniors pursuing higher education in the fine or performing arts. **Focus:** Art; Performing arts. **Qualif.:** Applicants must graduate from public or private high school in lee county and pursue a degree in the fine or performing arts. **Criteria:** Selection will be based on the committee's criteria.

Funds Avail.: $1,000. **Duration:** Annual. **Number Awarded:** 10. **To Apply:** Applicants must submit application via online; the federal student financial aid application (fafsa) opens for all individuals who are pursuing postsecondary education. the student aid report (sar) that shows each student's estimated family contribution (efc) score is required for all scholarships; the most up-to-date transcript, official or unofficial, will be required for all scholarships fall 2019 grades should be included in the transcript that you upload into your scholarship application; SAT and/or ACT test scores will be required; at least one reference letter is required. applicants should obtain a reference letter from a person who is outside of the applicant's family and can attest to the applicant's character while knowing the applicant well enough to pass judgement with credibility. **Deadline:** February 10. **Contact:** Phone: (239) 274-5900; Email: scholarships@floridacommunity.com.

10687 ■ Isabel Mayer Kirkpatrick Scholarship Fund *(Undergraduate/Scholarship)*

Purpose: To fund tuition for high school graduates with a "B" average of 2.7 to 3.3. **Focus:** General studies/Field of study not specified. **Qualif.:** Applicants must be graduates from public or private high school in lee county; be well-rounded in terms of education, community service, sports and leadership activities; and have a gpa of 2.7-3.3 unweighted (anything higher will disqualify the student). **Criteria:** Selection will be based on the committee's criteria.

Funds Avail.: $5,300. **Duration:** Annual. **Number Awarded:** 1. **To Apply:** Applicants must submit application via online;. the federal student financial aid application (fafsa) opens for all individuals who are pursuing postsecondary education. the student aid report (sar) that shows each student's estimated family contribution (efc) score is required for all scholarships; the most up-to-date transcript, official or unofficial, will be required for all scholarships fall 2019 grades should be included in the transcript that you upload into your scholarship application; SAT and/or ACT test scores will be required; at least one reference letter is required. applicants should obtain a reference letter from a person who is outside of the applicant's family and can attest to the applicant's character while knowing the applicant well enough to pass judgement with credibility. **Deadline:** February 10. **Contact:** Phone: (239) 274-5900; Email: scholarships@floridacommunity.com.

10688 ■ James Bilder Scholarship Fund *(Undergraduate/Scholarship)*

Purpose: To fund tuition for high school students intending to pursue vocational or technical studies. **Focus:** General

Awards are arranged alphabetically below their administering organizations

studies/Field of study not specified. **Qualif.:** Applicants must have graduated from public high school in lee county and able to demonstrate financial need. **Criteria:** Selection will be based on the committee's criteria.

Funds Avail.: $4,400 each. **Duration:** Annual. **Number Awarded:** 2. **To Apply:** Applicants must submit application via online; the federal student financial aid application (fafsa) opens for all individuals who are pursuing postsecondary education. the student aid report (sar) that shows each student's estimated family contribution (efc) score is required for all scholarships and the most up-to-date transcript, official or unofficial, will be required for all scholarships fall 2019 grades should be included in the transcript that you upload into your scholarship application with SAT and/or ACT test scores; at least one reference letter is required. applicants should obtain a reference letter from a person who is outside of the applicant's family and can attest to the applicant's character while knowing the applicant well enough to pass judgement with credibility. **Deadline:** February 24. **Contact:** Phone: (239) 274-5900; Email: scholarships@floridacommunity.com.

10689 ■ John I. & Madeleine R. Taeni Scholarship Fund *(Undergraduate/Scholarship)*

Purpose: To support students pursuing degrees in teaching, nursing, paramedic training, or emergency medical technician training. **Focus:** Emergency and disaster services; Nursing; Paramedics; Teaching. **Qualif.:** Applicants must be residents of charlotte, collier, glades, hendry or lee county; highly motivated; and, pursuing teaching, nursing paramedic training, or emergency medical technician training. **Criteria:** Selection will be based on the committee's criteria.

Duration: Annual. **Contact:** Phone: (239) 274-5900; Email: scholarships@floridacommunity.com.

10690 ■ John M. & Mary A. Shanley Memorial Scholarship *(Undergraduate, Graduate/Scholarship)*

Purpose: To fund students pursuing degrees or advanced degrees in medicine, law, dentistry, teaching (math and science), ministry, engineering, accounting, architecture and computer science. **Focus:** Accounting; Agriculture, Economic aspects; Architecture; Computer and information sciences; Dentistry; Engineering; Law; Medicine; Religion; Teaching. **Qualif.:** Applicants must be graduates from a high school in charlotte, hendry or lee counties and plan to pursue medicine, law, dentistry, teaching (math or science), ministry, engineering, accounting, Agriculture, architecture or computer science with document financial need; GPA of 3.0 or higher. **Criteria:** Selection will be based on the committee's criteria.

Funds Avail.: $5,000 each. **Duration:** Annual; up to 4 years. **Number Awarded:** Varies. **To Apply:** Applicants should submit a FAFSA Form; Applicants must submit application via online.**Deadline:** February 24. **Remarks:** The scholarship was established in honor of john m. & mary a. Shanley. **Contact:** Phone: (239) 274-5900; Email: scholarships@floridacommunity.com.

10691 ■ John & Ruth Childe Scholarship Fund *(Undergraduate/Scholarship)*

Purpose: To fund the education of students with physical disability intending to pursue higher education in a college, university or technical school. **Focus:** General studies/Field of study not specified. **Qualif.:** Applicants must be graduate from public or private high school in Lee County; Must have a physical disability and the ability to state and describe disability in the application's personal essay section. **Criteria:** Selection will be based on the committee's criteria.

Funds Avail.: $1,900. **Duration:** Annual. **To Apply:** Applicants should submit a FAFSA Form; Applicants must submit application via online.**Deadline:** February 10. **Contact:** Phone: (239) 274-5900; Email: scholarships@floridacommunity.com.

10692 ■ Jordan Abdo Memorial Scholarship Fund *(Undergraduate/Scholarship)*

Purpose: To fund scholarships for a north fort myers high school male or female student athlete. **Focus:** General studies/Field of study not specified. **Criteria:** Selection will be based on the committee's criteria.

Funds Avail.: $1,400. **Duration:** Annual. **Number Awarded:** 1. **Remarks:** The scholarship was established in honor of jordan abdo. **Contact:** Phone: (239) 274-5900; Email: scholarships@floridacommunity.com.

10693 ■ Judge Isaac Anderson, Jr. Scholarship Fund *(Undergraduate/Scholarship)*

Purpose: To provide a two-year or four-yea regionally accredited college or university scholarship to Lee County minority high school seniors who can demonstrate financial need. **Focus:** General studies/Field of study not specified. **Criteria:** Selection will be based on the committee's criteria.

Funds Avail.: $1,300. **Duration:** Annual. **To Apply:** Applicants must submit application via online; the federal student financial aid application (fafsa) opens for all individuals who are pursuing postsecondary education. the student aid report (sar) that shows each student's estimated family contribution (efc) score is required for all scholarships and the most up-to-date transcript, official or unofficial, will be required for all scholarships fall 2019 grades should be included in the transcript that you upload into your scholarship application with SAT and/or ACT test scores; at least one reference letter is required. applicants should obtain a reference letter from a person who is outside of the applicant's family and can attest to the applicant's character while knowing the applicant well enough to pass judgement with credibility. **Deadline:** February 24. **Contact:** Phone: (239) 274-5900; Email: scholarships@floridacommunity.com.

10694 ■ Judge William J. Nelson Scholarship Fund *(Undergraduate/Scholarship)*

Purpose: To provide financial assistance for qualified high school seniors who will be attending the university of florida. **Focus:** General studies/Field of study not specified. **Qualif.:** Applicants must be graduates from a high school in charlotte, collier, glades, hendry or lee county who have overcome adversity in some way. they must attend the university of Florida. **Criteria:** Selection will be based on the committee's criteria.

Funds Avail.: $1,800. **Duration:** Annual. **Number Awarded:** 1. **To Apply:** Applicants should submit a FAFSA Form; Applicants must submit application via online.**Deadline:** February 10. **Contact:** Phone: (239) 274-5900; Email: scholarships@floridacommunity.com.

10695 ■ Lewis B. Barber Memorial Scholarship Fund *(Undergraduate/Scholarship)*

Purpose: To fund books and tuition for students pursuing either of the following educational paths: (1) certification to teach the deaf and blind; (2) seminary or pre-seminary

Awards are arranged alphabetically below their administering organizations

school to study church, christian music or christian education. **Focus:** Christian education; Religion. **Qualif.:** Applicants must be graduates from public or private high school in charlotte, collier, glades, hendry or lee county; pursue certification to teach deaf/blind or attend seminary/ pre-seminary school to study church, Christian music or Christian education; maintain satisfactory grades; acknowledge and express Jesus Christ as lord and savior.**Criteria:** Selection will be based on the committee's criteria.

Funds Avail.: $5,000. **Duration:** Annual. **To Apply:** Applicants should submit a FAFSA Form; Applicants must submit application via online.**Deadline:** February 10. **Remarks:** The scholarship was established in honor of lewis b. Barber. **Contact:** Phone: (239) 274-5900; Email: scholarships@floridacommunity.com.

10696 ■ Love Of Bonita Empowerment Scholarship Fund *(Undergraduate/Scholarship)*

Purpose: To provide books, tuition, and/or course fees for Bonita Springs residents who have been out of school for at least two years to attend a college or technical school. **Focus:** General studies/Field of study not specified. **Qualif.:** Applicants must be residents of bonita springs who are able to document financial need; may be students who were out of high school at least 2 years or received a ged. **Criteria:** Selection will be based on the committee's criteria.

Funds Avail.: $1,000. **Duration:** Annual. **Deadline:** February 10. **Contact:** Phone: (239) 274-5900; Email: scholarships@floridacommunity.com.

10697 ■ Matt Harmon Memorial Scholarship Fund *(Undergraduate/Scholarship)*

Purpose: To fund books and tuition for college-bound male baseball players. **Focus:** General studies/Field of study not specified. **Qualif.:** Applicants must be graduates of a public school in lee county; males who have played baseball in high school; and, able to demonstrate financial need. **Criteria:** Selection will be based on the committee's criteria.

Funds Avail.: $900. **Duration:** Annual. **To Apply:** Applicants must submit application via online; the federal student financial aid application (fafsa) opens for all individuals who are pursuing postsecondary education. the student aid report (sar) that shows each student's estimated family contribution (efc) score is required for all scholarships; the most up-to-date transcript, official or unofficial, will be required for all scholarships fall 2019 grades should be included in the transcript that you upload into your scholarship application; SAT and/or ACT test scores will be required; at least one reference letter is required. applicants should obtain a reference letter from a person who is outside of the applicant's family and can attest to the applicant's character while knowing the applicant well enough to pass judgement with credibility. **Deadline:** February 24. **Remarks:** the scholarship was established in honor of matt harmon. **Contact:** Phone: (239) 274-5900; Email: scholarships@floridacommunity.com.

10698 ■ Paul B. & Aline Flynn Scholarship Fund *(Undergraduate/Scholarship)*

Purpose: To assist high school or undergraduate/graduate students planning to study at a 4-year accredited college in the area of communications or journalism. **Focus:** Communications; Journalism. **Qualif.:** Applicants must have graduated from a public or private high school in Charlotte, Collier, Glades, Hendry or Lee County; pursue a degree in Communications, English or Journalism; and, have a 3.0 or higher GPA. **Criteria:** Selection will be based on the committee's criteria.

Funds Avail.: $2,950 each. **Duration:** Annual. **Number Awarded:** 2. **To Apply:** Applicants must submit application via online; the federal student financial aid application (fafsa) opens for all individuals who are pursuing postsecondary education. the student aid report (sar) that shows each student's estimated family contribution (efc) score is required for all scholarships and the most up-to-date transcript, official or unofficial, will be required for all scholarships fall 2019 grades should be included in the transcript that you upload into your scholarship application with SAT and/or ACT test scores; at least one reference letter is required. applicants should obtain a reference letter from a person who is outside of the applicant's family and can attest to the applicant's character while knowing the applicant well enough to pass judgement with credibility. **Deadline:** February 10. **Contact:** Phone: (239) 274-5900; Email: scholarships@floridacommunity.com.

10699 ■ Robert A. Kleckner Scholarship Fund *(Undergraduate, Graduate/Scholarship)*

Purpose: To assist financially needy high school, undergraduate, or graduate students pursuing a career in finance or accounting. **Focus:** Accounting; Finance. **Qualif.:** Applicants must be graduates from a high school in charlotte, glades, hendry or lee counties pursuing a degree in finance or accounting, and have documented financial need. **Criteria:** Selection will be based on the committee's criteria.

Funds Avail.: $2,300. **Duration:** Annual. **Deadline:** February 10. **Contact:** Phone: (239) 274-5900; Email: scholarships@floridacommunity.com.

10700 ■ Robert B. And Dorothy Pence Scholarship Fund *(Undergraduate/Scholarship)*

Purpose: To fund tuition for economically-disadvantaged students to attend college or technical school. **Focus:** General studies/Field of study not specified. **Qualif.:** Applicants must have graduated from a public or private high school in lee county and industrious students with good moral character with documented financial need. **Criteria:** Selection will be based on the committee's criteria.

Funds Avail.: $1,800. **Duration:** Annual. **Number Awarded:** 1. **To Apply:** Applicants must submit application via online; the federal student financial aid application (fafsa) opens for all individuals who are pursuing postsecondary education. the student aid report (sar) that shows each student's estimated family contribution (efc) score is required for all scholarships and the most up-to-date transcript, official or unofficial, will be required for all scholarships fall 2019 grades should be included in the transcript that you upload into your scholarship application with SAT and/or ACT test scores; at least one reference letter is required. applicants should obtain a reference letter from a person who is outside of the applicant's family and can attest to the applicant's character while knowing the applicant well enough to pass judgement with credibility. **Deadline:** February 24. **Contact:** Phone: (239) 274-5900; Email: scholarships@floridacommunity.com.

10701 ■ Robert C. & Margaret A. Schikora Scholarship Fund *(Undergraduate/Scholarship)*

Purpose: To assist needy students who have previously graduated from high schools in lee county to pursue postsecondary educational opportunities. **Focus:** General studies/Field of study not specified. **Qualif.:** Applicants must graduate from a public or private high school in Lee County; Must have a documented 3.0 GPA; Must be well-rounded, in terms of education, community service, sports

Awards are arranged alphabetically below their administering organizations

and leadership; Must document financial need. **Criteria:** Selection will be based on the committee's criteria.

Funds Avail.: $1,200. **Duration:** Annual. **Number Awarded:** 1. **To Apply:** Applicants must submit application via online; the federal student financial aid application (fafsa) opens for all individuals who are pursuing postsecondary education. the student aid report (sar) that shows each student's estimated family contribution (efc) score is required for all scholarships and the most up-to-date transcript, official or unofficial, will be required for all scholarships fall 2019 grades should be included in the transcript that you upload into your scholarship application with SAT and/or ACT test scores; at least one reference letter is required. applicants should obtain a reference letter from a person who is outside of the applicant's family and can attest to the applicant's character while knowing the applicant well enough to pass judgement with credibility. **Deadline:** February 24. **Contact:** Phone: (239) 274-5900; Email: scholarships@floridacommunity.com.

10702 ■ Ruth Messmer Scholarship Fund
(Undergraduate/Scholarship)

Purpose: To support women pursuing a career in business. **Focus:** Business. **Qualif.:** Applicants must be graduates from a public or private high school in lee, charlotte, glades, hendry or collier counties with woman pursuing a business career in college; have well-rounded in terms of education, community service, and leadership activities. **Criteria:** Selection will be based on the committee's criteria.

Funds Avail.: $1,200. **Duration:** Annual. **Number Awarded:** 1. **To Apply:** Applicants should submit a FAFSA Form; Applicants must submit application via online. **Deadline:** February 10. **Contact:** Phone: (239) 274-5900; Email: scholarships@floridacommunity.com.

10703 ■ Southwest Florida Community Foundation College Assistance Scholarships *(Undergraduate/Scholarship)*

Purpose: To fund books, laboratory fees, or any expenses related to student's academic costs. **Focus:** General studies/Field of study not specified. **Qualif.:** Applicants must reside in Charlotte, Lee, Glades, Hendry or Collier County and must demonstrate financial need. **Criteria:** Application materials are reviewed by a member of the Community Foundation's Scholarship Reading Committee. Selection of applicants will be based on academic standing and financial need.

Funds Avail.: No specific amount. **Duration:** Annual. **To Apply:** Applicants must submit a letter of interest, transcript, personal essay and financial need documentation.

10704 ■ Southwest Florida Deputy Sheriffs Association Fund *(Undergraduate/Scholarship)*

Purpose: To provide financial funds for qualified high school students who are dependents of law enforcement officers. **Focus:** General studies/Field of study not specified. **Qualif.:** Applicants must be graduates from high school in charlotte, collier, lee, hendry or glades counties who are dependents of law enforcement officers in the above counties. **Criteria:** Selection will be based on the committee's criteria.

Funds Avail.: $1,500. **Duration:** Annual. **Number Awarded:** 1. **To Apply:** Applicants must submit application via online; the federal student financial aid application (fafsa) opens for all individuals who are pursuing postsecondary education. the student aid report (sar) that shows

each student's estimated family contribution (efc) score is required for all scholarships and the most up-to-date transcript, official or unofficial, will be required for all scholarships fall 2019 grades should be included in the transcript that you upload into your scholarship application with SAT and/or ACT test scores; at least one reference letter is required. applicants should obtain a reference letter from a person who is outside of the applicant's family and can attest to the applicant's character while knowing the applicant well enough to pass judgement with credibility. **Deadline:** February 10. **Contact:** Phone: (239) 274-5900; Email: scholarships@floridacommunity.com.

10705 ■ William L. Graddy Law School Scholarship Fund *(Graduate/Scholarship)*

Purpose: To fund scholarships for students who have completed their first year of course load at an accredited law school. **Focus:** Law. **Qualif.:** Applicants must have completed first year of law school; a GPA of 2.8 or above; been residents of charlotte, collier, glades, hendry or lee for at least 3 years; and, demonstrated financial need. **Criteria:** Selection will be based on the committee's criteria.

Funds Avail.: $1,800. **Duration:** Annual. **Number Awarded:** 1. **To Apply:** Applicants must submit application via online; the federal student financial aid application (fafsa) opens for all individuals who are pursuing postsecondary education. the student aid report (sar) that shows each student's estimated family contribution (efc) score is required for all scholarships and the most up-to-date transcript, official or unofficial, will be required for all scholarships fall 2019 grades should be included in the transcript that you upload into your scholarship application with SAT and/or ACT test scores; at least one reference letter is required. applicants should obtain a reference letter from a person who is outside of the applicant's family and can attest to the applicant's character while knowing the applicant well enough to pass judgement with credibility. **Deadline:** February 24. **Contact:** Phone: (239) 274-5900; Email: scholarships@floridacommunity.com.

10706 ■ Southwest Movers Association (SMA)
510 W 15th St.
Austin, TX 78701
Ph: (512)476-0107
Fax: (512)474-6494
Free: 800-759-2305
E-mail: info@southwestmovers.org
URL: www.mytexasmover.com
Social Media: www.facebook.com/Southwest-Movers
-Association-444028518982712
twitter.com/My_Texas_Mover

10707 ■ SMA Foundation Scholarship Fund
(Undergraduate/Scholarship)

Purpose: To provide financial assistance to those workers or dependents who are pursuing studies toward a higher education. **Focus:** General studies/Field of study not specified. **Qualif.:** Applicants must be high school seniors or college students; must be employees or dependents of someone who is currently employed by a company with membership in the Southwest Movers Association. **Criteria:** Recipients will be chosen by the members of the SMA Foundation Board of Trustees. The funds will be sent directly to the recipient's school.

Funds Avail.: No specific amount. **Duration:** Annual. **To Apply:** Applicants must submit completed application form;

Awards are arranged alphabetically below their administering organizations

recent photograph; official transcript (last midterm is acceptable); letter of intent; and two or more letters of recommendation. **Deadline:** March 27. **Contact:** SMA Foundation Scholarship Fund, 510 W, 15th St., Austin, Tx 78701; Phone: 800-759-2305.

10708 ■ The Southwest Native-American Foundation (SWNAF)
1261 N Edgewood St.
Flagstaff, AZ 86004
E-mail: briantnanaf@gmail.com
URL: swnaf.org
Social Media: www.facebook.com/TSWNAF
www.instagram.com/swnaf
twitter.com/SWNAF1

10709 ■ Southwest Native-American Foundation Scholarships *(Undergraduate, University, Four Year College/Scholarship)*

Purpose: To assist high school seniors who are matriculating to college with scholarships. **Focus:** General studies/Field of study not specified. **Qualif.:** Applicants must be freshmen, sophomores, or juniors in high school who are interested in attending a four-year college, community college, art school, or vocational school. **Criteria:** Applicants are evaluated based on merit and financial need.

Funds Avail.: Varies. **To Apply:** Applicants must answer the questions (at website) in a Word Document and return with printed responses, along with a copy of high school transcript, letter of acceptance from the college/university or summer program, and one recommendation letter from a high school teacher. **Deadline:** May 1. **Contact:** Mail: The Southwest Native-American Foundation, P.O. Box W., Boulder, Colorado 80302-9998.

10710 ■ SouthWest Sun Solar Inc.
13752 Harbor Blvd.
Garden Grove, CA 92840
Ph: (714)582-3909
E-mail: info@southwestsunsolar.com
URL: southwestsunsolar.com
Social Media: www.facebook.com/Southwestsunsolar
twitter.com/SWSunSolar

10711 ■ SouthWest Sun Solar $500 Scholarship *(Undergraduate/Scholarship)*

Purpose: To support students who have shown work and a passion for solar energy. **Focus:** General studies/Field of study not specified. **Qualif.:** Applicants must be undergraduate students at a university/college in the southern California area and have a GPA of at least 3.0. **Criteria:** Academic excellence, work in the community or school, in addition to their community service.

Funds Avail.: $500. **To Apply:** Applicant must fill out the application form, attach a resume and submit two recommendation letters from employers, professors, advisors, or community leaders. Applicant must also submit a 500-word personal statement about their work in the community. **Deadline:** March 31. **Contact:** Summer Tran, Utility Specialist; Phone: 714-582-3909; Email: summer.tran@southwestsunsolar.com; Jason Khoo, Marketing Director; Phone: 714-883-0118; Email: jason@southwestsunsolar.com.

10712 ■ Southwestern Rugs Depot
22773 Teppert Ave.
Eastpointe, MI 48021
Ph: (770)609-5798
E-mail: contact@southwesternrugsdepot.com
URL: www.southwesternrugsdepot.com
Social Media: facebook.com/southwesternrugsdepot

10713 ■ Why Decor Matters Scholarship *(Undergraduate/Scholarship)*

Purpose: To provide assistance to students trying to afford college. **Focus:** General studies/Field of study not specified. **Qualif.:** Applicant must be a full- or part-time enrolled college student at an accredited university. **Criteria:** Selection will be based on the quality and originality of essay.

Funds Avail.: $1,000. **Duration:** Annual. **Number Awarded:** 1. **To Apply:** Applicant must submit essay of at least 450 words on the following topic: Please describe why home decor matters to you, your favorite interior decorating tips, how you think about interior design, etc. Application can be completed at www.southwesternrugsdepot.com/scholarship/. **Deadline:** December 31.

10714 ■ Spangenberg Shibley & Liber LLP
1001 Lakeside Ave. E, Ste. 1700
Cleveland, OH 44114
Fax: (216)696-3924
Free: 877-696-3303
URL: www.spanglaw.com
Social Media: www.facebook.com/spangenberg.law.firm
www.linkedin.com/company/spangenberg-shibley-&-liber-llp
twitter.com/SpangenbergLaw
www.youtube.com/user/spanglawfirm

10715 ■ Spangenberg Shibley & Liber Video PSA Scholarship Awards *(Undergraduate/Scholarship)*

Purpose: To create awareness about various social topics. **Focus:** Law. **Qualif.:** Applicants must be U.S citizens or legal permanent U.S. residents; must be currently attending an educational institution or planning to attend a college university during academic year. **Criteria:** Selection will be evaluated on originality, creativity, strength of message and ability to inspire viewers.

Funds Avail.: $2,000 First prize; $1,000 Second prize; $500 Third prize. **To Apply:** Applicants must submit all required entry materials including the following: completed entry form; original 30-60 second SPA video on one of the Scholarship Program topics; headshot photo (.jpg or.png); and all required information by the deadline. Applicants must have read and agree to the General Rules & Disclaimers. **Deadline:** March 31.

10716 ■ Specialized Carriers and Rigging Association (SC&RA)
5870 Trinity Pky., Ste. 200
Centreville, VA 20120
Ph: (703)698-0291
E-mail: info@scranet.org
URL: www.scranet.org
Social Media: www.facebook.com/scranet
www.instagram.com/scra_net

Awards are arranged alphabetically below their administering organizations

www.linkedin.com/company/scranet
twitter.com/scranet
www.youtube.com/user/scranetorg

10717 ■ SC&R Foundation Grant Program
(Undergraduate/Grant)

Purpose: To support students and employees in the specialized carriers and rigging industry. **Focus:** Transportation. **Qualif.:** Applicants must open to anyone who currently works in the specialized transportation or crane and rigging industry; open to anyone who is interested in working in the above mentioned industry; open to SC&RA member company employees; courses or classes should be directly related to acquiring necessary skills to advance their career in the industry; (for example, diesel mechanics, welding, book keeping, driver school, crane operator certification, marketing, accounting). **Criteria:** Scholarship committee performed blind evaluations of all the applications.

Funds Avail.: Up to $5,000. **Duration:** Annual. **Number Awarded:** Varies. **To Apply:** Applicants must complete the application form together with two letters of recommendation (one letter from an academic advisor or employer); official transcripts; recent photograph; and contact information. **Deadline:** October 31. **Contact:** Jackie Roskos; Phone: 703-698-0291; Email: jroskos@scr-foundation.org.

10718 ■ SC&R Foundation Scholarship
(Undergraduate/Scholarship)

Purpose: To provide career opportunities and scholarship to its members. **Focus:** Transportation. **Qualif.:** Applicants must be an employee of an SC&RA member company; must be a direct relative (child, step child, spouse, grand child) of an employee of an SC&RA member company; scholarships are awarded to applicants pursuing 4 year degree, masters degree, or internship with an SC&RA member company; open to full-time and part-time students. **Criteria:** Scholarship committee performed blind evaluations of all the applications.

Funds Avail.: $3,000. **Duration:** Annual. **To Apply:** Applicants must complete the application form together with two letters of recommendation (one letter from an academic advisor or employer); official transcripts; recent photograph; and contact information. **Deadline:** January 21.

10719 ■ Specialty Equipment Market Association (SEMA)
1575 S Valley Vista Dr.
Diamond Bar, CA 91765-0910
Ph: (909)610-2030
Fax: (909)860-0184
URL: www.sema.org

10720 ■ SEMA Memorial Scholarship and Loan Forgiveness Award *(Graduate, Undergraduate/Loan, Scholarship)*

Purpose: To foster industry leadership by supporting the education of students pursuing careers in the automotive aftermarket. **Focus:** Automotive technology. **Qualif.:** Applicants must be employees of a SEMA member-company who have completed a certificate, associate, bachelor's or graduate level degree at an accredited university, college or vocational/training program in the United States; must have a minimum 2.5 GPA.

Duration: Annual. **To Apply:** Applicants must submit a official, sealed transcripts for all college or post-secondary

course work completed through the first quarter or semester of the current year; a statement of purpose and give us your best in 500 words or less; Demonstrate passion for the automotive industry. **Deadline:** March 1. **Contact:** Juliet Marshall, SEMA Mducation manager; Phone: 909-978-6655; Email: julietm@sema.org.

10721 ■ SEMA Memorial Scholarships *(Graduate, Undergraduate/Scholarship)*

Purpose: To support educational goals for students pursuing careers in the automotive aftermarkets. **Focus:** Automotive technology. **Qualif.:** Applicant must be a U.S. Citizen enrolled full-time in a program of study at an accredited university, college or post-secondary vocational/technical program located within the United States, at the time of application; must have a minimum 2.5 grade point average; must be pursuing studies leading to a career in the automotive industry or related field. **Criteria:** Selection will be based on academic performance.

Funds Avail.: Varies. **Duration:** Annual. **To Apply:** Applicant must upload a valid copy of school transcript or trade-school progress report; minimum of one (1) online recommendation; essay: statement of purpose. **Deadline:** March 1. **Remarks:** Established in 1984. **Contact:** SEMA Manager of Student Programs Juliet Marshall at 909-978-6655 or julietm@sema.org.

10722 ■ Specialty Equipment Market Association Scholarships *(Graduate, Undergraduate, Vocational/Occupational/Scholarship)*

Purpose: To foster industry leadership by supporting the education of students pursuing careers in the automotive aftermarket; to foster leadership in the specialty equipment marketplace. **Focus:** Automotive technology. **Criteria:** Selection will be based on academic performance.

Funds Avail.: $2,000 - $3,000; with $5,000 going to the top student. **Duration:** Annual. **To Apply:** Applicants must submit school transcripts; a minimum of one online recommendation; two 250-word essays; and personal background. **Deadline:** March 5.

10723 ■ SPIE
PO Box 10
Bellingham, WA 98227-0010
Ph: (360)676-3290
Fax: (360)647-1445
Free: 888-504-8171
E-mail: customerservice@spie.org
URL: spie.org
Social Media: www.facebook.com/SPIE.org
www.instagram.com/spiephotonics
www.linkedin.com/company/spie
twitter.com/SPIEtweets
www.youtube.com/spietv

10724 ■ BACUS Scholarship *(Graduate, Undergraduate/Scholarship)*

Purpose: To provide education assistance to students in field of microlithography. **Focus:** Engineering, Optical; Optics. **Qualif.:** Applicants must be student members of SPIE; must be enrolled full-time, undergraduate or graduate students in the field of microlithography emphasizing on optical tooling or semiconductor manufacturing technologies. **Criteria:** Selection will be based on merit, experiences and education level.

Awards are arranged alphabetically below their administering organizations

Funds Avail.: $5,000. **Duration:** Annual. **To Apply:** Applicants must submit a completed scholarship application form (available on the website) and two letters of recommendation sent separately by the recommender; completed application must be sent electronically; standard Student Membership fee is $20. **Deadline:** February 15. **Remarks:** Established in 1998. **Contact:** Email: scholarships@spie.org.

10725 ■ D.J. Lovell Scholarship *(Graduate, Undergraduate/Scholarship)*

Purpose: To provide education assistance to a student in optical design. **Focus:** Engineering, Optical; Optics. **Qualif.:** Applicants must be student members of SPIE; must be enrolled full-time in an optics photonics imaging or optoelectronics program or related discipline at an accredited school; must be in high school or secondary school, undergraduate or post-secondary school, or graduate school. **Criteria:** Selection will be based on merit, experiences and education level.

Funds Avail.: $11,000. **Duration:** Annual. **To Apply:** Applicants must submit a completed scholarship application form (available on the website) and two letters of recommendation sent separately by the recommender; completed application must be sent electronically; standard Student Membership fee is $20. **Deadline:** February 15. **Contact:** Email: scholarships@spie.org.

10726 ■ Michael Kidger Memorial Scholarship in Optical Design *(Undergraduate/Scholarship)*

Purpose: To provide education assistance to a student engaged in optical design of either imaging or non-imaging systems. **Focus:** Engineering, Optical; Optics. **Qualif.:** Applicants must be students of optical design; must meet the entry criteria for the chosen course of study or research; must have at least one year after the award to completion of their chosen course of study. **Criteria:** Selection will be based on merit, experiences and education level.

Duration: Annual. **To Apply:** Applicants must submit a summary (five pages maximum) of their academic background and interest in pursuing training or research in optical design; and two letters of recommendation. **Remarks:** Established in honor of Michael John Kidger, a well-respected educator and member of the optical science and engineering community. Established in 1998. **Contact:** Email: scholarships@spie.org.

10727 ■ Laser Technology, Engineering and Applications Scholarship *(Graduate, Undergraduate/Scholarship)*

Purpose: To recognize student's scholarly achievement in laser technology, engineering, or applications. **Focus:** Engineering; Technology. **Qualif.:** Applicants must be student members of SPIE; must be enrolled full-time in an optics photonics imaging or optoelectronics program or related discipline at an accredited school; must be in high school or secondary school, undergraduate or post-secondary school, or graduate school. **Criteria:** Selection will be based on merit, experiences and education level.

Funds Avail.: $5,000. **Duration:** Annual. **To Apply:** Applicants must submit a completed scholarship application form (available on the website) and two letters of recommendation sent separately by the recommender; completed application must be sent electronically; standard Student Membership fee is $20. **Deadline:** February 15. **Remarks:** Sponsored in part by a gift from the former Forum for Military Applications of Directed Energy. **Contact:** Email: scholarships@spie.org.

10728 ■ Optical Design and Engineering Scholarship *(Graduate, Undergraduate/Scholarship)*

Purpose: To provide education assistance to a student in optical design and engineering. **Focus:** Engineering, Optical; Optics. **Qualif.:** Applicants must be student members of SPIE; must be enrolled full-time, undergraduate or graduate in an optical design and engineering. **Criteria:** Selection will be based on merit, experiences and education level.

Funds Avail.: No specific amount. **Duration:** Annual. **To Apply:** Applicants must submit a completed scholarship application form (available on the website) and two letters of recommendation sent separately by the recommender; completed application must be sent electronically; standard Student Membership fee is $20. **Deadline:** February 15. **Remarks:** Established in honor of Bill Price and Warren Smith, both well-respected members of SPIE's technical community. **Contact:** Email: scholarships@spie.org.

10729 ■ SPIE Student Author Travel Grants *(Graduate, Undergraduate/Grant)*

Purpose: To provide supplement travel support for students presenting a paper at an SPIE meeting. **Focus:** Engineering, Optical; Optics. **Qualif.:** Applicants must be full-time student members of SPIE; must be a full-time student author in a high school, undergraduate, or graduate program, who will present their accepted paper at an SPIE conference and submit their manuscript to be published in the Proceedings of SPIE. **Criteria:** Selection will be based on merit, experiences and education level.

Funds Avail.: $250-$500 (domestic traveler); $300-$750 (international traveler). **Duration:** Annual. **To Apply:** Applicants must submit a completed scholarship application form (available on the website) and two letters of recommendation sent separately by the recommender; completed application must be sent electronically; standard Student Membership fee is $20. **Contact:** AuthorHelp@spie.org.

10730 ■ Spinal Cord Injury BC (SCIBC)
780 SW Marine Drive
Vancouver, BC, Canada V6P 5Y7
Ph: (604)324-3611
Fax: (604)326-1229
Free: 800-689-2477
E-mail: info@sci-bc.ca
URL: sci-bc.ca
Social Media: www.facebook.com/SpinalCordInjuryBC
www.instagram.com/sci_bc
www.linkedin.com/company/spinal-cord-injury-bc
twitter.com/sci_bc
www.youtube.com/user/BCParaplegic

10731 ■ BCPF Bursaries *(Undergraduate/Scholarship)*

Purpose: To provide educational funds to deserving students with disabilities. **Focus:** General studies/Field of study not specified. **Qualif.:** Applicants must be a student with a spinal cord injury; must be a Canadian citizen or landed immigrant, resident of BC and must be attending or planning to attend a post-secondary educational institution in BC. **Criteria:** Selection will be based on merit.

To Apply: Applicants must submit the completed application form available from the website; must include an official transcript of records, and a letter of reference from either an employer or educator. **Deadline:** May 13. **Con-**

Awards are arranged alphabetically below their administering organizations

tact: British Columbia Paraplegic Foundation Bursary Committee, 780 SW Marine Dr., Vancouver, BC, V6P 5Y7.

10732 ■ Spokeo Inc.
556 S Fair Oaks Ave., Ste. 101-179
Pasadena, CA 91105
E-mail: customercare@spokeo.com
URL: www.spokeo.com
Social Media: www.facebook.com/spokeo
www.linkedin.com/company/spokeo
twitter.com/spokeo
youtube.com/user/spokeo

10733 ■ Spokeo Connections Scholarships
(Undergraduate/Scholarship)

Purpose: To help students to find and achieve their own dreams. **Focus:** General studies/Field of study not specified. **Qualif.:** Applicants must be U.S. citizens or permanent residents of the United States; must be either an incoming college freshmen or a current undergraduate or graduate students of any accredited two- or four-year college or university; must have a GPA of 3.0 or higher.

Funds Avail.: $1,000. **Duration:** Annual. **To Apply:** Applicants must be entered through the official spokeo connections scholarship submission form online, essays must be written in English and uploaded in either a Word or PDF format. **Deadline:** July 1. **Contact:** URL: community.spokeo.com.

10734 ■ Sports Turf Managers Association (STMA)
805 New Hampshire St., Ste. E
Lawrence, KS 66044
Ph: (785)843-2549
Fax: (785)843-2977
Free: 800-323-3875
E-mail: kheck@stma.org
URL: www.stma.org
Social Media: www.facebook.com/FieldExperts
www.linkedin.com/company/fieldexperts
twitter.com/FieldExperts

10735 ■ Terry Mellor Continuing Education Grant
(Undergraduate/Grant)

Purpose: To fund a portion of the winner's attendance at the STMA Conference. **Focus:** Athletics. **Qualif.:** Applicants must be members of STMA Affiliated Chapter and nominators must be STMA National Members; self nominations are not permissible. **Criteria:** Selection will be based on the committees' criteria.

Funds Avail.: $1,000. **Duration:** Annual. **To Apply:** Applicants must submit letter of recommendation for the nominees. **Deadline:** October 15. **Contact:** STMA headquarter; Phone: 800-323-3875.

10736 ■ Safer Athletic Field Environments Scholarships (SAFE) *(Graduate, Undergraduate, Two Year College/Scholarship)*

Purpose: To assist students within the industry who are outstanding within the sports turf industry, both in sports turf management and research. **Focus:** Turfgrass management. **Qualif.:** Applicants must be enrolled in a two-year program, undergraduate program, or graduate program in a major/field related to sports turf management in the upcoming academic year; applicants must have at least one semester of study left; must be an STMA member. **Criteria:** Selection will be based on merit, not the basis of need; also evaluated on the basis of academic skills, potential within the industry, employment history, extracurricular activities, and the recommendations of faculty advisors and employers.

Duration: Annual. **To Apply:** Application must be completed online and at www.stma.org/scholarship-program/. **Deadline:** October 15. **Remarks:** SAFE awards three named scholarships: the Dr. James Watson Graduate Scholarship, the Dr. James Watson Undergraduate Scholarship, and the Dr. Fred Grau Scholarship. The Watson Scholarships are named in honor of long-time green industry researcher and consultant Dr. James Watson, are funded by the Toro Giving Program, and are presented to the top graduate and undergraduate scholarship recipients. The top recipient from a two-year program receives the Dr. Fred Grau scholarship, which is named in honor of the first turfgrass extension specialist in the United States. There is not a separate application for these named scholarships; they are awarded to the top graduate and undergraduate applicants. Established in 2000.

10737 ■ Gary Vanden Berg Internship Grant
(Undergraduate/Grant)

Purpose: To offset the costs a student may have incurred while interning. **Focus:** Sports studies. **Qualif.:** Applicants must be student members of STMA in good standing who are currently enrolled in a minimum of 6 credit hours or were enrolled in a minimum of 6 credit hours in the semester just prior to the internship and graduates who completed an internship after graduation are also eligible. **Criteria:** Selection will be based on the committees' criteria.

Funds Avail.: $1,000. **Duration:** Annual; late fall. **To Apply:** Applicants must submit a complete application form together with the following materials: 650 words or less, describing the value of the internship to the applicants' career and how the internship will help the applicants to achieve their goals; transcript (s) from all higher education institution (s) attended; letter of reference from the applicants' Internship Supervisor and; copy of resume. **Deadline:** October 15. **Contact:** Kim Heck, 800-323-3875.

10738 ■ SprayWorks Equipment Group
945 McKinley Ave., SW
Canton, OH 44707
Ph: (330)587-4141
URL: sprayworksequipment.com

10739 ■ The James Davidson Innovative Student Scholarship *(Graduate/Scholarship)*

Purpose: To encourage innovation in chemical science and awareness of the polyurethane industry. **Focus:** Chemistry. **Qualif.:** Applicant must be pursuing a degree in chemical sciences at a four-year university; must have a minimum 2.5 GPA. **Criteria:** Students must submit one academic letter of recommendation from a non-family member and 800 word or less essay, explaining how they are or plan to create innovation through chemical science.

Funds Avail.: $600. **Duration:** Annual. **Number Awarded:** 1. **To Apply:** Applicant must submit an 800-word or less essay explaining how they are or plan to create innovation through chemical science. Essay must be typed, double-

Awards are arranged alphabetically below their administering organizations

spaced, in times new roman font, on 8x11 paper, and written in English. Also must have a title page; application is available online at sprayworksequipment. **Deadline:** January 15. **Contact:** Email: Jennifer@sprayworksequipment.com.

10740 ■ The Charles B. Staats Memorial Foundation Inc.

1729 Manhasset Dr.
Dunwoody, GA 30338
Ph: (404)731-0594
E-mail: maggie@cbsmf.org
URL: www.cbsmf.org

10741 ■ The Charles B. Staat Memorial Scholarship *(Graduate/Scholarship)*

Purpose: To inspire and empower high school seniors to become future leaders and active members of their communities by serving as swim coaches to youth and adults. **Focus:** General studies/Field of study not specified. **Qualif.:** Applicant must be a high school senior in Georgia accepted into a four-year college or university for the upcoming school year; have a minimum 3.0 GPA; and have at least two years of demonstrated swim coach experience. **Criteria:** Five board members will evaluate the applications independently and then come together to review them. The following eight categories are considered: scholastic performance, quality of application, swimming reference, other reference, community involvement, community leadership, swimming involvement, and significance of coaching.

Funds Avail.: Variable, currently $2,000. **Duration:** Annual; Scholarship is good for up to four years, based on meeting scholarship contract annual criteria. **Number Awarded:** 1. **To Apply:** Application should be completed on website and submitted via email along with a swimming reference letter, a character reference letter, copy of ACT/SAT scores, official high school transcript, and proof of acceptance to a four-year college or university. **Deadline:** May 25. **Contact:** Margaret P. Staats; Email: maggie@cbsmf.org; URL: www.cbsmf.org/scholarship.html.

10742 ■ Stained Glass Association of America (SGAA)

255 Pratt St.
Buffalo, NY 14204
Ph: (816)737-2090
Free: 800-438-9581
E-mail: headquarters@sgaaonline.com
URL: stainedglass.org
Social Media: www.facebook.com/SGAA1
www.instagram.com/sgaa_hq
www.linkedin.com/company/stained-glass-association-of
-america

10743 ■ Albinas Elskus Scholarship *(Other/Scholarship)*

Purpose: To support artists who display the promise for creativity in the stained glass arts. **Focus:** Arts; Painting. **Qualif.:** Applicant must be an artist who displays the promise for creativity in the stained glass arts especially, but not limited to, the area of glass painting. **Funds Avail.:** Up to $1,000. **Duration:** Annual. **To Apply:** Application form and details available at stainedglass.org/

stained-glass-school/scholarships/.

10744 ■ Dorothy L. Maddy Academic Scholarship *(Undergraduate/Scholarship)*

Purpose: To support students and artists of stained glass. **Focus:** Art. **Qualif.:** Applicant must be a student enrolled in a full-time academic program and a stained glass artist. **Criteria:** Selection will be made by the SGS Scholarship Committee.

Funds Avail.: $1,000. **Duration:** Annual. **Number Awarded:** 1. **To Apply:** Application form and details available at stainedglass.org/stained-glass-school/scholarships/.

10745 ■ Dorothy L. Maddy Workshop/Seminar Scholarship *(Other/Scholarship)*

Purpose: To support stained glass artists in taking workshops and short-term classes. **Focus:** Arts; Design. **Qualif.:** Applicants must be stained glass artists looking to attend hands-on, short-term workshops and classes.

Funds Avail.: $600. **Duration:** Annual. **To Apply:** Application form and details available at stainedglass.org/stained-glass-school/scholarships/.

10746 ■ Stanford Advanced Materials

23661 Birtcher Dr.
Lake Forest, CA 92630
Ph: (949)407-8904
Fax: (949)812-6690
E-mail: sales@samaterials.com
URL: www.samaterials.com
Social Media: www.facebook.com/samaterials
www.linkedin.com/company/stanford-advanced-materials
twitter.com/SAMaterials

10747 ■ Stanford Advanced Materials $1,000 College Scholarship *(College/Scholarship)*

Purpose: To help needy students enhance their writing skills and contribute to the study of chemistry related to materials. **Focus:** Materials research/science.

Funds Avail.: $1,000. **Contact:** www.samaterials.com/content/315-stanford-advanced-materials-1000-college-scholarship.

10748 ■ Stark Community Foundation (SCF)

400 Market Ave. N, Ste. 200
Canton, OH 44702
Ph: (330)454-3426
Fax: (330)454-5855
E-mail: info@starkcf.org
URL: www.starkcf.org
Social Media: www.facebook.com/pages/Stark-Community
-Foundation/381913043984
www.instagram.com/starkcommfdn
www.youtube.com/channel/UCY_gFvbZjZCrm_AkD-
DREBxw

10749 ■ Wayne D. Ackerman Family Scholarship Fund *(Undergraduate/Scholarship)*

Purpose: To provide scholarship assistance to qualified individuals who want to pursue their studies. **Focus:** General studies/Field of study not specified. **Qualif.:** Applicants must be seniors attending a high school in Stark County,

Awards are arranged alphabetically below their administering organizations

Ohio who will graduate with their class in May or June; must be enrolled as full-time students and have a cumulative GPA of at least 3.0 on a 4.0 scale and have been accepted Into a four-year college or university.

Duration: Annual. **Number Awarded:** Varies. **To Apply:** Applicants must submit a copy of your Student Aid Report (SAR) from the Free Application for Federal Student Aid (FAFSA); two letters of recommendation; official transcript. **Deadline:** April 1. **Contact:** Phone: 330-454-3426; Email: scholarship@starkcf.org.

10750 ■ Alice J. Foit Scholarship Fund
(Undergraduate/Scholarship)

Purpose: To provide scholarship assistance to qualified individuals who want to pursue their studies. **Focus:** General studies/Field of study not specified. **Qualif.:** Applicants must be Carroll County High School graduates or graduates residing in German Township of Harrison County, Ohio enrolled as full-time students at a two or four-year college or university program leading to a degree; and if attending college, must intend to live in or work in either Carroll or Harrison County, Ohio for a minimum of two years after completion of their education. **Criteria:** Selection will be based on demonstrated involvement in both extracurricular activities and community and religious activities.

Funds Avail.: No specific amount. **Duration:** Annual. **Number Awarded:** Varies. **Remarks:** Established in 2001. **Contact:** Phone: 330-454-3426; Email: scholarship@starkcf.org.

10751 ■ American Guild of Organists, Canton Chapter Charitable Fund *(Undergraduate/Scholarship)*

Purpose: To provide scholarship assistance to qualified individuals who want to pursue their studies. **Focus:** Music.

Funds Avail.: No specific amount. **Remarks:** Established in 1992.

10752 ■ Bill McCarthy Boy Scout Scholarship Fund
(Undergraduate/Scholarship)

Purpose: To provide scholarship assistance to qualified individuals who want to pursue their studies. **Focus:** General studies/Field of study not specified.

Funds Avail.: No specific amount. **Duration:** Annual. **Number Awarded:** Varies. **To Apply:** Applicants must submit a copy of your Student Aid Report (SAR) from the Free Application for Federal Student Aid (FAFSA); two letters of recommendation; official transcript. **Remarks:** Established in 1997. **Contact:** Phone: 330-454-3426; Email: scholarship@starkcf.org.

10753 ■ Joan Blend Scholarship Fund *(Undergraduate, Graduate/Scholarship)*

Purpose: To assist students pursuing a degree in registered nursing. **Focus:** Nursing. **Qualif.:** Applicants must be students pursuing a degree in registered nursing; must be a Stark County resident attending or planning to attend a university or nursing school offering a registered nursing degree; must have a minimum GPA of 2.5 for undergraduate studies or 3.0 for graduate studies and demonstrate financial need. **Criteria:** Selection will be based on academic standing and financial need.

Funds Avail.: No specific amount. **Duration:** Annual. **To Apply:** Applicants must submit name and email address of a manager or supervisor who you would like to ask to submit a letter of recommendation on your behalf. If you have no work experience, please pick another professional who supervised you in a volunteer situation. He/She will be contacted automatically via email. **Deadline:** April 1. **Remarks:** Established in 2000.

10754 ■ Harry D. Callahan Educational Trust
(Undergraduate/Scholarship)

Purpose: To provide scholarship assistance to qualified individuals who want to pursue their studies. **Focus:** General studies/Field of study not specified. **Qualif.:** Applicants must be students who are residents of Stark County, in the last year at a Stark County high school or a Stark County high school graduate, and must have applied to or been accepted by a college or recognized educational institution of higher learning in the state of Ohio or within a 150 mile radius of the center of Canton, Ohio; may already be enrolled in college; must have a minimum cumulative GPA of 2.6.

Duration: Annual. **Number Awarded:** Varies. **To Apply:** Applicants must submit: completed application form; answered character reference questionnaires from at least four persons of recognized standing in the community; transcript of high school credits and all credits earned from an institution of higher learning. **Deadline:** April 1. **Remarks:** Established in 1985. **Contact:** Phone: 330-454-3426; Email: scholarship@starkcf.org.

10755 ■ George H. and Anna Casper Fund
(Undergraduate, Graduate/Scholarship, Loan)

Purpose: To provide scholarship assistance to qualified individuals who want to pursue their studies. **Focus:** General studies/Field of study not specified. **Qualif.:** Applicants must be Stark County graduates pursuing graduate-level studies. **Criteria:** Recipients will be selected based on financial need and academic standing.

Funds Avail.: No specific amount. **To Apply:** Applicants must complete and submit the application form. **Remarks:** Established in 1973. **Contact:** info@cantonstudentloan.org.

10756 ■ Robert Martz DiGiacomo Memorial Scholarship Fund *(Undergraduate/Scholarship)*

Purpose: To provide scholarship assistance to qualified individuals who want to pursue their studies. **Focus:** General studies/Field of study not specified.

Duration: Annual. **Number Awarded:** Varies. **To Apply:** Applications can be submitted online; essay (500 words or fewer); must submit a copy of your Student Aid Report (SAR) from the Free Application for Federal Student Aid (FAFSA); two letters of recommendation; official transcript. **Remarks:** Established in 1999. **Contact:** Phone: 330-454-3426; Email: scholarship@starkcf.org.

10757 ■ Don and Madalyn Sickafoose Educational Trust Fund *(Undergraduate/Scholarship, Loan)*

Purpose: To provide scholarship assistance to qualified individuals who want to pursue their studies. **Focus:** General studies/Field of study not specified. **Qualif.:** Applicants must be students living in southeastern Stark County, northwestern Carroll County and northern Tuscarawas County. **Criteria:** Selection is based on financial need; demonstrated aptitude for college work; a minimum GPA of 2.5.

Duration: Annual. **Number Awarded:** Varies. **To Apply:** Applicants must submit a copy of your Student Aid Report. **Deadline:** April 1. **Remarks:** Established in 1982. **Contact:** Phone: 330-454-3426; Email: scholarship@starkcf.org.

Awards are arranged alphabetically below their administering organizations

10758 ■ Jack B. Fisher Scholarship Fund *(Graduate/ Scholarship)*

Purpose: To assist graduates of Stark County high schools who are current employees of Fishers Foods in good standing. **Focus:** Fisheries sciences/management. **Qualif.:** Applicants must be graduates of Stark County High school and current employees of Fisher Foods in good standing; if employed during high school, a minimum of one year of employment is required; if employed after graduation from high school, a minimum of 2 years of employment is required; must have total of one year previous service as a fishers foods employee. **Criteria:** Selection is based on demonstrated financial need.

Duration: Annual. **Number Awarded:** Varies. **To Apply:** Applicants must provide the name and email address of a Fishers Foods store manager who you would like to ask to submit a letter of recommendation on your behalf. **Deadline:** April 1. **Remarks:** Established in 1997. **Contact:** Phone: 330-454-3426; Email: scholarship@starkcf.org.

10759 ■ David A. and Pamela A. Gault Charitable Fund *(Undergraduate/Scholarship)*

Purpose: To provide scholarship assistance to qualified individuals who want to pursue their studies. **Focus:** General studies/Field of study not specified.

Funds Avail.: No specific amount. **Duration:** Annual. **Number Awarded:** Varies. **To Apply:** Applicants must submit a copy of your Student Aid Report (SAR) from the Free Application for Federal Student Aid (FAFSA); two letters of recommendation; official transcript. **Deadline:** January 4. **Remarks:** Established in 1998. **Contact:** Phone: 330-454-3426; Email: scholarship@starkcf.org.

10760 ■ Margaret S. Gilbert Scholarship Fund *(Graduate/Scholarship)*

Purpose: To provide scholarship assistance to qualified individuals who want to pursue their studies. **Focus:** History; Mathematics and mathematical sciences; Natural sciences. **Qualif.:** Applicants must be Stark County public high school female graduates, who attend or will attend, Oberlin College and major in one of the sciences, mathematics or history.

Duration: Annual. **Number Awarded:** Varies. **To Apply:** Applicants must submit a copy of your Student Aid Report (SAR) from the Free Application for Federal Student Aid (FAFSA); two letters of recommendation; official transcript. **Remarks:** Established in 1992. **Contact:** Phone: 330-454-3426; Email: scholarship@starkcf.org.

10761 ■ James H. and Shirley L. Green Scholarship Fund *(Undergraduate/Scholarship)*

Purpose: To provide scholarship assistance to qualified individuals who want to pursue their studies. **Focus:** General studies/Field of study not specified.

Funds Avail.: No specific amount. **Duration:** Annual. **Remarks:** Established in 2000. **Contact:** Phone: 330-454-3426; Email: scholarship@starkcf.org.

10762 ■ Velma Shotwell Griffin Memorial Scholarship Fund *(Undergraduate/Scholarship)*

Purpose: To provide scholarship assistance to qualified individuals who want to pursue their studies. **Focus:** History; Music; Writing. **Qualif.:** Applicants must be graduates of Conotton Valley High School or Carrollton High School; must be planning to enroll, or currently enrolled, at an accredited college or university to pursue further education in the following fields; history; writing, not limited to, English journalism, language arts, communications and programs in mass media; music, not limited to vocal music, instrumental music, music history, music education and music performance; any other program or field of study approved by the selection committee. **Criteria:** Selection will be based on financial needs; vocal music, instrumental music, music history, music education, and music performance.

Funds Avail.: No specific amount. **Duration:** Annual. **Number Awarded:** Varies. **To Apply:** Applicants must submit a copy of your Student Aid Report (SAR) from the Free Application for Federal Student Aid (FAFSA); two letters of recommendation; official transcript. **Deadline:** March 1. **Remarks:** Established in 2000. **Contact:** Phone: 330-454-3426; Email: scholarship@starkcf.org.

10763 ■ Dr. James H. Heckman Memorial Scholarship Fund *(Undergraduate/Scholarship)*

Purpose: To provide scholarship assistance to qualified individuals who want to pursue their studies. **Focus:** General studies/Field of study not specified. **Qualif.:** Applicants must be Hoover High School graduating seniors; must have above average accomplishment in high school; must have demonstrated financial need; must be planning to a four-year degree program in any field of study; must demonstrate good moral and personal characteristics.

Funds Avail.: No specific amount. **Duration:** Annual. **Number Awarded:** Varies. **To Apply:** Applicants must submit a copy of your Student Aid Report (SAR) from the Free Application for Federal Student Aid (FAFSA); two letters of recommendation; official transcript. **Deadline:** April 1. **Contact:** Phone: 330-454-3426; Email: scholarship@ starkcf.org.

10764 ■ Dale O. Heimberger CRNA Memorial Scholarship Fund *(Graduate/Scholarship)*

Purpose: To provide scholarship assistance to qualified individuals who want to pursue their studies. **Focus:** Anesthesiology. **Qualif.:** Applicants must be accepted into the University of Akron, College of Nursing-Graduate Anesthesia Program. **Criteria:** Selection will be based on scholastic aptitude and demonstrated financial need.

Funds Avail.: No specific amount. **To Apply:** Applicants must submit a copy of your Student Aid Report (SAR) from the Free Application for Federal Student Aid (FAFSA); two letters of recommendation; official transcript. **Remarks:** Established in 1999. **Contact:** Phone: 330-454-3426; Email: scholarship@starkcf.org.

10765 ■ Raymond T. Hoge Scholarship Fund *(Undergraduate/Scholarship)*

Purpose: To provide scholarship assistance to qualified individuals who want to pursue their studies. **Focus:** Business; Education. **Qualif.:** Applicants must be Stark County residents, specifically, graduating seniors of Perry High School or alumni who plan to attend an institution of higher learning; must be enrolled, or will be enrolled as full-time students and must be planning to pursue a degree in the field of business or education.

Funds Avail.: No specific amount. **Duration:** Annual. **Number Awarded:** Varies. **To Apply:** Applicants must submit a copy of your Student Aid Report (SAR) from the Free Application for Federal Student Aid (FAFSA); two letters of recommendation; official transcript. **Deadline:** April 1. **Remarks:** Established in 2000. **Contact:** Phone: 330-454-3426; Email: scholarship@starkcf.org.

Awards are arranged alphabetically below their administering organizations

10766 ■ Judge and Mrs. Robert D. Horowitz Legal Scholarship Fund *(Graduate, Undergraduate/ Scholarship)*

Purpose: To provide scholarship assistance to qualified individuals who want to pursue their studies. **Focus:** Paralegal studies. **Criteria:** Selection will be based on the committee's criteria.

Funds Avail.: No specific amount. **Duration:** Annual. **Number Awarded:** Varies. **To Apply:** Applicants must have at least two letter of reference documenting their public service or volunteer activities and have completed a short essay on their personal public service or volunteer experience. **Deadline:** May 1. **Remarks:** Established in 2004. **Contact:** Phone: 330-454-3426; Email: scholarship@starkcf.org.

10767 ■ Ira G. Turpin Scholar Program Fund *(Undergraduate/Scholarship)*

Purpose: To provide scholarship assistance to qualified individuals who want to pursue their studies. **Focus:** General studies/Field of study not specified. **Qualif.:** Applicants must be seventh and eleventh grade minority students attending Stark County schools; who possess scholarship, perseverance, high standards and hard work toward achieving their career goals. **Criteria:** Selection will be based on committee's criteria.

Funds Avail.: No specific amount. **Duration:** Annual. **Number Awarded:** Varies. **To Apply:** Applicants must submit a copy of your Student Aid Report (SAR) from the Free Application for Federal Student Aid (FAFSA); two letters of recommendation; official transcript. **Deadline:** April 26. **Remarks:** Established in 1990. **Contact:** Phone: 330-454-3426; Email: scholarship@starkcf.org.

10768 ■ Jackson High School Alumni Scholarship Fund *(Graduate/Scholarship)*

Purpose: To provide scholarship assistance to qualified individuals who want to pursue their studies. **Focus:** General studies/Field of study not specified. **Qualif.:** Applicants must be graduating seniors at Jackson High School or Jackson High School graduates who are currently enrolled as full-time college students; must have minimum GPA of 2.5 or above. **Criteria:** Selection of applicants will be based on their demonstration of community service, involvement in extracurricular activities, academic standing and personal interview with selection committee.

Funds Avail.: No specific amount. **To Apply:** Application forms are available online. **Remarks:** Established in 2001.

10769 ■ Jay C. and B. Nadine Leggett Charitable Fund *(Undergraduate/Scholarship)*

Purpose: To assist qualified individuals who want to pursue their studies. **Focus:** General studies/Field of study not specified. **Criteria:** Selection will be based on extracurricular activities; personal characteristics, and demonstrate the requisite financial need.

Funds Avail.: No specific amount. **Duration:** Annual. **Number Awarded:** Varies. **To Apply:** Applicants must submit a copy of your Student Aid Report (SAR) from the Free Application for Federal Student Aid (FAFSA); two letters of recommendation; official transcript. **Deadline:** April 1. **Remarks:** Established in 1996. **Contact:** Phone: 330-454-3426; Email: scholarship@starkcf.org.

10770 ■ Julio C. Diaz Academic Scholarship Fund *(Undergraduate/Scholarship)*

Purpose: To provide scholarship assistance to qualified individuals who want to pursue their studies. **Focus:** General studies/Field of study not specified. **Qualif.:** Applicants must be students attending Saint Thomas Aquinas High School who have completed at least one year at the said institution and have achieved minimum cumulative GPA of at least 3.5 on a 4.0 scale; a record of school and community service. **Criteria:** Selection will be based on demonstration of involvement in extracurricular activities at St. Thomas Aquinas High School.

Duration: Annual. **Number Awarded:** Varies. **To Apply:** Applicant must Submit one reference from a current St. Thomas Aquinas teacher. **Deadline:** April 1. **Remarks:** The Scholarship was established in memory of Julio C. Diaz by family. Established in 2005. **Contact:** St. Thomas Aquinas High School, 2121 Reno Dr. NE, Louisville, OH, 44641.

10771 ■ The Junior Achievement of East Central Ohio, Inc. Scholarship Fund *(Undergraduate, High School/Scholarship)*

Purpose: To provide scholarship assistance to qualified individuals who want to pursue their studies. **Focus:** General studies/Field of study not specified. **Qualif.:** Applicant must be high school seniors who have participated in JA programs in Stark County, Tuscarawas and Carroll Counties. Applicants must have achieved a minimum 3.0 GPA. **Criteria:** Selection will be based on the committee criteria.

Duration: Annual. **Number Awarded:** Varies. **To Apply:** Applicants must submit a copy of your Student Aid Report (SAR) from the Free Application for Federal Student Aid (FAFSA); two letters of recommendation; official transcript. **Deadline:** April 1. **Remarks:** Established in 1987.

10772 ■ David A. Kaiser Memorial Scholarship Fund *(Undergraduate/Scholarship)*

Purpose: To provide scholarship assistance to qualified individuals who want to pursue their studies. **Focus:** General studies/Field of study not specified. **Qualif.:** Applicants must be students attending high school in the Canton City School District who will graduate with their class in May or June; who have been accepted into a four-year accredited college or university; enrolled as full-time students; are planning pursue a four-year degree; must have achieved a minimum GPA of 3.8. **Criteria:** Selection will be based on demonstrated outstanding achievement in academics; and demonstrated personal characteristics of integrity, leadership and scholarship.

Funds Avail.: $50,000. **Duration:** Annual. **Number Awarded:** Varies. **To Apply:** Applicants must submit a copy of your Student Aid Report (SAR) from the Free Application for Federal Student Aid (FAFSA); two letters of recommendation; official transcript; must submit essay(500 words or fewer). **Deadline:** April 1. **Remarks:** Established in 2001. **Contact:** Phone: 330-454-3426; Email: scholarship@starkcf.org.

10773 ■ Samuel Krugliak Legal Scholarship Fund *(Undergraduate/Scholarship)*

Purpose: To provide scholarship assistance to qualified individuals who want to pursue their studies. **Focus:** Paralegal studies.

Funds Avail.: No specific amount. **Duration:** Annual. **Number Awarded:** Varies. **Remarks:** Established in 2000. **Contact:** Phone: 330-454-3426; Email: scholarship@starkcf.org.

10774 ■ Lake Dollars for Scholars Endowment Fund *(Undergraduate/Scholarship)*

Purpose: To provide scholarship assistance to qualified individuals who want to pursue their studies. **Focus:** Educa-

---

Awards are arranged alphabetically below their administering organizations

tion, Vocational-technical; Nursing. **Qualif.:** Applicants must be graduating seniors residing within the boundaries of the Lake Local District, Lake Township and Stark County, Ohio; must have been accepted into a two-year or four-year college or university, nursing school, or other post high school vocational education program; must meet the requirements of the application form provided by Lake Dollars For Scholars. **Criteria:** Selection will be based on the scholarship application criteria.

Funds Avail.: No specific amount. **Number Awarded:** Varies. **To Apply:** Applicants must submit completed application form and are advised to contact the Lake High School Guidance Office.

10775 ■ Lester and Eleanor Webster Foundation Fund *(Undergraduate/Scholarship)*

Purpose: To provide scholarship assistance to qualified individuals who want to pursue their studies. **Focus:** General studies/Field of study not specified.

Funds Avail.: No specific amount. **Duration:** Annual. **Number Awarded:** Varies. **To Apply:** Applicants must submit a copy of your Student Aid Report (SAR) from the Free Application for Federal Student Aid (FAFSA); two letters of recommendation; official transcript. **Remarks:** Established in 1989. **Contact:** Phone: 330-454-3426; Email: scholarship@starkcf.org.

10776 ■ Lillian Grace Mahan Scholarship Fund *(Graduate/Scholarship)*

Purpose: To provide scholarship assistance to qualified individuals who want to pursue their studies. **Focus:** Library and archival sciences.

Funds Avail.: No specific amount. **Duration:** Annual. **Remarks:** Established in 1991. **Contact:** Phone: 330-454-3426; Email: scholarship@starkcf.org.

10777 ■ Manzer-Keener-Wefler Scholarship Fund *(Undergraduate/Scholarship)*

Purpose: To provide scholarship assistance to qualified individuals who want to pursue their studies. **Focus:** Photography; Visual arts. **Qualif.:** Applicants must be two-year or four-year college or university or art institute with a chosen field of study in or related to photography or visual arts; non-traditional college students originally from Stark County, Ohio, or counties contiguous to Stark; who are currently attending a two-year or four-year college or university or art institute part-time are also eligible; cumulative GPA of 2.5 on a 4.0 scale shall be required. **Criteria:** Recipients are selected based on academic potential and financial need.

Funds Avail.: No specific amount. **Duration:** Annual. **Number Awarded:** Varies. **To Apply:** Applicants must submit a copy of your Student Aid Report (SAR) from the Free Application for Federal Student Aid (FAFSA); two letters of recommendation; official transcript. **Remarks:** Established in 2006. **Contact:** Phone: 330-454-3426; Email: scholarship@starkcf.org.

10778 ■ Markley Family Scholarship Fund *(Undergraduate/Scholarship)*

Purpose: To provide scholarship assistance to qualified individuals who want to pursue their studies. **Focus:** General studies/Field of study not specified. **Qualif.:** Applicants must be full time undergraduate students of Walsh University, North Canton, OH; both residents and commuters are eligible to apply. **Criteria:** Applicants will be selected based on academic performance and financial need.

Funds Avail.: No specific amount. **Duration:** Annual. **Number Awarded:** Varies. **To Apply:** Applicants must submit a copy of your Student Aid Report (SAR) from the Free Application for Federal Student Aid (FAFSA); two letters of recommendation; official transcript. **Deadline:** April 1. **Remarks:** Established in 1993. **Contact:** Phone: 330-454-3426; Email: scholarship@starkcf.org.

10779 ■ Sanders J. Mestel Legal Scholarship Fund *(Undergraduate/Scholarship)*

Purpose: To provide scholarship assistance to qualified individuals who want to pursue their studies. **Focus:** Law. **Qualif.:** Applicants must be students beginning their third-year in law school. **Criteria:** Selection will be based on financial need; and a high degree of interest in trial advocacy.

Funds Avail.: No specific amount. **Duration:** Annual. **Number Awarded:** Varies. **Deadline:** Varies. **Remarks:** The Scholarship was established in memory of Sanders J. Mestel by his parents Harry and Anne Mestel. Established in 1985. **Contact:** Phone: 330-454-3426; Email: scholarship@starkcf.org.

10780 ■ Harry Mestel Memorial Accounting Scholarship Fund *(Undergraduate/Scholarship)*

Purpose: To provide scholarship assistance to qualified individuals who want to pursue their studies. **Focus:** Accounting. **Qualif.:** Applicants must be accounting students enrolled at an Ohio college or university in their third, fourth or fifth year of accounting studies (pursuing a Bachelor of Science in Accounting) whose permanent address is in Stark County, Ohio; and must have achieved a cumulative GPA of at least 3.0 on a 4.0 scale. **Criteria:** Selection will be based on demonstrated need for financial aid; and outstanding involvement in community activities.

Funds Avail.: No specific amount. **Duration:** Annual. **To Apply:** Applicants must upload certification by the Dean of the Business School that you are in good standing and in your, third, fourth or fifth year of accounting studies. **Deadline:** April 1. **Remarks:** Established in 2004.

10781 ■ John G. and Betty J. Mick Scholarship Fund *(Undergraduate/Scholarship)*

Purpose: To provide scholarship assistance to qualified individuals who want to pursue their studies. **Focus:** Engineering. **Qualif.:** Applicants must be seniors attending a high school in Stark County, OH; must have been accepted as full-time students in Stark State College of Technology engineering Program for a two-year degree which will also transfer to a four-year degree program at another university at the discretion of the students; must have been accepted as full-time students into the Engineering program at any university or college in the State of Ohio; non-traditional students furthering their education after entering the workforce will be considered secondarily; must have cumulative GPA of at least 2.0 on a 4.0 scale. **Criteria:** Recipients will be selected based on academic achievement, personal interview.

Funds Avail.: No specific amount. **Duration:** Annual. **Number Awarded:** Varies. **To Apply:** Applicants must provide the name and email address of a math, science or engineering teacher who they would like to ask to submit a letter of recommendation on their behalf. **Deadline:** April 1. **Remarks:** Established in 2005. **Contact:** Phone: 330-454-3426; Email: scholarship@starkcf.org.

Awards are arranged alphabetically below their administering organizations

10782 ■ Minnie Hopkins Scholarship Fund (Graduate/Scholarship)

Purpose: To assist applicants who have attended Lathrop/Compton School and/or successor schools for at least three years. **Focus:** General studies/Field of study not specified. **Qualif.:** Applicants must have graduated from lathrop or compton School and attended lathrop or compton for at least three years; must have graduated from Stark County public high school and been accepted into a college, university, or technical school; must have a cumulative GPA of at least 2.5 on a 4.0 scale.

Funds Avail.: No specific amount. **Number Awarded:** Varies. **To Apply:** Applicants must submit a copy of your Student Aid Report (SAR) from the Free Application for Federal Student Aid (FAFSA); two letters of recommendation; official transcript. **Deadline:** April 1. **Remarks:** Established in 1993.

10783 ■ Lt. Colonel Robert G. Moreland Vocational/Technical Fund (Undergraduate/Scholarship)

Purpose: To provide scholarship assistance to qualified individuals who want to pursue their studies. **Focus:** Education, Vocational-technical.

Funds Avail.: No specific amount. **Duration:** Annual. **Remarks:** Established in 1994. **Contact:** Phone: 330-454-3426; Email: scholarship@starkcf.org.

10784 ■ Norman J. Tschantz, Walter C. Deuble and Dominic J. Bagnoli, Jr. Caddie Scholarship Fund (Undergraduate/Scholarship)

Purpose: To provide scholarship assistance to qualified individuals who want to pursue their studies. **Focus:** General studies/Field of study not specified. **Qualif.:** Applicants must have served at least one year as a caddy at Congress Lake Country Club; must have academic achievement in high school, college, or trade school. **Criteria:** Selection will be based on academic standing, extracurricular activities, overall character and demonstration of responsibility and diligent effort.

Funds Avail.: No specific amount. **Duration:** Annual. **Number Awarded:** Varies. **To Apply:** Applicants must submit a copy of your Student Aid Report. **Deadline:** July 8. **Remarks:** Established in 1995. **Contact:** Phone: 330-454-3426; Email: scholarship@starkcf.org.

10785 ■ Notre Dame Club of Canton, Ohio Scholarship Fund (Undergraduate/Scholarship)

Purpose: To provide scholarship assistance to qualified individuals who want to pursue their studies. **Focus:** General studies/Field of study not specified. **Qualif.:** Applicants must be students who have attended Stark County or Tuscarawas County, Ohio High School, Dalton High School, or Orville High School in Wayne County, Ohio, or Central Kidron Christian School in Kidron, Ohio; must have GPA of at least 3.0 on a 4.0 scale while in high school; must demonstrate an outstanding involvement both in academics and extracurricular activities; must have been accepted to attend the University of Notre Dame, Notre Dame, Indiana. **Criteria:** Selection will be based on academic standing and extracurricular activities.

Funds Avail.: No specific amount. **Duration:** Annual. **Number Awarded:** Varies. **To Apply:** Applicants must submit a copy of your Student Aid Report (SAR) from the Free Application for Federal Student Aid (FAFSA); two letters of recommendation; official transcript. **Deadline:** April 1. **Contact:** Phone: 330-454-3426; Email: scholarship@starkcf.org.

10786 ■ O'Jay's Scholarship Fund (Undergraduate/Scholarship)

Purpose: To provide scholarship assistance to qualified individuals who want to pursue their studies. **Focus:** General studies/Field of study not specified. **Criteria:** Selection will be based on the committee's criteria.

Funds Avail.: No specific amount. **Duration:** Annual. **Number Awarded:** Varies. **To Apply:** Applicants must submit a copy of your Student Aid Report (SAR) from the Free Application for Federal Student Aid (FAFSA); two letters of recommendation; official transcript. **Deadline:** April 1. **Remarks:** Established in 2005. **Contact:** Phone: 330-454-3426; Email: scholarship@starkcf.org.

10787 ■ Perry Township School Memorial Scholarship Fund (Undergraduate/Scholarship)

Purpose: To provide scholarship assistance to qualified individuals who want to pursue their studies. **Focus:** General studies/Field of study not specified. **Qualif.:** Applicants must be high school graduates or high school seniors who have permanent residency in Perry Township, Carroll County, OH or who have permanent residency on the date they began their post-high school education; must have been accepted, currently enrolled, or planning to enroll at an accredited college, university, or technical school with at least a two year course of study to pursue further education.

Funds Avail.: No specific amount. **Duration:** Annual. **Number Awarded:** Varies. **To Apply:** Applicants must provide the name and email address of a teacher, coach, advisor or church pastor who they would like to ask to submit a letter of recommendation on their behalf. **Deadline:** April 1. **Contact:** Phone: 330-454-3426; Email: scholarship@starkcf.org.

10788 ■ August M. Rocco Scholarship Fund (Undergraduate/Scholarship)

Purpose: To provide scholarship assistance to qualified individuals who want to pursue their studies. **Focus:** General studies/Field of study not specified. **Qualif.:** Applicants must be male or female graduates of Canton Central Catholic High School or St. Thomas Aquinas High School and of the Catholic faith; must be accepted to attend college at University of Notre Dame, South Bend, IN; must have good scholastic record and character traits.

Funds Avail.: No specific amount. **Duration:** Annual. **Number Awarded:** Varies. **To Apply:** Applicants must submit a copy of your Student Aid Report (SAR) from the Free Application for Federal Student Aid (FAFSA); two letters of recommendation; official transcript. **Deadline:** January 4. **Remarks:** Established in 1961. **Contact:** Phone: 330-454-3426; Email: scholarship@starkcf.org.

10789 ■ Ruth M. Cogan Foundation Trust (Undergraduate/Scholarship)

Purpose: To provide scholarship assistance to qualified applicants from Stark County, Ohio in obtaining a college education, particularly in the field of music. **Focus:** Music. **Qualif.:** Applicants must be residents of Stark County, Ohio pursuing college-level study in the field of music. **Criteria:** Selection will be based on the committee's criteria.

Funds Avail.: Amount varies. **Duration:** Annual. **Number Awarded:** Varies. **To Apply:** Applicants must submit a copy of your Student Aid Report (SAR) from the Free Application for Federal Student Aid (FAFSA); two letters of recommendation; official transcript. **Deadline:** April 1. **Remarks:**

Awards are arranged alphabetically below their administering organizations

Established in 1990. **Contact:** Phone: 330-454-3426; Email: scholarship@starkcf.org.

10790 ■ Aaron Seesan Memorial Scholarship Fund
(Undergraduate/Scholarship)

Purpose: To provide scholarship assistance to qualified individuals who want to pursue their studies. **Focus:** General studies/Field of study not specified. **Qualif.:** Applicants must be graduating senior from Massillon Washington High School and one graduating senior from any other Stark County high school who has been accepted by or is attending a two-year or four-year college or university, a post-high school technical education program, or nursing school; and minimum 3.0 cumulative GPA on a 4.0 scale. **Criteria:** Selection will be based on demonstration of outstanding involvement in extracurricular activities and community activities outside of school; participation in community service activities and financial need.

Duration: Annual. **Number Awarded:** Varies. **To Apply:** Applicants must submit a copy of your Student Aid Report (SAR) from the Free Application for Federal Student Aid (FAFSA); two letters of recommendation; official transcript. **Deadline:** April 1. **Remarks:** Established in 2005. **Contact:** Phone: 330-454-3426; Email: scholarship@starkcf.org.

10791 ■ Sheriff W. Bruce Umpleby Law Enforcement Memorial Scholarship Fund *(Undergraduate/Scholarship)*

Purpose: To provide scholarship assistance to qualified individuals who want to pursue their studies. **Focus:** Law enforcement. **Qualif.:** Applicants must be students who are seniors attending high school either inside or outside Stark County, who will graduate with their class, or are graduates of a high school either inside or outside Stark County; must have been accepted, into a post secondary institution with plans to major in law enforcement. **Criteria:** Selection will be based on enrolled as a full-time student and have achieved a cumulative GPA of at least 3.0 on a 4.0 scale.

Funds Avail.: No specific amount. **Duration:** Annual. **Number Awarded:** Varies. **To Apply:** Applicants must submit a copy of your Student Aid Report (SAR) from the Free Application for Federal Student Aid (FAFSA); two letters of recommendation; official transcript. **Deadline:** January 1. **Remarks:** Established in 1999. **Contact:** Phone: 330-454-3426; Email: scholarship@starkcf.org.

10792 ■ Ruth Skeeles Memorial Scholarship Fund
(Undergraduate/Scholarship)

Purpose: To provide scholarship assistance to qualified individuals who want to pursue their studies. **Focus:** General studies/Field of study not specified.

Funds Avail.: No specific amount. **Duration:** Annual. **Number Awarded:** Varies. **To Apply:** Applicants must submit a copy of your Student Aid Report (SAR) from the Free Application for Federal Student Aid (FAFSA); two letters of recommendation; official transcript. **Remarks:** Established in 1995. **Contact:** Phone: 330-454-3426; Email: scholarship@starkcf.org.

10793 ■ Stark County Bar Association Scholarship Fund *(Undergraduate/Scholarship)*

Purpose: To provide scholarship assistance to qualified individuals who want to pursue their studies. **Focus:** Law. **Qualif.:** Applicants must be from the Stark County area. **Criteria:** Selection will be based on demonstration of financial need; students from the Stark County area;

students likely to return to the Stark County area to practice law.

Funds Avail.: No specific amount. **Duration:** Annual. **Number Awarded:** Varies. **To Apply:** Applicants must submit a copy of your Student Aid Report (SAR) from the Free Application for Federal Student Aid (FAFSA); two letters of recommendation; official transcript. **Remarks:** Established in 2004. **Contact:** Phone: 330-454-3426; Email: scholarship@starkcf.org.

10794 ■ Stark County Dairy Promoters Scholarship Fund *(Graduate/Scholarship)*

Purpose: To provide scholarship assistance to qualified individuals who want to pursue their studies. **Focus:** Animal science and behavior; Dairy science; Food science and technology; Nutrition; Veterinary science and medicine.

Funds Avail.: No specific amount. **Duration:** Annual. **Number Awarded:** Varies. **To Apply:** Applicants must submit a copy of your Student Aid Report (SAR) from the Free Application for Federal Student Aid (FAFSA); two letters of recommendation; official transcript. **Deadline:** January 4. **Remarks:** Established in 1990. **Contact:** Phone: 330-454-3426; Email: scholarship@starkcf.org.

10795 ■ Jeffrey Tyler Sweitzer Wrestling Memorial Scholarship Fund *(Undergraduate/Scholarship)*

Purpose: To provide scholarship assistance to qualified individuals who want to pursue their studies. **Focus:** General studies/Field of study not specified.

Funds Avail.: No specific amount. **Duration:** Annual. **Remarks:** Established in 2001. **Contact:** Phone: 330-454-3426; Email: scholarship@starkcf.org.

10796 ■ Timothy S. Sweterlitsch Memorial Scholarship Fund *(Undergraduate/Scholarship)*

Purpose: To provide scholarship assistance to qualified individuals who want to pursue their studies. **Focus:** General studies/Field of study not specified. **Qualif.:** Applicants must be graduates of Washington High School in Massillon, Ohio. **Criteria:** Selection will be based on good academic accomplishment; good athletic ability in high school; good moral and personal characteristics.

Funds Avail.: No specific amount. **Duration:** Annual. **Number Awarded:** Varies. **To Apply:** Applicants must submit a copy of your Student Aid Report (SAR) from the Free Application for Federal Student Aid (FAFSA); two letters of recommendation; official transcript. **Deadline:** April 1. **Remarks:** Established in 1994. **Contact:** Phone: 330-454-3426; Email: scholarship@starkcf.org.

10797 ■ Thomas W. Gallagher Scholarship Fund
(Undergraduate/Scholarship)

Purpose: To provide scholarship assistance to qualified individuals who want to pursue their studies. **Focus:** Pharmacy. **Qualif.:** Applicants must be students Minerva High School graduate who has been accepted in a pharmacy degree program or course of study in the field of science. **Criteria:** Selection will be consideration given to students pursuing a degree in pharmacy.

Duration: Annual. **Number Awarded:** Varies. **To Apply:** Applicants must submit a copy of your Student Aid Report (SAR) from the Free Application for Federal Student Aid (FAFSA); two letters of recommendation; official transcript. **Remarks:** Established in 2003. **Contact:** Phone: 330-454-3426; Email: scholarship@starkcf.org.

Awards are arranged alphabetically below their administering organizations

10798 ■ Tim Triner Letter Carriers Scholarship Fund
(Undergraduate/Scholarship)

Purpose: To provide scholarship assistance to qualified individuals who want to pursue their studies. **Focus:** General studies/Field of study not specified.

Funds Avail.: No specific amount. **Duration:** Annual. **Number Awarded:** Varies. **Remarks:** Established in 2001. **Contact:** Phone: 330-454-3426; Email: scholarship@starkcf.org.

10799 ■ US Acute Care Solutions Health Information Management Scholarship Fund *(Undergraduate/Scholarship)*

Purpose: To provide scholarship assistance to qualified individuals who want to pursue their studies. **Focus:** Health education.

Duration: Annual. **Contact:** Phone: 330-454-3426; Email: scholarship@starkcf.org.

10800 ■ Virginia C. Jack and Ralph L. Jack Scholarship Fund *(Undergraduate/Scholarship)*

Purpose: To provide scholarship assistance to qualified individuals who want to pursue their studies. **Focus:** Education, Vocational-technical; Nursing. **Qualif.:** Applicants must be Stark County residents; must be admitted to technical school, college or university, or school of nursing; must be full or part time students; must be traditional or non-traditional students; must have 2.50 or higher GPA on a 4.0 scale.

Duration: Annual. **Number Awarded:** Varies. **To Apply:** Applicants must submit a copy of your Student Aid Report (SAR) from the Free Application for Federal Student Aid (FAFSA); two letters of recommendation; official transcript. **Deadline:** April 1. **Remarks:** Established in 1999. **Contact:** Phone: 330-454-3426; Email: scholarship@starkcf.org.

10801 ■ John R. and Joan F. Werren Scholarships Fund *(Undergraduate/Scholarship)*

Purpose: To provide scholarship assistance to qualified individuals who want to pursue their studies. **Focus:** General studies/Field of study not specified. **Qualif.:** Applicants must be students planning to enroll or are presently enrolled at Grove City College. **Criteria:** Preferences are given to freshmen and current students who are Stark County residents. Recipients will be selected based on scholarship standards established by Grove City College.

To Apply: Applicants must contact the school's Financial Aid Office for more information. **Remarks:** Established in 2001.

10802 ■ Mary Kean White Memorial Scholarship Fund *(Undergraduate, Doctorate/Scholarship)*

Purpose: To provide scholarship assistance to qualified individuals who want to pursue their studies. **Focus:** Education, Elementary. **Qualif.:** Applicants must be graduates of Malvern High School or Carrollton High School; must be currently enrolled as full time students at an accredited college or university; must be pursuing a career in elementary education or related field.

To Apply: Applicants must submit a copy of your Student Aid Report (SAR) from the Free Application for Federal Student Aid (FAFSA); two letters of recommendation; official transcript. **Remarks:** The Scholarship was established in honor of Mary Kean White by Brothers David, Joseph, and Thomas Kean. Established in 2000. **Contact:** Phone:

330-454-3426; Email: scholarship@starkcf.org.

10803 ■ Workshops, Inc. and Stark MRDD Fostering Diversity Through Special Needs Scholarship Fund *(Undergraduate/Scholarship)*

Purpose: To provide scholarship assistance to qualified individuals who want to pursue their studies. **Focus:** Education, Special. **Qualif.:** Applicants must be full-time juniors or seniors majoring in special education or a related field in a four-year college or university in the area. **Criteria:** Selection will be based on the committee's criteria.

Funds Avail.: No specific amount. **Duration:** Annual. **To Apply:** Applicants must submit a copy of your Student Aid Report (SAR) from the Free Application for Federal Student Aid (FAFSA); two letters of recommendation; official transcript. **Remarks:** Established in 1998. **Contact:** Phone: 330-454-7992.

10804 ■ State of Idaho Board of Education
650 W State St., 3rd Fl.
Boise, ID 83702
Ph: (208)334-2270
Fax: (208)334-2632
E-mail: board@osbe.idaho.gov
URL: boardofed.idaho.gov

10805 ■ Idaho Opportunity Scholarship
(Undergraduate/Scholarship)

Purpose: To support students from Idaho in their pursuit of higher education. **Focus:** General studies/Field of study not specified. **Qualif.:** Applicants must be Idaho residents who have graduated from an Idaho high school or its equivalent (GED/HSE from Idaho); have an unweighted, cumulative GPA of 2.7 or above; must attend designated Idaho colleges or universities (see sponsor's website for list). **Criteria:** Selection will be based on financial need and GPA requirements.

Funds Avail.: $3,500 per year (for up to four years). **Duration:** Annual; up to 4 years. **To Apply:** Application details are available at: boardofed.idaho.gov/scholarships/idaho-opportunity-scholarship/. **Deadline:** March 1. **Contact:** Joy Miller, Scholarships Program Manager; Phone: 208-332-1595; Email: Joy.Miller@osbe.idaho.gov; Scholarship Programs Help at 208-334-2270.

10806 ■ State of New Jersey Department of Health - New Jersey Commission on Brain Injury Research (NJCBIR)
369 S. Warren St.
Trenton, NJ 08625
Ph: (609)633-6465
Fax: (609)943-4213
URL: www.state.nj.us

10807 ■ NJCBIR Individual Research Grants *(Graduate, Professional development, Postdoctorate, Doctorate/Grant)*

Purpose: To encourage investigators to undertake research on neural protection, repair and regeneration after traumatic brain injury; to encourage individuals to undertake research on the effectiveness of clinical interventions for traumatic brain injury; and to enable researchers with novel scientific and clinical ideas to test them and develop pilot data

Awards are arranged alphabetically below their administering organizations

needed to develop a programmatic area of research that can be supported by additional funding from the National Institutes of Health and other funding sources. **Focus:** Neurology.

Funds Avail.: Up to $3,000,000 per year. **Duration:** Annual. **To Apply:** Applicants must comply with the following requirements; terms and conditions for the administration of grants; general and specific grant compliance requirements issued by the awarding division or commission; submit a grant application, letter of intent, inquiry or concept paper as required in the RFA. **Deadline:** January 10. **Contact:** Christine Traynor, Program New Jersey Commission on Brain Injury Research, New jersey Department of Health, 225 E State st., 2nd Fl. W, Trenton, New Jersey, 08625; Phone: 609-633-6465; Email: NJCBIR@doh.nj.gov.

10808 ■ NJCBIR Pilot Research Grants (Other/Grant)

Purpose: To encourage investigators to undertake research on neural protection, repair and regeneration after traumatic brain injury; to encourage individuals to undertake research on the effectiveness of clinical interventions for traumatic brain injury; and to enable researchers with novel scientific and clinical ideas to test them and develop pilot data needed to develop a programmatic area of research that can be supported by additional funding from the National Institutes of Health and other funding sources. **Focus:** Neurology.

Funds Avail.: Up to $3,000,000 per year. **To Apply:** Applicants must comply with the following requirements; terms and conditions for the administration of grants; general and specific grant compliance requirements issued by the awarding division or commission; submit a grant application, letter of intent, inquiry or concept paper as required in the RFA. **Deadline:** October 1. **Contact:** Christine Traynor, Program New Jersey Commission on Brain Injury Research, New jersey Department of Health, 225 E State st., 2nd Fl. W, Trenton, New Jersey, 08625; Phone: 609-633-6465; Email: NJCBIR@doh.nj.gov.

10809 ■ NJCBIR Postdoctoral and Graduate Student Fellowships (Graduate, Postdoctorate, Professional development, Doctorate/Fellowship)

Purpose: To encourage investigators to undertake research on neural protection, repair and regeneration after traumatic brain injury; to encourage individuals to undertake research on the effectiveness of clinical interventions for traumatic brain injury; and to enable researchers with novel scientific and clinical ideas to test them and develop pilot data needed to develop a programmatic area of research that can be supported by additional funding from the National Institutes of Health and other funding sources. **Focus:** Neurology. **Criteria:** Selection will be reviewed by an independent scientific merit review panel and recommended to the NJCSCR for continued funding.

Funds Avail.: $50,000. **Duration:** Annual. **To Apply:** Applicants must comply with the following requirements; terms and conditions for the administration of grants; general and specific grant compliance requirements issued by the granting agency; applicable federal cost principles relating to the applicants; NJCBIR research guidelines governing grants are available for review and submission on the website; a letter of intent must also be filed with the NJCBIR office. **Contact:** Christine Traynor, Program New Jersey Commission on Brain Injury Research, New jersey Department of Health, 225 E State st., 2nd Fl. W, Trenton, New Jersey, 08625; Phone: 609-633-6465; Email: NJCBIR@doh.nj.gov.

10810 ■ NJCBIR Programmatic Multi-Investigator Project Grants (Other/Grant)

Purpose: To enhance in-depth mechanistic analysis and promote translational research. **Focus:** Neurology. **Criteria:** Selection will be based on the committee's criteria.

Funds Avail.: $600,000 per year. **Duration:** One to three years. **To Apply:** Applicants must comply with the following requirements; terms and conditions for the administration of grants; general and specific grant compliance requirements issued by the granting agency; applicable federal cost principles relating to the applicant and NJCBIR research guidelines governing grants are available for review and submission on the website at www.sage.nj.gov; a letter of intent must also be filed with the NJCBIR office. **Deadline:** August 1 for the Letter of Intent; October 3 for the applications.

10811 ■ State of Wisconsin Higher Educational Aids Board (HEAB)
4822 Madison Yards Way
Madison, WI 53705
Ph: (608)267-2206
Fax: (608)267-2808
E-mail: HEABmail@wi.gov
URL: www.heab.state.wi.us

10812 ■ Wisconsin Minority Teacher Loan (Undergraduate/Loan)

Purpose: To address the needs of Wisconsin students enrolled in a program leading to teacher licensure. **Focus:** Education; Teaching. **Qualif.:** Applicants must be Wisconsin residents, minorities, undergraduate sophomores, juniors, or seniors who are enrolled at least half-time in programs leading to teacher licensure at a University of Wisconsin System institution or a non-profit, independent college or university in the state of Wisconsin; must be enrolled in a program of study leading to a teacher's license in a discipline identified as a teacher shortage area for the state of Wisconsin by the federal Department of Education; must have a GPA of 2.5 or higher based on a 4.0 scale; must agree to teach in a public or private elementary or secondary school, or a tribal school, in a Wisconsin school district with a 40% or higher minority student population.

Funds Avail.: Up to $10,000 per year (maximum lifetime of $30,000). **To Apply:** Applicants must be nominated by the financial aid office at their school; nominated students must complete a Minority Teacher Loan Recipient Agreement and Minority Teacher Loan Information Sheet; the completed paperwork must be submitted to the Higher Educational Aids Board for processing; only original documents will be accepted. **Contact:** Joy Dyer, Grant Specialist-Higher Educational Aids Board, Phone: 608-267-2212; Email: joy.dyer@wisconsin.gov.

10813 ■ Wisconsin Nursing Student Loan (Graduate, Undergraduate, Doctorate/Loan)

Purpose: To address the needs of nursing students enrolled at an eligible Wisconsin institution that prepares them to be licensed as nurses, either RN or LPN. **Focus:** Nursing. **Qualif.:** Applicants must be students enrolled in a participating UW, Wisconsin Technical College or private, nonprofit post-secondary institution in the state; must be Wisconsin residents; must be enrolled at least half-time in a degree or certificate program leading to a nursing license, master's degree in nursing or doctoral degree in nursing;

Awards are arranged alphabetically below their administering organizations

must make satisfactory academic progress; must demonstrate financial need; applicants must agree to practice full-time as a licensed nurse and/or as a nurse educator in Wisconsin for the term of the forgiveness period. **Criteria:** Selection will be based on the committee's criteria.

Funds Avail.: $1,000-$3,000 per year (maximum $15,000 lifetime). **To Apply:** Applicants must complete and submit a FAFSA form each year; students should inform financial aid administrators of their interest in receiving a nursing student loan each year, so administrators will consider them when allocating this loan; the school financial aid administrator will designate students who show eligibility for the nursing student loan and will offer them a loan; the school financial aid administrator will forward to the higher educational aids board all student information and a signed loan agreement from each student. **Contact:** Peter Zammuto; Phone: 608-267-2209; Email: peter.zammuto@wisconsin.gov.

10814 ■ Wisconsin Teacher of the Visually Impaired Loan *(Undergraduate, Graduate/Loan)*

Purpose: To provide loans to individuals for their preparation to become licensed teachers of the visually impaired or orientation and mobility instructors. **Focus:** Education; Teaching; Visual impairment. **Qualif.:** Applicants must be undergraduate or graduate students enrolled at least half-time at an in-state or eligible out-of-state institution in a program that prepares them to be licensed as teachers of the visually impaired or as orientation and mobility instructors; must be Wisconsin residents; for each of the first two years the students teaches and meets the eligibility criteria, 25% of the loan is forgiven; for the third year, 50% is forgiven. If the student does not teach and meet the eligibility criteria, the loan must be repaid at an interest rate of 5%. **Criteria:** Selection will be based on the committee's criteria.

Funds Avail.: $250-$10,000. **Duration:** Annual. **To Apply:** Applicants may contact Nancy Wilkison for the application process and other information. **Contact:** Peter Zammuto; Phone: 608-267-2209; Email: peter.zammuto@wisconsin.gov.

10815 ■ Staunton Military Academy Alumni Foundation (SMA)
PO Box 958
Staunton, VA 24402-0958
Ph: (540)885-1309
E-mail: smaoffice@sma-alumni.org
URL: sma-alumni.org

10816 ■ SMA Alumni Foundation Legacy Scholarship Program *(Other/Scholarship)*

Purpose: To preserve and perpetuate the traditions of Truth, Duty, and Honor. **Focus:** General studies/Field of study not specified. **Qualif.:** Applicant must have been accepted by an accredited two or four year institution of higher learning. **Criteria:** Recipients will be selected based on the merits of their application by a scholarship selection committee.

Funds Avail.: $1,500. **Duration:** Annual. **Number Awarded:** 4. **To Apply:** Applicants must provide external supporting documentation listed on the application (including transcripts and two letters of recommendation); cover letter; copy of the letter of acceptance from the institution of higher learning; written request for each year enclosing a transcript from the school the applicant is attending which

shows a grade point average of no less than 3.0, on a scale of 1 - 4.0 or a B average for a different scale. **Deadline:** June 1.

10817 ■ STC Canada West Coast (STC)
597-4974 Kingsway St.
Burnaby, BC, Canada V5H 4M9
E-mail: president@stcwestcoast.ca
URL: stcwestcoast.ca
Social Media: twitter.com/stccwc

10818 ■ Julia Broderick Scholarships
(Undergraduate/Scholarship)

Purpose: To help students to establish their career in the profession after graduation. **Focus:** Technical communications. **Qualif.:** Applicant must be a technical writing student in the final year of study; pursuing a career in technical communication and must have a first-class standing or equivalent. **Criteria:** Selection is based on the strength of the instructors' recommendations in combination with the applicant's academic standing and achievements.

Funds Avail.: $500. **Number Awarded:** 1. **To Apply:** Applicants must submit a completed application form along with a copy of current transcripts (in PDF); a one-to-two page description (in MS Word format) of academic and career goals and achievements; and two letters of recommendation from faculty members in the field of technical communications (in PDF).

10819 ■ Steuben County Community Foundation (SCCF)
1701 N Wayne St.
Angola, IN 46703
Ph: (260)665-6656
Fax: (260)665-8420
E-mail: sccf@steubenfoundation.org
URL: www.steubenfoundation.org
Social Media: www.facebook.com/steubenfoundation

10820 ■ Clifford V. Abbott Memorial Scholarships
(Undergraduate/Scholarship)

Purpose: To provide financial support to outstanding students. **Focus:** General studies/Field of study not specified. **Qualif.:** Applicants must be residents of Steuben County; graduating seniors from Fremont High School. **Criteria:** Applicants are selected based on the committee's review of the application materials.

Funds Avail.: No specific amount. **Duration:** Annual. **To Apply:** Applicants must submit one character statement from an individual outside of the school environment, and one academic statement from a person at your school. Applicants must also submit their copy of school transcripts. **Deadline:** September 8. **Contact:** Steuben County Community Foundation, at the above address.

10821 ■ Dale Hughes Jr Memorial Scholarship
(Undergraduate/Scholarship)

Purpose: To provide support to Prairie Heights students in their continuing education. **Focus:** General studies/Field of study not specified.

To Apply: Applicants must be a student. **Remarks:** The Scholarship was established in memory of Dale Hughes, Jr. by his wife, Emilyn. Established in 2004. **Contact:** 1701

Awards are arranged alphabetically below their administering organizations

N Wayne St., Angola, IN, 46703; Phone: 260-665-6656.

10822 ■ Dr. J Glenn Radcliffe Scholarship Fund
(Undergraduate/Scholarship)

Purpose: To provide financial assistance to those students who are planning to attend Trine University. **Focus:** General studies/Field of study not specified.

Remarks: Established in 2001. **Contact:** 1701 N Wayne St., Angola, IN, 46703; Phone: 260-665-6656.

10823 ■ Don and Eileen Fulton Nursing Scholarship Fund *(Undergraduate/Scholarship)*

Purpose: To provide financial assistance to those students who will be continuing their education through an accredited nursing program at any Indiana institution of higher education. **Focus:** Nursing.

Remarks: Established in 2003. **Contact:** 1701 N Wayne St., Angola, IN, 46703; Phone: 260-665-6656.

10824 ■ Ed Haas Memorial Scholarship Fund
(Graduate/Scholarship)

Purpose: To provide a scholarship to any graduating Steuben County high school senior that will be pursuing a degree in education, humanities and/or the arts. **Focus:** Arts; Education--Curricula; Humanities.

Remarks: The Scholarship was established in memory of Ed Haas by family and friends. Established in 2000. **Contact:** 1701 N Wayne St., Angola, IN, 46703; Phone: 260-665-6656.

10825 ■ Ellen Eberhardt Memorial Scholarship Fund
(Undergraduate/Scholarship)

Purpose: To provide support for students pursuing degree in environmental education. **Focus:** Environmental conservation.

Deadline: September 8. **Contact:** 1701 N Wayne St., Angola, IN, 46703; Phone: 260-665-6656.

10826 ■ M.G. "Doc" Headley Scholarships
(Undergraduate/Scholarship)

Purpose: To provide support for students pursuing a degree in agricultural. **Focus:** Agriculture, Economic aspects; Veterinary science and medicine.

Remarks: Establishing memory of Dr. M. G. "Doc" Headley. Established in 2000. **Contact:** 1701 N Wayne St., Angola, IN, 46703; Phone: 260-665-6656.

10827 ■ Helen R Greenamyer Memorial Fund
(Undergraduate/Scholarship)

Purpose: To provide financial support to those students who are pursuing a career in Nursing. **Focus:** Nursing.

Contact: 1701 N Wayne St., Angola, IN, 46703; Phone: 260-665-6656.

10828 ■ John W. Kelley Memorial Scholarship Fund
(Undergraduate/Scholarship)

Purpose: To provide financial support to those students who are interested in earning a degree in Law Enforcement Education. **Focus:** Law enforcement.

Remarks: The Scholarship was established in memory of John Kelly by his friend and local businessman, Frank Baade. Established in 2004. **Contact:** 1701 N Wayne St., Angola, IN, 46703; Phone: 260-665-6656.

10829 ■ Mandel and Lauretta Abrahamer Scholarship Fund *(Undergraduate/Scholarship)*

Purpose: To provide financial support to those students pursuing education in health-related fields. **Focus:** Nursing.

Remarks: Established in 1995. **Contact:** 1701 N Wayne St., Angola, IN, 46703; Phone: 260-665-6656.

10830 ■ Nettie and Edward Shelah Scholarship Fund *(Undergraduate/Scholarship)*

Purpose: To provide financial assistance to graduates of Hamilton High School. **Focus:** General studies/Field of study not specified. **Qualif.:** Applicant must be a graduates of Hamilton High School.

Deadline: September 8. **Remarks:** Established in 1999. **Contact:** 1701 N Wayne St., Angola, IN, 46703; Phone: 260-665-6656.

10831 ■ Paul & Inger Friend 4-H Scholarship Fund
(Undergraduate/Scholarship)

Purpose: To provide support to 4-H members attending a 2 or 4 year college. **Focus:** General studies/Field of study not specified.

Remarks: Established in 2006. **Contact:** 1701 N Wayne St., Angola, IN, 46703; Phone: 260-665-6656.

10832 ■ Pauline Hand Memorial Scholarship *(Other/ Scholarship)*

Purpose: To provide financial support to Steuben County students going to a full-time university or college. **Focus:** General studies/Field of study not specified.

Remarks: Established in 2007. **Contact:** 1701 N Wayne St., Angola, IN, 46703; Phone: 260-665-6656.

10833 ■ Richard L. Baker Memorial Scholarship Fund *(Undergraduate/Scholarship)*

Purpose: To provide financial support to those graduating students of Fremont High School for their academic achievements. **Focus:** General studies/Field of study not specified.

Remarks: Established in 2006. **Contact:** 1701 N Wayne St., Angola, IN, 46703; Phone: 260-665-6656.

10834 ■ Tara Lynne Arnold Scholarship Fund
(Undergraduate/Scholarship)

Purpose: To provide financial support to those students who will be entering a four-year college or university with the intent of pursuing a Bachelor of Arts Degree. **Focus:** Psychology; Women's studies.

Remarks: The Scholarship was established in memory of Tara Lynne Arnold by family and friends. Established in 2006. **Contact:** 1701 N Wayne St., Angola, IN, 46703; Phone: 260-665-6656.

10835 ■ Verna Curry Boyer Scholarship Fund
(Undergraduate/Scholarship)

Purpose: To provide financial assistance to those students who are pursuing teaching. **Focus:** Teaching.

Remarks: Established in 2005. **Contact:** 1701 N Wayne St., Angola, IN, 46703; Phone: 260-665-6656.

10836 ■ Steven Titus & Associates PC
207 Gillette Ave.
Gillette, WY 82716
Ph: (307)317-0854

Awards are arranged alphabetically below their administering organizations

URL: www.steventituslaw.com
Social Media: www.facebook.com/steventituslaw
www.instagram.com/steventituslaw

10837 ■ Find Your Path Scholarship *(Graduate, College/Scholarship)*

Purpose: To help a deserving high school student in Wyoming pay for their college education. **Focus:** General studies/Field of study not specified. **Qualif.:** Applicant must be currently attending school in Wyoming, or planning on attending college or university in Wyoming; current high school students attending school in Wyoming and planning on attending a college outside of Wyoming may also apply. Applicant must also have a minimum 3.0 GPA and be a U.S. citizen or permanent resident (DACA recipients are welcome to apply). **Criteria:** Selection will be based write a short essay tell.

Funds Avail.: $500. **Number Awarded:** 1. **To Apply:** Applicant must submit essay and fill out application. Essay should cover who the applicant is and how going to college will help them achieve their goals. **Deadline:** May 28.

10838 ■ Stickler Involved People (SIP)
15 Angelina Dr.
Augusta, KS 67010
Ph: (316)259-5194
E-mail: sip@sticklers.org
URL: stickler.org
Social Media: www.facebook.com/Stickler-Involved-People
-326686947421856

10839 ■ Dr. Gunnar B. Stickler Scholarship *(Undergraduate, Vocational/Occupational/Scholarship)*

Purpose: To assist deserving college-bound adults afflicted with Stickler Syndrome to pursue their dreams and education goals. **Focus:** General studies/Field of study not specified. **Qualif.:** Applicants must be graduating students who have a minimum GPA of 3.0 on a 4.0 scale or equivalent from any American high school students who plan to enter any accredited public or private community, junior, or four-year college or university or vocational-technical school. **Criteria:** Applicants must be diagnosed with Stickler Syndrome by a primary care physicians or Geneticists.

Funds Avail.: $500. **Duration:** One year. **Number Awarded:** 1. **To Apply:** Applicants must fill out the application form (available on the website); must provide a physician letter diagnosing their Stickler Syndrome; and must enclose a high school transcript (sealed). **Deadline:** June 15. **Contact:** Submit the applications to stickler involved people, Gunnar B. Stickler Scholarship Award, PO Box 775, Cologne, NJ 08213.

10840 ■ Stockton University
101 Vera King Farris Dr.
Galloway, NJ 08205-9441
Ph: (609)652-4528
Fax: (609)626-3481
URL: intraweb.stockton.edu
Social Media: www.instagram.com/stocktonuniversity
www.linkedin.com/school/richard-stockton-college
twitter.com/Stockton_edu
www.youtube.com/c/StocktonUniversityNJ

10841 ■ The Achieve Physical Therapy & Fitness Scholarship *(Doctorate/Scholarship)*

Purpose: To provide financial assistance to qualified individuals who wish to pursue a doctoral degree. **Focus:** Physical therapy. **Qualif.:** Applicants must be enrolled in the doctorate level of a physical therapy course.

Funds Avail.: No specific amount. **Duration:** Annual. **Number Awarded:** Varies. **Deadline:** March 19. **Contact:** Email: foundationscholarships@stockton.edu; Phone: 609-626-3658.

10842 ■ The Joseph Berkman, and Michael and Sarah Chipkin Holocaust/Genocide Studies Award *(Graduate/Scholarship)*

Purpose: To provide financial assistance to qualified individuals who wish to pursue Holocaust genocide studies. **Focus:** General studies/Field of study not specified. **Qualif.:** Applicants must be students enrolled in a Master's Program in Holocaust genocide studies.

Funds Avail.: No specific amount. **Duration:** Annual. **Contact:** Email: foundationscholarships@stockton.edu; Phone: 609-626-3658.

10843 ■ Dr. Richard E. Bjork Memorial Graduate Study Award *(Graduate/Scholarship)*

Purpose: To provide financial assistance to qualified individuals who want to pursue a graduate degree. **Focus:** General studies/Field of study not specified. **Qualif.:** Applicants must be students pursuing a graduate studies work.

Funds Avail.: No specific amount. **Duration:** Annual. **Contact:** Email: foundationscholarships@stockton.edu; Phone: 609-626-3658.

10844 ■ Frances N. Christian Memorial Endowment Nursing Scholarship *(Graduate, Undergraduate/ Scholarship)*

Purpose: To provide financial assistance to qualified individuals who want to pursue a degree in the nursing profession. **Focus:** Nursing. **Qualif.:** Applicants must have a minimum cumulative GPA of 3.5 and must demonstrate commitment to the profession of nursing.

Funds Avail.: No specific amount. **Duration:** Annual. **Contact:** Email: foundationscholarships@stockton.edu; Phone: 609-626-3658.

10845 ■ The Shanon Newberry Physical Therapy Scholarship Endowment *(Doctorate/Scholarship)*

Purpose: To provide financial assistance to qualified individuals who want to pursue a degree in physical therapy. **Focus:** Physical therapy. **Qualif.:** Applicants must be in their fifth or sixth year of study in the Doctorate in a Physical Therapy Program.

Funds Avail.: No specific amount. **Duration:** Annual. **Contact:** Email: foundationscholarships@stockton.edu; Phone: 609-626-3658.

10846 ■ The Physical Therapy Faculty Scholarship Endowment *(Graduate/Scholarship)*

Purpose: To provide financial assistance to qualified individuals who want to pursue a degree in physical therapy. **Focus:** Physical therapy. **Qualif.:** Applicants must be in their final year of a physical therapy program and must exhibit a commitment to community service.

Funds Avail.: No specific amount. **Duration:** Annual. **Contact:** Email: foundationscholarships@stockton.edu; Phone: 609-626-3658.

10847 ■ The Bea and Harry Ross Scholarship Endowment *(Graduate/Scholarship)*

Purpose: To provide financial assistance to qualified individuals who want to pursue their education. **Focus:**

Awards are arranged alphabetically below their administering organizations

General studies/Field of study not specified. **Qualif.:** Applicants must be graduate or upper class students.

Funds Avail.: No specific amount. **Duration:** Annual. **Number Awarded:** Varies. **Deadline:** April 1. **Contact:** Email: foundationscholarships@stockton.edu; Phone: 609-626-3658.

10848 ■ The Richard Stockton College of New Jersey Foundation Alumni Association Graduate Awards (Graduate/Scholarship)

Purpose: To provide financial assistance to qualified individuals who wish to pursue their education. **Focus:** General studies/Field of study not specified. **Qualif.:** Applicants must be students who are pursuing a Master's Degree at Stockton. **Criteria:** Recipients will be selected based on the scholarship application materials.

Funds Avail.: No specific amount. **To Apply:** Applicants must complete the application form available on the website; submit two letters of recommendation (one must be from a Stockton faculty member), transcript and statement essay. **Contact:** Stockton Foundation Scholarship; E-mail: foundationscholarships@stockton.edu; Phone:609.652.4528.

10849 ■ Stonewall Community Foundation
1270 Broadway, Ste. 501
New York, NY 10001
Ph: (212)457-1341
E-mail: stonewall@stonewallfoundation.org
URL: stonewallfoundation.org
Social Media: www.facebook.com/StonewallCF
www.instagram.com/stonewallfoundation
twitter.com/stonewallcf

10850 ■ The Gene & John Athletic Fund
(Undergraduate/Scholarship)

Purpose: To provide emerging lesbian, gay, bisexual, transgender, and queer athletes with financial resources to help them reach their potential and realize their dreams. **Focus:** Athletics. **Qualif.:** Applicants must be LGBT athlete students who are looking to continue their education while pursuing athletics. **Criteria:** Selection is based on financial need.

Duration: Annual. **To Apply:** Applicants must submit a completed application form.

10851 ■ Traub-Dicker Rainbow Scholarships (TDRS)
(Undergraduate/Scholarship)

Purpose: To encourage and support women-identified lesbians in their pursuit of higher education. **Focus:** General studies/Field of study not specified. **Qualif.:** Applicants must be lesbians who are graduating high school seniors; must plan to attend a recognized college or university or be currently enrolled. **Criteria:** Selection is based on demonstrated academic excellence, community service and impacting LGBTQ issues.

Funds Avail.: $1,500 and $3,000. **Duration:** Annual. **Number Awarded:** 3. **Remarks:** Established in 2004. **Contact:** Email: scholarships@stonewallfoundation.org.

10852 ■ The Bee Winkler Weinstein Scholarship Fund (Undergraduate, Vocational/Occupational/Scholarship)

Purpose: To promote growth and self-sufficiency in young women by providing grants covering vocational or technical training, licensing fees, college application fees. **Focus:** General studies/Field of study not specified. **Qualif.:** Applicants must be lesbians, female bisexuals or transgender; must be between the ages of 16 to 26 and reside within the United States. **Criteria:** Selection is based on applicants financial need.

Funds Avail.: $25 - $650. **Duration:** Annual. **To Apply:** Applicants must submit a completed application form and letter of recommendation. **Contact:** 1270 Broadway, Ste. 501 New York, NY, 10001; Phone: 212-457-1341; Fax: 212-457-1351; Email: grants@stonewallfoundation.org.

10853 ■ The Stout Law Firm PLLC
201 W 16th St.
Houston, TX 77008
URL: www.divorcelawyerhouston.pro

10854 ■ Stout Law Firm Family Matters Scholarship
(College, University, Vocational/Occupational, Undergraduate/Scholarship)

Purpose: To help students reflect on the importance of family. **Focus:** General studies/Field of study not specified. **Qualif.:** Applicant must be graduating seniors enrolling in college, or current college, trade school, or university students. **Criteria:** Selection will be based on essay.

Funds Avail.: $1,000. **Number Awarded:** 1. **To Apply:** Applicant must write an essay of at least 5,00 words expressing what family means to them and how their family is important to them (applicant can be from any background or type of family). Application should send picture of ID, school information, and essay to contact. **Deadline:** December 1. **Contact:** Melissa Whitted; Email: Melissa@thestoutlawform.com; URL: www.divorcelawyer.pro/the-stout-law-firm-family-matters-scholarship.

10855 ■ Strada Education Network
10 W. Market St., Ste 1100
Indianapolis, IN 46204
Ph: (317)806-1200
URL: www.stradaeducation.org

10856 ■ The Thurgood Marshall College Fund
(Undergraduate/Scholarship)

Purpose: To offer financial assistance to outstanding students attending one of the 47 publicly-supported Historically Black Colleges and Universities (HBCUs) within the TMCF member-school network. **Focus:** General studies/Field of study not specified. **Criteria:** Selection shall be based on the aforementioned qualifications and compliance with the application details.

Funds Avail.: $6,200. **Duration:** Annual. **Number Awarded:** Varies. **To Apply:** Applicants may visit the website to verify the application process and other pieces of information. **Deadline:** June 4. **Contact:** URL: www.tmcf.org/our-scholarships/current-scholarships/tmcf-strada-education-scholarship/8986.

10857 ■ StraightForward Media
12337 N. 147th Dr.
Surprise, AZ 85379
Ph: (605)202-4169
URL: www.straightforwardmedia.com
Social Media: twitter.com/PPCoutlaw

Awards are arranged alphabetically below their administering organizations

10858 ■ Dale E. Fridell Memorial Scholarships
(Undergraduate, Vocational/Occupational/Scholarship)

Purpose: To financially assist students in their educational pursuits. **Focus:** General studies/Field of study not specified. **Qualif.:** Applicant must be a student currently enrolled or planning to enroll in a university, college, trade school, technical institute, vocational training or other post-secondary education program. **Criteria:** Selection will be based on the submitted application.

Funds Avail.: $1,000. **Duration:** Biennial. **Number Awarded:** 1. **To Apply:** Applicants must complete the Online Scholarship Application.

10859 ■ Mesothelioma Memorial Scholarships
(Undergraduate, Vocational/Occupational/Scholarship)

Purpose: To financially assist students in their educational pursuits. **Focus:** General studies/Field of study not specified. **Qualif.:** Applicants must be students currently enrolled or planning to enroll in a university, college, trade school, technical institute, vocational training or other post-secondary education program. **Criteria:** Selection will be based on merit.

Funds Avail.: $500. **Duration:** Quarterly. **Number Awarded:** 4. **To Apply:** Applicants must complete scholarship application online. **Deadline:** February 15. **Remarks:** Established in 2003.

10860 ■ Outlaw Student's Medical Professions Scholarships *(Undergraduate/Scholarship)*

Purpose: To financially assist students in their educational pursuits. **Focus:** Health care services. **Qualif.:** Applicants must be students planning to attend a medical profession field. **Criteria:** Selection will be based on merit.

Funds Avail.: $500. **Duration:** Quarterly. **Number Awarded:** 4. **To Apply:** Applicants must complete scholarship application online. **Deadline:** December 30.

10861 ■ Outlaw Student's Minority Scholarships
(Undergraduate/Scholarship)

Purpose: To financially assist students in their educational pursuits. **Focus:** General studies/Field of study not specified. **Qualif.:** Applicants must be college or soon-to-be college students who are members of racial or ethnic minority groups. **Criteria:** Selection will be based on merit.

Funds Avail.: $500. **Duration:** Quarterly. **Number Awarded:** 4. **To Apply:** Applicants must complete scholarship application online. **Deadline:** June 30.

10862 ■ Outlaw Student's Nursing School Scholarships *(Undergraduate/Scholarship)*

Purpose: To financially assist students in their educational pursuits. **Focus:** Nursing. **Qualif.:** Applicants must be nursing students. **Criteria:** Selection will be based on merit.

Funds Avail.: $500. **Duration:** Quarterly. **Number Awarded:** 4. **To Apply:** Applicants must complete the scholarship application online. **Deadline:** January 14.

10863 ■ Outlaw Student's Teacher Scholarships
(Undergraduate/Scholarship)

Purpose: To financially assist students in their educational pursuits. **Focus:** Teaching. **Qualif.:** Applicants must be students pursuing a degree or course of study with the intent of becoming a teacher. **Criteria:** Selection will be based on merit.

Funds Avail.: $500. **Duration:** Quarterly. **Number Awarded:** 4. **To Apply:** Applicants must complete the Online Scholarship Application. **Deadline:** January 14.

10864 ■ Student Osteopathic Medical Association (SOMA)
142 E Ontario St.
Chicago, IL 60611-2864
Ph: (312)202-8193
Fax: (312)202-8200
Free: 866-626-9262
E-mail: administration@studentdo.org
URL: www.studentdo.org
Social Media: www.facebook.com/NationalSOMA
instagram.com/National_SOMA
twitter.com/NationalSOMA
youtube.com/NationalSOMA

10865 ■ Humanism in Medicine Scholarships
(Undergraduate/Scholarship)

Purpose: To help medical students pursue their studies. **Focus:** Medicine, Osteopathic. **Qualif.:** Applicants must be third- or fourth-year osteopathic medical students attending any accredited osteopathic medical colleges; must be members of SOMA; and must not be previous recipients of the scholarship. **Criteria:** Selection will be based on how well they demonstrate their character in the philosophy of osteopathic medicine, love for their community and peers, leadership and dedication, compassion and empathy, spirit and enthusiasm.

Funds Avail.: $1,000. **Number Awarded:** 1.

10866 ■ Marvin H. and Kathleen G. Teget Leadership Scholarship *(Undergraduate/Scholarship)*

Purpose: To benefit students pursuing a career in specialty medicine. **Focus:** Medicine; Medicine, Osteopathic. **Qualif.:** Applicants must be pursuing specialty medicine career; must be members of SOMA; and must not be previous recipients of the scholarship; demonstrate a strong interest in leadership. **Criteria:** Selection is based on the students demonstrating leadership in a specialty field.

Funds Avail.: $1,000. **Number Awarded:** 2.

10867 ■ Osteopathic Medical Student Research Fellowship Program *(Undergraduate/Fellowship)*

Purpose: To provide funds for medical students who are currently or will be conducting a research project in the field of osteopathy. **Focus:** Medicine, Osteopathic.

Funds Avail.: Up to $5,000. **Duration:** Annual. **Deadline:** January 31. **Remarks:** Established in 2011.

10868 ■ Students of History
PO Box 4644
Broadlands, VA 20148
E-mail: luke@studentsofhistory.org
URL: studentsofhistory.org
Social Media: www.facebook.com/StudentsOfHistory/
www.instagram.com/studentsofhistory/
www.youtube.com/user/StudentsofHistory

10869 ■ Students of History Scholarship
(Undergraduate/Scholarship)

Purpose: To encourage students to continue their passion for social studies beyond high school, and to reward those

Awards are arranged alphabetically below their administering organizations

who show a dedication to learning history. **Focus:** General studies/Field of study not specified. **Qualif.:** Applicants must be graduating high school seniors with a love of history and learning; must have completed at least three social studies or history classes in high school. **Criteria:** Essay and teacher recommendations.

Funds Avail.: $1,000. **Duration:** Annual. **Number Awarded:** 1. **To Apply:** Application form and essay topic are available at www.studentsofhistory.com/scholarship. Form and essay should be mailed to the address above. **Deadline:** May 1.

10870 ■ Study.com
100 View St., Ste. 202
Mountain View, CA 94041
Free: 877-266-4919
URL: www.study.com
Social Media: www.facebook.com/StudyDotCom
www.instagram.com/studydotcom
www.linkedin.com/company/study-com
twitter.com/studydotcom

10871 ■ Study.com CLEP Scholarship *(Other/Scholarship)*

Purpose: To support students taking the CLEP (College Level Equivalency Program) exam. **Focus:** General studies/Field of study not specified. **Qualif.:** Applicant must be a U.S. citizen or permanent resident; must be planning on taking the CLEP exam. **Criteria:** Selection will be based on the quality of answers submitted on the application.

Funds Avail.: $250 to $500. **Duration:** Annual. **Number Awarded:** 3. **To Apply:** Application is available online at study.com/academy/popular/studycom-clep-scholarship-application-form-information.html. **Deadline:** April 1. **Contact:** Koby Wong; Email: koby@email.study.com.

10872 ■ Study.com Scholarship Florida Students *(Undergraduate, College/Scholarship)*

Purpose: To help a student pursuing their undergraduate degree from a college or university in Florida. **Focus:** General studies/Field of study not specified. **Qualif.:** Must be a U.S. citizen or permanent resident enrolled (or accepted) in an accredited college or university in Florida and planning to continue the next year; must have a minimum of 30 semester (or 40 quarter hours) still to be completed; must consent to provide a digital photograph of self and quote for display on Study.com if awarded the scholarship. **Criteria:** Selection will be based on the quality of answers submitted in the application.

Funds Avail.: $500. **Duration:** Annual. **Number Awarded:** 1. **To Apply:** Application is available online at study.com/pages/Scholarship_for_Florida_Students.html. **Deadline:** April 1. **Contact:** Koby Wong; Email: koby@email.study.com.

10873 ■ Study.com Scholarship Texas Students *(Undergraduate, College/Scholarship)*

Purpose: To help a student in pursuing an undergraduate degree in Texas. **Focus:** General studies/Field of study not specified. **Qualif.:** Applicant must be a U.S. citizen or permanent resident enrolled in an accredited college or university in the state of Texas and planning to continue the next year (or a high school senior who meets these criteria); must have a minimum of 30 credit hours (or 40 quarter

hours) still to complete; must consent to have a digital photograph of self and quote for display on Study.com if chosen as winner of scholarship. **Criteria:** Selection will be based on the quality of the answers submitted in the application.

Funds Avail.: $500. **Duration:** Annual. **Number Awarded:** 1. **To Apply:** Application is available online at study.com/pages/Scholarship_for_Texas_Students.html. **Deadline:** April 1. **Contact:** Koby Wong; Email: koby@email.study.com.

10874 ■ SugarSpunRun
5 S Broad St.
New Freedom, PA 17349
E-mail: samantha@sugarspunrun.com
URL: sugarspunrun.com
Social Media: www.facebook.com/Sugarspunrun
twitter.com/Sugarspunrun

10875 ■ Sugar Spun Scholarship *(Undergraduate, Graduate/Scholarship)*

Purpose: To help fund the cost of college tuition. **Focus:** General studies/Field of study not specified. **Qualif.:** Applicants must be students must be attending or accepted into a US college or university. **Criteria:** Essays are judged on originality, creativity, style, grammar, punctuation, and spelling, as well as adherence to the essay prompt.

Funds Avail.: $500. **Duration:** Annual. **To Apply:** Submit essay should be written in English and should not exceed 1,000 words; electronic submissions in Word or PDF format; must write an essay based on one of the following prompts: most memorable meal; life lesson learned through food; you could sit down to a meal with any person in history, living or dead, who would you choose, and why Include the food that you would serve; applications must include the following above the essay: full name; email address; Phone number; Mailing address; school that applicant attending or intend to attend. **Deadline:** August 1. **Remarks:** Established in 2017. **Contact:** Sugar Spun Run, 5 S Broad St., PO Box 521, New Freedom, PA, 17349; Email: scholarship@sugarspunrun.com.

10876 ■ Hatton W. Sumners Foundation, Inc.
325 N St. Paul St., Ste. 3920
Dallas, TX 75201
Ph: (214)220-2128
URL: www.hattonsumners.org
Social Media: linkedin.com/in/dara-m-derryberry-739939a5

10877 ■ Hatton W. Sumners Endowed Law Schools Scholarships *(Undergraduate, Graduate/Scholarship)*

Purpose: To support worthy students enrolled in a law school. **Focus:** Law. **Qualif.:** Applicants must be law students enrolled at the Oklahoma City University School of Law or Southern Methodist University's Dedman School of Law.

Funds Avail.: No specific amount. **Duration:** Annual. **To Apply:** Interested students may contact their school for the application process.

10878 ■ Hatton W. Sumners Endowed Undergraduate School Scholarships *(Undergraduate/Scholarship)*

Purpose: To provide educational assistance to students beginning their junior year. **Focus:** Education; History;

Awards are arranged alphabetically below their administering organizations

Journalism; Law; Political science. **Qualif.:** Applicants must be students beginning their junior year at Austin College, Howard Payne University's Douglas MacArthur Academy of Freedom, Schreiner University, Southern Methodist University's John G. Tower for Political Studies or Texas Wesleyan University; preferred majors are in the area of political science, although scholarships have been granted in education, history, journalism, pre-law and other disciplines.

Funds Avail.: No specific amount. **Duration:** Annual. **To Apply:** Applicants may contact their school for the application process.

10879 ■ Hatton W. Sumners Non-Endowed Undergraduate and Graduate Scholarships
(Undergraduate, Graduate/Scholarship)

Purpose: To provide students with a unique educational experience. **Focus:** Education; History; Journalism; Law; Political science. **Qualif.:** Applicants must be junior or senior students enrolled at Southwestern University, Huston-Tillotson University, St. Edwards University, The University of Dallas or Texas Christian University; preferred majors are in the area of political science, although scholarships have been granted in education, history, journalism, pre-law and other disciplines; the Foundation also supports Masters Students of Public Administration scholarships at the University of North Texas.

Funds Avail.: No specific amount. **Duration:** Annual. **To Apply:** Applicants may contact their school for the application process.

10880 ■ Sun Country Amateur Golf Association (SCAGA)
2316 Southern Blvd., Ste. D
Rio Rancho, NM 87124
URL: www.suncountrygolf.org
Social Media: www.facebook.com/Sun-Country-Golf
  -107678782626157
twitter.com/suncountrygolf
www.youtube.com/user/SunCountryGolfTV

10881 ■ Dwight Teed Scholarship Fund
(Undergraduate/Scholarship)

Purpose: To support students that achieved excellence in the classroom, present themselves as excellent citizens, have a connection with the game of golf, need financial assistance and are come highly recommended by credible sources. **Focus:** General studies/Field of study not specified. **Qualif.:** Applicants must have completed their junior year in high school or at least one year in college; achieved 3.0 or higher cumulative grade point average; and have a connection to golf. **Criteria:** Recipients are selected based on personal character as evidenced by students' participation in extracurricular activities or involvement in the local community; and financial need.

Funds Avail.: $1,500 each. **Duration:** Annual. **Number Awarded:** 4. **To Apply:** Applicants must submit a completed application form together with a letter outlining applicant's goals and objectives for college; three letters of recommendation, at least one must be from a SCAGA member; a copy of parents most current year tax return (form 1040, 1040A, or 1040EZ); current high school or college transcripts must be sent directly from the school to the SCAGA office (must include most current SAT or ACT exam results). **Deadline:** April. **Remarks:** Established in 1984. **Contact:** Sandra Campbell, 2316 Southern Blvd., Ste. D,

Rio Rancho, NM 87124; Email: sandra@suncountrygolf house.com.

10882 ■ Sure Oak
115 E 23rd St.
New York, NY 10010

10883 ■ The Sure Oak Scholarship *(College, University/Scholarship)*

Purpose: To help students achieve their goals. **Focus:** General studies/Field of study not specified. **Qualif.:** Applicant must be an undergraduate student enrolled in an accredited college or university. **Criteria:** Selection will be made by a panel of judges.

Funds Avail.: $1,000. **Duration:** Two years. **Number Awarded:** 1. **Deadline:** July 15. **Contact:** Email: lara@ sureoak.com.

10884 ■ The Surety & Fidelity Association of America (SFAA)
1140 19th St. NW, Ste. 500
Washington, DC 20036-6617
Ph: (202)463-0600
Fax: (202)463-0606
E-mail: information@surety.org
URL: www.surety.org
Social Media: www.facebook.com/SuretyFidelity
www.linkedin.com/company/the-surety-&-fidelity
  -association-of-america?trk=company_name
twitter.com/SuretyFidelity

10885 ■ Surety and Fidelity Industry Intern and Scholarship Program *(Undergraduate, Graduate/ Scholarship)*

Purpose: To support minority students whose studies are in the areas of insurance/risk management, accounting, or business/finance and to encourage their consideration of the surety industry and surety/fidelity underwriting as a career choice. **Focus:** Accounting; Business; Finance; Insurance and insurance-related fields; Management. **Criteria:** Applicants are evaluated based on academic achievement and financial need.

Funds Avail.: $5,000. **Duration:** Annual. **Contact:** Barbara Reiff; Email: breiff@surety.org.

10886 ■ SuretyBonds.com
3514 Interstate 70 Dr. SE, Ste. 102
Columbia, MO 65201
Free: 800-308-4358
E-mail: customercare@suretybonds.com
URL: www.suretybonds.com
Social Media: www.facebook.com/suretybond
www.linkedin.com/company/suretybonds-com
twitter.com/suretybonds
youtube.com/user/SuretyBonds

10887 ■ SuretyBonds.com Small Business Scholarship *(Undergraduate/Scholarship)*

Purpose: To support college students as a way of giving back to the small business community. **Focus:** General studies/Field of study not specified.

Awards are arranged alphabetically below their administering organizations

---

Funds Avail.: $1,500. **Duration:** Annual. **To Apply:** Application details available at www.suretybonds.com/scholarships/.

10888 ■ Surface Mount Technology Association (SMTA)

6600 City W Pky., Ste. 300
Eden Prairie, MN 55344
Ph: (952)920-7682
Fax: (952)926-1819
URL: www.smta.org
Social Media: www.facebook.com/SMTAorg
www.instagram.com/smtaorg
www.linkedin.com/company/smta---surface-mounte
 -technology-association
twitter.com/SMTAorg
www.youtube.com/user/SMTAorg

10889 ■ Charles Hutchins Educational Grant
(Graduate/Grant)

Purpose: To support a graduate-level student pursuing a degree and working on thesis research in electronic assembly, electronics packaging, or a related field. **Focus:** Electronics. **Qualif.:** Applicants must be a full-time graduate-level student; must working on thesis research in electronics assembly; electronics packaging, or a related field; attending a school in North America. **Criteria:** Selection will be based on the committee's criteria.

Funds Avail.: $5,000. **Duration:** Annual. **To Apply:** Applicants must provide a letter of recommendation from your advisor; submit an official copy of your graduate transcripts may take up to 1 month; must provide current resume including publication record; also submit copy of your undergraduate transcripts. **Remarks:** Established in 1998.

10890 ■ George Miksch Sutton Avian Research Center

393636 Gap Rd.
Bartlesville, OK 74005
Ph: (918)336-7778
E-mail: info@suttoncenter.org

10891 ■ Sutton Scholarship Award *(Undergraduate/Award, Scholarship)*

Purpose: To support the contributions of individuals anywhere who effectively use the visual arts to convey current conservation messages. **Focus:** Animal science and behavior; Communications; Wildlife conservation, management, and science. **Qualif.:** Applicants must be Oklahoma high school students grades 10-12. **Criteria:** Selection will be judged by the panel.

Funds Avail.: Up to $20,000. **Duration:** Annual. **To Apply:** Applicants should submit artwork and a 250-word essay that explains how their work communicates information about a current conservation issue. **Deadline:** January 10. **Contact:** Audra Fogle; Email: afogle@suttoncenter.org.

10892 ■ Sweep-All

450 Roblin Blvd. E.
Winkler, MB, Canada R6W 0H2
URL: sweep-all.com

Social Media: www.facebook.com/SweepAllTurf
www.instagram.com/sweepallturf
www.linkedin.com/company/sweep-all
www.pinterest.ca/SweepAllTurf
twitter.com/sweepallturf
www.youtube.com/c/SweepAll

10893 ■ Sweep All Scholarship *(College, University/Scholarship)*

Purpose: To provide financial aid to help students pursue an education. **Focus:** General studies/Field of study not specified. **Qualif.:** Applicant must be a U.S. citizen accepted, or currently attending, a college or university in the United States. **Criteria:** Selection is random.

Funds Avail.: $500. **To Apply:** Each applicant must submit a 200 word essay about an idea to help clean up and maintain local parks or university / college grounds; fill out on the application via the sponsor's website at sweep-all.com/scholarship. **Deadline:** November 30.

10894 ■ Swiss Benevolent Society of New York (SBS)

500 5th Ave., Rm. 1800
New York, NY 10110
Ph: (212)246-0655
Fax: (212)246-1366
URL: www.sbsny.org
Social Media: www.facebook.com/swiss.benevolent
www.linkedin.com/company/swiss-benevolent-society-of
 -new-york
twitter.com/swissbenevolent

10895 ■ Medicus Student Exchange Scholarship *(Graduate, Undergraduate/Scholarship)*

Purpose: To provide partial financial support for U.S. residents at the junior, senior or graduate college level who have been accepted to study at a Swiss University or Federal Institute of Technology. **Focus:** General studies/Field of study not specified. **Qualif.:** Applicants must be a U.S. Resident, permanently domiciled in the U.S., been accepted to a Swiss University or to a Federal Institute of Technology., study full-time at undergraduate (college junior or senior) or graduate school level. **Criteria:** Recipients are selected based on the committee's review of the application materials.

Funds Avail.: $5,000. **To Apply:** Application forms can be downloaded at the SBSNY web site. Applicants must submit the following required documents: general and scholastic pages of application packet; official transcripts of all high school, college and graduate grades when applying for the first time, official updates thereafter; SAT or GRE results when applying for the first time; proof of Swiss citizenship of applicant or one parent when applying for the first time; proof of U.S. citizenship or visa status when applying for the first time; letter of acceptance from Swiss University or Federal Institute of Technology or Technical College; two letters of recommendation from professors in the applicant's major area of study, on official letterhead; proof of proficiency in the language of instruction; statement of sufficient total funding. For studies in the U.S.: official transcript of records of at least one year of study in the U.S.; transcripts

Awards are arranged alphabetically below their administering organizations

of education in Switzerland; letter of recommendation from a professor in the applicant's major area of study, on official letterhead. **Deadline:** March 31.

10896 ■ Full Pellegrini Scholarship *(Undergraduate, Graduate/Scholarship)*

Purpose: To provide financial support to students who needs regular payment for their education. **Focus:** General studies/Field of study not specified. **Criteria:** Recipients are selected based on need and academic merit.

Funds Avail.: No specific amount. **To Apply:** Application forms can be downloaded at the SBSNY web site; must submit the following required documents: general and scholastic pages of application packet; official transcripts of all high school, college and graduate grades when applying for the first time, official updates thereafter; SAT or GRE results when applying for the first time; proof of Swiss citizenship of applicant or one parent when applying of the first time; proof of U.S. citizenship or visa status when applying for the first time; financial pages of application packet, including all requested information, unless applying for merit portion only; signed copy of all pages and schedules of Federal Income Tax returns and of W-2 forms of applicant and supporting party and/or spouse, where applicable; proof of cost for tuition and room and board, copy of bursar's bill (high school applicants provide figures of anticipated cost); letter of reference from a high school principal or a guidance counselor or from a professor in the applicant's major area of study, on official letterhead. **Deadline:** March 31.

10897 ■ Sonja S. Maguire Outstanding Scholastic Achievement Awards *(Graduate, Undergraduate/ Scholarship)*

Purpose: To provide financial support to college seniors or graduate students who are in need. **Focus:** General studies/Field of study not specified. **Criteria:** Recipients are selected based on the committee's review of the application materials.

Funds Avail.: No specific amount. **To Apply:** Application forms can be downloaded at the SBSNY web site; must submit the following required documents general and scholastic pages of application packet; official transcripts of all high school, college and graduate grades when applying for the first time, official updates thereafter; SAT or GRE results when applying for the first time; proof of Swiss citizenship of applicant or one parent when applying for the first time; proof of U.S. citizenship or visa status when applying for the first time; two letters of recommendation from professors in the applicant's major area of study, on official letterhead. **Deadline:** March 31.

10898 ■ Zimmermann Scholarship *(Graduate/ Scholarship)*

Purpose: To provide financial support to students who are in need. **Focus:** General studies/Field of study not specified. **Criteria:** Recipients are selected based on the committee's review of the application materials.

Funds Avail.: No specific amount. **To Apply:** Application forms can be downloaded at the SBSNY web site; must submit the following required documents general and scholastic pages of application packet; official transcripts of all high school, college and graduate grades when applying for the first time, official updates thereafter; SAT or GRE results when applying for the first time; proof of Swiss citizenship of applicant or one parent when applying for the first time; proof of U.S. citizenship or visa status when ap-

plying for the first time; two letters of recommendation from professors in the applicant's major area of study, on official letterhead. **Deadline:** March 31.

10899 ■ Sycamore Hills Dentistry
10082 Illinois Rd.
Fort Wayne, IN 46804
Ph: (260)213-4400
Fax: (260)213-4222
E-mail: office@sycamorehillsdentistry.com
URL: www.sycamorehillsdentistry.com
Social Media: www.facebook.com/sycamorehillsdentistry
twitter.com/SycHillsDent

10900 ■ Sycamore Hills Dentistry Scholarship *(College, University/Scholarship)*

Purpose: To provide financial assistance to students pursuing degrees in any dental field. **Focus:** Dental hygiene; Dental laboratory technology; Dentistry. **Qualif.:** Applicant must be a U.S. citizen and accepted to, or currently attending, an accredited program at a college or university in the United States for a degree or certificate in the dental field.

Funds Avail.: $1,000. **To Apply:** Must write an essay explaining why they are deserving of this scholarship; applications must be submitted via the web form only and essays must be hand delivered in person to the office; provide a college transcript or proof of acceptance to a college, university, or education program in dentistry. **Deadline:** November 30.

10901 ■ Syncrude Canada Ltd.
PO Box 1600 Stn. M
Calgary, AB, Canada T2P 1M5
Ph: (780)790-5911
E-mail: info@syncrude.com
URL: www.syncrude.ca
Social Media: www.instagram.com/syncrude_canada
www.linkedin.com/company/syncrude-canada-ltd-
twitter.com/SyncrudeCanada
www.youtube.com/user/syncrudecanada

10902 ■ Syncrude/Athabasca University Aboriginal Scholarships *(Undergraduate/Scholarship)*

Purpose: To provide support the education of Aboriginal students. **Focus:** Computer and information sciences; Industry and trade; Information science and technology; Management; Nursing. **Qualif.:** Applicants must be Alberta residents who are Aboriginal students studying in the following degree programs through Athabasca University: Bachelor of Arts, Bachelor of Administration, Bachelor of Administration-Post Diploma, Bachelor of Commerce, Bachelor of Science in Computing and Information Systems or Bachelor of Science-Post Diploma in Computing and Information Systems, and Bachelor of Nursing. **Criteria:** Selection is based on financial need, academic performance and potential and community/extracurricular activities; preference will be given to applicants entering the first year of full-time studies.

Funds Avail.: $2,000. **To Apply:** Applicants must submit a completed application form. **Deadline:** September 30. **Contact:** Student Awards Administrative Assistant, Office of Registrar, Athabasca University, 1 University Dr., Athabasca, AB, Canada, T9S 3A3; Phone: 800-788-9041 ext.

Awards are arranged alphabetically below their administering organizations

6197; Email: awardsinfo@athabascau.ca.

10903 ■ Tag and Label Manufacturers Institute (TLMI)

6 Main St.
Milford, OH 45150
Ph: (513)401-9042
Fax: (513)401-9437
E-mail: office@tlmi.com
URL: www.tlmi.com
Social Media: www.instagram.com/tlmi_official
www.linkedin.com/company/tlmi
twitter.com/tlmi
www.youtube.com/channel/UCnssdLvYvElMyqBxalMAljw/featured

10904 ■ Tag and Label Manufacturers Institute Scholarships - Four-Year Colleges *(Undergraduate/Scholarship)*

Purpose: To assist full-time college students in pursuing a degree to prepare for a career in the tag and label manufacturing industry. **Focus:** Graphic art and design; Management; Marketing and distribution. **Qualif.:** Applicant must be a second or third year full-time college student with a 3.00 or higher GPA. **Criteria:** Recipients are selected based on demonstrated interest in the field of tag and label industry.

Funds Avail.: $5,000. **Duration:** Annual. **To Apply:** Applicants must fill out the application online; must prepare a one-page personal statement on information sheet, work experiences, family financial report, career and educational goals and reasons why they deserve the award; a school transcript; three references; and samples of work (not mandatory). **Contact:** Email:office@tlmi.com.

10905 ■ Tag and Label Manufacturers Institute Scholarships - Two-Year Colleges *(Undergraduate/Scholarship)*

Purpose: To provide students the assistance they need in seeking career in the flexographic industry. **Focus:** Industrial design. **Qualif.:** Applicants must be enrolled full-time in a flexographic printing program at a two-year college or technical program that grants degrees; and must maintain a 3.00 or higher GPA. **Criteria:** Recipients will be selected based on the application materials and demonstrated interest in the chosen field.

Funds Avail.: $1,000. **Duration:** Annual. **To Apply:** Application forms are available at the website. Committee will not accept applications direct from a student, applicants must present the application form, official college transcript and a personal statement to their educators who will submit to TLMI office. **Contact:** Email:office@tlmi.com.

10906 ■ Tailhook Association (TA)

9696 Businesspark Ave.
San Diego, CA 92131-1643
Ph: (858)689-9223
Free: 800-322-4665
URL: www.tailhook.net
Social Media: www.facebook.com/Tailhook.Association
twitter.com/_tailhook_

10907 ■ Tailhook Educational Foundation Scholarship *(Undergraduate, Postdoctorate/Scholarship)*

Purpose: To support the education of people who are interested in learning about history and present day activi-

ties of US navy carrier aviation. **Focus:** Aviation. **Qualif.:** Applicants must be high school graduates and dependents of current or former (US Navy/US Marines Corps/US Coast Guards) Naval Aviators, Naval Flight Officers, or Naval Aircrew men; must be dependents of individuals who are serving or have served on board as US Navy Aircraft carriers.

Funds Avail.: No specific amount. **Duration:** Annual. **Deadline:** March 1.

10908 ■ Tailor Made Lawns, Inc. (TML)

1003 1st St. W
Conover, NC 28613
Ph: (828)358-4555
URL: www.tailormadelawns.com
Social Media: www.facebook.com/tailormadelawns
www.linkedin.com/company/tailor-made-lawn-svc
twitter.com/tailormadelawns

10909 ■ Tailor Made Lawns Scholarship Fund *(Undergraduate/Scholarship)*

Purpose: To award financial assistance to North Carolina students demonstrating academic excellence and passion for environmental engineering, plant sciences, environmental sciences, green technology, and related fields. **Focus:** Botany; Environmental science. **Qualif.:** Applicant must be a current North Carolina resident; currently pursuing studies in environmental engineering, plant sciences, environmental sciences, green technology, and related fields; currently enrolled, or planning to be enrolled, in an accredited college or university in the fall semester; GPA of 3.0 or higher. **Criteria:** Letter of intent written by the student, faculty references, academic transcripts, and SAT/ACT scores; passion for the environment.

Funds Avail.: $1,000. **Duration:** Annual. **To Apply:** Applicant must submit Completed application form; Letter of Intent: Showcasing applicants passion for the environment, intended career path and what inspired applicant to pursue environmental education; 2-3 letters of recommendation from teachers or faculty; School transcripts or SAT/ ACT scores. **Deadline:** June 30. **Contact:** Attn: Damon Milotte; Email: scholarship@tailormadelawns.com.

10910 ■ Taiwanese American Citizens League (TACL)

2443 Fillmore St., No. 380-9501
San Francisco, CA 94115
Ph: (201)901-8225
E-mail: tacl@tacl.org
URL: tacl.org
Social Media: www.facebook.com/tacl.org
www.instagram.com/taclorg
twitter.com/taclorg

10911 ■ TACL-LA Taiwanese American Community Scholarship (TACS) *(Undergraduate/Scholarship)*

Purpose: To support students with leadership qualities committed to public service. **Focus:** General studies/Field of study not specified. **Criteria:** Selection is based on the committee's criteria.

Funds Avail.: $500. **Duration:** Annual. **Deadline:** March 30. **Contact:** Lynn Wen, TACL- LA Community Scholarships, PO Box 80673, San Marino, CA, 91118-8673.

Awards are arranged alphabetically below their administering organizations

10912 ■ Robert M. Takasugi Public Interest Fellowship

245 5th St., Ste. 103
San Francisco, CA 94103
URL: takasugifellowship.org

10913 ■ Robert M. Takasugi Public Interest Fellowships *(Postgraduate/Fellowship)*

Purpose: To encourage dedicated lawyers to pursue public interest careers. **Focus:** Law. **Qualif.:** Applicants must be a post-graduate law student pursuing public interest careers. **Criteria:** Selection is based on the application.

Funds Avail.: $5,000. **Duration:** Annual; 10 weeks. **To Apply:** Applicants must submit a cover letter; resume; three references (without letters); and answers (no more than three pages) to the questions posted at the website. **Contact:** Edwin Prather at edwin@pratherlawoffices.com.

10914 ■ Tall Clubs International (TCI)

1555 CR 2103
Weimar, TX 78962
E-mail: tcifoundationscholarships@gmail.com
URL: www.tall.org

10915 ■ Tall Clubs International Student Scholarships *(Undergraduate/Scholarship)*

Purpose: To promote tall awareness among tall men and women, and in the community. **Focus:** General studies/ Field of study not specified. **Qualif.:** Applicants must be under 21 years of age and attending their first year of college in the following fall; must also meet the TCI height requirement minimums of 5'10 (178 cm) for women and 6'2 (188 cm) for men.

Funds Avail.: Up to $1,000. **Duration:** Annual. **To Apply:** Applicants must be selected by the closest Member Clubs. **Contact:** Scholarship Committee, Email: tcischolarships@ hotmail.com; Phone: 888-468-2552.

10916 ■ Tall Ships America (TSA)

221 3rd St., Bldg. 2, Ste. 101
Newport, RI 02840
Ph: (401)846-1775
Fax: (401)849-5400
URL: www.tallshipsamerica.org
Social Media: www.facebook.com/tallshipsamerica
www.instagram.com/tallshipsamerica/?hl=en
twitter.com/tallshipsfleet

10917 ■ Henry H. Anderson, Jr. Sail Training Scholarship *(Professional development/Scholarship, Recognition, Award)*

Purpose: To assist those who are genuinely interested in experiencing sail training and education under sail. **Focus:** Sports studies. **Criteria:** Selection will be based on the desire of the applicants, whether individuals or groups, to undergo sail training which the main theme of the award is; applicants must also show a demonstrated need for financial assistance.

Funds Avail.: Maximum awards of $750 for individuals; $1,500 for organized groups. **Duration:** Annual. **Number Awarded:** Varies. **To Apply:** Applicants must first select a sail training program to participate in; individuals or group

leaders must then contact that program, request a copy of its registration or application form, and advise that organization that they are applying for a tall ships American financial assistance scholarship; it is important for the applicants to establish a good, working contact with the selected sail training program and to be aware of that program's registration requirements; applicants must complete both the scholarship application and the sail training program application and submit copies of each to both tall ships America and the sail training program; applications should be typewritten or legibly printed; applicants may also use a computer to download an application form from the tall ships America website. scholarship applications must be completed in full and include the required signatures.

10918 ■ Alex Tanous Foundation

PO Box 3818
Portland, ME 04104-3818
Ph: (207)773-8328
E-mail: enlighten@alextanous.org
URL: www.alextanous.org
Social Media: www.facebook.com/alex.tanous.73
twitter.com/ATanous

10919 ■ Alex Tanous Scholarship Award *(Undergraduate/Scholarship)*

Purpose: To provide financial assistance to qualified students who want to pursue their academic study and or research in science related in the areas of physical and spiritual development. **Focus:** Parapsychology. **Qualif.:** Applicants must be student attending an accredited college or university, or participating in a certificate in Parapsychological studies. **Criteria:** Selection will be based on submitted applications.

Funds Avail.: $500. **Duration:** Annual. **To Apply:** Applicants must demonstrate a previous interest in the stated fields by including sample writing on the subject with the application form; must complete the application form available online; and letters of reference are also required from two individuals who are familiar with work and or studies or a detailed description of the conference to be sponsored; essays written, blogs or research may be submitted to the Alex Tanous Foundation as part of our mission to further the research and disseminate the work through the Alex Tanous Foundation for Scientific Research. **Deadline:** May 1.

10920 ■ Tarkio College Alumni Association (TCAA)

PO Box 111
Tarkio, MO 64491
Ph: (660)736-4208
E-mail: tcaa@tarkio.net
URL: www.tarkioalumni.org

10921 ■ Charles "Chuck" McAdams Memorial Scholarships *(Graduate, Undergraduate/Scholarship)*

Purpose: To provide financial assistance to the children or grandchildren of Tarkio College graduates in attending either an accredited undergraduate baccalaureate or graduate institution in the United States of America. **Focus:** General studies/Field of study not specified. **Criteria:** Selection is based on the evaluation of submitted documents and specific criteria.

Awards are arranged alphabetically below their administering organizations

Funds Avail.: No specific amount. **Duration:** Annual. **To Apply:** Applicants must submit a copy of high school transcript or certification of high school graduation; college transcript or certificate of baccalaureate degree; birth certificate showing that a parent or grandparent had gradu- ated from Tarkio College; two reference letters; statement of academic goals; essay on how to interpret and plan to fulfill the "Tarkio Experience"; two letters of reference as to character and scholarship (sent under separate cover or directly from writer). **Deadline:** February 15. **Contact:** Tarkio College Alumni Association, PO Box 111,Tarkio, MO, 64491.

10922 ■ TaskEasy, Inc
669 SW Temple.
Salt Lake City, UT 84101
Free: 800-518-4461
E-mail: help@taskeasy.com
URL: www.taskeasy.com
Social Media: www.facebook.com/taskeasy
www.linkedin.com/company/taskeasy/
twitter.com/taskeasy

10923 ■ TaskEasy Scholarships for Future Entrepreneurs *(Undergraduate/Scholarship)*

Purpose: To help young entrepreneurs achieve the goal of building their own businesses within the lawn care industry. **Focus:** Business.

Funds Avail.: $1,000.

10924 ■ Teacher.org
7120 Hayvenhurst Ave.
Van Nuys, CA 91406
E-mail: info@teacher.org
URL: www.teacher.org
Social Media: www.facebook.com/BecomeTeacher/
instagram.com/teacher_org
twitter.com/BecomeTeacher

10925 ■ Teacher.org's Inspire Our Future Scholar- ship *(All/Scholarship)*

Purpose: To encourage the aspirations of those in the teaching profession. **Focus:** Education; Teaching. **Qualif.:** Applicants must be legal residents of the United States; must be at least 18 years of age; must be currently enrolled in an accredited college or university in the United States, as listed on the U.S. Department of Education website; and must have a minimum GPA of 3.5 on a 4.0 scale. **Criteria:** Selection will be based on their essays that will be read by panels of teaching professionals and organization leaders.

Funds Avail.: $500. **Duration:** Annual. **To Apply:** Ap- plicants must go to the website to fill out the entry form and answer the question in the space allotted. **Deadline:** April 1. **Contact:** URL: www.teacher.org/scholarships-grants/.

10926 ■ Teachers Insurance and Annuity As- sociation of America (TIAA)
730 3rd Ave.
New York, NY 10017-3206
Fax: (800)914-8922
Free: 800-842-2252
URL: www.tiaa.org

Social Media: www.facebook.com/tiaa
www.linkedin.com/company/tiaa
twitter.com/tiaa
www.youtube.com/c/+tiaa

10927 ■ Ruth Simms Hamilton Research Fellowship *(Graduate/Fellowship)*

Purpose: To support cutting-edge, graduate-level research to further the study of the African diaspora. **Focus:** African studies; Social sciences. **Qualif.:** Applicants must be gradu- ate students enrolled in a social science program at an ac- credited U.S. college/university and studying the African Diaspora; must have successfully passed comprehensive exams.

Funds Avail.: Greater than $30,000. **Duration:** Annual. **Number Awarded:** 1. **To Apply:** Applicants must provide a 2-4 page summary of research; Curriculum Vitae; letter of support. **Deadline:** December 15. **Remarks:** Established to honor the memory and outstanding work of the late Dr. Ruth Simms Hamilton, the former Michigan State University professor and TIAA Trustee. Established in 2005. **Contact:** E-mail: fellowshipapps@grd.msu.edu.

10928 ■ Tear Film and Ocular Surface Society (TFOS)
PO Box 130146
Boston, MA 02113
URL: www.tearfilm.org
Social Media: youtube.com/user/TearFilmSociety

10929 ■ TFOS Fellowship Awards *(Graduate, Postdoctorate/Fellowship)*

Purpose: To present work (poster or oral presentation) and also to learn about a new scientific area at a small international meeting of the caliber of a Gordon Conference or Keystone Symposium. **Focus:** Filmmaking.

Funds Avail.: $1,500 each. **Duration:** Annual. **Number Awarded:** Total of 6. **To Apply:** Applicants should send a curriculum vitae; the submitted abstract; a brief 1-2 page statement discussing the importance of this meeting to their research activities; and a letter of support from the supervisor; and does not have to have an accepted abstract at the time of consideration, but proof of acceptance must be provided before travel awards are granted. **Contact:** Rose Sullivan; E-mail: rose@tearfilm.org.

10930 ■ TechChecks
138 Daniel Dr.
Lakewood, NJ 08701
Free: 866-527-3758
E-mail: sales@techchecks.net
URL: www.techchecks.net
Social Media: www.facebook.com/pages/Tech-Checks-Inc
 -Deluxe-Checks/187536314642898
twitter.com/Tech_Checks

10931 ■ TechChecks Business Leadership Scholar- ships *(Undergraduate/Scholarship)*

Purpose: To encourage minority and female students to not only attend college, but to enter and succeed in leader- ship positions in white male-dominated industries and companies. **Focus:** Business. **Qualif.:** Applicants who are high school seniors or college students pursuing a degree

Awards are arranged alphabetically below their administering organizations

in Business Administration, or other business-related field; must have an average SAT score of 1070, Match ACT 26 or higher and average GPA of 3.5 or above. **Criteria:** Selection will be based on the quality of research, originality and presentation of the submitted essay. Priority will be given to minority students.

Funds Avail.: $1,000. **Number Awarded:** Up to 4. **To Apply:** Applicants must visit the website to fill out an application and must be submitted via email. **Deadline:** June 15. **Contact:** The TechChecks Business Leadership Scholarship, 272 Lanes Mill Rd, Howell, NJ, 07731; Phone: 866-527-3758; Fax: 866-527-8883; Email: Sales@techchecks.net.

10932 ■ Technical Women's Organization (TWO)
6500 Air Cargo Rd.
Oklahoma City, OK 73195-0208
E-mail: info@technicalwomen.org
URL: www.technicalwomen.org
Social Media: www.facebook.com/Technical-Womens
 -Organization-TWO-of-the-Federal-Aviation
 -Administration-104692320966

10933 ■ Technical Women's Organization Education Scholarship *(Advanced Professional, Graduate/Scholarship)*
Purpose: to support educational opportunities for members of the Technical Women's Association. **Focus:** General studies/Field of study not specified. **Qualif.:** Applicants must be pursuing an aviation-related technical degree; non-FAA applicants need a two sponsor or can apply by becoming a two associate member. **Criteria:** Selection is based on how the applicant will benefit from completing the course, essay responses, length of time and service to the Technical Women's Organization.

Funds Avail.: Up to $1,000 each. **Number Awarded:** 2. **To Apply:** Applicants must submit completed application along with a signed TWO Scholarship Training Contract; two letters of recommendation from either a current or former supervisor, an instructor or advisor, an acquaintance that has known applicant for more than one year and is not a relative (Non FAA, an additional letter must be from a TWO sponsor); resume listing job history for last three years; biography; list formal training for the past three years: college, technical, agency, or directed studies (Non FAA applicants must supply the latest transcript). **Deadline:** August 1. **Contact:** Technical Women's Organization TWO Scholarship (In Honor of Bernadette Ohlemacher) Selection Committee Attn: Beverly Newsome 7520 Ashcroft Circle Fort Worth, TX 76120. Info@TechnicalWomen.org.

10934 ■ Technology First
714 E Monument Ave., Ste. 106
Dayton, OH 45402
Ph: (937)229-0054
E-mail: info@technologyfirst.org
URL: www.technologyfirst.org
Social Media: www.facebook.com/technologyfirst.org
www.linkedin.com/company/technologyfirst
twitter.com/technologyfirst

10935 ■ Technology First / ROBERT V. MCKENNA SCHOLARSHIP *(Undergraduate/Scholarship)*
Purpose: To provide financial support to those deserving students. **Focus:** Information science and technology. **Cri-**

teria: Selection will be based on the based on the committee's criteria.
Funds Avail.: Varies. **Contact:** Ann Gallaher, agallaher@technologyfirst.org.

10936 ■ Technology Student Association (TSA)
1904 Association Dr.
Reston, VA 20191-1540
Ph: (703)860-9000
Fax: (703)758-4852
Free: 888-860-9010
E-mail: general@tsaweb.org
URL: www.tsaweb.org
Social Media: www.facebook.com/nationalTSA
www.instagram.com/nationaltsa
twitter.com/NationalTSA

10937 ■ Future STEM Teacher Scholarship *(Undergraduate/Scholarship)*
Purpose: To support the STEM education profession by encouraging promising TSA students to pursue careers as K-12 STEM teachers. **Focus:** Technology. **Qualif.:** Applicants must have participated in an active TSA chapter for a minimum of two (2) consecutive years; served as a TSA officer at the local, state and/or national level for a minimum of one (1) academic year; attended and participated in at least one (1) TSA conference at the state or national level. Participated in an active TSA chapter for a minimum of two (2) consecutive years; served as a TSA officer at the local, state and/or national level for a minimum of one (1) academic year; attended and participated in at least one (1) TSA conference at the state or national level. **Criteria:** Selection shall be based on the aforementioned applicants' qualifications and compliance with the application details.

Funds Avail.: $3,500. **Duration:** Annual. **Number Awarded:** 1. **To Apply:** Applicants must submit: a signed cover letter that includes a detailed description of the applicant's involvement in TSA, based on the above criteria; SAT score and/or ACT score: high school class rank (indicate how many in the class); no more than three (3) letters of reference, one of which must come from a technology teacher; a single-sided, one-page typed essay on career plans for becoming a teacher in the technology education profession. **Deadline:** May 8.

10938 ■ William P. Elrod Memorial Scholarship *(Undergraduate/Scholarship)*
Purpose: To provide financial support to students pursuing undergraduate programs. **Focus:** Technology. **Criteria:** Selection will be evaluated by the Awards Committee.
Funds Avail.: $2,500. **Duration:** Annual. **To Apply:** Applicants must submit a completed application to the TSA Awards Committee; resume; short essay; A copy of your high school transcript; Three letters of reference. **Deadline:** May 1.

10939 ■ Telacu
5400 E Olympic Blvd., 3rd Fl.
Los Angeles, CA 90022
Ph: (323)721-1655
Fax: (323)724-3372
URL: telacu.com

10940 ■ Citi/TELACU Scholars Mentoring Program *(Undergraduate/Scholarship)*
Purpose: To assist undergraduate students pursuing careers in business-related fields with much more than

Awards are arranged alphabetically below their administering organizations

financial resources. **Focus:** Business. **Qualif.:** Applicants must be seniors in last year of undergraduate studies; must be pursuing degrees in business-related disciplines; must have 3.0 GPA; must demonstrate academic excellence; must have proven leadership qualities. **Criteria:** Selection is based on extracurricular involvement demonstrating a commitment to the community and a need for financial and academic support in order to successfully complete a post-secondary program.

Funds Avail.: No specific amount.

10941 ■ David C. Lizárraga Fellowship *(Graduate/ Fellowship)*

Purpose: To support students pursuing advanced degrees in business or engineering. **Focus:** Business; Engineering.

Funds Avail.: No specific amount. **To Apply:** The application process is online. **Deadline:** December.

10942 ■ Toyota/TELACU Scholarships *(Undergraduate/Scholarship)*

Purpose: To support Latino students in their educational pursuits. **Focus:** Business; Engineering. **Qualif.:** Applicants must be junior or senior and must be pursuing a degree in engineering fields. **Criteria:** Recipients are selected based on the committee's review of the application materials.

Funds Avail.: Up to $5,000.

10943 ■ Telecommunications Association of Michigan (TAM)
600 W Shiawassee St.
Lansing, MI 48933
Ph: (517)482-4166
URL: www.telecommich.org
Social Media: www.linkedin.com/company/
  telecommunications-association-of-michigan
twitter.com/TAMichigan

10944 ■ Telecommunications Association of Michigan - Category II - IV Scholarship *(Undergraduate/Scholarship)*

Purpose: To elevate the technical and business competence of young people by providing them with assistance to acquire meaningful and marketable skills; to provide educational incentive to deserving students who will ultimately provide leadership for the professions in business, education and public service. **Focus:** General studies/Field of study not specified. **Qualif.:** Applicant must be a Category II or Category III or Category IV member. Any student in a graduating class of a high school or any student now enrolled in an accredited, degree granting college or university, except for college seniors. **Criteria:** Selection is based on academic excellence, financial need and ability.

Funds Avail.: No specific amount.

10945 ■ Telluride Association (TA)
217 W Ave.
Ithaca, NY 14850
Ph: (607)273-5011
Fax: (607)272-2667
E-mail: telluride@cornell.edu
URL: www.tellurideassociation.org
Social Media: www.linkedin.com/groups/35439/profile

twitter.com/tellurideassoc

10946 ■ Telluride Association Summer Program Scholarships *(Undergraduate/Scholarship)*

Purpose: To bring together young people from around the world who share a passion for learning. **Focus:** General studies/Field of study not specified. **Qualif.:** Applicant must be a junior high school student and must be nominated by a teacher, counselor or other educator. **Criteria:** Applications that meet all requirements will be prioritized.

Funds Avail.: Stipend of up to $500. **To Apply:** Teachers, educators, or counselors can nominate up to five candidates. TASP Nomination Form is available on the website.

10947 ■ Telugu Association of North America (TANA)
26233 Taft Rd.
Novi, MI 48374
Free: 855-687-8262
E-mail: info@tana.org
URL: www.tana.org
Social Media: www.facebook.com/TANA-Telugu
  -Association-of-North-America-148580031842798
www.instagram.com/TANA_social
www.linkedin.com/company/tanasocial
twitter.com/TANAsocial

10948 ■ Chereddi NarayanaRao & Radhamanohari Scholarships *(Graduate/Scholarship)*

Purpose: To provide financial support to deserving Telugu students who want to pursue their education in the United States. **Focus:** General studies/Field of study not specified. **Qualif.:** Applicants must be Telugu students who are currently residing in Andhra Pradesh; must have been admitted to a graduate school in a U.S. university; must demonstrate financial need. **Criteria:** Selection of applicants will be based on the following criteria: (a) need; (b) merit, grades and recommendations; (c) scores in standardized tests like GRE, TOEFL; (d) reputation of the college/university in India from which the applicant is graduating; (e) reputation of the school in North America in which the applicant is planning to pursue the education; (f) the field of study in which the applicant is planning higher education; (g) extracurricular activities the applicant is proficient in, and (h) only if the applicant is a Telugu student from Andhra Pradesh.

Funds Avail.: $2,000. **To Apply:** Applicants must complete the following information name, address with pin code and phone number; profession and annual income; name, address, and phone number of parents; professions and annual incomes of parents; net worth of all assets of applicant and parents combined; high school and college educational qualifications and work experience of the applicant (enclose a copy of the transcripts); name, address and phone number of the department and the university in the United States where the applicant intends to enroll. **Contact:** Prasad Choudary Kakarala, 66 Harvest Ln., Tiffin, OH, 44883, USA; Email: prasadkakarala@yahoo.com.

10949 ■ Gadde Sitaramamma & Tirupataiah Scholarship *(Graduate/Scholarship)*

Purpose: To provide financial support to deserving Telugu students who want to pursue their education in the United States. **Focus:** General studies/Field of study not specified. **Qualif.:** Applicants must be Telugu students who are

Awards are arranged alphabetically below their administering organizations

currently residing in Andhra Pradesh; must have been admitted to a graduate school in a U.S. university; must demonstrate financial need. **Criteria:** Selection of applicants will be based on the following criteria: (a) need; (b) merit, grades and recommendations; (c) scores in standardized tests like GRE, TOEFL; (d) reputation of the college/university in India from which the applicant is graduating; (e) reputation of the school in North America in which the applicant is planning to pursue the education; (f) the field of study in which the applicant is planning higher education; (g) extracurricular activities the applicant is proficient in, and (h) only if the applicant is a Telugu student from Andhra Pradesh.

Funds Avail.: $2,000. **Number Awarded: 1. To Apply:** Applicants must complete the following information name, address with pin code and phone number; profession and annual income; name, address, and phone number of parents; professions and annual incomes of parents; net worth of all assets of applicant and parents combined; high school and college educational qualifications and work experience of the applicant (enclose a copy of the transcripts); name, address and phone number of the department and the university in the United States where the applicant intends to enroll. **Contact:** Prasad Choudary Kakarala, 66 Harvest Ln., Tiffin, OH, 44883, USA; Email: prasadkakarala@yahoo.com.

10950 ■ Guthikonda BasavapunnaRao & Umadevi Scholarship *(Graduate/Scholarship)*

Purpose: To provide financial support to deserving Telugu students who want to pursue their education in the United States. **Focus:** General studies/Field of study not specified.

Funds Avail.: $2,000. **To Apply:** Applicants must complete the following information name, address with pin code and phone number; profession and annual income; name, address, and phone number of parents; professions and annual incomes of parents; net worth of all assets of applicant and parents combined; high school and college educational qualifications and work experience of the applicant (enclose a copy of the transcripts); name, address and phone number of the department and the university in the United States where the applicant intends to enroll. **Contact:** Prasad Choudary Kakarala, 66 Harvest Ln., Tiffin, OH, 44883, USA; Email: prasadkakarala@yahoo.com.

10951 ■ Guthikonda Ramabrahmam & Balamani Scholarship *(Graduate/Scholarship)*

Purpose: To provide financial support to deserving Telugu students who want to pursue their education in the United States. **Focus:** General studies/Field of study not specified. **Qualif.:** Applicants must be Telugu students who are currently residing in Andhra Pradesh; must have been admitted to a graduate school in a U.S. university; must demonstrate financial need. **Criteria:** Selection of applicants will be based on the following criteria: (a) need; (b) merit, grades and recommendations; (c) scores in standardized tests like GRE, TOEFL; (d) reputation of the college/university in India from which the applicant is graduating; (e) reputation of the school in North America in which the applicant is planning to pursue the education; (f) the field of study in which the applicant is planning higher education; (g) extracurricular activities the applicant is proficient in, and (h) only if the applicant is a Telugu student from Andhra Pradesh.

Funds Avail.: $2,000. **To Apply:** Applicants must complete the following information name, address with pin code and

phone number; profession and annual income; name, address, and phone number of parents; professions and annual incomes of parents; net worth of all assets of applicant and parents combined; high school and college educational qualifications and work experience of the applicant (enclose a copy of the transcripts); name, address and phone number of the department and the university in the United States where the applicant intends to enroll. **Contact:** Prasad Choudary Kakarala, 66 Harvest Ln., Tiffin, OH, 44883, USA; Email: prasadkakarala@yahoo.com.

10952 ■ Kodali Veeraiah & Sarojini Scholarship *(Graduate/Scholarship)*

Purpose: To provide financial support to deserving Telugu students who want to pursue their education in the United States. **Focus:** General studies/Field of study not specified. **Qualif.:** Applicants must be Telugu students who are currently residing in Andhra Pradesh; must have been admitted to a graduate school in a U.S. university; must demonstrate financial need. **Criteria:** Selection will be based on need; merit, grades and recommendations; scores in standardized tests like GRE, TOEFL; reputation of the college/university in India from which the applicant is graduating; reputation of the school in North America in which the applicant is planning to pursue the education; the field of study in which planning higher education; and extracurricular activities.

Funds Avail.: $2,000. **To Apply:** Applicant must complete the following information name, address with pin code and phone number; profession and annual income; name, address, and phone number of parents; professions and annual incomes of parents; net worth of all assets of applicant and parents combined; high school and college educational qualifications and work experience of the applicant (enclose a copy of the transcripts); name, address and phone number of the department and the university in the United States where the applicant intends to enroll. **Contact:** Prasad Choudary Kakarala, 66 Harvest Ln., Tiffin, OH, 44883, USA; Email: prasadkakarala@yahoo.com.

10953 ■ TANA Foundation Graduate Scholarships *(Graduate/Scholarship)*

Purpose: To provide financial support to deserving Telugu students who want to pursue their education in the United States. **Focus:** General studies/Field of study not specified. **Qualif.:** Applicants must be Telugu students who are currently residing in Andhra Pradesh; must have been admitted to a graduate school in a U.S. university; must demonstrate financial need.

Funds Avail.: $2,000. **To Apply:** Applicant must complete the following information name, address with pin code and phone number; profession and annual income; name, address, and phone number of parents; professions and annual incomes of parents; net worth of all assets of applicant and parents combined; high school and college educational qualifications and work experience of the applicant (enclose a copy of the transcripts); name, address and phone number of the department and the university in the United States where the applicant intends to enroll. **Deadline:** September 30. **Contact:** Prasad Choudary Kakarala, 66 Harvest Ln., Tiffin, OH, 44883, USA; Email: prasadkakarala@yahoo.com.

10954 ■ Vallabhaneni Sukundamma & Lakshmaiah Scholarship *(Graduate/Scholarship)*

Purpose: To provide financial support to deserving Telugu students who want to pursue their education in the United

Awards are arranged alphabetically below their administering organizations

States. **Focus:** General studies/Field of study not specified. **Qualif.:** Applicants must be Telugu students who are currently residing in Andhra Pradesh; must have been admitted to a graduate school in a U.S. university; must demonstrate financial need.

Funds Avail.: $2,000. **To Apply:** Applicants must complete the following information name, address with pin code and phone number; profession and annual income; name, address, and phone number of parents; professions and annual incomes of parents; net worth of all assets of applicant and parents combined; high school and college educational qualifications and work experience of the applicant (enclose a copy of the transcripts); name, address and phone number of the department and the university in the United States where the applicant intends to enroll. **Deadline:** Sep 30. **Contact:** Prasad Choudary Kakarala, 66 Harvest Ln., Tiffin, OH, 44883, USA; Email: prasadkakarala@yahoo.com.

10955 ■ Temecula Valley Wine Society (TVWS)
PO Box 890598
Temecula, CA 92589-0598
URL: www.tvwinesociety.org

10956 ■ Nancy Johnston Memorial Scholarships
(Graduate, Undergraduate/Scholarship)

Purpose: To provide financial assistance to students majoring in Enology, Entomology, Viticulture or Wine Marketing. **Focus:** Enology; Entomology; Viticulture. **Qualif.:** Applicants must be upper division and graduate-level students at California Universities, who are majoring in Viticulture, Enology or Wine Marketing; California State College students pursuing two-year certification or A.S. Degrees in Winemaking; previous recipients may apply. **Criteria:** Selection will be based on submitted documents; grade point average; financial need; school and community involvement; work experience; and post-graduation goals.

Funds Avail.: No specific amount. **Duration:** Annual. **To Apply:** Applicants must submit a completed application form; a letter of recommendation from advisor or professor and an official copy of college transcript(s) including high school transcripts for A.S. candidates. **Deadline:** October 28.

10957 ■ Tenge Law Firm LLC
1738 Pearl St., Ste. 300
Boulder, CO 80302
Ph: (303)653-9043
URL: tengelaw.com
Social Media: www.facebook.com/TengeLawFirm
www.instagram.com/tengelawfirmllc
twitter.com/TengeLawFirmLLC
www.youtube.com/user/fortcollinslawyer

10958 ■ Your Time to Climb Scholarship
(Undergraduate/Scholarship)

Purpose: To pay it forward and help a deserving student attend college. **Focus:** General studies/Field of study not specified. **Qualif.:** Applicant must be a high school senior on track to graduate and planning to enroll in college, or a college student enrolled in an accredited four-year college or university, or currently enrolled in a two-year college or university and planning to transfer to a four-year college or university upon completion; have earned or will earn high

school diploma by this school year; have maintained a minimum 3.0 GPA; and are a U.S. citizen or permanent resident (DACA recipients are welcome to apply).

Funds Avail.: $1,000. **Number Awarded:** 1. **To Apply:** Application and essay must be submitted online. **Deadline:** April 28. **Contact:** tengelaw.com/scholarship/.

10959 ■ Tennessee Education Association (TEA)
801 2nd Ave. N
Nashville, TN 37201-1099
Ph: (615)242-8392
Free: 800-342-8367
E-mail: info@teateachers.org
URL: www.teateachers.org
Social Media: www.facebook.com/TennesseeEA
www.instagram.com/tea_teachers
twitter.com/TEA_teachers
www.youtube.com/user/TennesseeEA

10960 ■ Don Sahli-Kathy Woodall Graduate Scholarships *(Graduate/Scholarship)*
Purpose: To provide financial assistance to qualified students who wish to pursue a teaching profession. **Focus:** Teaching. **Qualif.:** Applicants must be students pursuing a degree in the teaching profession; must be involved or have past activities in the United Education Profession. **Criteria:** Selection of applicants will be based on past activities in the United Education Profession and on academic ability, need, leadership and potential as a leader and association leader within the teaching profession.

Funds Avail.: $1,000. **Duration:** Annual. **Number Awarded:** 1. **To Apply:** Applicants must complete the application form available on the website and must be submitted to the TEA Headquarters. **Remarks:** The award was established in honor of Dr. Donald G. Sahli, executive secretary of the Tennessee Education Association. Established in 1971. **Contact:** Tennessee Education Association, 801 Second Ave. N, Nashville, TN, 37201-1099; Phone: 615-242-8392, 800-342-8367.

10961 ■ Sons and Daughters Don Sahli-Kathy Woodall Scholarships *(Graduate, Undergraduate/Scholarship)*
Purpose: To provide financial support to students who wish to pursue a teaching profession. **Focus:** Teaching. **Qualif.:** Applicants must be TEA member's children who are high school seniors, undergraduate or graduate students planning to enroll in a Tennessee college, must major in education. **Criteria:** Selection will be given to students who have demonstrated their commitment to the teaching profession. Applicants will be selected based on academic excellence, leadership, economic need and recommendations.

Funds Avail.: $1,000. **Number Awarded:** 1. **To Apply:** Applicants must complete the application form available on the website; attach two recommendation letters, transcript of record, and a short essay of no more than 200 words on why they want to be a teacher. **Deadline:** March 1. **Remarks:** The award was established in honor of Dr. Donald G. Sahli, executive secretary of the Tennessee Education Association. Established in 1971. **Contact:** Jeanette DeMain, Don Sahli-Kathy Woodall Scholarships, Tennessee Education Association, 801 Second Ave. N, Nashville, TN, 37201-1099.

10962 ■ Terra Foundation for American Art
120 E Erie St.
Chicago, IL 60611

Awards are arranged alphabetically below their administering organizations

Ph: (312)664-3939
Fax: (312)664-2052
E-mail: contact@terraamericanart.org
URL: www.terraamericanart.org
Social Media: www.facebook.com/TerraAmericanArt
instagram.com/terraamericanart
twitter.com/TerraAmArt

10963 ■ Terra Foundation Fellowships at the Smithsonian American Art Museum *(Postdoctorate/Fellowship)*

Purpose: To support full-time independent and dissertation research by scholars from abroad or by US scholars. **Focus:** Arts; History. **Qualif.:** Applicants must be predoctoral, senior or postdoctoral fellows from US or abroad.**Criteria:** Selection will be based on the committee's criteria.

Funds Avail.: $32,700 at the predoctoral level; $48,000 at the postdoctoral and senior levels. **Duration:** Annual. **To Apply:** Applicants must visit the website to fill out an application and must be submitted via email. **Deadline:** November 1. **Contact:** Email: grants@terraamericanart.org.

10964 ■ Terra Foundation Postdoctoral Teaching Fellowships at the Institut National d'Histoire de l'Art, Paris *(Postdoctorate/Fellowship)*

Purpose: To promote education taught in English on the history of American art and transatlantic exchange, and structure a corresponding field of research. **Focus:** Arts; History.

Funds Avail.: No specific amount. **Contact:** Email: grants@terraamericanart.org.

10965 ■ Terra Foundation Research Travel Grants *(Doctorate, Undergraduate/Grant)*

Purpose: To enable scholars outside the United States to consult resources that are only available within the United States. **Focus:** Art. **Qualif.:** Applicants must be doctoral students and scholars who received their degree within ten years of the application deadline, outside the United States.**Criteria:** Selection will be based on the committee's criteria.

Funds Avail.: $6,000-$9,000. **Number Awarded:** Up to 13. **To Apply:** Research travel grant application can be downloaded online. The travel should be undertaken within one calendar year after the announcement of the selection results. The final report must be submitted within three months of completion of travel. The report should include a description of the travel undertaken as a result of the grant, an assessment of the research accomplished and a financial report detailing grant expenditures. **Contact:** Email: grants@terraamericanart.org.

10966 ■ Terra Summer Residency Fellowships *(Master's, Doctorate/Fellowship)*

Purpose: To provide an opportunity for participants to widen their academic and creative horizons, explore international cultural perspectives, and forge lifelong exchanged and professional networks. **Focus:** Arts; History. **Qualif.:** Applicants must be either visual artists with a master's degree or its equivalent at the time of application or doctoral candidates researching American art and visual culture or its role in a context of international artistic exchange prior to 1980. All applicants are expected to be fluent in English. Knowledge of French is desirable but not required. Preference will be given to applicants who have

completed their degree within the past five years. Doctoral candidates should be at an advanced stage of their doctoral research and writing.**Criteria:** Selection will be based on the committee's criteria.

Funds Avail.: A stipend of $5,000. **Duration:** Annual. **Number Awarded:** Up to 2. **To Apply:** Applicants must be nominated by their dissertation advisor, professor, or previous art school supervisor. Each professor may nominate a maximum of two students each year. Selected fellows are required to give a presentation outlining their research/artistic project; attend the seminars/lectures of all senior scholars and artists and other required meetings; and present their accomplishments at the end of the program. Application form can be obtained at the website. **Remarks:** Established in 2001. **Contact:** Email: grants@terraamericanart.org.

10967 ■ TESOL International Association

1925 Ballenger Ave., Ste. 550
Alexandria, VA 22314-6820
Ph: (703)836-0774
Fax: (703)836-7864
Free: 888-891-0041
E-mail: info@tesol.org
URL: www.tesol.org
Social Media: www.facebook.com/tesol.assn
www.instagram.com/tesol_assn
www.linkedin.com/company/tesol-international-association
twitter.com/TESOL_Assn

10968 ■ The Ruth Crymes TESOL Fellowship for Graduate Study *(Graduate/Fellowship, Monetary, Award)*

Purpose: To support current graduate students in the development of projects with direct application to ESOL classroom instruction. **Focus:** Linguistics. **Criteria:** Selection will be based on the merit of the graduate study project; clear goals of graduate studies relevant scholarship and experiences; demonstrated financial need related to completing the graduate study project.

Funds Avail.: $1,500. **Duration:** Annual. **Number Awarded:** 1. **To Apply:** Applicant complete the online application process; letter written by your graduate supervisor; describe your scholarship. **Deadline:** October 1. **Contact:** Email: awards@tesol.org.

10969 ■ The Albert H. Marckwardt Travel Grants *(Graduate, Doctorate/Grant)*

Purpose: To assist graduate students in their travel to the TESOL International Convention and English Language Expo. **Focus:** Linguistics; Teaching. **Qualif.:** Applicants must be TESOL members who are graduate students in TESL/TEFL programs worldwide.

Funds Avail.: $500. **Duration:** Annual. **Number Awarded:** Varies. **To Apply:** Application is via online. Applicants must submit essay/personal statement (1, 000 words), transcript, and one letter of recommendation. **Deadline:** October 1. **Remarks:** The award was established in honor of Mary Finocchiaro, a noted educator, author, and TESOL president. Established in 1976. **Contact:** Email: awards@tesol.org.

10970 ■ The TESOL/TEFL Travel Grant *(Advanced Professional/Grant, Monetary)*

Purpose: To help EFL professionals attend the annual TESOL International Convention & English Language Expo.

Awards are arranged alphabetically below their administering organizations

Focus: Linguistics; Teaching. **Qualif.:** Applicant must be any TESOL member who is a teacher, teacher trainer, supervisor, or who is otherwise engaged in some aspect of teaching English as a foreign language for a minimum of 5 years.

Funds Avail.: $2,500. **Duration:** Annual. **To Apply:** Applicant complete the online application process; letters submitted by the applicant will not be accepted; you can fill out the application completely, and you will not have to go back and fill in items later. **Deadline:** October 1. **Contact:** Email: awards@tesol.org.

10971 ■ Texas Association of Community Schools (TACS)

1011 San Jacinto Blvd., Ste. 204
Austin, TX 78701-2431
Ph: (512)440-8227
Fax: (512)442-6705
URL: www.tacsnet.org
Social Media: www.facebook.com/TexasACS
twitter.com/tacsnet

10972 ■ TACS/A. Bragas and Associates Student Scholarships *(Undergraduate/Scholarship)*

Purpose: To support students and develop excellence in student achievement through the collaboration of member schools. **Focus:** General studies/Field of study not specified. **Qualif.:** Applicants must be high school students whose District is an Institutional Member of TACS.

Funds Avail.: $1,000. **Duration:** Annual. **Number Awarded:** 2. **To Apply:** Applicants may submit their Basic Data Sheet accompanied by a one page letter to the committee, whereby the applicants indicate why they have chosen their career goal and how the scholarship will help them attain that goal; a small picture. **Deadline:** April 1.

10973 ■ TACS/Texas Tech University K-12 *(Undergraduate/Scholarship)*

Purpose: To support outstanding individuals who have the determination to attain their academic goals. **Focus:** General studies/Field of study not specified. **Qualif.:** Applicants must be high school students whose District is an Institutional Member of TACS and who are planning to attend at Texas Tech University for the upcoming school year. **Criteria:** Selection will be based on the committee's criteria.

Funds Avail.: $1,000. **Number Awarded:** 1. **To Apply:** Applicant must send a completed basic data sheet accompanied by one page letter to the committee, whereby the applicant indicates why they have chosen their career goal and how the scholarship will help them attain that goal; must also include a small picture of the applicant. **Deadline:** April 1.

10974 ■ Texas Association of Developing Colleges (TADC)

1140 Empire Central Dr., Ste. 550
Dallas, TX 75247
Ph: (214)630-2511
E-mail: info@txadc.org
URL: www.txadc.org

10975 ■ The Urban Scholarship Fund *(Graduate/Scholarship)*

Purpose: To provide funds for the graduating high school seniors, new and/ or returning college students attending any accredited nonprofit public or independent two or four-year college/university of technical school. **Focus:** General studies/Field of study not specified. **Qualif.:** Applicants must be U.S. citizens; must be Texas residents; must be graduating high school seniors, new and/or returning college students attending any accredited nonprofit public or independent two or four-year college/university or technical school. **Criteria:** Recipients are selected based on financial need.

Funds Avail.: $700 - $2,000. **Duration:** Annual. **To Apply:** Applicants must submit a completed application form and also must include 2018-2019 SAR, High School Transcript, GED Certification, I-551 (Green card = Permanent Resident ID Card) Copy of front and back.

10976 ■ Texas Computer Education Association (TCEA)

3100 Alvin Devane Blvd., Bldg. B
Austin, TX 78741
Ph: (512)476-8500
Fax: (512)476-8574
Free: 800-282-8232
E-mail: tceaoffice@tcea.org
URL: www.tcea.org
Social Media: www.facebook.com/tcea.org
twitter.com/tcea

10977 ■ Richard A. Brown Student Scholarship *(Undergraduate/Scholarship)*

Purpose: To provide support to deserving students who are pursuing a career in technology in education. **Focus:** Computer and information sciences; Education. **Qualif.:** Applicants must be full time students at an accredited college/university (12 hours or more); have successfully completed at least 24 hours of college; pursuing a career in education; have a cumulative GPA of at least 2.75 on a scale of 4.0; and have not previously received the scholarship. **Criteria:** Selection will be based on the submitted application materials.

Funds Avail.: $1,000. **Duration:** Annual. **To Apply:** Applicants must submit a completed Scholarship Entry Form together with a statement of personal and family information including financial need, if any; three letters of recommendation (not to exceed one page); a copy of college transcript to date; and a one page personal profile.

10978 ■ Jeri Hodges Leadership Scholarship *(Professional development/Scholarship)*

Purpose: To encourage and enhance learning and professional growth in educational technology for practicing and pre-service educators. **Focus:** Computer and information sciences; Education. **Qualif.:** Applicants must be a member of TCEA (non-members may submit membership and dues at the time of entry); be employed full time in the field of education; use the money to attend professional development activities that will increase knowledge of educational technology; and have not received the scholarship previously. **Criteria:** Selection is based on the submitted application materials.

Funds Avail.: $500. **Duration:** Annual. **To Apply:** Applicants must submit a completed Scholarship Entry Form together with two letters of recommendation (not to exceed one page), and a one page personal profile; each entry form must be accompanied with four copies of the supporting documents.

Awards are arranged alphabetically below their administering organizations

10979 ■ Robert E. Knight Professional Scholarship
(Graduate/Scholarship)

Purpose: To support and assist practicing educators in achieving a higher education degree in the field of educational or instructional technology. **Focus:** Computer and information sciences; Education. **Qualif.:** Applicants must be members of TCEA (non-members may submit membership and dues at the time of entry); must be employed full time in the field of education. **Criteria:** Selection is based on the submitted application materials.

Funds Avail.: $1,000. **Duration:** Annual. **Number Awarded:** 1. **To Apply:** Applicants must submit a completed Scholarship Entry Form along with two letters of recommendation (not to exceed one page); a one page personal profile; and proof of enrollment in master's or doctoral program in the field of educational technology; College transcript that indicates major. **Remarks:** Established in 2007.

10980 ■ Texas Counseling Association (TCA)
1204 San Antonio St., Ste. 201
Austin, TX 78701
Ph: (512)472-3403
Fax: (512)472-3756
Free: 800-580-8144
URL: www.txca.org
Social Media: www.facebook.com/
  TexasCounselingAssociation
www.linkedin.com/company/texas-counseling-association
twitter.com/TxCAtweets

10981 ■ TCA Outstanding Graduate Student Award
(Graduate/Award)

Purpose: To support graduate students who are showing dedication and academic excellence in the theory and practice of some significant area of counseling and exhibiting outstanding scholarships. **Focus:** Counseling/Guidance. **Qualif.:** Applicants must be students pursuing graduate degrees in counseling; must have compiled an outstanding academic record of their graduate studies in some significant area of counseling; must demonstrate a commitment to issue of counseling. **Criteria:** Selection will be based on academic excellence and commitment to the advancement of the profession of counseling.

Funds Avail.: No specific amount. **Duration:** Annual. **To Apply:** Applicants must have their work submitted by a colleague or professor or applicants may submit nominations on their behalf; nomination submissions include nomination form. **Contact:** Phone: 512-472-3403; Tollfree: 800-580-8144; Fax: 512-472-3756.

10982 ■ Texas Health Information Management Association (TXHIMA)
PO Box 1027
Leander, TX 78646
Ph: (512)540-4441
Fax: (512)692-2651
E-mail: txhima@txhima.org
URL: www.txhima.org
Social Media: www.facebook.com/
  TexasHealthInformationManagementAssociation/
www.linkedin.com/groups/2326865/profile
twitter.com/TxHIMA14ED

Awards are arranged alphabetically below their administering organizations

10983 ■ Evelyn L. Cockrell Memorial Scholarship
(Undergraduate/Scholarship)

Purpose: To support the professional development of individuals engaged in the study of health information technology or health information management. **Focus:** Health education. **Qualif.:** Applicants must be active student members of AHIMA with TxHIMA membership; citizens of the United States or hold resident status in the United States; and, enrolled in an AHIMA accredited educational program pursuing an HIT or HIA degree which leads to the RHIT or RHIA certification. **Criteria:** Selection will be based on the essay, 50 points (content, writing style, grammar, spelling, and punctuation) and financial need, 50 points.

Funds Avail.: No specific amount. **Duration:** Annual. **To Apply:** Applicants must complete and submit the application form; must provide a copy of official transcript or a copy of high school transcript if a first semester freshman; must have two (2) individuals to complete a letter of recommendation. One letter must be from an educational advisor or professor while the other letter of recommendation must also address perceived financial need of the student and how receiving this scholarship will benefit the student to continue their health information education; must submit an essay of 350-400 words about personal goals and how the scholarship money will help them to reach the goals. Enclose one current digital photograph which will be published with the winner's name at the discretion of the Board of Directors; the photograph will not be circulated to the Board of Directors until the recipient has been chosen; sign and date each item on the agreement form. **Deadline:** April 26.

10984 ■ TxHIMA HIA-HIT Scholarship
(Undergraduate/Scholarship)

Purpose: To support the professional development of individuals engaged in the undergraduate study of health information technology or health information management. **Focus:** Health education. **Qualif.:** Applicants must be active student members of AHIMA with TxHIMA membership; be residents of the state of Texas for at least one year; be citizens of U.S. or hold permanent resident status in the said country; have a major of Health Information Administration or Technology and a minimum GPA of 3.5 (on a 4.00 scale) in that major and a minimum cumulative GPA of 3.5 on a 4.0 scale. **Criteria:** Nominations are solicited from the Program Directors of each Texas school and voted on by the TxHIMA Board of Directors.

Funds Avail.: No specific amount. **Duration:** Annual. **Number Awarded:** 2. **To Apply:** Applicants must complete and submit the application form together with their college transcript and letters of recommendation; applicants must obtain the signature of the Program Director for the purpose of eligibility to apply for the scholarship; must submit their essay of 500 words or less, on a separate sheet of paper, on how they will use the scholarship money and why they feel they deserve it and must discuss what personal attributes, training, experience or goals that will make them an asset to the health information management profession; at the bottom of the essay in own handwriting, write the following statement: "This essay is my work and has not been written, composed, or edited for me by anyone." plus the signature and date the statement; lastly is current wallet-size photo for use in the TxHIMA Journal and the photo will not be shared with the Board of Directors until after the recipients have been selected; submitted online via online application form. **Deadline:** April 26.

10985 ■ TxHIMA Outstanding Student Scholarship (Undergraduate/Scholarship)

Purpose: To identify and honor an outstanding Health Information Technology and Health Information Administration student in Texas. **Focus:** Health education; Health services administration. **Qualif.:** Applicants must be graduating students in the last year of a HIA or HIT program; must have an overall cumulative grade point average (GPA) minimum of 3.0. and an overall major GPA of 3.5; must be full-time students in a health information program (12-semester hours minimum); TxHIMA Active Student membership (AHIMA member designating Texas as your Component State Association); Texas residency (minimum 1 year) prior to application; U.S. citizen or permanent resident status. **Criteria:** Selection will be based on the following criteria: leadership (35 points); scholarship (40 points); student essay (500 words - 25 points).

Funds Avail.: No specific amount. **Duration:** Annual. **To Apply:** Applicants must visit the website for the online application process and must submit the following requirements: at least two (2) letters of recommendation written by a faculty member, clinical site sponsor, co-worker or peer. One letter of recommendation must be written by the Program Director; a certified transcript of grades to be submitted with the online nomination form; a wallet size photo for recognition in the TxHIMA Newsletter and website. **Deadline:** April 26.

10986 ■ Texas Music Educators Association (TMEA)
7900 Centre Park Dr.
Austin, TX 78754
Ph: (512)452-0710
Fax: (512)451-9213
E-mail: zgersch@tmea.org
URL: www.tmea.org
Social Media: www.facebook.com/tmea.org
twitter.com/TMEA

10987 ■ Bill Cormack Scholarships (Undergraduate/Scholarship)

Purpose: To provide professional growth opportunities; to encourage interaction among music education professionals; to foster public support for music in school; to offer quality musical experiences for students; to cultivate universal appreciation and lifetime involvement in music; to develop and maintain productive working relationships with other professional organizations. **Focus:** Music. **Qualif.:** Applicants must be entering freshmen in a Texas college or university; must major in a music degree program leading to Texas teacher-certification with music as the primary teaching field. **Criteria:** Recipients are selected based on academic performance.

Funds Avail.: $3,000 per year for up to five years. **To Apply:** Applicants must submit: completed application form; a high school transcript; a one-to-two page essay that describes their reasons for becoming a teacher, commitment to music education and future career goals; three-to-five evaluations from individuals who can assess the applicant's potential for success in an undergraduate music education program and as a music educator, music skills and abilities, work ethic and other personal qualities; must submit a verification from student's advisor that the applicants will teach within the semester indicated on the application. **Deadline:** November 1.

10988 ■ Texas Music Educators Association Past-Presidents Memorial Scholarships (Undergraduate/Scholarship)

Purpose: To provide professional growth opportunities; to encourage interaction among music education professionals; to foster public support for music in school; to offer quality musical experiences for students; to cultivate universal appreciation and lifetime involvement in music; to develop and maintain productive working relationships with other professional organizations. **Focus:** Music. **Qualif.:** Applicants must be entering freshmen at a Texas college or university; must major in a music degree program leading to Texas teacher-certification with music as the primary teaching field. **Criteria:** Recipients are selected based on academic performance.

Funds Avail.: $2,500 per year for up to five years. **Duration:** Annual. **To Apply:** Applicants must submit: completed application form; high school transcript; a one-to-two-page essay that describes their reasons for becoming a teacher, commitment to music education and future career goals; three-to-five evaluations from individuals who can assess the applicant's potential for success in an undergraduate music education program and as a music educator, music skills and abilities, work ethic and other personal qualities; must submit a verification by student's advisor that the applicants will teach within the semester indicated on the application. **Deadline:** November 1.

10989 ■ Texas Mutual Insurance Co.
2200 Aldrich St.
Austin, TX 78723-3474
Ph: (512)224-3800
Fax: (800)359-0650
Free: 800-859-5995
E-mail: information@texasmutual.com
URL: www.texasmutual.com
Social Media: www.facebook.com/texasmutual
www.instagram.com/texasmutual
twitter.com/texasmutual
www.youtube.com/user/TexasMutual

10990 ■ Texas Mutual Scholarship Program (Undergraduate, Vocational/Occupational/Scholarship)

Purpose: To provide financial support for the surviving family members of employees who died from an on-the-job accident, and/or whose injuries qualify for lifetime income benefits, to have the chance to pursue education and training to help them build better futures. **Focus:** Education, Vocational-technical. **Criteria:** Selection will be based on the committee's criteria.

Funds Avail.: Up to $6,000 for tuition and up to $600 for course-related books and supplies. **Duration:** Annual. **To Apply:** Applicants must complete the application form available at the website of Texas Mutual Insurance Company; must include latest high school transcript of grades or college/technical school transcripts (if attended); letter of admission if entering freshman; letters of recommendation (optional); standardized test scores for college admission (SAT or ACT); detailed report of any financial aid awarded. **Deadline:** October 31. **Contact:** Texas Mutual Insurance Company, Office of the President, 6210 E Hwy. 290, Austin, Texas, 78723-1098.

10991 ■ Texas Society of Professional Engineers (TSPE)
1001 Congress Ave., Ste. 260
Austin, TX 78701

Awards are arranged alphabetically below their administering organizations

Ph: (512)472-9286
Free: 800-580-8973
E-mail: info@tspe.org
URL: www.tspe.org
Social Media: www.facebook.com/TSPEHQ
twitter.com/TSPE_HQ
www.youtube.com/user/TSPEVideo

10992 ■ Graduating Texas High School Seniors Scholarship *(Undergraduate/Scholarship)*

Purpose: To provide financial assistance to students studying to become engineers in an engineering program at an ABET-accredited college or university. **Focus:** Engineering. **Qualif.:** Applicants must be United States citizens; must be high school seniors with a 3.0 or higher GPA entering college in the coming school year; must have scored at least 600 in math, 550 in critical reading and 500 in writing on the SAT or a 29 in math and 25 in English on the ACT; and enrolled in an ABET program. **Criteria:** Selection are evaluated based on academic performance, achievements, leadership, and career goals.

Funds Avail.: No specific amount. **To Apply:** Applicants must submit the completed application form; essay; two recommendations from non-relatives (high school teachers preferred); and an official transcript; SAT or ACT scores; additional information as required by your Chapter Scholarship Coordinator. **Deadline:** January 19. **Contact:** Please call local Scholarship Coordinator or Nancy Rierson; Email: nancy@tspe.org.

10993 ■ Texas Space Grant Consortium

3925 W Braker Ln., Ste. 200
Austin, TX 78759
Fax: (512)471-3585
Free: 800-248-8742
E-mail: jurgens@tsgc.utexas.edu
URL: tsgc.utexas.edu
Social Media: www.facebook.com/NASATexasSpaceGrant
twitter.com/TexasSpaceGrant

10994 ■ TSGC Graduate Fellowships *(Graduate/Fellowship)*

Purpose: To encourage students to study in the fields of space science and engineering. **Focus:** Aerospace sciences. **Qualif.:** Applicants must be citizens of the United States; must be registered for full-time study in a graduate program at one (or more) of the consortium institutions; must be promised financial support at that institution, and must not have exceeded the time limit described under "duration". **Criteria:** Selection will be based competitive basis with consideration of excellence in academics; interest in space; recommendations from the institution.

Funds Avail.: $5,000. **Duration:** Annual. **To Apply:** Applications can be submitted online; must submit one online letter of recommendation; transcripts from all universities attended. **Deadline:** April 24.

10995 ■ Texas State Historical Association (TSHA)

3001 Lake Austin Blvd.
Austin, TX 78703
Ph: (512)471-2600
URL: tshaonline.org

Social Media: facebook.com/
  TexasStateHistoricalAssociation
twitter.com/txsthistassoc

10996 ■ Catarino and Evangelina Hernández Research Fellowships in Latino History *(Advanced Professional/Fellowship)*

Purpose: To provide support for the research proposal relating to the history of Latinos in Texas. **Focus:** Latin American studies. **Qualif.:** Applicants must have a research proposal relating to the history of Latinos in Texas State. **Criteria:** Recipients will be selected based on submitted research proposal.

Funds Avail.: $1,000. **Duration:** Annual. **Number Awarded:** 1. **To Apply:** Applicants must submit a complete vita electronically and four copies of the research proposal; application should specify the purpose of the research, the need for money and description of the end product. **Deadline:** October 15. **Contact:** amawards@tshaonline.org or call 512-471-2600.

10997 ■ Mary M. Hughes Research Fellowships in Texas History *(Professional development/Fellowship)*

Purpose: To assist individuals doing research relating to Texas history. **Focus:** History. **Qualif.:** Applicants must be individuals who have a research proposal on twentieth-century Texas history. **Criteria:** Recipients will be chosen based on submitted materials.

Funds Avail.: $2,000. **Duration:** Annual. **Number Awarded:** 1. **To Apply:** Applicants must include a complete vita and four copies of the research proposal; application should be no longer than one page, should specify the purpose of the research, the need for money and description of the end product. **Deadline:** October 15. **Remarks:** The fellowship was established by the thirteen children of Mary M. Hughes, to celebrate their mother's eighty-ninth birthday and her fiftieth year in Texas. **Contact:** Awards coordinator at AMawards@TSHAonline.org, 512-471-2600 or visit www.tshaonline.org.

10998 ■ John H. Jenkins Research Fellowships in Texas History *(Professional development/Fellowship)*

Purpose: To assist individuals doing research having to do with Texas history. **Focus:** History. **Qualif.:** Applicants must have a research proposal relating to Texas history. **Criteria:** Selection will be evaluated based on submitted research proposal.

Funds Avail.: $1,000. **Duration:** Annual. **Number Awarded:** 1. **To Apply:** Applicants must submit Individuals wishing to apply should submit an application form (and attach the proposal and a curriculum vita) electronic copies submitted through the above link; trouble submitting the form electronically. **Deadline:** October 15. **Remarks:** The fellowship was established to honor Mr. Jenkins for all that he accomplished on behalf of Texas history as an author, editor, bookseller, and Fellow and member of the Executive Council of the Texas State Historical Association. Established in 1994. **Contact:** Jenkins Research Fellowship Committee, Texas State Historical Association, 3001 Lake Austin Blvd., Ste. 3.116, Austin, TX 78703; Email: email us at: amawards@tshaonline.org.

10999 ■ Mary Jon and J. P. Bryan Leadership in Education Awards *(Advanced Professional/Award)*

Purpose: To recognize outstanding teachers in Texas. **Focus:** History; Teaching. **Qualif.:** Applicants must be full-

Awards are arranged alphabetically below their administering organizations

time teachers at the middle school, high school or college levels presently teaching history in a Texas school or college. **Criteria:** Preference will be given to applicants who best meet the judge's criteria and based on submitted materials.

Funds Avail.: $5,000. **Duration:** Annual. **To Apply:** Applicants must submit resume or curriculum vitae, a list of activities and accomplishments, awards/honors, publications, and description of programs. **Deadline:** December 8. **Remarks:** Established in 1985. **Contact:** Chairman, Mary Jon and J. P. Bryan, Leadership in Education Award, Texas State Historical Association, 3001 Lake Austin Blvd., Ste. 3.116, Austin, TX, 78703.

11000 ■ Cecilia Steinfeldt Fellowships for Research in the Arts and Material Culture (Professional development/Fellowship)

Purpose: To support research proposal in Arts and Material Culture. **Focus:** Art. **Qualif.:** Applicants must have a research proposal on decorative and fine arts, material culture, preservation and architecture in Texas from the seventh century to present. **Criteria:** Recipients will be given to individuals whose respective research proposals best meet the judge's criteria.

Funds Avail.: $1,000. **Duration:** Annual. **Number Awarded:** 1. **To Apply:** Applicants should submit an entry form, four (4) copies of vita, and four (4) copies of a proposal to the TSHA office by the fixed deadline. **Deadline:** October 15. **Remarks:** The fellowship was established to honor Cecilia Steinfeldt, the longtime curator of the Witte Museum of San Antonio, in recognition of her lifelong scholarly devotion to the arts in Texas. Established in 1996. **Contact:** coordinator, AMawards@TSHAonline.org; Phone:512-471-2600Email: amawards@tshaonline.org.

11001 ■ Texas Telephone Association (TTA)
7004 Bee Caves Rd., Bldg. 1, Ste. 100
Austin, TX 78746
Ph: (512)472-1183
Fax: (512)472-1293
E-mail: joannkam@tta.org
URL: www.tta.org
Social Media: www.facebook.com/texastelephone
www.linkedin.com/company/texas-telephone-association
twitter.com/Telecom4Texas

11002 ■ Texas Telephone Association Foundation Scholarships (Undergraduate/Scholarship)

Purpose: To provide financial assistance to those students with financial hardship. **Focus:** General studies/Field of study not specified. **Qualif.:** Applicants must be U.S citizens; must have earned a cumulative GPA of 3.0 or higher; must plan to attend a Texas college or university; must be graduating from a Texas high school. **Criteria:** Special consideration will be given to students who will be pursuing a college degree in fields of study relevant to telecommunications (math, business, engineering, and computer science).

Funds Avail.: $2,000. **Duration:** Quadrennial; up to four years. **Number Awarded:** 6. **To Apply:** Applicants must submit completed application; application must include a current transcript; a letter of acceptance from a Texas college or university; a copy of student's SAR (Student Aid Report). **Deadline:** April 10. **Contact:** Joann Kamerman; E-mail: joannkam@tta.org; Phone: 512- 472-1183.

11003 ■ Textile Care Allied Trades Association (TCATA)
27251 Wesley Chapel Blvd. Ste.,311
Wesley Chapel, FL 33544
Ph: (813)348-0075
URL: www.tcata.org
Social Media: www.facebook.com/TCATANJ
twitter.com/TextileCare

11004 ■ TCATA College Scholarship Fund (Undergraduate/Scholarship)

Purpose: To provide financial support for students interested in pursuing a degree at any accredited U.S. college or university on a full-time basis. **Focus:** General studies/Field of study not specified. **Criteria:** Selection will be selected based on academic achievement, leadership qualities and courses of study.

Funds Avail.: $2,000. **Duration:** Annual; up to four years. **To Apply:** Applicants must complete an application form and provide a copy of Scholarship Aptitude Test (SAT) or American College Test (ACT) scores; transcripts of all high school grades and any college grades if applicable; a letter from their high school principal - or other highest official equivalent - describing their leadership qualities, extra-curricular activities and other relevant information; and a letter describing past personal accomplishments, immediate goals and future academic and career objectives. **Deadline:** April 30. **Remarks:** Established in 1980. **Contact:** TCATA College Scholarship Program; 27251, Wesley Chapel Blvd., Ste. 311, Wesley Chapel, FL, 33544; Phone: 813-348-0075; fax: 813-348-0077.

11005 ■ ThanksUSA
1390 Chain Bridge Rd., Ste. 260
McLean, VA 22101
Free: 888-849-8720
E-mail: amandafolks@thanksusa.org
URL: www.thanksusa.org
Social Media: www.facebook.com/ThanksUSAorg
www.instagram.com/thanksusa
www.linkedin.com/company/thanksusa
twitter.com/ThanksUSA

11006 ■ ThanksUSA Scholarship (Undergraduate, Vocational/Occupational/Scholarship)

Purpose: To support the dependents and spouses of active duty U.S. military service personnel with their educational pursuits. **Focus:** General studies/Field of study not specified. **Criteria:** Recipients are selected based on financial need, academic record and demonstrated leadership and participation in school and community activities; preference is given to children or spouses of service personnel killed or injured during active duty.

Duration: Annual. **To Apply:** Applications can be submitted online; current and complete transcript of grades; unofficial and online transcripts must display student name, school name, grades and credit hours; photo; minimum 202x288 pixels, maximum 384x576 pixels (file size 2 mb or less); copy of current nursing license; copy of earned associate's degree. **Deadline:** April 15. **Contact:** Phone: 507-931-8209; Email: thanksusa@scholarshipamerica.org.

11007 ■ Theatre Communications Group (TCG)
520 8th Ave., 24th Fl.
New York, NY 10018-4156

Awards are arranged alphabetically below their administering organizations

E-mail: custserv@tcg.org
URL: www.tcg.org
Social Media: www.facebook.com/tcg.org
www.instagram.com/tcg_gram
twitter.com/tcg
www.youtube.com/user/IAmTheatre

11008 ■ NEA/TCG Career Development Program for Designers *(Professional development/Grant)*

Purpose: To provide financial support and creative opportunities to exceptional early-career scenic-lighting, costume and sound designers who seek a career in America's not-for-profit professional theatre. **Focus:** Theater arts. **Qualif.:** Applicants must be early-career theater designers.

Funds Avail.: $25,000. **Duration:** Annual. **Number Awarded:** 6. **Contact:** Jessica Lewis, Artistic Programs Project Coordinator; Email: jlewis@tcg.org.

11009 ■ NEA/TCG Career Development Program *(Professional development/Grant)*

Purpose: To provide financial support and creative opportunities to exceptional early-career stage directors who seek a career in America's not-for-profit professional theatre. **Focus:** Theater arts. **Qualif.:** Applicants must be early-career theatre directors. **Criteria:** Selection will be based on the committee criteria.

Funds Avail.: $25,000. **Duration:** Annual; up to two years. **Number Awarded:** 6. **Contact:** Email:webmgr@arts.gov.

11010 ■ Alan Schneider Director Award *(Professional development/Award, Grant)*

Purpose: To assist exceptional directors whose talent has been demonstrated through work in specific regions, but who are not known nationally. **Focus:** Theater arts.

Funds Avail.: $7,500. **Duration:** Periodic. **To Apply:** Nominees must submit application materials and two letters of recommendation, on their behalf. The letter must address why the nominee is a strong candidate for the Alan Schneider Director Award. Recommenders MUST submit their letters directly to TCG by email. **Deadline:** December 10. **Remarks:** The award was named in the honor of Alan Schneider. **Contact:** Email: artisticprograms@tcg.org.

11011 ■ Theatre Guild of Simsbury (TGS)
PO Box 92
Simsbury, CT 06070
E-mail: theatreguildsimsbury@gmail.com
URL: www.theatreguildsimsbury.org

11012 ■ Theatre Guild Scholarship *(Undergraduate/Scholarship)*

Purpose: To support high school students who are excellent in performing arts. **Focus:** Performing arts; Theater arts. **Qualif.:** Applicant must be a graduating senior of Simsbury High School who has demonstrated excellence in the performing arts.

Funds Avail.: No specific amount. **Duration:** Annual.

11013 ■ Theatre for Young Audiences USA (TYA/USA)
c/o New York City Children's Theater
340 E 46th St.
New York, NY 10017

Ph: (917)438-7010
E-mail: info@tyausa.org
URL: www.tyausa.org

11014 ■ The Ann Shaw International TYA Fellowship *(Professional development/Fellowship)*

Purpose: To support career development opportunities for theater artists and administrators committed to Theatre for Young Audiences. **Focus:** Theater arts. **Qualif.:** Applicants must be active ASSITEJ/USA members.

Funds Avail.: $3,000. **Duration:** Annual. **Number Awarded:** Varies. **To Apply:** Applicants submit a proposal for a research and discovery trip that will advance their understanding of the TYA field; Proposals may include meetings with practitioners, observation of work in action, attendance to a festival, or other possible activities. **Deadline:** February 14. **Remarks:** Established in 1996. **Contact:** TYA/USA; Email: info@tyausa.org.

11015 ■ Thermo Fisher Scientific Inc.
168 Third Ave.
Waltham, MA 02451
Free: 800-678-5599
URL: www.thermofisher.com
Social Media: www.facebook.com/ThermoFisher
www.linkedin.com/company/thermo-fisher-scientific
twitter.com/ThermoFisher

11016 ■ Thermo Fisher Scientific Antibody Scholarship *(Undergraduate, Graduate/Scholarship)*

Purpose: To provide educational opportunities to students in the life sciences. **Focus:** Biochemistry; Biology; Chemistry; Life sciences. **Qualif.:** Applicant must be a legal resident of the United States (student visa holders are eligible) and be at least 18 years old; must have a declared major of biology, chemistry, biochemistry, or related life science field; must have a cumulative GPA of at least 3.0; must be an undergraduate or graduate student at an accredited U.S. college or university. **Criteria:** Committee will select recipients who best fit one or more or the sponsor's values of integrity, intensity, innovation, or involvement.

Funds Avail.: $10,000 (1 award); $5,000 (5 awards). **Number Awarded:** 6. **To Apply:** Application is available online at www.thermofisher.com/AntibodyScholarship. **Deadline:** May 5. **Contact:** Email: AntibodyScholarship@thermofisher.com.

11017 ■ J. Walter Thompson Co.
466 Lexington Ave.
New York, NY 10017-3140
Ph: (212)210-7000
URL: www.jwt.com
Social Media: www.facebook.com/JWTWorldwide
www.instagram.com/wunthompson
www.linkedin.com/company/jwt
twitter.com/JWT_Worldwide
www.youtube.com/user/JWTWorldwide/featured

11018 ■ Helen Lansdowne Resor Scholarship *(Undergraduate, Graduate, Other/Scholarship)*

Purpose: To support creative female students. **Focus:** Art; Design; Filmmaking; Sculpture. **Qualif.:** Applicant must be a "badass" woman studying creativity; must be a registered

Awards are arranged alphabetically below their administering organizations

student in an undergraduate, graduate, or portfolio program; must show creative talent and potential in a course of study like art direction, copywriting, design, experimental design, sculpture, film, etc.; must maintain satisfactory academic and creative progress as determined by the school.

Funds Avail.: Up to $10,000. **Duration:** Varies; through completeion of recipient's degree. **Number Awarded:** 5. **To Apply:** Applicant must submit application form, personal statement, letter of recommendation, and 35 creative samples. **Deadline:** May 14. **Contact:** Email: hirscholarship@jwt.com.

11019 ■ Thunder Bay Community Foundation (TBCF)

The Chapple Bldg., Ste. 312-101 N Syndicate Ave.
Thunder Bay, ON, Canada P7C 3V4
Ph: (807)475-7279
Fax: (807)684-0793
URL: www.tbcf.org
Social Media: www.facebook.com/TBayCF
twitter.com/tbaycf?lang=en
www.youtube.com/channel/UCUu4ZUi
  -23W1c0YLPs7poCA

11020 ■ Helen L. Dewar Scholarship *(Undergraduate/ Scholarship)*

Purpose: To provide scholarship assistance to qualified graduating students from Northward School. **Focus:** General studies/Field of study not specified. **Criteria:** Selection will be based on academic performance, involvement in school and community activities, reference letter and the response to the essay question.

Funds Avail.: Varies. **Number Awarded:** Varies. **To Apply:** Applicants must submit three copies and one original of each application, stapled and 3 hole-punched including include wet or original signature; volunteer activities form; extracurricular activities form; work experience form; one reference from an adult in the community using the criteria in the reference letter details form; essay on why the applicant chose the particular field of study; high school transcript along with this semester's mid-term marks (submitted by the guidance Counsellor); students may not apply directly to the Foundation for this scholarship but to their school's Student Services. **Deadline:** April 14. **Remarks:** The Scholarship was established in honor of Miss Helen Lilodah Dewar. Established in 1991. **Contact:** Thunder Bay Community Foundation, Ste. 312, 101 Syndicate Ave., Thunder Bay, ON, P7C 3V4; Phone: 807-475-7279.

11021 ■ Joshua Dyke Family Scholarship *(Undergraduate/Scholarship)*

Purpose: To provide scholarship assistance to qualified graduating students from South Ward, Dennis Franklin Cromarty, Sir Winston Churchill, St. Patrick, and Westgate Schools. **Focus:** General studies/Field of study not specified. **Criteria:** Selection will be based on academic performance, involvement in school and community activities, reference letter and the response to the essay question.

Funds Avail.: Varies. **Duration:** Annual. **Number Awarded:** Varies. **To Apply:** Applicants must submit three copies and one original of each application, stapled and 3 hole-punched including include wet or original signature; volunteer activities form; extracurricular activities form; work experience form; one reference from an adult in the com-

munity using the criteria in the reference letter details form; essay on why the applicant chose the particular field of study; high school transcript along with this semester's mid-term marks (submitted by the guidance Counsellor); students may not apply directly to the Foundation for this scholarship but to their school's Student Services. **Deadline:** April 12. **Remarks:** The Scholarship was established in honor of late Rev. Joshua Dyke by Mrs. Edith Dyke. **Contact:** Thunder Bay Community Foundation, Ste. 312, 101 Syndicate Ave., Thunder Bay, ON, P7C 3V4; Phone: 807-475-7279.

11022 ■ John Alexander McLean Scholarship *(Undergraduate/Scholarship)*

Purpose: To provide scholarship assistance to qualified graduating students from the Bachelor of Education program at Lakehead University. **Focus:** Education.

Funds Avail.: Varies. **Number Awarded:** 1. **Deadline:** April 14. **Remarks:** The Scholarship was established by Thunder Bay Community Foundation received a bequest from Ms. Jean Elizabeth McLean to create a scholarship in memory of her late husband. Established in 2001. **Contact:** Thunder Bay Community Foundation, Ste. 312, 101 Syndicate Ave., Thunder Bay, ON, P7C 3V4; Phone: 807-475-7279.

11023 ■ Roy Seymour Rogers and Geraldine Ruth Rogers Scholarship *(Undergraduate/Scholarship)*

Purpose: To provide scholarship assistance to qualified graduating students from Geraldton Composite, Ecole secondaire chateau jeunesse, Lake Superior, Long Lac 58 First Nation, Manitouwadge, Marathon, and Nipigon-Red Rock District High School. **Focus:** General studies/Field of study not specified. **Criteria:** Selection will be based on academic performance, involvement in school and community activities, reference letter and the response to the essay question.

Funds Avail.: Varies. **Number Awarded:** 2. **To Apply:** Applicants must submit three copies and one original of each application, stapled and 3 hole-punched including include wet or original signature; volunteer activities form; extracurricular activities form; work experience form; one reference from an adult in the community using the criteria in the reference letter details form; essay on why the applicant chose the particular field of study; high school transcript along with this semester's mid-term marks (submitted by the guidance Counsellor); students may not apply directly to the Foundation for this scholarship but to their school's Student Services. **Deadline:** April 12. **Remarks:** The Scholarship was established in honor of Ms. Geraldine Ruth Rogers. Established in 2006. **Contact:** Thunder Bay Community Foundation, Ste. 312, 101 Syndicate Ave., Thunder Bay, ON, P7C 3V4; Phone: 807-475-7279.

11024 ■ Ross A. Wilson Science Scholarship *(Undergraduate/Scholarship)*

Purpose: To provide scholarship assistance to qualified graduating students at Hammarskjold High School who excel in science. **Focus:** Science. **Criteria:** Selection will be based on academic performance, involvement in school and community activities, reference letter and the response to the essay question.

Funds Avail.: Varies. **Number Awarded:** 2. **To Apply:** Applicants must submit three copies and one original of each application, stapled and 3 hole-punched including include wet or original signature; volunteer activities form; extracurricular activities form; work experience form; one reference from an adult in the community using the criteria in the

---

Awards are arranged alphabetically below their administering organizations

reference letter details form; essay on why the applicant chose the particular field of study; high school transcript along with this semester's mid-term marks (submitted by the guidance Counsellor); students may not apply directly to the Foundation for this scholarship but to their school's Student Services. **Deadline:** April 16. **Remarks:** Established in 2005. **Contact:** Thunder Bay Community Foundation, Ste. 312, 101 Syndicate Ave., Thunder Bay, ON, P7C 3V4; Phone: 807-475-7279.

11025 ■ Thurgood Marshall College Fund (TMCF)
901 F St. NW, Ste. 300
Washington, DC 20004
Ph: (202)507-4851
Fax: (202)652-2934
E-mail: info@tmcf.org
URL: tmcf.org
Social Media: www.facebook.com/
   ThurgoodMarshallCollegeFund
instagram.com/tmcf_hbcu
twitter.com/tmcf_hbcu
youtube.com/tmcftv1

11026 ■ McDonald's Inspiration Celebration Scholarship *(Undergraduate, Graduate/Scholarship)*

Purpose: To provide students seeking financial assistance to complete their education. **Focus:** General studies/Field of study not specified. **Qualif.:** Applicants must be 18 years or older; must be current undergraduate or graduate student; must be full-time student at one of TMCF's 47 member-schools; grade point average of 3.0 or higher; must have demonstrated involvement in music performance; education through a relevant music major and/or participation in band or similar musical activity. **Criteria:** Recipients will be evaluated based on their merit and financial need. In addition, the scholarship application process is highly competitive and most awards are limited to students attending TMCF member-schools, which are public Historically Black Colleges and Universities.

Funds Avail.: $10,000 for tuition, on-campus room, board. **Duration:** One semester. **To Apply:** Applicants must submit resume; college transcript (unofficial or official); Student Aid Report; essay in a minimum of 500 words in music. **Deadline:** June 17. **Contact:** Deshuandra Walker; E-mail: deshuandra.walker@tmcf.org.

11027 ■ Tidwell Law Firm
815 T L Townsend Dr., 106
Rockwall, TX 75087
Ph: (972)234-8208
URL: jerrytidwell.com

11028 ■ The Exoneration Education Initiative *(Undergraduate/Scholarship)*

Purpose: To encourage students to pursue a career in defense law and reclaim the rights of wrongfully convicted individuals. **Focus:** Law. **Qualif.:** Applicant must be either a graduating high school senior enrolling, or an undergraduate student currently enrolled, in a college, trade school, or university for the fall semester. Applicant must reside in the United States and plan to study in the United States. **Criteria:** Selection will be based on the best essay submitted.

Funds Avail.: $2,500. **Number Awarded:** 1. **To Apply:** Applicant must write an essay (500 words minimum) detail-

ing the case of a wrongfully accused individual who was released or is still imprisoned that inspired them to pursue a career in defense law. Applicants are encouraged to outline the case in a detailed way and artfully describe how it led them to choose a career in law. Essay should be submitted via email. **Deadline:** July 31. **Contact:** Jerry Tidwell; Email: jerry@jerrytidwell.com; URL: www.jerrytidwell.com/scholarship/.

11029 ■ Tiftickjian Law Firm, P.C.
1315 S. Clayton Street, Ste 100
Denver, CO 80210
Ph: (303)991-5896
URL: www.criminallawdenver.com
Social Media: www.facebook.com/TiftickjianLawFirm
www.linkedin.com/in/tiftickjianlawfirm
twitter.com/dui5280
www.youtube.com/channel/UCHT_fJLETTH7fkxwsGe1U3g

11030 ■ Tiftickjian Law Firm, P.C. Juvenile Justice Law School Scholarships *(Graduate/Scholarship)*

Purpose: To encourage and assist students with attending law school with an interest in juvenile justice, as well as raise awareness of the issue of prison sentences and reduced rights for minors that place youths on an institutionalized path towards spending a large part of their life in the criminal justice system. **Focus:** Criminal justice; Law; Youth. **Qualif.:** Applicants must be U.S. citizens or permanent residents; must be enrolled or accepted to an accredited law school within the United States; and must have a cumulative GPA of 3.50 or higher. **Criteria:** Selection will be based on the applicants' eligibility and compliance with the application process.

Funds Avail.: $1,000. **Duration:** Annual. **Number Awarded:** 1. **To Apply:** Applicants must be able to provide the following documents for consideration; proof of legal residency in the United States (i.e. birth certificate, passport, permanent resident card, etc.); a completed application; an official copy of a current academic transcript; and an essay of not more than three pages describing how they think juvenile justice could be improved to rehabilitate juveniles and keep them out of the criminal justice system.

11031 ■ Tikvah Center for Law and Jewish Civilization
40 Washington Sq. South
New York, NY 10012
Ph: (212)998-6100
URL: www.law.nyu.edu

11032 ■ Berkowitz Fellowship *(Professional development/Fellowship)*

Purpose: To facilitate research and scholarship into areas that examine historical, cultural and political forces that helped shape the intellectual atmosphere in which the integration of varying traditions of law into an operative jurisprudential system was affected. **Focus:** Jewish studies; Law. **Qualif.:** Applicants must be senior scholars.

Funds Avail.: No specific amount. **Number Awarded:** 1.

11033 ■ The Tikvah Fund
165 E 56th St., 4th Fl.
New York, NY 10022

Awards are arranged alphabetically below their administering organizations

Ph: (212)796-1672
Fax: (646)514-5915
E-mail: info@tikvahfund.org
URL: tikvahfund.org
Social Media: www.facebook.com/tikvahfund
www.linkedin.com/company/tikvah-fund
twitter.com/tikvahfund

11034 ■ The Tikvah Fellowship *(Undergraduate/Fellowship)*

Purpose: To support exceptional individuals interested in the political, religious, and intellectual future of the Jewish people. **Focus:** Jewish studies. **Qualif.:** Applicant must have a completed undergraduate degree from a college or university in the United States, Israel, or other country.**Criteria:** Selection will be on a highly selective basis.

11035 ■ Pat Tillman Foundation

222 W Merchandise Mart Pl., Ste. 1212
Chicago, IL 60654
Ph: (773)360-5277
E-mail: info@pattillmanfoundation.org
URL: pattillmanfoundation.org
Social Media: www.facebook.com/pattillmanfnd
www.linkedin.com/company/pat-tillman-foundation
twitter.com/pattillmanfnd

11036 ■ Tillman Scholars Program *(Undergraduate, Graduate/Scholarship)*

Purpose: To assist individuals with their academic expenses, including tuition and fees, books, and living expenses. **Focus:** General studies/Field of study not specified. **Qualif.:** Applicants must be veterans or active-duty military service members (honorably discharged of pre- and post-9/11 service; from all branches of the U.S. military including national guard and reserve); or current spouses of veterans or active-duty service members, including surviving spouses; or service members or spouses pursuing a degree as full-time students (undergraduate, graduate or professional degree students at a public or private, U.S.-based accredited institution). **Criteria:** Selection will be based on the committee's criteria.

Funds Avail.: No specific amount. **Duration:** Annual. **To Apply:** Applicants must visit the website to complete the online application process. **Remarks:** Established in 2008.

11037 ■ Timeshares Only

4700 Millenia Blvd., Ste. 250
Orlando, FL 32839
Ph: (407)465-1888
Fax: (407)465-5169
E-mail: info@timesharesonly.com
URL: www.timesharesonly.com
Social Media: facebook.com/TimesharesOnly
twitter.com/Timesharesonly

11038 ■ Hospitality Career Scholarship *(Undergraduate/Scholarship)*

Purpose: To support students who want to make a positive difference as a future leader in the hospitality community. **Focus:** Hotel, institutional, and restaurant management. **Qualif.:** Applicants must be currently enrolled in an undergraduate hospitality degree program or certificate program at an accredited college or university, or be a high school student who has been accepted to a college and plans to study a hospitality-related major; students in a hospitality certificate program at an accredited college are also eligible; must have a minimum cumulative grade point average of 3.0.; at least 18 years old; legal resident of the U.S.

To Apply: Provide a profile photo, a brief biography, and responses to a brief text interview at www.timesharesonly.com/hospitality-career-scholarship. **Contact:** Email: scholarships@timesharesonly.com.

11039 ■ Tingen & Williams PLLC

1801 Bayberry Crt., Ste. 203
Richmond, VA 23226
Ph: (804)477-1720
Fax: (804)505-0997
URL: tingenwilliams.com
Social Media: www.facebook.com/tingenlaw
www.linkedin.com/company/tingen-&-williams-pllc
twitter.com/tingenwilliams
www.youtube.com/channel/UCwx2HFrH-atRn3NxbI9-Pcw

11040 ■ The Tingen & Williams Undergraduate Scholarship *(Undergraduate/Scholarship)*

Purpose: To help students pay for undergraduate degrees. **Focus:** General studies/Field of study not specified. **Qualif.:** Applicant must be enrolled full-time in an undergraduate program at a Virginia college or university for the upcoming school year; must have a minimum 3.0 GPA; and be a U.S. citizen or permanent resident. **Criteria:** Selection will be based on prior academic achievement and the written essay.

Funds Avail.: $600. **Number Awarded:** 1. **To Apply:** Applicant must write an essay (no more than 1,000 words) that responds to the essay prompt on the application page. All materials can be submitted online. **Deadline:** May 29. **Contact:** tingenwilliams.com/scholarships.

11041 ■ Titan Web Agency

PO Box 1262
Riverton, UT 84065
Ph: (801)783-3101
URL: titanwebagency.com
Social Media: www.facebook.com/TitanWebAgency
www.linkedin.com/company/titan-web-agency
twitter.com/TitanWebAgency
www.youtube.com/user/titanwebagency

11042 ■ Titan Web Agency Bi-Annual Scholarship Program *(Community College, Four Year College, Two Year College/Scholarship)*

Purpose: To help students who have a desire to own their own business, and with a financial need for college. **Focus:** General studies/Field of study not specified. **Qualif.:** Applicants should have a desire to own their own business; must be attending a two-year community college or a four-year accredited university; must be U.S. resident; minorities are encouraged to apply.

Funds Avail.: $500. **Duration:** Biennial. **To Apply:** Submit essay of at least 1,000 words detailing why you want to be an entrepreneur. Include a creative photo that you feel represents you best, as well as your full name, address,

Awards are arranged alphabetically below their administering organizations

email address, phone number, and proof of school registration. **Deadline:** June 1; December 1. **Contact:** Titan Web Agency, PO Box 1262, Riverton, UT, 84065; Email: support@titanwebagency.com.

11043 ■ Tobi
530 Forbes Blvd.
South San Francisco, CA 94080
Ph: (516)331-3145
URL: www.tobi.com
Social Media: www.facebook.com/shopTOBI
www.instagram.com/shoptobi
www.pinterest.com/shopTOBI
twitter.com/shopTOBI

11044 ■ Tobi's Scholarship *(Undergraduate/ Scholarship)*
Purpose: To help finance higher education for female students. **Focus:** General studies/Field of study not specified. **Qualif.:** Applicant must be a woman enrolled or enrolling as an undergraduate student in a four-year college or community college in the United States.

Funds Avail.: $3,000. **Number Awarded:** 1. **To Apply:** Applicant must answer all questions on the application form and submit via email. **Contact:** www.tobi.com/tobi_cares/scholarship_program/application.

11045 ■ Tocris
614 McKinley Pl., NE
Minneapolis, MN 55413
Ph: (612)379-2956
Fax: (612)656-4400
Free: 800-343-7475
E-mail: customerservice.na@bio-techne.com
URL: www.tocris.com
Social Media: facebook.com/TocrisBioscience
www.linkedin.com/company/tocris-bioscience
twitter.com/Tocris

11046 ■ Tocris Scholarship Program *(All/Scholarship)*
Purpose: To aide a student pursuing a science related degree. **Focus:** Science. **Qualif.:** Applicant must be pursuing a science related degree. **Criteria:** Selection will be based on responses provided by applicant.

Funds Avail.: $1,500. **Number Awarded:** 1, twice a year. **Deadline:** July 29. **Contact:** Email: scholarship@novusbio.com.

11047 ■ Robert Toigo Foundation
180 Grand Ave., Ste. 925
Oakland, CA 94612
Ph: (510)763-5771
Fax: (510)763-5778
E-mail: info@toigofoundation.org
URL: www.toigofoundation.org
Social Media: www.facebook.com/toigofoundation
www.linkedin.com/company/robert-toigo-foundation
twitter.com/ToigoFoundation

11048 ■ Robert Toigo Foundation Fellowship *(Master's/Fellowship)*
Purpose: To support students committed to a career in finance. **Focus:** Finance. **Criteria:** Selection is based on

leadership potential, academic excellence and demonstrated commitment to social change and community responsibility.

Funds Avail.: No specific amount. **Duration:** Annual. **To Apply:** Applicants must complete the application form online. **Contact:** Email: apply@toigofoundation.org.

11049 ■ TonaLaw
870 Middle Country Rd.
Saint James, NY 11780
Ph: (631)780-5355
Fax: (631)780-5685
Free: 833-TONALAW
URL: www.tonalaw.com
Social Media: www.facebook.com/tonalawfirm
www.instagram.com/844tonalaw
www.linkedin.com/company/the-law-office-of-thomas-tona
 -p-c-/
twitter.com/tonalaw
www.youtube.com/channel/UCtgaj5o6TBWaipXTF5YmlSg

11050 ■ TonaLaw Veteran's Scholarship *(Undergraduate, Graduate, Professional development, Vocational/Occupational/Scholarship)*
Purpose: To assist U.S. veterans who are returning to higher education. **Focus:** General studies/Field of study not specified. **Qualif.:** Applicants must be veterans of any branch of the Armed Forces of the United States; be attending school in the United States; and be students at an accredited school, or accepted to begin school at an accredited school within 6 months of application. **Criteria:** Selection will be made by the selection committee.

Funds Avail.: $1,000. **Duration:** Semiannual. **To Apply:** Submit essay (300-600 words) answering the rubric, "Describe how your military service has made an impact on your life. How has it prepared you for college and what do you plan to do after you complete your education?". **Deadline:** July 31; November 30.

11051 ■ The Toolsy
412 N Main St., Ste. 100
Buffalo, WY 82834
Ph: (415)800-3878
URL: www.thetoolsy.com

11052 ■ The Toolsy Scholarship: The Importance of Craftship *(All/Scholarship)*
Purpose: To help students hone and improve their writing, artistic, and craftship skills, as well as leverage craftship to more than a label of a "dying art.". **Focus:** General studies/ Field of study not specified.

Funds Avail.: $500. **Duration:** Annual. **Number Awarded:** 1. **To Apply:** Applicant must submit an essay (1,000 to 1,500 words) answering the following subject: Craftship is as essential as ever in (scholarship year). Do you agree or disagree? Essay must be in a Word document. Application details are available online at www.thetoolsy.com. **Deadline:** Septermber 19.

11053 ■ Toptal, L.L.C.
548 Market St.,No. 36879
San Francisco, CA 94104

Awards are arranged alphabetically below their administering organizations

URL: www.toptal.com
Social Media: www.facebook.com/toptal
twitter.com/toptal

11054 ■ Toptal Scholarships for Women *(All/ Scholarship)*

Purpose: To provide assistance to female students from all majors and academic standings who have a passion for changing the guture. **Focus:** General studies/Field of study not specified. **Qualif.:** Applicant must be at least 16 years old and female. Not available to any resident or citizen in any country that prohibits the Scholarship Program or that is prohibited by U.S. law.

Funds Avail.: $10,000 plus one year mentorship from senior Toptal expert. **Duration:** Annual. **Number Awarded:** 5. **To Apply:** Applications must be completed online. **Deadline:** September 28 (Africa); October 30 (Oceania); November 30 (Asia); January 31 (Europe); March 31 (Americas). **Contact:** Email: scholarships@toptal.com; URL: www.toptal.com/scholarships-for-women.

11055 ■ TopTechGiant
70 N Lake Dr.
Orchard Park, NY 14127
E-mail: contact@toptechgiant.com
URL: toptechgiant.com

11056 ■ TopTechGiant $1,000 Scholarship *(Two Year College, Community College, Undergraduate, Graduate/Scholarship)*

Purpose: To help students pay their tuition fees. **Focus:** General studies/Field of study not specified. **Qualif.:** Applicant must be currently enrolled in a college or university and must have a passion for writing; the piece of content must be unique and creative; the language must be English; the words of your content must be able to convince anyone that you are correct. **Criteria:** To participate in this scholarship program you will have to research and create a piece of content between 300 – 1,000 words; the content language must be in English.

Funds Avail.: $1,000. **Duration:** Annual. **To Apply:** Applicant should submit writing piece and other information to online.

11057 ■ The Toro Company
8111 Lyndale Ave. S
Bloomington, MN 55420-1196
Ph: (952)888-8801
Free: 800-348-2424
E-mail: community@thetorocompany.com
URL: www.thetorocompany.com
Social Media: www.facebook.com/Toro.Company
www.instagram.com/thetorocompany
www.pinterest.com/thetorocompany
twitter.com/thetorocompany
www.youtube.com/user/toro

11058 ■ Dr. James Watson Fellowship Program *(Doctorate, Graduate/Fellowship)*

Purpose: To provide financial assistance for the future educators and researchers of the turfgrass industry. **Focus:** Turfgrass management. **Qualif.:** Applicants must be candidates for masters' or doctoral degrees in fields related

to golf course management. **Criteria:** Selection will be evaluated based on academic achievement, potential to become a leading professional, employment history, accomplishments in research and education, communication skills, peer recommendation.

Funds Avail.: $5,000. **Duration:** Annual. **Number Awarded:** 3. **To Apply:** Applicants must submit their transcript of records, advisor's report and superintendent's Report; the essay component must not exceed two double-spaced pages; additional application forms can be obtained from the environmental institute for golf or may visit the GCSAA website. **Deadline:** October 1. **Remarks:** Established in 1998. **Contact:** URL: www.gcsaa.org/education/ scholarships; Mischia Wright, Email: mwright@gcsaa.org; Phone: 785-832-4445.

11059 ■ Toronto and Region Conservation Authority (TRCA)
5 Shoreham Dr.
Downsview, ON, Canada M3N 1S4
Ph: (416)661-6600
Fax: (416)661-6898
E-mail: info@trca.on.ca
URL: trca.ca
Social Media: www.facebook.com/TorontoConservation
www.instagram.com/trca_hq
twitter.com/TRCA_HQ
www.youtube.com/channel/
UCuoB2mf6OUEaK8anhlxODIA

11060 ■ The B. Harper Bull Scholarship Awards *(Graduate, Doctorate, Postgraduate/Award)*

Purpose: To further the science of natural heritage management within the boundaries of Toronto and Region Conservation's (TRCA) jurisdiction. **Focus:** Ecology; Fisheries sciences/management; Forestry; Hydrology; Water resources; Wildlife conservation, management, and science. **Criteria:** Submissions will be reviewed by toronto and region conservation foundation's volunteer selection committee; special consideration will be given to students who demonstrate leadership through volunteer and extra-curricular activities.

Funds Avail.: First prize - $3,000; Second prize - $2,000; Third prize - $1,000. **Duration:** Annual. **To Apply:** Applicants must submit completed application form; 500-word essay outlining how the applicant demonstrates the values of the living city--where human settlement can flourish forever as part of nature's beauty and diversity; two letters of reference, including one academic reference and one work-related reference. **Deadline:** September 29. **Contact:** Debbie Pokornik, Coordinator II, Donor Stewardship; Phone: 416-661-6600 x5346; Email: dpokornik@trca.on.ca.

11061 ■ Toronto Rehabilitation Institute
550 University Ave.
Toronto, ON, Canada M5G 2A2
Ph: (416)597-3422
E-mail: kite@uhn.ca
URL: www.kite-uhn.com
Social Media: www.facebook.com/torontorehabinstitute
www.instagram.com/torontorehabinstitute/?hl=en
www.linkedin.com/company/toronto-rehabilitation-institute
www.linkedin.com/company/toronto-rehabilitation-institute/
about

Awards are arranged alphabetically below their administering organizations

twitter.com/UHN
twitter.com/TRI_UHN
youtube.com/UHNToronto
www.youtube.com/channel/
  UCMOs32lv0UHB2zXkblB2xyQ/videos

11062 ■ Annie Kirshenblatt Memorial Scholarship
(Graduate, Undergraduate/Scholarship)

Purpose: To provide support for study or research within programs related to the field of gerontology. **Focus:** Gerontology. **Qualif.:** Applicants must be enrolled in study or research within programs related to the field of gerontology. **Criteria:** Selection is based on submitted application materials.

Funds Avail.: 2,000 Canadian Dollars. **Duration:** Annual. **To Apply:** Applicants must submit a completed application form and references to The Kirshenblatt Memorial Scholarships, Toronto Rehabilitation Institute.

11063 ■ Shoshana Philipp (Kirshenblatt) R.N. Memorial Scholarships *(Graduate, Undergraduate/Scholarship)*

Purpose: To provide support for study or research within programs related to gerontological nursing. **Focus:** Gerontology; Nursing. **Qualif.:** Applicant must be a Canadian citizen or landed immigrant; have plans to work in Canada and be enrolled in a course or is conducting a research project within a program that is related to the field of Gerontology that will lead to a certificate, diploma or degree. **Criteria:** Selection is based on submitted application materials.

Funds Avail.: 2,000 Canadian Dollars. **Duration:** Annual. **To Apply:** Applicants must submit a completed application form and references to The Kirshenblatt Memorial Scholarships, Toronto Rehabilitation Institute.

11064 ■ Toronto Rehab Scholarships in Rehabilitation-Related Research *(Graduate/Scholarship)*

Purpose: To further the active involvement of people with disabilities in rehabilitation-related research. **Focus:** Medical research.
Funds Avail.: $20,000. **Duration:** Annual.

11065 ■ Toronto Rehabilitation Institute Graduate Student Scholarships - Ontario Student Opportunities Trust Fund (OSOTF) *(Graduate/Scholarship)*

Purpose: To provide financial support for doctoral stream (MSc/PhD) thesis degree program students at University of Toronto. **Focus:** Engineering; Health services administration. **Qualif.:** Applicants must be graduate students enrolled at the University of Toronto; must have a financial need; and must be in a research training either at Toronto Rehab or another suitable institution; now reside in Ontario. **Criteria:** Selection will be based on the submitted application materials.

Funds Avail.: No specific amount. **To Apply:** Applicants must submit a completed application form and required materials to Office of the Vice Dean, Graduate Affairs, Faculty of Medicine, University of Toronto. **Deadline:** May 2.

11066 ■ Tourette Association of America
42-40 Bell Blvd., Ste. 205
Bayside, NY 11361

Ph: (718)224-2999
Fax: (718)279-9596
E-mail: support@tourette.org
URL: www.tourette.org
Social Media: www.facebook.com/TouretteAssociation
www.instagram.com/touretteassociation
www.linkedin.com/company/tourette-association-of-america
twitter.com/TouretteAssn
www.youtube.com/channel/UC91zplYK_8Pwu48EZkLetUg

11067 ■ Tourette Association of America Research Grant Awards *(Master's, Doctorate/Grant)*

Purpose: To promote, enhance, and support the research regarding Tourette Syndrome. **Focus:** Tourette syndrome. **Qualif.:** Applicants must have a M.D., Ph.D., or equivalent; previous experience in the field of movement disorders is desirable, but not essential; applicants may reside outside the United States.

Funds Avail.: Up to $75,000 for one year or up to $150,000 for two years. **Duration:** Annual. **Remarks:** Established in 1984. **Contact:** E-mail: denise.walker@tourette.org; Phone: 718-224-2999.

11068 ■ Touro Synagogue Foundation (TSF)
85 Touro St.
Newport, RI 02840
Ph: (401)847-4794
URL: www.tourosynagogue.org

11069 ■ The Aaron and Rita Slom Scholarships
(Undergraduate/Scholarship)

Purpose: To educate future generations. **Focus:** Historic preservation. **Qualif.:** Applicants must be high school graduating students. **Criteria:** Recipients scholarships are for high school seniors who plan to enroll in an institute of higher learning for a minimum of six credits; The institution can be public or private, and has no geographic limitations.

Duration: Annual. **Number Awarded:** 2. **To Apply:** Applicants must submit an interpretative work (i.e. written submission, audio visual, documentary, film, PowerPoint) focusing on the George Washington letter in context with the present time; written submissions such as essays, stories, poems (no less than 500 words and no more than 1000 words), or audio-visual submissions such as documentaries, films or computer presentations (no more than 10 minutes) will be considered. **Deadline:** April 21. **Contact:** Touro Synagogue Foundation, Attention: Slom Scholarship, 85 Touro St., Newport, RI 02840; Phone: 401-847-4794 x207; Email: tours@tourosynagogue.org.

11070 ■ Tower Cancer Research Foundation (TCRF)
8767 Wilshire Blvd., Ste. 401
Beverly Hills, CA 90211
Ph: (310)299-8470
Fax: (310)861-5436
E-mail: tcrf@towercancer.org
URL: www.towercancer.org
Social Media: www.facebook.com/TowerCancerResearch
www.instagram.com/towercancerresearch
twitter.com/TowerCancer

Awards are arranged alphabetically below their administering organizations

11071 ■ Career Development Grant in molecular genetics *(Advanced Professional, Professional development/Grant)*

Purpose: To support forward thinking scientists from Southern California's premier academic medical centers. **Focus:** Oncology. **Criteria:** Evaluation of grants applications based on novelty of hypothesis; scientific quality; potential for revealing something meaningful about cancer; feasibility of the proposal; evidence of institutional support for the project.

Funds Avail.: $100,000. **Duration:** Irregular. **To Apply:** Applicant must submit the application Outlined as Basic Information, non-technical abstract, technical abstract, applicant's biographical sketch, sponsor's biographical sketch, description of proposed project, personal statement, letters of recommendation, sponsor letter, budget, certifications or statements of exemption, publication reprints; Completed applications must be submitted online as one PDF; title the PDF completed application document as listed below:last Name.career Development grant.institution. date of submission. **Deadline:** May 4. **Remarks:** Established in 2006. **Contact:** Tower Cancer Research Foundation, 8767 Wilshire Blvd. Ste. 401, Beverly Hills, CA, 90211; Kelli; Phone: 310-299-8470; Email: kelli@towercancer.org.

11072 ■ TranscriptionServices.com
Raleigh, NC
URL: www.transcriptionservices.com
Social Media: www.facebook.com/Transcriptionists

11073 ■ The TranscriptionServices.com Scholarship *(Undergraduate/Scholarship)*

Purpose: To help talented students pay for higher education. **Focus:** General studies/Field of study not specified. **Qualif.:** Applicants must be high school seniors or undergraduate students in the United States with a cumulative 3.0 GPA over the previous year.

Funds Avail.: $500. **Duration:** Annual. **Number Awarded:** 1. **To Apply:** Submit application online along with a 500 to 750 word essay on the following prompt: If you woke up tomorrow with permanent hearing loss, what would be the biggest challenge you would face? How would you address that challenge? **Deadline:** June 1. **Contact:** Email: scholarship@TranscriptionServices.com; URL: www.transcriptionservices.com/scholarship.

11074 ■ Transport Workers Union of America (TWU)
501 3rd St. NW, 9th Fl.
Washington, DC 20001
Ph: (202)719-3900
Fax: (202)347-0454
URL: www.twu.org
Social Media: www.facebook.com/transportworkersunion
twitter.com/transportworker

11075 ■ The Michael J. Quill Scholarship *(Undergraduate/Scholarship)*

Purpose: To provide professional legal, education, research and public relations services to the local and divisions. **Focus:** General studies/Field of study not specified. **Qualif.:** Applicants must be sons and daughters, dependent brothers and sisters (claimed with IRS) of a present, retired, or deceased TWU members who are high school seniors

and will enter an accredited college beginning with the fall term. **Criteria:** Recipients are selected based on applicant's capability to do the college work under the High School Principal certification.

Funds Avail.: $4,800. **Duration:** Annual. **Number Awarded:** 15. **To Apply:** Applicants fill out Section A by yourself. answer all questions; section B requires the signature of the relative, if alive, on whose TWU membership your eligibility depends; Section C should be filled out by either the TWU President or Secretary-Treasurer of the local union to which your parent belongs (brother or sister in case you are a dependent brother or sister of a TWU member); Section D should be completed by the principal of your high school. **Remarks:** Established in 1969.

11076 ■ Transportation Association of Canada (TAC)
401-1111 Prince of Wales Dr.
Ottawa, ON, Canada K2C 3T2
Ph: (613)736-1350
Fax: (613)736-1395
E-mail: secretariat@tac-atc.ca
URL: www.tac-atc.ca
Social Media: www.facebook.com/tac2014atc
www.linkedin.com/company/transportation-association-of-canada

11077 ■ TAC Foundation – 3M Canada "Bob Margison Memorial" Scholarship *(Graduate, Undergraduate/Scholarship)*

Purpose: To provide support and encouragement to those interested in pursuing a career in transportation planning or transportation engineering. **Focus:** Transportation. **Qualif.:** Applicants must be undergraduate or graduate students with transportation engineering as field of their studies; for community college students, they must be enrolled in full-time studies, entering their final year of a certified community college program and intend to pursue a career in the transportation field, as it relates to the foundation's primary focus; for university undergraduates, they must be enrolled in at least two semesters of full-time studies; for graduate students, they must be B average or equivalent in their previous academic year. **Criteria:** Selection will be based on TAC foundation scholarship committee evaluates and scores all qualifying applications.

Funds Avail.: $4,500. **To Apply:** Applicants must submit an official copy of the current academic transcript with official letterhead in an unalterable format; maximum two-page resume summarizing the education, employment experience, achievements and interests; and academic reference form. **Deadline:** February 28. **Remarks:** The scholarship was established in memory of Bob Margison. **Contact:** Foundation's Executive Director; Email: foundation@tac-atc.ca.

11078 ■ TAC Foundation-407 ETR Scholarships *(Undergraduate, Graduate/Scholarship)*

Purpose: To recognize the importance of investing in both highway infrastructure and transportation expertise for the future. **Focus:** Transportation. **Qualif.:** Applicants must be undergraduate or graduate students with transportation engineering as field of their studies; for community college students, they must be enrolled in full-time studies, entering their final year of a certified community college program and intend to pursue a career in the transportation field, as

Awards are arranged alphabetically below their administering organizations

it relates to the Foundation's primary focus; for University undergraduates, they must be enrolled in at least two semesters of full-time studies; for graduate students, they must be admissible to a full-time transportation-related graduate studies program or already registered as a full-time graduate student in the field; must be Canadian, Alberta, British Columbia, or Saskatchewan citizens or permanent residents and have achieved an overall B average or equivalent in their previous academic year. **Criteria:** Selection will be based on TAC Foundation Scholarship Committee evaluates and scores all qualifying applications. **Funds Avail.:** $5,000. **Deadline:** February 28. **Contact:** Foundation's Executive Director; Email: foundation@tac-atc.ca.

11079 ■ TAC Foundation-Amec Foster Wheeler Scholarships *(Undergraduate, Graduate/Scholarship)*

Purpose: To recognize the increasing complexity of transportation issues and the need for future professionals to have the education base needed to develop innovative and sustainable solutions. **Focus:** Transportation. **Qualif.:** Applicants must be undergraduate or graduate students with transportation-related disciplines as field of their studies; for community college students, they must be enrolled in full-time studies, entering their final year of a certified community college program and intend to pursue a career in the transportation field, as it relates to the Foundation's primary focus; for university undergraduates, they must be enrolled in at least two semesters of full-time studies; for Graduate students, they must be admissible to a full-time transportation-related graduate studies program or already registered as a full-time graduate student in the field; all applicants must be Canadian citizens or permanent residents and have achieved an overall B average or equivalent in their previous academic year. **Criteria:** Applicants are evaluated and scores all qualifying application. **Funds Avail.:** $5,000. **To Apply:** Applicants must submit the official copy of the current academic transcript with official letterhead in an unalterable format; maximum two-page resume summarizing the education, employment experience, achievements and interests; and academic reference form. **Deadline:** February 28. **Contact:** Foundation's Executive Director; Email: foundation@tac-atc.ca.

11080 ■ TAC Foundation-ATS Traffic Scholarships *(Undergraduate, Graduate/Scholarship)*

Purpose: To encourage and professional work environment with emphasis on work-life balance, professional development, and career growth. **Focus:** Transportation. **Qualif.:** Applicants must be undergraduate or graduate students with traffic engineering and planning (specializing in Intelligent Transportation System) as field of their studies. For community college students, they must be enrolled in full-time studies, entering their final year of a certified community college program and intend to pursue a career in the transportation field, as it relates to the Foundation's primary focus. For University undergraduates, they must be enrolled in at least two semesters of full-time studies. For Graduate students, they must be admissible to a full-time transportation-related graduate studies program or already registered as a full-time graduate student in the field. All applicants must be Canadian citizens or permanent residents and have achieved an overall B average or equivalent in their previous academic year. **Criteria:** TAC Foundation Scholarship Committee evaluates and scores all qualifying applications. Preference may be given to candidates with relevant work experience. **Funds Avail.:** $5,000. **To Apply:** Applicants must submit the following documents together with the application form:

official copy of the current academic transcript with official letterhead in an unalterable format; maximum two-page resume summarizing the education, employment experience, achievements and interests; and academic reference form. **Deadline:** February 28. **Contact:** Foundation's Executive Director; Email: foundation@tac-atc.ca.

11081 ■ TAC Foundation-Canadian Council of Independent Laboratories Graduate Student Scholarships (CCIL) *(Graduate/Scholarship)*

Purpose: To support transportation education in Canada, such as promoting careers in transportation to skilled students, and assisting transportation educators and researchers. **Focus:** Transportation. **Qualif.:** Applicants must be graduate students with materials engineering, concrete or asphalt technology, as field of their studies; must be admissible to a full-time transportation-related graduate studies program or already registered as a full-time graduate student in the field; must be Canadian citizens or permanent residents; and have achieved an overall B average or equivalent in their previous academic year. **Criteria:** TAC Foundation Scholarship Committee evaluates and scores all qualifying applications. Preference may be given to candidates with relevant work experience. **Funds Avail.:** $5,000. **To Apply:** Applicants must submit the following documents together with the application form: an official copy of the applicants' most current academic transcript provided on official letterhead in an unalterable format; a maximum two-page resume summarizing the applicant's education, relevant employment experience, achievements and interests; and academic reference form. **Deadline:** February 28. **Contact:** Foundation's Executive Director; Email: foundation@tac-atc.ca.

11082 ■ TAC Foundation-CCMTA Road Safety Scholarships *(Undergraduate, Graduate/Scholarship)*

Purpose: To provide educational support for professionals who wish to pursue a specialty in a holistic road safety education. **Focus:** Transportation. **Qualif.:** Applicants must be undergraduate or graduate students with transportation engineering as field of their studies; for community college students, they must be enrolled in full-time studies, entering their final year of a certified community college program and intend to pursue a career in the transportation field, as it relates to the Foundation's primary focus; for University undergraduates, they must be enrolled in at least two semesters of full-time studies; for graduate students, they must be admissible to a full-time transportation-related graduate studies program or already registered as a full-time graduate student in the field; must be Canadian, Alberta, British Columbia, or Saskatchewan citizens or permanent residents and have achieved an overall B average or equivalent in their previous academic year. **Criteria:** Selection will be based on the TAC Foundation Scholarship Committee evaluating and scoring all qualifying applications. **Funds Avail.:** $5,000. **To Apply:** Applicants must submit an official copy of the current academic transcript with official letterhead in an unalterable format; maximum two-page resume summarizing the education, employment experience, achievements and interests; and academic reference form. **Deadline:** February 28. **Contact:** Foundation's Executive Director; Email: foundation@tac-atc.ca.

11083 ■ TAC Foundation-Cement Association of Canada Scholarships *(Graduate, Undergraduate/Scholarship)*

Purpose: To provide support and encouragement to those interested in pursuing a career in transportation planning or

Awards are arranged alphabetically below their administering organizations

transportation engineering. **Focus:** Transportation. **Qualif.:** Applicants must be Canadian citizens or landed immigrants; and must be enrolled for the entire academic year. **Criteria:** Preference will be given to candidates with relevant work experience.

Funds Avail.: 5,000 Canadian Dollars. **To Apply:** Applicants must complete the application form available online; must provide academic references and relevant employment information; must have an electronic version of their transcript of records. Application form and requirements must be sent to the TAC Foundation. **Deadline:** February 13. **Contact:** Foundation's Executive Director at foundation@tac-atc.ca.

11084 ■ TAC Foundation-Dillon Consulting Scholarships *(Undergraduate, Graduate/Scholarship)*

Purpose: To provide support and encouragement to those interested in pursuing a career in transportation planning or transportation engineering. **Focus:** Transportation. **Qualif.:** Applicants must be undergraduate or graduate students with transportation engineering as field of their studies; for community college students, they must be enrolled in full-time studies, entering their final year of a certified community college program and intend to pursue a career in the transportation field, as it relates to the foundation's primary focus; for university undergraduates, they must be enrolled in at least two semesters of full-time studies; for graduate students, they must be B average or equivalent in their previous academic year. **Criteria:** Selection will be given to candidates with relevant work experience.

Funds Avail.: $5,000 Canadian Dollars. **To Apply:** Applicants must provide academic references and relevant employment information; must have an electronic version of transcript records. **Deadline:** February 28. **Contact:** Foundation's Executive Director at foundation@tac-atc.ca.

11085 ■ TAC Foundation-Dr. Ralph Haas Graduate Student Scholarships *(Graduate/Scholarship)*

Purpose: To continue the tradition of providing financial assistance to graduate students in the broad area of transportation. **Focus:** Transportation. **Qualif.:** Applicants must be graduate students with transportation-related disciplines as field of their studies; must be admissible to a full-time transportation-related graduate studies program or already registered as a full-time graduate student in the field; must be Canadian citizens or permanent residents; and have achieved an overall B average or equivalent in their previous academic year. **Criteria:** TAC Foundation Scholarship Committee evaluates and scores all qualifying applications. Preference may be given to candidates with relevant work experience.

Funds Avail.: $5,000. **To Apply:** Applicants must submit the following documents together with the application form: an official copy of the applicants' most current academic transcript provided on official letterhead in an unalterable format; a maximum two-page resume summarizing the applicant's education, relevant employment experience, achievements and interests; and academic reference form. **Deadline:** February 28. **Contact:** Foundation's Executive Director; Email: foundation@tac-atc.ca.

11086 ■ TAC Foundation-EllisDon Community College/CEGEP Scholarships *(Undergraduate/Scholarship)*

Purpose: To support transportation education in Canada, such as promoting careers in transportation to skilled students, and assisting transportation educators and

researchers. **Focus:** Transportation. **Qualif.:** Applicants must be undergraduate or graduate students with transportation engineering as field of their studies; for community college students, they must be enrolled in full-time studies, entering their final year of a certified community college program and intend to pursue a career in the transportation field, as it relates to the Foundation's primary focus; for University undergraduates, they must be enrolled in at least two semesters of full-time studies; for graduate students, they must be admissible to a full-time transportation-related graduate studies program or already registered as a full-time graduate student in the field; must be Canadian, Alberta, British Columbia, or Saskatchewan citizens or permanent residents and have achieved an overall B average or equivalent in their previous academic year. **Criteria:** Selection will be based on TAC Foundation Scholarship Committee evaluating and scoring all qualifying applications.

Funds Avail.: $2,500. **To Apply:** Applicants must submit an official copy of the current academic transcript with official letterhead in an unalterable format; maximum two-page resume summarizing the education, employment experience, achievements and interests; and academic reference form. **Deadline:** February 28. **Contact:** Foundation's Executive Director; Email: foundation@tac-atc.ca.

11087 ■ TAC Foundation-exp Scholarships *(Undergraduate, Graduate/Scholarship)*

Purpose: To support transportation education in Canada, such as promoting careers in transportation to skilled students, and assisting transportation educators and researchers. **Focus:** Transportation. **Qualif.:** Applicants must be undergraduate or graduate students with transportation planning and engineering disciplines as field of their studies. For community college students, they must be enrolled in full-time studies, entering their final year of a certified community college program and intend to pursue a career in the transportation field, as it relates to the Foundation's primary focus. For University undergraduates, they must be enrolled in at least two semesters of full-time studies. For Graduate students, they must be admissible to a full-time transportation-related graduate studies program or already registered as a full-time graduate student in the field. All applicants must be Canadian citizens or permanent residents and have achieved an overall B average or equivalent in their previous academic year. **Criteria:** TAC Foundation Scholarship Committee evaluates and scores all qualifying applications. Preference may be given to candidates with relevant work experience.

Funds Avail.: $5,000. **To Apply:** Applicants must submit the following documents together with the application form: official copy of the current academic transcript with official letterhead in an unalterable format; maximum two-page resume summarizing the education, employment experience, achievements and interests; and academic reference form. **Deadline:** March 2.

11088 ■ TAC Foundation-Golder Associates Ltd. Scholarships *(Undergraduate, Graduate/Scholarship)*

Purpose: To support transportation education in Canada, such as promoting careers in transportation to skilled students, and assisting transportation educators and researchers. **Focus:** Transportation. **Qualif.:** Applicants must be undergraduate or graduate students with transportation engineering as field of their studies; for community college students, they must be enrolled in full-time studies, entering their final year of a certified community college program and intend to pursue a career in the transportation

Awards are arranged alphabetically below their administering organizations

field, as it relates to the Foundation's primary focus; for University undergraduates, they must be enrolled in at least two semesters of full-time studies; for graduate students, they must be admissible to a full-time transportation-related graduate studies program or already registered as a full-time graduate student in the field; must be Canadian, Alberta, British Columbia, or Saskatchewan citizens or permanent residents and have achieved an overall B average or equivalent in their previous academic year. **Criteria:** Selection will be based on the TAC Foundation Scholarship Committee evaluating and scoring all qualifying applications.

Funds Avail.: $5,000. **To Apply:** Applicants must submit an official copy of the current academic transcript with official letterhead in an unalterable format; maximum two-page resume summarizing the education, employment experience, achievements and interests; and academic reference form. **Deadline:** February 28. **Contact:** Foundation's Executive Director; Email: foundation@tac-atc.ca.

11089 ■ TAC Foundation-HDR Corporation Graduate Student Scholarships (Graduate/Scholarship)

Purpose: To pursuing graduate studies in transportation planning and transportation engineering. **Focus:** Transportation. **Qualif.:** Applicants must be undergraduate or graduate students with transportation engineering as field of their studies; for community college students, they must be enrolled in full-time studies, entering their final year of a certified community college program and intend to pursue a career in the transportation field, as it relates to the Foundation's primary focus; for University undergraduates, they must be enrolled in at least two semesters of full-time studies; for graduate students, they must be admissible to a full-time transportation-related graduate studies program or already registered as a full-time graduate student in the field; must be Canadian, Alberta, British Columbia, or Saskatchewan citizens or permanent residents and have achieved an overall B average or equivalent in their previous academic year. **Criteria:** Selection will be based on TAC Foundation Scholarship Committee evaluating and scoring all qualifying applications.

Funds Avail.: $5,000. **To Apply:** Applicants must submit an official copy of the current academic transcript with official letterhead in an unalterable format; maximum two-page resume summarizing the education, employment experience, achievements and interests; and academic reference form. **Deadline:** February 28. **Contact:** Foundation's Executive Director; Email: foundation@tac-atc.ca.

11090 ■ TAC Foundation-IBI Group Scholarships (Undergraduate, Graduate/Scholarship)

Purpose: To provide scholarship to students who are pursuing a degree in transportation. **Focus:** Transportation. **Qualif.:** Applicants must be Canadian citizens or landed immigrants; and must be enrolled for the entire academic year. **Criteria:** Selection will be given to candidates with relevant work experience.

Funds Avail.: $4,500 Canadian Dollars. **To Apply:** Applicants must complete the application form (available online); must provide academic references and relevant employment information; must have an electronic version of their transcript of records. Application form and requirements must be sent to the TAC Foundation. **Deadline:** February 28. **Contact:** Foundation's Executive Director; Email: foundation@tac-atc.ca.

11091 ■ TAC Foundation-ISL Engineering Scholarships (Undergraduate, Graduate/Scholarship)

Purpose: To support transportation education in Canada, such as promoting careers in transportation to skilled students, and assisting transportation educators and researchers. **Focus:** Transportation. **Qualif.:** Applicants must be undergraduate or graduate students with transportation engineering as field of their studies. For community college students, they must be enrolled in full-time studies, entering their final year of a certified community college program and intend to pursue a career in the transportation field, as it relates to the Foundation's primary focus. For University undergraduates, they must be enrolled in at least two semesters of full-time studies. For Graduate students, they must be admissible to a full-time transportation-related graduate studies program or already registered as a full-time graduate student in the field. All applicants must be Canadian citizens or permanent residents and have achieved an overall B average or equivalent in their previous academic year. **Criteria:** Selection will be based on TAC Foundation Scholarship Committee evaluates and scores all qualifying applications.

Funds Avail.: $5,000. **To Apply:** Applicants must complete the application form (available online); must provide academic references and relevant employment information; must have an electronic version of their transcript of records. Application form and requirements must be sent to the TAC Foundation. **Deadline:** February 28. **Remarks:** In recognition of Gary W. Mack. **Contact:** Foundation's Executive Director; Email: foundation@tac-atc.ca.

11092 ■ TAC Foundation-LEA Consulting Ltd. Scholarships (Undergraduate, Graduate/Scholarship)

Purpose: To support transportation education in Canada, such as promoting careers in transportation to skilled students, and assisting transportation educators and researchers. **Focus:** Transportation. **Qualif.:** Applicants must be Canadian citizens or permanent residents; should be entering third or fourth year studies; must intend to pursue a career in some aspect of the transportation field and meet the conditions of the scholarships; must have achieved an overall B level or equivalent average mark in their previous academic year. **Criteria:** Selection will be based on TAC Foundation Scholarship Committee evaluates and scores all qualifying applications.

Funds Avail.: Varies. **Number Awarded:** Varies. **To Apply:** Applicants must provide academic references and relevant employment information; must have an electronic version of transcript records. **Deadline:** February 13.

11093 ■ TAC Foundation-MMM Group Limited Scholarships (Undergraduate, Graduate/Scholarship)

Purpose: To provide scholarship to students who are pursuing a degree in transportation. **Focus:** Transportation. **Qualif.:** Applicants must be undergraduate or graduate students with transportation engineering as field of their studies; for community college students, they must be enrolled in full-time studies, entering their final year of a certified community college program and intend to pursue a career in the transportation field, as it relates to the Foundation's primary focus; for University undergraduates, they must be enrolled in at least two semesters of full-time studies; for graduate students, they must be admissible to a full-time transportation-related graduate studies program or already registered as a full-time graduate student in the field; must be Canadian, Alberta, British Columbia, or Saskatchewan citizens or permanent residents and have

Awards are arranged alphabetically below their administering organizations

achieved an overall B average or equivalent in their previous academic year. **Criteria:** Selection will be based on TAC Foundation Scholarship Committee evaluates and scores all qualifying applications.

Funds Avail.: $5,000 Canadian Dollars. **To Apply:** Applicants must submit an official copy of the current academic transcript with official letterhead in an unalterable format; maximum two-page resume summarizing the education, employment experience, achievements and interests; and academic reference form. **Deadline:** February 13. **Contact:** Foundation's Executive Director at foundation@tac-atc.ca.

11094 ■ TAC Foundation-Municipalities Scholarships (Undergraduate, Graduate/Scholarship)

Purpose: To provide scholarship to students who are pursuing a degree in transportation. **Focus:** Transportation. **Qualif.:** Applicants must be Canadian citizens or landed immigrants, and must be enrolled for the entire academic year. **Criteria:** Selection will be based on TAC Foundation Scholarship Committee evaluations and scores for all qualifying applications.

Funds Avail.: $3,000 Canadian Dollars. **To Apply:** Applicants must submit an official copy of the current academic transcript with official letterhead in an unalterable format; maximum two-page resume summarizing the education, employment experience, achievements and interests; and academic reference form. **Deadline:** February 28. **Contact:** Foundation at foundation@tac-atc.ca.

11095 ■ TAC Foundation-Parsons Scholarships (Undergraduate, Graduate/Scholarship)

Purpose: To support transportation education in Canada, such as promoting careers in transportation to skilled students, and assisting transportation educators and researchers. **Focus:** Transportation. **Qualif.:** Applicants must be undergraduate or graduate students with transportation engineering as field of their studies; for community college students, they must be enrolled in full-time studies, entering their final year of a certified community college program and intend to pursue a career in the transportation field, as it relates to the Foundation's primary focus; for University undergraduates, they must be enrolled in at least two semesters of full-time studies; for graduate students, they must be admissible to a full-time transportation-related graduate studies program or already registered as a full-time graduate student in the field; must be Canadian, Alberta, British Columbia, or Saskatchewan citizens or permanent residents and have achieved an overall B average or equivalent in their previous academic year. **Criteria:** Selection will be based on TAC Foundation Scholarship Committee evaluates and scores all qualifying applications.

Funds Avail.: $5,000. **To Apply:** Applicants must submit an official copy of the current academic transcript with official letterhead in an unalterable format; maximum two-page resume summarizing the education, employment experience, achievements and interests; and academic reference form. **Deadline:** February 28. **Remarks:** In recognition of W.J. Malone. **Contact:** Foundation's Executive Director; Email: foundation@tac-atc.ca.

11096 ■ TAC Foundation-Peto MacCallum Undergraduate & College Scholarships (Undergraduate/Scholarship)

Purpose: To support transportation education in Canada, such as promoting careers in transportation to skilled students, and assisting transportation educators and researchers. **Focus:** Transportation. **Qualif.:** Applicants

must be university undergraduates enrolled in at least two semesters of full-time transportation-related disciplines studies; must be Canadian citizens or permanent residents; and have achieved an overall B average or equivalent in their previous academic year. **Criteria:** Selection will be based on TAC Foundation Scholarship Committee evaluating and scoring all qualifying applications.

Funds Avail.: $5,000. **To Apply:** Applicants must submit an official copy of the applicant's most current academic transcript provided on official letterhead in an unalterable format; a maximum two-page resume summarizing the applicant's education, relevant employment experience, achievements and interests; and academic reference form. **Deadline:** February 28. **Contact:** Foundation's Executive Director; Email: foundation@tac-atc.ca.

11097 ■ TAC Foundation-Provinces and Territories Scholarships (Undergraduate, Graduate/Scholarship)

Purpose: To provide scholarship to students who are pursuing a degree in transportation. **Focus:** Transportation. **Qualif.:** Applicants must be undergraduate or graduate students with transportation engineering as field of their studies; for community college students, they must be enrolled in full-time studies, entering their final year of a certified community college program and intend to pursue a career in the transportation field, as it relates to the foundation's primary focus; for university undergraduates, they must be enrolled in at least two semesters of full-time studies; for graduate students, they must be B average or equivalent in their previous academic year. **Criteria:** Selection will be given to candidates with relevant work experience.

Funds Avail.: $3,000 Canadian Dollars each. **To Apply:** Applicants must complete the application form (available online); must provide academic references and relevant employment information; must have an electronic version of their transcript of records. Application form and requirements must be sent to the TAC Foundation. **Deadline:** February 28. **Contact:** Foundation's Executive Director; Email: foundation@tac-atc.ca.

11098 ■ TAC Foundation-SNC Lavalin Scholarships (Undergraduate, Graduate/Scholarship)

Purpose: To encourage the development of future transportation professionals. **Focus:** Transportation. **Qualif.:** Applicants must be undergraduate or graduate students with transportation-related disciplines as field of their studies. For community college students, they must be enrolled in full-time studies, entering their final year of a certified community college program and intend to pursue a career in the transportation field, as it relates to the Foundation's primary focus. For University undergraduates, they must be enrolled in at least two semesters of full-time studies. For Graduate students, they must be admissible to a full-time transportation-related graduate studies program or already registered as a full-time graduate student in the field. All applicants must be Canadian citizens or permanent residents and have achieved an overall B average or equivalent in their previous academic year. **Criteria:** TAC Foundation Scholarship Committee evaluates and scores all qualifying applications. Preference may be given to candidates with relevant work experience.

Funds Avail.: $5,000. **To Apply:** Applicants must submit the following documents together with the application form: official copy of the current academic transcript with official letterhead in an unalterable format; maximum two-page resume summarizing the education, employment experi-

Awards are arranged alphabetically below their administering organizations

ence, achievements and interests; and academic reference form. **Deadline:** February 28. **Contact:** Foundation's Executive Director; Email: foundation@tac-atc.ca.

11099 ■ TAC Foundation-Stantec Consulting Dr. Ralph Haas Scholarships *(Graduate, Undergraduate/ Scholarship)*

Purpose: To encourage students to continue their post-graduate studies in the field of transportation engineering and to contribute to the cost-effective mobility upon which our society is based. **Focus:** Transportation. **Qualif.:** Applicants must be undergraduate or graduate students with transportation engineering as field of their studies; for community college students, they must be enrolled in full-time studies, entering their final year of a certified community college program and intend to pursue a career in the transportation field, as it relates to the foundation's primary focus; for university undergraduates, they must be enrolled in at least two semesters of full-time studies; for graduate students, they must be B average or equivalent in their previous academic year. **Criteria:** Selection will be given to candidates with relevant work experience.

Funds Avail.: $5,000 Canadian Dollars. **To Apply:** Applicants must complete the application form available online; must provide academic references and relevant employment information; must have an electronic version of their transcript of records. Application form and requirements must be sent to the TAC Foundation. **Deadline:** February 28. **Remarks:** The scholarship was established in memory of Dr. Ralph Haas. **Contact:** Foundation's Executive Director at foundation@tac-atc.ca.

11100 ■ TAC Foundation-Tetra Tech EBA Inc. Scholarships *(Undergraduate, Graduate/Scholarship)*

Purpose: To support transportation education in Canada, such as promoting careers in transportation to skilled students, and assisting transportation educators and researchers. **Focus:** Transportation. **Qualif.:** Applicants must be undergraduate or graduate students with transportation engineering as field of their studies. For community college students, they must be enrolled in full-time studies, entering their final year of a certified community college program and intend to pursue a career in the transportation field, as it relates to the Foundation's primary focus. For University undergraduates, they must be enrolled in at least two semesters of full-time studies. For Graduate students, they must be admissible to a full-time transportation-related graduate studies program or already registered as a full-time graduate student in the field. All applicants must be Canadian citizens or permanent residents and have achieved an overall B average or equivalent in their previous academic year. **Criteria:** TAC Foundation Scholarship Committee evaluates and scores all qualifying applications. Preference may be given to candidates with relevant work experience.

Funds Avail.: $5,000. **To Apply:** Applicants must submit the following documents together with the application form: official copy of the current academic transcript with official letterhead in an unalterable format; maximum two-page resume summarizing the education, employment experience, achievements and interests; and academic reference form. **Deadline:** February 28. **Contact:** Foundation's Executive Director; Email: foundation@tac-atc.ca.

11101 ■ Transportation Association of Canada Foundation Scholarships *(Graduate, Undergraduate/ Scholarship)*

Purpose: To provide support and encouragement to those interested in pursuing a career in transportation planning or

transportation engineering. **Focus:** Transportation. **Qualif.:** Applicants must be undergraduate or graduate students with transportation engineering as field of their studies; for community college students, they must be enrolled in full-time studies, entering their final year of a certified community college program and intend to pursue a career in the transportation field, as it relates to the foundation's primary focus; for university undergraduates, they must be enrolled in at least two semesters of full-time studies; for graduate students, they must be B average or equivalent in their previous academic year. **Criteria:** Selection will be given to candidates with relevant work experience.

Funds Avail.: $5,000 Canadian Dollars. **To Apply:** Applicants must provide academic references and relevant employment information; must have an electronic version of transcript records. **Deadline:** February 28. **Contact:** Foundation's Executive Director at foundation@tac-atc.ca.

11102 ■ Tri-County/City Soil & Water Conservation District (TCCSWCD)
4811 Carr Dr.
Fredericksburg, VA 22408
Ph: (540)656-2401
Fax: (540)656-2403
E-mail: tricountycity@tccswcd.org
URL: tccswcd.org

11103 ■ L. Gordon "Link" Linkous Scholarship *(Undergraduate/Scholarship)*

Purpose: To promote education of local students pursuing scientific and technical fields emphasizing natural resource conservation, environmental protection, and/or environmental studies. **Focus:** Agricultural sciences; Environmental conservation; Forestry; Hydrology; Wildlife conservation, management, and science. **Qualif.:** Applicants must be accepted to or already attending an accredited higher education institution for the upcoming academic year, on a part-time or full-time basis; must reside in the Virginia counties of King George, Spotsylvania, or Stafford, or the city of Fredericksburg; must be pursuing degrees in natural resource conservation, such as forestry, soils, hydrology, agriculture, wildlife, natural resources management, or environmental sciences; and must have a 3.0 or higher GPA. **Criteria:** Essay that best demonstrates how educational interest relates to the conservation of natural resources.

Funds Avail.: $500. **Duration:** Annual. **Number Awarded:** 1. **To Apply:** Must submit a completed application, copy of most recent transcripts/GED certification, three letters of recommendation, and a 100 to 350 word essay. **Deadline:** January 10. **Remarks:** The scholarship is named for Mr. L. Gordon Linkous, in honor of his 60 years of dedicated service to the conservation of natural resources.

11104 ■ VASWCD College Scholarship *(College, Four Year College, Two Year College, Undergraduate/ Scholarship)*

Purpose: To give financial support to Virginian students majoring in natural resource conservation and/or environmental studies. **Focus:** Environmental conservation. **Qualif.:** Applicants who are rising or current full-time freshman level curriculum students will be considered; must be studying in the fields of natural resource conservation and/or environmental studies.

Funds Avail.: $1,000. **Duration:** Annual. **Number Awarded:** 4. **To Apply:** Complete application, provide transcripts and letters of recommendation. **Deadline:** January 10. **Contact:** Mariya Hudick; Phone: 540-656-2401.

11105 ■ Triadex Services
5334 Primrose Lake Cir.
Tampa, FL 33647
Fax: (813)579-1390
Free: 877-874-2339
E-mail: info2@triadexservices.com
Social Media: www.facebook.com/triadexservices
www.linkedin.com/company/triadexservices

11106 ■ Triadex Scholarship (Undergraduate/ Scholarship)

Purpose: To provide financial aid to students with a passion for marketing, entrepreneurship, technology and making our communities better places. **Focus:** General studies/ Field of study not specified. **Qualif.:** Must be high school seniors or current college students in the U.S. with a minimum 3.3 GPA. **Criteria:** Selection will be based on a combination of academic record, personal and professional achievements, extracurricular activities, and need for financial aid.

Funds Avail.: $250 to $750. **Duration:** Quarterly. **Number Awarded:** 4 per year. **To Apply:** Applicant must download the application form and submit completed form along with academic records via email. **Deadline:** March 31; June 30; September 30; December 31. **Contact:** URL: www.triadexservices.com/triadex-scholarship.

11107 ■ Triangle Coalition for STEM Education
1840 Wilson Blvd., Ste. 201
Arlington, VA 22201
Ph: (703)516-5960
Fax: (703)516-5969
Free: 800-582-0115
URL: www.trianglecoalition.org

11108 ■ Albert Einstein Distinguished Educator Fellowships (AEF) (Graduate, Other/Fellowship)

Purpose: To provide a unique professional development opportunity for accomplished K-12 educators in the fields of science, technology, engineering, and mathematics (STEM) to serve in the national education arena. **Focus:** Education, Elementary; Education, Secondary. **Qualif.:** Applicants must be U.S. citizens; have a minimum of five years full-time classroom teaching experience prior to completing the application; have been teaching full-time in a public or private elementary or secondary school for at least five of the last seven years in a STEM discipline; and be currently employed full-time in a public or private elementary or secondary school or school district. **Criteria:** Selection is based on: excellence in teaching science, mathematics, or technology; experimental and innovative attitude in the approach to teaching; sustained professional growth in science or mathematics in the art of teaching; professional involvement and leadership; interpersonal and communication skills needed to serve in the public policy environment and knowledge of national, state and local policies which affect education.

Funds Avail.: No specific amount. **Number Awarded:** Varies. **To Apply:** Applicants may visit the website to verify the application process and other pieces of information. **Contact:** E-mail: sc.einstein@science.doe.gov.

11109 ■ Tribeca Film Institute
32 Ave. of the Americas, 27th Fl.
New York, NY 10013
Ph: (212)274-8080
Fax: (212)274-8081
E-mail: institute@tfiny.org
URL: www.tfiny.org
Social Media: www.facebook.com/TribecaFilmInstitute
twitter.com/TribecaFilmIns

11110 ■ TFI Latin America Media Arts Fund (Professional development/Grant)

Purpose: To support innovative filmmakers living and working in the Caribbean, Mexico, Central and South America who are working on feature-length scripted, documentary or hybrid films. **Focus:** Media arts. **Qualif.:** Applicants must be innovative film and video artists working and living in the Caribbean, Mexico, Central and South America who are 18 years of age, and whose works reflect their diverse cultures.

Funds Avail.: Up to $12,000. **Duration:** Annual. **To Apply:** Applicants must comply with all of the following rules and eligibility requirements; failure to comply with these rules will render a submission ineligible; submissions must be scripted, documentary, animation, and/or hybrid feature-length films with an intended length of at least 70 minutes; submissions must be in advanced development, production or post-production and must not have aired on any form of television, been screened publicly or have been distributed in theaters or via the internet prior to February the following year; submitted films must show enough footage to highlight unique access and storytelling ability; eligible projects should not have any existing US or Latin distribution in place; projects may be in any language or dialect, but if they are not in English, then they must be subtitled in English.

11111 ■ Trinity Education Foundation
215 W Mukilteo Blvd., Ste. 205
Everett, WA 98203
Ph: (425)249-4800
E-mail: info@tef-lbi.org
URL: www.tef-lbi.org
Social Media: www.facebook.com/trinitylbi
www.instagram.com/trinityeducationfoundation
www.linkedin.com/company/trinity-education-foundation

11112 ■ Trinity Education Foundation Seminary Scholarship (Graduate/Scholarship)

Purpose: To provide financial assistance to students attending seminary. **Focus:** Christian education; Religion. **Qualif.:** Applicant must be attending or accepted to a Christian seminary in the United States. **Criteria:** Based on need, academic performance, and service.

Funds Avail.: $1,000 (may vary from year to year). **Number Awarded:** 1. **To Apply:** Applications must be completed online at www.tef-lbi.org. **Deadline:** March 31. **Contact:** Email: info@tef-lbi.org.

11113 ■ Trinity Scholars Program (Undergraduate/ Scholarship)

Purpose: To provide four-year scholarships to the Trinity Scholars program, a holistic approach designed to identify individual "callings," provide one-on-one professional coaching and ensure educational and career success while

Awards are arranged alphabetically below their administering organizations

bridging the financial gap, which often derails a student's goals. **Focus:** General studies/Field of study not specified. **Qualif.:** Applicant must be attending a Christian college in any of the Northwest states (WA, OR, ID, or MT); show a strong desire to understand their calling in life and are willing to commit to the Trinity Scholars Program assessments and coaching support; meet the GPA and financial requirements to be a TSP GRAD. **Criteria:** Based on need, academic performance, and service.

Funds Avail.: $10,000. **Duration:** Scholarship is for four years. **Number Awarded:** 2. **To Apply:** Application must be completed online at www.tef-lbi.org. **Deadline:** March 31. **Contact:** Email: info@tef-lbi.org.

11114 ■ TRIUMF
4004 Wesbrook Mall
Vancouver, BC, Canada V6T 2A3
URL: www.triumf.ca
Social Media: www.facebook.com/TRIUMFLab
www.instagram.com/triumflab
www.linkedin.com/company/triumf
twitter.com/triumflab
www.youtube.com/triumflab

11115 ■ TRIUMF Summer Research Award
(Undergraduate/Award, Scholarship)

Purpose: To provide undergraduate students the opportunity to experience the excitement of research at a National Laboratory such as TRIUMF. **Focus:** Physics. **Qualif.:** Applicants must be enrolled at an accredited Canadian post-secondary institution and be legally entitled to work in Canada; must be currently enrolled in your second (first in Quebec), or higher, year of studies in the physical sciences or engineering; must have achieved a first-class standing.

Funds Avail.: $2,000. **Duration:** Annual. **Number Awarded:** 5. **To Apply:** Applicants must submit curriculum vitae and cover letter are in pdf format; reference letters; transcripts. **Deadline:** January 14.

11116 ■ Trolling Battery Advisor
786 Howard St. SE
Grand Rapids, MI 49507
Ph: (616)379-3791
URL: www.trollingbatteryadvisor.com

11117 ■ Trolling Battery Scholarship *(Undergraduate, Graduate/Scholarship)*

Purpose: To encourage students to build their career in the writing field. **Focus:** General studies/Field of study not specified. **Qualif.:** Applicant must have outstanding writing skills and must have a capability to write the engaging content. **Criteria:** Selection is based on the quality and uniqueness of the applicant's writing.

Funds Avail.: $1,000. **Duration:** Annual. **Number Awarded:** 1. **To Apply:** Applicants must submit their 1,500-2,000 word essay on one of the following subjects: Advantages And Disadvantages of Owning a Trolling Motor; Trolling Motor Battery Proper Care For Good Service; Using Electric Trolling Motors for Fishing; 5 Secrets of a Marine Battery Charger; Three Things to Know About Using a Marine Inverter. This essay should be submitted along with full name, email, and copy of college/university ID to scholarship@trollingbatteryadvisor.com or online at

www.trollingbatteryadvisor.com/scholarship. **Deadline:** March 25. **Contact:** Email: scholarship@trollingbatteryadvisor.com.

11118 ■ Truck Renting and Leasing Association (TRALA)
675 N Washington St., Ste. 410
Alexandria, VA 22314
Ph: (703)299-9120
URL: www.trala.org
Social Media: www.facebook.com/TRALAorg
www.linkedin.com/company/truck-renting-and-leasing-association
twitter.com/TRALAorg

11119 ■ TRALA Industry Scholarship Awards
(Undergraduate/Scholarship)

Purpose: To assist TRALA-member company employees or their dependents to pursue vocational training as diesel maintenance technicians. **Focus:** General studies/Field of study not specified. **Qualif.:** Applicants must be employees of TRALA member companies in North America, or dependents/children of full-time employees of TRALA member companies in North America pursuing a course of study related to the truck transportation industry at an accredited two-year vocational program. **Criteria:** Selection of recipients will be administered by Scholarship America.

Funds Avail.: $5,000 each. **Duration:** Annual; two years. **Number Awarded:** 4. **To Apply:** Applicants must submit the online application form. **Deadline:** November 1. **Contact:** Phone: 507-931-1682; Email: trala@scholarshipamerica.org.

11120 ■ Truckload Carriers Association (TCA)
555 E Braddock Rd.
Alexandria, VA 22314
Ph: (703)838-1950
Fax: (703)836-6610
E-mail: tca@truckload.org
URL: www.truckload.org
Social Media: www.facebook.com/Truckload-Carriers-Association-208489819183351
www.instagram.com/truckloadcarriersassociation/
www.linkedin.com/company/668155
twitter.com/TCANews
www.youtube.com/tcanews

11121 ■ TCA Scholarship Fund *(Undergraduate/Scholarship)*

Purpose: To support students associated with the truckload industry to reach their dreams. **Focus:** General studies/Field of study not specified. **Qualif.:** Applicants must be students in good standing who will be attending an accredited four-year college or university as a freshman, sophomore, junior, or senior and who is either the child, grandchild, or spouse of an employee, or an employee of a TCA member; or, the child, grandchild or spouse of an independent contractor or an independent contractor affiliated with a TCA member; must have a minimum grade point average of 3.0. **Criteria:** Selection will be based on the following criteria: financial need; scholastic achievement; student status; a individual of high character and integrity.

Awards are arranged alphabetically below their administering organizations

Funds Avail.: $6,250. **Duration:** Annual. **To Apply:** Applicants must complete the online application process and submit the following requirements: official transcript of all courses and grades; a course schedule (if available) for the upcoming term; the name, department, address and telephone number of the person at the college or university to which the scholarship check should be sent for disbursement; a headshot photo that must be a 300 dpi resolution or 1 MB in size. **Deadline:** July 31. **Remarks:** Established in 1973. **Contact:** Truckload Carriers Association, c/o TCA Scholarship Fund, 555 E. Braddock Rd., Alexandria, VA, 22314.

11122 ■ Truckload Carriers Association Scholarships (Undergraduate/Scholarship)

Purpose: To help students associated with the truckload industry reach their dreams. **Focus:** General studies/Field of study not specified. **Qualif.:** Applicants must be a college junior or senior in good standing, who is a child, grandchild, spouse of an employee, or an employee of TCA member; must either be the child, grandchild or spouse of an independent contractor or an independent contractor affiliated with a trucking company and attending an accredited four-year college or university. **Criteria:** Recipient will be selected based on financial need, excellence in scholastic achievement in freshman and sophomore years (minimum of 3.3 cumulative GPA), full-time student status with high character and integrity; students pursuing transportation and business degrees will be given special consideration.

Funds Avail.: $2,000 to $6,250. **To Apply:** Applicants must send their complete application, official complete transcript of all college courses and grades, course schedule including tuition and fees for upcoming term. **Deadline:** July 12.

11123 ■ Pierre Elliott Trudeau Foundation (PETF)
600 - 1980 Sherbrooke St. W
Montreal, QC, Canada H3H 1E8
Ph: (514)938-0001
Fax: (514)938-0046
E-mail: communications@fondationtrudeau.ca
URL: www.trudeaufoundation.ca
Social Media: www.facebook.com/
  fondationtrudeaufoundation
www.instagram.com/fdn_pierre_elliott_trudeau
www.linkedin.com/company/fondation-trudeau-foundation
www.youtube.com/user/FTrudeauF/videos?reload=9

11124 ■ Pierre Elliott Trudeau Foundation octoral Scholarships (Doctorate/Scholarship)

Purpose: To support qualified individuals who want to pursue their research on a present-day concern. **Focus:** Humanities; Social sciences. **Qualif.:** Applicants must be Canadian citizens and landed immigrants pursuing full-time doctoral studies in Canada; must be applying for the first year of a doctoral program, or be registered in the first or second year of such a program.

Duration: Annual. **To Apply:** Applicants must complete the application form available online; must submit the official transcript and reference letters. **Deadline:** January 22.

11125 ■ Trudeau Fellowships - Regular (Advanced Professional, Professional development/Fellowship)

Purpose: To support individuals in their research and professional development. **Focus:** General studies/Field of

study not specified. **Qualif.:** Applicants must be Canadian citizens or permanent residents or legally allowed to reside in Canada for the period that they will benefit from the funding; must be active in the social sciences and humanities and work in an area related to one or more of the Foundation's four themes; must be committed to contribute the equivalent of at least one day a week for an academic term to the Foundation's intellectual leadership; and must be nominated by a Canadian university or other entity whom the Foundation has invited to submit a nomination. **Criteria:** Selection will be based on the following: productivity; leadership and innovation; communication and engagement; and Trudeau projects; moreover, Trudeau fellows will be selected through a rigorous process comprised of the following stages: evaluation of all nominations files by an internal committee; selection of finalists by an external committee; approval of the finalists by the Application and Nomination Review Committee; and final approval by the Foundation's Board of Directors.

To Apply: Applicants must provide the following materials: a two-page backgrounder on the candidate (may visit the website for the template); a detailed letter from the nominator, outlining the candidates' academic achievements and their record of public engagement; a detailed project proposal from the candidates, outlining their proposal for a Trudeau project. The proposal is not required to include a budget, but if the candidate feels that a budget would help illustrate the proposal, a summary budget may be included; the proposal, including the budget if desired, should be between 5 and 10 pages; candidates' current resume; up to three publications, articles or book chapters written by the candidates; an optional, one or two testimonies or articles about the candidate containing substantially different elements than those contained in the letter of recommendation. **Contact:** Sarah Saublet, Program Director, Fellowships and Mentorships; Phone: 514 938-0001, extension 228; Email: ssaublet@trudeaufoundation.ca.

11126 ■ True & Co.
68 Jay St.
Brooklyn, NY 11201
Ph: (718)690-5570
URL: trueandco.com
Social Media: www.facebook.com/trueandco
twitter.com/trueandco_us

11127 ■ #thefutureisfemale scholarship (Undergraduate, Graduate, Four Year College, Two Year College/Scholarship)

Purpose: To empower young women to pursue careers they love. **Focus:** General studies/Field of study not specified. **Qualif.:** Applicants must be female; be a U.S. citizen or resident; have a GPA over 3.0.

Funds Avail.: $3,000. **Duration:** Annual. **Number Awarded:** 1. **Deadline:** June 29.

11128 ■ Harry S. Truman Scholarship Foundation (HSTSF)
712 Jackson Pl. NW
Washington, DC 20006
Ph: (202)395-4831
E-mail: office@truman.gov
URL: www.truman.gov

Awards are arranged alphabetically below their administering organizations

11129 ■ Harry S. Truman Scholarships *(Undergraduate, Graduate/Scholarship)*

Purpose: To provide financial assistance for students pursuing graduate degrees in public service fields. **Focus:** Public service. **Qualif.:** Applicants must first be nominated by the Truman Faculty Representative at their institution. Each accredited four-year institution may nominate up to four students for the 2021 awards. **Criteria:** Finalists are selected on the basis of: extent and quality of community service and government involvement; leadership record; academic performance, writing and analytical skills; and suitability of the nominee's proposed program of study for a career in public service.

Funds Avail.: $30,000 merit-based. **Duration:** Annual. **To Apply:** Applicants must submit an online application form and nomination materials. Once a Faculty Representative has decided to nominate a student, he or she must log in to the Foundation website and complete a Nomination Form. The candidate will then receive an email from the Foundation with the instructions on how to access the online application. In the meantime, candidates may use the sample application on the website as a guide. **Deadline:** February 2. **Contact:** The Harry S. Truman Scholarship Foundation; 712 Jackson Place, NW; Washington, DC 20006.

11130 ■ TrustedPros Inc.

111 Peter St., Ste. 901
Toronto, ON, Canada M5V 2H1
Free: 855-890-7767
E-mail: support@trustedpros.com
URL: trustedpros.com
Social Media: www.facebook.com/TrustedPros
www.linkedin.com/company/trustedpros
twitter.com/trustedpros
youtube.com/embed/Rjnu0fwuzcs

11131 ■ TrustedPros Scholarships *(Undergraduate/Scholarship)*

Purpose: To help lessen educational expenses of deserving students pursuing careers in the construction and skilled trades industries. **Focus:** Architecture; Construction; Heating, air conditioning, and refrigeration. **Qualif.:** Applicants must be Canadian or U.S. residents enrolled in an accredited Canadian or U.S. college, university or trade school; have a grade point average of 3.0 or higher; have demonstrated financial need.

Funds Avail.: $1,000 Canadian Dollars. **Duration:** Annual. **Number Awarded:** 2 (one to a Canadian resident, one to a U.S. resident). **To Apply:** Applicant must submit transcripts, a letter demonstrating financial need, and 1,000 minimum word essay about "how your field might be improved?" **Deadline:** December 15. **Contact:** scholarships@trustedpros.com.

11132 ■ Truthfinder

2534 State St., Ste. 473
San Diego, CA 92101
Ph: (858)242-1350
E-mail: info@truthfinder.com
URL: www.truthfinder.com
Social Media: www.facebook.com/TruthFinderInc
www.linkedin.com/company/truthfinder
www.pinterest.com/TruthFinderInc/

twitter.com/TruthFinder
www.youtube.com/+TruthfinderInc

11133 ■ Truthfinder Scholarship for Women in STEM *(Undergraduate, Graduate, Two Year College/Scholarship)*

Purpose: To encourage women in STEM fields. **Focus:** Engineering; Mathematics and mathematical sciences; Science; Technology. **Qualif.:** Applicants must be a woman currently enrolled in or attending a college or university; must be a US citizen; must be enrolled in a degree related to science, technology, engineering, or mathematics; must have a GPA of 3.00 or higher. **Criteria:** Selection based on essay or video essay of the following: Original voice; Unique style; Creativity; Interesting ideas; Clear presentment of the topic; Peer impact; Spelling/Grammar.

Funds Avail.: $2,500. **Duration:** Annual. **Number Awarded:** 1. **To Apply:** Applicants must submit an either a 750-word essay or a video on what inspires them about their career in STEM. Applications are available. **Contact:** 2534 State St., Ste. 473, San Diego, CA, 92101; Phone: 858-242-1350; Email: scholarship@truthfinder.com.

11134 ■ TSHP Research and Education Foundation

3000 Joe DiMaggio, Ste. 30-A
Round Rock, TX 78665
Ph: (512)906-0546
Fax: (512)852-8514
Free: 800-242-8747
E-mail: tshp@tshp.org
URL: www.tshp.org/tshp-re-foundation.html
Social Media: www.linkedin.com/groups/6576682/profile
twitter.com/TSHP_org

11135 ■ TSHP R&E Foundation Scholarship Program *(Undergraduate, Graduate/Scholarship)*

Purpose: To help students pursue their education in pharmacy field. **Focus:** Pharmacy. **Qualif.:** Applicants must be undergraduate and graduate students. **Criteria:** Recipients will be selected based on financial need, academic ability, and career interest.

Funds Avail.: Range from $500 to $1,500. **Duration:** Annual. **To Apply:** Applicants must complete the application form; submit a letter of application explaining how to meet the required criteria, future pharmacy practice goals and philosophy of pharmacy practice; submit a copy of the latest grade report verifying their current GPA; provide proof of residency for el paso, gene lake and central texas; and submit two letters of reference; two letters of reference. **Deadline:** February 10. **Contact:** Email: scholarship@tshp.org.

11136 ■ Turco Legal

29 Water St..Ste 301
Newburyport, MA 01950
Ph: (978)225-9030
Free: 866-995-6663
URL: turcolegal.com
Social Media: www.facebook.com/TurcoLegal
twitter.com/damianturco

11137 ■ Turco Munoz Domestic Violence Survivor Scholarship *(Undergraduate, Graduate/Scholarship)*

Purpose: To help the cause by supporting the education of those who intend to professionally help with the domestic

Awards are arranged alphabetically below their administering organizations

violence crisis. **Focus:** Law; Social work. **Qualif.:** Applicant must have some victim advocacy experience serving survivors of domestic violence (experience as a victim advocate, family law paralegal, social worker, investigator, or other employee of an organization whose mission is to serve DV survivors); be enrolled either in law school, or an undergraduate or graduate program, with a focus in an applicable field of study; and must have a genuine intention to focus their career after graduation serving survivors of domestic violence. **Criteria:** Scholarship Selection Committee will review all applications considering academic performance, employment and volunteer experience, financial needs, and plans after graduation. Committee may hold interviews to make a final selection.

Funds Avail.: $1,000. **Number Awarded:** 1. **To Apply:** Applications must be submitted online. **Deadline:** August 15. **Contact:** turcolegal.com/scholarship/.

11138 ■ Turf and Ornamental Communicators Association (TOCA)
605 Columbus Ave. S
New Prague, MN 56071-1935
Ph: (952)758-6340
Fax: (952)758-5813
E-mail: toca@gandgcomm.com
URL: www.toca.org
Social Media: www.facebook.com/TOCAorg
twitter.com/TOCAorg

11139 ■ Turf and Ornamental Communicators Association Scholarship Program *(Undergraduate/Scholarship)*

Purpose: To provide financial support for undergraduate college students pursuing a career in green industry communications. **Focus:** Communications. **Criteria:** Recipients will be evaluated by the Scholarship Committee.

Funds Avail.: $2,500. **Number Awarded:** 1. **To Apply:** Applicants must submit complete application form together with references (two academic/professional references), writing/editing sample (One news article published or prepared for publication), essay (500 words), resume, and transcript. **Deadline:** March 1. **Remarks:** Established in 1992. **Contact:** Barb Ulschmid at barbulschmid@gardnerandgardnercommunications.com; 952-758-6340.

11140 ■ Turkish Coalition of America (TCA)
1510 H St. NW, Ste. 900
Washington, DC 20005
Ph: (202)370-1399
Fax: (202)370-1398
E-mail: info@tc-america.org
URL: www.tc-america.org
Social Media: www.facebook.com/TurkishCoalitionofAmerica
twitter.com/TCAmerica
www.youtube.com/channel/UCgoda5bmWvAslTh81D1a66w

11141 ■ Arif Mardin Music Fellowship *(Other/Fellowship)*

Purpose: To provide financial assistance for promising musicians from Turkey and to give them the chance to study in the United States. **Focus:** Music. **Qualif.:** Applicant must be an individuals of Turkish descent or nationality, over the age of 15, with a minimum of six months experience playing their instrument or singing. **Criteria:** Selection committee will be given to applicants 18 years of age and younger.

Funds Avail.: $500. **Duration:** Annual. **To Apply:** Applications can be submitted online. **Deadline:** August 14.

11142 ■ TCA-ACBH Scholarship to Turkey Program *(Undergraduate/Scholarship)*

Purpose: To provide financial assistance to students who are pursuing their educational goal. **Focus:** General studies/Field of study not specified. **Qualif.:** Applicants full-time Bosnian-American undergraduates accepted to a study abroad program at a Turkish university. **Criteria:** Selection is based on merit.

Funds Avail.: $2,000. **Number Awarded:** 10. **To Apply:** Applicants must send a resume and a cover letter to ACBH with subject title "TCA Scholarship" via email. **Contact:** E-mail: baacbh@gmail.com with subject, TCA Scholarship.

11143 ■ TCA-UMD Scholarship to Turkey Program *(Undergraduate/Scholarship)*

Purpose: To provide financial assistance to students who are pursuing their educational goal. **Focus:** General studies/Field of study not specified. **Qualif.:** Applicants must be full-time Macedonian-American undergraduates accepted to a study abroad program at a Turkish university. **Criteria:** Preference will be given to those who meet the criteria.

Funds Avail.: $2,000. **Number Awarded:** 10. **To Apply:** Applicants should send their resume and cover letter.

11144 ■ TCAdvance Scholarship *(Undergraduate/Scholarship)*

Purpose: To fulfill the objective of engaging and cultivating a new generation of Young Turkish American leaders. **Focus:** Communications; International affairs and relations; Political science; Printing trades and industries; Public affairs; Public relations. **Criteria:** Selection will be selected based on academic achievement.

Funds Avail.: No specific amount. **Duration:** Annual. **To Apply:** Applicants must submit three (3) collated, non-stapled, paper clipped copies of each of the following items: (1) Completed Application Form (2) Resume: each copy should be submitted on one single-sided 8.5. **Contact:** E-mail: scholarships@tc-america.org.

11145 ■ J.L. Turner Legal Association (JLTLA)
2101 Ross Ave.
Dallas, TX 75201
URL: www.jltla.org

11146 ■ The Phyllis Lister-Brown Memorial Scholarship *(Undergraduate/Scholarship)*

Purpose: To award scholarship to a minority law student who has excelled academically. **Focus:** Law. **Qualif.:** Applicants must be either male or female law students; must be currently enrolled in an ABA accredited law school in the United States; must be in good academic standing at the law school; must be either second year or third year minority law students that is from the DFW Metroplex or a second or third year minority law students that attend law school in the DFW Metroplex. **Criteria:** Selection will be based on financial need and merit.

Awards are arranged alphabetically below their administering organizations

Funds Avail.: No specific amount. **Duration:** Annual. **To Apply:** Applicants must submit a completed application form. **Deadline:** September 15. **Remarks:** Established in 1982. **Contact:** Submissions Must Be Sent To The Following Address: J. L. Turner Legal Association Foundation, Scholarship Committee, PO Box 130987, Dallas, TX, 75313-0987; Email: Kandace@walterlegal.com.

11147 ■ The Fred Finch Scholarship (Undergraduate/Scholarship)

Purpose: To recognize the most outstanding male minority law students. **Focus:** Law. **Qualif.:** Applicants must be male minority law students; must be currently enrolled in an ABA accredited law school in the United States; must be in good academic standing at the law school; must be either second year or third year minority law students that is from the DFW Metroplex or a second or third year minority law students that attend law school in the DFW Metroplex. **Criteria:** Selection will be based on basis of merit and financial need.

Funds Avail.: No specific amount. **Duration:** Annual. **To Apply:** Applicants must submit a completed application form. **Deadline:** September 15. **Remarks:** Established in 1982. **Contact:** Submissions Must Be Sent To The Following Address: J. L. Turner Legal Association Foundation, Scholarship Committee, PO Box 130987, Dallas, TX, 75313-0987; Email: Kandace@walterlegal.com.

11148 ■ The Marie Trahan/Susman Godfrey Scholarship (Undergraduate/Scholarship)

Purpose: To support outstanding African-American male or female law student in continuing their studies. **Focus:** Law. **Qualif.:** Applicants must be African-American law students from the state of Texas; must be currently enrolled in an ABA accredited law school in the United States; must be in good academic standing at the law school; must be either second or third year minority law students that are from the DFW Metroplex or a second or third year minority law student that attends law school in the DFW Metroplex.**Criteria:** Selection will be based on basis of merit and financial need.

Funds Avail.: No specific amount. **Duration:** Annual. **To Apply:** Applicants must submit a completed application form. **Deadline:** September 15. **Remarks:** Established in 1982. **Contact:** Submissions Must Be Sent To The Following Address: J. L. Turner Legal Association Foundation, Scholarship Committee, PO Box 130987, Dallas, TX, 75313-0987; Email: Kandace@walterlegal.com.

11149 ■ Financial Need Minority Scholarships (Undergraduate/Scholarship)

Purpose: To inspire educational pursuits in the field of law among law students. **Focus:** Law. **Qualif.:** Applicants must be a United States citizen or permanent legal resident; must be currently enrolled in an ABA accredited law school in the United States; must be in good academic standing at the law school; must be either second year or third year minority law students that is from the DFW Metroplex or a second or third year minority law students that attend law school in the DFW Metroplex. **Criteria:** Selection will be based on financial need and merit.

Funds Avail.: No specific amount. **Duration:** Annual. **To Apply:** Applicants must submit a completed application form. **Deadline:** September 15. **Remarks:** Established in 1982. **Contact:** Oluwande Elam, phone: 214-780-1304, e-mail: wande@outlook.com; or LaKisha Camese, phone: 469-888-1845, e-mail: cameselg@hotmail.com.

11150 ■ The Barbara Jordan Scholarship (Undergraduate/Scholarship)

Purpose: To recognize the most outstanding female minority law student. **Focus:** Law. **Qualif.:** Applicants must be female minority students; must be currently enrolled in an ABA accredited law school in the United States; must be in good academic standing at the law school; must be either second year or third year minority law students that is from the DFW Metroplex or a second or third year minority law students that attend law school in the DFW Metroplex. **Criteria:** Selection will be based on basis of merit and financial need.

Funds Avail.: No specific amount. **Duration:** Annual. **To Apply:** Applicants must submit a completed application form. **Deadline:** September 15. **Remarks:** Established in 1982. **Contact:** Submissions Must Be Sent To The Following Address: J. L. Turner Legal Association Foundation, Scholarship Committee, PO Box 130987, Dallas, TX, 75313-0987; Email: Kandace@walterlegal.com.

11151 ■ Turner Solutions, LLC
2560 King Arthur Blvd., Ste. 124-107
Lewisville, TX 75056
E-mail: scott@scottalanturner.com
URL: scottalanturner.com
Social Media: www.facebook.com/scottalanturner23
instagram.com/scottalanturner
linkedin.com/in/scottalanturner
twitter.com/scottalanturner
youtube.com/c/scottalanturner

11152 ■ Scott Alan Turner Personal Finance Scholarship (High School, Undergraduate/Scholarship)

Purpose: To help provide personal finance education to students and to develop a deeper knowledge and appreciation of good money management. **Focus:** General studies/Field of study not specified. **Qualif.:** Applicants must: be graduating high school seniors or undergraduate college students; have minimum grade point average of 3.0; be between the ages of 16 and 25 years old; be planning to enroll or currently enrolled in a two- or four-year college or vocational school on a part-time or full-time basis; U.S. citizen or legal resident. **Criteria:** Quality of essay.

Funds Avail.: $1,000 to undergraduate student; $500 to high school senior. **Duration:** Annual. **To Apply:** Compose essay of at least 500 words discussing what your family taught you about money/personal finance and what you've learned about money on your own. **Deadline:** July 1. **Contact:** Email: scholarship@scottalanturner.com.

11153 ■ Turnkey Lender
1999 S Bascom Ave., Ste. 700
Campbell, CA 95008
Free: 888-299-4892
URL: www.turnkey-lender.com

11154 ■ The Turnkey Lender's Scholarship Program (Undergraduate/Scholarship)

Purpose: To create and nurture the correct attitude towards market forces through higher education. **Focus:** Finance. **Qualif.:** Applicant must be an undergraduate student at an accredited college or university. **Criteria:** Selection will be done by an internal committee of Turnkey Lenders' busi-

Awards are arranged alphabetically below their administering organizations

ness analytics team and will be based on the essay submitted.

Funds Avail.: $1,000. **Number Awarded:** 1. **To Apply:** Applicant must write an essay (1,000 words) on the topic provided and publish the post online publicly. **Deadline:** December 20. **Contact:** Email: scholarship@turnkey-lender.com; URL: www.turnkey-lender.com/scholarship/.

11155 ■ Twenty Four Seven Hotels
520 Newport Center Dr., No. 520
Newport Beach, CA 92660

11156 ■ Twenty Four Seven Hotels Scholarship Opportunity *(Undergraduate, College, University/Scholarship)*

Purpose: To help a student gain an education in a hospitality related field. **Focus:** Hotel, institutional, and restaurant management. **Qualif.:** Applicant must be a legal U.S. resident and is either enrolled or planning to enroll in an accredited U.S college or university in an undergraduate program in a hospitality related field. **Criteria:** Scholarship will be awarded to the applicant who best demonstrates a genuine desire and goal of using the scholarship to advance in hospitality related fields, and shows an overall passion for knowledge.

Funds Avail.: $500. **Number Awarded:** 1. **To Apply:** Applicant must submit an essay (500 words) on their future career and educational objectives in hospitality. Essay can be submitted via email to brett@mabventures.com. **Deadline:** July 1. **Contact:** URL: www.247hotels.com/scholarship-opportunity/.

11157 ■ TXG Capital
1000 W Morehead St., Ste. 150
Charlotte, NC 28208
URL: www.txgcapital.com

11158 ■ Ted Rollins Eco Scholarship *(Undergraduate/Scholarship)*

Purpose: To help a high school graduate or undergraduate looking to offset the cost of a business, sustainability, or marketing degree. **Focus:** Environmental conservation. **Qualif.:** Applicants must be high school seniors or college undergraduate students majoring (or planning to major) in a field related to sustainability; must plan to take at least 10 credit hours during the fall semester. **Criteria:** Selection will be made by a committee of three judges

Funds Avail.: $1,000. **Duration:** Annual. **Number Awarded:** 1. **To Apply:** Submit the application form at www.tedrollinsecoscholars.com. Use the "Your Story And Goals" field to share your interests, experience, and goals related to sustainability and ecopreneurism. **Deadline:** April 3. **Contact:** E-mail: scholarship@tedrollinseco scholars.com; URL: www.tedrollinsecoscholars.com.

11159 ■ Type Media Center
116 E 16th St., 8th Fl.
New York, NY 10003
Ph: (212)822-0250
Fax: (212)253-5356
E-mail: press@typemediacenter.org
URL: typemediacenter.org
Social Media: www.facebook.com/typemediacenter
twitter.com/TypeMediaCenter

11160 ■ The Robert Masur Fellowship in Civil Liberties *(Undergraduate/Fellowship)*

Purpose: To recognize a first-year law student who is currently involved in an internship in civil liberties or civil rights. **Focus:** Civil rights. **Qualif.:** Applicants must be students who intend to carry out significant activities during the summer (in between their first and second year) in the areas of civil rights and/or civil liberties.

Funds Avail.: $2,000. **Duration:** Annual. **Number Awarded:** Varies. **To Apply:** Applicants should send a proposal, no more than two pages, describing their intended summer project, along with a resume, a brief letter of recommendation.

Awards are arranged alphabetically below their administering organizations

CPSIA information can be obtained
at www.ICGtesting.com
Printed in the USA
BVHW050131200121
598186BV00007B/118

7